This book may be used to supplement the
**Osborne 16-Bit Microprocessor Handbook**
(formerly **An Introduction to Microcomputers: Volume 2 — Some Real Microprocessors)**
or as a stand alone reference.

OSBORNE

# 4 & 8-Bit Microprocessor Handbook

OSBORNE

# 4 & 8-Bit Microprocessor Handbook

Adam Osborne
Gerry Kane

OSBORNE/McGraw-Hill
Berkeley, California

**Published by**
**OSBORNE/McGraw-Hill**
**630 Bancroft Way**
**Berkeley, California 94710**
**U. S. A.**

For information on translations and book distributors outside of the U. S. A., please write OSBORNE/McGraw-Hill at the above address.

23456789 DODO 8987654321
ISBN 0-931988-42-X

Cover design by Marc Miyashiro.

**Contributing Authors**

The following persons have contributed to the writing of sections of this book in addition to its principal authors.

Bob Abromovitz
Janice K. Enger
Curtis A. Ingraham
Susanna Jacobson
Patrick L. McGuire
Allan H. Robbins

S.A.MANSI

## CONTENTS

# INTRODUCTION

This is one of two books that replace ***An Introduction to Microcomputers: Volume 2 — Some Real Microprocessors***. That volume went through several printings and in 1978 was printed loose-leaf. Six bimonthly updates to the loose-leaf version were published in 1979 and early 1980 to provide information on newly introduced microprocessor devices. The loose-leaf version proved, however, to be quite unpopular with bookstores because of packaging and handling considerations. It also became more and more difficult to maintain a timely flow of bimonthly updates. For these reasons, ***Volume 2*** is being replaced by two bound paperback books: ***The Osborne 4 & 8-Bit Microprocessor Handbook*** and the ***Osborne 16-Bit Microprocessor Handbook***. Together these handbooks include all of the information that was contained in ***Volume 2*** and the six updates. All known errors have been corrected and new data sheets have been added to the two handbooks. We have divided ***Volume 2*** into two separate handbooks because the single-volume version would be over 1800 pages in length and rather difficult to bind. In addition, the devices lend themselves to this grouping since the 16-bit microprocessors are generally much more powerful than the four- and eight-bit microprocessors and thus are directed toward different applications.

***Volume 2*** was part of a four-volume ***Introduction to Microcomputers*** series:

- ***Volume 0 — The Beginner's Book*** was written for readers who know nothing about computers.
- ***Volume 1 — Basic Concepts*** provides a detailed explanation of microprocessor concepts, including number systems, addressing modes, typical instruction sets, input/output techniques, and so on. The device descriptions in the ***4 & 8-Bit Microprocessor Handbook*** and the ***16-Bit Microprocessor Handbook*** assume that you have a working knowledge of the general concepts presented in ***Volume 1***, and we will occasionally make references to material presented in ***Volume 1***.
- ***Volume 2 — Some Real Microprocessors***, which is being replaced by these handbooks.
- ***Volume 3 — Some Real Support Devices***, which describes general support devices that may be used with any microprocessor. Some dedicated support devices are described in the ***4 & 8-Bit Microprocessor Handbook*** and the ***16-Bit Microprocessor Handbook***. We define a "dedicated" support device as one best used with its parent microprocessor. We define a "general" support device as one that can be used with any microprocessor. We will occasionally make references in this book to some of the general support devices described in ***Volume 3***. When designing a system based on one of the microprocessors described in this handbook, you should not automatically assume that the dedicated support devices described in this book are the only ones or the best ones to use with a particular microprocessor: you should always check the functionally equivalent parts described in ***Volume 3***.

In addition to this ***Introduction to Microcomputers*** series, we have begun publishing other individual handbooks. The first two handbooks of this series are: ***The 8089 I/O Processor Handbook***, which includes the 8289 bus arbiter, and the ***CRT Controller Handbook***, which describes LSI CRT controller devices. This individual handbook approach will be used in the future to maintain a convenient flow of detailed, objective information on new microprocessors and related support devices.

## SIGNAL CONVENTIONS

**Signals may be active high, active low or active in two states. An active high signal is one which, in the high state, causes events to occur, while in the low state has no significance. A signal that is active low causes events to occur when in the low state, but has no significance in the high state. A signal that has two active states will cause two different types of events to occur, depending upon whether the signal is high or low; this signal has no inactive state. Within this book a signal that is active low has a bar placed over the signal name. For example, $\overline{\text{WR}}$ identifies a "write strobe" signal which is pulsed low when data is ready for external logic to receive. A signal that is active high or has two active states has no bar over the signal name.**

# TIMING DIAGRAM CONVENTIONS

**Timing diagrams play an important part in the description of any microprocessor or support device. Timing diagrams are therefore used extensively in this book. All timing diagrams observe the following conventions:**

1) A low signal level is equivalent to no voltage. A high signal level is equivalent to voltage present:

2) A single signal making a low-to-high transition is illustrated like this:

3) A single signal making a high-to-low transition is illustrated like this:

4) When two or more parallel signals exist, the notation:

states that one or more of the parallel signals change level, but the transition (high-to-low or low-to-high) is unspecified.

5) A three-state single signal is shown floating thus:

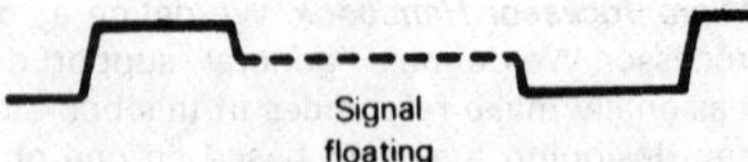


6) A three-state bus containing two or more signals is shown floating thus:

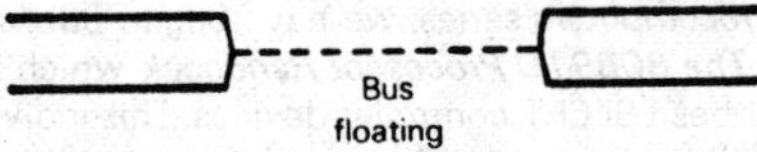


7) When one signal condition triggers other signal changes, an arrow indicates the relationship as follows:

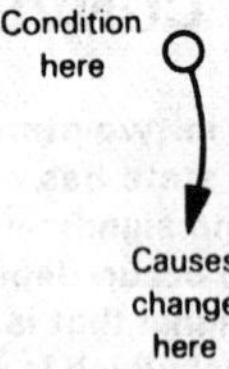

Thus a signal making a low-to-high transition would be illustrated triggering another signal making a high-to-low transition as follows:

A signal making a high-to-low transition triggering a bus change of state would be illustrated as follows:

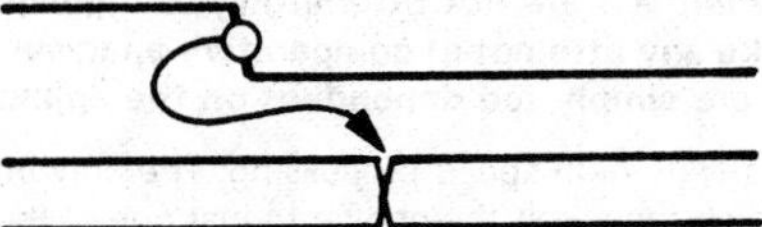

8) When two or more conditions must exist in order to trigger another logic event, the following illustration is used:

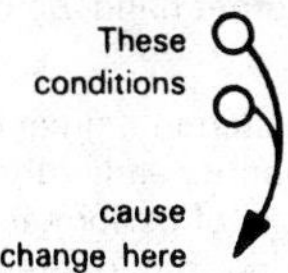


Thus a low-to-high transition of one signal occurring while another signal is low would be illustrated triggering a third event as follows:

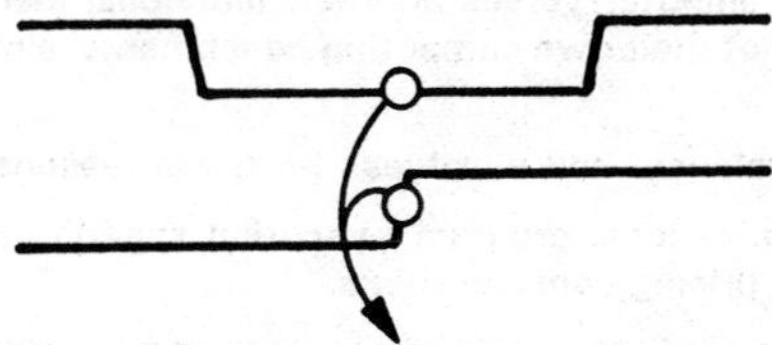

9) When a single triggering condition causes two or more events to occur, the following illustration is used:

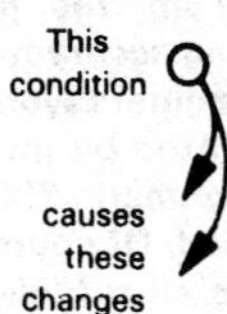


Thus a low-to-high transition of one signal triggering changes in two other signal levels would be illustrated as follows:

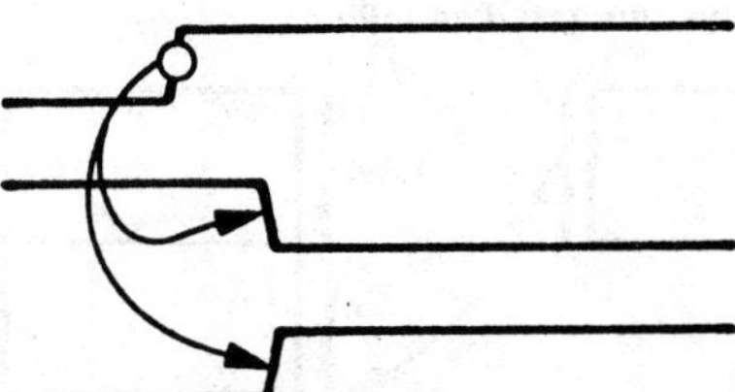

10) All signal level changes are shown as square waves. Thus rise and fall times are ignored. These times are given in the data sheets which appear at the end of every chapter.

# INSTRUCTION SET CONVENTIONS

**Every microcomputer instruction set is described with two tables. One table identifies the operations which occur when the instruction set is executed, while the second table defines object codes and instruction times.**

**Because of the wide differences that exist between one instruction set and another, we have elected not to use a single set of codes and symbols to describe the operations for all instructions in all instruction sets. We believe any type of universal convention is likely to confuse rather than clarify; therefore each instruction set table is preceded by a list of symbols as used within that table alone.**

**A short benchmark program is given to illustrate each instruction set. Some comments regarding benchmark programs in general are, however, in order. We are not attempting to highlight strengths or weaknesses of different devices, nor does this book make any attempt at comparative analyses, since the criteria which make one microcomputer better than another are simply too dependent on the application.**

**COMPARATIVE ANALYSIS**

Consider an application which requires relatively high speed processing. The only important criterion will be program execution speed, which may limit the choice to just one of the microcomputers we are describing.

Execution speeds of all of the microcomputers may, on the other hand, be quite adequate for a second application; in this case, price may be the only overriding factor.

In a third application, a manufacturer may have already invested in a great deal of engineering development expense, using one particular microcomputer that was available in quantity earlier than any others; the advantages or disadvantages of using a different microcomputer, based on minor cost of performance advantages, will likely be overwhelmed by the extra expense and time delays involved with switching in mid-stream.

**BENCHMARK PROGRAMS**

**And what about benchmark programs?**

**There have been a number of benchmark programs in the literature, purporting to show the strengths or weaknesses of one microcomputer versus another; individual manufacturers have added to the confusion by putting out their own competing benchmarks, aimed at showing their product to be superior to an immediate rival.**

**Benchmark programs are misleading, irrelevant and worthless for these reasons:**

1. **In a majority of microcomputer applications, program execution speed, and minor variations in program length, are simply overwhelmed by pricing considerations.**
2. **Even assuming that for some specific application, program length and execution speed are important, trivial changes in the benchmark program definition can profoundly alter the results that are obtained. This is one point we will demonstrate in this book, while describing individual instruction sets.**
3. **Benchmark programs are invariably written by the smartest programmers in an organization, and they take an enormous amount of time to ensure programming accuracy and excellence. This is not the level at which any user should anticipate "run of the mill" programmers working; indeed, a far more realistic evaluation of a microcomputer's instruction set could be generated by giving an average programmer too little time in which to implement an incompletely defined benchmark. This will more closely approximate the working conditions under which real products are developed. Of course, defining the "average programmer," "too little time" and an "incomplete specification" are all sufficiently subjective that they defy resolution.**

**We will demonstrate the capriciousness of benchmark programs via the following benchmark program:**

**Raw data has been input to a general purpose input buffer, beginning at IOBUF. This raw data is to be moved to a permanent table, which may be partially filled; the raw data is to be stored in the data table starting with the first unfilled byte. The benchmark may be illustrated as follows:**

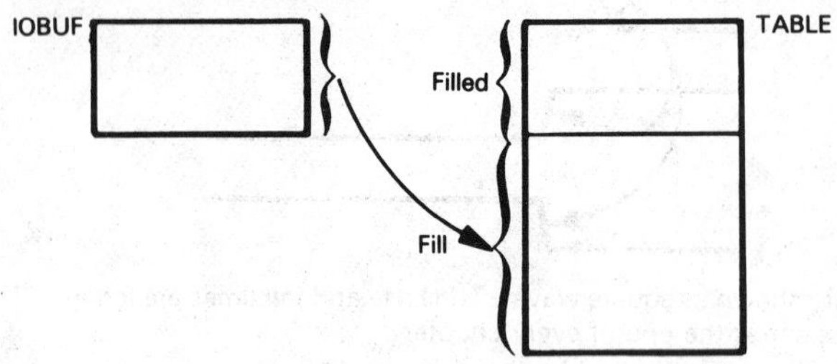

## HOW THIS BOOK HAS BEEN PRINTED

**Notice that text in this book has been printed in boldface type** and lightface type. **This has been done to help you skip those parts of the book that cover subject matter with which you are familiar. You can be sure that lightface type only expands on information presented in the previous boldface type.** Therefore, read only boldface type until you reach a subject about which you want to know more, at which point start reading the lightface type.

# Chapter 1
# 4-BIT MICROPROCESSORS

The earliest microprocessors were all 4-bit devices; that is to say, data was operated on in 4-bit units, frequently referred to as "nibbles". **Early microprocessors were 4-bit devices simply because the concept of an LSI CPU was ambitious enough; starting with an 8-bit CPU would have been foolhardy.**

But LSI technology has advanced so rapidly that there is an inconsequential difference between the cost of manufacturing an 8-bit CPU chip as against a 4-bit chip. Manufacturers attempted to maintain an artificial price differential between their 4-bit and 8-bit CPUs in order to prolong the life of the 4-bit product, but the pressure of competition has all but extinguished these price differentials — with the result that the 4-bit microprocessor is a dying product. Price is the only advantage that 4-bit microprocessors offer when compared to the more capable 8-bit microprocessor.

Early 4-bit microcomputers included such devices as the Intel 4004 and 4040, the Rockwell PPS4, and the National Semiconductor IMP-4. These early 4-bit microcomputers require package counts that exceed those of typical 8-bit microcomputers that are now available, therefore **the economics of today dictate that the Intel 4004, the Intel 4040, the Rockwell PPS4, and the IMP-4 offer less capability for more money. We consider these devices to be obsolete; therefore they are not described.** It is interesting to note that even though these four 4-bit microcomputers are obsolete, they will continue to have a significant market for many years to come, based on products that were designed around them before they became obsolete.

As mentioned above, a price differential, however small, does exist between the 4-bit and 8-bit microprocessors. This cost savings only becomes realistic in very high volumes. Manufacturers in the consumer and automotive markets fit this user profile. A cost savings of $1.00 over 500,000 to 1,000,000 units is well worth the increased effort of programming a 4-bit microcomputer. Note that this savings exists only for the 4-bit microcomputers (i.e., those chips which include processor, RAM, ROM, and I/O on one chip). All other 4-bit products are considered obsolete and will not be covered in this chapter. Today a number of manufacturers are offering 4-bit microcomputers. These microcomputers have from 1/2K to 2K of program memory, 32 to 128 bytes of data memory, and from 8 to 32 I/O pins. Computers of this level of complexity are extremely useful as dedicated controllers and are finding a myriad of uses. **This chapter will examine the following three processors in detail:**

**1) Texas Instruments TMS1000**

**2) Rockwell PPS4/1**

**3) National Semiconductor COP**

The TMS1000 is one of the oldest and most widely used microprocessors. It was originally released in 1972. Its longevity can be attributed to the fact that it was the first single-chip microcomputer ever offered. Rockwell's PPS4/1 is a single-chip version of their earlier PPS4 chip set. The new National Semiconductor COP (Controller Oriented Processor) is an offshoot of their earlier COP (Calculator Oriented Processor). One of the most remarkable features of the COP series is its price. Prices below $1.00 are quoted to high-volume users for the COP 411L (the 1/2K program memory version).

## TMS1000

**In reality, the TMS1000 is a family of six 4-bit microcomputers whose differences are summarized in Table 1-1. The various microcomputers are sufficiently similar for us to describe them together.** PMOS and CMOS versions are now available. Some CMOS versions manufactured by Motorola have the part number MC141000.

**Figure 1-1 illustrates that part of our general microcomputer system logic which is implemented by the TMS1000 series microcomputers. This figure is deceptive, since it would be hard to compare the primitive I/O capabilities of the TMS1000 with a device such as the 8255 Programmable Peripheral Interface device, which is described in Volume 3. Nevertheless, Figure 1-1 does indicate the logic which is provided by a TMS1000 series microcomputer, albeit in a primitive form.**

Table 1-1. TMS1000 Series Microcomputer Summary

| | TMS 1000 | TMS 1200 | TMS 1070 | TMS 1270 | TMS 1100 | TMS 1300 | TMS 1000C | TMS 1200C | MC 141000 | MC 141200 |
|---|---|---|---|---|---|---|---|---|---|---|
| Package Pin Count | 28 | 40 | 28 | 40 | 28 | 40 | 28 | 40 | 28 | 40 |
| ROM Program Bytes* | 1024 | 1024 | 1024 | 1024 | 2048 | 2048 | 1024 | 1024 | 1024 | 1024 |
| RAM Data Nibbles** | 64 | 64 | 64 | 64 | 128 | 128 | 64 | 64 | 64 | 64 |
| R Signal Outputs | 11 | 13 | 11 | 13 | 11 | 16 | 10 | 16 | 11 | 16 |
| O Data Outputs | 8 | 8 | 8 | 10 | 8 | 8 | 8 | 8 | 8 | 8 |
| Maximum Rated Voltage | 20 | 20 | 35 | 35 | 20 | 20 | 6 | 6 | 6.5 | 6.5 |
| Typical Power Dissipation | 15V/ 90mW | 15V/ 90mW | 15V/ 90mW | 15V/ 90mW | 15V/ 90mW | 15V/ 90mW | 5V/ 15mW | 5V/ 5mW | 5V/ 2.5mW 3V/ 0.5mW | 5V/ 2.5mW 3V/ 0.5mW |

*A Byte is eight bits **A Nibble is four bits

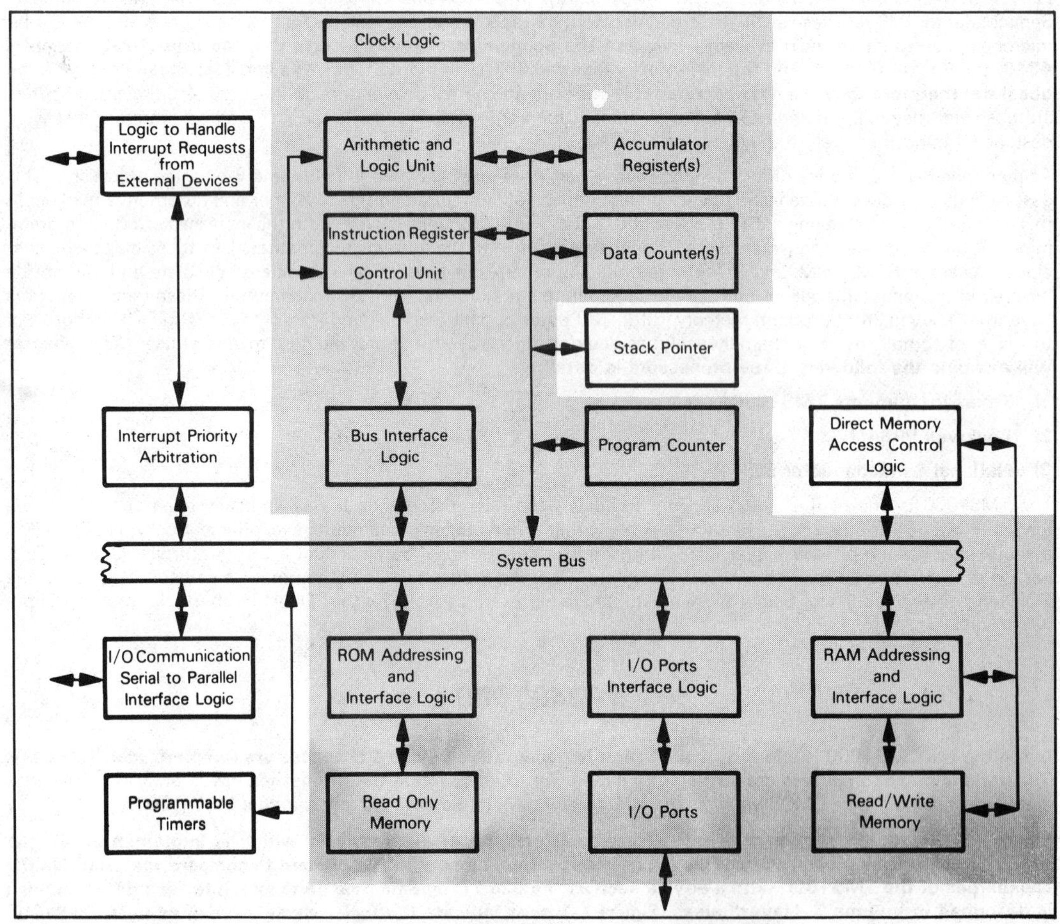


Figure 1-1. Logic of the TMS1000 Series Microcomputer

**The fact that the TMS1000 series microcomputers are single-chip devices has a number of secondary, non-obvious implications.** Most important of all, there are no such things as support devices. The 1024 or 2048 bytes of ROM represent the exact amount of program memory which will be present, there can be neither more nor less. Similarly, the 64 or 128 nibbles of RAM cannot be expanded. Direct memory access logic is not present — and its presence would make very little sense anyway; with the small total ROM and RAM memory available, there simply is not the opportunity to transfer blocks of data long enough to warrant bypassing the CPU.

**Interrupts are lacking in the TMS1000 series.** Initially this was dictated by space constraints on the chip. The fabrication technology of the early seventies was already being strained by the TMS1000. This lack of interrupt inputs is especially apparent in controller applications where asynchronous events are common. Most applications can be successfully coded by using a polling algorithm. The number of bytes consumed by this polling operation is typically less than 10% of the available program memory. However, the real rub is the time consumed while executing this code. In the consumer marketplace there is constant pressure for lower cost and greater functionality. The cost jump from a 4-bit to an 8-bit microcomputer can be as high as $3.00, so there is great cost pressure to stay with a 4-bit microcomputer. **The addition of interrupt logic, therefore, is significant in those applications that are already pushing the 4-bit microcomputers to their limits.**

All devices of the TMS1000 microcomputer family are implemented using PMOS technology. Selected CMOS parts are also available.

A single -15V power supply is required for PMOS parts. CMOS parts use power supplies in the range +3V to +6.5V.

The fastest clock frequency which can drive a TMS1000 series microcomputer has a 2.5 microsecond cycle time. All instructions execute in six clock cycles, or 15 microseconds; but beware of making direct execution speed comparisons between the TMS1000 and the 8-bit microcomputers which are described next. A TMS1000 program will usually be considerably longer than the 8-bit microcomputer equivalent because the TMS1000 instruction set is more primitive; but this is not always true. It is possible for the TMS1000 instruction set to equal or surpass many 8-bit microprocessors, in terms of instruction efficiency, for certain control applications.

The prime manufacturer of the TMS1000 is:

TEXAS INSTRUMENTS, INC.
P.O. Box 1443
Houston, Texas 77001

A second source for CMOS parts with MC14xxxx part numbers (see Table 1-1) is:

MOTOROLA INCORPORATED
CMOS Products Division
3501 Ed Bluestein Blvd.
Austin, Texas 78721

## TMS1000 PROGRAMMABLE REGISTERS

TMS1000 programmable registers may be illustrated as follows:

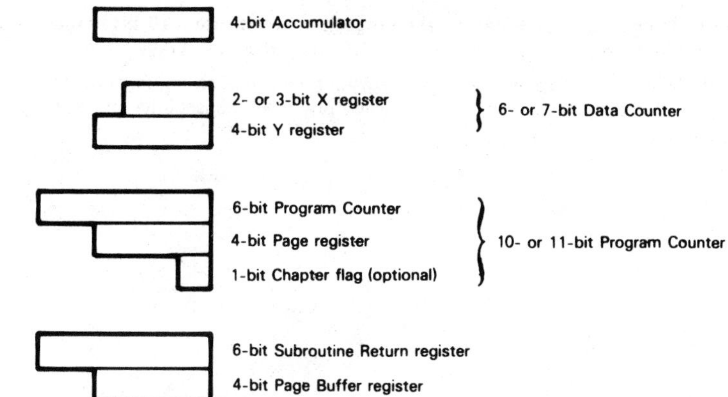


Apart from being only four bits wide, **the Accumulator is a typical primary Accumulator.** It is the principal source and destination for data that is being operated on.

Taken together, **the X and Y registers constitute a 6- or 7-bit Data Counter** which addresses the 64 or 128 nibbles of RAM. The X register is two or three bits wide and the Y register is four bits wide. Since the X and Y registers are indeed separate and distinct registers, RAM is effectively divided into four or eight pages, each of which is 16 nibbles long. A four-page RAM may be illustrated as follows:

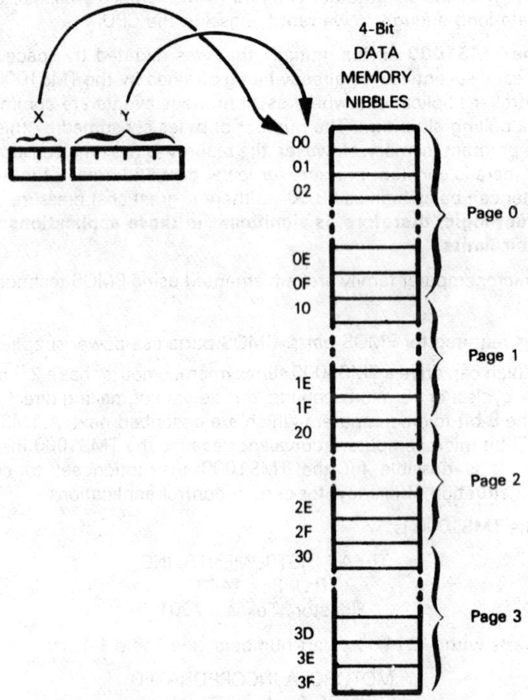


**The Y register, in addition, serves as a secondary Accumulator and an output Address register.** We will describe its use as an output Address register shortly.

Those TMS1000 series microcomputers that provide 128 nibbles of RAM have a 3-bit X register. RAM is then divided into eight 16-nibble pages.

**The Program Counter and Page Address register, taken together, constitute a 10-bit Program Counter.** They are, in reality separate and distinct registers, with the result that program memory is divided into sixteen 64-byte pages.

The Program Counter is implemented as a feedback shift register rather than as a binary counter. This means that the logically consecutive program memory locations do not reside physically consecutive in the program memory. This mapping is shown in Table 1-2.

Table 1-2. Map of TMS1000 Program Memory Page

| Logical Location | Physical Location | Logical Location | Physical Location | Logical Location | Physical Location |
|---|---|---|---|---|---|
| 0 | 0 | 1A | 21 | 34 | 26 |
| 1 | 01 | 1B | 02 | 35 | 0C |
| 2 | 03 | 1C | 05 | 36 | 19 |
| 3 | 07 | 1D | 0B | 37 | 32 |
| 4 | 0F | 1E | 17 | 38 | 25 |
| 5 | 1F | 1F | 2F | 39 | 0A |
| 6 | 3F | 20 | 1C | 3A | 15 |
| 7 | 3E | 21 | 38 | 3B | 2A |
| 8 | 3D | 22 | 31 | 3C | 14 |
| 9 | 3B | 23 | 23 | 3D | 28 |
| A | 37 | 24 | 06 | 3E | 10 |
| B | 2F | 25 | 0D | 3F | 20 |
| C | 1E | 26 | 1B | | |
| D | 3C | 27 | 36 | | |
| E | 39 | 28 | 2D | | |
| F | 33 | 29 | 1A | | |
| 10 | 27 | 2A | 34 | | |
| 11 | 0E | 2B | 29 | | |
| 12 | 1D | 2C | 12 | | |
| 13 | 3A | 2D | 24 | | |
| 14 | 35 | 2E | 08 | | |
| 15 | 2B | 2F | 11 | | |
| 16 | 16 | 30 | 22 | | |
| 17 | 2C | 31 | 04 | | |
| 18 | 18 | 32 | 09 | | |
| 19 | 30 | 33 | 13 | | |

**Those TMS1000 microcomputers that provide 2048 bytes of program memory have an additional 1-bit flag, referred to as Chapter Logic, which is used to select one of two alternate 1024-byte ROM chapters.**

**TMS1000 SUBROUTINES**

**The Subroutine Return register is simply a buffer for the Program Counter register. Similarly, the Page Buffer register is a simple buffer for the Page Address register.** These two buffer registers allow the TMS1000 a single level of subroutine call logic. **When a subroutine is called,** the contents of the Page Address and Page Buffer registers are exchanged, the Program Counter register contents are moved to the Subroutine Return register, and a new value provided by the subroutine Call instruction is loaded into the Program Counter. This may be illustrated as follows:

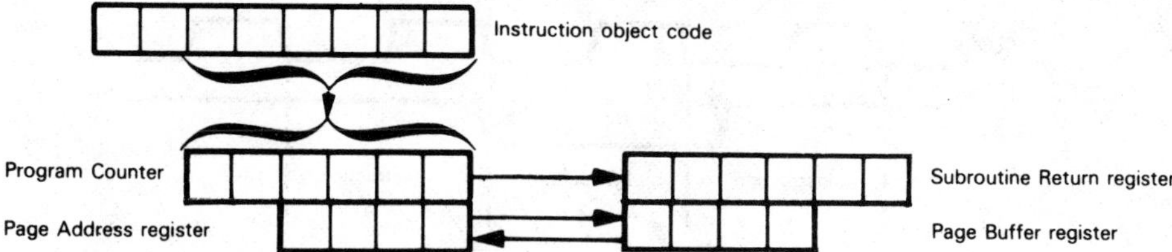

## TMS1000 MEMORY ADDRESSING MODE

**TMS1000 microcomputers have separate and distinct program and data memories.** There are no instructions capable of writing into program memory, and data memory cannot contain instruction object codes.

**Data memory is accessed using implied addressing.** The X and Y registers combine to serve as a Data Counter; we have just described this use of the X and Y registers.

**Only subroutine Call instructions and Branch instructions address program memory. These instructions address program memory using variations of absolute, paged direct addressing.**

We have already illustrated the addressing logic of a subroutine call.

A Branch instruction loads the Program Counter with a new address, which is provided by the instruction, just as a Call instruction does. If the Branch instruction occurs in a subroutine — that is, in the sequence between a subroutine Call instruction and a subroutine Return instruction — the Page Address register will not be affected. However, execution of a Branch instruction outside a subroutine will load the Page Address register from the Page Buffer register. The two types of program branches may be illustrated as follows:

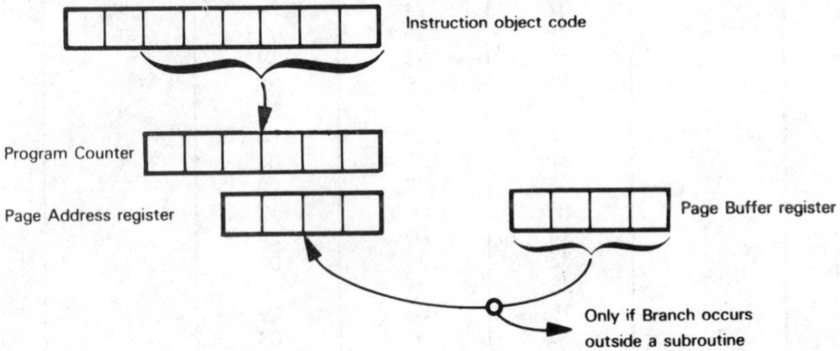


## TMS1000 STATUS FLAGS

**The TMS1000 series microcomputers have a single status flag which combines to serve as a Carry status and a simple logic decision status. All Branch and subroutine Call instructions are conditional;** the Branch or subroutine Call occurs only if the status flag is 1.

The unique feature of the status flag as compared to most status logic is that its passive level is high (1). **If an instruction causes the status flag to be reset to 0, it will revert to 1 after a single instruction cycle:**

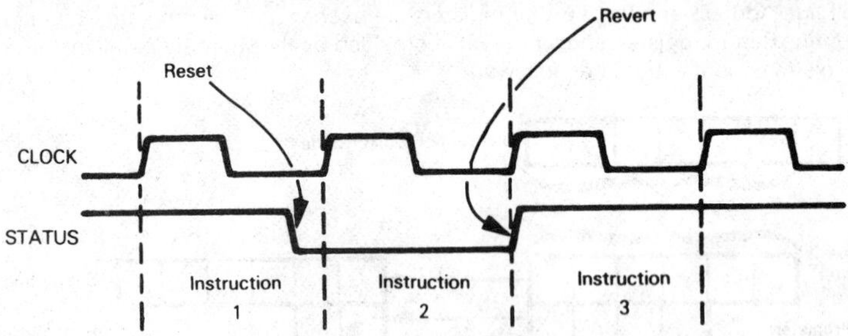


Instructions that test the condition of the status flag must directly follow the instruction which modifies the level of the status flag.

## TMS1000 INPUT AND OUTPUT LOGIC

**The only data input to a TMS1000 series microcomputer occurs as 4-bit nibbles, referred to in Texas Instruments literature as K inputs.** Instructions that access the K inputs simply input whatever signal levels exist at the time of the access.

**The TMS1200C has an additional 4-bit input port called the L port. It also has two additional control pins: K/L and MODE.** The chip possesses only a single 4-bit input bus. The K/L pin selects which set of inputs is connected to the internal bus. When the K/L pin is low the K inputs are connected to the internal bus, and when it is high the L inputs are connected to the internal bus. The K/L pin has an internal pull-down resistor which causes the K input lines to be selected if no input is applied to this pin. **The L input lines can be latched.** The latching is controlled by the MODE input pin. When the MODE input pin is high, any L lines going high are latched. When the MODE input is low, the latch is cleared and the current state of the L inputs passes through it. The MODE pin also has an internal pull-down resistor which causes the latch to be reset if no connection is made to the MODE pin.

**TMS1000 series microcomputers output data referred to as O outputs, and control signals referred to as R outputs.**

There are eight data or O outputs; but they are created in an unusual way. O output logic receives, as inputs, the contents of the Accumulator, plus the status flag. These five data bits create the eight O output signals according to a matrix which you must define when you order the TMS1000 microcomputer. This may be illustrated as follows:

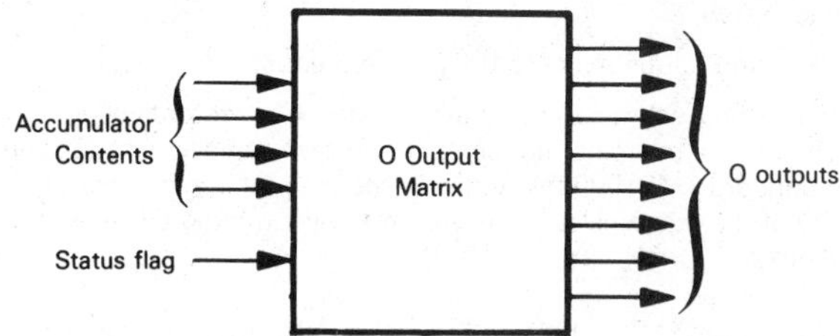


As the illustration above would imply, the five inputs select 32 of the possible 256 signal combinations which can be output via the eight O outputs.

This matrix is very handy for code conversion. For example, outputs to seven segment displays can be automatically converted to seven segment codes via a single output instruction. There is no need for the processor to perform any additional operations.

The control R outputs are treated as 11, 13 or 16 single control signals. Refer to Table 1-1, which identifies the number of R output signals available with each of the TMS1000 series microcomputers. **You can set or reset R output signals individually. The Y register is used to identify the individual R signal which is being set or reset.**

## TMS1000 INSTRUCTION PROGRAMMABLE LOGIC ARRAY

**The TMS1000 can be microprogrammed.** Only 12 of each processor's instructions are hardwired. The rest of the instructions are created out of 16 microinstructions. A 31 x 16 element PLA allows 31 instructions to be defined. The ability to program this PLA is provided as a mask option. If your application does not make use of all the instructions, or if certain often repeated operations appear exceptionally cumbersome, custom microprogramming may be the route for you. A word of caution: microcoding should only be undertaken by the most experienced programmers. It is difficult, and mistakes are costly and hard to find.

**The following elements are at your control:**

1) **Adder inputs**

2) **Adder function**

3) **Adder outputs**

4) **Memory write logic**

The adder has two inputs: the P input and the N input. The P input can consist of either the Y register, the memory location pointed to by the X and Y registers, or the CKI bus. The CKI bus consists of either a 4-bit constant formed by the low-order four bits of the instruction's opcode or the current state of the K inputs. The opcode of the instruction determines what is present on the CKI bus. If the opcode is in the range 0 - 7 or $40_{16}$ - $7F_{16}$ then the low-order four bits of the opcode are gated onto the CKI bus. If the opcode is in the range $8_{16}$ - $F_{16}$ then the K inputs are gated onto the

CKI bus. A 0 is gated onto the CKI bus if the opcode is in the range $20_{16}$ - $2F_{16}$. Opcodes in the range $30_{16}$ - $3F_{16}$ gate a bit mask onto the bus. This mask is created from the low-order two bits of the opcode, as shown below:

| Opcode | Bit Mask |
|---|---|
| XXXXXX00 | 1110 |
| XXXXXX01 | 1101 |
| XXXXXX10 | 1011 |
| XXXXXX11 | 0111 |

All other opcodes deactivate the CKI bus logic.

The N input of the adder can consist of either the Accumulator, the complement of the Accumulator, the memory location pointed to by the X and Y registers, a constant of all ones, or the CKI bus. The adder always adds the P and N inputs. It can also perform the following tasks:

1) Add 1 to the result of the addition
2) Send the carry to the status latch
3) Compare P and N inputs, setting status equal to 0 if they are equal

The adder's result can be gated to the Accumulator or the Y register. The contents of either the Accumulator or the CKI bus can be written out to memory. The microinstructions to perform the above functions are listed in Table 1-3. Table 1-4 is a breakdown of the 43 standard TMS1000 instructions, showing their microcoding. The priority column of Table 1-4 defines the relative priority of the microinstructions within the instruction cycle. Microinstructions with the same priority are executed in parallel.

Table 1-3. TMS1000 Series Programmable Microinstructions

| Mnemonic | Priority | Function |
|---|---|---|
| CKP | 1 | CKI to P adder input. |
| YTP | | Y register to P adder input. |
| MTP | | Memory (X,Y) to P adder input. |
| ATN | 1 | Accumulator to N adder input. |
| NATN | | Accumulator to N adder input. |
| MTN | | Memory (X,Y) to N adder input. |
| 15TN | | $F_{16}$ to N adder input. |
| CKN | | CKI to N adder input. |
| CIN | 1 | One is added to sum of P plus N inputs (P+N+1). |
| NE | | Adder compares P and N inputs. If they are identical, status is set to zero. |
| C8 | | Carry is sent to status (MSB only). |
| STO | 2 | Accumulator data to memory. |
| CKM | | CKI to memory. |
| AUTA | 3 | Adder result stored into Accumulator. |
| AUTY | | Adder result stored into Y register. |
| STSL | | Status is stored into status latch. |

Table 1-4. Microinstruction Index

| Mnemonic | Opcode | Microinstructions | |
|---|---|---|---|
| | | Fixed | Programmable |
| ALEC | 0 1 1 1 C | | CKP, NATN, CIN, C8 |
| ALEM | 0 0 1 0 1 0 0 1 | | MTP, NATN, CIN, C8 |
| AMAAC | 0 0 1 0 0 1 0 1 | | MTP, ATN, C8, AUTA |
| A6AAC | 0 0 0 0 0 1 1 0 | | CKP, ATN, C8, AUTA |
| A8AAC | 0 0 0 0 0 0 0 1 | | CKP, ATN, C8, AUTA |
| A10AAC | 0 0 0 0 0 1 0 1 | | CKP, ATN, C8, AUTA |
| BR | 1 0 W | BR | |
| CALL | 1 1 W | CALL | |
| CLA | 0 0 1 0 1 1 1 1 | | AUTA |
| CLO | 0 0 0 0 1 0 1 1 | CLO | |
| COMX | 0 0 0 0 0 0 0 0 | COMX | |
| CPAIZ | 0 0 1 0 1 1 0 1 | | NATN, CIN, C8, AUTA |
| DAN | 0 0 0 0 0 1 1 1 | | CKP, ATN, CIN, C8, AUTA |
| DMAN | 0 0 1 0 1 0 1 0 | | MTP, 15TN, C8, AUTA |
| DYN | 0 0 1 0 1 1 0 0 | | YTP, 15TN, C8, AUTY |
| IA | 0 0 0 0 1 1 1 0 | | ATN, CIN, AUTA |
| IMAC | 0 0 1 0 1 0 0 0 | | MTP, CIN, C8, AUTA |
| IYC | 0 0 1 0 1 0 1 1 | | YTP, CIN, C8, AUTY |
| KNEZ | 0 0 0 0 1 0 0 1 | | CKP, NE |
| LDP | 0 0 0 1 C | LDP | |
| LDX | 0 0 1 1 1 1 B | LDX | |
| MNEZ | 0 0 1 0 0 1 1 0 | | MTP, NE |
| RBIT | 0 0 1 1 0 1 B | RBIT | |
| RETN | 0 0 0 0 1 1 1 1 | RETN | |
| RSTR | 0 0 0 0 1 1 0 0 | RSTR | |
| SAMAN | 0 0 1 0 0 1 1 1 | | MTP, NATN, CIN, C8, AUTA |
| SBIT | 0 0 1 1 0 0 B | SBIT | |
| SETR | 0 0 0 0 1 1 0 1 | SETR | |
| TAM | 0 0 0 0 0 0 1 1 | | STO |
| TAMIY | 0 0 1 0 0 0 0 0 | | STO, YTP, CIN, AUTY |
| TAMZA | 0 0 0 0 0 1 0 0 | | STO, AUTA |
| TAY | 0 0 1 0 0 1 0 0 | | ATN, AUTY |
| TBIT 1 | 0 0 1 1 1 0 B | | CKP, CKN, MTP, NE |
| TCY | 0 1 0 0 C | | CKP, AUTY |
| TCMIY | 0 1 1 0 C | | CKM, YTP, CIN, AUTY |
| TDO | 0 0 0 0 1 0 1 0 | TDO | |
| TKA | 0 0 0 0 1 0 0 0 | | CKP, AUTA |
| TMA | 0 0 1 0 0 0 0 1 | | MTP, AUTA |
| TMY | 0 0 1 0 0 0 1 0 | | MTP, AUTY |
| TYA | 0 0 1 0 0 0 1 1 | | YTP, AUTA |
| XMA | 0 0 1 0 1 1 1 0 | | MTP, STO, AUTA |
| YNEA | 0 0 0 0 0 0 1 0 | | YTP, ATN, NE STSL |
| YNEC | 0 1 0 1 C | | YTP, CKN, NE |

## TMS1000 SERIES MICROCOMPUTER PINS AND SIGNALS

**Figures 1-2 through 1-9 illustrate the pins and signals of the TMS1000 series microcomputers.** Note that the TMS1000 and TMS1100 microcomputers have identical pins and signals. Since signals are consistent for the entire family of microcomputers, they will be described together.

**The four data inputs are provided by K1, K2, K4 and K8.** We would name these signals DI0, DI1, DI2 and DI3 to be consistent with common microcomputer terminology; however, Texas Instruments literature uses the signal names K1, K2, K4 and K8 to represent the binary level of each signal.

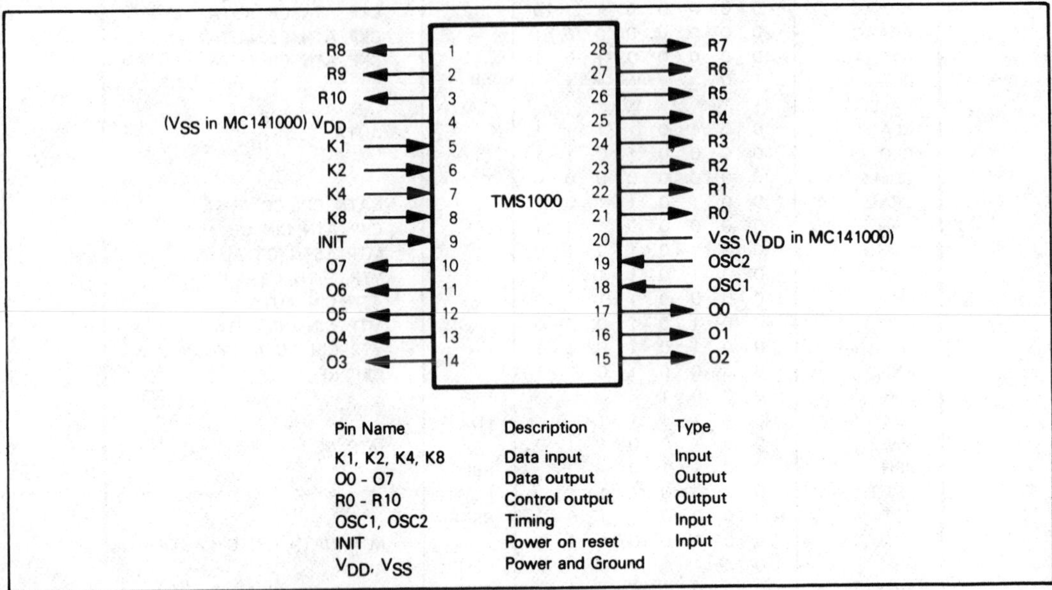


| Pin Name | Description | Type |
|---|---|---|
| K1, K2, K4, K8 | Data input | Input |
| O0 - O7 | Data output | Output |
| R0 - R10 | Control output | Output |
| OSC1, OSC2 | Timing | Input |
| INIT | Power on reset | Input |
| $V_{DD}$, $V_{SS}$ | Power and Ground | |

Figure 1-2. TMS1000 and MC141000 Microcomputer Signals and Pin Assignments

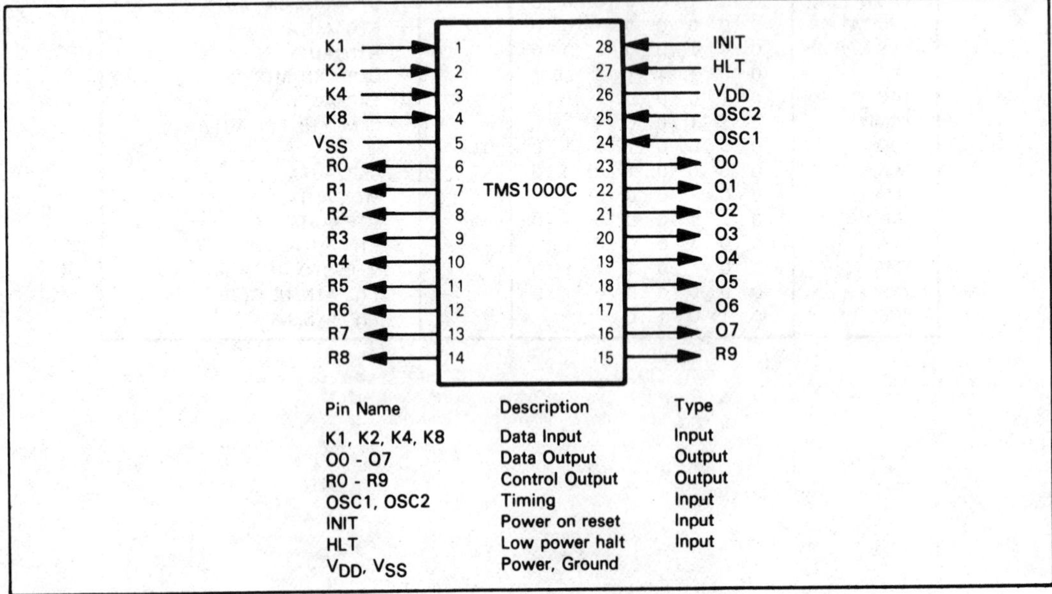


| Pin Name | Description | Type |
|---|---|---|
| K1, K2, K4, K8 | Data Input | Input |
| O0 - O7 | Data Output | Output |
| R0 - R9 | Control Output | Output |
| OSC1, OSC2 | Timing | Input |
| INIT | Power on reset | Input |
| HLT | Low power halt | Input |
| $V_{DD}$, $V_{SS}$ | Power, Ground | |

Figure 1-3. TMS1000C Signals and Pin Assignments

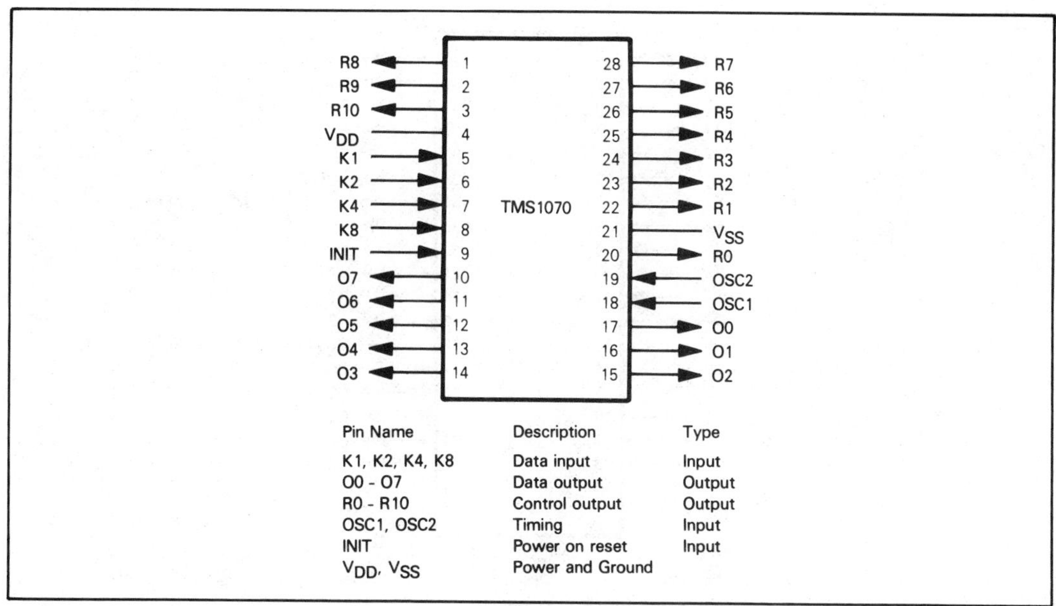


| Pin Name | Description | Type |
|---|---|---|
| K1, K2, K4, K8 | Data input | Input |
| O0 - O7 | Data output | Output |
| R0 - R10 | Control output | Output |
| OSC1, OSC2 | Timing | Input |
| INIT | Power on reset | Input |
| $V_{DD}$, $V_{SS}$ | Power and Ground | |

Figure 1-4. TMS1070 Microcomputer Signals and Pin Assignments

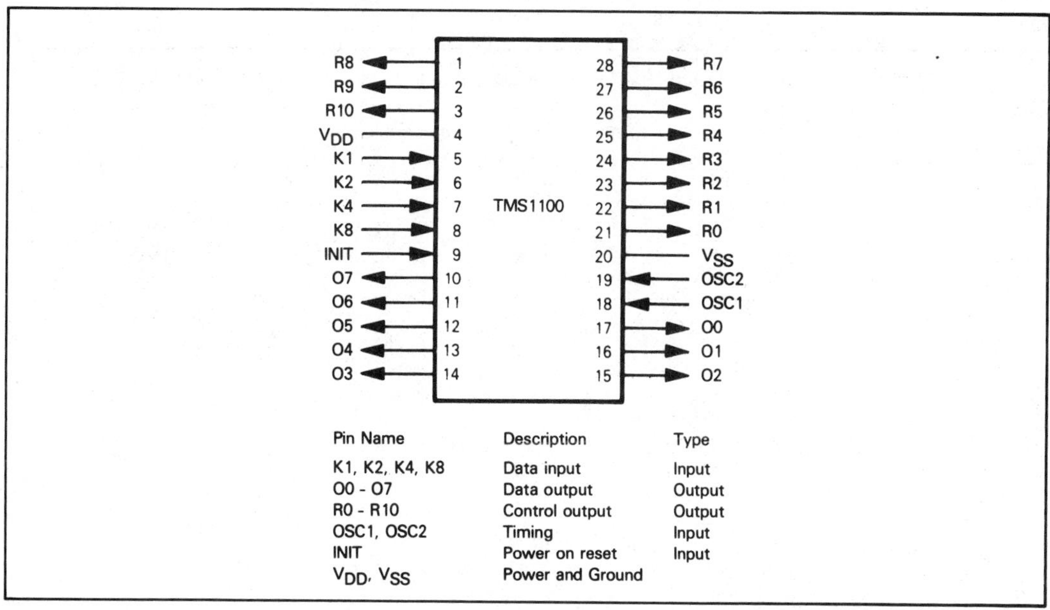


| Pin Name | Description | Type |
|---|---|---|
| K1, K2, K4, K8 | Data input | Input |
| O0 - O7 | Data output | Output |
| R0 - R10 | Control output | Output |
| OSC1, OSC2 | Timing | Input |
| INIT | Power on reset | Input |
| $V_{DD}$, $V_{SS}$ | Power and Ground | |

Figure 1-5. TMS1100 Microcomputer Signals and Pin Assignments

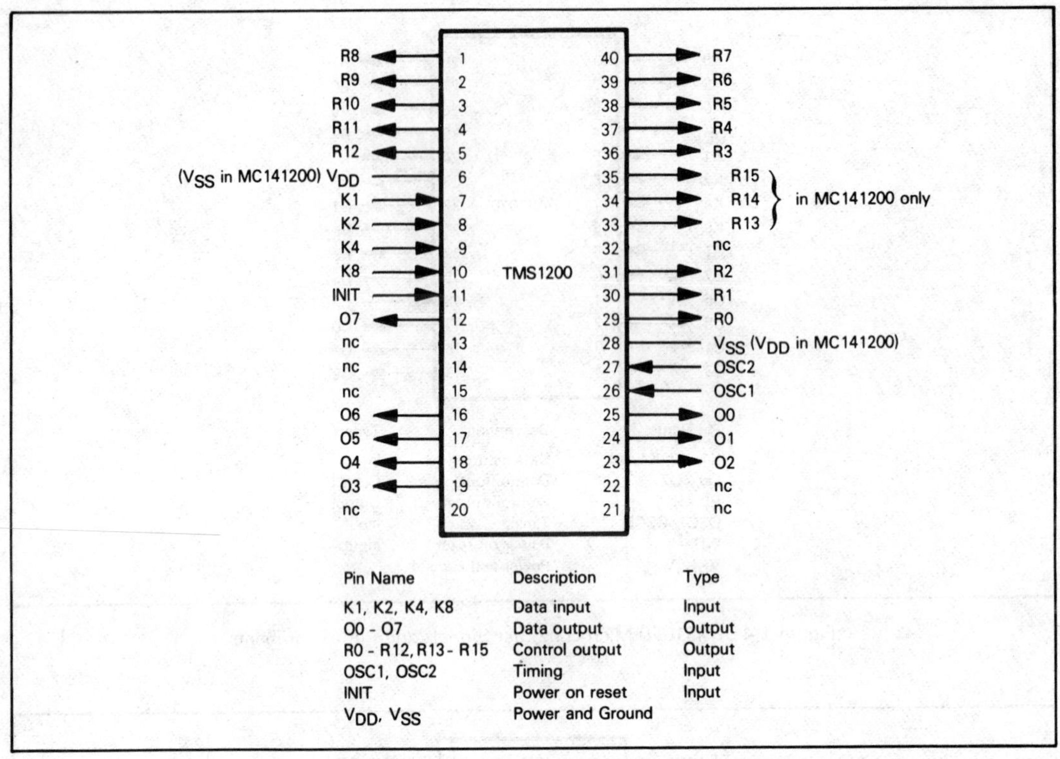


| Pin Name | Description | Type |
|---|---|---|
| K1, K2, K4, K8 | Data input | Input |
| O0 - O7 | Data output | Output |
| R0 - R12, R13 - R15 | Control output | Output |
| OSC1, OSC2 | Timing | Input |
| INIT | Power on reset | Input |
| $V_{DD}$, $V_{SS}$ | Power and Ground | |

Figure 1-6. TMS1200 and MC141200 Microcomputer Signals and Pin Assignments

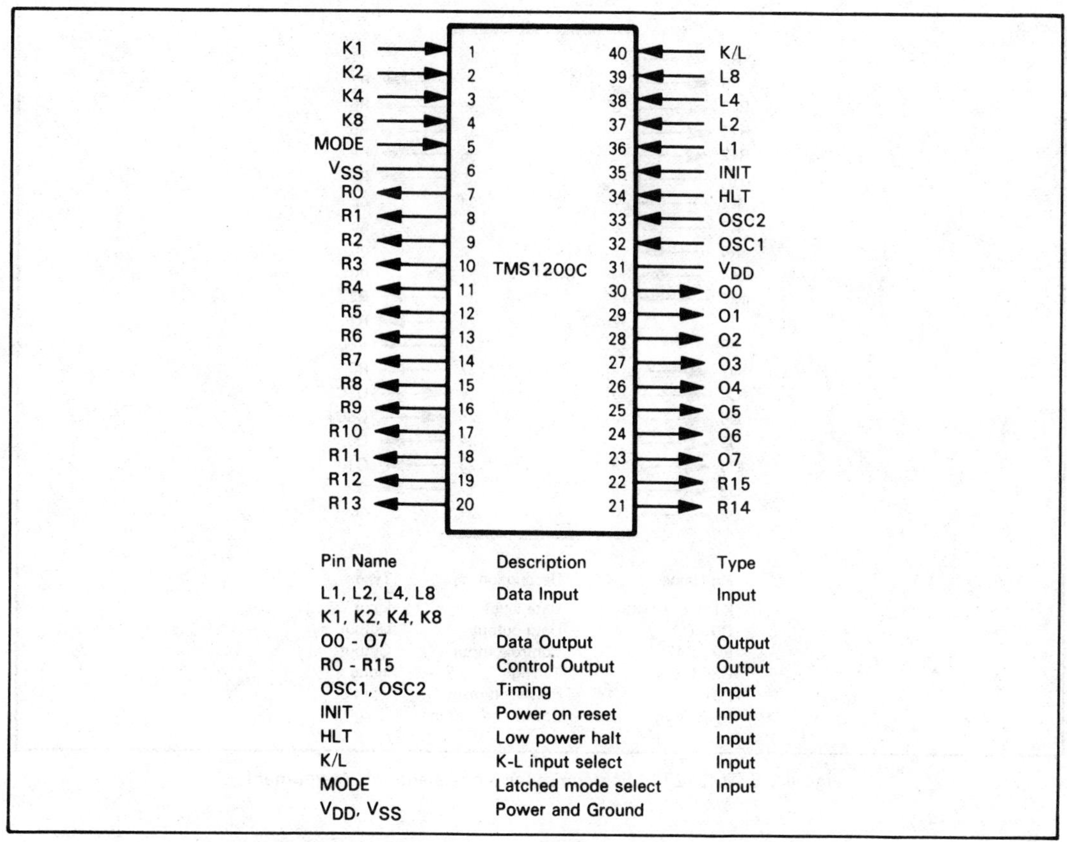


| Pin Name | Description | Type |
|---|---|---|
| L1, L2, L4, L8<br>K1, K2, K4, K8 | Data Input | Input |
| O0 - O7 | Data Output | Output |
| R0 - R15 | Control Output | Output |
| OSC1, OSC2 | Timing | Input |
| INIT | Power on reset | Input |
| HLT | Low power halt | Input |
| K/L | K-L input select | Input |
| MODE | Latched mode select | Input |
| $V_{DD}$, $V_{SS}$ | Power and Ground | |

Figure 1-7. TMS1200C Microcomputer Signals and Pin Assignments

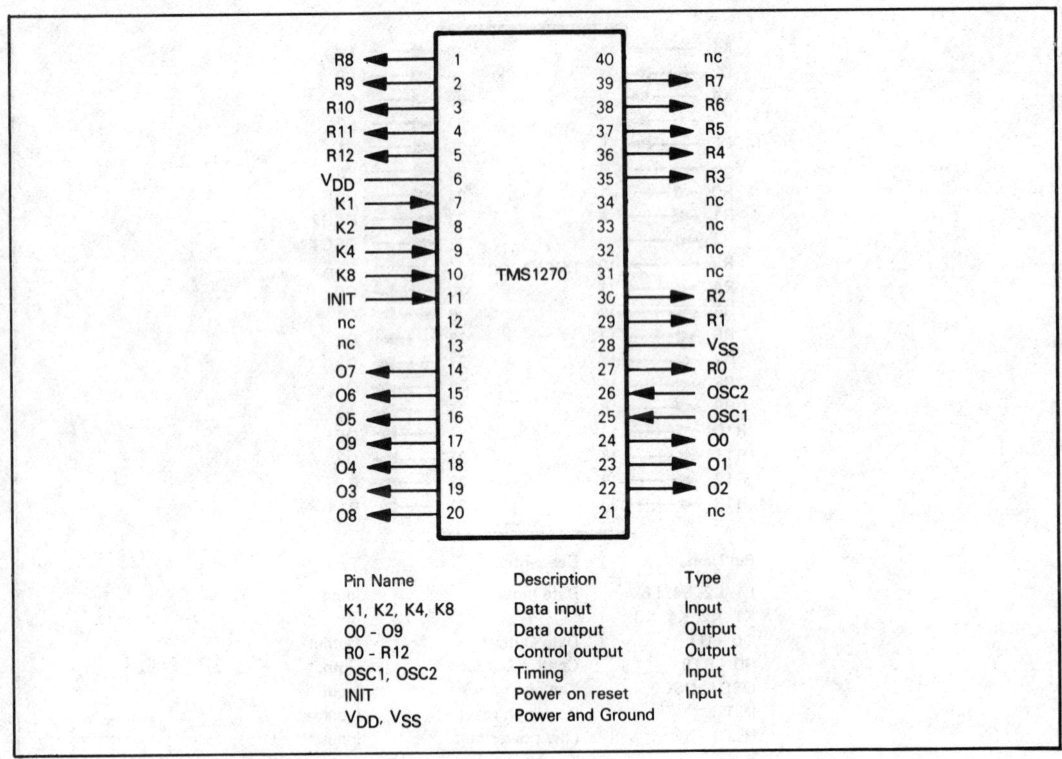


| Pin Name | Description | Type |
|---|---|---|
| K1, K2, K4, K8 | Data input | Input |
| O0 - O9 | Data output | Output |
| R0 - R12 | Control output | Output |
| OSC1, OSC2 | Timing | Input |
| INIT | Power on reset | Input |
| $V_{DD}$, $V_{SS}$ | Power and Ground | |

Figure 1-8. TMS1270 Microcomputer Signals and Pin Assignments

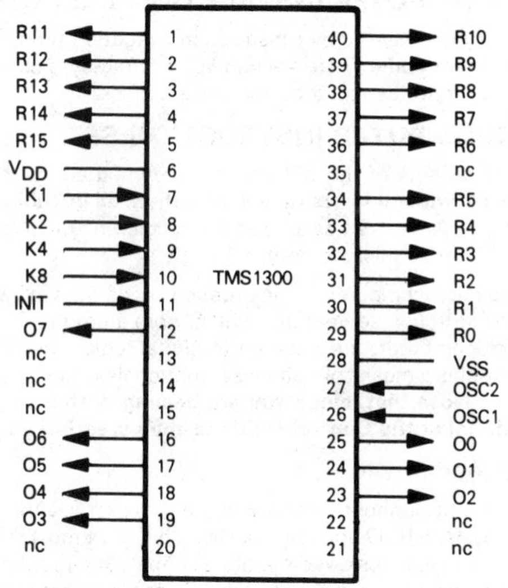

TMS1300
R11 1 — 40 R10
R12 2 — 39 R9
R13 3 — 38 R8
R14 4 — 37 R7
R15 5 — 36 R6
$V_{DD}$ 6 — 35 nc
K1 7 — 34 R5
K2 8 — 33 R4
K4 9 — 32 R3
K8 10 — 31 R2
INIT 11 — 30 R1
O7 12 — 29 R0
nc 13 — 28 $V_{SS}$
nc 14 — 27 OSC2
nc 15 — 26 OSC1
O6 16 — 25 O0
O5 17 — 24 O1
O4 18 — 23 O2
O3 19 — 22 nc
nc 20 — 21 nc

| Pin Name | Description | Type |
|---|---|---|
| K1, K2, K4, K8 | Data input | Input |
| O0 - O7 | Data output | Output |
| R0 - R15 | Control output | Output |
| OSC1, OSC2 | Timing | Input |
| INIT | Power on reset | Input |
| $V_{DD}$, $V_{SS}$ | Power and Ground | |

Figure 1-9. TMS1300 Microcomputer Signals and Pin Assignments

**The O outputs are provided by O0 - O7, or, in the case of the TMS1270, O0 - O9.**

**The R outputs occur at R0 - R15, or some smaller number of R outputs,** depending on the microcomputer.

**OSC1 and OSC2 are timing inputs and outputs.** A number of timing options are provided. All TMS1000 series microcomputers contain internal clock logic which you can access in conjunction with an external RC circuit as follows:

OSC1
OSC2
$V_{SS}$
$V_{DD}$

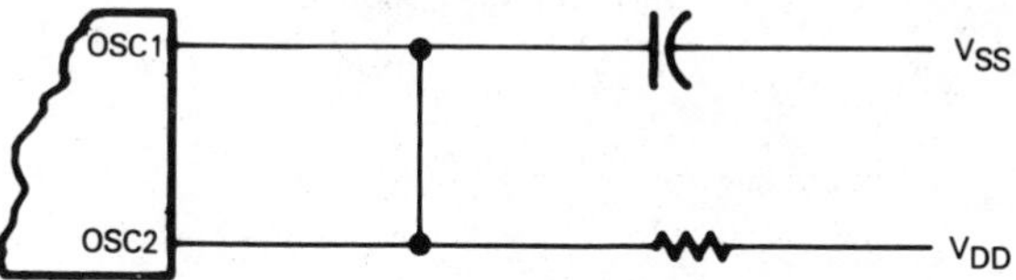

You can also input an externally created clock signal at OSC1, in which case OSC2 must be connected to ground ($V_{SS}$). When you have more than one TMS1000 series microcomputer in a configuration, it is a good idea to synchronize the many microcomputers by driving them with a single clock signal.

**INIT is a power on reset signal.** Following power on, INIT should be input high ($V_{SS}$) for at least six consecutive clock cycles. The Reset operation stores binary ones in the Page Address register and the Page Buffer register. The O outputs, the R outputs and the Program Counter are all zeroed. Thus, the first instruction executed will have the hexadecimal address $3C0_{16}$.

Page Address register
Program Counter
1 1 1 1 0 0 0 0 0 0
3 C 0

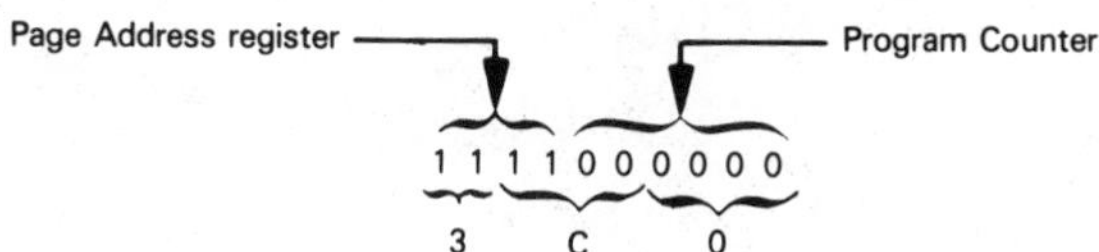

## TMS1000 SERIES MICROCOMPUTER INSTRUCTION EXECUTION

No microcomputer described in this book has simpler instruction execution timing than the TMS1000 series. **All instructions generate one byte of object code.** There are no two- or three-byte object codes. Similarly, **every instruction executes in a single machine cycle,** as timed by the system clock.

## TMS1000 SERIES MICROCOMPUTER INSTRUCTION SET

There are variations in the instruction sets of the different microcomputers in the TMS1000 series. However, **the different instruction sets are similar enough for us to describe them all in Table 1-5.** As compared to similar tables for other microcomputers in this book, Table 1-5 has an additional column which identifies the instructions which are available with each of the TMS1000 series microcomputers.

Within the confines of a single-chip microcomputer, the instruction set defined in Table 1-5 is both powerful and effective. It would be easy to point out instruction set features which, from a programmer's point of view, are undesirable; however, the TMS1000 series microcomputers are oriented to digital logic. The TMS1000 is not a product that gets programmed; rather, its instruction set is a means of defining an optional portion of the ROM mask. Within this context, the instruction set is very adequate. **Note that, since you are dealing with a single-chip microcomputer, there is nothing to prevent you from redefining the Control Unit and thus creating your own instruction set.**

## THE BENCHMARK PROGRAM

The benchmark program we are using throughout this book in order to exercise the various microcomputer instruction sets is essentially meaningless in any TMS1000 application. Given 64, or at most, 128 nibbles of RAM, the whole concept of moving data among tables is meaningless. We therefore simplify the problem and look upon IOBUF as external logic. Instead of reading from IOBUF, we will input K data. We will assume that each block of K data is preceded by a nibble which defines the number of data nibbles to follow:

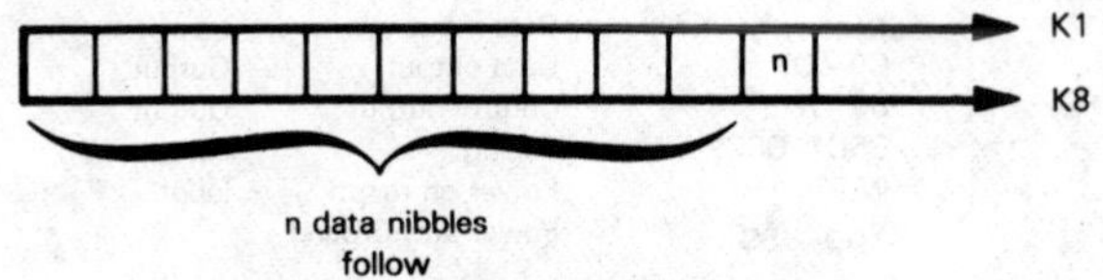


Thus, each block of data that is input must be fifteen nibbles or less in length.

```
        LDX     TBHI    LOAD TABLE PAGE ADDRESS
        TKA             INPUT FIRST K NIBBLE. IT EQUALS DATA NIBBLE TO FOLLOW
        TAY             MOVE TO Y. XY NOW ADDRESSES END OF TABLE
LOOP    TKA             INPUT NEXT DATA NIBBLE
        TAM             SAVE IN MEMORY
        DYN             DECREMENT Y
        BR      LOOP    IF Y NOT 0, RETURN FOR NEXT NIBBLE
```

Symbols are used in Table 1-5 as follows:

Registers:

- A - Accumulator
- X,Y - Data Counter. Y also serves as an output address.
- PC - Program Counter
- PA - Page Address register
- CF - Chapter Flag (one bit)
- SR - Subroutine Return register
- PB - Page Buffer

Statuses:

- ST - The Status Flag
- C - The status flag reflects a Carry. That is, it is set if there is a Carry from the most significant bit (MSB), and reset otherwise.
- NE - The status flag reflects "not equal". That is, it is set if the compared bits are not equal, and reset if they are equal.

Inputs and Outputs:

- K - the four input lines
- O - the five-bit Output register
- R - the control outputs

bb Two bits in the object code which specify one of the four bits of a RAM location:

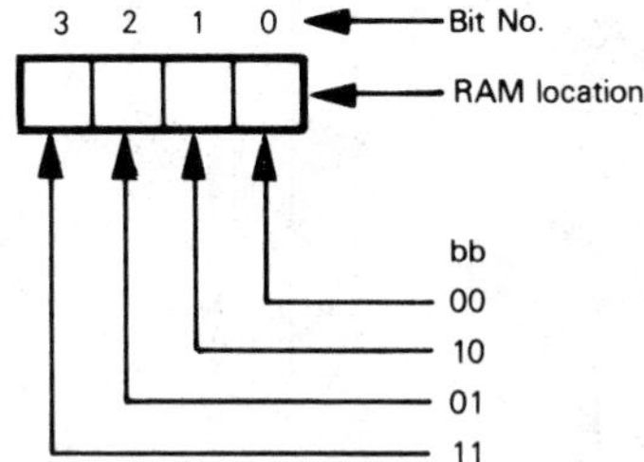


| | |
|---|---|
| b | Operand which specifies one bit of a RAM location |
| data | 2, 3, or 4 bits of immediate data |
| label | Destination of Branch instruction (6 bits of direct address in the object code) |
| R([Y]) | The control output line specified by the contents of the Y register. |
| x | One bit of immediate data or direct address in the object code. |
| [X](MSB) | The most significant bit of the X register |
| [[X,Y]] | The contents of the RAM location addressed by the contents of the Data Counter. |
| [[X,Y]](b) | The specified bit of the RAM location addressed by the contents of the Data Counter. |
| [ ] | Contents of location enclosed within brackets. If a register designation is enclosed within the brackets, then the designated register's contents are specified. If K or R is enclosed within the brackets, then the data at the inputs or control outputs is specified. |
| ← → | Data is transferred in the direction of the arrow. |
| ⟷ | Data is exchanged between the two locations designated on either side of the arrow. |

Where two object codes are given, the first is the code used in the TMS1000, TMS1200, TMS1070, and TMS1270, while the second is the object code used in the TMS1100 and TMS1300.

X in one of the rightmost three columns means that the instruction is implemented on the designated TMS1000 device.

Table 1-5. TMS1000 Series Instruction Set Summary

| TYPE | MNEMONIC | OPERAND | STATUSES C | STATUSES NE | OPERATION PERFORMED | OBJECT CODE | TMS1000(C) TMS1200(C) TMS1070 TMS1270 | TMS1100 TMS1300 | MC141000 MC141200 |
|---|---|---|---|---|---|---|---|---|---|
| I/O | KNEZ | | | X | If [K] ≠ 0, ST ← 1<br>Set status only if data on input lines is not 0. | 09 | X | | X |
| | | | | | | 0E | | X | |
| | TKA | | | | [K]→[A]<br>Load Accumulator with data on input lines. | 08 | X | X | X |
| | SETR | | | | R([Y]) ← 1<br>Set R output addressed by contents of Y. | 0D | X | X | X |
| | RSTR | | | | R([Y]) ← 0<br>Reset R output addressed by contents of Y. | 0C | X | X | X |
| | TDO | | | | [O] ← ([A],ST)<br>Transfer data from Accumulator and status flag to the O outputs. | 0A | X | X | X |
| | CLO | | | | [O] ← $00_{16}$<br>Clear the O Output register. | 0B | X | | X |
| PRIMARY MEMORY REFERENCE | TAM | | | | [A]→[[X,Y]]<br>Store Accumulator to RAM location addressed by contents of XY Data Counter. | 03 | X | | X |
| | | | | | | 27 | | X | |
| | TMY | | | | [[X,Y]]→[Y]<br>Load Register Y from RAM. | 22 | X | X | X |
| | TMA | | | | [[X,Y]]←[A]<br>Load Accumulator from RAM. | 21 | X | X | X |
| | XMA | | | | [[X,Y]]←→[A]<br>Exchange contents of RAM location addressed by Data Counter XY with those of Accumulator. | 2E | X | | |
| | | | | | | 03 | | X | X |
| PRIMARY MEMORY REFERENCE WITH REGISTER OPERATE | TAMIY | | | | [A]→[[X,Y]]; [Y]←[Y]+1<br>Store Accumulator to RAM and increment contents of Y register. | 20 | X | | X |
| | TAMIYC | | X | | [A]→[[X,Y]]; [Y]←[Y]+1; ST ← C<br>Store Accumulator to RAM and increment contents of Y register. Set status flag only if there is a carry. | 25 | | X | |
| | TAMDYN | | X | | [A]→[[X,Y]]; [Y]←[Y]-1; ST ← C<br>Store Accumulator to RAM and decrement contents of Y register. Set status flag only if there is no borrow. | 24 | | X | |
| | TAMZA | | | | [A]→[[X,Y]]; [A] ← 0<br>Store Accumulator to RAM and then clear Accumulator. | 04 | X | | |
| | | | | | | 26 | | X | X |
| SECONDARY MEMORY REFERENCE (MEMORY OPERATE) | AMAAC | | X | | [A]←[[X,Y]] + [A]; ST ← C<br>Add contents of RAM location to those of Accumulator. Set status flag only if there is a carry. | 25 | X | | X |
| | | | | | | 06 | | X | |
| | SAMAN | | X | | [A]←[[X,Y]]-[A]; ST ← C<br>Subtract Accumulator contents from those of RAM location. Set status flag only if there is no borrow. | 27 | X | | X |
| | | | | | | 3C | | X | |
| | IMAC | | X | | [A]←[[X,Y]] + 1; ST ← C<br>Load contents of RAM location to Accumulator and increment. Set status flag only if there is a carry. RAM contents are unchanged. | 28 | X | | X |
| | | | | | | 3E | | X | |

Table 1-5. TMS1000 Series Instruction Set Summary (Continued)

| TYPE | MNEMONIC | OPERAND | STATUSES C | STATUSES NE | OPERATION PERFORMED | OBJECT CODE | TMS1000(C) TMS1200(C) TMS1070 TMS1270 | TMS1100 TMS1300 | MC141000 MC141200 |
|---|---|---|---|---|---|---|---|---|---|
| SECONDARY MEMORY REFERENCE (MEMORY OPERATE) (CONTINUED) | DMAN | | X | | [A]←[[X,Y]]-1; ST ← C<br>Load contents of RAM location to Accumulator and decrement. Set status flag only if there is no borrow. RAM contents are unchanged. | 2A<br>07 | X | X | X |
| | ALEM | | X | | If [A] ≤ [[X,Y]], ST ← 1<br>Set status flag only if Accumulator contents are less than or equal to those of RAM location addressed by Data Counter XY. | 29<br>01 | X | X | X |
| | MNEA | | | X | If [[X,Y]] ≠ [A], ST ← 1<br>Set status flag only if contents of RAM location are not equal to those of Accumulator. | 00 | | X | |
| | MNEZ | | | X | If [[X,Y]] ≠ 0, ST ← 1<br>Set status flag only if contents of RAM location are not equal to zero. | 26<br>3F | X | X | X |
| | SBIT | b | | | [[X,Y]](b) ← 1<br>Set specified bit of RAM location addressed by contents of Data Counter XY. | 001100bb | X | X | X |
| | RBIT | b | | | [[X,Y]](b) ← 0<br>Reset specified bit of RAM location addressed by contents of Data Counter XY. | 001101bb | X | X | X |
| | TBIT1 | b | | X | ST ← [[X,Y]](b)<br>Test specified bit of RAM location and set status flag only if the bit is set. | 001110bb | X | X | X |
| IMMEDIATE | TCY | data | | | [Y]← data<br>Load Register Y immediate. | 0100xxxx | X | X | X |
| | TCMIY | data | | | [[X,Y]]← data; [Y]←[Y] + 1<br>Load RAM location immediate and increment contents of Register Y. | 0110xxxx | X | X | X |
| | LDX | data | | | [X]← data<br>Load Register X immediate. | 001111xx<br>00101xxx | X | X | X |
| | LDP | data | | | [PB]← data<br>Load Page Buffer register immediate. | 0001xxxx | X | X | |
| IMMEDIATE OPERATE | ALEC | data | X | | If [A] ≤ data, ST ← 1<br>Set status flag only if Accumulator contents are less than or equal to immediate data. | 0111xxxx | X | | X |
| | YNEC | data | | X | If [Y] ≠ data, ST ← 1<br>Set status flag only if contents of Register Y are not equal to immediate data. | 0101xxxx | X | X | X |
| | A2AAC | | X | | [A]←[A] + 2; ST ← C<br>Add 2 to Accumulator contents. Set status flag only if there is a carry. | 78 | | X | |
| | A3AAC | | X | | [A]←[A] + 3; ST ← C<br>Add 3 to Accumulator contents. Set status flag only if there is a carry. | 74 | | X | |
| | A4AAC | | X | | [A]←[A] + 4; ST ← C<br>Add 4 to Accumulator contents. Set status flag only if there is a carry. | 7C | | X | |
| | A5AAC | | X | | [A]←[A] + 5; ST ← C<br>Add 5 to Accumulator contents. Set status flag only if there is a carry. | 72 | | X | |
| | A6AAC | | X | | [A]←[A] + 6; ST ← C<br>Add 6 to Accumulator contents. Set status flag only if there is a carry. | 06<br>7A | X | X | X |
| | A7AAC | | X | | [A]←[A] + 7; ST ← C<br>Add 7 to Accumulator contents. Set status flag only if there is a carry. | 76 | | X | |

Table 1-5. TMS1000 Series Instruction Set Summary (Continued)

| TYPE | MNEMONIC | OPERAND | STATUSES C | STATUSES NE | OPERATION PERFORMED | OBJECT CODE | TMS1000(C) TMS1200(C) TMS1070 TMS1270 | TMS1100 TMS1300 | MC141000 MC141200 |
|---|---|---|---|---|---|---|---|---|---|
| IMMEDIATE OPERATE (CONTINUED) | A8AAC | | X | | [A]←[A]+8; ST ← C<br>Add 8 to Accumulator contents. Set status flag only if there is a carry. | 01<br>7E | X<br> | <br>X | X<br> |
| | A9AAC | | X | | [A]←[A]+9; ST ← C<br>Add 9 to Accumulator contents. Set status flag only if there is a carry. | 71 | | X | |
| | A10AAC | | X | | [A]←[A]+10; ST ← C<br>Add 10 to Accumulator contents. Set status flag only if there is a carry. | 05<br>79 | X<br> | <br>X | <br>X |
| | A11AAC | | X | | [A]←[A]+11; ST ← C<br>Add 11 to Accumulator contents. Set status flag only if there is a carry. | 75 | | X | |
| | A12AAC | | X | | [A]←[A]+12; ST ← C<br>Add 12 to Accumulator contents. Set status flag only if there is a carry. | 7D | | X | |
| | A13AAC | | X | | [A]←[A]+13; ST ← C<br>Add 13 to Accumulator contents. Set status flag only if there is a carry. | 73 | | X | |
| | A14AAC | | X | | [A]←[A]+14; ST ← C<br>Add 14 to Accumulator contents. Set status flag only if there is a carry. | 7B | | X | |
| JUMP | RETN | | | | [PC]←[SR], [PA]←[PB]<br>Return from subroutine. | 0F | X | X | X |
| BRANCH ON CONDITION | BR | label | | | If ST = 1, then [PC]← label;<br>outside subroutine, [PA]←[PB]<br>Branch if status flag is set. | 10xxxxxx | X | X | X |
| | CALL | label | | | If ST = 1, then [SR]←[PC]+1, [PB]⟷[PA], [PC]← label<br>Call subroutine if status flag is set. A subroutine call within a subroutine will act as a branch, and load the Page Buffer from the Page Address register:<br>[PC]← LABEL<br>[PB]←[PA] | 11xxxxxx | X | X | X |
| REGISTER–REGISTER MOVE | TAY | | | | [A]→[Y]<br>Transfer Accumulator contents to Register Y. | 24<br>20 | X<br> | <br>X | X<br> |
| | TYA | | | | [Y]→[A]<br>Transfer Register Y contents to Accumulator. | 23 | X | X | X |
| REGISTER–REGISTER OPERATE | YNEA | | | X | If [Y] ≠ [A], ST ← 1<br>Set status flag only if contents of Y register are not equal to those of Accumulator. | 02 | X | X | X |
| REGISTER OPERATE | CLA | | | | [A]← 0<br>Clear Accumulator. | 2F<br>7F | X<br> | <br>X | X<br> |
| | IA | | | | [A]←[A]+1<br>Increment Accumulator. No status affected. | 0E | X | | X |
| | IAC | | X | | [A]←[A]+1; ST ← C<br>Increment Accumulator. Set status flag only if there is a carry. | 70 | | X | |

Table 1-5. TMS1000 Series Instruction Set Summary (Continued)

| TYPE | MNEMONIC | OPERAND | STATUSES C | STATUSES NE | OPERATION PERFORMED | OBJECT CODE | TMS1000(C) TMS1200(C) TMS1070 TMS1270 | TMS1100 TMS1300 | MC141000 MC141200 |
|---|---|---|---|---|---|---|---|---|---|
| REGISTER OPERATE (CONTINUED) | DAN | | X | | [A]←[A]-1; ST ← C | 07 | X | | X |
| | | | | | Decrement Accumulator. Set status flag only if there is no borrow. | 77 | | X | |
| | IYC | | X | | [Y]←[Y]+1; ST ← C | 2B | X | | X |
| | | | | | Increment Register Y. Set status flag only if there is a carry. | 05 | | X | |
| | DYN | | X | | [Y]←[Y]-1; ST ← C | 2C | X | | X |
| | | | | | Decrement Register Y. Set status flag only if there is no borrow. | 04 | | X | |
| | CPAIZ | | X | | $[A] \leftarrow \overline{[A]} + 1$; if [A] = 0, ST ← 1 | 2D | X | | X |
| | | | | | Negate Accumulator contents (twos complement). Set status only if result is zero. | 3D | | X | |
| | COMX | | | | $[X] \leftarrow \overline{[X]}$ | 00 | X | | X |
| | | | | | Complement contents of X register (ones complement). | | | | |
| | COMX | | | | $[X](MSB) \leftarrow \overline{[X](MSB)}$ | 09 | | X | |
| | | | | | Complement most significant bit of X register. | | | | |
| | COMC | | | | $CF \leftarrow \overline{CF}$ | 0B | | X | |
| | | | | | Complement Chapter flag. | | | | |

# THE NATIONAL SEMICONDUCTOR COP400 SERIES SINGLE-CHIP MICROCOMPUTERS

The National Semiconductor COP (Controller Oriented Processor) family is a recent addition to the 4-bit microcomputer market. **There are currently 13 members of the COP family. Table 1-6 summarizes the capability of each processor. The COP411L is the low-end member of the COP family.** It is designed for low cost and has a price of under $1.00 when ordered in large quantities. This is truly remarkable. Use of the COP411L microcomputer makes an entire microcomputer-based control system available for what was previously the cost of only the microcomputer itself. **The different models in the COP400 series of microprocessors are very similar devices.** The few differences that do exist stem from differences in I/O configuration. The COP402M, COP420, COP420C, and COP440 can also have a MICROBUS® interface as a mask programmable option. MICROBUS® is National Semiconductor's chip level interface standard. It specifies a standard set of interface signals (chip enable, read/write, etc.) for interconnecting complex (although not necessarily intelligent) data manipulating circuits, such as D/A converters, UARTS, and microcomputers.

Table 1-6 provides an overview of the members of the COP400 family. The COP402, COP402M and COP404L are designed primarily for prototyping applications where it is necessary to be able to modify the program memory. The COP410L/411L series are the low-end models of the COP400 family. The COP421 series is a bonding option of the COP420 that does not bring out the four dedicated input lines IN0-IN3. The COP440 and COP444L are expanded memory versions of the COP420. The COP440 provides additional I/O capability as well.

Figure 1-10 illustrates that part of our general microcomputer system logic which is implemented by the COP400 microcomputers. The COP402, COP402M, and COP404L do not contain any on-board ROM, and the COP402M, COP410L, COP411L, COP421, COP421L, and COP421C have no interrupt capability. **Note that, unlike the TMS1000 or the PPS4/1, several COP400 devices provide a true interrupt capability.** This allows the user to implement more efficient and compact code. Applications that may be impossible within 1024 bytes on the TMS1000 or PPS4/1 may be feasible on a COP400 device. The lack of DMA capability is not a major drawback, since block data transfers into the small on-board RAM of a COP400 device would make little sense. A programmable timer would be a helpful addition to a COP400 system. Although the COP420 and COP421 series provide a "timer" capability, it is not programmable. An internal 10-bit counter sets a flag once each 1024 instruction cycles. This timer allows the COP to generate an internal fixed time base.

**All devices of the COP400 family are implemented via N-channel silicon gate MOS technology, except for the COP420C and COP421C, which are implemented via CMOS technology.**

**A single +5 volt supply is the only power supply required by the COP400 microcomputers. However, most models provide, as a mask option, a separate power supply for RAM, which sinks a maximum current of 3 mA at 3.3 V.**

**The fastest clock frequency that can drive a COP microcomputer is 4 MHz. Each instruction cycle will take 16 clock cycles, therefore the fastest instruction cycle time is 4 μs.** Although various COP models provide mask options of 32-, 8-, and 4-clock instruction cycles, the maximum clock frequency decreases accordingly; thus 4 μs remains the shortest instruction time.

The manufacturer of the COP400 series is:

NATIONAL SEMICONDUCTOR CORPORATION
2900 Semiconductor Drive
Santa Clara, CA 95051

Table 1-6. COP400 Series Microcomputer Summary

| Feature | Device | | | | | | | | | | | | |
|---|---|---|---|---|---|---|---|---|---|---|---|---|---|
| | **402** | **402M** | **404L** | **410L** | **411L** | **420** | **420L** | **420C** | **421** | **421L** | **421C** | **440** | **444L** |
| **Pins Per Package** | 40 | 40 | 40 | 24 | 20 | 28 | 28 | 28 | 24 | 24 | 24 | 40 | 28 |
| **ROM Program Bytes** | 0 | 0 | 0 | 512 | 512 | 1024 | 1024 | 1024 | 1024 | 1024 | 1024 | 2048 | 2048 |
| **RAM Data Nibbles** | 64 | 64 | 128 | 32 | 32 | 64 | 64 | 64 | 64 | 64 | 64 | 128 | 128 |
| **Dedicated Output Bits Available** | 6 | 6 | 6 | 6 | 4 | 6 | 6 | 6 | 6 | 6 | 6 | 10 | 6 |
| **Dedicated Input Bits Available** | 5 | 1 | 6 | 1 | 1 | 6 | 6 | 6 | 2 | 2 | 2 | 10 | 6 |
| **Bidirectional I/O Bits** | 12 | 12 | 12 | 12 | 11 | 12 | 12 | 12 | 12 | 12 | 12 | 16 | 12 |
| **Supply Voltage Range (V)** | 4.5 - 6.3 | 4.5 - 6.3 | 4.5 - 9.5 | 4.5 - 9.5 | 4.5 - 9.5 | 4.5 - 6.3 | 4.5 - 9.5 | 2.4 - 6.3 | 4.5 - 6.3 | 4.5 - 9.5 | 2.4 - 6.3 | 4.5 - 6.3 | 4.5 - 9.5 |
| **Separate RAM Power Supply Available** | No | No | No | Yes | Yes | Yes | Yes | No | Yes | Yes | No | Yes | Yes |
| **Stack Levels** | 3 | 3 | 3 | 2 | 2 | 3 | 3 | 3 | 3 | 3 | 3 | 3 | 3 |
| **Interrupt** | Yes | No | Yes | No | No | Yes | Yes | Yes | No | No | No | Yes | Yes |
| **MICROBUS® Interface Option** | No | Yes | No | No | No | Yes | No | Yes | No | No | No | Yes | No |
| **Instruction Cycle Time ($\mu s$)** | 4 | 4 | 16 | 16 | 16 | 4 | 16 | 16 | 4 | 16 | 16 | 4 | 16 |

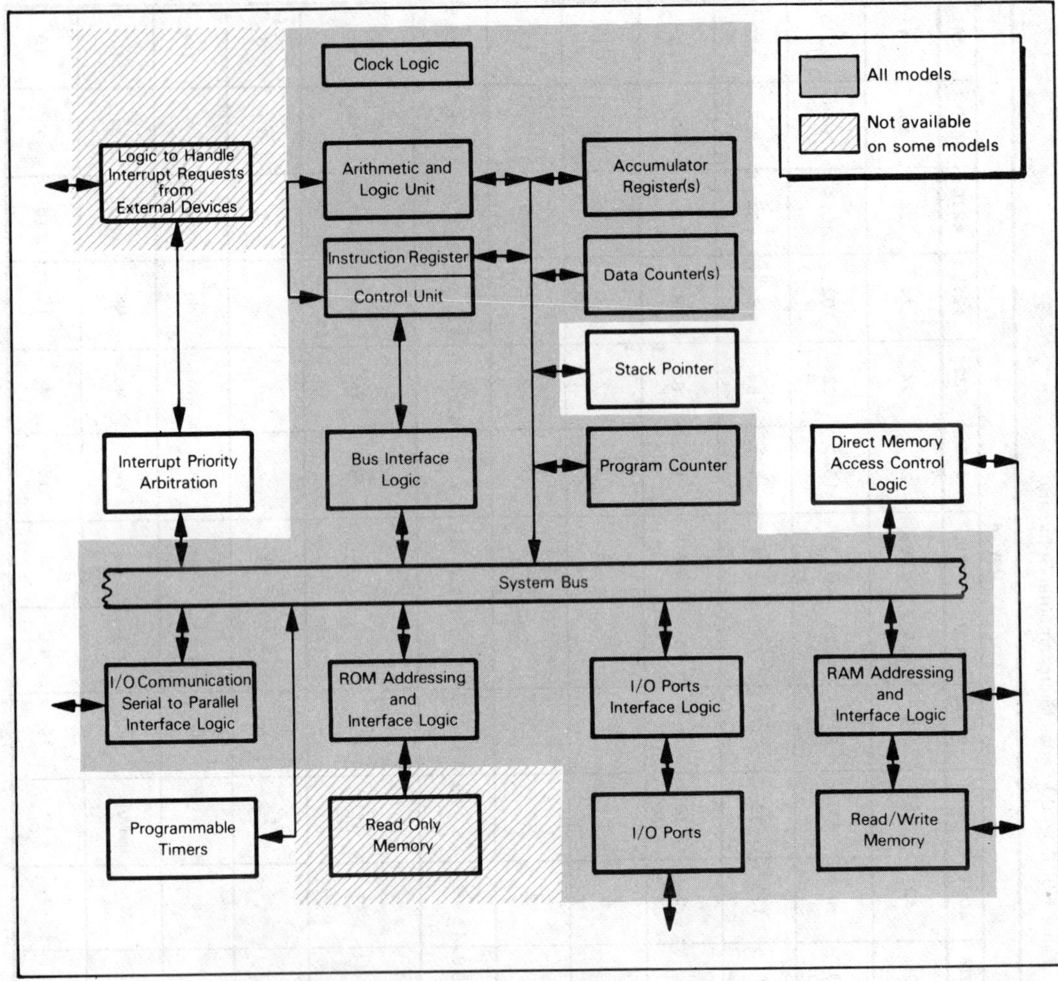

All models
Not available on some models
Clock Logic
Logic to Handle Interrupt Requests from External Devices
Arithmetic and Logic Unit
Accumulator Register(s)
Instruction Register
Control Unit
Data Counter(s)
Stack Pointer
Interrupt Priority Arbitration
Bus Interface Logic
Program Counter
Direct Memory Access Control Logic
System Bus
I/O Communication Serial to Parallel Interface Logic
ROM Addressing and Interface Logic
I/O Ports Interface Logic
RAM Addressing and Interface Logic
Programmable Timers
Read Only Memory
I/O Ports
Read/Write Memory

Figure 1-10. Logic of the COP400 Series of Microcomputers

## COP400 PROGRAMMABLE REGISTERS

COP programmable registers may be illustrated as follows:

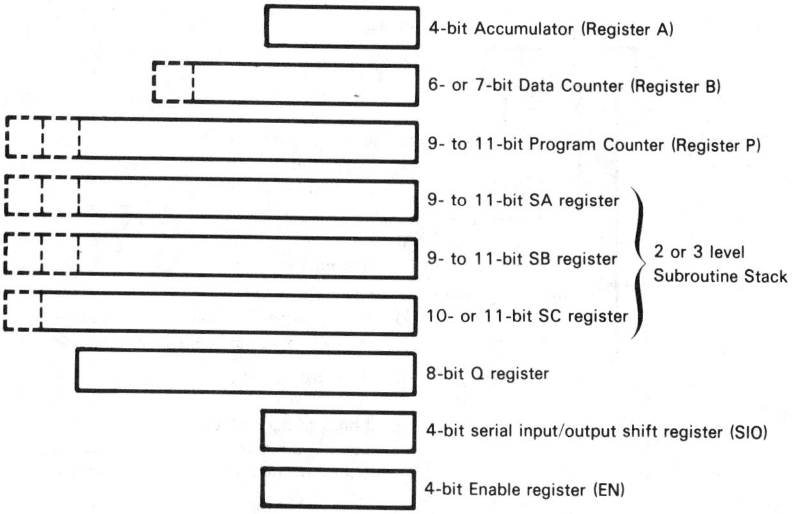

The COP microcomputers are all single address machines, and **the Accumulator is used as the implied primary source or destination register.**

**The B register is a 6- or 7-bit data counter,** depending on the COP400 model under consideration. The COP404L, COP440, and COP444L have 7-bit B registers; all other models' B registers are 6 bits wide. It is often treated as two distinct registers. The low-order four bits are referred to as Bd (digit) and the high-order bits are referred to as Br (register). These mnemonics will become clear after RAM memory organization is discussed. The location in RAM that the B register points to is referred to as Memory.

**The Program Counter is a 9- to 11-bit register providing direct access to a maximum of 2048 bytes of program memory.** Each COP400 model's program memory size determines its Program Counter width. Thus, the COP410L and COP411L have 9-bit Program Counters, while the COP404L, COP440, and COP444L have Program Counters 11 bits wide. Other models — COP402, COP402M, COP420, COP420L, COP420C, COP421, COP421L, and COP421C — have 10-bit Program Counters. Although some instructions do refer to ROM pages, no special Program Counter page register is provided. This greatly simplifies programming since the contents of this special page register do not have to be manipulated. The Program Counter is also used as a data pointer to ROM. This feature is useful for table look-up and other operations requiring ROM constants.

**COP400 RETURN ADDRESS STACK**

**The SA, SB, and SC registers provide a three-level subroutine return address stack.** They are all the same width as the Program Counter, and thus can reference all of the available memory. This organization precludes the need for a subroutine page register. None of the page boundary problems of the TMS100 arise. These registers are also used to save the current value of the Progam Counter (i.e., the next instruction to be executed) when the Program Counter is being used as a ROM data pointer. This implies that if ROM constants are being accessed via the Program Counter (LQID instruction) only two levels of subroutines can be supported, since saving the Program Counter causes the stack to be pushed one additional time. **The COP410L and COP411L have a two-level stack; therefore neither of these models implements Register SC.**

**The Q register is an 8-bit register that is used to allow the 4-bit COP microcomputer to process 8-bit data.** The 8-bit data in the Q register can originate from either the instruction ROM, the 8-bit L I/O port, or the Accumulator and Memory. Data is passed between the ALU and the Q register via Memory and the Accumulator. Memory holds the low-order four bits and the Accumulator holds the high-order four bits.

**The SIO register is a 4-bit register which can be used as a 4-bit serial in/serial out shift register or as an asynchronous binary counter.** The configuration of the SIO register is specified by the Enable (EN) register. The contents of the SIO register are accessed via an exchange with the Accumulator. This method can provide an uninterrupted stream of serial data.

**COP400 ENABLE REGISTER**

**The EN register is a 4-bit register that is used to configure the serial input/output logic, enable interrupts, and tristate the L I/O ports.** The bits in the EN register are assigned as shown below:

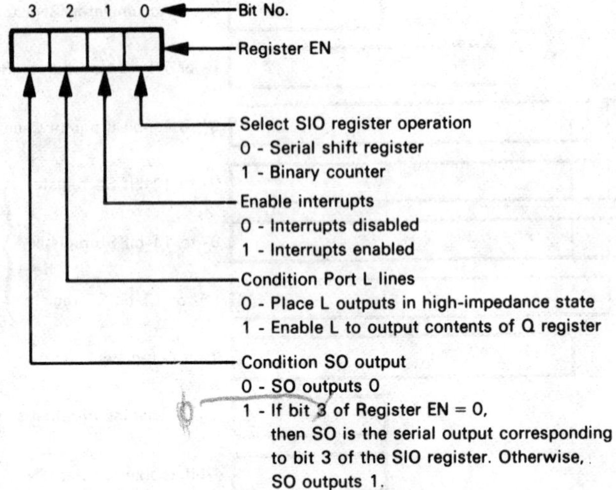


Bits 3 and 0 of the EN register are used to control the serial input/output logic. Detailed explanation of their use is provided in the section on COP serial I/O. Bit 1 of Register EN is a typical interrupt enable. If interrupts are enabled, bit 1 of the IN port is treated as an interrupt request line. Bit 2 of Register EN is used to tristate (float) the L bidirectional I/O ports. If the MICROBUS® option has been selected, setting or resetting EN bit 2 has no effect on the L I/O ports.

## COP MEMORY ADDRESSING

**The COP400, like all other 4-bit microcomputers, has separate and distinct program and data memories. There is no way for you to cause the COP400 to execute instructions out of data memory.**

**COP400 PROGRAM MEMORY**

The program memory of a COP400 microcontroller can be implemented either internally (i.e., on the microprocessor chip) or externally (i.e., on a separate chip). The COP402, COP402M, and COP404L support only external program memory. The COP402 and COP402M will allow up to 1024 bytes of external program memory while the COP404L allows up to 2048 bytes of external program memory. All the other members of the COP400 family have on-board ROMs that are used to implement program memory. The COP410L and COP411L have on-board program memories of 512 bytes. The COP440 and COP444L have on-board program memories of 2048 bytes. All other microprocessors in the COP400 family have on-board program memories of 1024 bytes.

Since some relative jumps are provided in the instruction set, it is often more convenient to consider program memory organized into pages of 64 bytes. The Program Counter can be used to reference data as well as instructions in the program memory. All of the program memory addressing registers (PC, SA, SB, SC) use the full program memory space width. This circumvents the need for special program memory page registers.

Some peculiarities of the program memory addressing scheme should be noted:

1) Although the page-relative jump instruction (JP) can transfer control within any page, the relative Jump-to-Subroutine (JSRP) only refers to page 2.
2) The page-relative jump instruction (JP) cannot pass control to the last byte on a page.
3) The page-relative jump instruction (JP) can pass control to any location on page 2 or page 3 if the Program Counter is currently on page 2 or page 3. In other words, when executing out of pages 2 or 3 a long jump (JMP) is not needed to pass control between pages 2 and 3.
4) The relative jump-to-subroutine instruction (JSRP) cannot be executed within pages 2 or 3.
5) The relative jump-to-subroutine instruction (JSRP) cannot pass control to the last byte on page 2.

**Data memory consists of 32, 64, or 128 4-bit nibbles.** Table 1-6 gives the data memory size for each model in the COP400 series. **Data memory is accessed via the B register.** It is convenient to view RAM as divided into registers of 16 digits each, corresponding to the bits of the B register as follows:

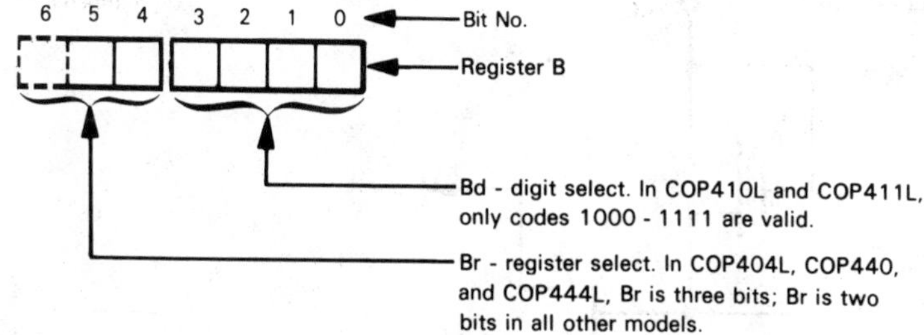


This scheme provides efficient 4-bit manipulation of the 6- or 7-bit data memory address. The memory location pointed to by B can be moved not only to the Accumulator but also directly to the Q register, the G port, or the L port.

## COP STATUS FLAGS

**The COP has only a single status bit — the Carry.** The Carry can be set by certain addition instructions and by set (SC) and reset (RC) instructions. In addition, there is a skip flag that is inaccessible to the programmer. If the skip flag is set during the course of execution of an instruction, the following instruction is skipped.

## COP400 PARALLEL INPUT/OUTPUT LOGIC

**The COP microcomputers all have the following standard parallel I/O ports:**

- **D port — 4-bit general purpose output port (2 bits on COP411L and 8 bits on COP440)**
- **G port — 4-bit general purpose bidirectional port (3 bits on COP411L and 8 bits on COP440)**
- **L port — 8-bit bidirectional tristate port**

In addition to the ports listed above, most COP400 models — COP402, COP402M, COP404L, COP420, COP420L, COP420C, and COP444L — have a 4-bit input port called the IN port. This port is eight bits wide on the COP440.

COP400 OUTPUT OPTIONS

A number of mask programmable options are available for these I/O ports. Each output of the G and D ports is available as either an enhancement mode device to ground in conjunction with a depletion mode device to $V_{CC}$, or as an open drain gate. These circuits are shown below.

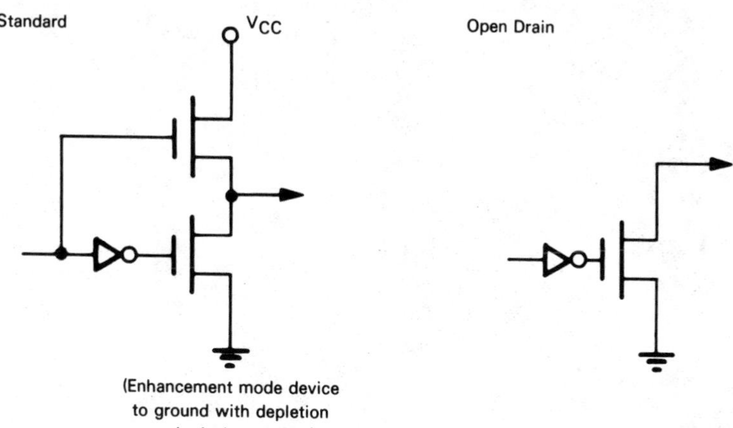


(Enhancement mode device to ground with depletion mode device to $V_{CC}$)

The L I/O port lines can be configured as either standard, open drain, push-pull, or high current source (for LED or TRIAC driver applications) outputs. All L port driver functions are tristateable. The IN port can be configured as either a loaded input or a high impedance input:

**COP400 INPUT OPTIONS**

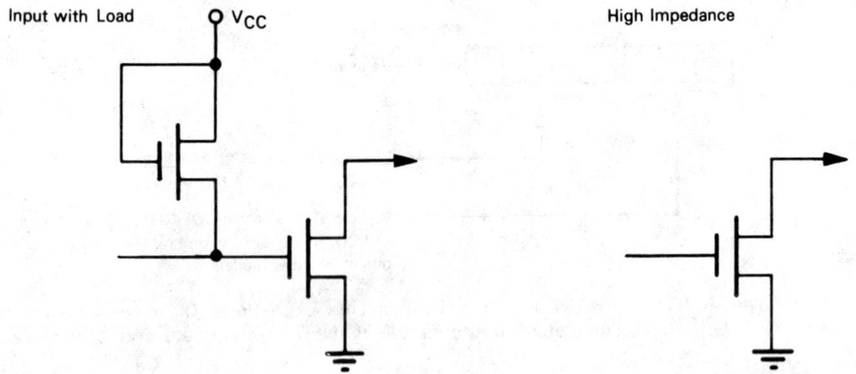


For each input line (ports G, L, and IN), you can specify whether input thresholds are to be standard TTL levels (0 $\leq$ 0.8 V, 1 $\geq$ 2.0 V) or higher voltage (0 $\leq$ 1.2 V, 1 $\geq$ 3.6 V).

**COP400 MICROBUS® INTERFACE**

**The COP402M, COP420, COP420C, and COP440 can also be mask programmed for a MICROBUS® interface.** When this option is selected, bits 1, 2, and 3 of IN are no longer general purpose inputs, and bit 0 of G becomes a dedicated output. The L port becomes an 8-bit bus port used for bidirectional data transfer. Line IN1 becomes a read control signal, designated $\overline{RD}$. When this line goes low it causes the COP to drive the transfer bus (L port) with the data currently in the Q register. IN3 is used as a write control signal, designated $\overline{WR}$. When this line goes low the current state of the transfer bus (L port) is latched into the Q register. IN2 becomes a chip select line, designated $\overline{CS}$. A low input at IN2 causes the COP to become selected. When it is selected, IN1 and IN3 act as read/write control signals, as outlined above. Line G0 becomes a ready output, designated INTR. This output is reset each time a $\overline{WR}$ pulse is accepted by the COP. INTR is used to provide the necessary synchronization between a host CPU and the COP during asynchronous data transfer. The timing of the MICROBUS® data transfers is quite simple. Figure 1-11 shows a read operation and Figure 1-12 shows a write operation. Detailed timing specifications appear in the data sheets at the end of this chapter.

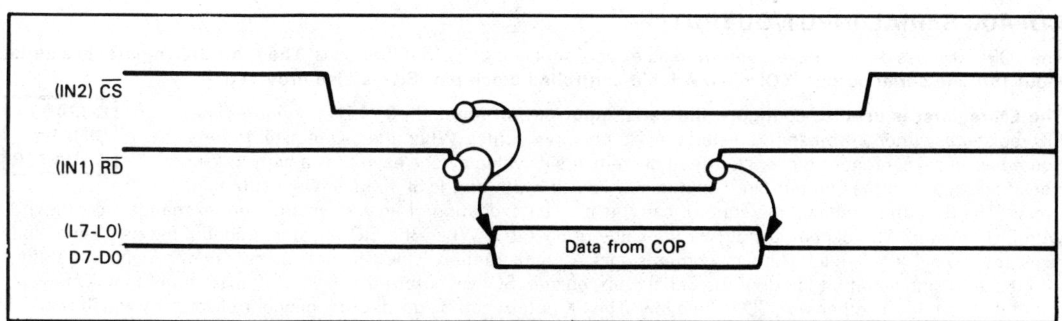


Figure 1-11. MICROBUS® Read Sequence

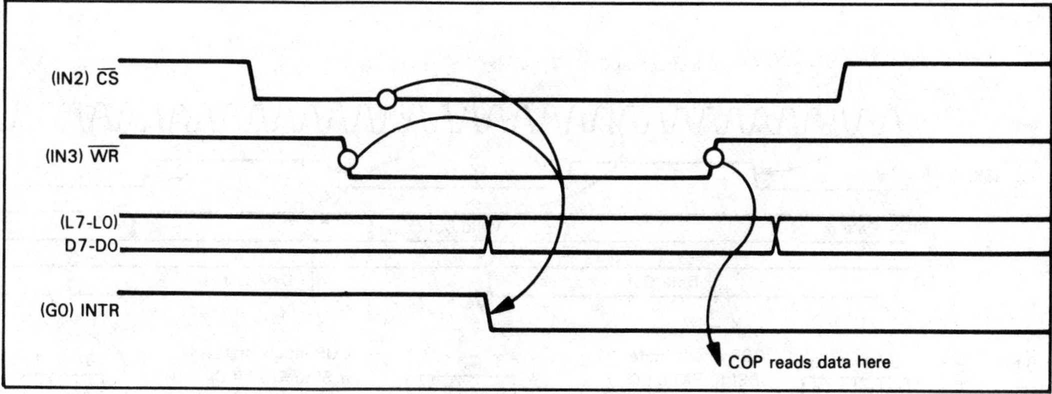


Figure 1-12. MICROBUS® Write Sequence

## COP400 SERIAL INPUT/OUTPUT

The COP400 series devices have a very workable set of serial input/output functions. **The 4-bit SIO register has serial input (SI) and serial output (SO) pins. A logic-controlled clock pin (SK) is also provided.**

**COP400 BINARY COUNTER**

**The EN register is used to configure the serial input/output logic.** Bit 0 of EN configures the SIO register as either a 4-bit shift register or a 4-bit binary counter. When the SIO register is configured as an asynchronous binary counter it decrements its value by one each time a high-to-low transition occurs on the SI input pin. The minimum pulse width on the SI input is two instruction cycles. The SK output reflects the state of carry at the last execution of an XAS instruction (exchange Accumulator with SIO register). The SO output follows the value of EN bit 3. When the SIO register is configured as a serial shift register (bit 0 of EN = 0) it left shifts its contents once each instruction cycle. The data present on the SI input is shifted into the least significant bit (bit 0) of the Serial Shift register. SO will output the most significant bit of the SIO register (bit 3) if EN bit 3 = 1; otherwise, SO is held low. The SK output can be used as a logic controlled clock which issues a pulse once each instruction cycle. This pulse is referred to as a SYNC pulse, since it is synchronized to the execution of each instruction. The generation of the SYNC pulse is initiated by an XAS instruction issued with Carry = 1 and is terminated by issuing an XAS instruction with Carry = 0; thus, if you wish to ensure that the serial data stream is continuous, every fourth instruction executed must be an XAS. Serial I/O timing is related to instruction cycle timing in the following way:

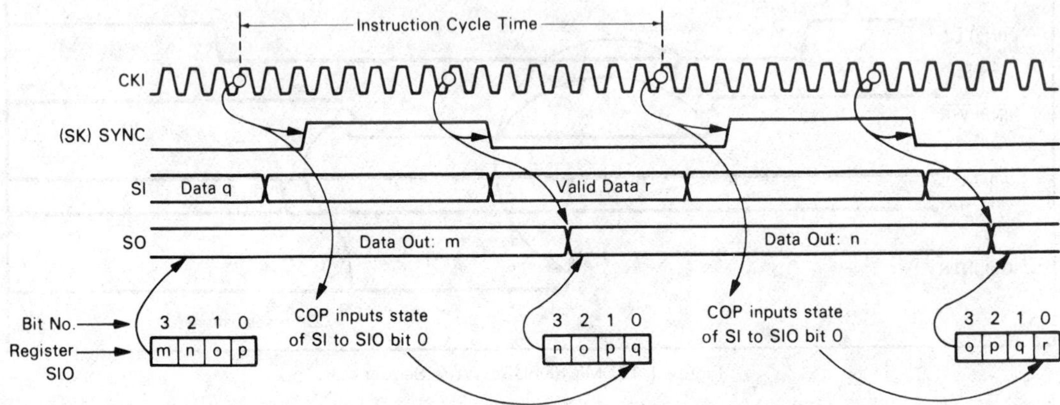


The first clock rising edge of the instruction cycle triggers the low-to-high transition of SYNC, output via SK; at this time the processor reads the state of SI into SIO bit 0, shifting the current bits 0-2 left. Halfway through the cycle (shown above as the eighth clock rising edge) SYNC (SK) is reset low and the new SIO bit 3 is output via SO.

Table 1-7 summarizes the serial I/O functions of the COP400 microcomputer.

Table 1-7. COP400 Serial I/O Functions

| $EN_3$ | $EN_0$ | SIO | SI | SO | SK after XAS |
|---|---|---|---|---|---|
| 0 | 0 | Shift Register | Input to Shift Register | 0 | If C = 1, SK = SYNC<br>If C = 0, SK = 0 |
| 1 | 0 | Shift Register | Input to Shift Register | Serial Out | If C = 1, SK = SYNC<br>If C = 0, SK = 0 |
| 0 | 1 | Binary Counter | Input to Binary Counter | 0 | If C = 1, SK = 1<br>If C = 0, SK = 0 |
| 1 | 1 | Binary Counter | Input to Binary Counter | 1 | If C = 1, SK = 1<br>If C = 0, SK = 0 |

## COP400 INTERRUPT LOGIC

**Many COP400 models have a true interrupt capability. They are the only products covered in this chapter which have a true interrupt.** Interrupts are not available on the COP402M, COP410L, COP411L, COP421, COP421L, and COP421C. An interrupt will only be acknowledged if the following conditions are true:

1) Interrupts have been enabled. This is accomplished by setting bit 1 of EN to 1.
2) An interrupt request has been issued. This consists of driving IN1 low for a minimum of two instruction cycles.
3) The execution of the current instruction has been completed.
4) Any chain of control transfers has been completed. This means any "jumps to jumps" (the jump instructions are JID, JMP, JP, JSR, and JSRL).
5) Any chain of LBI (Load B immediate) instructions has been completed.

Once all of the above conditions have been met, the interrupt is acknowledged. The CPU begins interrupt acknowledgement by first saving the current contents of the Program Counter in the SA register and pushing the rest of the subroutine save registers. The contents of the SC register are lost. The skip status is saved in a 1-bit Skip Status Save register. Next, interrupts are disabled (i.e., bit 1 of EN = 0). Finally, control is passed to location 0FFH. The first word of an interrupt service routine must be a NOP; therefore, if interrupts are employed the word at location $0FF_{16}$ must be a $44_{16}$ (NOP op-code). Interrupts can be re-enabled by executing a LEI (Load Enable register Immediate) at any point prior to the return instruction. It is good practice, however, to place this interrupt enable command immediately preceding the return to preclude the possibility of nested interrupt requests. Note that since an interrupt request must be present for two instruction cycles before it is acknowledged, the instruction immediately following the enable interrupts command will always be executed. Two further words of caution concerning the skip and carry statuses: **the skip status, although saved, is not pushed onto a Stack as the Program Counter is.** It is saved in a single 1-bit Save register. The skip status is restored by a Return instruction (RET). Any time a RET is executed a check is made for the restoration of the skip status. If the Skip Status Save register is set, the skip status will be set. This implies that **any use of a RET instruction within an interrupt service routine, other than as the return from the interrupt service routine, will cause the skip status to be lost.** Therefore, nested subroutines within interrupt service routines should be avoided at all costs. **Also note that the state of Carry is not saved when an interrupt is acknowledged.** You must either avoid the use of instructions which modify Carry within interrupt service routines or save the state of Carry.

## COP400 SERIES MICROCOMPUTER PINS AND SIGNALS

Figures 1-13 through 1-17 illustrate the signals and pin assignments of the members of the COP400 family of microcomputers. The signals that are consistent for the entire family of microcomputers will be described together.

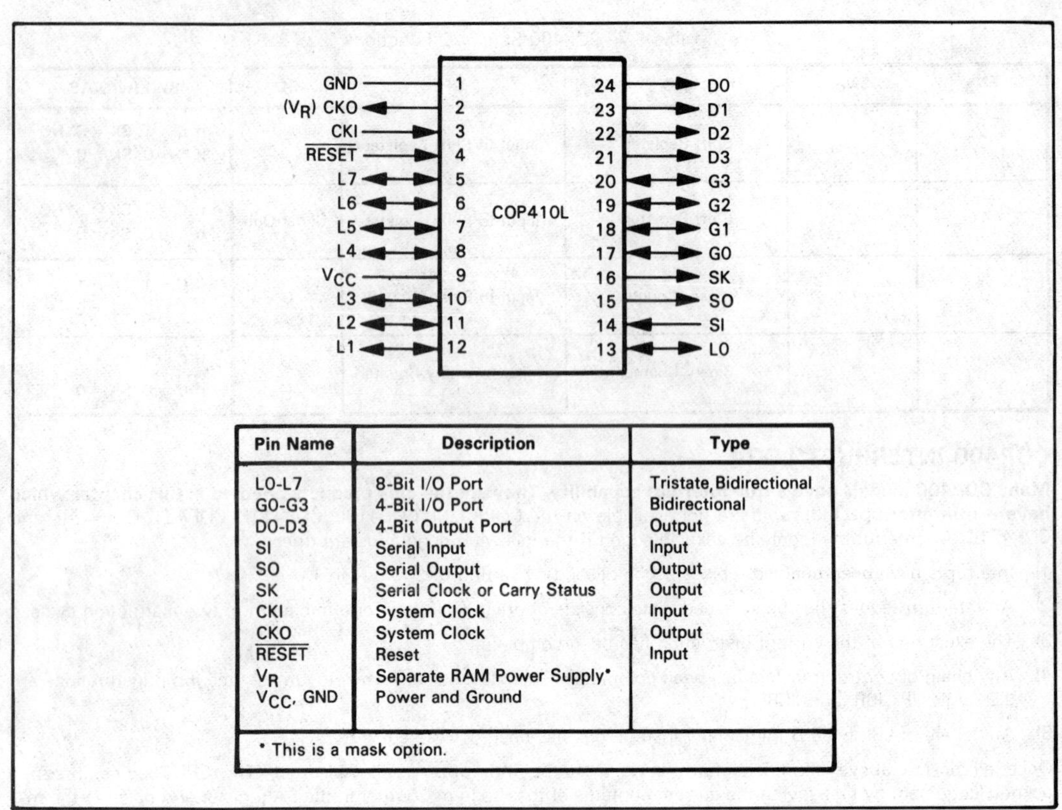


| Pin Name | Description | Type |
|---|---|---|
| L0-L7 | 8-Bit I/O Port | Tristate, Bidirectional |
| G0-G3 | 4-Bit I/O Port | Bidirectional |
| D0-D3 | 4-Bit Output Port | Output |
| SI | Serial Input | Input |
| SO | Serial Output | Output |
| SK | Serial Clock or Carry Status | Output |
| CKI | System Clock | Input |
| CKO | System Clock | Output |
| RESET | Reset | Input |
| $V_R$ | Separate RAM Power Supply* | |
| $V_{CC}$, GND | Power and Ground | |

* This is a mask option.

Figure 1-13. COP410L Signals and Pin Assignments

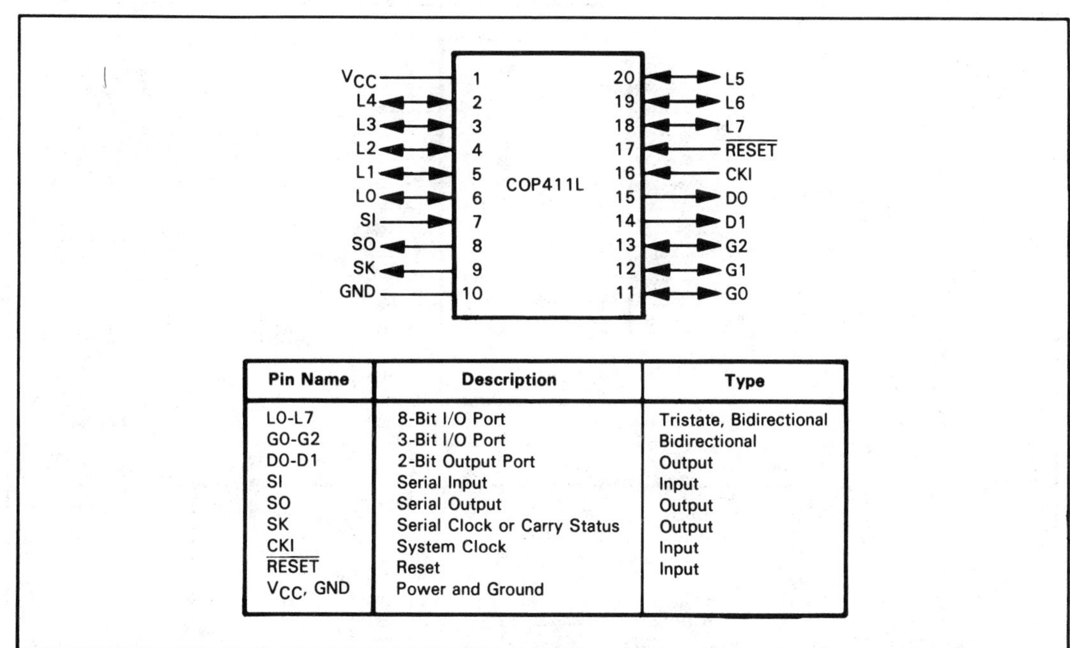


| Pin Name | Description | Type |
|---|---|---|
| L0-L7 | 8-Bit I/O Port | Tristate, Bidirectional |
| G0-G2 | 3-Bit I/O Port | Bidirectional |
| D0-D1 | 2-Bit Output Port | Output |
| SI | Serial Input | Input |
| SO | Serial Output | Output |
| SK | Serial Clock or Carry Status | Output |
| CKI | System Clock | Input |
| $\overline{\text{RESET}}$ | Reset | Input |
| $V_{CC}$, GND | Power and Ground | |

Figure 1-14. COP411L Signals and Pin Assignments

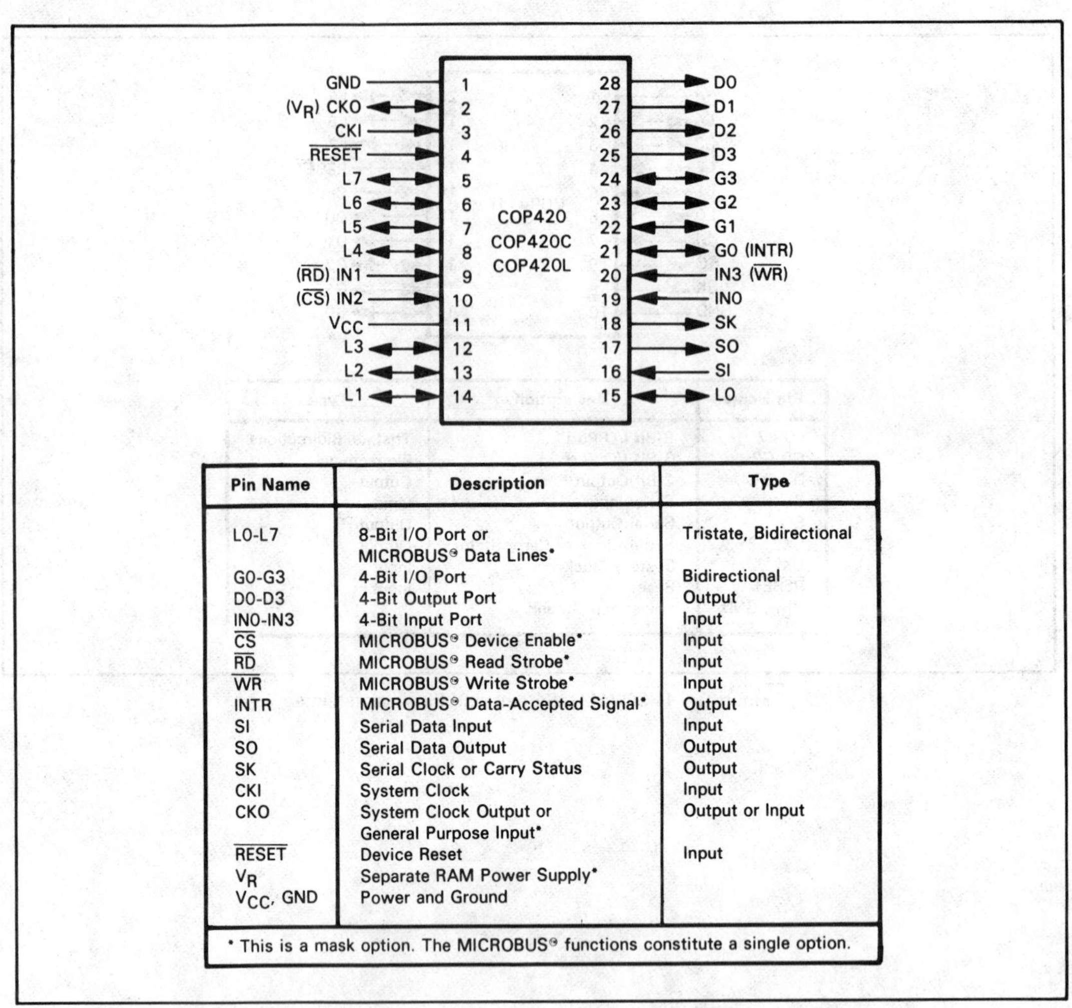


| Pin Name | Description | Type |
|---|---|---|
| L0-L7 | 8-Bit I/O Port or MICROBUS® Data Lines* | Tristate, Bidirectional |
| G0-G3 | 4-Bit I/O Port | Bidirectional |
| D0-D3 | 4-Bit Output Port | Output |
| IN0-IN3 | 4-Bit Input Port | Input |
| $\overline{CS}$ | MICROBUS® Device Enable* | Input |
| $\overline{RD}$ | MICROBUS® Read Strobe* | Input |
| $\overline{WR}$ | MICROBUS® Write Strobe* | Input |
| INTR | MICROBUS® Data-Accepted Signal* | Output |
| SI | Serial Data Input | Input |
| SO | Serial Data Output | Output |
| SK | Serial Clock or Carry Status | Output |
| CKI | System Clock | Input |
| CKO | System Clock Output or General Purpose Input* | Output or Input |
| $\overline{RESET}$ | Device Reset | Input |
| $V_R$ | Separate RAM Power Supply* | |
| $V_{CC}$, GND | Power and Ground | |

* This is a mask option. The MICROBUS® functions constitute a single option.

Figure 1-15. COP420, COP420C, and COP420L Signals and Pin Assignments

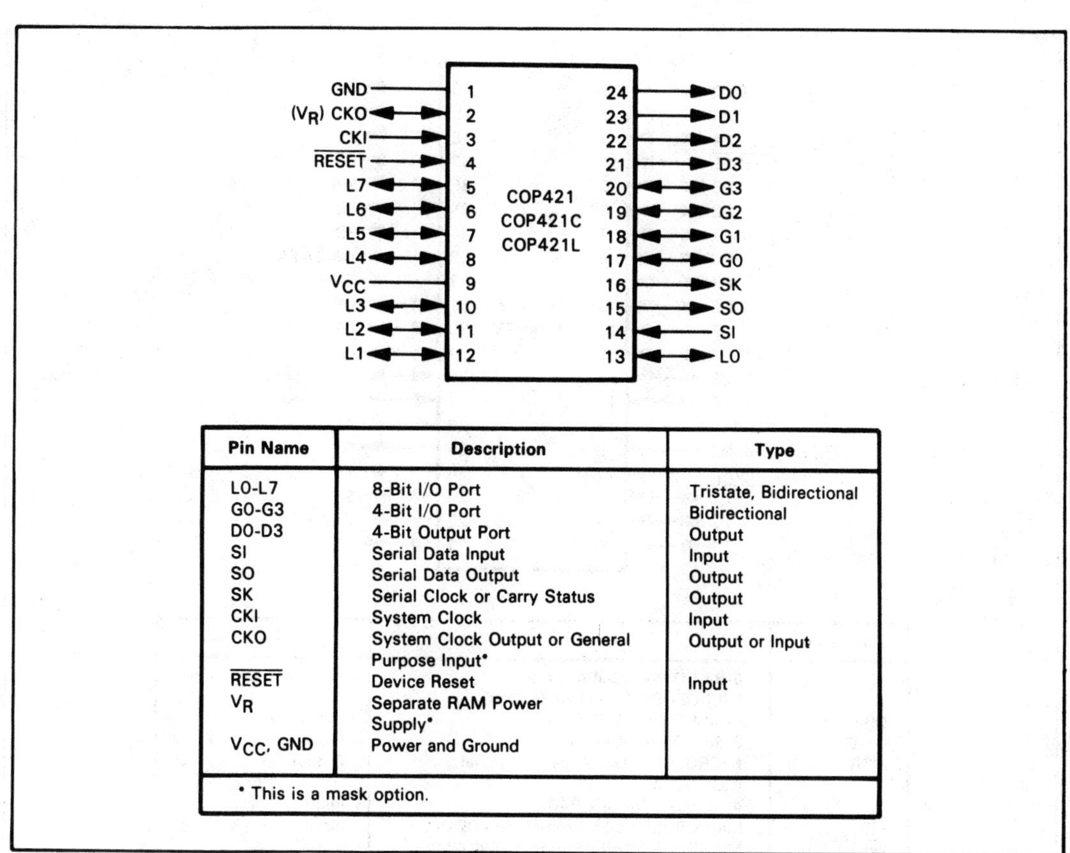


| Pin Name | Description | Type |
|---|---|---|
| L0-L7 | 8-Bit I/O Port | Tristate, Bidirectional |
| G0-G3 | 4-Bit I/O Port | Bidirectional |
| D0-D3 | 4-Bit Output Port | Output |
| SI | Serial Data Input | Input |
| SO | Serial Data Output | Output |
| SK | Serial Clock or Carry Status | Output |
| CKI | System Clock | Input |
| CKO | System Clock Output or General Purpose Input* | Output or Input |
| $\overline{\text{RESET}}$ | Device Reset | Input |
| $V_R$ | Separate RAM Power Supply* | |
| $V_{CC}$, GND | Power and Ground | |

* This is a mask option.

Figure 1-16. COP421, COP421C, and COP421L Signals and Pin Assignments

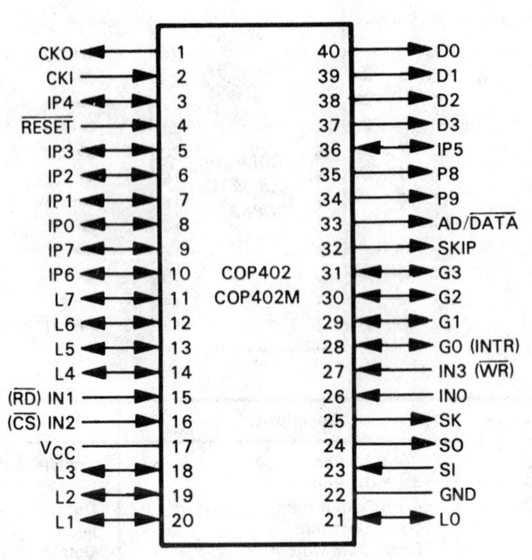


| Pin Name | Description | Type |
|---|---|---|
| L0-L7 | 8-Bit I/O Port (COP402) or MICROBUS® Data Lines (COP402M) | Tristate, Bidirectional |
| G0-G3 | 4-Bit I/O Port (COP402) | Bidirectional |
| G1-G3 | 3-Bit I/O Port (COP402M) | Bidirectional |
| INTR | MICROBUS® Data-Accepted Signal (COP402M) | Output |
| IN0-IN3 | 4-Bit Input Port (COP402) | Input |
| $\overline{RD}$ | MICROBUS® Read Strobe (COP402M) | Input |
| $\overline{WR}$ | MICROBUS® Write Strobe (COP402M) | Input |
| $\overline{CS}$ | MICROBUS® Device Enable (COP402M) | Input |
| D0-D3 | 4-Bit Output Port | Output |
| SI | Serial Input | Input |
| SO | Serial Output | Output |
| SK | Serial Clock or Carry Status | Output |
| AD/$\overline{DATA}$ | Address Out/Data In Indicator | Output |
| SKIP | Instruction Skip | Output |
| CKI | Clock or Crystal Input | Input |
| CKO | Crystal Connection | Output |
| IP0-IP7 | Multiplexed Program Address and Data Bus | Bidirectional |
| P8, P9 | High-order Two Program Address Bits | Output |
| $\overline{RESET}$ | Device Reset | Input |
| $V_{CC}$, GND | Power and Ground | |

Figure 1-17. COP402 and COP402M Signals and Pin Assignments

**The eight bidirectional L port pins are designated L0-L7.**

**The four pins of the G port are designated G0-G3.**

**The four pins of the D output port are designated D0-D3.**

**SI is the serial input pin, SO is the serial output pin, and SK is the logic controlled clock or Carry status output.**

**CKI (Clock Input) and CKO (Clock Output) are the two system timing pins.** There are four possible mask programmable options for these pins: crystal controlled oscillator, external oscillator, RC controlled oscillator, and externally synchronized oscillator. All of these options are illustrated in Figure 1-18.

**COP400 CKO OPTIONS**

If you choose the external oscillator option, then, **on some COP400 models, CKO is available for one of two other functions:**

- **A general purpose input line**
- **A separate RAM power supply ($V_R$)**

When CKO is mask-programmed as a data input line, you can read its state into bit 1 of the Accumulator by executing an INIL instruction. All COP420 and COP421 models provide this option. A separate RAM power supply is necessary in applications where you wish to preserve data during failure of the primary power supply ($V_{CC}$). Table 1-6 shows which COP400 models offer the $V_R$ option.

**$\overline{\text{RESET}}$ activates the initialization logic.** The $\overline{\text{RESET}}$ pin is configured as a Schmitt trigger for noise immunity. Initialization will occur if $\overline{\text{RESET}}$ is driven low for a minimum of two instruction cycles. Initialization performs the following tasks:

1) Program Counter is reset to 0
2) Accumulator is reset to 0
3) B register is reset to 0
4) Carry is reset to 0
5) Enable register bits are reset to 0
6) D port bits are reset to 0
7) G port bits are reset to 0
8) The SK output is configured to act as a SYNC output

Hence, after initialization, instruction execution will begin at program address 0. The instruction is this location must be a CLRA (code 00). The clearing of Register EN results in the following initial operating conditions:

- Register SIO functions as a serial shift register
- Serial output (SO) is held low
- Interrupts (if available) are disabled
- L port outputs are in high impedance state

**COP400 POWER-ON RESET**

**Power and Ground are represented by $V_{CC}$ and GND, respectively. If the power supply rise time is greater than one microsecond and less than one millisecond, then initialization will occur automatically,** with the same results as described above for $\overline{\text{RESET}}$. Therefore, if your design can guarantee the appropriate rise time for $V_{CC}$, you need not use $\overline{\text{RESET}}$ for power-on initialization.

**IN0-IN3 comprise a 4-bit input port which is available on some COP400 models.** As we described in the section on parallel I/O ports, **those COP400 models which possess the IN port also offer the MICROBUS® interface mask option. When the COP400 device interfaces to another microcomputer via the MICROBUS®, the system controller drives $\overline{\text{CS}}$, $\overline{\text{RD}}$, and $\overline{\text{WR}}$ to the COP, and the COP outputs INTR to the system controller.** Table 1-6 shows which COP400 models offer the MICROBUS® option. The only difference between the COP402 and COP402M is that the COP402M provides the MICROBUS® interface.

**The COP402 and COP402M have the ability to address external memory and therefore have a few signals that are not present on the other members of the COP400 family.**

**IP0-IP7 implement a bidirectional Data and Address Bus.** This bus is used to transfer instructions from program memory to the COP402 or COP402M microcontrollers. Instructions and data are multiplexed on the IP bus under the control of the AD/$\overline{\text{DATA}}$ line. **When the AD/$\overline{\text{DATA}}$ line is high, the COP402 or COP402M is driving the IP bus with the low-order eight bits of the instruction's address. When the AD/$\overline{\text{DATA}}$ line is low, the COP402 or COP402M expects external logic to drive the IP bus with the instruction whose address was previously output.** Great

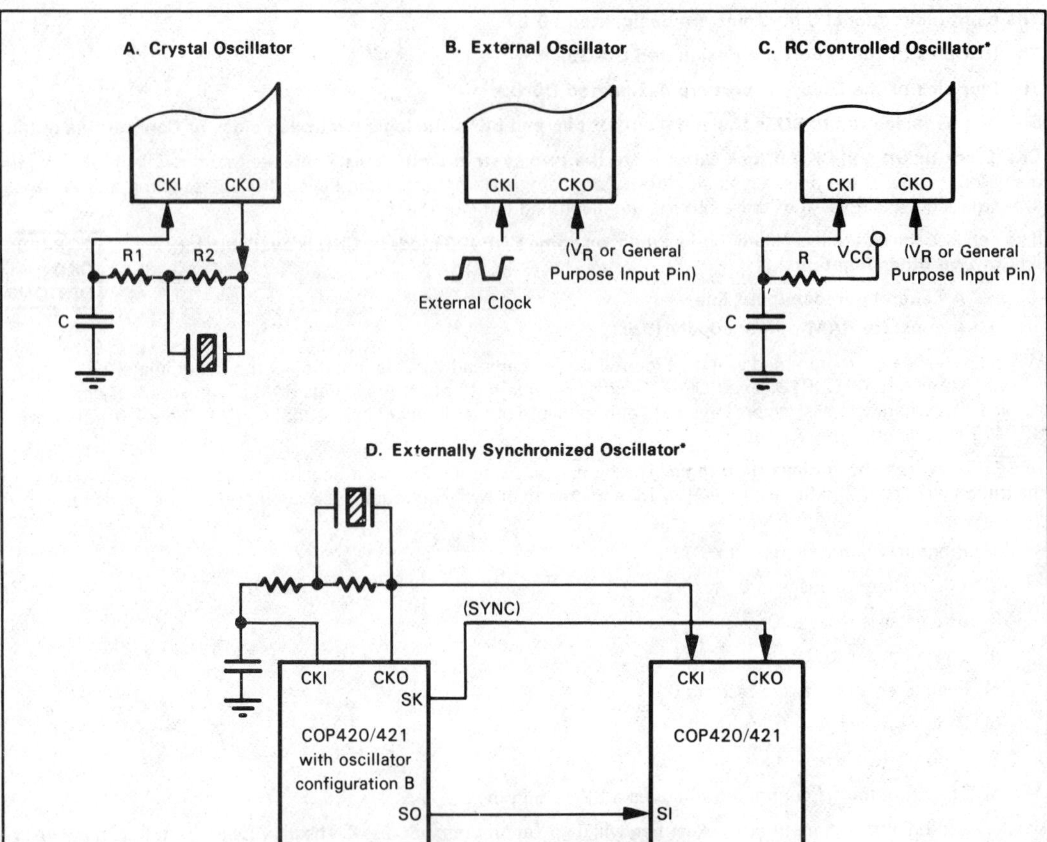


* Oscillator configurations C and D are not available on COP402 or COP402M.

| Crystal Oscillator | | | |
|---|---|---|---|
| Crystal Value (MHz) | Component Values | | |
| | R1 (kΩ) | R2 (MΩ) | C (pF) |
| 4 | 1 | 1 | 27 |
| 3.58 | 1 | 1 | 27 |
| 2.09 | 1 | 1 | 56 |

| RC Controlled Oscillator | | |
|---|---|---|
| R (kΩ) | C (pF) | Instruction Cycle Time In μs |
| 12 | 100 | 5 ± 20% |
| 6.8 | 220 | 5.3 ± 23% |
| 8.2 | 300 | 8 ± 29% |
| 22 | 100 | 8.6 ± 16% |

Figure 1-18. COP400 Clock Options

latitude is allowed in implementing the external memory. RAM, ROM or PROM may be employed. The only requirements for the external memory are:

- Random addressing (i.e., no serial memory devices such as bubble memories)
- TTL-compatible, tristate outputs
- TTL-compatible inputs
- Access time $\leq$ 1.7 $\mu$s

These requirements are quite liberal and will allow for most bipolar, MOS, or CMOS devices. The timing of the IP bus is quite simple and well suited to minimal hardware designs. Note that the address information on the IP bus should be latched on the high-to-low transition of the AD/$\overline{\text{DATA}}$ line.

**P8 and P9 provide the high-order two bits of the instruction address.** The low-order eight bits are supplied on the IP bus. P8 and P9 are dedicated lines and are not governed by the state of AD/$\overline{\text{DATA}}$. This means that P8 and P9 do not have to be latched.

**The SKIP output undergoes a low-to-high transition once each instruction cycle.** It is useful during debugging for synchronizing events to each instruction execution.

## COP400 SERIES MICROCOMPUTER INSTRUCTION EXECUTION

**All instructions generate one or two bytes of object code. Every instruction executes in a single instruction cycle of a fixed length.** The standard length of an instruction cycle is 16 clock periods; however, every COP400 model except the COP402 and COP402M offers other divisors as a mask option. You may choose a divisor of 8 on all models which have divisor options, and a divisor of 32 is available on the COP420L and COP421L. In addition, all L-suffix models offer a divisor of 4 if the input oscillator is RC controlled. Thus, **depending on the COP400 model and oscillator frequency you choose, an instruction cycle may consist of 4, 8, 16, or 32 clock periods.**

## COP400 SERIES MICROCOMPUTER INSTRUCTION SET

**The instruction set given in Tables 1-9 and 1-10 is that of the COP420; this is a subset of the full COP400 series instruction set, which will be available on the COP440.** Other COP400 models discussed in this chapter have instruction sets which are subsets of the COP420 instructions. The rightmost columns of Table 1-9 show which models execute the instructions discussed.

The COP400 series instruction set has some powerful instructions — compared to those of other 4-bit microcomputers — that perform multiple operations with a single instruction. In addition, the ability to move data directly between I/O ports is an especially convenient feature.

**There are almost no variations between the instruction sets of the COP420 and COP421. The only differences stem from the fact that the COP420 has the IN port. Two additional instructions are present in the COP420 instruction set to deal with this port.**

**The CMOS versions of the COP420 and COP421 have an additional instruction, the HLTT instruction.** Execution of HLTT places the microcomputer in a low-power-consumption halt state until the timer overflows. At that time execution resumes with the instruction following the HLTT.

The COP410L and COP411L have instruction sets that are subsets of that of the COP421. The COP410L and COP411L lack the following instructions:

- ADT
- CASC
- CQMA
- INIL
- ININ
- LDD
- OGI
- SKT
- XABR

Note that, other than the three instructions INIL, ININ, and SKT, all the deleted operations can be performed using the remaining instructions. Table 1-8 shows how this may be done.

Table 1-8. COP410L and COP411L Equivalents for Deleted Instructions

| Instruction | Equivalent Sequence | | |
|---|---|---|---|
| ADT | AISC | 10 | |
| | NOP | | ;defeats skip condition |
| CASC | COMP | | |
| | ASC | | |
| CQMA | INL | | |
| LDD reg,digit | LBI | reg,digit | ;note that B contents are lost |
| | LD | 0 | |
| OGI data4 | CLRA | | ;put data in A by adding it to 0 |
| | AISC | data4 | ;(original contents of A are lost) |
| | NOP | | |
| | X | 0 | ;output data to G from RAM |
| | OMG | | |
| | X | 0 | ;replace original RAM data |
| XABR | No direct replacement; however, LBI can be used to load the entire B register. You can also alter Br via the instructions LD, X, XDS, and XIS, which provide a bit pattern to be Exclusive-ORed with the contents of Br. | | |

The XAD instruction has been modified such that it can only access the last location of data memory (i.e., location register 3, digit 15). The LBI instruction has been modified to work with the reduced RAM area of the COP410L and COP411L; specifically, only digits 9-15 and 0 in registers 0-3 are valid RAM addresses. This change has the important side effect of making all LBI instructions single-byte instructions. The successive LBI skip condition (explained below) has been deleted, and successive LBIs will be executed.

**The first instruction of a COP400 program must be a Clear Accumulator instruction (CLRA). Therefore, location 0 of the program memory must be a 0 (CLRA op-code).**

**If multiple LBI instructions (Load B Immediate) appear consecutively in ROM, only the first one is executed.** All remaining consecutive occurrences are skipped. Instruction execution continues with the first non-LBI instruction encountered. This feature can be useful for making multiple use of a single routine. A number of LBIs can be placed in front of a common routine. Control is then passed to one of these LBI instructions, causing the B register to be set. Control then falls through to the common routine. As mentioned earlier, this LBI skip feature is not available on COP410L or COP411L.

## BENCHMARK PROGRAM

As stated in the TMS1000 section, the benchmark program used for the 4-bit microcomputers is different from the one used in the rest of this book. The special nature of the 4-bit microcomputers demands it. This benchmark program will input a block of data from the G port. The first byte of data is equal to one less than the number of nibbles that follow. Each block can contain up to 16 nibbles.

```
        LBI     REG,0   ;SET B POINTING TO THE START OF A RAM REGISTER
        ING             ;INPUT NUMBER OF NIBBLES TO FOLLOW
        CAB             ;SET UP B REGISTER TO FILL RAM FROM HIGH DIGIT TO LOW DIGIT
NEXT:   ING             ;GET DATA BYTE
        XDS     0       ;STORE TO MEMORY AND DECREMENT DIGIT ADDRESS
        JP      NEXT    ;SKIP THIS INSTRUCTION WHEN DONE
```

The following symbols are used in Tables 1-9 and 1-10:

A — 4-bit Accumulator

aaaa — Encoding of the values 0-3 as follows:

0 - 1101
1 - 0111
2 - 0110
3 - 1011

addr6 — 6-bit instruction address

addr7 — 7-bit instruction address

addr10 — 10-bit instruction address

addri — 10-bit indirect address formed from the contents of the Program Counter, the Accumulator, and data memory as follows:

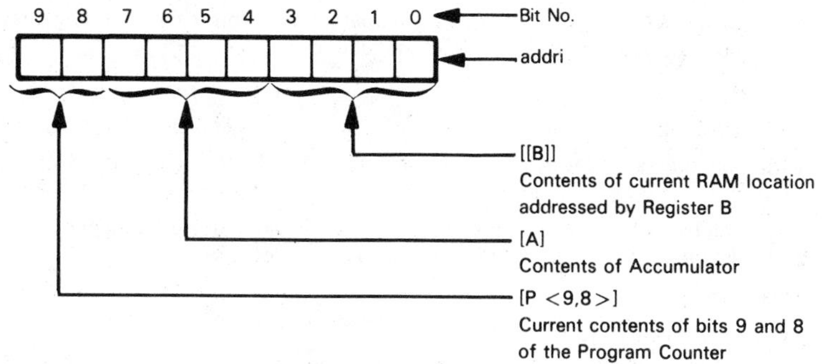


B — 6-bit RAM pointer register

bbbb — Encoding of the values 0-3 as follows:
0 - 1100
1 - 0101
2 - 0010
3 - 0011

Bd — Low-order four bits of Register B, which serve as a RAM digit pointer

bit — A 2-bit field which specifies an individual bit of a register, port, or RAM location

Br — High-order bits of Register B, which serve as a RAM register pointer

C — Carry status flag

cccc — Encoding of the values 0-3 as follows:
0 - 0000
1 - 1000
2 - 0001
3 - 1001

CKO — The clock line which may serve instead as a data input line

D — 4-bit output port

data4 — 4-bit immediate data

dddd — Immediate data in the range $0_{16}$-$F_{16}$

digit — 4-bit RAM digit select

digitp — 4-bit RAM digit select limited to the values 9-15 and 0

eeee — Immediate data specified by the operand "digitp" and encoded as the value of "digitp" decremented by 1:

| digitp | eeee |
|---|---|
| 9 | 1000 |
| A | 1001 |
| - | - |
| - | - |
| - | - |
| E | 1101 |
| F | 1110 |
| 0 | 1111 |

EN 4-bit enable register

G 4-bit latched I/O port

IL Latched pins of IN port; IL<0> latches IN<0>, and IL<3> latches IN<3>

IN 4-bit input port

**INSTRUCTION CYCLES**
Instruction cycle time is fixed when the device is manufactured. This instruction time may be 4, 8, 16, or 32 input clock periods, depending on the COP model chosen.

L 8-bit I/O port

mm The low-order eight bits of a 10-bit address

nnnnnnn A 7-bit instruction address, appearing only in memory pages 2 and 3. nnnnnnn $\neq 7F_{16}$

**OBJECT CODE**
We represent each byte of the object code as either two hex digits or eight binary digits. Explanations of variable bit fields appear in alphabetic order in this list.

P 10-bit Program Counter

pp The high-order two bits of a 10-bit address

Q 8-bit latch for L port

qqqqqq A 6-bit instruction address. qqqqqq $\neq 3F_{16}$

reg 2-bit RAM register select

SA 10-bit subroutine Save Register A

SB 10-bit subroutine Save Register B

SC 10-bit subroutine Save Register C

SIO Serial I/O register or 4-bit counter

SK Serial clock or Carry status output line

STATUS The following symbols represent the operation's effect on the Carry status:
- (blank) no effect
X - affected by the operation
0 - always reset by the operation
1 - always set by the operation

SYNC Serial I/O synchronization pulse output via SK. See our discussion of serial I/O for timing and function details.

TF Internal timer overflow flag. This flag is set every 1024 instruction cycles.

x<y,z> Bits y through z of the quantity x. For example, B<3, 0> means the low-order four bits of the RAM pointer register. If the z term is omitted then only the bit selected by y is being referenced: thus A<0> means the least significant bit of the Accumulator.

← Data moves in the direction of the arrow

←→ Exchange data between two locations

[ ] The contents of the register, I/O port, or memory location designated inside the brackets. Hence, [A] means the contents of the Accumulator, and [reg,digit] means the contents of the RAM location addressed by the operands "reg" and "digit."

[[ ]] The contents of the memory location addressed via a register: [[B]] means the contents of a RAM location and [[P]] means data from program memory.

[$\overline{A}$] The complement of the Accumulator contents.

Table 1-9. Summary of the National Semiconductor COP400 Series Instruction Set

| TYPE | MNEMONIC | OPERAND(S) | OBJECT CODE | BYTES | INST. CYCLES | STATUS C | OPERATION PERFORMED | IMPLEMENTED ON COP MODEL: 410L 411L | 420 420L 402 402M | 420C | 421 421L | 421C |
|---|---|---|---|---|---|---|---|---|---|---|---|---|
| I/O | ING | | 33 2A | 2 | 1 | | [A] ← [G]<br>Input G port to Accumulator. | X | X | X | X | X |
| | ININ | | 33 28 | 2 | 1 | | [A] ← [IN]<br>Input IN port to Accumulator. | | X | X | | |
| | INIL | | 33 29 | 2 | 1 | | [A<0>] ← [IL<0>] if IN port is present; else 0<br>[A<1>] ← 0<br>[A<2>] ← [CKO] if CKO is an input; else 1<br>[A<3>] ← [IL<3>] if IN port is present; else 0<br>If available, input IL latches to Accumulator bits 3 and 0, otherwise clear those bits. Input CKO to Accumulator bit 2; set that bit if CKO serves as a clock line. | | X | X | X | X |
| | INL | | 33 2E | 2 | 1 | | [A] ← [L<0,3>]<br>[[B]] ← [L<4,7>]<br>Input low-order four bits of L port to Accumulator and high-order four bits to RAM location. | X | X | X | X | X |
| | OBD | | 33 3E | 2 | 1 | | [D] ← [Bd]<br>Output Bd register to D port. | X | X | X | X | X |
| | OMG | | 33 3A | 2 | 1 | | [G] ← [[B]]<br>Output RAM location contents to G port. | X | X | X | X | X |
| | XAS | | 4F | 1 | 1 | | [A] ← [SIO]<br>[SK] ← [C] if [C] = 0 or if [EN<0>] = 1;<br>[SK] ← SYNC pulse otherwise<br>Exchange Accumulator contents with those of serial I/O register. Execution of this instruction affects output line SK as described in the main text. | X | X | X | X | X |
| PRIMARY MEMORY REF. | CAMQ | | 33 3C | 2 | 1 | | [Q<0,3>] ← [[B]]<br>[Q<4,7>] ← [A]<br>Copy Accumulator and RAM data to L port latch. | X | X | X | X | X |
| | CQMA | | 33 2C | 2 | 1 | | [A] ← [Q<0,3>]<br>[[B]] ← [Q<4,7>]<br>Send contents of L port latch to RAM location and Accumulator. | | X | X | X | X |
| | LD | reg | 00rr0101 | 1 | 1 | | [A] ← [[B]]<br>[Br] ← [Br] XOR reg<br>Load Accumulator from RAM location and modify RAM register pointer. | X | X | X | X | X |
| | LDD | reg,digit | 23<br>00rrdddd | 2 | 1 | | [A] ← [reg,digit]<br>Load Accumulator from RAM location addressed by the operands "reg" and "digit". | | X | X | X | X |

Table 1-9. Summary of the National Semiconductor COP400 Series Instruction Set (Continued)

| TYPE | MNEMONIC | OPERAND(S) | OBJECT CODE | BYTES | INST. CYCLES | STATUS C | OPERATION PERFORMED | IMPLEMENTED ON COP MODEL 410L 411L | 420 420L 402 402M | 420C | 421 421L | 421C |
|---|---|---|---|---|---|---|---|---|---|---|---|---|
| PRIMARY MEMORY REFERENCE (Continued) | LQID | | BF | 1 | 1 | | [SC] ← [SB]<br>[SB] ← [SA]<br>[SA] ← [P] + 1<br>[P] ← addri<br>[Q] ← [[P]]<br>[P] ← [SA]<br>[SA] ← [SB]<br>[SB] ← [SC]<br>Load L port latch with ROM constant. Previous contents of stack register SC are lost. | X | X | X | X | X |
| | X | reg | 00rr0110 | 1 | 1 | | [A] ←→ [[B]]<br>[Br] ← [Br] XOR reg<br>Exchange Accumulator with RAM location and modify RAM register pointer. | X | X | X | X | X |
| | XAD | reg,digit | 23<br>10rrdddd | 2 | 1 | | [A] ←→ [reg,digit]<br>Exchange Accumulator with RAM location addressed by "reg" and "digit". Only XAD 3,15 is valid on COP410L and COP411L. | X | X | X | X | X |
| | XDS | reg | 00rr0111 | 1 | 1 | | [A] ←→ [[B]]<br>[Bd] ← [Bd] − 1<br>[Br] ← [Br] XOR reg<br>Exchange Accumulator with RAM location, decrement RAM digit pointer, and modify RAM register pointer. Skip next instruction if Bd decrements past 0. | X | X | X | X | X |
| | XIS | reg | 00rr0100 | 1 | 1 | | [A] ←→ [[B]]<br>[Bd] ← [Bd] + 1<br>[Br] ← [Br] XOR reg<br>Exchange Accumulator with RAM location, increment RAM digit pointer and modify RAM register pointer. Skip next instruction if Bd increments past $F_{16}$. | X | X | X | X | X |
| BIT MANIPULATION | RMB | bit | 0100bbbb | 1 | 1 | | [[B]<bit>] ← 0<br>Reset the specified RAM bit to 0. | X | X | X | X | X |
| | SMB | bit | 0100aaaa | 1 | 1 | | [[B]<bit>] ← 1<br>Set the specified RAM bit to 1. | X | X | X | X | X |

Table 1-9. Summary of the National Semiconductor COP400 Series Instruction Set (Continued)

| TYPE | MNEMONIC | OPERAND(S) | OBJECT CODE | BYTES | INST. CYCLES | STATUS C | OPERATION PERFORMED | IMPLEMENTED ON COP MODEL | | | | |
|---|---|---|---|---|---|---|---|---|---|---|---|---|
| | | | | | | | | 410L 411L | 420 420L 402 402M | 420C | 421 421L | 421C |
| SECONDARY MEMORY REF | ASC | | 30 | 1 | 1 | X | [A] ← [A] + [[B]] + [C]<br>Add contents of RAM location to the Accumulator with carry. Skip next instruction if execution of ASC sets Carry status. | X | X | X | X | X |
| | ADD | | 31 | 1 | 1 | | [A] ← [A] + [[B]]<br>Add contents of RAM location to the Accumulator. | X | X | X | X | X |
| | CASC | | 10 | 1 | 1 | X | [A] ← $\overline{[A]}$ + [[B]] + [C]<br>Add contents of RAM location plus carry to the complement of the Accumulator. Skip next instruction if result sets Carry status, indicating no borrow. | | X | X | X | X |
| | XOR | | 02 | 1 | 1 | | [A] ← [A] XOR [[B]]<br>Exclusive-OR Accumulator contents with those of RAM location. | X | X | X | X | X |
| IMMEDIATE | OGI | data4 | 33<br>0101dddd | 2 | 1 | | [G] ← data4<br>Output immediate data to G port. | | X | X | X | X |
| | STII | data4 | 0111dddd | 1 | 1 | | [[B]] ← data4<br>[Bd] ← [Bd] + 1<br>Store immediate data in RAM location and increment RAM digit pointer. | X | X | X | X | X |
| | LBI | reg,digitp | 00rreeee | 1 | 1 | | [Bd] ← digitp<br>[Br] ← reg<br>Load B register immediate. Skip next instructions if they are LBIs. COP410L and COP411L do not skip subsequent LBIs. | X | X | X | X | X |
| | LBI | reg,digit | 33<br>10rrdddd | 2 | 1 | | [Bd] ← digit<br>[Br] ← reg<br>Load B register immediate. Skip contiguous LBI instructions. | | X | X | X | X |
| | LEI | data4 | 33<br>0110dddd | 2 | 1 | | [EN] ← data4<br>Load the Enable register immediate. | X | X | X | X | X |
| IMMEDIATE OPERATE | AISC | data4 | 0101dddd | 1 | 1 | | [A] ← [A] + data4<br>Add immediate data to Accumulator. Skip next instruction if execution generates a carry. Note that Carry status is not affected. | X | X | X | X | X |

Table 1-9. Summary of the National Semiconductor COP400 Series Instruction Set (Continued)

| TYPE | MNEMONIC | OPERAND(S) | OBJECT CODE | BYTES | INST. CYCLES | STATUS C | OPERATION PERFORMED | IMPLEMENTED ON COP MODEL | | | | |
|---|---|---|---|---|---|---|---|---|---|---|---|---|
| | | | | | | | | 410L 411L | 420 420L 402 402M | 420C | 421 421L | 421C |
| JUMP | JID | | FF | 1 | 1 | | [P] ← [addri]<br>Jump to address contained in ROM. | X | X | X | X | X |
| | JMP | addr10 | 011000pp mm | 2 | 1 | | [P] ← addr10<br>Jump to address specified by operand. | X | X | X | X | X |
| | JP | addr6 | 11qqqqqq | 1 | 1 | | [P<0,5>] ← addr6<br>Jump within page. May not address the last word ($3F_{16}$) of the page. | X | X | X | X | X |
| | JP | addr7 | 1nnnnnnn | 1 | 1 | | [P<0,6>] ← addr7<br>Jump within pages 2 and 3. Only valid when executing from pages 2 and 3. May not address locations $0BF_{16}$ or $0FF_{16}$. | X | X | X | X | X |
| SUBROUTINE CALL AND RETURN | JSRP | addr6 | 10qqqqqq | 1 | 1 | | [SC] ← [SB]<br>[SB] ← [SA]<br>[SA] ← [P] + 1<br>[P<0,5>] ← addr6<br>[P<6,9>] ← 0010<br>Jump to subroutine on page 2, saving return address on the Stack. JSRP cannot be executed from pages 2 and 3 and may not pass control to address $0BF_{16}$. | X | X | X | X | X |
| | JSR | addr10 | 011010pp mm | 2 | 1 | | [SC] ← [SB]<br>[SB] ← [SA]<br>[SA] ← [P] + 1<br>[P] ← addr10<br>Jump to subroutine, saving return address on the Stack. | X | X | X | X | X |
| | RET | | 48 | 1 | 1 | | [P] ← [SA]<br>[SA] ← [SB]<br>[SB] ← [SC]<br>Return from subroutine. | X | X | X | X | X |
| | RETSK | | 49 | 1 | 1 | | [P] ← [SA]<br>[SA] ← [SB]<br>[SB] ← [SC]<br>Return from subroutine and skip next instruction. | X | X | X | X | X |

Table 1-9. Summary of the National Semiconductor COP400 Series Instruction Set (Continued)

| TYPE | MNEMONIC | OPERAND(S) | OBJECT CODE | BYTES | INST. CYCLES | STATUS C | OPERATION PERFORMED | IMPLEMENTED ON COP MODEL | | | | |
|---|---|---|---|---|---|---|---|---|---|---|---|---|
| | | | | | | | | 410L 411L | 420 420L 402 402M | 420C | 421 421L | 421C |
| BRANCH ON CONDITION | SKC | | 20 | 1 | 1 | | Skip on [C] = 1<br>Skip next instruction if Carry is set. | X | X | X | X | X |
| | SKE | | 21 | 1 | 1 | | Skip on [A] = [[B]]<br>Skip next instruction if Accumulator contents equal those of addressed RAM location. | X | X | X | X | X |
| | SKGZ | | 33 21 | 2 | 1 | | Skip on [G] = 0<br>Skip next instruction if all bits of I/O Port G contain 0. | X | X | X | X | X |
| | SKGBZ | bit | 33<br>000cccc1 | 2 | 1 | | Skip on [G<bit>] = 0<br>Skip next instruction if the specified bit of I/O Port G contains 0. | X | X | X | X | X |
| | SKMBZ | bit | 000cccc1 | 1 | 1 | | Skip on [[B]<bit>] = 0<br>Skip next instruction if the specified RAM bit contains 0. | X | X | X | X | X |
| | SKT | | 41 | 1 | 1 | | Skip on [TF] = 1; [TF] ← 0<br>Skip next instruction if internal timer overflow has occurred. Reset overflow indicator if skip is performed. The internal timer overflows once every 1024 instruction cycles. | | X | X | X | X |
| REGISTER-REGISTER MOVE | CAB | | 50 | 1 | 1 | | [Bd] ← [A]<br>Move Accumulator contents to RAM digit pointer register. | X | X | X | X | X |
| | CBA | | 4E | 1 | 1 | | [A] ← [Bd]<br>Move RAM digit pointer value to Accumulator. | X | X | X | X | X |
| | XABR | | 12 | 1 | 1 | | [A<0,1>] ←→ [Br]<br>[A<2,3>] ← 00<br>Exchange low-order bits of Accumulator with RAM register pointer. | | X | X | X | X |

Table 1-9. Summary of the National Semiconductor COP400 Series Instruction Set (Continued)

| TYPE | MNEMONIC | OPERAND(S) | OBJECT CODE | BYTES | INST. CYCLES | STATUS C | OPERATION PERFORMED | IMPLEMENTED ON COP MODEL | | | | |
|---|---|---|---|---|---|---|---|---|---|---|---|---|
| | | | | | | | | 410L 411L | 420 420L 402 402M | 420C | 421 421L | 421C |
| REGISTER OPERATE | CLRA | | 00 | 1 | 1 | | [A] ← 0000<br>Reset Accumulator contents to 0. | X | X | X | X | X |
| | COMP | | 40 | 1 | 1 | | [A] ← $\overline{[A]}$<br>Complement Accumulator contents. | X | X | X | X | X |
| | ADT | | 4A | 1 | 1 | | [A] ← [A] + 1010<br>Add ten to contents of Accumulator. | | X | X | X | X |
| INTERRUPT | LEI | data4 | 33<br>0110dddd | 2 | 1 | | [EN] ← data4<br>Load the Enable register immediate. | X | X | X | X | X |
| STATUS | RC | | 32 | 1 | 1 | 0 | [C] ← 0<br>Reset Carry to 0. | X | X | X | X | X |
| | SC | | 22 | 1 | 1 | 1 | [C] ← 1<br>Set Carry to 1. | X | X | X | X | X |
| | NOP | | 44 | 1 | 1 | | No operation. | X | X | X | X | X |
| | HLTT | | 33 39 | 2 | * | | Halt until timer overflows. | | | X | | X |

*Halt state will last from 1 to 1024 instruction cycles.

Table 1-10. National Semiconductor COP400 Series Instruction Object Codes

| INSTRUCTION | | OBJECT CODE | BYTES | |
|---|---|---|---|---|
| ADD | | 31 | 1 | |
| ADT | | 4A | 1 | * |
| AISC | data4 | 0101dddd | 1 | |
| ASC | | 30 | 1 | |
| CAB | | 50 | 1 | |
| CAMQ | | 33 3C | 2 | |
| CASC | | 10 | 1 | * |
| CBA | | 4E | 1 | |
| CLRA | | 00 | 1 | |
| COMP | | 40 | 1 | |
| CQMA | | 33 2C | 2 | * |
| HLTT | | 33 39 | 2 | * |
| ING | | 33 2A | 2 | |
| INIL | | 33 29 | 2 | * |
| ININ | | 33 28 | 2 | * |
| INL | | 33 2E | 2 | |
| JID | | FF | 1 | |
| JMP | addr10 | 011000pp | 2 | |
| | | mm | | |
| JP | addr6 | 11qqqqqq | 1 | |
| JP | addr7 | 1nnnnnnn | 1 | |
| JSR | addr10 | 011010pp | 2 | * |
| | | mm | | |
| JSRP | addr6 | 10qqqqqq | 1 | |
| LBI | reg,digit | 33 | 2 | * |
| | | 10rrdddd | | |
| LBI | reg,digitp | 00rreeee | 1 | |
| LD | reg | 00rr0101 | 1 | |
| LDD | reg,digit | 23 | 2 | |
| | | 00rrdddd | | |

* This instruction is not available on all COP400 models.

| INSTRUCTION | | OBJECT CODE | BYTES | |
|---|---|---|---|---|
| LEI | data4 | 33 | 2 | |
| | | 0110dddd | | |
| LQID | | BF | 1 | |
| NOP | | 44 | 1 | |
| OBD | | 33 3E | 2 | |
| OGI | data4 | 33 | 2 | * |
| | | 0101dddd | | |
| OMG | | 33 3A | 2 | |
| RC | | 32 | 1 | |
| RET | | 48 | 1 | |
| RETSK | | 49 | 1 | |
| RMB | bit | 0100bbbb | 1 | |
| SC | | 22 | 1 | |
| SKC | | 20 | 1 | |
| SKE | | 21 | 1 | |
| SKGBZ | bit | 33 | 2 | |
| | | 000cccc1 | | |
| SKGZ | | 33 21 | 2 | |
| SKMBZ | bit | 000cccc1 | 1 | |
| SKT | | 41 | 1 | * |
| SMB | bit | 0100aaaa | 1 | |
| STII | data4 | 0111dddd | 1 | |
| X | reg | 00rr0110 | 1 | |
| XABR | | 12 | 1 | * |
| XAD | reg,digit | 23 | 2 | |
| | | 10rrdddd | | |
| XAS | | 4F | 1 | |
| XDS | reg | 00rr0111 | 1 | |
| XIS | reg | 00rr0100 | 1 | |
| XOR | | 02 | 1 | |

* This instruction is not available on all COP400 models.

# THE PPS4/1

**The PPS4/1 family of microcomputers was developed as the single-chip replacement for the Rockwell PPS4 family.** The PPS4/1 family has been used extensively in consumer products. Its sales, like those of the other established 4-bit microcomputers, number in the millions. The PPS4/1 is very similar to the TMS1000. Both share similar approaches to memory organization, both have a similar I/O structure, and both lack a true interrupt capability. The major differences between the two families are:

1) Most models of the PPS4/1 family have a serial I/O capability.

2) The PPS4/1 microcomputers are not microprogrammable, as is the TMS1000.

3) The PPS4/1 family has a special purpose member, the PPS4/1 MM76C, which handles high-speed counting. The TMS1000 has no counterpart to this processor.

There are ten members of the PPS4/1 family. They are summarized in Table 1-11.

Figure 1-19 illustrates those parts of our general microcomputer model implemented by the PPS4/1 microcomputer. This figure is deceptive, since it would appear that a PPS4/1 has a System Bus. This is not the case. The bus illustrated is purely internal. The only means available to a PPS4/1 for communication to the outside world is via its I/O pins. **No provision for external RAM or ROM has been made.** Furthermore, the operations provided are primitive compared to those in 8-bit microprocessors or their support devices. For example, the serial I/O logic of the PPS4/1 cannot be compared to that of the Intel 8251 USART, or even the 1602 UART. The serial I/O logic merely serializes a 4-bit nibble into a bit stream (and the inverse). No provision is made for synchronization or for detecting framing or overrun errors. Buffering must be explicitly performed by the software. Nonetheless, the serial I/O interface is a very useful feature.

Table 1-11. Summary of the PPS4/1 Family of Microcomputers

| | **MM75** | **MM76** | **MM76C** | **MM76E** | **MM76EL** | **MM76L** | **MM77** | **MM77L** | **MM78** | **MM78L** |
|---|---|---|---|---|---|---|---|---|---|---|
| **ROM (bytes)** | 640 | 640 | 640 | 1024 | 1024 | 640 | 1344 | 1536 | 2048 | 2048 |
| **RAM (nibbles)** | 48 | 48 | 48 | 48 | 48 | 48 | 96 | 96 | 128 | 128 |
| **Total I/O Lines** | 22 | 31 | 39 | 31 | 31 | 31 | 31 | 31 | 31 | 31 |
| **Conditional Interrupt** | 1 | 2 | 2 | 2 | 2 | 2 | 2 | 2 | 2 | 2 |
| **Input** | 4 | 8 | 8 | 8 | 8 | 8 | 8 | 8 | 8 | 8 |
| **Bidirectional** | 17 | 18 | 18 | 18 | 18 | 18 | 18 | 18 | 18 | 18 |
| **Serial** | -- | 3 | 3 | 3 | 3 | 3 | 3 | 3 | 3 | 3 |
| **Package (Dual In-Line or Quad In-Line)** | 28-pin dual | 42-pin quad | 52-pin quad | 42-pin quad | 40-pin dual | 40-pin dual | 42-pin quad | 40-pin dual | 42-pin quad | 40-pin dual |
| **Supply Voltage (V)** | -15 | -15 | -15 | -15 | -11 to -6.5 | -11 to -6.5 | -15 | -11 to -6.5 | -15 | -11 to -6.5 |
| **Supply Current (mA)** | 8 | 8 | 12 | 3 | 3 | 3 | 8 | 3 | 8 | 3 |

**All devices of the PPS4/1 family are implemented using PMOS technology.**

**A single -15 volt power supply is required for all members of the PPS4/1 family except the L series parts (MM76EL, MM76L, MM77L, and MM78L). The L series parts will work with a power supply in the range of -11.0 to -6.5 volts with as little as 3 mA of current.** This makes them quite suitable for battery powered applications.

**Most members of the PPS4/1 family operate at a maximum clock frequency of 80 kHz, which gives a 12.5 microsecond cycle time. The L series parts can run at up to 100 kHz, yielding a 10 microsecond cycle time.** Since all instructions execute in one or two clock cycles, the PPS4/1 has a slight speed advantage over the TMS1000, but is at a severe speed disadvantage to the COP series.

**The primary manufacturer of the PPS4/1 series is:**

ROCKWELL INTERNATIONAL
Microelectronic Device Division
P.O. Box 3669
Anaheim, CA 92803

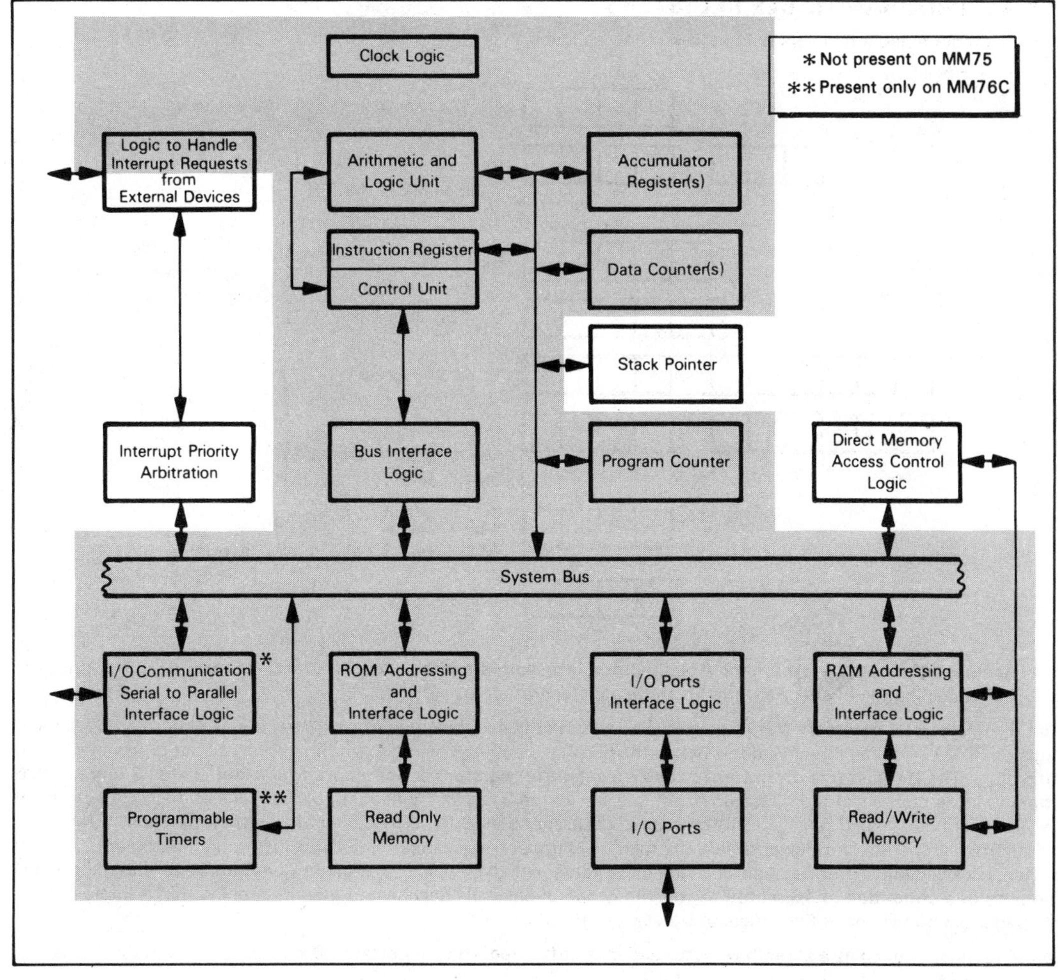


Figure 1-19. Logic of the PPS4/1 Family of Microcomputers

## PPS4/1 PROGRAMMABLE REGISTERS

PPS4/1 programmable registers may be illustrated as follows:

4-bit Accumulator

Data Counter

6- or 7-bit B register (7-bit on MM77, MM77L, MM78, MM78L)

5-bit Page register

6-bit Offset register

11-bit Program Counter

11-bit SA register

11-bit SB register (MM77, MM77L, MM78, MM78L only)

One or Two level subroutine stack

4-bit X register (MM77, MM77L, MM78, MM78L only)

4-bit S register

**The Accumulator acts as a primary Accumulator in a single-address machine architecture.** It is the principal source and destination of every arithmetic and logical operation.

**The B register is the primary Data Counter.** The only way to access locations in RAM is implied addressing via the B register. RAM cannot be directly addressed on the PPS4/1. The RAM memory is addressed as a contiguous block of 4-bit nibbles. **The B register is often treated as two separate registers concatenated together, called B lower and B upper.** B lower consists of the least significant four bits of the B register, while B upper consists of the most significant two or three bits of the B register. This division is necessary due to the 4-bit data paths within the PPS4/1. Many instructions will operate on B lower differently than on B upper. For example, the INCB instruction increments B lower while exclusive-ORing B upper with an immediate value. For this reason **it is often convenient to view the RAM memory as a collection of 16-nibble pages.** Many operations will show a wrap-around effect within a single 16-nibble page, since these operations modify B lower but not B upper.

**The X register is used as a scratch register and as a buffer register for certain I/O operations.** The X register is present on the MM77, MM77L, MM78, and MM78L models of the PPS4/1 family.

**The S register** is used by serial I/O logic. It **holds parallel data that is being shifted in or shifted out.**

**The P register is the Program Counter.** It consists of two parts, a 5-bit Page register and a 6-bit Offset register. Program memory is separate from data memory and is read-only. **Program memory is organized as 32 pages of 64 bytes each.** Single-byte subroutine call instructions always transfer to the two highest pages of the program address space, i.e., pages 30 and 31 (addresses $780_{16}$ - $7FF_{16}$). The PPS4/1 uses circular shift logic rather than an adder to increment the Program Counter. This means that the instructions in a given page are not in sequential order. This is of no significance except to the assembler and other program development software. Table 1-12 lists the correspondence between execution sequence and physical addresses within a page.

**The SA register is a return address save register.** It is used for saving the return address during a subroutine call. The MM77, MM77L, MM78, and MM78L all have an additional save register called the SB register. The SA and SB registers function as a two-level Stack. Hence the MM77, MM77L, MM78, and MM78L can have two levels of subroutine nesting rather than just one.

Table 1-12. PPS4/1 ROM Addressing Sequence

| Execution Sequence | Address | |
|---|---|---|
| | Binary Value | Hex Value |
| 0 | 000000 | 00 |
| 1 | 100000 | 20 |
| 2 | 010000 | 10 |
| 3 | 001000 | 08 |
| 4 | 000100 | 04 |
| 5 | 000010 | 02 |
| 6 | 100001 | 21 |
| 7 | 110000 | 30 |
| 8 | 011000 | 18 |
| 9 | 001100 | 0C |
| 10 | 000110 | 06 |
| 11 | 100011 | 23 |
| 12 | 010001 | 11 |
| 13 | 101000 | 28 |
| 14 | 010100 | 14 |
| 15 | 001010 | 0A |
| 16 | 100101 | 25 |
| 17 | 110010 | 32 |
| 18 | 111001 | 39 |
| 19 | 111100 | 3C |
| 20 | 011110 | 1E |
| 21 | 101111 | 2F |
| 22 | 010111 | 17 |
| 23 | 001011 | 0B |
| 24 | 000101 | 05 |
| 25 | 100010 | 22 |
| 26 | 110001 | 31 |
| 27 | 111000 | 38 |
| 28 | 011100 | 1C |
| 29 | 001110 | 0E |
| 30 | 100111 | 27 |
| 31 | 010011 | 13 |
| 32 | 001001 | 09 |
| 33 | 100100 | 24 |
| 34 | 010010 | 12 |
| 35 | 101001 | 29 |
| 36 | 110100 | 34 |
| 37 | 011010 | 1A |
| 38 | 101101 | 2D |
| 39 | 110110 | 36 |
| 40 | 111011 | 3B |
| 41 | 011101 | 1D |
| 42 | 101110 | 2E |
| 43 | 110111 | 37 |
| 44 | 011011 | 1B |
| 45 | 001101 | 0D |
| 46 | 100110 | 26 |
| 47 | 110011 | 33 |
| 48 | 011001 | 19 |
| 49 | 101100 | 2C |
| 50 | 010110 | 16 |
| 51 | 101011 | 2B |
| 52 | 010101 | 15 |
| 53 | 101010 | 2A |
| 54 | 110101 | 35 |
| 55 | 111010 | 3A |
| 56 | 111101 | 3D |
| 57 | 111110 | 3E |
| 58 | 111111 | 3F |
| 59 | 011111 | 1F |
| 60 | 001111 | 0F |
| 61 | 000111 | 07 |
| 62 | 000011 | 03 |
| 63 | 000001 | 01 |

## PPS4/1 MEMORY ADDRESSING

**PPS4/1 MEMORY ADDRESSING**

**The PPS4/1 contains separate and distinct program and data memories.** Program memory is strictly read-only. Instructions cannot be executed out of data memory. **Program memory can be addressed only by instruction execution.** No means of storing constants in program memory has been provided other than as the operand of immediate instructions. The branch instructions provided allow program memory to be addressed in its entirety, in banks of 16 pages or as 64-byte pages. The top two pages of program memory are the primitive subroutine pages. These pages can be addressed from anywhere in the program address space by the TM instruction with only a 6-bit address. Frequently used subroutines should be located in these pages.

**Data memory is addressed via implied addressing. The B register is used as a data counter which addresses data memory.** There are no other means of accessing data memory.

## PPS4/1 STATUS FLAGS

**PPS4/1 STATUS FLAGS**

The PPS4/1 has only one program-accessible status flag — the Carry.

There is also an internal skip status bit; if this bit is set during an instruction execution, the following instruction will be skipped.

## PPS4/1 INPUT AND OUTPUT LOGIC

All members of the PPS4/1 family have parallel I/O capability. All members of the PPS4/1 family except the MM75 also have a serial I/O capability.

**PPS4/1 PARALLEL I/O**

There are four types of parallel I/O available in the PPS4/1 series. They are:

1) 4-bit parallel input ports
2) 4-bit bidirectional ports
3) Discrete I/O lines
4) Conditional interrupts

**All members of the PPS4/1 family except the MM75 have two parallel input ports.** The MM75 has only one parallel input port. These 4-bit ports are **referred to as the P inputs.** The two P ports are referred to as Channel 1 (pins P1 - P4) and Channel 2 (pins P5 - P8). The signals entering Channel 2 are internally inverted before reaching the Accumulator. The MM75 implements only Channel 1.

**PPS4/1 DECODE MATRIX**

**All members of the PPS4/1 family have two bidirectional 4-bit ports, referred to as the R ports.** On all PPS4/1 microprocessors pins R1 - R4 are called Channel A. On the MM75, MM76, MM76E, MM76EL, and MM76L pins R5 - R8 are called Channel B. On the MM75, MM76, MM76E, MM76EL, and MM76L both the A and B channels' outputs can be obtained from a 16 x 8 decode matrix. This matrix allows a 4-bit quantity in the Accumulator to generate an 8-bit output. This is very helpful for applications using seven-segment displays. The contents of the decode matrix are alterable as a mask option. The standard chip comes with a BCD to seven-segment conversion table in the decode matrix. Loading the Accumulator with the digits 0 - $F_{16}$ allows Channels A and B to output the seven-segment codes for 0 - 9, A, -, P, D, E, and blank, respectively. The MM77, MM77L, MM78, and MM78L lack this decode matrix capability. On these processors R5 - R8 are referred to as Channel X. Channel X is routed through the X register on both input and output. Channel A functions normally except for the lack of the decode matrix on output.

**All members of the PPS4/1 family except the MM75 have a 10-bit discrete I/O port called the D port. The MM75 has a 9-bit D port.** The lines comprising the D port can be read or written independently (i.e., individual bits of the port can be manipulated). This port is designed for use with asynchronous inputs.

**PPS4/1 INTERRUPT INPUTS**

**All members of the PPS4/1 family have two conditional interrupt lines.** The MM75 has only one dedicated conditional interrupt input. However, R8 can be used as either an R input or an interrupt line. The conditional interrupt lines INT0 and INT1 are very similar to the D port lines, except that they can be tested by a single instruction. This feature allows the rapid testing of the conditional interrupt lines. Note that **this is not a true interrupt capability.** The microprocessor is not interrupted asynchronously. Instead, **the program must test for the interrupt condition and take appropriate action.**

**PPS4/1 SERIAL I/O**

All members of the PPS4/1 family except the MM75 have a serial I/O facility. This facility is implemented via three I/O lines connected to the S register: a serial input line, a serial output line, and a bidirectional serial shift clock line. The serial output line is connected to the high-order bit of the S register. Data to be shifted out is first transferred from the Accumulator to the S register. When the S register is shifted, the new high-order bit appears on the serial output line, and the value of the serial input line is shifted into the low-order bit of S. Two types of serial I/O timing are allowed: internal and external. If operation with the internal shift clock is selected, then the shift operation begins after an IOS instruction and takes two cycles of the internal clock ($CLK_A$) for each bit or eight cycles for four bits. A data clock is output on the Shift Clock line. The timing can be illustrated as follows:

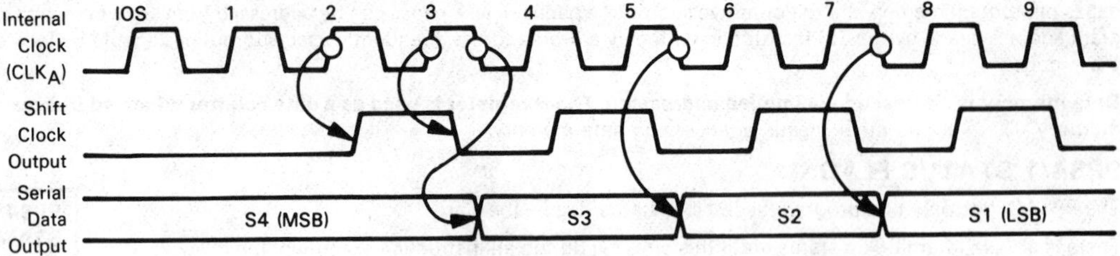

If an externally supplied shift clock is provided, the S register is shifted left once for each $CLK_A$ cycle that the shift clock is input high. This timing is shown below:

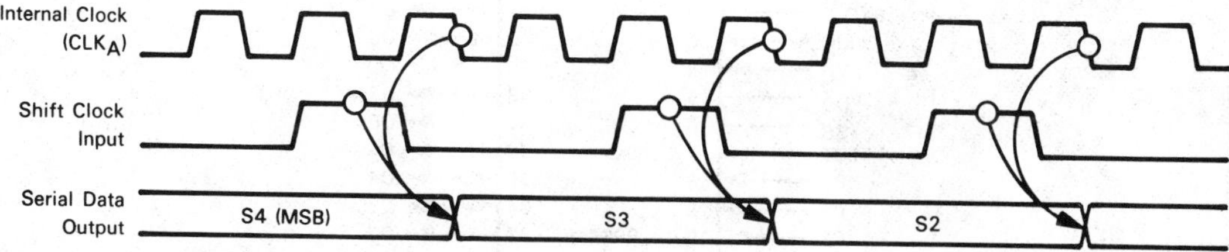


## PPS4/1 PINS AND SIGNALS

**Figures 1-20 through 1-23 illustrate the pins and signals for most members of the PPS4/1 family.** Note that the majority of the signals are consistent across the entire PPS4/1 family. For this reason we will combine the discussions of pins and signals for all members of the PPS4/1 family. The MM76C and its pins and signals are described later in this section.

Data inputs are provided by P1 - P8. P1 - P4 constitute the Channel 1 input port, while P5 - P8 constitute the Channel 2 input port.

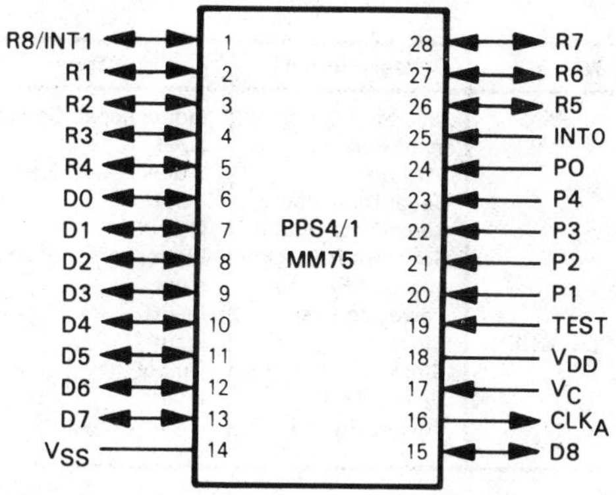

PPS4/1
MM75

| | | | |
|---|---|---|---|
| R8/INT1 | 1 | 28 | R7 |
| R1 | 2 | 27 | R6 |
| R2 | 3 | 26 | R5 |
| R3 | 4 | 25 | INTO |
| R4 | 5 | 24 | PO |
| DO | 6 | 23 | P4 |
| D1 | 7 | 22 | P3 |
| D2 | 8 | 21 | P2 |
| D3 | 9 | 20 | P1 |
| D4 | 10 | 19 | TEST |
| D5 | 11 | 18 | $V_{DD}$ |
| D6 | 12 | 17 | $V_C$ |
| D7 | 13 | 16 | $CLK_A$ |
| $V_{SS}$ | 14 | 15 | D8 |

| Pin Name | Description | Type |
|---|---|---|
| DO-D8 | Discrete I/O Pins | Bidirectional, Open Drain |
| P1-P4 | Input Port | Input |
| R1-R8/INT1 | I/O Port | Bidirectional, Open Drain |
| INTO,R8/INT1 | Interrupt Request | Input |
| PO | Power-on Reset | Input |
| $V_C$ | Clock | Input |
| $CLK_A$ | Clock | Output |
| TEST | Device Test | Input |
| $V_{DD}$,$V_{SS}$ | Power, Ground | |

Figure 1-20. PPS4/1 MM75 Pins and Signals

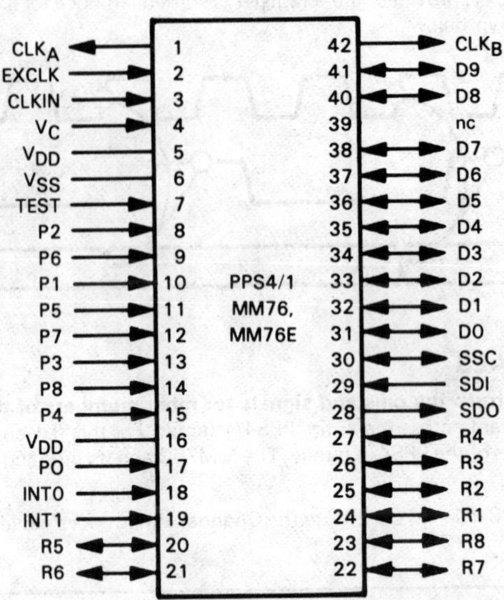


| Pin Name | Description | Type |
|---|---|---|
| D0-D9 | Discrete I/O Pins | Bidirectional, Open Drain |
| P1-P8 | Input Port | Input |
| R1-R8 | I/O Port | Bidirectional, Open Drain |
| SDI | Serial Data Input | Input |
| SDO | Serial Data Output | Output |
| SSC | Serial Shift Clock | Bidirectional, Open Drain |
| INT0, INT1 | Interrupt Request | Input |
| PO | Power-on Reset | Input |
| $V_C$, EXCLK, CLKIN | Clock | Input |
| $CLK_A$, $CLK_B$ | Clock | Output |
| TEST | Device Test | Input |
| $V_{DD}$, $V_{SS}$ | Power, Ground | |

Figure 1-21. PPS4/1 MM76 and MM76E Pins and Signals

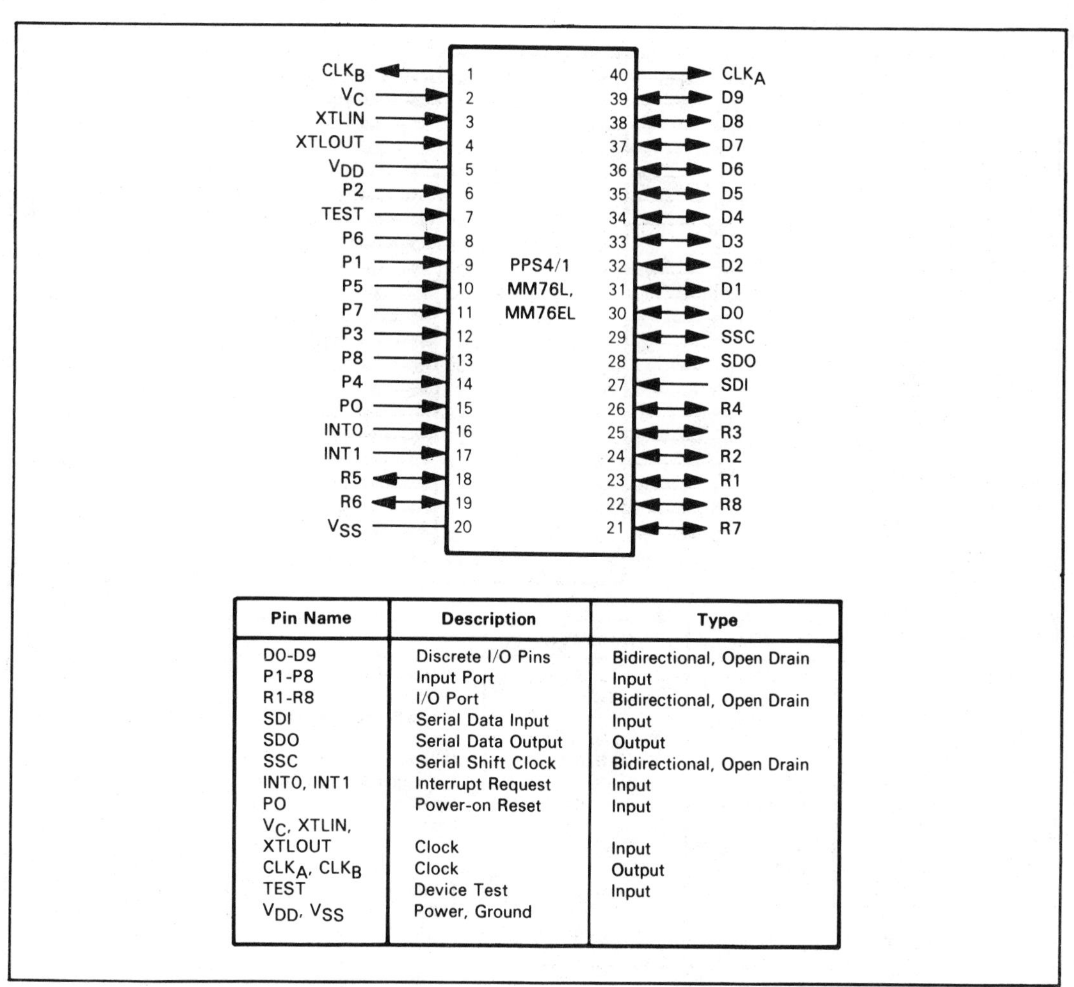


| Pin Name | Description | Type |
|---|---|---|
| DO-D9 | Discrete I/O Pins | Bidirectional, Open Drain |
| P1-P8 | Input Port | Input |
| R1-R8 | I/O Port | Bidirectional, Open Drain |
| SDI | Serial Data Input | Input |
| SDO | Serial Data Output | Output |
| SSC | Serial Shift Clock | Bidirectional, Open Drain |
| INTO, INT1 | Interrupt Request | Input |
| PO | Power-on Reset | Input |
| $V_C$, XTLIN, XTLOUT | Clock | Input |
| $CLK_A$, $CLK_B$ | Clock | Output |
| TEST | Device Test | Input |
| $V_{DD}$, $V_{SS}$ | Power, Ground | |

Figure 1-22. PPS4/1 MM76L and MM76EL Pins and Signals

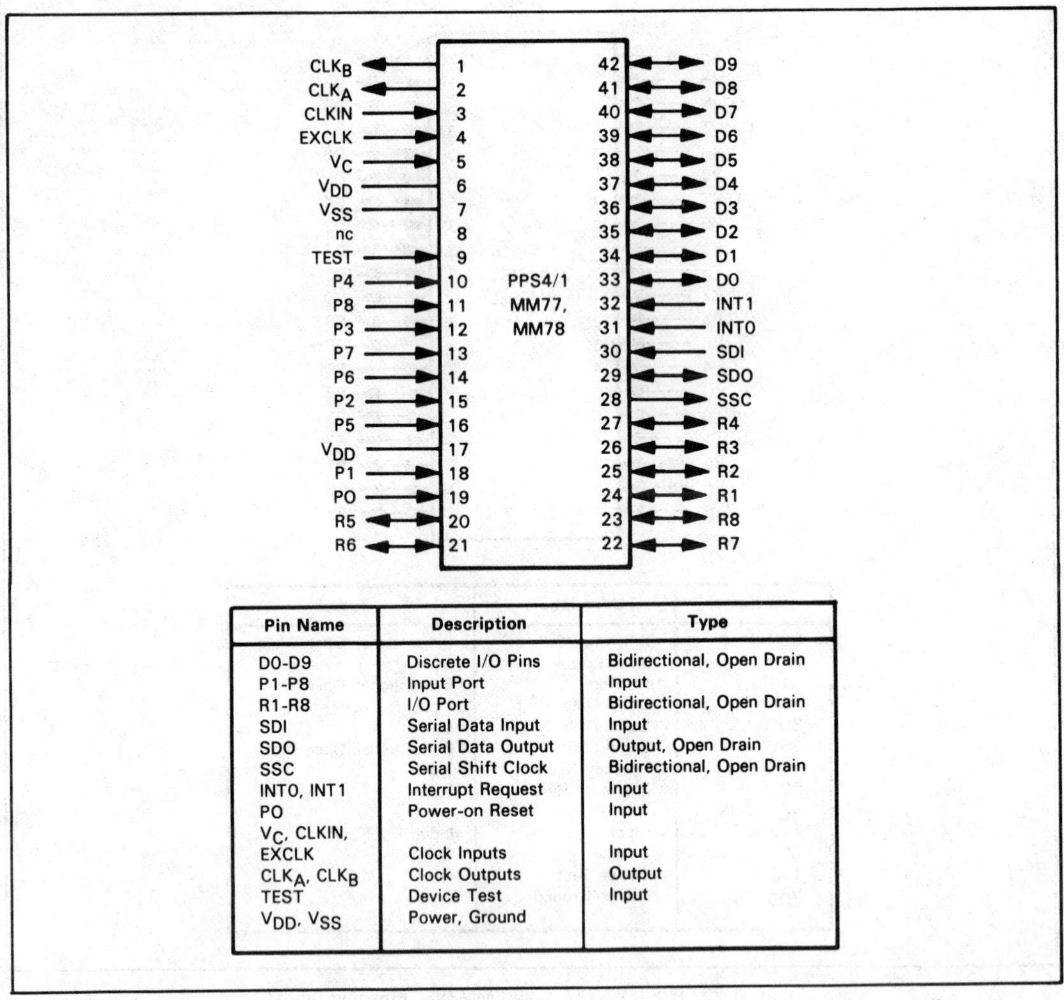


| Pin Name | Description | Type |
|---|---|---|
| DO-D9 | Discrete I/O Pins | Bidirectional, Open Drain |
| P1-P8 | Input Port | Input |
| R1-R8 | I/O Port | Bidirectional, Open Drain |
| SDI | Serial Data Input | Input |
| SDO | Serial Data Output | Output, Open Drain |
| SSC | Serial Shift Clock | Bidirectional, Open Drain |
| INTO, INT1 | Interrupt Request | Input |
| PO | Power-on Reset | Input |
| $V_C$, CLKIN, EXCLK | Clock Inputs | Input |
| $CLK_A$, $CLK_B$ | Clock Outputs | Output |
| TEST | Device Test | Input |
| $V_{DD}$, $V_{SS}$ | Power, Ground | |

Figure 1-23. PPS4/1 MM77 and MM78 Pins and Signals

The bidirectional I/O port is provided by pins R1 - R8. R1 - R4 implement the A port while R5 - R8 implement the B or X port, depending on the microcomputer.

The discrete I/O lines are provided by D0 - D9.

Serial I/O logic is implemented via the SDO, SDI, and SSC pins. SDO is the Serial Data Output line, SDI is the Serial Data Input line, and SSC is the Serial Shift Clock line.

**PPS4/1 CLOCK LOGIC**

$CLK_A$, $CLK_B$ (except MM75), $V_C$, and PO are common timing and reset pins present on all members of the PPS4/1 family. There are differences in the clock oscillator options for the low power L series. The L series uses two pins, called XTLOUT and XTLIN, while the other members of the PPS4/1 family use EXCLK and CLKIN. The standard PPS4/1 (except the MM75) can be connected for either an internal or an external clock. To use the internal clock, a resistor is connected between $V_C$ and $V_{DD}$. A 56 k$\Omega$ resistor will set the clock frequency to a nominal 80 kHz ±50%. If more precise timing is required, a precision external oscillator can be used. The external oscillator is connected to CLKIN, and the EXCLK pin is tied to $V_{DD}$. Frequencies within the range 40 kHz to 80 kHz are allowed.

The L series microcomputers have four timing options available: internal oscillator, external oscillator, crystal, and slave. The internal oscillator and external oscillator options are the same as the standard internal and external clock modes. The crystal mode allows connection of a crystal to drive the internal oscillator. Slave mode is used to synchronize two microcomputers. In this mode $CLK_A$ and $CLK_B$ are employed as inputs which accept the $CLK_A$ and $CLK_B$ outputs from another PPS4. The table below shows how an L series device is connected for the four clock options.

| Mode | $V_C$ | XTLIN | XTLOUT | $CLK_A$, $CLK_B$ | Frequency (kHz @ $V_{DD}$ = -8 V) |
|---|---|---|---|---|---|
| Internal | $V_{DD}$ | $V_{SS}$ | nc | Outputs | 70-130 |
| External Clock | $V_{SS}$ | Clock Input | nc | Outputs | 400-800 |
| External Crystal | $V_{SS}$ | One side of crystal | Other side of crystal | Outputs | ≈800 |
| Slave | $V_{DD}$ | $V_{DD}$ | nc | Inputs | 50-100 |

The PO input pin is the standard power-on reset input. The following circuit will generate a proper reset pulse:

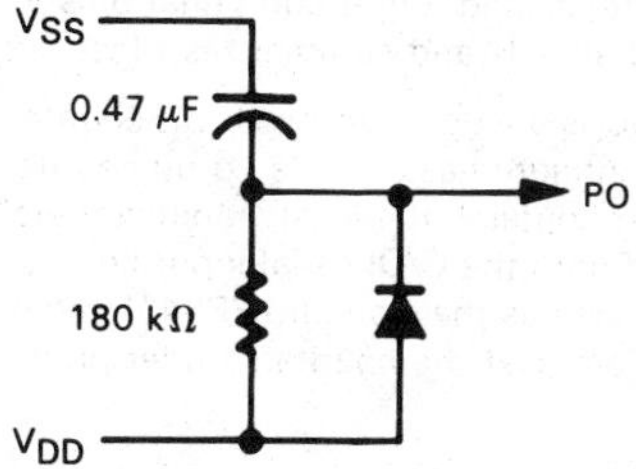


The standard power-on reset causes the microprocessor to start execution at location $3C0_{16}$. This location must contain either a NOP, a Reset Carry, or a Set Carry instruction. The following location may contain any valid PPS4/1 instruction.

The INT0 and INT1 inputs can cause conditional branching when tested by the INT0L, INT0H, INT1L, INT1H, DIN0, and DIN1 instructions.

The TEST input is normally connected to $V_{SS}$. ROM, RAM, and instruction logic can be tested by connecting TEST to $V_{DD}$.

## PPS4/1 MM76C HIGH-SPEED COUNTER OPTION

The PPS4/1 MM76C is an enhanced version of the standard PPS4/1 MM76 that contains 16 bits of high-speed counter capability. Fourteen programmable modes of counter operation are available. The options available include:

1) Single 16-bit counter
2) Dual 8-bit counters
3) Quadrature input
4) Event input
5) Up or down counting
6) Automatic preset of counters
7) Shifting of counters

Counter control is provided by assigning special meanings to five of the standard PPS4/1 MM76 I/O instructions when the microprocessor is executing in the special counter mode. The rich variety of counter configurations makes the PPS4/1 MM76C a very powerful tool in producing minimal hardware systems. Applications for the PPS4/1 MM76C include motor control with direction sensing, frequency counting, digital-to-analog conversion, and frequency synthesis. Entire control systems can be implemented with only a PPS4/1 MM76C microcomputer.

## Description of PPS4/1 MM76C Counter Subsystem

In addition to the standard PPS4/1 MM76 hardware the PPS4/1 MM76C contains logic for the counters. This logic consists of the following functional blocks:

1) Input circuitry
2) Lower counter register (8 bits)
3) Lower data register (8 bits)
4) Lower carry
5) Upper counter register (8 bits)
6) Upper data register (8 bits)
7) Upper carry
8) Control register (4 bits)
9) Control flip-flops (3 bits)

Figure 1-24 shows the relationship of each of these functional blocks to the architecture of the PPS4/1 MM76. The additions to the standard PPS4/1 MM76 are shaded. Eight additional pins are provided for counter control and status. Figure 1-25 shows the device's pins and signals and summarizes those signals not present on the PPS4/1 MM76.

The 16-bit counter of the PPS4/1 MM76C is divided into two 8-bit counters called the Upper Counter and the Lower Counter. When the counter circuitry is configured as a single 16-bit counter the Upper Counter contains the most significant eight bits and the Lower Counter contains the least significant eight bits. Both counters can be preset using the C/DI serial input line. Data is clocked onto the C/DI serial input line by the serial shift clock SCC/D. The timing of this serial input operation is exactly the same as the standard PPS4/1 serial I/O explained above. By this arrangement, external logic can preset the counters. To preset the counters under program control by the PPS4/1 MM76C, simply wire the microprocessor as shown below:

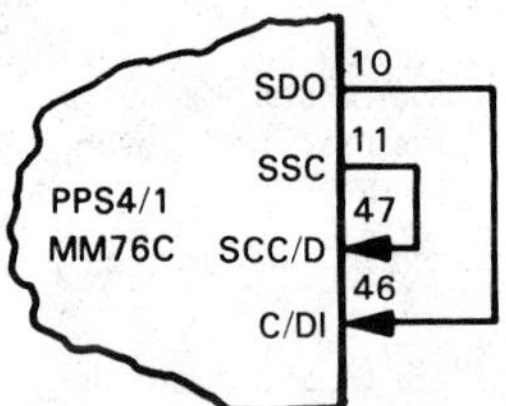


Since the PPS4/1 serial I/O logic handles only four bits at a time, two serial transmissions must be executed to load an 8-bit counter. The first serial transmission loads the least significant four bits of the Lower Counter; the second loads the most significant four bits of the Lower Counter; the third loads the least significant four bits of the Upper Counter; and the fourth loads the most significant four bits of the Upper Counter. Note that the serial input line C/DI will also be used to load the Control register. Care should be taken to preset the counters only when the PPS4/1 MM76C expects to receive counter data on the C/DI line. Each counter has a carry bit that is set whenever the counter overflows or underflows. The state of these carries is made available to external logic at the CA8 (Lower Counter) and CA16/D (Upper Counter) pins. Associated with each counter is an 8-bit buffer register; these are called the Upper Data register and the Lower Data register. Via the Data registers, the Counters may be read while counting is taking place. The Upper Data register has two special functions not implemented in the Lower Data register: shifting and presetting. Shifting of the Upper Data register can occur in only two of the 14 operational modes. Data can be shifted into the Upper Data register via the control/data serial input pin (C/DI) and out of the Upper Data register via the Upper Counter's carry bit (CA16/D). Control of all shifting operations is governed by the control/data serial shift clock (SCC/D). The presetting function automatically transfers the contents of the Upper Data register to the Upper Counter register whenever the Upper Counter overflows.

Two input modes are implemented: these are event input and quadrature input. Event input simply counts transitions on the input line. PC1 is the event input for the Lower Counter and SYEV is the event input for the Upper Counter. Both the Upper and Lower Counters can count up or down. The control of up or down counting on the Lower Counter is set by PC2. When PC2 is high the Lower Counter will count up; when PC2 is low the Lower Counter counts down. The Upper Counter can be set by the program to count either up or down. If the Upper Counter has been configured as the most significant eight bits of a 16-bit counter, its counting direction follows that of the Lower Counter. Event counting can take place at rates up to 2 MHz.

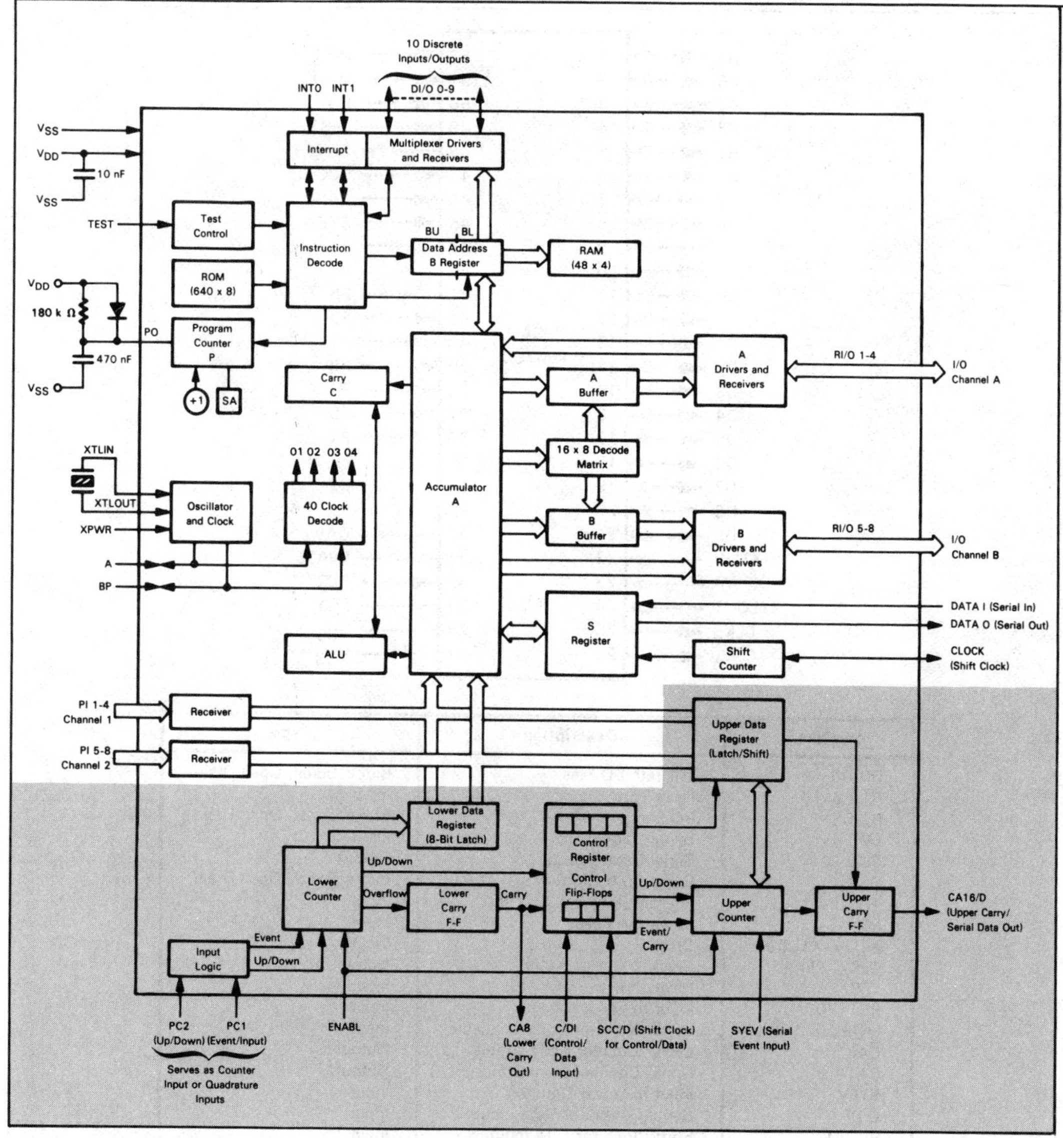


Figure 1-24. MM76C Counter Logic

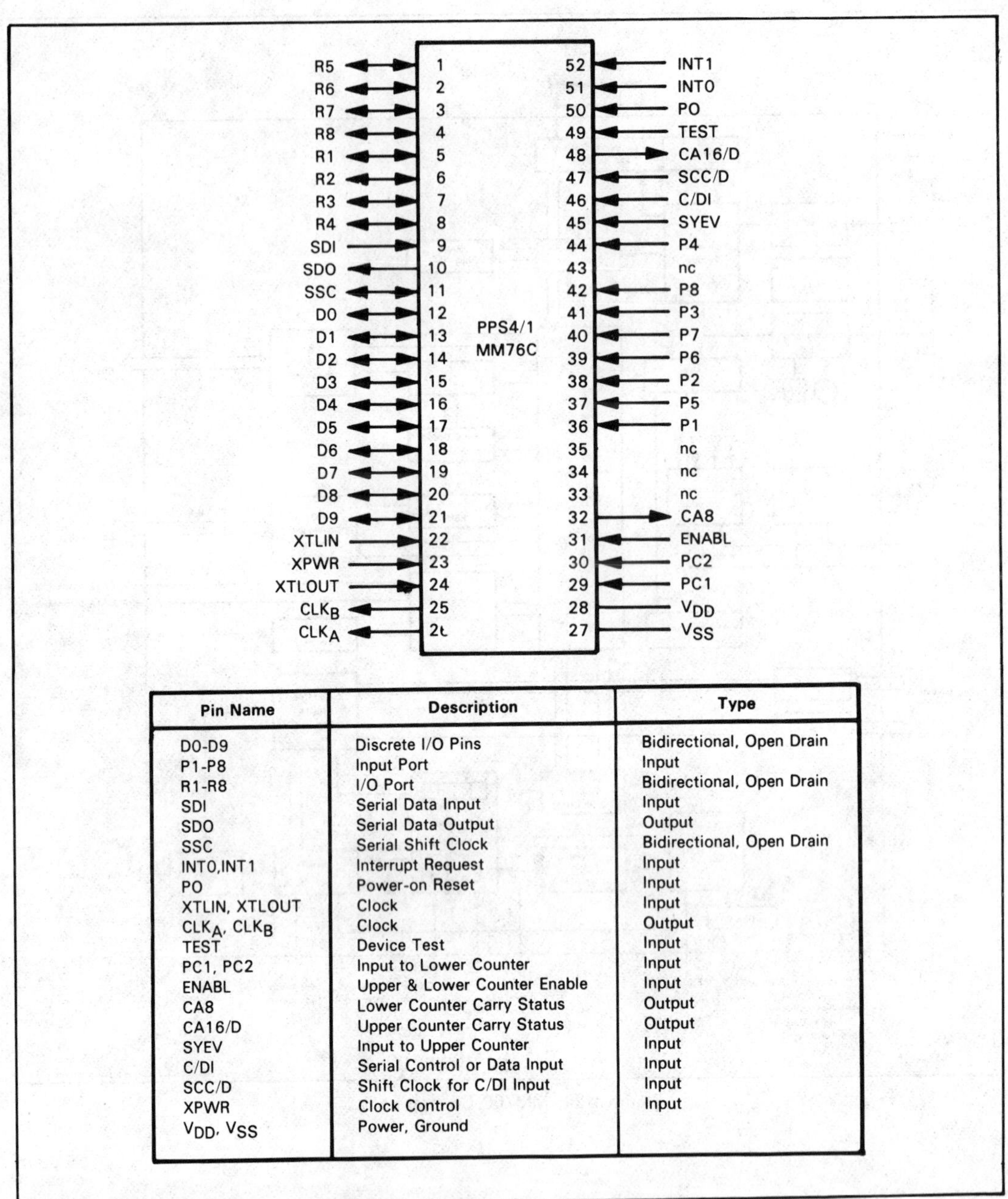


| Pin Name | Description | Type |
|---|---|---|
| DO-D9 | Discrete I/O Pins | Bidirectional, Open Drain |
| P1-P8 | Input Port | Input |
| R1-R8 | I/O Port | Bidirectional, Open Drain |
| SDI | Serial Data Input | Input |
| SDO | Serial Data Output | Output |
| SSC | Serial Shift Clock | Bidirectional, Open Drain |
| INTO,INT1 | Interrupt Request | Input |
| PO | Power-on Reset | Input |
| XTLIN, XTLOUT | Clock | Input |
| $CLK_A$, $CLK_B$ | Clock | Output |
| TEST | Device Test | Input |
| PC1, PC2 | Input to Lower Counter | Input |
| ENABL | Upper & Lower Counter Enable | Input |
| CA8 | Lower Counter Carry Status | Output |
| CA16/D | Upper Counter Carry Status | Output |
| SYEV | Input to Upper Counter | Input |
| C/DI | Serial Control or Data Input | Input |
| SCC/D | Shift Clock for C/DI Input | Input |
| XPWR | Clock Control | Input |
| $V_{DD}$, $V_{SS}$ | Power, Ground | |

Figure 1-25. PPS4/1 MM76C Pins and Signals

Quadrature input mode measures the frequency and relative phase relationship of two input signals. It uses two signals 90 degrees out of phase at PC1 and PC2. Input signals of this type are commonly generated by standard incremental rotation sensors. (See Figure 1-26.) A count is generated any time a transition occurs at PC1 or PC2. The counting direction is determined by the phase relationship between the two inputs. If the signal at PC1 leads the signal at PC2, the counter counts up; if the signal at PC1 lags the signal at PC2, the counter counts down. In systems such as the one outlined in Figure 1-26, a change of phase indicates a change of direction of rotation. The count recorded in the counter over a fixed period is proportional to the rotational velocity.

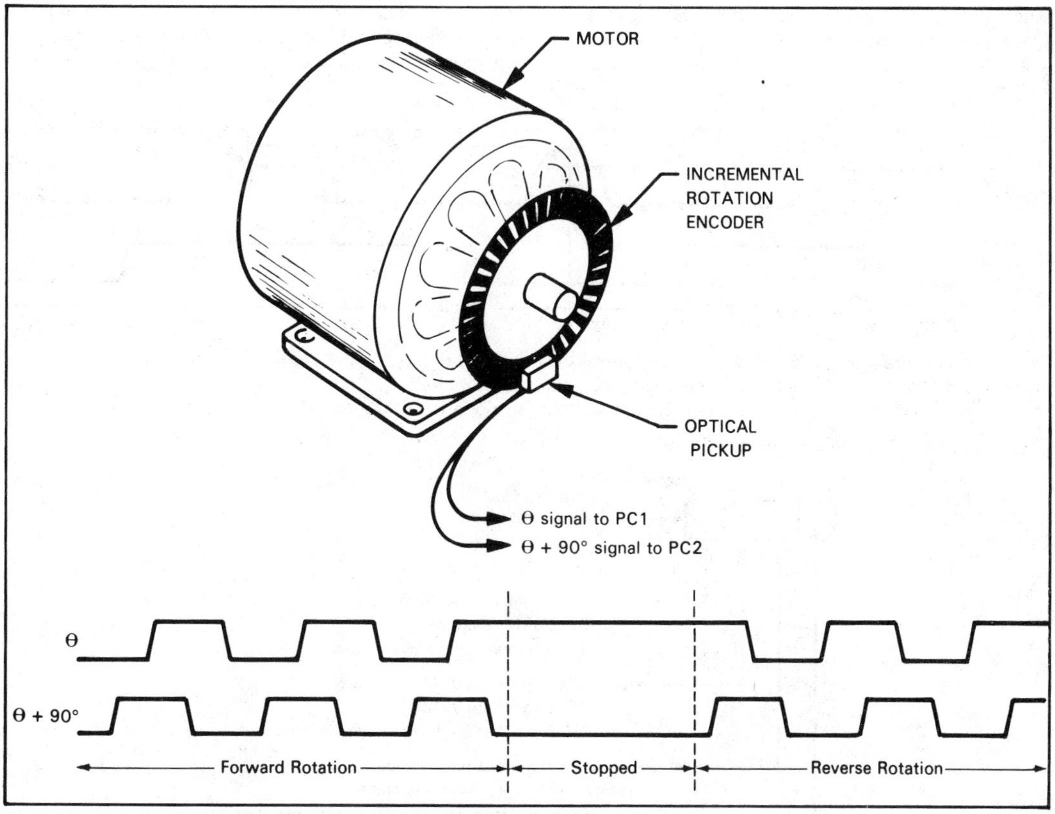

MOTOR
INCREMENTAL
ROTATION
ENCODER
OPTICAL
PICKUP
Θ signal to PC1
Θ + 90° signal to PC2
Θ
Θ + 90°
Forward Rotation
Stopped
Reverse Rotation

Figure 1-26. Generation of Quadrature Inputs

In quadrature input mode a maximum input frequency of 500 kHz on each input is allowed. Quadrature input imposes a few timing constraints that must be maintained to ensure proper operation of the input logic. A count reversal must not occur sooner than 500 ns after the last count. This timing is illustrated below:

Last Up Count
First Down Count
PC1
PC2
500 ns minimum
Count Up
Count Down

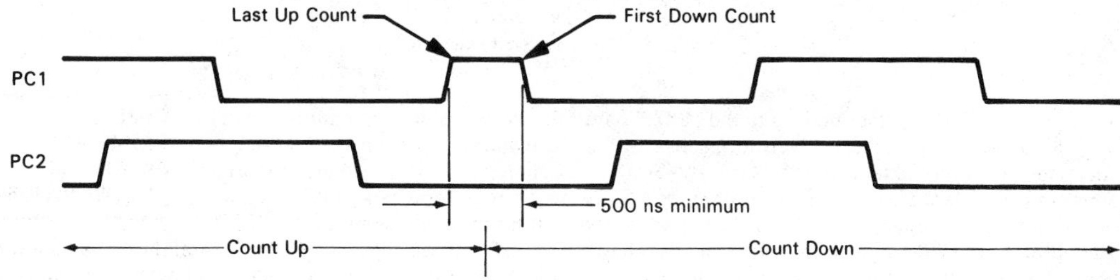

Another constraint exists when quadrature input is used with a 16-bit counter. When a carry is produced from the Lower Counter to the Upper Counter, a single phase reversal is handled as outlined above. However, any subsequent phase reversals must not occur for at least three cycles of the microprocessor's $CLK_A$. This timing may be illustrated as follows:

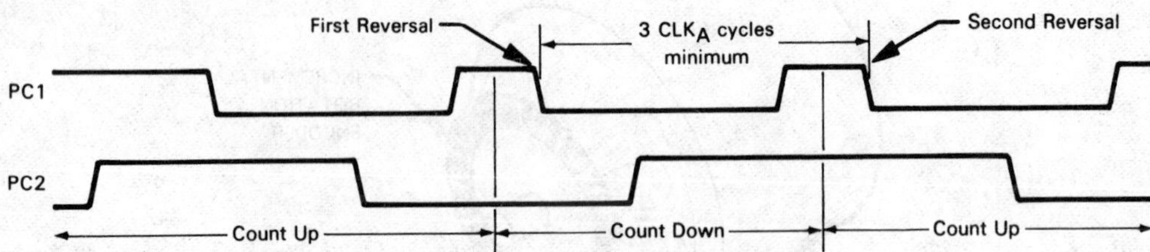


The Control register and the Control flip-flops control the operation of the counter logic. One of the 14 possible modes of counter operation is selected by writing an appropriate bit pattern into the Control register. The Control flip-flops are set and reset by the special I/O instructions used in counter mode to control the state of the counter logic.

Control register contents are interpreted as illustrated below:

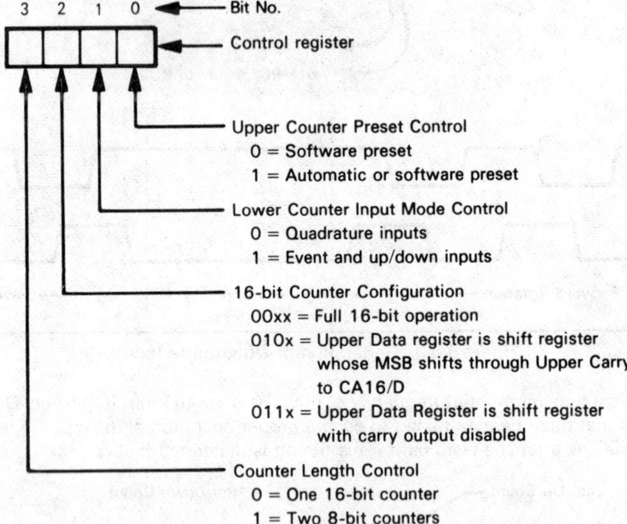


**PPS4/1 MM76C COUNTER INSTRUCTIONS**

Rather than adding new instructions to the MM76 instruction set to control the counter on the MM76C, a second meaning is given to a subset of MM76 instructions when the MM76C is operated in counter mode. On the MM76C the SEG1 instruction performs the combined functions of the standard SEG1 and SEG2 instructions. SEG2 does not perform its regular function; rather, it initiates the counter mode of operation. In the counter mode the instructions SEG2, IAM, IBM, I1, and I2C are used to control the counter logic. You must use these instructions carefully since their function depends on their sequence in the program. For example, I1 transfers the lower bits of the Lower Data register to the Accumulator if it precedes an I2C instruction, while it transfers the lower bits of the Upper Data register if it follows an I2C instruction.

The PPS4/1 MM76C internal clock provides a slightly different set of operating modes than the rest of the PPS4/1 family. These operating modes are summarized below:

**PPS4/1 MM76C CLOCK LOGIC**

| Mode | XPWR | XTLIN | XTLOUT | $CLK_A$ $CLK_B$ | Frequency (kHz) |
|---|---|---|---|---|---|
| Internal | $V_{SS}$ | $V_{DD}$ | No Connection | Outputs | 75-125 |
| External Crystal | $V_{DD}$ | One side of 3.57 MHz crystal | Other side of 3.57 MHz crystal | Outputs | 89 |
| Slave | $V_{SS}$ | $V_{SS}$ | No Connection | Inputs | Unspecified |

## PPS4/1 SERIES MICROCOMPUTER INSTRUCTION EXECUTION

Almost all PPS4/1 instructions execute in a single clock cycle. Notable exceptions are transfer, conditional transfer, and macro instructions.

## PPS4/1 SERIES MICROCOMPUTER INSTRUCTION SET

There are variations in the instruction sets of the different microcomputers of the PPS4/1 series. However, the similarities outweigh the differences, so all the instruction sets are described in Table 1-13. Separate columns have been provided to show which instructions correspond to which microcomputer.

The PPS4/1 instruction set is weak when compared to that of other microprocessors. However, the PPS4/1 series was designed as a low-cost digital logic replacement and functions more than adequately in this role. The economics of its use in a high-volume product make any programmer inconvenience irrelevant. The type of product for which the PPS4/1 is designed is produced in the tens of thousands. An extra week or two of programming effort is insignificant in such an application.

## THE BENCHMARK PROGRAM

As stated in the TMS1000 section of this chapter, a special benchmark more suited to the 4-bit microcomputers will be used. This benchmark consists of inputting a 1- to 16-nibble packet of data from an input port.

```
        LBL     BUFFER  GET BUFFER ADDRESS
        I1              INPUT BUFFER LENGTH
        LBA             SAVE BUFFER LENGTH
LOOP    I1              INPUT DATA
        XDSK    0       STORE DATA
        T       LOOP    GET MORE DATA
```

## PPS4/1 INSTRUCTION MNEMONICS

**Table 1-13 summarizes the PPS4/1 instruction set. The MNEMONIC column shows the instruction mnemonic, and the operands, if any, are shown in the OPERAND column. Macro instructions (combinations of basic instructions) are not included.**

**The fixed part of an assembly language instruction is shown in UPPER CASE. The variable part (immediate data, label or address) is shown in lower case.**

## PPS4/1 INSTRUCTION OBJECT CODES

**For instruction bytes without variations, object codes are represented as two hexadecimal digits (e.g., 4D).**

**For instruction bytes with variations in one of the two digits, the object code is shown as one 4-bit binary number and one hexadecimal digit (e.g., 5 dddd). For other instruction bytes with variations, the object code is shown as eight binary digits (e.g., 11aa aaaa).**

**The object code, execution time, and instruction length in bytes is shown in Table 1-14 for each instruction. Tables 1-15 and 1-16 list the object codes in numerical order.**

## PPS4/1 INSTRUCTION EXECUTION TIMES

**Tables 1-13 and 1-14 list the instruction execution times in clock periods.** Real time can be obtained by dividing the given number of clock periods by the clock frequency. For example, for an instruction that requires one clock period, a 100 kHz clock will result in a 10 microsecond execution time.

## PPS4/1 ABBREVIATIONS

These are the abbreviations used in this chapter:

| | |
|---|---|
| A | The 4-bit Accumulator |
| aaaaaa | A 6-bit address used to specify an offset within a page (low-order address bits) |
| AB | The 4-bit Accumulator Buffer register |
| addr6 | A 6-bit address constant |
| addr7 | A 7-bit address constant |
| addr10x | A 10-bit address constant in the range 0-$37F_{16}$ |
| addr10y | A 10-bit address constant in the range 0-$3FF_{16}$ |
| addr10z | A 10-bit address constant in the range $400_{16}$ - $77F_{16}$ |
| B | The 6-bit Data Counter (7 bits in MM77, MM78) |
| bit2,bb | A 2-bit immediate field used to specify a single bit in a 4-bit nibble as follows:<br>$00_2$ - selects least significant bit<br>$01_2$ - selects next to least significant bit<br>$10_2$ - selects next to most significant bit<br>$11_2$ - selects most significant bit |
| C | Carry flag |
| CR | The 4-bit Control register (MM76C only) |
| CR1 | Control flip-flop 1 (MM76C only) |
| CR2 | Control flip-flop 2 (MM76C only) |
| CR3 | Control flip-flop 3 (MM76C only) |
| D | The 10-bit discrete I/O port (9 bits on MM75) |
| data2 | A 2-bit immediate field |
| data3 | A 3-bit immediate field |
| data4 | A 4-bit immediate field |
| data4x | A 4-bit non-zero immediate field |
| dd | Two bits of immediate data |
| ddd | Three bits of immediate data |
| dddd | Four bits of immediate data |
| DM | The 128-bit Decode Matrix (not on MM77, MM78) |
| eeee | A 4-bit non-zero immediate field |
| ffff | Least significant four bits of an immediate data field wider than four bits |
| gg | Most significant two bits of a 6-bit immediate value |
| ggg | Most significant three bits of a 7-bit immediate value |
| hhhh | Four bits of non-zero immediate data |
| [INT0] | The INT0 flip-flop |
| [INT1] | The INT1 flip-flop |
| LC | The 8-bit Lower Counter register |
| LDR | The 8-bit Lower Data register |
| P | The 8-bit Input Port (4 bits on MM75) |
| PC | The 10-bit Program Counter (11 bits in MM77, MM78) |
| PPPP | A 4-bit page address (high-order address bits) |
| R | The 8-bit Input/Output port |
| S | The 4-bit Serial Input/Output register |
| SA | The 10-bit Subroutine Save register (11 bits in MM77, MM78) |
| SB | The 11-bit Subroutine Save register (MM77, MM78 only) |
| UC | The 8-bit Upper Counter register (MM76C only) |
| UDR | The 8-bit Upper Data register (MM76C only) |
| X | The 4-bit X register (MM77, MM78 only) |
| XB | The 4-bit X register buffer |
| xx | A 2-bit "don't care" |
| xxxx | A 4-bit "don't care." Values of $0000_2$ and $0001_2$ are not allowed. |
| [ ] | Contents of the location within brackets. If a register is enclosed by brackets, then the contents of that register |

| Symbol | Meaning |
|---|---|
| < > | Subfield specifier. Specifies a subset for a register or memory location. A single digit enclosed by angle brackets specifies only a single bit. Two numbers separated by a comma and enclosed by angle brackets specify a range of bits. The first number specifies the least significant bit position of the subfield, while the second digit specifies the most significant bit. All bits are numbered from least to most significant, with bit 0 being the least significant bit. For example:<br>A<0> specifies the least significant bit of the Accumulator<br>UC<4,7> specifies the most significant four bits of the Upper Counter register |
| ← | Data is transferred in the direction of the arrow |
| ←→ | Data is exchanged between two locations |
| iff | If and only if |
| = | Test for equality between two values |
| $\Lambda$ | Logical AND |
| * | Multiplication |
| + | Addition |
| $\overline{x}$ | Complement of x |
| ⊕ | Exclusive OR |
| * | New carry not valid until second cycle after instruction execution completes |
| ** | Value of Carry during previous cycle is used |
| *** | New B register contents may not be valid until second cycle following execution of this instruction |
| **** | IOS executes in one cycle. I/O register shifting continues for 8 more cycles. |

Table 1-13. A Summary of the PPS4/1 Microcomputer Instruction Set

| TYPE | MNEMONIC | OPERAND(S) | OBJECT CODE MM75 MM76 | OBJECT CODE MM77 MM78 | CLOCK CYCLES | STATUS C | STATUS SKIP | OPERATION PERFORMED |
|---|---|---|---|---|---|---|---|---|
| I/O | IAM | | 1A | | 1 | | | $[A] \leftarrow [R] <0,3> \wedge [A]$<br>Input least significant 4 bits of the R port, ANDed with A, to A. |
| | IBM | | 1B | | 1 | | | $[A] \leftarrow [R] <4,7> \wedge [A]$<br>Input most significant 4 bits of the R port, ANDed with A, to A. |
| | IOA | | | 7B | 1 | | | $[A]_{new} \leftarrow [AB]_{old} \wedge [R]_{old} <0,3>$<br>$[AB]_{new} \leftarrow [A]_{old}$<br>$[R]_{new} <0,3> \leftarrow [AB]_{new}$<br>Simultaneously input the least significant 4 bits of the R port, ANDed with the A buffer, to A while transferring the contents of A to the least significant 4 bits of the R port via the A buffer. |
| | I1 | | 4A | | 1 | | | $[A] \leftarrow [P] <0,3>$<br>Input least significant 4 bits of the P port to A. |
| | I1SK | | | 60 | 1 | | X | $[A] \leftarrow [P] <0,3> + [A]$<br>Input and add least significant 4 bits of the P port to A. Skip if no overflow. |
| | IOS | | 4D | 2D | 1•••• | | | Serial<br>Serial Out ← [3 ← 0] ← Serial In<br>Shift the Serial I/O register left 4 times. Shifting takes 8 cycles after IOS executes. |
| | I2C | | 4B | 78 | 1 | | | $[A] \leftarrow \overline{[P] <4,7>}$<br>Input the complement of the most significant 4 bits of the P port to A. |
| | IX | | | 72 | 1 | | | $[X] \leftarrow [XB] \wedge [R] <4,7>$<br>Input most significant 4 bits of the R port, ANDed with the X register buffer, to the X register. |
| | OA | | 18 | | 1 | | | $[R] <0,3> \leftarrow [A]$<br>Output Accumulator to least significant 4 bits of the R port. |
| | OB | | 19 | | 1 | | | $[R] <4,7> \leftarrow [A]$<br>Output Accumulator to most significant 4 bits of the R port. |
| | OX | | | 73 | 1 | | | $[XB] \leftarrow [X]$<br>$[R] <4,7> \leftarrow [XB]$<br>Output X register to 4 most significant bits of the R port via the X buffer. |
| | ROS | | 1 01xx | 71 | 1 | | | $[D] <[B] <0,3>> \leftarrow 0$<br>Reset the discrete I/O pin selected by the least significant 4 bits of B when $B <4,5> = 11_2$ (MM75, MM76) or $B <6> = 0$ (MM77, MM78). If $B <0,3> = 1010_2$, reset INT1 flip-flop. If $B <0,3> = 1011_2$, reset INTO flip-flop. |

Table 1-13. A Summary of the PPS4/1 Microcomputer Instruction Set (Continued)

| TYPE | MNEMONIC | OPERAND(S) | OBJECT CODE MM75 MM76 | OBJECT CODE MM77 MM78 | CLOCK CYCLES | STATUS C | STATUS SKIP | OPERATION PERFORMED |
|---|---|---|---|---|---|---|---|---|
| I/O (Continued) | SEG1 | | 0E | | 1 | | | [R] <0,3> ← [DM] < [A] •8, ([A] •8) +3 ><br>Output the lower order 4 bits of the Decode Matrix entry selected by A to the least significant 4 bits of the R port. B must point to the complement of A. (Except MM76C). |
| | SEG1 | | 0E | | 1 | | | [R] ← [DM] < [A] •8, ([A] •8) +7 ><br>Output to the R port the 8 bits selected from the Decode Matrix by the contents of the Accumulator. The B register must point to a RAM location that holds the complement of A. A mask option allows the most significant bit of R to display the current state of C. (MM76C only) |
| | SEG2 | | 0F | | 1 | | | [R] <4,7> ← [DM] < ([A] •8) +4, ([A] •8) +7 ><br>Output the higher order 4 bits of the Decode Matrix entry selected by A to the most significant 4 bits of the R port. B must point to the complement of A. Also, a mask option allows R <7> to be set to the current state of C. (Except MM76C) |
| | SOS | | 1 00xx | 70 | 1 | | | [D < [B] <0,3>> ← 1<br>Set the discrete I/O pin selected by the least significant 4 bits of B when B <4,5> = $11_2$ (MM75, MM76) or B <6> = 0 (MM77, MM78). If B <0,3> = $1010_2$, reset INT1 flip-flop. If B <0,3> = $1011_2$, reset INT0 flip-flop. |
| MM76C COUNTER I/O | IAM | | 1A | | 1 | | | [A] ← [R] <0,3> Λ [A]<br>[UC] ← [LC] ← 0 iff modes 1-5 (16-bit counter modes)<br>[UC] ← 0 iff modes 6-14 Λ [CR2] = 1 (8-bit counter modes)<br>[LC] ← 0 iff modes 6-14 Λ [CR1] = 1 (8-bit counter modes)<br>Input least significant 4 bits of R port, ANDed with A, to A. Clear both counters if configured as a single 16-bit counter. If configured as two 8-bit counters clear Lower Counter register if CR1 flip-flop set, and clear Upper Counter register if CR2 set. |
| | IBM | | 1B | | 1 | | | [A] ← [R] <4,7> Λ [A]<br>[UC] ← [UDR]<br>Input most significant 4 bits of R port, ANDed with A, to A. Load Upper Counter register from Upper Data register. |
| | I1 | | 4A | | 1 | | | [A] ← [LDR] <0,3> iff [CR1] = 1 Λ [CR2] = 0<br>[A] ← [UDR] <0,3> iff [CR1] = 0 Λ [CR2] = 1<br>If no I2C instruction has been executed, then load A with the least significant 4 bits of the Lower Data register. If an I2C instruction has been executed, then load A with the least significant 4 bits of the Upper Data register. |

Table 1-13. A Summary of the PPS4/1 Microcomputer Instruction Set (Continued)

| TYPE | MNEMONIC | OPERAND(S) | OBJECT CODE MM75 MM76 | OBJECT CODE MM77 MM78 | CLOCK CYCLES | STATUS C | STATUS SKIP | OPERATION PERFORMED |
|---|---|---|---|---|---|---|---|---|
| MM76C COUNTER I/O (Continued) | I2C | | 4B | | 1 | | | [A] ← [LDR] <4,7> iff [CR1] = 1 Λ [CR2] = 0<br>or<br>[A] ← [UDR] <4,7> iff [CR1] = 1 Λ [CR2] = 0<br>[CR1] ← 0<br>[CR2] ← $\overline{[CR2]}$<br>[CR3] ← 0<br>The first I2C instruction will load A with the most significant 4 bits of the Lower Data register. The second I2C will load A with the most significant 4 bits of the Upper Data register and exit counter mode. |
| | SEG2 | | 0F | | 1 | | | Enables counter logic iff [CR1] = 0<br>[LDR] ← [LC] iff [CR1] = 0<br>[UDR] ← [UC] iff [CR1] = 0<br>Gate serial data input to UDR iff [CR1] = 0<br>Gate serial data input to CR iff [CR1] ≠ 0<br>UC configured to count up iff [CR1] ≠ 0<br>Disable UC enable input iff [CR1] ≠ 0<br>Disable UC preset iff [CR1] ≠ 0<br>LC configured to quadrature mode iff [CR1] ≠ 0<br>[CR3] ← 1 iff [CR1] = 0<br>[CR1] ← 1<br>First SEG2 executed enables counter logic, loads the Upper and Lower Data registers from their respective counters, gates the serial control/data input to the Upper Data register, and sets the CR1 flip-flop. The second and all subsequent SEG2s executed (until counter mode terminates) cause the Upper Counter register to be configured as an up counter, the Lower Counter register to be configured for quadrature inputs, the serial control/data input to be gated to the Control register, the Upper Counter register enable input and preset control to be disabled, and the CR1 and CR3 flip-flops to be set (MM76C only). |
| PRIMARY MEMORY REFERENCE | L | data2 | 5 00dd | 5 00dd | 1 | | | [A] ← [[B]];<br>[B] <4,5> ← [B] <4,5> + data2<br>Load the Accumulator from the RAM location addressed by B. Exclusive-OR bits 4,5 of B with data2. |
| | X | data2 | 5 10dd | 5 11dd | 1 | | | [A] ←→ [[B]];<br>[B] <4,5> ← [B] <4,5> + data2.<br>Exchange the Accumulator with the RAM location addressed by B. Exclusive-OR bits 4,5 of B with data2 |

Table 1-13. A Summary of the PPS4/1 Microcomputer Instruction Set (Continued)

| TYPE | MNEMONIC | OPERAND(S) | OBJECT CODE MM75 MM76 | OBJECT CODE MM77 MM78 | CLOCK CYCLES | STATUS C | STATUS SKIP | OPERATION PERFORMED |
|---|---|---|---|---|---|---|---|---|
| PRIMARY MEMORY REFERENCE (Continued) | XDSK | data2 | 5 11dd | 5 10dd | 1••• | | X | [A] ←→ [[B]]; [B] <0,3> ← [B] <0,3> - 1 [B] <4,5> ← [B] <4,5> ⊕ data2 Exchange the Accumulator with the RAM location addressed by B. Exclusive-OR bits 4,5 of B with data2. Decrement least significant 4 bits of B. Skip if least significant 4 bits of B equal $1111_2$. |
| | XNSK | data2 | 5 01dd | 5 01dd | 1••• | | X | [A] ←→ [[B]]; [B] <0,3> -1 [B] <0,3> ← [B] <4,5> ← [B] <4,5> ⊕ data2 Exchange the Accumulator with the RAM location addressed by B. Exclusive-OR bits 4,5 of B with data2. Increment least significant 4 bits of B. Skip if least significant 4 bits of B equal $0000_2$. |
| SECONDARY MEMORY REFERENCE | A | | 42 | 7E | 1 | | | [A] ← [A] + [[B]] Add contents of RAM location addressed by B to Accumulator. |
| | AC | | 40 | 7C | 1• | X | | [A] ← [A] + [[B]] + C Add contents of RAM location addressed by B with Carry to Accumulator. Carry not valid for one additional cycle. |
| | ACSK | | 41 | 7D | 1• | X | X | [A] ← [A] + [[B]] + C Add contents of RAM location addressed by B with Carry to Accumulator. Skip if no carry (overflow). Carry not valid for one additional cycle. |
| | ASK | | 43 | | 1 | | X | [A] ← [A] + [[B]] Add contents of RAM location addressed by B to Accumulator. |
| | RB | bit2 | 1 01bb | 2 01bb | 1 | | | [[B]] <bit2> ← 0 Reset bit bit2 of the RAM location addressed by B. |
| | SB | bit2 | 1 00bb | 2 00bb | 1 | | | [[B]] <bit2> ← 1 Set bit bit2 of the RAM location addressed by B. |
| IMMEDIATE OPERATE | AISK | data4x | 6 eeee | 6 eeee | 1 | | X | [A] ← [A] +data4 Add immediate to Accumulator. Skip if no overflow. |
| | DC | | 66,00 | 66,00 | 2 | | X | Same as AISK 6. Must always be followed by NOP as shown. |
| | EOB | data2 | 1 11dd | | 1 | | X | [B] <4,5> ← [B] <4,5> ⊕ data2 Exclusive-OR data2 with most significant 2 bits of B. Skip until next non-LB, -EOB or -LBL instruction. |
| | EOB | data3 | | 0 1ddd | 1 | | X | [B] <4,6> ← [B]<4,6> ⊕ data3 Exclusive-OR data3 with most significant 3 bits of B. Skip until next non-LB, -EOB or -LBL instruction. |
| | LAI | data4 | 7 dddd | 4 dddd | 1 | | X | [A] ← data4 Load Accumulator immediate. Skip until first non-LAI instruction. |

Table 1-13. A Summary of the PPS4/1 Microcomputer Instruction Set (Continued)

| TYPE | MNEMONIC | OPERAND(S) | OBJECT CODE MM75 MM76 | OBJECT CODE MM77 MM78 | CLOCK CYCLES | STATUS C | STATUS SKIP | OPERATION PERFORMED |
|---|---|---|---|---|---|---|---|---|
| IMMEDIATE OPERATE (Continued) | LB | data4 | 2 dddd | 1 dddd | 1 | | X | $[B] <0,3> \leftarrow \text{data4}$<br>$[B] <4,5> \leftarrow 0$<br>Clear bits 4,5 of B and load least significant 4 bits with data4. Execute any EOB instruction that immediately follows. Skip until next non-LB,-EOB, or -LBL instruction. |
| JUMP | T | addr6 | 11aa aaaa | | 2 | | | $[PC] <0,5> \leftarrow \overline{\text{addr6}}$<br>$[PC] <6,9> \leftarrow 1110_2$ iff PC is $380_{16}$ - $3FF_{16}$<br>On-page transfer if executing from pages 0-13. If executing on pages 14-15, always jump to page 14. |
| | T | addr6 | | 11aa aaaa | 2 | | | $[PC] <0,5> \leftarrow \overline{\text{addr6}}$<br>$[PC] <6,10> \leftarrow 11110_2$ if PC is $780_{16}$ - $7FF_{16}$<br>On-page transfer if executing on pages 0-29. If executing on pages 30-31, always jump to page 30. |
| | TL | addr10x | 3 pppp<br>11aa aaaa | | 3 | | | $[PC] \leftarrow \overline{\text{addr10x}}$<br>Transfer to an address on pages 0-13. |
| | TL | addr10y | | 3 pppp<br>11aa aaaa | 3 | | | $[PC] \leftarrow \overline{\text{addr10y}}$<br>Transfer to an address on pages 0-15. |
| | TLB | addr10z | | 3 pppp<br>3 xxxx<br>11aa aaaa | 4 | | | $[PC] \leftarrow \overline{\text{addr10z}}$<br>Transfer to an address on pages 16-29. |
| SUBROUTINE CALL AND RETURN | RT | | 02 | 2F | 2 | | | $[PC] \leftarrow [SA]$<br>$[SA] \leftarrow [SB]$ (MM77, MM78 only)<br>Return from subroutine. |
| | RTSK | | 03 | 2E | 2 | | X | $[PC] \leftarrow [SA]$<br>$[SA] \leftarrow [SB]$ (MM77, MM78 only)<br>Return from subroutine and skip next instruction. |
| | TM | addr6 | 10aa aaaa | | 2 | | | $[SA] \leftarrow [PC] + 1$ iff executing from 0 - $37F_{16}$<br>$[PC] <0,5> \leftarrow \overline{\text{addr6}}$<br>$[PC] <6,9> \leftarrow 1111_2$<br>Subroutine call to primitive subroutine page (page 15) if executing on pages 0-13. Jump to primitive subroutine page if executing on pages 14-15. |
| | TM | addr6 | | 10aa aaaa | 2 | | | $[SB] \leftarrow [SA]$ iff executing from 0-$77F_{16}$<br>$[SA] \leftarrow [PC] + 1$ iff executing from 0-$77F_{16}$ |

Table 1-13. A Summary of the PPS4/1 Microcomputer Instruction Set (Continued)

| TYPE | MNEMONIC | OPERAND(S) | OBJECT CODE MM75 MM76 | OBJECT CODE MM77 MM78 | CLOCK CYCLES | STATUS C | STATUS SKIP | OPERATION PERFORMED |
|---|---|---|---|---|---|---|---|---|
| SUBROUTINE CALL AND RETURN (Continued) | TML | addr10x | 3 pppp<br>10aa aaaa | | 3 | | | $[PC] <0,5> \leftarrow \overline{addr6}$<br>$[PC] <6,10>$ $11111_2$<br>Subroutine call to primitive subroutine page (page 31) if executing on pages 0-29. Jump to primitive subroutine page if executing on pages 30-31.<br>$[SA] \leftarrow [PC] + 1$<br>$[PC] \leftarrow \overline{addr10x}$<br>Subroutine call to pages 0-13. |
| | TML | addr10y | | 3 pppp<br>10aa aaaa | 3 | | | $[SB] \leftarrow [SA]$<br>$[SA] \leftarrow [PC] + 1$<br>$[PC] \leftarrow \overline{addr10y}$<br>Subroutine call to pages 0-15. |
| | TMLB | addr10z | | 30<br>3 pppp<br>10aa aaaa | 4 | | | $[SB] \leftarrow [SA]$<br>$[SA] \leftarrow [PC] + 1$<br>$[PC] \leftarrow \overline{addr10z}$<br>Subroutine call to pages 16-29. |
| BRANCH ON CONDITION | DINO | | 07 | | 1 | | X | $[INTO] \leftarrow 1$<br>Skip next instruction if INTO = 0. Set INTO = 1. |
| | DIN1 | | 06 | | 1 | | X | $[INT1] \leftarrow 1$<br>Skip next instruction if INT1 = 0. Set INT1 = 1. |
| | INTOH | | | 03 | 1 | | X | Skip next instruction if INTO = 1. |
| | INTOL | | 04 | | 1 | | X | Skip next instruction if INTO = 0. |
| | INT1H | | 05 | | 1 | | X | Skip next instruction if INT1 = 1. |
| | INT1L | | | 04 | 1 | | X | Skip next instruction if INT1 = 0. |
| | SKBF | bit2 | 0 10bb | 2 10bb | 1 | | X | Skip if bit of RAM location addressed by B and selected by bit2 is 0. |
| | SKISL | | 0 10xx | | 1 | | X | Skip if discrete input selected by least significant 4 bits of B is 0. $B <4,5>$ must be $11_2$. |
| | SKISL | | | 01 | 1 | | X | Skip if discrete input selected by least significant 4 bits of B is 0. $B <6>$ must be 0.<br>$B <0,3> = 1010_2$ selects INT1 flip-flop.<br>$B <0,3> = 1011_2$ selects INTO flip-flop. |
| | SKMEA | | 47 | 7F | 1 | | X | Skip if A equals contents of RAM location addressed by B. |
| | SKNC | | 01 | 02 | 1** | | X | Skip if Carry = 0. |
| | TAB | | | 2C | 3+[A] | | X | Table lookup based on contents of A. Executes the next instruction, which must be a NOP, TM, T, RT, RTSK, SC, RC, SB, RB, SOS, ROS, OX, IX, or TL. Then skips the next [A] + 1 instructions.<br>$[A] \leftarrow 1111_2$ |

Table 1-13. A Summary of the PPS4/1 Microcomputer Instruction Set (Continued)

| TYPE | MNEMONIC | OPERAND(S) | OBJECT CODE MM75 MM76 | OBJECT CODE MM77 MM78 | CLOCK CYCLES | STATUS C | STATUS SKIP | OPERATION PERFORMED |
|---|---|---|---|---|---|---|---|---|
| REGISTER OPERATE | COM | | 45 | 77 | 1 | | | [A] ← $[\overline{A}]$<br>Complement Accumulator. |
| | DC | | 66,00 | 66,00 | 2 | | X | [A] ← [A] + 6<br>Decimal correct Accumulator by adding 6. |
| REGISTER-REGISTER MOVE | LBA | | 44 | 76 | 1*** | | | [B] <0,3> ← [A]<br>Load least significant 4 bits of B from A. |
| | LSA | | 4C | | 1 | | | [S] ← [A]<br>Load S register from A. |
| | LXA | | | 75 | 1 | | | [X] ← [A]<br>Load X register from A. |
| | SAG | | | 07 | 1 | | | [B] <4,6> $011_2$ (for next instruction only)<br>Causes B to address row 3 for the next instruction only. The contents of B are not modified. |
| | XAB | | 46 | 7A | 1*** | | | [B] ←→ [A]<br>Exchange B with A. |
| | XAS | | 4E | 74 | 1 | | | [S] ←→ [A]<br>Exchange S with A. |
| | XAX | | | 79 | 1 | | | [X] ←→ [A]<br>Exchange X with A. |
| STATUS | RC | | 0D | 05 | 1 | 0 | | [C] ← 0<br>Reset Carry. |
| | SC | | 0C | 06 | 1 | 1 | | [C] ← 1<br>Set Carry. |
| | NOP | | 00 | 00 | 1 | | | No operation. |

Table 1-14. PPS4/1 Instruction Mnemonics

| MNEMONIC | MM75, MM76 OBJECT CODE | MM77, MM78 OBJECT CODE | BYTES | CLOCK |
|---|---|---|---|---|
| A | 42 | 7E | 1 | 1 |
| AC | 40 | 7C | 1 | 1* |
| ACSK | 41 | 7D | 1 | 1* |
| AISK data4x | 6 eeee | 6 eeee | 1 | 1 |
| ASK | 43 | | | |
| COM | 45 | 77 | 1 | 1 |
| DC | 66,00 | 66,00 | 2 | 2 |
| DIN0 | 07 | | 1 | 1 |
| DIN1 | 06 | | 1 | 1 |
| EOB data2 | 1 11dd | | 1 | 1 |
| EOB data3 | | 0 1ddd | 1 | 1 |
| IAM | 1A | | 1 | 1 |
| IBM | 1B | | 1 | 1 |
| INT0L | 04 | | 1 | 1 |
| INT0H | | 03 | 1 | 1 |
| INT1L | | 04 | 1 | 1 |
| INT1H | 05 | | 1 | 1 |
| IOA | | 7B | 1 | 1 |
| IOS | 4D | 2D | 1 | 1**** |
| IX | | 72 | 1 | 1 |
| I1 | 4A | | 1 | 1 |
| I1SK | | 60 | 1 | 1 |
| I2C | 4B | 78 | 1 | 1 |
| L data2 | 5 00dd | 5 00dd | 1 | 1 |
| LAI data4 | 7 dddd | 4 dddd | 1 | 1 |
| LB data4 | 2 dddd | 1 dddd | 1 | 1 |
| LBA | 44 | 76 | 1 | 1*** |
| LSA | 4C | | 1 | 1 |
| LXA | | 75 | 1 | 1 |
| NOP | 00 | 00 | 1 | 1 |
| OA | 18 | | 1 | 1 |
| OB | 19 | | 1 | 1 |
| OX | | 73 | 1 | 1 |
| RB bit2 | 1 01bb | 2 01bb | 1 | 1 |
| RC | 0D | 05 | 1 | 1 |
| ROS | 1 01xx | 71 | 1 | 1 |
| RT | 02 | 2F | 1 | 1 |
| RTSK | 03 | 2E | 1 | 2 |
| SAG | | 07 | 1 | 1 |
| SB bit2 | 1 00bb | 2 00bb | 1 | 1 |
| SC | 0C | 06 | 1 | 1 |
| SEG1 | 0E | | 1 | 1 |
| SEG2 | 0F | | 1 | 1 |
| SKBF bit2 | 0 10bb | 2 10bb | 1 | 1 |
| SKISL | 0 10xx | 01 | 1 | 1 |
| SKMEA | 47 | 7F | 1 | 1 |
| SKNC | 01 | 02 | 1 | 1** |
| SOS | 1 00xx | 70 | 1 | 1 |
| T addr6 | 11aa aaaa | 11aa aaaa | 1 | 2 |
| TAB | | 2C | 1 | 3 + [A] |
| TL addr10x | 3 pppp<br>11aa aaaa | | 2 | 3 |
| TL addr10y | | 3 pppp<br>11aa aaaa | 2 | 3 |
| TLB addr10z | | 3 pppp<br>3 xxxx<br>11aa aaaa | 3 | 4 |
| TM addr6 | 10aa aaaa | 10aa aaaa | 1 | 2 |
| TML addr10x | 3 pppp<br>10aa aaaa | | 2 | 3 |
| TML addr10y | | 3 pppp<br>10aa aaaa | 2 | 3 |
| TMLB addr10z | | 30<br>3 pppp<br>10aa aaaa | 3 | 4 |
| X data2 | 5 10dd | 5 11dd | 1 | 1 |
| XAB | 46 | 7A | 1 | 1*** |
| XAS | 4E | 74 | 1 | 1 |
| XAX | | 79 | 1 | 1 |
| XDSK data2 | 5 11dd | 5 10dd | 1 | 1*** |
| XNSK data2 | 5 01dd | 5 01dd | 1 | 1*** |

Table 1-15. PPS4/1 MM75, MM76 Instruction Object Codes

| OBJECT CODE | MNEMONIC |
|---|---|
| 00 | NOP |
| 01 | SKNC |
| 02 | RT |
| 03 | RTSK |
| 04 | INT0L |
| 05 | INT1H |
| 06 | DIN1 |
| 07 | DIN0 |
| 08 - 0B | SKISL or SKBF 0 - SKBF 3 |
| 0C | SC |
| 0D | RC |
| 0E | SEG1 |
| 0F | SEG2 |
| 10 - 13 | SOS or SB 0 - SB 3 |
| 14 - 17 | ROS or RB 0 - RB 3 |
| 18 | OA |
| 19 | OB |
| 1A | IAM |
| 1B | IBM |
| 1C - 1F | EOB 0 - EOB 3 |
| 20 - 2F | LB 0 - LB F |
| 3 pppp 10aa aaaa | TML pp ppaa aaaa |
| 3 pppp 11aa aaaa | TL pp ppaa aaaa |
| 40 | AC |
| 41 | ACSK |

| OBJECT CODE | MNEMONIC |
|---|---|
| 42 | A |
| 43 | ASK |
| 44 | LBA |
| 45 | COM |
| 46 | XAB |
| 47 | SKMEA |
| 48, 49 | not used |
| 4A | I1 |
| 4B | I2C |
| 4C | LSA |
| 4D | IOS |
| 4E | XAS |
| 4F | not used |
| 50 - 53 | L 0 - L 3 |
| 54 - 57 | XNSK 0 - XNSK 3 |
| 58 - 5B | X 0 - X 3 |
| 5C - 5F | XDSK 0 - XDSK 3 |
| 60 - 6F | AISK 0 - AISK F |
| 66,00 | DC,NOP |
| 70 - 7F | LAI 0 - LAI F |
| 80 - 8F | TM 3F - TM 30 |
| 90 - 9F | TM 2F - TM 20 |
| A0 - AF | TM 1F - TM 10 |
| B0 - BF | TM 0F - TM 00 |
| C0 - CF | T 3F - T 30 |
| D0 - DF | T 2F - T 20 |
| E0 - EF | T 1F - T 10 |
| F0 - FF | T 0F - T 00 |

Table 1-16. PPS4/1 MM77, MM78 Instruction Object Codes

| OBJECT CODE | MNEMONIC | OBJECT CODE | MNEMONIC |
|---|---|---|---|
| 00 | NOP | 61 - 6F | AISK 1 - AISK F |
| 01 | SKISL | 66,00 | DC |
| 02 | SKNC | 70 | SOS |
| 03 | INTOH | 71 | ROS |
| 04 | INT1L | 72 | IX |
| 05 | RC | 73 | OX |
| 06 | SC | 74 | XAS |
| 07 | SAG | 75 | LXA |
| 08 - 0F | EOB 0 - EOB 7 | 76 | LBA |
| 10 - 1F | LB 0 - LB F | 77 | COM |
| 20 - 23 | SB 0 - SB 3 | 78 | I2C |
| 24 - 27 | RB 0 - RB 3 | 79 | XAX |
| 28 - 2B | SKBF 0 - SKBF 3 | 7A | XAB |
| 2C | TAB | 7B | IOA |
| 2D | IOS | 7C | AC |
| 2E | RTSK | 7D | ACSK |
| 2F | RT | 7E | A |
| 30, 3 pppp, 10aa aaaa | TMLB 01pp ppaa aaaa | 7F | SKMEA |
| 30, 3 pppp, 11aa aaaa | TLB 01pp ppaa aaaa | 80 - 8F | TM 3F - TM 30 |
| 3 pppp, 10aa aaaa | TML 00pp ppaa aaaa | 90 - 9F | TM 2F - TM 20 |
| 3 pppp, 11aa aaaa | TL 00pp ppaa aaaa | A0 - AF | TM 1F - TM 10 |
| 40 - 4F | LAI 0 - LAI F | B0 - BF | TM 0F - TM 00 |
| 50 - 53 | L 0 - L 3 | C0 - CF | T 3F - T 30 |
| 54 - 57 | XNSK 0 - XNSK 3 | D0 - DF | T 2F - T 20 |
| 58 - 5B | XDSK 0 - XDSK 3 | E0 - EF | T 1F - T 10 |
| 5C - 5F | X 0 - X 3 | F0 - FF | T 0F - T 00 |
| 60 | I1SK | | |

# DATA SHEETS

This section contains specific electrical and timing data for the following devices:

- TMS1000 series microcomputer
- COP420/421 microcomputers
- COP402/COP402M ROMless microcomputers
- PPS4/1 Series Microcomputers

## ABSOLUTE MAXIMUM RATINGS OVER OPERATING FREE-AIR TEMPERATURE RANGE (UNLESS OTHERWISE NOTED)*

| | |
|---|---|
| Voltage applied to any device terminal (see Note 1) | −20 V |
| Supply voltage, $V_{DD}$ | −20 V to 0.3 V |
| Data input voltage | −20 V to 0.3 V |
| Clock input voltage | −20 V to 0.3 V |
| Average output current (see Note 2): O outputs | −24 mA |
| R outputs | −14 mA |
| Peak output current: O outputs | −48 mA |
| R outputs | −28 mA |
| Continuous power dissipation: TMS 1000/1100 NL | 400 mW |
| TMS 1200/1300 NL | 600 mW |
| Operating free-air temperature range | 0°C to 70°C |
| Storage temperature range | −55°C to 150°C |

*Stresses beyond those listed under "Absolute Maximum Ratings" may cause permanent damage to the device. This is a stress rating only and functional operation of the device at these or any other conditions beyond those indicated in the "Recommended Operating Conditions" section of this specification is not implied. Exposure to absolute-maximum-rated conditions for extended periods may affect device reliability.

## RECOMMENDED OPERATING CONDITIONS

| PARAMETER | | MIN | NOM | MAX | UNIT |
|---|---|---|---|---|---|
| Supply voltage, $V_{DD}$ (see Note 3) | | −14 | −15 | −17.5 | V |
| High-level input voltage, $V_{IH}$ (see Note 4) | K | −1.3 | −1 | 0.3 | V |
| | INIT or Clock | −1.3 | −1 | 0.3 | |
| Low-level input voltage, $V_{IL}$ (see Note 4) | K | $V_{DD}$ | | −4 | V |
| | INIT or Clock | $V_{DD}$ | −15 | −8 | |
| Clock cycle time, $t_{c(\phi)}$ | | 2.5 | 3 | 10 | μs |
| Instruction cycle time, $t_c$ | | 15 | | 60 | μs |
| Pulse width, clock high, $t_{w(\phi H)}$ | | 1 | | | μs |
| Pulse width, clock low, $t_{w(\phi L)}$ | | 1 | | | μs |
| Sum of rise time and pulse width, clock high, $t_r + t_{w(\phi H)}$ | | 1.25 | | | μs |
| Sum of fall time and pulse width, clock low, $t_f + t_{w(\phi L)}$ | | 1.25 | | | μs |
| Oscillator frequency, $f_{osc}$ | | 100 | | 400 | kHz |
| Operating free-air temperature, $T_A$ | | 0 | | 70 | °C |

NOTES: 1. Unless otherwise noted, all voltages are with respect to $V_{SS}$.
2. These average values apply for any 100-ms period.
3. Ripple must not exceed 0.2 volts peak-to-peak in the operating frequency range.
4. The algebraic convention where the most-positive (least-negative) limit is designated as maximum is used in this specification for logic voltage levels only.

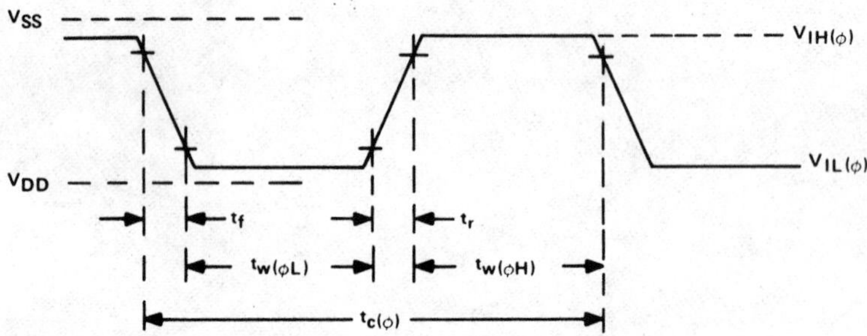


NOTE: Timing points are 90% (high) and 10% (low).

**EXTERNALLY DRIVEN CLOCK INPUT WAVEFORM**

# TMS 1000/1200 AND TMS 1100/1300

## ELECTRICAL CHARACTERISTICS OVER RECOMMENDED OPERATING FREE-AIR TEMPERATURE RANGE (UNLESS OTHERWISE NOTED)

| PARAMETER | | | TEST CONDITIONS | | MIN | TYP† | MAX | UNIT |
|---|---|---|---|---|---|---|---|---|
| $I_I$ | Input current, K inputs | | $V_I = 0$ V | | 50 | 300 | 500 | μA |
| $V_{OH}$ | High-level output voltage (see Note 1) | O outputs | $I_O = -10$ mA | | −1.1‡ | −0.6‡ | | V |
| | | R outputs | $I_O = -2$ mA | | −0.75 | −0.4 | | V |
| $I_{OL}$ | Low-level output current | | $V_{OL} = V_{DD}$ | | | | −100 | μA |
| $I_{DD(av)}$ | Average supply current from $V_{DD}$ TMS 1000/1200 (see Note 2) | | All outputs open | | | −6 | −10 | mA |
| $I_{DD(av)}$ | Average supply current from $V_{DD}$ TMS1100/1300 (see Note 2) | | All outputs open | | | −7 | −11 | mA |
| $P_{(AV)}$ | Average power dissipation TMS 1000/1200 (see Note 2 | | All outputs open | | | 90 | 175 | mW |
| $P_{(AV)}$ | Average power dissipation TMS1100/1300 (see Note 2) | | All outputs open | | | 105 | 193 | mW |
| $f_{osc}$ | Internal oscillator frequency | | $R_{ext} = 50$ kΩ, | $C_{ext} = 47$ pF | 250 | 300 | 350 | kHz |
| $C_i$ | Small-signal input capacitance, K inputs | | $V_I = 0$, | f = 1 kHz | | 10 | | pF |
| $C_{i(\phi)}$ | Input capacitance, clock input | | $V_I = 0$, | f = 100 kHz | | 25 | | pF |

†All typical values are at $V_{DD} = -15$ V, $T_A = 25°$C.

‡Parts with $V_{OH}$ of −2 V minimum, −1.3 V typical, are available if requested.

NOTES: 1. The algebraic convention where the most-positive (least-negative) limit is designated as maximum is used in this specification for logic voltage levels only.

2. Values are given for the open-drain O and R output configurations. Pull-down resistors are optionally available on all outputs and increase $I_{DD}$ (see Section 4.4).

## SCHEMATICS OF INPUTS AND OUTPUTS

TYPICAL OF ALL K INPUTS

INPUT

$V_{SS}$

R ≈ 50 kΩ

$V_{DD}$

TYPICAL OF ALL O AND R OPEN-DRAIN OUTPUTS

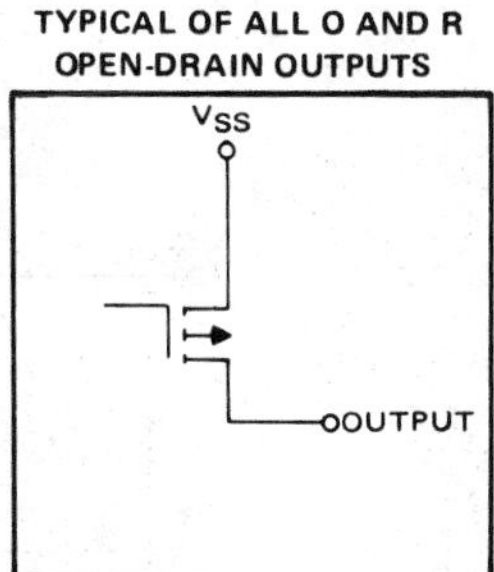


TYPICAL OF ALL O AND R OUTPUTS WITH OPTIONAL PULL-DOWN RESISTORS

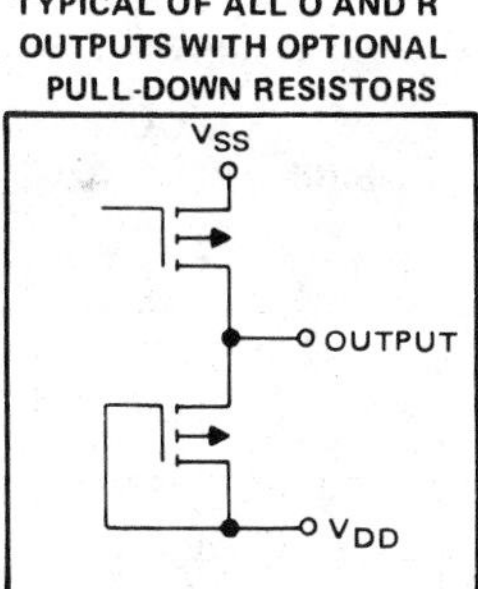


The O outputs have nominally 60 Ω on-state impedance; however, upon request a 130-Ω buffer can be mask programmed (see note [‡] section 4.3).

The value of the pull-down resistors is mask alterable and provides the following nominal short-circuit output currents (outputs shorted to $V_{SS}$):

O outputs: 100, 200, 300, 500, or 900 μA

R outputs: 100, 150, or 200 μA.

## TMS 1000/1200 AND TMS 1100/1300

### INTERNAL OR EXTERNAL CLOCK

If the internal oscillator is used, the OSC1 and OSC2 terminals are shorted together and tied to an external resistor to $V_{DD}$ and a capacitor to $V_{SS}$. If an external clock is desired, the clock source may be connected to OSC1 and OSC2 shorted to $V_{SS}$.

**CONNECTION FOR INTERNAL OSCILLATOR**

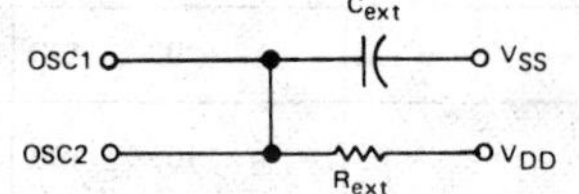


**TYPICAL INTERNAL OSCILLATOR FREQUENCY vs EXTERNAL RESISTANCE**

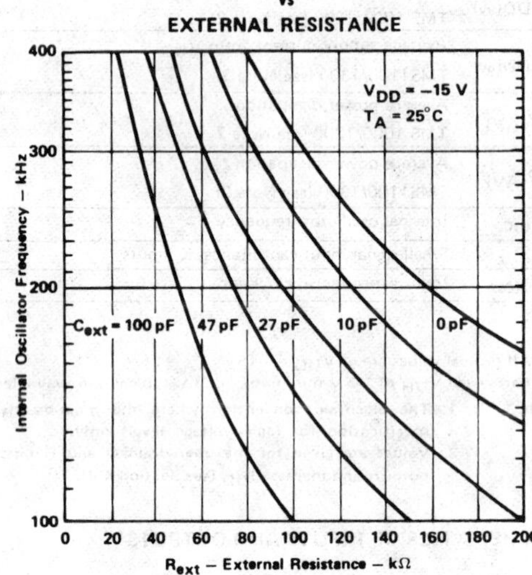


**TYPICAL BUFFER CHARACTERISTICS**

**O OUTPUTS**
**HIGH-LEVEL OUTPUT CURRENT vs HIGH-LEVEL OUTPUT VOLTAGE**

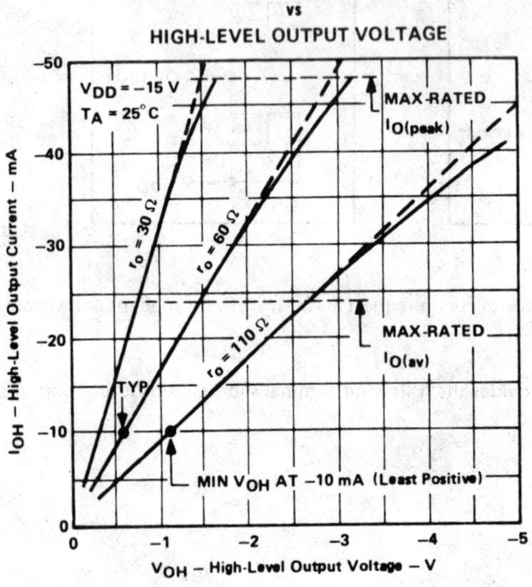


**R OUTPUTS**
**HIGH-LEVEL OUTPUT CURRENT vs HIGH-LEVEL OUTPUT VOLTAGE**

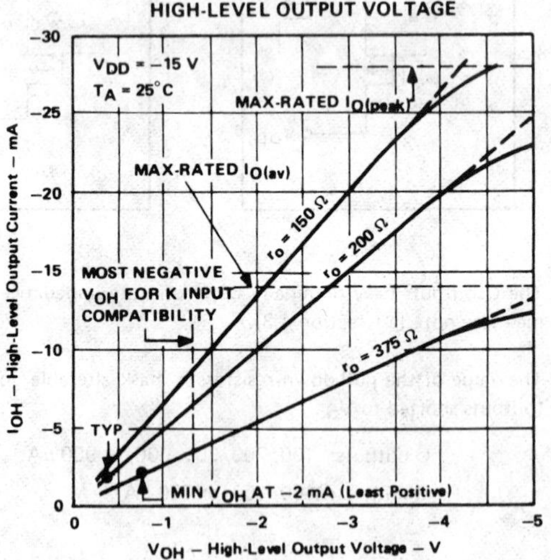

## ABSOLUTE MAXIMUM RATINGS OVER OPERATING FREE-AIR TEMPERATURE RANGE (UNLESS OTHERWISE NOTED)*

| | |
|---|---|
| Voltage applied to any device terminal (see Note 1) | −20 V |
| Supply voltage, $V_{DD}$ | −20 V to 0.3 V |
| Data input and output voltage with $V_{DD}$ applied (see Note 2) | −35 V to 0.3 V |
| Clock input and INIT input voltage | −20 V to 0.3 V |
| Average output current (see Note 3): O outputs | −2.5 mA |
| R outputs | −12 mA |
| Peak output current: O outputs | −5 mA |
| R outputs | −24 mA |
| Continuous power dissipation: TMS 1070 NL | 400 mW |
| TMS 1270 NL | 600 mW |
| Operating free-air temperature range | 0°C to 70°C |
| Storage temperature range | −55°C to 150°C |

*Stresses beyond those listed under "Absolute Maximum Ratings" may cause permanent damage to the device. This is a stress rating only and functional operation of the device at these or any other conditions beyond those indicated in the "Recommended Operating Conditions" section of this specification is not implied. Exposure to absolute-maximum-rated conditions for extended periods may affect device reliability.

## RECOMMENDED OPERATING CONDITIONS

| PARAMETER | | MIN | NOM | MAX | UNIT |
|---|---|---|---|---|---|
| Supply voltage, $V_{DD}$ (see Note 4) | | −14 | −15 | −17.5 | V |
| High-level input voltage, $V_{IH}$ (see Note 5) | K | −6 | | 0.3 | V |
| | INIT or Clock | −1.3 | −1 | 0.3 | |
| Low-level input voltage, $V_{IL}$ (see Note 5) | K (See Note 2) | −35 | | −8 | V |
| | INIT or Clock | $V_{DD}$ | −15 | −8 | |
| Clock cycle time, $t_{c(\phi)}$ | | 2.5 | 3 | 10 | μs |
| Instruction cycle time, $t_c$ | | 15 | | 60 | μs |
| Pulse width, clock high, $t_{w(\phi H)}$ | | 1 | | | μs |
| Pulse width, clock low, $t_{w(\phi L)}$ | | 1 | | | μs |
| Sum of rise time and pulse width, clock high, $t_r + t_{w(\phi H)}$ | | 1.25 | | | μs |
| Sum of fall time and pulse width, clock low, $t_f + t_{w(\phi L)}$ | | 1.25 | | | μs |
| Oscillator frequency, $f_{osc}$ | | 100 | | 400 | kHz |
| Operating free-air temperature, $T_A$ | | 0 | | 70 | °C |

NOTES:
1. Unless otherwise noted, all voltages are with respect to $V_{SS}$.
2. $V_{DD}$ must be within the recommended operating conditions specified in 5.4.
3. These average values apply for any 100-ms period.
4. Ripple must not exceed 0.2 volts peak-to-peak in the operating frequency range.
5. The algebraic convention where the most-positive (least-negative) limit is designated as maximum is used in this specification for logic voltage levels only.

## ELECTRICAL CHARACTERISTICS OVER RECOMMENDED OPERATING FREE-AIR TEMPERATURE RANGE (UNLESS OTHERWISE NOTED)

| PARAMETER | | | TEST CONDITIONS | | MIN | TYP† | MAX | UNIT |
|---|---|---|---|---|---|---|---|---|
| $I_I$ | Input current, K inputs | | $V_I$ = 0 V | | 40 | 100 | 300 | μA |
| $V_{OH}$ | High-level output voltage (see Note 1) | O outputs | $I_O$ = −1 mA | | −1 | −0.5 | | V |
| | | R outputs | $I_O$ = −10 mA | | −4.5 | −2.25 | | |
| $I_{OL}$ | Low-level output current | | $V_{OL}$ = $V_{DD}$ | | | | −100 | μA |
| $I_{DD(av)}$ | Average supply current from $V_{DD}$ | | All outputs open | | | −6 | −10 | mA |
| $P_{(AV)}$ | Average power dissipation | | All outputs open | | | 90 | 175 | mW |
| $f_{osc}$ | Internal oscillator frequency | | $R_{ext}$ = 50 kΩ, | $C_{ext}$ = 47 pF | 250 | 300 | 350 | kHz |
| $C_i$ | Small-signal input capacitance, K inputs | | $V_I$ = 0 V, | f = 1 kHz | | 10 | | pF |
| $C_{i(\phi)}$ | Input capacitance, clock input | | $V_I$ = 0 V, | f = 100 kHz | | 25 | | pF |

†All typical values are at $V_{DD}$ = −15 V, $T_A$ = 25°C.

NOTE 1: The algebraic convention where the most-positive (least-negative) limit is designated as maximum is used in this specification for logic voltage levels only.

# TMS1000C/1200C PRELIMINARY ELECTRICAL SPECIFICATIONS

## ABSOLUTE MAXIMUM RATINGS

Voltage applied to any device terminal . . . . . . . . . . 6 V
Supply voltage, $V_{DD}$ . . . . . . . . . . -0.3 V to 6 V
Data input voltage . . . . . . . . . . -0.3 V to 6 V
Clock input voltage . . . . . . . . . . -0.3 V to 6 V
Input current . . . . . . . . . . ±10 mA
Output current . . . . . . . . . . ±40 mA
Continuous power dissipation . . . . . . . . . . 200 mW
Operating free-air temperature range . . . . . . . . . . 0 to 70°C
Storage temperature range . . . . . . . . . . -55°C to +150°C

## RECOMMENDED OPERATING CONDITIONS

| | MIN | NOM | MAX | UNIT |
|---|---|---|---|---|
| Supply voltage, $V_{DD}$ | 3.0 | | 6.0 | V |
| High level input voltage: $V_{IH}$ | | | | |
| K/L input | 4.0 | | $V_{DD}$ | V |
| Init, Clock | 4.0 | | $V_{DD}$ | V |
| Low level input voltage: $V_{IL}$ | | | | |
| K/L input | $V_{SS}$ | | 1 | V |
| Init, Clock | $V_{SS}$ | | 1 | V |
| Clock cycle time: $t_{c(\phi)}$ | 1 | | 20 | μsec |
| Instruction cycle time | 6 | | 120 | μsec |
| Pulse width, clock high: $t_{w(\phi H)}$ | 0.3 | | | μsec |
| Pulse width, clock low: $t_{w(\phi L)}$ | 0.3 | | | μsec |
| Clock rise and fall time: $t_f$ and $t_r$ | | | 1 | μsec |
| Clock frequency: $F(\phi)$ | 0.05 | | 1 | MHZ |
| Operating free air temperature | 0 | | +70 | °C |

NOTE: Tests at $V_{DD}$ = 5 Volts

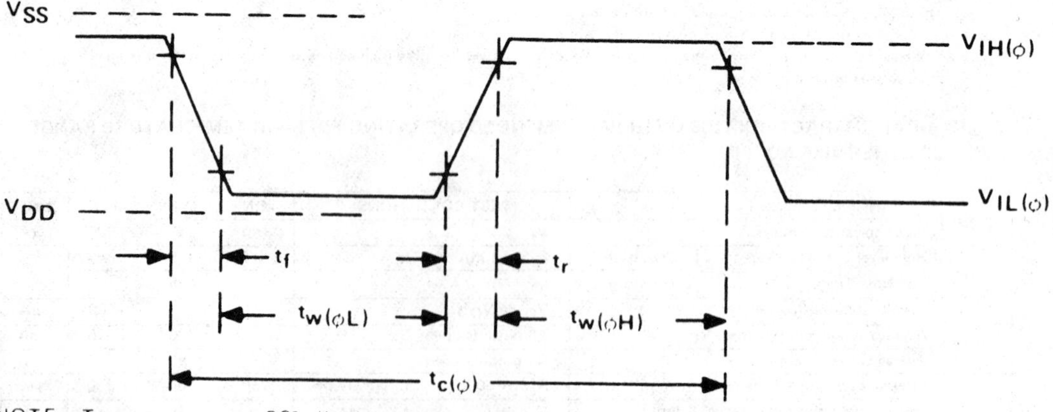


NOTE: Timing points are 90% (high) and 10% (low).

**EXTERNALLY DRIVEN CLOCK INPUT WAVEFORM**

## TMS1000C/1200C ELECTRICAL CHARACTERISTICS

| PARAMETER | MIN | TYP | MAX | UNIT |
|---|---|---|---|---|
| Input current, K/L inputs $V_I = 5$ V | | 100 | | μA |
| High level output voltage: $V_{OH}$ O and R outputs IO = -2 mA | 2.5 | | | V |
| Low level output voltage: $V_{OL}$ O and R outputs IO = 2 mA | | | 0.4 | V |
| Average supply current from $V_{DD}$: $I_{DD}(AV)$ All outputs open: Operating mode FOSC = 1 MHZ | | 3 | | ma |
| Quiescent supply current from $V_{DD}$: $I_{DD}(Q)$ All outputs open: HALT mode | | 10 | | μA |
| Internal oscillator frequency | 0.05 | | 1.0 | MHZ |

## TMS 1000/1200C SCHEMATICS OF INPUTS AND OUTPUTS

TYPICAL OF ALL INPUTS

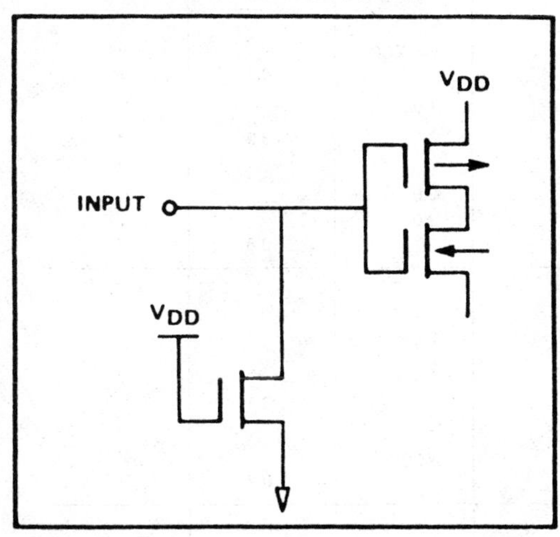


TYPICAL OF ALL O & R OUTPUTS

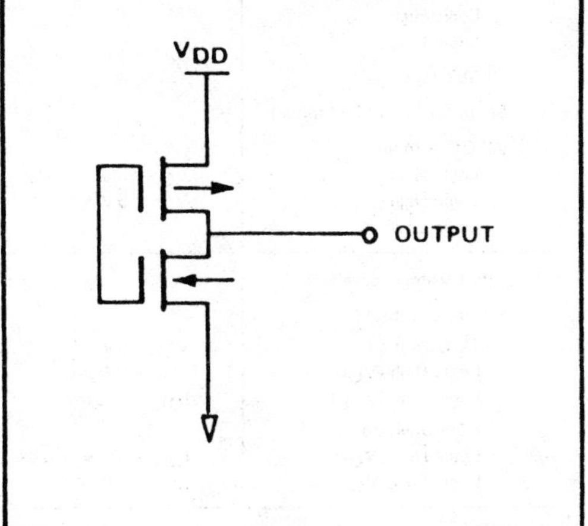

## Absolute Maximum Ratings

| | |
|---|---|
| Voltage at Any Pin Relative to GND | −0.5V to +7V |
| Ambient Operating Temperature (note 1) | 0°C to +70°C |
| Ambient Storage Temperature | −65°C to +150°C |
| Lead Temperature (Soldering, 10 seconds) | 300°C |
| Power Dissipation | 0.75 Watt at 25°C<br>0.4 Watt at 70°C |

*Absolute maximum ratings indicate limits beyond which damage to the device may occur. DC and AC electrical specifications are not ensured when operating the device at absolute maximum ratings.*

## DC Electrical Characteristics

$0°C \leq T_A \leq +70°C$, $4.5V \leq V_{CC} \leq 6.3V$ unless otherwise noted.

| Parameter | Conditions | Min | Max | Units |
|---|---|---|---|---|
| Operating Voltage ($V_{CC}$) | | 4.5 | 6.3 | V |
| Operating Supply Current | $V_{CC}$ = 5V, $T_A$ = 25°C (all inputs and outputs open) | | 30 | mA |
| Input Voltage Levels | | | | |
| CKI Input Levels | | | | |
| Crystal Input | | | | |
| Logic High ($V_{IH}$) | | 2.0 | | V |
| Logic Low ($V_{IL}$) | | | 0.4 | V |
| TTL Input | $V_{CC}$ = 5V ± 5% | | | |
| Logic High ($V_{IH}$) | | 2.0 | | V |
| Logic Low ($V_{IL}$) | | | 0.8 | V |
| Schmitt Trigger Input | | | | |
| Logic High ($V_{IH}$) | | 0.7 $V_{CC}$ | | V |
| Logic Low ($V_{IL}$) | | | 0.6 | V |
| $\overline{\text{RESET}}$ Input Levels | | | | |
| Logic High | | 0.7 $V_{CC}$ | | V |
| Logic Low | | | 0.6 | V |
| $\overline{\text{RESET}}$ Hysteresis | | 1.0 | | V |
| SO Input Level (Test mode) | | 2.0 | 3.0 | V |
| All Other Inputs | | | | |
| Logic High | $V_{CC}$ = max | 3.0 | | V |
| Logic High | $V_{CC}$ = 5V ± 5% | 2.0 | | V |
| Logic Low | | | 0.8 | V |
| Output Voltage Levels | | | | |
| Standard Output | | | | |
| TTL Operation | $V_{CC}$ = 5V ± 5% | | | |
| Logic High ($V_{OH}$) | $I_{OH}$ = 100 μA | 2.4 | | V |
| Logic Low ($V_{OL}$) | $I_{OL}$ = −1.6 mA | | 0.4 | V |
| CMOS Operation | | | | |
| Logic High ($V_{OH}$) | $I_{OH}$ = 10 μA | $V_{CC}$ − 1 | | V |
| Logic Low ($V_{OL}$) | $I_{OL}$ = −10 μA | | 0.2 | V |
| Output Current Levels | | | | |
| LED Direct Drive Output | $V_{CC}$ = 6V | | | |
| Logic High ($I_{OH}$) | $V_{OH}$ = 2.0V | 2.5 | 14 | mA |
| TRI-STATE® Output Leakage Current | | −10 | +10 | μA |
| CKO Output | | | | |
| $V_R$ Power Saving Option | | | | |
| Power Requirements | $V_R$ = 3.3V | | 3 | mA |

## AC Electrical Characteristics $0°C \leq T_A \leq +70°C$, $4.5V \leq V_{CC} \leq 6.3V$ unless otherwise stated.

| Parameter | Conditions | Min | Max | Units |
|---|---|---|---|---|
| Instruction Cycle Time — $t_C$ | figure 3 | 4 | 10 | μs |
| CKI Using Crystal (figure 8A) | | | | |
| Input Frequency — $f_I$ | ÷16 mode | 1.6 | 4 | MHz |
| | ÷8 mode | 0.8 | 2 | MHz |
| Duty Cycle (Note 2) | figure 3A | 30 | 55 | % |
| CKI Using External Clock (figure 8B) | | | | |
| Input Frequency | ÷16 mode | 1.6 | 4 | MHz |
| | ÷8 mode | 0.8 | 2 | MHz |
| Duty Cycle (Note 2) | | 30 | 60 | % |
| Rise Time | $f_I$ = 4 MHz | | 60 | ns |
| Fall Time | $f_I$ = 4 MHz | | 40 | ns |
| CKI Using RC (figure 8c) | | | | |
| Frequency | R = 15k ± 5%, C = 100 pF ± 10% | 0.5 | 1.0 | MHz |
| Instruction Cycle Time | | 4 | 8 | μs |
| CKO as SYNC Input (figure 8d) | | | | |
| $t_{SYNO}$ | figure 3A | 50 | | ns |
| INPUTS: (figure 3) | | | | |
| $IN_3$-$IN_0$, $G_3$-$G_0$, $L_7$-$L_0$ | | | | |
| $t_{SETUP}$ | | 1.7 | | μs |
| $t_{HOLD}$ | | 100 | | ns |
| SI | | | | |
| $t_{SETUP}$ | | 0.3 | | μs |
| $t_{HOLD}$ | | 100 | | ns |
| OUTPUTS: | | | | |
| COP TO CMOS PROPAGATION DELAY | $4.5V \leq V_{CC} \leq 6.3V$, $C_L$ = 50 pF, $V_{OH} = 0.7 V_{CC}$, $V_{OL} = 0.3 V_{CC}$ | | | |
| SK as a Logic-Controlled Clock | | | | |
| $t_{PD1}$ | | | 1.1 | μs |
| $t_{PD0}$ | | | 0.3 | μs |
| S0, SK as a Data Output | | | | |
| $t_{PD1}$ | | | 1.4 | μs |
| $t_{PD0}$ | | | 0.3 | μs |
| $t_{PD1}$ | $V_{OH}$ = 2V | | 0.7 | μs |
| $D_3$-$D_0$, $G_3$-$G_0$ | | | | |
| $t_{PD1}$ | | | 1.6 | μs |
| $t_{PD0}$ | | | 0.6 | μs |
| $L_7$-$L_0$ (Standard) | | | | |
| $t_{PD1}$ | | | 1.4 | μs |
| $t_{PD0}$ | | | 0.3 | μs |
| $L_7$-$L_0$ (LED Direct Drive) | | | | |
| $t_{PD1}$ | $V_{OH}$ = 2V | | 2.4 | μs |
| $t_{PD0}$ | | | 0.4 | μs |

## AC Electrical Characteristics (continued) $0°C \leq T_A \leq +70°C$, $4.5V \leq V_{CC} \leq 6.3V$ unless otherwise stated.

| Parameter | Conditions | Min | Max | Units |
|---|---|---|---|---|
| OUTPUTS (cont.): | | | | |
| COP TO TTL PROPAGATION DELAY | fanout = 1 Standard TTL Load $V_{CC} = 5V \pm 5\%$, $C_L = 50\,pF$, $V_{OH} = 2.4V$, $V_{OL} = 0.4V$ | | | |
| SK as a Logic-Controlled Clock | | | | |
| $t_{PD1}$ | | | 0.8 | μs |
| $t_{PD0}$ | | | 0.8 | μs |
| SK as a Data Output, SO | | | | |
| $t_{PD1}$ | | | 1.0 | μs |
| $t_{PD0}$ | | | 1.0 | μs |
| $D_3$-$D_0$, $G_3$-$G_0$ | | | | |
| $t_{PD1}$ | | | 1.3 | μs |
| $t_{PD0}$ | | | 1.3 | μs |
| $L_7$-$L_0$ | | | | |
| $t_{PD1}$ | | | 1.4 | μs |
| $t_{PD0}$ | | | 0.4 | μs |
| $L_7$-$L_0$ (Push-Pull) | | | | |
| $t_{PD1}$ | | | 0.4 | μs |
| $t_{PD0}$ | | | 0.3 | μs |
| CKO (figure 3b) | | | | |
| $t_{PD1}$ | | | 0.2 | μs |
| $t_{PD0}$ | | | 0.2 | μs |
| MICROBUS™ TIMING | $C_L = 50\,pF$, $V_{CC} = 5V \pm 5\%$ | | | |
| A. Read Operation (figure 4) | | | | |
| Chip Select Stable Before $\overline{RD}$ – $t_{CSR}$ | | 50 | | ns |
| Chip Select Hold Time for $\overline{RD}$ – $t_{RCS}$ | | 5 | | ns |
| $\overline{RD}$ Pulse Width – $t_{RR}$ | | 300 | | ns |
| Data Delay from $\overline{RD}$ – $t_{RD}$ | | | 250 | ns |
| $\overline{RD}$ to Data Floating – $t_{DF}$ | | | 200 | ns |
| Write Operation (figure 5) | | | | |
| Chip Select Stable Before $\overline{WR}$ – $t_{CSW}$ | | 20 | | ns |
| Chip Select Hold Time for $\overline{WR}$ – $t_{WCS}$ | | 20 | | ns |
| $\overline{WR}$ Pulse Width – $t_{WW}$ | | 300 | | ns |
| Data Set-Up Time for $\overline{WR}$ – $t_{DW}$ | | 200 | | ns |
| Data Hold Time for $\overline{WR}$ – $t_{WD}$ | | 40 | | ns |
| INTR Transition Time from $\overline{WR}$ – $t_{WI}$ | | | 700 | ns |

**Note 1:** An extended temperature range COP420/421 is available which will operate within an ambient temperature range of –40°C to +85°C.

**Note 2:** Duty Cycle = $t_{WI}/(t_{WI} + t_{WO})$.

**Note 3:** See figure 9 for additional I/O characteristics.

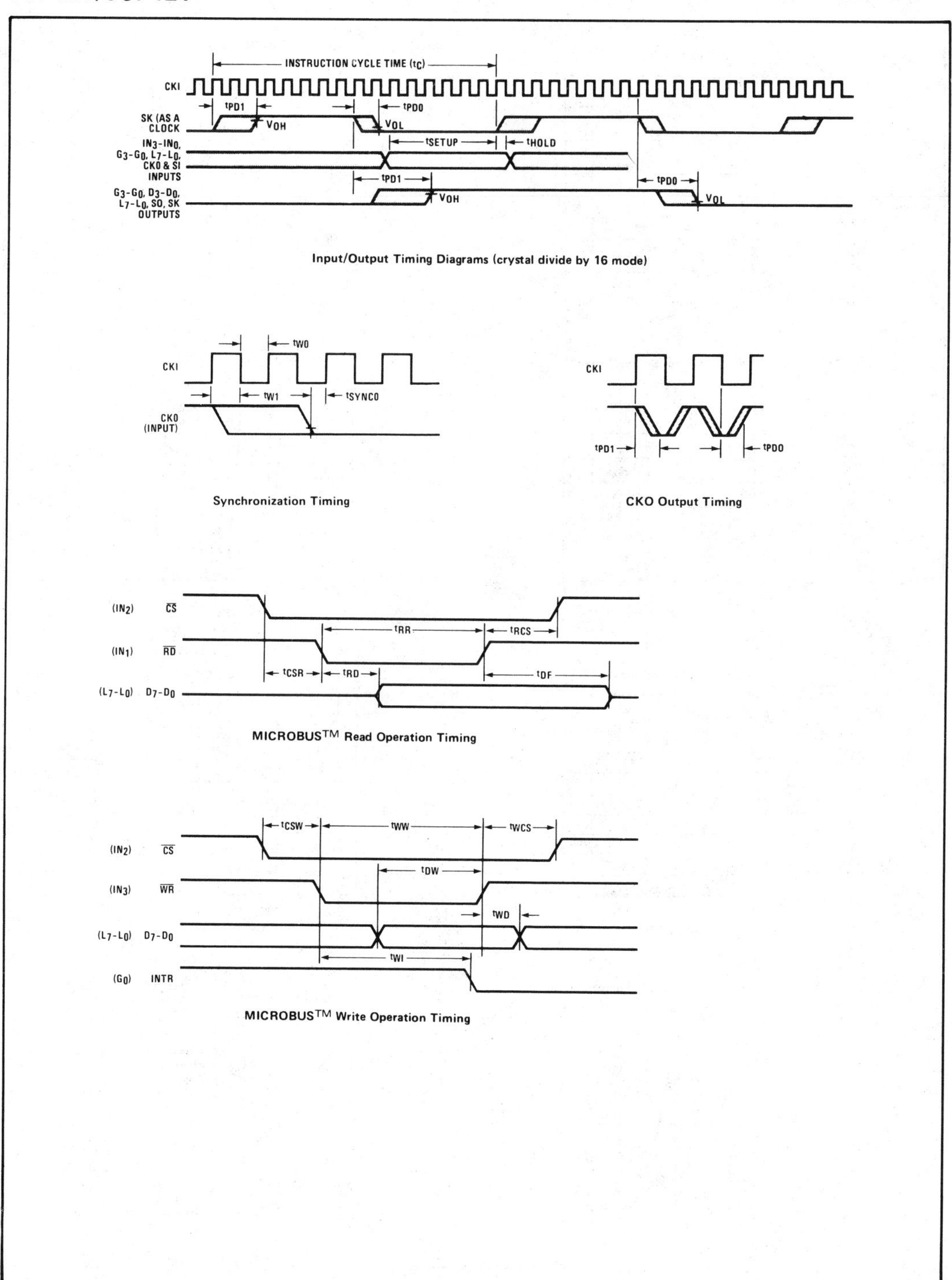


Input/Output Timing Diagrams (crystal divide by 16 mode)

Synchronization Timing

CKO Output Timing

MICROBUS™ Read Operation Timing

MICROBUS™ Write Operation Timing

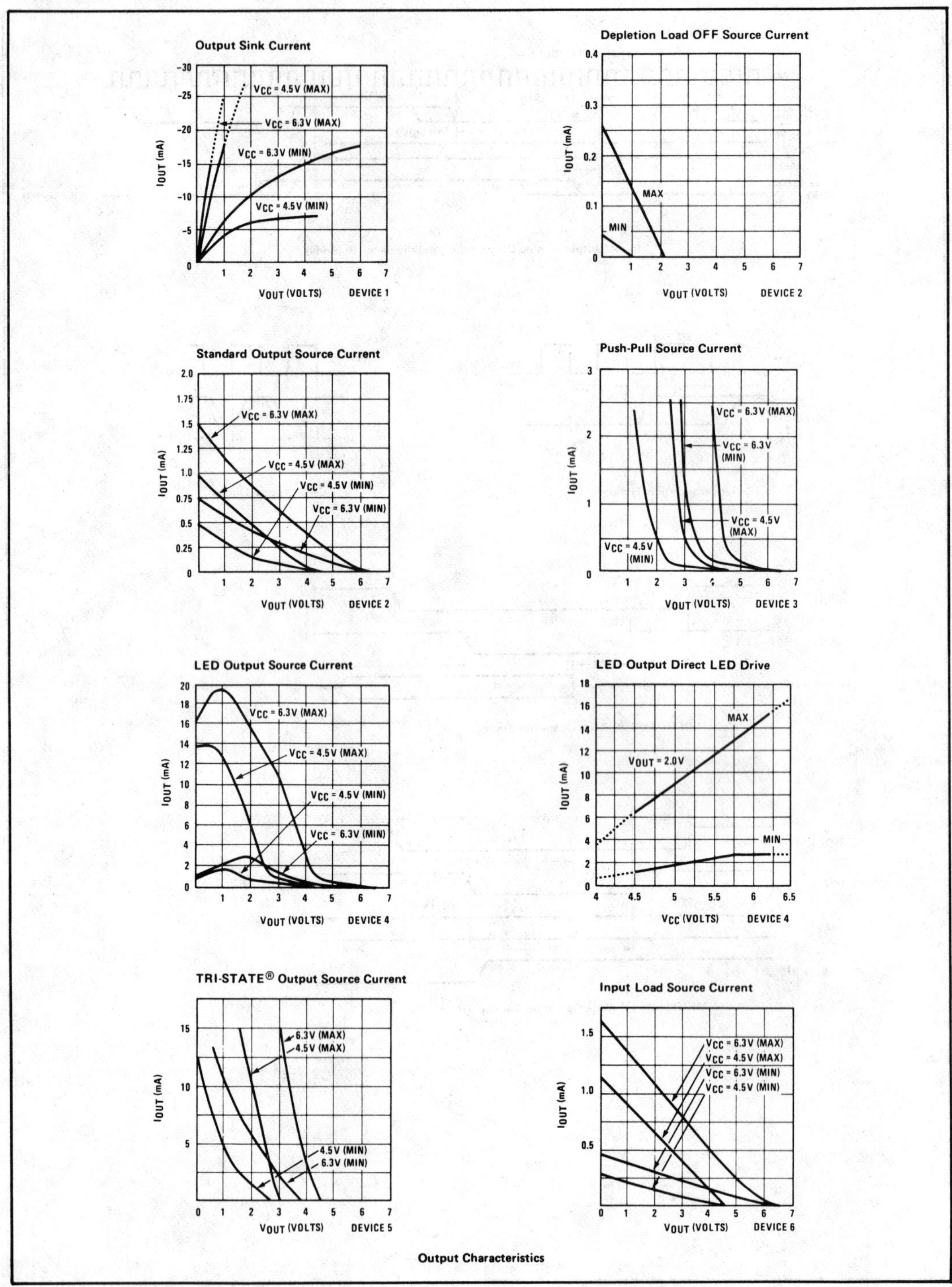


Output Characteristics

## Absolute Maximum Ratings

| | |
|---|---|
| Voltage at Any Pin Relative to GND | −0.5V to +7V |
| Ambient Operating Temperature | 0°C to +70°C |
| Ambient Storage Temperature | −65°C to +150°C |
| Lead Temperature (Soldering, 10 seconds) | 300°C |
| Power Dissipation | 0.75 Watt at 25°C<br>0.4 Watt at 70°C |

*Absolute maximum ratings indicate limits beyond which damage to the device may occur. DC and AC electrical specifications are not ensured when operating the device at absolute maximum ratings.*

## DC Electrical Characteristics $0°C \leq T_A \leq +70°C$, $4.5V \leq V_{CC} \leq 6.3V$ unless otherwise noted.

| Parameter | Conditions | Min | Max | Units |
|---|---|---|---|---|
| Operating Voltage ($V_{CC}$) | | 4.5 | 6.3 | V |
| Operating Supply Current | $V_{CC}$ = 5V, $T_A$ = 25°C (all inputs and outputs open) | | 30 | mA |
| Input Voltage Levels | | | | |
| CKI Input Levels | | | | |
| Logic High ($V_{IH}$) | | 2.0 | | V |
| Logic Low ($V_{IL}$) | | | 0.4 | V |
| RESET Input Levels | | | | |
| Logic High | | 0.7 $V_{CC}$ | | V |
| Logic Low | | | 0.6 | V |
| RESET Hysteresis | | 1.0 | | V |
| SO Input Level (Test mode) | | 2.0 | 3.0 | V |
| All Other Inputs | | | | |
| Logic High | $V_{CC}$ = max | 3.0 | | V |
| Logic High | $V_{CC}$ = 5V ± 5% | 2.0 | | V |
| Logic Low | | | 0.8 | V |
| Output Voltage Levels (Note 2) | | | | |
| TTL Operation | $V_{CC}$ = 5V ± 5% | | | |
| Logic High ($V_{OH}$) | $I_{OH}$ = 100μA | 2.4 | | V |
| Logic Low ($V_{OL}$) | $I_{OL}$ = −1.6mA | | 0.4 | V |
| CMOS Operation | | | | |
| Logic High ($V_{OH}$) | $I_{OH}$ = 10μA | $V_{CC}$ − 1 | | V |
| Logic Low ($V_{OL}$) | $I_{OL}$ = −10μA | | 0.2 | V |
| Output Current Levels | | | | |
| LED Direct Drive Output | $V_{CC}$ = 6V | | | |
| Logic High ($I_{OH}$) | $V_{OH}$ = 2.0V | 2.5 | 14 | mA |
| TRI-STATE® Output Leakage Current | | −10 | +10 | μA |

## AC Electrical Characteristics $0°C \leq T_A \leq +70°C$, $4.5V \leq V_{CC} \leq 6.3V$ unless otherwise noted.

| Parameter | Conditions | Min | Max | Units |
|---|---|---|---|---|
| Instruction Cycle Time — $t_C$ | figure 3 | 4 | 10 | μs |
| CKI Using Crystal (figure 8) | | | | |
| Input Frequency — $f_I$ | ÷16 mode | 1.6 | 4 | MHz |
| Duty Cycle (Note 2) | figure 3a | 30 | 55 | % |
| INPUTS: (figure 3a) | | | | |
| $IN_3-IN_0$, $G_3-G_0$, $L_7-L_0$ | | | | |
| $t_{SETUP}$ | | 1.7 | | μs |
| $t_{HOLD}$ | | 100 | | ns |
| SI, $IP_7-IP_0$ | | | | |
| $t_{SETUP}$ | | 0.3 | | μs |
| $t_{HOLD}$ | | 100 | | ns |
| OUTPUTS: | | | | |
| COP TO CMOS PROPAGATION DELAY | $4.5V \leq V_{CC} \leq 6.3V$, $C_L = 50pF$, $V_{OH} = 0.7V_{CC}$, $V_{OL} = 0.3V_{CC}$ | | | |
| SK as a Logic-Controlled Clock | | | | |
| $t_{PD1}$ | | | 1.1 | μs |
| $t_{PD0}$ | | | 0.3 | μs |
| SO, SK as a Data Output | | | | |
| $t_{PD1}$ | | | 1.4 | μs |
| $t_{PD0}$ | | | 0.3 | μs |
| $t_{PD1}$ | $V_{OH} = 2V$ | | 0.7 | μs |
| $D_3-D_0$, $G_3-G_0$ | | | | |
| $t_{PD1}$ | | | 1.6 | μs |
| $t_{PD0}$ | | | 0.6 | μs |
| $L_7-L_0$ (LED Direct Drive) | | | | |
| $t_{PD1}$ | $V_{OH} = 2V$ | | 2.4 | μs |
| $t_{PD0}$ | | | 0.4 | μs |
| COP TO TTL PROPAGATION DELAY | fanout = 1 Standard TTL Load $V_{CC} = 5V \pm 5\%$, $C_L = 50pF$, $V_{OH} = 2.4V$, $V_{OL} = 0.4V$ | | | |
| $AD/\overline{DATA}$ | | | | |
| $t_{PD1}$ | | | 0.5 | μs |
| $t_{PD0}$ | | | 0.5 | μs |
| SKIP | | | | |
| $t_{PD1}$ | | | 0.6 | μs |
| $t_{PD0}$ | | | 0.6 | μs |

## AC Electrical Characteristics (continued) 0°C ≤ $T_A$ ≤ +70°C, 4.5V ≤ $V_{CC}$ ≤ 6.3V unless otherwise noted.

| Parameter | Conditions | Min | Max | Units |
|---|---|---|---|---|
| OUTPUTS (cont.): | | | | |
| SK as a Logic-Controlled Clock | | | | |
| $t_{PD1}$ | | | 0.8 | μs |
| $t_{PD0}$ | | | 0.8 | μs |
| SK as a Data Output, SO | | | | |
| $t_{PD1}$ | | | 1.0 | μs |
| $t_{PD0}$ | | | 1.0 | μs |
| $D_3$-$D_0$, $G_3$-$G_0$ | | | | |
| $t_{PD1}$ | | | 1.3 | μs |
| $t_{PD0}$ | | | 1.3 | μs |
| $L_7$-$L_0$ | | | | |
| $t_{PD1}$ | | | 1.4 | μs |
| $t_{PD0}$ | | | 0.4 | μs |
| $IP_7$-$IP_0$, $P_9$, $P_8$ | | | | |
| $t_{PD1}$ | | | 1.5 | μs |
| $t_{PD0}$ | | | 1.5 | μs |
| CKO (figure 3a) | | | | |
| $t_{PD1}$ | | | 0.2 | μs |
| $t_{PD0}$ | | | 0.2 | μs |
| MICROBUS™ TIMING (COP402M) | $C_L$ = 50pF, $V_{CC}$ = 5V ± 5% | | | |
| A. Read Operation (figure 4) | | | | |
| Chip Select Stable before $\overline{RD}$ — $t_{CSR}$ | | 50 | | ns |
| Chip Select Hold Time for $\overline{RD}$ — $t_{RCS}$ | | 5 | | ns |
| $\overline{RD}$ Pulse Width — $t_{RR}$ | | 300 | | ns |
| Data Delay from $\overline{RD}$ — $t_{RD}$ | | | 250 | ns |
| $\overline{RD}$ to Data Floating — $t_{DF}$ | | | 200 | ns |
| B. Write Operation (figure 5) | | | | |
| Chip Select Stable before $\overline{WR}$ — $t_{CSW}$ | | 20 | | ns |
| Chip Select Hold Time for $\overline{WR}$ — $t_{WCS}$ | | 20 | | ns |
| $\overline{WR}$ Pulse Width — $t_{WW}$ | | 300 | | ns |
| Data Setup Time for $\overline{WR}$ — $t_{DW}$ | | 200 | | ns |
| Data Hold Time for $\overline{WR}$ — $t_{WD}$ | | 40 | | ns |
| INTR Transition Time from $\overline{WR}$ — $t_{WI}$ | | | 700 | ns |

**Note 1:** Duty Cycle = $t_{WI}/(t_{WI} + t_{WO})$.

**Note 2:** See figure 11 for additional I/O characteristics.

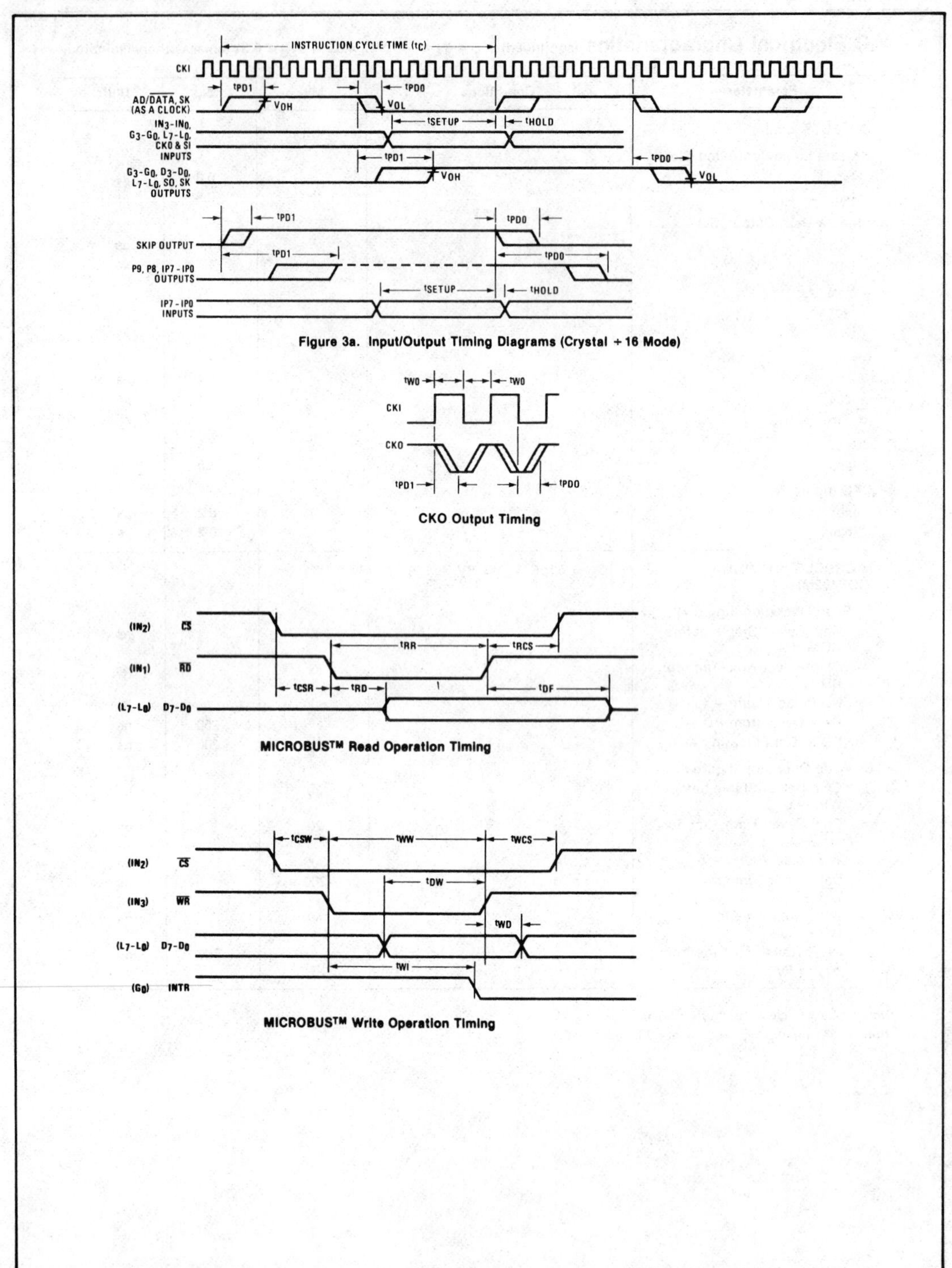


Figure 3a. Input/Output Timing Diagrams (Crystal ÷ 16 Mode)

CKO Output Timing

MICROBUS™ Read Operation Timing

MICROBUS™ Write Operation Timing

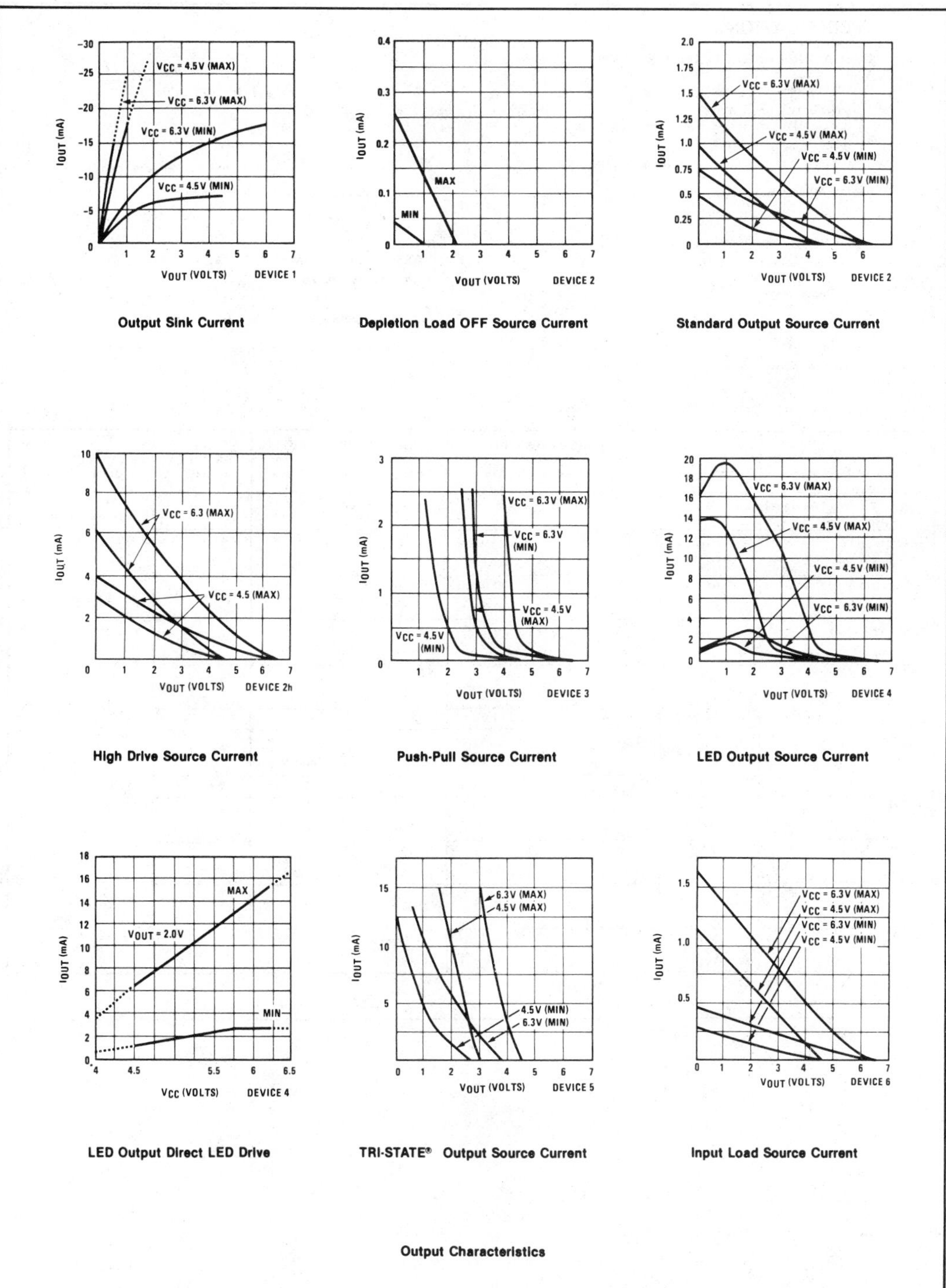


Output Characteristics

## SPECIFICATIONS

### OPERATING CHARACTERISTICS

Supply Voltage:

VDD = 15 Volts ±5%
(Logic "1" = most negative voltage $V_{IL}$ and $V_{OL}$.)

VSS = 0 Volts (Gnd.)
(Logic "0" = most positive voltage $V_{IH}$ and $V_{OH}$.)

System Operating Frequencies:

80 kHz ±50% with external resistor

Device Power Consumption:

75 mw, typical

Input Capacitance:

$<5$ pf

Input Leakage:

$<10$ μa

Open Drain Driver Leakage (R OFF):

$\leqslant 10$ μa at -30 Volts

Operating Ambient Temperature (TA):

0°C to 70°C (TA = 25°C unless otherwise specified.)

Storage Temperature:

-55°C to 120°C

### ABSOLUTE MAXIMUM VOLTAGE RATINGS (with respect to VSS)

Maximum negative voltage on any pin -30 volts.

Maximum positive voltage on any pin +0.3 volts.

| INPUT/OUTPUT | SYMBOL | LIMITS (VSS = 0) | | | LIMITS (VSS = +5V) | | | TIMING (SAMPLE/ GOOD) | TEST CONDITIONS |
|---|---|---|---|---|---|---|---|---|---|
| | | MIN | TYP | MAX | MIN | TYP | MAX | | |
| Supply Current (Average) for VDD | IDD | | 5 ma | 8 ma | | 5 ma | 8 ma | | VDD = -15.75V T = 25°C |
| Discrete I/O's | $V_{IH}$ | -1.0V | | | +4.0V | | | φ34 | |
| DI/O 0-DI/O 8 | $V_{IL}$ | | | -4.2V | | | +0.8V | | |
| DI/O 0-5 | RON | | | 500 ohms | | | 500 ohms | φ2* | 3.0 ma max. |
| DI/O 6-8 | RON | | | 400 ohms | | | 400 ohms | | |
| Channel 1 Input | $V_{IH}$ | -1.5V | | | +3.5V | | | φ1 | |
| PI1-PI4 | $V_{IL}$ | | | -4.2V | | | +0.8V | | |
| I/O Channel A | $V_{IH}$ | -1.5V | | | +3.5V | | | φ3 | |
| RI/O1-RI/O4 | $V_{IL}$ | | | -4.2V | | | +0.8V | | |
| | RON | | | 250 ohms | | | 250 ohms | φ2* | 6.0 ma max. |
| I/O Channel B | $V_{IH}$ | -1.5V | | | +3.5V | | | φ3 | |
| RI/O5-RI/O8 | $V_{IL}$ | | | -4.2V | | | +0.8V | | |
| | RON | | | 250 ohms | | | 250 ohms | φ2* | 6.0 ma max. |
| INTO | $V_{IH}$ | -1.5V | | | +3.5V | | | φ3 | |
| | $V_{IL}$ | | | -4.2V | | | +0.8V | | |
| Clock | $V_{OH}$ | -1.0V | | | +4.0V | | | -5.0V | CL = 50 pf (max) |
| A | $V_{OL}$ | | | -10.0V | | | -5.0V | | |
| VC | $V_{IH}$ | | | | | | | | 56K ±5% |
| | $V_{IL}$ | | | | | | | | |
| PO | $V_{IH}$ | -2.0V | | | +3.0V | | | | Special circuit |
| | $V_{IL}$ | | | -6.0V | | | -1.0V | | |

*State established by φ2 (minimum impedance after φ4).
**Same as above except φ4 minimum at φ2 of next cycle.

# PPS4/1 MM76 and MM76E

## SPECIFICATIONS

### OPERATING CHARACTERISTICS

Supply Voltage:

VDD = 15 Volts ±5%
(Logic "1" = most negative voltage $V_{IL}$ and $V_{OL}$.)

VSS = 0 Volts (Gnd.)
(Logic "0" = most positive voltage $V_{IH}$ and $V_{OH}$.)

System Operating Frequencies:

80 kHz ±50% with external resistor

Device Power Consumption:

75 mw, typical

Input Capacitance:

<5 pf

Input Leakage:

<10 μa

Open Drain Driver Leakage (R OFF):

⩽10 μa at -30 Volts

Operating Ambient Temperature (TA):

0°C to 70°C (TA = 25°C unless otherwise specified.)

Storage Temperature:

-55°C to 120°C

### ABSOLUTE MAXIMUM VOLTAGE RATINGS (with respect to VSS)

Maximum negative voltage on any pin -30 volts.

Maximum positive voltage on any pin +0.3 volts.

| INPUT/OUTPUT | SYMBOL | LIMITS (VSS = 0) | | | LIMITS (VSS = +5V) | | | TIMING (SAMPLE/ GOOD) | TEST CONDITIONS |
|---|---|---|---|---|---|---|---|---|---|
| | | MIN | TYP | MAX | MIN | TYP | MAX | | |
| Supply Current (Average) for VDD | IDD | | 5 ma | 8 ma | | 5 ma | 8 ma | | VDD = -15.75V T = 25°C |
| Discrete I/O's | $V_{IH}$ | -1.0V | | | +4.0V | | | ϕ34 | |
| DI/O 0-DI/O 9 | $V_{IL}$ | | | -4.2V | | | +0.8V | | |
| DI/O 0-5 | RON | | | 500 ohms | | | 500 ohms | ϕ2* | 3.0 ma max. |
| DI/O 6-9 | RON | | | 400 ohms | | | 400 ohms | | |
| Channel 1 Input | $V_{IH}$ | -1.5V | | | +3.5V | | | ϕ1 | |
| PI1-PI4 | $V_{IL}$ | | | -4.2V | | | +0.8V | | |
| Channel 2 Input | $V_{IH}$ | -1.5V | | | +3.5V | | | ϕ3 | |
| PI5-PI8 | $V_{IL}$ | | | -4.2V | | | +0.8V | | |
| I/O Channel A | $V_{IH}$ | -1.5V | | | +3.5V | | | ϕ3 | |
| RI/O1-RI/O4 | $V_{IL}$ | | | -4.2V | | | +0.8V | | |
| | RON | | | 250 ohms | | | 250 ohms | ϕ2* | 6.0 ma max. |
| I/O Channel B | $V_{IH}$ | -1.5V | | | +3.5V | | | ϕ3 | |
| RI/O5-RI/O8 | $V_{IL}$ | | | -4.2V | | | +0.8V | | |
| | RON | | | 250 ohms | | | 250 ohms | ϕ2* | 6.0 ma max. |
| DATA I | $V_{IH}$ | -1.0V | | | +4.0V | | | ϕ4 | |
| | $V_{IL}$ | | | -4.2V | | | +0.8V | | |
| DATA O | RON | | | 500 ohms | | | 500 ohms | ϕ4** | 3.0 ma max. |
| INTO | $V_{IH}$ | -1.5V | | | +3.5V | | | ϕ3 | |
| | $V_{IL}$ | | | -4.2V | | | +0.8V | | |
| INT1 | $V_{IH}$ | -1.5V | | | +3.5V | | | ϕ1 | |
| | $V_{IL}$ | | | -4.2V | | | +0.8V | | |
| Clock | $V_{OH}$ | -1.0V | | | +4.0V | | | -5.0V | CL = 50 pf (max) |
| A, BP, ($\bar{B}$) | $V_{OL}$ | | | -10.0V | | | -5.0V | | |
| EXCLK*** | $V_{IH}$ | -1.5V | | | +3.5V | | | -4.0V | F max. = 80 kHz |
| | $V_{IL}$ | | | -9.0V | | | -4.0V | | |
| CLK IN | $V_{IH}$ | -1.0V | | | +4.0V | | | | |
| | $V_{IL}$ | | | -10.0V | | | -5.0V | | |
| Shift Clock | $V_{IH}$ | -1.0V | | | +4.0V | | | ϕ34 | |
| Clock | $V_{IL}$ | | | -4.2V | | | +0.8V | | |
| | RON | | | 500 ohms | | | 500 ohms | ϕ4** | 2.0 ma max. |
| VC | $V_{IH}$ | | | | | | | | 56K ±5% |
| | $V_{IL}$ | | | | | | | | |
| PO | $V_{IH}$ | -2.0V | | | +3.0V | | | | Special circuit |
| | $V_{IL}$ | | | -6.0V | | | -1.0V | | |

*State established by ϕ2 (minimum impedance after ϕ4).
**Same as above except ϕ4 minimum at ϕ2 of next cycle.
***Requires selected resistor at VC. Contact Rockwell for specific requirements when using external oscillator.

# PPS4/1 MM76C

## SPECIFICATIONS

**52-PIN IN-LINE SOCKET**
Burndy P/N: DILE-52P1
Burndy Corp., 931 S. Douglas
El Segundo, Calif. 90245

**OPERATING CHARACTERISTICS**
VDD = -15 Volts ±5%
(Logic "1" = most negative voltage $V_{IL}$ and $V_{OL}$)
VSS = 0 Volts (GND)
(Logic "0" = most positive voltage $V_{IH}$ and $V_{OH}$)

System Operating Frequencies:
89 kHz ±25% (internal clock)

Device Power Consumption:
200 mw, typical

Input Capacitance:
<5 pf

Input Leakage:
<10 μa

Open Drain Driver Leakage (R OFF):
⩽10 μa at -30 Volts

Operating Ambient Temperature (TA):
$0^oC$ to $70^oC$ (TA = $25^oC$ unless otherwise specified)

Storage Temperature:
$-55^oC$ to $120^oC$

**ABSOLUTE MAXIMUM VOLTAGE RATINGS**
**(with respect to VSS)**
Maximum negative voltage on any pin -30 volts.
Maximum positive voltage on any pin +0.3 volt.

| Input/Output | Symbol | Limits (VSS = 0) | | | Limits (VSS = +5V) | | | Timing (Sample/ Good) | Test Conditions |
|---|---|---|---|---|---|---|---|---|---|
| | | Min | Typ | Max | Min | Typ | Max | | |
| Supply Current (Average) for VDD | $I_{DD}$ | | 12 ma | | | | | | VDD = -15.75V<br>T = $25^oC$ |
| Discrete I/O's<br>DI/O 0-DI/O 9 | $V_{IH}$<br>$V_{IL}$ | -1.0V | | <br>-4.2V | +4.0V | | <br>+0.8V | Ø3 & Ø4 | |
| DI/O 0-5 | $R_{ON}$ | | | 500 ohms | | | 500 ohms | Ø2* | 3.0 ma max. |
| DI/O 6-9 | $R_{ON}$ | | | 400 ohms | | | 400 ohms | | |
| Channel 1 Input<br>PI1-PI4 | $V_{IH}$<br>$V_{IL}$ | -1.5V | | <br>-4.2V | +3.5V | | <br>+0.8V | Ø1 | |
| Channel 2 Input<br>PI5-PI8 | $V_{IH}$<br>$V_{IL}$ | -1.5V | | <br>-4.2V | +3.5V | | <br>+0.8V | Ø3 | |
| I/O Channel A<br>RI/O1-RI/O4 | $V_{IH}$<br>$V_{IL}$ | -1.5V | | <br>-4.2V | +3.[illegible]V | | <br>+0.8V | Ø3 | |
| | $R_{ON}$ | | | 250 ohms | | | 250 ohms | Ø2* | 6.0 ma max. |
| I/O Channel B<br>RI/O5-RI/O8 | $V_{IH}$<br>$V_{IL}$ | -1.5V | | <br>-4.2V | +3.5V | | <br>+0.8V | Ø3 | |
| | $R_{ON}$ | | | 250 ohms | | | 250 ohms | Ø2* | 6.0 ma max. |
| DATAI | $V_{IH}$<br>$V_{IL}$ | -1.0V | | <br>-4.2V | +4.0V | | <br>+0.8V | Ø4 | |
| DATAO | $R_{ON}$ | | | 500 ohms | | | 500 ohms | Ø4** | 3.0 ma max. |
| INT0 | $V_{IH}$<br>$V_{IL}$ | -1.5V | | <br>-4.2V | +3.5V | | <br>+0.8V | Ø3 | |
| INT1 | $V_{IH}$<br>$V_{IL}$ | -1.5V | | <br>-4.2V | +3.5V | | <br>+0.8V | Ø1 | |
| Clock<br>A, BP, ($\bar{B}$) | $V_{OH}$<br>$V_{OL}$ | -1.0V | | <br>-10.0V | +4.0V | | <br>-5.0V | -5.0V | CL ≠ 50 pf (max) |
| XPWR | $V_{IH}$<br>$V_{IL}$ | VSS | | <br>VDD | VSS | | <br>VDD | | |
| XTLIN, XTLOUT | $V_{IH}$<br>$V_{IL}$ | | | | | | | | Crystal<br>3.579 MHz |
| Shift Clock<br>CLOCK | $V_{IH}$<br>$V_{IL}$ | -1.0V | | <br>-4.2V | +4.0V | | <br>+0.8V | Ø3 & Ø4 | |
| | $R_{ON}$ | | | 500 ohms | | | 500 ohms | Ø4** | 2.0 ma max. |
| PO | $V_{IH}$<br>$V_{IL}$ | -2.0V | | <br>-6.0V | +3.0V | | <br>-1.0V | | Special circuit |
| PC1 | $V_{IH}$<br>$V_{IL}$ | -1.5V | | <br>-4.2V | +4.5V | | <br>+0.8V | DC | |
| PC2 | $V_{IH}$<br>$V_{IL}$ | -1.5V | | <br>-4.2V | +4.5V | | <br>+0.8V | DC | |
| CA8 LOWER CARRY OUT | $R_{ON}$ | | | 500 ohms | | | 500 ohms | DC | |
| CA16/D UPPER CARRY SERIAL DATA OUT | $R_{ON}$ | | | 500 ohms | | | 500 ohms | Ø3 & Ø4 | |
| SYEV SERIAL EVENT INPUT | $V_{IH}$<br>$V_{IL}$ | -1.5V | | <br>-4.2V | +3.5V | | <br>+0.8V | Ø3 | |
| SCC/D SHIFT CLOCK CONTROL/DATA | $V_{IH}$<br>$V_{IL}$ | -1.0V | | <br>-10.0V | +4.0V | | <br>+0.8V | Ø3 & Ø4 | |
| C/DI CONTROL/DATA INPUT | $V_{IH}$<br>$V_{IL}$ | -1.0V | | <br>-10.0V | +4.0V | | <br>+0.8V | Ø3 | |
| ENABL | $V_{IH}$<br>$V_{IL}$ | -1.5V | | <br>-4.2V | +3.5V | | <br>+0.8V | DC | |

*State established by Ø2 (minimum impedance after Ø4)
**Same as above except Ø4 minimum at Ø2 of next cycle.

## SPECIFICATIONS

### OPERATING CHARACTERISTICS

Supply Voltage:

$V_{DD}$ = -8.5 Volts -2.5, +2.0 Volts
(Logic "1" = most negative voltage $V_{IL}$ and $V_{OL}$.)
$V_{SS}$ = 0 Volts (Gnd.)
(Logic "0" = most positive voltage $V_{IH}$ and $V_{OH}$.)

System Operating Frequencies:

(1) Internal: 100 kHz Nominal at $V_{DD}$ = -8.5V
(2) External 800 kHz Crystal: 100 kHz

Device Power Consumption: 15 mw, typical

Input Capacitance: <5 pf

Input Leakage: <10 $\mu$a

Open Drain Driver Leakage (R OFF): <10 $\mu$a at -30 Volts

Operating Ambient Temperature ($T_A$)

$0^{o}$C to $+70^{o}$C (Commercial): MM76L and MM76EL
$-40^{o}$C to $+85^{o}$C (Industrial): MM76L-2 and MM76EL-2

Storage Temperature: $-55^{o}$C to $120^{o}$C

### ABSOLUTE MAXIMUM VOLTAGE RATINGS
**(with respect to VSS)**

Maximum negative voltage on any pin -30 volts.

Maximum positive voltage on any pin +0.3 volts.

### TEST CONDITIONS: $V_{DD}$ = -8.5V, $T_A$ = $25^{o}$C

| INPUT/OUTPUT | SYMBOL | LIMITS (VSS = 0) MIN | TYP | MAX | LIMITS (VSS = +5V) MIN | TYP | MAX | TIMING (SAMPLE/ GOOD) | TEST CONDITIONS |
|---|---|---|---|---|---|---|---|---|---|
| Supply Current (Average) for VDD | IDD | | 1.75 ma | 3 ma | | 1.75 ma | 3 ma | | |
| Discrete I/O's DI/O 0-9 | $V_{IH}$ | -1.0V | | | +4.0V | | | $\phi$34 | |
| | $V_{IL}$ | | | -4.2V | | | +0.8V | | |
| | RON | | | 100 ohms | | | 100 ohms | $\phi$2* | 10.0 ma max. |
| Channel 1 Input PI1-PI4 | $V_{IH}$ | -1.5V | | | +3.5V | | | $\phi$1 | |
| | $V_{IL}$ | | | -4.2V | | | +0.8V | | |
| Channel 2 Input PI5-PI8 | $V_{IH}$ | -1.5V | | | +3.5V | | | $\phi$3 | |
| | $V_{IL}$ | | | -4.2V | | | +0.8V | | |
| I/O Channel A RIO1-RIO4 | $V_{IH}$ | -1.5V | | | +3.5V | | | $\phi$4 | |
| | $V_{IL}$ | | | -4.2V | | | +0.8V | | |
| | RON | | | 250 ohms | | | 250 ohms | $\phi$2* | 6.0 ma max. |
| I/O Channel B RIO5-RIO8 | $V_{IH}$ | -1.5V | | | +3.5V | | | $\phi$4 | |
| | $V_{IL}$ | | | -4.2V | | | +0.8V | | |
| | RON | | | 250 ohms | | | 250 ohms | $\phi$2* | 6.0 ma max. |
| DATA I | $V_{IH}$ | -1.0V | | | +4.0V | | | $\phi$4 | |
| | $V_{IL}$ | | | -4.2V | | | +0.8V | | |
| DATA O | RON | | | 500 ohms | | | 500 ohms | $\phi$4** | 3.0 ma max. |
| INT0 | $V_{IH}$ | -1.5V | | | +3.5V | | | $\phi$3 | |
| | $V_{IL}$ | | | -4.2V | | | +0.8V | | |
| INT1 | $V_{IH}$ | -1.5V | | | +3.5V | | | $\phi$1 | |
| | $V_{IL}$ | | | -4.2V | | | +0.8V | | |
| Clock A, BP, ($\overline{B}$) | $V_{OH}$ | -1.0V | | | +4.0V | | | | CL = 50 pf (max) |
| | $V_{OL}$ | | | -6.0V | | | -1.0V | | |
| XTLIN | $V_{IH}$ | -1.5V | | | +3.5V | | | -4.0V | |
| | $V_{IL}$ | | | -6.0V | | | -1.0V | | |
| Shift Clock | $V_{IH}$ | -1.0V | | | +4.0V | | | $\phi$34 | |
| | $V_{IL}$ | | | -4.2V | | | +0.8V | | |
| | RON | | | 500 ohms | | | 500 ohms | $\phi$4** | 2.0 ma max. |
| VC | $V_{IH}$ | | | | | | | | V = 11.0V max. |
| | $V_{IL}$ | | | | | | | | |
| PO | $V_{IH}$ | -1.5V | | | +3.0V | | | | Special circuit |
| | $V_{IL}$ | | | -4.2V | | | -1.0V | | |

*State established by $\phi$2 (minimum impedance after $\phi$4).
**Same as above except $\phi$4 minimum at $\phi$2 of next cycle.

### NOTES:

#### MASK PROGRAMMED PULL-UP RESISTORS ON OUTPUTS

Resistor pull-ups are available as an option on all RIO and DI/O outputs. These pull-ups are connected to $V_{DD}$. The following values ± 25% are available: 3K, 5K, 10K, 15K, 25K, and Open Circuit.

#### PULL-UPS ON INPUTS

MOS FET Pull-ups are also available on the PI, INT, and DATA I inputs. The connection of this pull-up is optional. The output current is 50 $\mu$a ± 25 $\mu$a with the input grounded and $V_{DD}$ at -8.5 volts.

# PP24/1 MM77 and MM78

## SPECIFICATIONS

### OPERATING CHARACTERISTICS

Supply Voltage:

VDD = 15 Volts ±5%
(Logic "1" = most negative voltage $V_{IL}$ and $V_{OL}$.)

VSS = 0 Volts (Gnd.)
(Logic "0" = most positive voltage $V_{IH}$ and $V_{OH}$.)

System Operating Frequencies:

80 kHz ±50% with external resistor

Device Power Consumption:

75 mw, typical

Input Capacitance:

<5 pf

Input Leakage:

<10 μa

Open Drain Driver Leakage (R OFF):

≤10 μa at -30 Volts

Operating Ambient Temperature (TA):

0°C to 70°C (TA = 25°C unless otherwise specified.)

Storage Temperature:

-55°C to 120°C

### ABSOLUTE MAXIMUM VOLTAGE RATINGS
**(with respect to VSS)**

Maximum negative voltage on any pin -30 volts.

Maximum positive voltage on any pin +0.3 volts.

| FUNCTION | SYMBOL | LIMITS (VSS = 0) MIN | TYP | MAX | LIMITS (VSS = +5V) MIN | TYP | MAX | TIMING (SAMPLE/ GOOD) | TEST CONDITIONS |
|---|---|---|---|---|---|---|---|---|---|
| Supply Current (Average) for VDD | IDD | | 5 ma | 8 ma | | 5 ma | 8 ma | | VDD = -15.75V T = 25°C |
| Discrete I/O's DI/O 0-DI/O 9 | $V_{IH}$ | -1.0V | | | +4.0V | | | φ3 | |
| | $V_{IL}$ | | | -4.2V | | | +0.8V | | |
| | RON | | | 500 ohms | | | 500 ohms | φ2* | 3.0 ma max. |
| Channel 1 Input PI1-PI4 | $V_{IH}$ | -1.5V | | | +3.5V | | | φ1 | |
| | $V_{IL}$ | | | -4.2V | | | +0.8V | | |
| Channel 2 Input PI5-PI8 | $V_{IH}$ | -1.5V | | | +3.5V | | | φ3 | |
| | $V_{IL}$ | | | -4.2V | | | +0.8V | | |
| I/O Channel A RI/O1-RI/O4 | $V_{IH}$ | -1.5V | | | +3.5V | | | φ3 | |
| | $V_{IL}$ | | | -4.2V | | | +0.8V | | |
| | RON | | | 500 ohms | | | 500 ohms | φ2* | 3.0 ma max. |
| I/O Channel X RI/O5-RI/O8 | $V_{IH}$ | -1.0V | | | +4.0V | | | Not sync. Must be stable at φ1 and 2. | |
| | $V_{IL}$ | | | -4.2V | | | +0.8V | | |
| | RON | | | 500 ohms | | | 500 ohms | φ2* | 3.0 ma max. |
| DATA I | $V_{IH}$ | -1.0V | | | +4.0V | | | φ4 | |
| | $V_{IL}$ | | | -4.2V | | | +0.8V | | |
| DATA O | RON | | | | | | | φ4** | |
| INT0 | $V_{IH}$ | -1.5V | | | +3.5V | | | φ3 | |
| | $V_{IL}$ | | | -4.2V | | | +0.8V | | |
| INT1 | $V_{IH}$ | -1.5V | | | +3.5V | | | φ1 | |
| | $V_{IL}$ | | | -4.2V | | | +0.8V | | |
| Clock A, BP, ($\bar{B}$) | $V_{OH}$ | -1.0V | | | +4.0V | | | | CL = 50 pf (max.) |
| | $V_{OL}$ | | | -10.0V | | | -5.0V | | |
| EXCLK*** | $V_{IH}$ | -1.5V | | | +3.5V | | | STRAP | F max = 80 kHz |
| | $V_{IL}$ | | | -7.0V | | | -2.0V | | |
| CLK IN | $V_{IH}$ | -1.0V | | | +4.0V | | | | |
| | $V_{IL}$ | | | -10.0V | | | -5.0V | | |
| Shift Clock Clock | $V_{IH}$ | -1.0V | | | +4.0V | | | φ34 | |
| | $V_{IL}$ | | | -4.2V | | | +0.8V | | |
| | RON | | | 500 ohms | | | 500 ohms | φ4** | 2.0 ma max. |
| VC | $V_{IH}$ | | | | | | | | 56K ±5% |
| | $V_{IL}$ | | | | | | | | |
| PO | $V_{IH}$ | -2.0V | | | +3.0V | | | | Special circuit |
| | $V_{IL}$ | | | -6.0V | | | -1.0V | | |

*State established by φ2 (minimum impedance after φ4).
**Same as above except φ4 minimum at φ2 of next cycle.
***Requires selected resistor at VC. Contact Rockwell for specific requirements when using external oscillator.

# Chapter 2
# THE MOSTEK 3870
# (AND FAIRCHILD F8)

**The F8 has had a profound impact on the microcomputer industry. When it first appeared, the F8 was discussed as an off-beat product with a strange set of chips and a ridiculous instruction set. The chip set was strange because logic was organized with the goal of minimizing chip counts; in contrast, microprocessors such as the 8080A and 6800 were designed with logic distributed functionally on chips - one traditional CPU logic function per chip. The F8 instruction set is indeed strange, and in some cases quite limiting, but it reflects the simple chip design of the F8 CPU.**

**Many microprocessors are now going into consumer products. In this marketplace, the two-chip F8 system provided by a 3850 CPU and a 3851 PSU gained an early dominant position. Other microprocessors available when the F8 was introduced required seven or more chips to provide the same capabilities as the two-chip F8. The economics of consumer product volumes rendered the inefficiencies of the F8 instruction set inconsequential; as a result, in 1977 the F8 was the world's leading microprocessor in terms of CPU sales.**

**In recognition of the F8 success story, most microprocessor manufacturers have introduced one-chip and two-chip microcomputer systems.**

Since the F8 3850 CPU/3851 PSU configuration was the world's first two-chip 8-bit microcomputer system, the F8 was the easiest 8-bit microprocessor to convert into a one-chip microcomputer. **Fairchild, the F8 prime source, and Mostek, the F8 second source, both designed one-chip microcomputers around the F8. Fairchild designed the 3859, which was a simple combination of the 3850 CPU and 3851 PSU on a single chip. Mostek developed a more ambitious one-chip microcomputer, the 3870. Mostek developed the 3870 ahead of the Fairchild 3859; therefore, Fairchild dropped the 3859 and became a second source for the 3870.** Thus, the original F8 second source, Mostek, is now the new prime source, while the original prime source, Fairchild, is now a second source.

The majority of F8 customers have small configurations which convert readily to the 3870. This being the case, **the 3870 is the F8 product being actively marketed,** while the old F8 chip set is now manufactured to meet the needs of existing customers and to represent a possible expansion for any customer whose application will no longer fit within the confines of the 3870. **In this chapter, therefore, we begin by examining the 3870 in detail. Descriptions of the F8 CPU and its support devices follow.**

**THE FAIRCHILD F8 DEVICE SET**

**These are the F8 devices described:**

- **The 3850 CPU.**
- **The 3851 Programmable Storage Unit (PSU), which provides read-only memory plus various additional logic functions.**
- **The 3852 Dynamic Memory Interface (DMI), which primarily provides interface logic for dynamic or static read-write memory.**
- **The 3853 Static Memory Interface (SMI), which primarily provides interface logic for static read/write memory.**
- **The 3854 Direct Memory Access (DMA), which, in conjunction with the 3852 DMI, implements Direct Memory Access logic.**
- **The 3856 and 3857 16K Programmable Storage Units (PSU 16), which are variations of the 3851 PSU but provide more read-only memory.**
- **The 3861 PIO, which provides the additional logic functions of the 3851 PSU but has no read-only memory.**
- **The 3871 PIO, which is equivalent to the 3861 PIO but has logic characteristics identical to the 3870.**

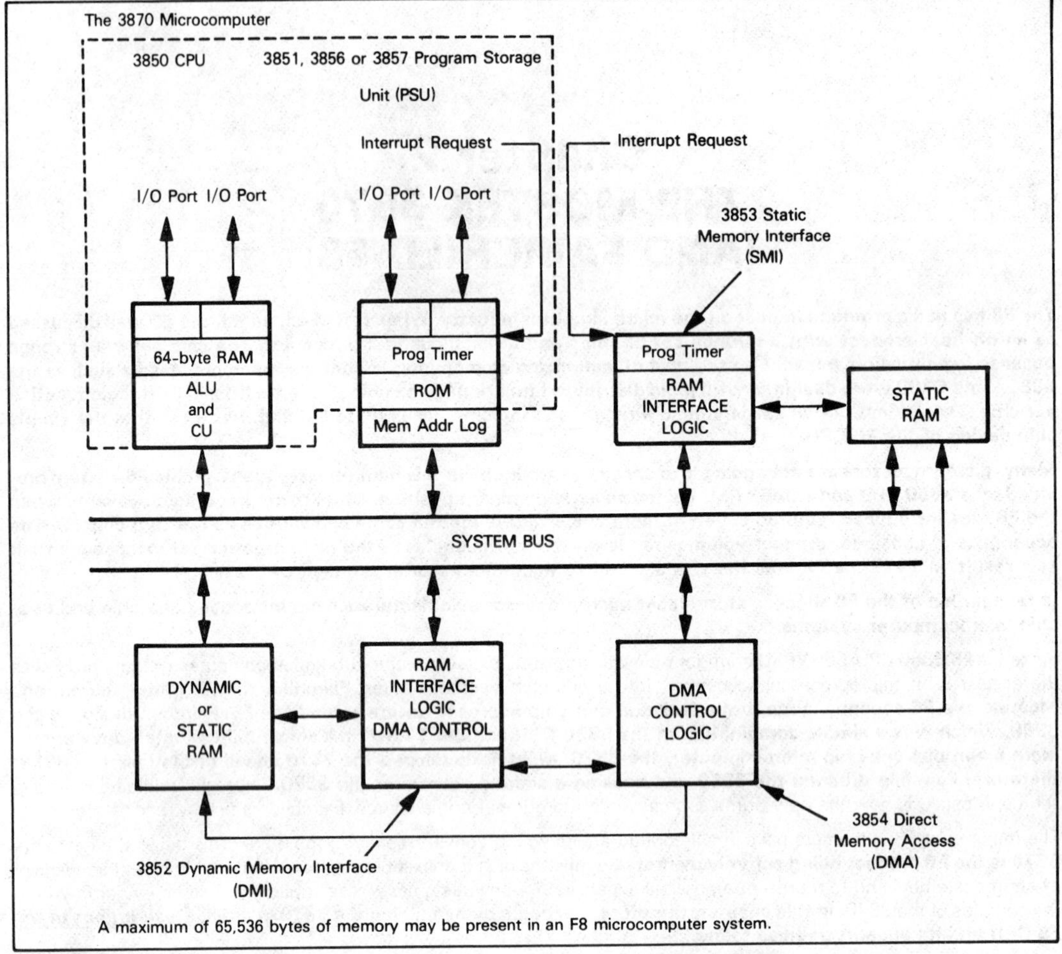


Figure 2-1. A Fairchild/Mostek F8 Microcomputer System

**Figure 2-1 illustrates logic associated with individual F8 devices, and the 3870 one-chip microcomputer.**

All devices of the F8 family require +5V and +12V power supplies. The 3870, however, uses a single +5V power supply.

Using a 500 ns clock, instruction cycle time is 2 μsec. Instruction execution times range from 1 to 6.5 instruction cycles, or 2 to 13 μsec.

N-channel isoplanar MOS technology is used for the F8.

N-channel ion injection technology is used for the 3870.

The principal manufacturer for the F8 is:

FAIRCHILD SEMICONDUCTOR
464 Ellis Street
Mountain View, CA 94040

The second source is:

MOSTEK, INC.
P.O. Box 169
Carrollton, TX 75006

The principal manufacturer for the 3870 is:

MOSTEK, INC.
P.O. Box 169
Carrollton, TX 75006

Second sources are:

FAIRCHILD SEMICONDUCTOR
464 Ellis Street
Mountain View, CA 94040

MOTOROLA, INC.
Semiconductor Products Division
3501 Ed Bluestein Blvd.
Austin, TX 78721

## THE 3870 ONE-CHIP MICROCOMPUTER

**Functions implemented on the 3870 microcomputer are illustrated in Figure 2-2.**

**Some caution must be exercised when looking at Figure 2-2;** functions shown as present should not always be considered equal to larger systems. For example, read/write memory and memory addressing are shown as completely present; however, only 64 bytes of read/write memory are provided, with no possibility of expansion. I/O ports and interface logic are shown as provided, but the 3870 itself has only four I/O ports. Programmable timers and interrupt handling logic are shown as present, yet only one interrupt request line is available and only one programmable timer is present -- again with no possibility for expansion.

**3870 EXPANSION**

There is, in fact, a sharp contrast between the expansion philosophy of the 3870 as compared to the Intel 8048. The 3870 is simply not expandable; **if your application overflows the 3870 you can keep your programs, but you must revert to the F8 chip set.** In contrast, the 8048 is expandable, albeit in a somewhat clumsy fashion. Thus, when an application overflows a 3870, you can keep your programs but you must throw away your 3870 chips. When an application overflows the 8048, you can keep the 8048 already in hand, using expansion capabilities to support new functions.

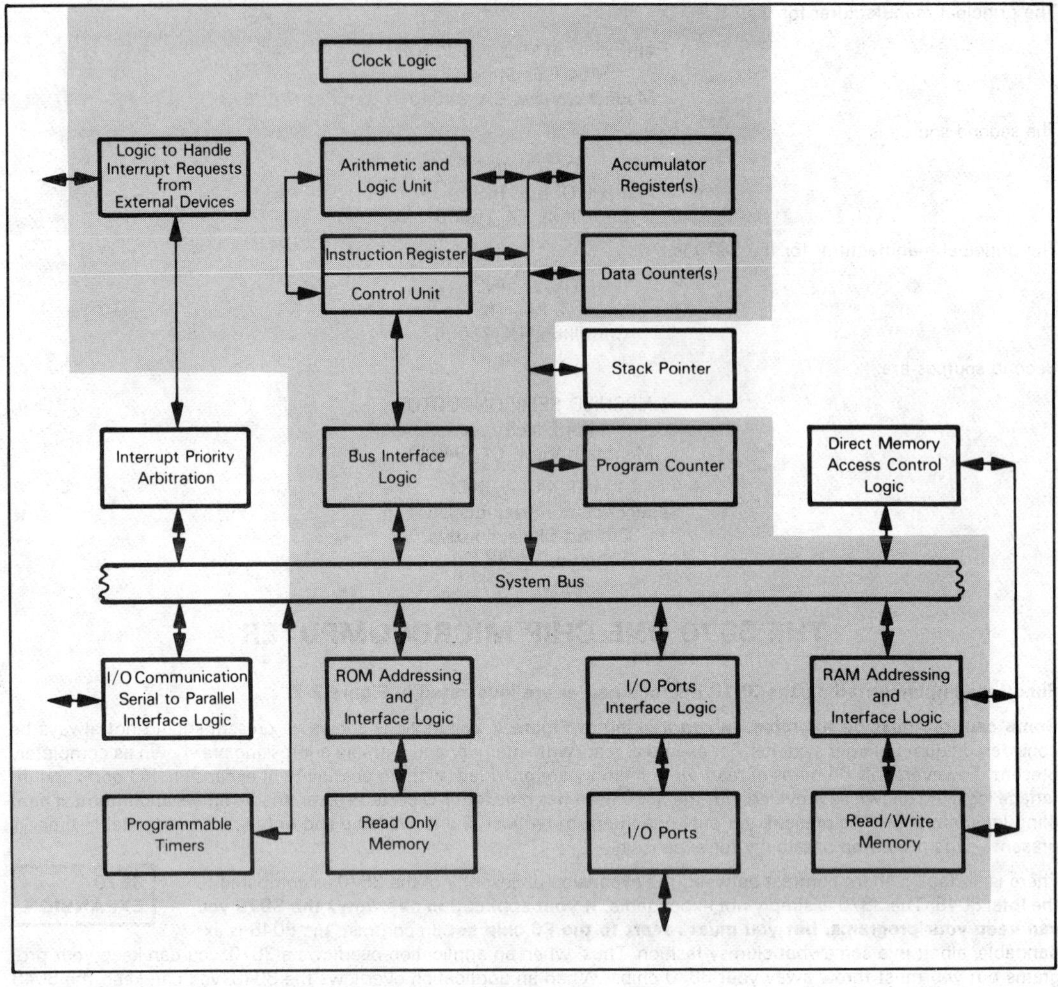


Figure 2-2. Logic of the Fairchild/Mostek 3870 Microcomputer

## 3870/F8 PROGRAMMABLE REGISTERS

**These are the programmable registers of the 3870 and F8:**

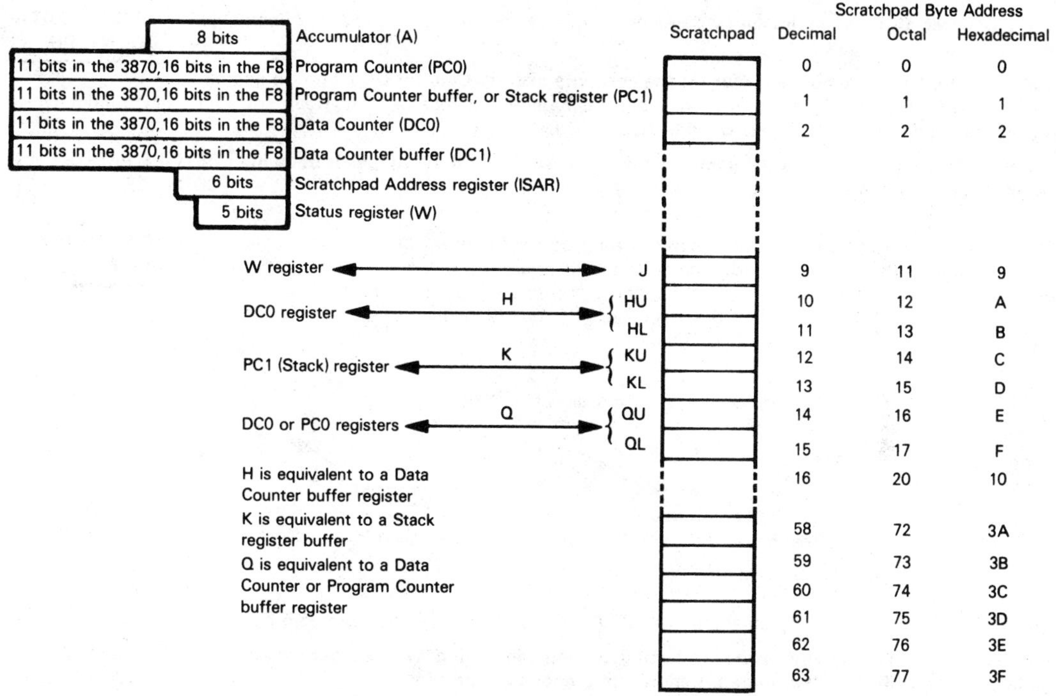


| Decimal | Octal | Hexadecimal |
|---|---|---|
| 0 | 0 | 0 |
| 1 | 1 | 1 |
| 2 | 2 | 2 |
| 9 | 11 | 9 |
| 10 | 12 | A |
| 11 | 13 | B |
| 12 | 14 | C |
| 13 | 15 | D |
| 14 | 16 | E |
| 15 | 17 | F |
| 16 | 20 | 10 |
| 58 | 72 | 3A |
| 59 | 73 | 3B |
| 60 | 74 | 3C |
| 61 | 75 | 3D |
| 62 | 76 | 3E |
| 63 | 77 | 3F |

**3870/F8 ACCUMULATOR**

**There is one 8-bit Accumulator,** which may be likened to the Primary Accumulator (A0) of our hypothetical microcomputer. Wherever there is a choice, this Accumulator is the usual source or destination for data operations associated with any instruction's execution.

**3870/F8 SCRATCHPAD**

**The 64-byte scratchpad may be viewed either as a small read-write memory, or as 64 8-bit secondary Accumulators.** The first 11 scratchpad bytes may be accessed directly, as though they were secondary Accumulators. Remaining RAM bytes can only be accessed using a form of implied memory addressing, where a 6-bit register (identified as the ISAR register) must provide the address of the byte being accessed. The ISAR register is in every way identical to a 6-bit Data Counter.

**3870/F8 DATA COUNTERS**

**Data Counter DC0 is an implied addressing register,** as described for our hypothetical microcomputer.

**Data Counter DC1 is simply a buffer for the contents of Data Counter DC0.** Implied addressing via Data Counter DC1 is not allowed. The only instruction that accesses Data Counter DC1 is an instruction which will exchange the contents of Data Counters DC0 and DC1.

**3870/F8 PROGRAM COUNTER**

**Program Counter PC0 serves the same function in a 3870 or F8 system as it does in our hypothetical microcomputer.**

**3870/F8 STACK REGISTER**

**The Stack register (PC1) is, in reality, a buffer for Program Counter PC0;** the Stack register does not address an area in read-write memory, and there are no Push or Pop instructions as described in Volume I, Chapter 6. Interrupts and Jump-to-Subroutine instructions save the contents of Program Counter PC0 in Stack register PC1, before loading a new address into Program Counter PC0:

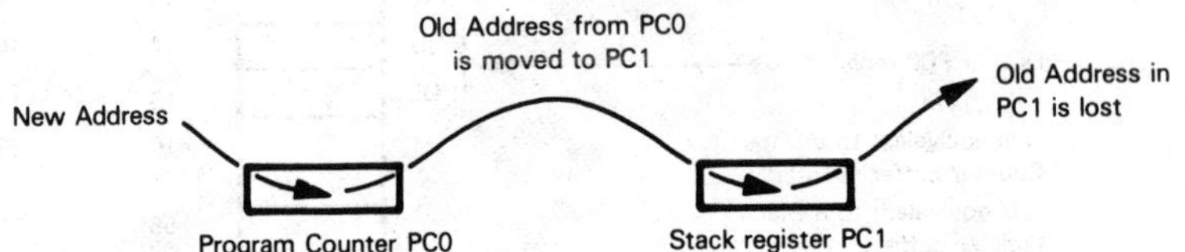


The classical Stack can be implemented in a 3870 or F8 system, but a short program needs to be written to do this.

**MEMORY ADDRESSING**

**Read-only memory is always addressed using implied addressing, with auto-increment, via Data Counter DC0. No other memory addressing modes are provided.**

There are a number of instructions which load immediate data into Data Counter DC0; data may also be transferred between Data Counter DC0 and scratchpad bytes, and it is possible to add the contents of the Accumulator to Data Counter DC0.

**SCRATCHPAD MEMORY ADDRESSING**

**In order to understand scratchpad addressing, one has to view it as representing neither 64 Accumulators nor 64 bytes of read-write memory, but rather as something between the two.**

## 3870 MEMORY ADDRESSING MODES

**The 3870 microcomputer has two separate and distinct memories:**

1) There is the 64-byte scratchpad, which is the only read/write memory available.

2) There are 2048 bytes of read-only memory, which must contain all programs, but may also contain constant data.

**We will refer to addressing of the 64-byte scratchpad as "scratchpad addressing", while "memory addressing" refers to the 2048 read-only memory bytes.**

It is important to note that the scratchpad and the read-only memory have separate and distinct address spaces. Scratchpad locations have addresses in the range 0 through $63_{10}$, while read-only memory locations have addresses in the range 0 through $2047_{10}$. Thus, addresses 0 through $63_{10}$ can access both a scratchpad byte and a read-only memory location; however, this will never cause confusion since separate and distinct instructions access scratchpad as against read-only memory. Since no one instruction can access both scratchpad and read-only memory, there is no possibility for confusion.

Instructions which access scratchpad memory use the four low-order object code bits to identify Scratchpad Addressing mode, as follows:

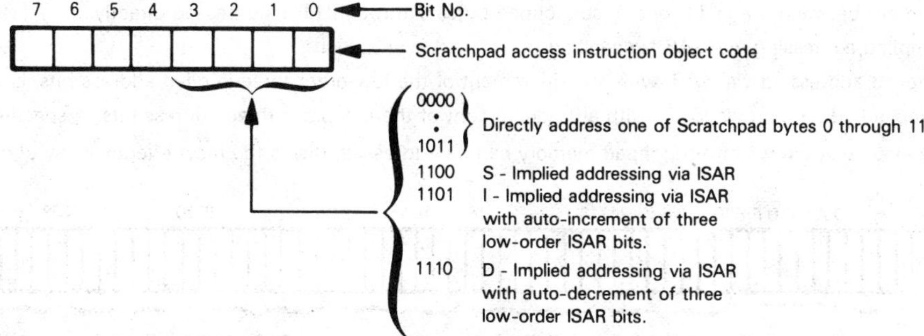


**There are a number of register-register instructions that operate on the Accumulator and on one of the first 12 scratchpad bytes, using object codes as follows:**

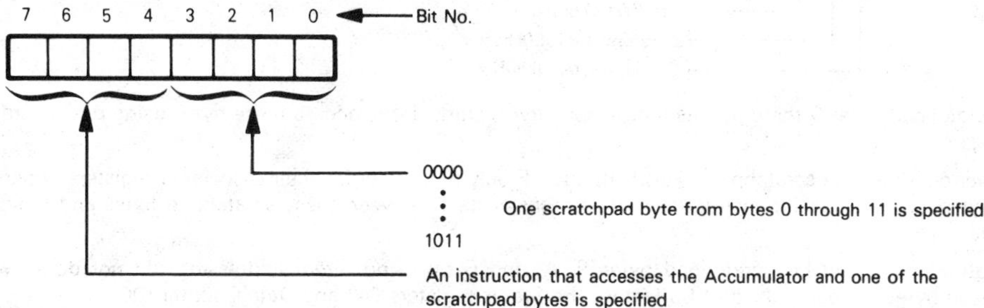


**DIRECT SCRATCHPAD ADDRESSING**

**This type of object code treats the first 12 scratchpad bytes as secondary Accumulators.**

**Any scratchpad byte may be addressed via the ISAR register using implied addressing;** that is to say, the 6-bit number in the ISAR (which can have a value in the range 0 through 63) identifies the one scratchpad byte which will be accessed by the next scratchpad referencing instruction.

**IMPLIED SCRATCHPAD ADDRESSING**

The ISAR register provides implied addressing, and implied addressing with auto-increment or auto-decrement; however, only the low-order three bits of the ISAR register are involved in the auto-increment or auto-decrement operation:

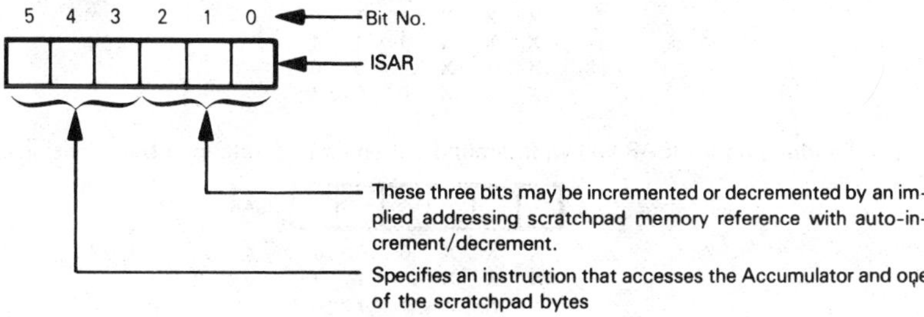


F8 scratchpad bytes may therefore be accessed as contiguous 8-byte buffers, with wraparound auto-increment or auto-decrement within each 8-byte buffer.

**r SCRATCHPAD ADDRESSING**

**Instructions shown in Table 2-2 use the symbol r in the operand to represent scratchpad addressing.** This is what the symbol r represents:

- If r is a number between 0 and 11, one of scratchpad bytes 0 through 11 is addressed directly.
- If r is S, implied addressing via ISAR is specified.
- If r is I, implied addressing via ISAR, with auto-increment of the low-order three implied address bits, is specified.
- If r is D, implied addressing via ISAR, with auto-decrement of the low-order three address bits, is specified.

Given the various ways in which scratchpad memory can be addressed, this is the most effective way of configuring scratchpad:

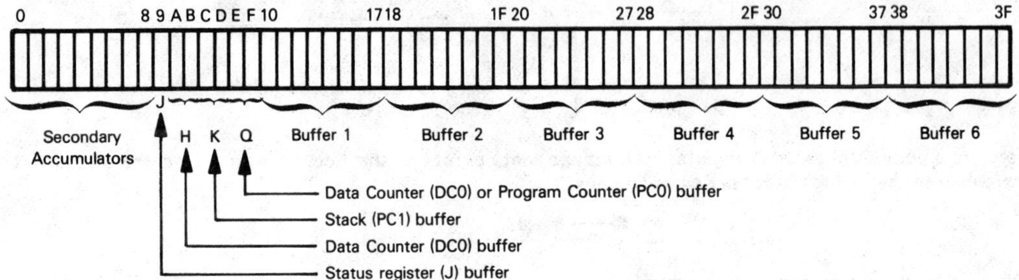


Treat scratchpad bytes 0 through 8 as nine secondary Accumulators; access these bytes using direct scratchpad addressing.

Wherever possible, use scratchpad bytes 9 through F only as buffers for their associated registers; when accessing these bytes, use the specific instructions which transfer data between these scratchpad bytes and their associated registers.

Although you can address scratchpad bytes 9, A, and B by using direct addressing, do not do so when these scratchpad bytes are being used as buffers for the Status registers (W) and Data Counter (DCO).

While indirect addressing via ISAR can access any scratchpad byte, you should avoid addressing scratchpad bytes 0 through F in this fashion. Wherever possible, use ISAR only to address scratch bytes $10_{16}$ through $3F_{16}$; divide this area into 8-byte buffers as illustrated. Because I addressing auto-increments only the three low-order ISAR bits, this form of scratchpad byte addressing will wrap around within one 8-byte buffer, as follows:

| ISAR | | | | | |
|---|---|---|---|---|---|
| X | X | X | 0 | 0 | 0 |
| X | X | X | 0 | 0 | 1 |
| X | X | X | 0 | 1 | 0 |
| X | X | X | 0 | 1 | 1 |
| X | X | X | 1 | 0 | 0 |
| X | X | X | 1 | 0 | 1 |
| X | X | X | 1 | 1 | 0 |
| X | X | X | 1 | 1 | 1 |
| X | X | X | 0 | 0 | 0 |
| X | X | X | 0 | 0 | 1 |

etc.

Similarly, D implied addressing via ISAR will wrap around within eight scratchpad byte divisions, as follows:

| ISAR | | | | | |
|---|---|---|---|---|---|
| X | X | X | 0 | 0 | 0 |
| X | X | X | 1 | 1 | 1 |
| X | X | X | 1 | 1 | 0 |
| X | X | X | 1 | 0 | 1 |
| X | X | X | 1 | 0 | 0 |
| X | X | X | 0 | 1 | 1 |
| X | X | X | 0 | 1 | 0 |
| X | X | X | 0 | 0 | 1 |
| X | X | X | 0 | 0 | 0 |
| X | X | X | 1 | 1 | 1 |

etc.

## 3870/F8 STATUS FLAGS

**The Status register, also called the W register, holds five status flags, as follows:**

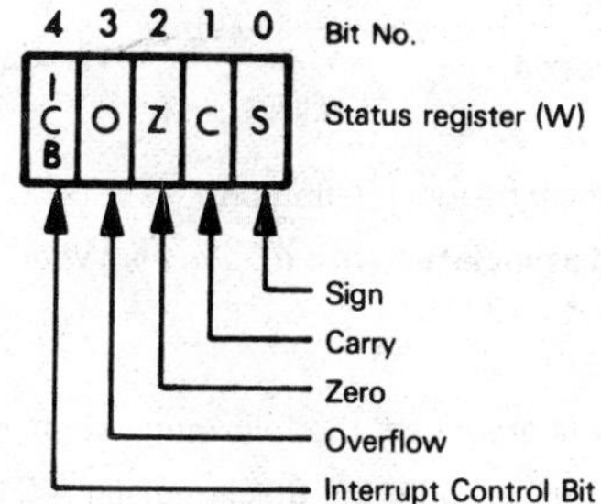


The O, Z, C and S status flags are identical to the flags with equivalent symbols, as described in Volume I, Chapter 6 for our hypothetical microcomputer.

The Interrupt Control bit is treated as a fifth status; this status will not be modified by arithmetic or logic operations, but it will be transferred, as a unit with the other four status flags, to or from Scratchpad byte 0.

## 3870 PINS AND SIGNALS

**3870 pins and signals are illustrated in Figure 2-3.**

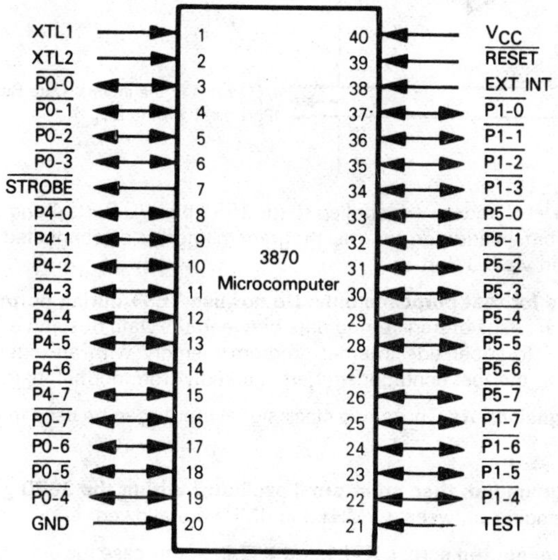

3870 Microcomputer

| Signal | Pin | Pin | Signal |
|---|---|---|---|
| XTL1 | 1 | 40 | $V_{CC}$ |
| XTL2 | 2 | 39 | RESET |
| P0-0 | 3 | 38 | EXT INT |
| P0-1 | 4 | 37 | P1-0 |
| P0-2 | 5 | 36 | P1-1 |
| P0-3 | 6 | 35 | P1-2 |
| STROBE | 7 | 34 | P1-3 |
| P4-0 | 8 | 33 | P5-0 |
| P4-1 | 9 | 32 | P5-1 |
| P4-2 | 10 | 31 | P5-2 |
| P4-3 | 11 | 30 | P5-3 |
| P4-4 | 12 | 29 | P5-4 |
| P4-5 | 13 | 28 | P5-5 |
| P4-6 | 14 | 27 | P5-6 |
| P4-7 | 15 | 26 | P5-7 |
| P0-7 | 16 | 25 | P1-7 |
| P0-6 | 17 | 24 | P1-6 |
| P0-5 | 18 | 23 | P1-5 |
| P0-4 | 19 | 22 | P1-4 |
| GND | 20 | 21 | TEST |

| Pin Name | Description | Type |
|---|---|---|
| P0-0 - P0-7 | I/O Port 0 | Bidirectional |
| P1-0 - P1-7 | I/O Port 1 | Bidirectional |
| P4-0 - P4-7 | I/O Port 4 | Bidirectional |
| P5-0 - P5-7 | I/O Port 5 | Bidirectional |
| STROBE | Ready Strobe | Output |
| EXT INT | External Interrupt | Input |
| RESET | External Reset | Input |
| TEST | Test Line | Input |
| XTL1, XTL2 | Time/Clock | Input |
| $V_{CC}$, GND | Power Supply Lines | Input |

Figure 2-3. 3870 Microcomputer Signals and Pin Assignments

32 of the 40 signals implement four 8-bit I/O ports, which are addressed as I/O Ports 0, 1, 4 and 5.

**Pins $\overline{\text{P00}}$ through $\overline{\text{P07}}$ implement I/O Port 0.**

**Pins $\overline{\text{P10}}$ through $\overline{\text{P17}}$ implement I/O Port 1.**

**Pins $\overline{\text{P40}}$ through $\overline{\text{P47}}$ implement I/O Port 4.**

**Pins $\overline{\text{P50}}$ through $\overline{\text{P57}}$ implement I/O Port 5.**

I/O port characteristics are described following signal definitions.

**$\overline{\text{STROBE}}$ is a handshaking control signal associated with I/O Port 4.** Whenever data is output to I/O Port 4, $\overline{\text{STROBE}}$ is pulsed low for approximately three clock periods.

External interrupt requests are input via EXT INT.

**3870 RESET**

**$\overline{\text{RESET}}$ is a master reset input.** When it is grounded, the following events occur:

1) Program Counter contents (PC0) are pushed onto the Stack register (PC1).
2) The ICB bit of the Status register is reset to 0; this disables all interrupts.
3) I/O Port 4 and 5 pins all output +5V. Reset does not affect I/O Port 0 and 1 pins.
4) Other internal registers are not affected.

**The TEST input is used to test hardware.** Normally the TEST pin is connected to ground, or it is left unconnected. When a voltage between 2V and 2.6V is connected to TEST, I/O Ports 4 and 5 become output and input connections to the internal Data Bus, as follows:

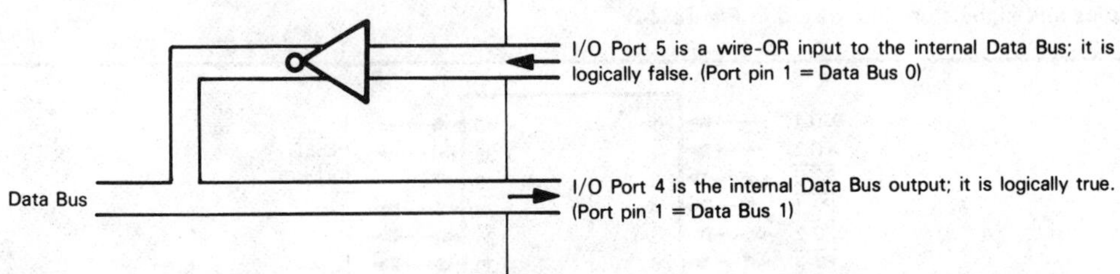
I/O Port 5 is a wire-OR input to the internal Data Bus; it is logically false. (Port pin 1 = Data Bus 0)
Data Bus
I/O Port 4 is the internal Data Bus output; it is logically true. (Port pin 1 = Data Bus 1)

When a voltage level between +6V and +7V is applied to the TEST pin, I/O Ports 4 and 5 are connected to the internal Data Bus as illustrated above; but, in addition, internal program memory is disconnected from the Data Bus. This allows instruction codes to be entered via I/O Port 5.

**The TEST pin should be used for test purposes only. Do not use TEST during normal 3870 operations.** You cannot, for example, use TEST as a means of transferring data between the Data Bus and external logic via I/O Ports 4 and 5. Also, you cannot use TEST to supercede internal program memory with an external program memory. This is because timing associated with the test conditions differs markedly from normal instruction execution timing.

**3870 CLOCK LOGIC**

**XTL1 and XTL2 are clock signal inputs.** These two clock signal inputs can be used in one of four ways.

**If XTL1 and XTL2 are both grounded, then an internal oscillator within the 3870 generates the clock signal.** Internal oscillator frequencies ranging between 1.7MHz and 4MHz are allowed.

**An external crystal may be connected across XTL1 and XTL2;** in this case the external crystal determines clock frequency. Any frequency in the range 1 MHz to 4 MHz is allowed. There are internal 20 pF capacitors between XTL1 and ground and XTL2 and ground; therefore, external capacitors are not required. This may be illustrated as follows:

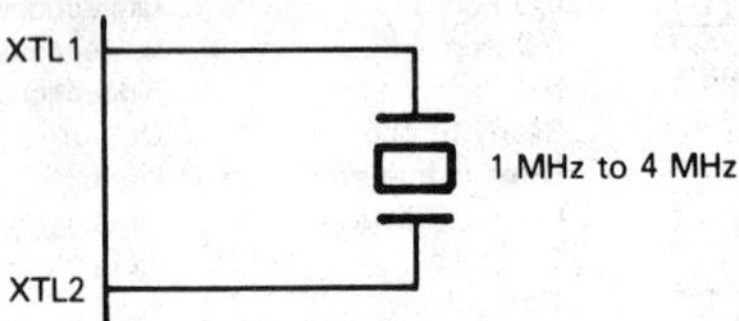
XTL1
1 MHz to 4 MHz
XTL2

**If an external clock signal is used, then it should be applied to pin XTL2, and pin XTL1 should be left open.**

The internal clock signal generated will have a frequency that is half of the external clock signal frequency. For example, in order to generate a 1 MHz internal clock signal, a 2 MHz external clock signal must be applied to pin XTL2.

**It is also possible to generate the internal 3870 clock signal using resistor capacitor (RC) or inductor capacitor (LC) circuits.** The RC mode may be illustrated as follows:

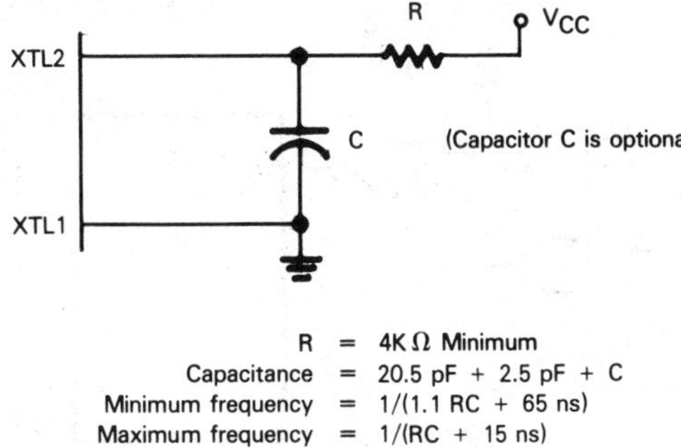


R = 4K Ω Minimum
Capacitance = 20.5 pF + 2.5 pF + C
Minimum frequency = 1/(1.1 RC + 65 ns)
Maximum frequency = 1/(RC + 15 ns)

The external capacitor C is optional, since there is a 20.5 pF internal capacitor.

The LC mode may be illustrated as follows:

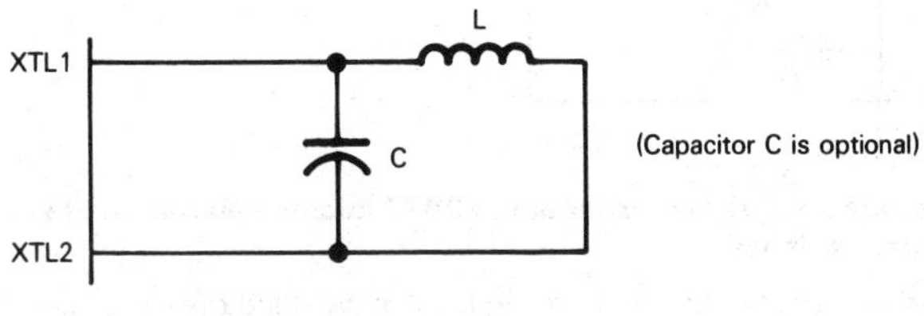


Inductor L = 0.1 mH (minimum)
Inductor quality = (Q) = 40
If the external capacitor (C) is present, it must be 30 pF or less.
Capacitance = 10 pF ± 1.3 pF + C
Frequency = $1/(2\pi\sqrt{LC})$

# 3870 INSTRUCTION TIMING AND EXECUTION

**All 3870 instructions execute as a sequence of "long" and "short" machine cycles. A long machine cycle lasts six clock periods. A short machine cycle lasts four clock periods.** For each 3870 instruction, Table 2-2 identifies the sequence of long and short machine cycles via which the instruction executes. By referring to this table, you can compute instruction execution times as a function of clock frequency.

Note that Table 2-2 refers to ROMC states. ROMC states have no meaning when you are using a 3870; however, they constitute five signals output by the 3850 CPU in an F8 configuration, as described later in this chapter. Since Table 2-2 applies to both the 3870 and the F8, ROMC states are identified.

## 3870 I/O PORTS

**The 3870 has four 8-bit I/O ports, which we defined when describing 3870 pins and signals. I/O ports are addressed via port numbers 0, 1, 4, and 5. I/O port addresses 6 and 7 are also reserved by the 3870; I/O Port 6 is used to output control codes and to input interrupt status. I/O Port 7 is used to access interval timer logic.**

0, 1, 4, 5, 6, and 7 are the only I/O port addresses which have any meaning within a 3870. Output instructions that address any other I/O port act as "no operation" instructions. Input instructions that address any other port will clear the Accumulator. Nevertheless, the 3870 instruction set, as defined in Table 2-1, includes both long-form and short-form I/O instructions, allowing any I/O port to be accessed with addresses in the range 0 through 255. This permits the 3870 instruction set to be completely compatible with the full F8 instruction set -- a necessity if 3870 programs are to be transportable to larger F8 configurations.

**Every one of the 3870 I/O port pins is truly bidirectional. Logic associated with each pin may be illustrated as follows:**

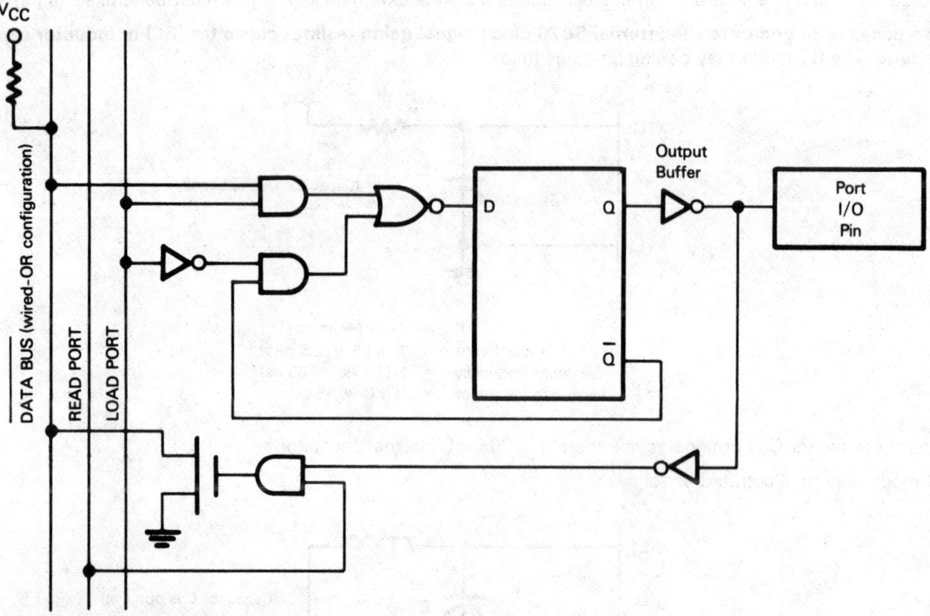


**The pin logic illustrated above is present in the 3870 microcomputer and the 3871 PIO only; other devices have the F8 I/O pin characteristics.**

If you do not understand digital logic, then you will not understand the illustration above, but that is not particularly important. The above illustration explains exactly how bidirectional I/O port pin logic works. From a programmer's point of view, this simply translates into the fact that you can freely input and output data without worrying about prior I/O port contents. However, **all I/O port pins have inverted logic.** This means that when you write 1 to an I/O port pin a 0 voltage will be generated, while a +5V voltage will be generated if you output 0 to the pin. Conversely, external logic will cause your program to input 1 if it grounds a pin, while it will cause your program to input 0 if it applies +5V to the pin.

**The output buffer portion of I/O port pin logic determines the pin characteristics. Standard TTL logic is provided by the standard output buffer,** which may be illustrated as follows:

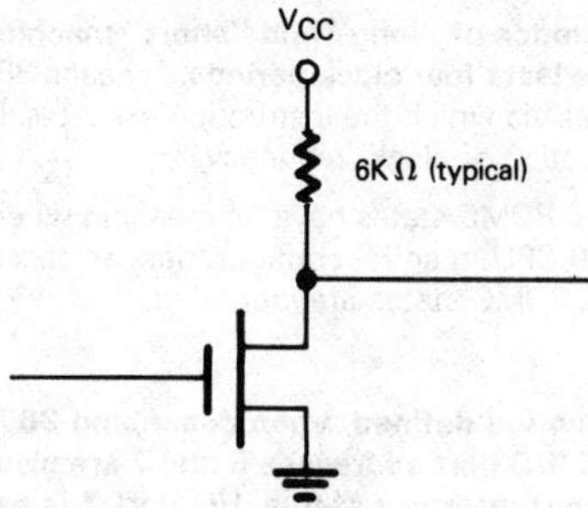

You can buy 3870 devices with different output buffers at I/O Ports 4 and 5, but not at I/O Ports 0 and 1. I/O Ports 0 and 1 pins can only have the standard output buffer illustrated above. **There are two optional output buffer designs available for pins of I/O Ports 4 and 5.** A direct drive output is similar to the standard output, but it sources more current. Logic is illustrated as follows:

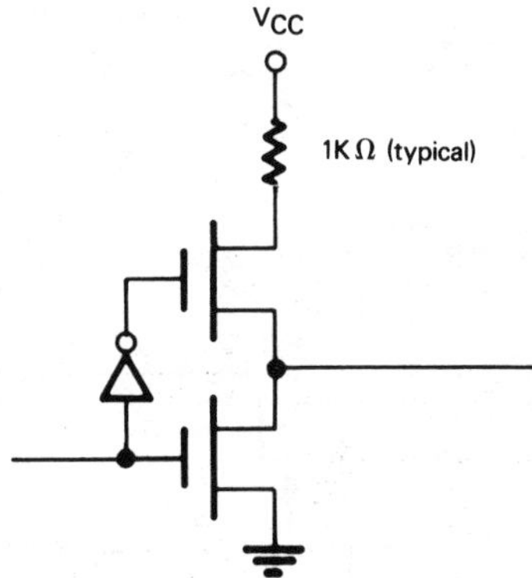


The other option is an open drain output, which may be illustrated as follows:

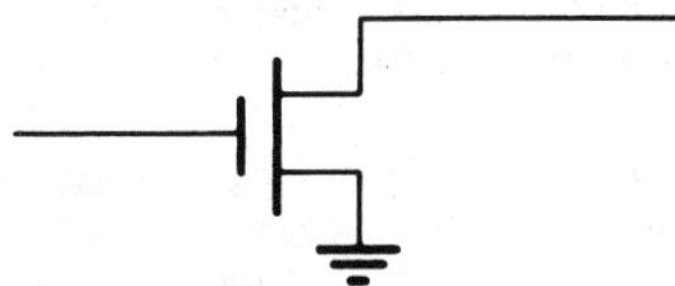

The open drain output allows you to tie pins together; you can then wire-AND two or more pins when data is output. Consider the following configurations:

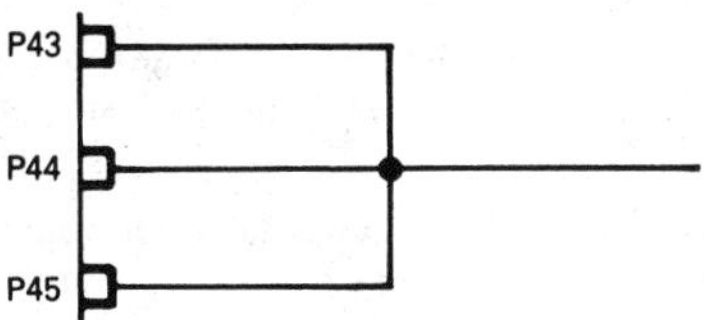


If all outputs are high, then the wire-AND will be high; however, if any one of the three outputs goes low, then the wire-AND resulting from all three outputs will also go low.

## 3870 INTERRUPT LOGIC

**External logic can input an interrupt request to the 3870 via the EXT INT signal.**

**Interrupt requests may also be generated internally by timer/counter logic.**

**3870 INTERRUPT DISABLE**

**There are two levels of interrupt enable/disable logic within the 3870. There is a Control register (described later in this chapter) which has bits 0 and 1 set aside to selectively enable or disable external interrupts and timer/counter interrupts, respectively.** If one or both of these interrupts are enabled, then **any interrupt request is still subject to master ena-**

**ble/disable logic, which is specified by the Interrupt Control bit of the Status register** (bit 4 of the W register). This may be illustrated as follows:

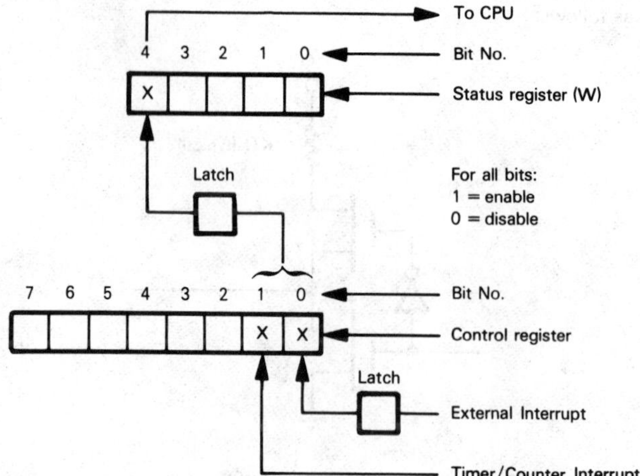


**A timer/counter interrupt request is latched.** If timer/counter interrupt logic has been disabled via Control register bit 1, then an interrupt request will be held until timer/counter interrupts are subsequently enabled; the interrupt request will then occur.

**External interrupt requests are not latched.** An external interrupt request will only occur if the EXT INT signal makes an active transition while external interrupts have been enabled by Control register bit 0.

**Any interrupt request that reaches Status register logic will be latched.** Thus, if Status register bit 4 is 0 when either an external interrupt request or a timer/counter interrupt request occurs, then the interrupt request will be held pending until Status register bit 4 is subsequently set to 1.

**A reset or power-on operation disables all interrupts; the Status and Control registers are cleared.**

**Timer/counter interrupt requests have priority over external interrupt requests.** Thus, if a timer/counter interrupt request and external interrupt request occur simultaneously and both are enabled, then the timer/counter interrupt request will be acknowledged.

**When any interrupt request is acknowledged, further interrupts are disabled via the Status register;** however, interrupt enable/disable logic associated with the Control register is not affected. Thus, an external interrupt request will be held pending for the duration of a timer/counter interrupt service routine's execution. However, the external interrupt request will be removed if, at any time while it is held pending, external interrupts are specifically disabled via bit 0 of the Control register.

If a timer/counter interrupt request is generated while an external interrupt service routine is being executed, then Status register interrupt disable logic will prevent the timer/counter interrupt request from interrupting the external interrupt service routine. However, the timer/counter interrupt request will be held pending until interrupts are subsequently enabled at the Status register. If for any reason timer/counter interrupts have been specifically disabled via Control register bit 1, then any subsequent timer/counter interrupt request will be delayed until timer/counter interrupt logic is specifically enabled via bit 1 of the Control register.

When an interrupt request is acknowledged, the Program Counter (PC0) contents are saved on the Stack register (PC1). For a Timer interrupt request, a new value, $020_{16}$, is loaded into the Program Counter:

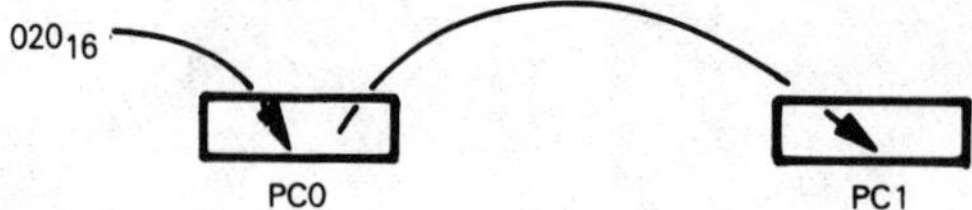

When an external interrupt request is acknowledged, Program Counter (PC0) contents are saved in the Stack register (PC1), then the new value $0A0_{16}$ is loaded into the Program Counter (PC0). Thus, interrupt service routines for timer and external interrupts must originate at memory locations $020_{16}$ and $0A0_{16}$, respectively.

Since a reset or power-on clears the Program Counter, the beginning of program memory must be allocated thus:

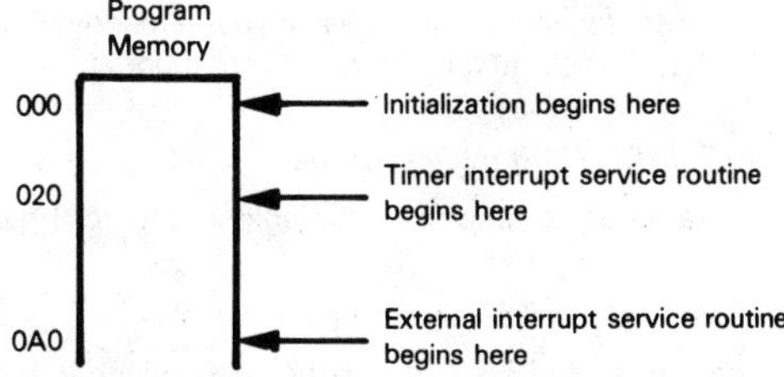


## TIMER/COUNTER LOGIC

**3870 timer/counter logic represents a significant enhancement over prior F8 logic.**

**3870 timer/event counter logic consists of an 8-bit binary Counter register together with a Buffer register and associated logic. The two registers are accessed as I/O Port 7.** Data output to I/O Port 7 is written into the Counter register and the Buffer register. Data input from Port 7 is read from the Counter register only. **This may be illustrated as follows:**

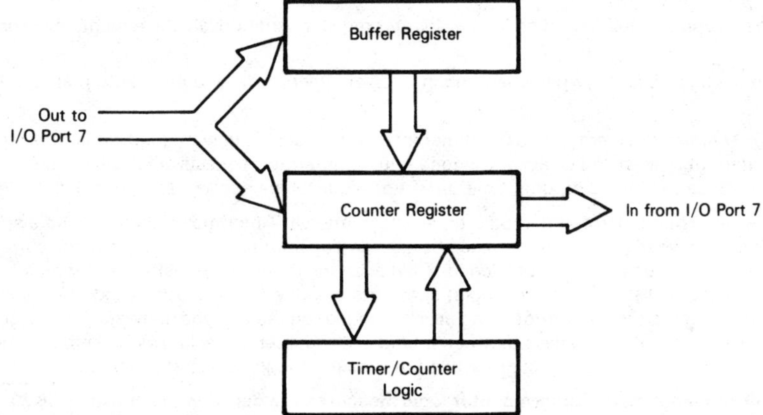


The scheme illustrated above allows timer/counter logic to operate in a "free running" mode. Whenever the contents of the Counter register decrement to 0, the new Counter register contents are taken from the Buffer register, and a timer interrupt request occurs. This may be illustrated as follows:

| Counter Register Contents | Buffer Register Contents | |
|---|---|---|
| 02 | xx | |
| 01 | xx | |
| | | → Timer interrupt request |
| 00 | xx | |
| xx | xx | |
| xx-1 | xx | |
| xx-2 | xx | |
| etc. | etc. | |

You can read Counter register contents at any time, even while the timer/counter is operating, by inputting from I/O Port 7; Counter register contents will be input.

**Timer/counter logic can be operated in Interval Timer mode, in Pulse Width Measurement mode, or in Event Counter mode. The contents of a Control register (which is accessed as I/O Port 6) determine the mode in which timer/counter logic will operate. We will describe the Control register after discussing timer/counter operating modes.**

**3870 INTERVAL TIMER MODE**

**In Interval Timer mode, timer/counter logic is used to compute time intervals. In order to compute a time interval, the timer/counter register contents are decremented at fixed "decrement" intervals.** The decrement interval is equal to a number of clock periods, as specified by the control code. The decrement interval may range between a low of two clock periods and a high of 400 clock periods. If, for example, a 500 nanosecond clock is employed and the decrement interval is 100 clock periods, then the Counter register contents will be decremented once every 50 microseconds. If the initial value output to I/O Port 7 is $200_{10}$ ($C8_{16}$), then in Interval Timer mode, timer/counter logic will time out once every 10 milliseconds.

Time interval = 0.5 x 100 x 200 microseconds

The time delays which can be generated using timer/counter logic in Interval Timer mode are given by the following equation:

Time interval = Reset value x Decrement time interval

The reset value is the value written out to I/O Port 7; it may have any value in the range 0 through 255. 0 is in fact equivalent to a count of 256, since the decrement ends with a Timer interrupt request when Counter register contents decrement from 1 to 0.

**In Interval Timer mode, timer/counter logic operates as follows:**

1) An initial value must be output to I/O Port 7. This becomes the reset value.
2) Using an appropriate control code, you select Interval Timer mode and options. The control code also starts and stops timer/counter logic in Interval Timer mode.
3) Once started by an appropriate control code, the Counter register continuously decrements, reloads, and redecrements.
4) In order to stop the timer/counter when operating in Interval Timer mode, you must output an appropriate control code.

Each time the Counter register decrements to 0, a timer interrupt request is generated. If timer interrupt requests are enabled, then the interrupt request will be acknowledged; if timer interrupt requests are disabled, the interrupt request will be latched and will be held pending until timer interrupt requests are subsequently enabled.

If interrupts are enabled when timer/counter logic times out in Interval Timer mode, there will be a small time delay before the interrupt is acknowledged; no interrupt can be acknowledged until the conclusion of the currently executing instruction, plus the next instruction if it is privileged. (Privileged instructions are instructions which cannot be interrupted; they are identified in Table 2-1.) In the worst case, it is possible for 49 clock periods to elapse between the timer/counter timing out and a timer interrupt being acknowledged; on the average, between 24 and 30 clock periods will separate these two events. If long delays between a time-out and interrupt acknowledge are not acceptable, then you must avoid executing privileged instructions while timer/counter logic is operating in Interval Timer mode.

**3870 PULSE WIDTH MEASUREMENT MODE**

**In Pulse Width Measurement mode, timer/counter logic measures the duration of a pulse which is input on the EXT INT pin.** Under program control, you can measure a low pulse:

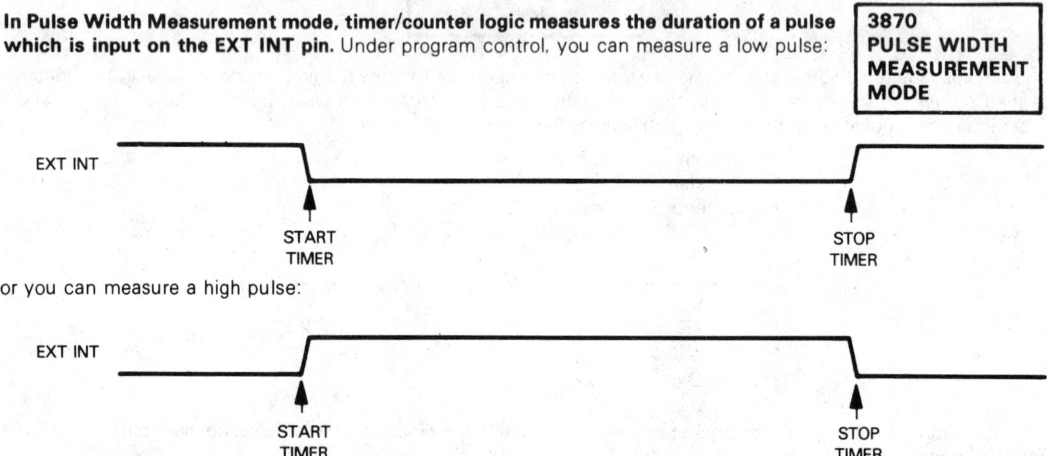


Stop and start logic represents the only difference between Pulse Width Measurement mode and Interval Timer mode. As illustrated above, it is EXT INT signal transitions that start and stop timer/counter logic in Pulse Width mode. In addition, you can use control codes to stop timer/counter logic in Pulse Width mode.

An external interrupt request occurs at the trailing edge of the EXT INT pulse. This external interrupt request will be acknowledged only if external interrupts have been enabled. If external interrupts are disabled, no interrupt request occurs. That is to say, if external interrupts are enabled at some point after the end of a pulse, no interrupt request will be pending.

Within the pulse itself, timer/counter decrement logic works exactly as described for Interval Timer mode. The Counter register contents are decremented once each decrement interval; the decrement interval is defined in Interval Timer mode. If the timer/counter does not time-out within the pulse width, then on the trailing edge of the pulse the timer/counter is stopped. By inputting from I/O Port 7, you read the contents of the Counter register at the trailing edge of the pulse; the difference between this input value and the initial reset value can be used to compute the pulse duration, as follows:

Pulse duration = (Initial reset value - final Counter register contents) x decrement time interval

For example, suppose the initial reset value output to I/O Port 7 is $100_{10}$ ($64_{16}$), while the final value input from I/O Port 7 is $16_{10}$ ($10_{16}$); if the control code has set timer/counter logic to decrement once every 100 microseconds, then the pulse width must be 8.4 milliseconds:

Pulse width = (100 - 16) x 100 microseconds

If the Counter register does time-out within a pulse, then a timer interrupt request occurs, the Buffer register contents are loaded into the Counter register, and decrementing restarts. Program logic must respond to the timer interrupt request by incrementing a scratchpad counter; the total pulse time is computed as follows:

Pulse duration = (Initial reset value - final Counter register contents)
x decrement time interval
x initial reset value x decrement time interval
x scratchpad counter contents

Suppose, for example, that the initial reset value output to I/O Port 7 is $200_{10}$ ($C8_{16}$), and that the Counter register has timed out three times within the pulse width; the scratchpad counter will now contain 3. If the final value input from I/O Port 7 is $53_{10}$ ($35_{16}$) and the decrement time interval specified by the control code is 50 microseconds, then the total pulse timer interval is 37.35 milliseconds:

Pulse interval = (200 - 53) x 50 + 200 x 3 x 50
= 37,350 microseconds

**3870 EVENT COUNTER MODE**

**In Event Counter mode, the Counter register contents are decremented on "active" transitions of the EXT INT input.** An "active" transition on this signal may be high-to-low or low-to-high, as selected by the control code.

In the Event Counter mode, when the Counter register decrements to 0 a timer interrupt request is latched, as described for the Interval Timer mode. Thus, if the timer interrupts are enabled, the interrupt request will be acknowledged following execution of the next non-privileged instruction; if timer interrupts are disabled, the interrupt request will be held until interrupt requests are re-enabled. Active transitions on the EXT INT signal, while decrementing the Counter register contents, also cause interrupt requests to occur if external interrupts are enabled. Since it would be pointless to have an external interrupt request occur on every decrement, external interrupts are normally disabled in Event Counter mode.

## THE 3870 CONTROL CODE

**Operation of 3870 timer/counter logic and interrupt logic is controlled via an 8-bit control code which must be output to I/O Port 6. I/O Port 6 is a write-only location. When you input from I/O Port 6, you do not read the contents of the Control register; rather, the level on the EXT INT pin appears at bit 7 of the Accumulator. This may be illustrated as follows:**

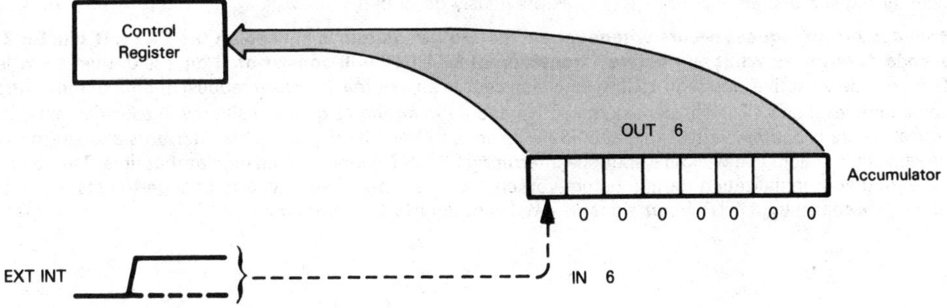

If you need to read the control code after writing it out, then you must keep a copy of it in one of the scratchpad bytes. Control code bits are assigned as follows:

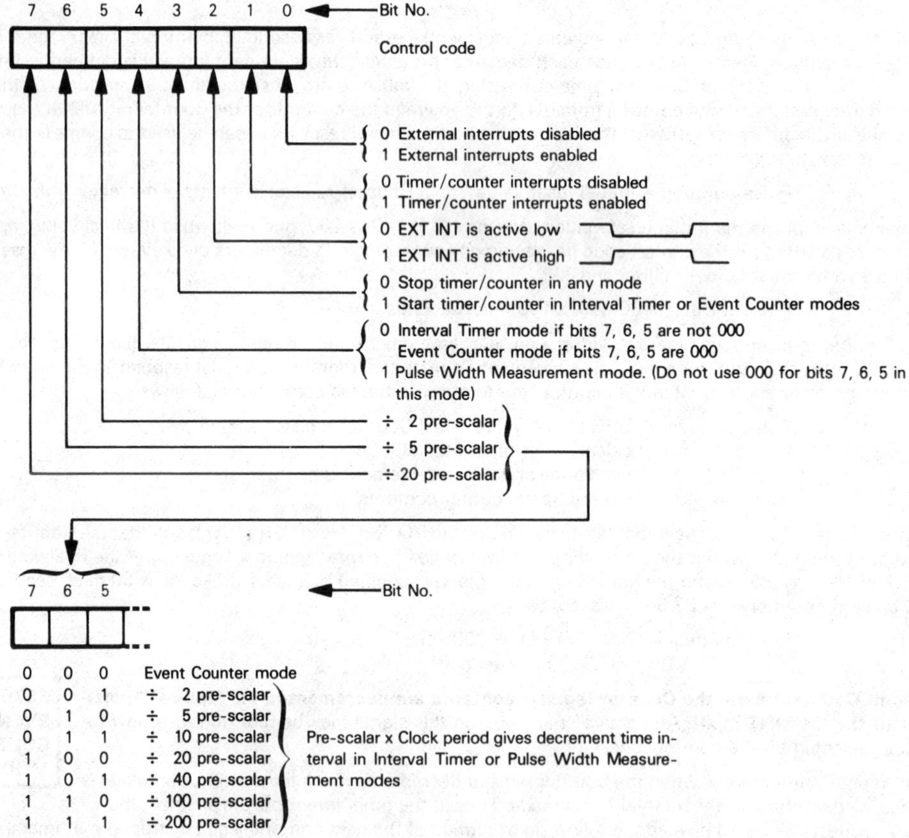


| 7 | 6 | 5 | | |
|---|---|---|---|---|
| 0 | 0 | 0 | Event Counter mode | |
| 0 | 0 | 1 | ÷ 2 pre-scalar | Pre-scalar x Clock period gives decrement time interval in Interval Timer or Pulse Width Measurement modes |
| 0 | 1 | 0 | ÷ 5 pre-scalar | |
| 0 | 1 | 1 | ÷ 10 pre-scalar | |
| 1 | 0 | 0 | ÷ 20 pre-scalar | |
| 1 | 0 | 1 | ÷ 40 pre-scalar | |
| 1 | 1 | 0 | ÷ 100 pre-scalar | |
| 1 | 1 | 1 | ÷ 200 pre-scalar | |

**Bits 0 and 1 are used to selectively enable or disable interrupt requests. External interrupt requests occur via active transitions on the EXT INT input signal; timer/counter interrupt requests are generated within timer/counter logic. You have the option of enabling both external interrupts and timer/counter interrupts; you can enable one but not the other, or you can disable both.**

Recall that timer/counter interrupt requests are latched; if timer/counter interrupt logic is disabled (control code bit 1 is 0) when the timer/counter interrupt request occurs, then the interrupt request will remain pending until timer/counter interrupts are subsequently enabled (control code bit 1 is 1), or until the 3870 is reset. A reset removes the latched interrupt request. External interrupts are not latched; an external interrupt request will be generated only as EXT INT makes an active transition while control code bit 0 is 1. A timer/counter interrupt request occurs whenever the timer/counter register decrements from 1 to 0, as previously described.

**An external interrupt request occurs whenever an "active" transition is sensed on the EXT INT pin. Bit 2 of the control code determines what an "active" transition of EXT INT will consist of.** If bit 2 is 0, then a low level on EXT INT is considered active, and high-to-low transition causes an external interrupt request. If bit 2 of the control code is 1, then a high level on EXT INT is considered active and a low-to-high signal transition will cause an external interrupt request. There is one precaution that should be taken with this bit: if you enable interrupts and set this bit high with the same instruction, you will get a spurious interrupt if EXT INT happens to be high at that time. The solution is to set bit 2 during your initialization routine before you enable interrupts. If you need to change the state of bit 2, you must first check that the EXT INT input signal is low (using an INS 6 instruction).

Control code bit 3 is the start/stop bit. This bit must be used to start and stop timer/counter logic when operating in Interval Timer mode or Event Counter mode. When timer/counter logic is operating in Pulse Width Measurement mode, then leading and trailing edges of an active EXT INT pulse start and stop timer/counter logic; within a pulse, however, the start/stop bit of the Control code can be used to stop and then restart timer/counter logic.

In Interval Timer mode or Pulse Width mode, bits 5, 6 and 7 select the decrement time interval. The important point to note is that bits 5, 6 and 7 are cumulative. Thus, you have seven pre-scalar options shown with the control code.

In Interval Timer mode or in Pulse Width mode, the Counter register contents are decremented once every decrement time interval. A decrement time interval is equal to the internal clock pulse time multiplied by the pre-scalar. Assuming a 500 nanosecond internal clock pulse width, 010 in Control register bits 7, 6 and 5 would generate a decrement time interval of 2.5 microseconds. A decrement time interval of 50 microseconds would be generated by 110 in Control register bits 7, 6 and 5.

## THE 3870/F8 INSTRUCTION SET

**Table 2-1 summarizes the 3870/F8 instruction set; instructions are grouped into categories that conform with our hypothetical microcomputer instruction set, as described in Volume 1, Chapter 7.**

With reference to Table 2-1, refer to the addressing modes description for an explanation of "r", which occurs in the operand column to represent some of the scratchpad addressing options.

One of the more confusing aspects of 3870/F8 programming is understanding the ways in which data may be moved between different registers; this information is therefore summarized in Figure 2-4.

The following symbols are used in Table 2-1:

| | |
|---|---|
| A | The Accumulator |
| addr | A 16-bit memory address |
| C | Carry status |
| data3 | A 3-bit binary data unit |
| data4 | A 4-bit binary data unit |
| data5 | A 5-bit binary data unit |
| DC0 | Data Counter register |
| DC1 | Data Counter buffer |
| dpchr | Scratchpad Data or Program Counter Half Registers. These are KU (Register 12), KL (Register 13), QU (Register 14) and QL (Register 15). |
| disp | An 8-bit signed binary address displacement |
| FMASK | A 4-bit mask composed of a portion of the Status register (W): |

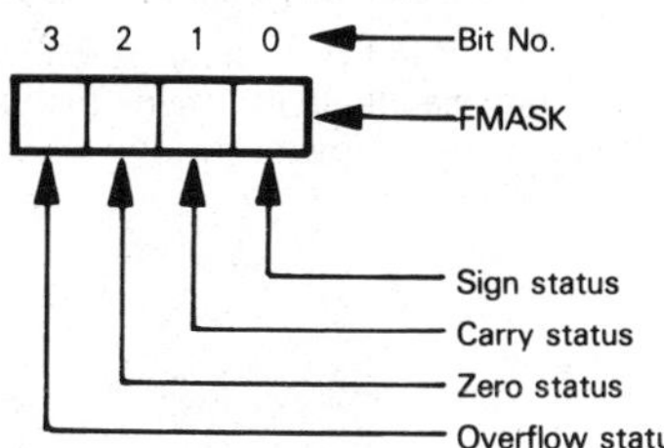


| | |
|---|---|
| H | Scratchpad Data Counter Register H (Registers 10 and 11). |
| I | The Interrupt Control Bit in the Status register (W). |
| ISAR | Indirect Scratchpad Address Register |
| J | Scratchpad Register 9 |
| K | Scratchpad Registers 12 and 13 |
| O | Overflow status |
| p4 | A 4-bit I/O port number |
| p8 | An 8-bit I/O port number |
| PC0 | Program Counter |
| PC1 | Stack register |
| Q | Scratchpad Registers 14 and 15 |

r — Any of the following operands and Scratchpad addressing modes:

- R direct address of bytes 0 through 11
- S implied addressing via ISAR
- I implied addressing via ISAR, with auto-increment of the low-order three ISAR bits
- D implied addressing via ISAR, with auto-decrement of the low-order three ISAR bits

S — Sign status

sr — The register specified by the r argument

TMASK — A 3-bit mask composed of a portion of the Status register (W):

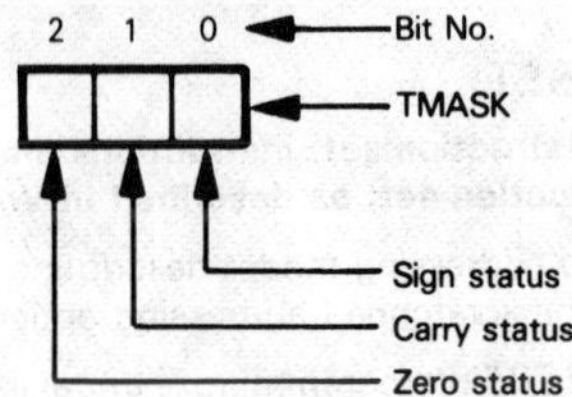


W — The CPU Status register

Z — Zero status

x<y,z> — Bits y through z of the quantity x. For example, A <3,0> represents the low-order four bits of the Accumulator; addr <15,8> represents the high-order eight bits of a 16-bit memory address

[ ] — Contents of location enclosed within brackets. If a register designation is enclosed within the brackets, then the designated register's contents are specified. If an I/O port number is enclosed within the brackets, then the I/O port contents are specified. If a memory address is enclosed within the brackets, then the contents of the addressed memory location are specified.

[[ ]] — Implied memory addressing; the contents of the memory location or register designated by the contents of a register

Λ — Logical AND

V — Logical OR

⊻ — Logical Exclusive OR

← — Data is transferred in the direction of the arrow

←→ — Data is exchanged between the two locations designated on either side of the arrow

Under the heading of STATUSES in Table 2-1, an X indicates statuses which are modified in the course of the instructions' execution. If there is no X, it means that the status maintains the value it had before the instruction was executed. A 0 or 1 means the status is cleared or set, respectively.

Table 2-1. 3870/F8 Instruction Set Summary

| TYPE | MNEMONIC | OPERAND(S) | BYTES | STATUSES | | | | | | OPERATION PERFORMED |
|---|---|---|---|---|---|---|---|---|---|---|
| | | | | C | Z | S | O | | | |
| I/O | INS | P4 | 1 | 0 | X | X | 0 | | | [A]←[P4]<br>Input to Accumulator from I/O port. |
| | IN | P8 | 2 | 0 | X | X | 0 | | | [A]←[P8]<br>Input to Accumulator from I/O port. |
| | OUTS | P4 | 1 | | | | | | | [P4]←[A]<br>Output to I/O port from Accumulator. |
| | OUT | P8 | 2 | | | | | | | [P8]←[A]<br>Output to I/O port from Accumulator. |
| PRIMARY MEMORY REFERENCE | LM | | 1 | | | | | | | [A]←[[DC0]], [DC0]←[DC0] + 1<br>Load the Accumulator via DC0 and auto-increment DC0. |
| | ST | | 1 | | | | | | | [[DC0]]←[A], [DC0]←[DC0 + 1]<br>Store the Accumulator via DC0 and auto-increment DC0. |
| | LR | A,r | 1 | | | | | | | [A]←[SR]<br>Load the contents of the specified register, SR, into the Accumulator. Increment or decrement ISAR if specified by r. |
| | LR | A,DPCHR | 1 | | | | | | | [A]←[DPCHR]<br>Load Accumulator with the contents of the specified DPCHR. |
| | LR | r,A | | | | | | | | [SR]←[A]<br>Load the contents of the Accumulator into the specified register. Increment or decrement ISAR if specified by r. |
| | LR | DPCHR,A | 1 | | | | | | | [DPCHR]←[A]<br>Load the contents of the Accumulator into the specified DPCHR. |
| | LR | DC0,H | 1 | | | | | | | [DC0]←[H]<br>Load the contents of Scratchpad registers 10 and 11 into DC0. |
| | LR | DC0,Q | 1 | | | | | | | [DC0]←[Q]<br>Load the contents of Scratchpad registers 14 and 15 into DC0. |
| | LR | H,DC0 | 1 | | | | | | | [H]←[DC0]<br>Load the contents of DC0 into Scratchpad registers 10 and 11. |
| | LR | Q,DC0 | 1 | | | | | | | [Q]←[DC0]<br>Load the contents of DC0 into Scratchpad registers 14 and 15. |
| | LR | PC1,K | 1 | | | | | | | [PC1]←[K]<br>Load the contents of Register K into the Stack register. |
| | LR | K,PC1 | 1 | | | | | | | [K]←[PC1]<br>Load the contents of the Stack register into Register K. |
| | LR | PC0,Q | 1 | | | | | | | [PC0]←[Q]<br>Load the contents of Register Q into the Program Counter. |
| | PK | | 1 | | | | | | | [PC1]←[PC0], [PC0]←[Q]<br>Save the contents of the Program Counter in the Stack register, then load the contents of Register Q into the Program Counter. |

Table 2-1. 3870/F8 Instruction Set Summary (Continued)

| TYPE | MNEMONIC | OPERAND(S) | BYTES | STATUSES | | | | | | OPERATION PERFORMED |
|---|---|---|---|---|---|---|---|---|---|---|
| | | | | C | Z | S | O | | | |
| SECONDARY MEMORY REFERENCE (SCRATCHPAD OPERATE) | AS | r | 1 | X | X | X | X | | | [A]←[A] + [SR]<br>Add binary the contents of the specified register to the contents of the Accumulator. Increment or decrement ISAR if specified by r. |
| | ASD | r | 1 | X | X | X | X | | | [A]←[A] + [SR]<br>Add decimal the contents of the specified register to the contents of the Accumulator; that is, both numbers are assumed to be BCD digits. Increment or decrement ISAR if specified by r. |
| | NS | r | 1 | 0 | X | X | 0 | | | [A]←[A] Λ [SR]<br>AND the contents of the specified register with the contents of the Accumulator. Increment or decrement ISAR if specified by r. |
| | XS | r | | 0 | X | X | 0 | | | [A]←[A] ⊻ [SR]<br>Exclusive-OR the contents of the specified register with the contents of the Accumulator. Increment or decrement the ISAR if specified by r. |
| | DS | r | 1 | X | X | X | X | | | [SR]←[SR] - 1<br>Decrement the specified register. Increment or decrement ISAR if specified by r. |
| SECONDARY MEMORY REFERENCE (MEMORY OPERATE) | AM | | 1 | X | X | X | X | | | [A]←[A] + [[DC0]], [DC0]←[DC0] + 1<br>Add Accumulator contents to the contents of the memory location addressed by DC0. Increment DC0. |
| | AMD | | 1 | X | X | X | X | | | [A]←[A] + [[DC0]], [DC0]←[DC0] + 1<br>Decimal add Accumulator contents to the contents of the memory location addressed by DC0. Increment DC0. |
| | NM | | 1 | 0 | X | X | 0 | | | [A]←[A] Λ [[DC0]], [DC0]←[DC0] + 1<br>AND Accumulator contents with the contents of the memory location addressed by DC0. Increment DC0. |
| | OM | | 1 | 0 | X | X | 0 | | | [A]←[A] V [[DC0]], [DC0]←[DC0] + 1<br>OR Accumulator contents with the contents of the memory location addressed by DC0. Increment DC0. |
| | XM | | 1 | 0 | X | X | 0 | | | [A]←[A] ⊻ [[DC0]], [DC0]←[DC0] + 1<br>Exclusive-OR Accumulator contents with the contents of the memory location addressed by DC0. Increment DC0. |
| | CM | | 1 | X | X | X | X | | | [[DC0]] - [A], [DC0]←[DC0] + 1<br>Subtract the contents of the Accumulator from the contents of the memory location addressed by DC0. Only the status flags are affected. Increment DC0. |
| IMMEDIATE | LISU | DATA3 | 1 | | | | | | | [ISAR <5,3>]←DATA3<br>Load immediate into the upper three bits of the ISAR. |
| | LISL | DATA3 | 1 | | | | | | | [ISAR <2,0>]←DATA3<br>Load immediate into the lower three bits of the ISAR. |
| | DCI | ADDR | 3 | | | | | | | [DC0]← ADDR<br>Load immediate data into the DC0. |
| | LIS | DATA4 | 1 | | | | | | | [A <3,0>]← DATA4<br>Load immediate data into the lower four bits of the Accumulator. Clear the high four bits of the Accumulator. |
| | LI | DATA8 | 2 | | | | | | | [A]← DATA8<br>Load immediate data into Accumulator. |

Table 2-1. 3870/F8 Instruction Set Summary (Continued)

| TYPE | MNEMONIC | OPERAND(S) | BYTES | STATUSES C | STATUSES Z | STATUSES S | STATUSES O | | | OPERATION PERFORMED |
|---|---|---|---|---|---|---|---|---|---|---|
| IMMEDIATE OPERATE | AI | DATA8 | 2 | X | X | X | X | | | [A]←[A] + DATA8<br>Add immediate to Accumulator. |
| | NI | DATA8 | 2 | 0 | X | X | 0 | | | [A]←[A] Λ DATA8<br>AND immediate with Accumulator. |
| | OI | DATA8 | 2 | 0 | X | X | 0 | | | [A]←[A] V DATA8<br>OR immediate with Accumulator. |
| | XI | DATA8 | 2 | 0 | X | X | 0 | | | [A]←[A] ⊻ DATA8<br>Exclusive-OR immediate with Accumulator. |
| | CI | DATA8 | 2 | X | X | X | X | | | DATA8 - [A]<br>Compare immediate: subtract Accumulator contents from immediate data, but only the status flags are affected. |
| JUMP | PI | ADDR | 3 | | | | | | | [PC1]←[PC0], [PC0]← ADDR<br>Save Program Counter in Stack register, then load immediate address into Program Counter. |
| | BR | DISP | 2 | | | | | | | [PC0]←[PC0] + DISP<br>Add immediate displacement to contents of Program Counter. |
| | JMP | ADDR | 3 | | | | | | | [PC0]← ADDR, [A]← ADDR <15,8><br>Load immediate address into Program Counter. Load the high order byte of the address into the Accumulator. |
| BRANCH ON CONDITION | BT | DATA3,DISP | 2 | | | | | | | If DATA3 V TMASK ≠ 0 then [PC0]←[PC0] + DISP<br>OR the 3 bits of immediate data with the current TMASK. If any resulting bit is a 1, add the displacement to PC0. |
| | BF | DATA4,DISP | 2 | | | | | | | If DATA4 = FMASK, then [PC0]←[PC0] + DISP<br>If the 4 bits of immediate data are equal to FMASK, add the displacement to PC0. |
| | BP | DISP | 2 | | | | | | | If [S] = 1 then [PC0]←[PC0] + DISP<br>Branch relative if the Sign bit is set. |
| | BC | DISP | 2 | | | | | | | If [C] = 1 then [PC0]←[PC0] + DISP<br>Branch relative if the Carry bit is set. |
| | BZ | DISP | 2 | | | | | | | If [Z] = 1 then [PC0]←[PC0] + DISP<br>Branch relative if the Zero bit is set. |
| | BM | DISP | 2 | | | | | | | If [S] = 0 then [PC0]←[PC0] + DISP<br>Branch relative if the Sign bit is reset. |
| | BNC | DISP | 2 | | | | | | | If [C] = 0 then [PC0]←[PC0] + DISP<br>Branch relative if the Carry bit is reset. |
| | BNZ | DISP | 2 | | | | | | | If [Z] = 0 then [PC0]←[PC0] + DISP<br>Branch relative if the Zero bit is reset. |
| | BNO | DISP | 2 | | | | | | | If [O] = 0 then [PC0]←[PC0] + DISP<br>Branch relative if the Overflow bit is reset. |
| | BR7 | DISP | 2 | | | | | | | If [ISAR <2,0>] = 7 then [PC0]←[PC0] + DISP<br>If the low three bits of the ISAR are not all 1s, branch relative. |

Table 2-1. 3870/F8 Instruction Set Summary (Continued)

| TYPE | MNEMONIC | OPERAND(S) | BYTES | STATUSES C | STATUSES Z | STATUSES S | STATUSES O | OPERATION PERFORMED |
|---|---|---|---|---|---|---|---|---|
| REGISTER-REGISTER MOVE | XDC | | 1 | | | | | [DC0]⟷[DC1] Exchange the contents of DC0 with the contents of DC1. |
| | LR | A,IS | 1 | | | | | [A]←[ISAR] Load the contents of ISAR into the Accumulator. |
| | LR | IS,A | 1 | | | | | [ISAR]←[A] Load the contents of the Accumulator into the ISAR. |
| | POP | | 1 | | | | | [PC0]←[PC1] Load the contents of the Stack register into the Program Counter. |
| REGISTER-REGISTER OPERATE | ADC | | 1 | 0 | X | 1 | 0 | [DC0]←[DC0] + [A] Add the contents of DC0 to the contents of the Accumulator, which is treated as a signed binary number. Store the result in DC0. |
| REGISTER OPERATE | SR | 1 | 1 | 0 | X | 1 | 0 |  0→[7 … 0]→ Shift the contents of the Accumulator right one bit. The most significant bit becomes a 0. |
| | SR | 4 | 1 | 0 | X | 1 | 0 | 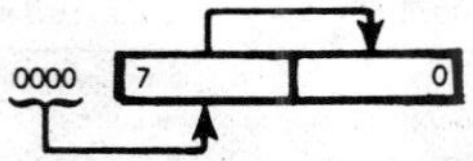 0000→[7 … 0] Shift the contents of the Accumulator right four bits. The most significant four bits become 0s. |
| | SL | 1 | 1 | 0 | X | X | 0 | ←[7 … 0]←0 Shift the contents of the Accumulator left one bit. The least significant bit becomes a 0. |
| | SL | 4 | 1 | 0 | X | X | 0 | 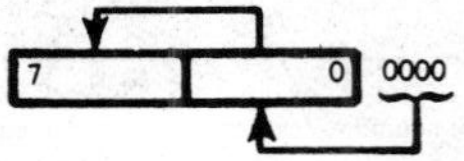 [7 … 0]←0000 Shift the contents of the Accumulator left four bits. The least significant four bits become 0s. |
| | COM | | 1 | 0 | X | X | 0 | [A]←[$\overline{A}$] Complement Accumulator contents. |
| | LNK | | 1 | X | X | X | X | [A]←[A] + C Add the Carry to the contents of the Accumulator. |
| | INC | | 1 | X | X | X | X | [A]←[A] + 1 Increment the contents of the Accumulator. |
| | CLR | | 1 | | | | | [A]←0 Clear the Accumulator. |

Table 2-1. 3870/F8 Instruction Set Summary (Continued)

| TYPE | MNEMONIC | OPERAND(S) | BYTES | STATUSES | | | | | | OPERATION PERFORMED |
|---|---|---|---|---|---|---|---|---|---|---|
| | | | | C | Z | S | O | | | |
| INTERRUPT | DI | | 1 | | | | | | | [I]←0<br>Set the interrupt enable bit in the Status register, W, to 0. |
| | EI | | 1 | | | | | | | [I]←1<br>Set the interrupt enable bit in the Status register, W, to 1. |
| STATUS | LR | W,J | 1 | | | | | | | [W]←[J]<br>Move the contents of Scratchpad register 9 into the Status register, W. |
| | LR | J,W | 1 | | | | | | | [J]←[W]<br>Move the contents of the Status register, W, into Scratchpad register 9. |
| | NOP | | 1 | | | | | | | No operation is performed. This is not a Halt. |

## THE 3870 BENCHMARK PROGRAM

**The fact that the 3870 has just 64 bytes of read/write memory makes the benchmark program used in this book somewhat meaningless. We will therefore substitute a program similar to the one given in Chapter 1 for the TMS1000.** A block of data is to be input via I/O Port 0. The first byte of data identifies the length of the data block to follow: this data block must be less than 48 bytes in length so that it will fit into scratchpad memory starting at scratchpad byte $10_{16}$. Here is the necessary program:

```
        INS    0       INPUT FIRST BLOCK LENGTH BYTE
        LR     0,A     SAVE IN SCRATCHPAD BYTE 0
        LISU   1       INITIALIZE ISAR
        LISL   0
LOOP    INS    0       INPUT DATA BYTE
        LR     S,A     SAVE IN NEXT SCRATCHPAD BYTE
        LR     A,IS    INCREMENT ALL SIX ISAR BITS
        INC
        LR     IS,A
        DS     0       DECREMENT SCRATCHPAD BYTE 0
        BNZ    LOOP    RETURN IF NOT ZERO
```

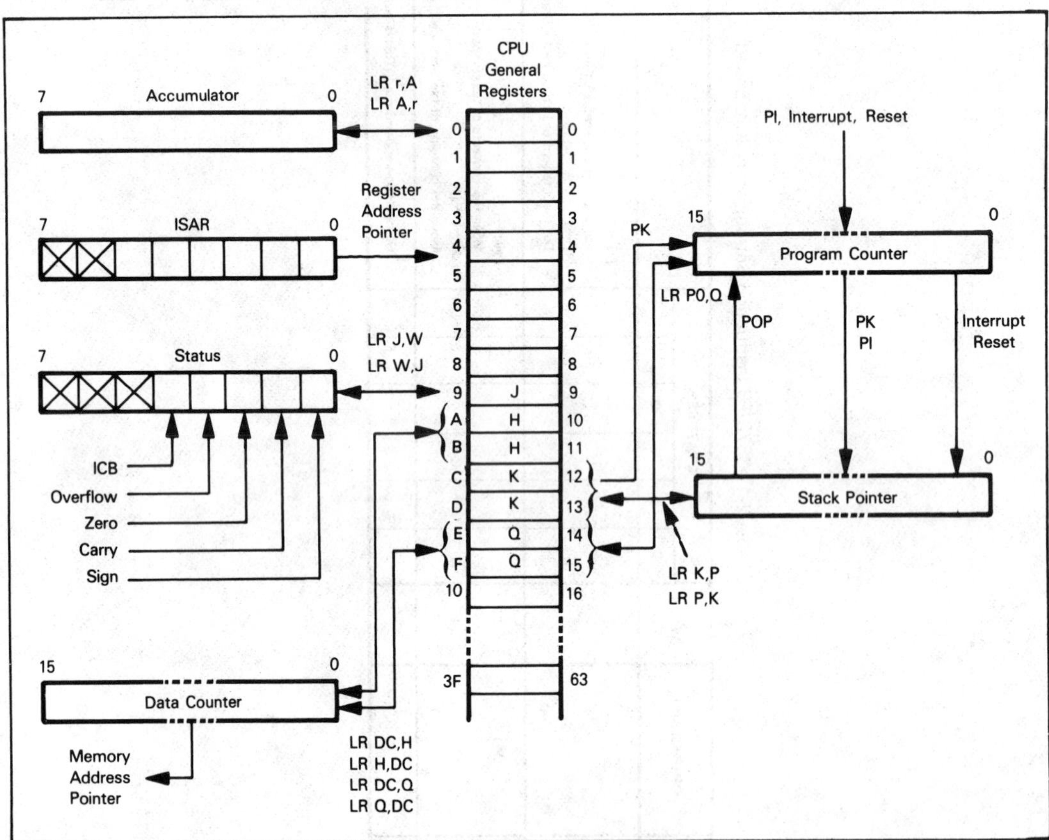


Figure 2-4. Instructions That Move Data Between the Scratchpad and Various Registers

Table 2-2. Timing and ROMC States for F8 Instruction Set

| MNEMONIC | OPERAND(S) | CYCLE | ROMC STATE |
|---|---|---|---|
| ADC | | L | A |
| | | S | 0 |
| AI | DATA8 | L | 3 |
| | | S | 0 |
| AM | | L | 2 |
| | | S | 0 |
| AMD | | L | 2 |
| | | S | 0 |
| AS | r | S | 0 |
| ASD | r | S | 1C |
| | | S | 0 |
| BF | DATA4,DISP | S | 1C |
| Branch | | L | 1 |
| | | S | 0 |
| | | S | 1C |
| No | | S | 3 |
| Branch | | S | 0 |
| BR7 | DISP | S | 3 |
| No Branch | | S | 0 |
| Branch | | L | 1 |
| | | S | 0 |
| BT | DATA3,DISP | S | 1C |
| No | | S | 3 |
| Branch | | S | 0 |
| | | S | 1C |
| Branch | | L | 1 |
| | | S | 0 |
| CI | DATA8 | L | 3 |
| | | S | 0 |
| CM | | L | 2 |
| | | S | 0 |
| COM | | S | 0 |
| DCI | ADDR | L | 11 |
| | | S | 3 |
| | | L | E |
| | | S | 3 |
| | | S | 0 |
| DI | | S | 1C |
| | | S | 0 |
| DS | r | L | 0 |
| EI | | S | 1C |
| | | S | 0 |
| IN | P8 | L | 3 |
| | | L | 1B |
| | | S | 0 |
| INC | | S | 0 |
| INS | 0 or 1 | S | 1C |
| | | S | 0 |
| INS | 2 | L | 1C |
| | through | L | 1B |
| | 15 | S | 0 |
| (INTERRUPT) | | L | 1C |
| | | L | 08 |
| | | L | 13 |
| | | S | 0 |
| JMP | ADDR | L | 3 |
| | | L | C |
| | | L | 14 |
| | | S | 0 |
| LI | DATA8 | L | 3 |
| | | S | 0 |
| LIS | DATA4 | S | 0 |
| LISL | DATA3 | S | 0 |

| MNEMONIC | OPERAND(S) | CYCLE | ROMC STATE |
|---|---|---|---|
| LISU | DATA3 | S | 0 |
| LM | | L | 2 |
| | | S | 0 |
| LNK | | S | 0 |
| LR | A,IS | S | 0 |
| LR | A,KL | S | 0 |
| LR | A,KU | S | 0 |
| LR | A,QL | S | 0 |
| LR | A,QU | S | 0 |
| LR | A,r | S | 0 |
| LR | DC0,H | L | 16 |
| | | L | 19 |
| | | S | 0 |
| LR | DC0,Q | L | 16 |
| | | L | 19 |
| | | S | 0 |
| LR | H,DC0 | L | 6 |
| | | L | 9 |
| | | S | 0 |
| LR | IS,A | S | 0 |
| LR | J,W | S | 0 |
| LR | K,P | L | 7 |
| | | L | B |
| | | S | 0 |
| LR | KL,A | S | 0 |
| LR | KU,A | S | 0 |
| LR | P,K | L | 15 |
| | | L | 18 |
| | | S | 0 |
| LR | PC0,Q | L | |
| | | L | |
| | | S | |
| LR | Q,DC0 | L | 6 |
| | | L | 9 |
| | | S | 0 |
| LR | QL,A | S | 0 |
| LR | QU,A | S | 0 |
| LR | r,A | S | 0 |
| LR | W,J | S | 1C |
| | | S | 0 |
| NI | DATA8 | L | 3 |
| | | S | 0 |
| NM | | L | 2 |
| | | S | 0 |
| NS | r | S | 0 |
| OI | DATA8 | L | 3 |
| | | S | 0 |
| OM | | L | 2 |
| | | S | 0 |
| OUT | P8 | L | 3 |
| | | L | 1A |
| | | S | 0 |
| OUTS | 0 or 1 | S | 1C |
| | | S | 0 |
| OUTS | 2 | L | 1C |
| | through | L | 1A |
| | 15 | S | 0 |
| PI | ADDR | L | 3 |
| | | S | D |
| | | L | C |
| | | L | 14 |
| | | S | 0 |

Table 2-2. Timing and ROMC States for F8 Instruction Set (Continued)

| MNEMONIC | OPERAND(S) | CYCLE | ROMC STATE |
|---|---|---|---|
| PK | | L | 12 |
| | | L | 14 |
| | | S | 0 |
| POP | | S | 4 |
| | | S | 0 |
| (RESET) | | S | 1C |
| | | L | 8 |
| | | S | 0 |
| SL | 1 | S | 0 |
| SL | 4 | S | 0 |
| SR | 1 | S | 0 |
| SR | 4 | S | 0 |
| ST | | L | 5 |
| | | S | 0 |
| XI | DATA8 | L | 3 |
| | | S | 0 |
| XM | | L | 2 |
| | | S | 0 |
| XS | r | S | 0 |

The following symbols are used in Table 2-3:

aaaa Four bits choosing the register addressing mode:
- 0000-1011 Registers 0 - B directly addressed
- 1100 ISAR addresses the register
- 1101 ISAR addresses the register. Increment low three bits of ISAR.
- 1110 ISAR addresses the register. Decrement low three bits of ISAR.
- 1111 NOP. No operation is performed if aaaa=$F_{16}$.

cc Two bits choosing a Scratchpad register:
- 00--KU Scratchpad Register 12
- 01--KL Scratchpad Register 13
- 10--QU Scratchpad Register 14
- 11--QL Scratchpad Register 15

d One bit of immediate data.

eeee A 4-bit port number.

qqqq A 16-bit address.

rr An 8-bit signed displacement.

ss An 8-bit port number.

yy One byte (8 bits) of immediate data.

When two numbers are given in the "Machine Cycles" column (for example, 3/3.5), the first is the execution time if no branch is taken, and the second is execution time if the branch is taken.

Table 2-3. 3870/F8 Instruction Set Object Code

| INSTRUCTION | OBJECT CODE | BYTES | MACHINE CYCLES |
|---|---|---|---|
| ADC | 8E | 1 | 2.5 |
| AI DATA8 | 24 YY | 2 | 2.5 |
| AM | 88 | 1 | 2.5 |
| AMD | 89 | 1 | 2.5 |
| AS r | 1100aaaa | 1 | 1 |
| ASD r | 1101aaaa | 1 | 2 |
| BC DISP | 82 RR | 2 | 3/3.5 |
| BF DATA4,DISP | 1001dddd RR | 2 | 3/3.5 |
| BM DISP | 91 RR | 2 | 3/3.5 |
| BNC DISP | 92 RR | 2 | 3/3.5 |
| BNO DISP | 98 RR | 2 | 3/3.5 |
| BNZ DISP | 94 RR | 2 | 3/3.5 |
| BP DISP | 81 RR | 2 | 3/3.5 |
| BR DISP | 90 RR | 2 | 3.5 |
| BR7 DISP | 8F RR | 2 | 3/3.5 |
| BT DATA3,DISP | 10000ddd RR | 2 | 3/3.5 |
| BZ DISP | 84 RR | 2 | 3/3.5 |
| CI DATA8 | 25 YY | 2 | 2.5 |
| CLR | 70 | 1 | 1 |
| CM | 8D | 1 | 2.5 |
| COM | 18 | 1 | 1 |
| DCI ADDR | 2A QQQQ | 3 | 6 |
| DI | 1A | 1 | 2 |
| DS r | 0011aaaa | 1 | 1.5 |
| EI | 1B | 1 | 2 |
| IN P8 | 26 SS | 2 | 4 |
| INC | 1F | 1 | 1 |
| INS P4 | 1010eeee | 1 | 4 |
| JMP ADDR | 29 QQQQ | 3 | 5.5 |
| LI DATA8 | 20 YY | 2 | 2.5 |
| LIS DATA4 | 0111dddd | 1 | 1 |
| LISL DATA3 | 01101ddd | 1 | 1 |
| LISU DATA3 | 01100ddd | 1 | 1 |
| LM | 16 | 1 | 2.5 |

| INSTRUCTION | OBJECT CODE | BYTES | MACHINE CYCLES |
|---|---|---|---|
| LNK | 19 | 1 | 1 |
| LR A,DPCHR | 000000cc | 1 | 1 |
| LR A,IS | 0A | 1 | 1 |
| LR A,r | 0100aaaa | 1 | 1 |
| LR DC,H | 10 | 1 | 4 |
| LR DC,Q | 0F | 1 | 4 |
| LR DPCHR,A | 000001cc | 1 | 1 |
| LR H,DC | 11 | 1 | 4 |
| LR IS,A | 0B | 1 | 1 |
| LR J,W | 1E | 1 | 1 |
| LR K,PC1 | 08 | 1 | 4 |
| LR PC0,Q | 0D | 1 | 4 |
| LR PC1,K | 09 | 1 | 4 |
| LR Q,DC | 0E | 1 | 4 |
| LR r,A | 0101aaaa | 1 | 1 |
| LR W,J | 1D | 1 | 2 |
| NI DATA8 | 21 YY | 2 | 2.5 |
| NM | 8A | 1 | 2.5 |
| NOP | 2B | 1 | 1 |
| NS r | 1111aaaa | 1 | 1 |
| OI DATA8 | 22 YY | 2 | 2.5 |
| OM | 8B | 1 | 2.5 |
| OUT P8 | 27 SS | 2 | 4 |
| OUTS P4 | 1011eeee | 1 | 4 |
| PI ADDR | 28 QQQQ | 3 | 6.5 |
| PK | 0C | 1 | 4 |
| POP | 1C | 1 | 2 |
| SL 1 | 13 | 1 | 1 |
| SL 4 | 15 | 1 | 1 |
| SR 1 | 12 | 1 | 1 |
| SR 4 | 14 | 1 | 1 |
| ST | 17 | 1 | 2.5 |
| XDC | 2C | 1 | 2 |
| XI DATA8 | 23 YY | 2 | 2.5 |
| XM | 8C | 1 | 2.5 |
| XS r | 1110aaaa | 1 | 1 |

# THE 3850 CPU

**Beginning with the 3850 CPU, we are going to describe the individual devices of the F8 microcomputer system. The 3850 CPU and the 3851 PSU descriptions depend on the preceding 3870 discussion for a frame of reference. That is to say, these two F8 devices are described as variations of the 3870, rather than as stand-alone devices.**

**Functions implemented on the 3850 CPU are illustrated in Figure 2-5.**

**These are the functions which one would expect to find on a CPU chip, and which are on the 3850 CPU:**

- The Arithmetic and Logic Unit
- The Control Unit and Instruction register
- Logic needed to interface the System Bus with the control signals which are input and output by the CPU
- Accumulator register

**There is no memory addressing logic, and there are no memory addressing registers on the 3850 CPU. Stack Pointer, Program Counter and Data Counter registers are all maintained on memory chips and memory interface chips.**

**With the F8 scheme, memory addressing logic will be duplicated if more than one memory device is present in an F8 microcomputer system. We will discuss shortly how potential contention problems are resolved under these circumstances.**

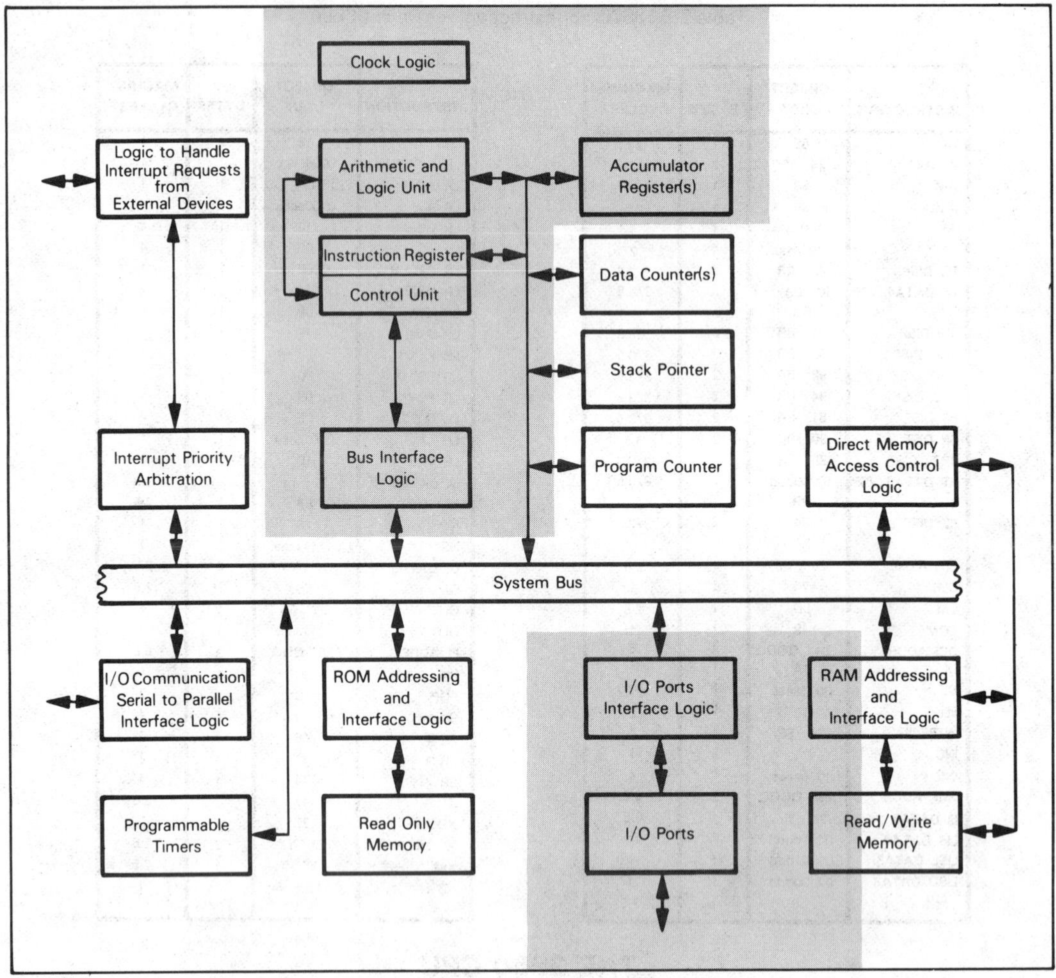


Figure 2-5. Logic of the Fairchild F8 3850 CPU

**Two advantages accrue from having no memory address logic on the CPU chip:**

1) No address lines are needed on the System Bus, so neither the CPU nor connecting devices need 16 address pins. These 16 pins are used instead to implement two 8-bit I/O ports at each device.

2) The real estate on the CPU chip which would have been used by Address registers and memory addressing logic is available for other purposes; it is used to implement 64 bytes of read/write memory.

**Having I/O ports and read/write memory on the CPU chip paves the way for some very low-cost small microcomputer configurations;** for example, the 3850 CPU and the 3851 PSU form a two-device microcomputer system, with all of the necessary prerequisites for reasonable performance. Until the advent of the 3870 single-chip microcomputer, this two-chip configuration represented the lowest cost 8-bit microcomputer on the market.

**The disadvantage of removing memory addressing logic from the CPU chip is that standard memory devices can no longer connect directly to the System Bus.** This bus has no address lines; therefore, separate logic devices must create the interface needed by standard memories. In the F8 system this is done by the 3852 DMI and the 3853 SMI devices.

**Clock signal generation logic is also part of the 3850 CPU.** This is now standard among microcomputers.

## F8 PROGRAMMABLE REGISTERS AND STATUS FLAGS

**F8 programmable registers and status flags are identical to the 3870. For details, refer to the earlier discussion.**

## F8 ADDRESSING MODES

**3870 and F8 addressing modes are identical, both for scratchpad memory and for external program memory. But memory addressing logic is implemented on F8 memory devices, not on the 3850 CPU.**

Every 3851 PSU contains its own Program Counter (PC0), Stack register (PS1), and Data Counter (DC0). The 3851 PSU has no Data Counter buffer (DC1).

The 3852 DMI and 3853 SMI devices contain all four Address registers: PC0, PC1, DC0 and DC1.

**Since Address registers are present on every PSU, DMI or SMI device in an F8 microcomputer system, these registers will be duplicated in any F8 system that contains more than a minimum amount of memory.** So long as the microcomputer system has been correctly configured, this presents no problem. Every memory device contains identical connections to the common System Bus, and instructions that modify the contents of any Address register do so identically for all memory devices. For example, if there are three memory devices, and therefore three Program Counters in an F8 system, every Program Counter is incremented identically after a byte of object code is fetched. This being the case, Address registers on different memory devices will always contain identical address information.

**Every F8 device that contains memory addressing logic also contains a memory address mask which you must define when ordering the device.** This mask identifies the device's addressed space. Thus, a memory device will only respond to memory accesses within its address space. **So long as no two devices have overlapping address spaces** (and if they do, that is a logic design error) **there is no chance for memory contentions to arise.** In order to illustrate this point, consider the very simple example of an F8 configuration that contains two 3851 PSUs. Each 3851 PSU contains 1024 bytes of read-only memory. Let us assume that 3851 PSU #1 responds to memory addresses in the range $0000_{16}$ through $03FF_{16}$, while PSU #2 responds to memory addresses in the range $0400_{16}$ through $07FF_{16}$. This may be illustrated as follows:

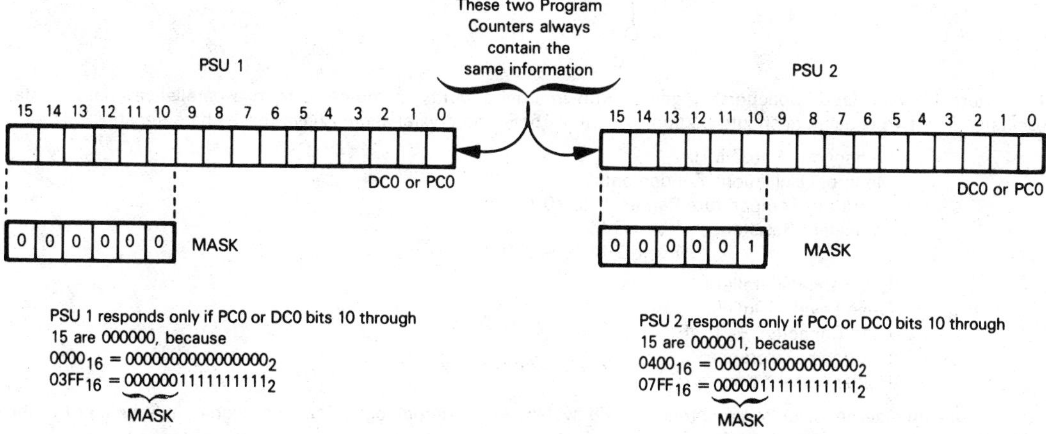


Any memory reference instruction will identify a memory address as the contents of either the Program Counter (PC0) or the Data Counter (DC0). When this address is in the range $0000_{16}$ through $03FF_{16}$, PSU #1 will respond but PSU #2 will not. If this address is in the range $0400_{16}$ through $07FF_{16}$, then PSU #2 will respond but PSU #1 will not. A memory address of $0800_{16}$ or more will result in neither PSU responding.

There is one circumstance under which memory addressing contentions can arise. Since the 3851 PSU does not contain a DC1 register, it does not respond to the XDC instruction which exchanges the contents of the DC0 and DC1 registers. Therefore, in an F8 configuration that contains 3851 PSUs together with 3852 DMI and/or 3853 SMI devices, execution of an XDC instruction will result in 3851 PSU DC0 registers containing different information from 3852 DMI or 3853 SMI DC0 registers. If an external data memory reference instruction is now executed, it is possible for a 3851 PSU and 3852 DMI or 3853 SMI device to simultaneously consider itself selected. For example, consider an F8 configuration which contains a 3851 PSU and 3853 SMI. Suppose the 3851 PSU mask causes it to respond to addresses in the range $0000_{16}$ through $03FF_{16}$, while the 3853 SMI responds to all other memory addresses. Now, if Data Counter DC0 contains $02A3_{16}$ while the Data Counter buffer (DC1) contains $0A7F_{16}$, then, following execution of an XDC instruction, nothing will happen to the contents of the 3851 PSU DC0 register; however, the 3853 SMI DC0 register will contain $0A7F_{16}$. Any instruction that accesses data memory via DC0 will now cause both the 3851 PSU and the 3853 SMI to consider themselves selected.

In F8 configurations that include the 3851 PSU together with 3852 DMI or 3853 SMI devices, the best way of avoiding memory addressing problems is to not use the XDC instruction. If you do use the XDC instruction, you must be particularly careful to ensure that DC0 is never within a 3851 PSU's address space when the XDC instruction is executed.

## F8 CLOCK CIRCUITS

**Three ways of generating an F8 system clock have been advertised; these are the RC mode, Crystal mode, and External mode. Only Crystal mode has worked consistently in practice.**

**Using the Crystal mode, a crystal in the 1 to 2 MHz range connects across the XTLX and XTLY pins;** along with two capacitors ($C_1$ and $C_2$), which provide a highly precise clock frequency:

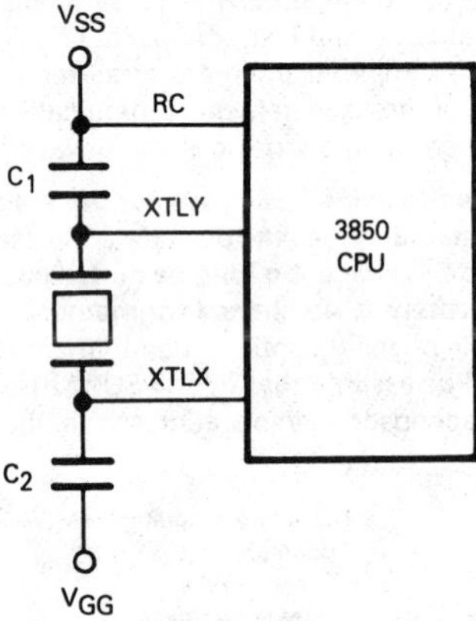


The external crystal (and capacitors), together with internal circuitry, combine to form a parallel resonant crystal oscillator. The two capacitors should be approximately 15pF. The crystal should have these characteristics:

Frequency: 1 to 2 MHz
Mode of Oscillation: Fundamental
Operating Temperature Range: 0 to 70°C
Equivalent Resistance: 1 to 1.5 MHz ~ 475Ω
1.5 to 2 MHz ~ 350Ω

Resonance: Parallel
Drive Level: 10mW
Load Capacity: ~ 15pF
Frequency Tolerance: Per customer's requirements
Holder (case) Style: Per customer's requirements

You can use an external clock to synchronize an F8 system with external logic. The clock signal must be input to the 3850 XTLY pin as follows:

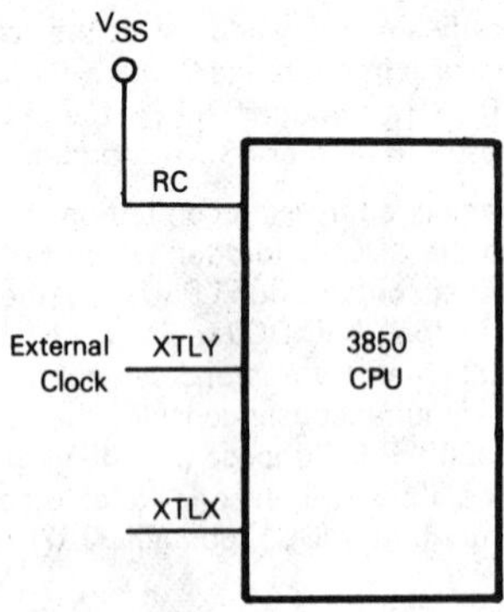

Table 2-4. ROMC Signals and What They Imply

| ROMC 4 3 2 1 0 | HEX | CYCLE LENGTH | FUNCTION |
|---|---|---|---|
| 0 0 0 0 0 | 00 | S,L | Instruction Fetch. The device whose address space includes the contents of the PC0 register must place on the Data Bus the op code addressed by PC0. Then all devices increment the contents of PC0. |
| 0 0 0 0 1 | 01 | L | The device whose address space includes the contents of the PC0 register must place on the Data Bus the contents of the memory location addressed by PC0. Then all devices add the 8-bit value on the Data Bus, as a signed binary number, to PC0. |
| 0 0 0 1 0 | 02 | L | The device whose DC0 addresses a memory word within the address space of that device must place on the Data Bus the contents of the memory location addressed by DC0. Then all devices increment DC0. |
| 0 0 0 1 1 | 03 | L,S | Similar to 00, except that it is used for Immediate Operand fetches (using PC0) instead of instruction fetches. |
| 0 0 1 0 0 | 04 | S | Copy the contents of PC1 into PC0. |
| 0 0 1 0 1 | 05 | L | Store the Data Bus contents or write bus contents into the memory location pointed to by DC0. Increment DC0. |
| 0 0 1 1 0 | 06 | L | Place the high order byte of DC0 on the Data Bus. |
| 0 0 1 1 1 | 07 | L | Place the high order byte of PC1 on the Data Bus. |
| 0 1 0 0 0 | 08 | L | All devices copy the contents of PC0 into PC1. The CPU outputs zero on the Data Bus in this ROMC state. Load the Data Bus into both halves of PC0 thus clearing the register. |
| 0 1 0 0 1 | 09 | L | The device whose address space includes the contents of the DC0 register must place the low order byte of DC0 onto the Data Bus. |
| 0 1 0 1 0 | 0A | L | All devices add the 8-bit value on the Data Bus, treated as a signed binary number, to the Data Counter. |
| 0 1 0 1 1 | 0B | L | The device whose address space includes the value in PC1 must place the low order byte of PC1 on the Data Bus. |
| 0 1 1 0 0 | 0C | L | The device whose address space includes the contents of the PC0 register must place the contents of the memory word addressed by PC0 onto the Data Bus. Then all devices move the value which has just been placed on the Data Bus into the low order byte of PC0. |
| 0 1 1 0 1 | 0D | S | All devices store in PC1 the current contents of PC0, incremented by 1. PC0 is unaltered. |
| 0 1 1 1 0 | 0E | L | The device whose address space includes the contents of PC0 must place the contents of the word addressed by PC0 onto the Data Bus. The value on the Data Bus is then moved to the low order byte of DC0 by all devices. |
| 0 1 1 1 1 | 0F | L | The interrupting device with highest priority must place the low order byte of the interrupt vector on the Data Bus. All devices must copy the contents of PC0 into PC1. All devices must move the contents of the Data Bus into the low order byte of PC0. |
| 1 0 0 0 0 | 10 | L | Inhibit any modification to the interrupt priority logic. |
| 1 0 0 0 1 | 11 | L | The device whose memory space includes the contents of PC0 must place the contents of the addressed memory word on the Data Bus. All devices must then move the contents of the Data Bus to the upper byte of DC0. |
| 1 0 0 1 0 | 12 | L | All devices copy the contents of PC0 into PC1. All devices then move the contents of the Data Bus into the low order byte of PC0. |
| 1 0 0 1 1 | 13 | L | The interrupting device with highest priority must move the high order half of the interrupt vector onto the Data Bus. All devices must move the contents of the Data Bus into the high order byte of PC0. The interrupting device will reset its interrupt circuitry (so that it is no longer requesting CPU servicing and can respond to another interrupt). |
| 1 0 1 0 0 | 14 | L | All devices move the contents of the Data Bus into the high order byte of PC0. |
| 1 0 1 0 1 | 15 | L | All devices move the contents of the Data Bus into the high order byte of PC1. |
| 1 0 1 1 0 | 16 | L | All devices move the contents of the Data Bus into the high order byte of DC0. |
| 1 0 1 1 1 | 17 | L | All devices move the contents of the Data Bus into the low order byte of PC0. |
| 1 1 0 0 0 | 18 | L | All devices move the contents of the Data Bus into the low order byte of PC1. |
| 1 1 0 0 1 | 19 | L | All devices move the contents of the Data Bus into the low order byte of DC0. |
| 1 1 0 1 0 | 1A | L | During the prior cycle an I/O port timer or interrupt control register was addressed. The device containing the addressed port must move the current contents of the Data Bus into the addressed port. |
| 1 1 0 1 1 | 1B | L | During the prior cycle the Data Bus specified the address of an I/O port. The device containing the addressed I/O port must place the contents of the I/O port on the Data Bus. (Note that the contents of timer and interrupt control registers cannot be read back onto the Data Bus.) |
| 1 1 1 0 0 | 1C | L or S | None. |
| 1 1 1 0 1 | 1D | S | Devices with DC0 and DC1 registers must switch registers. Devices without a DC1 register perform no operation. |
| 1 1 1 1 0 | 1E | L | The device whose address space includes the contents of PC0 must place the low order byte of PC0 onto the Data Bus. |
| 1 1 1 1 1 | 1F | L | The device whose address space includes the contents of PC0 must place the high order byte of PC0 on the Data Bus. |

## F8 CPU PINS AND SIGNALS

**3850 CPU pins and signals are illustrated in Figure 2-6. A description of these signals is useful as a guide to the way in which the F8 microcomputer system works.**

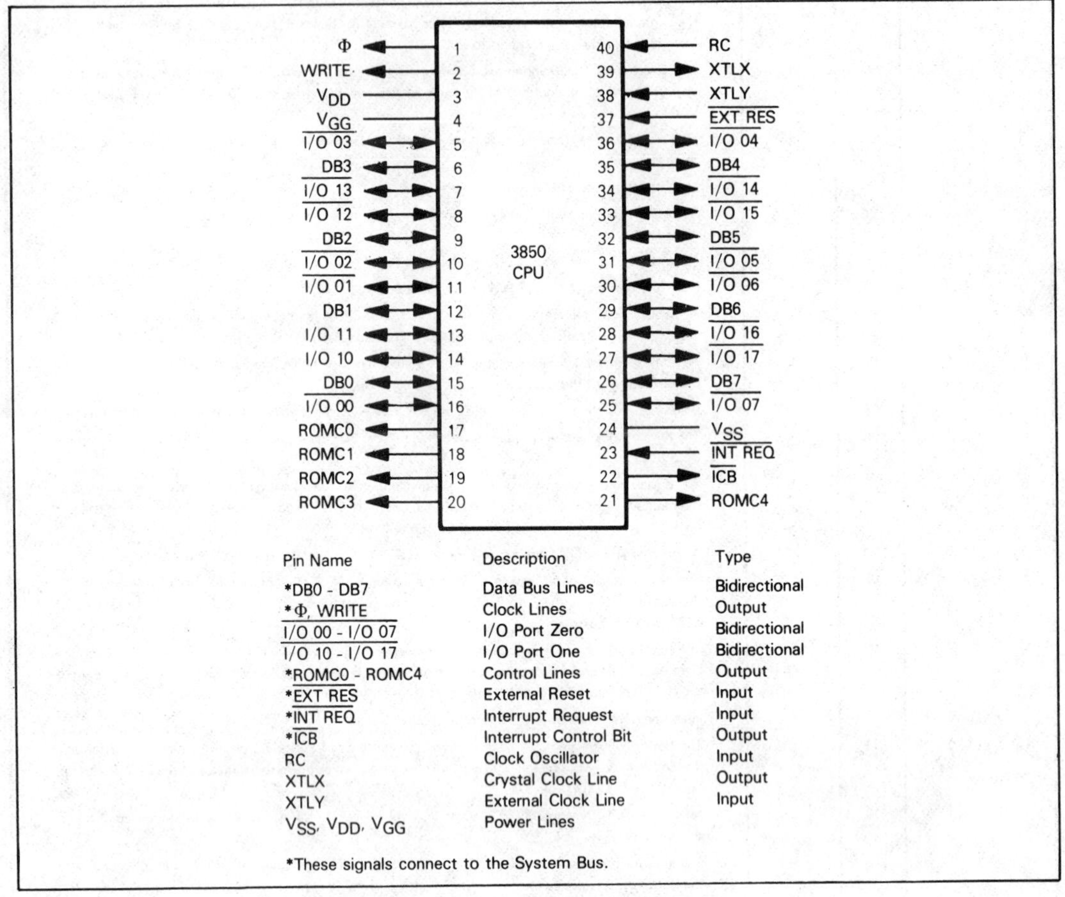


| Pin Name | Description | Type |
|---|---|---|
| *DB0 - DB7 | Data Bus Lines | Bidirectional |
| *Φ, WRITE | Clock Lines | Output |
| I/O 00 - I/O 07 | I/O Port Zero | Bidirectional |
| I/O 10 - I/O 17 | I/O Port One | Bidirectional |
| *ROMC0 - ROMC4 | Control Lines | Output |
| *EXT RES | External Reset | Input |
| *INT REQ | Interrupt Request | Input |
| *ICB | Interrupt Control Bit | Output |
| RC | Clock Oscillator | Input |
| XTLX | Crystal Clock Line | Output |
| XTLY | External Clock Line | Input |
| $V_{SS}$, $V_{DD}$, $V_{GG}$ | Power Lines | |

*These signals connect to the System Bus.

Figure 2-6. Fairchild 3850 CPU Signals and Pin Assignments

**The Data Bus lines (DB0 - DB7) and the control lines (ROMC0 - ROMC4) provide the heart of all data and control information flow.**

The Data Bus lines are common, bidirectional lines, and are the only conduit for data to be transmitted between devices of an F8 microcomputer system.

**A lack of address lines on the System Bus usually means that data and addresses must be multiplexed on a single set of eight lines — which slows down all memory reference operations; they must now proceed in three serial increments, rather than in one parallel increment. In the F8 System Bus, multiplexing is rarely needed, since addresses originate within memory devices, or memory interface devices, whence they are transmitted directly to memory.** In other words, the only time addresses are ever transmitted on the Data Bus is when they are being transmitted as data.

Refer to Figure 2-1. Suppose a memory reference instruction needs to access a byte of dynamic RAM. ROMC control signals (described in the next paragraph) specify that the memory byte whose address is implied by the Data Counters (DC0) is to be referenced. Every memory device receives the ROMC control signals, but only the 3852 DMI finds that its address space includes the Data Counter implied address; therefore, only the 3852 DMI will respond to the memory reference instruction. The 3852 DMI then outputs an address directly to dynamic RAM; this address is not transmitted via the System Bus. If the memory reference instruction requires data to be input to or output from dynamic RAM, the data transfer occurs directly between the System Bus and Dynamic RAM, bypassing the 3852 DMI entirely.

**ROMC STATE**

Since the 3851 PSU, the 3852 DMI and the 3853 SMI devices all contain Address registers and address generation logic, they also contain rudimentary Arithmetic and Logic Units equivalent to very primitive CPUs. These primitive CPUs are driven by 5-bit instructions called ROMC states. **ROMC states are output by the 3850 CPU via five control lines, ROMC0 - ROMC4.** Each five-bit combination of ROMC signal states identifies one of 32 possible operations which the memory devices may have to perform to accomplish one step of an instruction's execution. For example, ROMC state 00000 causes the contents of memory bytes addressed by the Program Counter to be transmitted to the CPU; this is the "instruction fetch" ROMC state. Table 2-4 summarizes the interpretation of ROMC states.

**Φ and WRITE are two timing signals** output by the 3850 CPU to synchronize events within the rest of the F8 system.

**The $\overline{\text{EXT RES}}$ line disables interrupts** and loads a 0 address into all Program Counters, causing program execution to restart with the instruction code stored in external memory byte 0.

**$\overline{\text{INT REQ}}$ and $\overline{\text{ICB}}$ are signals used for overall interrupt control.** $\overline{\text{INT REQ}}$ is the master line on which all interrupt requests are transmitted to the 3850 CPU. $\overline{\text{ICB}}$ is output low by the CPU if interrupts are enabled, and it is output high by the CPU if interrupts are disabled.

**The two I/O ports which are part of the 3850 CPU device use pins I/O00 - I/O07 and I/O10 - I/O17, respectively.**

**RC, XTLX and XTLY are the three pins used for clock inputs.**

## F8 TIMING AND INSTRUCTION EXECUTION

**All instructions are executed in cycles, which are timed by the trailing edge of WRITE.**

**There are two types of instruction cycle, the short cycle** which is four Φ clock periods long, **and the long cycle** which is six Φ clock periods long. The long cycle is sometimes referred to as 1.5 cycles. WRITE high appears only at the end of an instruction cycle. Timing may be illustrated as follows:

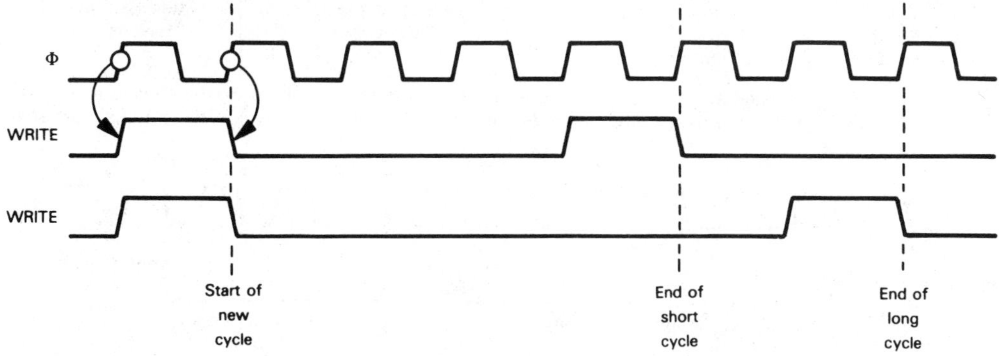


The simplest instructions of the F8 instruction set execute in one short cycle. The most complex instruction (PI) requires two short cycles plus three long cycles.

**Table 2-2 summarizes the sequence in which short (S) and long (L) machine cycles are executed for each F8 instruction. ROMC states defining operations performed during each machine cycle are summarized in Table 2-4.**

The trailing edge of the WRITE pulse triggers the next ROMC state to be output on the ROMC0 - ROMC4 lines:

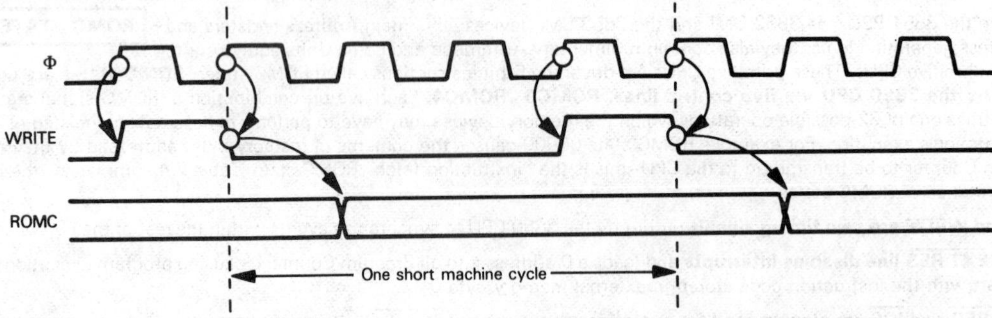


For any instruction that only accesses the Accumulator or scratchpad memory, no further System Bus activity is required, since all subsequent operations will occur within the F8 CPU. This inactivity on the System Bus is used to overlap the last (or only) machine cycle of one instruction with the instruction fetch for the next instruction. For instructions that execute in a single machine cycle, accessing only logic within the 3850 CPU, timing may be illustrated as follows:

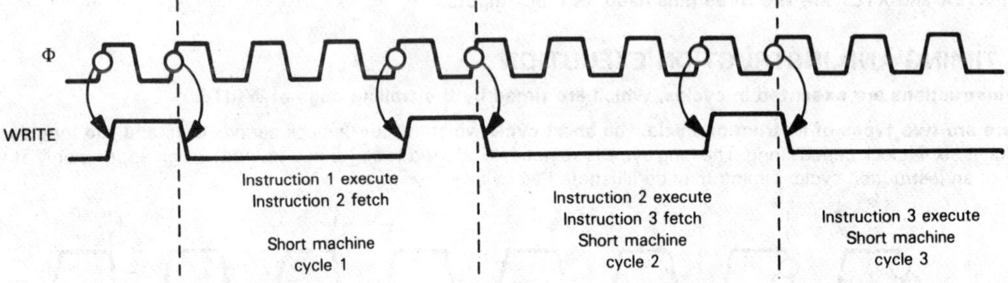


Instructions that do access external memory or I/O ports will always terminate with a machine cycle that does not cause any System Bus activity; the next instruction is fetched during this machine cycle. This may be illustrated as follows:

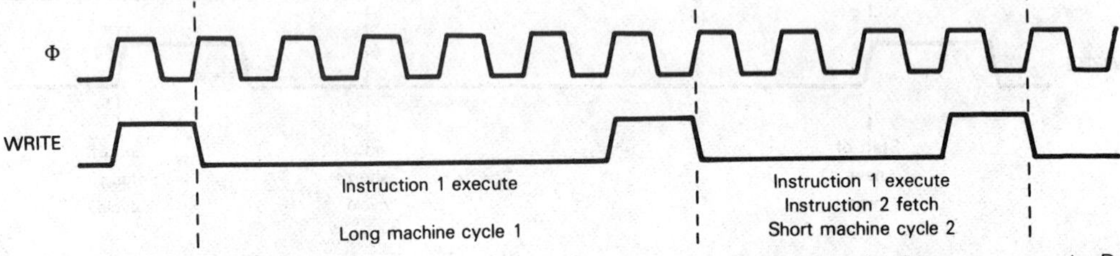


If for any reason data is to be transferred via the Data Bus during a machine cycle, then the data appears on the Data Bus at some time which depends on the data source or destination. For details, see the data sheets at the end of this chapter. There are no accompanying control signals since none are needed; the ROMC state identifies events which are occurring. Timing for any machine cycle that involves data transfer via the Data Bus may be illustrated as follows:

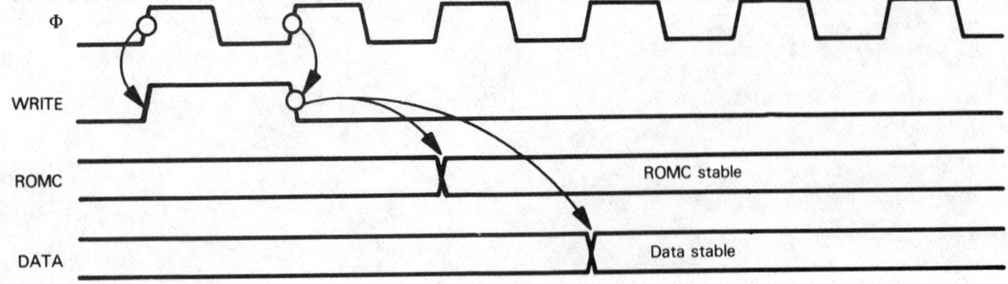

## F8 I/O PORTS

**Logic associated with each F8 I/O port pin may be illustrated as follows:**

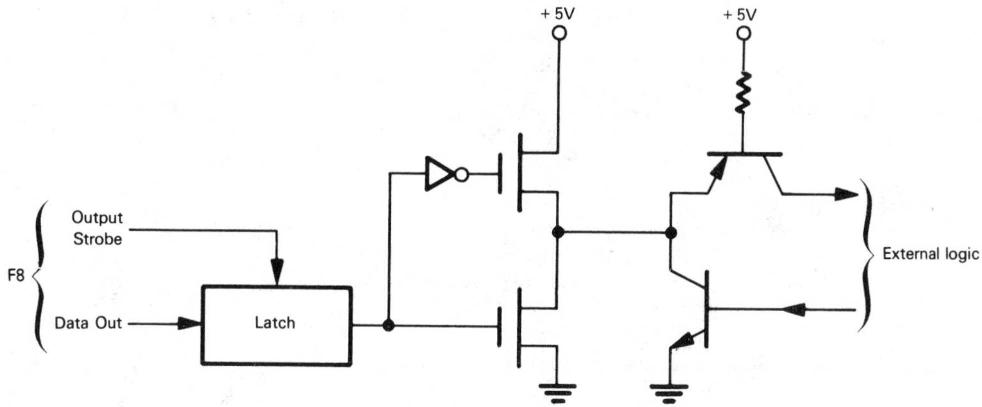


The characteristics of F8 I/O port pins differ markedly from the 3870. The only point of similarity is the fact that both have inverse logic; when you output a 1-bit, 0V is output to external logic; when you write a 0-bit, a +5V voltage is output to external logic. Conversely, external logic must input 0V for a 1 input bit and +5V for a 0 input bit.

On reset or power up, F8 I/O port pins are indeterminate. You must therefore start every Reset instruction sequence with instructions that initialize all I/O port pins. In contrast, the 3870 clears I/O Port 4 and 5 pins on reset; this generates +5V outputs since logic is inverted.

When using 3870 or F8 I/O ports, the following restrictions apply:

1) You must write 0 to every I/O port pin that is to receive data input. This is because external logic cannot write a 0 to any I/O port pin that previously had a 1 bit output by the CPU.
2) The CPU cannot output a 0 bit (+5V output) to an I/O port pin if the pin is connected to external logic that is inputting a 1 bit (0V input).

## A SUMMARY OF F8 INTERRUPT PROCESSING

**The interrupt handling capabilities of the F8 system are described with the 3851 PSU and 3853 SMI devices. Although many different interrupt priority arbitration schemes could be implemented, the simplest scheme would be to daisy chain 3851 PSUs, terminating the daisy chain with a 3853 SMI if present.**

As soon as an interrupt is acknowledged, the contents of Program Counters (PC0) are saved in Stack registers (PC1); then an interrupt vector address is loaded into the Program Counters. This address is a permanent mask option for PSUs, with the exception of bit 7, which discriminates between timer interrupts and external interrupts. The interrupt address vector is completely programmable for the 3853 SMI, again with the exception of bit 7, which discriminates between timer interrupts and external device interrupts.

Post-interrupt housekeeping operations must be handled via an appropriate program. Defining just what this program consists of is not simple; an F8 system has only the Accumulator and Status register which must be saved, but at the other extreme, it has the entire scratchpad which could be saved.

## THE F8 INSTRUCTION SET

**The F8 and 3870 instruction sets are identical; for details see Table 2-1 and associated text.**

## THE BENCHMARK PROGRAM

**Now consider our benchmark program; for the F8 it looks like this:**

```
        DCI    TABLE   LOAD TABLE BASE ADDRESS
        LM             LOAD DISPLACEMENT TO FIRST FREE BYTE
        ADC            ADD TO BASE ADDRESS
        XDC            SAVE THIS ADDRESS IN DC1
        DCI    IOBUF   LOAD I/O BUFFER BASE ADDRESS
LOOP    LM             LOAD NEXT BYTE FROM I/O BUFFER
        XDC            SWITCH ADDRESSES
        ST             STORE IN NEXT BYTE OF TABLE
        XDC            SWITCH ADDRESSES
        DS     0       DECREMENT I/O BUFFER LENGTH
        BNZ    LOOP    RETURN IF NOT END
        LR     H,DC    IF END, STORE SECOND BYTE OF CURRENT
        LR     A,HL    TABLE ADDRESS AS DISPLACEMENT TO
        DCI    TABLE   FIRST FREE BYTE
        ST
```

**The benchmark program above makes the following assumptions:**

1) The I/O buffer can be located anywhere in read/write memory.
2) The number of occupied bytes in the I/O buffer is maintained in scratchpad byte 0. Thus, decrementing scratchpad byte 0 to zero provides the I/O buffer length.
3) The permanent data table beginning memory address has all 0s for the low-order eight bits:

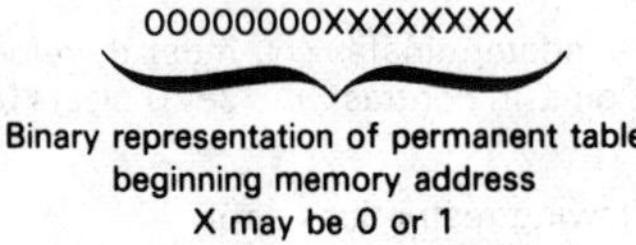


Binary representation of permanent table beginning memory address
X may be 0 or 1

The table is not more than 256 bytes long, and the displacement to the first free byte is stored in the first byte of the table. Since the table beginning address has 0s in the low-order eight bits, the displacement to the first free byte also becomes the low-order eight bits of the first free byte address:

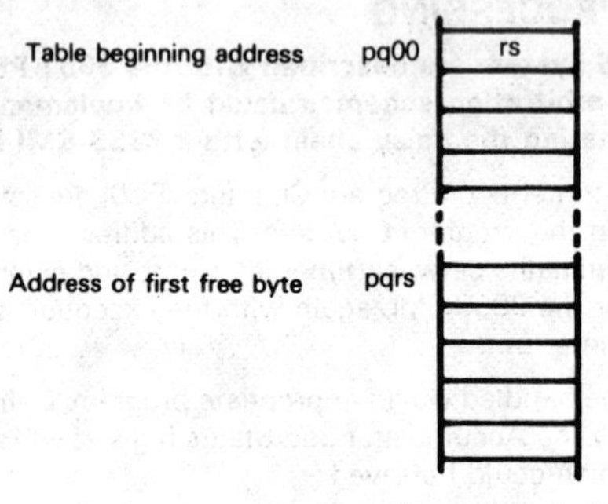


pq and rs are hexadecimal digits

All of the above assumptions are valid — and, depending upon the application, may also be realistic. Removing any of the above assumptions will make the F8 program longer, by removing one of the inherent strengths of the F8 instruction set.

# THE 3851 PROGRAM STORAGE UNIT (PSU)

**The 3851 PSU has been the principal read-only memory program storage device in small F8 microcomputer systems. In addition to providing 1024 bytes of read-only memory, the 3851 PSU has two 8-bit I/O ports, a programmable timer, and interrupt logic.**

**The 3851 PSU can also be used in non-F8 microcomputer systems.** The most important and non-obvious advantage of including a 3851 PSU in a non-F8 microcomputer system is the fact that 3851 PSU memory will lie outside of the microcomputer address space. This is because the 3851 PSU relies on its own memory addressing logic, which exists independent of and parallel to any other memory addressing logic.

Figure 2-7 illustrates functions provided by the 3851 PSU. Device pins and signals are given in Figure 2-8. Pins and signals which are unique to the 3851 PSU are described as part of the general 3851 PSU discussion.

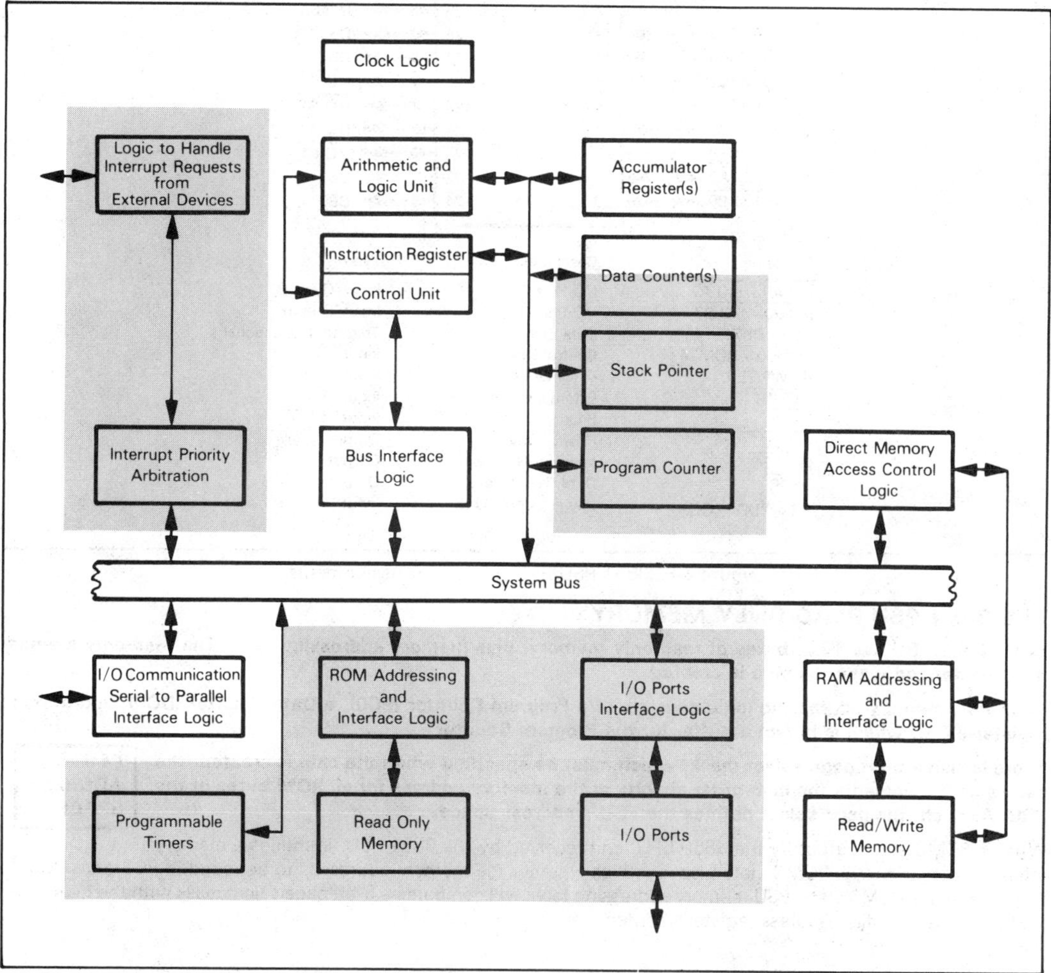


Figure 2-7. Logic of the Fairchild F8 3851, 3856 and 3857 Programmable Storage Unit

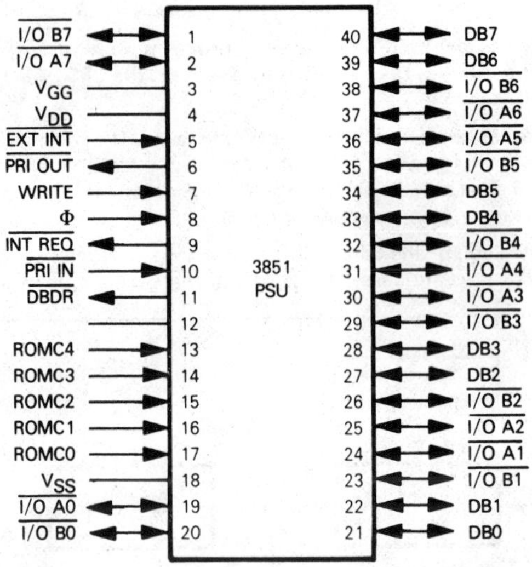

| Signal | Pin | 3851 PSU | Pin | Signal |
|---|---|---|---|---|
| $\overline{\text{I/O B7}}$ | 1 | | 40 | DB7 |
| $\overline{\text{I/O A7}}$ | 2 | | 39 | DB6 |
| $V_{GG}$ | 3 | | 38 | $\overline{\text{I/O B6}}$ |
| $V_{DD}$ | 4 | | 37 | $\overline{\text{I/O A6}}$ |
| $\overline{\text{EXT INT}}$ | 5 | | 36 | $\overline{\text{I/O A5}}$ |
| $\overline{\text{PRI OUT}}$ | 6 | | 35 | $\overline{\text{I/O B5}}$ |
| WRITE | 7 | | 34 | DB5 |
| Φ | 8 | | 33 | DB4 |
| $\overline{\text{INT REQ}}$ | 9 | | 32 | $\overline{\text{I/O B4}}$ |
| $\overline{\text{PRI IN}}$ | 10 | 3851 | 31 | $\overline{\text{I/O A4}}$ |
| $\overline{\text{DBDR}}$ | 11 | PSU | 30 | $\overline{\text{I/O A3}}$ |
| | 12 | | 29 | $\overline{\text{I/O B3}}$ |
| ROMC4 | 13 | | 28 | DB3 |
| ROMC3 | 14 | | 27 | DB2 |
| ROMC2 | 15 | | 26 | $\overline{\text{I/O B2}}$ |
| ROMC1 | 16 | | 25 | $\overline{\text{I/O A2}}$ |
| ROMC0 | 17 | | 24 | $\overline{\text{I/O A1}}$ |
| $V_{SS}$ | 18 | | 23 | $\overline{\text{I/O B1}}$ |
| $\overline{\text{I/O A0}}$ | 19 | | 22 | DB1 |
| $\overline{\text{I/O B0}}$ | 20 | | 21 | DB0 |

| Pin Name | Description | Type |
|---|---|---|
| $\overline{\text{I/O A0}}$ - $\overline{\text{I/O A7}}$ | I/O Port A | Input/Output |
| $\overline{\text{I/O B0}}$ - $\overline{\text{I/O B7}}$ | I/O Port B | Input/Output |
| DB0 - DB7 | Data Bus | Tristate, Bidirectional |
| ROMC0 - ROMC4 | Control Lines | Input |
| Φ, $\overline{\text{WRITE}}$ | Clock Lines | Input |
| $\overline{\text{EXT INT}}$ | External Interrupt | Input |
| $\overline{\text{PRI IN}}$ | Priority In | Input |
| $\overline{\text{PRI OUT}}$ | Priority Out | Output |
| $\overline{\text{INT REQ}}$ | Interrupt Request | Output |
| $\overline{\text{DBDR}}$ | Data Bus Drive | Output |
| $V_{SS}$, $V_{DD}$, $V_{GG}$ | Power Supply Lines | Input |

Figure 2-8. 3851 PSU Signals and Pin Assignments

## THE 3851 PSU READ-ONLY MEMORY

**Every 3851 PSU has 1024 bytes of read-only memory, plus memory addressing logic. The read-only memory must be defined when the chip is created.**

**3851 PSU memory addressing logic consists of a Program Counter (PC0), a Data Counter (DC0), and a Stack register (PC1), which is in fact a buffer for the Program Counter.**

**PSU ADDRESS SPACE**

**There is also a 6-bit page select mask, which must be specified when the chip is created; the page select represents the high-order six bits of the memory address for all ROM bytes of the PSU. As such, the page select defines the PSU's address space.**

When a ROMC state output by the 3850 CPU, and received by the 3851 PSU, identifies a memory reference operation, the ROMC state also identifies whether the memory address is to be found in PC0 or in DC0. In response to this ROMC state, PSU memory addressing logic will compare its 6-bit page select mask with the high-order six bits of the specified Address register's contents:

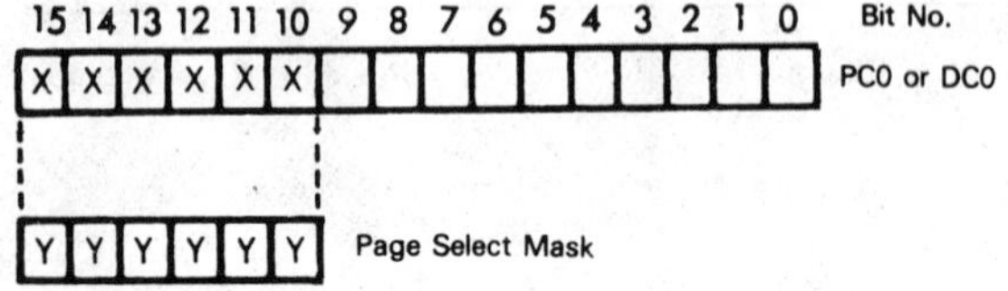

If there is coincidence, the 3851 PSU will respond to the memory reference operation; if there is no coincidence, the 3851 PSU addressing logic modifies the contents of Address registers, as might be required by the ROMC state, but it does not respond to the actual memory reference instruction.

## 3851 PSU INPUT/OUTPUT LOGIC

**Every 3851 PSU has four I/O port addresses assigned to it. These four I/O ports have addresses which are specified via a 6-bit I/O port address mask,** which you must define when you order a 3851 PSU. This mask is interpreted as the 6 high-order bits of an 8-bit I/O port address. These are the four addressable I/O ports:

| I/O port address mask: | XXXXXX | |
|---|---|---|
| | XXXXXX00 | I/O Port A |
| | XXXXXX01 | I/O Port B |
| | XXXXXX10 | Interrupt control port |
| | XXXXXX11 | Programmable Timer register |

Suppose the 6-bit I/O port mask is specified as $000011_2$. I/O Ports $0C_{16}$, $0D_{16}$, $0E_{16}$ and $0F_{16}$ will then be selected.

An I/O port mask of 000000 is illegal, since I/O port addresses 0 and 1 are reserved for the two 3850 CPU I/O ports.

**The two 8-bit I/O ports of a 3851 PSU are identical to the 3850 CPU I/O ports** which we have already described, except for one detail: **there are three optional I/O port pin logic configurations available with a 3851 PSU.**

The first option is the standard configuration which we described for the 3850 CPU I/O port pins.

The second option is open drain configuration, which may be illustrated as follows:

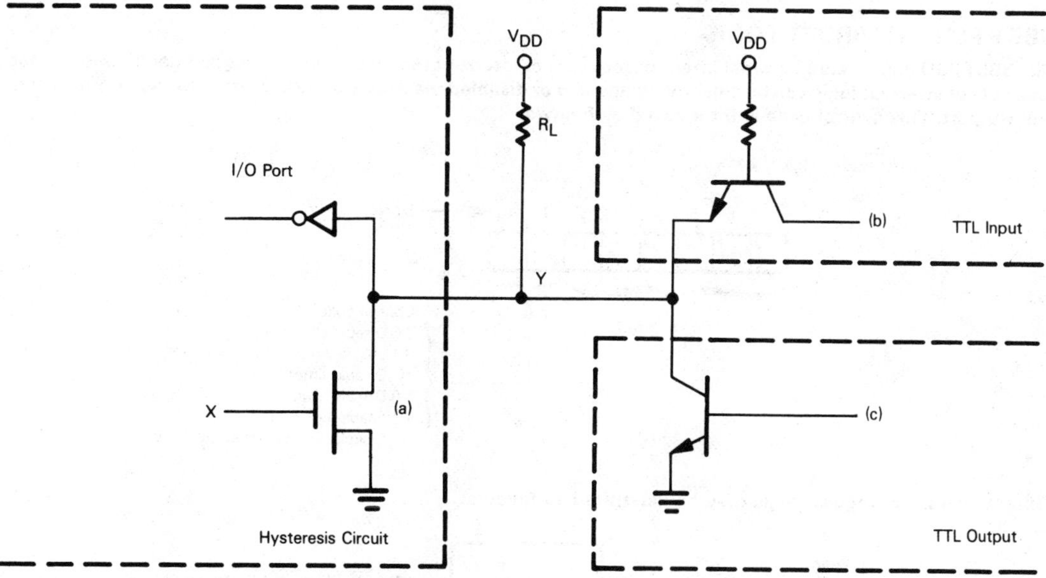


This open drain configuration allows you to wire-OR outputs from a number of pins.

The third option is a driver pull-up configuration designed specifically to drive LED displays. This configuration may be illustrated as follows:

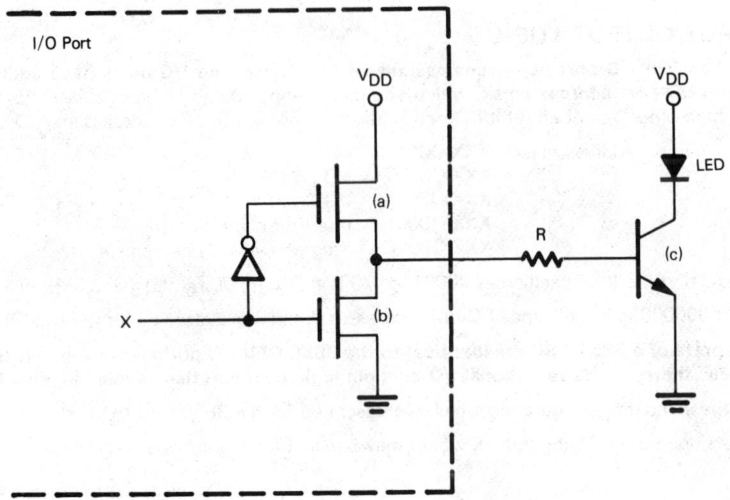


## 3851 PSU INTERRUPT LOGIC

**The 3851 PSU can receive external interrupt requests or interrupt requests from its programmable timer. These two sets of interrupt logic can be selectively enabled or disabled via a control code written to the interrupt control I/O port. This control code is interpreted as follows:**

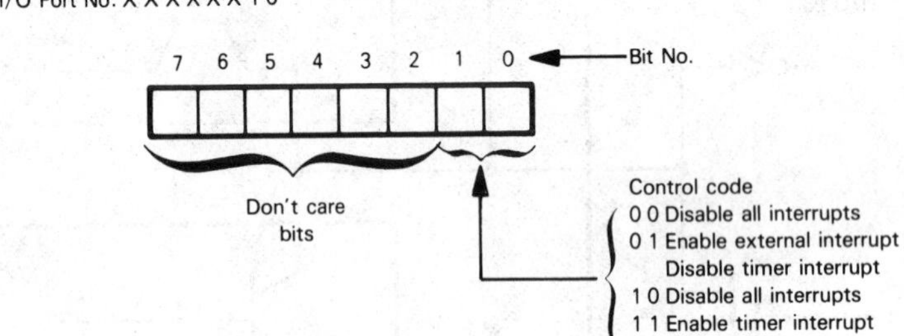


**External interrupt request logic may be illustrated as follows:**

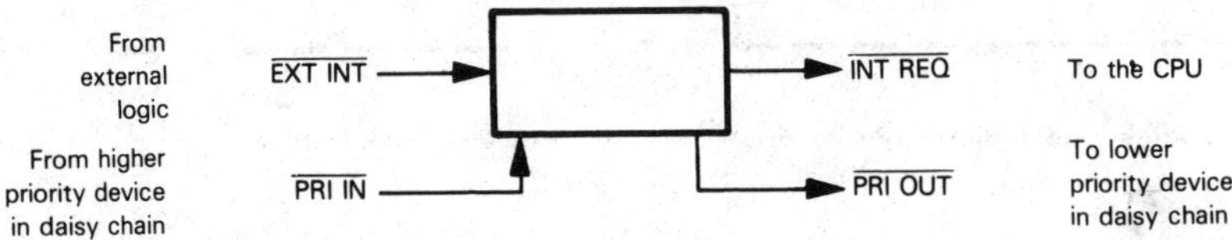


An external interrupt request is generated by external logic pulling $\overline{\text{EXT INT}}$ low. The interrupt request will be passed on to the CPU by outputting $\overline{\text{INT REQ}}$ low, providing these two conditions are met:

1) External interrupts have been enabled via the interrupt control code (01 in the two low-order bits).

2) The $\overline{\text{PRI IN}}$ signal is low.

If $\overline{EXT\ INT}$ is low and external interrupts are enabled, an interrupt is being requested; whether or not it is acknowledged, $\overline{PRI\ OUT}$ is output high. The combination of the $\overline{PRI\ IN}$ and $\overline{PRI\ OUT}$ signals is designed to implement daisy chain interrupt priority logic, which may be illustrated as follows:

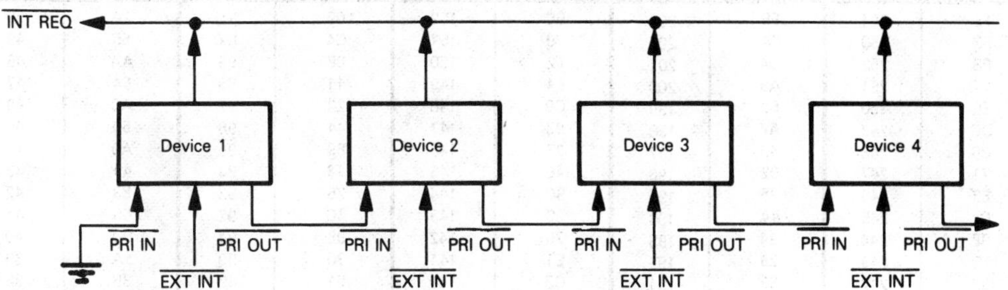


When an active interrupt request occurs at one device, outputting PRI OUT high disables external interrupt logic at all lower priority devices in the daisy chain.

**An interval timer interrupt request is generated when the programmable timer I/O port decrements to zero.** This interrupt request will be acknowledged if programmable timer interrupts have been enabled via the interrupt control I/O port (11 in the two low-order bits).

There is no priority arbitration between external interrupts and programmable timer interrupts, since one or the other but not both can be enabled at any time.

**When the CPU acknowledges an interrupt request, the 3851 PSU responds by saving Program Counter (PC0) contents in the Stack register (PC1), then loading an interrupt service routine starting address into the Program Counter (PC0). This interrupt service routine starting address is a mask option which you must specify when ordering the 3851 PSU. One bit of the interrupt address vector (it is bit 7) is set aside to identify the interrupt request as external or as coming from the programmable timer.** This may be illustrated as follows:

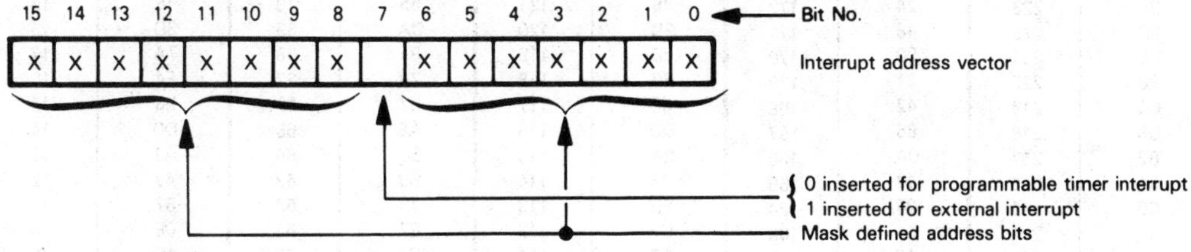


The actual interrupt response sequence consists of five machine cycles, during which ROMC states are output in the order $10_{16}$, $1C_{16}$, $0F_{16}$, $13_{16}$, $00_{16}$. Table 2-4 identifies functions performed in response to each ROMC state.

Table 2-5. Relationship Between Programmable Timer Contents and Effective Timer Counts

| TIMER CONTENTS | TIMER COUNTS | TIMER CONTENTS | TIMER COUNTS | TIMER CONTENTS | TIMER COUNTS | TIMER CONTENTS | TIMER COUNTS | TIMER CONTENTS | TIMER COUNTS |
|---|---|---|---|---|---|---|---|---|---|
| FE | 254 | F5 | 203 | BC | 152 | 62 | 101 | 2A | 50 |
| FD | 253 | EA | 202 | 79 | 151 | C4 | 100 | 55 | 49 |
| FB | 252 | D4 | 201 | F2 | 150 | 88 | 99 | AA | 48 |
| F7 | 251 | A9 | 200 | E4 | 149 | 11 | 98 | 54 | 47 |
| EE | 250 | 52 | 199 | C9 | 148 | 22 | 97 | A8 | 46 |
| DC | 249 | A4 | 198 | 93 | 147 | 44 | 96 | 50 | 45 |
| B8 | 248 | 49 | 197 | 27 | 146 | 89 | 95 | A0 | 44 |
| 71 | 247 | 92 | 196 | 4E | 145 | 13 | 94 | 41 | 43 |
| E3 | 246 | 25 | 195 | 9C | 144 | 26 | 93 | 83 | 42 |
| C7 | 245 | 4A | 194 | 38 | 143 | 4C | 92 | 06 | 41 |
| 8E | 244 | 94 | 193 | 70 | 142 | 98 | 91 | 0D | 40 |
| 1D | 243 | 29 | 192 | E1 | 141 | 30 | 90 | 1A | 39 |
| 3B | 242 | 53 | 191 | C3 | 140 | 61 | 89 | 35 | 38 |
| 76 | 241 | A6 | 190 | 86 | 139 | C2 | 88 | 6B | 37 |
| ED | 240 | 4D | 189 | 0C | 138 | 84 | 87 | D7 | 36 |
| DA | 239 | 9A | 188 | 18 | 137 | 08 | 86 | AF | 35 |
| B4 | 238 | 34 | 187 | 31 | 136 | 10 | 85 | 5E | 34 |
| 68 | 237 | 69 | 186 | 63 | 135 | 20 | 84 | BD | 33 |
| D1 | 236 | D3 | 185 | C6 | 134 | 40 | 83 | 7B | 32 |
| A3 | 235 | A7 | 184 | 8C | 133 | 81 | 82 | F6 | 31 |
| 47 | 234 | 4F | 183 | 19 | 132 | 02 | 81 | EC | 30 |
| 8F | 233 | 9E | 182 | 33 | 131 | 05 | 80 | D8 | 29 |
| 1F | 232 | 3C | 181 | 67 | 130 | 0B | 79 | B0 | 28 |
| 3F | 231 | 78 | 180 | CE | 129 | 16 | 78 | 60 | 27 |
| 7E | 230 | F0 | 179 | 9D | 128 | 2C | 77 | C0 | 26 |
| FC | 229 | E0 | 178 | 3A | 127 | 59 | 76 | 80 | 25 |
| F9 | 228 | C1 | 177 | 74 | 126 | B3 | 75 | 00 | 24 |
| F3 | 227 | 82 | 176 | E9 | 125 | 66 | 74 | 01 | 23 |
| E6 | 226 | 04 | 175 | D2 | 124 | CC | 73 | 03 | 22 |
| CD | 225 | 09 | 174 | A5 | 123 | 99 | 72 | 07 | 21 |
| 9B | 224 | 12 | 173 | 4B | 122 | 32 | 71 | 0F | 20 |
| 36 | 223 | 24 | 172 | 96 | 121 | 65 | 70 | 1E | 19 |
| 6D | 222 | 48 | 171 | 2D | 120 | CA | 69 | 3D | 18 |
| DB | 221 | 90 | 170 | 5B | 119 | 95 | 68 | 7A | 17 |
| B6 | 220 | 21 | 169 | B7 | 118 | 2B | 67 | F4 | 16 |
| 6C | 219 | 42 | 168 | 6E | 117 | 57 | 66 | E8 | 15 |
| D9 | 218 | 85 | 167 | DD | 116 | AE | 65 | D0 | 14 |
| B2 | 217 | 0A | 166 | BA | 115 | 5C | 64 | A1 | 13 |
| 64 | 216 | 14 | 165 | 75 | 114 | B9 | 63 | 43 | 12 |
| C8 | 215 | 28 | 164 | EB | 113 | 73 | 62 | 87 | 11 |
| 91 | 214 | 51 | 163 | D6 | 112 | E7 | 61 | 0E | 10 |
| 23 | 213 | A2 | 162 | AD | 111 | CF | 60 | 1C | 9 |
| 46 | 212 | 45 | 161 | 5A | 110 | 9F | 59 | 39 | 8 |
| 8D | 211 | 8B | 160 | B5 | 109 | 3E | 58 | 72 | 7 |
| 1B | 210 | 17 | 159 | 6A | 108 | 7C | 57 | E5 | 6 |
| 37 | 209 | 2E | 158 | D5 | 107 | F8 | 56 | CB | 5 |
| 6F | 208 | 5D | 157 | AB | 106 | F1 | 55 | 97 | 4 |
| DF | 207 | BB | 156 | 56 | 105 | E2 | 54 | 2F | 3 |
| BE | 206 | 77 | 155 | AC | 104 | C5 | 53 | 5F | 2 |
| 7D | 205 | EF | 154 | 58 | 103 | 8A | 52 | BF | 1 |
| FA | 204 | DE | 153 | B1 | 102 | 15 | 51 | 7F | 0 |

Timer counts are decimal numbers
Timer contents are hexadecimal numbers

## 3851 PSU PROGRAMMABLE TIMER LOGIC

**The 3851 PSU has a single programmable timer which is addressed as the fourth I/O port (XXXXXX11$_2$).** This timer is free running unless it contains the value FF$_{16}$. **The value FF$_{16}$ stops the timer.**

**The interval timer is a polynomial shift register. Table 2-5 gives the correlation between timer counts and timer register contents.**

The programmable timer decrements once every 31 clock periods. Using a 500 nanosecond clock, therefore, the timer register will decrement once every 15.5 microseconds.

In order to generate any specific time interval, you must load an initial value into the programmable timer register by outputting the appropriate timer contents to the programmable timer I/O port address. For example, in order to have an initial value of 100$_{16}$, you must load the programmable timer I/O port with the value C4$_{16}$. Loading the programmable timer with the initial value 28$_{16}$ will generate an initial count of 164$_{10}$. These correlations can be read off Table 2-5.

Once the programmable timer times out, it reloads the value FE$_{16}$, representing 254$_{10}$ counts, and starts to decrement again.

## 3851 PSU DATA TRANSFER TIMING

**When data is input to the 3851 PSU from the Data Bus, no control signals are needed** since the ROMC state signals identify the presence of data on the Data Bus. **When data is output by the 3851 PSU, however, the control output DBDR is low.** Timing may be illustrated as follows:

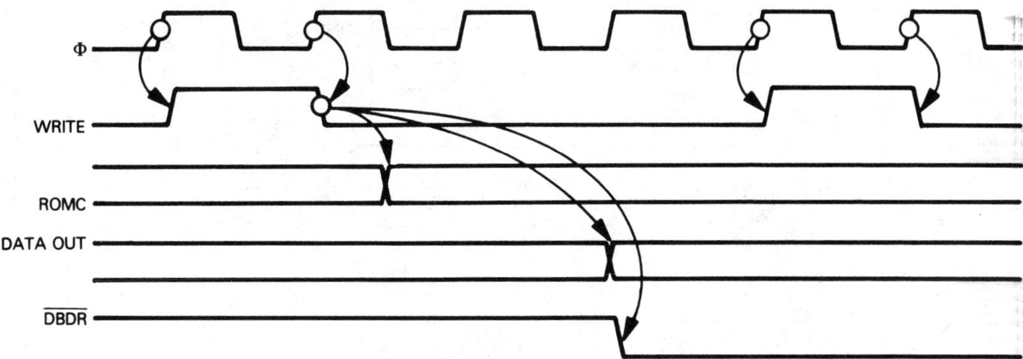


The purpose of the low $\overline{DBDR}$ signal is to prevent Data Bus contentions from ever arising. This is also a very useful signal in non-F8 microcomputer systems that include a 3851 PSU, since it can be used as a data read strobe.

## USING THE 3851 PSU IN NON-F8 CONFIGURATIONS

**The 3851 PSU is easily included in non-F8 microcomputer configurations. The trick is to generate ROMC states as memory addresses. A ROMC state of 1C idles the 3851 PSU.** Appropriate logic is illustrated in Figure 2-9.

Let us consider some examples. For simplicity, we will use 8080A assembly language mnemonics and assume that the 3851 PSU is selected by addresses FFED$_{16}$ through FFFF$_{16}$. This is how data input and data output via 3851 PSU I/O ports could be implemented, in conjunction with the logic of Figure 2-9:

| F8 Instructions | | ROMC States | 8080A Instructions | |
|---|---|---|---|---|
| IN | PORT | 03 | MVI | A,PORT |
| | | 1B | STA | 0FFE3H |
| | | 00 | LDA | 0FFFBH |
| OUT | PORT | 03 | MVI | A,PORT |
| | | 1A | LXI | 0FFFAH |
| | | | MVI | B,DATA |
| | | | STA | 0FFE3H |
| | | | MOV | M,B |

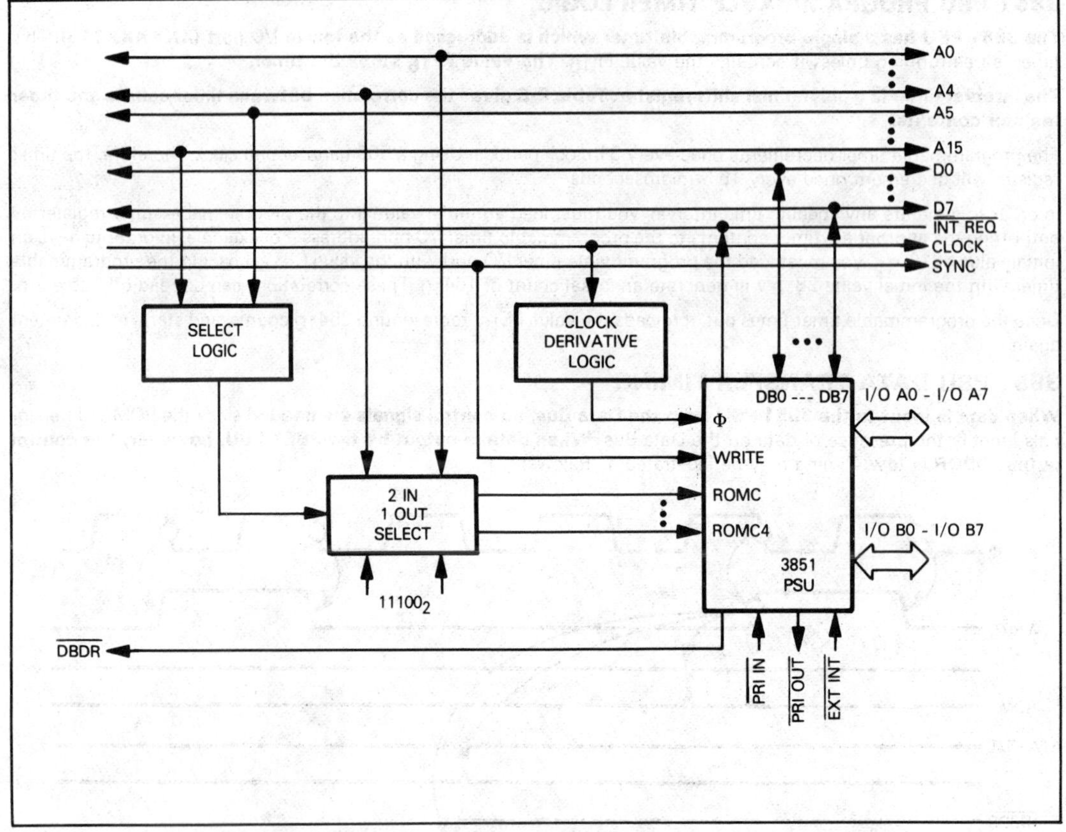


Figure 2-9. Conceptual Logic to Include a 3851 PSU in a Non-F8 Microcomputer System

**Possibly the most useful application for a 3851 PSU in some other microcomputer system would be to implement lookup tables.** The 1024 bytes of read-only memory could store data tables of that size. The Program Counter and Data Counter are active Address registers which can be used to identify the location which must be looked up.

By way of illustration, consider a decimal multiplication table look-up program. 100 bytes of read-only memory could be set aside to store the product of any two single decimal digits. This may be illustrated as follows:

Memory location: 00---09 10 11 12---19 20 21 22---29 30 31 etc.
Contents: 00---00 00 01 02---09 00 02 04---18 00 03 etc.

Now, in order to compute any decimal multiplication, the two decimal digits are loaded into the eight low-order Data Counter bits; the contents of the memory location addressed by the Data Counter are then read. Again assuming that the 3851 PSU is selected by memory addresses $FFED_{16}$ through $FFFF_{16}$, and using 8080A assembly language mnemonics in conjunction with Figure 2-9, appropriate instructions may be illustrated as follows:

| ROMC States | 8080A Instructions | |
|---|---|---|
| 19 | | |
| 02 | MVI | 46H |
| | STA | 0FFF9H |
| | LDA | 0FFE2H |

These instructions seek 4 x 6; 24 will be returned to the Accumulator.

These are just some conceptual examples of how the 3851 PSU can be used in non-F8 configurations. Clearly, the specific microprocessor being used to drive the 3851 PSU will have a significant influence on the exact interface used and the 3851 logic capabilities which are or are not accessible.

## THE 3861 AND 3871 PARALLEL I/O (PIO) DEVICES

**The 3861 PIO contains the I/O ports, programmable timer, and interrupt logic of the 3851 PSU. This device contains no memory; it is otherwise identical to the 3851 PSU. Figure 2-8 provides 3861 PIO signals and pin assignments.**

**The 3871 has the I/O ports, timer/counter and interrupt logic of the 3870 single-chip microcomputer. 3871 PIO signals and pin assignments are identical to the 3851 PSU illustrated in Figure 2-8, with the exception that the 3870 STROBE signal associated with I/O Port 4 is output at pin 12.**

## THE 3856 AND 3857 16K PROGRAMMABLE STORAGE UNITS (16K PSU)

**These two devices are enhancements of and replacements for the 3851 PSU which we have just described.**

Superficially, Figure 2-7 represents the logic implemented on all three PSUs — the 3851, 3856 and 3857. **Table 2-6 summarizes the differences between the devices. These are the most significant features of the 3856 and 3857 PSUs:**

1) RESET sets all I/O port pins and address lines to zero. In the 3851, PSU RESET leaves I/O port pins indeterminate — and this has caused problems in many applications.
2) The interval timers of the 3856 and 3857 PSUs are binary decrementers rather than polynomial shifters — with the result that you can read timer contents directly and determine lapsed times. Also, a programmable option allows you to measure pulse widths being input to the PSU.
3) The 3857 PSU uses the 16 pins of the two 8-bit I/O ports for 16 address lines, so that additional ROM or RAM can be interfaced directly to a 3857 PSU — without requiring a 3852 DMI or 3853 SMI, as was the case with the 3851 PSU.
4) The 3856 and 3857 PSUs both provide 2K bytes of ROM for program storage; this is twice the program memory available on the 3851 PSU. This significantly increases the scope of two-device F8 microcomputer systems.

Figures 2-10 and 2-11 illustrate the pins and signals of the 3856 and 3857 16K PSUs respectively.

Table 2-6. A Summary of Differences Between 3851, 3856 and 3857 PSUs

| FUNCTION | 3851 PSU | 3856 PSU | 3857 PSU |
|---|---|---|---|
| ROM | 1024 bytes | 2048 bytes | 2048 bytes |
| I/O Ports | 2 x 8 bits | 2 x 8 bits | None |
| Address lines | None | None | 16 |
| Interrupt signals | Priority in and Priority out | Priority in and Priority out | Priority in only. Must be end of daisy chain. |
| Interrupt options | Enable timer or external, but not both | Enable timer and/or external | Enable timer and/or external |
| Timer register | 8-bit Polynomial | 8-bit Count down | 8-bit Count down |
| Timer decrement interval | 31 clock cycles | 2, 8, 32 or 128 clock cycles | 2, 8, 32 or 128 clock cycles |
| Timer stop/start control | No | Yes | Yes |
| Timer readback | No | Yes | Yes |
| Timer read pulse width? | No | Yes | Yes |
| RESET zero I/O ports? | No | Yes | No I/O ports |

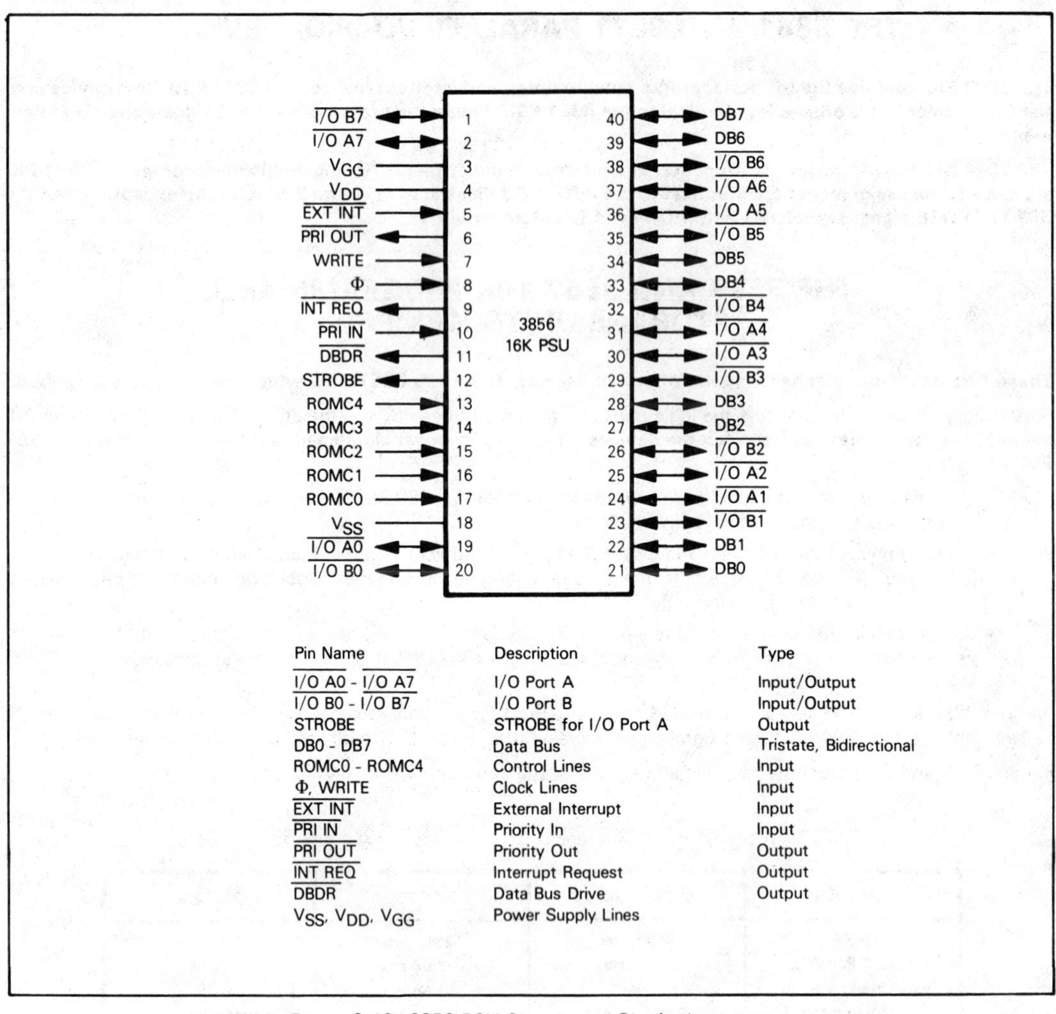


| Pin Name | Description | Type |
|---|---|---|
| I/O A0 - I/O A7 | I/O Port A | Input/Output |
| I/O B0 - I/O B7 | I/O Port B | Input/Output |
| STROBE | STROBE for I/O Port A | Output |
| DB0 - DB7 | Data Bus | Tristate, Bidirectional |
| ROMC0 - ROMC4 | Control Lines | Input |
| Φ, WRITE | Clock Lines | Input |
| EXT INT | External Interrupt | Input |
| PRI IN | Priority In | Input |
| PRI OUT | Priority Out | Output |
| INT REQ | Interrupt Request | Output |
| DBDR | Data Bus Drive | Output |
| $V_{SS}$, $V_{DD}$, $V_{GG}$ | Power Supply Lines | |

Figure 2-10. 3856 PSU Signals and Pin Assignments

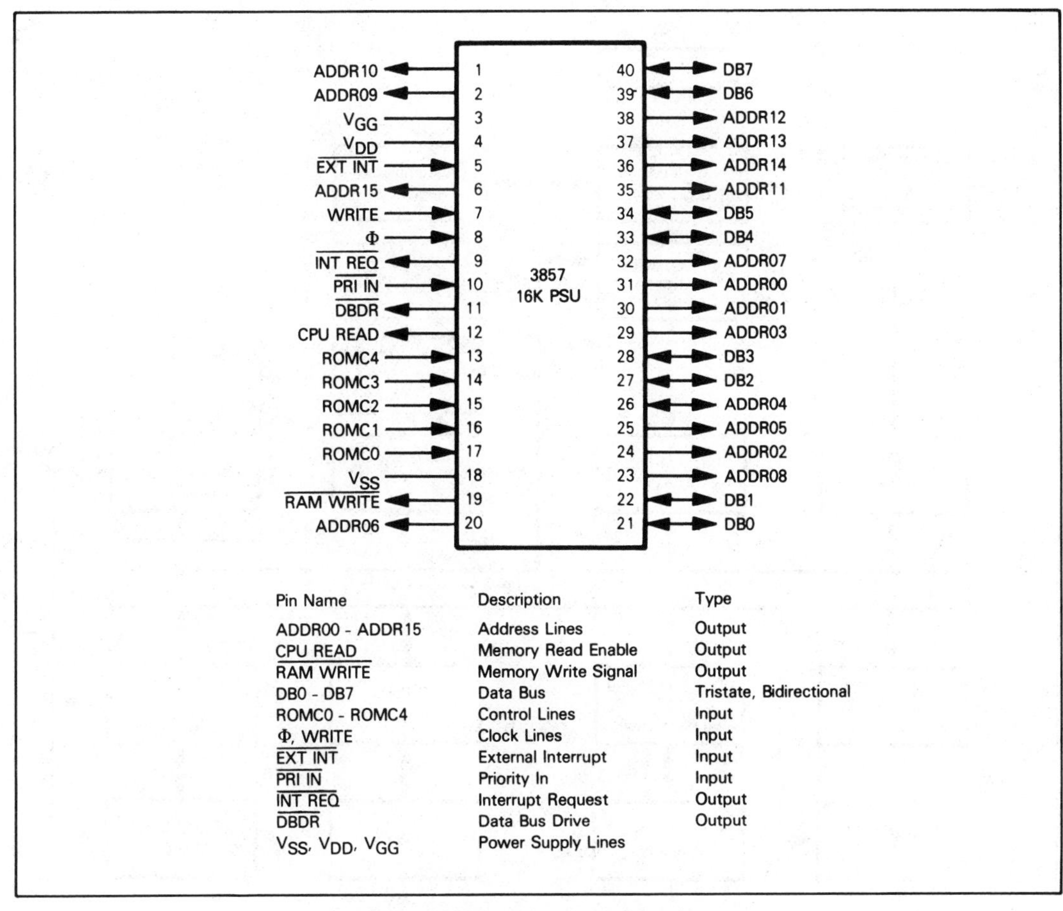


| Pin Name | Description | Type |
|---|---|---|
| ADDR00 - ADDR15 | Address Lines | Output |
| CPU READ | Memory Read Enable | Output |
| RAM WRITE | Memory Write Signal | Output |
| DB0 - DB7 | Data Bus | Tristate, Bidirectional |
| ROMC0 - ROMC4 | Control Lines | Input |
| Φ, WRITE | Clock Lines | Input |
| EXT INT | External Interrupt | Input |
| PRI IN | Priority In | Input |
| INT REQ | Interrupt Request | Output |
| DBDR | Data Bus Drive | Output |
| $V_{SS}$, $V_{DD}$, $V_{GG}$ | Power Supply Lines | |

Figure 2-11. 3857 PSU Signals and Pin Assignments

# ADDITIONAL F8 SUPPORT DEVICES

**There are three additional F8 support devices: the 3852 Dynamic Memory Interface, the 3853 Static Memory Interface, and the 3854 Direct Memory Access device. We are going to summarize these devices rather than give complete descriptions, since these devices are infrequently used.**

Only F8 configurations with a substantial amount of memory use these devices — and there are very few such F8 configurations; however, in every case there are better alternatives. For example, the 3854 Direct Memory Access device should not be used to implement direct memory access logic in non-F8 configurations; the Z80 DMA device is clearly superior. In fact, signal peculiarities and timing problems associated with the 3852 DMI, 3853 SMI and 3854 DMA devices make them unattractive components in non-F8 configurations.

If you do need to use the 3852 DMI, the 3853 SMI, or the 3854 DMA devices, you will have to refer to vendor literature, since the discussion which follows provides performance summaries only — not product detail.

## THE 3852 DYNAMIC MEMORY INTERFACE (DMI)

**Primarily, this device contains the necessary address generation and memory refresh logic needed to include dynamic read/write memory in an F8 system.**

**Because of the way in which the F8 microcomputer system is organized, however, memory refresh and direct memory access logic are closely related. That is why, in Figure 2-12, a small part of the direct memory access control logic is shown as being implemented on the 3852 DMI chip.**

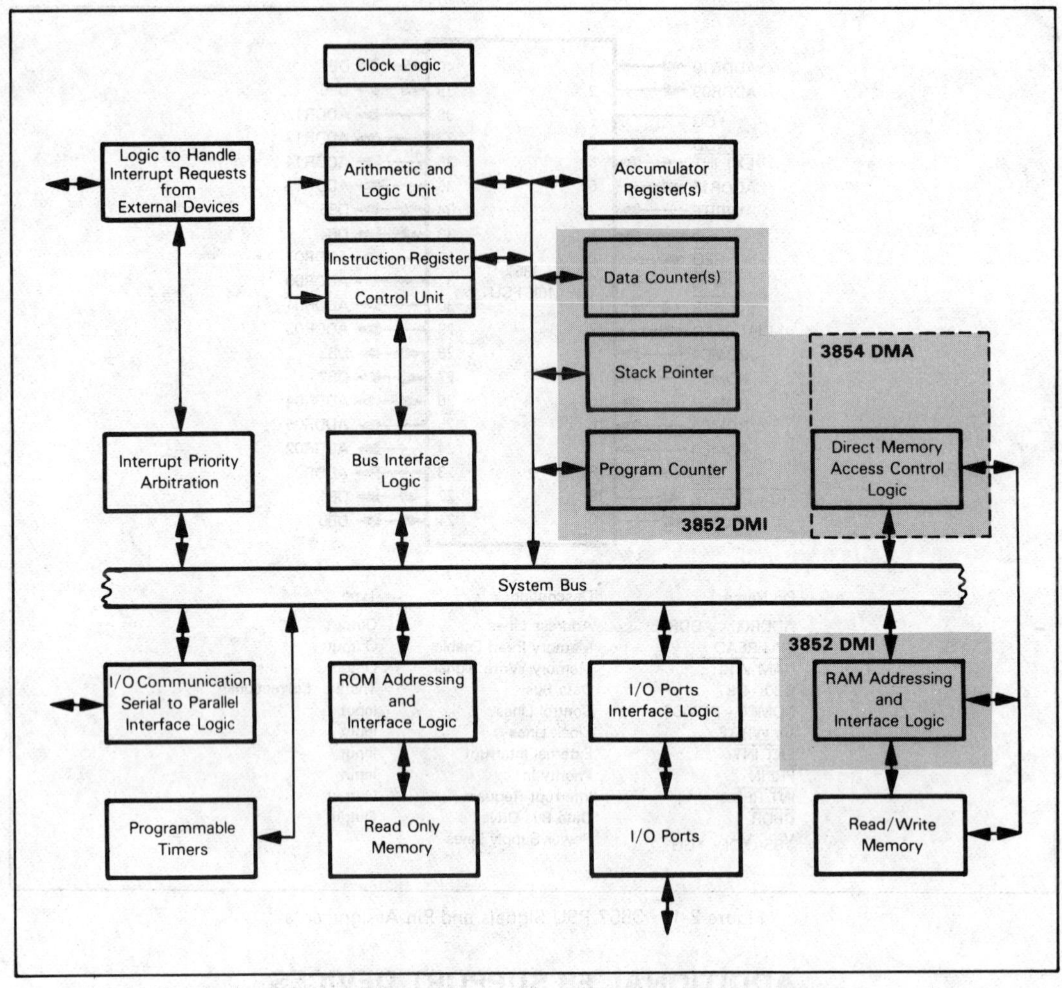


Figure 2-12. Logic of the Fairchild F8 3852 Dynamic Memory Interface (DMI), and of the 3854 Direct Memory Access (DMA) Devices

Figure 2-13 illustrates pins and signals of the 3852 DMI.

**Conceptually, memory addressing logic of the 3852 DMI is very similar to 3857 PSU memory addressing logic; there are, however, some differences between the 3852 DMI memory addressing and the 3851 or 3856 PSU:**

1) The 3852 DMI contains two Data Counters, DC0 and DC1. The presence of the auxiliary Data Counter (DC1) has no immediate impact on memory addressing logic within the 3852 DMI. However, as we discussed earlier, its presence in an F8 system that also includes a 3851 PSU calls for programming caution.

2) Data and address flows surrounding a 3852 DMI are totally unlike the 3851 or 3856 PSU. In the case of these PSUs, addresses are transmitted entirely within the logic of the PSU; the only communication needed between a PSU and the CPU is via the eight Data Bus lines of the System Bus. The DMI, on the other hand, generates a 16-bit address, which it outputs directly to the read/write memory which it is controlling.

   These address pins are equivalent to 3857 PSU address pins — that is, the address pins which a CPU would have, if the CPU contained memory addressing logic for the microcomputer system. In other words, the 3852 DMI creates the address lines and control signals, which, so far as the read/write memory is concerned, are lacking on the F8 System Bus. The F8 System Bus does, however, contain data lines needed by the read/write memory to actually transmit data to or from the CPU.

   Data and address flows around the 3852 DMI may be illustrated as follows:

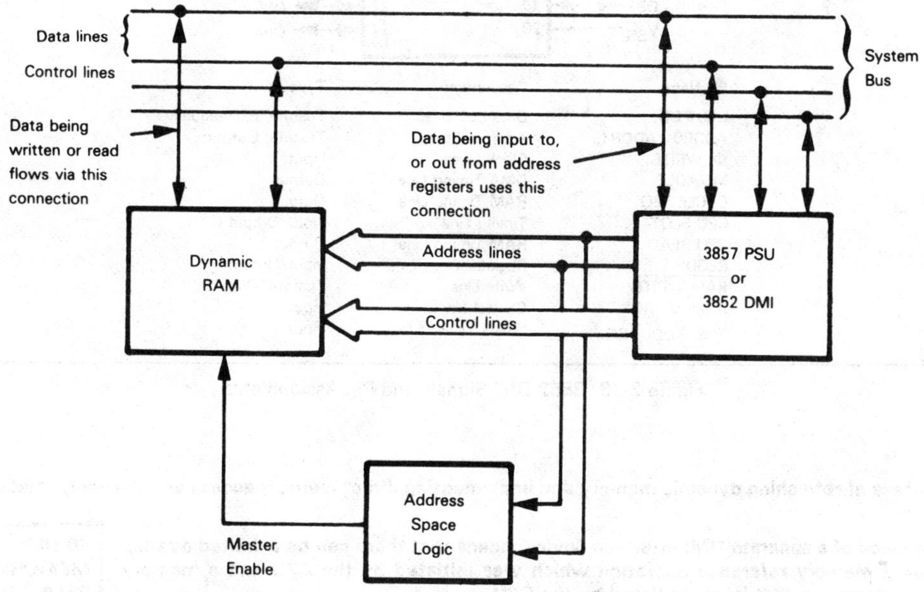


3) Unlike the 3851, 3856 or 3857 PSU, the 3852 DMI has no on-chip logic to determine address space for read/write memory which the DMI is controlling. Address space determination is made by logic in between the DMI and the read/write memory. Typically, selected high-order address lines output by the DMI are gated through elementary Boolean logic components to create the master enable signal used to strobe attached read/write memory. This is illustrated above.

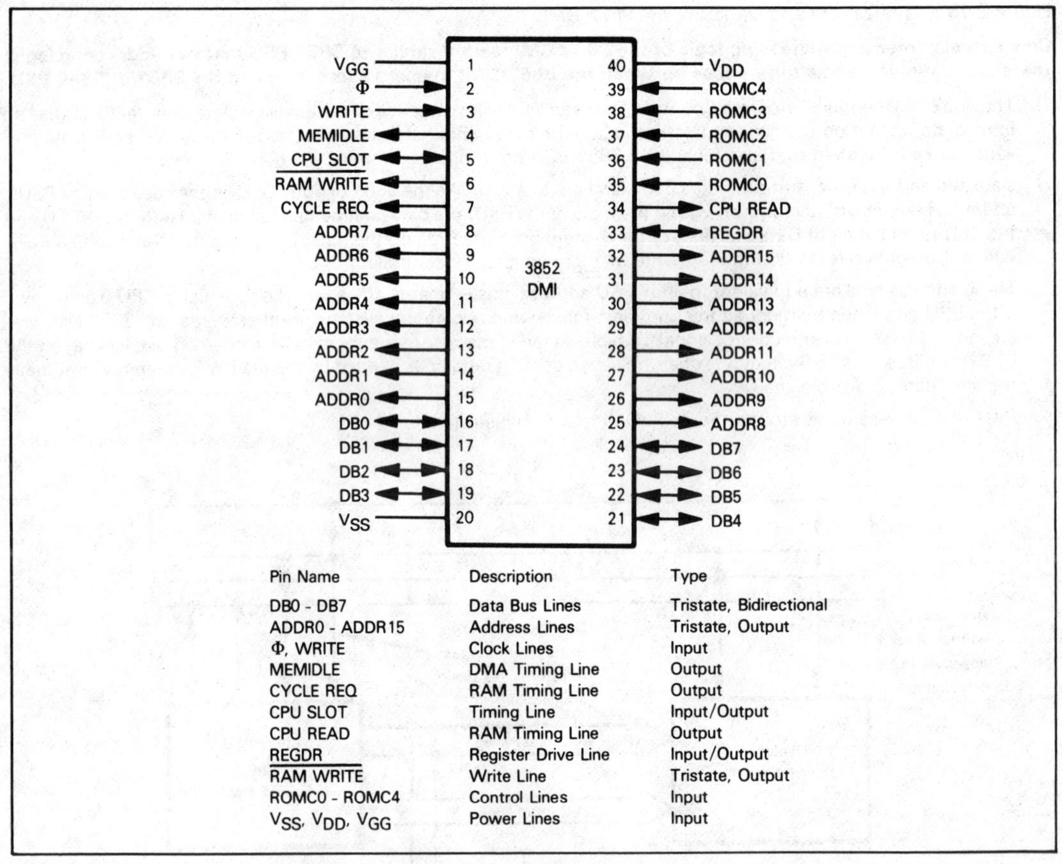


| Pin Name | Description | Type |
|---|---|---|
| DB0 - DB7 | Data Bus Lines | Tristate, Bidirectional |
| ADDR0 - ADDR15 | Address Lines | Tristate, Output |
| Φ, WRITE | Clock Lines | Input |
| MEMIDLE | DMA Timing Line | Output |
| CYCLE REQ | RAM Timing Line | Output |
| CPU SLOT | Timing Line | Input/Output |
| CPU READ | RAM Timing Line | Output |
| REGDR | Register Drive Line | Input/Output |
| RAM WRITE | Write Line | Tristate, Output |
| ROMC0 - ROMC4 | Control Lines | Input |
| $V_{SS}$, $V_{DD}$, $V_{GG}$ | Power Lines | Input |

Figure 2-13. 3852 DMI Signals and Pin Assignments

**The process of refreshing dynamic memory and implementing direct memory access are integrally related in an F8 system.**

**F8 DMI MEMORY REFRESH**

**The presence of a separate DMI interface device means that there can be a limited overlap between a memory reference operation which was initiated by the CPU and a memory reference operation that is not initiated by the CPU.**

**Two types of memory reference operations are not initiated by the CPU: memory refresh and direct memory access.**

**Let us consider how a direct memory access may follow a CPU-initiated memory read operation. These are the events which occur:**

1) Upon receiving an appropriate ROMC state from the CPU, the 3852 DMI outputs a 16-bit memory address, together with a read strobe; these outputs from the 3852 DMI are received by read/write memory.

2) Read/write memory responds by placing data directly on the Data Bus. The data must remain stable on the Data Bus until the CPU has had time to read the data.

3) While data is stable on the Data Bus, DMA logic may apply a new memory address to read/write memory. Following the arrival of address and control signals at read/write memory, there is a fixed time delay before read/write memory responds by placing data on the Data Bus. This time delay can overlap with time when prior data must be stable on the Data Bus. This may be illustrated as follows:

**F8 DIRECT MEMORY ACCESS**

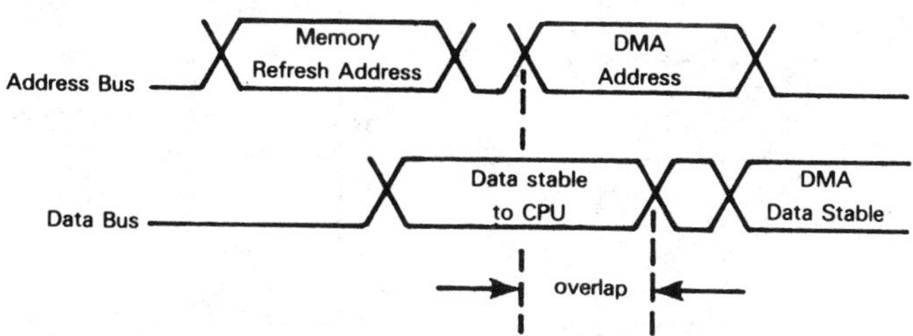


**DMI logic outputs control signals which identify the way in which each memory access period is being used;** there are three possibilities:

1) Memory is communicating with the F8 System Bus.
2) Memory is not communicating with the System Bus, but since it is dynamic memory it is being refreshed.
3) Memory is not communicating with the System Bus and is available for external access.

Cases 2 or 3 above may follow case 1 in separate memory access periods of the same instruction cycle.

## THE 3854 DIRECT MEMORY ACCESS (DMA) DEVICE

**This device receives memory access period identification signals output by the 3852 DMI. Based on the direct memory access requirements specified by the currently executing program, the DMA device accesses read/write memory, during available memory access periods, as defined by the 3852 DMI. Figure 2-14 illustrates 3854 DMA pins and signals.**

**These are the variables which must be specified for a direct memory access operation:**

1) The beginning address for the memory buffer into which data must be written, or out of which data must be read.
2) The length of the buffer.
3) Whether data is to be written or read out of the buffer.

**Once a direct memory access operation has been initiated, it proceeds in parallel with other events occurring within the F8 microcomputer system, using memory access periods which are defined by the 3852 DMI as available for direct memory access.** In other words, direct memory access operations in no way slow down program execution that may be occurring in parallel.

**DMA data transfer may be high-speed or low-speed.** Low-speed DMA transfer means that each DMA access is enabled by a signal from the external device, stating that it is ready to transmit or receive data. High-speed access assumes that the external device will always be ready to transmit or receive data; therefore, every single available memory access period is utilized.

As a direct memory access operation proceeds, after each access the memory address is incremented and the buffer length is decremented. Memory address, buffer length and DMA controls are stored in buffers which the CPU accesses as though they were I/O ports. The contents of these I/O ports may be written into, or read at any time. **This means that the F8 DMA system allows total flexibility for every type of programmable DMA operation;** these include such things as stopping a DMA operation temporarily, or interrogating a DMA operation to determine how far it has progressed.

**Indefinite DMA transfer may also be specified.** In this case, no buffer length is given; rather, the DMA operation will proceed until stopped.

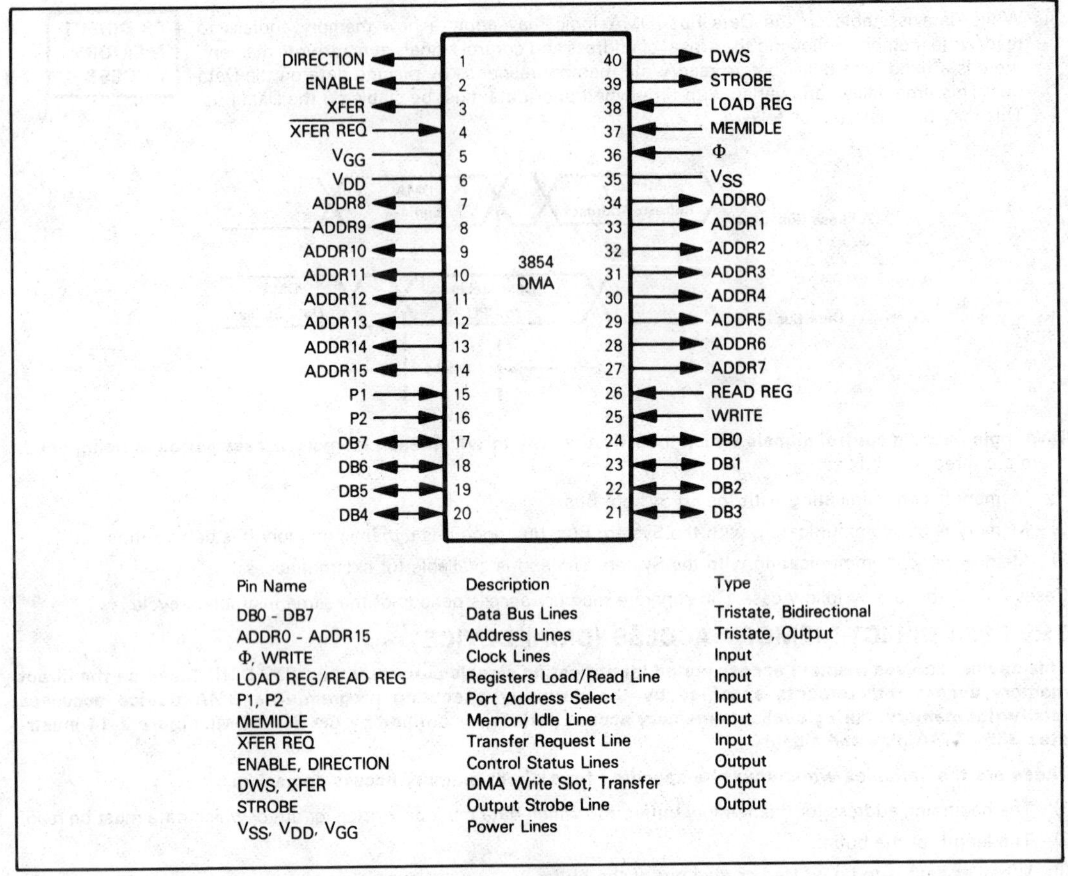


| Pin Name | Description | Type |
|---|---|---|
| DB0 - DB7 | Data Bus Lines | Tristate, Bidirectional |
| ADDR0 - ADDR15 | Address Lines | Tristate, Output |
| Φ, WRITE | Clock Lines | Input |
| LOAD REG/READ REG | Registers Load/Read Line | Input |
| P1, P2 | Port Address Select | Input |
| MEMIDLE | Memory Idle Line | Input |
| XFER REQ | Transfer Request Line | Input |
| ENABLE, DIRECTION | Control Status Lines | Output |
| DWS, XFER | DMA Write Slot, Transfer | Output |
| STROBE | Output Strobe Line | Output |
| $V_{SS}$, $V_{DD}$, $V_{GG}$ | Power Lines | |

Figure 2-14. 3854 DMA Signals and Pin Assignments

## THE 3853 STATIC MEMORY INTERFACE (SMI)

**The 3853 SMI provides interface logic for static read/write memory, that is, for memory which does not need to be refreshed. Logic implemented on this device is illustrated in Figure 2-15, and is a simple combination of functions which have already been described for the 3851 PSU and for the 3852 DMI. Figure 2-16 illustrates 3853 SMI pins and signals.**

**The description of memory interface logic which was given for the 3852 DMI applies also for the 3853 SMI. The 3853 SMI, however, does not identify memory access periods, and cannot be used to implement direct memory access.**

Because the 3853 SMI does not have memory refresh or direct memory access support logic, there is unused real estate on the SMI chip. The real estate is used to implement a programmable timer and interrupt processing logic, as described for the 3851 PSU. There are, however, two small differences between interrupt logic as implemented on the PSU and the SMI devices; they are:

1) The 3853 SMI interrupt address vector is not a permanent mask option as it is on the PSU; rather, it is programmable.
2) The 3853 SMI has no priority output line, which means that in a daisy chain interrupt configuration it must have lowest priority; that is, it must come at the end of the daisy chain.

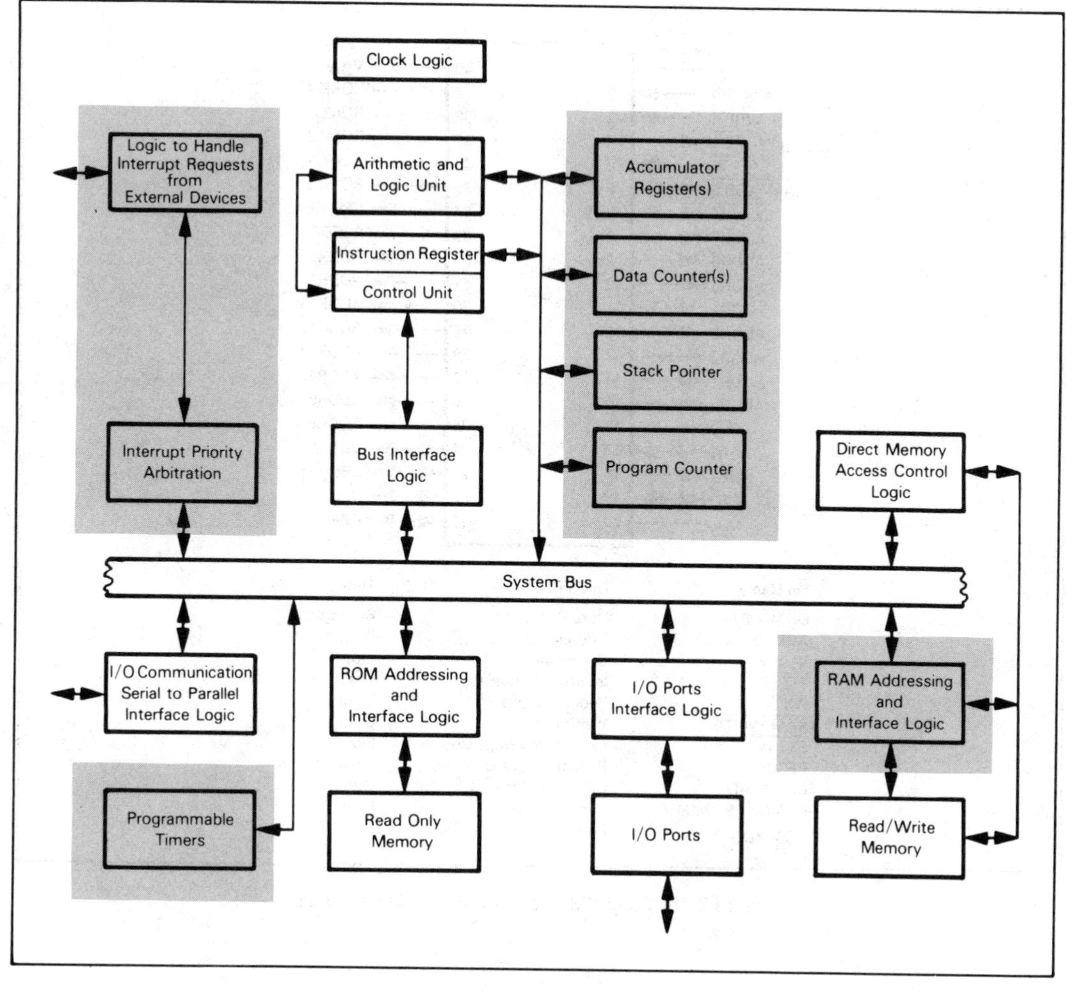


Figure 2-15. Logic of the F8 3853 Static Memory Interface (SMI) Device

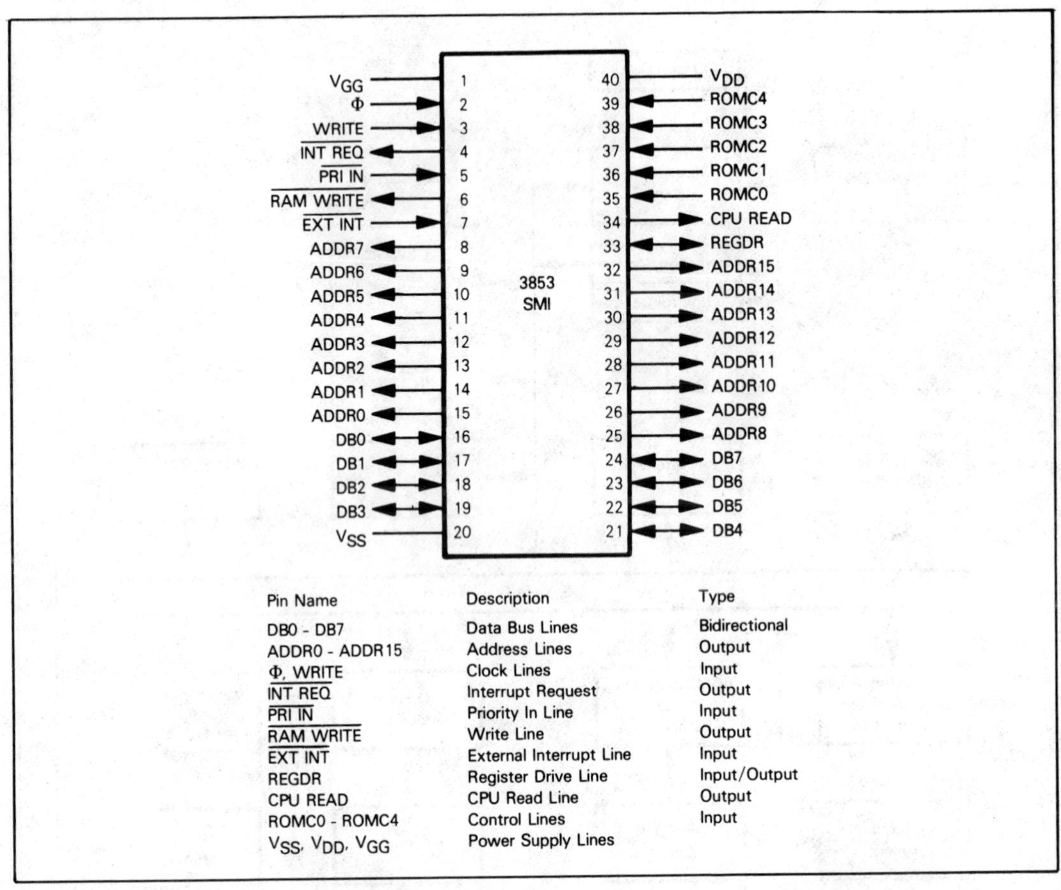


| Pin Name | Description | Type |
|---|---|---|
| DB0 - DB7 | Data Bus Lines | Bidirectional |
| ADDR0 - ADDR15 | Address Lines | Output |
| Φ, $\overline{\text{WRITE}}$ | Clock Lines | Input |
| $\overline{\text{INT REQ}}$ | Interrupt Request | Output |
| $\overline{\text{PRI IN}}$ | Priority In Line | Input |
| $\overline{\text{RAM WRITE}}$ | Write Line | Output |
| $\overline{\text{EXT INT}}$ | External Interrupt Line | Input |
| REGDR | Register Drive Line | Input/Output |
| CPU READ | CPU Read Line | Output |
| ROMC0 - ROMC4 | Control Lines | Input |
| $V_{SS}$, $V_{DD}$, $V_{GG}$ | Power Supply Lines | |

Figure 2-16. 3853 SMI Signals and Pin Assignments

# DATA SHEETS

This section contains specific electrical and timing data for the following devices:

- 3870 One-Chip Microcomputer
- 3850 CPU
- 3851 PSU
- 3852 DMI
- 3853 SMI
- 3854 DMA
- 3856 2K PSU
- 3861 PIO

## 3870

### ELECTRICAL SPECIFICATIONS

### ABSOLUTE MAXIMUM RATINGS*

Temperature Under Bias .......... 0°C to 70°C
Storage Temperature .......... −65°C to +150°C
Voltage On Any Pin With Respect To Ground .......... −1.0V to + 7V
Power Dissipation .......... 1.0W

### DC CHARACTERISTICS

$T_A$ = 0°C to 70°C, $V_{CC}$ = 5V ± 10%

| SYMBOL | PARAMETER | MIN | MAX | UNIT | TEST CONDITIONS |
|---|---|---|---|---|---|
| $I_{CC}$ | Power Supply Current | | TBD | mA | Outputs Open |
| $P_D$ | Power Dissipation | | TBD | mW | Outputs Open |
| $V_{IHEX}$ | External Clock Input High Level | 2.4 | 5.8 | V | |
| $V_{ILHEX}$ | External Clock Input Low Level | −0.3 | 0.6 | V | |
| $I_{IHEX}$ | External Clock Input High Current | | 100 | μA | $V_{IHEX}$= 2.4V |
| $I_{ILEX}$ | External Clock Input Low Current | | −100 | μA | $V_{ILEX}$= 0.6V |
| $V_{IH}$ | Input High Level | 2.0 | 5.8 | V | |
| $V_{IL}$ | Input Low Level | −0.3 | 0.8 | V | |
| $I_{IH}$ | Input High Current (except open drain and direct drive I/O ports) | | 100 | μA | $V_{IH}$= 2.4V internal pull-up |
| $I_{IL}$ | Input Low Current (except open drain and direct drive ports) | | −1.6 | mA | $V_{IL}$= 0.4V |
| $I_{LOD}$ | Leakage Current (open drain ports) | | 10 | μA | Pull-down device off |
| $I_{OH}$ | Output High Current (except open drain and direct drive ports) | −100 | | μA | $V_{OH}$= 2.4V |
| $I_{OHDD}$ | Output Drive Current (direct drive ports) | −1.5 | −8 | mA | $V_{OH}$= 0.7V to 1.5V |
| $I_{OL}$ | Output Low Current | 1.8 | | mA | $V_{OL}$= 0.4V |
| $I_{OHS}$ | Output High Current ($\overline{STROBE}$ Output) | −300 | | μA | $V_{OH}$= 2.4V |
| $I_{OLS}$ | Output Low Current ($\overline{STROBE}$ Output) | 5.0 | | mA | $V_{OL}$= 0.4V |

*Stresses above those listed under "Absolute Maximum Ratings" may cause permanent damage to the device. This is a stress rating only and functional operation of the device at these or any other condition above those indicated in the operational sections of this specification is not implied. Exposure to absolute maximum rating conditions for extended periods may affect device reliability.

**Data sheets on pages 2-D2 through 2-D5 reprinted by permission of Mostek Corporation.**

## AC CHARACTERISTICS

$T_A$ = 0℃ to 70℃, $V_{CC}$ = +5V ± 10%

| SIGNAL | SYMBOL | PARAMETER | MIN | MAX | UNIT | COMMENTS |
|---|---|---|---|---|---|---|
| | $t_{0(XTL)}$ | Time Base Period, Crystal Mode | 250 | 1000 | ns | 4MHz-1MHz |
| | $t_{0(LC)}$ | Time Base Period, LC Mode | 250 | 1000 | ns | 4MHz-1MHz |
| XTL 1 | $t_{0(RC)}$ | Time Base Period, RC Mode | 250 | 2000 | ns | 4MHz-500kHz |
| XTL 2 | $t_{0(INT)}$ | Time Base Period, Internal Mode | 250 | 590 | ns | 4MHz-1.7MHz |
| | $t_{0(EX)}$ | Time Base Period, External Mode | 250 | 2500 | ns | 4MHz-400kHz |
| | $t_{EX(H)}$ | External Clock Pulse Width, High | 90 | 2000 | ns | |
| | $t_{EX(L)}$ | External Clock Pulse Width, Low | 90 | 2000 | ns | |
| Φ | $t_\Phi$ | Internal Φ Clock Period | $2t_0$ | typ. | ns | 0.5 μs @ 4MHz ext. time base |
| $\overline{\text{STROBE}}$ | $t_{I/O-S}$ | Port Output to $\overline{\text{STROBE}}$ Delay | 3tΦ-1000 min.<br>3tΦ+250 max. | | ns | Note 1 |
| | $t_{SL}$ | $\overline{\text{STROBE}}$ Pulse Width, Low | 8tΦ -250 min.<br>12tΦ +250 max. | | ns | |
| $\overline{\text{RESET}}$ | $t_{RH}$ | $\overline{\text{RESET}}$ Hold Time, Low | 6tΦ +750 min. | | ns | |
| EXT INT | $t_{EH}$ | EXT INT Hold Time, Active State | 6tΦ +750 min. | | ns | Note 2 |

NOTES:
1. Load is 50pF plus 1 standard TTL input.
2. Specification is applicable when the timer is in the Interval Timer Mode. See "Timer Characteristics" for EXT INT requirements when in the Pulse Width Measurement Mode or the Event Counter Mode.
3. The AC Timing Diagrams are given in Figure 5.

## CAPACITANCE

$T_A$ = 25℃, f = 2MHz

| SYMBOL | PARAMETER | MIN | MAX | UNIT | TEST CONDITION |
|---|---|---|---|---|---|
| $C_{IN}$ | Input Capacitance: I/O Ports, $\overline{\text{RESET}}$, EXT INT | | 7 | pF | Unmeasured pins returned to GND |
| $C_{XTL}$ | Input Capacitance: XTL 1, XTL 2 | 18 | 23 | pF | |

## TIMER CHARACTERISTICS

Definitions:

Error = Indicated time value - actual time value

tpsc = t Φ x Prescale Value

**Interval Timer Mode:**

Single interval error, free running (Note 3) .......................................... ±6tΦ
Cumulative interval error, free running (Note 3) .......................................... 0
Error between two Timer reads (Note 2) .......................................... ±(tpsc + tΦ)
Start Timer to stop Timer error (Notes 1,4) .......................... +tΦ to −(tpsc +tΦ)
Start Timer to read Timer error (Notes 1,2) .......................... −5tΦ to −(tpsc + 7tΦ)
Start Timer to interrupt request error (Notes 1,3) .......................... −2tΦ to −8tΦ
Load Timer to stop Timer error (Note 1) .......................... +tΦ to −(tpsc + 2tΦ)
Load Timer to read Timer error (Notes 1,2) .......................... −5tΦ to −(tpsc + 8tΦ)
Load Timer to interrupt request error (Notes 1,3) .......................... −2t Φ to −9tΦ

**Pulse Width Measurement Mode:**

Measurement accuracy (Note 4) .......................................... +t Φ to −(tpsc +2t Φ)
Minimum pulse width of EXT INT pin .......................................... 2t Φ

**Event Counter Mode:**

Minimum active time of EXT INT pin .......................................... 2tΦ
Minimum inactive time of EXT INT pin .......................................... 2tΦ

**Notes:**

1. All times which entail loading, starting, or stopping the Timer are referenced from the end of the last machine cycle of the OUT or OUTS instruction.

2. All times which entail reading the Timer are referenced from the end of the last machine cycle of the IN or INS instruction.

3. All times which entail the generation of an interrupt request are referenced from the start of the machine cycle in which the appropriate interrupt request latch is set. Additional time may elapse if the interrupt request occurs during a privileged or multicycle instruction.

4. Error may be cumulative if operation is repetitively performed.

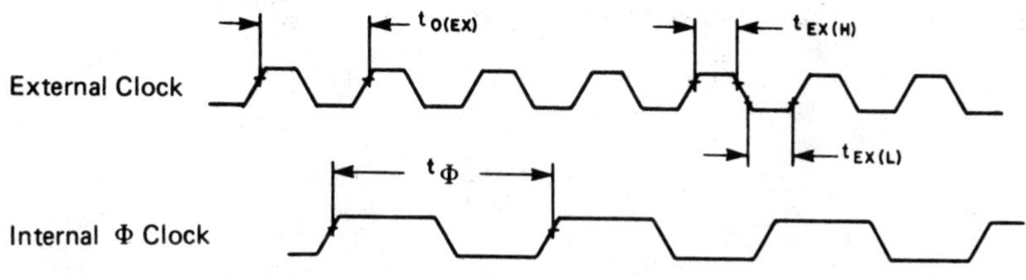


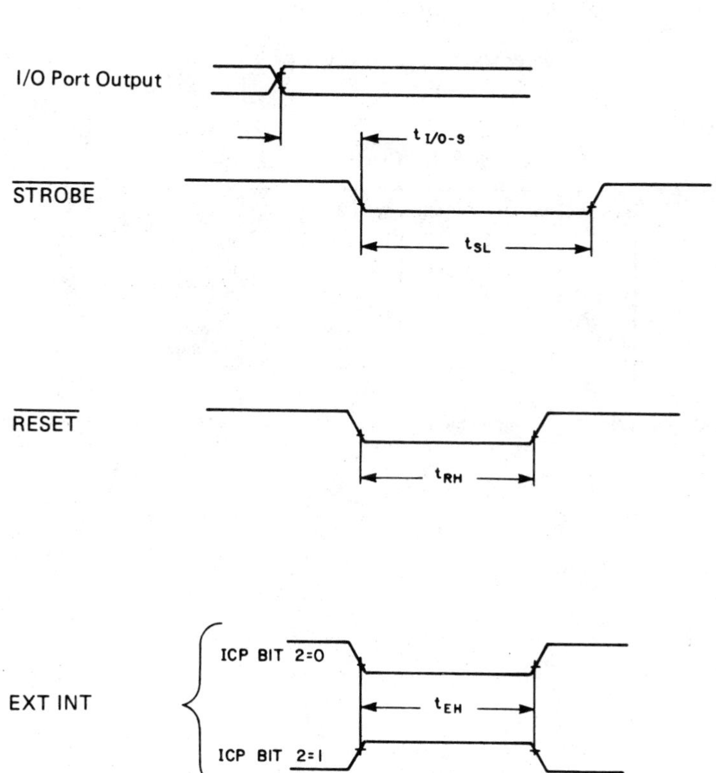


Note: All measurements are referenced to $V_{IL}$ max., $V_{IH}$ min., $V_{OL}$ max., or $V_{OH}$ min.

FIGURE 5. AC TIMING DIAGRAMS

### 2.2.2 Electrical Specifications

*Absolute maximum ratings (above which useful life may be impaired)*

| | |
|---|---|
| $V_{GG}$ | +15V to -0.3V |
| $V_{DD}$ | +7V to -0.3V |
| RC, XTLX and XTLY | +15V to -0.3V (RC with 5KΩ series resistor) |
| All other inputs | +7V to -0.3V |
| Storage temperature | -55°C to +150°C |
| Operating temperature | 0°C to +70°C |

**Note:** All voltages with respect to $V_{SS}$.

*DC Characteristics:* $V_{SS}$ = 0V, $V_{DD}$ = +5V ± 5%, $V_{GG}$ = +12V ± 5%, $T_A$ = 0°C to +70°C

**SUPPLY CURRENTS**

| SYMBOL | PARAMETER | MIN. | TYP. | MAX. | UNITS | TEST CONDITIONS |
|---|---|---|---|---|---|---|
| $I_{DD}$ | $V_{DD}$ Current | | 45 | 75 | mA | f = 2 MHz, Outputs unloaded |
| $I_{GG}$ | $V_{GG}$ Current | | 12 | 30 | mA | f - 2 MHz, Outputs unloaded |

*Table 2-3. A Summary of 3850 CPU Signal DC Characteristics*

| SIGNAL | SYMBOL | PARAMETER | MIN. | MAX. | UNITS | TEST CONDITIONS |
|---|---|---|---|---|---|---|
| Φ, WRITE | $V_{OH}$ | Output High Voltage | 4.4 | $V_{DD}$ | Volts | $I_{OH}$ = -50 μA |
| | $V_{OL}$ | Output Low Voltage | $V_{SS}$ | 0.4 | Volts | $I_{OL}$ = 1.6 mA |
| | $V_{OH}$ | Output High Voltage | 2.9 | | Volts | $I_{OH}$ = -100 μA |
| XTLY | $V_{IH}$ | Input High Voltage | 4.5 | $V_{GG}$ | Volts | |
| | $V_{IL}$ | Input Low Voltage | $V_{SS}$ | 0.8 | Volts | |
| | $I_{IH}$ | Input High Current | 5 | 50 | μA | $V_{IN} = V_{DD}$ |
| | $I_{IL}$ | Input Low Current | -10 | -120 | μA | $V_{IN} = V_{SS}$ |
| ROMC0 ⋮ ROMC4 | $V_{OH}$ | Output High Voltage | 3.9 | $V_{DD}$ | Volts | $I_{OH}$ = -100 μA |
| | $V_{OL}$ | Output Low Voltage | $V_{SS}$ | 0.4 | Volts | $I_{OL}$ = 1.6 mA |
| DB0 ⋮ DB7 | $V_{IH}$ | Input High Voltage | 2.9 | $V_{DD}$ | Volts | |
| | $V_{IL}$ | Input Low Voltage | $V_{SS}$ | 0.8 | Volts | |
| | $V_{OH}$ | Output High Voltage | 3.9 | $V_{DD}$ | Volts | $I_{OH}$ = -100 μA |
| | $V_{OL}$ | Output Low Voltage | $V_{SS}$ | 0.4 | Volts | $I_{OL}$ = 1.6 mA |
| | $I_{IH}$ | Input High Current | | 3 | μA | $V_{IN}$ = 7V 3-State mode |
| | $I_{IL}$ | Input Low Current | | -3 | μA | $V_{IN} = V_{SS}$, 3-State mode |
| I/O 0 ⋮ I/O 17 | $V_{OH}$ | Output High Voltage | 3.9 | $V_{DD}$ | Volts | $I_{OH}$ = -30 μA |
| | $V_{OH}$ | Output High Voltage | 2.9 | $V_{DD}$ | Volts | $I_{OH}$ = -150 μA |
| | $V_{OL}$ | Output Low Voltage | $V_{SS}$ | 0.4 | Volts | $I_{OL}$ = 1.6 mA |
| | $V_{IH}$ | Input High Voltage (1) | 2.9 | $V_{DD}$ | Volts | Internal pull-up to $V_{DD}$ |
| | $V_{IL}$ | Input Low Voltage | $V_{SS}$ | 0.8 | Volts | |
| | $I_{IL}$ | Input Low Current | | -1.6 | mA | $V_{IN}$ = 0.4V (2) |
| $\overline{\text{EXT RES}}$ | $V_{IH}$ | Input High Voltage | 3.5 | $V_{DD}$ | Volts | Internal pull-up to $V_{DD}$ |
| | $V_{IL}$ | Input Low Voltage | $V_{SS}$ | 0.8 | Volts | |
| | $I_{IL}$ | Input Low Current | -0.1 | -1.0 | mA | $V_{IN} = V_{SS}$ |
| $\overline{\text{INT REQ}}$ | $V_{IH}$ | Input High Voltage | 3.5 | $V_{DD}$ | Volts | Internal pull-up to $V_{DD}$ |
| | $V_{IL}$ | Input Low Voltage | $V_{SS}$ | 0.8 | Volts | |
| | $I_{IL}$ | Input Low Current | -0.1 | -1.0 | mA | $V_{IN} = V_{SS}$ |
| $\overline{\text{ICB}}$ | $V_{OH}$ | Output High Voltage | 3.9 | $V_{DD}$ | Volts | IOH = -10 μA |
| | $V_{OH}$ | Output High Voltage | 2.9 | $V_{DD}$ | Volts | $I_{OH}$ = -100 μA |
| | $V_{OL}$ | Output Low Voltage | $V_{SS}$ | 0.4 | Volts | $I_{OL}$ = 100 μA |

(1) Hysteresis input circuit provides additional 0.3V noise immunity while internal pull-up provides TTL compatability.

(2) Measured while F8 port is outputting a high level.

**Note:**

Positive current is defined as conventional current flowing into the pin referenced.

(3) Guaranteed but not tested.

*Table 2-4. A Summary of 3850 CPU Signal AC Characteristics*

*AC Characteristics:* $V_{SS}$ = 0V, $V_{DD}$ = +5V ± 5%, $V_{GG}$ = +12V ± 5%, $T_A$ = 0°C to +70°C

Symbols in this table are used by all figures in Section 2.

| SYMBOL | PARAMETER | MIN. | TYP. | MAX. | UNITS | TEST CONDITIONS |
|---|---|---|---|---|---|---|
| $P_x$* | External Input Period | 0.5 | | 10 | μS | |
| $PW_x$* | External Pulse Width | 200 | | $P_x$-200 | nS | $t_r$, $t_f \leq$ 30 nS |
| $tx_1$ | Ext. to Φ - to - Delay | | | 250 | nS | CL = 100 pf |
| $tx_2$ | Ext. to Φ + to + Delay | | | 250 | nS | CL = 100 pf |
| PΦ | Φ Period | 0.5 | | 10 | μS | |
| $PW_1$ | Φ Pulse Width | 180 | | PΦ-180 | nS | $t_r$, $t_f$ = 50 nS; $C_L$ = 100 pf |
| $td_1$ | Φ to WRITE + Delay | | 150 | 250 | nS | $C_L$ = 100 pf |
| $td_2$ | Φ to WRITE - Delay | | 150 | 250 | nS | $C_L$ = 100 pf |
| $PW_2$ | WRITE Pulse Width | PΦ-100 | | PΦ | nS | $t_r$, $t_f$ = 50 nS typ; $C_L$ = 100 pf |
| $PW_S$ | WRITE Period; Short | | 4PΦ | | | |
| $PW_L$ | WRITE Period; Long | | 6PΦ | | | |
| $td_3$ | WRITE to ROMC Delay | 80 | 300 | 550 | nS | $C_L$ = 100 pf |
| $td_4$* | WRITE to $\overline{\text{ICB}}$ Delay | | | 350 | nS | $C_L$ = 50 pf |
| $td_5$ | WRITE to $\overline{\text{INT REQ}}$ Delay | | | 430 (2) | nS | $C_L$ = 100 pf |
| $t_{sx}$* | $\overline{\text{EXT RES}}$ set-up time | 1.0 | | | μS | $C_L$ = 20 pf |
| $t_{su}$* | I/O set-up time | 300 | | | nS | |
| $t_h$* | I/O hold time | 50 | | | nS | |
| $t_o$* | I/O Output Delay | | | 2.5 | μS | $C_L$ = 50 pf |
| $tdb_1$* | WRITE to Data Bus Stable | | 0.6 | 1.3 | μS | $C_L$ = 100 pf |
| $tdb_2$ | WRITE to Data Bus Stable | 2PΦ | | 2PΦ+1.0 | μS | $C_L$ = 100 pf |
| $tdb_3$* | Data Bus Set-up | 200 | | | nS | |
| $tdb_4$* | Data Bus Set-up | 500 | | | nS | |
| $tdb_5$ | Data Bus Set-up | 500 | | | nS | |
| $tdb_6$* | Data Bus Set-up | 500 | | | nS | |

*The parameters which are starred in the table above represent those which are most frequently of importance when interfacing to an F8 system. These encompass I/O timing, external timing generation and possible external RAM timing. The remaining parameters are typically those that are only relevant between F8 chips and not normally of concern to the user.

(1) Input and output capacitance is 3 to 5 pf typical on all pins except $V_{DD}$, $V_{GG}$, and $V_{SS}$.

(2) If $\overline{\text{INTREQ}}$ is being supplied asynchronously, it can be pulled down at any time except during a fetch cycle that has been preceded by a non-priviledged instruction. In that case $\overline{\text{INTREQ}}$ must go down according to the requirements of $td_5$.

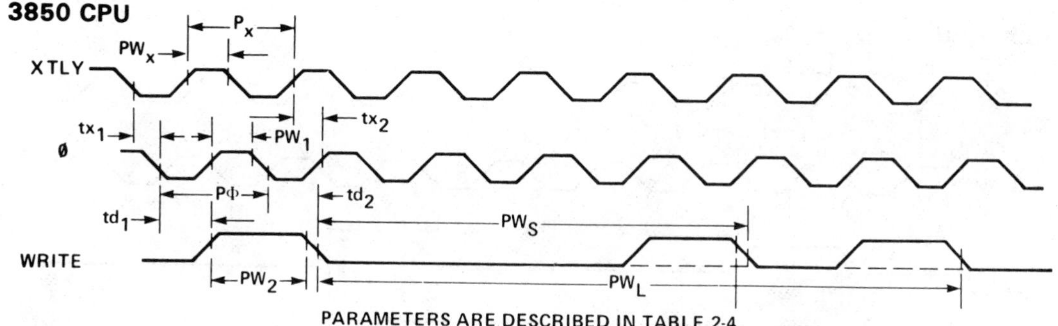


*Figure 2-8. Timing Signal Specifications*

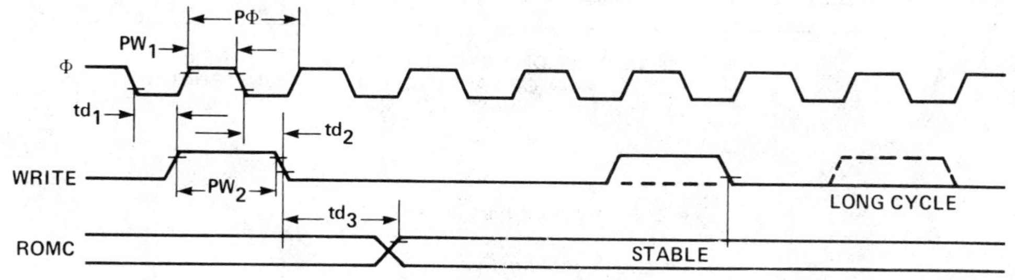


*Figure 2-9. ROMC Signals Output by 3850 CPU*

## 3850 CPU

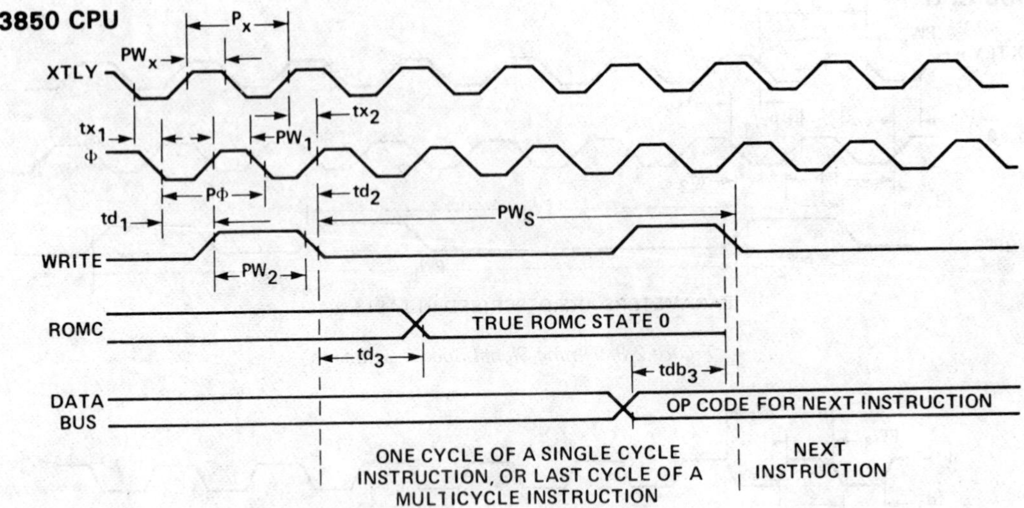


Symbols are defined in Table 2-4

*Figure 2-10A. A Short Cycle Instruction Fetch*

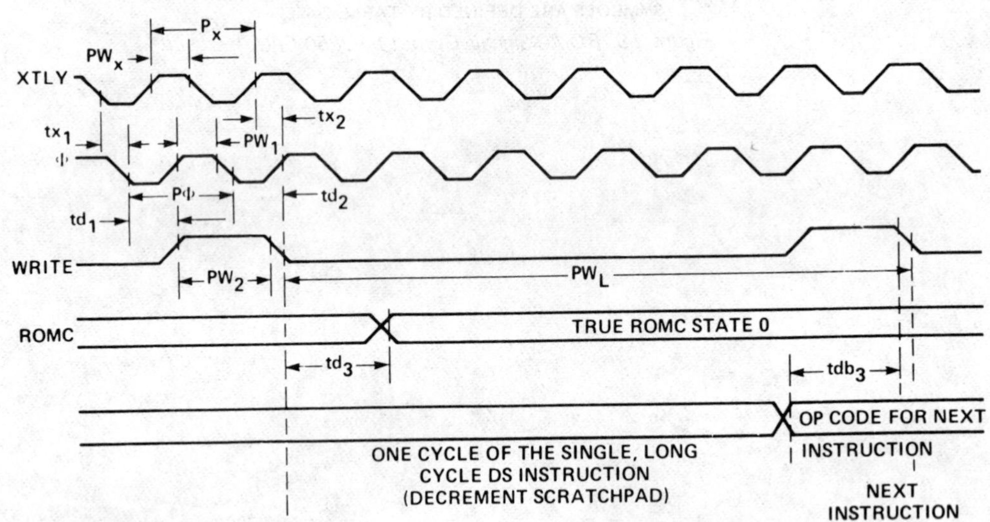


Symbols are defined in Table 2-4

*Figure 2-10B. A Long Cycle Instruction Fetch (During DS Only)*

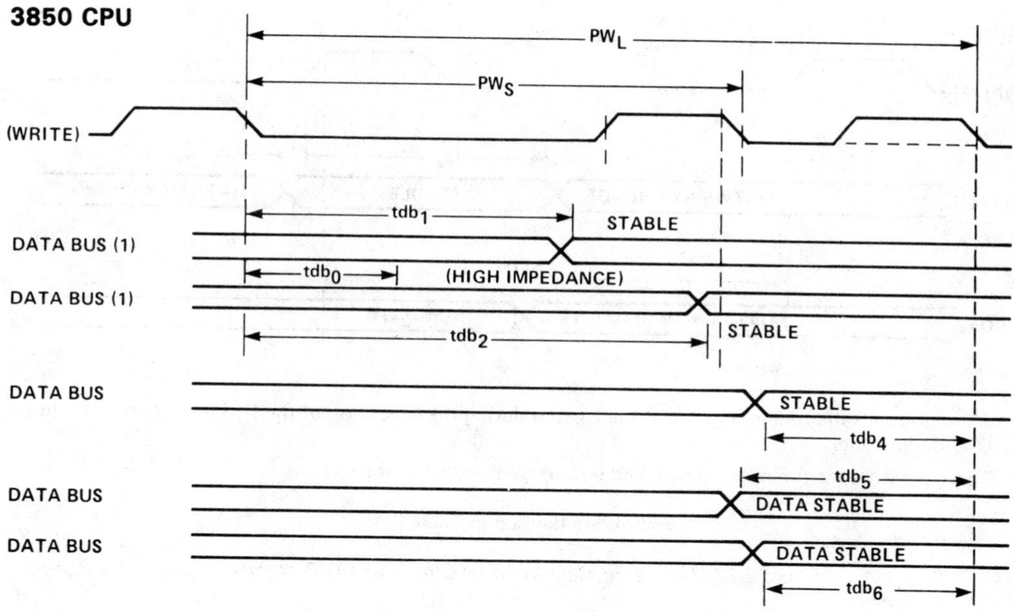


1. Timing for CPU outputting data onto the data bus.

   Delay $tdb_1$ is the delay when data is coming from the accumulator.

   Delay $tdb_2$ is the delay when data is coming from the scratchpad (or from a memory device).

   Delay $tdb_0$ is the delay for the CPU to stop driving the data bus.

2. There are four possible cases when inputting data to the CPU, via the data bus lines: they depend on the data path and the destination in the CPU, as follows:

   $tdb_3$; Destination – IR (instruction Fetch) – See Figure 2-10 for details.
   $tdb_4$; Destination – Accumulator (with ALU operation – AM)
   $tdb_5$; Destination – Scratchpad (LR K,P etc.)
   $tdb_6$; Destination – Accumulator (no ALU operation – LM)

   In each case a stable data hold time of 50 nS from the WRITE refrence point is required.

**Symbols are defined in Table 2-4**

*Figure 2-11. Memory Reference Timing*

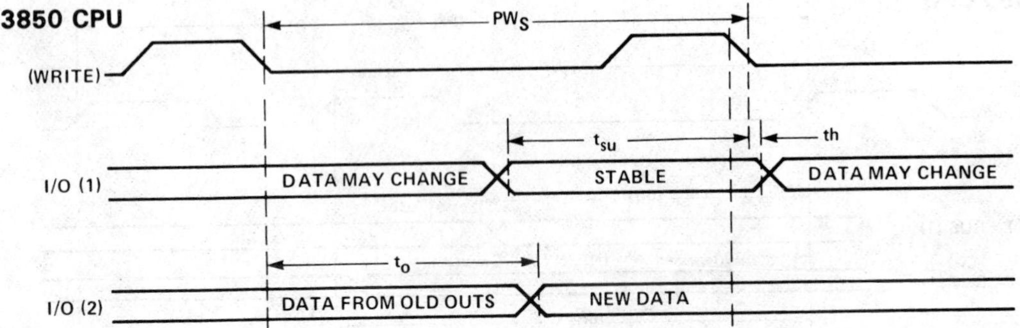


(1) This represents the timing for data at the I/O pin during the execution of the INS instruction, i.e., the CPU is inputting.

(2) This represents the timing for data being output by the CPU at the I/O pin.

Symbols are defined in Table 2-4

*Figure 2-13. Timing for Data Input or Output at I/O Port Pins*

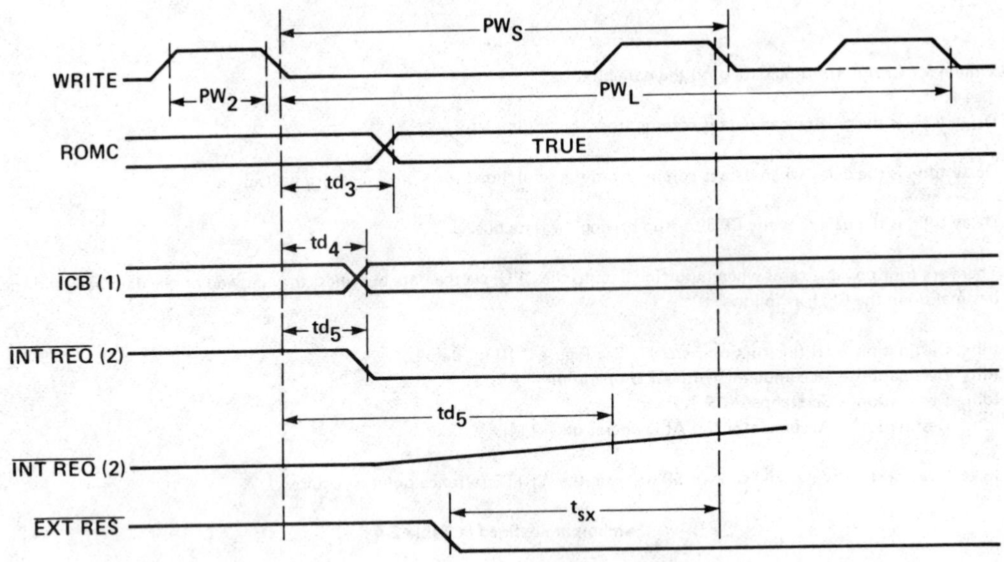


(1) $\overline{ICB}$ will go from a 1 to a 0 following the execution of the EI instruction and will go from a 0 to 1 following either the execution of the DI instruction or the CPU's acknowledgement of an interrupt.

(2) This is an input to the CPU chip and is generated by a PSU or 3853 MI chip. The open drain outputs of these chips are all wire "ANDed" together on this line with the pull-up being located on the CPU chip. For a 0 to 1 transition the delay is measured to 2.0V.

Symbols are defined in Table 2-4

*Figure 2-14. Interrupt Signals Timing*

### 3.2.5 Electrical Specifications

*Absolute Maximum Ratings* (Above which useful life may be impaired)

| | |
|---|---|
| $V_{GG}$ | +15V to -0.3V |
| $V_{DD}$ | +7V to -0.3V |
| I/O Port Open Drain Option | +15V to -0.3V |
| External Interrupt Input | -600 μA to +225 μA |
| All other inputs & outputs | +7V to -0.3V |
| Storage Temperature | -55°C to +150°C |
| Operating Temperature | 0°C to +70°C |

**Note:** All voltages with respect to $V_{SS}$.

*DC Characteristics:* $V_{SS}$ = 0V, $V_{DD}$ = +5V ± 5%,
$V_{GG}$ = +12V ± 5%,
$T_A$ = 0°C to +70°C

*SUPPLY CURRENTS*

| SYMBOL | PARAMETER | MIN. | TYP. | MAX. | UNITS | TEST CONDITIONS |
|---|---|---|---|---|---|---|
| $I_{DD}$ | $V_{DD}$ Current | | 28 | 60 | mA | f = 2 MHz, Outputs Unloaded |
| $I_{GG}$ | $V_{GG}$ Current | | 10 | 30 | mA | f = 2 MHz, Outputs Unloaded |

*Table 3-2. A Summary of 3851 PSU Signal Characteristics*

| SIGNAL | SYMBOL | PARAMETER | MIN. | MAX. | UNITS | TEST CONDITIONS |
|---|---|---|---|---|---|---|
| DATA BUS (DB0-DB7) | $V_{IH}$ | Input High Voltage | 2.9 | $V_{DD}$ | Volts | |
| | $V_{IL}$ | Input Low Voltage | $V_{SS}$ | 0.8 | Volts | |
| | $V_{OH}$ | Output High Voltage | 3.9 | $V_{DD}$ | Volts | $I_{OH}$ = -100 µA |
| | $V_{OL}$ | Output Low Voltage | $V_{SS}$ | 0.4 | Volts | $I_{OL}$ = 1.6 mA |
| | $I_{IH}$ | Input High Current | | 1 | µA | $V_{IN} = V_{DD}$, 3-State mode |
| | $I_{OL}$ | Input Low Current | | -1 | µA | $V_{IN} = V_{SS}$, 3-State mode |
| CLOCK LINES (Φ, WRITE) | $V_{IH}$ | Input High Voltage | 4.0 | $V_{DD}$ | Volts | |
| | $V_{IL}$ | Input Low Voltage | $V_{SS}$ | 0.8 | Volts | |
| | $I_L$ | Leakage Current | | 3 | µA | $V_{IN} = V_{DD}$ |
| PRIORITY IN AND CONTROL LINES ($\overline{\text{PRI IN}}$, ROMC0-ROMC4) | $V_{IH}$ | Input High Voltage | 3.5 | $V_{DD}$ | Volts | |
| | $V_{IL}$ | Input Low Voltage | $V_{SS}$ | 0.8 | Volts | |
| | $I_L$ | Leakage Current | | 3 | µA | $V_{IN} = V_{DD}$ |
| PRIORITY OUT ($\overline{\text{PRI OUT}}$) | $V_{OH}$ | Output High Voltage | 3.9 | $V_{DD}$ | Volts | $I_{OH}$ = -100 µA |
| | $V_{OL}$ | Output Low Voltage | $V_{SS}$ | 0.4 | Volts | $I_{OL}$ = 100 µA |
| INTERRUPT REQUEST ($\overline{\text{INT REQ}}$) | $V_{OH}$ | Output High Voltage | | | Volts | Open Drain Output [1] |
| | $V_{OL}$ | Output Low Voltage | $V_{SS}$ | 0.4 | Volts | $I_{OL}$ = 1 mA |
| | $I_L$ | Leakage Current | | 3 | µA | $V_{IN} = V_{DD}$ |
| DATA BUS DRIVE ($\overline{\text{DBDR}}$) | $V_{OH}$ | Output High Voltage | | | | External Pull-up |
| | $V_{OL}$ | Output Low Voltage | $V_{SS}$ | 0.4 | Volts | $I_{OL}$ = 2 mA |
| | $I_L$ | Leakage Current | | 3 | µA | $V_{IN} = V_{DD}$ |
| EXTERNAL INTERRUPT ($\overline{\text{EXT INT}}$) | $V_{IH}$ | Input High Voltage | 3.5 | | Volts | |
| | $V_{IL}$ | Input Low Voltage | | 0.8 | Volts | |
| | $V_{IC}$ | Input Clamp Voltage | | 15 | Volts | $I_{IH}$ = 185 µA |
| | $I_{IH}$ | Input High Current | | 10 | µA | $V_{IN} = V_{DD}$ |
| | $I_{IL}$ | Input Low Current | | -225 | µA | $V_{IN}$ = 2V |
| | $I_{IL}$ | Input Low Current | -150 | -500 | µA | $V_{IN} = V_{SS}$ |
| I/O PORT OPTION A (STANDARD PULL-UP) | $V_{OH}$ | Output High Voltage | 3.9(5) | $V_{DD}$ | Volts | $I_{OH}$ = -30 µA |
| | $V_{OH}$ | Output High Voltage | 2.9 | $V_{DD}$ | Volts | $I_{OH}$ = -150 µA |
| | $V_{OL}$ | Output Low Voltage | $V_{SS}$ | 0.4 | Volts | $I_{OL}$ = 1.6 mA |
| | $V_{IH}$ | Input High Voltage | 2.9(3) | $V_{DD}$ | Volts | Internal Pull-up to $V_{DD}$ [3] |
| | $V_{IL}$ | Input Low Voltage | $V_{SS}$ | 0.8 | Volts | |
| | $I_L$ | Leakage Current | | 1 | µA | $V_{IN} = V_{DD}$ |
| | $I_{IL}$ | Input Low Current | | -1.6 | mA | $V_{IN}$ = 0.4V [4] |
| I/O PORT OPTION B (OPEN DRAIN) | $V_{OH}$ | Output High Voltage | | | | External Pull-up |
| | $V_{OL}$ | Output Low Voltage | $V_{SS}$ | 0.4 | Volts | $I_{OL}$ = 2 mA |
| | $V_{IH}$ | Input High Voltage | 2.9(3) | $V_{DD}$ | Volts | [3] |
| | $V_{IL}$ | Input Low Voltage | $V_{SS}$ | 0.8 | Volts | |
| | $I_{IL}$ | Leakage Current | | 2 | µA | $V_{IN}$ = + 12V |

*Table 3-2. A Summary of 3851 PSU Signal Characteristics (Continued)*

| SIGNAL | SYMBOL | PARAMETER | MIN. | MAX. | UNITS | TEST CONDITIONS |
|---|---|---|---|---|---|---|
| I/O PORT OPTION C (DRIVER PULL-UP) | $V_{OH}$ | Output High Voltage | 3.75 | $V_{DD}$ | Volts | $I_{OH}$ = -1 mA |
| | $V_{OL}$ | Output Low Voltage | $V_{SS}$ | 0.4 | Volts | $I_{OL}$ = 1.6 mA |

**Notes:**

1. Pull-up resistor to $V_{DD}$ on CPU.
2. Positive current is defined as conventional current flowing into the pin referenced.
3. Hysteresis input circuit provides additional 0.3V noise immunity while internal/external pull-up provides TTL compatibility.
4. Measured while I/O port is outputting a high level.
5. Guaranteed but not tested.

*Table 3-3. A Summary of 3851 PSU Signal AC Characteristics*

*AC Characteristics:* $V_{SS}$ = 0V, $V_{DD}$ = +5V ± 5%, $V_{GG}$ = +12V ± 5%, $T_A$ = 0°C to +70°C

Symbols in this table are used by all figures in Section 3.

| SYMBOL | PARAMETER | MIN. | TYP. | MAX. | UNITS | TEST CONDITIONS |
|---|---|---|---|---|---|---|
| $P\phi$ | $\phi$ Period | 0.5 | | 10 | μS | |
| $PW_1$ | $\phi$ Pulse Width | 180 | | $P\phi$-180 | nS | $t_r$, $t_f$ = 50 nS typ. |
| $td_1$ | $\phi$ to WRITE + Delay | | | 250 | nS | $C_L$ = 100 pf |
| $td_2$ | $\phi$ to WRITE-Delay | | | 250 | nS | $C_L$ = 100 pf |
| $td_4$ | WRITE to DB Input Delay | | | $2P\phi$ + 1.0 | μS | |
| $PW_2$ | WRITE Pulse Width | $P\phi$-100 | | $P\phi$ | nS | $t_r$, $t_f$ = 50 nS typ. |
| $PW_S$ | WRITE Period; Short | | $4P\phi$ | | | |
| $PW_L$ | WRITE Period; Long | | $6P\phi$ | | | |
| $td_3$ | WRITE to ROMC Delay | | | 550 | nS | |
| $td_7$ | WRITE to DB Output Delay<br>WRITE to $\overline{DBDR}$ — Delay | $2P\phi$ + 100 - $td_2$ | $2P\phi$ + 200 | $2P\phi$ + 850 - $td_2$ | nS | $C_L$ = 100 pf |
| $td_8$ | WRITE to $\overline{DBDR}$ + Delay | | 200 | | nS | Open Drain |
| $tr_1$ | WRITE to $\overline{INT\ REQ}$ — Delay | | | 430 | nS | $C_L$ = 100 pf [1] |
| $tr_2$ | WRITE to $\overline{INT\ REQ}$ + Delay | | | 430 | nS | $C_L$ = 100 pf [3] |
| $tpr_1$ | PRI IN to $\overline{INT\ REQ}$ — Delay | | 200 | | nS | $C_L$ = 100 pf [2] |
| $tpd_1$ | PRI IN to $\overline{PRI\ OUT}$ — Delay | | | 300 | nS | $C_L$ = 50 pf |
| $tpd_2$ | PRI IN to $\overline{PRI\ OUT}$ + Delay | | | 300 | nS | $C_L$ = 50 pf |
| $tpd_3$ | WRITE to $\overline{PRI\ OUT}$ + Delay | | | 600 | nS | $C_L$ = 50 pf |
| $tpd_4$ | WRITE to $\overline{PRI\ OUT}$ — Delay | | | 600 | nS | $C_L$ = 50 pf |
| $t_{sp}$ | WRITE to Output Stable | | | 1.0 (3) | μS | $C_L$ = 50 pf, Standard Pull-up |
| $t_{od}$ | WRITE to Output Stable | | | 1.0 (3) | μS | $C_L$ = 50 pf, $R_L$ = 12.5 KΩ to $V_{DD}$ plus TTL load |
| $t_{dp}$ | WRITE to Output Stable | | 200 | 400 | nS | $C_L$ = 50 pf, Driver Pull-up |
| $t_{su}$ | I/O Setup Time | 1.3 | | | μS | |
| $t_h$ | I/O Hold Time | 0 | | | nS | |
| $t_{ex}$ | $\overline{EXT\ INT}$ Setup Time | 400 | | | nS | |

**Notes:**

1. Assume Priority In was enabled ($\overline{PRI\ IN}$ = 0) in previous F8 cycle before interrupt is detected in the PSU.
2. PSU has interrupt pending before priority in is enabled.
3. Assume pin tied to $\overline{INT\ REQ}$ input of the 3850 CPU.
4. The parameters which are shaded in the table above represent those which are most frequently of importance when interfacing to an F8 system. Unshaded parameters are typically those that are relevant only between F8 chips and not normally of concern to the user.
5. Input and output capacitance is 3 to 5 pf typical on all pins except $V_{DD}$, $V_{GG}$, and $V_{SS}$.

## 3851 PSU

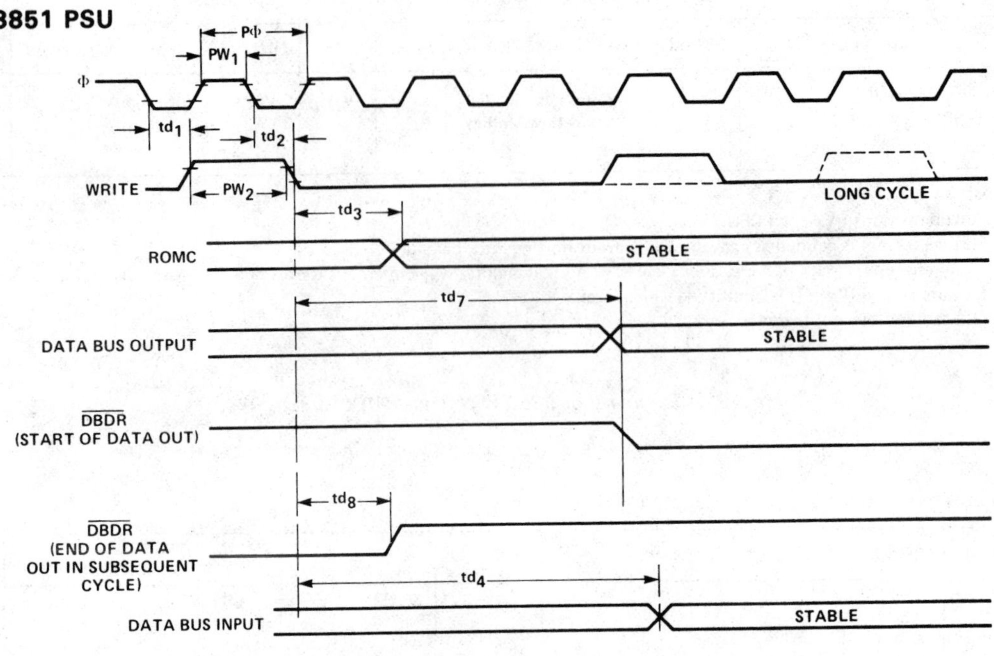


SYMBOLS ARE DEFINED IN TABLE 3-3

*Figure 3-3. 3851 PSU Data Bus Timing*

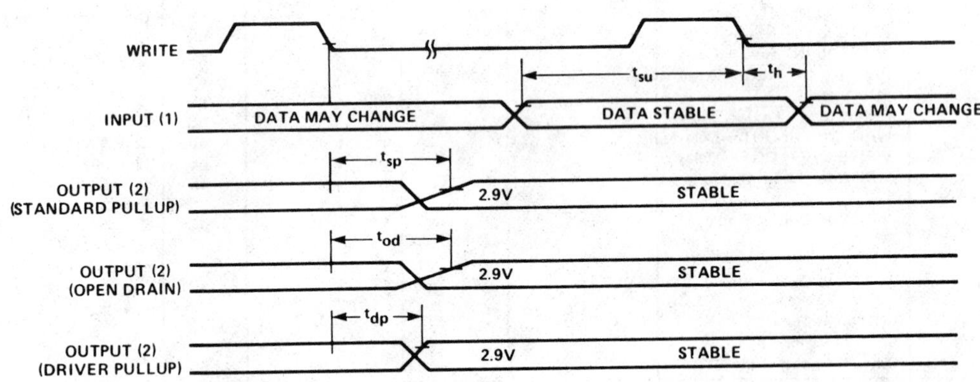


SYMBOLS ARE DEFINED IN TABLE 3-3

1. The set-up and hold times specified are with respect to the end of the second long cycle during execution of the three cycle IN or INS instruction.
2. All delay times are specified with respect to the end of the second long cycle during execution of the three cycle OUT or OUTS instruction.

*Figure 3-7. Timing at PSU I/O Ports*

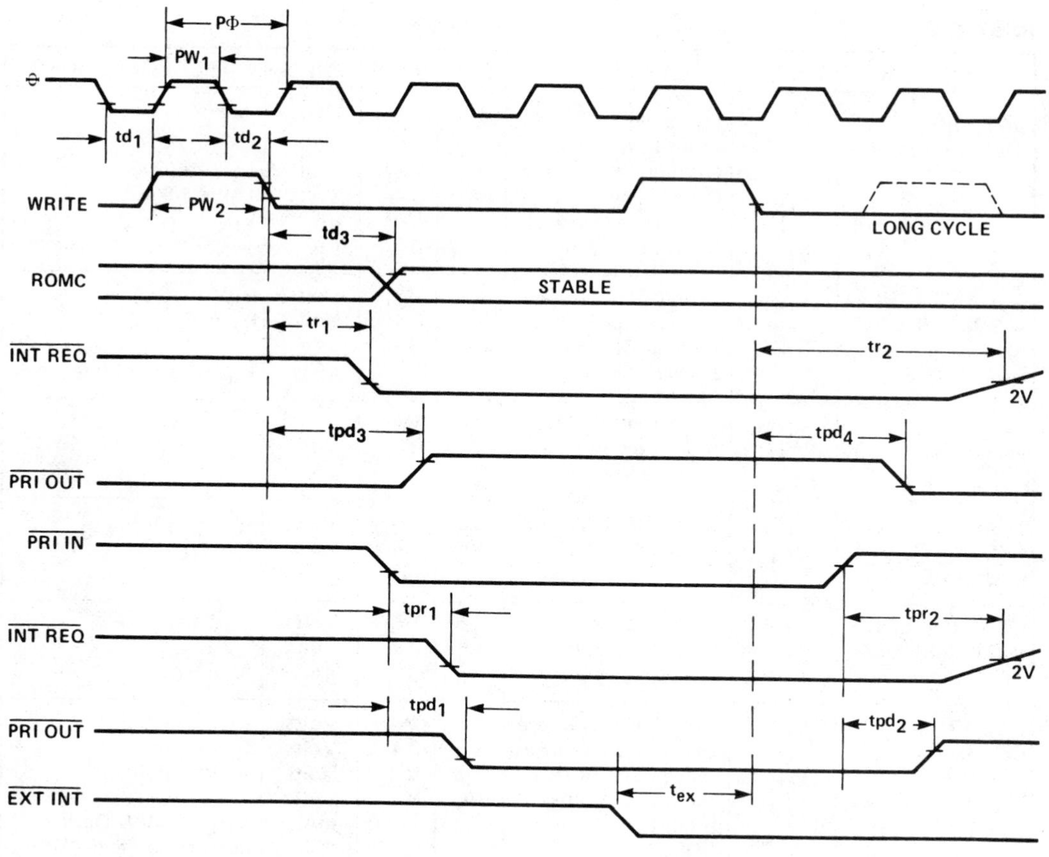


NOTE: TIMING MEASUREMENTS ARE MADE AT VALID LOGIC LEVEL OF THE SIGNALS REFERENCED UNLESS OTHERWISE NOTED.

SYMBOLS ARE DEFINED IN TABLE 3-3

*Figure 3-13. Interrupt Logic Signals' Timing*

*Table 4-2. Summary of 3852 DMI Signal Characteristics*

| SIGNAL | SYMBOL | PARAMETER | MIN. | MAX. | UNITS | TEST CONDITIONS |
|---|---|---|---|---|---|---|
| DATA BUS (DB0-DB7) | $V_{IH}$ | Input High Voltage | 2.9 | $V_{DD}$ | Volts | |
| | $V_{IL}$ | Input Low Voltage | $V_{SS}$ | 0.8 | Volts | |
| | $V_{OH}$ | Output High Voltage | 3.9 | $V_{DD}$ | Volts | $I_{OH}$ = -100 μA |
| | $V_{OL}$ | Output Low Voltage | $V_{SS}$ | 0.4 | Volts | $I_{OL}$ = 1.6 mA |
| | $I_{IH}$ | Input High Current | | 3 | μA | $V_{IN} = V_{DD}$, 3-State mode |
| | $I_{IL}$ | Input Low Current | | -3 | μA | $V_{IN} = V_{SS}$, 3-State mode |
| ADDRESS LINES (ADDR0-ADDR15) AND RAM WRITE (overlined) | $V_{OH}$ | Output High Voltage | 4.0 | $V_{DD}$ | Volts | $I_{OH}$ = -1 mA |
| | $V_{OL}$ | Output Low Voltage | $V_{SS}$ | 0.4 | Volts | $I_{OL}$ = 3.2 mA |
| | $I_L$ | Leakage Current | | 3 | μA | $V_{IN} = V_{DD}$, 3-State mode |
| | $I_L$ | Leakage Current | | -3 | μA | $V_{IN} = V_{SS}$, 3-State mode |
| CLOCK (Φ, WRITE) | $V_{IH}$ | Input High Voltage | 4.0 | $V_{DD}$ | Volts | |
| | $V_{IL}$ | Input Low Voltage | $V_{SS}$ | 0.8 | Volts | |
| | $I_L$ | Leakage Current | | 3 | μA | $V_{IN} = V_{DD}$ |
| MEMIDLE, CYCLE REQ, CPU READ | $V_{OH}$ | Output High Voltage | 3.9 | $V_{DD}$ | Volts | $I_{OH}$ = -1 mA |
| | $V_{OL}$ | Output Low Voltage | $V_{SS}$ | 0.4 | Volts | $I_{OL}$ = 2 mA |
| CONTROL LINES (ROMC0-ROMC4) | $V_{IH}$ | Input High Voltage | 3.5 | $V_{DD}$ | Volts | |
| | $V_{IL}$ | Input Low Voltage | $V_{SS}$ | 0.8 | Volts | |
| | $I_L$ | Leakage Current | | 3 | μA | $V_{IN}$ = 6V |
| REGDR, CPU SLOT | $V_{OH}$ | Output High Voltage | 3.9 | $V_{DD}$ | Volts | $I_{OH}$ = -300 μA |
| | $V_{OL}$ | Output Low Voltage | $V_{SS}$ | 0.4 | Volts | $I_{OL}$ = 2 mA |
| | $V_{IH}$ | Input High Voltage | 3.5 | $V_{DD}$ | Volts | Internal Pull-up |
| | $V_{IL}$ | Input Low Voltage | $V_{SS}$ | 0.8 | Volts | |
| | $I_{IL}$ | Input Low Current (REGDR) | -3.5 | -14.0 | mA | $V_{IN}$ = 0.4V & Device outputting a logic "1" |
| | $I_L$ | Leakage Current | | 3 | μA | $V_{IN}$ = 6V |

*Table 4-3. 3852 DMI Output Signals Timing Summary*

| SYMBOL | PARAMETER | MIN. | TYP. | MAX. | UNITS | NOTES |
|---|---|---|---|---|---|---|
| PΦ | Φ clock period | 0.5 | | 10 | μS | Fig. 2-9 |
| $td_2$ | Φ to WRITE - Delay | | | 250 | nS | |
| $tad_1$ | Address delay if PC0 | 50 | 300 | 500 | nS | 3 |
| $tad_2$ | Address delay to high Z (short cycle with DMA on) | $tcs_2$+50 | | $tcs_2$+200 | nS | 3 |
| $tad_3$ | Address delay to refresh (short cycle with REF on) | $tcs_2$+50 | | $tcs_2$+400 | nS | 3 |
| $tad_4$ | Address delay if DC | 2PΦ+50-$td_2$ | | 2PΦ+400-$td_2$ | nS | 3 |
| $tad_5$ | Address delay to high Z (long cycle with DMA on) | $tcs_3$+50 | | $tcs_3$+200 | nS | 3 |
| $tad_6$ | Address delay to refresh (long cycle with REF on) | $tcs_3$+50 | | $tcs_3$+400 | nS | 3 |
| $tcr_1$ | CPU READ – Delay | 50 | 250 | 450 | nS | 1 |
| $tcr_2$ | CPU READ + Delay | 2PΦ+50-$td_2$ | | 2PΦ+400-$td_2$ | nS | 1 |
| $tcs_1$ | CPU SLOT + Delay | 80-$td_2$ | | 320-$td_2$ | nS | 1 |
| $tcs_2$ | CPU SLOT – Delay (PC0 access) | 2PΦ+60-$td_2$ | | 2PΦ+420-$td_2$ | nS | 1 |
| $tcs_3$ | CPU SLOT – Delay (DC access) | 4PΦ+60-$td_2$ | | 2PΦ+420-$td_2$ | nS | 1 |
| $tm_1$ | MEMIDLE + Delay (PC0 access) | 2PΦ+50-$td_2$ | | 4PΦ+400-$td_2$ | nS | 1 |
| $tm_2$ | MEMIDLE – Delay (PC0 access) | 4PΦ+50-$td_2$ | | 4PΦ+350-$td_2$ | nS | 1 |
| $tm_3$ | MEMIDLE + Delay (DC access) | 4PΦ+50-$td_2$ | | 4PΦ+400-$td_2$ | nS | 1 |
| $tm_4$ | MEMIDLE – Delay (DC access) | 6PΦ+50-$td_2$ | | 6PΦ+350-$td_2$ | nS | 1 |
| $tcy_1$ | WRITE to CYCLE REQ – Delay | 80-$td_2$ | | 400-$td_2$ | nS | 1, 4 |
| $tcy_2$ | WRITE to CYCLE REQ + Delay | PΦ+80-$td_2$ | | PΦ+400-$td_2$ | nS | 1, 4 |
| $tcy_3$ | CYCLE REQ + to + Edge Delay | | 2PΦ | | | 1, 4 |
| $tcy_4$ | CYCLE REQ – to – Edge Delay | | 2PΦ | | | 1, 4 |
| $twr_1$ | $\overline{\text{RAM WRITE}}$ – Delay | 4PΦ+50-$td_2$ | | 4PΦ+450-$td_2$ | nS | 3 |
| $twr_2$ | $\overline{\text{RAM WRITE}}$ + Delay | 5PΦ+50-$td_2$ | | 5PΦ+300-$td_2$ | nS | 3 |
| $twr_3$ | $\overline{\text{RAM WRITE}}$ Pulse Width | 350 | | PΦ | nS | 3 |
| $twr_4$ | $\overline{\text{RAM WRITE}}$ to High Z Delay | $tcs_2$+40 | | $tcs_2$+200 | nS | 3 |
| $trg_1$ | REGDR – Delay | 70 | 300 | 500 | nS | 1 |
| $trg_2$ | REGDR + Delay | 2PΦ+80-$td_2$ | | 2PΦ+500-$td_2$ | nS | 1 |
| $td_4$ | WRITE to Data Bus Input Delay | | | 2PΦ+1000 | nS | |
| $td_7$ | WRITE to Data Bus Output Delay | 2PΦ+100-$td_2$ | | 2PΦ+850-$td_2$ | | 2 |

**Notes:**

1. $C_L$ = 50 pf.

2. $C_L$ = 100 pf.

3. $C_L$ = 500 pf.

4. CYCLE REQ is a divide-by-2 of Φ for all instructions except the STORE instruction.

5. On a given chip, the timing for all signals will tend to track. For example, if CPU SLOT for a particular chip is fairly slow and its timing falls out near the MAX delay value specified, then the timing for all signals on that chip will tend to be out near the MAX delay values. Likewise for a fast chip whose signals fall near the MIN values. This is a result of the fact that processing parameters (which affect device speed) are quite uniform over small physical areas on the surface of a wafer.

6. Input and output capacitance is 3 to 5 pf typical on all pins except $V_{DD}$, $V_{GG}$, and $V_{SS}$.

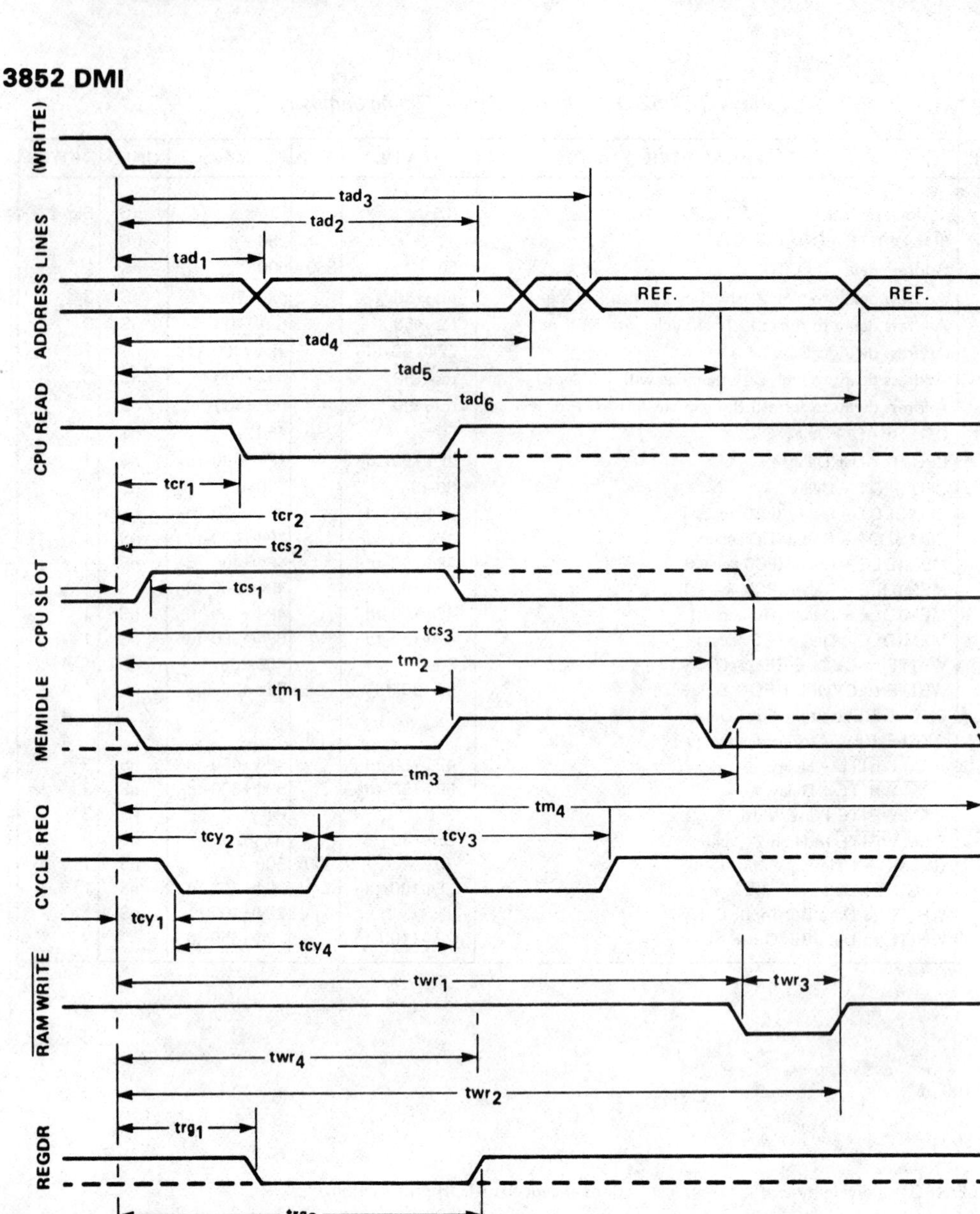


*Figure 4-4. Timing Characteristics for 3852 DMI Output Signals*

#### 4.2.2 DC Electrical Specifications

*Absolute Maximum Ratings* (Above which useful life may be impaired).

| | |
|---|---|
| $V_{GG}$ | +15V to -0.3V |
| $V_{DD}$ | +7V to -0.3V |
| All other inputs & outputs | +7V to -0.3V |
| Storage Temperature | −55°C to +150°C |
| Operating Temperature | 0°C to +70°C |

**Note:** All voltages with respect to $V_{SS}$.

*DC Characteristics:* $V_{SS}$ = 0V, $V_{DD}$ = +5V ± 5%, $V_{GG}$ = +12V ± 5%, $T_A$ = 0°C to +70°C

*SUPPLY CURRENTS*

| SYMBOL | PARAMETER | MIN. | TYP. | MAX. | UNITS | TEST CONDITIONS |
|---|---|---|---|---|---|---|
| $I_{DD}$ | $V_{DD}$ Current | | 35 | 70 | mA | f = 2 MHz, Outputs unloaded |
| $I_{GG}$ | $V_{GG}$ Current | | 13 | 30 | mA | f = 2 MHz, Outputs unloaded |

*Table 5-2. 3853 SMI Output Signals Timing Summary*

| SYMBOL | PARAMETER | MIN. | TYP. | MAX. | UNITS | NOTES |
|---|---|---|---|---|---|---|
| PΦ | Φ clock period | 0.5 | | 10 | μS | Fig. 2-9 |
| $td_2$ | Φ to WRITE - Delay | | | 250 | nS | 2 |
| $tad_1$ | Address delay if PC0 | 50 | 300 | 500 | nS | 3 |
| $tad_4$ | Address delay if DC0 | 2PΦ+50-$td_2$ | | 2PΦ+400-$td_2$ | nS | 3 |
| $tcr_1$ | CPU READ – Delay | 50 | 250 | 450 | nS | 1 |
| $tcr_2$ | CPU READ + Delay | 2PΦ+50-$td_2$ | | 2PΦ+400-$td_2$ | nS | 1 |
| $twr_1$ | $\overline{\text{RAM WRITE}}$ – Delay | 4PΦ+50-$td_2$ | | 4PΦ+450-$td_2$ | nS | 3 |
| $twr_2$ | $\overline{\text{RAM WRITE}}$ + Delay | 5PΦ+50-$td_2$ | | 5PΦ+300-$td_2$ | nS | 3 |
| $twr_3$ | $\overline{\text{RAM WRITE}}$ Pulse | 350 | | PΦ | nS | 3 |
| $trg_1$ | REGDR – Delay | 70 | 300 | 500 | nS | 1 |
| $trg_2$ | REGDR + Delay | 2PΦ+80-$td_2$ | | 2PΦ+500-$td_2$ | nS | 1 |
| $td_4$ | WRITE to Data Bus Input Delay | | | 2PΦ+1000 | nS | |
| $td_7$ | WRITE to Data Bus Output Delay | 2PΦ+100-$td_2$ | | 2PΦ+850-$td_2$ | nS | 2 |
| $tr_1$ | WRITE to $\overline{\text{INT REQ}}$ – Delay | | | 430 | nS | 2, 6 |
| $tpr_1$ | $\overline{\text{PRI IN}}$ to $\overline{\text{INT REQ}}$ – Delay | | 200 | 240 | nS | 2, 7 |
| $t_{ex}$ | $\overline{\text{EXT INT}}$ Set-up Time | 400 | | | nS | |

**Notes:**

1. $C_L$ = 50 pf.
2. $C_L$ = 100 pf.
3. $C_L$ = 500 pf.
4. On a given chip, the timing for all signals will tend to track. For example, if CPU SLOT for a particular chip is fairly slow and its timing falls out near the MAX delay value specified, then the timing for all signals on that chip will tend to be out near the MAX delay values. Likewise for a fast chip whose signals fall out near the MIN values. This is a result of the fact that processing parameters (which affect device speed) are quite uniform.
5. Input and output capacitance is 3 to 5 pf typical on all pins except $V_{DD}$, $V_{GG}$, and $V_{SS}$.
6. Assume Priority In was enabled ($\overline{\text{PRI IN}}$ = 0) in previous F8 cycle before interrupt is detected in the PSU.
7. PSU has interrupt pending before priority in is enabled.

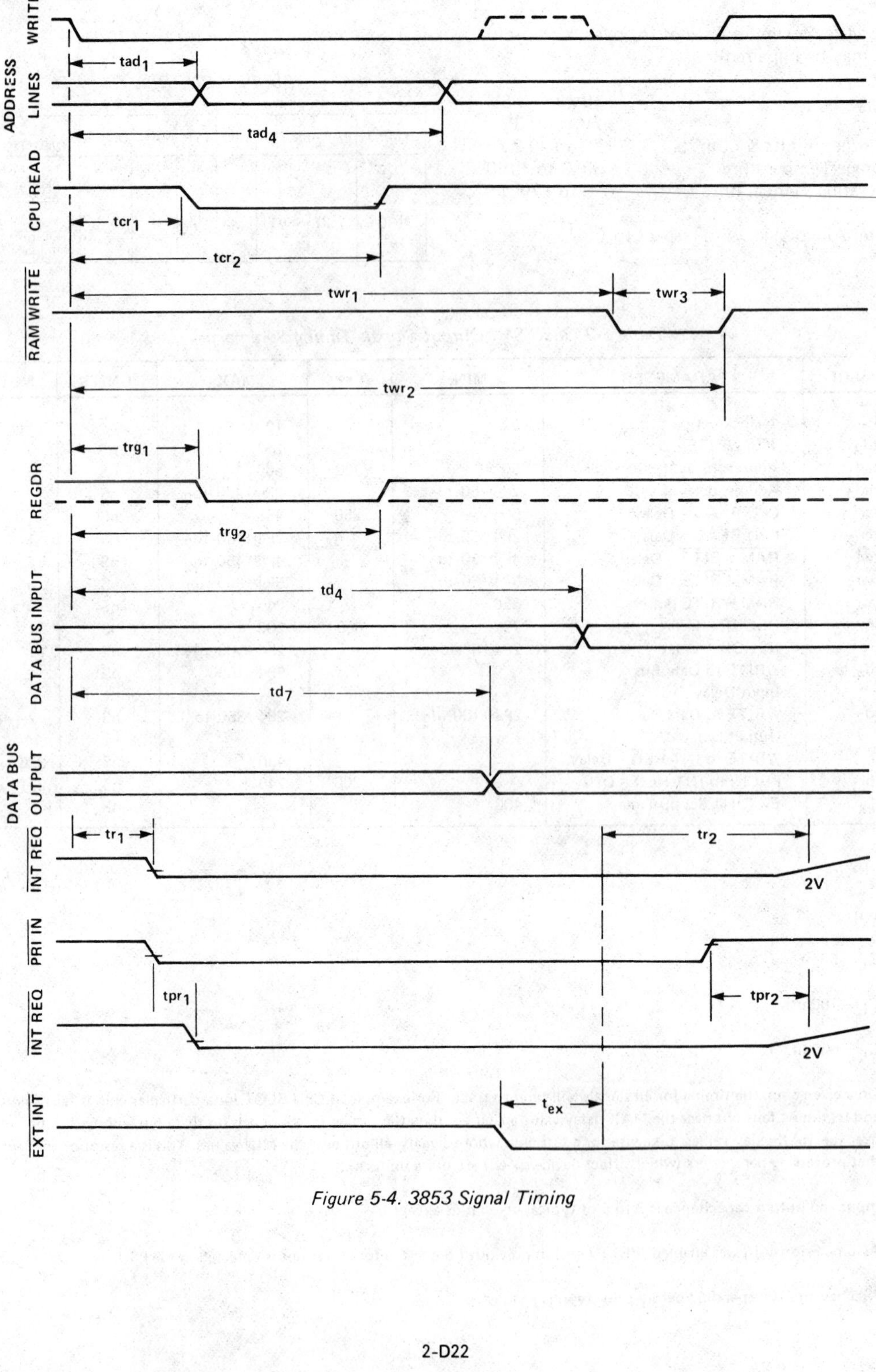

*Figure 5-4. 3853 Signal Timing*

*Table 6-3. Summary of 3854 DMA Signal Characteristics*

*ELECTRICAL SPECIFICATIONS*

*Absolute Maximum Ratings (Above which useful life may be impaired)*

| | |
|---|---|
| $V_{GG}$ | +15V to -0.3V |
| $V_{DD}$ | +7V to -0.3V |
| All other Inputs & Outputs | +7V to -0.3V |
| Storage Temperature | -55°C to +150°C |
| Operating Temperature | 0°C to +70°C |

**Note:** All voltages with respect to $V_{SS}$.

DC CHARACTERISTICS: $V_{SS}$ = 0V, $V_{DD}$ = +5V ± 5%, $V_{GG}$ = +12V ± 5%, $T_A$ = 0 to +70°C

**SUPPLY CURRENTS**

| SYMBOL | PARAMETER | MIN. | TYP. | MAX. | UNITS | TEST CONDITIONS |
|---|---|---|---|---|---|---|
| $I_{DD}$ | $V_{DD}$ Current | | 20 | 40 | mA | f = 2 MHz, Outputs Unloaded |
| $I_{GG}$ | $V_{GG}$ Current | | 15 | 28 | mA | f = 2 MHz, Outputs Unloaded |

| SIGNAL | SYMBOL | PARAMETER | MIN. | MAX. | UNITS | TEST CONDITIONS |
|---|---|---|---|---|---|---|
| DATA BUS (DB0-DB7) | $V_{IH}$ | Input High Voltage | 3.5 | $V_{DD}$ | Volts | |
| | $V_{IL}$ | Input Low Voltage | $V_{SS}$ | 0.8 | Volts | |
| | $V_{OH}$ | Output High Voltage | 3.9 | $V_{DD}$ | Volts | $I_{OH}$ = -100 μA |
| | $V_{OL}$ | Output Low Voltage | $V_{SS}$ | 0.4 | Volts | $I_{OL}$ = 1.6 mA |
| | $I_{IH}$ | Input High Current | | 1 | μA | $V_{IN}$ = 6V, 3-State mode |
| | $I_{IL}$ | Input Low Current | | -1 | μA | $V_{IN}$ = $V_{SS}$, 3-State mode |
| ADDRESS LINES (ADDR0-ADDR15) | $V_{OH}$ | Output High Voltage | 4.0 | $V_{DD}$ | Volts | $I_{OH}$ = -1 mA |
| | $V_{OL}$ | Output Low Voltage | $V_{SS}$ | 0.4 | Volts | $I_{OL}$ = 3.2 mA |
| | $I_L$ | Leakage Current | | 1 | μA | $V_{IN}$ = 6V, 3-State mode |
| ENABLE, DIRECTION DWS (DMA WRITE SLOT), XFER, STROBE | $V_{OH}$ | Output High Voltage | 3.9 | $V_{DD}$ | Volts | $I_{OH}$ = -100 μA |
| | $V_{OL}$ | Output Low Voltage | $V_{SS}$ | 0.4 | Volts | $I_{OL}$ = 2 mA |
| | $I_L$ | Leakage Current | | 1 | μA | $V_{IN}$ = 6V |

| SIGNAL | SYMBOL | PARAMETER | MIN. | MAX. | UNITS | TEST CONDITIONS |
|---|---|---|---|---|---|---|
| MEM IDLE, $\overline{\text{XFER REQ}}$ | $V_{IH}$ | Input High Voltage | 3.5 | $V_{DD}$ | Volts | |
| | $V_{IL}$ | Input Low Voltage | $V_{SS}$ | 0.8 | Volts | |
| | $I_L$ | Leakage Current | | 1 | μA | $V_{IN}$ = 6V |
| LOAD REG, READ REG, P1, P2 | $V_{IH}$ | Input High Voltage | 3.5 | $V_{DD}$ | Volts | |
| | $V_{IL}$ | Input Low Voltage | $V_{SS}$ | 0.8 | Volts | |
| | $I_L$ | Leakage Current | 0 | 1 | μA | $V_{IN}$ = 6V |
| WRITE, Φ | $V_{IH}$ | Input High Voltage | 4.0 | $V_{DD}$ | Volts | |
| | $V_{IL}$ | Input Low Voltage | $V_{SS}$ | 0.8 | Volts | |
| | $I_L$ | Leakage Current | 0 | 1 | μA | $V_{IN}$ = 6V |

**Note:**

Positive current is defined as conventional current flowing into the pin referenced.

*Table 6-4. 3854 DMA Device Signals Summary*

| SYMBOL | PARAMETER | MIN. | TYP. | MAX. | UNITS | NOTES |
|---|---|---|---|---|---|---|
| PΦ | Φ Clock Period | 0.5 | | 10 | μS | Note 1 |
| $PW_1$ | Φ Pulse Width | 180 | | PΦ-180 | nS | $t_r$, $t_f$ = 50 nS typ. |
| $td_1$ | Φ to WRITE + Delay | 60 | | 300 | nS | Note 1 |
| $td_2$ | Φ to WRITE – Delay | 60 | | 250 | nS | Note 1 |
| $PW_2$ | WRITE Pulse Width | PΦ-100 | | PΦ | nS | $t_r$, $t_f$ = 50 nS typ. |
| $td_3$ | WRITE to READ/LOAD REG Delay | | | 600 | nS | |
| $td_4$ | DB Input Set-up Time | | | 300 | nS | |
| $td_6$ | $\overline{\text{XFER REQ}}$ to MEM IDLE Set-up | 200 | | | nS | |
| $td_7$ | MEM IDLE to ADDR True | 50 | 200 | 500 | nS | $C_L$ = 500 pf |
| $td_7'$ | MEM IDLE to ADDR 3-State | 30 | | 250 | nS | $C_L$ = 500 pf |
| $td_8$ | READ REG to DB Output | 40 | | 300 | nS | $C_L$ = 100 pf |
| $td_9$ | WRITE to ENABLE & DIRECTION + Delay | | | 450 | nS | $C_L$ = 50 pf |
| $td_9'$ | MEM IDLE to ENABLE - Delay | | | 400 | nS | $C_L$ = 50 pf |
| $td_{10}$ | MEM IDLE to XFER & DWS + Delay | | | 300 | nS | $C_L$ = 50 pf |
| $td_{10}$ | MEM IDLE to XFER & DWS – Delay | | | 300 | nS | $C_L$ = 50 pf |
| $td_{11}$ | Φ to STROBE + Delay | 30 | | 200 | nS | $C_L$ = 50 pf |
| $td_{11}$ | Φ to STROBE – Delay | 30 | | 200 | nS | $C_L$ = 50 pf |

**Notes:**

1. These specifications are those of Φ and WRITE as supplied by the 3850 CPU.
2. Input and output capacitance is 3 to 5 pf typical on all pins except $V_{DD}$, $V_{GG}$, and $V_{SS}$.

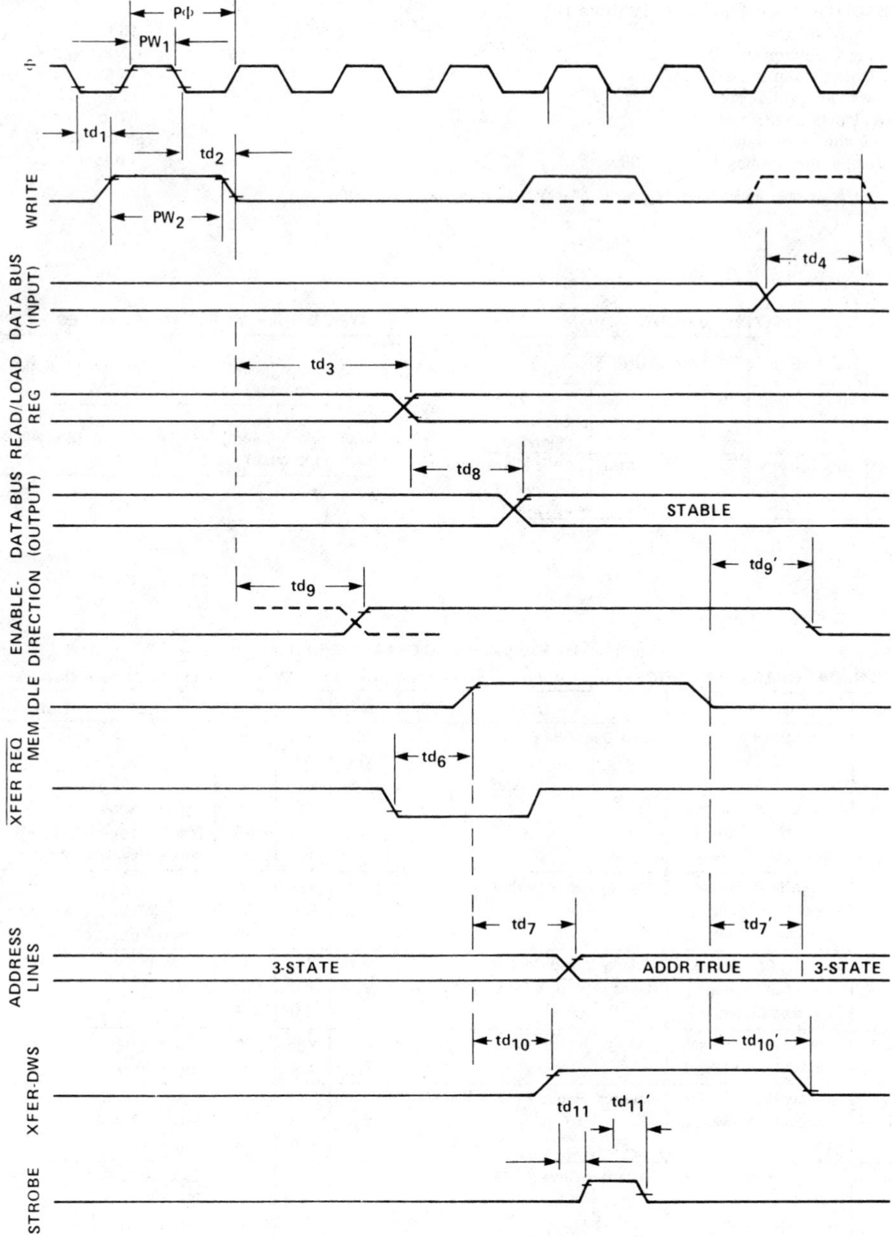


*Figure 6-5. 3854 DMA Device Signals and Timing*

## 3856 2K PSU

**ABSOLUTE MAXIMUM RATINGS** (Note 1)

| | |
|---|---|
| Supply Voltage $V_{GG}$ | +15 to −0.3 V |
| Supply Voltage $V_{DD}$ | +7 to −0.3 V |
| I/O Port Open Drain Option | +15 to −0.3 V |
| Other I/O Port Options | +7 to −0.3 V |
| All Inputs and Outputs | +7 to −0.3 V |
| Storage Temperature | −55 to +150°C |
| Temperature (Ambient) Under Bias | 0 to +70°C |

NOTE 1. Above which useful life may be impaired. All voltages measured with respect to $V_{SS}$.

**SUPPLY CURRENTS**

| SYMBOL | PARAMETER | TYP | MAX | UNITS | TEST CONDITIONS |
|---|---|---|---|---|---|
| $I_{DD}$ | $V_{DD}$ Current | 75 | 125 | mA | f = 2 MHz, Outputs unloaded |
| $I_{GG}$ | $V_{GG}$ Current | 30 | 45 | mA | f = 2 MHz, Outputs unloaded |

**TYPICAL THERMAL RESISTANCE VALUES**

| | |
|---|---|
| PLASTIC: | |
| $\theta_{JA}$ (Junction to ambient) | = 60°C/W (Still Air) |
| $\theta_{JC}$ (Junction to case) | = 42°C/W |
| CERAMIC: | |
| $\theta_{JA}$ (Junction to ambient) | = 48°C/W (Still Air) |
| $\theta_{JC}$ (Junction to case) | = 33°C/W |

**TABLE 1. 3856 PSU SIGNAL DC CHARACTERISTICS**

**DC ELECTRICAL CHARACTERISTICS:** $V_{SS}$ = 0 V, $V_{DD}$ = +5.0 V ±5%, $V_{GG}$ = +12 V ±5%, $T_A$ = 0°C to +70°C unless otherwise noted.

| SYMBOL | PARAMETER | SIGNAL | MIN | MAX | UNITS | TEST CONDITIONS |
|---|---|---|---|---|---|---|
| $V_{IH}$ | Input HIGH Voltage | Data Bus ($DB_0$-$DB_7$) | 2.9 | $V_{DD}$ | V | |
| $V_{IL}$ | Input LOW Voltage | | $V_{SS}$ | 0.8 | V | |
| $V_{OH}$ | Output HIGH Voltage | | 3.9 | $V_{DD}$ | V | $I_{OH}$ = −100 μA |
| $V_{OL}$ | Output LOW Voltage | | $V_{SS}$ | 0.4 | V | $I_{OL}$ = 1.6 mA |
| $I_{IH}$ | Input HIGH Current | | | 3.0 | μA | $V_{IN}$ = $V_{DD}$, 3-State Mode |
| $I_{OL}$ | Input LOW Current | | | −3.0 | μA | $V_{IN}$ = $V_{SS}$, 3-State Mode |
| $V_{IH}$ | Input HIGH Voltage | Clock Lines (ϕ, Write) | 4.0 | $V_{DD}$ | V | |
| $V_{IL}$ | Input LOW Voltage | | $V_{SS}$ | 0.8 | V | |
| $I_L$ | Leakage Current | | | 3.0 | μA | $V_{IN}$ = $V_{DD}$ |
| $V_{IH}$ | Input HIGH Voltage | Priority In and Control | 3.5 | $V_{DD}$ | V | |
| $V_{IL}$ | Input LOW Voltage | Lines ($\overline{\text{PRI IN}}$, ROM $C_0$-ROM $C_4$) | $V_{SS}$ | 0.8 | V | |
| $I_L$ | Leakage Current | | | 3.0 | μA | $V_{IN}$ = $V_{DD}$ |
| $V_{OH}$ | Output HIGH Voltage | Priority Out ($\overline{\text{PRI OUT}}$) | 3.9 | $V_{DD}$ | V | $I_{OH}$ = −100 μA |
| $V_{OL}$ | Output LOW Voltage | | $V_{SS}$ | 0.4 | V | $I_{OL}$ = 100 μA |
| $V_{OH}$ | Output HIGH Voltage | Interrupt Request ($\overline{\text{INT REQ}}$) | | | V | Open Drain Output (Note 1) |
| $V_{OL}$ | Output LOW Voltage | | $V_{SS}$ | 0.4 | V | $I_{OL}$ = 1.0 mA |
| $I_L$ | Leakage Current | | | 3.0 | μA | $V_{IN}$ = $V_{DD}$ |
| $V_{OH}$ | Output HIGH Voltage | Data Bus Drive ($\overline{\text{DBDR}}$) | | | | External Pull-up |
| $V_{OL}$ | Output LOW Voltage | | $V_{SS}$ | 0.4 | V | $I_{OL}$ = 2.0 mA |
| $I_L$ | Leakage Current | | | 3.0 | μA | $V_{IN}$ = $V_{DD}$ |

### TABLE 1. 3856 PSU SIGNAL DC CHARACTERISTICS

**DC ELECTRICAL CHARACTERISTICS:** $V_{SS} = 0\,V$, $V_{DD} = +5.0\,V \pm 5\%$, $V_{GG} = +12\,V \pm 5\%$, $T_A = 0°C$ to $+70°C$ unless otherwise noted.

| SYMBOL | PARAMETER | SIGNAL | MIN | MAX | UNITS | TEST CONDITIONS |
|---|---|---|---|---|---|---|
| $V_{OH}$ | Input HIGH Voltage | Strobe | 3.9 | $V_{DD}$ | V | $I_{OH} = 1.0$ mA |
| $V_{OL}$ | Output LOW Voltage | | $V_{SS}$ | 0.4 | V | $I_{OL} = 2.0$ mA |
| $V_{IH}$ | Input HIGH Voltage | External Interrupt ($\overline{EXT\ INT}$) | 2.9 | $V_{DD}$ | V | $I_{IN} = -130\ \mu A$ (Internal Pull-up) |
| $V_{IL}$ | Input LOW Voltage | | $V_{SS}$ | 0.8 | V | |
| $I_{IL}$ | Input LOW Current | | | −1.6 | mA | $V_{IN} = 0.4$ V |
| $V_{OH}$ | Output HIGH Voltage | I/O Port Option A | 3.9 | $V_{DD}$ | V | $I_{OH} = -30\ \mu A$, Note 5 |
| $V_{OH}$ | Output HIGH Voltage | (Standard Pull-Up) | 2.9 | $V_{DD}$ | V | $I_{OH} = -150\ \mu A$ |
| $V_{OL}$ | Output LOW Voltage | | $V_{SS}$ | 0.4 | V | $I_{OL} = 1.6$ mA |
| $V_{IH}$ | Input HIGH Voltage | | 2.9 | $V_{DD}$ | V | Internal Pull-up to $V_{DD}$, Note 3 |
| $V_{IL}$ | Input LOW Voltage | | $V_{SS}$ | 0.8 | V | |
| $I_{IL}$ | Input LOW Current | | | −1.6 | mA | $V_{IN} = 0.4$ V, Note 4 |
| $V_{OH}$ | Output HIGH Voltage | I/O Port Option B | | • | | External Pull-up |
| $V_{OL}$ | Output LOW Voltage | (Open Drain) | $V_{SS}$ | 0.4 | V | $I_{OL} = 2.0$ mA, Note 3 |
| $V_{IH}$ | Input HIGH Voltage | | 2.9 | $V_{DD}$ | V | |
| $V_{IL}$ | Input LOW Voltage | | $V_{SS}$ | 0.8 | V | |
| $V_{OH}$ | Output HIGH Voltage | I/O Port Option C | 4.0 | $V_{DD}$ | V | $I_{OH} = -1.0$ mA |
| $V_{OL}$ | Output LOW Voltage | (Driver Pull-Up) | $V_{SS}$ | 0.4 | V | $I_{OL} = 2.0$ mA |

NOTES:
1. Pull-up resistor to $V_{DD}$ on CPU.
2. Positive current is defined as conventional current flowing into the pin referenced.
3. Hysteresis input circuit provides additional 0.3 V noise immunity while internal/external pull-up provides TTL compatibility.
4. Measured while I/O port is outputting a high level.
5. Guaranteed, but not tested.

### TABLE 2. 3856 PSU SIGNAL AC CHARACTERISTICS

**AC ELECTRICAL CHARACTERISTICS:** $V_{SS} = 0\,V$, $V_{DD} = +5.0\,V \pm 5\%$, $V_{GG} = +12\,V \pm 5\%$, $T_A = 0°C$ to $+70°C$ unless otherwise noted.

| SYMBOL | PARAMETER | MIN | TYP | MAX | UNITS | TEST CONDITIONS |
|---|---|---|---|---|---|---|
| $P\phi$ | $\phi$ Period | 0.5 | | 10 | μs | |
| $PW_1$ | $\phi$ Pulse Width | 180 | | $P\phi-180$ | ns | $t_r$, $t_f$ = 50 ns Typ |
| $td_1$, $td_2$ | $\phi$ to Write + Delay | | | 250 | ns | $C_L$ = 100 pF |
| $td_4$ | Write to DB Input Delay | | | $2P\phi+1.0$ | μs | |
| $PW_2$ | Write Pulse Width | $P\phi-100$ | | $P\phi$ | ns | $t_r$, $t_f$ = 50 ns Typ |
| $PW_S$ | Write Period; Short | | $4P\phi$ | | | |
| $PW_L$ | Write Period; Long | | | | ns | |
| $td_3$ | Write to ROMC Delay | | | 550 | ns | |
| $td_7$ | Write to DB Output Delay | $2P\phi+100-td_2$ | $2P\phi+200$ | $2P\phi+850-td_2$ | ns | $C_L$ = 100 pF |
| | Write to DBDR − Delay | | | | | |
| $td_8$ | Write to DBDR + Delay | | 200 | | ns | Open Drain |
| $tr_1$ | Write to INT Req − Delay | | | 430 | ns | $C_L$ = 100 pF, Note 1 |
| $tpr_1$ | PRI In to INT Req − Delay | | 200 | | ns | $C_L$ = 100 pF, Note 2 |
| $tpd_1$, $tpd_2$ | PRI In to PRI Out Delay | | 800 | | ns | $C_L$ = 50 pF |
| $tpd_3$, $tpd_4$ | Write to PRI Out Delay | | 600 | | ns | $C_L$ = 50 pF |
| $t_{sp}$ | Write to Output Stable | | | 1.0 | μs | $C_L$ = 50 pF, Standard Pull-up Note 3 |
| $t_{od}$ | Write to Output Stable | | | 2.5 | μs | $C_L$ = 50 pF, $R_L$ = 12.5 kΩ Open Drain, Note 5 |
| $t_{dp}$ | Write to Output Stable | | 200 | 400 | ns | $C_L$ = 50 pF, Driver Pull-up |
| $t_{su}$ | I/O Set-up Time | 1.3 | | | μs | |
| $t_h$ | I/O Hold Time | 0 | | | ns | |
| $t_{ax}$ | Ext Int Set-up Time | 400 | | | ns | |
| $t_sB_1$ | Write to Strobe + Delay | | | $5P\phi+300$ | ns | $C_L$ = 50 pF |
| $t_sB_2$ | Write to Strobe − Delay | | | $6P\phi+410$ | ns | $C_L$ = 50 pF |

NOTES:
1. Assume Priority In was enabled ($\overline{PRI\ IN}$ = 0) in previous F8 cycle before interrupt is detected in the PSU.
2. PSU has interrupt pending before priority in is enabled.
3. Assume pin tied to $\overline{INT\ REQ}$ input of the 3850 CPU.
4. The parameters which are shaded in the table above represent those which are most frequently of importance when interfacing to an F8 system. Unshaded parameters are typically those that are relevant only between F8 chips and not normally of concern to the user.
5. Input and output capacitance is 3 to 5 of typical on all pins except $V_{DD}$, $V_{CC}$ and $V_{SS}$.

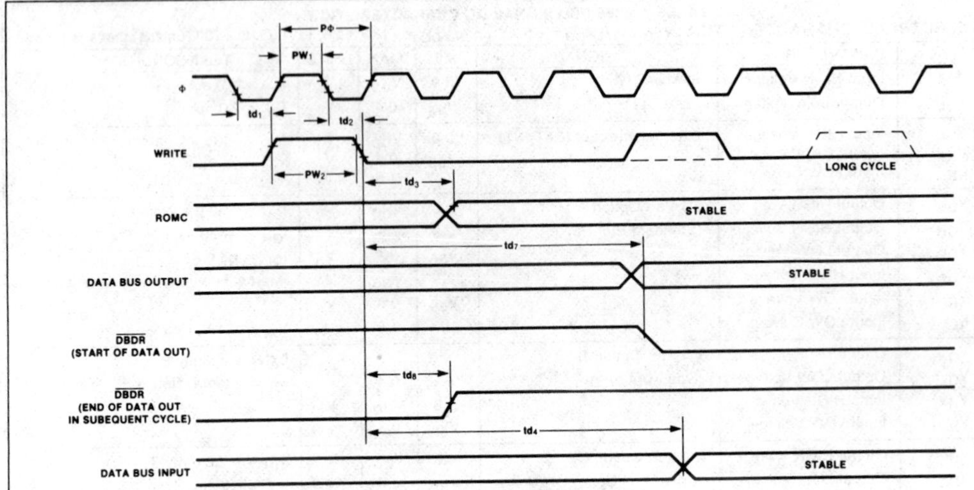


**Fig. 2 DATA BUS TIMING**

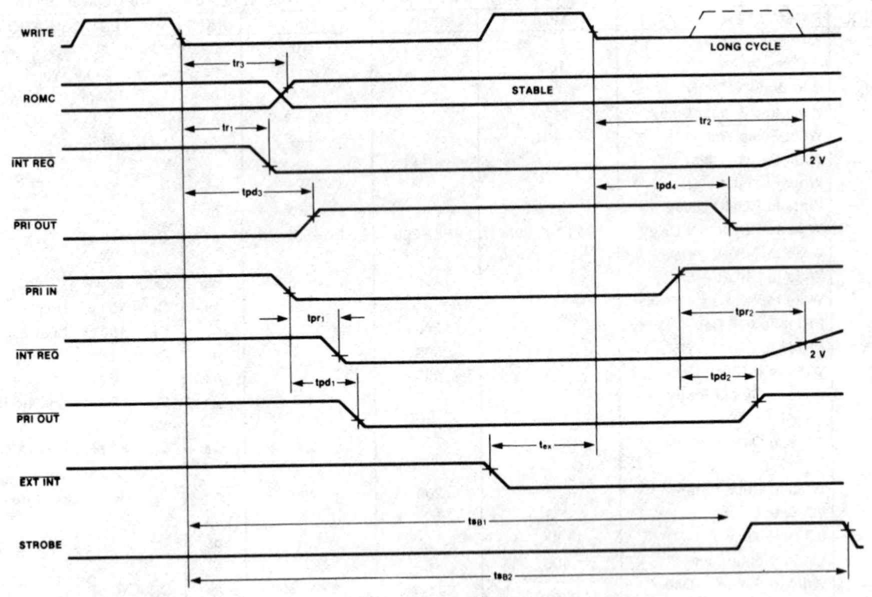


**Fig. 3 INTERRUPT LOGIC SIGNALS I/O STROBE**

NOTES:
1. Timing measurements are made at valid logic level to valid logic level of the signals referenced unless otherwise noted.
2. Symbols are defined in Table 2.

I/O operations that use the two PSU I/O ports execute in three instruction cycles. During the first cycle, the port address is transmitted to the Data Bus. During the second cycle, data is either sent from the Accumulator to the I/O latch or enabled from the I/O pin to the Accumulator depending on whether the instruction is an output or an input. At the falling edge or Write (marking the end of the second cycle and beginning of the third cycle) the data is strobed into either the Latch (OUTS) or the Accumulator (INS) respectively. The third cycle is then used by the CPU for its next instruction fetch. *Figure 4* indicates I/O timing.

Data Bus timing associated with execution of I/O instructions does not differ from Data Bus timing associated with any other data transfer to, or from the PSU. However, timing at the I/O port itself depends on which port option is being used. *Figures 5a, 5b, and 5c* illustrate the three ports options. *Figure 4* illustrates timing for the three cases.

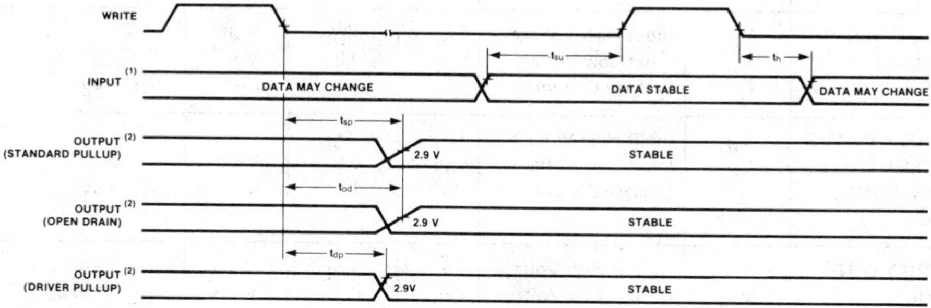


**Fig. 4 TIMING AT PSU I/O PORTS**

(1.) The set-up and hold times specified are with respect to the end of the second long cycle during execution of the three cycle IN or INS instruction.

(2.) All delay times are specified with respect to the end of the second long cycle during execution of the three cycle OUT or OUTS instruction.

### 7.2.2 Electrical Specifications

*Absolute Maximum Ratings (Above which useful life may be impaired)*

| | |
|---|---|
| $V_{GG}$ | +15V to -0.3V |
| $V_{DD}$ | +7V to -0.3V |
| External Interrupt Input | -600 μA to +225 μA |
| All other Inputs & Outputs | +7V to -0.3V |
| Storage Temperature | -55°C to +150°C |
| Operating Temperature | 0°C to +70°C |

*SUPPLY CURRENTS*

| SYMBOL | PARAMETER | MIN. | TYP. | MAX. | UNITS | TEST CONDITIONS |
|---|---|---|---|---|---|---|
| $I_{DD}$ | $V_{DD}$ Current | | 30 | 70 | mA | f = 2 MHz, Outputs Unloaded |
| $I_{GG}$ | $V_{GG}$ Current | | 10 | 18 | mA | f = 2 MHz, Outputs Unloaded |

Supply currents measured with $V_{DD}$ = +5V ± 5%, $V_{GG}$ = +12V ± 5%, $T_A$ = 0°C to +70°C. All other electrical specifications are in Table 7-4. All voltages measured with respect to $V_{SS}$.

*Table 7-4. A Summary of 3861 PIO Signal Characteristics*

| SIGNAL | SYMBOL | PARAMETER | MIN. | MAX. | UNITS | TEST CONDITIONS |
|---|---|---|---|---|---|---|
| DATA BUS (DB0-DB7) | $V_{IH}$ | Input High Voltage | 3.5 | $V_{DD}$ | Volts | |
| | $V_{IL}$ | Input Low Voltage | $V_{SS}$ | 0.8 | Volts | |
| | $V_{OH}$ | Output High Voltage | 3.9 | $V_{DD}$ | Volts | $I_{OH}$ = -100 μA |
| | $V_{OL}$ | Output Low Voltage | $V_{SS}$ | 0.4 | Volts | $I_{OL}$ = 1.6 mA |
| | $I_{IH}$ | Input High Current | | 1 | μA | $V_{IN}$ = 6V, 3-State mode |
| | $I_{OL}$ | Input Low Current | | -1 | μA | $V_{IN}$ = $V_{SS}$, 3-State mode |
| CLOCK LINES (Φ, WRITE) | $V_{IH}$ | Input High Voltage | 4.0 | $V_{DD}$ | Volts | |
| | $V_{IL}$ | Input Low Voltage | $V_{SS}$ | 0.8 | Volts | |
| | $I_L$ | Leakage Current | | 1 | μA | $V_{IN}$ = 6V |
| PRIORITY IN AND CONTROL LINES ($\overline{\text{PRI IN}}$, ROMC0-ROMC4) | $V_{IH}$ | Input High Voltage | 3.5 | $V_{DD}$ | Volts | |
| | $V_{IL}$ | Input Low Voltage | $V_{SS}$ | 0.8 | Volts | |
| | $I_L$ | Leakage Current | | 1 | μA | $V_{IN}$ = 6V |
| PRIORITY OUT ($\overline{\text{PRI OUT}}$) | $V_{OH}$ | Output High Voltage | 3.9 | $V_{DD}$ | Volts | $I_{OH}$ = -100 μA |
| | $V_{OL}$ | Output Low Voltage | $V_{SS}$ | 0.4 | Volts | $I_{OL}$ = 100 μA |
| INTERRUPT REQUEST ($\overline{\text{INT REQ}}$) | $V_{OH}$ | Output High Voltage | | | Volts | Open Drain Output [1] |
| | $V_{OL}$ | Output Low Voltage | $V_{SS}$ | 0.4 | Volts | $I_{OL}$ = 1 mA |
| | $I_L$ | Leakage Current | | 1 | μA | $V_{IN}$ = 6V |
| DATA BUS DRIVE ($\overline{\text{DBDR}}$) | $V_{OH}$ | Output High Voltage | | | | External Pull-up |
| | $V_{OL}$ | Output Low Voltage | $V_{SS}$ | 0.4 | Volts | $I_{OL}$ = 2 mA |
| | $I_L$ | Leakage Current | | 1 | μA | $V_{IN}$ = 6V |
| EXTERNAL INTERRUPT ($\overline{\text{EXT INT}}$) | $V_{IH}$ | Input High Voltage | 3.5 | | Volts | |
| | $V_{IL}$ | Input Low Voltage | | 1.2 | Volts | |
| | $V_{IC}$ | Input Clamp Voltage | | 15 | Volts | $I_{IH}$ = 185 μA |
| | $I_{IH}$ | Input High Current | | 10 | μA | $V_{IN}$ = $V_{DD}$ |
| | $I_{IL}$ | Input Low Current | | -225 | μA | $V_{IN}$ = 2V |
| | $I_{IL}$ | Input Low Current | -150 | -500 | μA | $V_{IN}$ = $V_{SS}$ |
| I/O PORT (STANDARD PULL-UP) | $V_{OH}$ | Output High Voltage | 3.9 | $V_{DD}$ | Volts | $I_{OH}$ = -30 μA |
| | $V_{OH}$ | Output High Voltage | 2.9 | $V_{DD}$ | Volts | $I_{OH}$ = -100 μA |
| | $V_{OL}$ | Output Low Voltage | $V_{SS}$ | 0.4 | Volts | $I_{OL}$ = 2 mA |
| | $V_{IH}$ | Input High Voltage | 2.9 | $V_{DD}$ | Volts | Internal Pull-up to $V_{DD}$ [3] |
| | $V_{IL}$ | Input Low Voltage | $V_{SS}$ | 0.8 | Volts | |
| | $I_{IL}$ | Leakage Current | | 1 | μA | $V_{IN}$ = 6V |
| | $I_L$ | Input Low Current | | -1.6 | mA | $V_{IN}$ = 0.4V [4] |

**Notes:**

1. Pull-up resistor to $V_{DD}$ on CPU.
2. Positive current is defined as conventional current flowing into the pin referenced.
3. Hysteresis input circuit provides additional 0.3V noise immunity while internal/external pull-up provides TTL compatibility.
4. Measured while I/O port is outputting a high level.
5. $V_{SS}$ = 0V, $V_{DD}$ = +5V ± 5%, $V_{GG}$ = +12V ± 5%, $T_A$ = 0°C to +70°C.
6. Output device off.

*Table 7-5. A Summary of 3861 PIO Signal AC Characteristics*

*AC Characteristics:* $V_{SS}$ = 0V, $V_{CC}$ = +5V ± 5%, $T_A$ = 0 C to +70°C

Symbols in this table are used by all figures in Section 7.

| SYMBOL | PARAMETER | MIN. | TYP. | MAX. | UNITS | TEST CONDITIONS |
|---|---|---|---|---|---|---|
| PΦ | Φ Period | 0.5 | | 10 | μS | |
| $PW_1$ | Φ Pulse Width | 180 | | PΦ-180 | nS | $t_r$, $t_f$ = 50 nS typ. |
| $td_1$ | Φ to WRITE + Delay | 60 | | 250 | nS | $C_L$ = 100 pf |
| $td_2$ | Φ to WRITE – Delay | 60 | | 225 | nS | $C_L$ = 100 pf |
| $td_4$ | WRITE to DB Input Delay | | | 2PΦ+1.0 | μS | |
| $PW_2$ | WRITE Pulse Width | PΦ-100 | | PΦ | nS | $t_r$, $t_f$ = 50 nS typ. |
| $PW_S$ | WRITE Period; Short | | 4PΦ | | | |
| $PW_L$ | WRITE Period; Long | | 6PΦ | | | |
| $td_3$ | WRITE to ROMC Delay | | | 550 | nS | |
| $td_7$ | WRITE to DB Output Delay<br>WRITE to $\overline{DBDR}$ – Delay | 2PΦ+100-$td_2$ | 2PΦ+200 | 2PΦ+850-$td_2$ | nS | $C_L$ = 100 pf |
| $td_8$ | WRITE to $\overline{DBDR}$ + Delay | | 200 | | nS | Open Drain |
| $tr_1$ | WRITE to $\overline{INT\ REQ}$ – Delay | | | 430 | nS | $C_L$ = 100 pf [1] |
| $tr_2$ | WRITE to $\overline{INT\ REQ}$ + Delay | | | 430 | nS | $C_L$ = 100 pf [3] |
| $tpr_1$ | $\overline{PRI\ IN}$ to $\overline{INT\ REQ}$ – Delay | | | 240 | nS | $C_L$ = 100 pf [2] |
| $tpr_2$ | $\overline{PRI\ IN}$ to $\overline{INT\ REQ}$ + Delay | | | 240 | nS | $C_L$ = 100 pf |
| $tpd_1$ | $\overline{PRI\ IN}$ to $\overline{PRI\ OUT}$ – Delay | | | 300 | nS | $C_L$ = 50 pf |
| $tpd_2$ | $\overline{PRI\ IN}$ to $\overline{PRI\ OUT}$ + Delay | | | 365 | nS | $C_L$ = 50 pf |
| $tpd_3$ | WRITE to $\overline{PRI\ OUT}$ + Delay | | | 700 | nS | $C_L$ = 50 pf |
| $tpd_4$ | WRITE to $\overline{PRI\ OUT}$ – Delay | | | 640 | nS | $C_L$ = 50 pf |
| *$t_{sp}$ | WRITE to Output Stable | | | 2.5 | μS | $C_L$ = 50 pf, Standard Pull-up |
| *$t_{su}$ | I/O Set-up Time | 1.3 | | | μS | |
| *$t_h$ | I/O Hold Time | 0 | | | nS | |
| *$t_{ex}$ | $\overline{EXT\ INT}$ Set-up Time | 400 | | | nS | |

Notes:

1. Assume Priority In was enabled ($\overline{PRI\ IN}$ = 0) in previous F8 cycle before interrupt is detected in the PIO.
2. PSU has interrupt pending before priority in is enabled.
3. Assume pin tied to $\overline{INT\ REQ}$ input of the 3850 CPU.

*4. The parameters which are starred in the table above represent those which are most frequently of importance when interfacing to an F8 system. Other parameters are typically those that are relevant only between F8 chips and not normally of concern to the user.

5. Input and output capacitance is 3 to 5 pf typical on all pins except $V_{DD}$, $V_{GG}$, and $V_{SS}$.

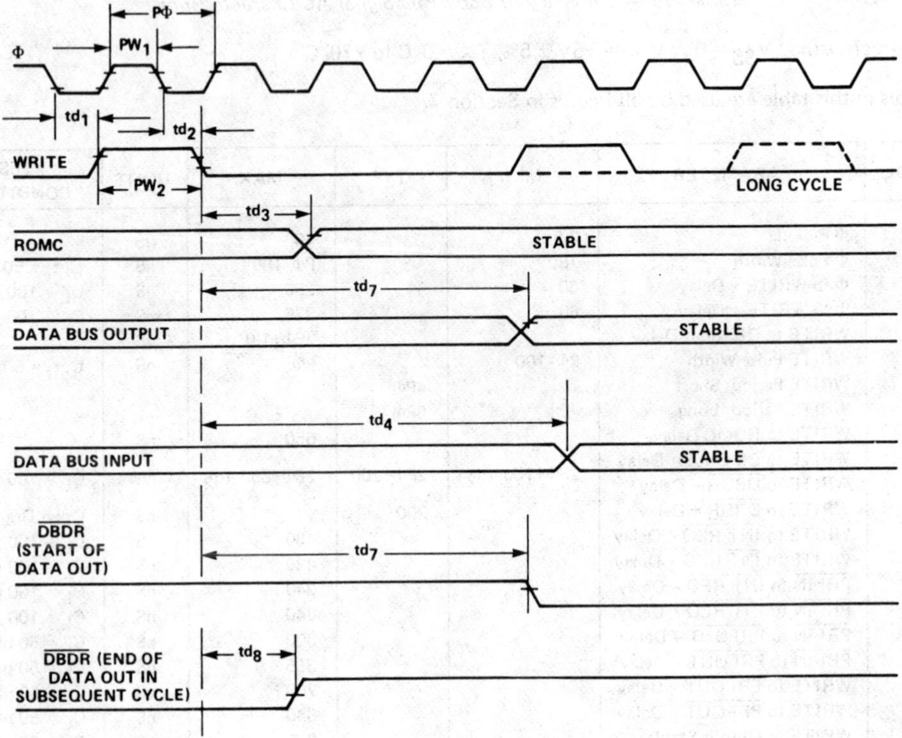


*Figure 7-3. 3861 PIO Data Bus Timing*

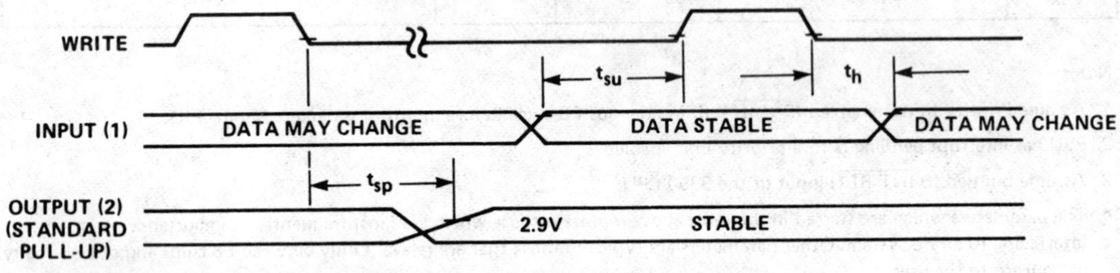


**SYMBOLS USED ARE DEFINED IN TABLE 7-5**

**Notes:**

1. Data from the I/O port is strobed into the accumulator of the CPU at the end of the second instruction cycle during execution of an IN or INS instruction.
2. During an OUT or OUTS instruction, data is strobed into the port latch at the end of the second instruction cycle; thus the cycle shown is the second cycle within the execution of the instruction.
3. Input and output capacitance of 3 to 5 pf typical on all pins except $V_{DD}$, $V_{GG}$, and $V_{SS}$.

*Figure 7-4. Timing at PIO I/O Ports*

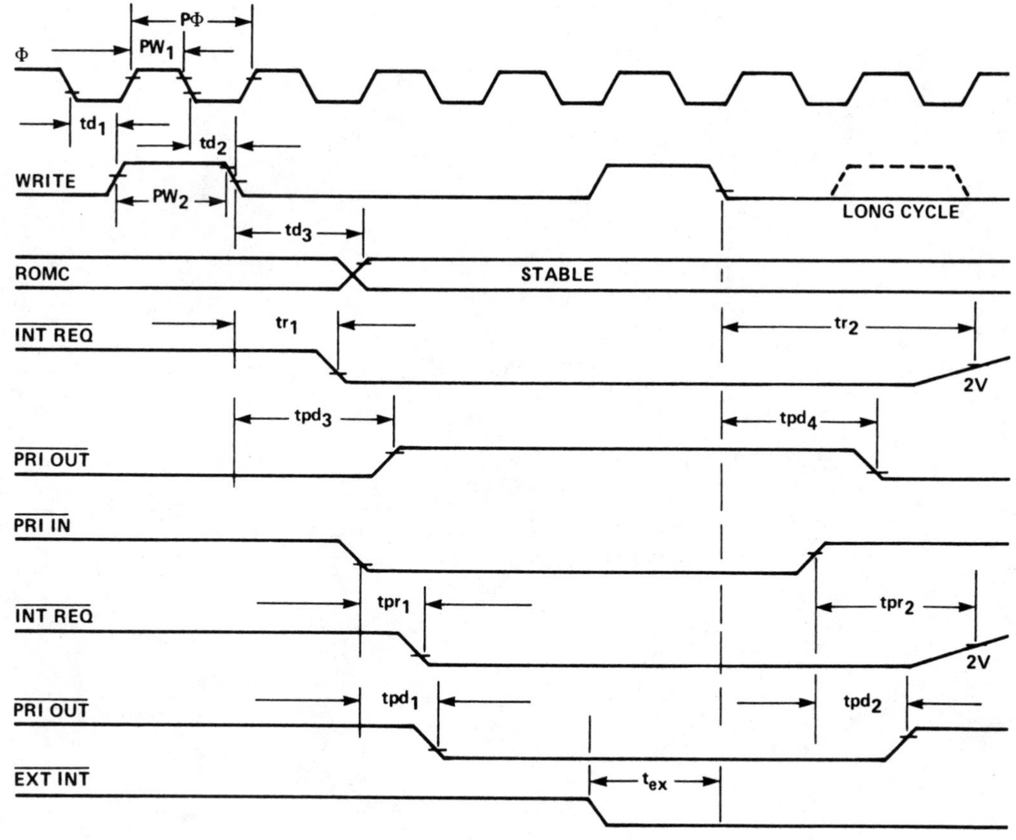


SYMBOLS ARE DEFINED IN TABLE 7-5

**Note:**

Timing measurements are made at valid logic level to valid logic level of the signals referenced unless otherwise noted.

*Figure 7-6. Interrupt Logic Signals's Timing*

# Chapter 3
# THE NATIONAL SEMICONDUCTOR SC/MP

**SC/MP is a low-cost microprocessor that has been designed to operate easily in multi-microprocessor configurations. The most interesting characteristic of SC/MP is its bus interface logic. Most microprocessors are designed to always operate as bus master in any microcomputer system. SC/MP, in contrast, has the bus interface logic of a support device; it does not assume that it has any more right to a System Bus than any other device. Bus request/acknowledge logic coupled with bus access priority logic makes SC/MP the slave microprocessor of choice in any multi-microprocessor application.**

**The very open bus interface logic of SC/MP results in it having no special support devices; it shares the support devices of other National Semiconductor microprocessors. These support devices are described in Volume 3.**

The prime source is:

NATIONAL SEMICONDUCTOR INC.
2900 Semiconductor Drive
Santa Clara, CA 95050

The authorized second source for SC/MP is:

SIGNETICS
811 East Arques Avenue
Sunnyvale, CA 94043

Although Signetics is authorized as an SC/MP second source, they have never actually manufactured SC/MP.

## THE SC/MP CPU

**Figure 3-1 conceptually illustrates the logic functions which are implemented on the SC/MP chip. One of the weaknesses of Figure 3-1, and the equivalent figures for the other microcomputers, is that the way in which logic functions are implemented cannot be identified. SC/MP, for example, implements non-CPU logic at a very elementary level, well suited for simple applications only.**

**SC/MP SERIAL I/O**

**Nonetheless, Figure 3-1 does reveal a few of the rather unusual capabilities provided by SC/MP. Notice that Serial-to-Parallel Interface Logic is shown as implemented by the SC/MP chip.** SC/MP has two serial I/O device pins, one for serial binary input data, the other for serial binary output data. The assembly and disassembly of serial-to-parallel data is accomplished by one SC/MP instruction.

**Figure 3-1 also shows Programmable Timer logic as being implemented by the SC/MP chip. This is barely justifiable** — the SC/MP instruction set includes a Delay instruction that is used to generate timed durations ranging from 13 to 131,593 microcycles. Note, however, that during this delay interval the CPU can be performing no other actions: the CPU is, in effect, operating solely as a programmable timer. This is obviously quite different from having a separate logic device that performs this timer function within a system. Once again, this points out the weakness of a generalized representation such as Figure 3-1.

**SC/MP DMA AND MULTIPROCESSOR LOGIC**

One other area of non-CPU logic shown as being implemented by SC/MP further illustrates this point. **A portion of the Direct Memory Access (DMA) logic is provided by SC/MP using a few signals to control bus access.** A significant amount of external logic would still be required to obtain an operational DMA system. Therefore, Figure 3-1 can be misleading because it cannot indicate the way in which the CPU implements a particular function. In this particular case there is also a significant area of non-CPU logic provided by SC/MP that is nowhere indicated by Figure

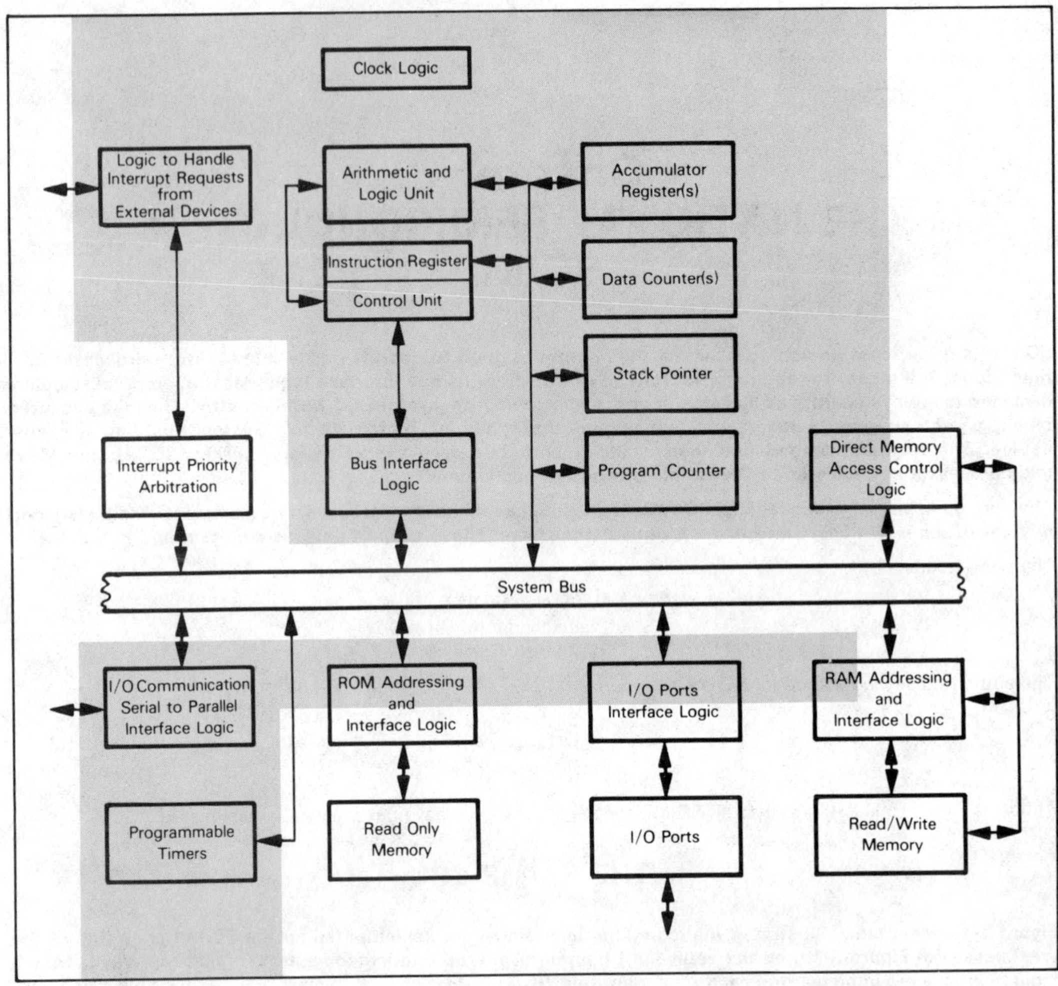


Figure 3-1. Logic of the SC/MP Microcomputer

3-1: **The signals that can be used for DMA are primarily intended to simplify the design of multiprocessor systems.** This is a very unusual logic function for a CPU to provide and therefore is not even suggested in Figure 3-1. But for SC/MP, the inclusion of this multiprocessor-oriented logic makes a lot of sense: its low cost and modest performance make it a likely candidate for multiprocessor systems.

**SC/MP AND SC/MP-II**

**There are two versions of the SC/MP CPU: the original version uses P-channel silicon-gate MOS/LSI technology and its part number is ISP-8A/500; the new version (SC/MP-II) uses N-channel technology and its part number is ISP-8A/600. The two versions are functionally equivalent and fully compatible in terms of object code and pin configuration.** (A few minor signal level conversions are required for complete signal compatibility: see Figure 3-3.) **The SC/MP-II provides some significant advantages over the original version — it is twice as fast and uses only one-fourth the power of the original P-channel version. Additionally, while SC/MP requires two power sources (a +5 volt and a -7 volt supply), SC/MP-II needs only a single +5 volt supply.** Throughout this chapter, we will simply refer to the CPU as SC/MP: all the descriptions apply to both versions of the CPU unless we specifically mention SC/MP-II.

**SC/MP INSTRUCTION EXECUTION SPEED**

**Both versions of the SC/MP CPU have an on-chip clock oscillator and can use a capacitor, crystal, or TTL clock input to drive the clock.** The P-channel SC/MP can run at a maximum frequency of 1 megahertz, which results in instruction execution times in the range of 10 to 50 microseconds. SC/MP-II can operate at frequencies up to 4 megahertz with resulting instruction execution times in the range of 5 to 25 microseconds. Notice that although the input frequency for SC/MP-II can be four times that of SC/MP, the instruction execution time for SC/MP-II is twice as fast (not four times as fast): this is because of internal differences in the way the on-chip clock oscillator uses the timing inputs.

**SC/MP LOGIC LEVEL**

**Both versions of SC/MP provide TTL-compatible input and output signals.**

## SC/MP PROGRAMMABLE REGISTERS

**SC/MP has an 8-bit Accumulator, an 8-bit Extension register, a 16-bit Program Counter, three 16-bit Pointer registers, and an 8-bit Status register. These programmable registers are illustrated as follows:**

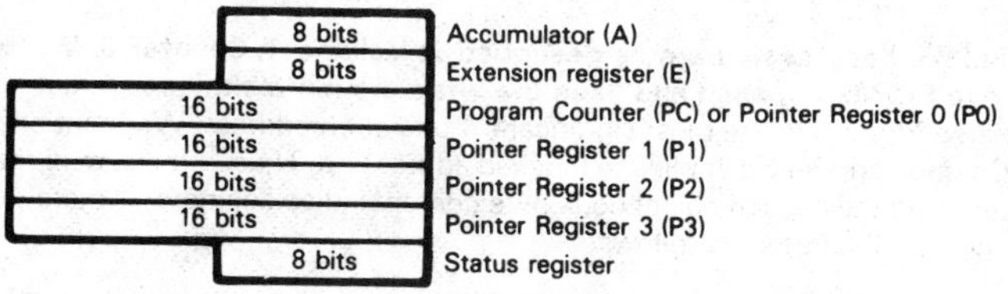

|  |  |
|---|---|
| 8 bits | Accumulator (A) |
| 8 bits | Extension register (E) |
| 16 bits | Program Counter (PC) or Pointer Register 0 (P0) |
| 16 bits | Pointer Register 1 (P1) |
| 16 bits | Pointer Register 2 (P2) |
| 16 bits | Pointer Register 3 (P3) |
| 8 bits | Status register |

**The Accumulator is a single, primary Accumulator, as described for our hypothetical microcomputer.**

**The Extension register is used to assemble or disassemble serial-to-parallel data for serial data input and output. This register is also used as a buffer for the Accumulator.**

**SC/MP MEMORY PAGES**

**The Program Counter is 16 bits wide; therefore up to 65,536 bytes of memory may be addressed in the normal course of events. The four high-order bits of the Program Counter represent page select bits; therefore the memory of an SC/MP system is divided into 16 pages of 4096 words each.**

Notice that the Program Counter is shown as Pointer Register 0; this is done because some instructions move data between Pointer registers including the Program Counter. There is one other unusual fact about the SC/MP Program Counter: **the four most significant bits (the page select bits) of the Program Counter are never incremented during the instruction fetch sequence. Instead, when the last address of a page is reached, the Program Counter "wraps-around" to the first address of the current page.** For example, if the Program Counter contains $2FFF_{16}$, when it is incremented the new contents of the Program Counter will be $2000_{16}$ instead of $3000_{16}$. The page select bits of the Program Counter can only be changed by executing an instruction that loads a new value into the most significant bits of the Program Counter.

Note that the four high-order address bits are not output on separate address pins; instead they are output on the data lines at the beginning of an input/output cycle and must be demultiplexed by external logic in order to generate page select signals.

**The three Pointer registers are also used as Index registers or Stack Pointers.** Typically, you would assign a specific function to each register. For example, the following assignments might be used:

P1 - ROM Pointer
P2 - Stack Pointer
P3 - Subroutine Pointer

These arbitrary assignments also reveal several interesting facts about the architecture of SC/MP. First, the SC/MP CPU does not provide an on-chip stack; instead, a stack can be maintained in memory using one of the Pointer registers as a Stack Pointer. Secondly, the SC/MP instruction set does not include a Jump-to-Subroutine instruction: one of the Pointer registers must be used to hold subroutine addresses which can then be swapped with the Program Counter. We will discuss this in detail when we describe the SC/MP instruction set.

## ADDRESSING MODES

**The SC/MP memory reference instructions use program-relative direct addressing, indexed addressing, and auto-indexed addressing. All memory reference instructions are two-byte instructions and have the following object code format:**

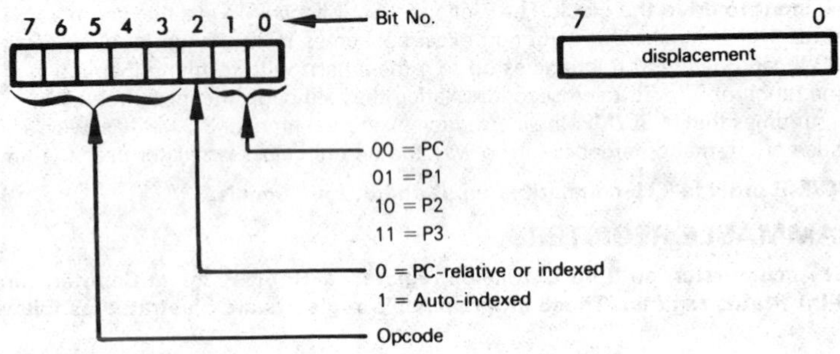


**Program relative and indexed addressing are as described in Volume 1, Chapter 6. We will just re-emphasize here that all addressing in SC/MP is paged and uses the wrap-around technique** — that is, there is no carry from the low order 12 bits of an address into the most significant 4 bits of an address. We mentioned this earlier when we discussed the Program Counter, and it also applies to indexed addressing. Thus, if the sum of the Index register (that is, one of the Pointer registers) and the second object code byte contents (displacement) is more than $FFF_{16}$, the Carry bit will be discarded. This may be illustrated as follows:

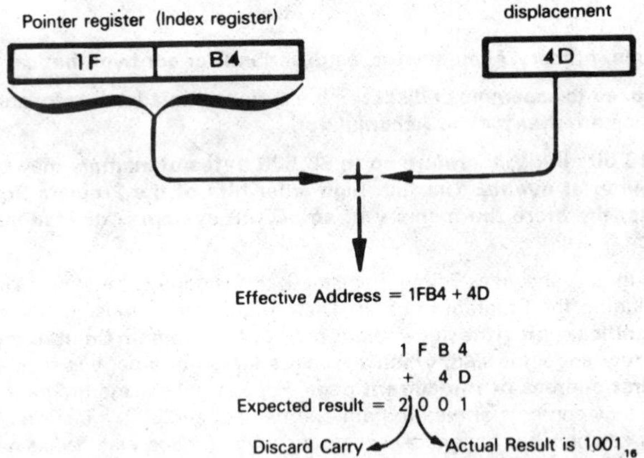


**Remember, all arithmetic operations during address formation, regardless of the addressing mode, obey this wrap-around technique: there is never a carry from bit 11 into bit 12.**

**The auto-indexing mode of addressing provided by SC/MP instructions is actually an auto-increment/auto-decrement operation.** When auto-indexing is specified, the displacement, as a signed binary number, is added to the contents of a Pointer register in order to compute an effective address. If the displacement is less than zero, the Pointer register is decremented by the displacement before the memory access. If the displacement is equal to or greater than zero, then the contents of the Pointer register is the effective address and the Pointer register contents are incremented by the displacement after the memory access. **This method of auto-increment and auto-decrement addressing is the same as that described in Volume I with one significant difference: SC/MP allows an address to be incremented or decremented by any value in the range 0 - 127 instead of just by a value of one.**

## SC/MP STATUS REGISTER

**SC/MP has a programmable 8-bit Status register which may be illustrated as follows:**

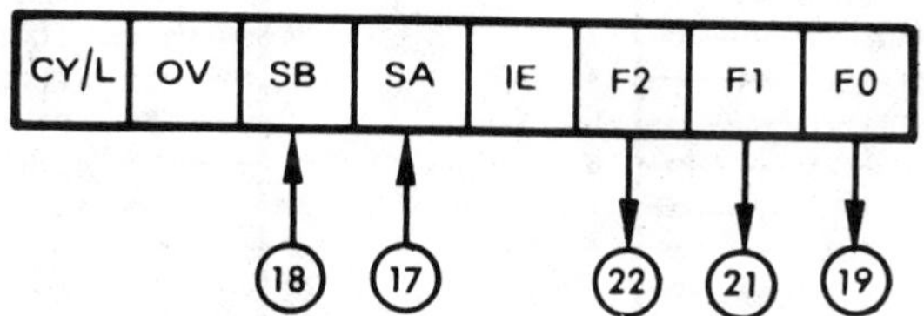


Circled numbers represent device pin numbers to which bits of the Status register are connected.

**The Carry (CY), Link (L) and Overflow (OV) status bits are typical microcomputer status bits as were described in Volume 1, Chapter 7.**

**The two sense bits, SB and SA, are tied to SC/MP device pins. These two bits directly reflect the state of the logic signals applied to the device pins and thus can be used to detect external events.** Although there are no SC/MP instructions that allow you to directly jump or branch on the condition of one of these bits, a sequence of masking and testing instructions can be used to accomplish the same effect, albeit more slowly. **The SA and SB bits are read-only bits. Instructions may read the status of these two bits, but only incoming signals may change their condition.** For example, an instruction that moves the contents of the Accumulator to the Status register may modify any of the other status bits, but bits 4 and 5 will not change. **The SA bit serves a dual function. If the Interrupt Enable (IE) bit is set to one, the SA input serves as the interrupt input.** We will discuss interrupt processing later in this chapter.

**F0, F1 and F2 are control flags that are tied to SC/MP device pins. The state of these three flags may be changed under program control and may be used to control external devices.** When the state of any of these flags is changed, it is immediately reflected by a change in the signal level at the associated device pin.

## SC/MP CPU SIGNALS AND PIN ASSIGNMENTS

**Figure 3-2 illustrates the SC/MP pins and signals. A description of these signals is useful as a guide to the way in which an SC/MP microcomputer system works.**

**The 12 address lines AD00 - AD11 output memory and I/O device addresses. These are tristate lines, and may be floated, giving external logic control of the Address Bus. The four most significant address bits (AD12 - AD15) are time multiplexed on the data lines.**

**The eight Data Bus lines DB0 - DB7 are multiplexed, bidirectional data lines through which 8-bit data units are input and output, and on which statuses and address bits are output at the beginning of any input/output cycle. Statuses on Data Bus lines DB4 - DB7 identify the type or purpose of the input/output cycle. The address bits on Data Bus lines DB0 - DB3 are the four most significant address bits (AD12 - AD15) which must be used to generate page select signals for memory or peripheral devices. Table 3-1 describes the status and address information that is output on the Data Bus. Like the address lines, the data lines are tristate.**

**SENSEA, SENSEB, FLAG0, 1, and 2 are pin connections for the similarly named Status register bits described earlier.**

**SIN and SOUT are used in combination with the SIO instruction for serial input of data to the Extension register and serial output of data from the Extension register.**

The remaining signals (excluding clock, power and ground) may be divided into bus access, Data Bus definition, and timing control signals.

**SIGNAL DIFFERENCES BETWEEN SC/MP (P-CHANNEL) AND SC/MP-II (N-CHANNEL)**

**You will notice that some of the SC/MP pins in Figure 3-2 have two sets of signal names: the names enclosed in parentheses reflect the nomenclature used with SC/MP-II.** Aside from the clock and power signals which we shall discuss separately, the only difference between SC/MP and SC/MP-II is in the polarity of bus access signals: Bus Request (BREQ/NBREQ), Enable In (ENIN/NENIN), and Enable Out (ENOUT/NENOUT). The "N" prefix to each of the SC/MP-II signals indicates that these signals are negative-true — as opposed to the positive- (or logic "1") true signals for the P-channel SC/MP. **In the descriptions that follow, we will use P-channel SC/MP nomenclature.** If you are using the N-channel SC/MP-II version, you must simply invert these signals.

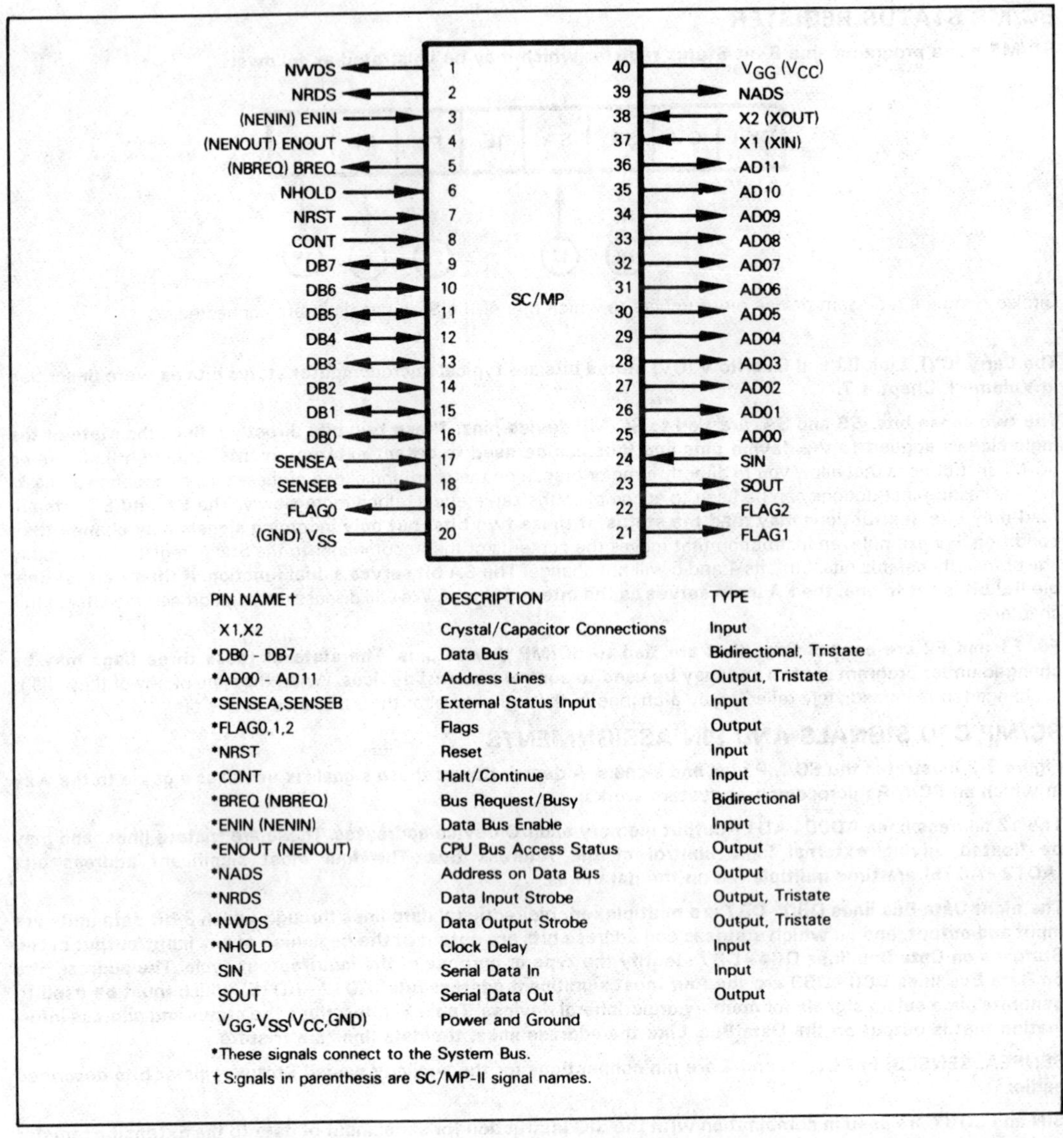


| PIN NAME† | DESCRIPTION | TYPE |
|---|---|---|
| X1,X2 | Crystal/Capacitor Connections | Input |
| •DB0 - DB7 | Data Bus | Bidirectional, Tristate |
| •AD00 - AD11 | Address Lines | Output, Tristate |
| •SENSEA,SENSEB | External Status Input | Input |
| •FLAG0,1,2 | Flags | Output |
| •NRST | Reset | Input |
| •CONT | Halt/Continue | Input |
| •BREQ (NBREQ) | Bus Request/Busy | Bidirectional |
| •ENIN (NENIN) | Data Bus Enable | Input |
| •ENOUT (NENOUT) | CPU Bus Access Status | Output |
| •NADS | Address on Data Bus | Output |
| •NRDS | Data Input Strobe | Output, Tristate |
| •NWDS | Data Output Strobe | Output, Tristate |
| •NHOLD | Clock Delay | Input |
| SIN | Serial Data In | Input |
| SOUT | Serial Data Out | Output |
| $V_{GG}$, $V_{SS}$ ($V_{CC}$, GND) | Power and Ground | |

•These signals connect to the System Bus.

† Signals in parenthesis are SC/MP-II signal names.

Figure 3-2. SC/MP CPU Signals and Pin Assignments

**SC/MP BUS ACCESS CONTROL SIGNALS**

**Before the SC/MP CPU can begin any input/output operation, it must gain access to the System Busses.** This approach reflects the design philosophy behind SC/MP. It is a relatively low-cost, low-performance CPU and the designers anticipated that it would frequently be used in multiprocessor systems or in systems utilizing Direct Memory Access. Accordingly, three signals are provided to control access to the System Busses.

**BREQ is used as a bus busy input indicating that some other device is using the System Busses; as an output, BREQ is a bus request which is output when the System Busses are free and SC/MP requires access to the busses.**

**ENIN is a control signal which is input to the CPU by external logic. When ENIN is low, the CPU is denied access to the System Busses and the SC/MP address and data lines are held in tristate mode.**

**ENOUT is the CPU's output response to ENIN.** When output high, ENOUT indicates that ENIN is high; therefore, the CPU can gain access to the System Busses, but it has not done so. If ENOUT is low, it indicates either that ENIN is low, therefore the CPU is being denied access to the System Busses or, if ENIN is high, then it indicates that the CPU is using the System Busses.

**SC/MP DATA BUS DEFINITION SIGNALS**

**When the CPU has gained access to the System Busses, three signals identify the way in which the CPU is using the Data Bus.**

**NADS is output to indicate that a valid address has been output on the address lines and that the low-order four bits of the Data Bus contain the high-order four bits of a 16-bit address. NADS also indicates that status information is being output on the high-order four bits of the Data Bus.**

**NRDS, when output by the CPU, indicates that the CPU wishes to receive data on the Data Bus.**

**NWDS, when output by the CPU, indicates that data is being output by the CPU on the Data Bus.** NWDS may be used by external logic as a write strobe.

**SC/MP TIMING CONTROL SIGNALS**

**There are three signals which control CPU timing.**

**NRST is a system reset signal.** When input low, it aborts any in-process operations. When returned high, all programmable registers are cleared, and program execution begins with the instruction fetched from memory location $0001_{16}$.

**CONT may be input to stop the CPU between instructions.** When CONT is input low, all CPU operations are halted after the current instruction execution has been completed. The CPU remains halted until CONT goes high.

**NHOLD is an input signal used during input/output operations to lengthen the allowed time interval for devices to respond to CPU access requests.**

## SC/MP TIMING AND INSTRUCTION EXECUTION

**The SC/MP timing for instruction execution is very simple. Instruction execution times are expressed in terms of microcycles.** A typical instruction is executed in 10 microcycles; one (the first) or more of these microcycles is an input/output cycle. The length of a microcycle depends on the frequency of the clock inputs to the CPU: with the P-channel SC/MP, the minimum microcycle length is 2 microseconds; for SC/MP-II, the N-channel version, minimum microcycle length is 1 microsecond. Thus, typical instruction execution time is 20 microseconds for the P-channel SC/MP, and 10 microseconds for SC/MP-II. **All microcycles, whether internal machine cycles or input/output cycles, are of the same length: the only variance occurs when the NHOLD signal is used to stretch an input or output cycle.**

**There are basically only three types of SC/MP machine (or micro) cycles: data input (read) cycles, data output (write) cycles, and internal microcycles.** The execution of each instruction is merely a concatenation of these three types of microcycles.

**SC/MP I/O CYCLE STATUS INFORMATION**

SC/MP does, however, output some status information at the beginning of every input or output cycle; this status information provides a more precise definition of the events that will occur during that microcycle. Table 3-1 lists the information which may be output on the Data Bus at the beginning of an I/O cycle (when NADS is low). Table 3-2 defines the status information for non-I/O cycles.

Table 3-1. Status and Address Output via the Data Lines at the Beginning of an I/O Cycle

| SYMBOLS | DATA BUS BIT | DEFINITION |
|---|---|---|
| H-Flag | 7 | Indicates that a Halt instruction has been executed. |
| D-Flag | 6 | Indicates that a Delay instruction has been executed and that a delay cycle is starting. |
| I-Flag | 5 | Indicates that the CPU is in the fetch cycle for the first byte of an instruction. |
| R-Flag | 4 | When high, indicates that the I/O cycle is a read cycle and that input data should be placed on the Data Bus when NRDS is active. When low, indicates that the I/O cycle is a write cycle and that the Data Bus will contain output data when NWDS is active. |
| AD15 | 3 | The four most significant bits of a 16-bit address. Can be used as page select signals. |
| AD14 | 2 | |
| AD13 | 1 | |
| AD12 | 0 | |

Table 3-2. Statuses Output on the Data Bus for Various Types of Machine Cycles

| Status Information | Data Bus Bit | TYPE OF MACHINE CYCLE | | | | |
|---|---|---|---|---|---|---|
| | | Instruction Fetch | Halt Instruction | Delay Instruction | Data Input (Read) | Data Output (Write) |
| H-Flag | 7 | 0 | 1 | 0 | 0 | 0 |
| D-Flag | 6 | 0 | 0 | 1 | 0 | 0 |
| I-Flag | 5 | 1 | 1 | 0 | 0 | 0 |
| R-Flag | 4 | 1 | 1 | 1 | 1 | 0 |

## SC/MP BUS ACCESS LOGIC

**Since the SC/MP CPU must gain access to the System Busses before it can perform an input or output cycle, we will describe the bus access logic before discussing input/output cycles.**

**Figure 3-3 illustrates the bus access logic processing sequence that occurs whenever the SC/MP CPU is going to perform an input/output cycle.**

First, the bidirectional BREQ line is tested. If the BREQ input is high, it indicates that the System Bus is currently in use: the CPU holds the outputs of the address and data lines, and the NRDS and NWDS signals in the high-impedance (tristate) mode.

When the BREQ input signal is low (or goes low) it indicates that the System Bus is free, and the CPU then outputs a logic "1" on the BREQ line. This informs external devices (for example, other SC/MP CPUs or a DMA controller) that a request for bus access has been initiated.

The CPU next tests the state of the ENIN input line. ENIN is essentially the "bus grant" signal: if it is low, it indicates the Bus Request (BREQ) is denied and the CPU remains in an idle state with its output held in the high impedance mode. When the ENIN input is high (or goes high) it indicates that the CPU's bus request has been granted and the I/O cycle can now be initiated.

When the I/O cycle has been completed, the CPU sets the BREQ output low to indicate that it has finished using the System Bus and that its outputs are once again in the high impedance mode.

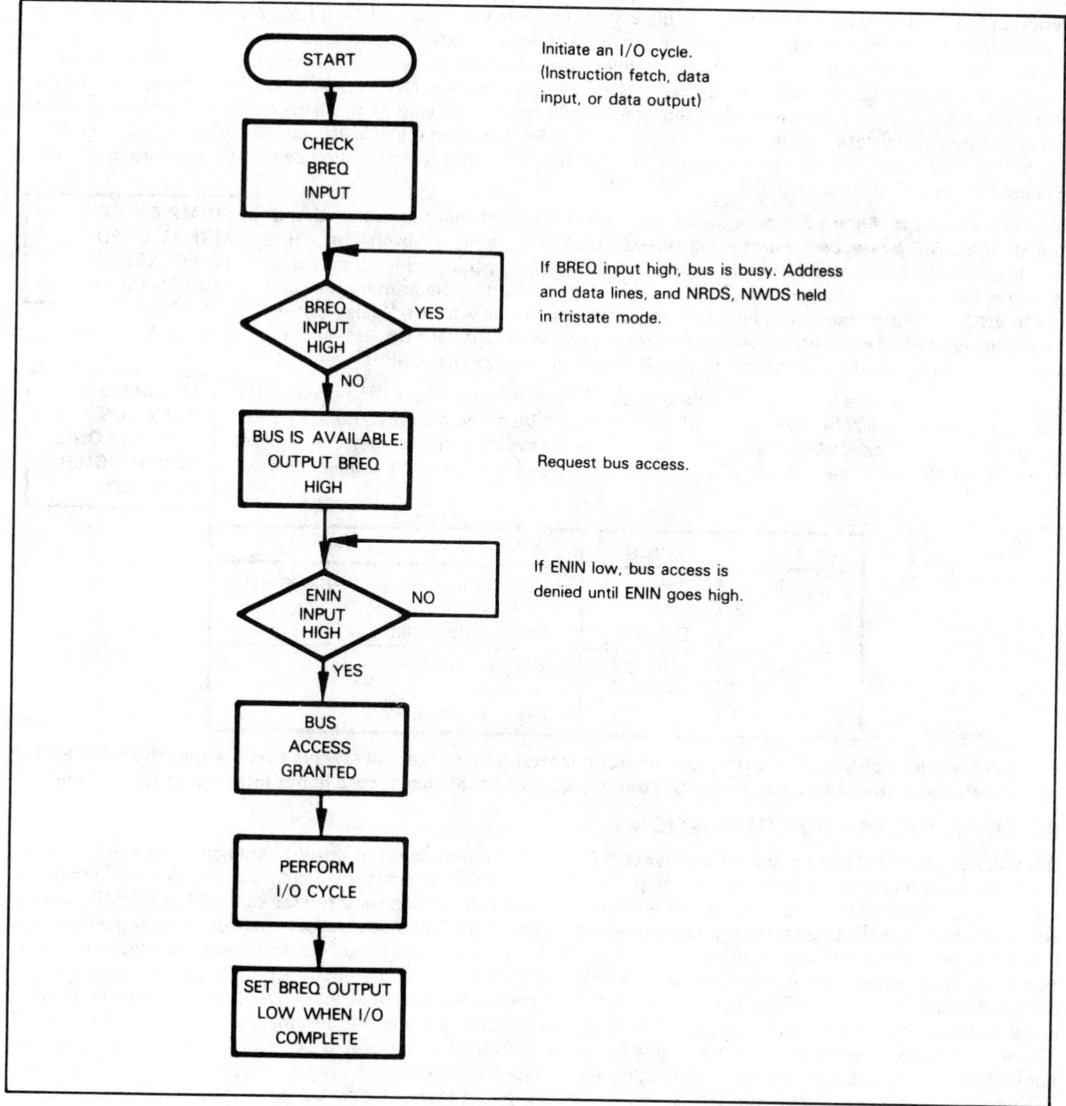


Figure 3-3. SC/MP Bus Access Logic Processing Sequence

**SUSPENSION OF AN SC/MP I/O CYCLE**

**There are a couple of aspects of the bus access sequence which are not revealed by Figure 3-3.**

**First, the SC/MP CPU has the rather unusual capability of suspending an I/O operation after it has already begun.** If the ENIN input line goes low while the CPU has access to the bus, the SC/MP address and data lines will go to the high impedance state, thus relinquishing access to the System Busses. The BREQ output signal will remain high and, when the ENIN input line subsequently goes high once more, the input/output cycle which had been suspended will begin again.

This ability to suspend an I/O cycle might be quite useful in a system where bus access is granted on a priority basis. In such a system, it is conceivable that one or more of the system devices (another CPU, for example) might have overriding priorities and require immediate access to the System Busses. The SC/MP bus access logic we've just described allows this to be accomplished with no difficulty whatsoever. **There is, however, one gray area in this I/O-suspend**

**function.** If an SC/MP I/O cycle is nearly complete, it would seem to be more efficient to go ahead and complete the cycle rather than suspending it and then restarting the entire cycle later. This is precisely what SC/MP does. Unfortunately, the SC/MP literature does not tell us where this "point-of-no-return" lies within an I/O cycle. One would assume, or at least hope that this point is prior to the time when NRDS or NWDS is sent out. These signals are the read and write strobe signals; if they were repeated when an I/O cycle was restarted, the same data might be read or written twice — a potentially vexing situation. However, you are at least assured that if ENIN goes low while SC/MP is performing an I/O cycle, the cycle will be performed — either by continuing to completion or by being restarted when the System Busses are again available.

**SC/MP ENOUT SIGNAL USED TO ESTABLISH ACCESS PRIORITIES**

**If you refer back to Figure 3-3 once again, you will notice that there is no mention of the third SC/MP bus access control signal — ENOUT.** This is not an oversight — it is simply due to the fact that the ENOUT signal performs a rather specialized function which is not necessary to an understanding of the SC/MP bus access logic. **The primary function of the ENOUT output signal is as an enabling signal in systems where a "daisy chain" technique is used to establish priorities for bus access.** We will defer a discussion of this use of ENOUT until later in this chapter when we discuss the use of SC/MP in multiprocessor and DMA systems.

**SC/MP I/O WITH BUS ACCESS LOGIC CONTINUOUSLY ENABLED**

If the SC/MP CPU is used in a single-processor, non-DMA system then there is no need for the built-in bus access logic. In these cases, which may in fact be in the majority, the bus access signals should be connected so that the SC/MP CPU is always guaranteed immediate access to the System Busses. This is easily accomplished by making the following connections:

| | SIGNAL | CONNECT TO |
|---|---|---|
| SC/MP | BREQ<br>ENIN<br>ENOUT | $V_{GG}$ through a pull-down resistor.<br>$V_{SS}$<br>Leave unterminated |
| SC/MP-II | NBREQ<br>NENIN<br>NENOUT | $V_{CC}$ via external resistor<br>Ground<br>Leave unterminated |

**In the descriptions of SC/MP input/output operations that follow, we will always assume that the SC/MP CPU has already been granted access to the System Busses, and that this access is not interrupted (or suspended).**

## SC/MP INPUT/OUTPUT OPERATIONS

**Once the SC/MP CPU has control of the System Busses, an actual input or output cycle can begin.** As we mentioned earlier in this chapter, the execution of any SC/MP instruction includes some combinations of input/output cycles and internal machine cycles. **Figure 3-4 illustrates the bus utilization required for each of the SC/MP instructions, and also reveals an interesting, non-obvious fact about SC/MP input/output operations.** Observe that each bus utilization interval is shown as being two microcycles in duration. This is true because **each input/output operation effectively requires two microcycles.** The CPU spends a portion of the first microcycle gaining access to the System Bus and placing address and status information on the address and data lines. The actual data transfer (read or write) occurs during the second microcycle. This can be confusing if you are designing a DMA or multiprocessor system: the actual time that the bus is available is a great deal less than you would expect if you based your computations solely on the number of read and write cycles required for each instruction. To make this more clear, refer to Table 3-3, which lists the read cycles, write cycles, and total microcycles required for execution of each SC/MP instruction. If you total up each of the columns from this table, you come up with the following figures:

| | | |
|---|---|---|
| Total Read Cycles | = | 79 |
| Total Write Cycles | = | 3 |
| Total Input/Output Cycles | = | 82 |
| Total Microcycles | = | 466 |

Based on these figures, it would appear that bus utilization is less than 20% (82/466). However, since the CPU maintains control of the bus for approximately two microcycles each time a read or write cycle is performed, the actual bus utilization is quite a bit greater than you would have expected. For precise timing parameters refer to the data sheets at the end of this chapter. Keep in mind that bus utilization computations should be based not only on these data sheets, but also on the actual program being used, since bus utilization is directly related to the composition of instructions which comprise your program — these calculations can differ significantly from any theoretical calculations based solely on a CPU's complete instruction set.

Now, having discussed those areas of SC/MP bus access and utilization which might be confusing, let us proceed to examine the actual data input/output operations — we will find that these SC/MP operations are quite straightforward.

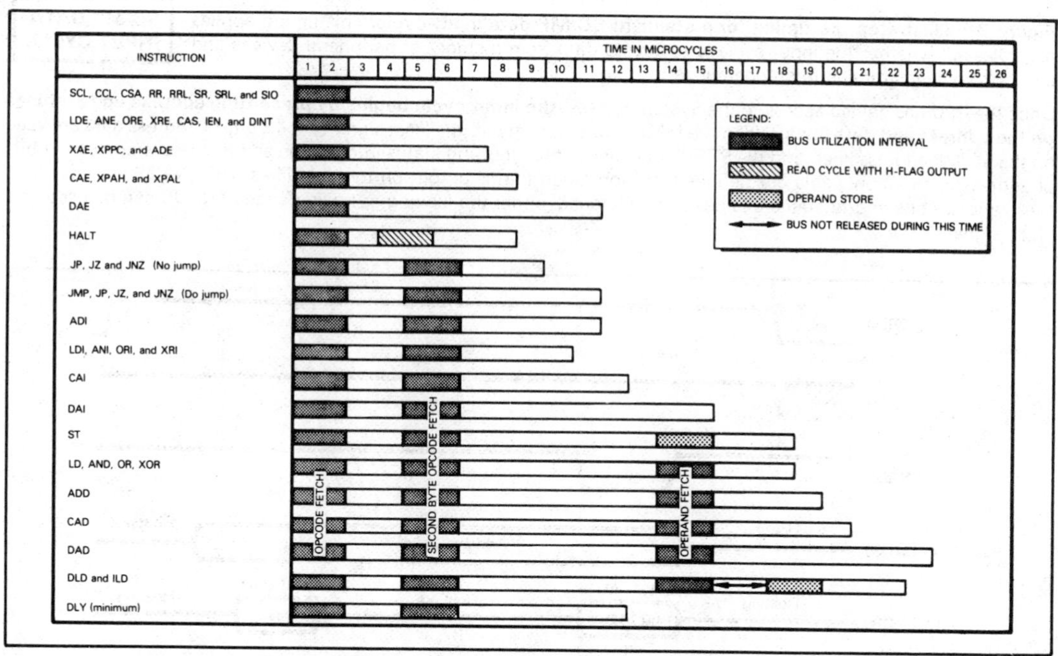


Figure 3-4. Bus Utilization of Each SC/MP Instruction

Table 3-3. SC/MP Instruction Execution Times

| INSTRUCTION | READ CYCLES | WRITE CYCLES | TOTAL MICROCYCLES |
|---|---|---|---|
| ADD | 3 | 0 | 19 |
| ADE | 1 | 0 | 7 |
| ADI | 2 | 0 | 11 |
| AND | 3 | 0 | 18 |
| ANE | 1 | 0 | 6 |
| ANI | 2 | 0 | 10 |
| CAD | 3 | 0 | 20 |
| CAE | 1 | 0 | 8 |
| CAI | 2 | 0 | 12 |
| CAS | 1 | 0 | 6 |
| CCL | 1 | 0 | 5 |
| CSA | 1 | 0 | 5 |
| DAD | 3 | 0 | 23 |
| DAE | 1 | 0 | 11 |
| DAI | 2 | 0 | 15 |
| DINT | 1 | 0 | 6 |
| DLD | 3 | 1 | 22 |
| DLY | 2 | 0 | 13 - 131593 |
| HALT | 2 | 0 | 8 |
| IEN | 1 | 0 | 6 |
| ILD | 3 | 1 | 22 |
| JMP | 2 | 0 | 11 |
| JNZ | 2 | 0 | 9, 11 for Jump |

| INSTRUCTION | READ CYCLES | WRITE CYCLES | TOTAL MICROCYCLES |
|---|---|---|---|
| JP | 2 | 0 | 9, 11 for Jump |
| JZ | 2 | 0 | 9, 11 for Jump |
| LD | 3 | 0 | 18 |
| LDE | 1 | 0 | 6 |
| LDI | 2 | 0 | 10 |
| NOP | 1 | 0 | 5 |
| OR | 3 | 0 | 18 |
| ORE | 1 | 0 | 6 |
| ORI | 2 | 0 | 10 |
| RR | 1 | 0 | 5 |
| RRL | 1 | 0 | 5 |
| SCL | 1 | 0 | 5 |
| SIO | 1 | 0 | 5 |
| SR | 1 | 0 | 5 |
| SRL | 1 | 0 | 5 |
| ST | 2 | 1 | 18 |
| XAE | 1 | 0 | 7 |
| XOR | 3 | 0 | 18 |
| XPAH | 1 | 0 | 8 |
| XPAL | 1 | 0 | 8 |
| XPPC | 1 | 0 | 7 |
| XRE | 1 | 0 | 6 |
| XRI | 2 | 0 | 10 |

Note: If slow memory is being used, the appropriate delay should be added for each read or write cycle.

**Figure 3-5 illustrates the timing for a standard SC/MP data input cycle.** This timing applies regardless of whether the input cycle is to access data from memory or peripheral devices and also applies to instruction fetch operations.

**SC/MP DATA INPUT CYCLE**

Once the CPU has gained access to the System Busses, **the input cycle begins by presenting address and statuses on the address and data lines.** When the NADS signal is sent out, the least significant 12 bits of address data are valid on the SC/MP address lines, and the SC/MP data lines are outputting status information and the most significant 4 bits of address information. Table 3-1 defines the information that is output on the data lines while NADS is true. When these address bits and/or status bits need to be latched, either the leading or trailing edge of NADS can be used as a clock signal.

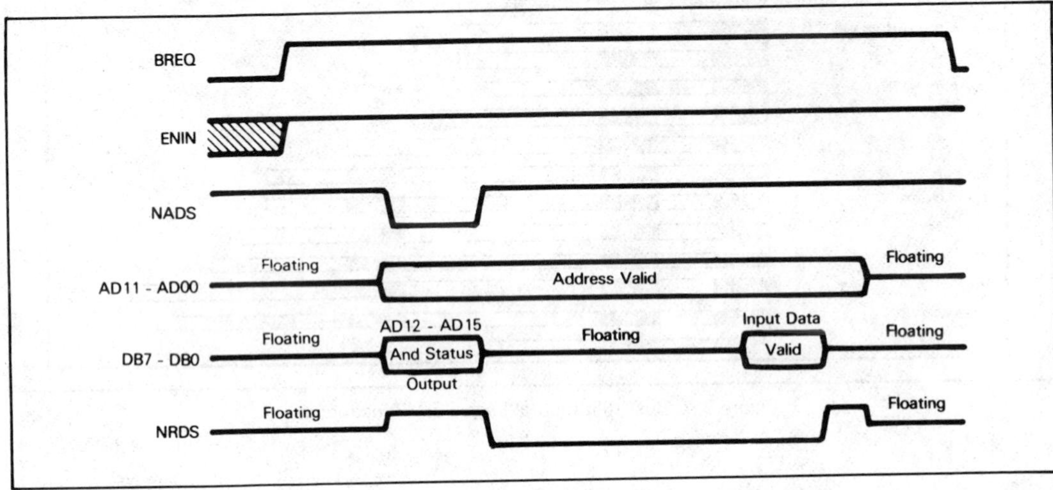


Figure 3-5. SC/MP Data Input Cycle

**Shortly after the trailing edge of NADS, the Data Bus is floated and the Read Data Strobe (NRDS) signal is output. Valid input data is expected prior to the trailing edge of NRDS.**

**SC/MP DATA OUTPUT CYCLE**

**The SC/MP data output cycle begins in the same way as the data input cycle. The only difference is that immediately after the status/address information is output on the data lines, the write or output data is placed on the data lines.** As shown in Figure 3-6, the NWDS signal is sent out to indicate when valid output data is present. Either the leading or trailing edge of NWDS could be used to latch the output data into external data latches.

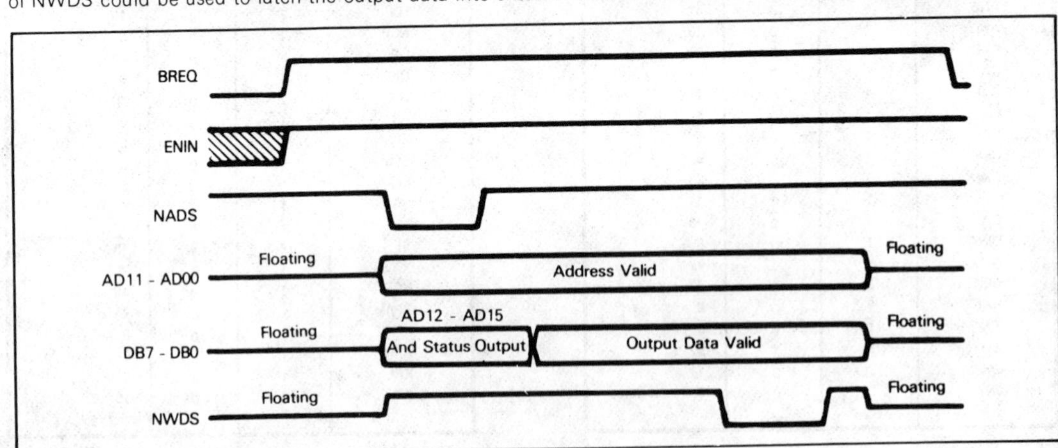


Figure 3-6. SC/MP Data Output Cycle

**SC/MP NHOLD SIGNAL FOR SLOW I/O OPERATIONS**

**The data input/output cycles just described allow approximately one microcycle for external logic to respond. If additional access time is required, the NHOLD input signal to the CPU can be used to lengthen an input/output cycle.** The NHOLD signal can be set low any time prior to the trailing edge of NRDS or NWDS as shown in Figure 3-7; this causes the trailing edge of NRDS or NWDS to be delayed until after NHOLD has been returned high. On data input cycles, the time until valid input data must be presented is simply delayed. On data output cycles, the valid output data is maintained on the data lines by the CPU until the delayed trailing edge of NWDS.

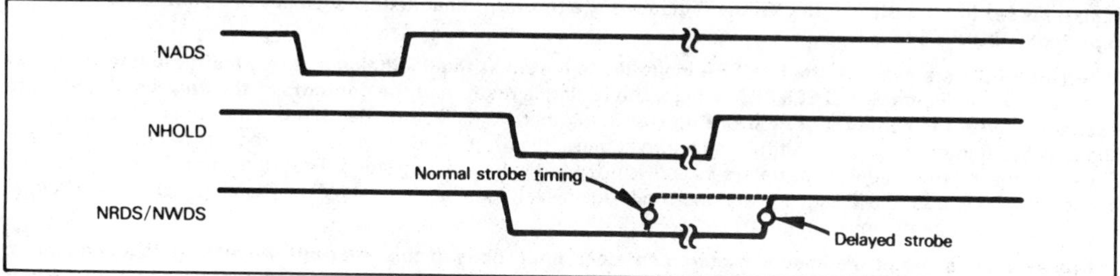


Figure 3-7. NHOLD Signal Used to Lengthen SC/MP I/O Operation

**The NHOLD signal causes the I/O cycle to be lengthened in increments of 1/2 microcycle. There is no limit on the duration of the NHOLD signal.**

## THE SC/MP HALT STATE

**The SC/MP Halt state differs from those described for other microprocessors in this book in one significant and unusual way — execution of the SC/MP Halt instruction does not cause the CPU to enter the Halt state.** Instead, when SC/MP executes a Halt instruction, it simply outputs the H-Flag status on data line 7 (DB7) when NADS is true.

**In order to actually place the CPU in the Halt state the CONT input signal to the CPU must be forced low.**

You can use external logic to force CONT low either in response to the H-Flag or completely asynchronously: whenever a low is applied to the CONT input, the CPU enters the Halt state upon completion of the current instruction. Figure 3-8 shows a circuit that can be used to force the CPU into the Halt state when a Halt instruction is executed. When DB7 is output high while NADS is true, it indicates the Halt instruction has been executed: this combination of events is used to generate a low-going pulse (NHALT) which is applied to the clear (CLR) input of a D flip-flop. The Q output of the flip-flop is applied to the CONT input signal to the CPU. Thus, whenever a Halt instruction is executed, the CPU will be forced into the Halt mode. CPU operation is resumed when the start switch S1 is momentarily closed to the NO contacts. This causes a positive-going clock pulse that sets the D flip-flop and returns the CONT input to the CPU high.

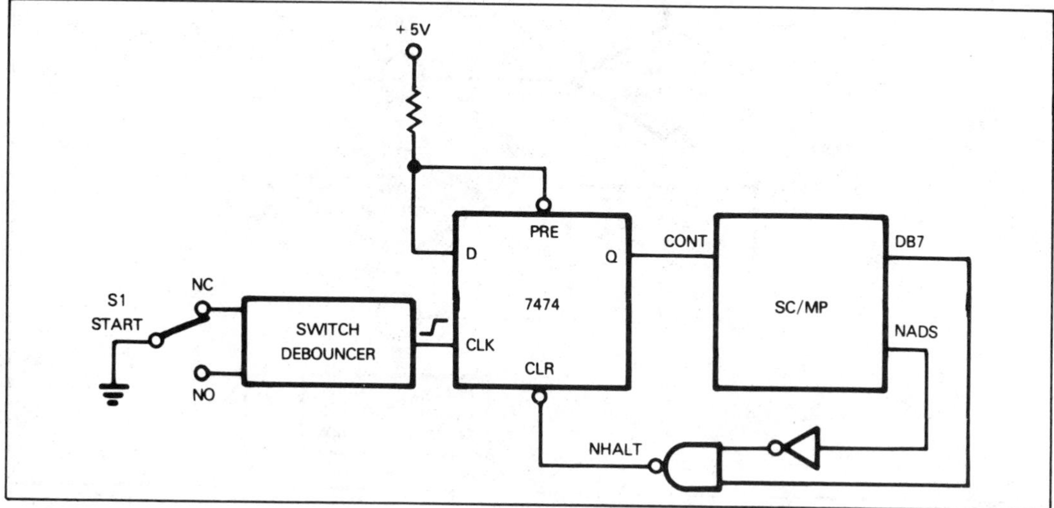


Figure 3-8. Circuit to Cause Programmed Halt for SC/MP CPU

**While the SC/MP CPU is in the Halt state, the address and data lines are floated. The CPU remains in the Halt state until the CONT input is returned high. There is one exception to this rule: if an interrupt request is detected while in the Halt state, the CPU responds to the interrupt by executing a single instruction.** Thus, you could use the first instruction of your interrupt service routine to reset the external CONT input signal, and thereby terminate the Halt state.

## SC/MP INTERRUPT PROCESSING

**The SENSEA input signal to the SC/MP CPU serves as the interrupt request line if bit 3 of the CPU's Status register is set to "1". Bit 3 of the Status register is the Interrupt Enable (IE) flag and can be set using the Interrupt Enable (IEN) instruction.**

**When interrupts are enabled, the SENSEA input line is tested at the beginning of every instruction fetch operation as shown in Figure 3-9. If SENSEA is high, the IE flag is reset, and the contents of the Program Counter are exchanged with the contents of Pointer Register 3.** In other words, Pointer Register 3 must contain the beginning address of your interrupt service routine. The return address, that is, the address at which program execution must continue after the interrupt request has been serviced, is now held in Pointer Register 3. Thus, the return-from-interrupt sequence would be to set the IE flag high and then once again exchange the contents of the Program Counter and Pointer Register 3 to resume the main program.

**Let us examine some of the special requirements and limitations of this interrupt processing sequence. First, before enabling interrupts you must load Pointer Register 3 (P3) with the beginning address of your interrupt service routine. Notice that the contents of P3 should actually be one less than the beginning address of the first instruction since the new contents of the Program Counter will be incremented prior to fetching the instruction.**

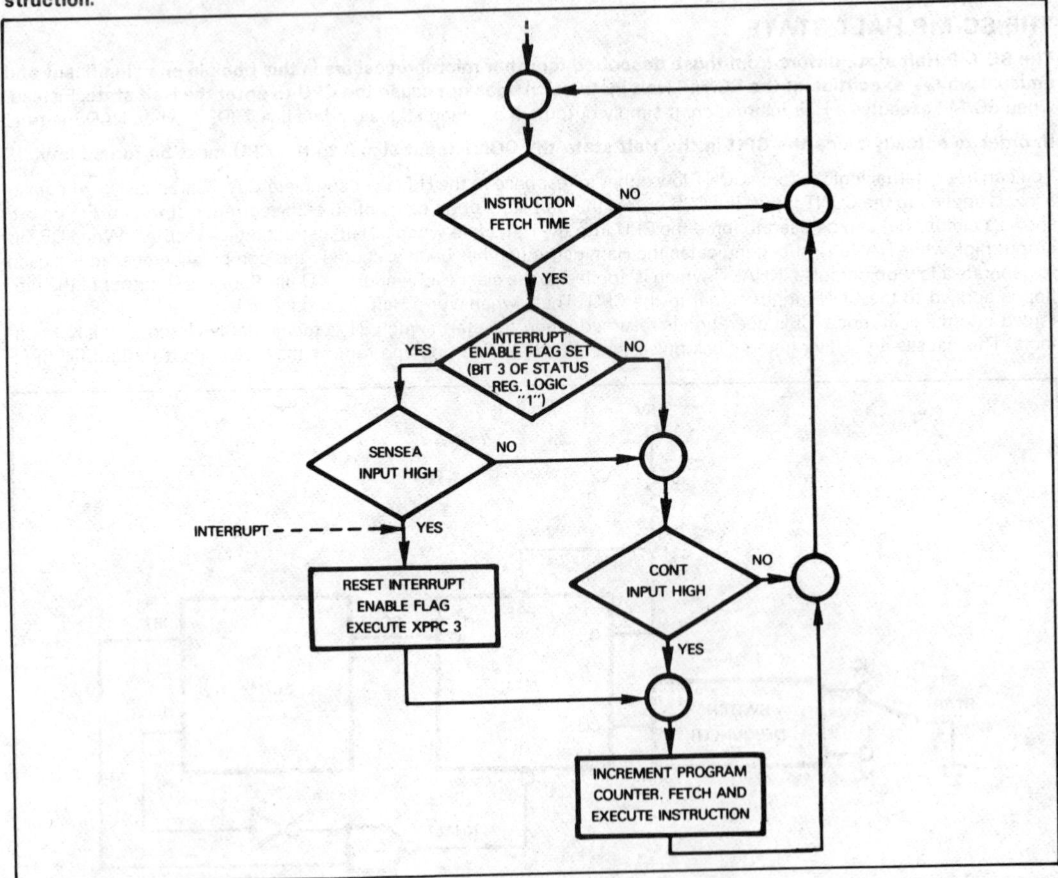


Figure 3-9. SC/MP Interrupt Instruction Fetch Process

**Next, if you compare the interrupt response of SC/MP to those of most other microcomputers or to our hypothetical microcomputer described in Volume 1, you will notice that the following two steps are missing:**

**1) There is no interrupt acknowledge signal.**

**2) None of the SC/MP register contents are saved.**

**In an SC/MP system, both of these functions are left up to your interrupt service routine.** For example, you might provide an interrupt acknowledge indication using one of the CPU Flag outputs or by outputting a specially defined address. If it is necessary to save the contents of the SC/MP registers, this must also be done by your program using a software stack or a predefined area of read/write memory. You must also provide the instructions necessary to restore the contents of any "saved" registers since, as we shall discuss next, the return-from-interrupt sequence used by SC/MP is also quite primitive.

**SC/MP RETURN-FROM-INTERRUPT TECHNIQUE**

**The final unusual aspect of the SC/MP interrupt system is that there is no Return-From-Interrupt instruction. Instead, as we mentioned earlier, the last instruction of your interrupt service routine must be an XPPC P3 instruction which restores the original contents of the Program Counter by exchanging the contents of PC and P3. This might seem quite straightforward, but it will require some special programming considerations.**

The XPPC P3 instruction, which we just mentioned, restores the correct value to the Program Counter — but what about P3? Remember that P3 is always supposed to point to the beginning address (minus 1) of your interrupt service routine (if interrupts are enabled). Yet, the interrupt response sequence we just described loaded the contents of P3 into the Program Counter (PC) and then incremented the PC. And, as our interrupt service routine is executed, the contents of PC will be incremented each time an instruction is executed. Thus, when we complete the interrupt service routine and again exchange the contents of PC and P3, we will be loading P3 (our service routine pointer) with a value that has been altered. So, the problem is — how do we perform an interrupt service routine and ensure that P3 will contain the correct pointer value upon completion of the service routine?

The solution to this quandary requires a closer examination of interrupt service routines. A typical interrupt service routine might consist of three primary segments. One segment would be the entry point to the routine and would include such things as register save operations: let us call this segment "S1". The second segment would be the instruction sequence which actually services the device which requested the interrupt: we will call this segment "S2". The final segment would restore registers and other system elements to their 'pre-interrupt' values, and then return control to the main (interrupted) program: we will call this segment "S3". Thus, the entire interrupt recognition/response/return sequence might be represented as follows:

(We will use arbitrary addresses to simplify our discussion.)

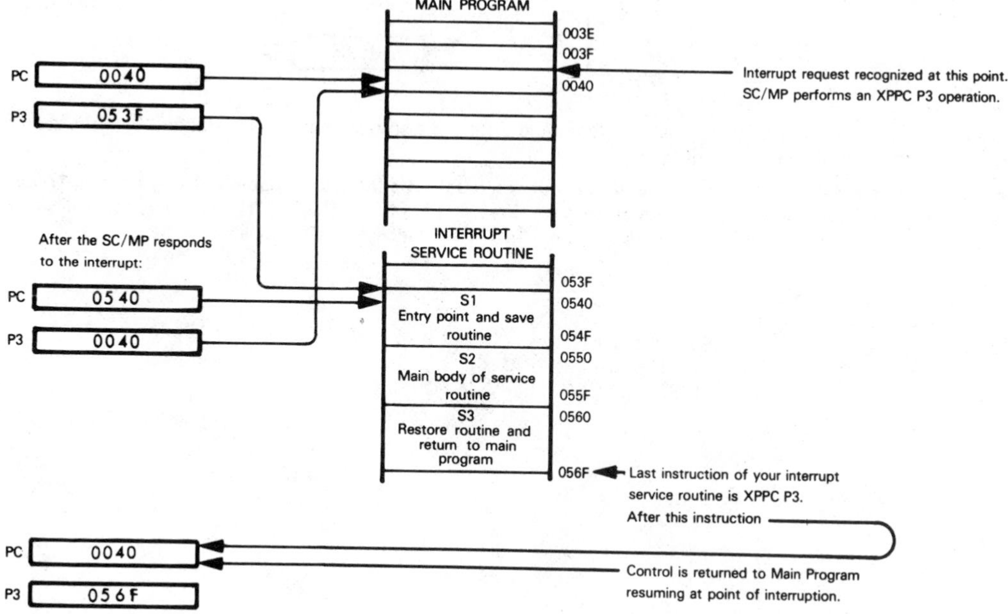

This sequence causes a proper return to the interrupted program but, as we have discussed, does not leave us with our desired pointer value (053F in this example) in P3. The solution requires us to rearrange the segments of our interrupt service routine as follows:

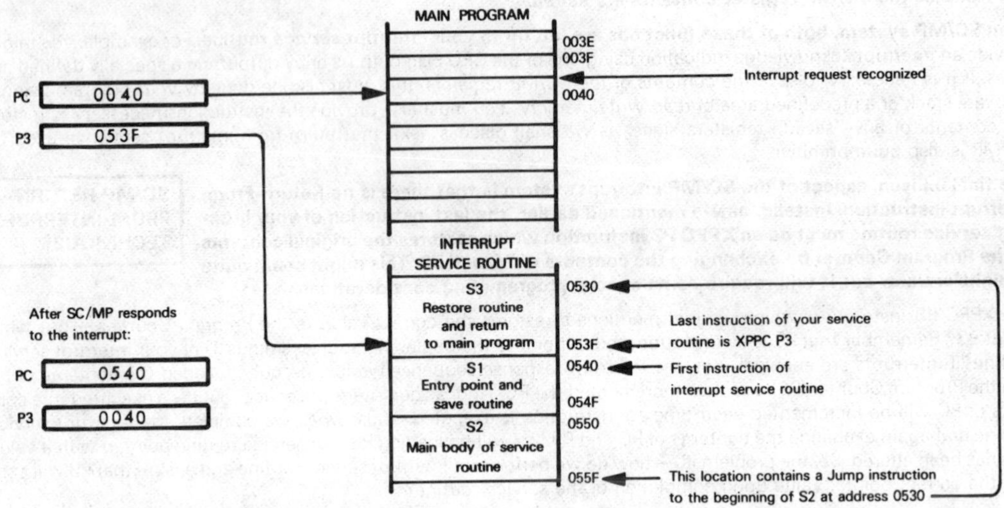


Now, our entry point for the interrupt service routine is still 0540, so we load P3 with a pointer of 053F as before. However, by rearranging the segments and adding a Jump instruction at the end of the second segment (S2), we can have the last instruction of our interrupt service routine located at 053F. When this instruction (XPPC P3) is executed the following operation occurs:

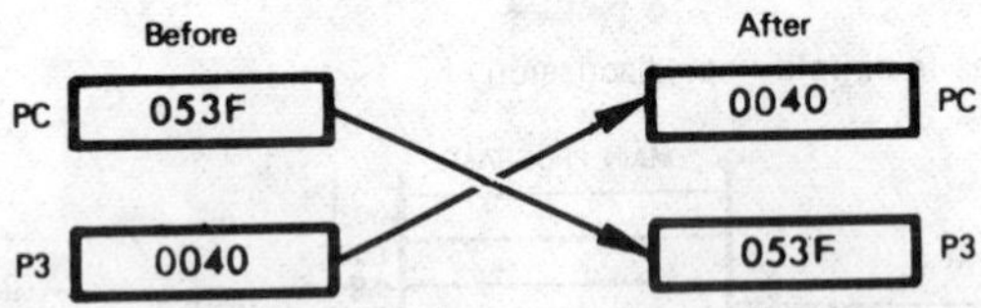


We have now returned control to the main program and we have also restored the contents of P3 to the required pointer value to allow servicing of subsequent interrupts.

**One final point: the CPU's interrupt processing sequence resets the Interrupt Enable (IE) flag to zero. To allow subsequent interrupts to be serviced, your service routine must set the IE flag to "1".** This would typically be the next to last instruction of your interrupt service routine. So the sequence of instructions would be:

```
-
-
-
IEN                 SET IE FLAG TO 1
XPPC      P3        RETURN TO MAIN PROGRAM
                    FIRST INSTRUCTION OF SERVICE ROUTINE
```

## SC/MP DMA AND MULTIPROCESSOR OPERATIONS

Because the SC/MP CPU is a low-cost, low-performance microprocessor, its designers anticipated that it would frequently be used in systems which include other devices of equal or greater intelligence and processing power. Accordingly, **logic is provided on the CPU which provides a simple yet effective method of operating in systems where the System Busses are shared.** The logic required to implement a shared-bus system is essentially the same regardless of whether the purpose is to allow another device (such as a high-speed peripheral) to perform a DMA operation or if it is required because there is more than one CPU operating in the system. There are a few rather subtle differences between the techniques used, and we shall point these out as we proceed with our discussion.

**SC/MP BUS-SHARING CONTROL SIGNALS**

As we have already described, **three SC/MP signals are dedicated to bus-sharing activities: BREQ is an input/output signal which serves both as a bus-request and bus-busy signal, ENIN is effectively a bus-grant input signal, and ENOUT is an output signal that can be used to establish priorities in daisy chained configurations.** Let us begin by seeing how SC/MP might operate in a system which includes a DMA controller.

**The DMA logic provided by the SC/MP CPU is nearly the inverse of that provided by other microcomputers in this book.** Most CPUs assume that they always have control of the System Busses. If another system device requires access to the System Busses, it makes a request to a DMA controller which, in turn, inputs a signal to the CPU requesting that the CPU yield control of the busses. When the CPU has no need for the bus, it outputs an acknowledgement signal to the DMA controller which then sends a bus-grant signal to the requesting device. **The SC/MP CPU, however, competes for the System Busses just as any other system device:** it never assumes that it has control of the busses. Thus, there are really no special considerations that need be accounted for when designing DMA logic for systems that include the SC/MP CPU. The DMA controller can treat the CPU as simply another device (no different from a peripheral device, although the CPU might be assigned to a higher priority) that requires access to the System Busses. Therefore, a typical DMA application would only require the use of the SC/MP BREQ and ENIN signals as shown in Figure 3-10.

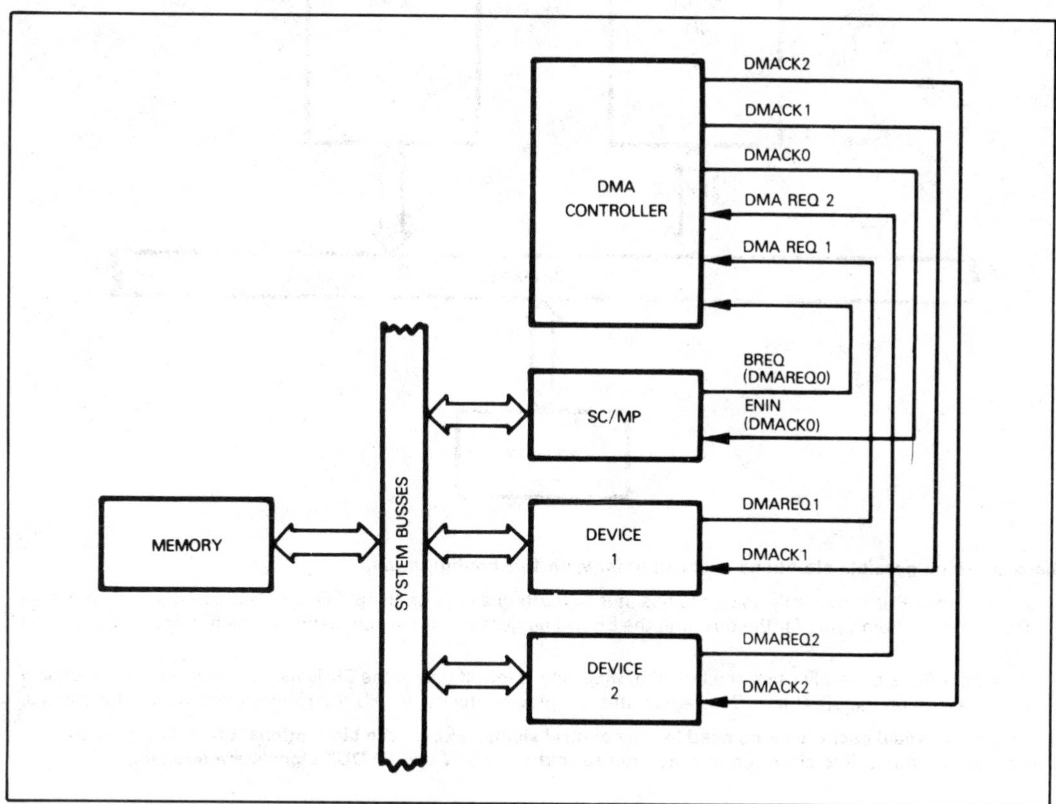


Figure 3-10. Using SC/MP in a System with Direct Memory Access

**Now let us look at how the SC/MP bus-sharing logic might be used in a multiprocessor system. It is in such a system that the CPU's bus-sharing logic can be most appreciated. First, let us restate the rules which govern the conditions of the SC/MP ENOUT output signal.**

**SC/MP IN MULTIPROCESSOR SYSTEMS**

**1) ENOUT is always low while SC/MP is actually using the System Busses; that is, while the ENIN input and BREQ output are both high.**

**2) When SC/MP is not using the System Busses (either BREQ output or ENIN input low), ENOUT is held in the same state as the ENIN input.**

**The effect of these rules may not be immediately obvious. To see how they function to simplify bus-sharing, let us construct a simple multiprocessor system consisting of two SC/MP CPUs and some memory.**

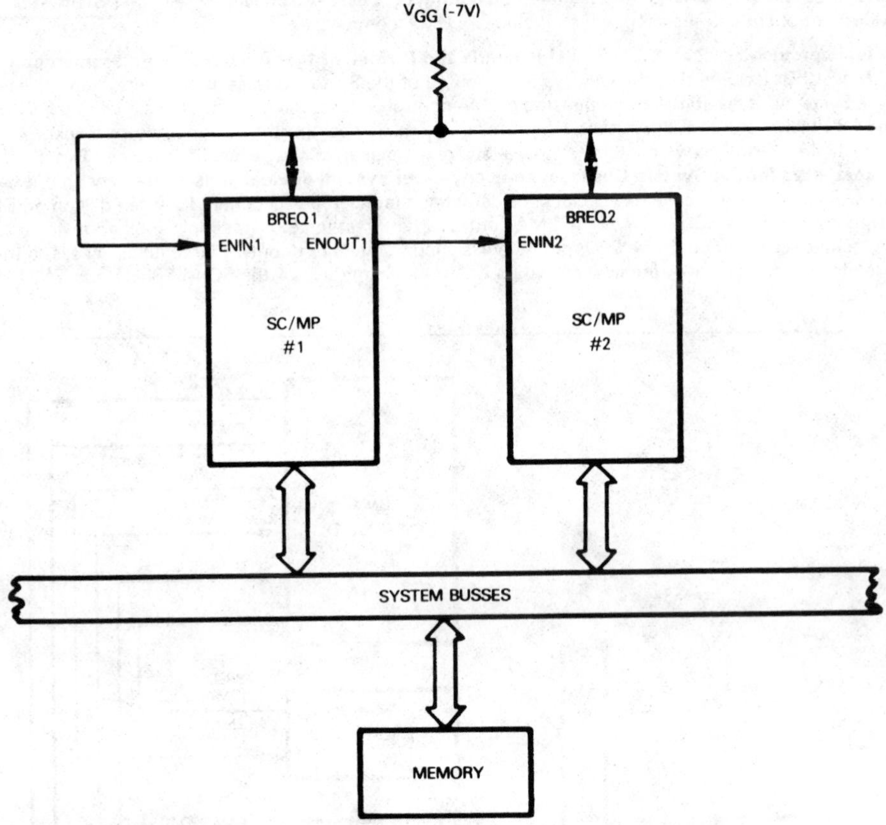


**There are three possible situations that can exist with this configuration.**

1) If one of the CPUs is currently using the bus, it is outputting a high on the BREQ line. This automatically prevents the other CPU from vying for the bus until the BREQ line goes low upon completion of the bus access by the first CPU.

2) If neither CPU is currently using the bus, the BREQ line is low. If one of the CPUs requires bus access, it can now output a high on the BREQ line. Once again, this will prevent the other CPU from subsequently vying for the bus.

**Thus far there would seem to be no need for any control signals except the bidirectional BREQ line. However, it is when the third possible situation is encountered that the ENIN and ENOUT signals are needed.**

3) If both CPUs require bus access at the same time, each will test the BREQ line and, finding it low, will output a high on BREQ. This simultaneous occurrence of requests for bus access is resolved by using the ENIN and ENOUT signals. The operation of these bus access signals to resolve this situation can be illustrated as follows:

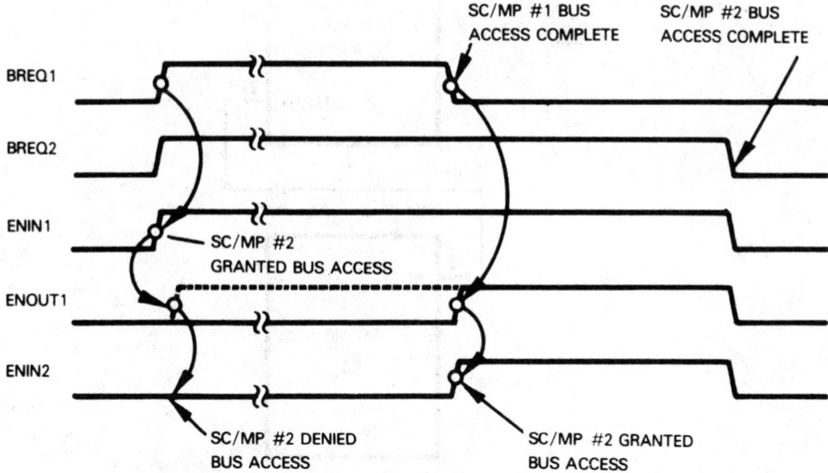


When the BREQ line goes high it applies a high input to the ENIN1 input of SC/MP #1. Since BREQ1 is also high at this time, SC/MP #1 now has access to the bus and it outputs a low on ENOUT1. This is applied to the ENIN2 input to SC/MP #2 and thus denies bus access by SC/MP #2. Notice that SC/MP #2 holds its BREQ2 output signal high even though its request has not yet been granted. When SC/MP #1 has finished its bus access, the BREQ1 output returns low. However, since the BREQ2 output is still high, ENIN1 remains high. This condition of BREQ1 low and ENIN1 high causes the ENOUT1 signal to go high, thus enabling SC/MP #2.

**This arrangement allows the first CPU in a daisy-chain string to have the highest priority for bus access and also automatically allows any other CPU to gain immediate access to the busses whenever they become available.**

**SC/MP CONTROL TECHNIQUES IN MULTIPROCESSOR APPLICATIONS**

Now that we have described the way in which the bus-sharing logic of the SC/MP CPU can be used in a multiprocessor system, let us continue just a bit further and describe a few more common considerations that you must deal with if you are designing a multiprocessor system. We will limit this discussion primarily to hardware and control considerations since programming in a multiprocessor system can become quite complex and is beyond the scope of this book. However, the techniques we will describe here are the first step towards simplifying the programming for such a system.

**The first operation that you must deal with in any microcomputer system is initialization of the system. This operation requires some additional thought when designing a multiprocessor system.** Typically, one CPU will be the primary or controlling CPU: how do you ensure that this CPU has control of the system when power is first applied?

**Figure 3-11 illustrates an easy method of establishing system control upon initialization.** The system reset signal (NRST), which is generated at power-up, is applied to SC/MP #1. The FLAG1 output from SC/MP #1 is then applied to the NRST input of SC/MP #2. Since the FLAG1 line is connected to a bit in the CPU's Status register which is set to zero on power-up, SC/MP #2 will be held in a reset condition until SC/MP #1 executes an instruction which sets that bit (and thus, the FLAG1 output line) high.

Of course, this method requires the FLAG1 output from SC/MP #1 to be dedicated to this initialization operation. If this is a problem, you could use two separate initialization circuits with, for example, the RC time constant for the SC/MP #2 circuitry being greater than that of the circuitry for SC/MP #1. This approach, however, does not provide the positive control of the first method we described.

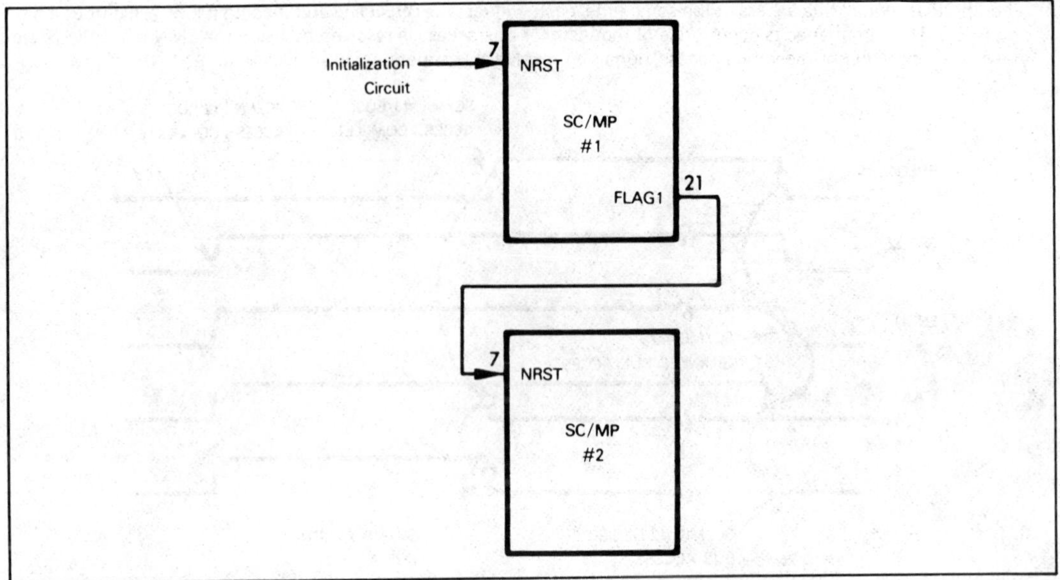


Figure 3-11. One Method of Initializing an SC/MP Multiprocessor System

Once the multiprocessor system has been initialized and is running, the bus-sharing logic that we've already described will resolve contentions between the CPUs as far as access to System Busses is concerned. However, **there might be situations where we want to assure that one of the CPUs will be guaranteed immediate and extended access to the System Busses. This can also be accomplished quite easily with SC/MP as illustrated in Figure 3-12.**

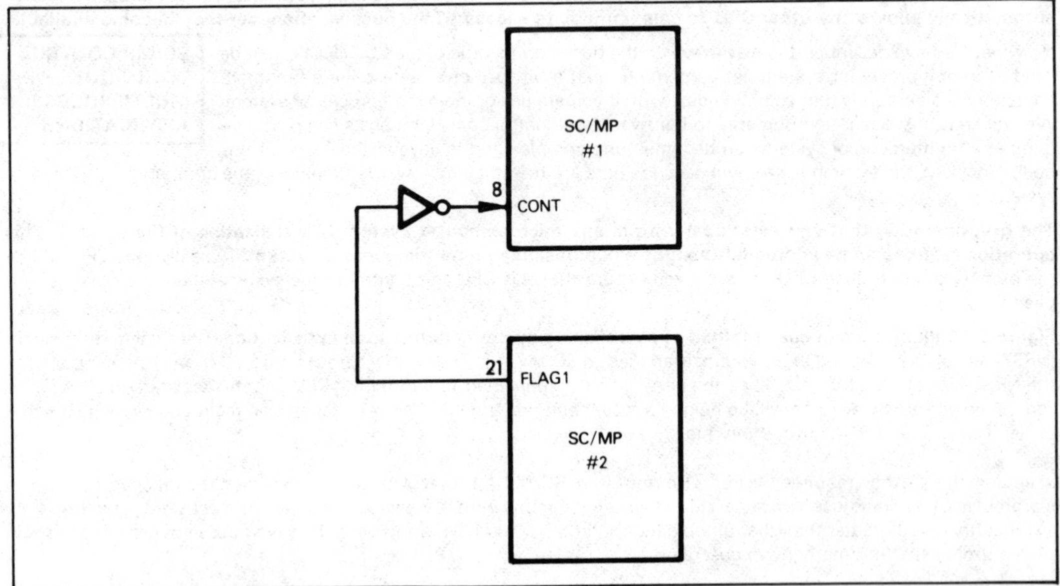


Figure 3-12. Forcing the Halt State in an SC/MP Multiprocessor System

In this illustration the FLAG 1 output of SC/MP #2 is inverted and applied to the CONT input of SC/MP #1. Now, if the F1 bit in the Status register of SC/MP #2 is set to "1", SC/MP #1 will be forced into the Halt state and is effectively removed from the system until the F1 bit is reset under program control.

## THE SC/MP RESET OPERATION

**An NRST low signal input to the SC/MP CPU initializes the microprocessor.** While NRST is low, any in-process operations are automatically aborted and the CPU's strobes and address and data lines are floated. NRST must be held low for a minimum of two microcycles. After NRST goes high again, this is what happens:

1) All of the programmable registers are cleared.
2) The first instruction is fetched from memory location $0001_{16}$.
3) The Bus Request (BREQ) for this first input/output operation occurs within 6-1/2 microcycles after NRST goes high.

**The NRST signal can be used at any time to reset the CPU, and must be used following power-up since SC/MP may power up in a random condition.** After power has first been applied to the CPU, you should allow approximately 100 milliseconds for the oscillator and internal clocks to stabilize before applying the NRST signal.

## SC/MP SERIAL INPUT/OUTPUT OPERATIONS

**The SC/MP CPU not only has two of its 40 pins designated primarily for serial input/output operations, it also dedicates one instruction from its rather limited instruction set solely to serial I/O.** Allocation of this amount of a CPU's resources for this purpose would seem unwarranted with most microprocessors; however, keep in mind that SC/MP is a very low-cost device and intended primarily for use in slow-speed applications. It is quite likely that SC/MP will frequently be used to transfer data serially, so it is therefore not only reasonable but advantageous to provide straightforward methods of performing these operations. Let us look now at how this is done with SC/MP.

In our description of SC/MP's programmable registers, we described the Extension (E) register as an 8-bit register. **When the E register is used for serial I/O, it is actually a 9-bit register with connections to two of the device pins as shown in the figure below.**

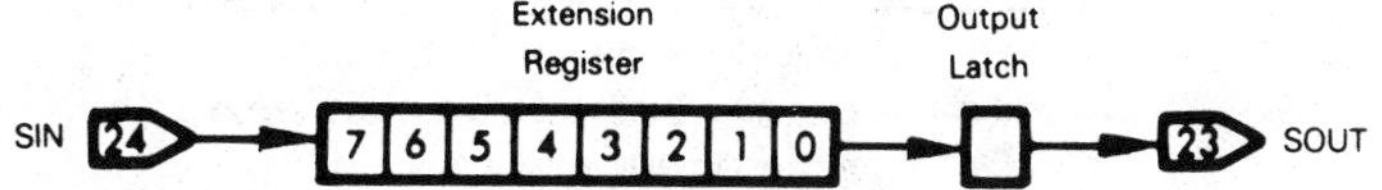


**When the SC/MP SIO (Serial Input/Output) instruction is executed, the contents of the Extension register are shifted right one bit position:** the previous contents of bit 0 are loaded into the output latch and output on the SOUT pin, and the level (1 or 0) present at the SIN pin is loaded into bit 7 of the Extension register. The Extension register can be loaded from, and its contents can be transferred to the Accumulator. A typical serial output operation would thus consist of:

1) Loading the Accumulator with the data byte that is to be transmitted.
2) Transferring the contents of the Accumulator into the Extension register.
3) Performing eight SIO instructions to shift the contents of the Extension register into the output latch and out onto the SOUT pin.

Of course, this sequence does not cover all the programming requirements for serial data transfers. For example, your program must provide some method of timing the bit transmission. This is easily accomplished with SC/MP by using the Delay (DLY) instruction, which can generate variable time delays ranging from 13 to 131,593 microcycles. For asynchronous operations, one of the SC/MP Flags which are connected to device pins can be pulsed each time a new bit is shifted out (or in) and one of the sense conditions inputs (SENSEA or SENSEB) can be tested to detect bit received/ready.

## THE SC/MP INSTRUCTION SET

**Table 3-4 lists the SC/MP instruction set.**

Memory reference instructions are shown as having either full or limited addressing capability. Full addressing capability is identified in the operand as follows:

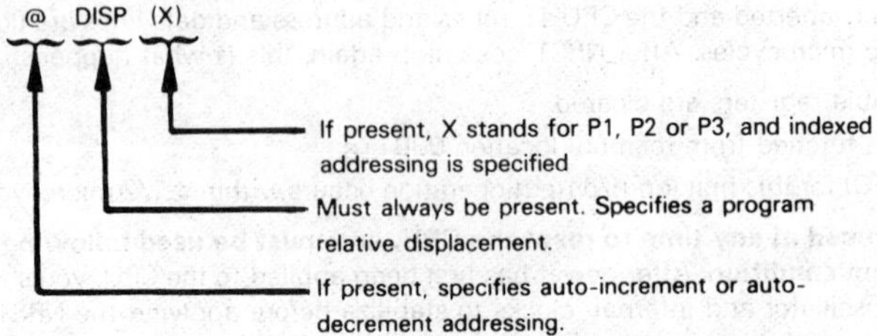


Thus, the real options associated with full addressing capability are:

| | |
|---|---|
| DISP | Direct, program relative addressing |
| DISP(X) | Direct, indexed addressing |
| @DISP(X) | Auto-increment or auto-decrement addressing |

Limited addressing capabilities do not include the auto-increment and auto-decrement feature. The operand field for instructions with limited addressing capability is shown as follows:

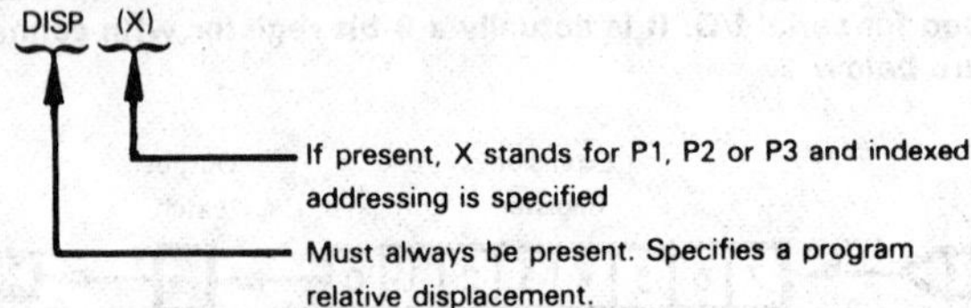


The serial I/O instruction inputs serial data via the high-order bit of the Extension register, and/or outputs serial data via the low-order bit of the Extension register.

The serial I/O instruction works as a one-bit right shift of the Extension register contents, with bit 0 being shifted to the SOUT pin and the SIN pin being shifted into bit 7. This has been illustrated along with the logic description.

It is worth noting that SC/MP has no Jump-to-Subroutine instruction; rather, the XPPC instruction is used to exchange the contents of the Program Counter with the contents of a Pointer register. In very simple applications (and those are the applications for which SC/MP is intended) this is a very effective scheme. Providing subroutines are not nested, a subroutine's beginning address may be stored in a Pointer register, then execution of XPPC moves the subroutine's starting address to the Program Counter, thereby executing the subroutine — but at the same time, the Program Counter contents are stored in the Pointer register, thus preserving the return address. At the conclusion of the subroutine, execution of another XPPC instruction is all that is needed to return from the subroutine. The only penalty paid is that one Pointer register is out of service while the subroutine is being executed. If all Pointer registers are needed by the subroutine, or if subroutines are nested, then the return address which is stored in the Pointer register must be saved in memory. In these more complicated applications, one of the Pointer registers will probably be used as a Stack Pointer, and addresses will be saved on the Stack.

This type of subroutine access, while it may appear primitive to a minicomputer programmer, is very effective in simple microcomputer applications.

The following symbols are used in Table 3-4.

| | |
|---|---|
| AC | Accumulator |
| C | Carry status |
| DATA | An 8-bit binary data unit |
| DISP | An 8-bit signed binary displacement |
| E | The Extension register |

| Symbol | Meaning |
|---|---|
| EA | Effective address, determined by the instruction. Options are:<br>DISP EA is [PC] + DISP<br>DISP(X) EA is [X] + DISP<br>@DISP(X) EA is [X] if DISP ≥ 0,<br>EA is [X] + DISP if DISP < 0;<br>in both cases [X]←[X] + DISP after EA is calculated. |
| E<i> | The ith bit of the Extension register |
| IE | Interrupt Enable |
| O | Overflow status |
| PC | Program Counter |
| X | One of the three Pointer registers |
| SIN | Serial Input pin |
| SOUT | Serial Output pin |
| SR | Status register |
| Z | Zero status |
| @ | Auto-increment flag |
| X<y,z> | Bits y through z of a Pointer register. For example, P3<7,0> represents the low-order byte of Pointer register P3. |
| @DISP(X) | This designates the available addressing modes for the SC/MP, as described above. In all three of the addressing modes, if -128 is specified for DISP, the contents of the Extension register are used instead of DISP. |
| [ ] | Contents of location enclosed within brackets. If a register designation is enclosed within the brackets, then the designated register's contents are specified. If a memory address is enclosed within the brackets, then the contents of the addressed memory location are specified. |
| [[ ]] | Implied memory addressing; the contents of the memory location designated by the contents of a register. |
| Λ | Logical AND |
| V | Logical OR |
| ∀ | Logical Exclusive-OR |
| ← | Data is transferred in the direction of the arrow. |
| ←→ | Data is exchanged between the two locations designated on either side of the arrow. |

Under the heading of STATUSES in Table 3-4, an X indicates statuses which are modified in the course of the instruction's execution. If there is no X, it means that the status maintains the value it had before the instruction was executed.

Table 3-4. SC/MP Instruction Set Summary

| TYPE | MNEMONIC | OPERAND(S) | BYTES | STATUSES C | STATUSES O | | | | | OPERATION PERFORMED |
|---|---|---|---|---|---|---|---|---|---|---|
| I/O | SIO | | 1 | | | | | | | [E<i-1>]←[E<i>]<br>SOUT ← [E0]<br>[E7] ← SIN<br>Shift the Extension register right one bit. Shift bit 0 of the Extension register to the output pin SOUT. Shift the data at input pin SIN into bit 7 of the Extension register. |
| PRIMARY MEMORY REF AND I/O | LD | @ DISP(X) | 2 | | | | | | | [AC]←[EA]<br>Load Accumulator from addressed memory location. |
| | ST | @ DISP(X) | 2 | | | | | | | [EA]←[AC]<br>Store Accumulator contents in addressed memory location. |
| SECONDARY MEMORY REFERENCE AND MEMORY OPERATE | ADD | @ DISP(X) | 2 | X | X | | | | | [AC]←[AC] + [EA] + [C]<br>Add binary to Accumulator the addressed memory location's contents with Carry. |
| | DAD | @ DISP(X) | 2 | X | | | | | | [AC]←[AC] + [EA] + [C]<br>Add decimal to Accumulator the addressed memory location's contents with Carry. |
| | CAD | @ DISP(X) | 2 | X | X | | | | | [AC]←[AC] + [$\overline{EA}$] + [C]<br>Add complement of addressed memory location's contents with Carry to Accumulator. |
| | AND | @ DISP(X) | 2 | | | | | | | [AC]←[AC] ∧ [EA]<br>AND Accumulator with addressed memory location's contents. |
| | OR | @ DISP(X) | 2 | | | | | | | [AC]←[AC] V [EA]<br>OR Accumulator with addressed memory location's contents. |
| | XOR | @ DISP(X) | 2 | | | | | | | [AC]←[AC] ⊻ [EA]<br>Exclusive-OR Accumulator with addressed memory location's contents. |
| | ILD | @ DISP(X) | 2 | | | | | | | [EA]←[EA] + 1; [AC]←[EA]<br>Increment addressed memory location's contents, then load into Accumulator. |
| | DLD | @ DISP(X) | 2 | | | | | | | [EA]←[EA] - 1; [AC]←[EA]<br>Decrement addressed memory location's contents, then load into Accumulator. |
| IMMEDIATE | LDI | DATA | 2 | | | | | | | [AC] ← DATA<br>Load immediate into Accumulator. |
| IMMEDIATE OPERATE | ADI | DATA | 2 | X | X | | | | | [AC]←[AC] + DATA + [C]<br>Add binary immediate. Add Carry to result. |
| | DAI | DATA | 2 | X | | | | | | [AC]←[AC] + DATA + [C]<br>Decimal add immediate. Add Carry to result. |
| | CAI | DATA | 2 | X | X | | | | | [AC]←[AC] + $\overline{DATA}$ + [C]<br>Add the contents of the Accumulator to the complement of the immediate data value. Add Carry to result. |
| | ANI | DATA | 2 | | | | | | | [AC]←[AC] ∧ DATA<br>AND immediate. |

Table 3-4. SC/MP Instruction Set Summary (Continued)

| TYPE | MNEMONIC | OPERAND(S) | BYTES | STATUSES | | | | | | OPERATION PERFORMED |
|---|---|---|---|---|---|---|---|---|---|---|
| | | | | C | O | | | | | |
| IMMEDIATE OPERATE (CONTINUED) | ORI | DATA | 2 | | | | | | | [AC]←[AC] V DATA<br>OR immediate. |
| | XRI | DATA | 2 | | | | | | | [AC]←[AC] ⊻ DATA<br>Exclusive-OR immediate. |
| JUMP | JMP | DISP(X) | 2 | | | | | | | [PC]←EA<br>Unconditional jump to effective address. |
| JUMP ON CONDITION | JP | DISP(X) | 2 | | | | | | | If [AC] ≥ 0; [PC]←EA<br>If the Accumulator contents are greater than 0, jump to effective address. |
| | JZ | DISP(X) | 2 | | | | | | | If [AC] = 0; [PC]←EA<br>If the Accumulator contents equal 0, jump to effective address. |
| | JNZ | DISP(X) | 2 | | | | | | | If [AC] = 0; [PC]←EA<br>If the Accumulator contents are not 0, jump to effective address. |
| REGISTER-REGISTER MOVE | LDE | | 1 | | | | | | | [AC]←[E]<br>Load the contents of the Extension register into the Accumulator. |
| | XPAL | X | 1 | | | | | | | [AC]←→[X<7,0>]<br>Exchange the contents of the Accumulator with the low order byte of the specified Pointer register. |
| | XPAH | X | 1 | | | | | | | [AC]←→[X<15,8>]<br>Exchange the contents of the Accumulator with the high order byte of the specified Pointer register. |
| | XPPC | X | 1 | | | | | | | [PC]←→[X]<br>Exchange the contents of the Program Counter with those of the specified Pointer register. |
| | XAE | | 1 | | | | | | | [AC]←→[E]<br>Exchange the contents of the Accumulator with those of the Extension register. |
| REGISTER-REGISTER OPERATE | ADE | | 1 | X | X | | | | | [AC]←[AC] + [E] + [C]<br>Add binary the contents of the Accumulator and the contents of the Extension register. Add Carry to this result. |
| | DAE | | 1 | X | | | | | | [AC]←[AC] + [E] + [C]<br>Add decimal the contents of the Extension register to those of the Accumulator. Add Carry to this result. |
| | CAE | | 1 | X | X | | | | | [AC]←[AC] + [$\overline{E}$] + [C]<br>Add binary the contents of the Accumulator and the complement of the Extension register contents. Add Carry to this result. |
| | ANE | | 1 | | | | | | | [AC]←[AC] Λ [E]<br>AND the contents of the Accumulator with those of the Extension register. |

Table 3-4. SC/MP Instruction Set Summary (Continued)

| TYPE | MNEMONIC | OPERAND(S) | BYTES | STATUSES C | O |  |  |  |  | OPERATION PERFORMED |
|---|---|---|---|---|---|---|---|---|---|---|
| REGISTER-REGISTER OPERATE (CONTINUED) | ORE | | 1 | | | | | | | [AC]←[AC] V [E]<br>OR the contents of the Accumulator with those of the Extension register. |
| | XRE | | 1 | | | | | | | [AC]←[AC] ⊻ [E]<br>Exclusive-OR the contents of the Accumulator with those of the Extension register. |
| REGISTER OPERATE | SR | | 1 | | | | | | | 0 → [7 → 0] →<br>Shift Accumulator contents right one bit. The high order bit becomes a 0. The low order bit is lost. |
| | SRL | | 1 | | | | | | | C → [7 → 0] →<br>Shift Accumulator contents right one bit. The Carry bit is shifted into the high order bit of the Accumulator. The low order bit is lost. |
| | RR | | 1 | | | | | | | [7 → 0] (0 → 7)<br>Rotate Accumulator contents right one bit. Rotate the low order bit of the Accumulator into the high order bit. |
| | RRL | | 1 | | | | | | | C → [7 → 0] (0 → C)<br>Rotate Accumulator contents right through Carry. |
| INTERRUPT | DINT | | 1 | | | | | | | [IE]←0<br>Disable interrupts. |
| | IEN | | 1 | | | | | | | [IE]←1<br>Enable interrupts. |
| STATUS | CCL | | 1 | 0 | | | | | | [C]←0<br>Clear Carry. |
| | SCL | | 1 | 1 | | | | | | [C]←1<br>Set Carry. |
| | CSA | | 1 | | | | | | | [AC]←[SR]<br>Load the contents of the Status register into the Accumulator. |
| | CAS | | 1 | | | | | | | [SR]←[AC]<br>Load the contents of the Accumulator into the Status register. |
| | HALT | | 1 | | | | | | | Pulse the H-Flag |
| | NOP | | 1 | | | | | | | No Operation. |
| | DLY | DATA | 1 | | | | | | | Delays CPU for a number of cycles equal to:<br>$13 + 2(AC) + 2DATA + 2^9DATA$ |

The following symbols are used in Table 3-5:

aa Two binary digits designating the Pointer register:
- 00 Program Counter
- 01 Pointer Register 1
- 10 Pointer Register 2
- 11 Pointer Register 3

m One binary digit specifying address mode:
- 0 Program Relative or Indexed
- 1 Immediate or Auto-increment or Auto-decrement

PP Two hexadecimal digits representing an 8-bit, signed displacement

QQ Two hexadecimal digits representing 8 bits of immediate data

Where two numbers are given — for example, 9/11, the first is execution time when no jump is taken; the second is execution time when there is a jump.

Table 3-5. SC/MP Instruction Set Object Codes and Execution Times

| INSTRUCTION | OBJECT CODE | BYTES | MACHINE CYCLES |
|---|---|---|---|
| ADD @DISP(X) | 11110maa | 2 | 19 |
| | PP | | |
| ADE | 70 | 1 | 7 |
| ADI DATA | F4 | | |
| | QQ | | |
| AND @DISP(X) | 11010maa | 2 | 18 |
| | PP | | |
| ANE | 50 | 1 | 6 |
| ANI DATA | D4 | 2 | 10 |
| | QQ | | |
| CAD DISP(X) | 11111maa | 2 | 20 |
| | PP | | |
| CAE | 78 | 1 | 8 |
| CAI DATA | FC | 2 | 12 |
| | QQ | | |
| CAS | 07 | 1 | 6 |
| CCL | 02 | 1 | 5 |
| CSA | 06 | 1 | 5 |
| DAD @DISP(X) | 11101maa | 2 | 23 |
| DAE | 68 | 1 | 11 |
| DAI DATA | EC | 2 | 15 |
| | QQ | | |
| DINT | 04 | 1 | 6 |
| DLY DATA | 101110aa | 2 | 22 |
| | PP | | |
| DLY DISP | 4F | 2 | 13-131, 593* |
| | PP | | |
| HALT | 00 | 1 | 8 |
| IEN | 05 | 1 | 6 |
| ILD DISP(X) | 101010aa | 2 | 22 |
| | PP | | |
| JMP DISP(X) | 100000aa | 2 | 11 |
| | PP | | |

| INSTRUCTION | OBJECT CODE | BYTES | MACHINE CYCLES |
|---|---|---|---|
| JNZ DISP(X) | 100011aa | 2 | 9/11 |
| | PP | | |
| JP DISP(X) | 100001aa | 2 | 9/11 |
| | PP | | |
| JZ DISP(X) | 100010aa | 2 | 9/11 |
| | PP | | |
| LD @DISP(X) | 11000maa | 2 | 18 |
| | PP | | |
| LDE | 40 | 1 | 6 |
| LDI DATA | C4 | 2 | 10 |
| | QQ | | |
| NOP | 08 | 1 | 5-10 |
| OR @DISP(X) | 11011maa | 2 | 18 |
| | PP | | |
| ORE | 58 | 1 | 6 |
| ORI DATA | DC | 2 | 10 |
| | QQ | | |
| RR | 1E | 1 | 5 |
| RRL | 1F | 1 | 5 |
| SCL | 03 | 1 | 5 |
| SIO | 19 | 1 | 5 |
| SR | 1C | 1 | 5 |
| SRL | 1D | 1 | 5 |
| ST @DISP(X) | 11001maa | 2 | 18 |
| | PP | | |
| XAE | 01 | 1 | 7 |
| XOR @DISP(X) | 11100maa | 2 | 18 |
| | PP | | |
| XPAH X | 001101aa | 1 | 8 |
| XPAL X | 001100aa | 1 | 8 |
| XPPC X | 001111aa | 1 | 7 |
| XRE | 60 | 1 | 6 |
| XRI DATA | E4 | 2 | 10 |
| | QQ | | |

*Delay time depends on the value of DATA.

## THE BENCHMARK PROGRAM

**For SC/MP, the benchmark program looks like this:**

```
        LD      TABLE(P3)     LOAD HIGH BYTE OF FIRST FREE TABLE BYTE
        XPAH    P1            ADDRESS MOVE TO PR1 HIGH-ORDER BYTE
        LD      TABLE+1(P3)   REPEAT FOR LOW-ORDER BYTE
        XPAL    P1
        LDI     IOHI          LOAD HIGH BYTE OF I/O BUFFER BASE ADDRESS
        XPAH    P2            MOVE TO PR2 HIGH-ORDER BYTE
        LDI     IOLO          REPEAT FOR LOW-ORDER BYTE
        XPAL    P2
LOOP    LD      @0(P2)        LOAD NEXT BYTE FROM I/O BUFFER
                              AUTO-INCREMENT
        ST      @0(P1)        STORE IN NEXT FREE TABLE BYTE
        DLD     IOCNT(P3)     DECREMENT I/O BUFFER COUNT AND LOAD
        JNZ     LOOP          RETURN TO LOOP IF NOT ZERO
        XPAL    P1            LOAD LOW-ORDER TABLE ADDRESS INTO A
        ST      TABLE+1(P3)   SAVE IN FIRST FREE TABLE BYTE ADDRESS
```

The SC/MP benchmark program makes the following assumptions.

The address of the first free table byte is not stored at the beginning of the table; rather, it is stored in two bytes of a data area, addressed by Pointer Register 3, plus a displacement. The addresses of these two bytes are given by the displacement TABLE and TABLE+1.

It is assumed that TABLE begins at a memory address with 0s for the low order eight binary digits (as for the F8 benchmark program); therefore, the contents of the data area byte with address TABLE+1(PC3) becomes the displacement to the first free byte of TABLE. Assuming that TABLE has a maximum length of 256 bytes, it is only necessary at the end of the data move operation to store a new byte address into TABLE+1, in order to update the address of the first free table byte. This scheme is illustrated below.

The I/O buffer beginning address is stored in two immediate instructions, which load the two halves of the I/O buffer beginning address into the Accumulator; each half is then exchanged into a Pointer register.

The SC/MP benchmark program assumptions may be illustrated as follows:

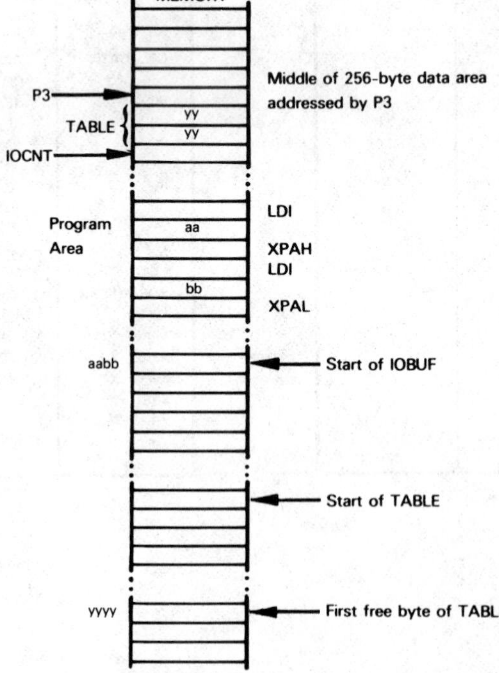

# SUPPORT DEVICES FOR THE SC/MP CPU

**SC/MP support devices are general-purpose and are therefore described in Volume 3. You may also use standard off-the-shelf buffers, bidirectional drivers, RAM and ROM to implement any supporting functions needed. Figure 3-13 illustrates an SC/MP system and the type of supporting devices that might be needed.** Notice that the buffers, latches and I/O ports are all indicated by dotted lines. We have done this because it is quite feasible that some SC/MP systems might consist only of the CPU and a small amount of memory. In such a system, there would not necessarily be any need for buffering the SC/MP input/output lines, nor demultiplexing status and page-select bits from the Data Bus. Many systems, however, will require some of the supporting devices indicated by Figure 3-13. In the remainder of this chapter we will briefly describe how some of the commonly required support functions for SC/MP can be implemented using both standard off-the-shelf devices and devices from other microcomputer families.

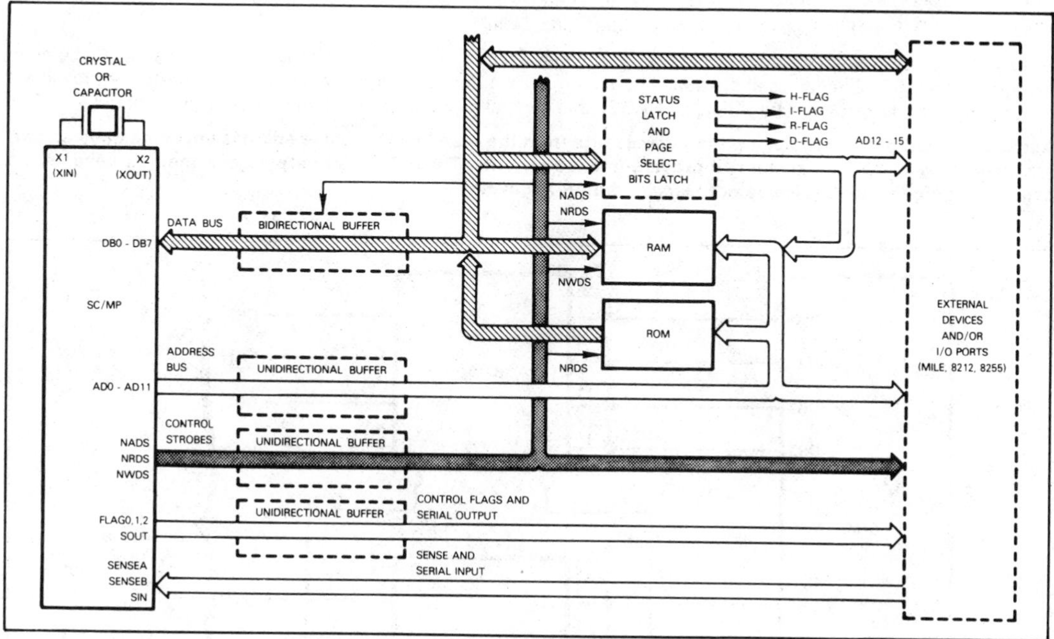


Figure 3-13. An SC/MP System Showing Typical Support Devices that may be Required

**BUFFERING SC/MP BUSSES**

As we mentioned earlier, the SC/MP output lines can each drive one TTL load. Some systems, especially those which utilize low-power external devices, may not require any buffering. **When buffering is needed, it can be provided using standard logic devices. The only area that requires any special attention is when you are buffering the data lines: since these lines are used both for input and output of data, you must provide bidirectional control of these buffering devices. Figure 3-14 shows one easy method of implementing bidirectional buffers for the SC/MP data lines using 8216 bidirectional bus drivers.** (The 8216 is a support device from the 8080 family and is described in Chapter 4.) The SC/MP NRDS signal is inverted and used to provide directional control of the buffers. When the SC/MP is performing a read operation, NRDS is output low: this causes the contents of the system Data Bus to be gated through the buffers and onto the SC/MP data lines. At all other times, NRDS is high and whatever is on the SC/MP data lines is passed onto the system Data Bus.

**DEMULTIPLEXING THE SC/MP DATA BUS**

**If you need to use the four most significant address bits (AD12 - AD15) for page select functions or if you are going to make use of the I/O cycle status information that SC/MP outputs, you must demultiplex this information from the SC/MP data lines. The most straightforward way of doing this is to use D-type flip-flops or data registers with the SC/MP NADS signal as the clock pulse.** Here are some standard 7400 family devices that might be used:

- 7475 Double 2-Bit Gated Latches with Q and $\overline{Q}$ Outputs
- 7477 Double 2-Bit Gated Latches with Q Output Only
- 74100 Double 4-Bit Gated Latches
- 74166 Dual 4-Bit Gated Latches with Clear
- 74174 Hex D-Type Flip-Flops with Common Clock and Clear
- 74175 Quad D-Type Flip-Flops with Common Clock and Clear

Some of these devices require that the NADS signal be inverted to provide the necessary clocking signal. Remember, though, that the SC/MP address and status information is valid during both the leading edge (high-to-low transition) and trailing edge (low-to-high transition) of NADS: this generally simplifies the demultiplexing operation.

**Another method of demultiplexing the address bits from the data lines is to use address decoding devices that are clocked by the NADS signal and provide latched outputs. These latched outputs can then be used as the page select signals (or device select signals) during I/O cycles.**

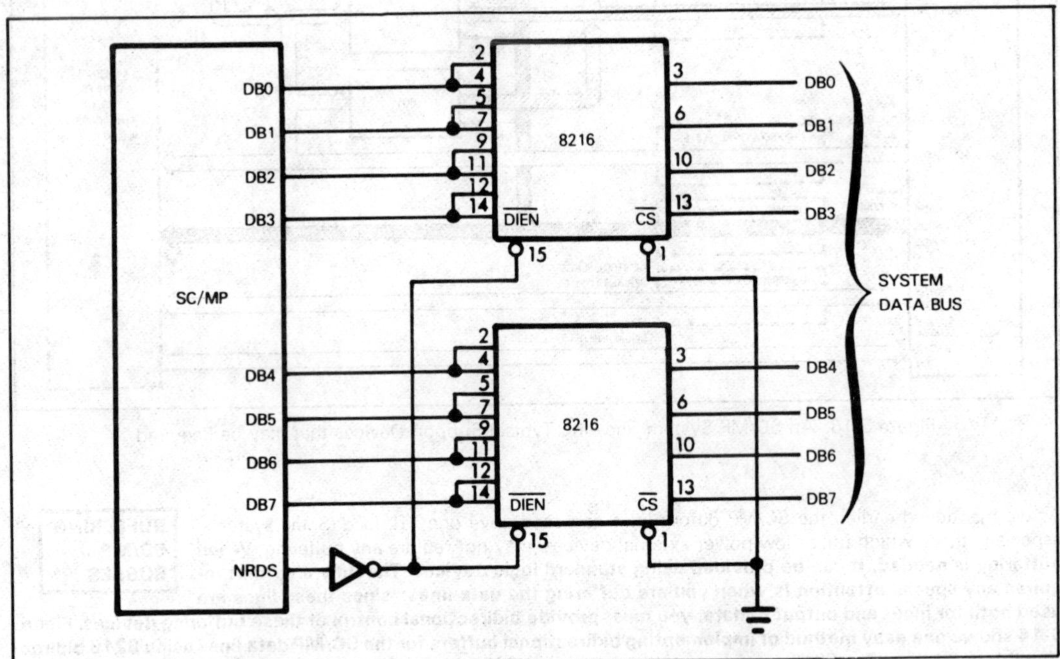


Figure 3-14. SC/MP Data Lines Buffered Using 8216 Devices

# USING OTHER MICROCOMPUTER SUPPORT DEVICES WITH THE SC/MP CPU

**There is nothing to prevent SC/MP from using support devices from other microcomputer "families". We have already shown one simple example — the use of 8216 bidirectional bus drivers to buffer the SC/MP data lines. The SC/MP CPU provides numerous control signals which allow general-purpose microcomputer support devices to be included in an SC/MP system. We will now describe a couple of specific examples of how this can be done — these examples will serve as guidelines for interfacing SC/MP to other support devices.**

**THE PACE MILE USED IN AN SC/MP SYSTEM**

**The Microprocessor Interface Latch Element (MILE) is a support device from the PACE microcomputer family and is described in detail in Volume 3. The MILE can be used to provide an 8-bit, bidirectional I/O port in an SC/MP system as shown in the figure below.**

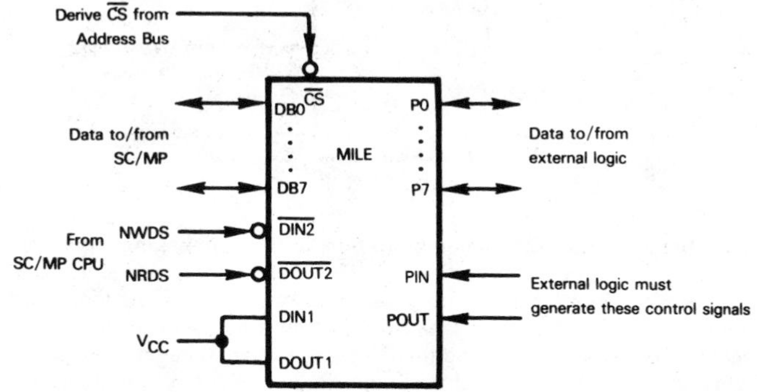


The chip select ($\overline{CS}$) signal must be derived from the Address Bus and could consist of a single address line, a page select signal, or the output of address decoding logic. Remember that the SC/MP CPU does not differentiate between memory and I/O devices: it treats the MILE simply as a memory location.

Directional control of the MILE is provided by the SC/MP read strobe (NRDS) and write strobe (NWDS) signals. NRDS is connected to the MILE's $\overline{DOUT2}$ input signal: when NRDS and $\overline{CS}$ are both low, the contents of the MILE's data latches are gated out onto the SC/MP data lines for input to the CPU. The SC/MP NWDS signal is connected to the MILE's $\overline{DIN2}$ input: when NWDS and $\overline{CS}$ are both low, the data output on the SC/MP data lines is latched into the MILE.

**In the figure above, the MILE's DIN1 and DOUT1 signals are continuously enabled by connecting them to +5V. An alternate method of using these two signals would be to connect them to address lines in order to simplify the address decoding requirements of the SC/MP system as shown in the figure below.**

**In this example, data transfers between the MILE and SC/MP are enabled when address bit 11 (AD11) is a zero and AD10 is a one. This figure also shows the two handshaking signals (STD and STP) provided by the MILE. These signals can be applied to the SENSEA or SENSEB inputs to SC/MP to implement simple I/O handshaking schemes.**

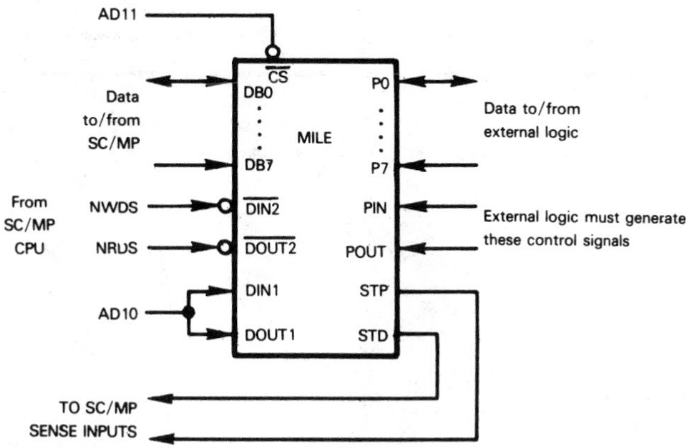

**THE 8212 I/O PORT USED IN SC/MP SYSTEMS**

**The 8212 I/O port from the 8080A microcomputer family is a device similar to the MILE: the only difference is that while the MILE can operate bidirectionally, the 8212 is unidirectional. The signal connections required to use the 8212 with SC/MP are quite simple:**

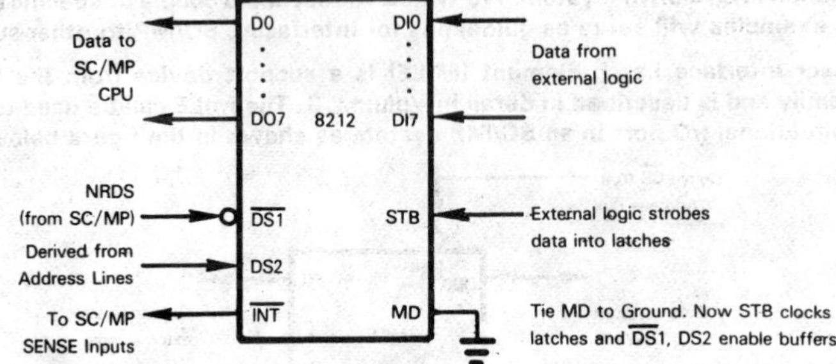


**The connections shown here use the 8212 as an input port with handshaking logic provided.** When the external logic latches data into the 8212 using the STB signal, the $\overline{INT}$ signal goes low; this signal can be applied to the SC/MP SENSEA or SENSEB input to inform the CPU that input data is ready. SC/MP would then execute a service routine program that would include an instruction to read data from the input port. This instruction would send out the input port's address, thus generating the DS2 signal, and then gate the latched data onto the CPU data lines when the NRDS signal is generated. When the latched data is read out of the 8212, the $\overline{INT}$ signal returns high to complete the transaction. This sequence is summarized by the following timing diagram:

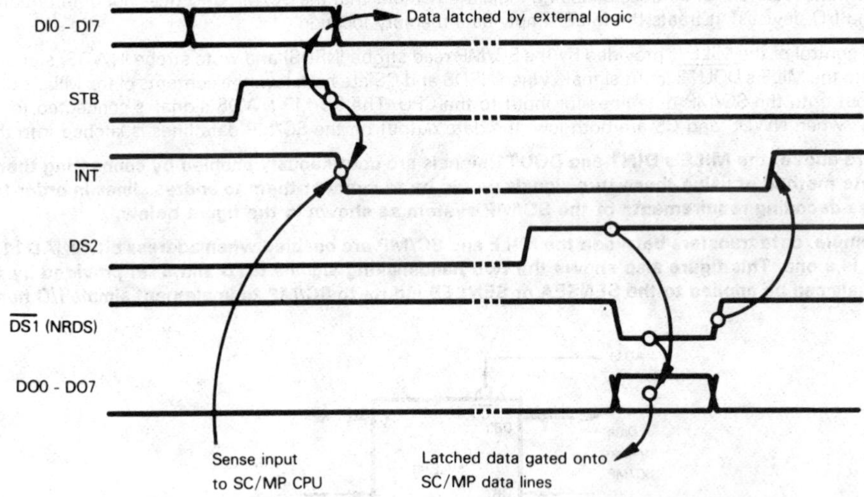

**Using the 8212 as an output port in an SC/MP system requires a simple reversal of the connections we described in the preceding example.**

**THE 8212 USED AS AN OUTPUT PORT IN AN SC/MP SYSTEM**

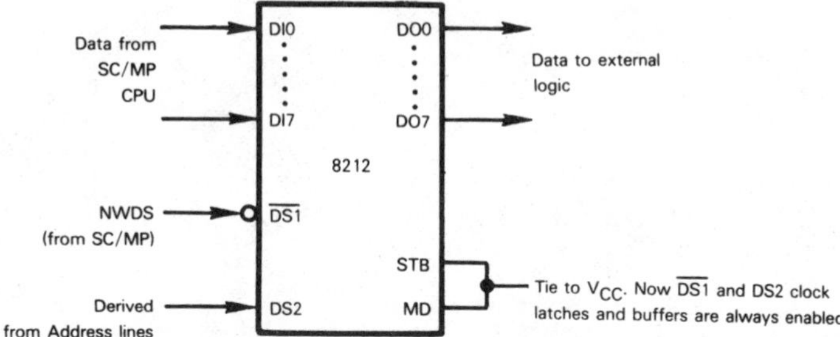


With this arrangement, data from the CPU will be loaded into the 8212 latches when the required address is generated to apply a high to DS2 and SC/MP outputs the NWDS strobe signal. Data that is latched into the 8212 is immediately gated out onto DO0 - DO7 and presented to external logic.

**We will conclude our discussion of support devices that may be used with SC/MP with the following observation. The MILE and 8212 devices, which we have used as examples, are both relatively simple support devices. However, more complex general-purpose support devices are usually no more difficult to interface to an SC/MP CPU. In fact, the interface is often simpler, from a hardware point of view, because such things as mode control are handled by software.**

# DATA SHEETS

This section contains specific electrical and timing data for both the SC/MP and SC/MP II (INS8060).

## applications

- Test Systems and Instrumentation
- Machine Tool Control
- Small Business Machines
- Word Processing Systems
- Educational Systems
- Multiprocessor Systems
- Process Controllers
- Terminals
- Traffic Controls
- Laboratory Controllers
- Sophisticated Games
- Automotive

## absolute maximum ratings

| | |
|---|---|
| Voltage at Any Pin | $V_{SS}$ + 0.3V to $V_{SS}$ − 20V |
| Operating Temperature Range | 0°C to +70°C |
| Storage Temperature Range | −65°C to +150°C |
| Lead Temperature (Soldering, 10 seconds) | 300°C |

## electrical characteristics ($T_A$ = 0°C to +70°C, $V_{SS}$ = +5V ± 5%, $V_{GG}$ = −7V ± 5%)

| Parameter | Conditions | Min. | Typ.* | Max. | Units |
|---|---|---|---|---|---|
| INPUT SPECIFICATIONS | | | | | |
| ENIN, NHOLD, NRST, SENSE A, SENSE B, SIN, DB0-DB7 (TTL Compatible) (Note 2) | | | | | |
| Logic "1" Input Voltage | | $V_{SS}$ − 1 | | $V_{SS}$ + 0.3 | V |
| Logic "0" Input Voltage | | $V_{SS}$ − 10 | | 0.8 | V |
| Pullup Transistor "ON" Resistance (Note 2) | $V_{IN}$ = ($V_{SS}$ − 1) V | | 7.5 | 12 | kΩ |
| Logic "0" Input Current | $V_{IN}$ = 0V | | | −1.6 | mA |
| BREQ (Note 3) | | | | | |
| Logic "1" Input Voltage | | $V_{SS}$ − 1 | | $V_{SS}$ + 0.3 | V |
| Logic "0" Input Voltage | | | | 0.8 | V |
| X1, X2 (Note 4) | | | | | |
| Logic "1" Input Voltage | | 3.0 | | $V_{SS}$ + 0.3 | V |
| Logic "0" Input Voltage | | | | 0.4 | V |
| Logic "1" Input Current | $V_{IN}$ = 3.0V | | | 5.0 | mA |
| Logic "0" Input Current | $V_{IN}$ = 0.4V | −5.5 | | | mA |
| Input Capacitance (All pins except $V_{GG}$ and $V_{SS}$) | | | | 10 | pF |
| Supply Current | | | | | |
| $I_{GG}$ (See Typical Plot of Normalized $I_{GG}$ [and $I_{SS}$] Versus Ambient Temperature on page 6.) | $T_A$ = 0°C, loads on all outputs: $I_{SINK}$ = 1.6mA (See diagram, Simulated Current Load, on page 6.) | | 100 | 135 | mA |
| $I_{SS}$ | | | 90 | 125 | mA |
| OUTPUT SPECIFICATIONS | | | | | |
| BREQ (Note 3) | | | | | |
| Logic "1" Output Current | $V_{OUT}$ = ($V_{SS}$ − 1) V | −2.0 | | | mA |
| Logic "0" Output Current | $V_{GG} \leqslant V_{OUT} \leqslant V_{SS}$ | | | ±10 | μA |
| External Load Capacitance | | | | 50 | pF |
| All Other Outputs | | | | | |
| Logic "1" Output Voltage | $I_{OUT}$ = −80μA | $V_{SS}$ − 1 | | | V |
| | $I_{OUT}$ = −200μA | 2.4 | | | V |
| Logic "0" Output Voltage | $I_{OUT}$ = 1.6mA | | | 0.4 | V |
| Logic "0" Output Current | $V_{OUT}$ = −0.5V | | | 4.0 | mA |
| Logic "0" Output Voltage | $I_{OUT}$ = 0mA (unloaded) | −3.0 | −0.7 | | V |

*Typical parameters correspond to nominal supply voltage at 25°C.

**Data sheets on pages 3-D2 through 3-D10 reproduced by permission of National Semiconductor Corporation.**

## electrical characteristics ($T_A$ = 0°C to +70°C, $V_{SS}$ = +5V ± 5%, $V_{GG}$ = −7V ± 5%) (continued)

| Parameter | Conditions | Min. | Typ.* | Max. | Units |
|---|---|---|---|---|---|
| TIMING SPECIFICATIONS (Note 5) | | | | | |
| $T_x$ (Notes 4 and 6) | | 1.0 | | 10.0 | μs |
| | 820pF ± 10% across X1 & X2 | 1.0 | | 4.0 | μs |
| $f_{res}$ | crystal with equivalent series resistance ⩽ 600Ω | 900 | | 1000 | kHz |
| Address and Input/Output Status (See figures 5 and 6.) | | | | | |
| $T_{D1}$ (ADS) | | $(3T_x/2) - 150$ | $3T_x/2$ | $(3T_x/2) + 200$ | ns |
| $T_W$ (ADS) | | $(T_x/2) - 250$ | | | ns |
| $T_S$ (ADDR) | | $(T_x/2) - 300$ | | | ns |
| $T_H$ (ADDR) | | 30 | 50 | | ns |
| $T_S$ (STAT) | | $(T_x/2) - 300$ | | | ns |
| $T_H$ (STAT) | | 30 | 50 | | ns |
| Data Input Cycle (See figure 5.) | | | | | |
| $T_D$ (RDS) | | -80 | -50 | | ns |
| $T_W$ (RDS) | | $(3T_x/2) - 400$ | | | ns |
| $T_S$ (RD) | | 300 | | | ns |
| $T_H$ (RD) | | 0 | | | ns |
| $T_{ACC}$ (RD) | | $2T_x - 400$ | | | ns |
| Data Output Cycle (See figure 6.) | | | | | |
| $T_D$ (WDS) | | $T_x - 250$ | | | ns |
| $T_W$ (WDS) | | $T_x - 250$ | | | ns |
| $T_S$ (WD) | | $(T_x/2) - 300$ | | | ns |
| $T_H$ (WD) | | 60 | 100 | | ns |
| Input/Output Cycle Extend (See figure 7.) | | | | | |
| $T_S$ (HOLD) | | 300 | | | ns |
| $T_{D1}$ (HOLD) | | | | 300 | ns |
| $T_{D2}$ (HOLD) | | | | 500 | ns |
| $T_W$ (HOLD) | | | | ∞ | ns |
| Bus Access (See figure 4.) | | | | | |
| $T_D$ (ENOUT) | | | | 300 | ns |
| $T_{D2}$ (ADS) | | $(T_x/2) - 350$ | | $T_x + 500$ | ns |
| OUTPUT LOAD CAPACITANCE | | | | | |
| External Load Capacitance | | | | 75 | pF |

**Note 1:** Maximum ratings indicate limits beyond which permanent damage may occur. Continuous operation at these limits is not intended and should be limited to those conditions specified under electrical characteristics.

**Note 2:** Pullup transistors provided on chip for TTL compatibility.

**Note 3:** BREQ is an input/output signal that requires an external resistor to $V_{GG}$ or ground.

**Note 4:** $X_1$ and $X_2$ are master timing inputs that are normally connected to a 1-megahertz crystal or an external capacitor to control the frequency of the on-chip oscillator.

A hermetically sealed quartz crystal is recommended. The crystal must be a series-resonant type and its equivalent series resistance must not exceed 600 ohms. Suppression of third harmonic oscillations may be required depending on the characteristics of the crystal. Typically, a 500-picofarad capacitor across pin $X_1$ or $X_2$ and an AC ground minimizes third harmonic effects.

If use of an external oscillator is desired, the circuit shown in figure 3 or an equivalent may be used.

**Note 5:** All times measured from valid Logic "0" or Logic "1" level.

**Note 6:** $T_x$ is the time period for one clock cycle of the on-chip or external oscillator. Refer to paragraph titled Timing Control for detailed definition.

*Typical parameters correspond to nominal supply voltage at 25°C.

# SC/MP

## DRIVERS AND RECEIVERS

Equivalent circuits for SC/MP drivers and receivers are shown below. All inputs have static charge protection circuits consisting of an RC filter and voltage clamp. These devices still should be handled with care, as the protection circuits can be destroyed by excessive static charge.

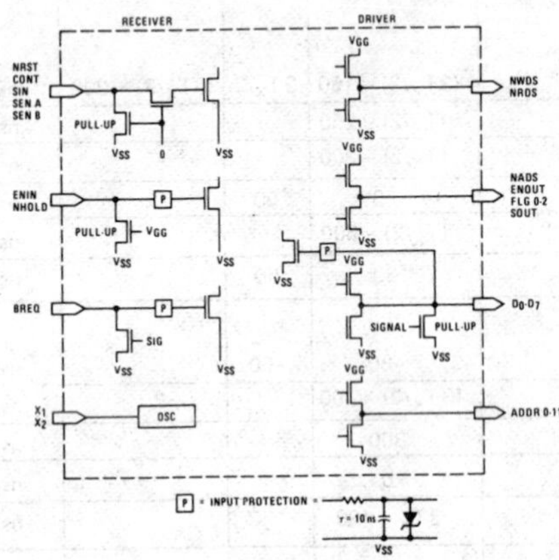


SC/MP Driver and Receiver Equivalent Circuits

## SUPPLY CURRENT DATA

Below are the two diagrams referenced from the parametric specification for the supply current, page 2.

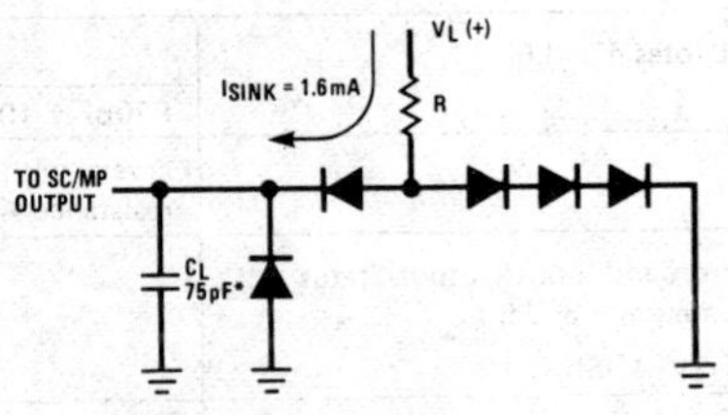


*INCLUDES JIG CAPACITANCE.

Simulated Current Load

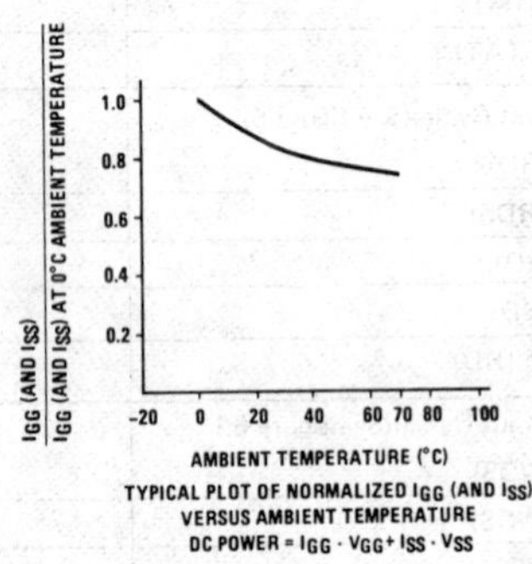


TYPICAL PLOT OF NORMALIZED $I_{GG}$ (AND $I_{SS}$) VERSUS AMBIENT TEMPERATURE

DC POWER = $I_{GG} \cdot V_{GG} + I_{SS} \cdot V_{SS}$

**B. BREQ, ENIN, and ENOUT Timing**

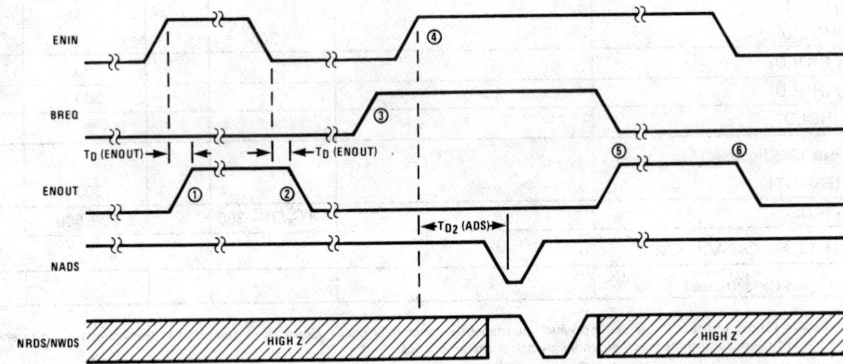


**Note 1:** ENOUT goes high to indicate that SC/MP was granted access to bus (ENIN high) but is not using bus.

**Note 2:** ENOUT goes low in response to low ENIN input.

**Note 3:** SC/MP generates bus request; bus access not granted because ENIN low.

**Note 4:** ENIN goes high. Bus access now granted and input/output cycle actually initiated. If ENIN is set low while SC/MP has access to the bus, the address and data ports will go to the high-impedance (TRI-STATE®) state, but BREQ will remain high. When ENIN is subsequently set high, the input/output cycle will begin again.

**Note 5:** I/O cycle completed. ENOUT goes high to indicate that SC/MP granted access to bus but not using bus. If ENIN had been set low before completion of input/output cycle, ENOUT would have remained low.

**Note 6:** ENOUT goes low to indicate that system busses are available for use by highest-priority requestor.

**FIGURE 4. Bus Access Control**

## SC/MP

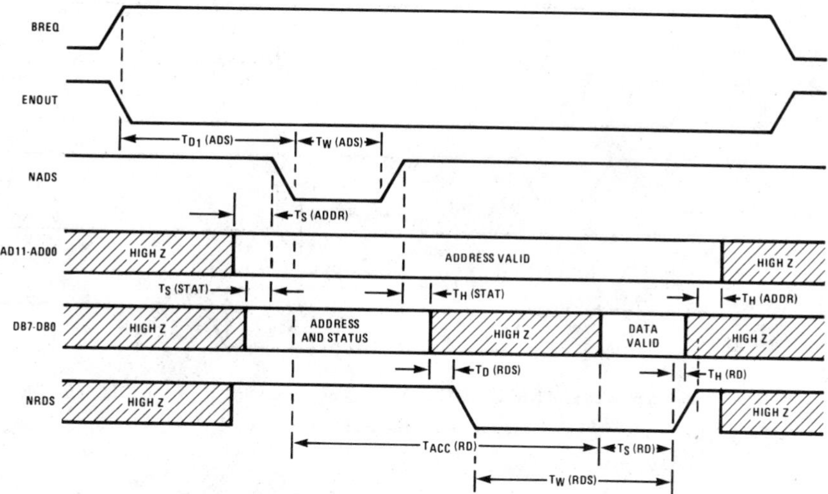


**Note:** Timing is valid when ENIN is wired high or is set high before BREQ is set high by SC/MP; see figure 4 for NADS timing when ENIN is set high after BREQ.

**FIGURE 5. SC/MP Data Input Timing**

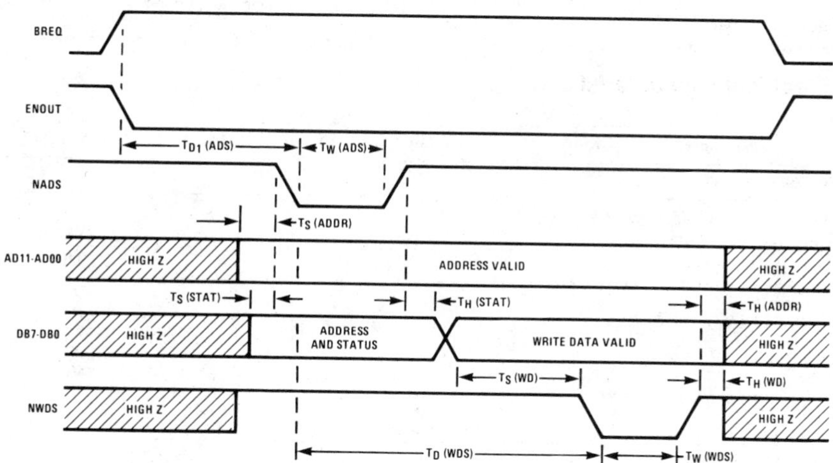


**FIGURE 6. SC/MP Data Output Timing**

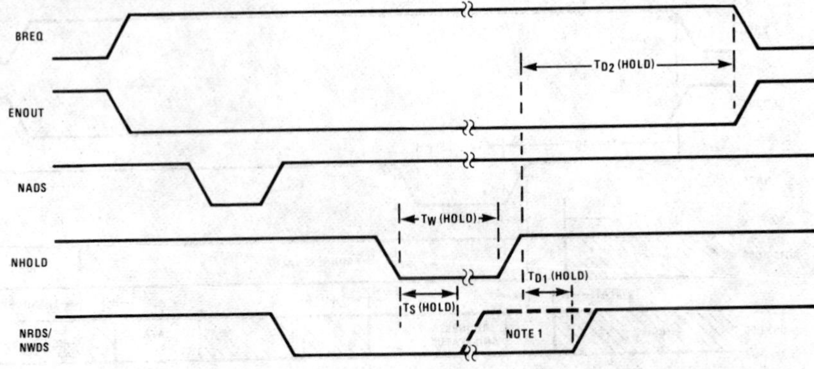


**Note:** Dashed trailing edge of NRDS/NWDS indicates normal strobe timing when NHOLD is not active.

**FIGURE 7. Extended Input/Output Timing**

## Applications

- Test Systems and Instrumentation
- Machine Tool Control
- Small Business Machines
- Word Processing Systems
- Educational Systems
- Multiprocessor Systems
- Process Controllers
- Terminals
- Traffic Controls
- Laboratory Controllers
- Sophisticated Games
- Automotive

## Absolute Maximum Ratings (Note 1)

Voltage at Any Pin . . . . . . . . . . . . . −0.5V to +7.0V

Operating Temperature Range . . . . . . . . 0°C to +70°C

Storage Temperature Range. . . . . . . −65°C to +150°C

Lead Temperature (Soldering, 10 seconds) . . . . . 300°C

## DC Electrical Characteristics ($T_A$ = 0°C to +70°C, $V_{CC}$ = +5V ± 5%)

| Parameter | Conditions | Min. | Max. | Units |
|---|---|---|---|---|
| INPUT SPECIFICATIONS | | | | |
| All Input Pins Except $V_{CC}$ and GND<br>Logic "1" Input Voltage | | 2.0 | $V_{CC}$ | V |
| Logic "0" Input Voltage | | −0.5 | 0.8 | V |
| Input Capacitance<br>(All pins except $V_{CC}$ and GND) | | | 10 | pF |
| Supply Current<br>$I_{CC}$ | $T_A$ = 25°C<br>outputs unloaded | | 45 | mA |
| | $T_A$ = 0°C<br>outputs unloaded | | 50 | mA |
| OUTPUT SPECIFICATIONS | | | | |
| "TRI-STATE®" Pins (NWDS, NRDS, DB0 - DB7, AD00 - AD11)<br>Logic "1" Output Voltage | $I_{OUT}$ = −100μA | 2.4 | | V |
| Logic "0" Output Voltage | $I_{OUT}$ = 2.0mA | | 0.4 | V |
| NADS, FLAG 0 - 2, SOUT, NENOUT<br>Logic "1" Output Voltage | $I_{OUT}$ = −100μA | $V_{CC}$ − 1 | | V |
| Logic "1" Output Voltage | $I_{OUT}$ = −1mA | 1.5 | | V |
| Logic "0" Output Voltage | $I_{OUT}$ = 2.0mA | | 0.4 | V |
| NBREQ (Note 2)<br>Logic "0" Output Voltage | $I_{OUT}$ = 2.0mA | | 0.4 | V |
| Logic "1" Output Current | $0 \leqslant V_{OUT} \leqslant V_{CC}$ | | ±10 | μA |
| XOUT<br>Logic "1" Output Voltage | $I_{OUT}$ = −100μA | 2.4 | | V |
| Logic "0" Output Voltage | $I_{OUT}$ = 1.6mA | | 0.4 | V |

## AC Electrical Characteristics [$T_A$ = 0°C to +70°C, $V_{CC}$ = +5 V ± 5%, 1 TTL Load (Note 3)]

| Parameter | Conditions | Min. | Max. | Units |
|---|---|---|---|---|
| $f_x$ | | 0.1 | 4.0 | MHz |
| | R = 240Ω ± 5% (figure 2B)<br>C = 300pF ± 10% | 2.0 | 4.0 | MHz |
| $T_C$ (Note 4) | | 500 | | ns |
| Microcycle | | 1 | | μs |
| External Clock Input (see figure 2A) | | | | |
| $T_{W0}$ | | 120 | | ns |
| $T_{W1}$ | | 120 | | ns |
| XOUT/ADS Timing Relationship (see figure 3) | | | | |
| $T_H$ (ADS) | | 100 | 225 | ns |
| Address and Input/Output Status (see figures 5 and 6) | | | | |
| $T_{D1}$ (ADS) | | | $3T_C/2$ | ns |
| $T_W$ (ADS) | | $(T_C/2) - 50$ | | ns |
| $T_S$ (ADDR) | | $(T_C/2) - 165$ | | ns |
| $T_H$ (ADDR) | | 50 | | ns |
| $T_S$ (STAT) | | $(T_C/2) - 150$ | | ns |
| $T_H$ (STAT) | | 50 | | ns |
| $T_H$ (NBREQ) | | 0 | | ns |
| Data Input Cycle (see figure 5) | | | | |
| $T_D$ (RDS) | | 0 | | ns |
| $T_W$ (RDS) | | $T_C + 50$ | | ns |
| $T_S$ (RD) | | 175 | | ns |
| $T_H$ (RD) | | 0 | | ns |
| $T_{ACC}$ (RD) | | $2T_C - 200$ | | ns |
| Data Output Cycle (see figure 6) | | | | |
| $T_D$ (WDS) | | $T_C - 50$ | | ns |
| $T_W$ (WDS) | | $T_C$ | | ns |
| $T_S$ (WD) | | $(T_C/2) - 200$ | | ns |
| $T_H$ (WD) | | 100 | | ns |
| Input/Output Cycle Extend (see figure 7) | | | | |
| $T_S$ (HOLD) | | 200 | | ns |
| $T_{D1}$ (HOLD) | | 130 | 275 | ns |
| $T_{D2}$ (HOLD) | | | 350 | ns |
| $T_W$ (HOLD) | | | ∞ | ns |
| $T_H$ (HOLD) | | 0 | | ns |
| Bus Access (see figure 4) | | | | |
| $T_D$ (NENOUT) | | | 150 | ns |
| $T_{D2}$ (ADS) | | $T_C/2$ | $3T_C/2$ | ns |
| $T_H$ (NENIN) | | 0 | | ns |
| Output Load Capacitance | | | | |
| XOUT | | | 30 | pF |
| All Other Output Pins | | | 75 | pF |

**Note 1:** Maximum ratings indicate limits beyond which damage may occur. Continuous operation at these limits is not intended and should be limited to those conditions specified under electrical characteristics.

**Note 2:** NBREQ is an input/output signal that requires an external resistor to $V_{CC}$.

**Note 3:** All times measured from valid Logic "0" level = 0.8 V or valid Logic "1" level = 2.0 V.

**Note 4:** $T_C$ is the time period for two clock cycles of the on-chip or external oscillator ($T_C = 2/f_x$). Refer to paragraph titled Timing Control for detailed definition.

**Note 5:** All times measured with a 50% duty cycle on the external clock.

The time interval of a microcycle is four times the period of the oscillator; that is:

period of one microcycle = $2T_C$

$$T_C = 2\left(\frac{1}{f_{osc}}\right) = 2\left(\frac{1}{f_{res}}\right) = 2\left(\frac{1}{f_{XIN}}\right)$$

where:

$T_C$ = time period for two cycles of on-chip or external oscillator

$f_{osc}$ = frequency of on-chip oscillator

$f_{res}$ = resonant frequency of crystal connected between XIN and XOUT pins

$f_{XIN}$ = frequency of external clock applied to XIN pin

**A. External Clock Input**

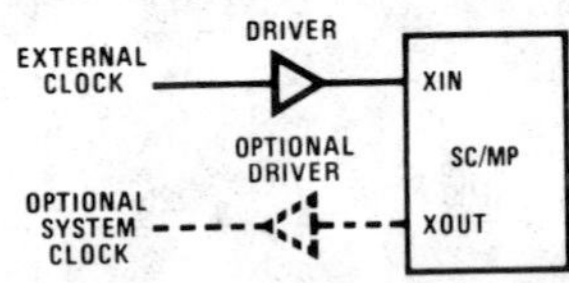


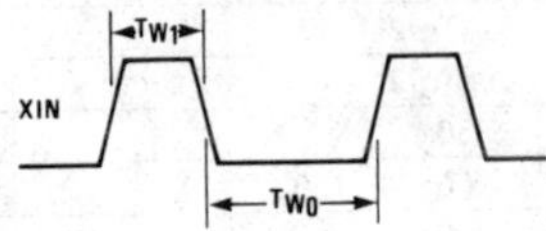


**B. Resistor-Capacitor Feedback Network**

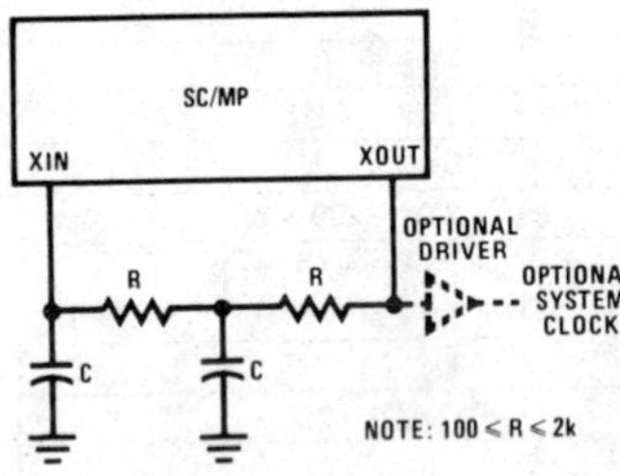


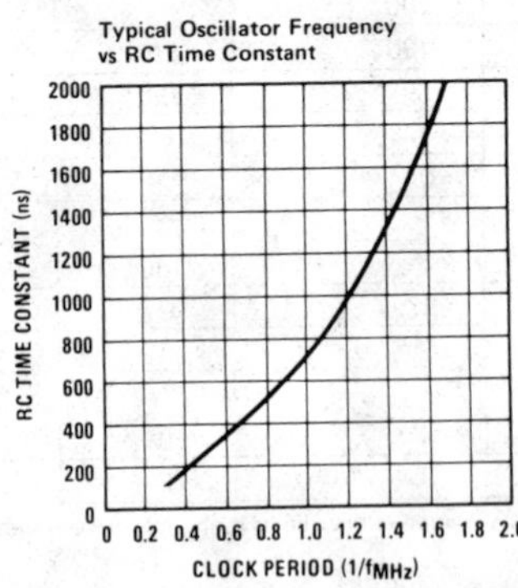


FIGURE 2. Frequency Control Networks for On-Chip Oscillator

**C. Crystal with Low-Pass Filter (Above 1 MHz)**

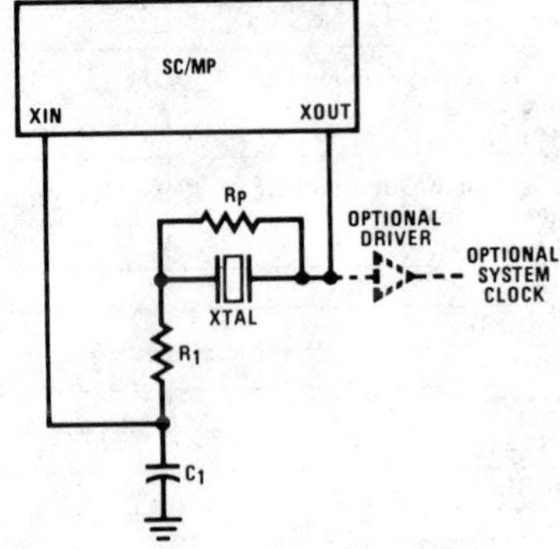


Suggested values for Crystal with Low-Pass Filter Network.

| Crystal | $R_P$ | $C_1$ | $R_1$ |
|---|---|---|---|
| 2MHz | 100kΩ | 56pF | 1kΩ |
| 3.58MHz | 100kΩ | 27pF | 1kΩ |
| 4MHz | 100kΩ | 27pF | 1kΩ |

XTAL is parallel resonant with maximum series resonance equal to 1kΩ.

**D. Crystal with Low-Pass Filter (1 MHz or Below)**

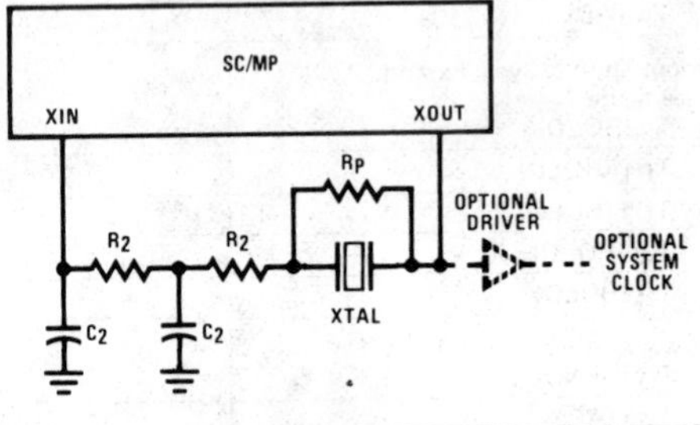


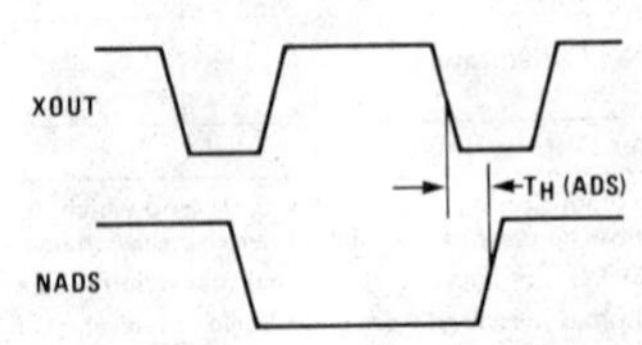


FIGURE 3. XOUT/NADS Timing Relationship

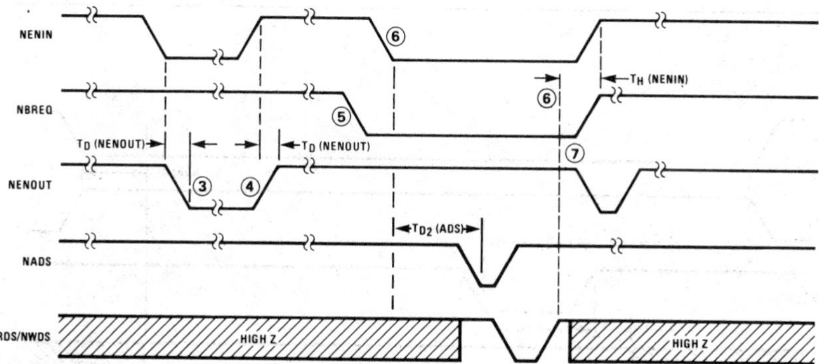


B. NBREQ, NENIN, and NENOUT Timing

**Note 1:** NENOUT is always high while SC/MP is actually using bus; that is, NENIN input and NBREQ output are low.

**Note 2:** When SC/MP is not using bus (NBREQ output or NENIN input high), NENOUT is held in same state as NENIN input.

**Note 3:** NENOUT goes low to indicate that SC/MP was granted access to bus (NENIN low) but is not using bus.

**Note 4:** NENOUT goes high in response to high NENIN input.

**Note 5:** SC/MP generates bus request; bus access not granted because NENIN high.

**Note 6:** NENIN goes low. Bus access now granted and input/output cycle actually initiated. If NENIN is set high while SC/MP has access to the bus, the address and data ports will go to the high-impedance (Tri-State®) state, but NBREQ will remain low. When NENIN is subsequently set low, the input/output cycle will begin again.

**Note 7:** Input/output cycle completed. NENOUT goes low to indicate that SC/MP granted access to bus but not using bus. If NENIN had been set high before completion of input/output cycle, NENOUT would have remained high.

**FIGURE 4. Bus Access Control**

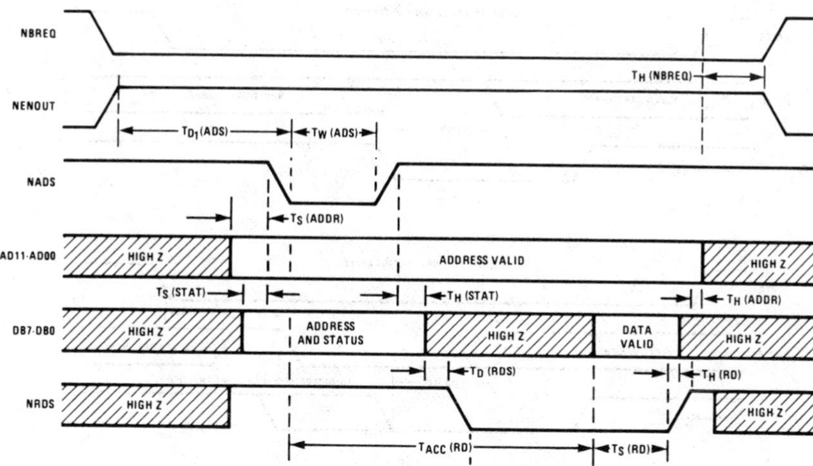


Note: Timing is valid when NENIN is low before NBREQ is set low by SC/MP; see figure 4 for NADS timing when NENIN is set low after NBREQ.

**FIGURE 5. SC/MP Data Input Timing**

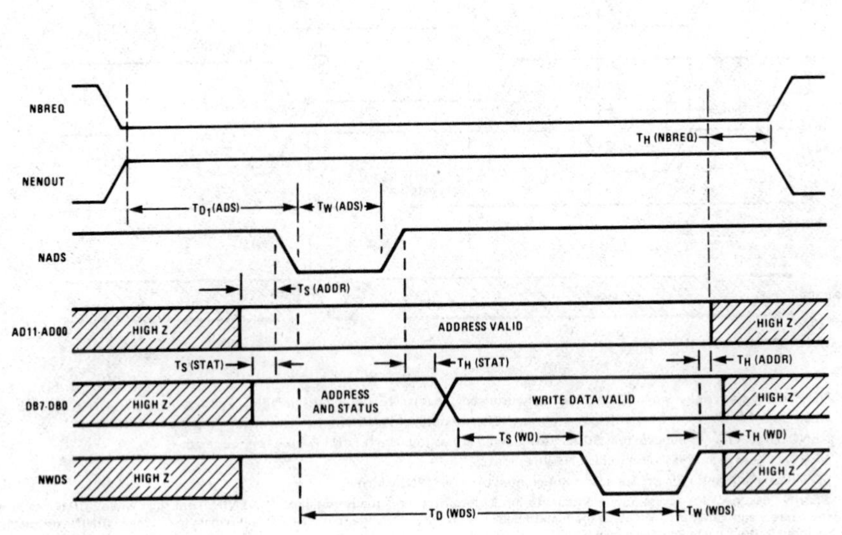


**FIGURE 6. Data Output Timing**

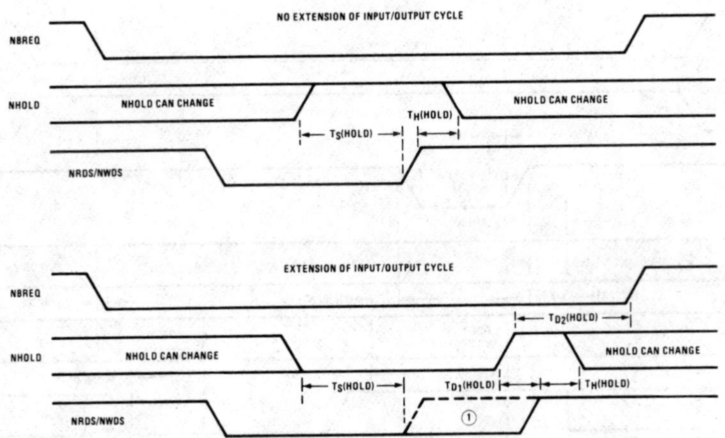


**Note 1:** In order to extend the input/output cycle, NHOLD must remain low until the point where NRDS/NWDS would have made a low-to-high transition with NHOLD inactive. Dashed line indicates the trailing edge of NRDS/NWDS when NHOLD is not active.

**FIGURE 7. NHOLD Timing**

# Chapter 4
# THE 8080A

**The 8080A is the most widely known of the microcomputers described in this book; as such, it becomes the frame of reference in many peoples' minds as to what a microcomputer should be.**

**The 8080A CPU is the direct descendant of the 8008, which was developed to Datapoint's specification for a device that would provide intelligent terminal data processing logic.**

**It should be borne in mind that the 8080A was designed as an enhancement of the 8008, at a time when no definable microcomputer user public had established itself;** therefore, many of the design features in the 8080A can be looked upon as astute shots in the dark. The success of this microcomputer is due either to the farsighted genius of its designers, or to the fact that the power of most microcomputers so overwhelms the needs of microcomputer applications, that CPU design becomes almost irrelevant when compared to product costs and product availability.

**An enhanced version of the 8080A, the 8085, is now available. The 8085 is described along with its support devices in Chapter 5.** Note that in many cases it will be possible to use 8080A support devices with the 8085 CPU. You are unlikely to use 8085 support devices with the 8080A; if your design is new enough to be looking at the 8085 support devices, then in all probability you would be using the 8085 CPU in preference to the 8080A.

**There is also a family of one-chip microcomputers currently available from Intel only — the 8048 family. Where the 8085 is an enhancement of the 8080 with many similarities, the 8048 is a somewhat different product. The 8048 devices are described in Chapter 6.**

The 8080A has more support devices than any other microprocessor on the market today. A few of these support devices are specific to the 8080A; however, the majority of them are used just as easily with almost any microprocessor. Only devices specific to the 8080A are described in this chapter; devices that can be used with any microprocessor are described in Volume 3. **The following is a list of 8080A support devices; a · at the left margin identifies a device described in this chapter, while an * in the left margin identifies a device which is described in Volume 3.**

- · **The 8080A/9080A CPU**
- · **The 8224 System Clock Generator and Driver. This device generates timing signals for the entire 8080A microcomputer system.**
- · **The 8228 System Controller (SC). This device demultiplexes the data lines of the 8080A CPU which are used for bidirectional data transfer and to output control and status signals.**
- * **The 8251 and 8251A Serial I/O Communication Interface, which provides a variety of synchronous and asynchronous serial data communication options.**
- * **The 8273 SDLC Protocol Serial I/O Controller.**
- * **The μPD379 and the μPD369. These devices provide synchronous and asynchronous serial I/O interfaces, respectively.**
- * **The 8255 and 8255A Parallel I/O interfaces, which provide programmable parallel I/O communication with external devices.**
- * **The 8212 Input/Output port, which can be used as an address buffer/decoder, a priority interrupt arbitrator, or an I/O peripheral interface.**
- * **The 8257 Direct Memory Access control device, which enables data to be transferred between memory and external logic, bypassing the CPU.**
- * **The 8253 Programmable Timer, which is accessed as an I/O device to create delays and timed pulses.**
- · **The 8259 Priority Interrupt Control Unit, which arbitrates priority among eight interrupts and creates appropriate CALL instructions in response to an interrupt acknowledge.**
- * **The 8214 priority interrupt device, which allows a number of interrupt requests to be received and processed under program control.**

* **The 8205, 8216 and 8226 address buffer decoders, which provide the logic needed to decode address spaces out of the 8080A address lines.**
* **The 8271 Programmable Floppy Disk Controller. This device provides a good deal of the logic needed to interface a floppy disk to a microprocessor.**
* **The 8275 Programmable CRT Controller. This device provides a great deal of the logic needed to interface industry standard CRT terminals to a microprocessor.**

**Table 4-1 lists the sources for each of the products described.** Device numbers in each column are the individual manufacturers' device numbers, which may differ for the same device.

Table 4-1. Devices of the 8080A Microcomputer Family

| DEVICE | AMD | INTEL | NEC | TI | NS | SIGNETICS*** |
|---|---|---|---|---|---|---|
| 8080A | 9080A** | 8080A | 8080A | TMS 8080A | 8080A | 8080A |
| 8224 | 8224 | 8224 | 8224 | SN74LS424 | 8224 | 8224 |
| 8228 | 8228/38 | 8228/38 | 8228/38 | SN74S428 | 8228/38 | 8228/38 |
| 8251 | 9551* | 8251 | 8251 | | | |
| | | | μPD379 | | | |
| | | | μPD369 | | | |
| 8255 | 9555* | 8255 | 8255 | | 8255 | |
| 8214 | | 8214 | 8214 | | | |
| 8216/26 | 8216/26 | | 8216 | | | |
| 8205 | 25LS138* | 8205 | | | | |
| 8212 | 8212 | 8212 | 8212 | SN74S412 | | |
| 8253 | | 8253 | 8253 | | | |
| 8259 | | 8259 | 8259 | | | |
| 8257 | | 8257 | 8257 | | | |
| TMS 5501 | | | | TMS 5501 | | |

* Some parameters vary, but pin-for-pin compatible

** Five CPU options are available offering clock speeds as fast as 250 ns, and wide temperature ranges

*** Signetics second sources National Semiconductor products

Companies manufacturing these microcomputer devices are:

INTEL CORPORATION
3065 Bowers Avenue
Santa Clara, CA 95051

ADVANCED MICRO DEVICES
901 Thompson Place
Sunnyvale, CA 94086

TEXAS INSTRUMENTS INC
P.O. Box 1444
Houston, TX 77001

NEC MICROCOMPUTERS INC
5 Militia Drive
Lexington, MA 02173

NATIONAL SEMICONDUCTOR CORP
2900 Semiconductor Drive
Santa Clara, CA 95050

SIGNETICS
811 East Arques Avenue
Sunnyvale, CA 94043

SIEMENS A.G.
Components Group
Balanstrasse 73, D8000
Munich 80, West Germany

**Siemens is manufacturing the 8080A family of devices in Europe with the active support of Intel. AMD is an authorized second source; however, most of their products were developed prior to the second source agreement. All other 8080A manufacturers are unauthorized. In consequence, some differences exist between Intel**

**and second source parts; differences are in some cases designed by the second source manufacturer, while in other cases differences are accidents. Differences we know about are described.**

The 8080A uses three levels of power supply: +5V, +12V and -5V.

Using a 500 ns clock, instruction execution times range from 2 to 9 $\mu$sec.

All 8080A devices have TTL compatible signals.

## THE 8080A CPU

**Of the 8080A devices available on the market, the NEC 8080A is the only one that differs significantly from the Intel 8080A.** The NEC 8080A is advertised as "an upward enhancement". Some of the NEC 8080A upward enhancements result in programs written for Intel 8080A not executing correctly on the NEC 8080A; therefore you should check carefully for incompatibilities when using the NEC 8080A. **NEC now manufactures an exact 8080A reproduction as well;** be sure you select the correct product if you buy from NEC.

Most differences between Intel and second source 8080A devices pertain to maximum clock frequency, environmental constraints and electrical characteristics. For details see the data sheets at the end of this chapter.

**Functions implemented on the 8080A CPU are illustrated in Figure 4-1; they represent "typical" CPU logic.** The 8080A has an Arithmetic and Logic Unit, Control Unit, Accumulator and registers.

N-Channel, silicon gate MOS technology is used by all 8080A manufacturers.

**The two most noticeable features of the 8080A CPU are the exclusion of clock logic and bus interface logic from the CPU chip.**

The need for a separate clock logic chip simply reflects the fact that the 8080A was a relatively early microprocessor. Other microprocessors developed at the same time also required external clock logic.

Bus interface logic must also be provided externally since the 8080A outputs an inadequate set of control signals. These control signals are augmented by instruction status information output on the Data Bus. External bus interface logic must combine the control signals with the instruction status signals to create an adequate Control Bus.

These characteristics of the 8080A CPU are described in detail on the following pages.

**The 8085 CPU incorporates clock logic and bus interface logic onto the CPU chip.**

### 8080A PROGRAMMABLE REGISTERS

The 8080A has seven 8-bit programmable registers, a 16-bit Stack Pointer, and a 16-bit Program Counter. These may be illustrated as follows:

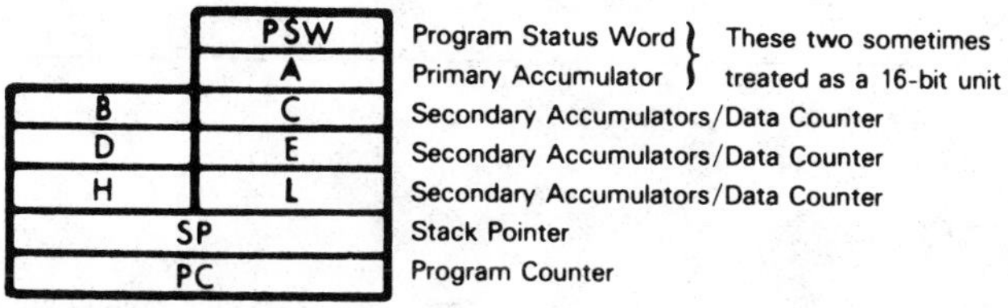

| | | |
|---|---|---|
| | PSW | Program Status Word } These two sometimes |
| | A | Primary Accumulator } treated as a 16-bit unit |
| B | C | Secondary Accumulators/Data Counter |
| D | E | Secondary Accumulators/Data Counter |
| H | L | Secondary Accumulators/Data Counter |
| SP | | Stack Pointer |
| PC | | Program Counter |

The A register is an 8-bit primary Accumulator. The remaining six Accumulator registers may be treated as six individual, 8-bit secondary Accumulators, or else they may be treated as three, 16-bit Data Counters, which we will refer to as BC, DE, and HL registers. The 16-bit HL register is the primary Data Counter, and provides the implied memory address for most memory reference instructions; a limited number of memory reference instructions use the BC and DE registers as Data Counters.

The 8080A uses a memory Stack, addressed by the Stack Pointer.

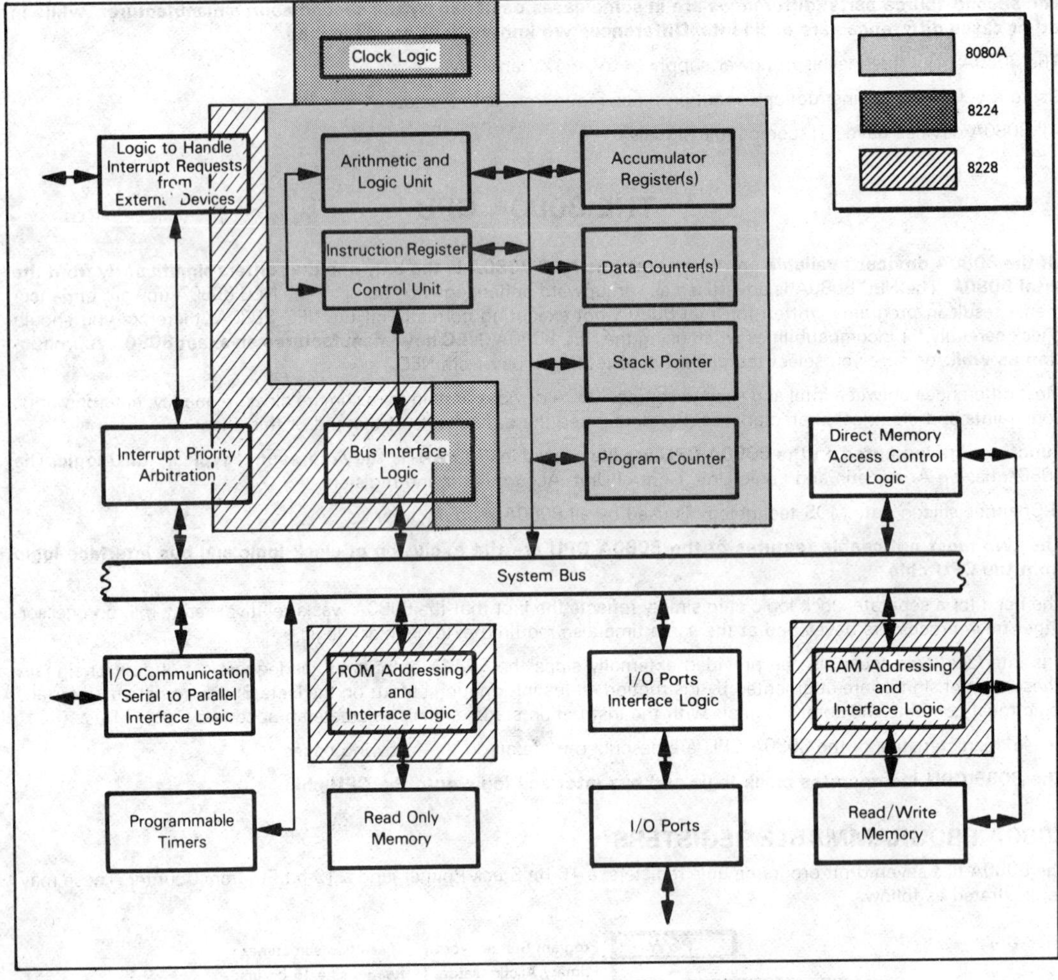


Figure 4-1. The 8080A CPU, 8224 Clock and 8228 System Controller. Forming a Three-Device Microprocessor

## 8080A ADDRESSING MODES

The memory addressing used by the 8080A is very straightforward; direct addressing and implied addressing are provided.

**8080A IMPLIED ADDRESSING**

The most frequently used memory addressing mode is implied addressing, via the HL register. This was the only memory addressing mode available on the predecessor microcomputer, the 8008.

Register-register Move, and Register-register Operate instructions allocate three bits to specify one of eight registers; since there are only seven registers, the eighth code becomes a memory reference specification, using implied addressing via the HL register, as follows:

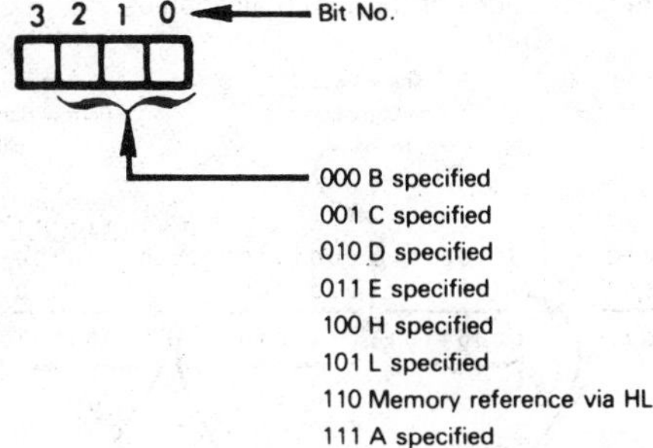


**8080A DIRECT ADDRESSING**

**With one exception, direct addressing is the only addressing mode provided for Jump and Branch instructions;** the exception is the instruction with the mnemonic PCHL, which provides a jump using implied addressing. **Direct addressing is also available for a limited number of memory reference instructions. All direct addressing instructions are three bytes long; a two-byte (16-bit) direct address is always specified.**

## 8080A STATUS

**The 8080A has a Status register with the following status flags:**

Zero (Z)
Sign (S)
Parity (P)
Carry (C)
Auxiliary Carry ($A_C$)
SUB, present in the NEC 8080A only

These status flags may be accessed by some instructions as a single Program Status Word (PSW). PSW bits are assigned as follows:

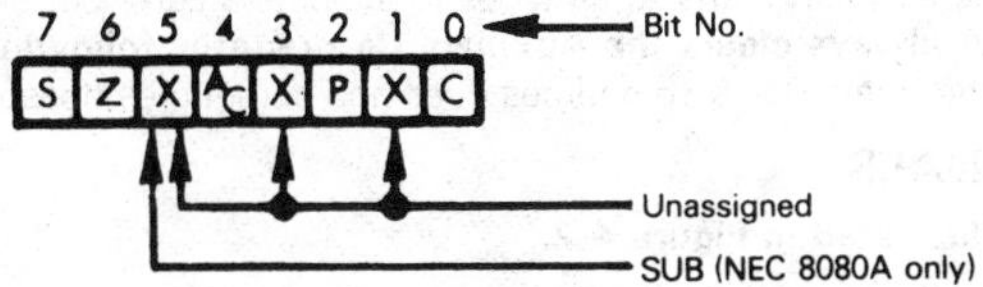


Instructions that access register pairs treat PSW and the Accumulator as a register pair.

The 8080A uses its Sign status as described for the hypothetical microcomputer in Volume 1, Chapter 7.

**CARRY STATUS BORROW LOGIC**

**The Carry status is not completely standard.** When an addition instruction is executed, any carry out of the high-order bit causes the Carry status to be set to 1, while no carry causes the Carry status to be reset to 0. This is standard Carry logic, also known as Add Carry logic. When a subtraction instruction is executed, however, the Carry logic is inverted.

A subtraction is actually the twos complement addition of the subtrahend to the minuend. The use of the Carry status is different: if there is a carry out of the high-order bit, then the Carry status is reset to 0; if there is no carry out of the high-order bit, then the Carry status is set to 1. This philosophy is known as Borrow Carry logic and is used only during subtraction operations. Here are illustrations of the two philosophies:

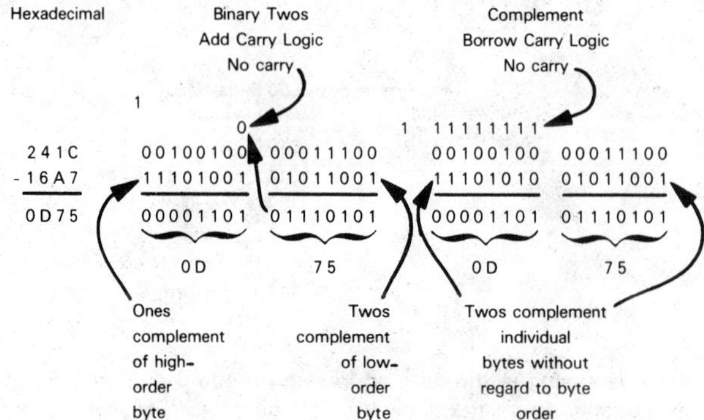


In a CPU which uses Add Carry logic, the twos complement of the low-order subtrahend byte is added to the minuend low-order byte. However, the ones complements of higher order subtrahend bytes are added to minuend bytes when the CPU executes a "Subtract with Carry". This logic adds the unaltered Carry status. This is equivalent to initially assuming that there is no carry from the lower order byte; if there is a carry from the lower order byte, then the ones complement addition is incremented.

In a CPU which uses Borrow Carry logic, the twos complement of every subtrahend byte is added to every minuend byte, irrespective of whether we are dealing with the low-order or any other subtrahend byte. This is equivalent to assuming that there will always be a carry from the lower order byte — hence the twos complement add. If there is no carry, the sum must be decremented. When a lower order byte borrows from the next high-order byte, there will be no carry; therefore, no carry causes the Carry status to be set to 1. However, the "Subtract-with-Carry" instruction subtracts the 1 Carry status from the result rather than adding it.

**AMD 9080A STATUS DIFFERENCE**

**The Auxiliary Carry status is set and reset by the NEC 8080A following execution of any subtract instruction** to correctly indicate whether a borrow from bit 4 occurred during the subtraction. The Intel 8080A uses the Auxiliary Carry at all times to indicate a carry out of bit 3 following addition. **The AMD 9080A always clears the Auxiliary Carry status following execution of a Boolean instruction;** the Intel 8080A sometimes does and sometimes does not.

## 8080A CPU PINS AND SIGNALS

**8080A CPU pins and signals are illustrated in Figure 4-2.**

**The 16 address lines A0 - A15 output memory and I/O device addresses.** These are tristate lines, and may be floated, giving external logic control of the Address Bus.

**The eight Data Bus lines D0 - D7 are multiplexed, bidirectional data lines via which 8-bit data units are input and output, and on which statuses are output during the first clock period of any machine cycle;** statuses on the Data Bus identify events which are to occur during the balance of the machine cycle, as described in Table 4-2. Like the address lines, the data lines are tristate.

**Remaining signals (excluding power and ground) may be divided into timing control, Data Bus definition, and interrupt control signals.**

**These are the timing control signals:**

**8080A TIMING CONTROL SIGNALS**

**A device which cannot respond to a CPU access request within the allowed time interval extends the time interval by pulling the READY input control low.** In response to READY low, the 8080A enters a Wait state, during which the CPU inserts an integral number of clock periods; **WAIT is output high, and all operations are suspended within the CPU,** but the address remains stable on the Address Bus.

**CPU logic can be stopped between the end of one instruction's execution, and the beginning of the next, by inputting a high level on HOLD.** This causes the CPU to float the Data and Address Busses, allowing external logic to access these busses, usually to perform direct memory access operations.

**The CPU responds to a HOLD request by outputting a Hold Acknowledge, HLDA, high;** this signal can be used by external logic to identify the beginning of the time when the CPU has actually floated external busses, and external logic can take control of the microcomputer system.

**RESET is a typical reset signal;** if held high for a minimum of three clock periods, it will zero the contents of all registers (excluding the status flags which maintain previous values), thus causing program execution to start with the instruction stored at memory location 0000.

**8080A DATA BUS DEFINITION SIGNALS**

**Two signals identify the condition of the Data Bus:**

**When DBIN is output high, data from an addressed memory location, or I/O port, must be placed on the Data Bus; DBIN may be used as a data input strobe.**

**$\overline{WR}$ is output low when data on the Data Bus is stable; $\overline{WR}$ may be used as a write strobe.**

**8080A INTERRUPT CONTROL SIGNALS**

**The two interrupt control lines are INT and INTE.** An external device requests an interrupt by inputting INT high. The CPU uses INTE to indicate whether interrupts are enabled or disabled.

# 8080A TIMING AND INSTRUCTION EXECUTION

**An 8080A instruction's execution is timed by a complex sequence of MACHINE CYCLES each of which is subdivided into CLOCK PERIODS.**

**8080A MACHINE CYCLES**

An instruction's execution may require from 1 to 5 machine cycles. Machine cycles are labeled MC1, MC2, MC3, MC4 and MC5.

**8080A CLOCK PERIODS**

A machine cycle is made up of 3, 4, or 5 clock periods; the first machine cycle of an instruction must have 4 or 5 clock periods. Clock periods are labeled $T_1$, $T_2$, $T_3$, $T_4$, $T_5$:

| MC1 | | | | | MC2 | | | | | MC3 | | | | | MC4 | | | | | MC5 | | | | |
|---|---|---|---|---|---|---|---|---|---|---|---|---|---|---|---|---|---|---|---|---|---|---|---|---|
| $T_1$ | $T_2$ | $T_3$ | $T_4$ | $T_5$ | $T_1$ | $T_2$ | $T_3$ | $T_4$ | $T_5$ | $T_1$ | $T_2$ | $T_3$ | $T_4$ | $T_5$ | $T_1$ | $T_2$ | $T_3$ | $T_4$ | $T_5$ | $T_1$ | $T_2$ | $T_3$ | $T_4$ | $T_5$ |

Where MC is shaded, the entire machine cycle is optional. Where T is shaded, the clock period is optional within its machine cycle.

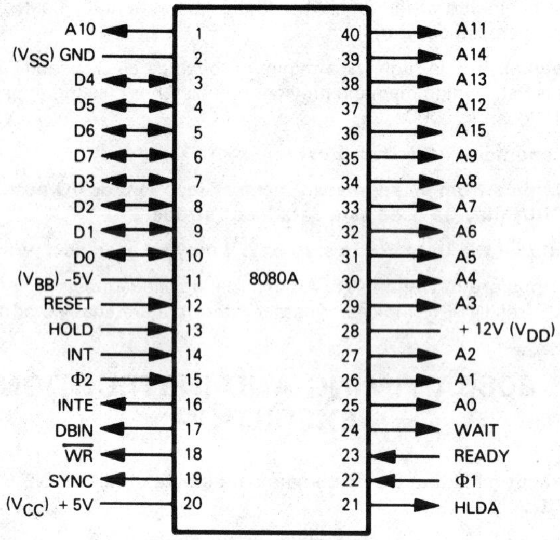

| Signal | Pin | Pin | Signal |
|---|---|---|---|
| A10 | 1 | 40 | A11 |
| ($V_{SS}$) GND | 2 | 39 | A14 |
| D4 | 3 | 38 | A13 |
| D5 | 4 | 37 | A12 |
| D6 | 5 | 36 | A15 |
| D7 | 6 | 35 | A9 |
| D3 | 7 | 34 | A8 |
| D2 | 8 | 33 | A7 |
| D1 | 9 | 32 | A6 |
| D0 | 10 | 31 | A5 |
| ($V_{BB}$) -5V | 11 | 30 | A4 |
| RESET | 12 | 29 | A3 |
| HOLD | 13 | 28 | + 12V ($V_{DD}$) |
| INT | 14 | 27 | A2 |
| Φ2 | 15 | 26 | A1 |
| INTE | 16 | 25 | A0 |
| DBIN | 17 | 24 | WAIT |
| $\overline{WR}$ | 18 | 23 | READY |
| SYNC | 19 | 22 | Φ1 |
| ($V_{CC}$) + 5V | 20 | 21 | HLDA |

8080A

| PIN NAME | DESCRIPTION | TYPE |
|---|---|---|
| *A0 - A15 | Address Lines | Output, Tristate |
| *D0 - D7 | Data Bus Lines | Bidirectional, Tristate |
| SYNC | Machine Cycle Synchronizer | Output |
| *DBIN | Data Input Strobe | Output |
| *READY | Data Input Stable | Input |
| *WAIT | CPU In Wait State | Output |
| *$\overline{WR}$ | Data Output Strobe | Output |
| *HOLD | Enter Hold State | Input |
| *HLDA | Hold Acknowledge | Output |
| *INT | Interrupt Request | Input |
| *INTE | Interrupt Enable | Output |
| *RESET | Reset CPU | Input |
| Φ1, Φ2 | Clock Signals | Input |
| $V_{SS}$, $V_{DD}$, $V_{CC}$, $V_{BB}$ | Power and Ground | |

*These signals connect to the System Bus.

Figure 4-2. 8080A CPU Signals and Pin Assignments

## CLOCK SIGNALS

Two clocks, Φ1 and Φ2, provide the CPU with its timing.

**Figure 4-3 illustrates the way in which clock signals Φ1 and Φ2 are used to generate a machine cycle consisting of five clock periods. A SYNC pulse identifies the first clock period of every machine cycle.**

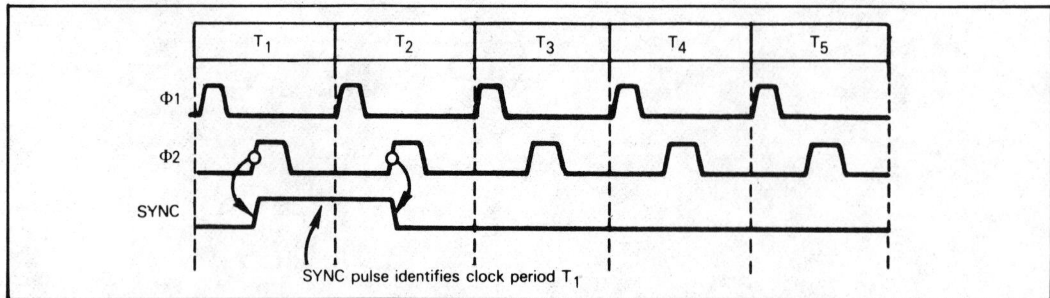


Figure 4-3. A Machine Cycle Consisting of Five Clock Periods

**A 9-segment clock is specified for the 8080A** where the Φ1 and Φ2 signals are generated out of 9 segments as follows:

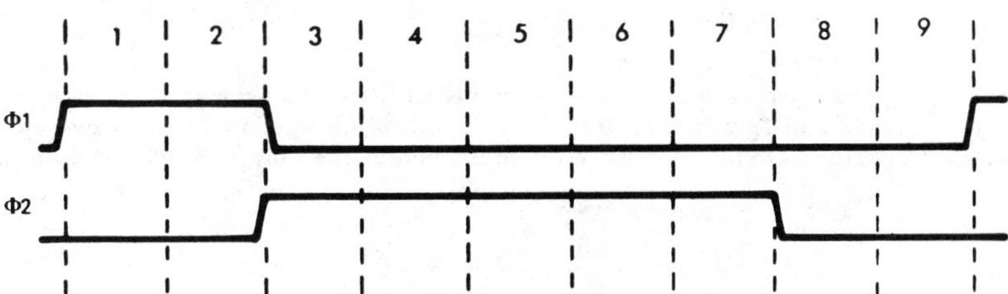


**The following alternative segmentations will also work:**

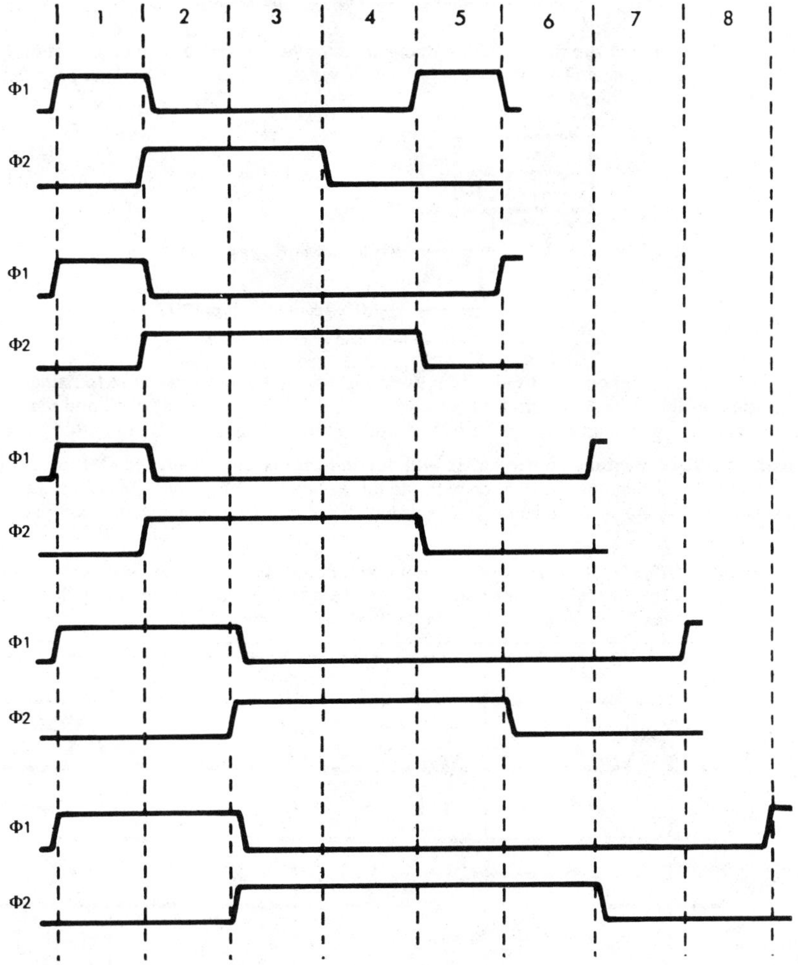

Irrespective of the segmentation used, note that the total clock period time must remain the same. For example, suppose you have a 500 nanosecond clock; individual segments must be timed as follows:

| Number of Segments | 9 | 8 | 7 | 6 | 5 |
|---|---|---|---|---|---|
| Duration of one segment (nanoseconds) | 55.55 | 62.5 | 71.43 | 83.33 | 100.00 |

In summary, therefore, a clock period will normally have 9 segments, but may have 4, 5, 6, 7 or 8 segments.

Note that **the only time you ever need to know about clock segmentation is when you are creating your own clock signals.** If you use the 8224 Clock Signal Generator (described later in this chapter) you can ignore clock signal segmentation.

**Clock periods $T_1$, $T_2$ and $T_3$ of each machine cycle are used (with one exception) for memory reference operations. During periods $T_4$ and $T_5$ functions internal to the CPU are executed. These two clock periods can be used by external logic for a limited number of approved operations that do not involve the CPU:**

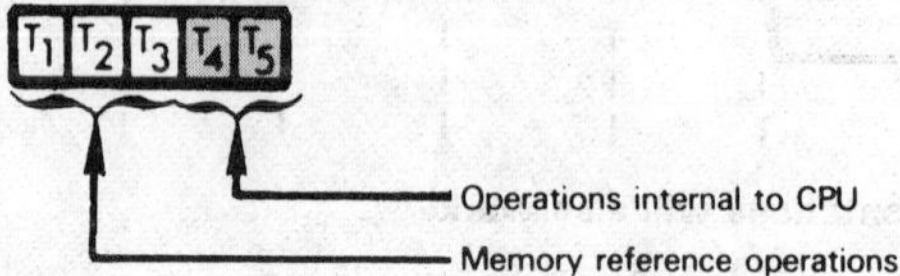


**The first three clock periods of the first machine cycle are always used to fetch an instruction from memory,** and load it into the Instruction register. The first machine cycle always has at least four clock periods, with the Program Counter being incremented during $T_4$:

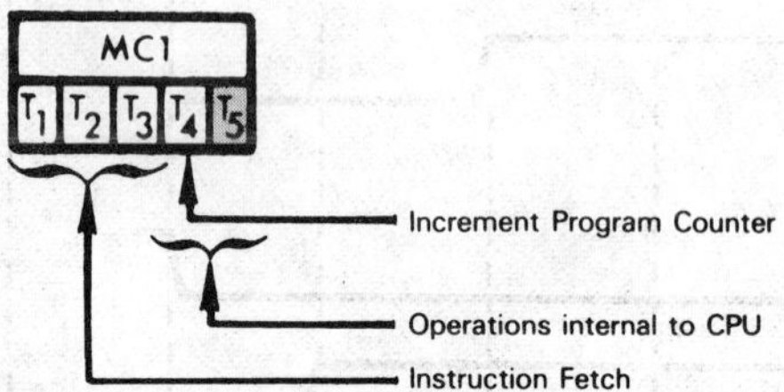


**8080A INSTRUCTION STATUS**

**The CPU identifies the operations that will occur during every machine cycle by outputting status information on the Data Bus during clock period $T_2$.** External logic uses SYNC and the Φ1 pulse at the start of $T_2$ to read status off the Data Bus. Timing is illustrated in Figure 4-4.

**If you are using an 8228 System Controller, it will decode status output on the Data Bus during $T_2$.** By combining this status information with the three control signals: $\overline{WR}$, DBIN and HLDA, the 8228 System Controller is able to generate a set of bus control signals which will interface industry standard memory devices and external logic.

**If you are not using an 8228 System Controller, then you must provide external logic that decodes the Data Bus during Φ1 of $T_2$. Your external logic must generate control signals which will be active during subsequent clock periods, at which time the Data Bus no longer holds status information.**

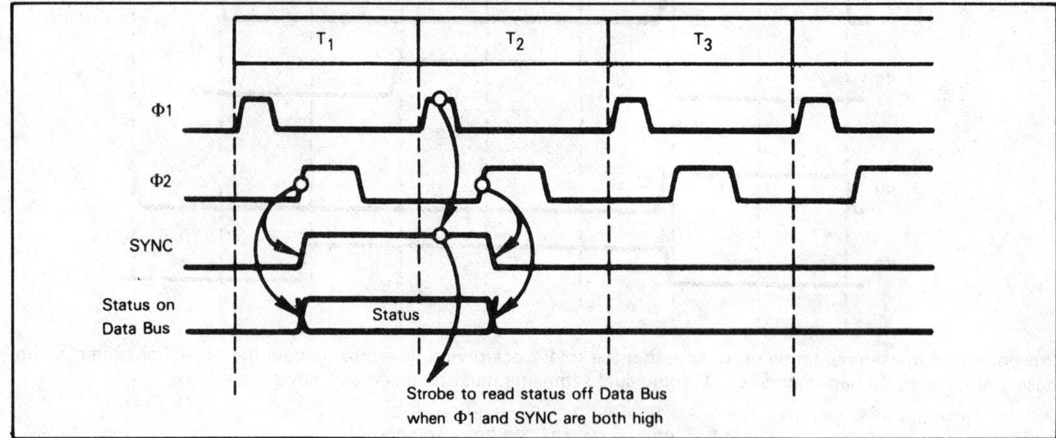


Figure 4-4. Status Output During $T_2$ of Every Machine Cycle

Table 4-2 defines the statuses which may be output during clock period $T_2$. Table 4-3 defines the way in which statuses should be interpreted to identify the various possible types of machine cycles.

Table 4-2. Statuses Output Via the Data Lines During the Second Clock Cycle of an 8080A Machine Cycle

| SYMBOLS | DATA BUS BIT | DEFINITION |
|---|---|---|
| HLTA | D3 | Acknowledge signal for Halt instruction |
| INTA* | D0 | Acknowledge signal for INTERRUPT request. Signal should be used to gate a Restart instruction onto the Data Bus when DBIN is active. |
| INP* | D6 | Indicates that the Address Bus contains the address of an input device and the input device should be placed on the Data Bus when DBIN is active. |
| OUT | D4 | Indicates that the Address Bus contains the address of an output device and the Data Bus will contain the output data when $\overline{WR}$ is active. |
| MEMR* | D7 | Designates that the Data Bus will be used for memory read data. |
| M1 | D5 | Provides a signal to indicate that the CPU is in the fetch cycle for the first byte of an instruction. |
| STACK | D2 | Indicates that the Address Bus holds the pushdown stack address from the Stack Pointer. |
| $\overline{WO}$ | D1 | Indicates that the operation in the current machine cycle will be a WRITE memory or OUTPUT function ($\overline{WO}$ = 0). Otherwise a READ memory, INPUT operation, or interrupt or Halt acknowledge will be executed. |

*These three status bits can be used to control the flow of data onto the 8080A Data Bus.

Table 4-3. Statuses Output on the Data Bus for Various Types of Machine Cycle

| | | TYPE OF MACHINE CYCLE | | | | | | | | | |
|---|---|---|---|---|---|---|---|---|---|---|---|
| DATA BUS BIT | STATUS INFORMATION | INSTRUCTION FETCH | MEMORY READ | MEMORY WRITE | STACK READ | STACK WRITE | INPUT READ | OUTPUT WRITE | INTERRUPT ACKNOWLEDGE | HALT ACKNOWLEDGE | INTERRUPT ACKNOWLEDGE WHILE HALT |
| D0 | INTA | 0 | 0 | 0 | 0 | 0 | 0 | 0 | 1* | 0 | 1 |
| D1 | $\overline{WO}$ | 1 | 1 | 0 | 1 | 0 | 1 | 0 | 1 | 1 | 1 |
| D2 | STACK | 0 | 0 | 0 | 1 | 1 | 0 | 0 | 0 | 0 | 0 |
| D3 | HLTA | 0 | 0 | 0 | 0 | 0 | 0 | 0 | 0 | 1 | 1 (0) |
| D4 | OUT | 0 | 0 | 0 | 0 | 0 | 0 | 1 | 0 | 0 | 0 |
| D5 | M1 | 1 | 0 | 0 | 0 | 0 | 0 | 0 | 1 | 0 | 1 |
| D6 | INP | 0 | 0 | 0 | 0 | 0 | 1 | 0 | 0 | 0 | 0 |
| D7 | MEMR | 1 | 1 | 0 | 1 | 0 | 0 | 0 | 0 | 1 (0) | 0 |

(0) Identifies status outputs of the NEC 8080A which differ from those of the Intel 8080A.

* This status is output as 0 by the NEC 8080A during a Call instruction being executed within the interrupt acknowledge process.

## INSTRUCTION FETCH SEQUENCE

**Instruction fetch timing is illustrated in Figure 4-5; events occur as follows:**

Period $T_1$ The leading edge of $\Phi 2$ triggers the SYNC high pulse, identifying period $T_1$.

WAIT is low, since the CPU is not in the Wait state.

$\overline{WR}$ remains high since this is an instruction fetch cycle; data is not being written to memory.

The leading edge of $\Phi 2$ is used to set selected Data Bus lines high, providing external logic with status information as follows:

| | |
|---|---|
| RI/$\overline{WO}$ (D1) | The CPU is expecting data input. |
| M1 (D5) | This is an instruction fetch period. |
| MEMR (D7) | Data input is expected from memory. |

The leading edge of $\Phi 2$ is used to set the required memory address on the address lines A0 to A15.

Period $T_2$ External logic uses the $\Phi 1$ pulse of time period $T_2$ to read status off the Data Bus. The read status strobe may be created as follows:

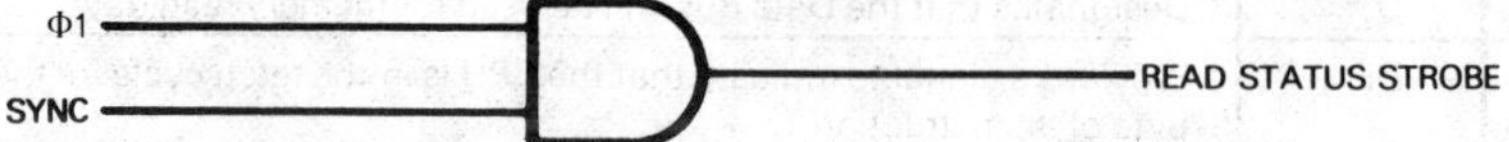


Remember, if you are using an 8228 System Controller, it reads and decodes status for you.

Immediately after status has been output on the Data Bus, the Data Bus is free to receive the instruction object code. The address for the instruction object code will be on the Address Bus; this address appears on the Address Bus during $T_1$, beginning with the rising edge of $\Phi 2$. The fact that status has been output and the Data Bus is free to receive the instruction object code is indicated by DBIN being pulsed high. The DBIN high pulse begins with the rising edge of $\Phi 2$ in $T_2$ and lasts exactly one clock period.

Period $T_3$ While DBIN is high, external logic must place the addressed instruction code on the Data Bus. The CPU will store this data in the Instruction register—whence the Control Unit interprets it as an instruction code.

The Data Bus is floated at $\Phi 2$ during $T_3$. This means that the Data Bus has been disconnected from the CPU and can be used in any way by logic external to the CPU.

Period $T_4$ The Address Bus is floated at $\Phi 2$ during $T_4$.

**The 8080A uses 1, 2 and 3 byte instructions. Each byte of a multibyte instruction requires its own instruction fetch.** Exact timing for multibyte instructions is given later in this chapter, after the 8080A instruction set has been described.

## A MEMORY READ OR WRITE OPERATION

So far as external logic is concerned, there is no difference between "read from memory" timing and instruction fetch timing — except that the M1 status (D5 on the Data Bus) is high during an instruction fetch only. **Figure 4-5** therefore **applies to a memory read operation also.**

**Since a memory read operation is executed during time periods $T_1$, $T_2$ and $T_3$ of a machine cycle, the presence of a memory read operation in an instruction's execution sequence will add one machine cycle to instruction execution time.**

**Figure 4-6 shows timing and signal sequences for a memory write operation. The signal sequences are identical to the instruction fetch sequence with the exception that DBIN remains low during $T_2$ and $T_3$, and different status signals are output on the Data Bus during $T_1$.**

## SEPARATE STACK MEMORY MODULES

**One 8080A CPU can access two memory modules with overlapping memory addresses: a stack memory module and a nonstack memory module.** Overlapping memory addresses can be used by the two memory modules, since Stack status (D2 high at $\Phi 1$ in $T_2$) can be used to select the stack memory, while lack of Stack status (D2 low at $\Phi 1$ in $T_2$) can be used to select nonstack memory. External logic must decode the address as referencing stack or nonstack memory.

Note that the 8228 System Controller does not generate a STACK control signal. Nevertheless, if you wish, you may implement separate stack and nonstack memory, with overlapping addresses; this requires your own status decode logic to isolate the Stack status. Such logic is quite simple, and may be illustrated as follows:

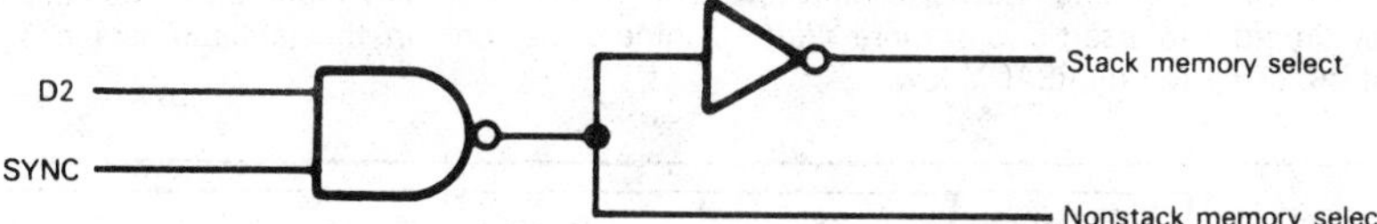


The only disadvantage associated with having a separate stack memory is that nonstack instructions cannot reference the stack memory.

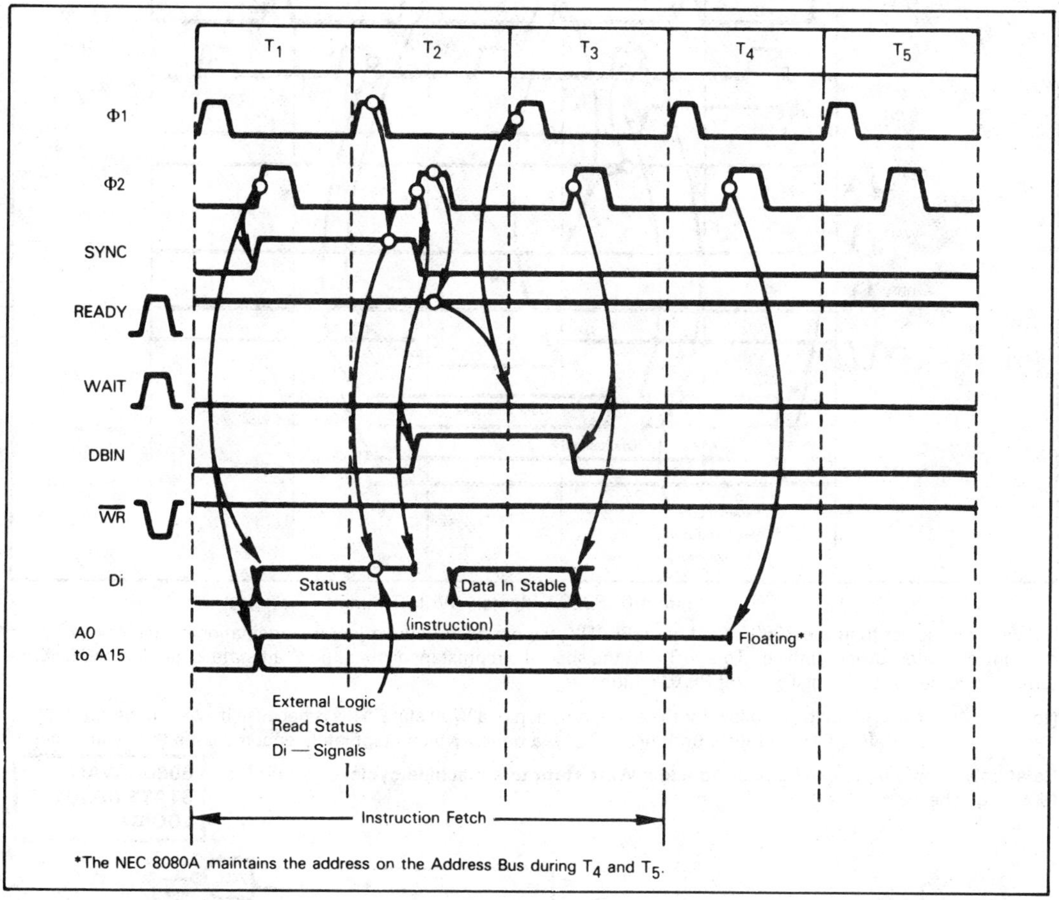

T1 T2 T3 T4 T5
Φ1
Φ2
SYNC
READY
WAIT
DBIN
$\overline{WR}$
Di
Status
Data In Stable
(instruction)
A0 to A15
Floating*
External Logic Read Status Di — Signals
Instruction Fetch

*The NEC 8080A maintains the address on the Address Bus during $T_4$ and $T_5$.

Figure 4-5. 8080A Instruction Fetch Sequence

## THE WAIT STATE

**8080A SLOW MEMORIES**

**A Wait state may occur between clock periods $T_2$ and $T_3$. The Wait state frees external logic or memory from having to operate at CPU speed.** Wait state timing is illustrated in Figure 4-7 and Figure 4-8.

If READY is low during Φ2 of $T_2$, the 8080A CPU will enter the Wait state following $T_2$. The Wait state consists of any number of clock periods during which the CPU performs no operations and maintains the levels of all output signals. The Wait state ends when READY is input high. The CPU samples READY during every Φ2 pulse within the Wait state; the Wait state will therefore end with the Φ1 pulse which follows a Φ2 pulse during which READY is sensed high.

**Memory interface logic in any 8080A microcomputer system must be designed to anticipate that every memory access either will, or will not require a Wait state.**

If memory is as fast as the 8080A CPU, then READY will normally be held high, in anticipation of no Wait state. In Figures 4-7 and 4-8 a broken line is used to represent this "READY normally high" case. Memory interface logic will pull READY low in order to insert one or more Wait machine cycles only in special circumstances; memory interface logic has until $\Phi 2$ of $T_2$ to pull READY low.

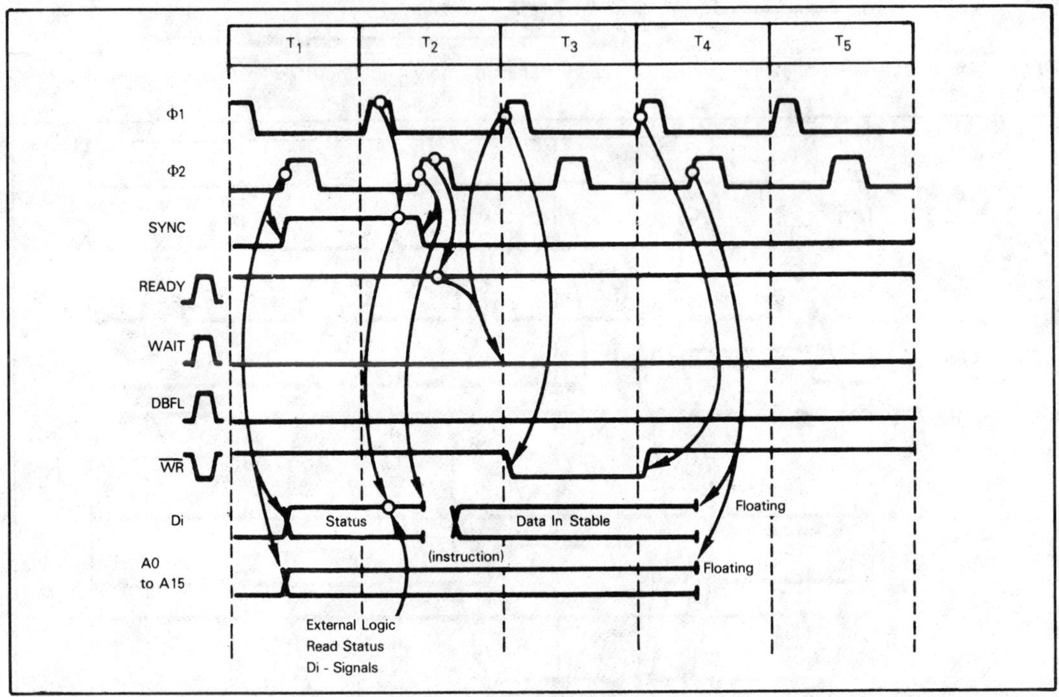


Figure 4-6. 8080A Memory Write Timing

If memory is slower than the 8080A CPU, then READY will normally be held low in anticipation of one or more Wait machine cycles occurring between $T_2$ and $T_3$. In the special circumstance where no Wait state is needed, memory interface logic has until $\Phi 2$ of $T_2$ to set READY high.

Note that $\overline{WR}$, if active, will be held low for the entire duration of a Wait state. This is because if $\overline{WR}$ is to be set low, the transition occurs at $\Phi 1$ of $T_2$ and lasts until $\Phi 1$ of $T_4$ — a period which completely encompasses the Wait state.

**8080A WAIT STATE REQUEST LOGIC**

**Relatively simple logic can be used to add a Wait state to a machine cycle.** Consider the following scheme:

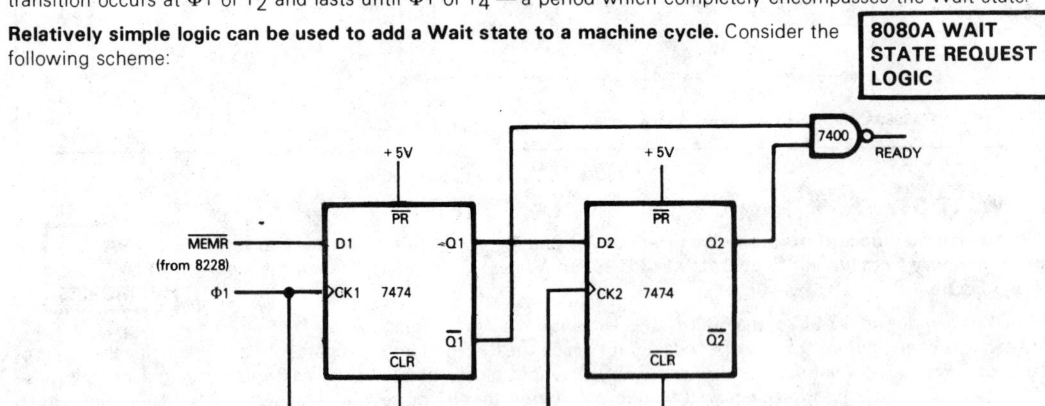

Our goal, using the logic above, is to create a low READY pulse, which is one clock period wide, whenever $\overline{MEMR}$ makes a high-to-low transition.

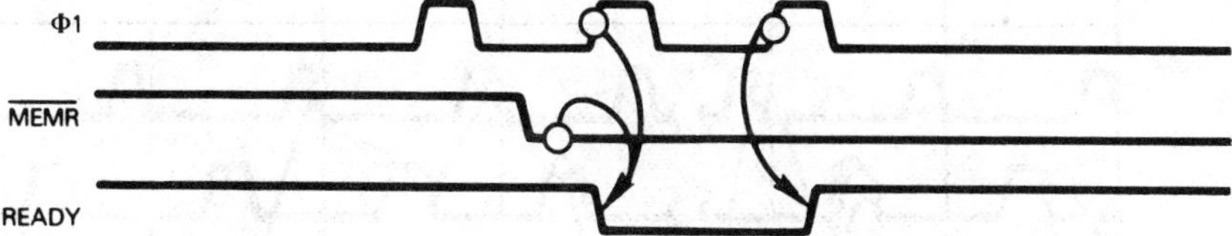


Consider the sequence of signal transitions in the logic we have illustrated above. At each Φ1 clock pulse, transitions will occur as follows:

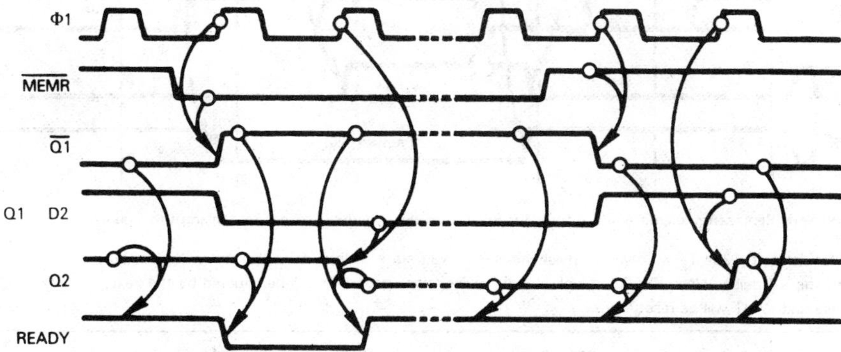


It requires $\overline{Q1}$ and Q2 to be high simultaneously for READY to be low; and that condition exists for a single clock pulse.
**Observe that you can use READY to trigger a one-shot in order to create a low READY input of any duration.**

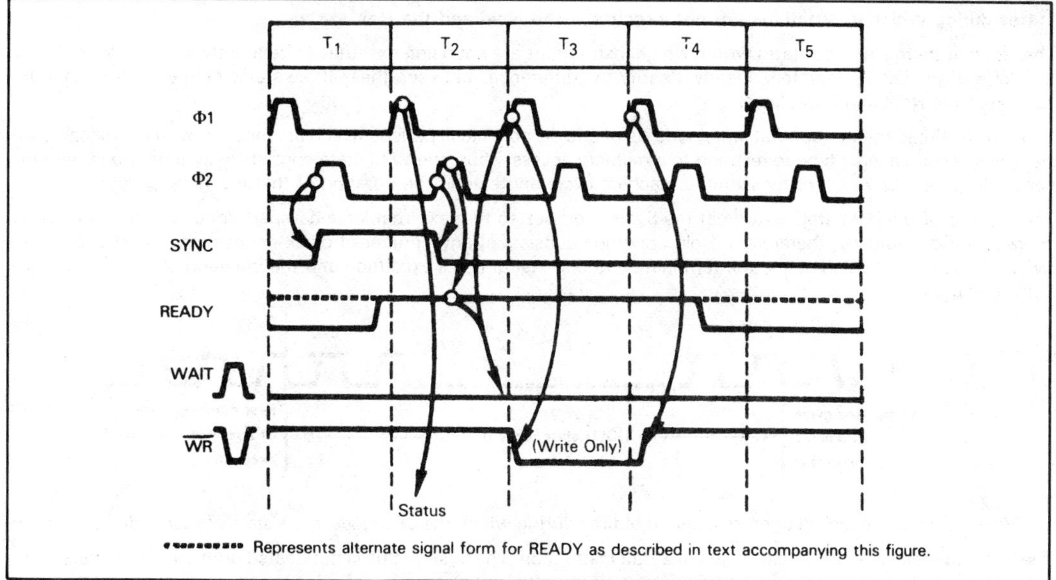


Figure 4-7. The 8080A CPU Operating With Fast Memory and No Wait State

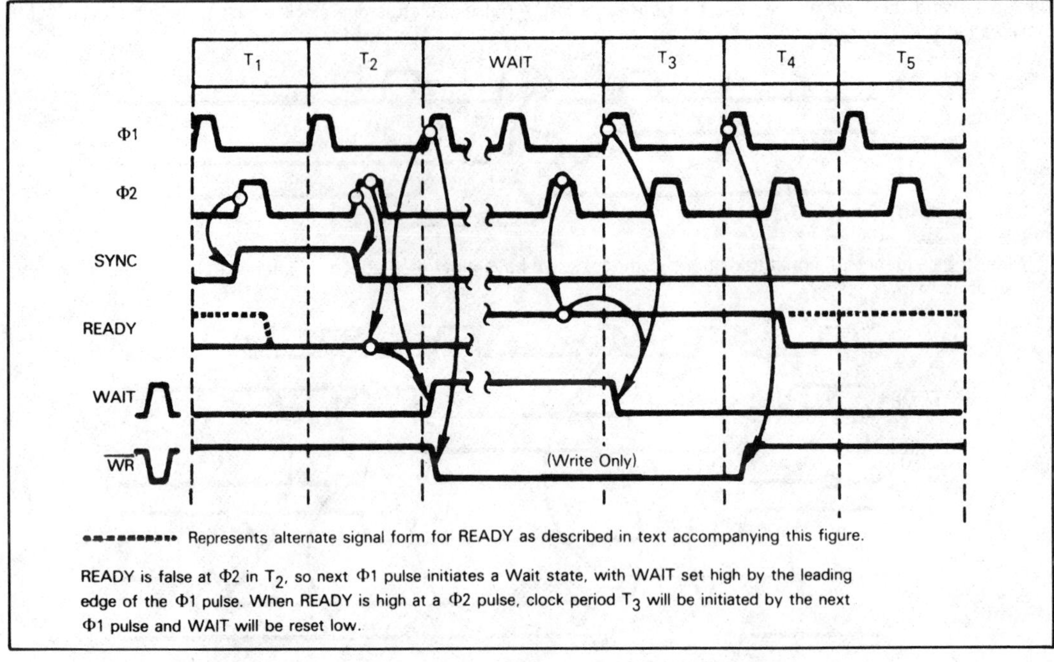


READY is false at Φ2 in $T_2$, so next Φ1 pulse initiates a Wait state, with WAIT set high by the leading edge of the Φ1 pulse. When READY is high at a Φ2 pulse, clock period $T_3$ will be initiated by the next Φ1 pulse and WAIT will be reset low.

Figure 4-8. The 8080A CPU Operating With Slow Memory and a Normal Wait State

## THE WAIT, HOLD AND HALT STATES

**We have discussed the Wait state within an 8080A microcomputer system, now we have to look at two further states during which instructions are not executed: the Hold and the Halt states.**

The fact that there are three states within which instructions are not being executed is frequently a source of confusion to 8080A users. Let us, therefore, clearly identify the differences between these three states before continuing a discussion of the Hold and Halt states.

As we have already seen, the Wait state consists of one or more clock periods which are inserted within a machine cycle, giving external logic time to respond to a memory access. Thus, the Wait state consists of an indeterminate number of clock periods which occur within a machine cycle and extend the duration of that machine cycle.

The purpose of the Hold state is to float the System busses so that external logic can perform direct memory access operations. Conceptually, therefore, a Hold condition consists of any number of clock periods, occurring in between two machine cycles which define the termination of one instruction's execution and the initiation of the next instruction's execution:

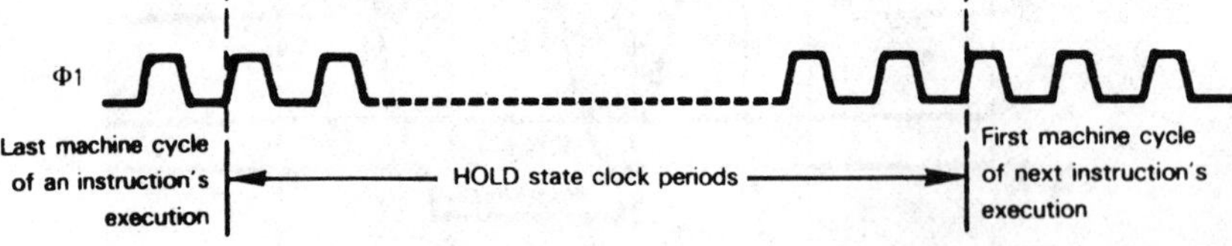


The Hold state may be looked upon as a period of time during which the CPU goes into a state of suspended animation.

The Halt state results from the execution of a Halt instruction. The System Bus is not floated during a Halt state. During the Halt state, the CPU simply marks time. The purpose of a Halt state is to define those time intervals when there is nothing for the CPU to do; now when the CPU has nothing to do, it is only logical to assume that the CPU cannot know how long it will be before it has something useful to do. Typically a Halt condition will end when some external logic demands the service of the CPU. One method that external logic uses to demand CPU service is the interrupt request. The 8080A therefore requires an interrupt request to terminate the Halt state.

Let us now look at the Hold and Halt states in more detail.

## THE HOLD STATE

**The Hold state allows external logic to stop the CPU.**

**The Hold state is similar to the Wait state. During both states, signals output by the CPU are held constant; but the Data and Address Busses are floated in the Hold state only, not in the Wait state.**

**The Hold and Wait states are also initiated in different ways and they serve different functions.**

The Wait state is initiated if external operations will not be completed during $T_3$. The purpose of the Wait state is to allow the CPU to operate with slow memories or external logic, therefore a Wait always occurs between clock periods $T_2$ and $T_3$.

A Hold state is initiated by the hold request input signal HOLD. The CPU acknowledges the onset of the Hold state by outputting HLDA high. If a HOLD is requested during a read or input operation ($RI/\overline{WO}$ (D1) high in $T_2$), then HLDA is set high by the leading edge of $\Phi 1$ in $T_3$. If a HOLD is requested during a write or output operation, then HLDA is set high by the leading edge of $\Phi 1$ in the cycle following $T_3$.

Note that even though HOLD is acknowledged and the Hold state is initiated in $T_3$ during a read memory or input data machine cycle, logic must still hold data steady on the Data Bus until the leading edge of $\Phi 2$ in $T_3$. This is because operations internal to the CPU will be executed normally during a HOLD. Operations internal to the CPU will only cease if the Hold state lasts for more cycles than would normally be present before the onset of the next $T_1$ cycle.

HOLD low will cause the end of the Hold state. HOLD low must coincide with the leading edge of $\Phi 1$ or $\Phi 2$, and will terminate the Hold state at the $\Phi 1$ pulse of the next machine cycle's $T_1$ clock period. The 8080A CPU will signal the end of the Hold state with HLDA false.

During the Hold state, the Data Bus and the Address Bus are floated. Floating begins at $\Phi 2$ in $T_3$ for a read operation and at $\Phi 2$ in the clock period following $T_3$ otherwise.

Figures 4-9 and 4-10 illustrate some variations on the Hold state.

**NEC 8080A HOLD DIFFERENCES**

**The NEC 8080A and the Intel 8080A differ when a Hold is requested during a DAD instruction's execution.** The NEC 8080A initiates the Hold as though a read operation was occurring, while the Intel 8080A initiates the Hold operation as though a write operation was occurring.

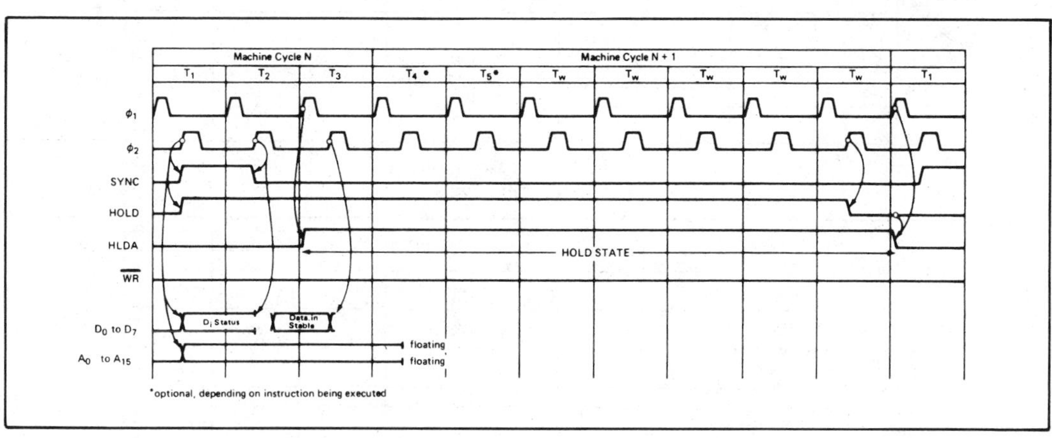


Figure 4-9A. Floating of Data and Address Busses at $\Phi 2$ in $T_3$, for READ Operation Being Completed Prior to Onset of Hold State

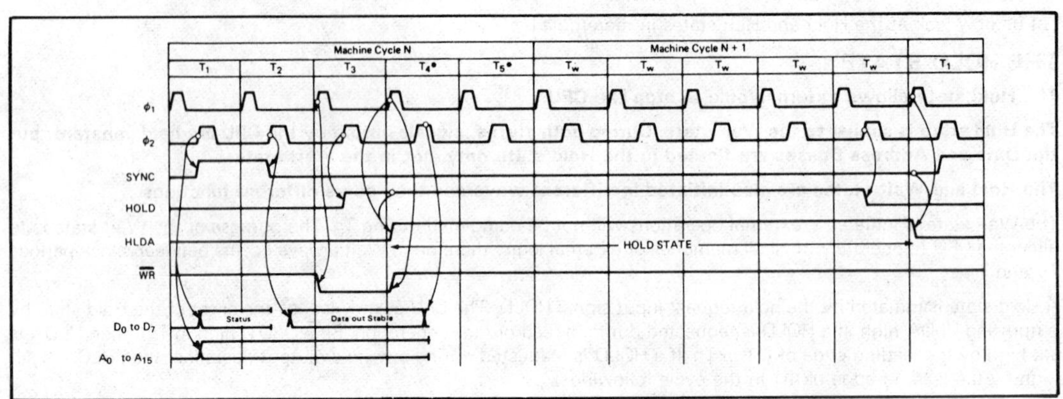


Figure 4-9B. Floating of Data and Address Busses at $\Phi 2$ in $T_4$, for a WRITE, or Any Non-READ Operation (RI/$\overline{WO}$=False)

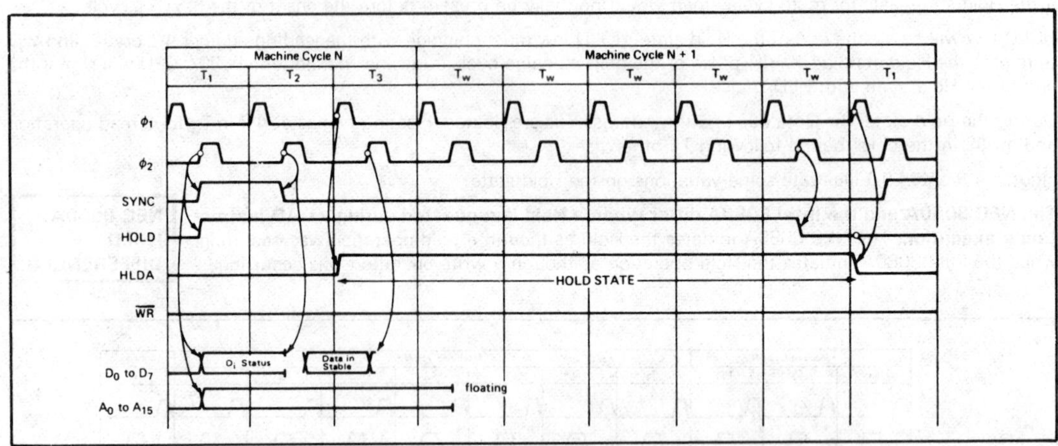


Figure 4-10A. Floating of Data and Address Busses for READ Operation in a Three Clock Period Machine Cycle

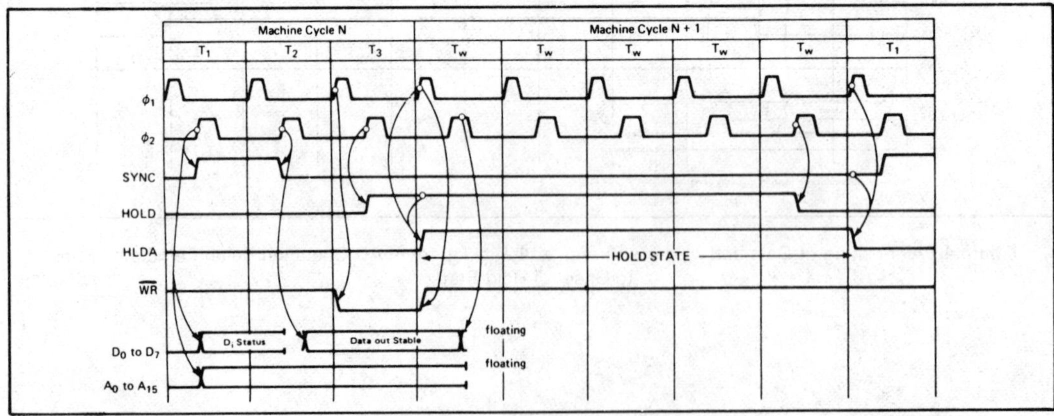


Figure 4-10B. Floating of Data and Address Busses at $\Phi 2$ in $T_1$, for WRITE or Any Non-READ Operation Being Completed Prior to Onset of Hold State

## THE HALT STATE AND INSTRUCTION

**The Halt state is similar to the Wait state, except that it is initiated by a Halt instruction.**

The Halt state is not initiated by READY low, although READY low is a necessary requirement for the onset of the Halt state. This means that READY high cannot be used to terminate a Halt state. Instead, **an interrupt request (INT high) must be used to terminate the Halt state.**

**Note that if interrupts have been inhibited, the interrupt request (INT high) will never be acknowledged, and the only way to get out of a Halt state is to power down, then power up the CPU.**

An anomaly of the Halt state is that the Data and Address Busses may be floated by entering the Hold state after entering the Halt state; that is, you can move into, and out of the Hold state while in the Halt state.

If the Hold state is entered after the Halt state, then the Hold state must be exited by setting HOLD low before exiting the Halt state.

During a HALT, a hold request signaled by HOLD will not be acknowledged if an interrupt has been requested (INT high) but not acknowledged (INTE high); i.e., the CPU will not enter the Hold state in the time between an interrupt being requested and acknowledged. Once the interrupt has been acknowledged (INTE low), the CPU may enter the Hold state.

Figure 4-30 illustrates signal sequences and timing for the Halt instruction (and state).

## THE RESET OPERATION

**A RESET high signal input to the 8080A CPU will clear the Program Counter and disable interrupts.**

**To properly perform the reset operation, RESET should be held high for at least three clock periods.** During these three clock periods, reset operations are executed in the following sequence:

1) The Program Counter is cleared.
2) All interrupt requests are disabled.
3) Internal interrupt acknowledge logic (associated with signal INTE) is cleared.
4) Internal hold acknowledge logic (associated with signal HLDA) is cleared.

**For as long as RESET is high, all 8080A CPU operations will be suspended.**

When RESET is reset low, instruction execution will resume with a $T_1$ clock period at the next $\Phi 1$ pulse. Since the Program Counter contains 0000, the first instruction executed following RESET will be the instruction stored in memory location $0000_{16}$.

Interrupts remain disabled when program execution resumes.

**When you power up any 8080A system you must simultaneously reset it.** Powering up does not reset or change anything within the 8080A. If you power up without resetting, then registers, including the Program Counter, will contain undefined data; thus program execution will immediately and erroneously begin at some random location of memory.

Here are two possible reset on power up logic implementations:

First a simple logic sequence:

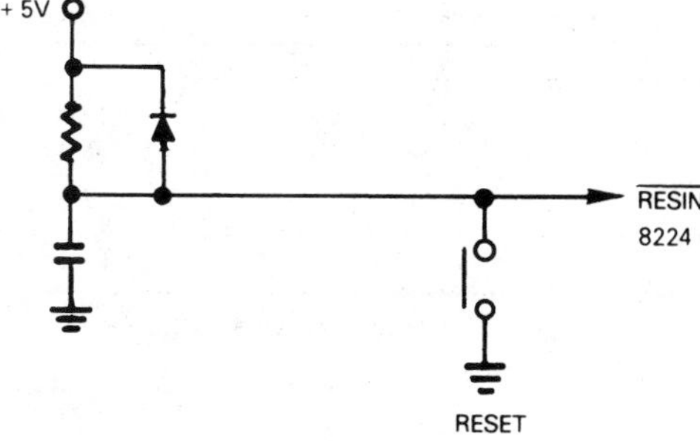

Next a more complex, and more reliable one:

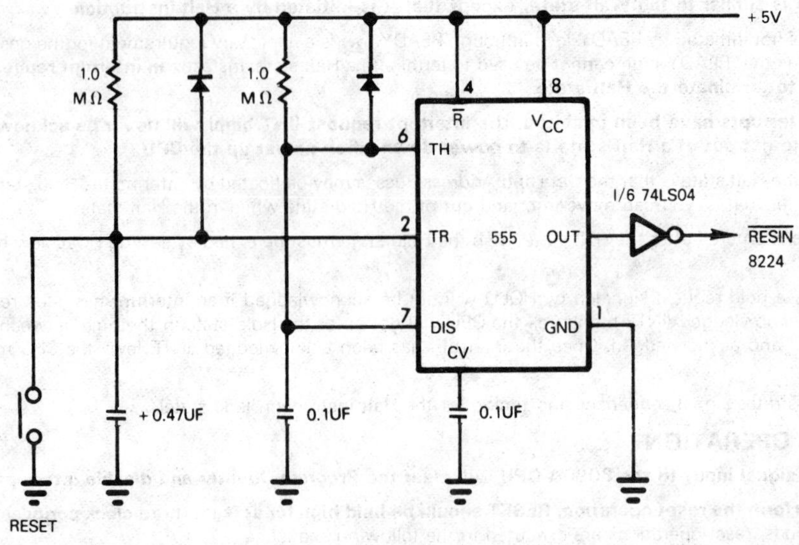


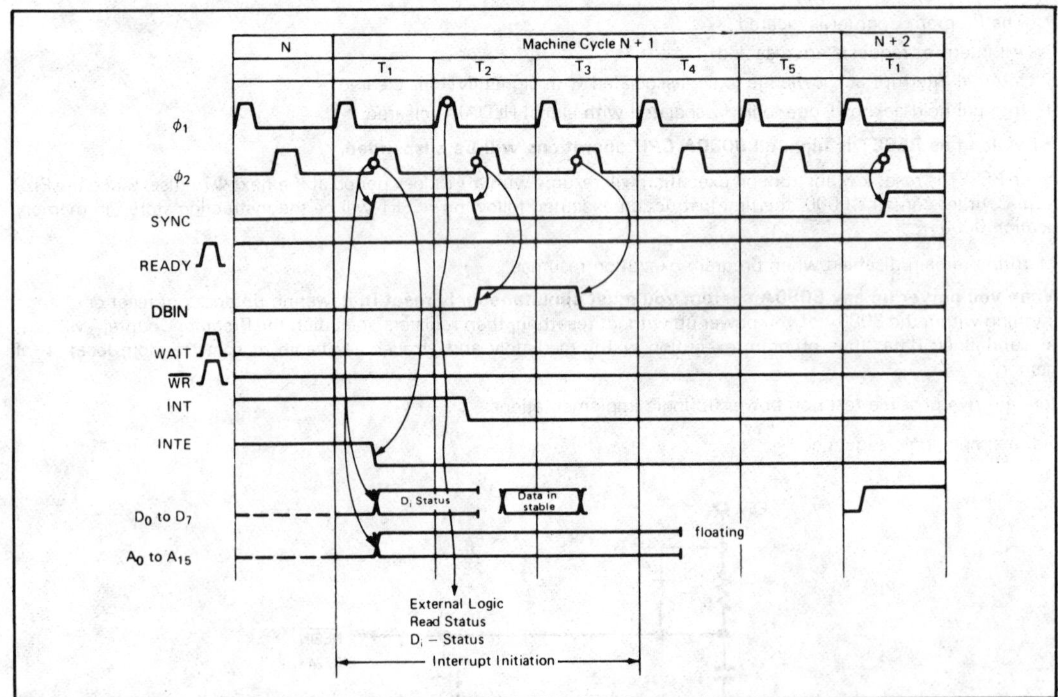


Figure 4-11. Interrupt Initiation Sequence

## EXTERNAL INTERRUPTS

**External logic may request an interrupt at any time by setting the INT input high. An interrupt request will only be acknowledged if interrupts have been enabled.** Normally the EI (Enable Interrupts) and DI (Disable Interrupts) instructions are executed to enable and disable interrupts; however, interrupts are automatically disabled by the CPU during the RESET condition, and following an interrupt acknowledge.

The 8080A CPU outputs INTE high when interrupts have been enabled, and low when interrupts are disabled. If interrupts are enabled, then the 8080A CPU will acknowledge an interrupt request during the next $T_1$ clock period, on the rising edge of $\Phi 2$. At this time INTE is set low to reflect the fact that an interrupt acknowledge automatically disables interrupts. **Timing is illustrated in Figure 4-11.**

**The 8080A CPU informs external logic that an interrupt has been acknowledged by outputting this status on the Data Bus:**

D0 - INTA
D1 - RI/$\overline{\text{WO}}$
D5 - M1

**INTA is the principal interrupt acknowledge status; it is converted into a separate interrupt acknowledge control signal by the 8228 System Controller.**

**Once an interrupt has been acknowledged, the 8080A CPU enters an instruction fetch sequence — but with two differences:**

1) Program Counter increment logic is suppressed.
2) Different statuses are output on the Data Bus during $T_2$. The statuses output on the Data Bus during various machine cycles are summarized in Table 4-3.

**The different statuses output during $T_2$ of a normal, or a post-interrupt acknowledge instruction fetch are very important.**

During a normal instruction fetch sequence, MEMR is output true on D7.

During the instruction fetch sequence which follows an interrupt acknowledge, MEMR is not output true on D7, but INTA is output true on D0.

Thus, external logic can differentiate between a normal instruction fetch and the instruction fetch sequence which follows an interrupt acknowledge.

It is very important that external logic be able to differentiate between a normal instruction fetch and an interrupt acknowledge instruction fetch. When the interrupt is acknowledged, the Program Counter is addressing an instruction which will not get executed until the interrupt service routine has completed execution:

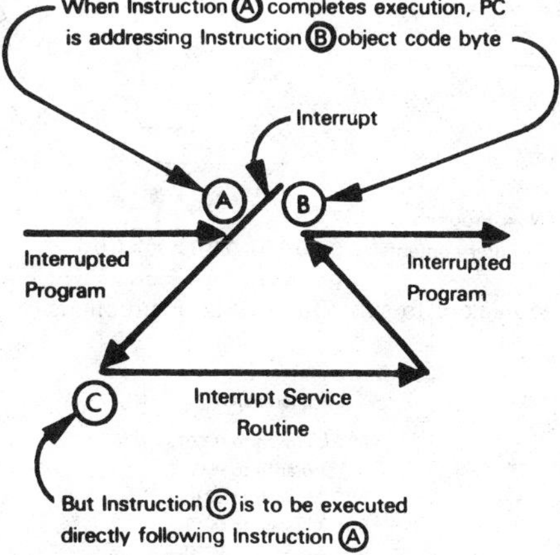

**Therefore the first instruction executed following the interrupt acknowledge must save the Program Counter contents. The last instruction executed within the interrupt service routine restores the Program Counter contents.During the instruction fetch which follows an interrupt acknowledge, the Program Counter increment logic is suppressed, because the 8080A CPU expects the object code for the first interrupt service routine instruction to be supplied by the interrupting device instead of memory:**

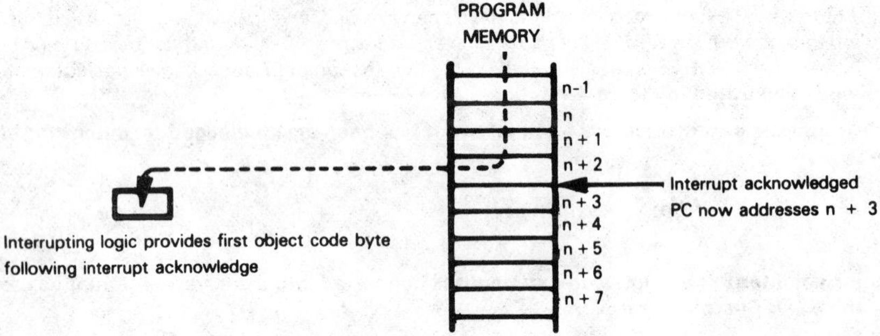


**The object code provided by external logic during the instruction fetch which follows the interrupt acknowledge must be the object code for an instruction which will save the Program Counter contents for subsequent retrieval. There is only one instruction which will do this and that is a subroutine CALL instruction.** Recall from Volume I that the subroutine CALL instruction will save the current Program Counter contents on the Stack, then will load a new starting address into the Program Counter. Thus, a subroutine CALL instruction satisfies the logical requirements for interrupt service routine initiation.

**The normal way of terminating a subroutine is via a Return instruction.** This instruction loads the Program Counter from the top of the Stack. The Return instruction will, therefore, satisfy the logical requirements for interrupt service routine termination.

There are two types of 8080A subroutine CALL instruction: the RESTART (RST) and the CALL. **The RST instruction is a one-byte subroutine CALL with the following object code:**

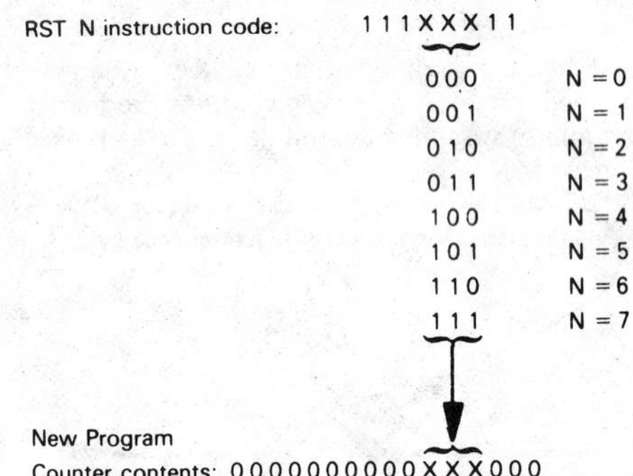


Therefore RST n instructions are equivalent to subroutine CALL instructions, with program execution branching as follows:

Subroutine

RST 0 branch to $0000_{16}$
RST 1 branch to $0008_{16}$
RST 2 branch to $0010_{16}$
RST 3 branch to $0018_{16}$
RST 4 branch to $0020_{16}$
RST 5 branch to $0028_{16}$
RST 6 branch to $0030_{16}$
RST 7 branch to $0038_{16}$

**The CALL instruction is a typical three-byte, direct memory addressing subroutine call:**

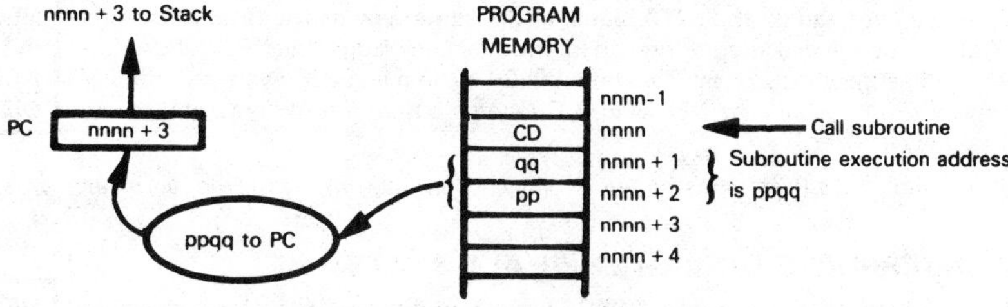


The address of the instruction following the subroutine call (nnnn+3) is saved on the Stack, to be retrieved subsequently by a Return instruction. The second and third CALL instruction object code bytes provide the address of the subroutine's first instruction; this address (ppqq) therefore is loaded into the Program Counter.

**What is not clearly understood by many 8080A users is that external logic can respond to an interrupt acknowledge by inserting either an RST or a subroutine CALL instruction.**

**Responding to an interrupt acknowledge by inserting an RST instruction is very straightforward.** The INTA status output during $T_2$ can be used to select external logic as the source of an object code, while the lack of an MEMR status can be used to suppress the normal instruction fetch which would occur from program memory. Thus, a simple 8-bit I/O buffer will generate a Restart instruction as follows:

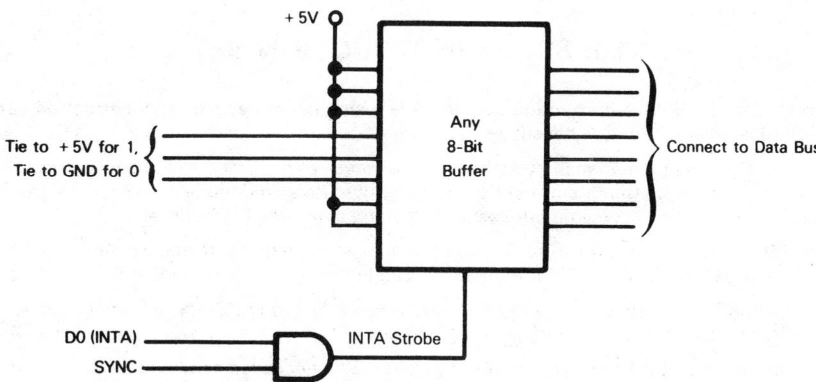


**With a little more effort, external logic can be designed to provide a subroutine CALL instruction's object code following the interrupt acknowledge.** Providing the INTA status is used to suppress normal program memory accesses for the next three machine cycles, logic associated with the external interrupt request can supply the three consecutive object code bytes of a normal subroutine CALL instruction.

In a configuration that includes an 8228 System Controller, if the first object code byte received following INTA output is a CALL ($CD_{16}$), then the 8228 System Controller outputs two more INTA statuses for the next two machine cycles. Now external logic can use INTA as a signal which disables normal memory accesses, selecting external logic instead. For more details, see the 8228 System Controller description given later in this chapter.

If your configuration does not include an 8228 System Controller, then external logic must be quite complex if it responds to an interrupt acknowledge with a CALL instruction. These are the operations external logic must perform:

1) In response to INTA true, suppress normal memory references and transmit the code $CD_{16}$ to the CPU. This code must be transmitted at the proper time, as an instruction code on the Data Bus.
2) Suppress normal memory accesses for the next two clock periods. Remember, there is no INTA true for these two periods.
3) During the next two clock periods, transmit the low order half, then the high order half of the interrupt service routine starting address. These two address bytes must be provided out of external logic, and their timing on the Data Bus must conform exactly to the second and third bytes of a CALL instruction.

If your configuration includes an 8259 Priority Interrupt Control Unit, then this device takes care of all logic associated with responding to an interrupt acknowledge with a CALL; the 8259 is described later in this chapter.

**NEC 8080A INTERRUPT ACKNOWLEDGE DIFFERENCES**

**The NEC 8080A does not handle the INTA signal in the same way as the Intel 8080A.** In response to a Call instruction executed during an interrupt acknowledge, the NEC 8080A outputs INTA true for three machine cycles; in an Intel 8080A system an 8228 System Controller must be present for this to occur. The NEC 8080A D0 status output also differs at this time; see Table 4-3 for details.

The NEC 8080A responds to Restart instructions following an interrupt acknowledge in the same way as the Intel 8080A.

## EXTERNAL INTERRUPTS DURING THE HALT STATE

**NEC 8080A EXTERNAL INTERRUPT DIFFERENCES**

**With all 8080A devices except the NEC 8080A, interrupt acknowledge logic during a Halt state is as illustrated in Figure 4-11. For the NEC 8080A, however, the interrupt acknowledge sequence differs slightly during the Halt state only.** INTE is reset low by the NEC 8080A on the rising edge of $\Phi 2$ in clock period $T_2$; this is one clock period later than illustrated in Figure 4-11. Note that this difference in NEC 8080A response applies only to the interrupt acknowledge process occurring within a Halt state.

## WAIT AND HOLD CONDITIONS FOLLOWING AN INTERRUPT

An interrupt cannot be acknowledged during a WAIT or HOLD condition. However, either of these conditions may occur following the interrupt acknowledge. For example, if there is insufficient time between $\Phi 1$ in $T_2$ and $\Phi 2$ in $T_2$ for external logic to fetch the required RST or CALL instruction, more time may be acquired by using the READY signal to generate a Wait state, as with any instruction's execution.

# THE 8080A INSTRUCTION SET

**Table 4-4 summarizes the 8080A instruction set; there is a significant departure in instruction set philosophy from the hypothetical microcomputer described in Volume 1.**

The 8080A is most efficiently programmed by making extensive use of the Stack and of subroutines. By providing a variety of Jump-to-Subroutine on Condition, and Return-from-Subroutine on Condition instructions, the 8080A allows the execution of subroutines to become an integral part of programmed logic sequences.

Observe that the 8080A has a number of 16-bit instructions; that is, instructions that operate on the 16-bit contents of the BC, DE or HL registers. These include 16-bit increment and decrement, 16-bit add, and 16-bit data moves.

The 16-bit instruction XTHL is particularly useful, since by allowing the top two Stack bytes to be exchanged with the HL registers, an easy method is provided for switching addresses.

The DAA instruction modifies the A register contents to generate a binary coded decimal equivalent of the original binary value. If carries out of bit 3 or bit 7 result, these are reported in the Auxiliary Carry and Carry statuses, respectively. See Volume 1 for a discussion of the decimal adjust operation.

**NEC 8080A INSTRUCTION SET DIFFERENCES**

**There are a few differences between NEC 8080A and Intel 8080A instruction execution.**

For binary subtraction and BCD arithmetic the NEC 8080A performs operations in what is theoretically the "correct" fashion — which differs from the actual implementation of the Intel 8080A. Specifically, the NEC 8080A has a Subtract status (SUB) which is set after any addition is performed. Only the NEC 8080A has a Subtract status.

The NEC 8080A correctly sets and resets the Auxiliary Carry status (AC) during subtract operations, identifying any borrow by the low order digit as follows:

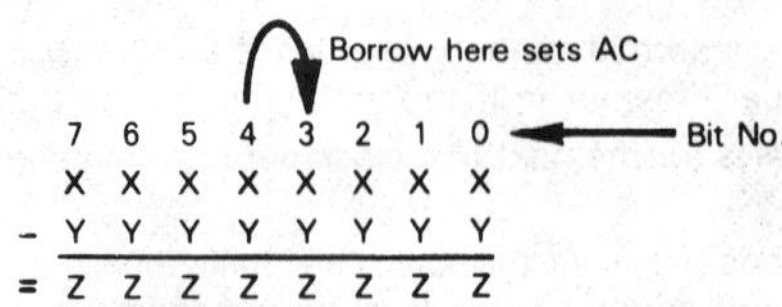

X, Y and Z represent any binary digits.

Decimal subtraction for the Intel 8080A and NEC 8080A may be illustrated as follows, assuming the contents of Register B are to be subtracted from the contents of Register C:

```
INTEL 8080A           NEC 8080A
MVI    A,99H          MOV    A,B
SUB    C              SUB    C
ADD    B              DAA
DAA
```

In the instruction sequence illustrated above for the Intel 8080A, you cannot use the Subtract instruction directly since it works for binary arithmetic only. You must create the nine's complement of the subtrahend by subtracting it from 99. Then you add the minuend to the nine's complement of the subtrahend. Finally you decimal adjust the result.

In the case of the NEC 8080A you may use the Subtract instruction for either binary or BCD data.

For a complete discussion of decimal subtraction using the Intel 8080A, see 8080 Programming for Logic Design, Chapter 7.

**The Carry and Auxiliary Carry statuses are also treated differently by the NEC and Intel 8080A. When Boolean instructions are executed by the Intel 8080A, the Carry status (C) is always reset; the Auxiliary Carry status (AC) is sometimes reset. The NEC 8080A leaves the Carry and Auxiliary Carry statuses alone when executing Boolean instructions.**

**When the AMD 9080A executes Boolean instructions it always clears both the Carry and Auxiliary Carry statuses.**

## THE BENCHMARK PROGRAM

Our benchmark program is coded for the 8080A as follows:

```
        LHLD    TABLE    ;LOAD ADDRESS OF FIRST FREE TABLE BYTE IN HL
        LXI     D,IOBUF  ;LOAD STARTING ADDRESS OF IOBUF IN DE
        LDA     IOCNT    ;LOAD I/O BUFFER LENGTH
        MOV     B,A      ;SAVE IN B
LOOP    LDAX    D        ;LOAD NEXT I/O BYTE
        INX     D        ;INCREMENT BUFFER ADDRESS
        MOV     M,A      ;STORE IN TABLE
        INX     H        ;INCREMENT TABLE ADDRESS
        DCR     B        ;DECREMENT BYTE COUNT
        JNZ     LOOP     ;RETURN FOR MORE BYTES
        SHLD    TABLE    ;AT END, RESTORE ADDRESS OF FIRST FREE TABLE BYTE
```

**The 8080A makes very few assumptions regarding the benchmark program.**

The address of the first free byte in the data table is assumed to be stored in the first two bytes of the data table — addressed by the label TABLE. The immediate addressing instruction LHLD loads the contents of the first two bytes of the data table into the H and L registers. At the end of the program, the incremented table address is restored with the direct addressing instruction SHLD.

Since the I/O buffer starting address does not change, an Immediate instruction is used to load this address into the DE registers.

Since the number of occupied bytes in the I/O buffer may change, a direct addressing instruction, LDA, is used to load this buffer length into the Accumulator. It is then moved to the B register, since the Accumulator is used to transfer data within the program loop.

The 8080A program makes no assumptions regarding the location of either the I/O buffer, or the data table, but it does assume that the table is not more than 256 bytes long.

**These are the abbreviations used in Table 4-4:**

| | | |
|---|---|---|
| A | The Accumulator | |
| B | The B register | These are sometimes treated as a register pair |
| C | The C register | |
| D | The D register | These are sometimes treated as a register pair |
| E | The E register | |

| | |
|---|---|
| H | The H register } This register pair provides the implied memory address |
| L | The L register } |
| C | Carry status. In Table 4-4 C refers to Carry status, not to the C register. |
| $A_C$ | Auxiliary Carry status |
| Z | Zero status |
| S | Sign status |
| P | Parity status |
| SUB | Subtract status (present in the NEC 8080A only) |
| I | The Instruction register |
| I2 | Second object code byte |
| I3 | Third object code byte |
| PC | The Program Counter |
| SP | The Stack Pointer |
| PSW | The Program Status Word, which has bits assigned to status flags as follows: |

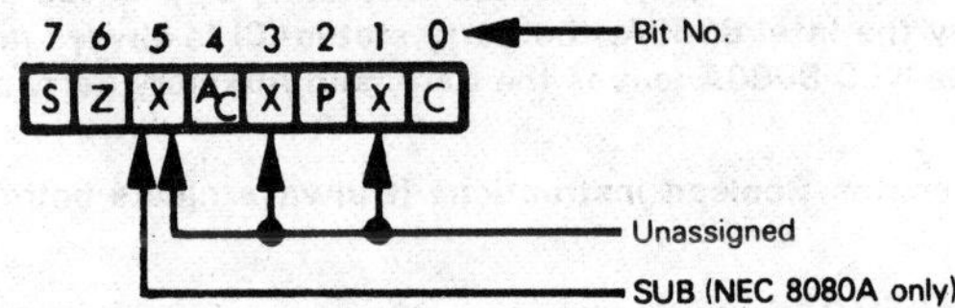


| | |
|---|---|
| DATA | 8-bit immediate data |
| DATA16 | 16-bit immediate data |
| DEV | An I/O device |
| REG | Register A, B, C, D, E, H or L |
| s | Source register |
| d | Destination register |
| M | Memory, address implied by HL |
| LABEL | A 16-bit address, specifying an instruction label |
| RP | A register pair: B for BC, D for DE, H for HL, SP for Stack Pointer |
| PORT | An I/O port, identified by a number between 0 and $FF_{16}$ |
| ADDR | A 16-bit address, specifying a data memory byte |
| [ ] | Contents of location identified within brackets |
| [[ ]] | Memory byte addressed by location identified within brackets |
| $\overline{[\ ]}$ | Complement of the contents of |
| ← | Move data in direction of arrow |
| ←→ | Exchange contents of locations on either side of arrow |
| + | Add |
| — | Subtract |
| Λ | AND |
| V | OR |
| $\forall$ | XOR |

**The letter C is used to identify Carry status.** Although C also identifies one of the 8080A registers, registers are always referenced generically in Table 4-4.

**8080A CARRY STATUS NOMENCLATURE**

Table 4-4. A Summary of 8080A/9080A Microcomputer Instruction Set

| TYPE | MNEMONIC | OPERAND(S) | BYTES | STATUSES | | | | | | OPERATION PERFORMED |
|---|---|---|---|---|---|---|---|---|---|---|
| | | | | C | AC | Z | S | P | SUB* | |
| I/O | IN | DEV | 2 | | | | | | | [A]←[DEV]<br>Input to A from device DEV (DEV = 0 to 255) |
| | OUT | DEV | 2 | | | | | | | [DEV]←[A]<br>Output from A to device DEV (DEV = 0 to 255) |
| PRIMARY MEMORY REFERENCE | LDAX | RP | 1 | | | | | | | [A]←[[RP]]<br>Load A using address implied by BC (RP = B) or DE (RP = D) |
| | STAX | RP | 1 | | | | | | | [[RP]]←[A]<br>Store A using implied addressing as for LDAX |
| | MOV | REG,M | 1 | | | | | | | [REG]←[[H,L]]<br>Load any register using address implied by HL |
| | MOV | M,REG | 1 | | | | | | | [[H,L]]←[REG]<br>Store any register using address implied by HL |
| | LDA | ADDR | 3 | | | | | | | [A]←[ADDR], i.e., [A]←[[I3, I2]]<br>Load A, use direct addressing |
| | STA | ADDR | 3 | | | | | | | [ADDR]←[A], i.e., [[I3, I2]]←[A]<br>Store A, use direct addressing |
| | LHLD | ADDR | 3 | | | | | | | [L]←[ADDR], [H]←[ADDR + 1], i.e., [L]←[[I3, I2]], [H]←[[I3, I2] + 1]<br>Load H and L registers, use direct addressing |
| | SHLD | ADDR | 3 | | | | | | | [ADDR]←[L], [ADDR + 1]←[H] i.e., [[I3, I2]]←[L], [[I3, I2] + 1]←[H]<br>Store H and L registers, use direct addressing |
| SECONDARY MEMORY REFERENCE (MEMORY OPERATE) | ADD | M | 1 | X | X | X | X | X | 0 | [A]←[A] + [[H,L]]<br>Add to A |
| | ADC | M | 1 | X | X | X | X | X | 0 | [A]←[A] + [[H,L]] + [C]<br>Add with Carry to A |
| | SUB | M | 1 | X | X | X | X | X | 1 | [A]←[A] - [[H,L]]<br>Subtract from A |
| | SBB | M | 1 | X | X | X | X | X | 1 | [A]←[A] - [[H,L]] - [C]<br>Subtract from A with borrow |
| | ANA | M | 1 | 0** | X†** | X | X | X | | [A]←[A] ∧ [H,L]]<br>AND with A |
| | XRA | M | 1 | 0** | 0†** | X | X | X | | [A]←[A] ⊻ [[H,L]]<br>Exclusive-OR with A |
| | ORA | M | 1 | 0** | 0†** | X | X | X | | [A]←[A] V [[H,L]]<br>OR with A |
| | CMP | M | 1 | X | X | X | X | X | 1 | [A] - [[H,L]]. Discard result but set flags.<br>Compare with A |
| | INR | M | 1 | | X** | X | X | X | 0 | [[H,L]]←[[H,L]] + 1<br>Increment memory |
| | DCR | M | 1 | | X** | X | X | X | 1 | [[H,L]]←[[H,L]]-1<br>Decrement memory |

Table 4-4. A Summary of 8080A/9080A Microcomputer Instruction Set (Continued)

| TYPE | MNEMONIC | OPERAND(S) | BYTES | STATUSES C | AC | Z | S | P | SUB* | OPERATION PERFORMED |
|---|---|---|---|---|---|---|---|---|---|---|
| IMMEDIATE | LXI | RP,DATA16 | 3 | | | | | | | [RP]←DATA16<br>Load 16-bit immediate data into BC (RP = B), DE (RP = D), HL (RP = H) or SP (RP = SP) |
| | MVI | M,DATA | 2 | | | | | | | [[H,L]]←DATA<br>Load 8-bit immediate data into memory location with address implied by HL |
| | MVI | REG,DATA | 2 | | | | | | | [REG]←DATA<br>Load 8-bit immediate data into any register |
| JUMP | JMP | ADDR | 3 | | | | | | | [PC]←ADDR<br>Jump to instruction with label ADDR |
| | PCHL | | 1 | | | | | | | [PC]←[H,L]<br>Jump to instruction at location implied by HL |
| SUBROUTINE CALL AND RETURN (IMMEDIATE AND STACK) | CALL | ADDR | 3 | | | | | | | [[SP]]←[PC], [PC]←ADDR, [SP]←[SP]-2<br>Jump to subroutine starting at ADDR |
| | CC | ADDR | 3 | | | | | | | [[SP]]←[PC], [PC]←ADDR, [SP]←[SP]-2<br>Jump to subroutine if C = 1 |
| | CNC | ADDR | 3 | | | | | | | [[SP]]←[PC], [PC]←ADDR, [SP]←[SP]-2<br>Jump to subroutine if C = 0 |
| | CZ | ADDR | 3 | | | | | | | [[SP]]←[PC], [PC]←ADDR, [SP]←[SP]-2<br>Jump to subroutine if Z = 1 |
| | CNZ | ADDR | 3 | | | | | | | [[SP]]←[PC], [PC]←ADDR, [SP]←[SP]-2<br>Jump to subroutine if Z = 0 |
| | CP | ADDR | 3 | | | | | | | [[SP]]←[PC], [PC]←ADDR, [SP]←[SP]-2<br>Jump to subroutine if S = 0 |
| | CM | ADDR | 3 | | | | | | | [[SP]]←[PC], [PC]←ADDR, [SP]←[SP]-2<br>Jump to subroutine if S = 1 |
| | CPE | ADDR | 3 | | | | | | | [[SP]]←[PC], [PC]←ADDR, [SP]←[SP]-2<br>Jump to subroutine if even parity |
| | CPO | ADDR | 3 | | | | | | | [[SP]]←[PC], [PC]←ADDR, [SP]←[SP]-2<br>Jump to subroutine if odd parity |
| | RET | | 1 | | | | | | | [PC]←[[SP]],[SP]←[SP]+2<br>Return from subroutine |
| | RC | | 1 | | | | | | | [PC]←[[SP]], [SP]←[SP]+2<br>Return from subroutine if C = 1 |
| | RNC | | 1 | | | | | | | [PC]←[[SP]], [SP]←[SP]+2<br>Return from subroutine if C = 0 |
| | RZ | | 1 | | | | | | | [PC]←[[SP]], [SP]←[SP]+2<br>Return from subroutine if Z = 1 |
| | RNZ | | 1 | | | | | | | [PC]←[[SP]], [SP]←[SP]+2<br>Return from subroutine if Z = 0 |
| | RM | | 1 | | | | | | | [PC]←[[SP]], [SP]←[SP]+2<br>Return from subroutine if S = 1 |

Table 4-4. A Summary of 8080A/9080A Microcomputer Instruction Set (Continued)

| TYPE | MNEMONIC | OPERAND(S) | BYTES | STATUSES | | | | | | OPERATION PERFORMED |
|---|---|---|---|---|---|---|---|---|---|---|
| | | | | C | AC | Z | S | P | SUB* | |
| SUBROUTINE CALL AND RETURN (IMMEDIATE AND STACK) (CONTINUED) | RP | | 1 | | | | | | | [PC]←[[SP]], [SP]←[SP]+2 Return from subroutine if S = 0 |
| | RPE | | 1 | | | | | | | [PC]←[[SP]], [SP]←[SP]+2 Return from subroutine if even parity |
| | RPO | | 1 | | | | | | | [PC]←[[SP]], [SP]←[SP]+2 Return from subroutine if odd parity |
| IMMEDIATE OPERATE | ADI | DATA | 2 | X | X | X | X | X | 0 | [A]←[A]+DATA Add immediate to A |
| | ACI | DATA | 2 | X | X | X | X | X | 0 | [A]←[A]+DATA+[C] Add with carry immediate to A |
| | SUI | DATA | 2 | X | X | X | X | X | 1 | [A]←[A]-DATA Subtract immediate from A |
| | SBI | DATA | 2 | X | X | X | X | X | 1 | [A]←[A]-DATA-[C] Subtract immediate with borrow from A |
| | ANI | DATA | 2 | 0** | X† | X | X | X | | [A]←[A] ∧ DATA AND immediate with A |
| | XRI | DATA | 2 | 0** | 0** | X | X | X | | [A]←[A] ⊻ DATA Exclusive-OR immediate with A |
| | ORI | DATA | 2 | 0** | 0** | X | X | X | | [A]←[A] V DATA OR immediate with A |
| | CPI | DATA | 2 | X | X | X | X | X | | Compare immediate with A |
| JUMP ON CONDITION | JC | ADDR | 3 | | | | | | | [PC]←ADDR Jump if C = 1 |
| | JNC | ADDR | 3 | | | | | | | [PC]←ADDR Jump if C = 0 |
| | JZ | ADDR | 3 | | | | | | | [PC]←ADDR Jump if Z = 1 |
| | JNZ | ADDR | 3 | | | | | | | [PC]←ADDR Jump if Z = 0 |
| | JP | ADDR | 3 | | | | | | | [PC]←ADDR Jump if S = 0 |
| | JM | ADDR | 3 | | | | | | | [PC]←ADDR Jump if S = 1 |
| | JPE | ADDR | 3 | | | | | | | [PC]←ADDR Jump on even parity |
| | JPO | ADDR | 3 | | | | | | | [PC]←ADDR Jump on odd parity |

Table 4-4. A Summary of 8080A/9080A Microcomputer Instruction Set (Continued)

| TYPE | MNEMONIC | OPERAND(S) | BYTES | STATUSES | | | | | | OPERATION PERFORMED |
|---|---|---|---|---|---|---|---|---|---|---|
| | | | | C | AC | Z | S | P | SUB* | |
| REG-REG MOVE | MOV | ds | 1 | | | | | | | [REG]←[REG]<br>Move any register (s) to any register (d) |
| | XCHG | | 1 | | | | | | | [D]←→[H], [E]←→[L]<br>Exchange DE with HL |
| | SPHL | | 1 | | | | | | | [SP]←[HL]<br>Transfer HL to SP |
| REGISTER-REGISTER OPERATE | ADD | REG | 1 | X | X | X | X | X | 0 | [A]←[A] + [REG]<br>Add any register to A |
| | ADC | REG | 1 | X | X | X | X | X | 0 | [A]←[A] + [REG] + [C]<br>Add with Carry any register to A |
| | SUB | REG | 1 | X | X | X | X | X | 1 | [A]←[A] - [REG]<br>Subtract any register from A |
| | SBB | REG | 1 | X | X | X | X | X | 1 | [A]←[A] - [REG] - [C]<br>Subtract any register with borrow from A |
| | ANA | REG | 1 | 0** | X† | X | X | X | | [A]←[A] ∧ [REG]<br>AND any register with A |
| | XRA | REG | 1 | 0** | 0†** | X | X | X | | [A]←[A] ⊻ [REG]<br>Exclusive-OR any register with A |
| | ORA | REG | 1 | 0** | 0†** | X | X | X | | [A]←[A] V [REG]<br>OR any register with A |
| | CMP | REG | 1 | X | X | X | X | X | 1 | [A] - [REG]. Discard result but set flags.<br>Compare any register with A |
| | DAD | RP | 1 | X | | | | | 0 | [H,L]←[H,L] + [RP]<br>Add to HL |
| REGISTER OPERATE | INR | REG | 1 | | X** | X | X | X | 0 | [REG]←[REG] + 1<br>Increment any register |
| | DCR | REG | 1 | | X** | X | X | X | 1 | [REG]←[REG] - 1<br>Decrement any register |
| | CMA | | 1 | | | | | | | [A]←[$\overline{A}$]<br>Complement A |
| | DAA | | 1 | X | X** | X | X | X | | Decimal adjust A |
| | RLC | | 1 | X | | | | | | 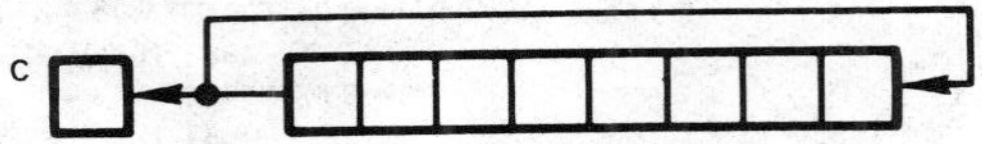<br>Rotate A left with branch carry |
| | RRC | | 1 | X | | | | | | 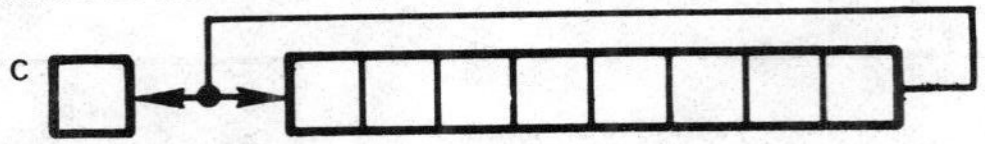<br>Rotate A right with branch carry |

Table 4-4. A Summary of 8080A/9080A Microcomputer Instruction Set (Continued)

| TYPE | MNEMONIC | OPERAND(S) | BYTES | STATUSES C | AC | Z | S | P | SUB* | OPERATION PERFORMED |
|---|---|---|---|---|---|---|---|---|---|---|
| REGISTER OPERATE (CONTINUED) | RAL | | 1 | X | | | | | | Rotate A left with carry |
| | RAR | | 1 | X | | | | | | Rotate A right with carry |
| | INX | RP | 1 | | | | | | | [RP]←[RP] + 1<br>Increment RP. RP = BC, DE, HL or SP |
| | DCX | RP | 1 | | | | | | | [RP]←[RP] - 1<br>Decrement RP |
| STACK | PUSH | RP | 1 | | | | | | | [[SP]]←[RP], [SP]←[SP] - 2<br>Push RP contents onto stack (RP = BC, DE, HL or PSW) |
| | POP | RP | 1 | | | | | | | [RP]←[[SP]], [SP]←[SP] + 2<br>Pop stack into RP (RP = BC, DE, HL or PSW) |
| | XTHL | | 1 | | | | | | | [H,L]←→[[SP]]<br>Exchange HL with top of stack |
| INTERRUPT | EI | | 1 | | | | | | | Enable interrupts |
| | DI | | 1 | | | | | | | Disable interrupts |
| | RST | N | 1 | | | | | | | Restart at addresses 8•N. N = 0 through 7. |
| STATUS | STC | | 1 | 1 | | | | | | [C]←1<br>Set Carry |
| | CMC | | 1 | X | | | | | | $[C] \leftarrow \overline{[C]}$<br>Complement Carry |
| | NOP | | 1 | | | | | | | No operation |
| | HLT | | 1 | | | | | | | Halt |

Statuses:
- C = Carry
- $A_C$ = Carry out of bit 3
- Z = Zero
- S = Sign
- P = Parity
- X = Status set or reset
- 0 = Status reset
- 1 = Status Set
- Blank = Status unchanged

* SUB status is present in NEC 8080A only

** NEC 8080A does not modify these status flags

† The AMD 9080A always resets $A_C$ to 0 for all Boolean instructions. The Intel 8085 sets $A_C$ to 1 for all AND instructions, and resets $A_C$ to 0 for all other Boolean instructions.

Table 4-5. A Summary of Instruction Object Codes and Execution Cycles

| INSTRUCTION | OBJECT CODE | BYTES | CLOCK PERIODS | FIGURE |
|---|---|---|---|---|
| ACI DATA | CE YY | 2 | 7 | 4-15 |
| ADC REG | 10001XXX | 1 | 4 | 4-12 |
| ADC M | 8E | 1 | 7 | 4-15 |
| ADD REG | 10000XXX | 1 | 4 | 4-12 |
| ADD M | 86 | 1 | 7 | 4-15 |
| ADI DATA | C6 YY | 2 | 7 | 4-15 |
| ANA REG | 10100XXX | 1 | 4 | 4-12 |
| ANA M | A6 | 1 | 7 | 4-15 |
| ANI DATA | E6 YY | 2 | 7 | 4-15 |
| CALL LABEL | CD ppqq | 3 | 17 | 4-26 |
| CC LABEL | DC ppqq | 3 | 11/17 | 4-26 |
| CM LABEL | FC ppqq | 3 | 11/17 | 4-26 |
| CMA | 2F | 1 | 4 | 4-12 |
| CMC | 3F | 1 | 4 | 4-12 |
| CMP REG | 10111XXX | 1 | 4 | 4-12 |
| CMP M | BE | 1 | 7 | 4-15 |
| CNC LABEL | D4 ppqq | 3 | 11/17 | 4-26 |
| CNZ LABEL | C4 ppqq | 3 | 11/17 | 4-26 |
| CP LABEL | F4 ppqq | 3 | 11/17 | 4-26 |
| CPE LABEL | EC ppqq | 3 | 11/17 | 4-26 |
| CPI DATA | FE YY | 2 | 7 | 4-15 |
| CPO LABEL | E4 ppqq | 3 | 11/17 | 4-26 |
| CZ LABEL | CC ppqq | 3 | 11/17 | 4-26 |
| DAA | 27 | 1 | 4 | 4-12 |
| DAD RP | 00XX1001 | 1 | 10(11)* | 4-20 |
| DCR REG | 00XXX101 | 1 | 5 | 4-13 |
| DCR M | 35 | 1 | 10 | 4-14 |
| DCX RP | 00XX1011 | 1 | 5 | 4-13 |
| DI | F3 | 1 | 4 | 4-12 |
| EI | FB | 1 | 4 | 4-12 |
| HLT | 76 | 1 | 7 | 4-30 |
| IN PORT | DB YY | 2 | 10 | 4-28 |
| INR REG | 00XXX100 | 1 | 5 | 4-13 |
| INR M | 34 | 1 | 10 | 4-14 |
| INX RP | 00XX0011 | 1 | 5 | 4-13 |
| JC LABEL | DA ppqq | 3 | 10 | 4-22 |
| JM LABEL | FA ppqq | 3 | 10 | 4-22 |
| JMP LABEL | C3 ppqq | 3 | 10 | 4-22 |
| JNC LABEL | D2 ppqq | 3 | 10 | 4-22 |
| JNZ LABEL | C2 ppqq | 3 | 10 | 4-22 |
| JP LABEL | F2 ppqq | 3 | 10 | 4-22 |
| JPE LABEL | EA ppqq | 3 | 10 | 4-22 |
| JPO LABEL | E2 ppqq | 3 | 10 | 4-22 |
| JZ LABEL | CA ppqq | 3 | 10 | 4-22 |
| LDA ADDR | 3A ppqq | 3 | 13 | 4-24 |
| LDAX RP | 000X1010 | 1 | 7 | 4-15 |
| LHLD ADDR | 2A ppqq | 3 | 16 | 4-17 |

| INSTRUCTION | OBJECT CODE | BYTES | CLOCK PERIODS | FIGURE |
|---|---|---|---|---|
| LXI RP,DATA16 | 00XX0001 | 3 | 10 | 4-22 |
| | YYYY | | | |
| MOV REG,REG | 01dddsss | 1 | 5(4)* | 4-13 |
| MOV M,REG | 01110sss | 1 | 7 | 4-16 |
| MOV REG,M | 01ddd110 | 1 | 7 | 4-15 |
| MVI REG,DATA | 00ddd110 | 2 | 7 | 4-15 |
| | YY | | | |
| MVI M,DATA | 36 YY | 2 | 10 | 4-14 |
| NOP | 00 | 1 | 4 | 4-12 |
| ORA REG | 10110XXX | 1 | 4 | 4-12 |
| ORA M | B6 | 1 | 7 | 4-15 |
| ORI DATA | F6 YY | 2 | 7 | 4-15 |
| OUT PORT | D3 YY | 2 | 10 | 4-29 |
| PCHL | E9 | 1 | 5 | 4-13 |
| POP RP | 11XX0001 | 1 | 10 | 4-19 |
| PUSH RP | 11XX0101 | 1 | 11 | 4-18 |
| RAL | 17 | 1 | 4 | 4-12 |
| RAR | 1F | 1 | 4 | 4-12 |
| RC | D8 | 1 | 5/11 | 4-27 |
| RET | C9 | 1 | 10(11)* | 4-19 |
| RLC | 07 | 1 | 4 | 4-12 |
| RM | F8 | 1 | 5/11 | 4-27 |
| RNC | D0 | 1 | 5/11 | 4-27 |
| RNZ | C0 | 1 | 5/11 | 4-27 |
| RP | F0 | 1 | 5/11 | 4-27 |
| RPE | E8 | 1 | 5/11 | 4-27 |
| RPO | E0 | 1 | 5/11 | 4-27 |
| RRC | 0F | 1 | 4 | 4-12 |
| RST N | 11XXX111 | 1 | 11 | 4-18 |
| RZ | C8 | 1 | 5/11 | 4-27 |
| SBB REG | 10011XXX | 1 | 4 | 4-12 |
| SBB M | 9E | 1 | 7 | 4-15 |
| SBI DATA | DE YY | 2 | 7 | 4-15 |
| SHLD ADDR | 22 ppqq | 3 | 16 | 4-25 |
| SPHL | F9 | 1 | 5(4)* | 4-13 |
| STA ADDR | 32 ppqq | 3 | 13 | 4-23 |
| STAX RP | 000X0010 | 1 | 7 | 4-16 |
| STC | 37 | 1 | 4 | 4-12 |
| SUB REG | 10010XXX | 1 | 4 | 4-12 |
| SUB M | 96 | 1 | 7 | 4-15 |
| SUI DATA | D6 YY | 2 | 7 | 4-15 |
| XCHG | EB | | 4 | 4-12 |
| XRA REG | 10101XXX | 1 | 4 | 4-12 |
| XRA M | AE | 1 | 7 | 4-15 |
| XRI DATA | EE YY | 2 | 7 | 4-15 |
| XTHL | E3 | 1 | 18(17)* | 4-21 |

ppqq represents four hexadecimal digit memory address
YY represents two hexadecimal data digits
YYYY represents four hexadecimal data digits
X represents an optional binary digit
ddd represents optional binary digits identifying a destination register
sss represents optional binary digits identifying a source register

* The NEC 8080A has five instructions with unique execution times, defined above by :(N)* where N is the number of NEC 8080A instruction cycles.

## INSTRUCTION EXECUTION TIMES AND CODES

**Table 4-5 lists instructions in alphabetic order, showing object codes and execution times, expressed as machine cycles.**

**Where two instruction cycles are shown, the first is for "condition not met" whereas the second is for "condition met".**

Detailed timing for instructions is provided by Figures 4-12 through 4-30. Table 4-5 identifies the timing diagram that applies to each instruction.

**Instruction object codes are represented as two hexadecimal digits for instructions without variations.**

**Instruction object codes are represented as eight binary digits for instructions with variations; the binary digit representation of variations is then identifiable.**

**NEC 8080A INSTRUCTION EXECUTION TIME DIFFERENCES**

**The NEC 8080A has four instructions with execution times that differ from the Intel 8080A.** These four instructions are the Register Move (MOV), the Return (RET), the 16-bit Add (DAD), and the Exchange instructions XTHL and SPHL.

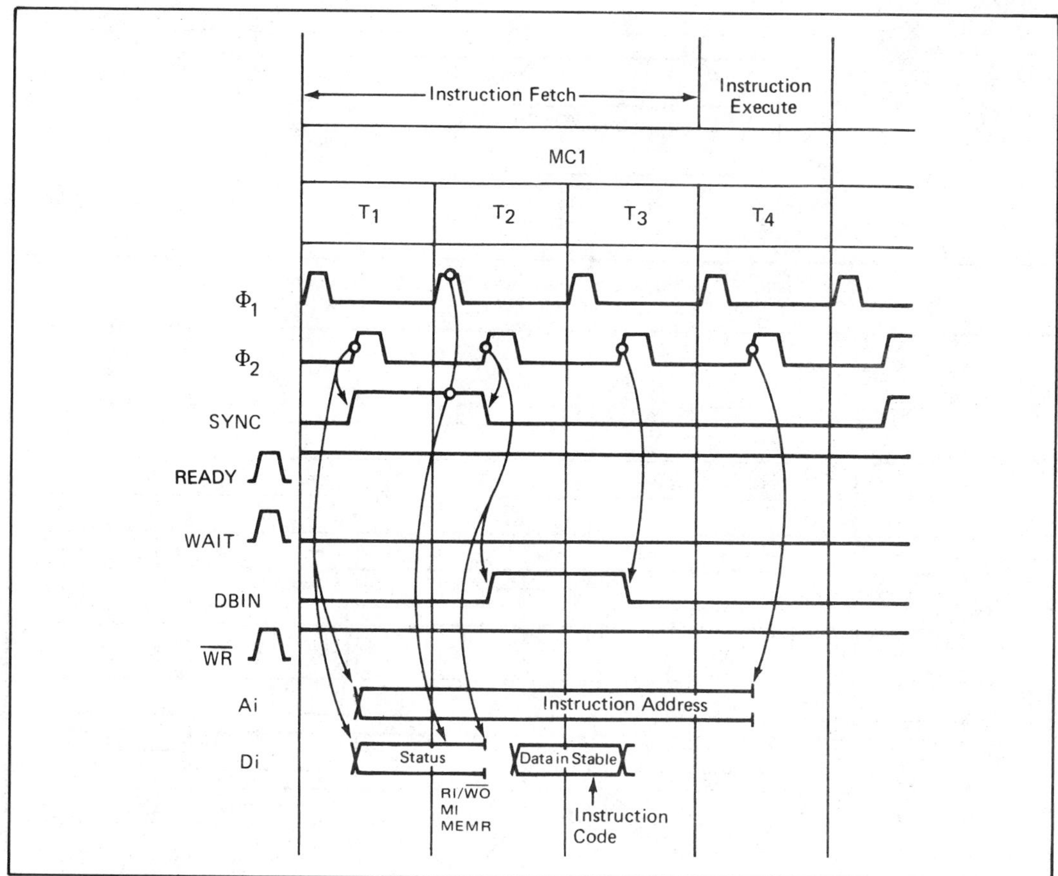


Figure 4-12. Signal Sequences and Timing for Instructions:
STC, CMC, CMA, NOP, RLC, RRC, RAL, RAR, XCHG, EI,
DI, DAA, ADD R, ADC R, SUB R, SBB R, ANA R, XRA R, ORA R, CMP R

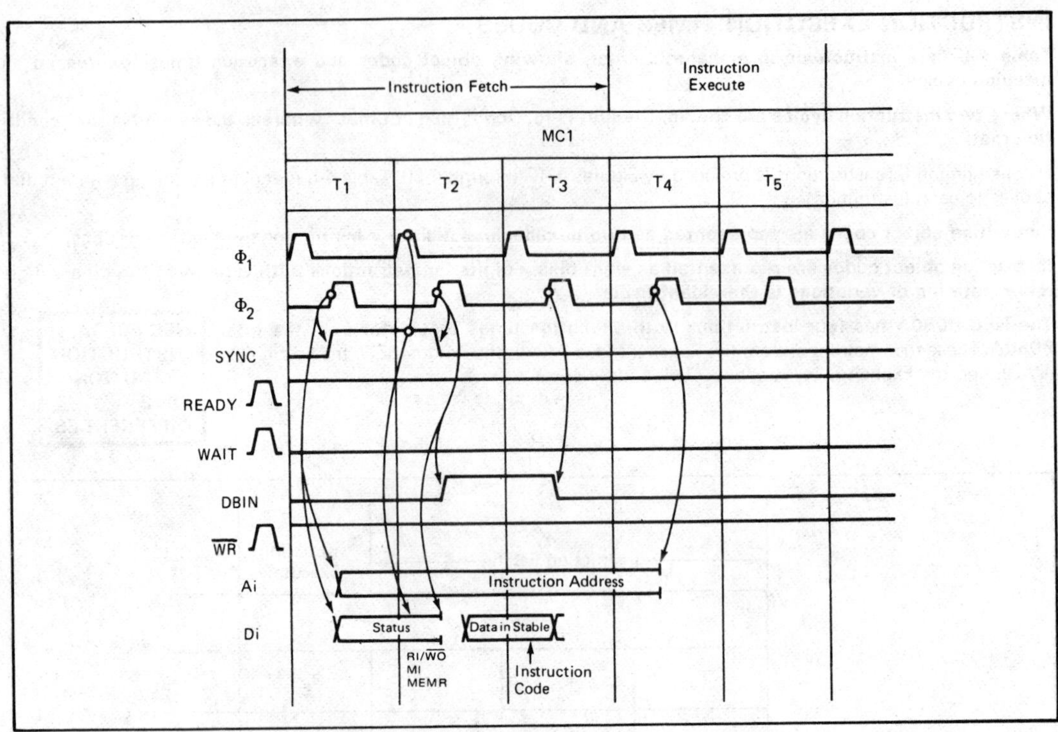


Figure 4-13. Signal Sequences and Timing for Instructions:
INR, DCR, MOV REG REG, SPHL, PCHL, DCX, INX

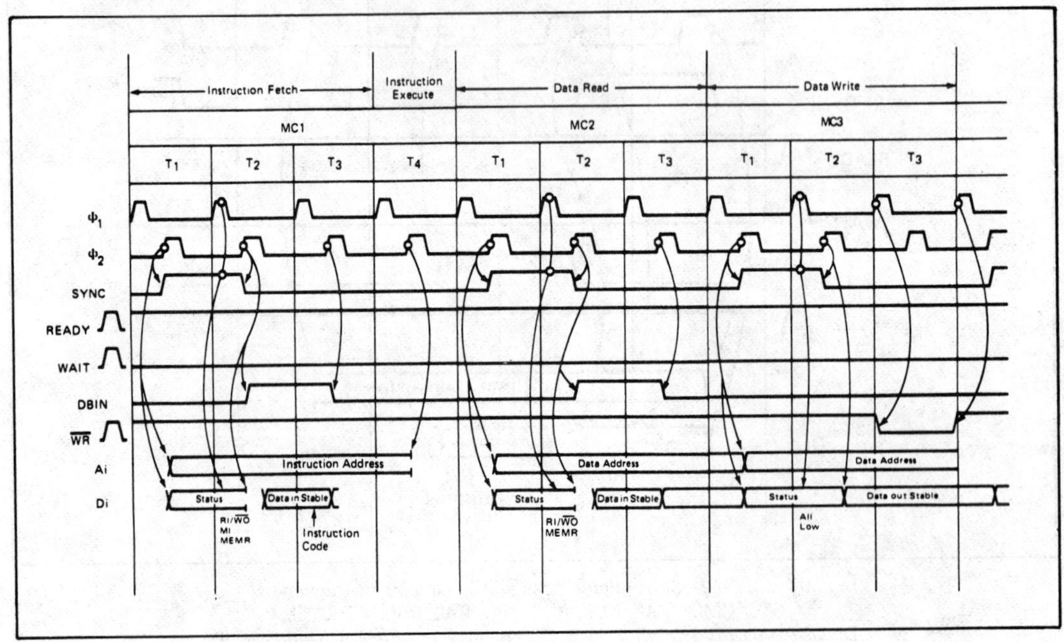


Figure 4-14. Signal Sequences and Timing for Instructions:
DCR, INR, MVI M

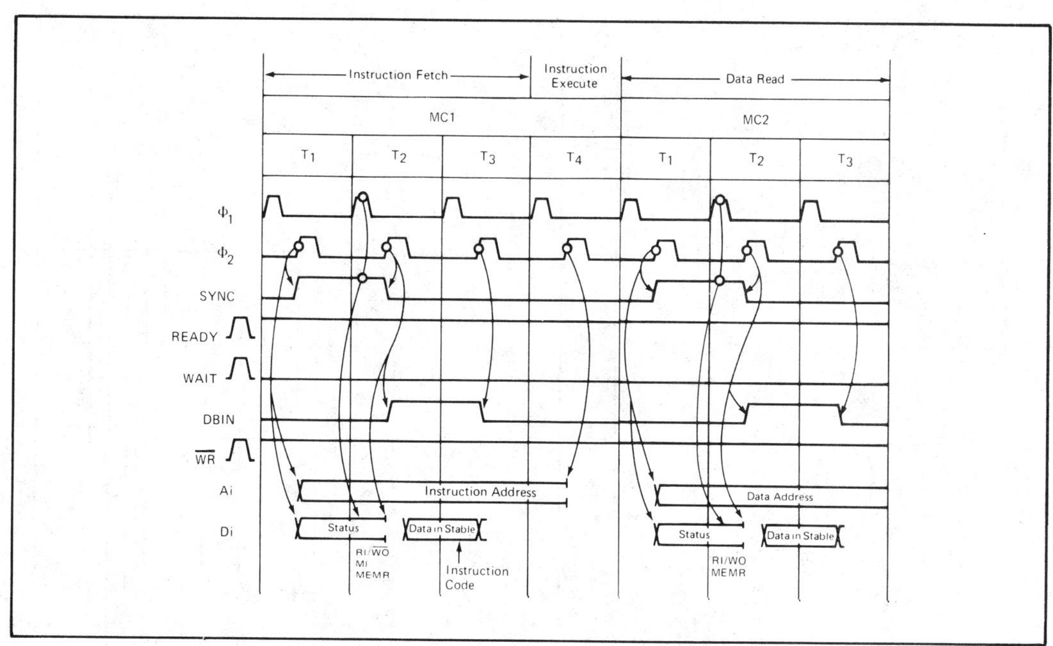


Figure 4-15. Signal Sequences and Timing for Instructions:
LDAX, MOV REG M, ADI, ACI, SUI, SBI, ANI, XRI, ORI, CPI, MVI R, ADD M, ADC M, SUB M, SBB M, ANA M, XRA M, ORA M, CMP M

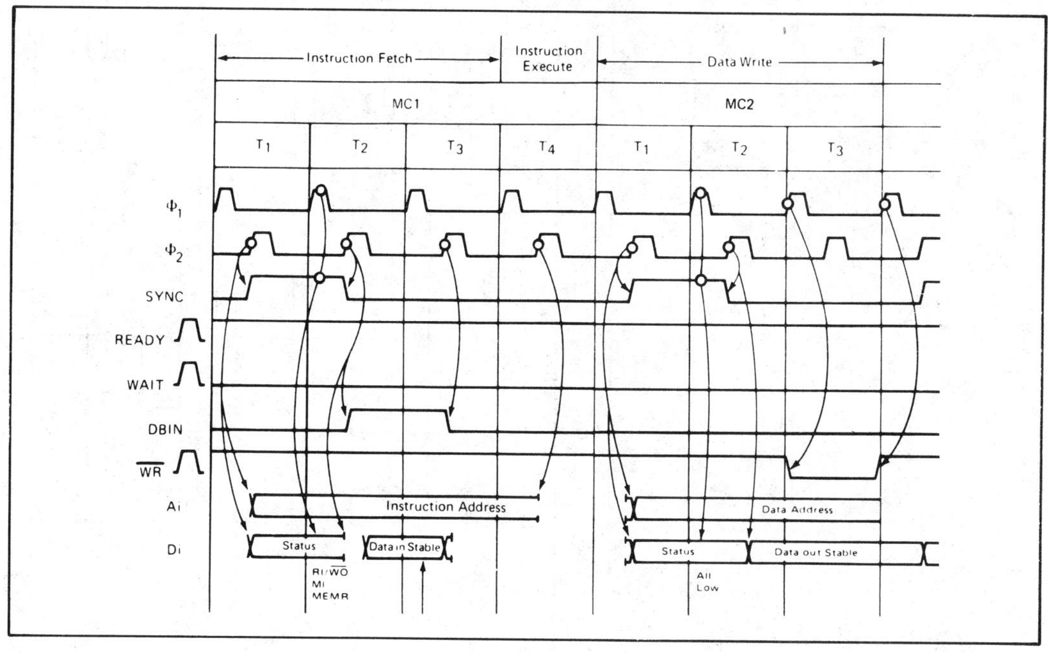


Figure 4-16. Signal Sequences and Timing for Instructions:
STAX, MOV M REG

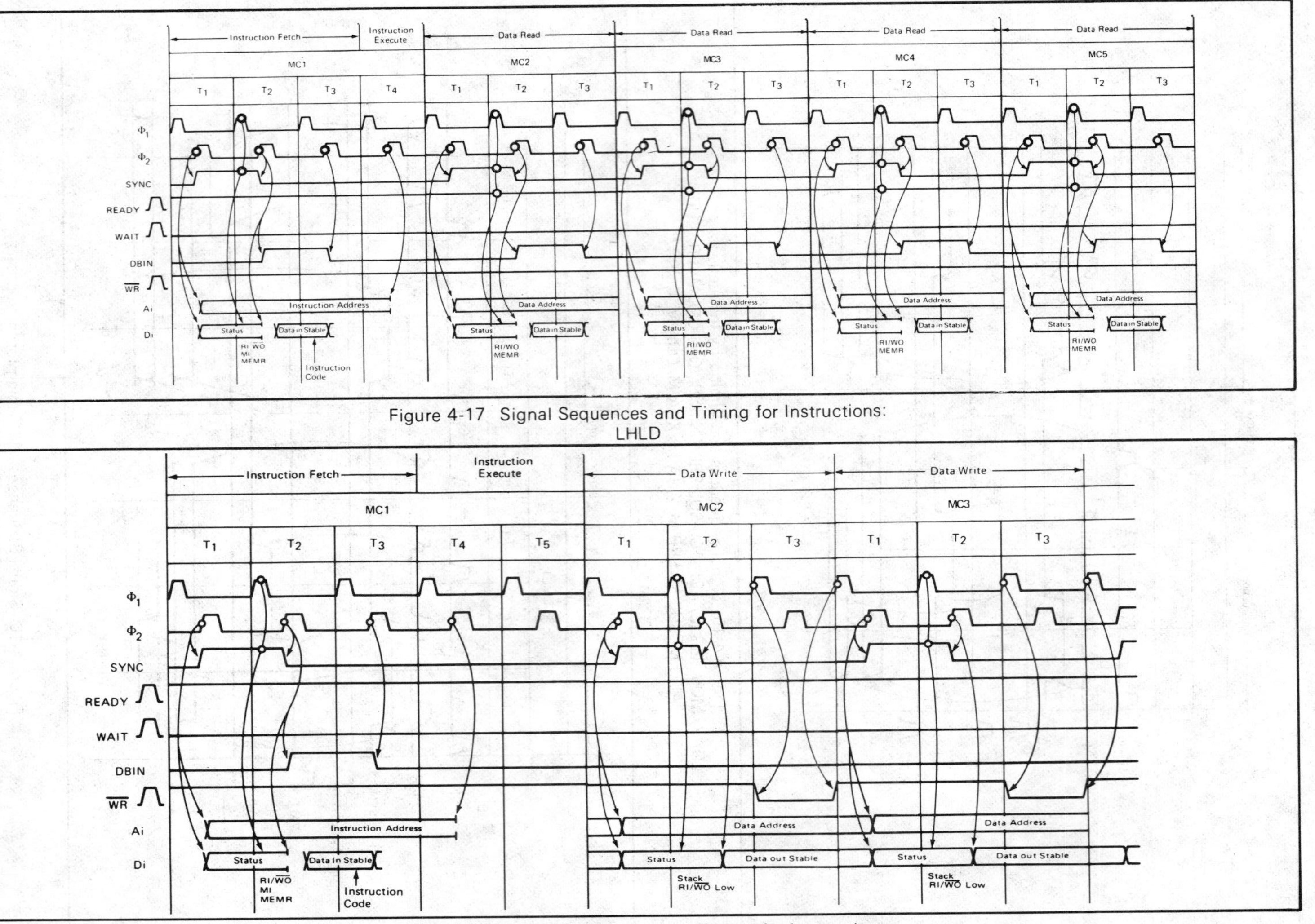


Figure 4-17 Signal Sequences and Timing for Instructions: LHLD



Figure 4-18. Signal Sequences and Timing for Instructions: PUSH, RST

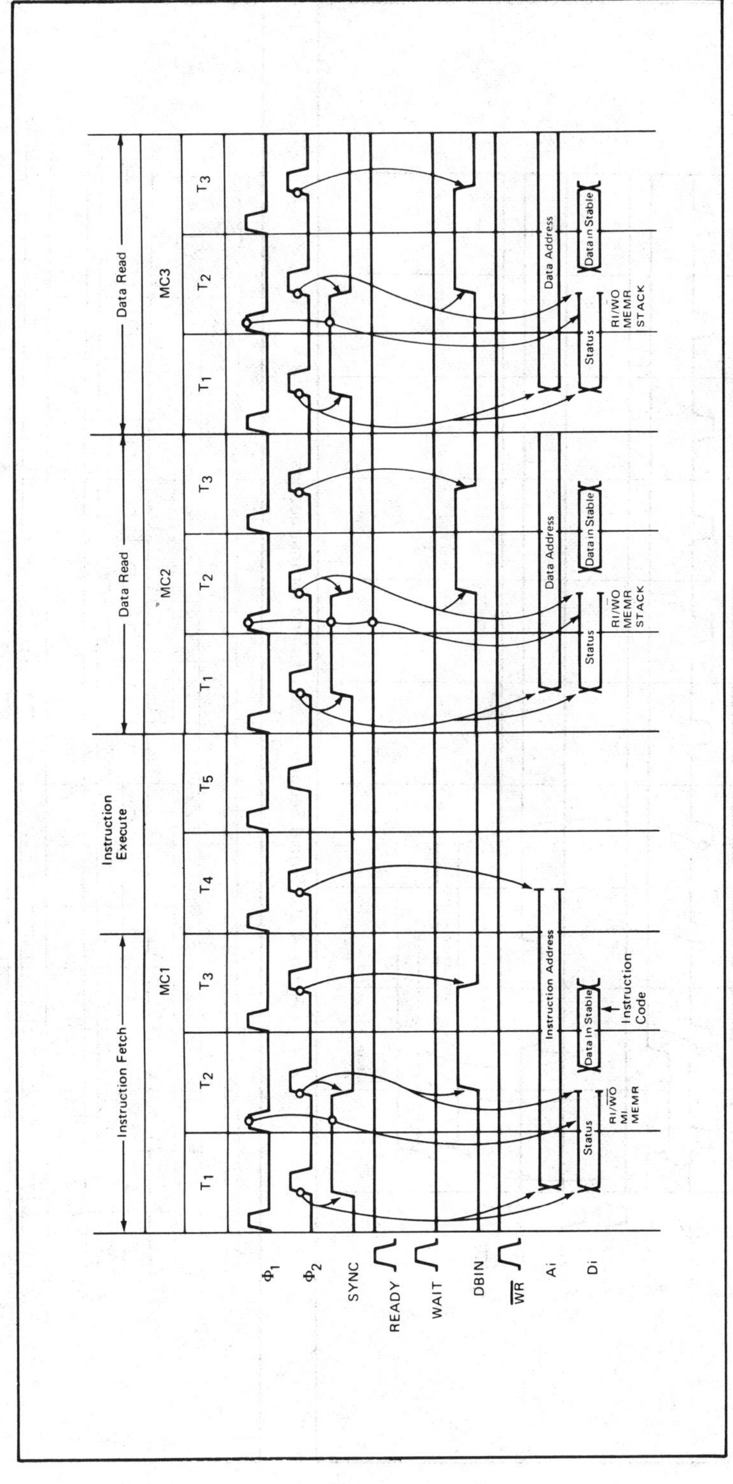


Figure 4-19. Signal Sequences and Timing for Instructions: POP, RET

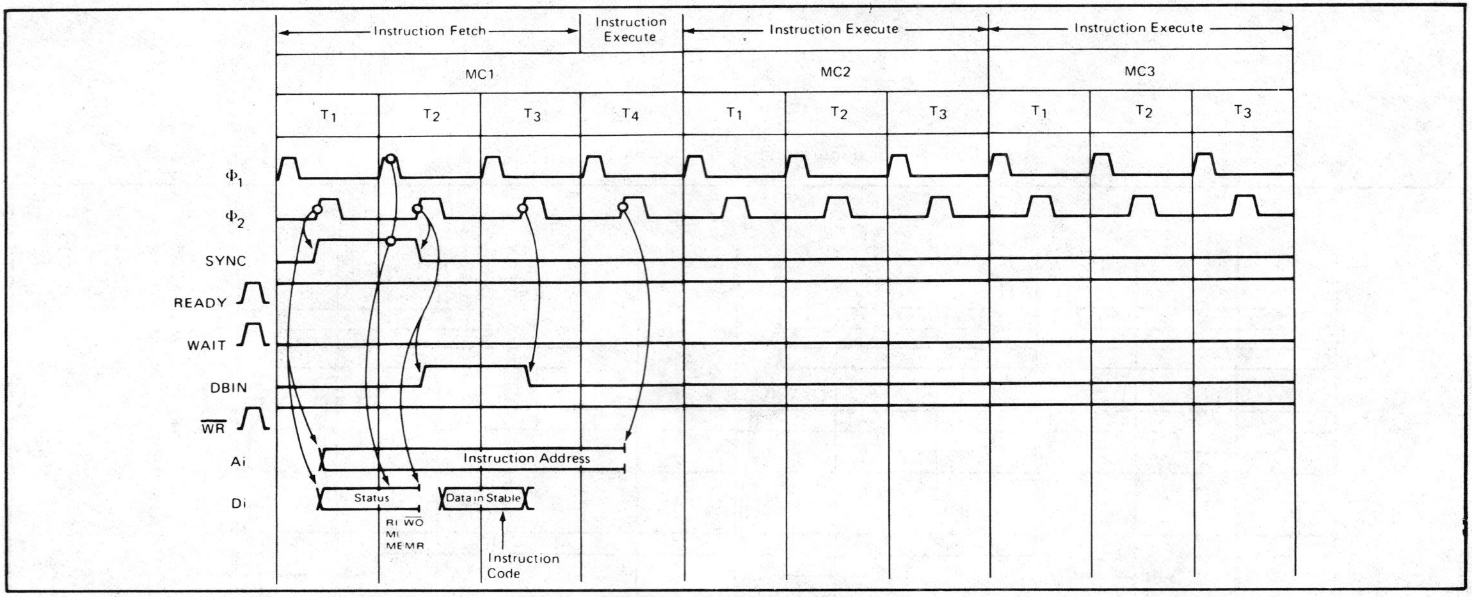

Instruction Fetch
Instruction Execute
Instruction Execute
Instruction Execute
MC1
MC2
MC3
$T_1$ $T_2$ $T_3$ $T_4$ $T_1$ $T_2$ $T_3$ $T_1$ $T_2$ $T_3$
$\Phi_1$
$\Phi_2$
SYNC
READY
WAIT
DBIN
$\overline{WR}$
Ai
Di
Instruction Address
Status
Data in Stable
RI $\overline{WO}$
MI
MEMR
Instruction Code

Figure 4-20. Signal Sequences and Timing for Instructions: DAD

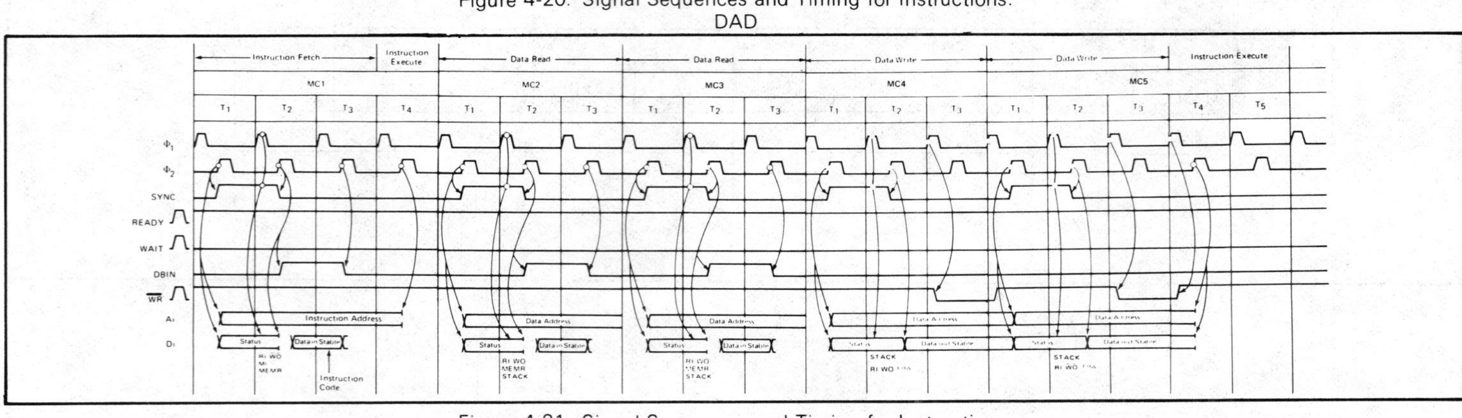


Figure 4-21. Signal Sequences and Timing for Instructions: XTHL

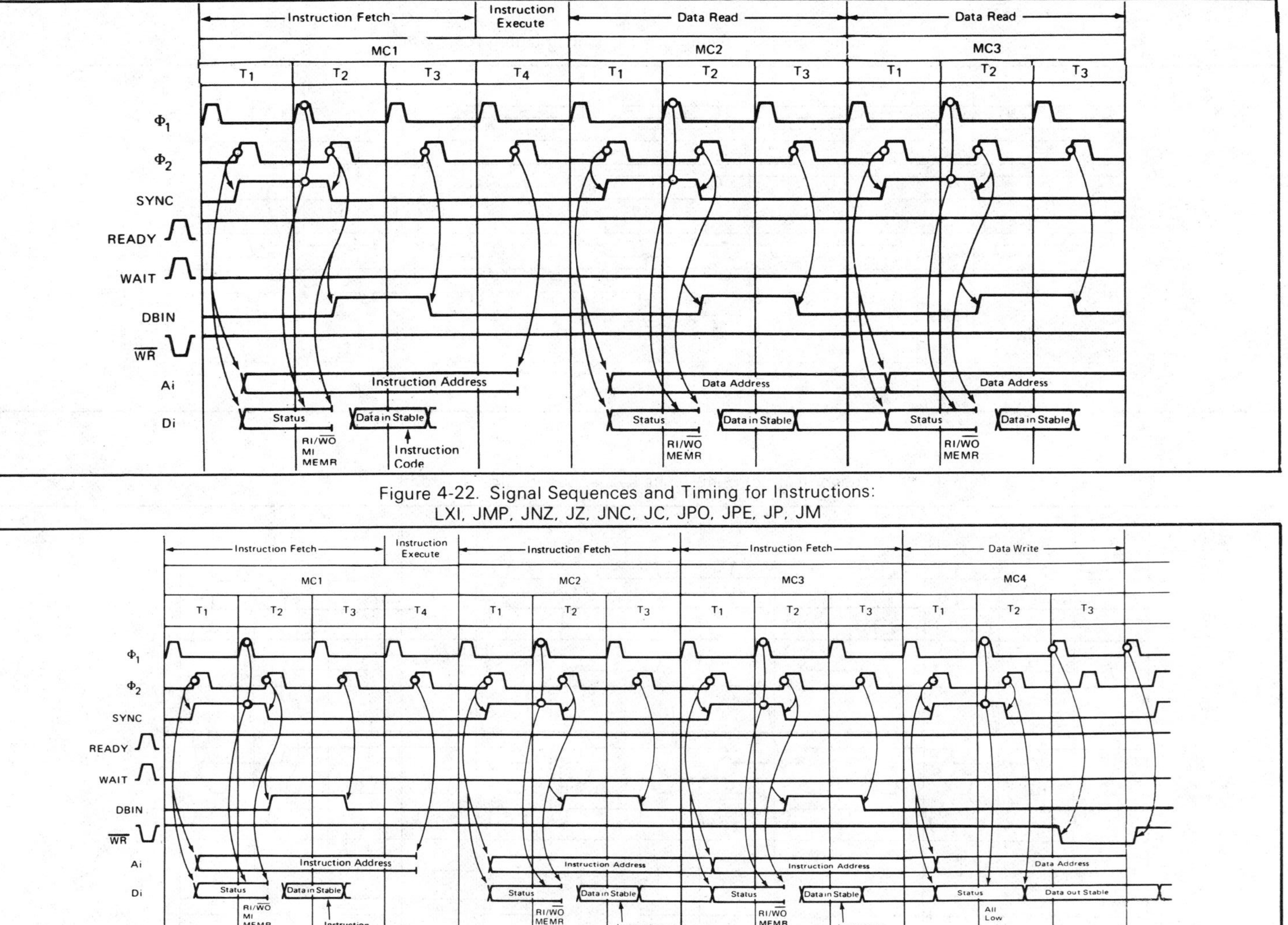


Figure 4-22. Signal Sequences and Timing for Instructions:
LXI, JMP, JNZ, JZ, JNC, JC, JPO, JPE, JP, JM



Figure 4-23. Signal Sequences and Timing for Instructions:
STA

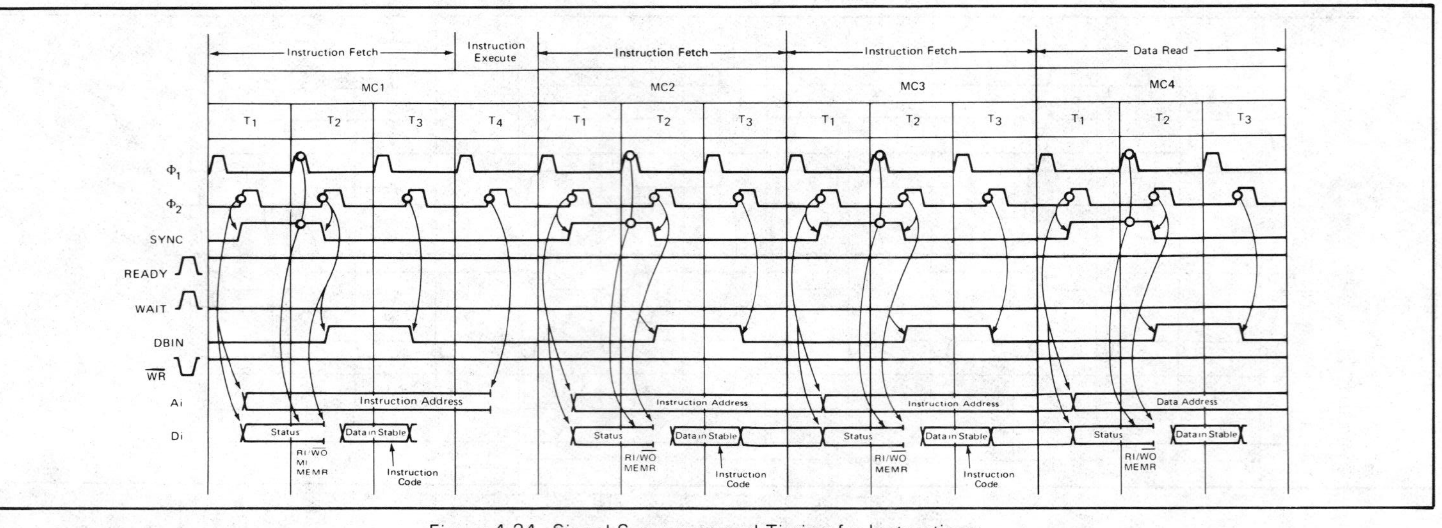


Figure 4-24. Signal Sequences and Timing for Instructions: LDA

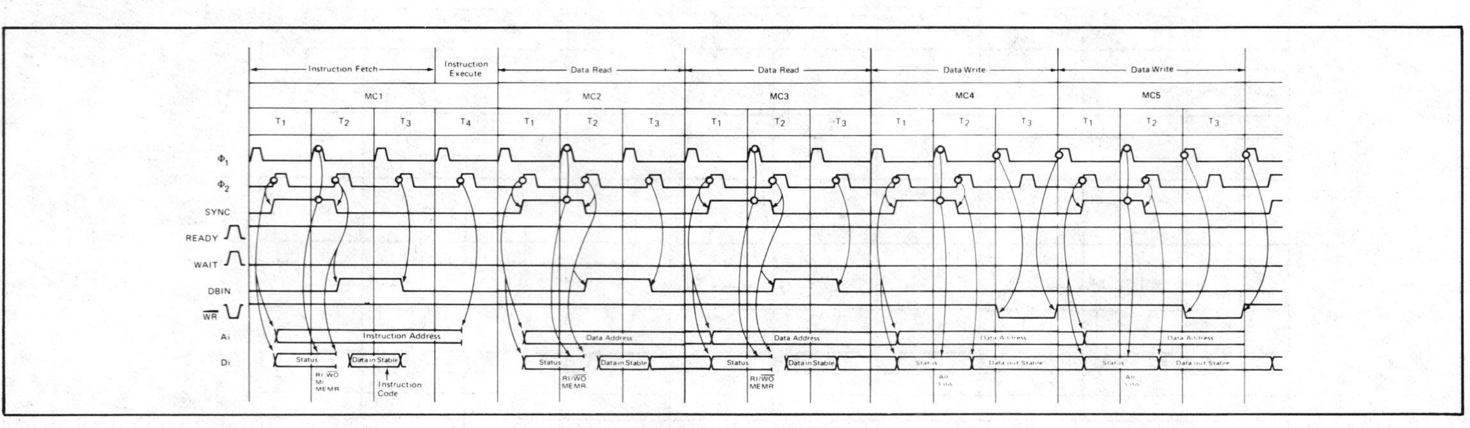


Figure 4-25. Signal Sequences and Timing for Instructions: SHLD

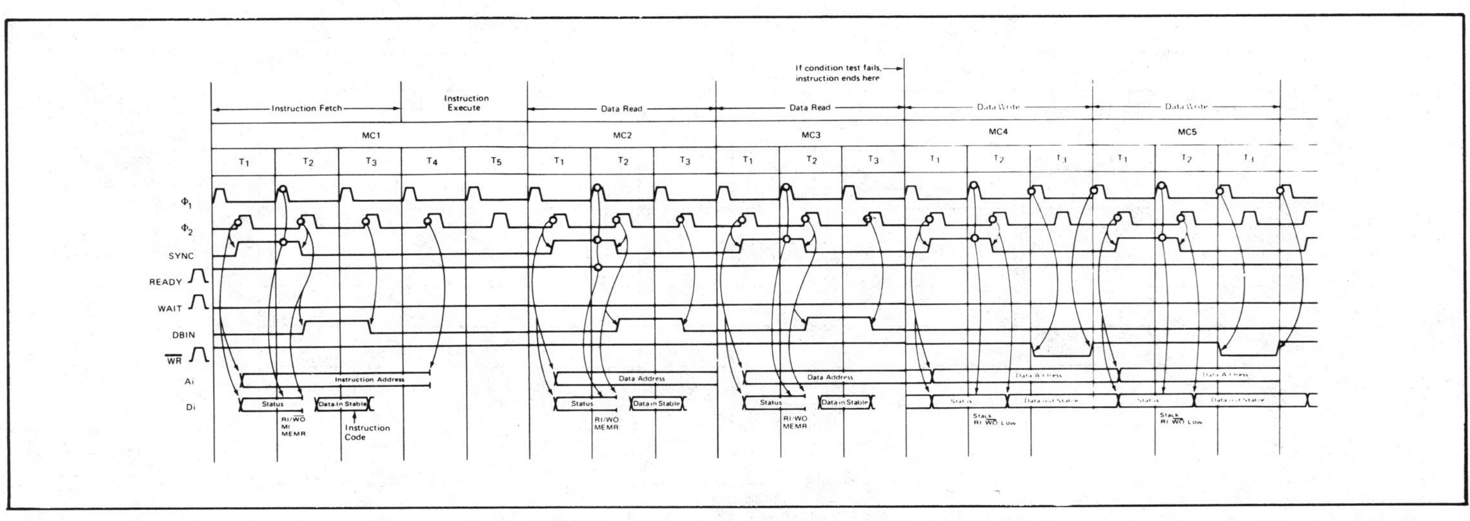


Figure 4-26. Signal Sequences and Timing for Instructions:
CALL, CNZ, CZ, CNC, CC, CPO, CPE, CP, CM

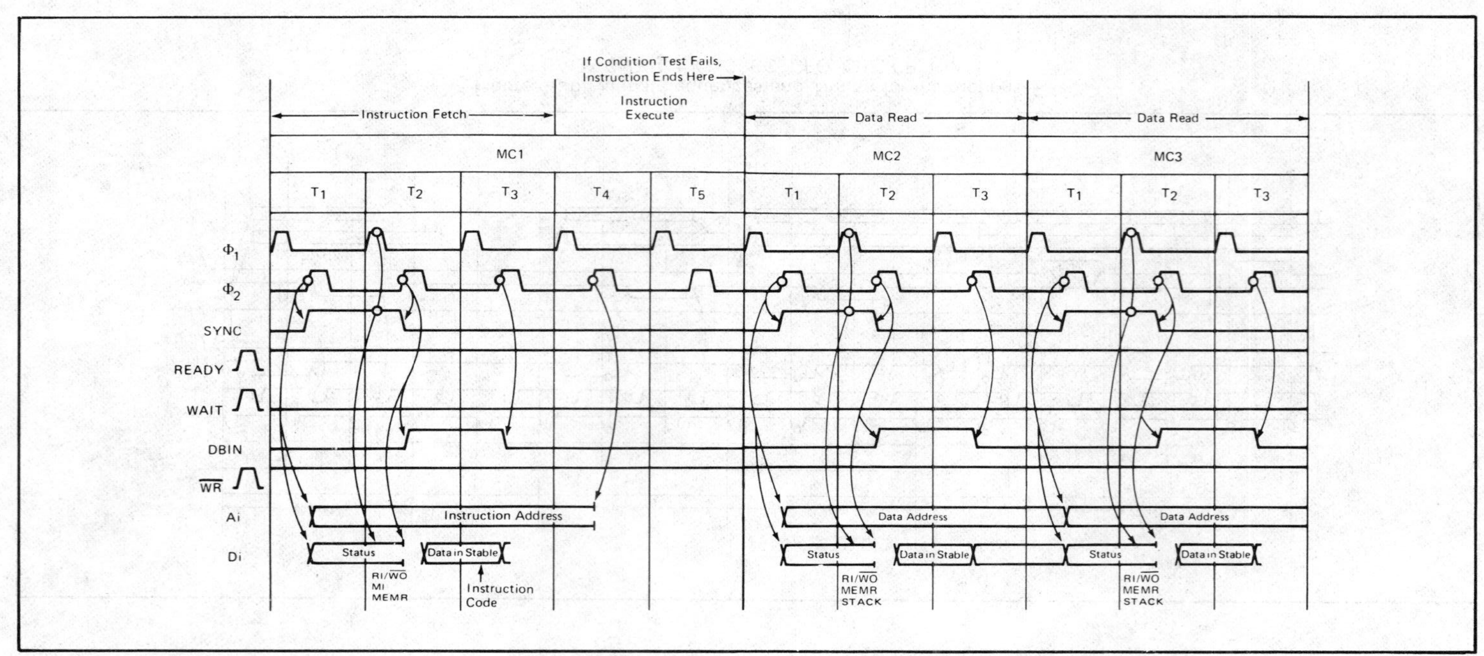


Figure 4-27. Signal Sequences and Timing for Instructions:
RNZ, RZ, RNC, RC, RPO, RPE, RP, RM

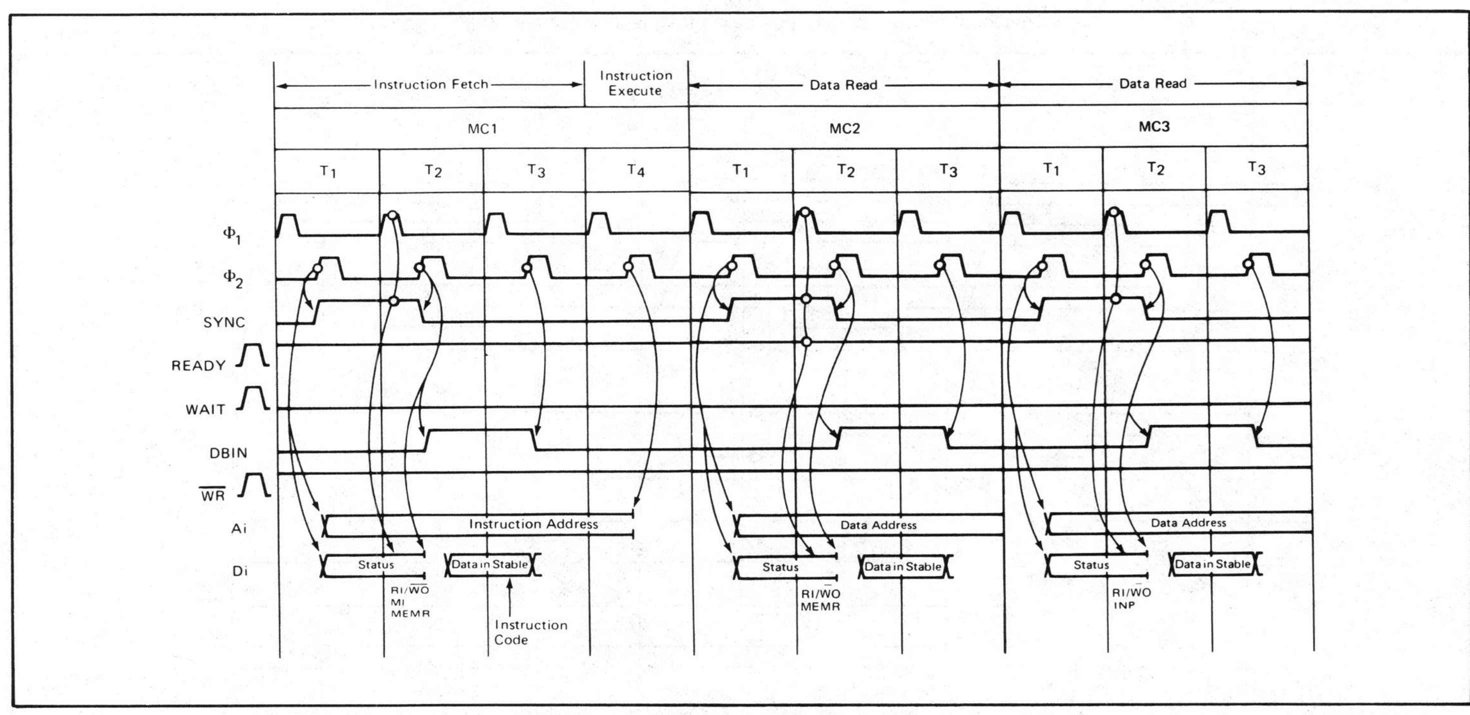


Figure 4-28. Signal Sequences and Timing for Instructions:
IN

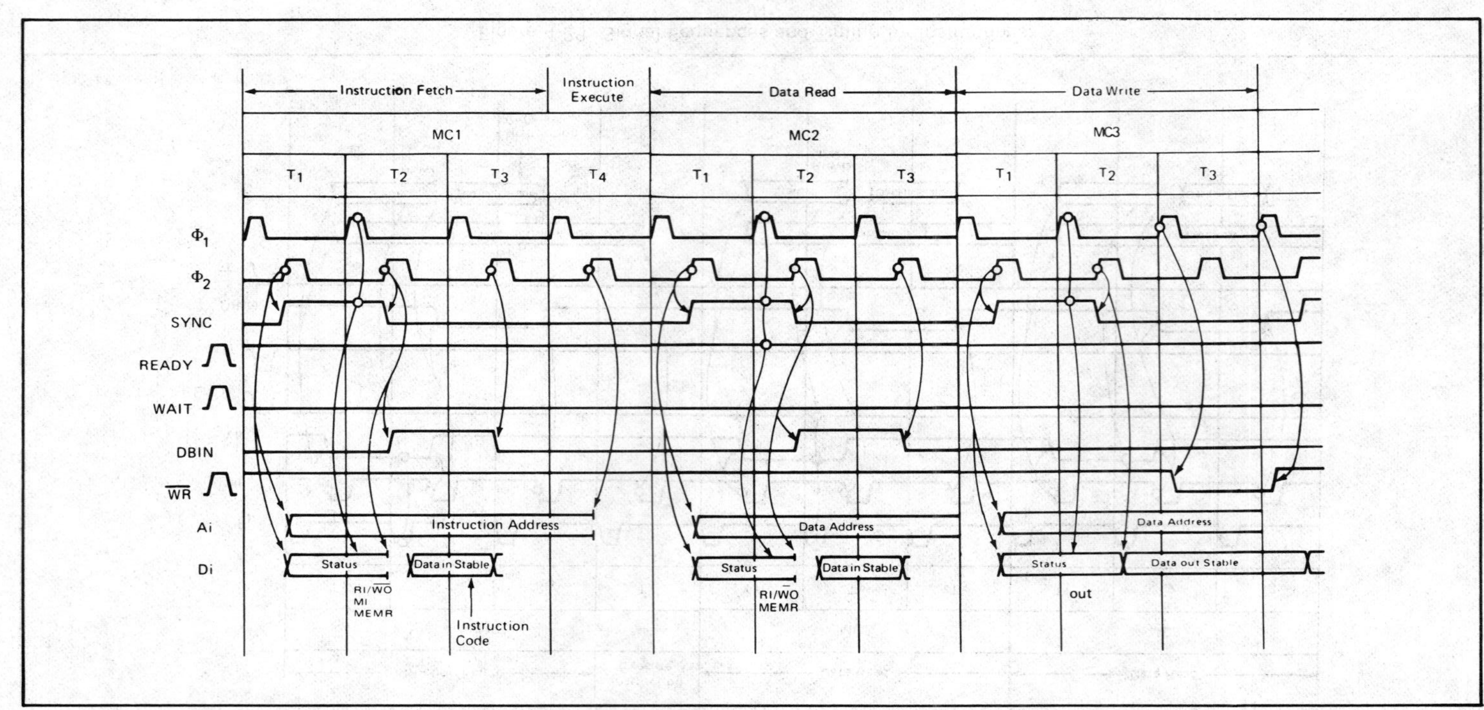


Figure 4-29. Signal Sequences and Timing for Instructions: OUT

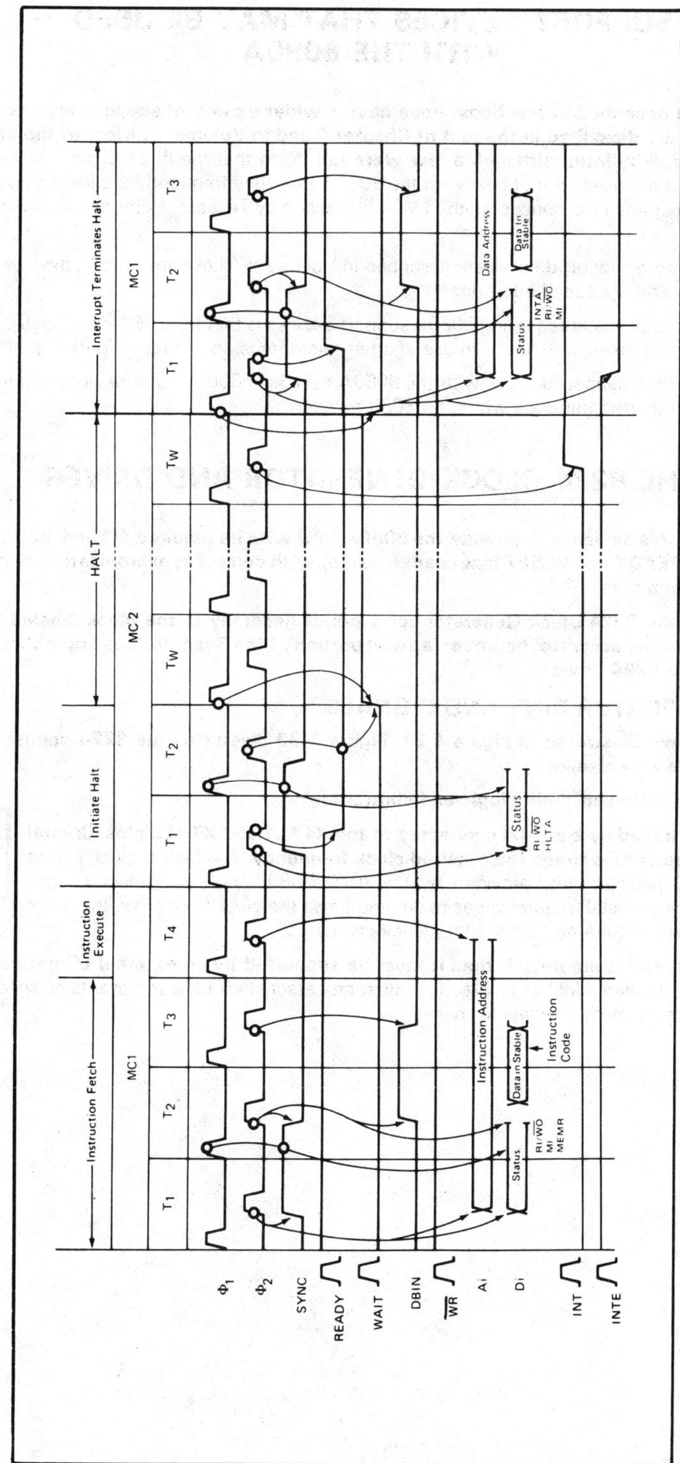


Figure 4-30. Signal Sequences and Timing for Instructions: HLT

# SUPPORT DEVICES THAT MAY BE USED WITH THE 8080A

**Of the microprocessors described in this book, none have a wider variety of support devices than the 8080A. These support devices are described in the rest of Chapter 4 and in Volume 3. Most of the devices described were originally developed by Intel, although a few were not.** Note that the 8224 Clock Generator and the 8228 System Controller devices are used so routinely with the 8080A that they frequently are looked upon as a three-chip CPU. An exception to this three-chip concept is the TMS 5501 made by Texas Instruments; it cannot be used with an 8228 System Controller.

A number of general-purpose support devices are described in Volume 3. These are support devices that may be used with any microprocessor and are specific to none.

One generalization that can be made regarding 8080A support devices is that the 8080A is so well endowed with support logic that it will rarely make much sense to use another microprocessor's support part in preference.

It is very difficult to use 6800 support devices with the 8080A because 6800 support devices require a synchronizing strobe signal which is difficult to generate within an 8080A system.

# THE 8224 CLOCK GENERATOR AND DRIVER

**The primary purpose of this device is to provide the 8080A CPU with its required Φ1 and Φ2 clock signals. Coincidentally, the 8080A READY and RESET inputs are created, with correct synchronization.** Recall that these two signals must be synchronized with Φ2.

**Logic implemented on the 8224 Clock Generator corresponds generally to the block labeled "Clock Logic" in Figure 4-1. To be completely accurate, however, a small portion of the Bus Interface Logic should also be illustrated as provided by the 8224 device.**

## 8224 CLOCK GENERATOR PINS AND SIGNALS

**8224 pins and signals are illustrated in Figure 4-31. Figure 4-33 illustrates the 8224 connected to an 8080A CPU and an 8228 System Controller.**

**Signals may be divided between timing logic and control logic.**

**8224 CLOCK SIGNALS**

**Clock frequency is controlled by a crystal connected to the XTAL1 and XTAL2 pins. Crystal frequency must be exactly nine times the required clock frequency.** The fastest clock period supported today is 250 nanoseconds, provided by the AMD 9080A. 500 nanosecond clock periods are standard. Since crystal frequency has to be nine times the clock frequency, the usual 500 nanosecond clock will require an 18 MHz frequency crystal.

**If an overtone mode crystal is employed, then it must be supported by an external LC network, connected to the TANK input.** This is standard clock logic practice; microprocessor clock logic represents no special case, therefore we will not discuss overtone mode crystals further.

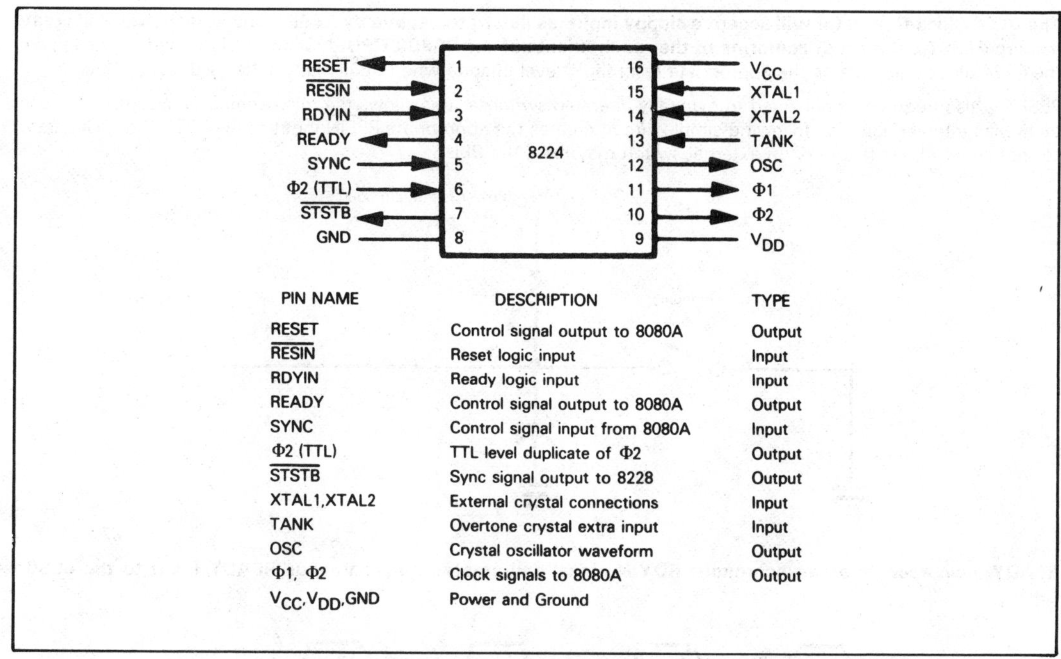


| PIN NAME | DESCRIPTION | TYPE |
|---|---|---|
| RESET | Control signal output to 8080A | Output |
| $\overline{\text{RESIN}}$ | Reset logic input | Input |
| RDYIN | Ready logic input | Input |
| READY | Control signal output to 8080A | Output |
| SYNC | Control signal input from 8080A | Input |
| Φ2 (TTL) | TTL level duplicate of Φ2 | Output |
| $\overline{\text{STSTB}}$ | Sync signal output to 8228 | Output |
| XTAL1,XTAL2 | External crystal connections | Input |
| TANK | Overtone crystal extra input | Input |
| OSC | Crystal oscillator waveform | Output |
| Φ1, Φ2 | Clock signals to 8080A | Output |
| $V_{CC}$,$V_{DD}$,GND | Power and Ground | |

Figure 4-31. 8224 Clock Generator Signals and Pin Assignments

**The principal clock signals output are Φ1 and Φ2, as required by the 8080A CPU.** These two clock signals are derived from a divide-by-nine counter that defines Φ1 and Φ2 as follows:

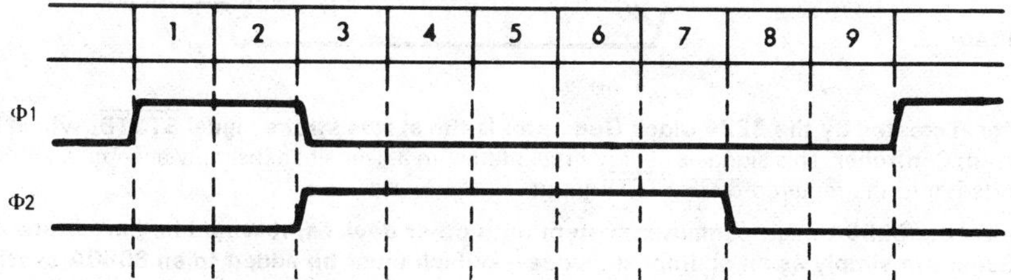


Two additional timing signals are output:

**The crystal oscillator frequency is output as OSC.**

**A TTL level duplicate of Φ2 is also output** for general use within the microcomputer system.

**The RESET input signal required by the 8080A CPU is usually generated by special external logic to provide sharp signal edges and synchronization with the Φ2 clock pulse.** Consider one common use of RESET — to detect power failure. A vague input may have to be converted into a crisp RESET as follows:

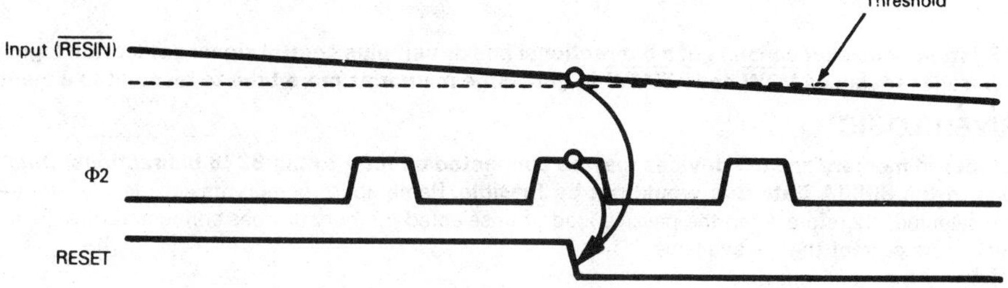

**The 8224 Clock Generator will accept a sloppy input, as illustrated above by $\overline{\text{RESIN}}$, and in response will create a sharp RESET output that conforms to the requirements of the 8080A CPU.** A Schmitt trigger within the logic of the 8224 clock chip creates the appropriate reset logic level change when $\overline{\text{RESIN}}$ falls below a threshold level.

RESET is also frequently connected to manually operated switches; this allows the microcomputer system to be reset by human intervention. The following simple circuit creates the appropriate $\overline{\text{RESIN}}$ input to the 8224 Clock Generator so that either power failure or an external switch may reset the CPU:

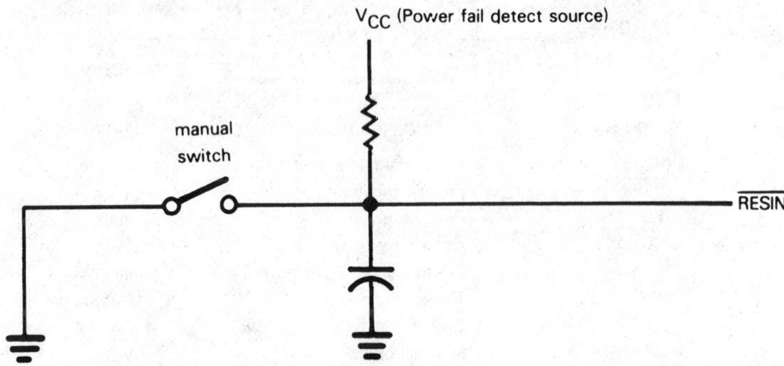


**READY logic accepts an asynchronous RDYIN signal and creates a synchronous READY input to the 8080A CPU:**

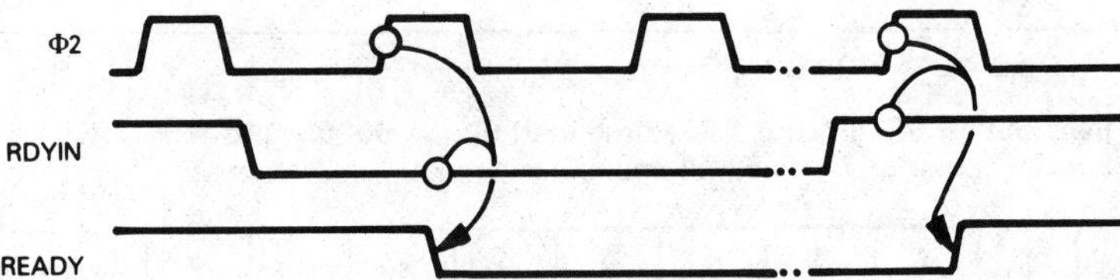


**One further signal created by the 8224 Clock Generator is the status strobe signal $\overline{\text{STSTB}}$, which is required by the 8228 System Controller.** This signal is of very little interest to a user since it simply accepts an 8080A SYNC output and converts it into the required 8228 $\overline{\text{STSTB}}$ input.

**When comparing the 8080A microcomputer system with other devices, it would be inaccurate to dismiss the 8224 Clock Generator simply as an additional device — which must be added to an 8080A system, supplying logic which is commonly found on competing CPU chips.** Do not forget the reset logic capability provided by the 8224 Clock Generator.

It can be argued that the 8080A CPU creates an artificial restriction — that RESET and READY inputs must be synchronized with Φ2; therefore the fact that the 8224 does this for you, simply eliminates a self imposed problem that should never have been there in the first place. This reasoning has merit, but the ability of the 8224 to receive a ragged $\overline{\text{RESIN}}$ input is a valuable feature that should not be overlooked.

# THE 8228 AND 8238 SYSTEM CONTROLLER AND BUS DRIVER

**The 8228 System Controller consists of a bidirectional bus driver, plus control signal generation logic. The 8238 System Controller advances $\overline{\text{I/OW}}$ and $\overline{\text{MEMW}}$ to give large memories more time to respond to a memory write.**

## BUS DRIVER LOGIC

**A large number of memory and I/O devices may be connected directly to the 8228 bidirectional Data Bus; such connections to the 8080A Data Bus would not be feasible.** Remember, memory devices leak current even when they are not selected; therefore, even the passive load of unselected memory devices connected directly to an 8080A CPU will leak more current than is available.

**When comparing the 8080A microcomputer system with an alternate microcomputer system, you should look carefully at the fan out provided by the alternate CPU.**

If the alternate CPU busses need to be buffered, then the 8228 System Controller becomes the equivalent 8080A system device; as such it does not represent an economic liability.

If the alternate CPU busses do not need to be buffered, then the 8228 System Controller represents an additional device, peculiar to the 8080A system.

## CONTROL SIGNAL LOGIC

**The 8228 combines the three 8080A control signals: $\overline{\text{WR}}$, DBIN and HLDA, with the statuses output on the Data Bus during $T_2$ in order to generate bus control signals as follows:**

MEMR status on D7 true, with DBIN true generates $\overline{\text{MEMR}}$ true
OUT status on D4 false, with $\overline{\text{WR}}$ true generates $\overline{\text{MEMW}}$ true
INP status on D6 true, with DBIN true generates $\overline{\text{I/OR}}$ true
OUT status on D4 true, with $\overline{\text{WR}}$ true generates $\overline{\text{I/OW}}$ true
INTA status on D0 true generates $\overline{\text{INTA}}$ true

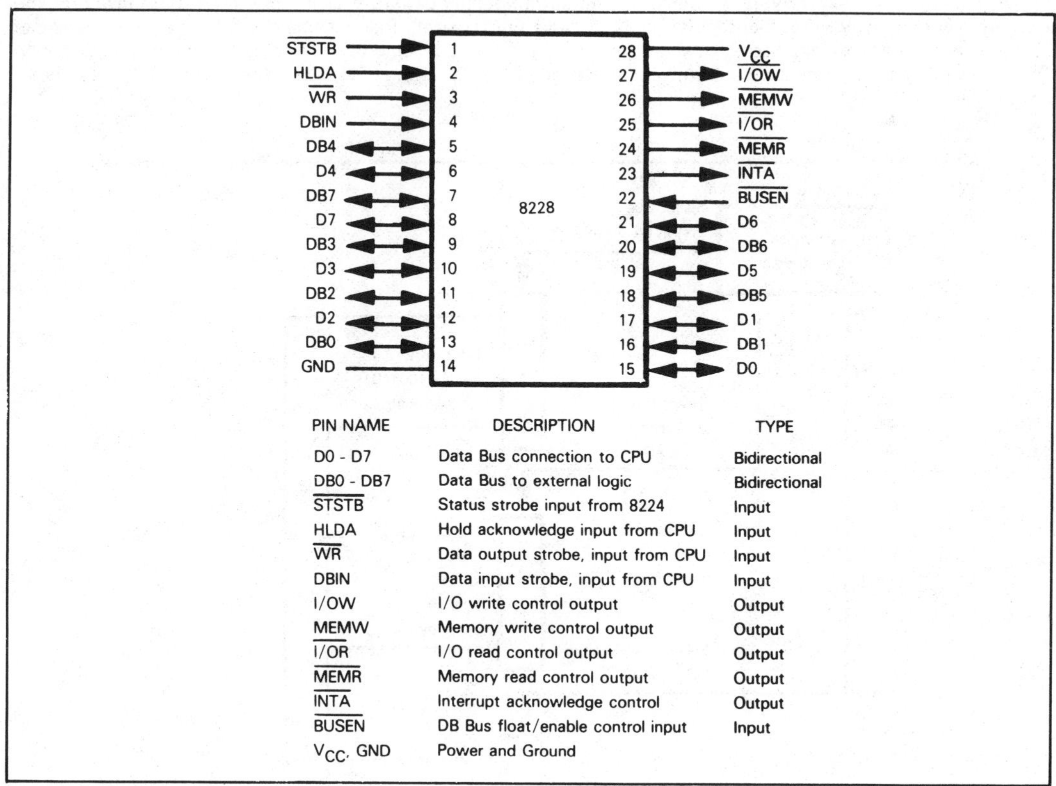


| PIN NAME | DESCRIPTION | TYPE |
|---|---|---|
| D0 - D7 | Data Bus connection to CPU | Bidirectional |
| DB0 - DB7 | Data Bus to external logic | Bidirectional |
| $\overline{\text{STSTB}}$ | Status strobe input from 8224 | Input |
| HLDA | Hold acknowledge input from CPU | Input |
| $\overline{\text{WR}}$ | Data output strobe, input from CPU | Input |
| DBIN | Data input strobe, input from CPU | Input |
| I/OW | I/O write control output | Output |
| MEMW | Memory write control output | Output |
| $\overline{\text{I/OR}}$ | I/O read control output | Output |
| $\overline{\text{MEMR}}$ | Memory read control output | Output |
| $\overline{\text{INTA}}$ | Interrupt acknowledge control | Output |
| $\overline{\text{BUSEN}}$ | DB Bus float/enable control input | Input |
| $V_{CC}$, GND | Power and Ground | |

Figure 4-32. 8228 System Controller Signals and Pin Assignments

## 8228 SYSTEM CONTROLLER PINS AND SIGNALS

**8228 pins and signals are illustrated in Figure 4-32.**

**D0 through D7** represent the bidirectional Data Bus connection between the 8228 System Controller and the 8080A CPU; it is referred to as the "Processor Data Bus".

**DB0 through DB7** represent the high fan out, bidirectional Data Bus accessed by external logic; it is referred to as the "System Data Bus".

**$\overline{WR}$, DBIN and HLDA** represent the control signals of the same name that are output by the 8080A CPU

All control bus signals use active low logic and may be defined as follows:

- $\overline{MEMR}$ — a read from memory strobe
- $\overline{MEMW}$ — a write to memory strobe
- $\overline{I/OR}$ — a read from external I/O strobe
- $\overline{I/OW}$ — a write to external I/O strobe
- $\overline{INTA}$ — interrupt acknowledge

Control signal timing is given in Figure 4-34.

**The interrupt acknowledge signal $\overline{INTA}$ has two special features which need to be explained. This signal may be tied to a +12 Volt power supply through a 1K Ohm resistor,** in which case 8228 logic assumes that there is only one possible interrupting source within the microcomputer system. **Now the 8228 will automatically insert the object code for an RST 7 instruction in response to the interrupt acknowledge.** This means that external logic does not need to supply the first post-interrupt instruction's object code. Of course, this means that all interrupt service routines effectively begin with the execution of an RST 7 instruction.

**If external logic responds to the $\overline{INTA}$ low pulse by supplying the first byte of a CALL instruction's object code (11001101), then the 8228 System Controller will automatically generate two more $\overline{INTA}$ low pulses for the next two machine cycles.** See Figure 4-34 for $\overline{INTA}$ pulse timing within the machine cycle. Now external logic can use the $\overline{INTA}$ pulse as a memory deselect and an interrupt acknowledge logic select. Here is a very general illustration of external logic that responds to an interrupt acknowledge by supplying the CPU with a three-byte CALL instruction's object code:

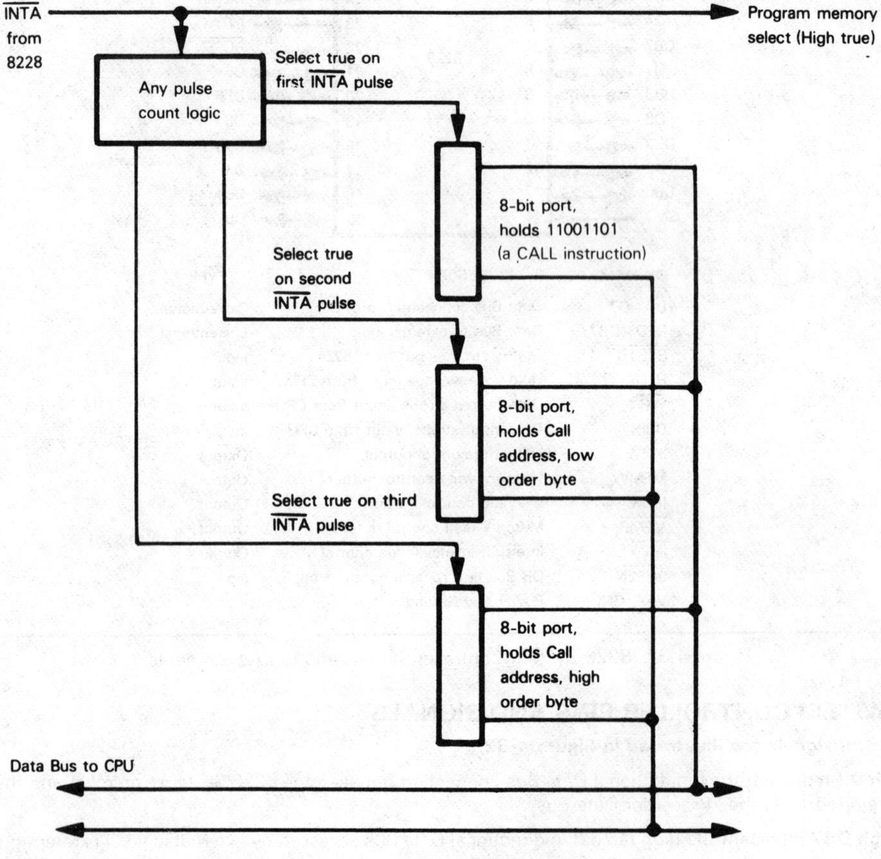

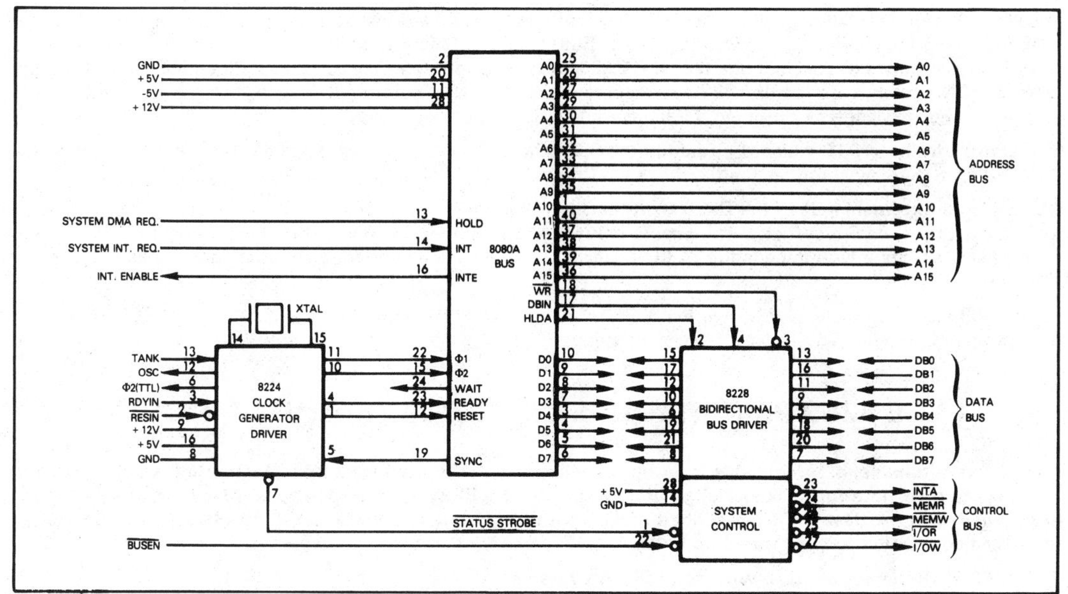


Figure 4-33. A Standard, Three Device 8080A Microcomputer System

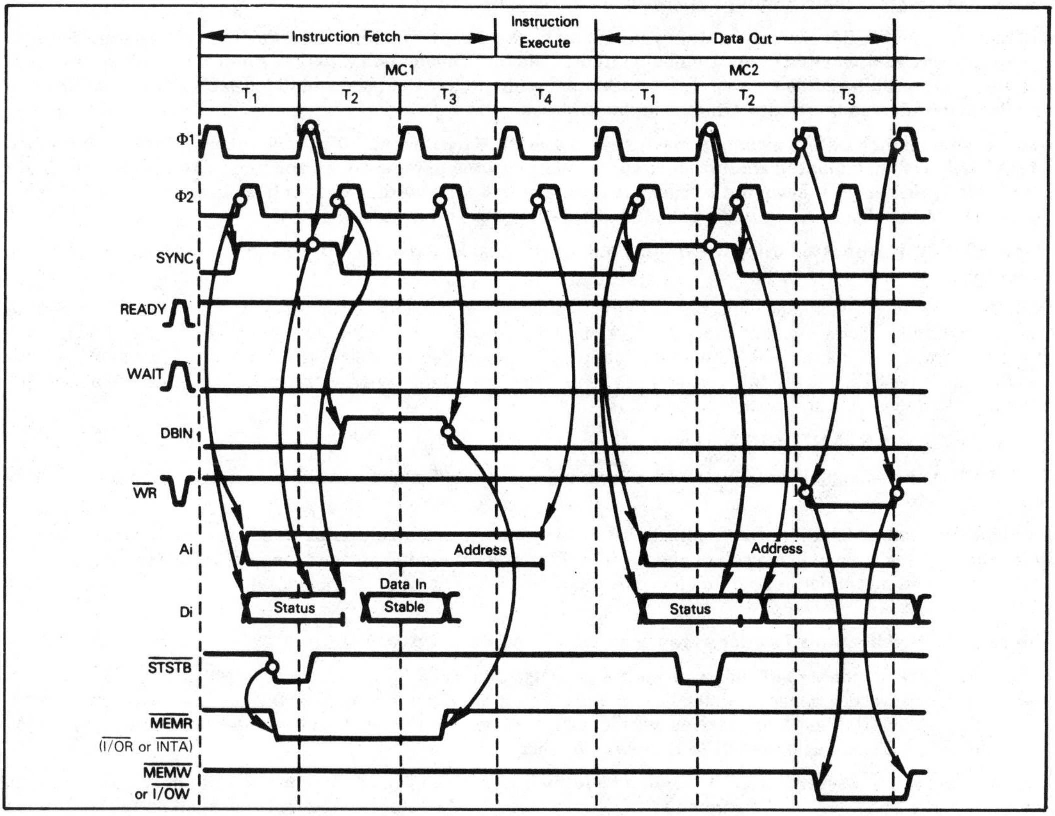

Figure 4-34. Timing for Control Signals Output by the 8228 System Controller

Recall that the NEC 8080A generates three INTA low output pulses in response to a Call instruction object code being returned during the interrupt acknowledge process. But the NEC 8228 System Controller does not assume that these three low INTA pulses will occur. Thus **the NEC 8228 System Controller may be used with an NEC 8080A or any other 8080A.** In every case the NEC 8228 will generate three low INTA output pulses when external logic responds to an interrupt acknowledge by providing a Call instruction object code.

**The status strobe STSTB** which is output by the 8224 Clock Generator is a variation of the SYNC output from the 8080A CPU. STSTB synchronizes the 8228 System Controller and is of no other concern to an 8080A user.

**BUSEN is an external input to the 8228 System Controller.** This is a very useful signal because it allows external logic to float the Data Bus. **When this signal is input low, the bidirectional bus driver logic of the 8228 System Controller presents a high impedance to the external Data Bus, thus allowing external logic to gain access to this bus.**

Figure 4-33 illustrates the way in which the 8080A CPU normally combines with the 8224 Clock Generator and the 8228 System Controller. These three devices are frequently looked upon as a single entity.

# THE 8259 PRIORITY INTERRUPT CONTROL UNIT (PICU)

**This is a very flexible, programmable interrupt handling device; it provides a CALL instruction's object code in response to three interrupt acknowledge (INTA) signals; the 8228 System Controller responds to an interrupt acknowledge in this fashion, as described earlier in this chapter. Therefore the 8259 PICU should be looked upon as a companion to the three-chip (8080A, 8224, 8228) microprocessor system.**

**The 8259 PICU cannot be used with non-8080A systems.**

**A single 8259 PICU with an 8080A microcomputer system will handle up to eight external interrupts, providing a variety of programmable interrupt priority arbitration schemes.**

**Alternatively, an 8080A microcomputer system may have a single 8259 PICU designated as a master, controlling up to eight additional 8259 PICUs designated as slaves. This allows a maximum of 64 levels of interrupt priority. Priority arbitration schemes may be set independently for the master and for each slave, resulting in a bewildering profusion of priority arbitration possibilities.**

**Use extreme caution before including master and slave PICUs within an 8080A microcomputer system. When an application is implemented around a microprocessor with the general speed and performance characteristics of an 8080A, then it is usually more efficient to handle numerous external request lines using multiple CPU configurations and/or programmed polling techniques, rather than interrupts.**

**The 8259 PICU is fabricated using NMOS technology; it is packaged in a 28-pin plastic DIP. All outputs are TTL compatible.**

With reference to the standard logic functions' illustration used throughout this book, the box marked "Interrupt Priority Arbitration" represents the functions implemented by the 8259 PICU. But it is hard to equate the large number of options provided by the 8259 PICU with the interrupt logic provided by other microcomputer systems. An application that needs the 8259 PICU would certainly not be satisfied by Interrupt Priority control logic provided by almost any other device described in this book.

## 8259 PICU PINS AND SIGNALS

**8259 PICU pins and signals are illustrated in Figure 4-35; we will summarize these signals, then discuss how the PICU is used.**

**From the programmer's point of view, the 8259 PICU will be accessed either as two I/O ports, or as two memory locations. CS is a typical chip select and A0 identifies one of two I/O ports or memory locations.** The way you, as a programmer, must interpret the function of each 8259 PICU I/O port or memory location depends on an intricate logical sequence.

**The two 8259 addressable locations are accessed via the Data Bus (D0 - D7).**

**IOR and IOW are standard read and write control signals.** If the 8259 PICU is being accessed as two I/O ports, then these two signals will be connected to the I/OR and I/OW controls output by the 8228 System Controller; on the other hand, if the 8259 PICU is being accessed as two memory locations, then IOR and IOW must be connected to the MEMR and MEMW controls output by the 8228 System Controller.

**External devices requesting interrupt service have their request signals connected to IR0 - IR7.** A high level on any one of these signals will be interpreted as an interrupt request. **An interrupt request is passed on to the CPU via the INT signal.** This is illustrated in Figure 4-36.

**In a configuration that includes master and slave 8259 PICUs** external logic will connect to the interrupt request signals (IR0 - IR7) of the slave PICUs only. The INT outputs of the slave PICUs will be connected to the interrupt requests (IR0 - IR7) of the master PICU. This is illustrated in Figure 4-37.

When more than one 8259 PICU is present in a system, **$\overline{\text{SP}}$ identifies the master and slave units.** $\overline{\text{SP}}$ high defines the master, while $\overline{\text{SP}}$ low forces an 8259 PICU to operate as a slave. **$\overline{\text{SP}}$ also determines the sense of the three cascade lines (C0, C1, C2);** these are output lines from the master and input lines to a slave.

**The 8080A CPU provides the standard interrupt acknowledge via $\overline{\text{INTA}}$.** This interrupt acknowledge will be received by all 8259 PICUs in the system, master or slave.

**In a system that includes a master 8259 PICU only, the three bytes of a CALL instruction's object code are output via the Data Bus in response to the three $\overline{\text{INTA}}$ control signals arriving from the 8228 System Controller.** The second and third bytes of the CALL instruction's object code provide an address which is unique to the selected interrupt request.

**In a configuration that includes master and slave 8259 PICUs, the master PICU outputs the first byte of a CALL instruction's object code; the master also outputs a value between 000 and 111 via the three cascade lines (C0 - C2). This three-bit binary value identifies the interrupt request level being acknowledged — and therefore the slave PICU being selected. The selected slave PICU provides the second and third bytes of the CALL instruction's object code in response to the second and third $\overline{\text{INTA}}$ pulses output by the 8228 System Controller. Thus the slave PICU identifies the interrupt request level it is acknowledging.**

**The interrupt acknowledge logic of the 8259 PICU is referred to as "Vectoring". Let us examine 8259 vectoring in more detail.**

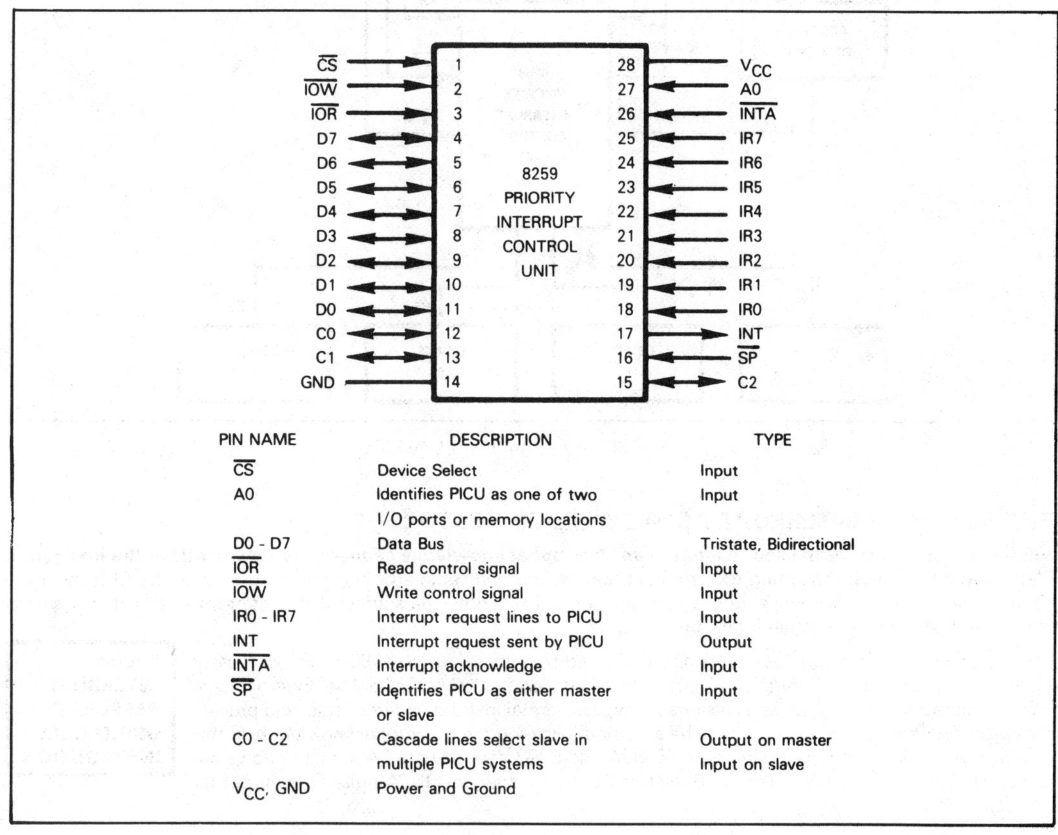


| PIN NAME | DESCRIPTION | TYPE |
|---|---|---|
| $\overline{\text{CS}}$ | Device Select | Input |
| A0 | Identifies PICU as one of two I/O ports or memory locations | Input |
| D0 - D7 | Data Bus | Tristate, Bidirectional |
| $\overline{\text{IOR}}$ | Read control signal | Input |
| $\overline{\text{IOW}}$ | Write control signal | Input |
| IR0 - IR7 | Interrupt request lines to PICU | Input |
| INT | Interrupt request sent by PICU | Output |
| $\overline{\text{INTA}}$ | Interrupt acknowledge | Input |
| $\overline{\text{SP}}$ | Identifies PICU as either master or slave | Input |
| C0 - C2 | Cascade lines select slave in multiple PICU systems | Output on master<br>Input on slave |
| $V_{CC}$, GND | Power and Ground | |

Figure 4-35. 8259 Priority Interrupt Control Unit Signals And Pin Assignments

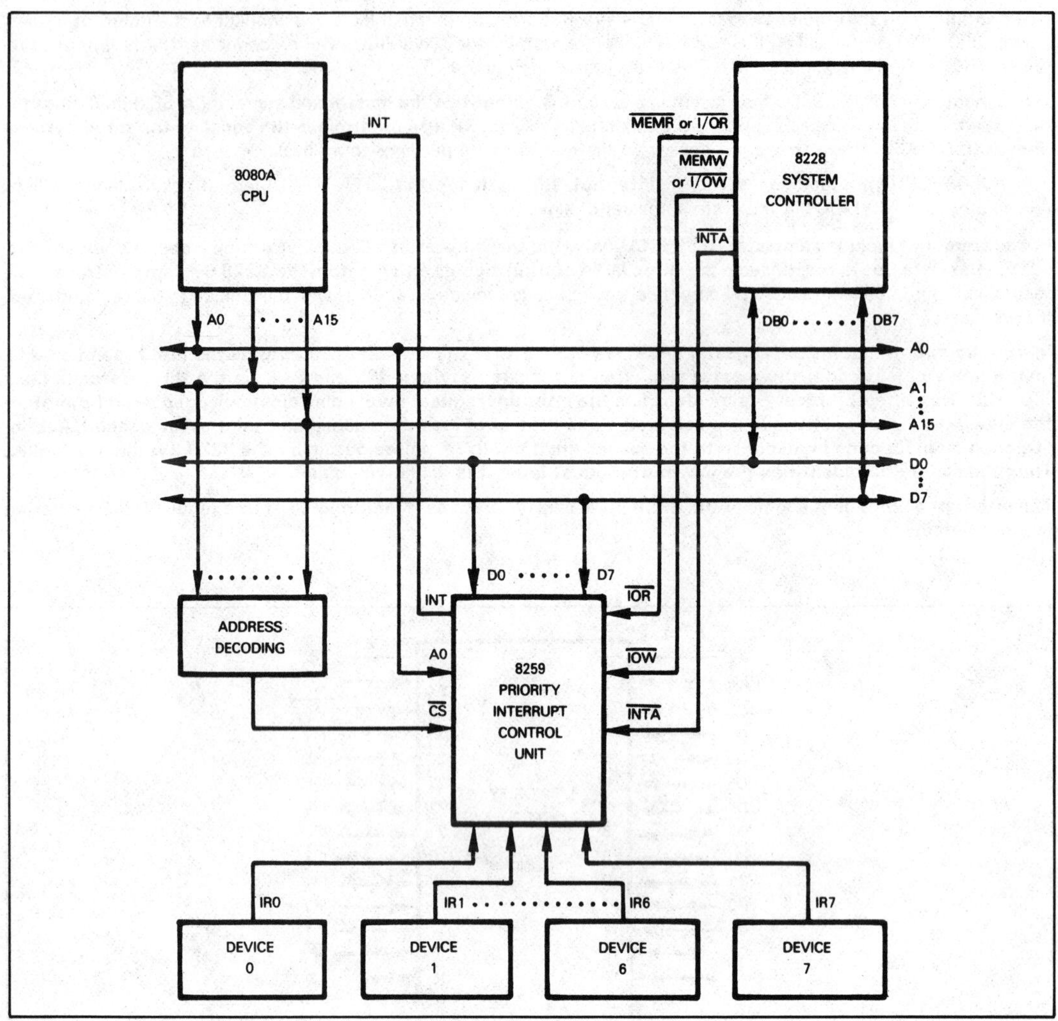


Figure 4-36. A System With One PICU

## THE 8259 PICU INTERRUPT ACKNOWLEDGE VECTOR

**Vectoring is a general term used to identify an interrupt acknowledge sequence which results in the immediate identification of the interrupting external source.** With a non-vectored interrupt acknowledge, the CPU must execute some instruction sequence whose sole purpose is to identify the source of the interrupt — and that assumes more than one possible external interrupting source.

**8080A INTERRUPT RESPONSE USING CALL INSTRUCTION**

Recall that when an interrupt request is acknowledged by a three-device 8080A microprocessor system, the 8228 System Controller outputs a low pulse on the $\overline{INTA}$ control line. External logic must interpret the low $\overline{INTA}$ pulse as a signal to bypass normal instruction fetch logic, and provide the object code for the first instruction to be executed following the interrupt acknowledge. (If this is new to you, refer to our discussion of the 8080A and 8228 devices.) If a CALL instruction's object code ($CD_{16}$) is returned to the 8228 System Controller, then low $\overline{INTA}$ pulses are output for the next two machine cycles — thus making it easy for external logic to fetch all three bytes of a CALL instruction's object code. **The 8259 PICU uses** this **8228 logic to supply a three-byte CALL instruction's object code as the first instruction executed following an interrupt acknowledge. But a CALL instruction's object code is interpreted thus:**

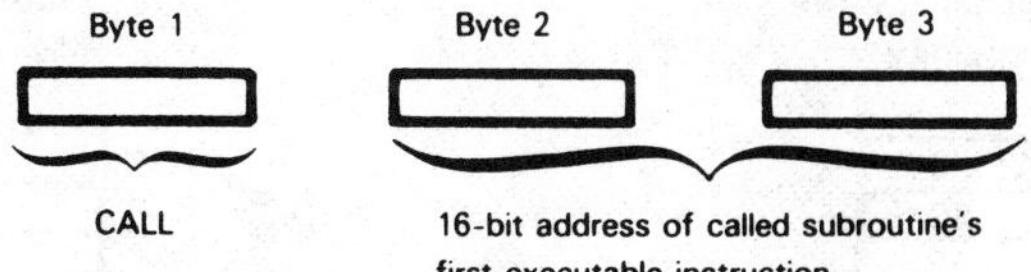


**There are two ways in which the 8259 PICU can compute the address portion of the CALL instruction object code (bytes 2 and 3). These are the two options:**

| Option 1 | Option 2 |
|---|---|
| XXXXXXXXXXXYYY00 | XXXXXXXXXXYYY000 |

X represents binary digits which are defined, under program control, to be a constant portion of the Call address.

Y represents binary digits which identify the interrupt priority level (000 through 111).

Since the CALL is the first instruction executed following an interrupt acknowledge, it causes program logic to branch to a memory location which is uniquely set aside for a single external interrupting source. **Suppose you have selected CALL instruction Option 1, as illustrated above.** You would then set aside an area of memory for a jump table, as follows:

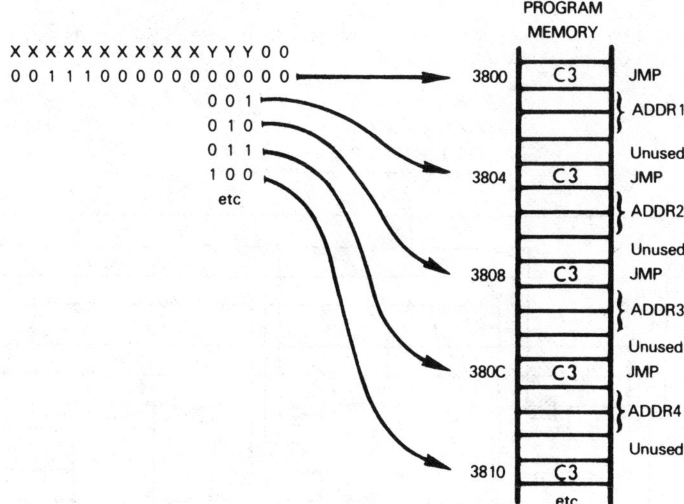


Memory addresses have been selected arbitrarily in the illustration above.

Program logic does not have to determine the source of an interrupt. You simply origin separate interrupt service routines at starting addresses specified by the Jump instructions in the jump table. This may be illustrated as follows:

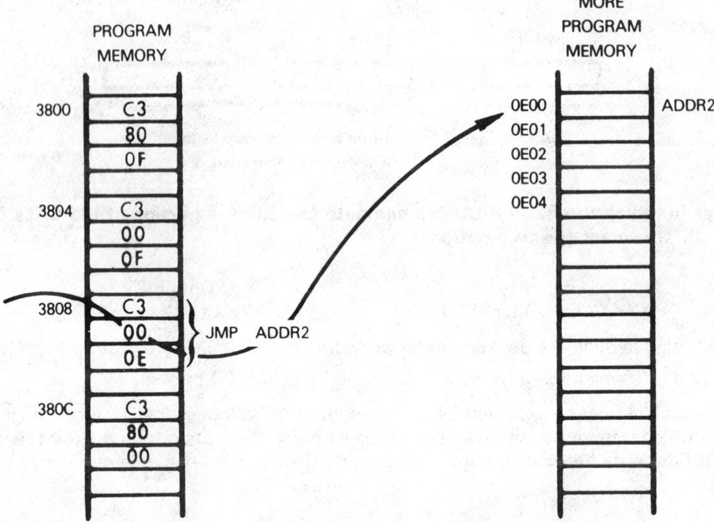


The illustration above arbitrarily assumes that the interrupt request arriving at IR2 has its service routine origined at $0E00_{16}$. In this example, the address vector provided by the 8259 is $3808_{16}$:

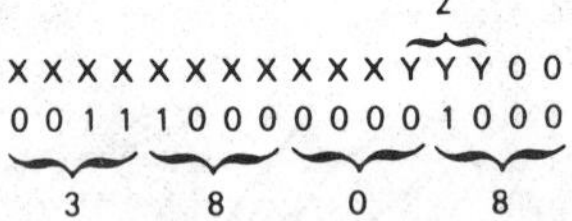


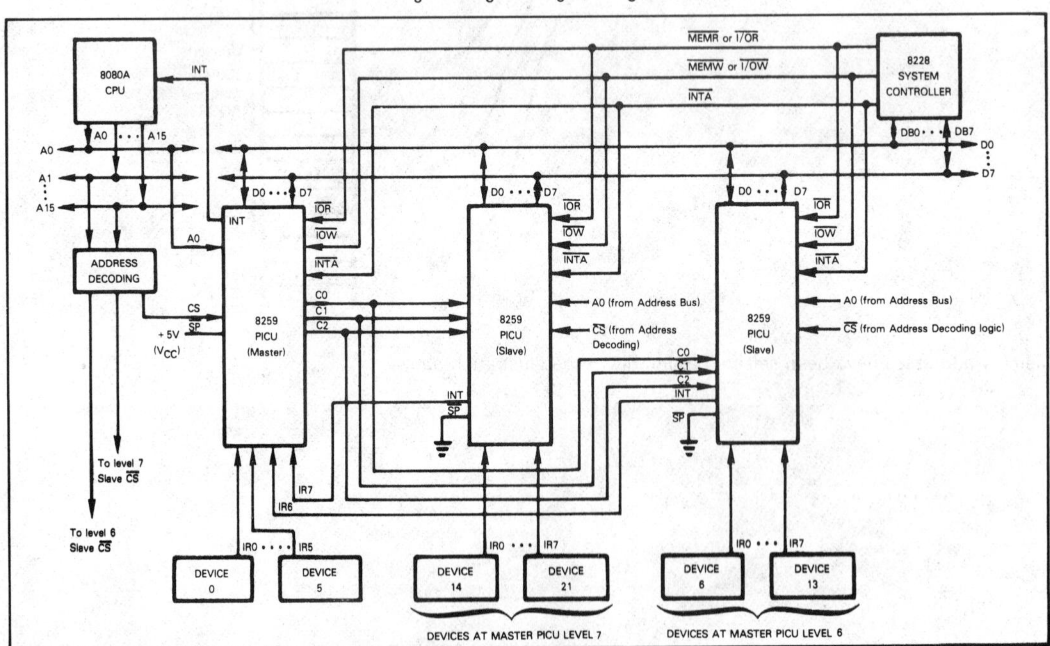


Figure 4-37. A System With Three PICUs — One Master And Two Slaves

At memory location $3808_{16}$, the object code for the instruction:

```
JMP     ADDR2
```

takes us directly to the required interrupt service routine.

## 8259 PICU PRIORITY ARBITRATION OPTIONS

**Priority arbitration logic is used to determine which interrupt request will be acknowledged when two or more interrupt requests exist simultaneously. The 8259 PICU allows interrupt priorities to be specified at two levels — which need to be clearly separated and identified.**

As discussed in Volume 1 — Basic Concepts, interrupt priority arbitration usually applies to simultaneous interrupt requests; at the instant an interrupt is acknowledged, **if more than one external requesting source is requesting an interrupt, priority arbitration logic decides which single interrupt request will be acknowledged.** Once an interrupt has been acknowledged, priority arbitration has nothing to do with whether the interrupt service routine can itself be interrupted, or by whom.

**The 8259 PICU extends interrupt priorities to the service routines themselves.** Once an interrupt has been acknowledged, its service routine can only be interrupted by a higher priority interrupt.

If you are unsure of the difference between interrupt priority arbitration at the point when interrupts are acknowledged, as against priority arbitration for the entire duration of an interrupt service routine, then refer to Volume 1 — Basic Concepts, where this subject is covered thoroughly.

Let us now look at the various priority arbitration options provided by the 8259 PICU.

**The Fully Nested Mode is the default case.** Interrupt priorities are set sequentially from 0 (highest) to 7 (lowest).

As we will describe shortly, **the 8259 PICU must be initialized by an appropriate instruction sequence** before it can be used in any way. **Upon completing programmed initialization, Fully Nested Mode is the priority arbitration option in force.** It takes additional instructions to specify any other priority arbitration option.

**8259 PICU INTERRUPT SERVICE ROUTINE PRIORITIES**

In Fully Nested Mode, interrupt priorities will never change. An interrupt request arriving at an IR line will never be acknowledged if an interrupt request exists at a higher priority line, or if an interrupt service routine is being executed in response to a higher priority interrupt request. Conversely, once an interrupt has been acknowledged, the interrupt service routine which is subsequently executed may be interrupted only by a higher priority interrupt. It makes no difference whether interrupts have, or have not been disabled, the 8259 PICU will ignore all interrupt requests at priority levels below that of an interrupt service routine currently being executed. For example, suppose interrupts are being requested simultaneously at levels 2 and 5. The level 2 interrupt will be acknowledged and its interrupt service routine will be executed. While the level 2 interrupt is being executed, the level 5 interrupt request will be denied by the 8259 PICU, whether or not interrupts have been disabled at the CPU. However, if an interrupt request arrives at priority level 1, the PICU will acknowledge this interrupt request, and will allow the level 2 interrupt service routine to be interrupted. This may be illustrated as follows:

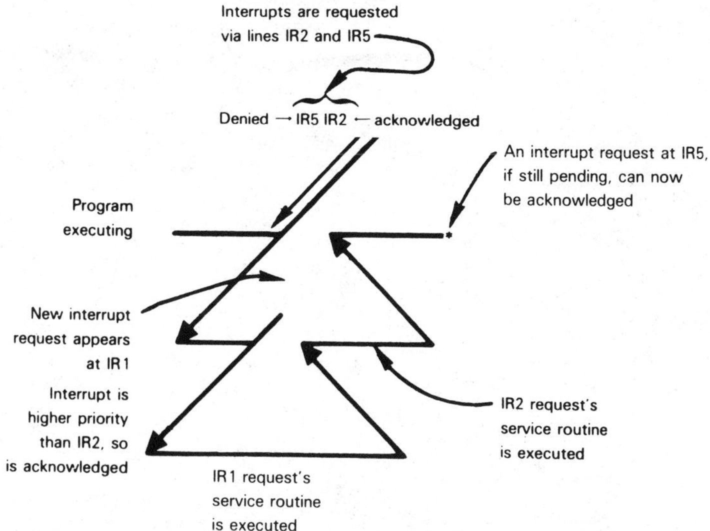

Interrupts are requested
via lines IR2 and IR5
Denied → IR5 IR2 ← acknowledged
An interrupt request at IR5,
if still pending, can now
be acknowledged
Program
executing
New interrupt
request appears
at IR1
Interrupt is
higher priority
than IR2, so
is acknowledged
IR2 request's
service routine
is executed
IR1 request's
service routine
is executed

It is very important to understand that the 8259 PICU extends interrupt priority logic beyond the interrupt acknowledge, to the interrupt service routine itself. Standard priority arbitration logic does not extend to the interrupt service routine. Thus, in the standard case if interrupts were being requested at priorities 2 and 5, then the priority level 2 request would be acknowledged, but the priority level 2 interrupt service routine could be interrupted by the level 5 interrupt request, unless all interrupts were disabled at the CPU — in which case an interrupt request at level 1 would also be denied.

If you do not want to extend interrupt priorities to the interrupt service routines, you can output a Special Mask Mode command (which we will describe shortly) to selectively enable interrupt requests of lower priority than the currently executing interrupt service routine.

**8259 PICU ROTATING INTERRUPT PRIORITIES**

**Rotating Priority, Mode A is the next option.** This differs from the Fully Nested Priority Mode, which we just described, in that after being serviced, a request is immediately relegated to lowest priority. This may be illustrated as follows:

| | Priorities assigned to IR lines | | | | | | | |
|---|---|---|---|---|---|---|---|---|
| | Lowest | | | | | | Highest | |
| | 7 | 6 | 5 | 4 | 3 | 2 | 1 | 0 |
| Before first acknowledge | IR7 | IR6 | IR5* | IR4 | IR3 | IR2* | IR1 | IR0 |
| After first acknowledge | IR2 | IR1 | IR0 | IR7 | IR6 | IR5* | IR4 | IR3 |
| After second acknowledge | IR5 | IR4 | IR3 | IR2 | IR1 | IR0 | IR7 | IR6 |

* identifies active interrupt requests.

In a microcomputer system that makes heavy use of interrupts, Rotating Run in Priority Mode A may be a necessary replacement for the default Fully Nested Priority Mode. In the default case, the lowest priority levels may get little or no service if there is heavy interrupt traffic. In an application that does not have a well defined hierarchy of interrupt priorities, a rotation of priorities, as illustrated above, is superior — because it has the effect of giving every priority level equal service.

Rotating Priority Mode A is implemented as a sequence of single programmed events. The microprocessor outputs an appropriate Control code to the 8259 PICU upon completing every interrupt service routine. Thus Rotating Priority Mode A is not a permanently specified PICU condition; each rotation represents a single response to a single Control code — unconnected to previous or future priority selections. For the moment, however, it is not necessary that you understand the programming techniques employed when selecting 8259 interrupt priority modes; that is a subject we will cover after completing the description of all available priority options.

**Rotating Priority Mode B gives you some flexibility in determining future priorities.** Now under program control you can fix the next division between top and bottom priorities at any time. This may be illustrated as follows:

| | Priority assigned to IR lines | | | | | | | |
|---|---|---|---|---|---|---|---|---|
| | | Lowest | | | | Highest | | |
| | 7 | 6 | 5 | 4 | 3 | 2 | 1 | 0 |
| Before first acknowledge | IR7 | IR6 | IR5 | IR4 | IR3 | IR2 | IR1 | IR0 |
| After first acknowledge<br>IR5 is defined as<br>lowest priority | IR5 | IR4 | IR3 | IR2 | IR1 | IR0 | IR7 | IR6 |
| After next acknowledge<br>IR3 is defined as<br>lowest priority | IR3 | IR2 | IR1 | IR0 | IR7 | IR6 | IR5 | IR4 |
| -<br>-<br>-<br>etc. | | | | -<br>-<br>-<br>etc. | | | | |

Rotating Priority Mode B allows program logic to determine subsequent interrupt priorities based upon transient system conditions. Rotating Priority Mode B rotates priorities any number of positions to the right, much as you might rotate the bits of an Accumulator.

Like Rotating Priority Mode A, Rotating Priority Mode B depends on the microprocessor outputting an appropriate Control code to the 8259 PICU. However, in Rotating Priority Mode A, rotation can be done only at the conclusion of an interrupt service routine, whereas in Rotating Priority Mode B, priorities can be changed at any time.

**8259 PICU INTERRUPT MASKING**

**Two mask modes allow individual priorities to be selectively disabled. A Simple Mask Mode allows the microprocessor to output an 8-bit mask, where 1 bits will cause corresponding interrupt request lines to be disabled.** For example, the mask value $CA_{16}$ will disable interrupt lines IR7, IR6, IR3 and IR1:

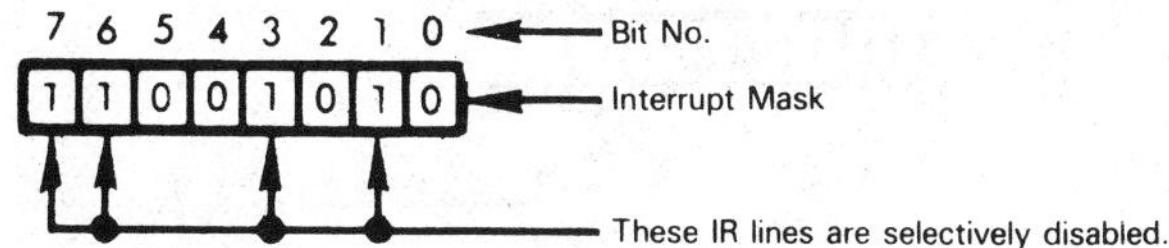


**A Special Mask Mode** is also provided; it **allows you to enable interrupts at a lower priority level than that of the currently executing interrupt service routine.** By writing a 1 to the appropriate bit of the Mask register, an interrupt level can be disabled while its interrupt service routine is executing. Even though the level is masked, all lower level interrupts will remain disabled until the conclusion of the service routine. Once the current level is masked, however, entering Special Mask Mode will enable all unmasked lower priority interrupt levels. Thus a request can interrupt a service routine operating on a higher priority level.

Masks may be superimposed on Rotating Priority Mode A or Mode B without restriction. This allows you to selectively enable and disable individual interrupt request lines, then rotate priorities for the enabled lines. Special Mask Mode also allows you to selectively enable interrupts of lower priority than a currently executing interrupt service routine.

**8259 PICU POLLING**

**Polled Mode bypasses priority arbitration altogether. If you select Polled Mode, then you must poll the 8259 PICU.** You will interpret the polled data as follows:

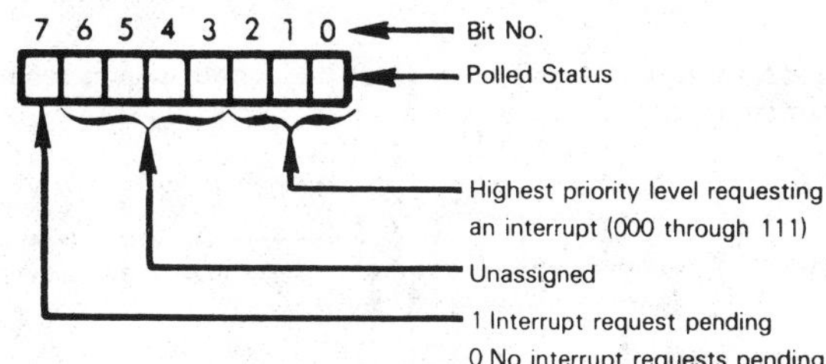


In a configuration that includes master and slave 8259 PICUs, you will first read status from the master PICU. Upon detecting a 1 bit in bit 7, you will poll the slave PICU which is identified by bits 2, 1 and 0 of the master's polled data. The slave poll identifies the highest priority interrupt request. This may be illustrated as follows:

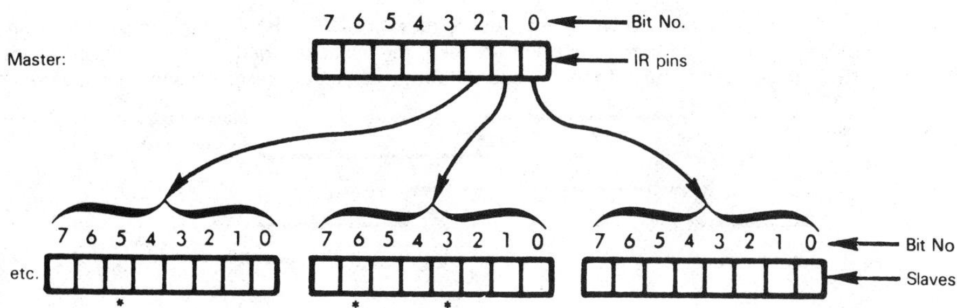

Suppose the * represents interrupt requests. The master poll would return:

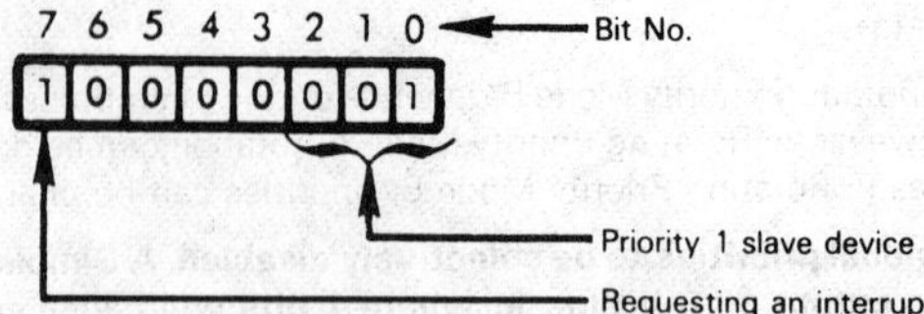


The polling program must now poll slave 1; it will read:

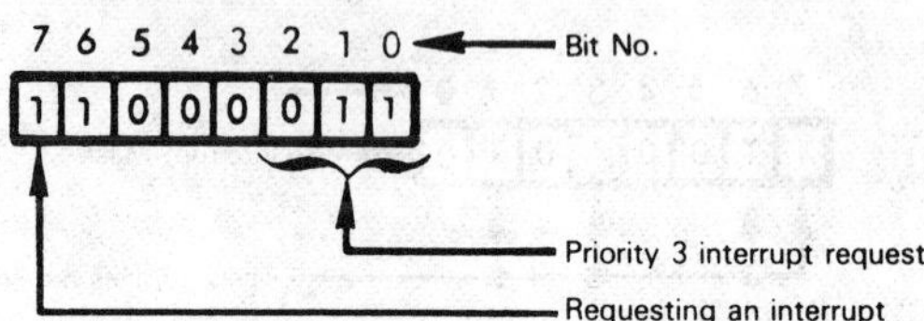


In Polled Mode, the 8259 PICU is not being used as an interrupt processing device at all. In effect, interrupt requests are reduced to status flags, which will be processed by the CPU when it is ready to do so. External logic is no longer able to force the CPU to suspend current program execution; thus the key concept of an interrupt is missing.

**While it may not immediately appear obvious, using the 8259 PICU in Polled Mode is possibly one of the most effective ways of utilizing this device.** A point we have frequently made is that the average microprocessor is simply too slow to efficiently handle random, nested interrupts in a traditional minicomputer fashion. It is faster and more efficient to poll status on a round-robin basis, branching to appropriate subroutines upon detecting a status flag via which external logic has requested service. A detailed discussion of this point may be found in the book 8080 Programming for Logic Design.

## HOW INTERRUPT REQUESTS AND PRIORITY STATUS ARE RECORDED

**Internal to the 8259 PICU there are two registers: an Interrupt Request (IR) register and an Interrupt Status (IS) register.**

**The Interrupt Request and Interrupt Status registers may be looked upon as receiving external interrupt request status in a cascaded fashion** as follows:

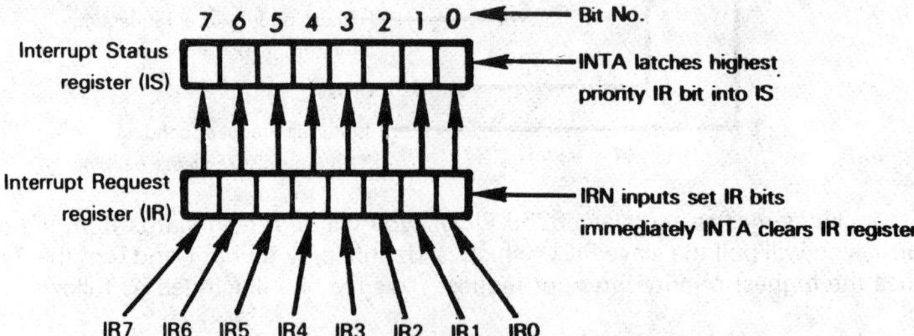


Any active interrupt request appearing on the interrupt request lines IR0 - IR7 will set corresponding bits of the Interrupt Request register. When any interrupt is acknowledged, the acknowledged interrupt's bit in the Interrupt Status register is set; simultaneously, all bits of the Interrupt Request register are reset. This may be illustrated as follows:

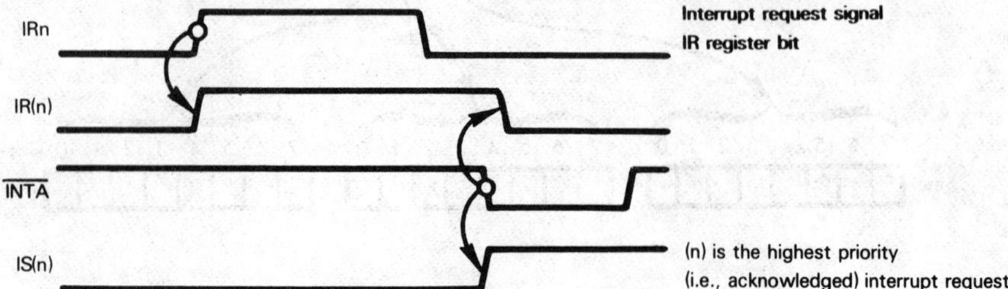

In order to reset any bit of the Interrupt Status register you must issue a specific "End-Of-Interrupt" instruction which we will describe shortly.

You may therefore look upon the Interrupt Request register as identifying active, but unacknowledged interrupt requests. Notice that Interrupt Request status is not preserved across an acknowledge. This means external logic must hold its Interrupt Request true until it has been selected and acknowledged.

You may look upon the Interrupt Status register as identifying the interrupt requests which are currently being serviced. If you do not nest interrupts, then only one bit of the Interrupt Status register will be set at any time. If you do nest interrupts, then more than one bit of the Interrupt Status register may be set — for the interrupt request being serviced currently and for any interrupt requests which were being serviced, but were themselves interrupted. But remember you can misuse the Interrupt Status register. If you do not end interrupt service routines by outputting an "End-Of-Interrupt" command to the 8259 PICU, then bits of the Interrupt Status register will remain set after the appropriate interrupt has been serviced.

If you use a mask to inhibit interrupt levels, then the inhibit logic will prevent bits of the Interrupt Request and Interrupt Status register from being set for the inhibited interrupt levels.

The Interrupt Request (IR) register stores a 1 bit at every requesting level; it may be visualized as a simple reflection of IR input signals:

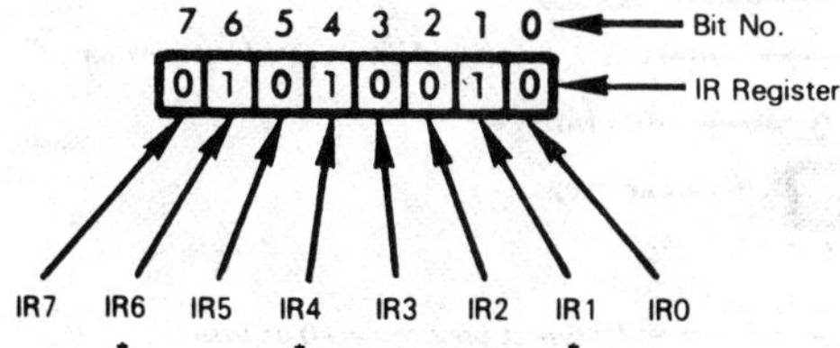


The Interrupt Status (IS) register reflects the status of current interrupt priority arbitration logic. Whenever an interrupt is acknowledged, the IS bit corresponding to the interrupt level is set. This bit is reset by the End-Of-Interrupt (EOI) instruction at the end of the interrupt service routine. We will tell you how to issue an EOI instruction shortly.

Suppose the 8259 PICU is operating in the default mode: fully nested interrupts, no mask bits set. An interrupt request is made at level 4. When this interrupt is acknowledged, bit 4 of the IS register is set:

| 7 | 6 | 5 | 4 | 3 | 2 | 1 | 0 | ← Bit No. |
|---|---|---|---|---|---|---|---|---|
| 0 | 0 | 0 | 1 | 0 | 0 | 0 | 0 | ← IS |

and interrupts at levels 5, 6 and 7 are disabled, since they are of lower priority than level 4. While the level 4 request is being serviced, a request is made at level 1. Since level 1 has higher priority, it will be acknowledged, interrupting the level 4 service routine. IS will look like this:

| 7 | 6 | 5 | 4 | 3 | 2 | 1 | 0 | ← Bit No. |
|---|---|---|---|---|---|---|---|---|
| 0 | 0 | 0 | 1 | 0 | 0 | 1 | 0 | ← IS |

Now interrupt levels 2 through 7 are disabled. At the conclusion of the level 1 service routine, EOI will reset bit 1:

| 7 | 6 | 5 | 4 | 3 | 2 | 1 | 0 | ← Bit No. |
|---|---|---|---|---|---|---|---|---|
| 0 | 0 | 0 | 1 | 0 | 0 | 0 | 0 | ← IS |

thus enabling interrupt levels 2 and 3 — and level 4, whose service routine can now continue. On the next EOI, assuming no further interruptions, bit 4 of IS will be reset, at which time levels 5, 6 and 7 will again be enabled.

In priority modes other than the Fully Nested Mode (Rotating Priorities A and B and Special Mask Mode) the 8259 PICU cannot be depended on to reset the correct IS bit when it receives the usual EOI. Therefore, it is sent a special EOI which specifies which level's service routine is ending — and therefore which IS bit is to be reset.

## PROGRAMMING THE 8259 PICU

**As we have already stated, the 8259 PICU appears to the programmer as two I/O ports, or memory locations. However, there are a number of ways in which data written to, or read from either location may be interpreted. Let us begin by defining these interpretations; then we will explain the sequence in which Control codes should be written, and statuses read, in order to access the many capabilities of the 8259 PICU.**

Control codes output to the lower I/O port or memory address (A0 = 0) may be interpreted in one of three ways, labeled Initialization Control Word 1 (ICW1) and Operation Control Words 2 and 3 (OCW2 and OCW3):

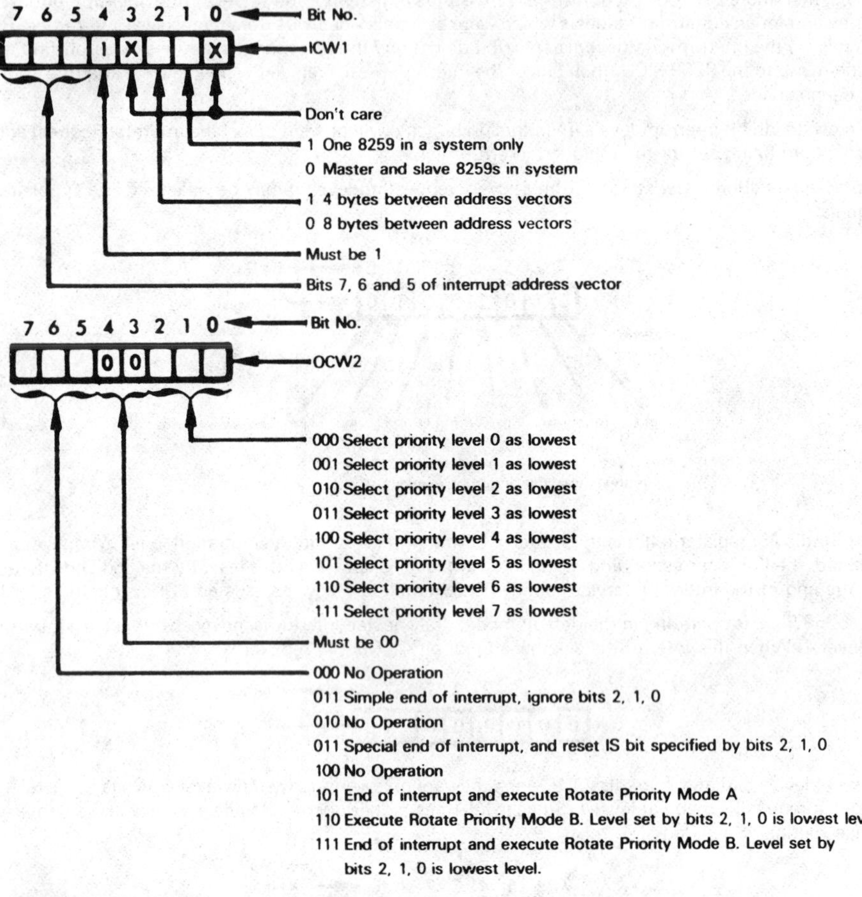


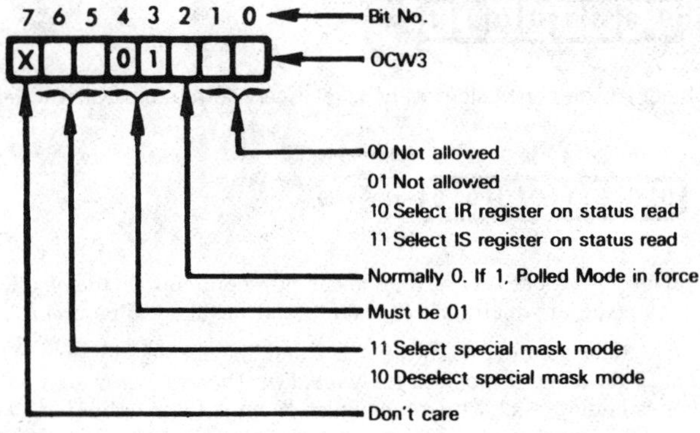

When reading from the lower address (A0 = 0), the condition of the most recently issued OCW3 bits 0 and 1 determine what will be read. If these two bits were 01, the Interrupt Request register (IR) is read; if these two bits are 11, the Interrupt Status register (IS) is read.

**Control codes output to the higher I/O port or memory address (A0 = 1) may also be interpreted in one of three ways.** After an ICW1 control has been output to the lower address (A0 = 0), either one, or two Control codes must be output to the higher address (A0 = 1). If ICW1, bit 1 is 1, a second Control code (ICW2) must be output to the higher address (A0 = 1) of the master 8259 PICU, and to every slave 8259 PICU, that may be present. This is the format of ICW2:

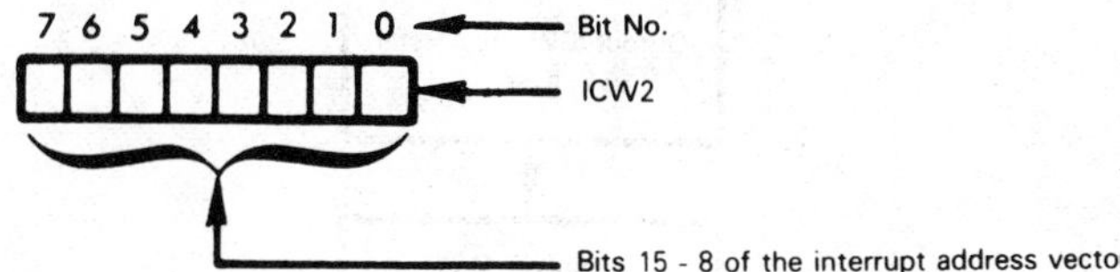


If ICW1, bit 1 is 0, ICW2, as illustrated above, must be output — and it must be followed by a second Control code (ICW3), output to the higher address (A0 = 1) of the master 8259 PICU, and then to each slave 8259 PICU. The master 8259 will interpret ICW3 as follows:

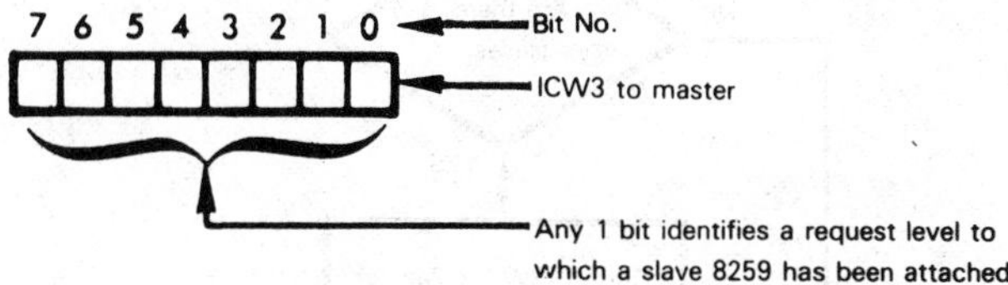


A slave 8259 will interpret ICW3 as follows:

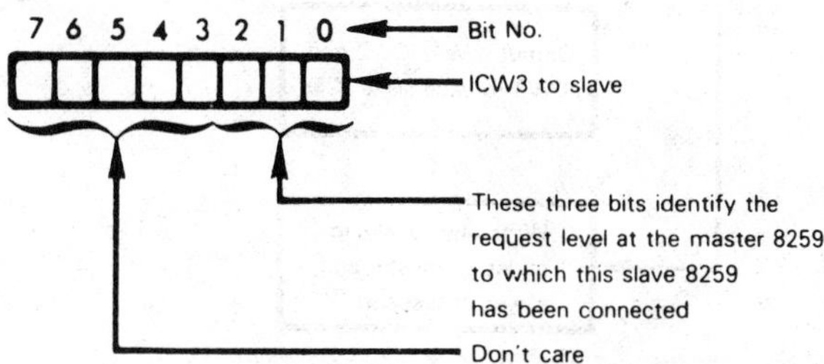


A system with a single 8259, therefore, has ICW1, then ICW2 output to it.

A system with master and slave 8259 devices must have ICW1, ICW2 and ICW3 output to the master, then ICW1, ICW2 and ICW3 output to each slave.

**8259 PICU INTERRUPT MASK**

**After the initiation sequence has been completed, when reading or writing to the higher I/O port address (A0 = 1), the Interrupt Mask register is accessed. Writing a 1 into any bit position will disable corresponding IR line requests. 0 bits enable interrupt requests at corresponding IR lines. When you return to the initiation sequence, the higher I/O port address again accesses ICW2 or ICW3.**

We will now examine the normal sequence in which the 8259 PICU will be programmed. Programming logic may be defined as follows:

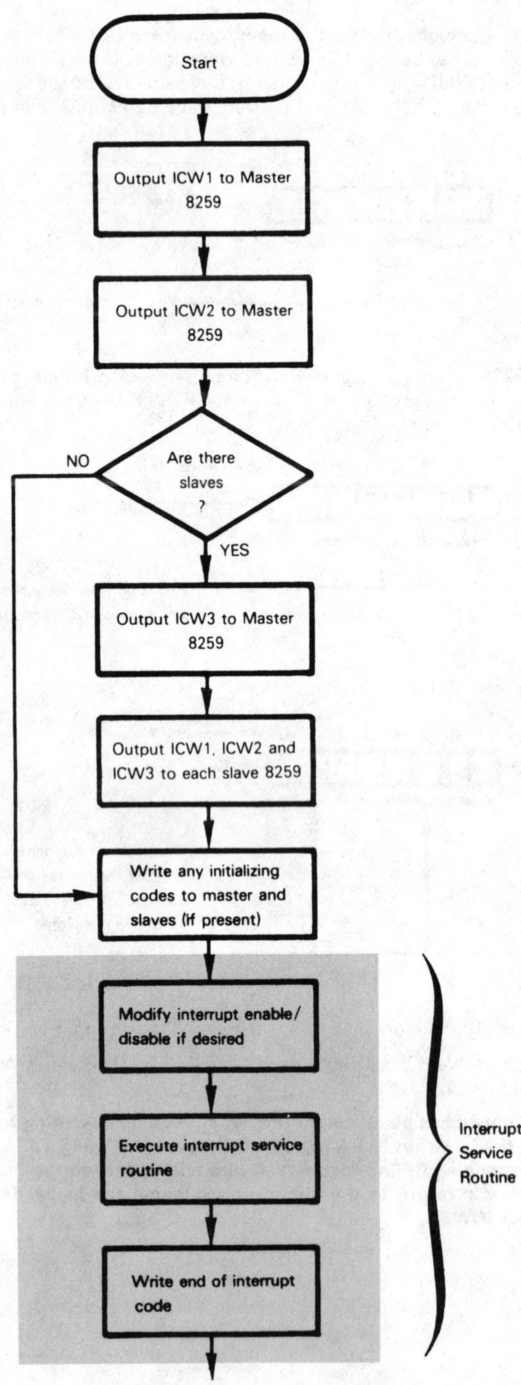

Using arbitrary data, the initiation sequence for a single 8259 PICU system may be illustrated as follows:

```
        MVI     PICUL,12H       ;WRITE OUT ICW1
        MVI     PICUH,40H       ;WRITE OUT ICW2
```

The labels PICUL and PICUH address the lower and higher 8259 PICU addressable locations, respectively.

The two instructions above assume that the 8259 PICU is being addressed as memory. The two immediate data bytes specify an interrupt address vector beginning at location $4000_{16}$, incrementing eight bytes with each priority level.

Now consider a configuration where there is a master PICU and three slave PICUs connected to IR0, IR1 and IR2. Here is the initiating instruction sequence required:

```
;INITIALIZE MASTER PICU
        MVI     PICUL,14H       ;WRITE OUT ICW1
        MVI     PICUH,40H       ;WRITE OUT ICW2
        MVI     PICUH,07H       ;IDENTIFY SLAVES TO MASTER
;INITIALIZE FIRST SLAVE PICU
        MVI     SPCL1,10H       ;WRITE OUT ICW1
        MVI     SPCH1,48H       ;WRITE OUT ICW2
        MVI     SPCH1,0         ;IDENTIFY PRIORITY TO SLAVE
;INITIALIZE SECOND SLAVE PICU
        MVI     SPCL2,30H       ;WRITE OUT ICW1
        MVI     SPCH2,48H       ;WRITE OUT ICW2
        MVI     SPCH2,1         ;IDENTIFY PRIORITY TO SLAVE
;INITIALIZE THIRD SLAVE PICU
        MVI     SPCL3,52H       ;WRITE OUT ICW1
        MVI     SPCH3,48H       ;WRITE OUT ICW2
        MVI     SPCH3,2         ;IDENTIFY PRIORITY TO SLAVE
```

Since there is a single master, and three slaves, there must be four sets of initiating instructions.

First, we initiate the master. Again, the interrupt address vector is origined at $4000_{16}$. This origin and the specification that four bytes will separate each vector will be used when interrupts are requested on levels to which no slave 8259 PICUs are connected. In this case the value $07_{16}$ is output indicating that IR0, IR1 and IR2 have connected slaves.

Slave initiation is straightforward. The first slave PICU has labels SPCL1 and SPCH1, representing the lower and higher addressable locations. SPCL2 and SPCH2 are second slave PICU labels, while SPCL3 and SPCH3 are third slave PICU labels.

All three slave PICUs specify a four-byte displacement between interrupt address vectors. Initial origins of $4800_{16}$, $4820_{16}$ and $4840_{16}$ are specified for slave 1, 2 and 3, respectively. Notice that the second byte written out to the high order address SPCH1, SPCH2 or SPCH3 identifies the slave's priority.

**Once 8259 PICUs have been initiated, programmable features are controlled by outputting appropriate Control codes and inputting appropriate status. Every interrupt service program must end by outputting an "End-Of-Interrupt" Control code to the 8259 PICU. Any form of "End-Of-Interrupt" Control code will do. Otherwise, there is no well defined sequence in which controls and status should be used.**

Table 4-6. A Summary of 8259 PICU Operations

| OPERATION | INSTRUCTION SEQUENCE |
|---|---|
| Select Fully Nested Mode | None. This is selected after initiation. |
| Issue simple End Of Interrupt command | Output $20_{16}$ (OCW2) to PICUL. |
| Rotate Priorities Mode A with End Of Interrupt | Output $A0_{16}$ (OCW2) to PICUL. |
| Rotate Priorities Mode B without End Of Interrupt | Output $Cn_{16}$ (OCW2) to PICUL. n is the new lowest priority. |
| Rotate Priorities Mode B with End Of Interrupt | Output $En_{16}$ (OCW2) to PICUL. n is the new lowest priority. |
| Output an interrupt mask | Output mask byte to PICUL any time after initiation sequence. |
| Read interrupt mask | Input PICUH. |
| Enter special mask mode | Output OCW3 to PICUL with $68_{16}$ in lower 7 bits. |
| Exit special mask mode | Output OCW3 to PICUL with $48_{16}$ in lower 7 bits. |
| Specify Polled Mode | Output OCW3 to PICUL with $0C_{16}$ in lower 7 bits. |
| Poll any PICU | Output OCW3 to PICUL with 011 in bits 4, 3, 2, then immediately read from PICUL. |
| Read IR Status | Output OCW3 to PICUL with $0A_{16}$ in lower 7 bits. Then read from PICUL. |
| Read IS Status | Output OCW3 to PICUL with $0B_{16}$ in lower 7 bits. Then read from PICUL. |
| Reset an IS status bit | Output $6N_{16}$ (OCW2) to PICUL if End Of Interrupt. N is the IS status bit to be reset. |
| PICUL identifies the PICU lower address (A0 = 0). PICUH identifies the PICU higher address (A0 = 1). | |

Here is an example of the end of an interrupt service routine:

```
MVI     PICUL,20H      ;SIMPLE END OF INTERRUPT
RET                    ;RETURN TO INTERRUPTED SEQUENCE
```

The simplest "End-Of-Interrupt" (EOI) is sent as OCW3. This command will reset the highest set bit in the IS register. Notice that we thus assume that this interrupt occurred in Fully Nested Priority Mode, where the highest bit corresponds to the highest priority level.

In other priority schemes, however, the interrupt level being serviced may not correspond to the highest set bit of the IS register. Suppose the interrupt handling scheme is Rotating Priority Mode B with level 2 the lowest priority and a level 0 request being serviced:

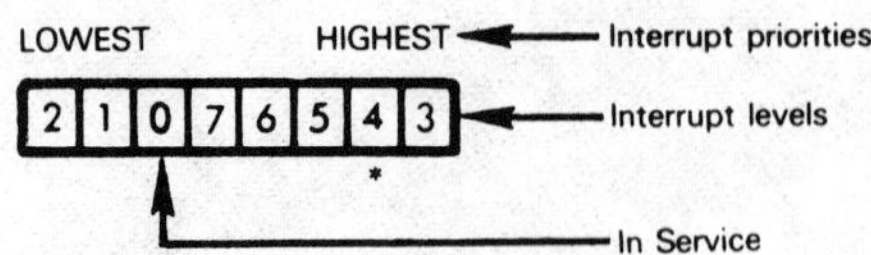

A request at level 4 (*) will interrupt the level 0 routine. The IS register would look like this:

| 7 | 6 | 5 | 4 | 3 | 2 | 1 | 0 | ← Bit No. |
|---|---|---|---|---|---|---|---|---|
| 0 | 0 | 0 | 1 | 0 | 0 | 0 | 1 | ← IS Register |

A simple EOI in the level 4 service routine will now reset bit 0 — which is wrong. The following instruction sequence will reset the correct IS bit and return:

```
MVI     PICUL,64H      ;END LEVEL 4 INTERRUPT
RET                    ;RETURN TO INTERRUPTED SEQUENCE
```

Since we are rotating priorities, the following would be preferable:

```
MVI     PICUL,E4       ;END LEVEL 4 INTERRUPT AND MAKE
                       ;LEVEL 4 LOWEST PRIORITY
RET                    ;RETURN TO INTERRUPTED SEQUENCE
```

The priorities and IS register now look like this:

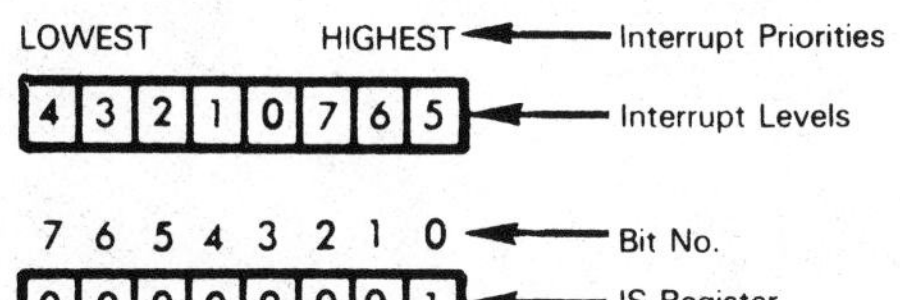


Either of the suggested EOI instructions would allow the level 0 routine to resume.

# DATA SHEETS

This section contains specific electrical and timing data for the following devices:

- 8080A/8080A-1/8080A-2 CPU
- 8224 Clock Device
- 8228/8238 System Controller
- 8259APIC

## ABSOLUTE MAXIMUM RATINGS*

Temperature Under Bias . . . . . . . . . . . 0°C to +70° C
Storage Temperature . . . . . . . . . . . . -65°C to +150°C
All Input or Output Voltages
With Respect to $V_{BB}$ . . . . . . . . . . . -0.3V to +20V
$V_{CC}$, $V_{DD}$ and $V_{SS}$ With Respect to $V_{BB}$ -0.3V to +20V
Power Dissipation . . . . . . . . . . . . . . . . . . . . . 1.5W

**COMMENT: Stresses above those listed under "Absolute Maximum Ratings" may cause permanent damage to the device. This is a stress rating only and functional operation of the device at these or any other conditions above those indicated in the operational sections of this specification is not implied. Exposure to absolute maximum rating conditions for extended periods may affect device reliability.*

## D.C. CHARACTERISTICS

$T_A$ = 0°C to 70°C, $V_{DD}$ = +12V ± 5%, $V_{CC}$ = +5V ± 5%, $V_{BB}$ = -5V ± 5%, $V_{SS}$ = 0V, Unless Otherwise Noted.

| Symbol | Parameter | Min. | Typ. | Max. | Unit | Test Condition |
|---|---|---|---|---|---|---|
| $V_{ILC}$ | Clock Input Low Voltage | $V_{SS}-1$ | | $V_{SS}+0.8$ | V | |
| $V_{IHC}$ | Clock Input High Voltage | 9.0 | | $V_{DD}+1$ | V | |
| $V_{IL}$ | Input Low Voltage | $V_{SS}-1$ | | $V_{SS}+0.8$ | V | |
| $V_{IH}$ | Input High Voltage | 3.3 | | $V_{CC}+1$ | V | |
| $V_{OL}$ | Output Low Voltage | | | 0.45 | V | $I_{OL}$ = 1.9mA on all outputs, |
| $V_{OH}$ | Output High Voltage | 3.7 | | | V | $I_{OH}$ = -150μA. |
| $I_{DD\,(AV)}$ | Avg. Power Supply Current ($V_{DD}$) | | 40 | 70 | mA | Operation |
| $I_{CC\,(AV)}$ | Avg. Power Supply Current ($V_{CC}$) | | 60 | 80 | mA | $T_{CY}$ = .48 μsec |
| $I_{BB\,(AV)}$ | Avg. Power Supply Current ($V_{BB}$) | | .01 | 1 | mA | |
| $I_{IL}$ | Input Leakage | | | ±10 | μA | $V_{SS} \leq V_{IN} \leq V_{CC}$ |
| $I_{CL}$ | Clock Leakage | | | ±10 | μA | $V_{SS} \leq V_{CLOCK} \leq V_{DD}$ |
| $I_{DL}$ [2] | Data Bus Leakage in Input Mode | | | -100<br>-2.0 | μA<br>mA | $V_{SS} \leq V_{IN} \leq V_{SS}+0.8V$<br>$V_{SS}+0.8V \leq V_{IN} \leq V_{CC}$ |
| $I_{FL}$ | Address and Data Bus Leakage During HOLD | | | +10<br>-100 | μA | $V_{ADDR/DATA} = V_{CC}$<br>$V_{ADDR/DATA} = V_{SS} + 0.45V$ |

## CAPACITANCE

$T_A$ = 25°C $V_{CC} = V_{DD} = V_{SS}$ = 0V, $V_{BB}$ = -5V

| Symbol | Parameter | Typ. | Max. | Unit | Test Condition |
|---|---|---|---|---|---|
| $C_\phi$ | Clock Capacitance | 17 | 25 | pf | $f_c$ = 1 MHz |
| $C_{IN}$ | Input Capacitance | 6 | 10 | pf | Unmeasured Pins |
| $C_{OUT}$ | Output Capacitance | 10 | 20 | pf | Returned to $V_{SS}$ |

NOTES:
1. The RESET signal must be active for a minimum of 3 clock cycles.
2. ΔI supply / $\Delta T_A$ = -0.45%/°C.

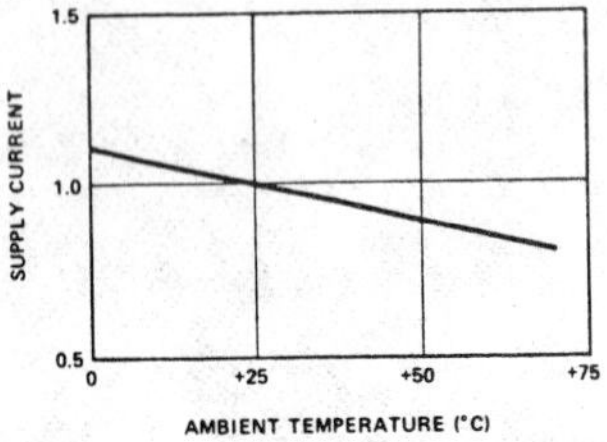


**Figure 2. Typical Supply Current vs. Temperature, Normalized[3]**

## A.C. CHARACTERISTICS (8080A)

$T_A$ = 0°C to 70°C, $V_{DD}$ = +12V ± 5%, $V_{CC}$ = +5V ± 5%, $V_{BB}$ = -5V ± 5%, $V_{SS}$ = 0V, Unless Otherwise Noted

| Symbol | Parameter | Min. | Max. | -1 Min. | -1 Max. | -2 Min. | -2 Max. | Unit | Test Condition |
|---|---|---|---|---|---|---|---|---|---|
| $t_{CY}$[3] | Clock Period | 0.48 | 2.0 | 0.32 | 2.0 | 0.38 | 2.0 | μsec | |
| $t_r, t_f$ | Clock Rise and Fall Time | 0 | 50 | 0 | 25 | 0 | 50 | nsec | |
| $t_{\phi 1}$ | ø1 Pulse Width | 60 | | 50 | | 60 | | nsec | |
| $t_{\phi 2}$ | ø2 Pulse Width | 220 | | 145 | | 175 | | nsec | |
| $t_{D1}$ | Delay ø1 to ø2 | 0 | | 0 | | 0 | | nsec | |
| $t_{D2}$ | Delay ø2 to ø1 | 70 | | 60 | | 70 | | nsec | |
| $t_{D3}$ | Delay ø1 to ø2 Leading Edges | 80 | | 60 | | 70 | | nsec | |
| $t_{DA}$[2] | Address Output Delay From ø2 | | 200 | | 150 | | 175 | nsec | $C_L$ = 100 pF |
| $t_{DD}$[2] | Data Output Delay From ø2 | | 220 | | 180 | | 200 | nsec | $C_L$ = 100 pF |
| $t_{DC}$[2] | Signal Output Delay From ø2 or ø2 (SYNC, WR, WAIT, HLDA) | | 120 | | 110 | | 120 | nsec | $C_L$ = 50 pF |
| $t_{DF}$[2] | DBIN Delay From ø2 | 25 | 140 | 25 | 130 | 25 | 140 | nsec | $C_L$ = 50 pF |
| $t_{DI}$[1] | Delay for Input Bus to Enter Input Mode | | $t_{DF}$ | | $t_{DF}$ | | $t_{DF}$ | nsec | |
| $t_{DS1}$ | Data Setup Time During ø1 and DBIN | 30 | | 10 | | 20 | | nsec | |

## WAVEFORMS

(Note: Timing measurements are made at the following reference voltages: CLOCK "1" = 8.0V "0" = 1.0V; INPUTS "1" = 3.3V, "0" = 0.8V; OUTPUTS "1" = 2.0V, "0" = 0.8V.)

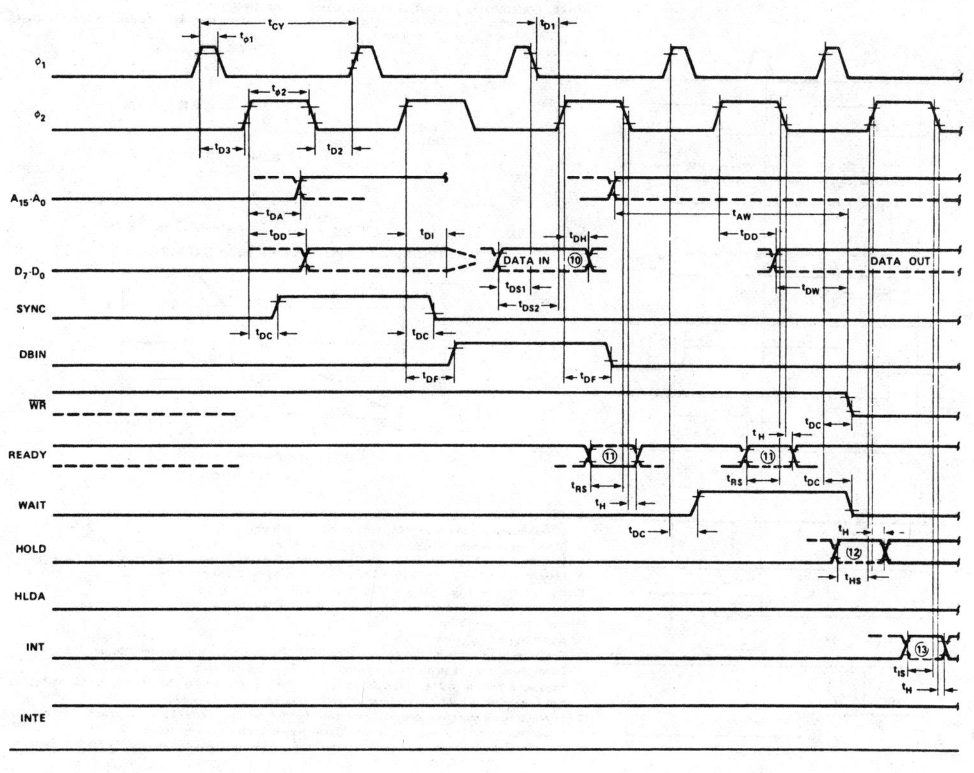

## A.C. CHARACTERISTICS (8080A)

$T_A = 0°C$ to $70°C$, $V_{DD} = +12V \pm 5\%$, $V_{CC} = +5V \pm 5\%$, $V_{BB} = -5V \pm 5\%$, $V_{SS} = 0V$, Unless Otherwise Noted

| Symbol | Parameter | Min. | Max. | -1 Min. | -1 Max. | -2 Min. | -2 Max. | Unit | Test Condition |
|---|---|---|---|---|---|---|---|---|---|
| $t_{DS2}$ | Data Setup Time to Ø2 During DBIN | 150 | | 120 | | 130 | | nsec | |
| $t_{DH}$[1] | Data Holt time From Ø2 During DBIN | [1] | | [1] | | [1] | | nsec | |
| $t_{IE}$[2] | INTE Output Delay From Ø2 | | 200 | | 200 | | 200 | nsec | $C_L = 50$ pF |
| $t_{RS}$ | READY Setup Time During Ø2 | 120 | | 90 | | 90 | | nsec | |
| $t_{HS}$ | HOLD Setup Time to Ø2 | 140 | | 120 | | 120 | | nsec | |
| $t_{IS}$ | INT Setup Time During Ø2 | 120 | | 100 | | 100 | | nsec | |
| $t_H$ | Hold Time From Ø2 (READY, INT, HOLD) | 0 | | 0 | | 0 | | nsec | |
| $t_{FD}$ | Delay to Float During Hold (Address and Data Bus) | | 120 | | 120 | | 120 | nsec | |
| $t_{AW}$[2] | Address Stable Prior to WR | [5] | | [5] | | [5] | | nsec | $C_L = 100$ pF: Address, Data; $C_L = 50$ pF: $\overline{WR}$,HLDA,DBIN |
| $t_{DW}$[2] | Output Data Stable Prior to WR | [6] | | [6] | | [6] | | nsec | |
| $t_{WD}$[2] | Output Data Stable From WR | [7] | | [7] | | [7] | | nsec | |
| $t_{WA}$[2] | Address Stable From WR | [7] | | [7] | | [7] | | nsec | |
| $t_{HF}$[2] | HLDA to Float Delay | [8] | | [8] | | [8] | | nsec | |
| $t_{WF}$[2] | WR to Float Delay | [9] | | [9] | | [9] | | nsec | |
| $t_{AH}$[2] | Address Hold Time After DBIN During HLDA | – 20 | | – 20 | | – 20 | | nsec | |

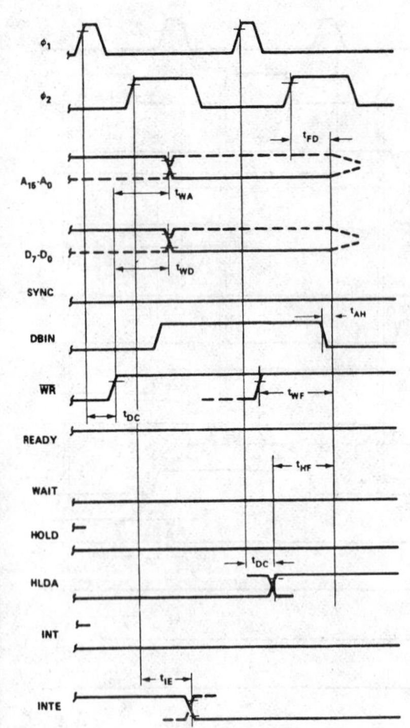


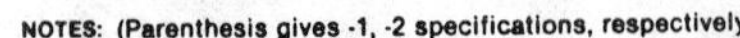

**NOTES: (Parenthesis gives -1, -2 specifications, respectively)**

1. Data input should be enabled with DBIN status. No bus conflict can then occur and data hold time is assured. $t_{DH}$ = 50 ns or $t_{DF}$, whichever is less.
2. Load Circuit.

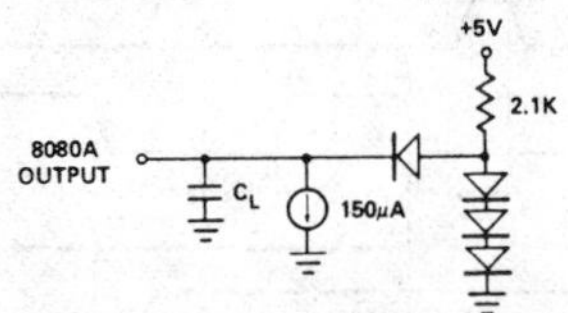


3. $t_{CY} = t_{D3} + t_{r\phi2} + t_{\phi2} + t_{f\phi2} + t_{D2} + t_{r\phi1} \geq 480$ ns (– 1:320 ns, – 2:380 ns).

**TYPICAL Δ OUTPUT DELAY VS. Δ CAPACITANCE**

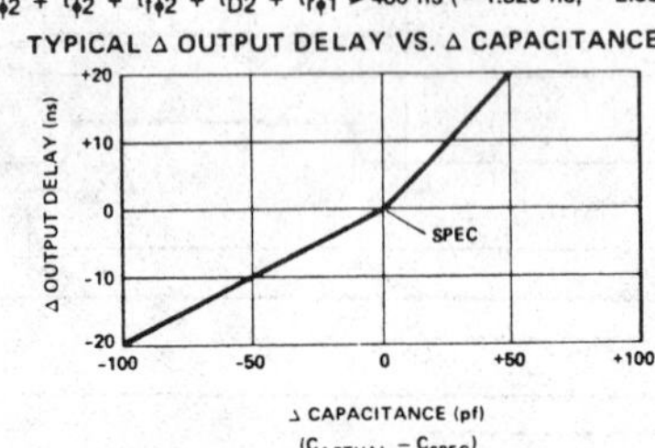


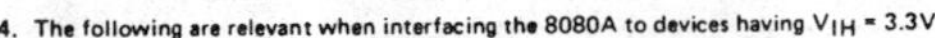

4. The following are relevant when interfacing the 8080A to devices having $V_{IH}$ = 3.3V:
   a) Maximum output rise time from .8V to 3.3V = 100ns @ $C_L$ = SPEC.
   b) Output delay when measured to 3.0V = SPEC +60ns @ $C_L$ = SPEC.
   c) If $C_L \neq$ SPEC, add .6ns/pF if $C_L > C_{SPEC}$, subtract .3ns/pF (from modified delay) if $C_L < C_{SPEC}$.
5. $t_{AW} = 2\,t_{CY} - t_{D3} - t_{r\phi2} - 140$ ns (– 1:110 ns, – 2:130 ns).
6. $t_{DW} = t_{CY} - t_{D3} - t_{r\phi2} - 170$ ns (– 1:150 ns, – 2:170 ns).
7. If not HLDA, $t_{WD} = t_{WA} = t_{D3} + t_{r\phi2}$ +10ns. If HLDA, $t_{WD} = t_{WA} = t_{WF}$.
8. $t_{HF} = t_{D3} + t_{r\phi2}$ -50ns.
9. $t_{WF} = t_{D3} + t_{r\phi2}$ -10ns
10. Data in must be stable for this period during DBIN $\cdot T_3$. Both $t_{DS1}$ and $t_{DS2}$ must be satisfied.
11. Ready signal must be stable for this period during $T_2$ or $T_W$. (Must be externally synchronized.)
12. Hold signal must be stable for this period during $T_2$ or $T_W$ when entering hold mode, and during $T_3$, $T_4$, $T_5$ and $T_{WH}$ when in hold mode. (External synchronization is not required.)
13. Interrupt signal must be stable during this period of the last clock cycle of any instruction in order to be recognized on the following instruction. (External synchronization is not required.)
14. This timing diagram shows timing relationships only; it does not represent any specific machine cycle.

## ABSOLUTE MAXIMUM RATINGS*

Temperature Under Bias . . . . . . . . . . . . . . . 0°C to 70°C
Storage Temperature . . . . . . . . . . . . . . −65°C to 150°C
Supply Voltage, $V_{CC}$ . . . . . . . . . . . . . . . . −0.5V to +7V
Supply Voltage, $V_{DD}$ . . . . . . . . . . . . . . −0.5V to +13.5V
Input Voltage . . . . . . . . . . . . . . . . . . . . . −1.5V to +7V
Output Current . . . . . . . . . . . . . . . . . . . . . . . . 100mA

**COMMENT: Stresses above those listed under "Absolute Maximum Ratings" may cause permanent damage to the device. This is a stress rating only and functional operation of the device at these or any other conditions above those indicated in the operational sections of this specification is not implied. Exposure to absolute maximum rating conditions for extended periods may affect device reliability.*

## D.C. CHARACTERISTICS

$T_A$ = 0°C to 70°C; $V_{CC}$ = +5.0V ±5%; $V_{DD}$ = +12V ±5%.

| Symbol | Parameter | Limits Min. | Limits Typ. | Limits Max. | Units | Test Conditions |
|---|---|---|---|---|---|---|
| $I_F$ | Input Current Loading | | | -.25 | mA | $V_F$ = .45V |
| $I_R$ | Input Leakage Current | | | 10 | μA | $V_R$ = 5.25V |
| $V_C$ | Input Forward Clamp Voltage | | | 1.0 | V | $I_C$ = -5mA |
| $V_{IL}$ | Input "Low" Voltage | | | .8 | V | $V_{CC}$ = 5.0V |
| $V_{IH}$ | Input "High" Voltage | 2.6<br>2.0 | | | V | Reset Input<br>All Other Inputs |
| $V_{IH}$-$V_{IL}$ | RESIN Input Hysteresis | .25 | | | V | $V_{CC}$ = 5.0V |
| $V_{OL}$ | Output "Low" Voltage | | | .45<br><br>.45 | V<br><br>V | ($\phi_1$,$\phi_2$), Ready, Reset, $\overline{STSTB}$<br>$I_{OL}$ =2.5mA<br>All Other Outputs<br>$I_{OL}$ = 15mA |
| $V_{OH}$ | Output "High" Voltage<br>$\phi_1$ , $\phi_2$<br>READY, RESET<br>All Other Outputs | <br>9.4<br>3.6<br>2.4 | | | <br>V<br>V<br>V | <br>$I_{OH}$ = -100μA<br>$I_{OH}$ = -100μA<br>$I_{OH}$ = -1mA |
| $I_{SC}$[1] | Output Short Circuit Current<br>(All Low Voltage Outputs Only) | -10 | | -60 | mA | $V_O$ = 0V<br>$V_{CC}$ = 5.0V |
| $I_{CC}$ | Power Supply Current | | | 115 | mA | |
| $I_{DD}$ | Power Supply Current | | | 12 | mA | |

Note: 1. Caution, $\phi_1$ and $\phi_2$ output drivers do not have short circuit protection

**Crystal Requirements**

Tolerance: 0.005% at 0°C-70°C
Resonance: Series (Fundamental)*
Load Capacitance: 20-35 pF
Equivalent Resistance: 75-20 ohms
Power Dissipation (Min): 4 mW

*With tank circuit use 3rd overtone mode.

## A.C. CHARACTERISTICS

$V_{CC}$ = +5.0V ± 5%; $V_{DD}$ = +12.0V ± 5%; $T_A$ = 0°C to 70°C

| Symbol | Parameter | Limits Min. | Limits Typ. | Limits Max. | Units | Test Conditions |
|---|---|---|---|---|---|---|
| $t_{\phi 1}$ | $\phi_1$ Pulse Width | $\frac{2tcy}{9}$ - 20ns | | | ns | $C_L$ = 20pF to 50pF |
| $t_{\phi 2}$ | $\phi_2$ Pulse Width | $\frac{5tcy}{9}$ - 35ns | | | | |
| $t_{D1}$ | $\phi_1$ to $\phi_2$ Delay | 0 | | | | |
| $t_{D2}$ | $\phi_2$ to $\phi_1$ Delay | $\frac{2tcy}{9}$ - 14ns | | | | |
| $t_{D3}$ | $\phi_1$ to $\phi_2$ Delay | $\frac{2tcy}{9}$ | | $\frac{2tcy}{9}$ + 20ns | | |
| $t_R$ | $\phi_1$ and $\phi_2$ Rise Time | | | 20 | | |
| $t_F$ | $\phi_1$ and $\phi_2$ Fall Time | | | 20 | | |
| $t_{D\phi 2}$ | $\phi_2$ to $\phi_2$ (TTL) Delay | -5 | | +15 | ns | $\phi_2$TTL,CL=30 $R_1$=300Ω $R_2$=600Ω |
| $t_{DSS}$ | $\phi_2$ to $\overline{STSTB}$ Delay | $\frac{6tcy}{9}$ - 30ns | | $\frac{6tcy}{9}$ | | $\overline{STSTB}$, CL=15pF $R_1$ = 2K $R_2$ = 4K |
| $t_{PW}$ | $\overline{STSTB}$ Pulse Width | $\frac{tcy}{9}$ - 15ns | | | | |
| $t_{DRS}$ | RDYIN Setup Time to Status Strobe | 50ns - $\frac{4tcy}{9}$ | | | | |
| $t_{DRH}$ | RDYIN Hold Time After $\overline{STSTB}$ | $\frac{4tcy}{9}$ | | | | |
| $t_{DR}$ | RDYIN or RESIN to $\phi_2$ Delay | $\frac{4tcy}{9}$ - 25ns | | | | Ready & Reset CL=10pF $R_1$=2K $R_2$=4K |
| $t_{CLK}$ | CLK Period | | $\frac{tcy}{9}$ | | | |
| $f_{max}$ | Maximum Oscillating Frequency | | | 27 | MHz | |
| $C_{in}$ | Input Capacitance | | | 8 | pF | $V_{CC}$=+5.0V $V_{DD}$=+12V $V_{BIAS}$=2.5V f=1MHz |

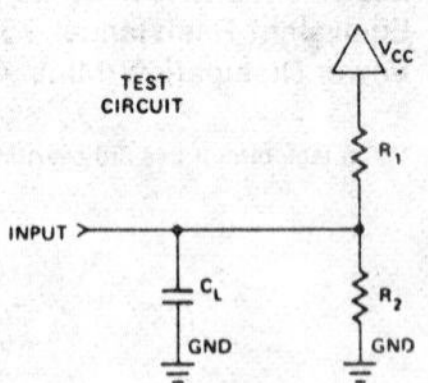

## WAVEFORMS

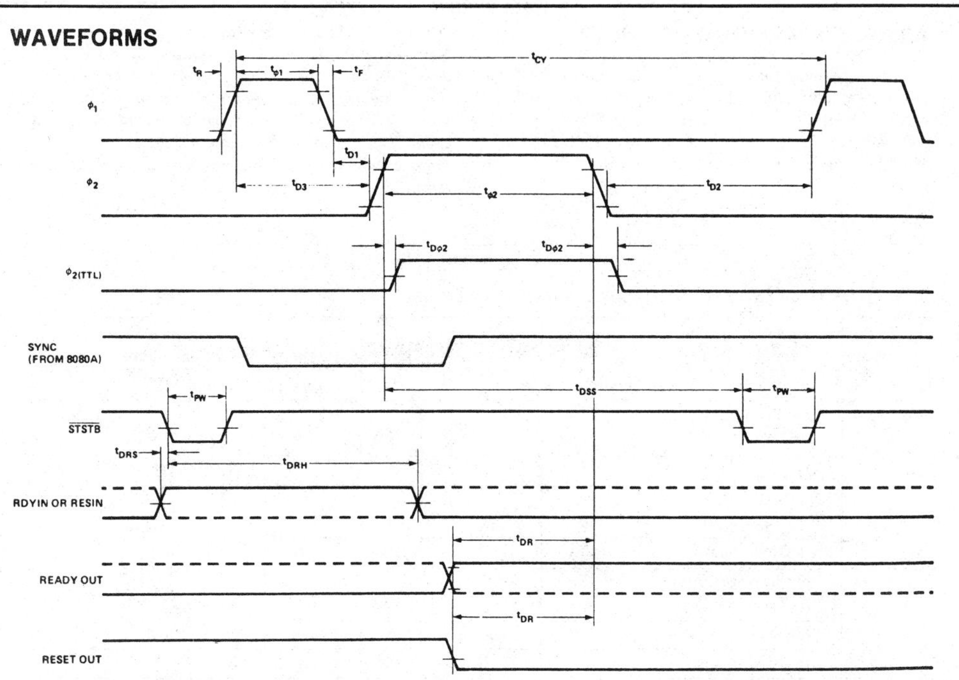


VOLTAGE MEASUREMENT POINTS: $\phi_1$, $\phi_2$ Logic "0" = 1.0V, Logic "1" = 8.0V. All other signals measured at 1.5V.

### EXAMPLE:

### A.C. CHARACTERISTICS (For $t_{CY}$ = 488.28 ns)

$T_A$ = 0°C to 70°C; $V_{DD}$ = +5V ±5%; $V_{DD}$ = +12V ±5%.

| Symbol | Parameter | Limits Min. | Limits Typ. | Limits Max. | Units | Test Conditions |
|---|---|---|---|---|---|---|
| $t_{\phi 1}$ | $\phi_1$ Pulse Width | 89 | | | ns | $t_{CY}$=488.28ns |
| $t_{\phi 2}$ | $\phi_2$ Pulse Width | 236 | | | ns | |
| $t_{D1}$ | Delay $\phi_1$ to $\phi_2$ | 0 | | | ns | |
| $t_{D2}$ | Delay $\phi_2$ to $\phi_1$ | 95 | | | ns | $\phi_1$ & $\phi_2$ Loaded to $C_L$ = 20 to 50pF |
| $t_{D3}$ | Delay $\phi_1$ to $\phi_2$ Leading Edges | 109 | | 129 | ns | |
| $t_r$ | Output Rise Time | | | 20 | ns | |
| $t_f$ | Output Fall Time | | | 20 | ns | |
| $t_{DSS}$ | $\phi_2$ to $\overline{STSTB}$ Delay | 296 | | 326 | ns | |
| $t_{D\phi 2}$ | $\phi_2$ to $\phi_2$ (TTL) Delay | -5 | | +15 | ns | |
| $t_{PW}$ | Status Strobe Pulse Width | 40 | | | ns | Ready & Reset Loaded to 2mA/10pF |
| $t_{DRS}$ | RDYIN Setup Time to $\overline{STSTB}$ | -167 | | | ns | All measurements referenced to 1.5V unless specified otherwise. |
| $t_{DRH}$ | RDYIN Hold Time after $\overline{STSTB}$ | 217 | | | ns | |
| $t_{DR}$ | READY or RESET to $\phi_2$ Delay | 192 | | | ns | |
| $f_{MAX}$ | Oscillator Frequency | | | 18.432 | MHz | |

## ABSOLUTE MAXIMUM RATINGS*

Temperature Under Bias . . . . . . . . . . . . . . −0°C to 70°C
Storage Temperature . . . . . . . . . . . . . . −65°C to 150°C
Supply Voltage, $V_{CC}$ . . . . . . . . . . . . . . . . . −0.5V to +7V
Input Voltage . . . . . . . . . . . . . . . . . . . . . . −1.5V to +7V
Output Current . . . . . . . . . . . . . . . . . . . . . . . . . . 100 mA

**COMMENT: Stresses above those listed under "Absolute Maximum Ratings" may cause permanent damage to the device. This is a stress rating only and functional operation of the device at these or any other conditions above those indicated in the operational sections of this specification is not implied. Exposure to absolute maximum rating conditions for extended periods may affect device reliability.*

## D.C. CHARACTERISTICS $T_A = 0°C$ to $70°C$; $V_{CC} = 5V \pm 5\%$.

| Symbol | Parameter | Limits Min. | Limits Typ.[1] | Limits Max. | Unit | Test Conditions |
|---|---|---|---|---|---|---|
| $V_C$ | Input Clamp Voltage, All Inputs | | .75 | -1.0 | V | $V_{CC}$=4.75V; $I_C$=-5mA |
| $I_F$ | Input Load Current, $\overline{\text{STSTB}}$ | | | 500 | μA | $V_{CC}$ = 5.25V |
| | $D_2$ & $D_6$ | | | 750 | μA | $V_F$ = 0.45V |
| | $D_0$, $D_1$, $D_4$, $D_5$, & $D_7$ | | | 250 | μA | |
| | All Other Inputs | | | 250 | μA | |
| $I_R$ | Input Leakage Current $\overline{\text{STSTB}}$ | | | 100 | μA | $V_{CC}$ = 5.25V |
| | $DB_0$-$DB_7$ | | | 20 | μA | $V_R$ = 5.25V |
| | All Other Inputs | | | 100 | μA | |
| $V_{TH}$ | Input Threshold Voltage, All Inputs | 0.8 | | 2.0 | V | $V_{CC}$ = 5V |
| $I_{CC}$ | Power Supply Current | | 140 | 190 | mA | $V_{CC}$=5.25V |
| $V_{OL}$ | Output Low Voltage, $D_0$-$D_7$ | | | .45 | V | $V_{CC}$=4.75V; $I_{OL}$=2mA |
| | All Other Outputs | | | .45 | V | $I_{OL}$ = 10mA |
| $V_{OH}$ | Output High Voltage, $D_0$-$D_7$ | 3.6 | 3.8 | | V | $V_{CC}$=4.75V; $I_{OH}$=-10μA |
| | All Other Outputs | 2.4 | | | V | $I_{OH}$ = -1mA |
| $I_{OS}$ | Short Circuit Current, All Outputs | 15 | | 90 | mA | $V_{CC}$=5V |
| $I_{O(off)}$ | Off State Output Current, All Control Outputs | | | 100 | μA | $V_{CC}$=5.25V; $V_O$=5.25 |
| | | | | -100 | μA | $V_O$=.45V |
| $I_{INT}$ | INTA Current | | | 5 | mA | (See Figure below) |

Note 1: Typical values are for $T_A$ = 25°C and nominal supply voltages.

## WAVEFORMS

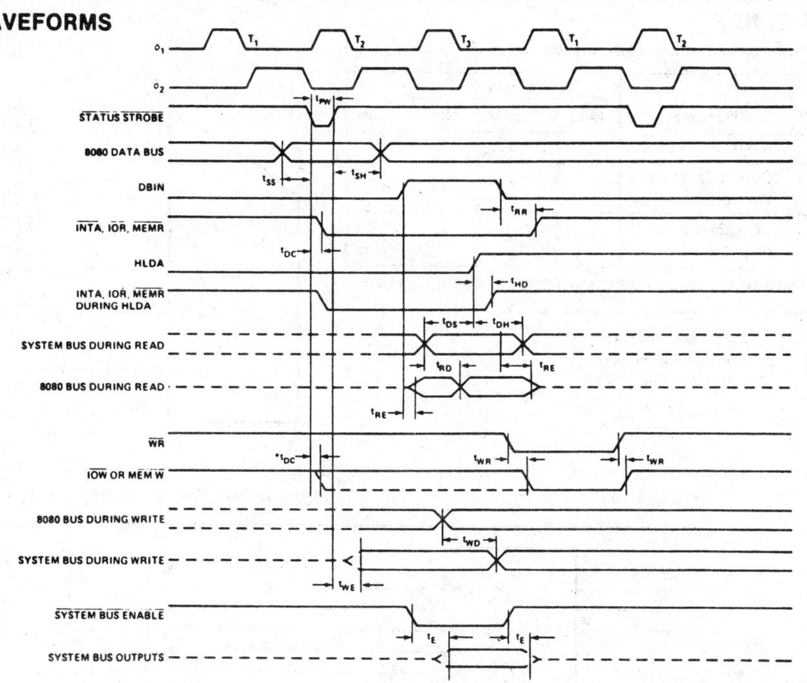


VOLTAGE MEASUREMENT POINTS: $D_0$-$D_7$ (when outputs) Logic "0" = 0.8V, Logic "1" = 3.0V. All other signals measured at 1.5V.

*ADVANCED $\overline{IOW}/\overline{MEMW}$ FOR 8238 ONLY.

## A.C. CHARACTERISTICS $T_A = 0°C$ to $70°C$, $V_{CC} = 5V \pm 5\%$

| Symbol | Parameter | Limits Min. | Limits Max. | Units | Condition |
|---|---|---|---|---|---|
| $t_{PW}$ | Width of Status Strobe | 22 | | ns | |
| $t_{SS}$ | Setup Time, Status Inputs $D_0$-$D_7$ | 8 | | ns | |
| $t_{SH}$ | Hold Time, Status Inputs $D_0$-$D_7$ | 5 | | ns | |
| $t_{DC}$ | Delay from $\overline{STSTB}$ to any Control Signal | 20 | 60 | ns | $C_L$ = 100pF |
| $t_{RR}$ | Delay from DBIN to Control Outputs | | 30 | ns | $C_L$ = 100pF |
| $t_{RE}$ | Delay from DBIN to Enable/Disable 8080 Bus | | 45 | ns | $C_L$ = 25pF |
| $t_{RD}$ | Delay from System Bus to 8080 Bus during Read | | 30 | ns | $C_L$ = 25pF |
| $t_{WR}$ | Delay from $\overline{WR}$ to Control Outputs | 5 | 45 | ns | $C_L$ = 100pF |
| $t_{WE}$ | Delay to Enable System Bus $DB_0$-$DB_7$ after $\overline{STSTB}$ | | 30 | ns | $C_L$ = 100pF |
| $t_{WD}$ | Delay from 8080 Bus $D_0$-$D_7$ to System Bus $DB_0$-$DB_7$ during Write | 5 | 40 | ns | $C_L$ = 100pF |
| $t_E$ | Delay from $\overline{\text{System Bus Enable}}$ to System Bus $DB_0$-$DB_7$ | | 30 | ns | $C_L$ = 100pF |
| $t_{HD}$ | HLDA to Read Status Outputs | | 25 | ns | |
| $t_{DS}$ | Setup Time, System Bus Inputs to HLDA | 10 | | ns | |
| $t_{DH}$ | Hold Time, System Bus Inputs to HLDA | 20 | | ns | $C_L$ = 100pF |

## CAPACITANCE

This parameter is periodically sampled and not 100% tested.

| Symbol | Parameter | Limits | | | Unit |
|---|---|---|---|---|---|
| | | Min. | Typ.[1] | Max. | |
| $C_{IN}$ | Input Capacitance | | 8 | 12 | pF |
| $C_{OUT}$ | Output Capacitance Control Signals | | 7 | 15 | pF |
| I/O | I/O Capacitance (D or DB) | | 8 | 15 | pF |

**Test Conditions:** NS: $V_{BIAS} = 2.5V$, $V_{CC} = 5.0V$, $T_A = 25°C$, f = 1MHz.

Note 2: For $D_0$-$D_7$: $R_1 = 4K\Omega$, $R_2 = \infty\Omega$, $C_L = 25pF$. For all other outputs: $R_1 = 500\Omega$, $R_2 = 1K\Omega$, $C_L = 100pF$.

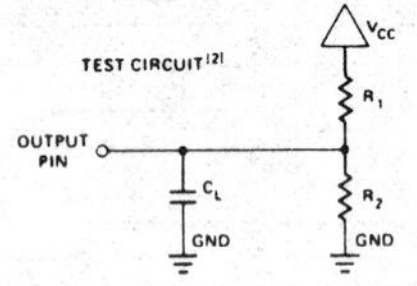


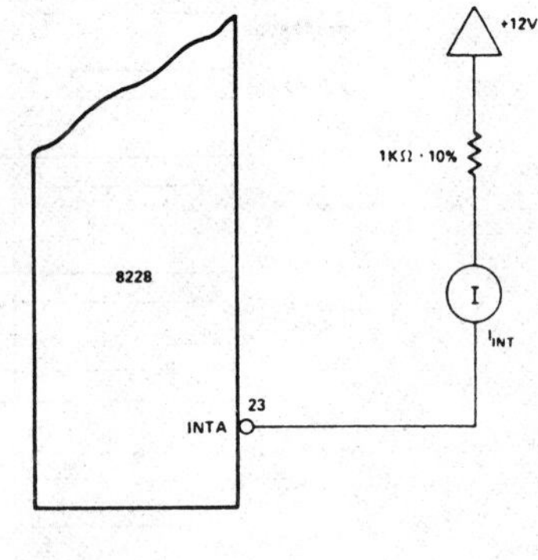


**Figure 1. INTA Test Circuit (for RST 7)**

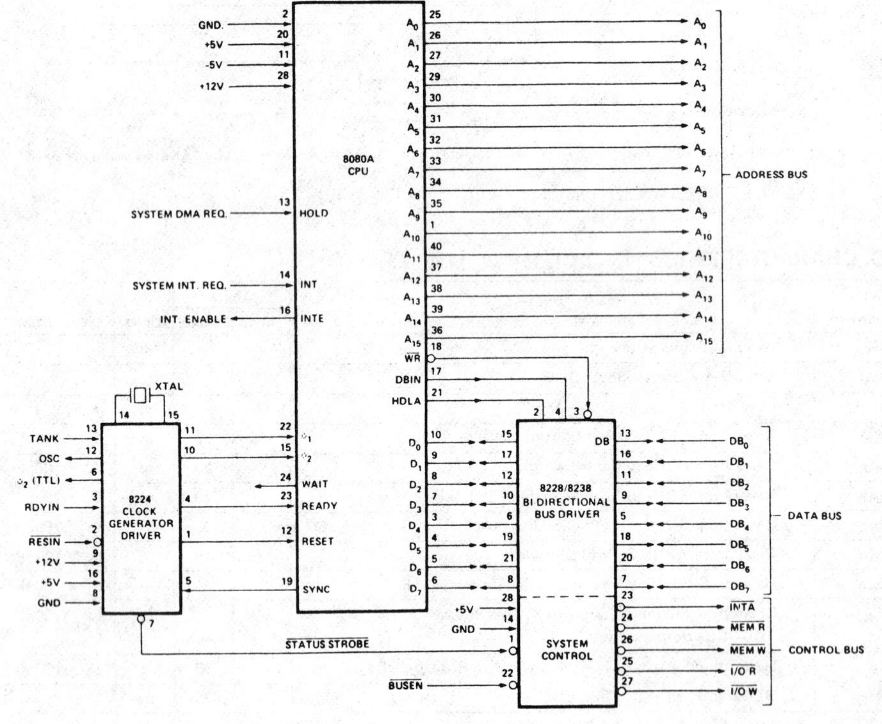

## ABSOLUTE MAXIMUM RATINGS*

Ambient Temperature Under Bias ...... −40°C to 85°C
Storage Temperature .............. −65°C to +150°C
Voltage on Any Pin
with Respect to Ground ............. −0.5V to +7V
Power Dissipation ......................... 1 Watt

*COMMENT:
Stresses above those listed under "Absolute Maximum Ratings" may cause permanent damage to the device. This is a stress rating only and functional operation of the device at these or any other conditions above those indicated in the operational sections of this specification is not implied.

## D.C. CHARACTERISTICS

$T_A$ = 0°C to 70°C, $V_{CC}$ = 5V ± 10% (8259-A), $V_{CC}$ = 5V ± 10% (8259A)

| Symbol | Parameter | Min. | Max. | Units | Test Conditions |
|---|---|---|---|---|---|
| $V_{IL}$ | Input Low Voltage | −0.5 | | V | |
| $V_{IH}$ | Input High Voltage | 2.0 | $V_{CC}$ + 0.5V | V | |
| $V_{OL}$ | Output Low Voltage | | 0.45 | V | $I_{OL}$ = 2.2 mA |
| $V_{OH}$ | Output High Voltage | 2.4 | | V | $I_{OH}$ = −400 μA |
| $V_{OH(INT)}$ | Interrupt Output High Voltage | 3.5 | | V | $I_{OH}$ = −100 μA |
| | | 2.4 | | V | $I_{OH}$ = −400 μA |
| $I_{LI}$ | Input Load Current | | 10 | μA | $V_{IN}$ = $V_{CC}$ to 0V |
| $I_{LOL}$ | Output Leakage Current | | −10 | μA | $V_{OUT}$ = 0.45V |
| $I_{CC}$ | $V_{CC}$ Supply Current | | 85 | mA | |
| $I_{LIR}$ | IR Input Load Current | | −300 | μA | $V_{IN}$ = 0 |
| | | | 10 | μA | $V_{IN}$ = $V_{CC}$ |

## 8259A A.C. CHARACTERISTICS

$T_A = 0°C$ to $70°C$ $V_{CC} = 5V \pm 5\%$ (8259A-8) $V_{CC} = 5V \pm 10\%$ (8259A)

### TIMING REQUIREMENTS

| Symbol | Parameter | 8259A-8 | | 8259A | | 8259A-2 | | Units | Test Conditions |
|---|---|---|---|---|---|---|---|---|---|
| | | Min. | Max. | Min. | Max. | Min. | Max. | | |
| TAHRL | AO/$\overline{CS}$ Setup to $\overline{RD}$/$\overline{INTA}$↓ | 50 | | 0 | | 0 | | ns | |
| TRHAX | AO/$\overline{CS}$ Hold after $\overline{RD}$/$\overline{INTA}$↑ | 5 | | 0 | | 0 | | ns | |
| TRLRH | $\overline{RD}$ Pulse Width | 420 | | 235 | | 160 | | ns | |
| TAHWL | AO/$\overline{CS}$ Setup to $\overline{WR}$↓ | 50 | | 0 | | 0 | | ns | |
| TWHAX | AO/$\overline{CS}$ Hold after $\overline{WR}$↑ | 20 | | 0 | | 0 | | ns | |
| TWLWH | $\overline{WR}$ Pulse Width | 400 | | 290 | | 190 | | ns | |
| TDVWH | Data Setup to $\overline{WR}$↑ | 300 | | 240 | | 160 | | ns | |
| TWHDX | Data Hold after $\overline{WR}$↑ | 40 | | 0 | | 0 | | ns | |
| TJLJH | Interrupt Request Width (Low) | 100 | | 100 | | 100 | | ns | See Note 1 |
| TCVIAL | Cascade Setup to Second or Third $\overline{INTA}$↓ (Slave Only) | 55 | | 55 | | 40 | | ns | |
| TRHRL | End of $\overline{RD}$ to Next Command | 160 | | 160 | | 160 | | ns | |
| TWHRL | End of $\overline{WR}$ to Next Command | 190 | | 190 | | 190 | | ns | |

**Note:** This is the low time required to clear the input latch in the edge triggered mode.

### TIMING RESPONSES

| Symbol | Parameter | 8259A-8 | | 8259A | | 8259A-2 | | Units | Test Conditions |
|---|---|---|---|---|---|---|---|---|---|
| | | Min. | Max. | Min. | Max. | Min. | Max. | | |
| TRLDV | Data Valid from $\overline{RD}$/$\overline{INTA}$↓ | | 300 | | 200 | | 120 | ns | C of Data Bus = 100 pF |
| TRHDZ | Data Float after $\overline{RD}$/$\overline{INTA}$↑ | 10 | 200 | | 100 | | 85 | ns | C of Data Bus Max text C = 100 pF Min. test C = 15 pF |
| TJHIH | Interrupt Output Delay | | 400 | | 350 | | 300 | ns | |
| TIAHCV | Cascade Valid from First $\overline{INTA}$↓ (Master Only) | | 565 | | 565 | | 360 | ns | $C_{INT}$ = 100 pF |
| TRLEL | Enable Active from $\overline{RD}$↓ or $\overline{INTA}$↓ | | 160 | | 125 | | 100 | ns | $C_{CASCADE}$ = 100 pF |
| TRHEH | Enable Inactive from $\overline{RD}$↑ or $\overline{INTA}$↑ | | 325 | | 150 | | d150 | ns | |
| TAHDV | Data Valid from Stable Address | | 350 | | 200 | | 200 | ns | |
| TCVDV | Cascade Valid to Valid Data | | 300 | | 300 | | 200 | ns | |

## CAPACITANCE

$T_A = 25°C$; $V_{CC} = GND = 0V$

| Symbol | Parameter | Min. | Typ. | Max. | Unit | Test Conditions |
|---|---|---|---|---|---|---|
| $C_{IN}$ | Input Capacitance | | | 10 | pF | fc = 1 MHz |
| $C_{I/O}$ | I/O Capacitance | | | 20 | pF | Unmeasured pins returned to $V_{SS}$ |

**Input and Output Waveforms for A.C. Tests**

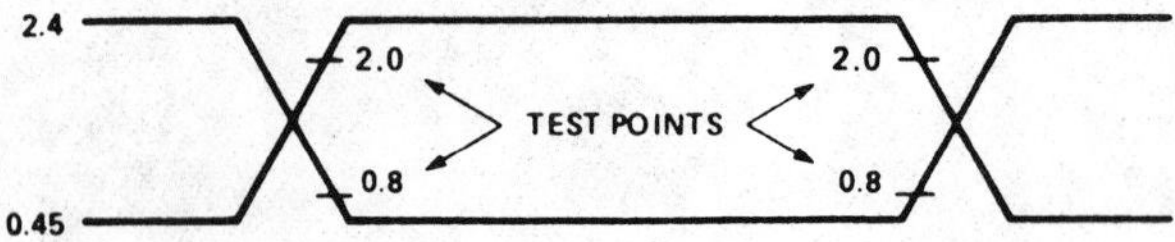

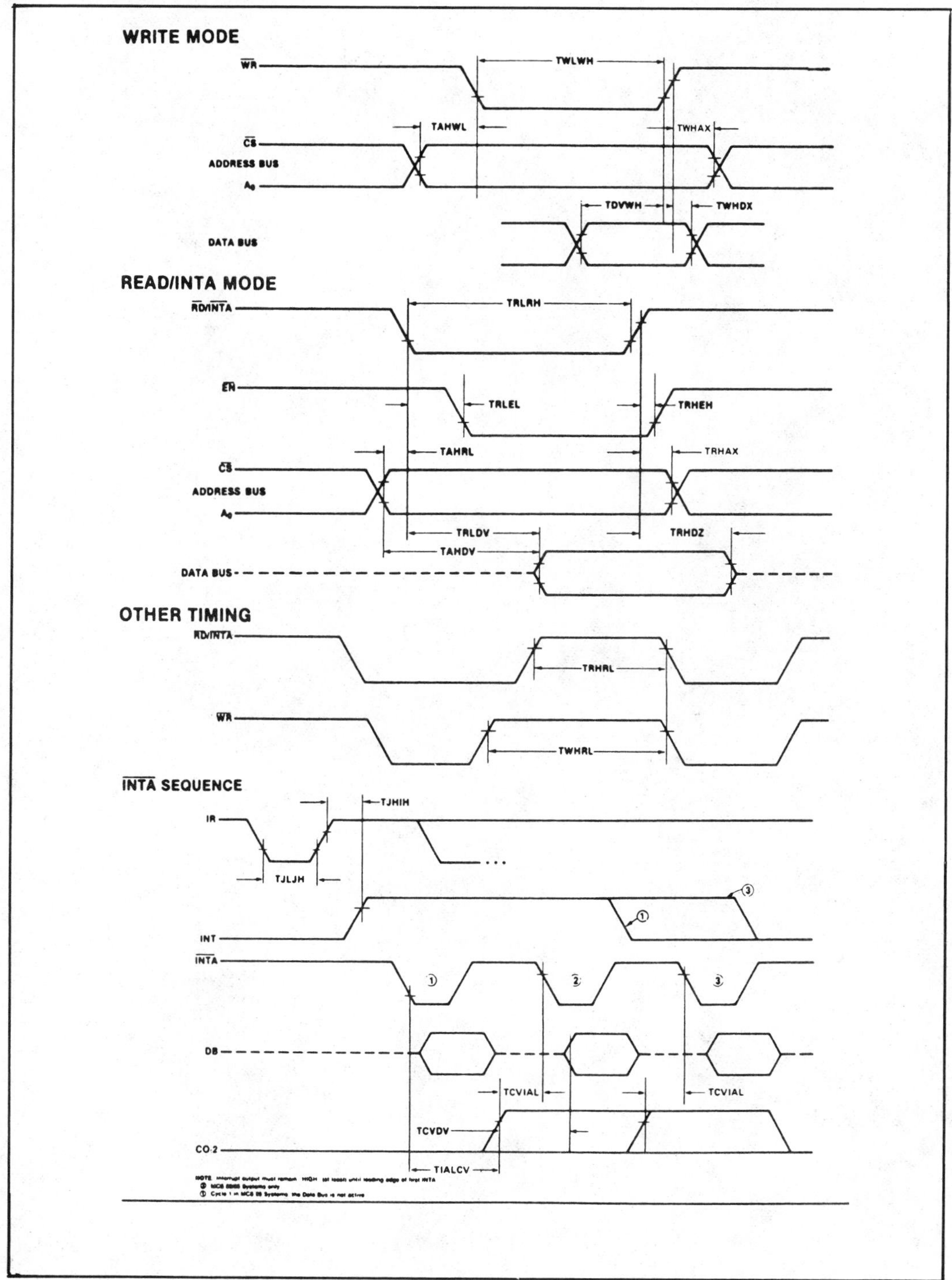
WRITE MODE
WR
TWLWH
TAHWL
TWHAX
CS
ADDRESS BUS
A0
TDVWH
TWHDX
DATA BUS
READ/INTA MODE
RD/INTA
TRLRH
EN
TRLEL
TRHEH
TAHRL
TRHAX
CS
ADDRESS BUS
A0
TRLDV
TRHDZ
TAHDV
DATA BUS
OTHER TIMING
RD/INTA
TRHRL
WR
TWHRL
INTA SEQUENCE
TJHIH
IR
TJLJH
INT
INTA
DB
TCVIAL
TCVIAL
TCVDV
CO-2
TIALCV

# Chapter 5
# THE 8085A

**The 8085A is Intel's enhancement of the 8080A — just as the Z80 is Zilog's enhancement of the 8080A. The Z80 is described in Chapter 7.**

**Intel is the developer of the 8085A; Intel is also the principal manufacturer of the 8080A. But the individuals at Zilog who developed the Z80 were previously employed by Intel, at which time they developed the 8080A from the 8008. The Z80 and the 8085A therefore have equal claim to be the legitimate descendent of the 8080A.**

**The 8085A provides the same logic as the 8080A, 8224 and 8228 three-chip CPU. The 8085A has the following additional enhancements:**

1) The 8085A requires a single +5V power supply.
2) The 8085A uses a single clock signal.
3) The 8085A has a primitive on-chip serial I/O capability which may also be used to input status and output control signals.
4) The 8085A has interrupt request pins with hardware-generated interrupt vectoring.
5) The 8085A operates with a standard 320 nanosecond clock as against the standard 500 nanosecond clock of the 8080A. But recall that there are versions of the 8080A that operate with a 250 nanosecond clock.

**The 8085A instruction set is almost identical to the 8080A instruction set; in contrast, the Z80 has a massively expanded instruction set.** The large Z80 instruction set has been criticized for its complexity, but one could argue that since the Z80 also provides the complete 8080A instruction set, anyone who does not want to use the additional instructions can simply ignore them.

**The 8085A multiplexes its Data Bus with the low-order Address Bus lines.** Such multiplexing demands custom support devices, or external demultiplexing logic.

**Figure 5-3 and associated text provide a direct comparison of 8085A and 8080A signal interfaces.**

**In addition to the 8085A microprocessor, support devices described in this chapter include:**

- The 8155/8156 static RAM with I/O ports and timer. This device provides 256 bytes of static read/write memory.
- The 8355 ROM with I/O ports. This device provides 2048 bytes of read-only memory plus I/O logic.
- The 8755A EPROM with I/O ports. This device provides 2048 bytes of erasable programmable read-only memory with I/O logic.

**Standard 8080A support devices described in Chapter 4 and in Volume 3 cannot be used with the 8085A unless the 8085A is operating with a 500 ns clock. If you are using the 8085A with a 320 ns clock, you must use the special -5 series of support parts.**

The 8085A prime source is:

INTEL CORPORATION
3065 Bowers Avenue
Santa Clara, California 95051

The 8085A second source is:

ADVANCED MICRO DEVICES
901 Thompson Place
Sunnyvale, California 94086

The 8085A uses a single +5V power supply; it is packaged as a 40-pin DIP.

Using a 320 nanosecond clock, instruction execution times range from 1.3 microseconds to 5.75 microseconds.

All 8085A devices have TTL compatible signals.

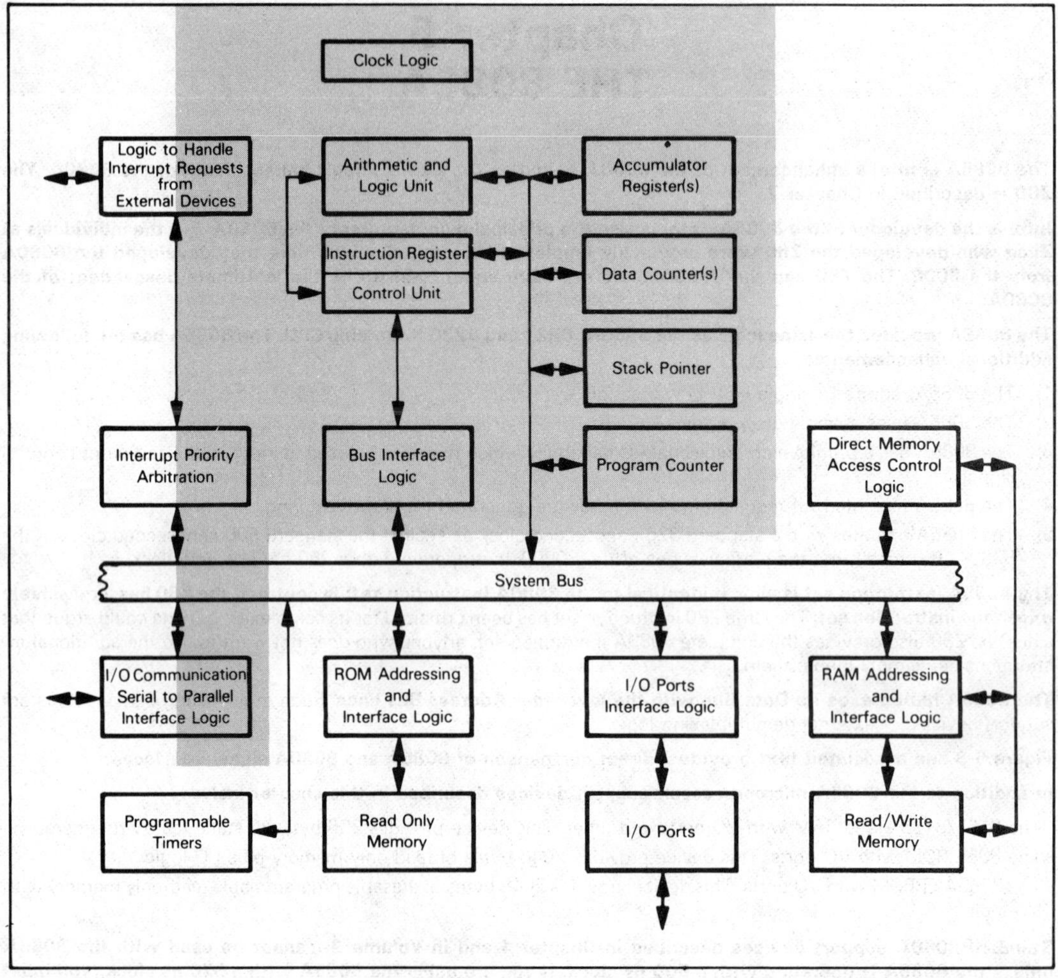


Figure 5-1. Logic of the 8085A Microprocessor

## THE 8085A CPU

**Functions implemented on the 8085A CPU are illustrated in Figure 5-1; they represent typical CPU logic.** The 8085A has an Arithmetic and Logic Unit, a Control Unit, Accumulators and registers.

Clock logic is on the 8085A CPU chip; only an external crystal or RC network is needed.

Bus interface logic which was excluded on the 8080A is provided by the 8085A.

N-channel silicon gate technology is used by all 8085A devices.

## 8085A PROGRAMMABLE REGISTERS

**The 8085A programmable registers are identical to the 8080A programmable registers. They may be illustrated as follows:**

| | | |
|---|---|---|
| | PSW | Program Status Word } These two sometimes |
| | A | Primary Accumulator } treated as a 16-bit unit |
| B | C | Secondary Accumulators/Data Counter |
| D | E | Secondary Accumulators/Data Counter |
| H | L | Secondary Accumulators/Data Counter |
| SP | | Stack Pointer |
| PC | | Program Counter |

**For a discussion of 8085A programmable registers refer to the 8080A CPU description given in Chapter 4.**

## 8085A ADDRESSING MODES

**The 8085A uses exactly the same memory addressing modes as the 8080A. Direct and implied memory addressing are available. See the 8080A addressing modes description given in Chapter 4 for details.**

## 8085A STATUS

**The 8085A has the same set of status flags as the 8080A; status flags are stored in the same bits of the Program Status Words. The five status flags provided are:**

Zero (Z)
Sign (S)
Parity (P)
Carry (C)
Auxiliary Carry (AC)

Status flags are assigned to bits of the Program Status Words as follows:

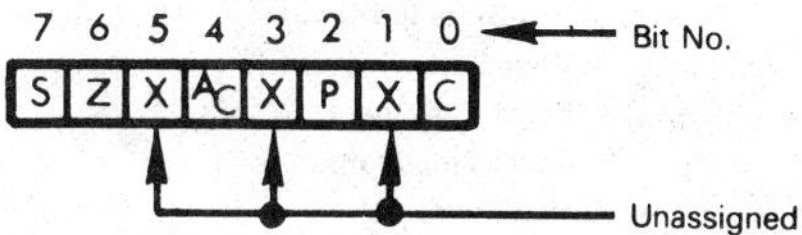


**For a discussion of status flags refer to the 8080A status description given in Chapter 4.**

## 8085A CPU PINS AND SIGNALS

**8085A CPU pins and signals are illustrated in Figure 5-2.**

Whereas the internal architecture and the instruction sets of the 8080A and the 8085A are very similar, pins and signals are not. We will therefore begin by describing 8085A signals without reference to, or comparison with, the 8080A; then we will compare the two interfaces.

**The Address and Data Busses of the 8085A are multiplexed.** Pins A8 - A15 are output-only lines which carry the high-order byte of memory addresses. AD0 - AD7 are bidirectional lines which output the low-order byte of memory addresses; AD0 - AD7 also serve as a bidirectional Data Bus.

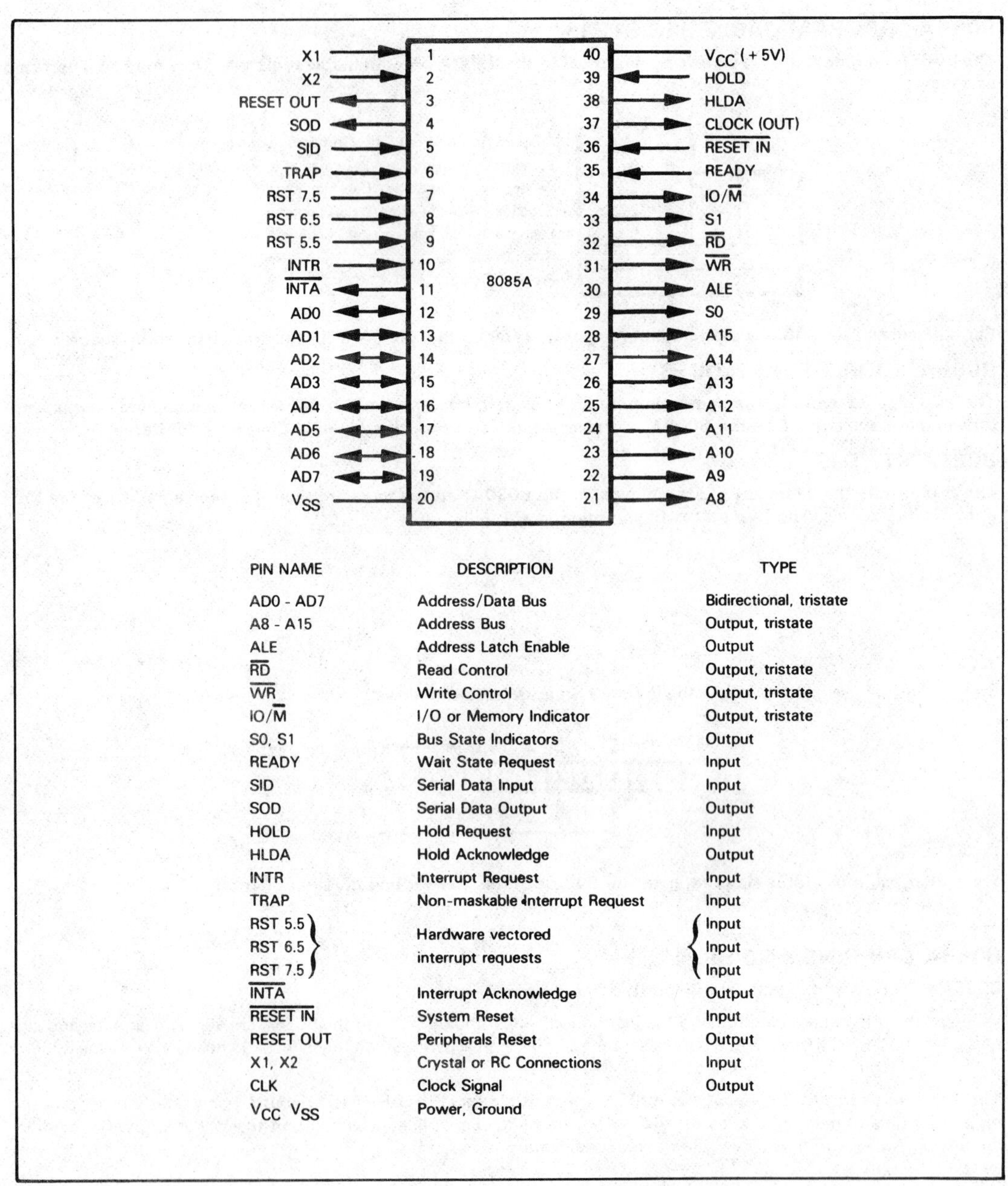


| PIN NAME | DESCRIPTION | TYPE |
|---|---|---|
| AD0 - AD7 | Address/Data Bus | Bidirectional, tristate |
| A8 - A15 | Address Bus | Output, tristate |
| ALE | Address Latch Enable | Output |
| $\overline{\text{RD}}$ | Read Control | Output, tristate |
| $\overline{\text{WR}}$ | Write Control | Output, tristate |
| IO/$\overline{\text{M}}$ | I/O or Memory Indicator | Output, tristate |
| S0, S1 | Bus State Indicators | Output |
| READY | Wait State Request | Input |
| SID | Serial Data Input | Input |
| SOD | Serial Data Output | Output |
| HOLD | Hold Request | Input |
| HLDA | Hold Acknowledge | Output |
| INTR | Interrupt Request | Input |
| TRAP | Non-maskable Interrupt Request | Input |
| RST 5.5 | Hardware vectored interrupt requests | Input |
| RST 6.5 | | Input |
| RST 7.5 | | Input |
| $\overline{\text{INTA}}$ | Interrupt Acknowledge | Output |
| $\overline{\text{RESET IN}}$ | System Reset | Input |
| RESET OUT | Peripherals Reset | Output |
| X1, X2 | Crystal or RC Connections | Input |
| CLK | Clock Signal | Output |
| $V_{CC}$ $V_{SS}$ | Power, Ground | |

Figure 5-2. 8085A CPU Signals and Pin Assignments

**ALE is an address latch enable signal** which pulses high when address data is being output on AD0 - AD7. You may use the falling edge of ALE to strobe the address off AD0 - AD7 into external latches if you are demultiplexing AD0 - AD7 into separate Address and Data Busses.

**Five control signals control memory and I/O accesses.**

**8085A CONTROL SIGNALS**

**$\overline{\text{RD}}$ is pulsed low for a memory or I/O read operation.**

**$\overline{\text{WR}}$ is pulsed low for a memory or I/O write operation.**

**IO/$\overline{\text{M}}$ is output high in conjunction with $\overline{\text{RD}}$ or $\overline{\text{WR}}$ for an I/O access.**

**IO/$\overline{\text{M}}$ is output low in conjunction with $\overline{\text{RD}}$ or $\overline{\text{WR}}$ for a memory read or write operation.**

**8085A DATA BUS DEFINITION SIGNALS**

**The state of the System Bus is further defined by the S0 and S1 status signals as follows:**

| S1 | S0 | OPERATION SPECIFIED |
|---|---|---|
| 0 | 0 | Halt |
| 0 | 1 | Memory or I/O write |
| 1 | 0 | Memory or I/O read |
| 1 | 1 | Instruction fetch |

External logic that does not have sufficient time to respond to an access can gain additional time by using the READY input signal. **The READY input can be used to insert Wait state clock periods in any machine cycle.** Timing and logic associated with Wait states is described later in this chapter.

**8085A SERIAL I/O**

Two signals allow a primitive serial I/O capability. **The high-order Accumulator bit may be output via SOD. The signal level at SID may be input to the high-order bit of the Accumulator.** SID and SOD may also be used to input status and to output control signals.

**Two signals allow external logic to take control of the System Bus.**

**8085A BUS CONTROL SIGNALS**

**HOLD, when input high, floats the Address Bus plus the $\overline{\text{RD}}$, $\overline{\text{WR}}$, IO/$\overline{\text{M}}$ and ALE control signals. HLDA is output high to acknowledge this Hold condition.**

**8085A INTERRUPT SIGNALS**

**There are six signals associated with interrupt logic. Interrupts may be requested via INTR, RST 5.5, RST 6.5, RST 7.5 and TRAP. An interrupt request made via INTR is acknowledged via the $\overline{\text{INTA}}$ output.**

INTR is the general purpose interrupt request used by external logic; it is equivalent to the 8080A INTR signal.

TRAP is a non-maskable, highest priority interrupt request. TRAP is used for catastrophic failure interrupts.

RST 5.5, RST 6.5 and RST 7.5 are three interrupt request signals supported by hardware-implemented vectoring.

**Interrupt capabilities of the 8085A are described in detail later in this chapter.**

**8085A RESET SIGNALS**

**There are two signals associated with 8085A Reset logic.**

$\overline{\text{RESET IN}}$ is the Reset input signal. This signal need not be synchronized with the clock. RESET OUT is a Reset signal output by the 8085A for use throughout the rest of the 8085A microcomputer system.

**X1 and X2 connect an external crystal or RC network to drive clock logic internal to the 8085A.** A crystal will be connected as follows:

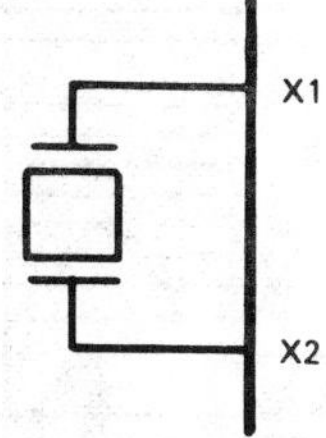

An RC network will be connected as follows:

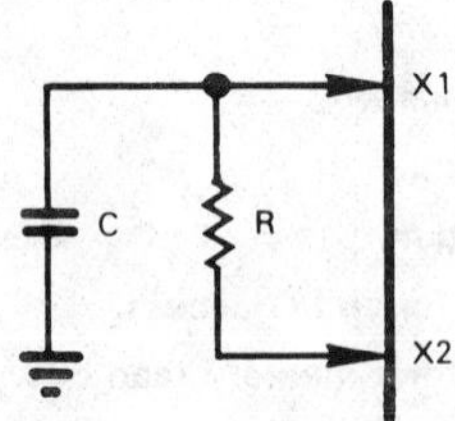


You can apply a clock signal directly to X1:

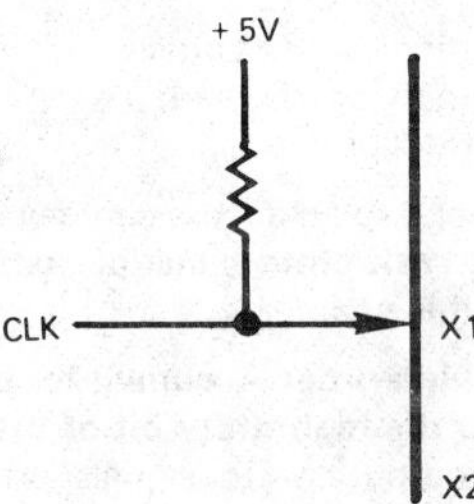


**The input frequency must be twice the operating frequency.** Thus, to obtain a 320 nanosecond clock, or 3.125 MHz, the input frequency must be 6.25 MHz.

Slave 8085A devices in a multiple CPU system will usually be driven directly by a clock signal.

A TTL level clock signal (CLK) is output by the 8085A. It may be used to drive slave CPUs, or for any other synchronization purpose within the microcomputer system. The frequency of CLK is the operating frequency of the 8085A; that is, the CLK frequency is half the input frequency.

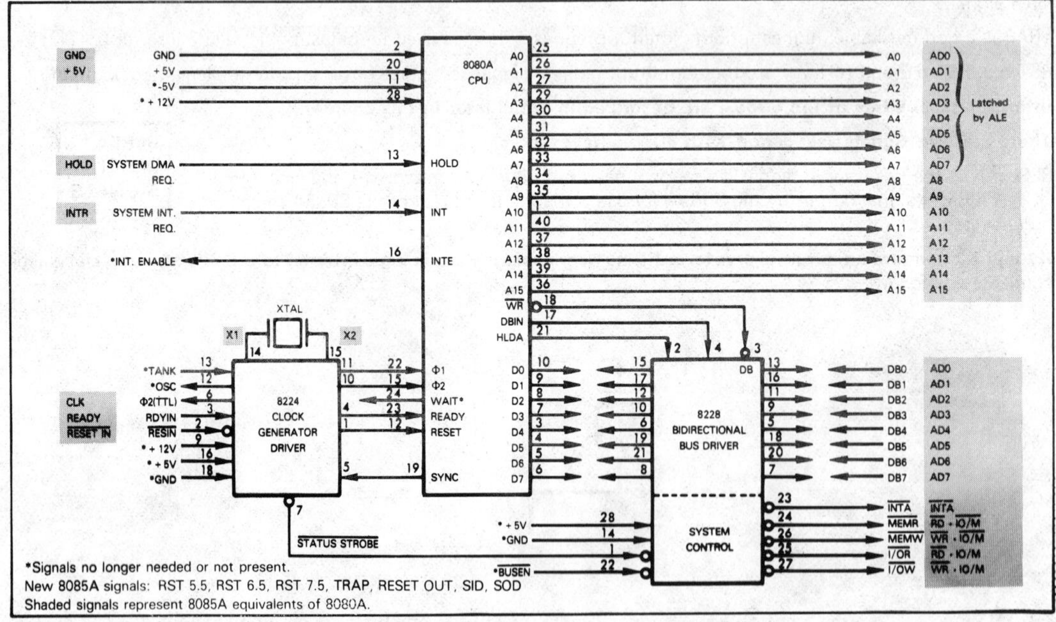


Figure 5-3. A Comparison of 8085A and 8080A/8224/8228 Signal Interface

## A COMPARISON OF 8085A AND 8080A SIGNALS

**No attempt has been made to maintain any kind of pin compatibility between the 8085A and the 8080A. Nevertheless, as illustrated in Figure 5-3, it is relatively simple to derive equivalent system busses when using the 8085A or 8080A.** But look at Figure 5-3 with an element of caution. Many logical combinations of 8085A signals are shown reproducing 8080A signals; in reality you will never generate such logical combinations — a point which will become clear as the chapter proceeds. **The purpose of Figure 5-3 is to illustrate the equivalence of the system busses generated by the 8085A and the 8080A without indicating that creation of equivalent busses is desirable.**

The 8080A signals which are shown as having direct 8085A equivalents are either obvious, or will become so after you have read this chapter.

What is more interesting is to look at the 8080A signals which no longer exist and the new 8085A signals which have been added.

**Let us first look at the signals which have been dropped.**

There are the surplus power supplies -5V and +12V, plus the secondary power supplies required by the 8224 Clock Generator and the 8228 System Controller. Elimination of these signals is self-evident.

INTE is an 8080A signal that indicates to external logic when interrupts have or have not been enabled internally by the 8080A. This signal is not very useful, since external logic cannot use the information it provides. Apart from illuminating an appropriate indicator on a minicomputer-like control panel, the INTE signal of the 8080A serves little useful purpose.

WAIT is a signal which is output high by the 8080A while Wait states are being inserted within a machine cycle. There is little that external logic can do with this signal, therefore its elimination in the 8085A carries no penalty.

$\overline{\text{BUSEN}}$ is a control input to the 8228 System Controller; it causes the 8228 to float its output signals. This signal is no longer required in the 8085A since the Hold state floats all equivalent 8085A output signals — with the exception of $\overline{\text{INTA}}$, which does not need to be floated.

The 8224 Clock Generator outputs two synchronizing clock signals — OSC and $\Phi$2 (TTL). $\Phi$2 (TTL) is approximately reproduced by CLK; OSC has no equivalent 8085A signal.

The TANK input to the 8224 Clock Generator allows overtones of the external crystal to be used. No such signal exists with the 8085A — which simply means that you have to use the primary frequency of any crystal connected across the X1 and X2 inputs.

**Seven new signals have been added to the 8085A; it would have been possible to provide separate Data and Address Busses by eliminating these seven signals, plus the ALE control signal** whose presence is a direct consequence of having multiplexed Data and Address Busses. Intel has chosen to provide the seven new signals, paying the price of having multiplexed Data and Address Busses.

**Let us examine the new signals.**

RST 5.5, RST 6.5, RST 7.5 and TRAP represent additional interrupt request inputs. TRAP is a non-maskable, high priority interrupt; the other three interrupt requests are supported by hardware-implemented vectoring.

RESET OUT is a Reset signal output by the 8085A; it may be used to reset support devices around the 8085A.

SID and SOD are control signals which provide a primitive serial input and output capability. These signals can also be used as a general purpose status input (SID) and a control output (SOD).

## 8085A TIMING AND INSTRUCTION EXECUTION

**An 8085A instruction's execution is timed by a sequence of machine cycles, each of which is divided into clock periods.**

**8085A MACHINE CYCLES**

An instruction is executed in from one to five machine cycles labeled MC1, MC2, MC3, MC4 and MC5.

**8085A CLOCK PERIODS**

The first machine cycle of any instruction's execution will have either four or six clock periods. Subsequent machine cycles will have three clock periods only. This may be illustrated as follows:

| MC1 | | | | | | MC2 | | | MC3 | | | MC4 | | | MC5 | | |
|---|---|---|---|---|---|---|---|---|---|---|---|---|---|---|---|---|---|
| $T_1$ | $T_2$ | $T_3$ | $T_4$ | $T_5$ | $T_6$ | $T_1$ | $T_2$ | $T_3$ | $T_1$ | $T_2$ | $T_3$ | $T_1$ | $T_2$ | $T_3$ | $T_1$ | $T_2$ | $T_3$ |

Where MC is shaded, the entire machine cycle is optional. Where T is shaded, the clock period is optional within its machine cycle.

8085A machine cycles and clock periods are very similar to those of the 8080A. You will find in Table 5-1 that the number of clock periods required to execute 8085A instructions is equal to the number of clock periods required by the 8080A to execute the same instructions, or differs by one clock period only.

## THE CLOCK SIGNALS

**The 8085A times its machine cycles using this simple clock signal:**

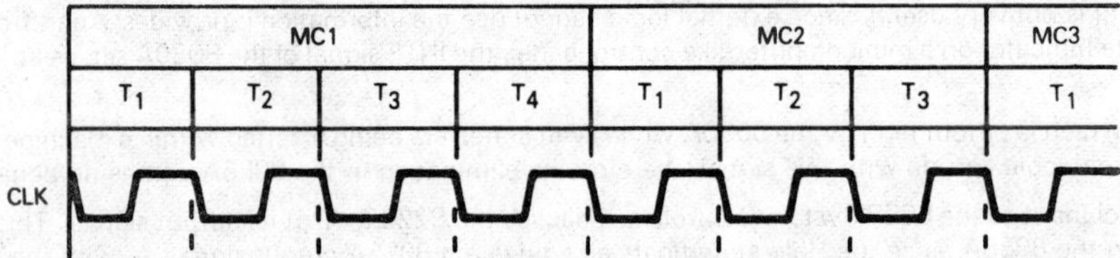


**Although the 8085A has no SYNC signal to identify the start of a new machine cycle, you can use the 8085A ALE signal for the same purpose.** This signal is output true during the first clock period of every machine cycle — at which time the AD0 - AD7 lines are outputting address data. In addition, you can identify the first (instruction fetch) cycle of any instruction's execution. S0 and S1 will both be output high during an instruction fetch machine cycle. Clock periods and machine cycles may therefore be identified as follows:

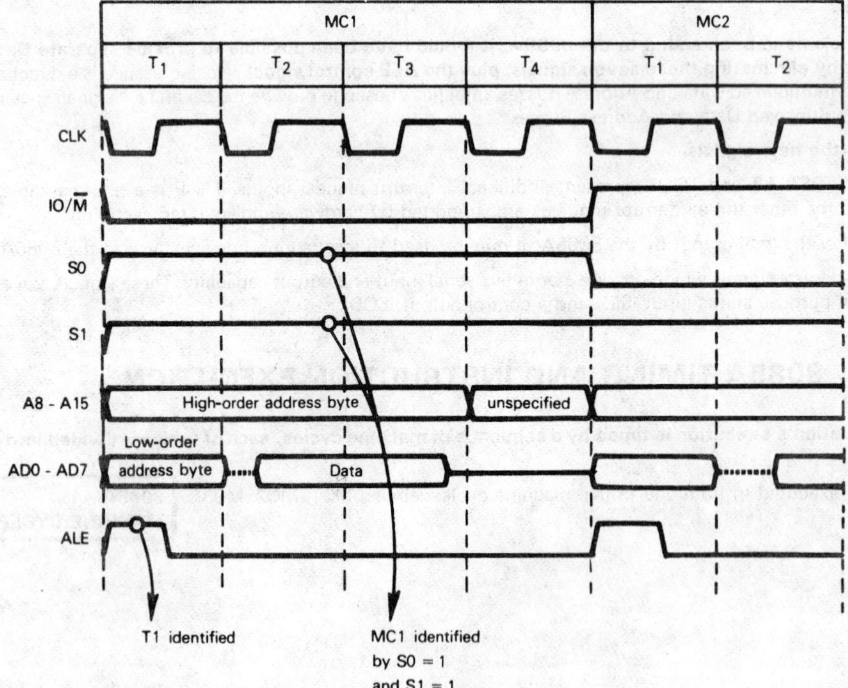

## MEMORY ACCESS SEQUENCES

**So far as external logic is concerned, there is very little difference between an instruction fetch, a memory read, and a memory write. We will therefore examine timing for these operations together.**

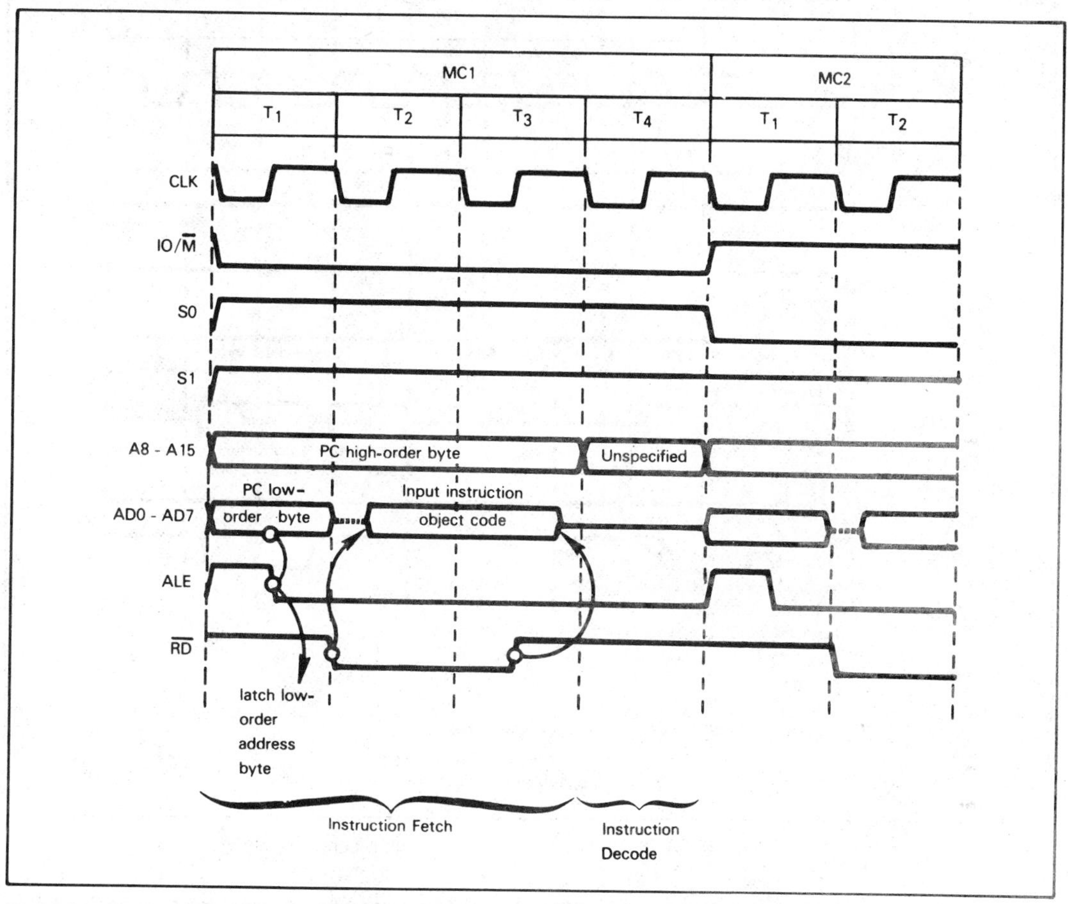


Figure 5-4. A Four Clock Period Instruction Fetch Machine Cycle

**Let us first consider an instruction fetch. Timing is illustrated in Figure 5-4 for a four clock period machine cycle, and in Figure 5-5 for a six clock period machine cycle.**

The most important aspect of the instruction fetch machine cycle is the fact that it will have either four or six clock periods, as against three for all subsequent machine cycles. The instruction fetch machine cycle must have at least four clock periods, since the fourth clock period is needed to decode the instruction object code which has been fetched. If the instruction requires no subsequent memory accesses, then a fifth and sixth clock period may be needed to perform the internal operation specified by the fetched instruction. If additional memory accesses will be required, then the fourth clock period of the first machine cycle is sufficient.

At the end of the first clock period, AD0 - AD7 is floated transiently; then it is turned around to act as a Data Input Bus. $\overline{RD}$ is pulsed low to strobe data onto the Data Bus.

The memory read must occur within three clock periods. Since this is an instruction fetch machine cycle, the CPU will place the input in the Instruction register. If external logic requires more time to respond to the memory access, then it can generate additional Wait clock periods. We will describe the 8085A Wait state shortly.

During the fourth clock period of the instruction fetch machine cycle the instruction object code is interpreted by logic of the 8085A CPU. Fifth and sixth clock periods will be required by some instructions to execute required internal operations.

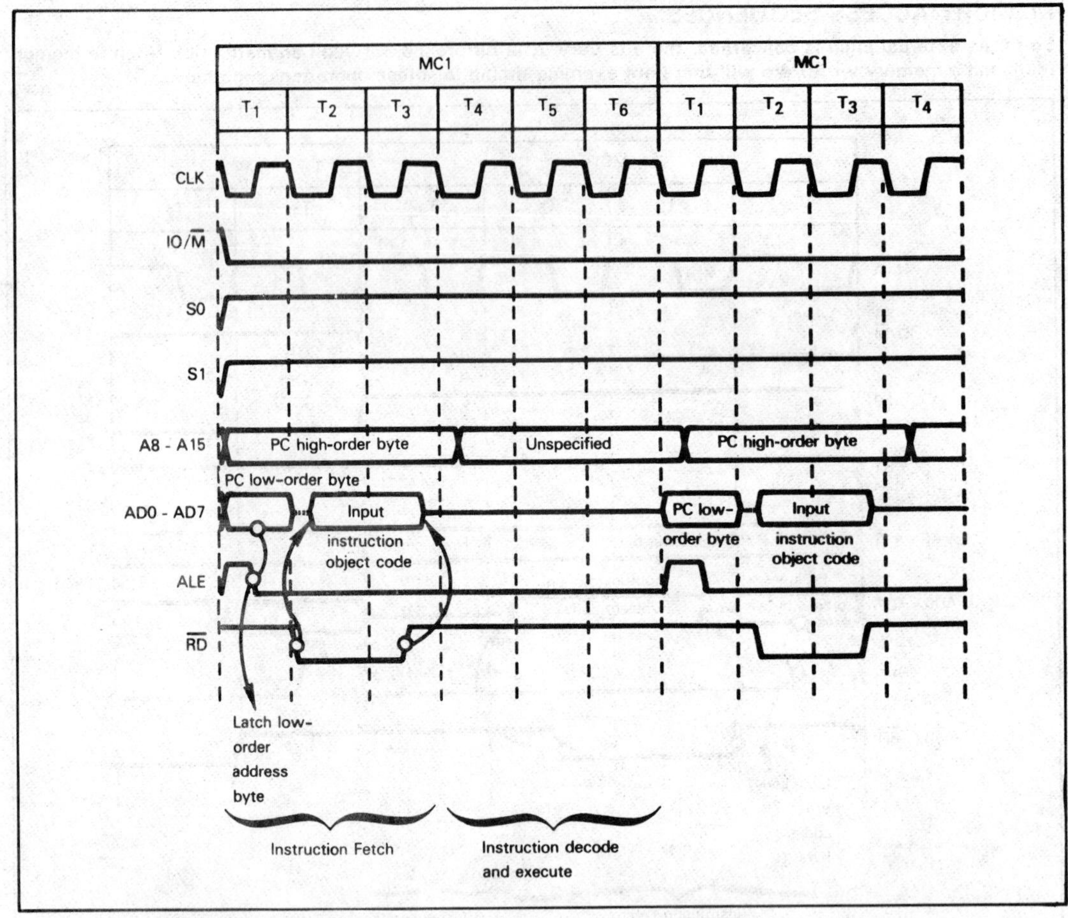


Figure 5-5. A Six Clock Period Instruction Fetch Machine Cycle

**During the fourth and subsequent clock periods, AD0 - AD7 is floated and A8 - A15 contains unspecified data.**

**8085A DEVICE SELECT LOGIC**

**The fact that AD0 - AD7 and A8 - A15 are unknown data during the fourth and subsequent clock periods of an instruction fetch machine cycle must be taken into account when you create memory select and I/O device select logic.**

In Figures 5-4 and 5-5 S0 and S1 are both high, identifying this as an instruction fetch machine cycle. IO/$\overline{M}$ is low since the instruction object code is to be fetched from memory. An instruction fetch is thus equivalent to a memory read.

The address of the memory location to be accessed is fetched from the Program Counter (PC) and is output on AD0 - AD7 (low-order byte) and A8 - A15 (high-order byte). **The low-order byte of this memory address is stable on AD0 - AD7 during the first clock period.** ALE is pulsed high at this time. **The trailing edge of ALE is designed to** act as a strobe signal which external logic can use to **latch the low-order address byte** off AD0 - AD7. **If you are using one of the 8085A support devices (the 8155, the 8156 the 8344 or the or the 8755A), then the low-order byte**

**of the memory address is latched off the AD0 - AD7 lines for you. If you are using standard memory devices, then you must demultiplex AD0 - AD7. Any simple latched buffer can be used for this purpose; here is an example of the 8212 I/O port being used as a demultiplexer:**

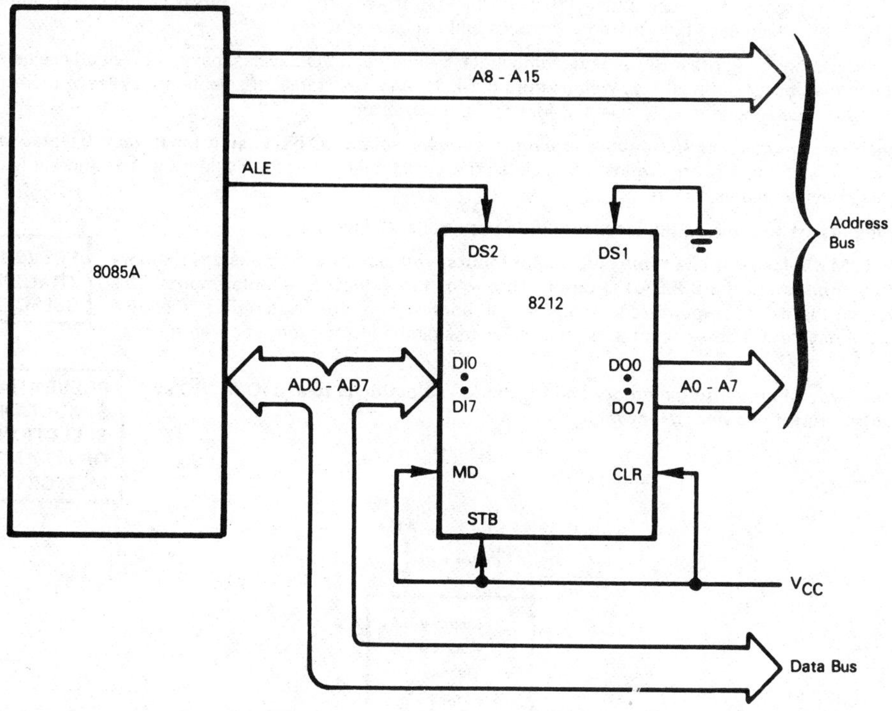


**You might argue that there is no harm done if memory or I/O devices select themselves when the System Bus is supposed to be idle; if neither the read nor write strobe is present, data transfer between the System Bus and the selected device cannot occur.**

**MULTIPLE DEVICE SELECTS AND BUS LOADING**

**Unfortunately, the problem is not so simple.**

It is possible for more than one memory or I/O device to consider itself selected while the bus is idle; this may occur under the following conditions:

1) If I/O devices are being selected as I/O ports, then the Address Bus lines may select an I/O port while simultaneously selecting a memory device.
2) In microcomputer systems that use only a small portion of the total allowed memory — and most microcomputer systems fall into this category — memory select logic need not decode unique memory addresses. Here is an example of two 4096-byte memory modules, each of which uses a single line of the Address Bus in order to create device selects:

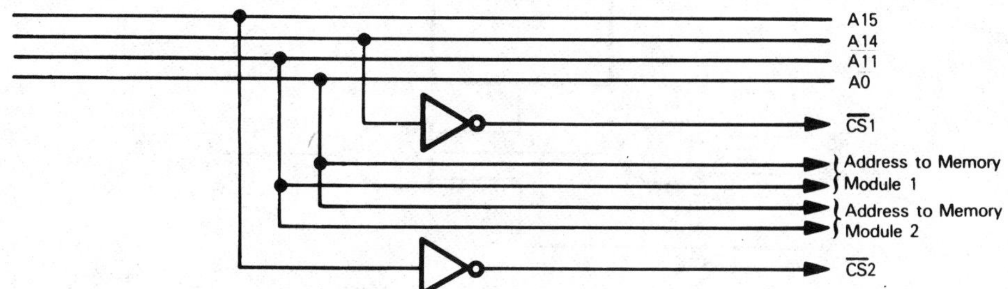

Memory module 1 will be assigned the address space $8000_{16}$ through $8FFF_{16}$. Memory module 2 will be assigned the address space $4000_{16}$ through $4FFF_{16}$. In reality a variety of other addresses will select memory modules 1 or 2. Addresses $C000_{16}$ through $CFFF_{16}$ will select memory modules 1 and 2.

A correctly written program will keep either A15 or A14 low; but while the System Bus is floating, both address lines could be high — in which case both memory modules will become selected.

While signal levels on the Address Bus are changing state, memory and I/O devices may be transiently selected. Transient selection may occur during T1 as well as during T4, T5 and T6. Transient selection may leave more than one memory or I/O device simultaneously selected for short periods of time.

**If more than one memory or I/O device is simultaneously selected, excessive loads may be placed on the System Bus.** At best, these excessive loads will cause devices connected to the System Bus to temporarily malfunction; at worst, device failures may result.

**It is very important to prevent devices from being spuriously selected.**

**PREVENTING TRANSIENT SELECTION**

**If you use ROM devices with multiple chip select inputs, you can prevent transient memory selection by connecting the 8085A $\overline{RD}$ output to one of the select (or enable) inputs.** This will ensure that the device responds only when a valid address is on the System Bus; therefore only one ROM device will be selected at a time. Refer to Volume III for information on memory devices.

**PREVENTING SIMULTANEOUS SELECTION OF I/O AND MEMORY**

**The simplest way of preventing memory and I/O device selection is to use IO/$\overline{M}$, $\overline{RD}$ and $\overline{WR}$ as contributors to device select logic:**

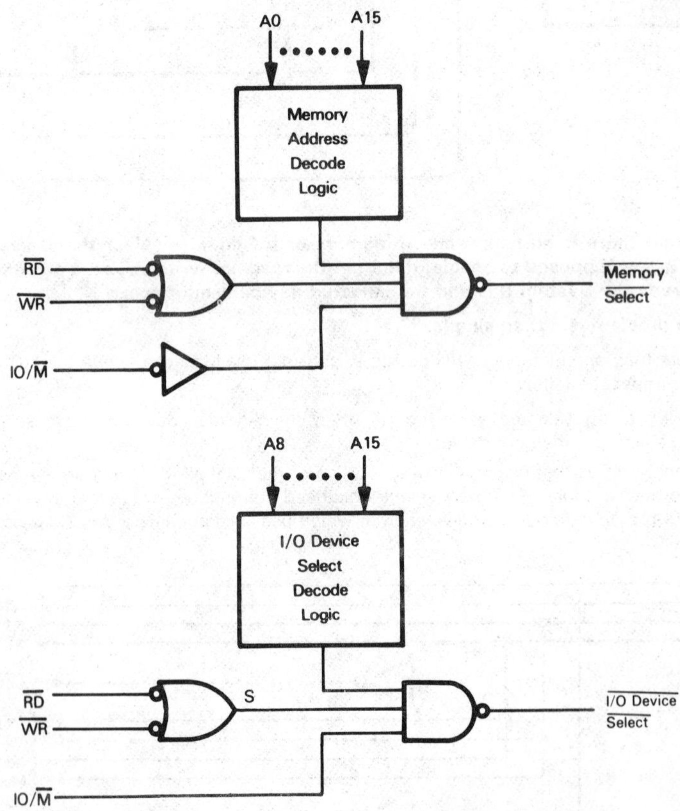

Timing for the memory select illustrated above may be illustrated as follows:

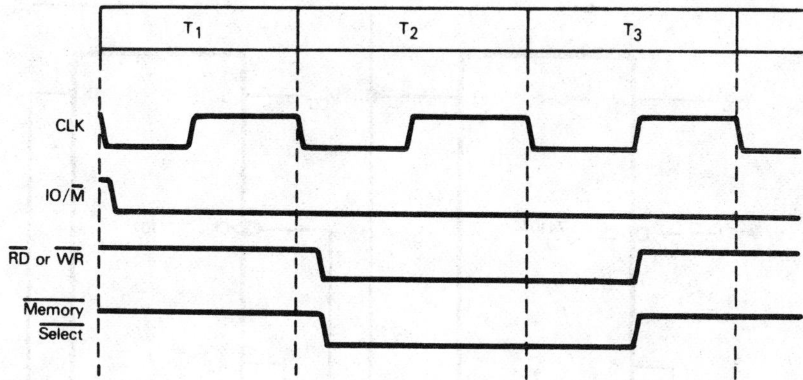


I/O device select logic timing differs only in the level of IO/$\overline{M}$.

IO/$\overline{M}$ distinguishes between memory and I/O devices. When $\overline{RD}$ or $\overline{WR}$ is low, memory or I/O device addresses must be valid. Thus the logic illustrated above will guarantee that spurious memory and I/O device selects never occur.

But there is a problem associated with the solution illustrated; memory and I/O devices do not receive a valid select signal until early in the second clock period. This is unfortunate, since valid addresses are available early in the first clock period. Delaying memory select logic until the second clock period may require Wait states to be added between clock periods 2 and 3 — and that unnecessarily slows down CPU operations. If execution speed is not a problem to you, then the simple select logic illustrated above will do. **If execution speed is a problem, then you must replace:**

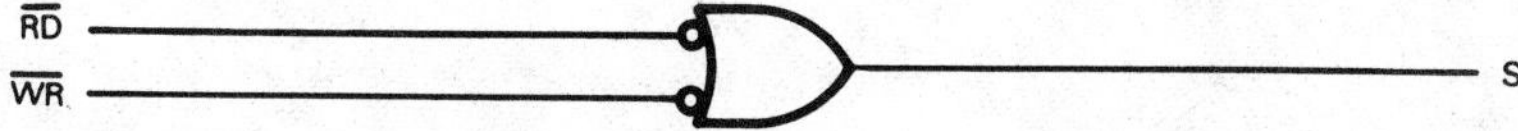


**in the simple select logic with alternative logic that may be defined as follows:**

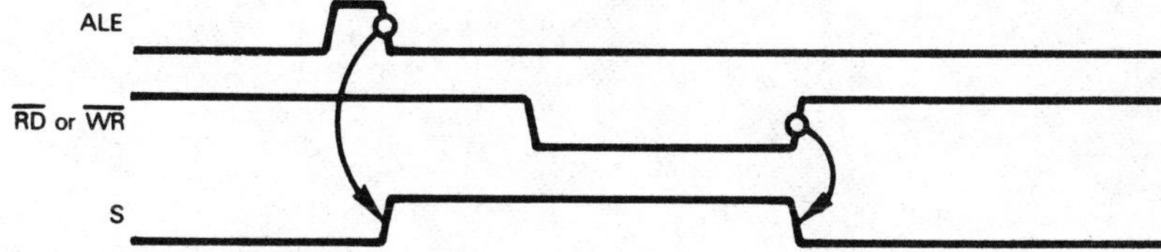

The required S output may be generated using two flip-flops as follows:

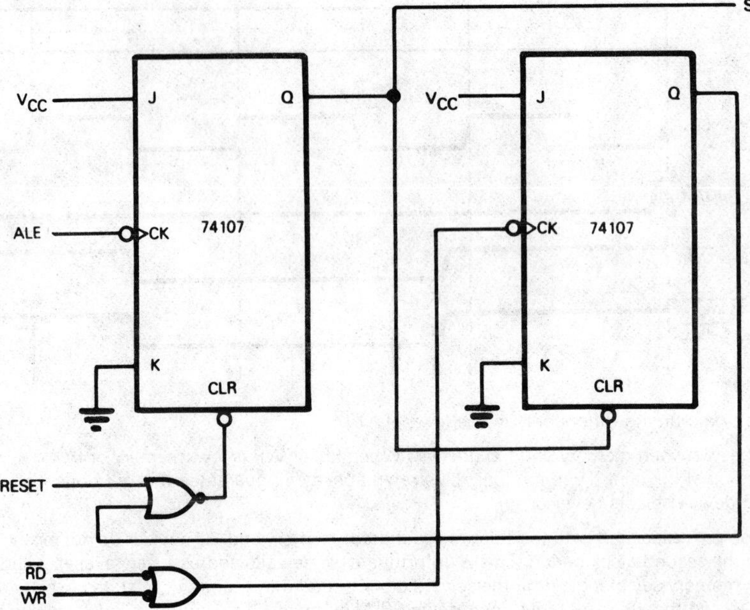

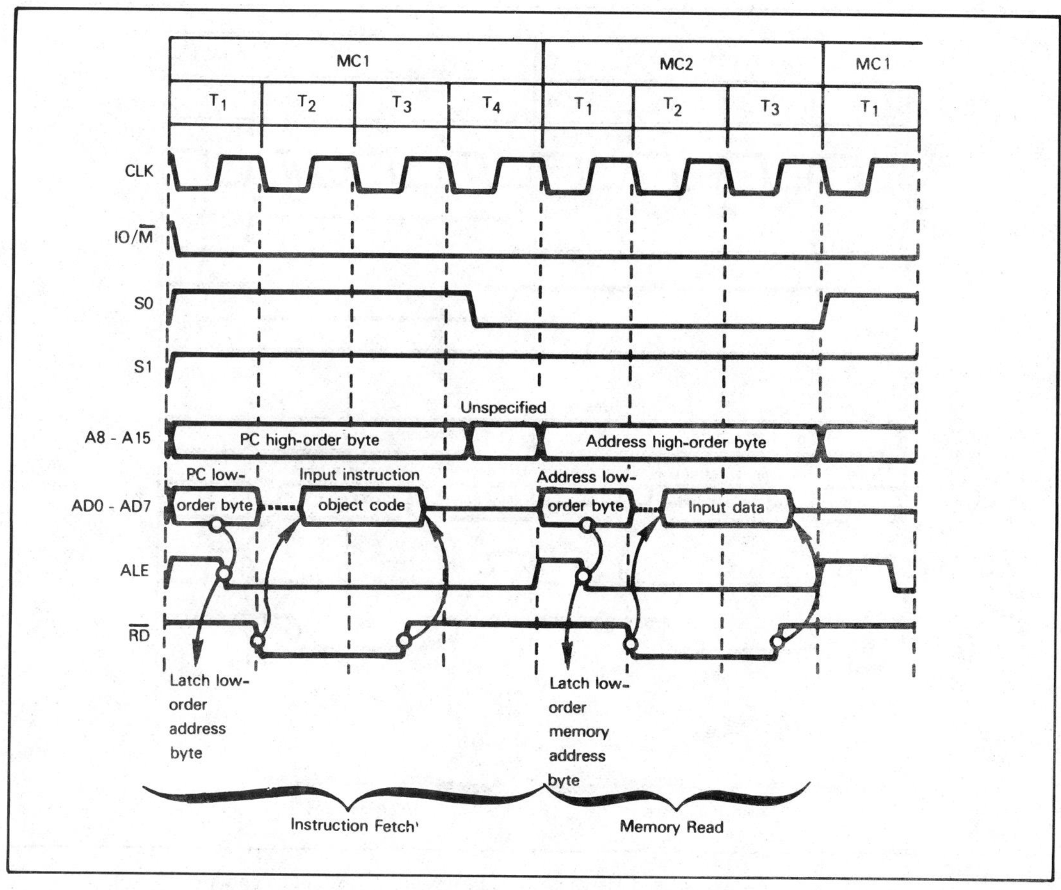


Figure 5-6. A Memory Read Machine Cycle Following an Instruction Fetch

**8085A MEMORY READ TIMING**

**Let us now consider a memory read operation; timing is illustrated in Figure 5-6.** So far as external logic is concerned, the only difference between a memory read and an instruction fetch is the S0 and S1 signal levels; they are both high for an instruction fetch, but S0 is low during a memory read. Also, the instruction fetch has four or six clock periods, while the memory read has three; but the extra instruction fetch clock periods occur after the memory access is completed. Therefore, so far as external logic is concerned, the extra clock periods of the instruction fetch machine cycle are irrelevant.

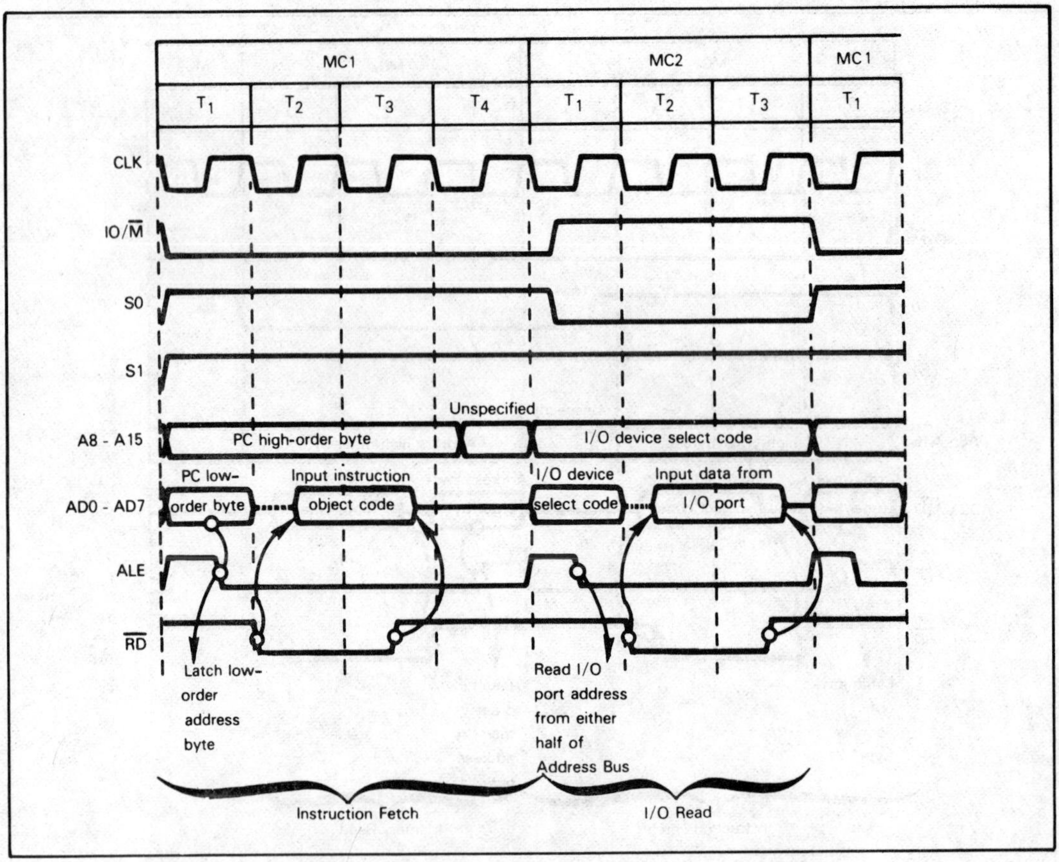

Figure 5-7. An I/O Read Machine Cycle Following an Instruction Fetch

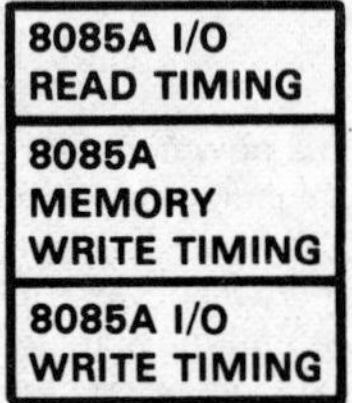

**Figure 5-7 illustrates I/O read timing.** Only the IO/$\overline{\text{M}}$ signal level in Figure 5-7 differs from Figure 5-6.

**8085A I/O READ TIMING**

**Memory write timing, illustrated in Figure 5-8, is very similar to memory read timing.** The principal difference is that during a memory write $\overline{\text{WR}}$ is output low, whereas during a memory read $\overline{\text{RD}}$ is output low. Also, during a memory write operation S1 is output low while S0 is output high.

**8085A MEMORY WRITE TIMING**

An I/O write operation is illustrated in Figure 5-9. As compared to Figure 5-8, IO/$\overline{\text{M}}$ is high in Figure 5-9 during the write machine cycle; there are no other timing differences.

**8085A I/O WRITE TIMING**

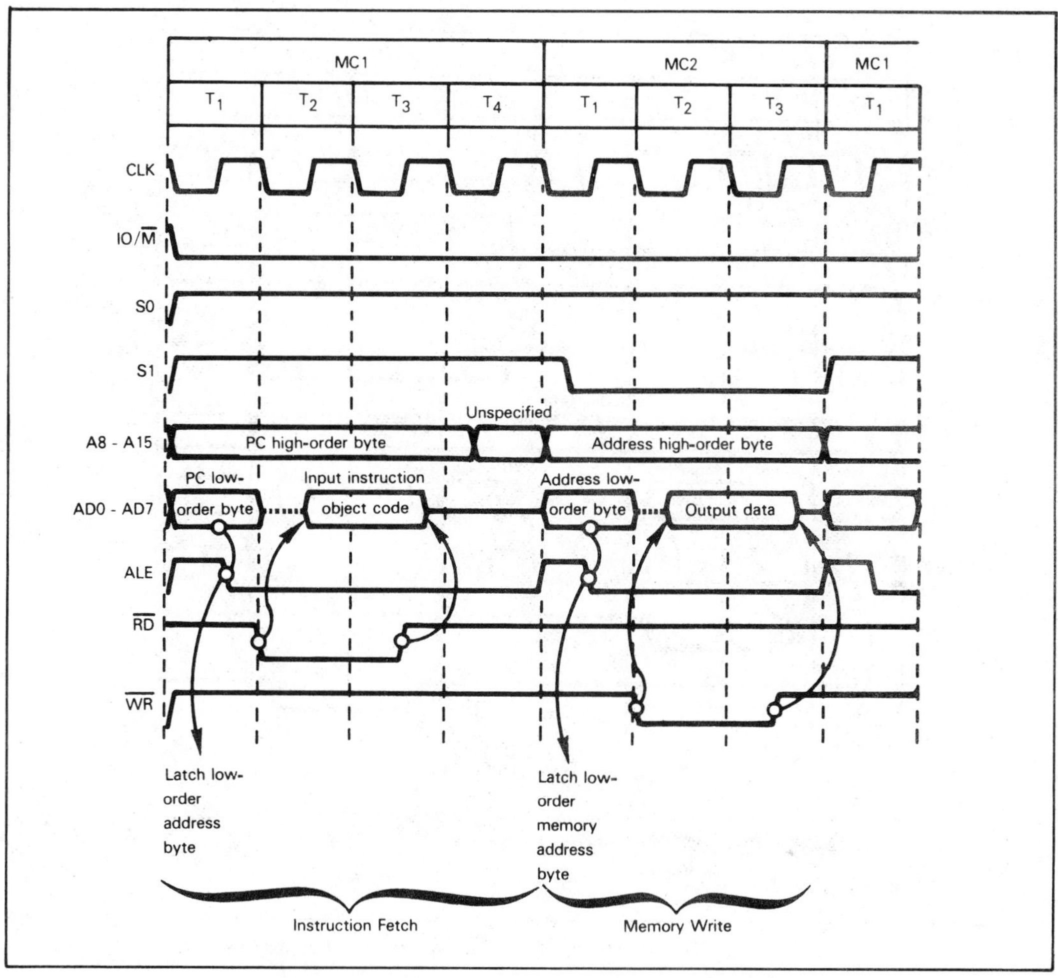


Figure 5-8. A Memory Write Machine Cycle Following an Instruction Fetch

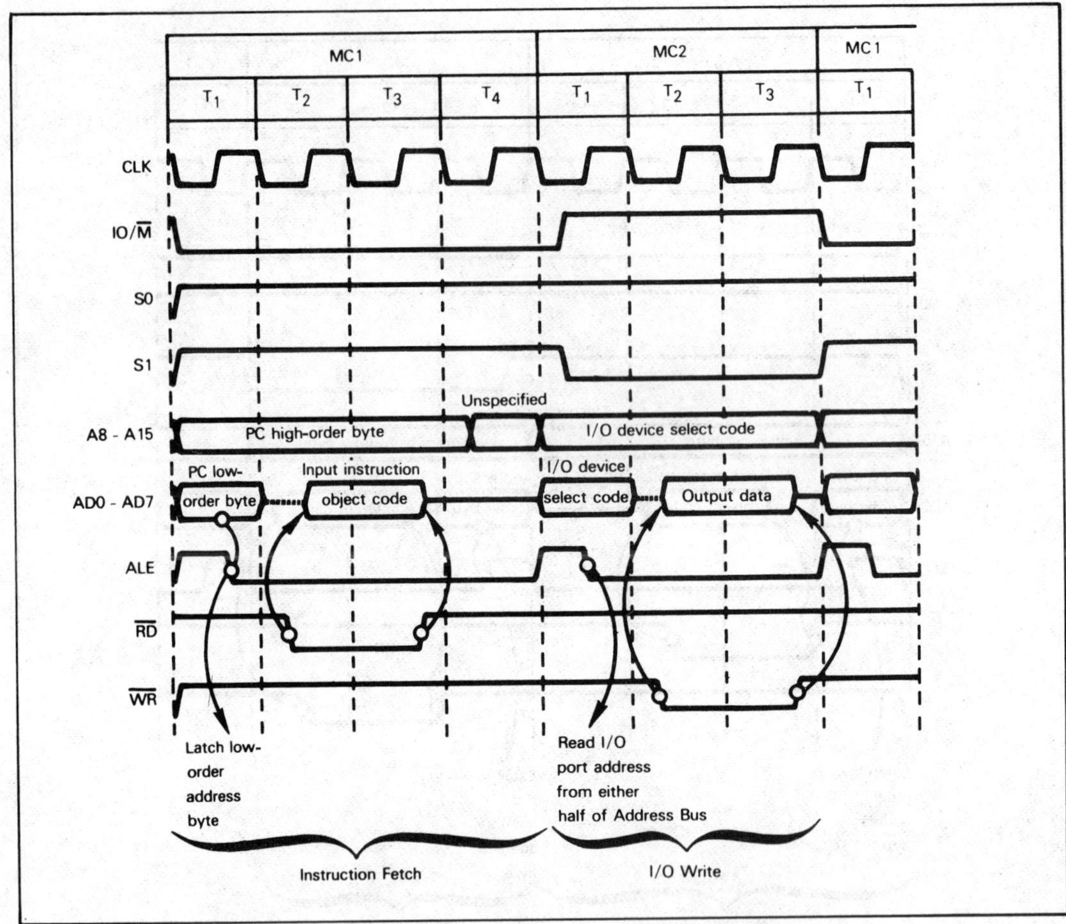


Figure 5-9. An I/O Write Machine Cycle Following an Instruction Fetch

## BUS IDLE MACHINE CYCLES

**8085A BUS IDLE MACHINE CYCLE**

**During a Bus Idle machine cycle no control signals change state on the System Bus.**

**There are three types of Bus Idle machine cycles:**

1) An instruction fetch Bus Idle machine cycle. The 8085A CPU acknowledges an interrupt from TRAP, RST 5.5, RST 6.5, and RST 7.5 by generating a Restart instruction internally. No external instruction fetch operations occur; however, logic internal to the CPU requires time to create the instruction object code. Therefore a Bus Idle instruction fetch machine cycle is executed. Timing is illustrated in Figure 5-17.

2) The instruction execute Bus Idle machine cycle. Only the DAD instruction uses this machine cycle. The DAD instruction adds the contents of two CPU registers to two other CPU registers. It takes six clock periods for logic internal to the 8085A CPU to complete these operations. The six clock periods are generated via two instruction execute Bus Idle machine cycles. Timing is illustrated in Figure 5-10.

3) The Halt Bus Idle machine cycle. Following execution of a Halt instruction an indeterminate number of Bus Idle machine cycles are executed for the duration of the Halt condition. Timing is illustrated in Figure 5-14.

**The condition of the IO/M, S1 and S2 signals during a Bus Idle machine cycle varies with the type of Bus Idle machine cycle.** These three signals will conform to instruction fetch level during an instruction fetch Bus Idle machine cycle. During an instruction execute Bus Idle machine cycle, Memory Read signal levels are maintained, but the RD control signal is not pulse low.

During a Halt Bus Idle machine cycle, S0 and S1 are both low but IO/$\overline{M}$, along with other tristate signals, is floated.

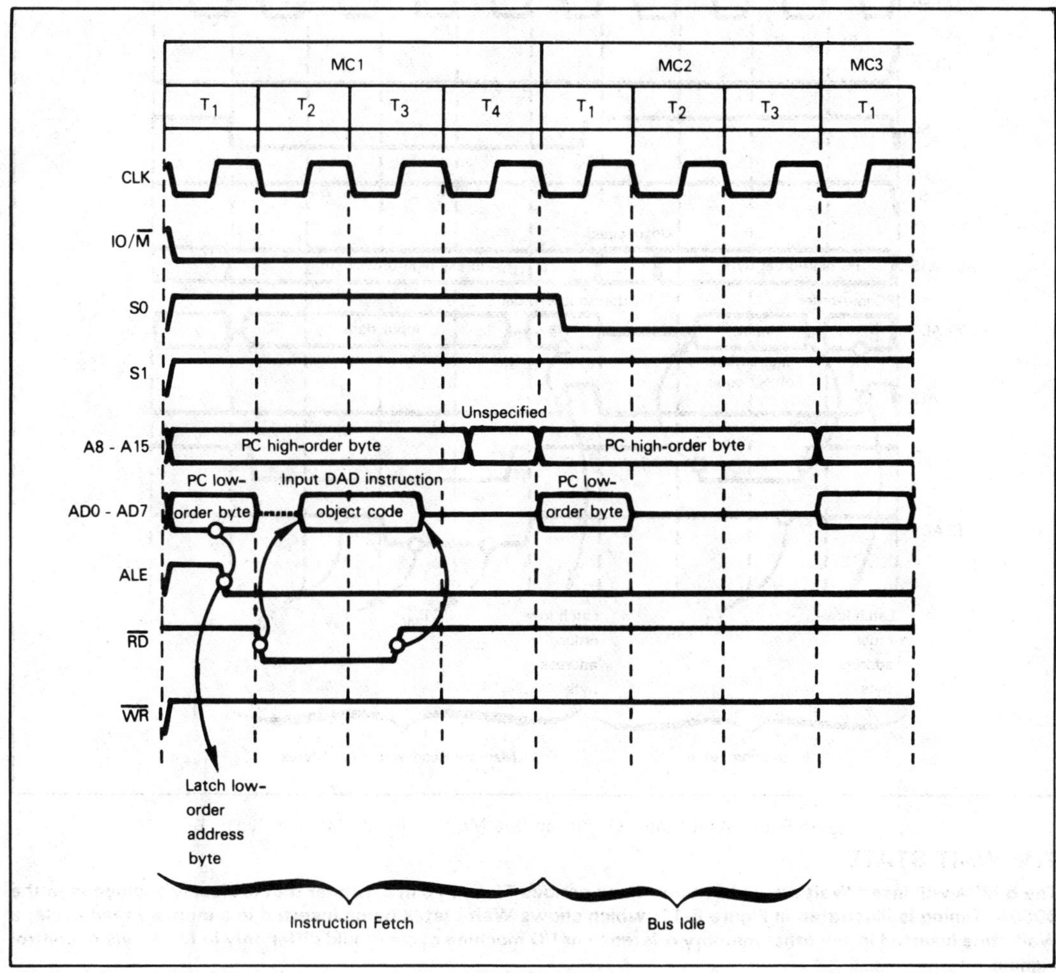


Figure 5-10. A Bus Idle Machine Cycle Following an Instruction Fetch During Execution of a DAD Instruction

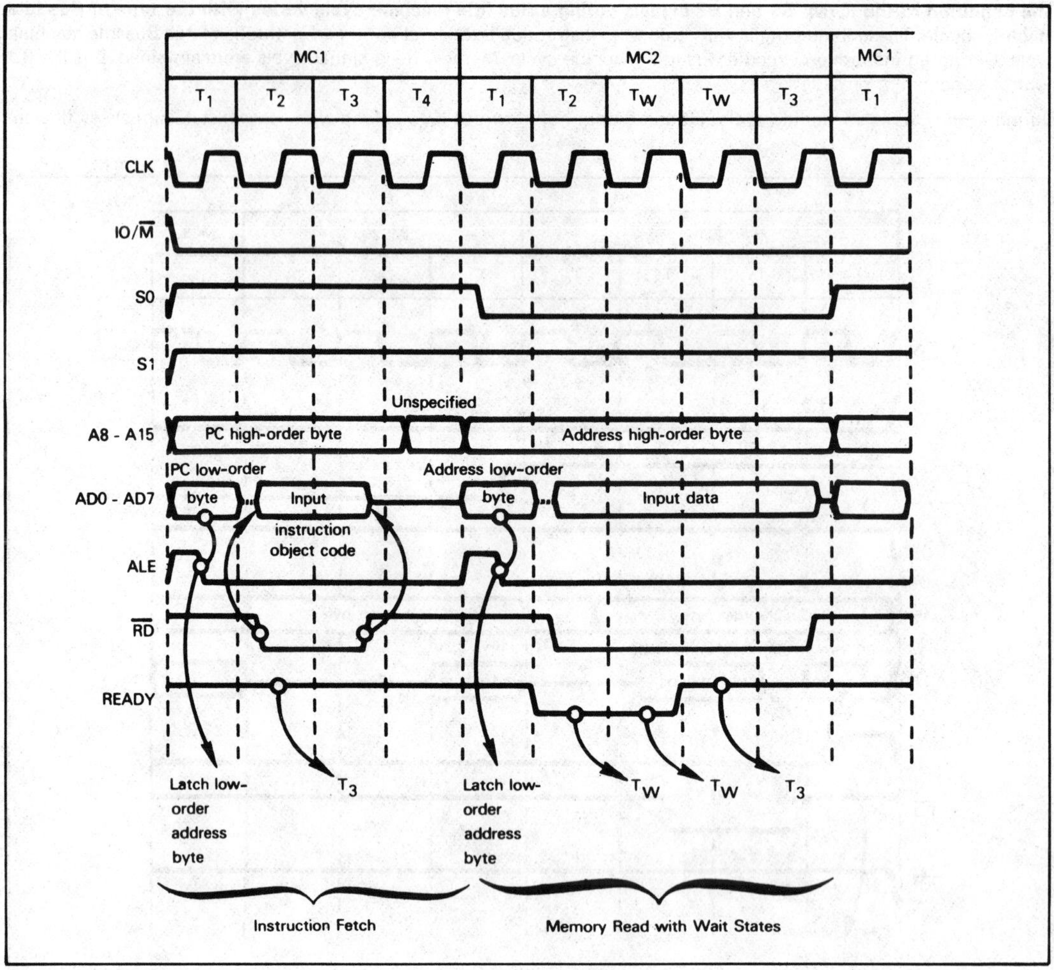

Figure 5-11. Wait States Occurring in a Memory Read Machine Cycle

## THE WAIT STATE

**The 8085A will insert Wait states between clock periods T2 and T3 in a manner that is closely analogous to the 8080A. Timing is illustrated in Figure 5-11, which shows Wait states being inserted in a memory read cycle; a Wait state inserted in any other memory reference or I/O machine cycle would differ only in the levels of control signals.**

The 8085A samples the READY line during T2. If READY is low during T2, then a Wait clock period will follow T2. The READY line is sampled in the middle of each Wait clock period; Wait clock periods continue to be inserted until READY is sampled high. As soon as READY is sampled high, the next clock period will be a T3 clock period — and normal program execution continues. This sampling may be illustrated as follows:

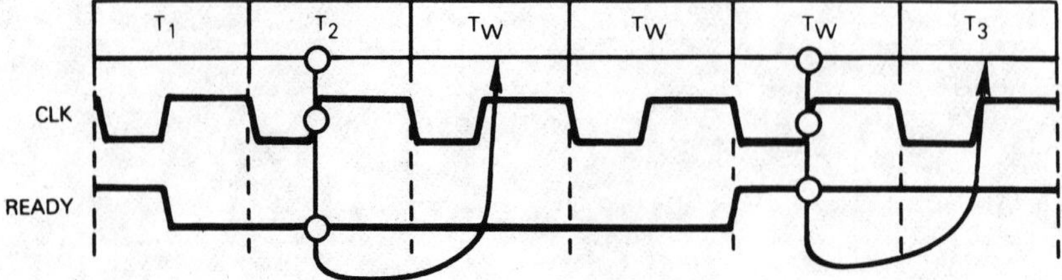

Wait states are used in an 8085A system exactly as described for the 8080A in Chapter 4 — to give slow memories and I/O devices more time in order to respond to an access. Thus the discussion of Wait states provided in Chapter 4 applies equally to the 8085A.

In Chapter 4 a pair of 7474 flip-flops are shown creating a low READY pulse that generates a single Wait state in a memory read machine cycle. For the 8085A the following variation applies:

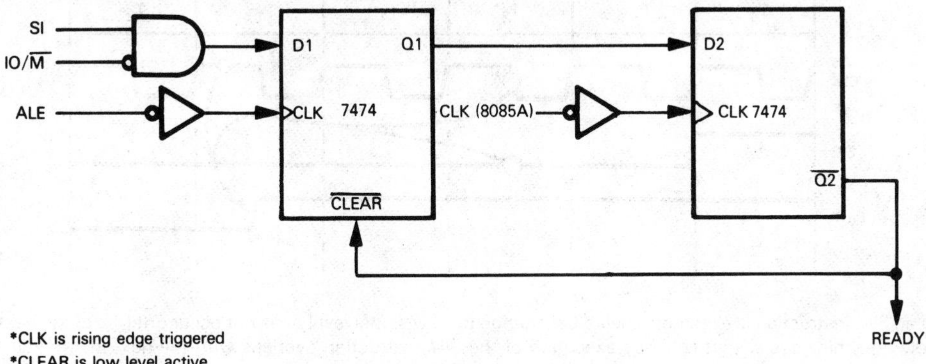


*CLK is rising edge triggered
*CLEAR is low level active

The circuit will operate with the following timing:

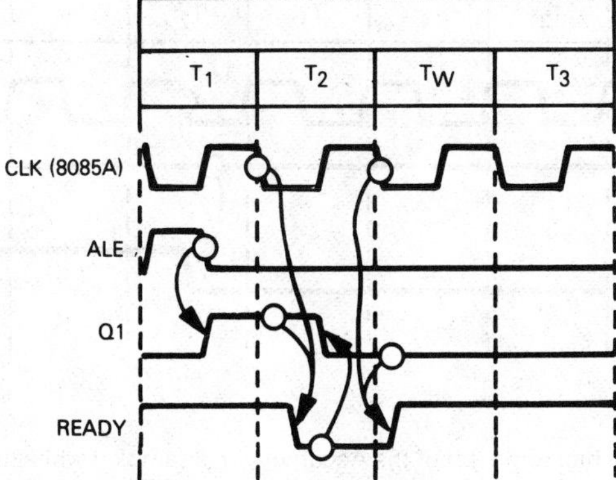


If the cycle is a memory read (S = 1, S0 = 0) or an instruction fetch (S1 = 1, S0 = 1), Q1 will go high at the falling edge of ALE. This will cause flip-flop 2 to go on at the next falling edge of the 8085A clock, thereby forcing READY low. The low on READY will clear flip-flop 1, so that READY will return high on the next falling edge of the 8085A clock.

## THE SID AND SOD SIGNALS

**The 8085A has two instructions which handle single-bit data.**

**The RIM instruction inputs data from the SID pin to the high-order bit of the Accumulator. The SIM instruction outputs the high-order bit of the Accumulator to the SOD pin.**

You may use the RIM and SIM instructions in order to implement a primitive serial I/O capability. A more useful application of these instructions is to read single signal status and to output single-signal controls.

When the RIM instruction is executed, the SID signal level is sampled on the rising edge of the clock signal during clock period T3 of the instruction fetch machine cycle. The high-order bit of the Accumulator is modified while the clock signal is high during T1 of the next instruction fetch machine cycle. Timing may be illustrated as follows:

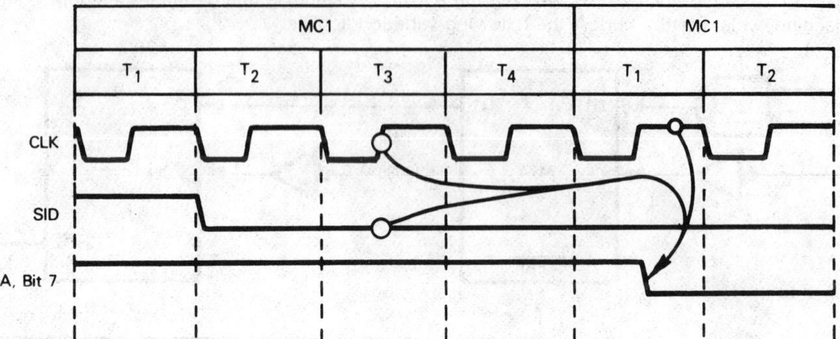


When an SIM instruction is executed, the actual change in SOD signal level does not occur until T2 of the next instruction fetch machine cycle; that is to say execution of the SIM instruction overlaps with the next instruction fetch.

This may be illustrated as follows:

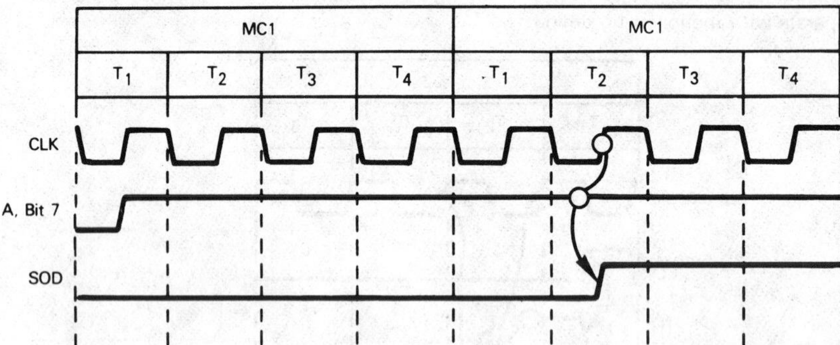


Following an SIM instruction fetch, the high-order bit of the Accumulator is sampled while the clock is low during T2 of the next instruction fetch machine cycle. During the same clock period, the SOD signal level is modified to reflect the contents of the high-order Accumulator bit. This overlap is feasible since neither the SOD signal nor the Accumulator contents are modified while an instruction is being fetched. Note that SOD must be enabled before it can be accessed or changed; you use bit 6 of the Accumulator to enable SOD, as detailed later in this chapter when we describe the 8085A instruction set.

**Figure 5-12 illustrates SID and SOD signal timing during execution of a RIM instruction followed by a SIM instruction.**

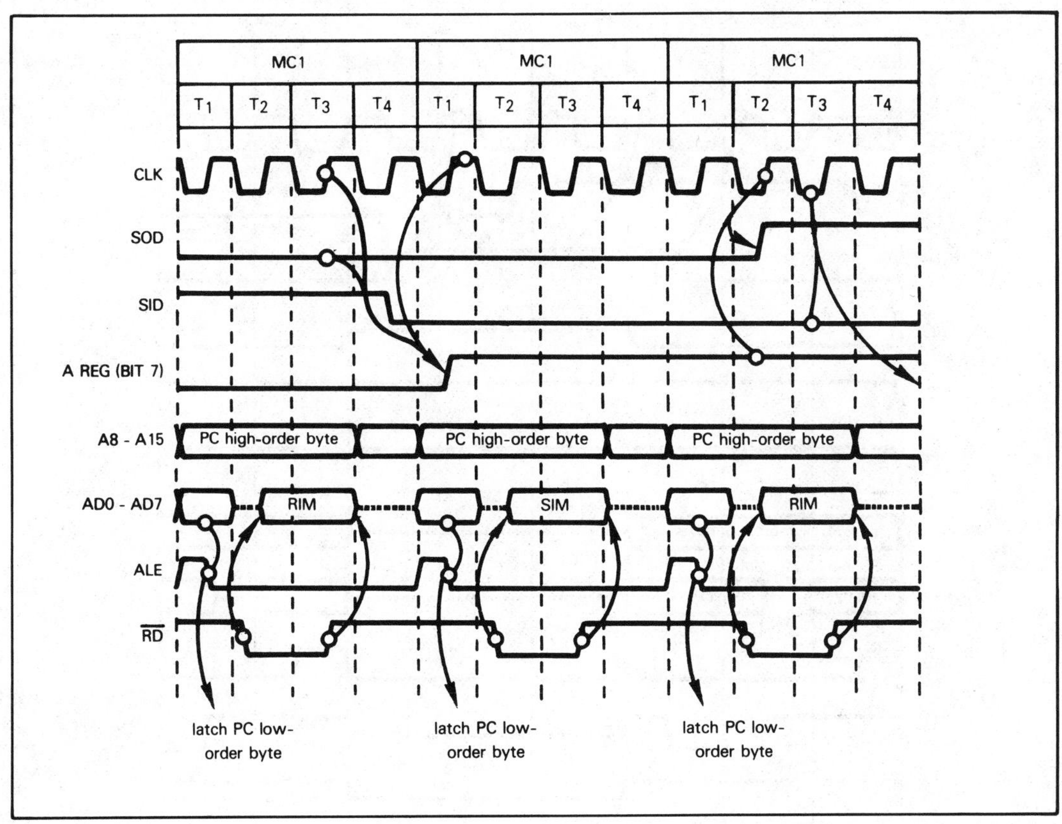


Figure 5-12. A RIM Instruction Followed by a SIM Instruction

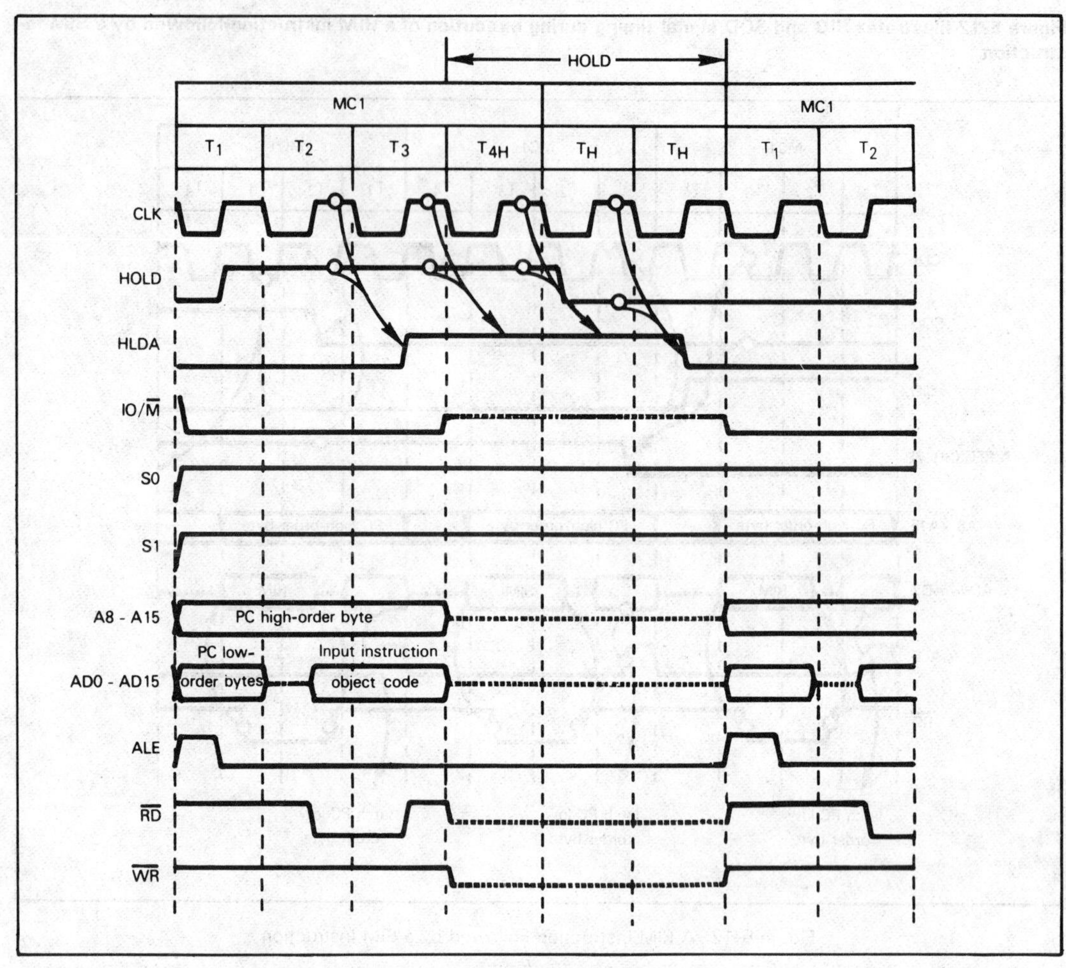


Figure 5-13. A Hold State Following a Single Machine Cycle Instruction Execution

## THE HOLD STATE

**The 8080A and the 8085A both use the Hold state as a means of transiently floating the System Bus. During a Hold, external logic gains bus control, usually to perform direct memory access operations.**

External logic requests a Hold state by inputting HOLD high. The microprocessor responds by entering the Hold state and outputting HLDA high. During a Hold state the microprocessor floats all tristate signals.

Both the 8080A and the 8085A initiate the Hold state at the conclusion of an instruction's execution. But there are significant differences between Hold state initiation logic for the 8085A as against the 8080A.

The 8080A initiates a Hold state following T3 for a Read machine cycle, or following T4 for a Write machine cycle. Timing is illustrated in Figures 4-9 and 4-10.

**The 8085A** in contrast, **has a fixed, two machine cycle sequence for Hold state initiation;** it may be illustrated as follows:

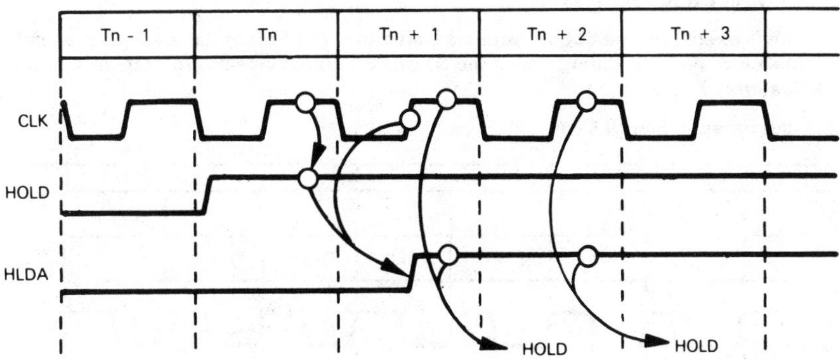


**During every machine cycle, Hold is sampled during T2; if Hold is high at this time, Hold acknowledge is output high during T3 and the Hold state begins during T4. Timing is illustrated in Figure 5-13.**

**During a six clock period machine cycle, if Hold is low when sampled during T2, then Hold will be sampled again during T4.** If Hold is sampled high during T4, then a Hold state will be initiated during T6. This may be illustrated as follows:

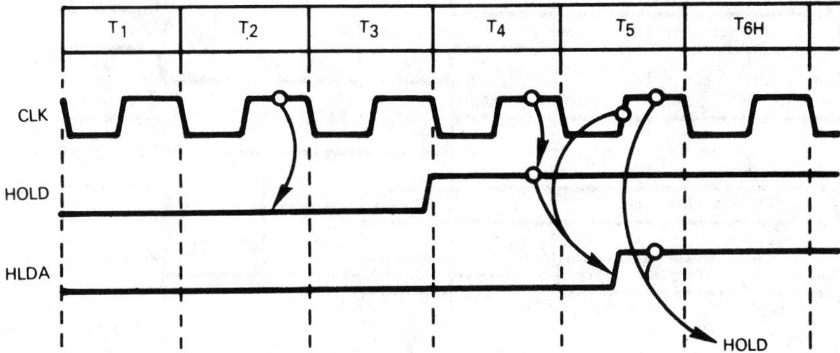


**Hold is sampled during every clock period of a Halt state.** As soon as Hold is detected high, a two clock period Hold state initiation sequence begins. Figures 5-14 and 5-15 illustrate the onset of Hold states within and before Halt states.

**A Hold state terminates two clock periods after the Hold signal goes low.**

There are no restrictions placed by 8085A logic on the duration of a Hold state. The Hold state lasts for as long as the HOLD input is high. Here is an example of a one clock period Hold state occurring during T4 and a three clock period Hold state beginning during T6 of a six clock period machine cycle:

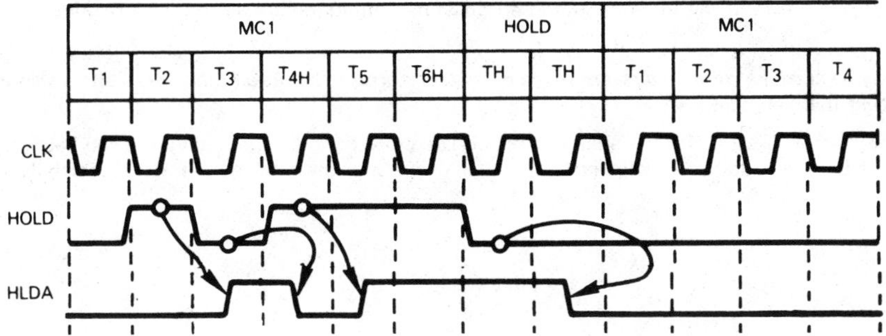

Figure 5-13 illustrates a Hold state lasting three clock periods, beginning during T4 of a four clock period machine cycle.

## THE HALT STATE AND INSTRUCTION

**When a Halt instruction is executed, the 8085A enters a Halt state. The Halt state consists of an indeterminate number of Halt Bus Idle clock periods, during which the S1 and S0 status signals are both output low while the tristate signals are floated.**

**Halt state timing is illustrated in Figure 5-14.**

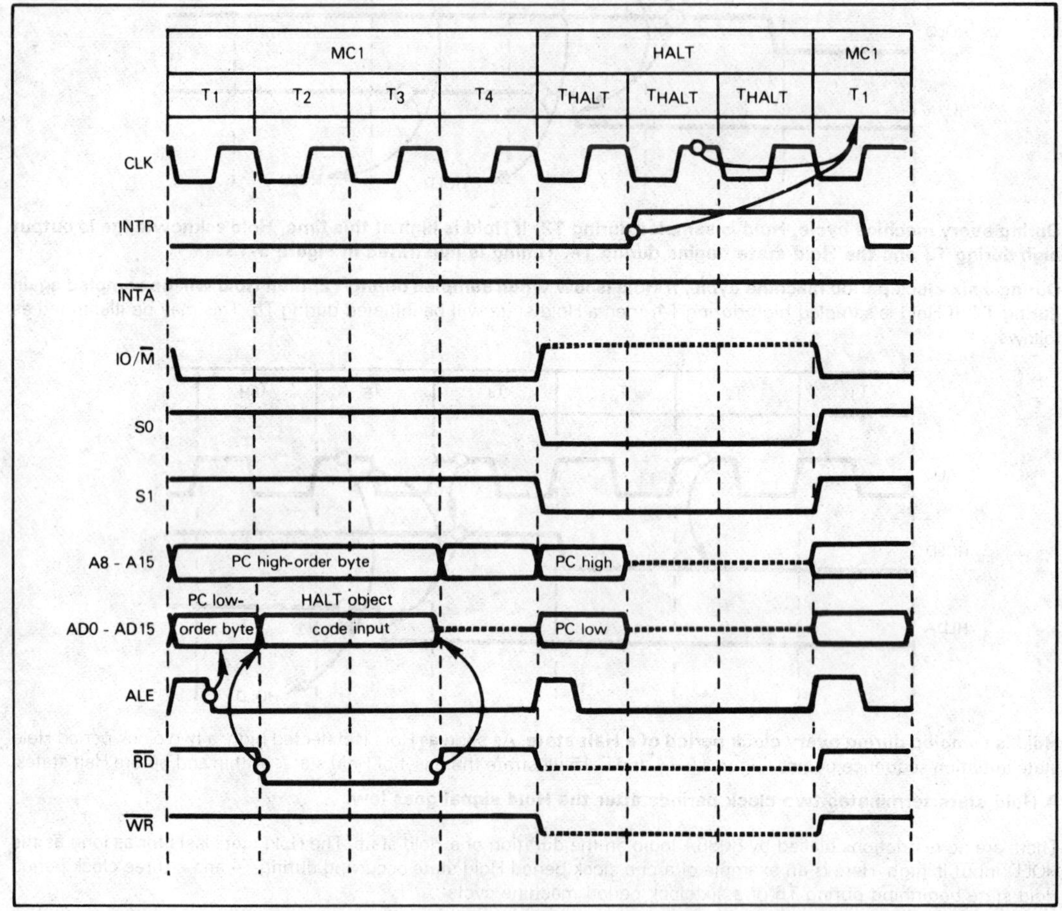


Figure 5-14. A Halt Instruction and a Halt State Terminated by an Interrupt Request

**A Halt state may be terminated by a system reset or by an interrupt request. Figure 5-14 shows an interrupt request terminating the Halt state.**

Note that the INTR signal, like the HOLD signal, is sampled two clock periods before anything can happen. Thus, as illustrated in Figure 5-14, an additional Halt clock period will occur after the clock period within which INTR goes high.

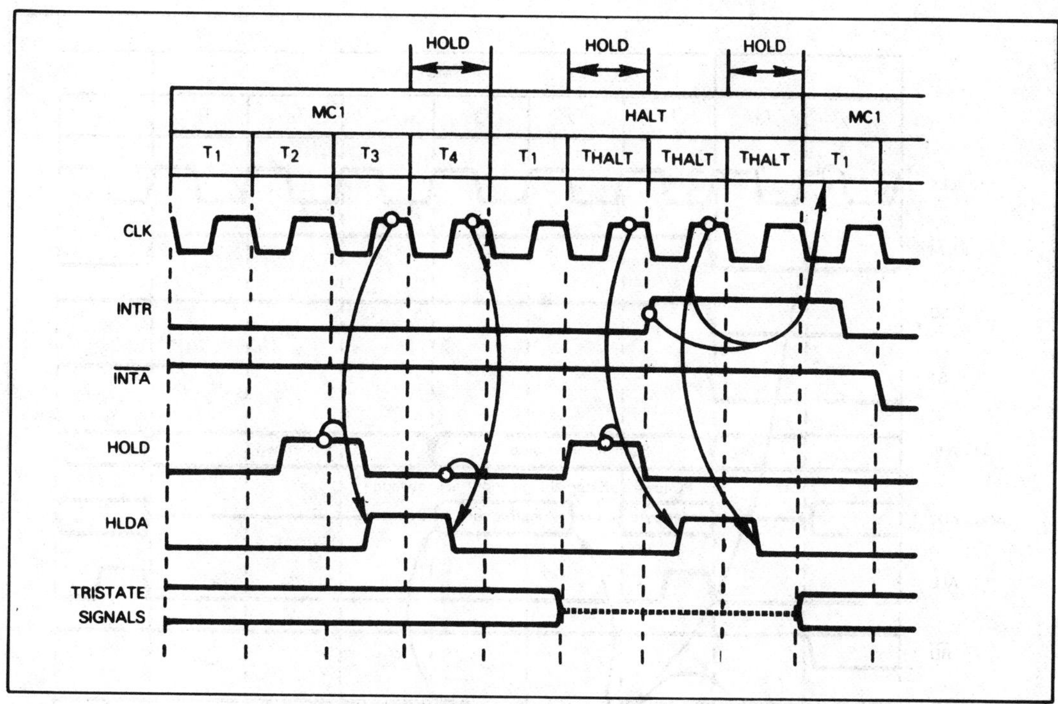


Figure 5-15. Hold States Occurring Within a Halt State

An interrupt request will only be executed if interrupts are enabled; however, the 8085A has a TRAP non-maskable interrupt. Thus you can always exit an 8085A Halt state via a TRAP interrupt request or by resetting the system.

**8085A HOLD WITHIN A HALT STATE**

**While in a Halt state you can enter and exit the Hold state. Figure 5-15 illustrates timing for the Hold state existing within the Halt state.** Notice that the Hold state only lasts for as long as the HOLD input is kept high.

Entering a Hold state within a Halt state also prevents you from terminating the 8085A Halt state with an interrupt request; this is because a HOLD request has priority over any interrupt request. Thus, if an interrupt request occurs while the 8085A is entering a Hold state, or is in a Hold state, the interrupt request will be ignored until the end of the Hold state. At that time, the interrupt request will be acknowledged — providing interrupts are enabled.

**Resetting the 8085A will terminate a Halt state at any time, whether or not you are in a Hold state.**

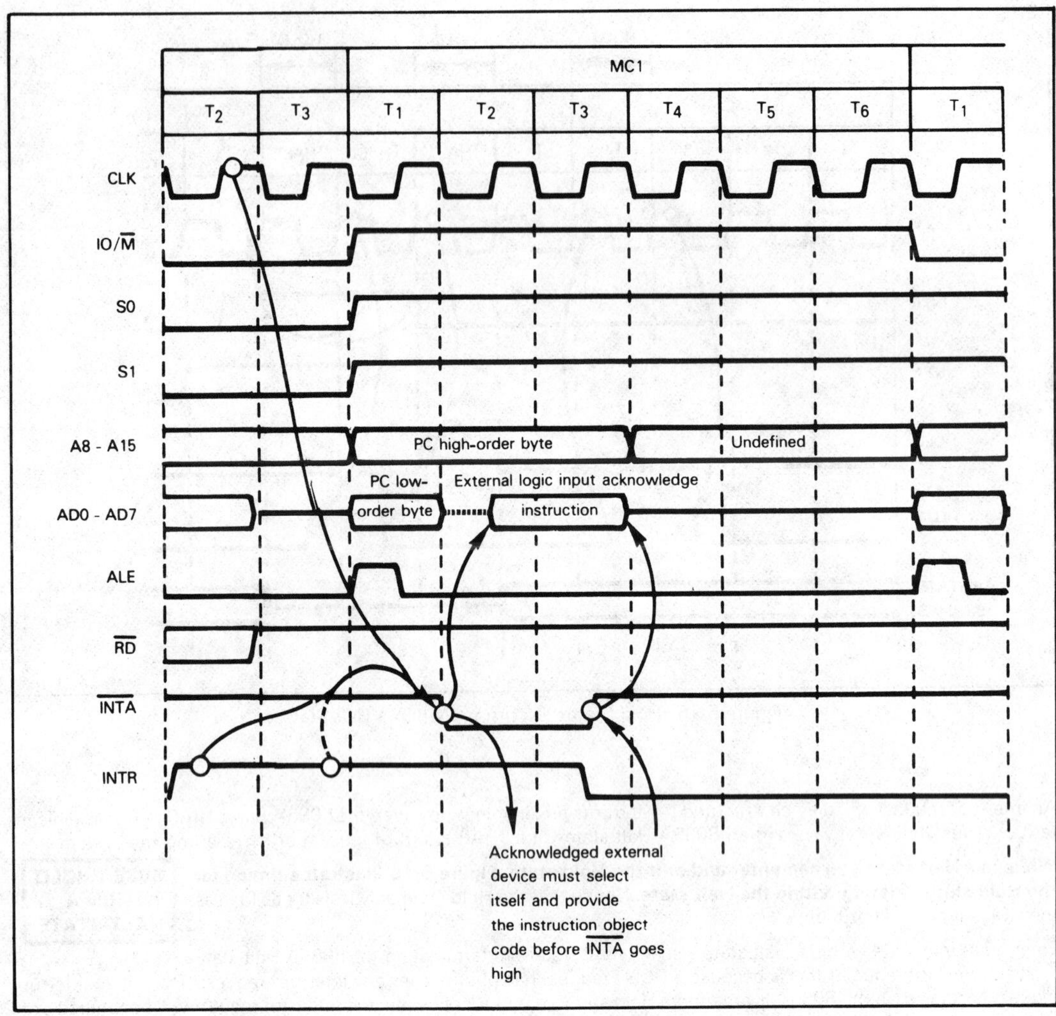


Figure 5-16. An Interrupt Being Acknowledged Using a Single Byte Instruction

## EXTERNAL INTERRUPTS

**There are some differences between the interrupt acknowledge logic of the 8085A as compared with the 8080A; however, the 8080A interrupt acknowledge logic is a subset of 8085A capabilities.**

Providing a valid interrupt request has been applied and interrupts are enabled, **the 8085A acknowledges the interrupt request on terminating execution of the current instruction.** The 8085A then executes an interrupt acknowledge machine cycle.

An interrupt acknowledge machine cycle is very similar to a six clock period instruction fetch machine cycle; however, during the interrupt acknowledge machine cycle the 8085A, like the 8080A, anticipates receiving an instruction object code from an I/O device — presumably the device whose interrupt request is being acknowledged. Since an I/O device is supposed to provide the object code during an interrupt acknowledge instruction fetch, $\overline{INTA}$ is pulsed low instead of $\overline{RD}$. Timing is illustrated in Figure 5-16.

**Note that even though memory is not being accessed, Program Counter contents are output on the Address Bus during an interrupt acknowledge instruction fetch; providing memory select logic uses IO/$\overline{M}$ and $\overline{RD}$, no harm will be done by having a valid address on the Address Bus during an interrupt acknowledge instruction fetch.**

The Program Counter contents are not incremented during the interrupt acknowledge process.

**8085A INTERRUPT ACKNOWLEDGE**

**In the 8085A, interrupt acknowledge has the same S1, S0, and IO/$\overline{M}$ levels as an instruction fetch. This means the interrupt acknowledge signal $\overline{INTA}$ serves both as an interrupt acknowledge and a read strobe.** External logic must use $\overline{INTA}$ both as a device select signal and a strobe signal identifying the time interval during which the interrupt acknowledge instruction code must be placed on the Data Bus. This can cause a timing problem. For any other instruction fetch, the trailing edge of ALE can be used to initiate device select timing; thus during any other instruction fetch you have from the middle of T1 until the middle of T2 to resolve the device select and wait for the read strobe. But you cannot use ALE in this fashion following an interrupt acknowledge, since external logic does not know that the interrupt has been acknowledged until $\overline{INTA}$ goes low. On the trailing edge of ALE during an interrupt acknowledge instruction fetch machine cycle, the Program Counter contents are being output on the Address Bus even though this address is irrelevant. **You must** therefore **use $\overline{INTA}$ as a signal which disables all I/O device select logic with the exception of the device whose interrupt request is being acknowledged.**

**WAIT STATES DURING 8085A INTERRUPT ACKNOWLEDGE**

**You may well have to insert Wait states during an interrupt acknowledge instruction fetch machine cycle;** the acknowledged external logic has the duration of the low $\overline{INTA}$ pulse within which it must resolve its select logic and place an instruction object code on the Data Bus.

Earlier in this chapter we showed you how you can create a one clock period low READY pulse using two 7474 D-type flip-flops. The circuit shown would generate the low READY pulse during a memory read or instruction fetch. The same circuit will also cause a Wait state during an 8085A interrupt acknowledge, which is identical to an instruction fetch as far as our small circuit is concerned.

**You can respond to an interrupt acknowledge by transmitting any instruction object code to the 8085A. Usually a Restart (RST) or a Call instruction object code will be transmitted.**

Figure 5-16 illustrates timing for a Restart instruction being transmitted following an interrupt acknowledge. The Restart instruction has been described in detail in Chapter 4 together with circuits which allow a Restart instruction to be created.

**8085A MULTIBYTE ACKNOWLEDGE**

**The 8085A contains internal logic to cope with multibyte instruction object codes transmitted during the interrupt acknowledge process.** During the second and third instruction fetch machine cycles, $\overline{INTA}$ is pulsed low while IO/$\overline{M}$ is output high. Thus responding to an interrupt acknowledge with a Call instruction simply involves creating a Call instruction's object code.

**The 8085A has four interrupt request pins which the 8080A does not have. These are TRAP, RST 5.5, RST 6.5 and RST 7.5. Interrupts requested via these pins cause the 8085A to generate its own internal interrupt acknowledge instruction.**

The internal interrupt acknowledge instruction results in subroutine calls to the following addresses:

| Interrupt | CALL Address |
|---|---|
| TRAP | $24_{16}$ |
| RST 5.5 | $2C_{16}$ |
| RST 6.5 | $34_{16}$ |
| RST 7.5 | $3C_{16}$ |

**TRAP is a non-maskable interrupt.**

**RST 5.5 and RST6.5 are level sensitive;**that means a high level input at these pins generates an interrupt request.

**RST 7.5 is edge sensitive;** an interrupt request occurs when the input to RST 7.5 makes a low-to-high transition.

**TRAP is both level and edge sensitive;** the low-to-high transition and the subsequent high level generate an interrupt request.

If an interrupt request is generated at RST 7.5 by a low-to-high transition, the 8085A will remember the interrupt request, whether or not the RST 7.5 input remains high. **You can thus generate an interrupt request via RST 7.5 using a high pulse.**

**Since you can request an interrupt via an RST 7.5 low-to-high transition, the RST 7.5 interrupt request signal itself cannot reset the interrupt request.** This may be illustrated as follows:

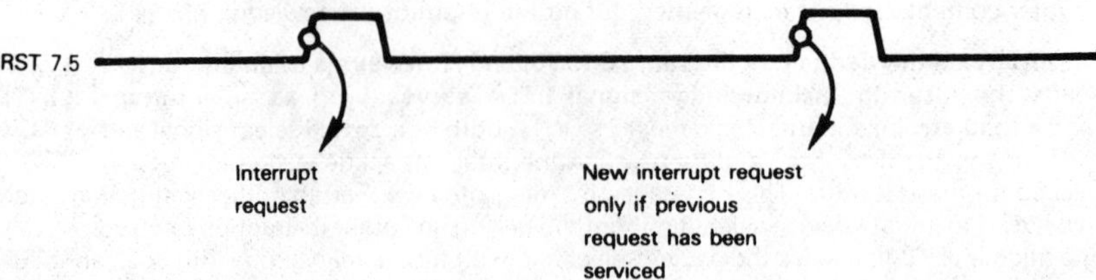


**You need not terminate service of an RST 7.5 interrupt request by executing an SIM instruction with bit 4 of the Accumulator set to 1; the CPU does this automatically when it recognizes the interrupt.**

**A low-to-high transition of the TRAP input creates an interrupt request.** The interrupt request will only be acknowledged while the TRAP input remains high; however, once a TRAP interrupt request has been acknowledged, **TRAP must go low and then high again before another interrupt request will be acknowledged.**

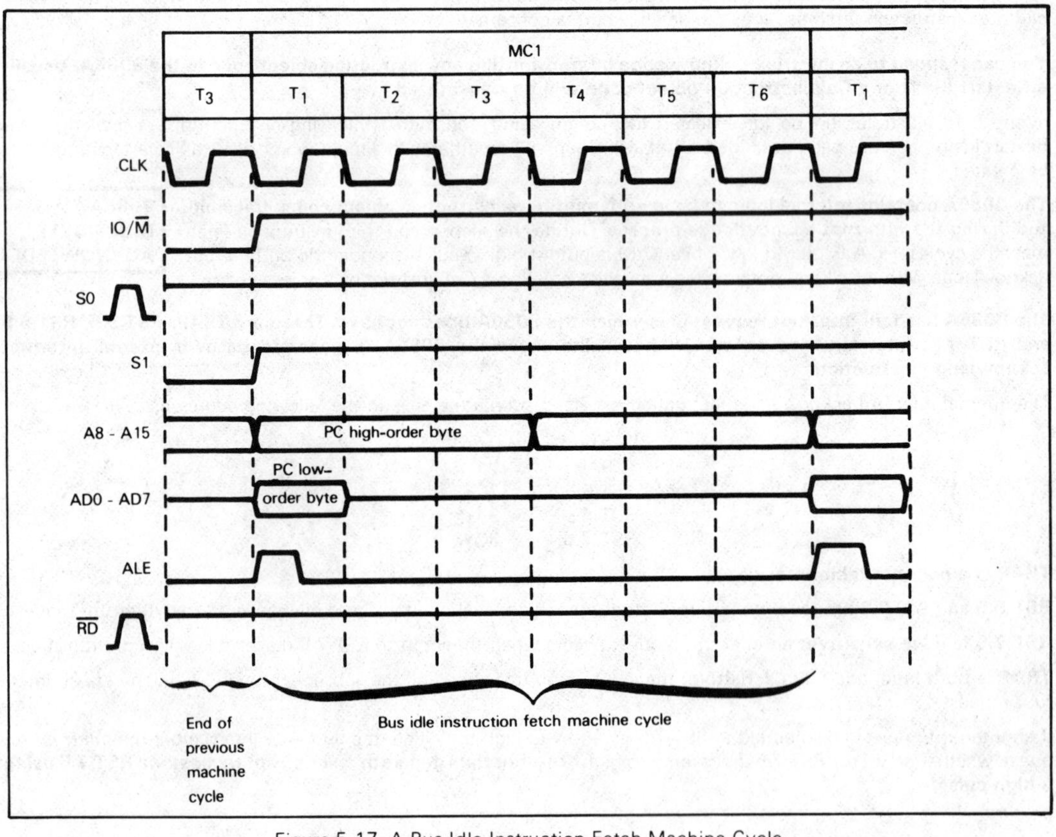

Figure 5-17. A Bus Idle Instruction Fetch Machine Cycle

**8085A interrupt priorities are as follows:**

| | |
|---|---|
| Highest | HOLD |
| | TRAP |
| | RST 7.5 |
| | RST6.5 |
| | RST 5.5 |
| Lowest | INTR |

**The 8085A executes an instruction fetch Bus Idle machine cycle after acknowledging a TRAP, RST 5.5, RST 6.5 or RST 7.5 interrupt request. Timing is given in Figure 5-17.**

**8085A TRAP INTERRUPT**

The TRAP interrupt request cannot be disabled. **The TRAP interrupt preserves the state of the interrupt enable flag.** This allows the user to restore the interrupt enable status after a TRAP interrupt.

**The RST 5.5, RST6.5, and RST 7.5 interrupt requests can be individually enabled and disabled using the SIM instruction. All interrupts except the TRAP can be enabled and disabled via the EL and DI instructions.**

**You may at any time examine interrupt enable/disable status by executying the RIM instruction.**

**8085A RIM AFTER TRAP**

**The first RIM instruction executed after a TRAP interrupt will show what the interrupt status was just before the TRAP, no matter how many IEs and DIs have been executed since the TRAP acknowledge. You must perform RIM after every TRAP to ensure that subsequent RIMs will provide accurate interrupt enable status.**

**The RIM and SIM instructions are described in detail later in this chapter.**

**You will service interrupts in an 8085A system exactly as described for the 8080A system. For a discussion of an interrupt acknowledge see Chapter 4.**

**Remember that a Hold request has priority over an interrupt request.** Thus, an interrupt will not be acknowledged while a Hold state exists and the 8085A will respond to a Hold request following an interrupt acknowledge.

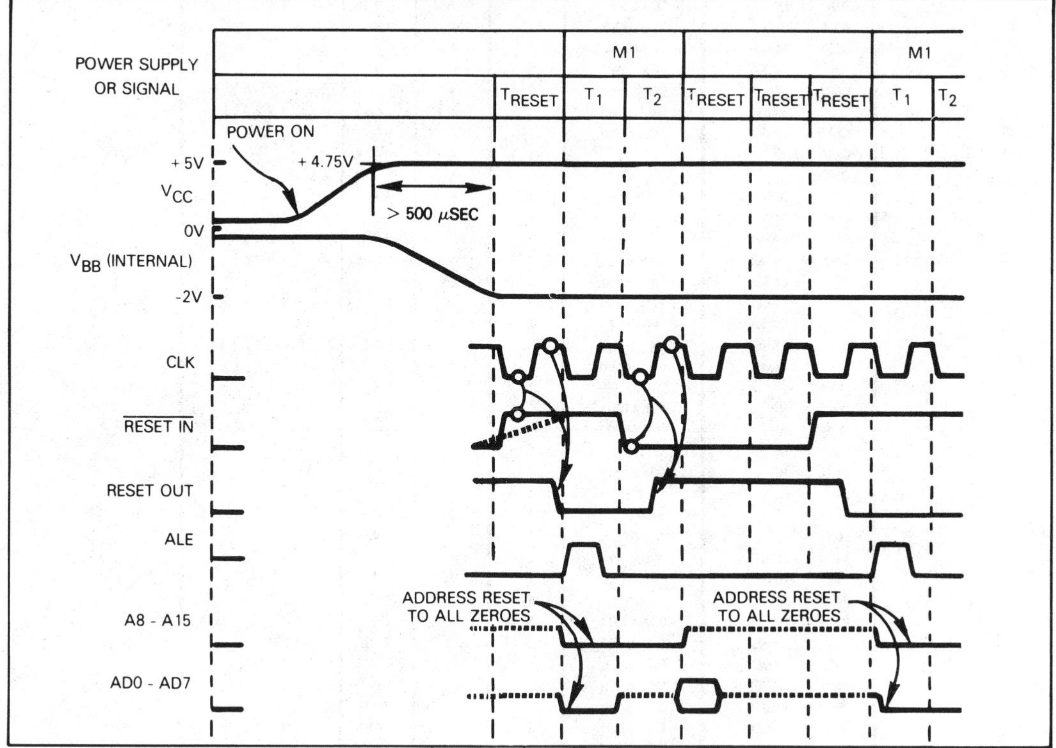


Figure 5-18. Power On and $\overline{\text{RESET IN}}$ Timing for the 8085A

## THE RESET OPERATION

**You reset an 8085A by inputting a low signal via $\overline{\text{RESET IN}}$.**

**When power is first turned on, the $\overline{\text{RESET IN}}$ pulse must last at least 500 nanoseconds (3 full clock cycles); no further requirements are imposed on the $\overline{\text{RESET IN}}$ signal. Logic internal to the 8085A will synchronize the $\overline{\text{RESET IN}}$ pulse with the internal clock. Timing for a Reset following a powerup is given in Figure 5-18.**

**Notice that a RESET OUT signal is provided. You can use this signal to reset other devices in the 8085A microcomputer system.**

**When the 8085A is reset the following events occur:**

1) The Program Counter is cleared; thus the first instruction executed following a reset must have its object code stored in memory location 0.
2) The Instruction register is cleared.
3) Interrupts are disabled.
4) The RST 7.5, RST 6.5 and RST 5.5 interrupts are masked out and thus disabled.
5) All tristate bus lines except ALE are floated.

Table 5-1. A Summary of 8085A Instruction Object Codes and Execution Cycles

| INSTRUCTION | | OBJECT CODE | BYTES | CLOCK PERIODS | | 8085A MACHINE CYCLES |
|---|---|---|---|---|---|---|
| | | | | 8080A | 8085A | |
| ACI | DATA | CE YY | 2 | 7 | 7 | 1 3 |
| ADC | REG | 10001XXX | 1 | 4 | 4 | 1 |
| ADC | M | 8E | 1 | 7 | 7 | 1 3 |
| ADD | REG | 10000XXX | 1 | 4 | 4 | 1 |
| ADD | M | 86 | 1 | 7 | 7 | 1 3 |
| ADI | DATA | C6 YY | 2 | 7 | 7 | 1 3 |
| ANA | REG | 10100XXX | 1 | 4 | 4 | 1 |
| ANA | M | A6 | 1 | 7 | 7 | 1 3 |
| ANI | DATA | E6 YY | 2 | 7 | 7 | 1 3 |
| CALL | LABEL | CD ppqq | 3 | 17 | 18 | 2 3 3 5 5 |
| CC | LABEL | DC ppqq | 3 | 11/17 | 9/18 | 2 3, 2 3 3 5 5 |
| CM | LABEL | FC ppqq | 3 | 11/17 | 9/18 | 2 3, 2 3 3 5 5 |
| CMA | | 2F | 1 | 4 | 4 | 1 |
| CMC | | 3F | 1 | 4 | 4 | 1 |
| CMP | REG | 10111XXX | 1 | 4 | 4 | 1 |
| CMP | M | BE | 1 | 7 | 7 | 1 3 |
| CNC | LABEL | D4 ppqq | 3 | 11/17 | 9/18 | 2 3, 2 3 3 5 5 |
| CNZ | LABEL | C4 ppqq | 3 | 11/17 | 9/18 | 2 3, 2 3 3 5 5 |
| CP | LABEL | F4 ppqq | 3 | 11/17 | 9/18 | 2 3, 2 3 3 5 5 |
| CPE | LABEL | EC ppqq | 3 | 11/17 | 9/18 | 2 3, 2 3 3 5 5 |
| CPI | DATA | FE YY | 2 | 7 | 7 | 1 3 |
| CPO | LABEL | E4 ppqq | 3 | 11/17 | 9/18 | 2 3, 2 3 3 5 5 |
| CZ | LABEL | CC ppqq | 3 | 11/17 | 9/18 | 2 3, 2 3 3 5 5 |
| DAA | | 27 | 1 | 4 | 4 | 1 |
| DAD | RP | 00XX1001 | 1 | 10 | 10 | 1 7 7 |
| DCR | REG | 00XXX101 | 1 | 5 | 4 | 1 |
| DCR | M | 35 | 1 | 10 | 10 | 1 3 5 |
| DCX | RP | 00XX1011 | 1 | 5 | 6 | 2 |
| DI | | F3 | 1 | 4 | 4 | 1 |
| EI | | FB | 1 | 4 | 4 | 1 |
| HLT | | 76 | 1 | 4 | 4 | 1 |
| IN | PORT | DB YY | 2 | 10 | 10 | 1 3 4 |
| INR | REG | 00XXX100 | 1 | 5 | 4 | 1 |
| INR | M | 34 | 1 | 10 | 10 | 1 3 5 |
| INX | RP | 00XX0011 | 1 | 5 | 6 | 2 |
| JC | LABEL | DA ppqq | 3 | 10 | 7/10 | 1 3, 1 3 3 |
| JM | LABEL | FA ppqq | 3 | 10 | 7/10 | 1 3, 1 3 3 |
| JMP | LABEL | C3 ppqq | 3 | 10 | 10 | 1 3 3 |
| JNC | LABEL | D2 ppqq | 3 | 10 | 7/10 | 1 3, 1 3 3 |
| JNZ | LABEL | C2 ppqq | 3 | 10 | 7/10 | 1 3, 1 3 3 |
| JP | LABEL | F2 ppqq | 3 | 10 | 7/10 | 1 3, 1 3 3 |

Table 5-1. A Summary of 8085A Instruction Object Codes and Execution Cycles (Continued)

| INSTRUCTION | | OBJECT CODE | BYTES | CLOCK PERIODS | | 8085A MACHINE CYCLES |
|---|---|---|---|---|---|---|
| | | | | 8080A | 8085A | |
| JPE | LABEL | EA ppqq | 3 | 10 | 7/10 | 1 3, 1 3 3 |
| JPO | LABEL | E2 ppqq | 3 | 10 | 7/10 | 1 3, 1 3 3 |
| JZ | LABEL | CA ppqq | 3 | 10 | 7/10 | 1 3, 1 3 3 |
| LDA | ADDR | 3A ppqq | 3 | 13 | 13 | 1 3 3 3 |
| LDAX | RP | 000X1010 | 1 | 7 | 7 | 1 3 |
| LHLD | ADDR | 2A ppqq | 3 | 16 | 16 | 1 3 3 3 3 |
| LXI | RP,DATA16 | 00XX0001<br>YYYY | 3 | 10 | 10 | 1 3 3 |
| MOV | REG,REG | 01dddsss | 1 | 5 | 4 | 1 |
| MOV | M,REG | 01110sss | 1 | 7 | 7 | 1 5 |
| MOV | REG,M | 01ddd110 | 1 | 7 | 7 | 1 3 |
| MVI | REG,DATA | 00ddd110<br>YY | 2 | 7 | 7 | 1 3 |
| MVI | M,DATA | 36 YY | 2 | 10 | 10 | 1 3 5 |
| NOP | | 00 | 1 | 4 | 4 | 1 |
| ORA | REG | 10110XXX | 1 | 5 | 4 | 1 |
| ORA | M | B6 | 1 | 7 | 7 | 1 3 |
| ORI | DATA | F6 YY | 2 | 7 | 7 | 1 3 |
| OUT | PORT | D3 YY | 2 | 10 | 10 | 1 3 6 |
| PCHL | | E9 | 1 | 5 | 6 | 2 |
| POP | RP | 11XX0001 | 1 | 10 | 10 | 1 3 3 |
| PUSH | RP | 11XX0101 | 1 | 11 | 12 | 2 5 5 |
| RAL | | 17 | 1 | 4 | 4 | 1 |
| RAR | | 1F | 1 | 4 | 4 | 1 |
| RC | | D8 | 1 | 5/11 | 6/12 | 2, 2 3 3 |
| RET | | C9 | 1 | 10 | 10 | 1 3 3 |
| RIM | | 20 | 1 | | 4 | 1 |
| RLC | | 07 | 1 | 4 | 4 | 1 |
| RM | | F8 | 1 | 5/11 | 6/12 | 2, 2 3 3 |
| RNC | | D0 | 1 | 5/11 | 6/12 | 2, 2 3 3 |
| RNZ | | C0 | 1 | 5/11 | 6/12 | 2, 2 3 3 |
| RP | | F0 | 1 | 5/11 | 6/12 | 2, 2 3 3 |
| RPE | | E8 | 1 | 5/11 | 6/12 | 2, 2 3 3 |
| RPO | | E0 | 1 | 5/11 | 6/12 | 2, 2 3 3 |
| RCC | | 0F | 1 | 4 | 4 | 1 |
| RST | N | 11XXX111 | 1 | 11 | 12 | 2 3 3 |
| RZ | | C8 | 1 | 5/11 | 6/12 | 2, 2 3 3 |
| SBB | REG | 10011XXX | 1 | 4 | 4 | 1 |
| SBB | M | 9E | 1 | 7 | 7 | 1 3 |
| SBI | DATA | DE YY | 2 | 7 | 7 | 1 3 |
| SHLD | ADDR | 22 ppqq | 3 | 16 | 16 | 1 3 3 5 5 |
| SIM | | 30 | 1 | | 4 | 1 |
| SPHL | | F9 | 1 | 5 | 6 | 2 |
| STA | ADDR | 32 ppqq | 3 | 13 | 13 | 1 3 3 5 |
| STAX | RP | 000X0010 | 1 | 7 | 7 | 1 5 |
| STC | | 37 | 1 | 4 | 4 | 1 |
| SUB | REG | 10010XXX | 1 | 4 | 4 | 1 |
| SUB | M | 96 | 1 | 7 | 7 | 1 3 |
| SUI | DATA | D6 YY | 2 | 7 | 7 | 1 3 |
| XCHG | | EB | 1 | 4 | 4 | 1 |
| XRA | REG | 10101XXX | 1 | 4 | 4 | 1 |
| XRA | M | AE | 1 | 7 | 7 | 1 3 |
| XRI | DATA | EE YY | 2 | 7 | 7 | 1 3 |
| XTHL | | E3 | 1 | 18 | 16 | 1 3 3 5 5 |

ppqq represents four hexadecimal digit memory address
YY represents two hexadecimal data digits
YYYY represents four hexadecimal data digits
X represents an optional binary digit
ddd represents optional binary digits identifying a destination register
sss represents optional binary digits identifying a source register

Machine cycle types:

1 - Four clock period instruction fetch (Figure 5-4)
2 - Six clock period instruction fetch (Figure 5-5)
3 - Memory read (Figure 5-6)
4 - I/O read (Figure 5-7)
5 - Memory write (Figure 5-8)
6 - I/O write (Figure 5-9)
7 - Bus idle (Figure 5-10)

# THE 8085A INSTRUCTION SET

**There are just three differences between the 8085A and the 8080A instruction sets:**

1) The 8085A has two additional instructions — RIM and SIM.
2) The number of clock periods required to execute instructions differs in some cases; Table 5-1 summarizes these differences.
3) Following a Halt instruction's execution, the 8085A floats tristate bus lines in the ensuing Halt state; the 8080A does not.

**Because the 8085A and 8080A instruction sets are so similar, the same benchmark program applies to both microprocessors.** Refer to Chapter 4 for a discussion of this benchmark program.

**Refer to Table 4-4 for a summary of the 8085A instruction set. The only two 8085A instructions not present in Table 4-4 are the RIM and SIM instructions.**

When the RIM instruction is executed, the following data is loaded into the Accumulator:

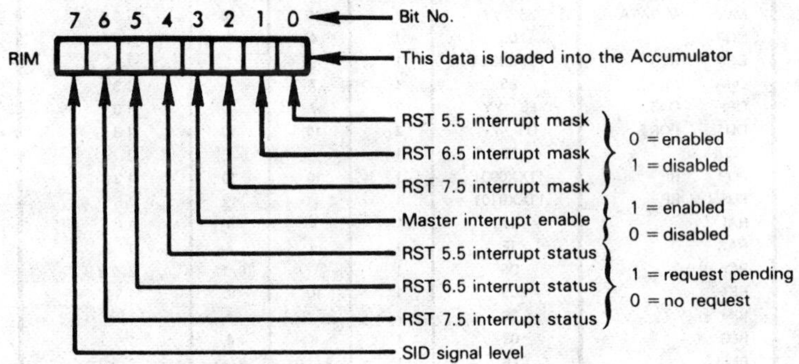


Thus, the RIM instruction allows you to examine interrupt and external status.

When the SIM instruction is executed the contents of the Accumulator are interpreted as follows:

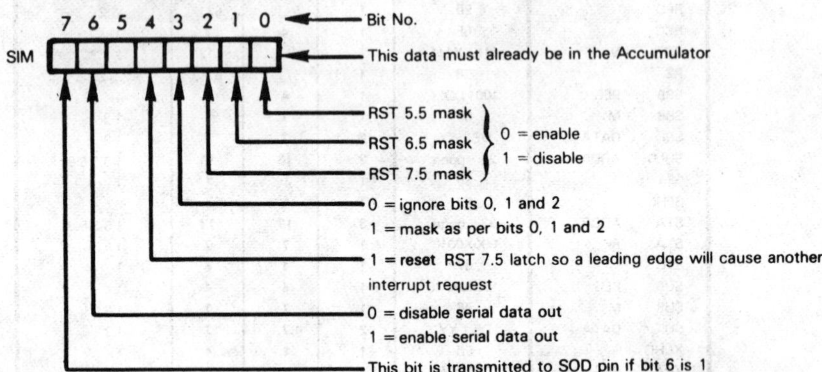


Thus the SIM instruction is used to selectively mask interrupts and to output a control signal via the SOD pin.

Note that if bit 6 of the Accumulator is 0 when the SIM instruction is executed, then the contents of bit 7 will not be transferred to the SOD pin.

From our discussion of the 8085A reset, recall that following a reset RST 5.5, RST 6.5 and RST 7.5 are all disabled; also, reset sets the SOD output to 0. Thus, following a reset an RIM instruction would input the following data to the Accumulator:

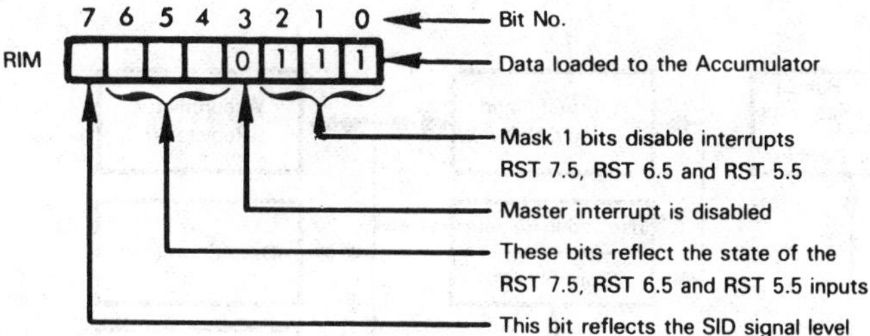


# 8085A MICROPROCESSOR SUPPORT DEVICES

**The 8085A has four special purpose multifunction support devices; they are described in this chapter.**

**The 8085A can use any -5 version of the 8080A support devices described in Chapter 4 and Volume 3. If you use the low-order eight 8085A address lines, you must demultiplex the 8085A Address and Data Busses to use 8080A support devices.**

# THE 8155/8156 STATIC READ/WRITE MEMORY WITH I/O PORTS AND TIMER

**The 8155 and 8156 are custom circuits designed specifically for the 8085A microprocessor. Each device provides 256 bytes of static read/write memory, two or three parallel I/O ports, and a programmable timer. The 8155 and 8156 devices differ only in the active level of the chip enable signal.**

**Figure 5-19 illustrates that part of general microcomputer system logic which has been implemented on the 8155 /8156 devices.**

**Figure 5-20 provides a functional diagram of 8155/8156 logic.**

**The 8155 or 8156 device is packaged as a 40-pin DIP. It uses a single +5V power supply. All inputs and outputs are TTL compatible.**

## 8155/8156 DEVICE PINS AND SIGNALS

**8155/8156 pins and signals are illustrated in Figure 5-21. Signals may be divided into the following categories:**

1) CPU interface and control
2) Parallel I/O
3) Programmable Timer

**We will first consider CPU interface and control signals.**

**AD0 - AD7 connect to a bidirectional, multiplexed Data and Address Bus.** As illustrated in Figure 5-22, these pins connect to the AD0 - AD7 bus lines output by the 8085A microprocessor.

**ALE is the Address Latch Enable control signal** output by the 8085A microprocessor to identify addresses on the multiplexed Data and Address Bus.

The 8155 or 8156 has both a memory space and an I/O address space. **When IO/$\overline{M}$ is high, I/O port addresses are decoded off AD0 - AD7** on the high-to-low transition of ALE; this may be illustrated as follows:

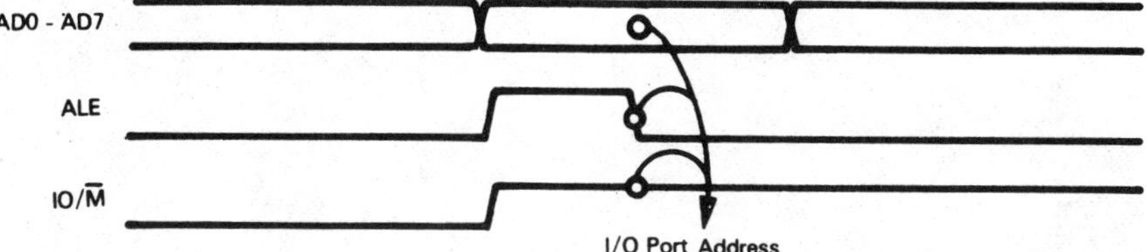

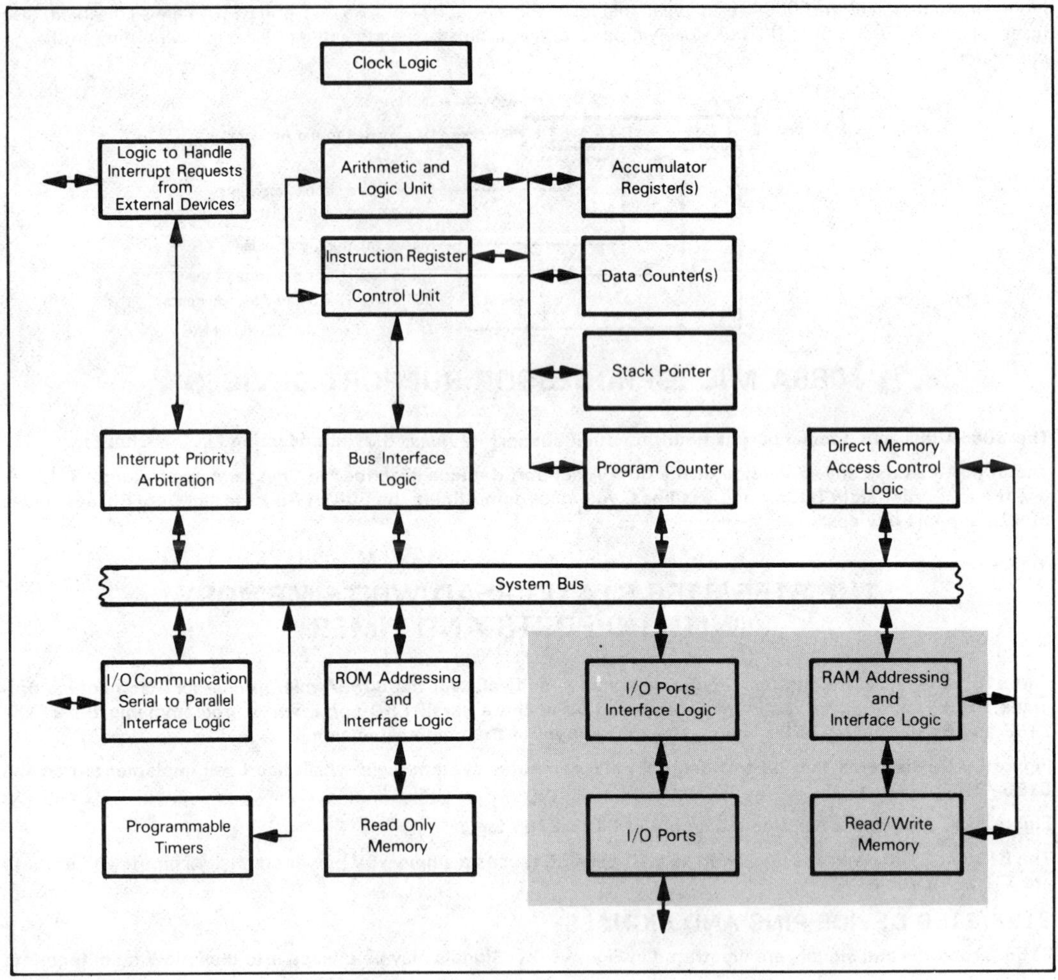


Figure 5-19. Logic of the 8155 and 8156 Multifunction Devices

**When IO/$\overline{\text{M}}$ is low, the address strobed off AD0 - AD7 is interpreted as a memory address.**

**CE is active high in the 8156 device; it is active low in the 8155. There is no other difference between the 8155 and 8156 devices.**

**The 8155 or 8156 device uses standard 8085A control signals on its CPU interface. These signals are $\overline{\text{RD}}$, $\overline{\text{WR}}$, ALE and IO/$\overline{\text{M}}$.** Refer to the description of these control signals given in the 8085A section of this chapter.

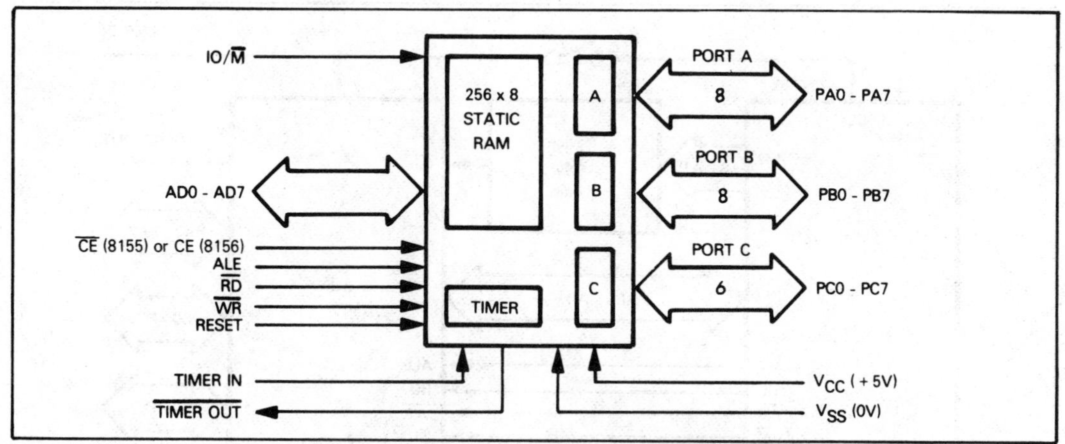


Figure 5-20. Logic Functions of the 8155/8156 Device

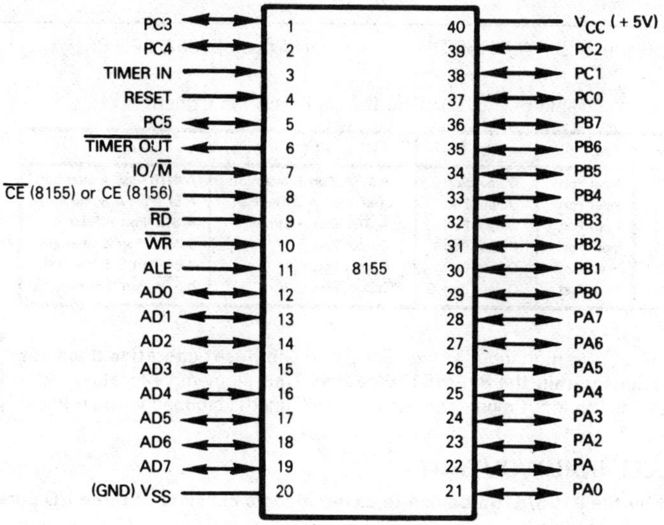

| Signal | Pin | 8155 | Pin | Signal |
|---|---|---|---|---|
| PC3 | 1 | | 40 | $V_{CC}$ (+5V) |
| PC4 | 2 | | 39 | PC2 |
| TIMER IN | 3 | | 38 | PC1 |
| RESET | 4 | | 37 | PC0 |
| PC5 | 5 | | 36 | PB7 |
| $\overline{TIMER\ OUT}$ | 6 | | 35 | PB6 |
| IO/$\overline{M}$ | 7 | | 34 | PB5 |
| $\overline{CE}$ (8155) or CE (8156) | 8 | | 33 | PB4 |
| $\overline{RD}$ | 9 | | 32 | PB3 |
| $\overline{WR}$ | 10 | | 31 | PB2 |
| ALE | 11 | 8155 | 30 | PB1 |
| AD0 | 12 | | 29 | PB0 |
| AD1 | 13 | | 28 | PA7 |
| AD2 | 14 | | 27 | PA6 |
| AD3 | 15 | | 26 | PA5 |
| AD4 | 16 | | 25 | PA4 |
| AD5 | 17 | | 24 | PA3 |
| AD6 | 18 | | 23 | PA2 |
| AD7 | 19 | | 22 | PA |
| (GND) $V_{SS}$ | 20 | | 21 | PA0 |

| PIN NAME | DESCRIPTION | TYPE |
|---|---|---|
| AD0 - AD7 | Multiplexed Address and Data Bus | Bidirectional |
| PA0 - PA7 | Eight I/O pins, designated as Port A | Bidirectional |
| PB0 - PB7 | Eight I/O pins, designated as Port B | Bidirectional |
| PC0 - PC5 | Six I/O pins, designated as Port C | Bidirectional |
| $\overline{RD}$ | Read from device control | Input |
| $\overline{WR}$ | Write to device control | Input |
| IO/$\overline{M}$ | I/O ports or memory select | Input |
| ALE | Address latch enable | Input |
| RESET | System reset | Input |
| CE/$\overline{CE}$ | Chip enable | Input |
| TIMER IN | Timer clock | Input |
| $\overline{TIMER\ OUT}$ | Timer output signal | Output |
| $V_{SS}$ $V_{CC}$ | Ground, Power | |

Figure 5-21. 8155/8156 Multifunction Device Signals and Pin Assignments

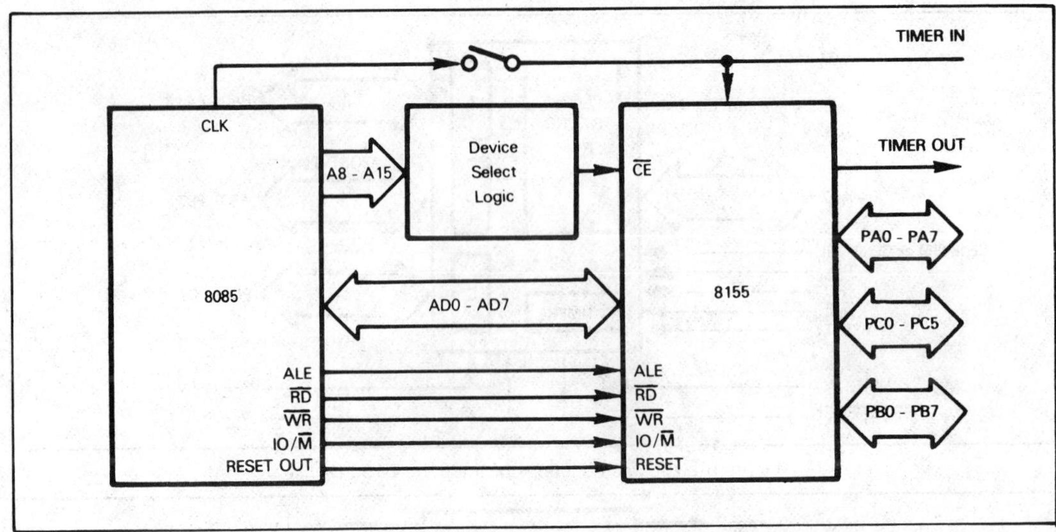


Figure 5-22. An 8155 Device Connected to an 8085A CPU Bus

Table 5-2. 8155/8156 Device Port C Pin Options

| Pin | ALT 1 | ALT 2 | ALT 3 | ALT 4 |
|---|---|---|---|---|
| PC0 | Input Port | Output Port | A INTR (Port A Interrupt) | A INTR (Port A Interrupt) |
| PC1 | Input Port | Output Port | A BF (Port A Buffer Full) | A BF (Port A Buffer Full) |
| PC2 | Input Port | Output Port | A $\overline{STB}$ (Port A Strobe) | A $\overline{STB}$ (Port A Strobe) |
| PC3 | Input Port | Output Port | Output Port | B INTR (Port B Interrupt) |
| PC4 | Input Port | Output Port | Output Port | B BF (Port B Buffer Full) |
| PC5 | Input Port | Output Port | Output Port | B $\overline{STB}$ (Port B Strobe) |

The 8155/8156 device is reset by a high input at the RESET pin. **The Reset operation does not clear memory or I/O locations within the 8155/8156 device.** Thus all memory locations contain zero, I/O ports are assigned to input mode and the Counter/Timer is stopped with an initial zero value.

**8155 DEVICE RESET**

## 8155/8156 PARALLEL INPUT/OUTPUT

**The interface presented by the 8155/8156 device to external logic consists of three I/O ports and two signals associated with Counter/Timer logic.**

**We will examine the I/O port logic and then the Counter/Timer logic.**

I/O Ports A and B are 8-bit parallel ports; each may be defined as an input port or an output port.

I/O Port C is a 6-bit parallel I/O port; it may be used to input or output parallel data, or Port C pins may support handshaking control signals for Ports A and B. Table 5-2 defines the four ways in which I/O Port C may be used.

**When I/O Ports A and B are used for simple parallel input or output, then their operation is identical to Mode 0 as described in Chapter 4 for the 8255 PPI. Handshaking mode is identical to 8255 Mode 1.** We will therefore discuss 8155 input and output with handshaking briefly. For a more detailed discussion refer to the 8255 PPI description given in Volume 3.

**8155/8156 I/O MODE 0**

**8155/8156 I/O MODE 1**

**Input with handshaking may be illustrated as follows:**

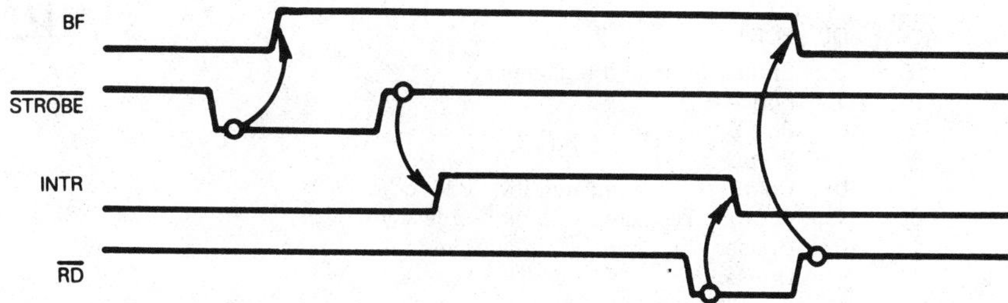


An event sequence begins with external logic inputting parallel data to I/O Port A or B; **external logic must pulse STROBE low, at which time the parallel data is loaded into the I/O port buffer.** This causes BF, the Buffer Full signal, to go high.

**External logic uses the BF signal as an indicator that no more data can be written.**

As soon as the externally provided low STROBE pulse is over, the interrupt request signal INTR goes high. This allows the 8085A to be interrupted once data has been loaded into the input buffer of the I/O port.

BF and INTR remain high until the CPU reads the contents of the I/O port. The read operation will be identified by a low RD pulse input to the 8155/8156 device. INTR is reset at the beginning of the RD pulse, while BF is reset at the end of the RD pulse. BF therefore is high while data is waiting to be read and while data is being loaded into the I/O port buffer or read out of the I/O port buffer. INTR is high only while data is waiting to be read.

BF and INTR have associated bits in the Status register of the 8155/8156 device.

**You connect INTR to an 8085A interrupt request if you want an interrupt-driven system. You write a program which polls the Status register of the 8155/8156 if you want to operate the system under program control.**

**Strobed output timing may be illustrated as follows:**

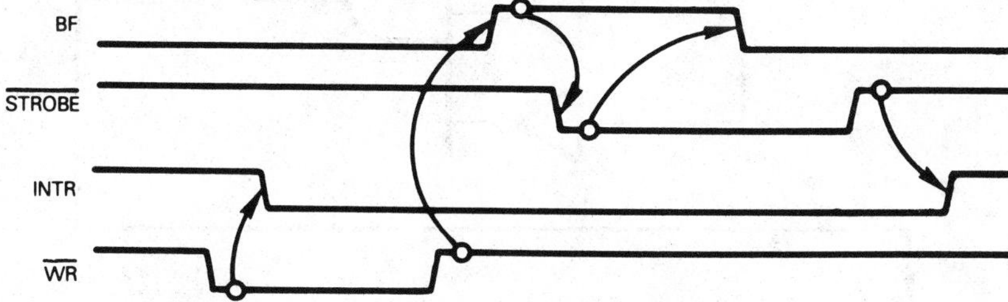


In output mode the I/O port buffer is initially empty, which means that the CPU must transmit data to the I/O port. Therefore INTR is initially high.

As soon as the CPU writes data to the I/O port, the interrupt request signal INTR is reset low; this occurs on the leading edge of the WR pulse. On the trailing edge of the WR pulse **BF is output high, telling external logic that data is in the I/O port buffer and may be read.**

**External logic strobes the data out by providing a low pulse at STROBE.** The leading edge of STROBE resets BF low, while the trailing edge of STROBE sets INTR high, causing the CPU to again output parallel data.

**You connect INTR to an appropriate 8085A interrupt request pin if you want an interrupt-driven system. You write a program to poll the Status register if you want to operate the 8155/8156 under program control.**

A simple method of using the 8155/8156 device parallel input/output with handshaking in interrupt mode would be to connect INTRA and INTRB to RST 5.5 and RST 6.5.

## 8155/8156 DEVICE ADDRESSING

**Having discussed 8155/8156 device memory and I/O ports, we must now look at device addressing.**

The 8155/8156 has 256 bytes of static read/write memory which are addressed by AD0 - AD7 while Chip Enable is true, and $IO/\overline{M} = 0$.

The 8155/8156 has eight addressable I/O ports. AD0, AD1 and AD2 select I/O ports while Chip Enable is true and IO/$\overline{M}$ = 1. **These are the eight addressable I/O ports:**

**8155/8156 I/O PORT ADDRESSES**

| AD2 | AD1 | AD0 | PORT |
|---|---|---|---|
| 0 | 0 | 0 | Status/Command registers |
| 0 | 0 | 1 | Port A |
| 0 | 1 | 0 | Port B |
| 0 | 1 | 1 | Port C |
| 1 | 0 | 0 | Counter/Timer register, low-order byte |
| 1 | 0 | 1 | Counter/Timer register, high-order byte |
| 1 | 1 | 0 | Unused |
| 1 | 1 | 1 | Unused |

Chip Enable is derived from A8 - A15, which holds the high-order byte of a memory address, or the I/O device number. **Chip Enable** thus **defines the exact address and I/O space for the 8155/8156 device.** Here is one possible configuration:

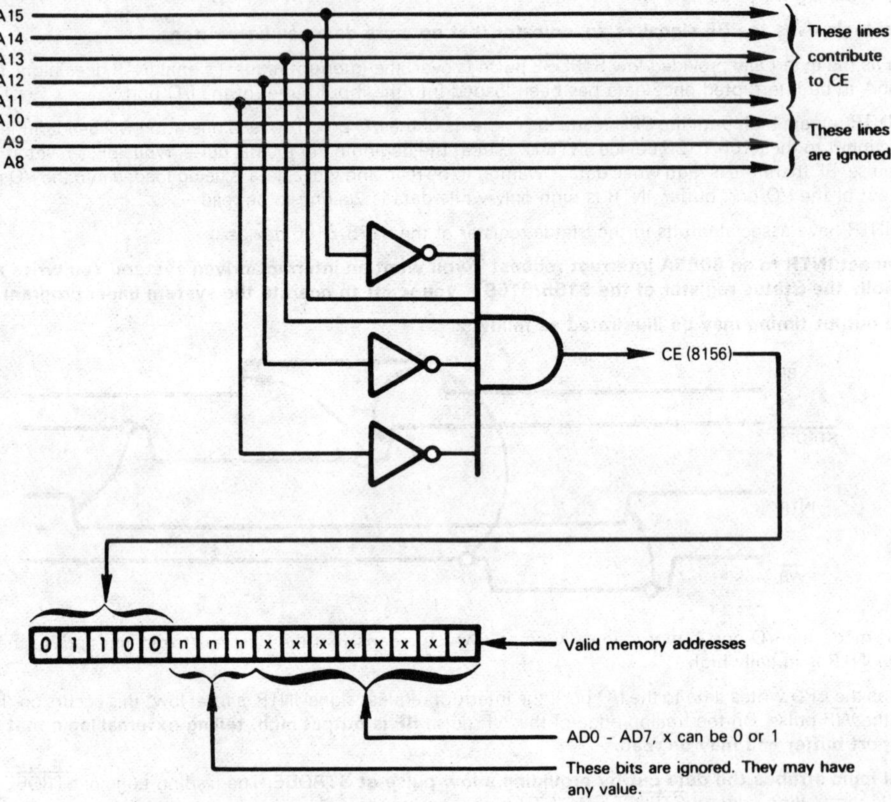


8155/8156 memory bytes will be selected by any memory addresses in the range $6n00_{16}$ through $6nFF_{16}$. "n" represents any digit in the range 0 through 7. Let us assume that programs access 8155/8156 memory bytes via addresses in the range $6000_{16}$ through $60FF_{16}$; we must further assume that addresses created by values of n in the range 1 through 7 never occur.

Now **the same chip select that you use to define your memory address space is also going to define your I/O address space.** Recall that the 8-bit I/O device number is output twice following execution of an I/O instruction — once on the high-order eight address lines A8 - A15 and again on the low-order Address/Data Bus lines AD0 - AD7. Thus the device select code which you generate from the eight high-order address lines for a memory address is the same device select code which you generate for the 8155/8156 I/O space.

But whereas the 8155/8156 has 256 addressable memory locations, it has eight addressable I/O ports; I/O ports are selected as follows:

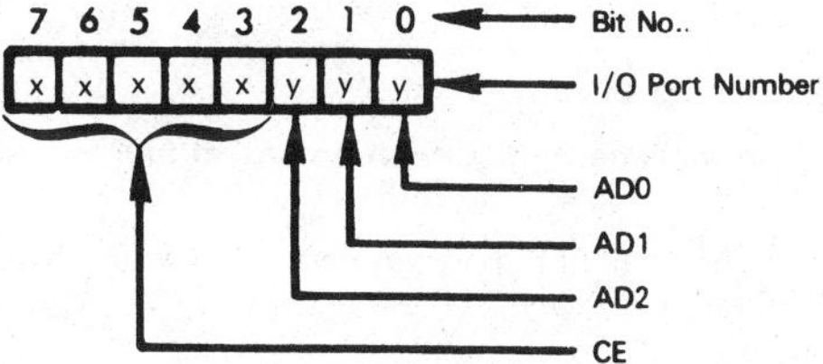


If Chip Enable is true when A15 - A11 is $01100_2$, then I/O port addresses will be $60_{16}$ through $67_{16}$.

Address lines A15 - A11 represent I/O device number bits 7 through 3. This is because the I/O device number is output on A15 - A8 following execution of an I/O instruction. It is therefore fortunate that we only used address lines A15 - A11 to create Chip Enable. Had we used A8, A9 or A10, the low-order three I/O device code bits would have served a double purpose — with strange results.

Suppose A10 = 0 is a prerequisite for device select logic to be true; these are the memory and I/O port selects which will result:

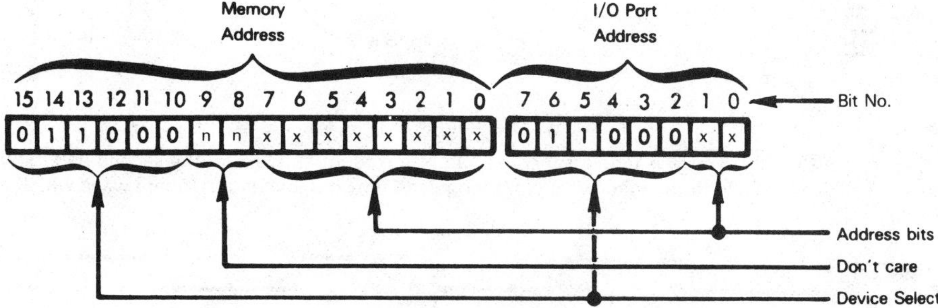


**You can now address only four of the eight 8155/8156 I/O Ports. You cannot include address lines A8, A9 or A10 in the device select logic that you use for any 8155/8156 device; if you do, you will limit the I/O capabilities of the device.**

**IO/$\overline{M}$ discriminates between exectuion of I/O instructions and memory reference instructions.**

## THE 8155/8156 COUNTER/TIMER

**Counter/Timer logic consists of a 16-bit register, addressed as two 8-bit I/O ports, an input clock signal and an output timer signal.** This may be illustrated as follows:

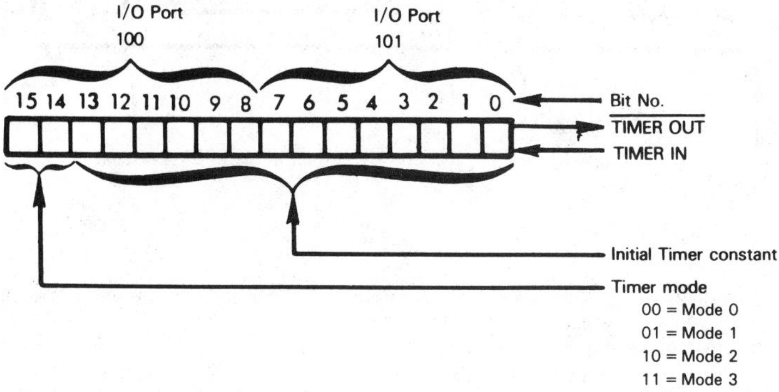

**The low-order 14 bits of the Counter/Timer register must be initialized with a 14-bit binary value that will decrement on low-to-high transitions of TIMER IN.** If TIMER IN is connected to the 8085A clock output signal CLK, then the timer is computing real time. TIMER IN can alternatively be connected to any external logic in which case the timer is counting external events.

**The timer times out when it decrements to zero.**

**The two high-order bits of the Counter/Timer register define one of four ways in which the TIMER OUT signal may be created.**

**8155/8156 TIMER MODE 0**

In **Mode 0,** TIMER OUT is high for the first half of the time interval and low for the second half of the time interval. This may be illustrated as follows:

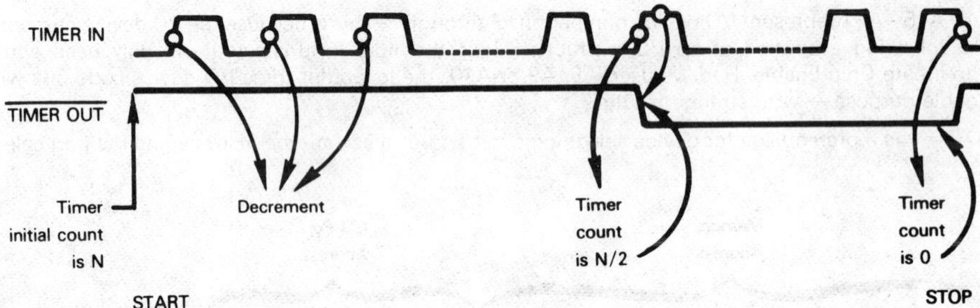


If N is odd, the extra pulse will occur while $\overline{\text{TIMER OUT}}$ is high.

In **Mode 1,** as in Mode 0, $\overline{\text{TIMER OUT}}$ is high for the first half of the count and low for the second half. However, the timer is automatically reloaded with the initial value following each time out, creating a square wave which may be illustrated as follows:

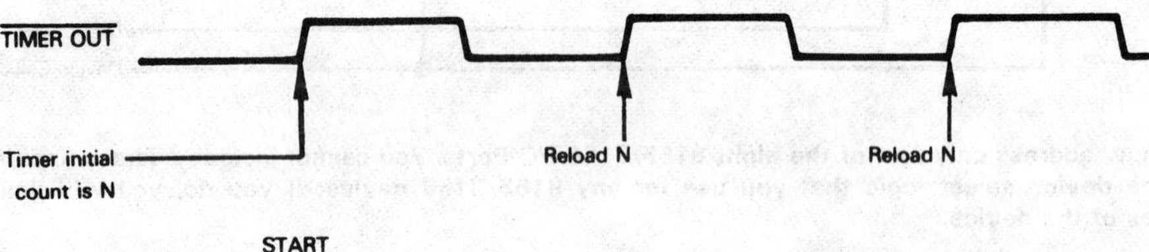


**Mode 2** outputs a single low clock pulse on the terminal count, then stops the timer. Timing may be illustrated as follows:

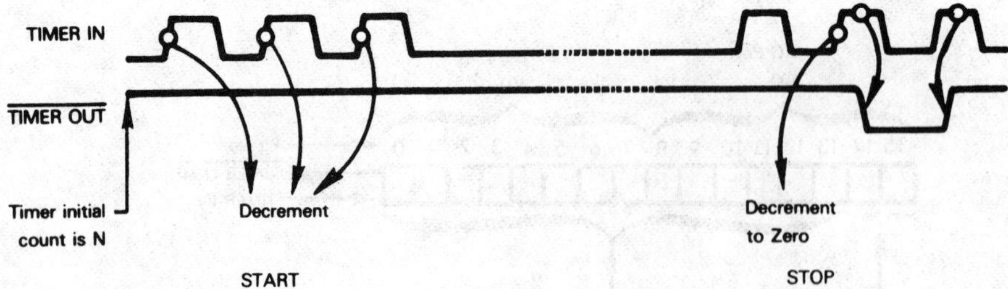


**Mode 3** is identical to Mode 2, except that when the timer times out the initial counter value is automatically reloaded.

## 8155/8156 CONTROL AND STATUS REGISTERS

**The Control and Status registers of the 8155/8156 are used to control both timer and parallel I/O logic. Let us now examine these registers.**

**The Control and Status registers of the 8155/8156 device are accessed via a single I/O port address. This is the lowest of the 8155/8156 I/O port addresses. When you write to this address you access the Control register; when you read from this address you access the Status register.**

**8155/8156 internal logic will interpret Control register bits as follows:**

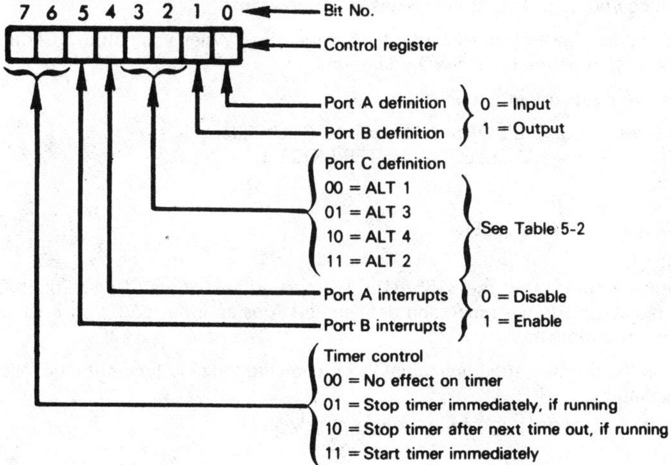


**Status register bits are set and reset as follows:**

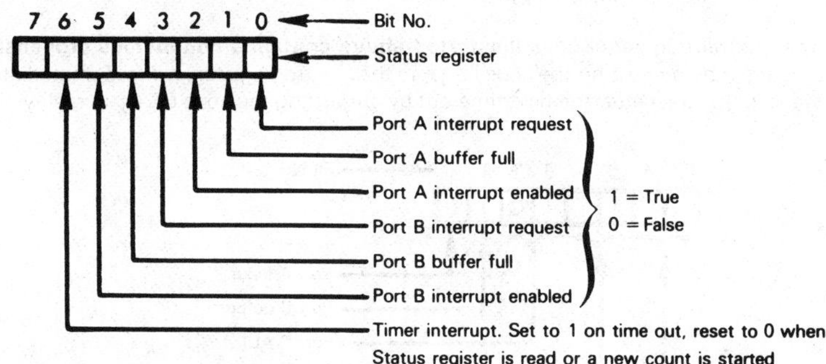


## 8155/8156 DEVICE PROGRAMMING

**Accessing 8155/8156 read/write memory is self-evident.** If you execute a memory reference instruction that specifies an address within the 8155/8156 address space, you will access an 8155/8156 memory byte.

**Parallel I/O programming is also self-evident;** you begin by outputting an appropriate code to the Control register in order to define the modes in which various ports will operate, and to enable or disable Mode 1 interrupts. Your only caution at this time must be to ensure that the two high-order bits of the Control code are 0; this prevents initiation of any timer operations.

**If you are using I/O ports without handshaking, the Status register is not affected by I/O operations.** No control signals or status indicate that new data has been input to, or has been read from I/O ports.

If you are operating the 8155/8156 in handshaking mode under program control, then you must poll the Status register in order to determine whether data is waiting to be read or must be written. Your program will consist of a series of input instructions which read status, followed by conditional branches that read or write data.

If you are operating the 8155/8156 parallel I/O in handshaking mode under interrupt control, then whenever data is waiting to be read or must be written, the high INTR control signal will vector program execution to an appropriate interrupt service routine.

**You can at any time read the contents of an I/O port that has been declared an output port.** You will simply read back whatever data was most recently written out to that I/O port. Reading the contents of an output port will have no effect on handshaking control signals associated with that port.

**Let us now examine programming associated with 8155/8156 Counter/Timer logic.**

You must first initialize the 16-bit Counter/Timer register by outputting two bytes that specify timer mode and initial count. The order in which you output these two bytes is unimportant.

Next you output an appropriate Control code in order to start the timer. When you output a Control code, remember not to modify any control bits that define parallel I/O operations.

Here is an appropriate initialization instruction sequence:

```
MVI     A,80H      LOAD 6080H AS AN INITIAL COUNTER
OUT     0C4H       VALUE. SELECT COUNTER MODE 1
MVI     A,60H
OUT     0C5H
MVI     A,0FAH     START TIMER
OUT     0C0H
```

This instruction sequence assumes that the 8155/8156 I/O port addresses are $C0_{16}$ through $C5_{16}$. The code $FA_{16}$ output to the Control register starts the timer, and defines Port A as an input port, Port B as an output port, both in handshaking mode with interrupts enabled.

You can at any time stop the counter, either immediately or following the next time-out. The following instructions will stop the counter immediately:

```
MVI     A,7AH      STOP THE TIMER IMMEDIATELY
OUT     C0H
```

The following instructions will stop the counter after the next time-out:

```
MVI     A,BAH      STOP THE TIMER AFTER THE
OUT     C0H        NEXT TIME OUT
```

**The Counter/Timer instruction sequences illustrated above contain a nonobvious propensity for programming errors.** We start the timer by outputting the code $FA_{16}$ to the Control register; we stop immediately by outputting the code $7A_{16}$ and we stop the timer after the next time-out by outputting the code $BA_{16}$. In reality, this is the code we are outputting:

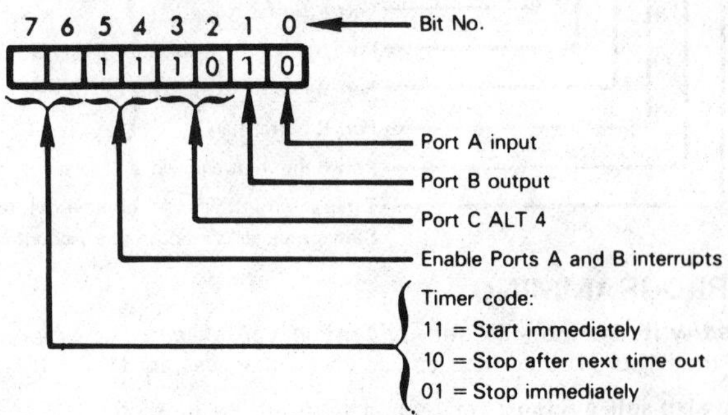


Whenever you output Control codes to modify 8155/8156 timer operation, you must always remember to output bits 0 through 5 correctly, in order to maintain previously defined parallel I/O options. **A commonly used programming technique that frees you from having to remember the condition of irrelevant bits in a control word is to use AND and OR masks.** Consider this general purpose instruction sequence:

```
IN      C0H        INPUT PRESENT CONTROL CODE
ANI     3FH        CLEAR TIMER BITS
(ORI    C0H        SET TIMER BITS)
OUT     C0H        RESTORE CONTROL CODE
```

**This technique will not work with the 8155/8156 device, since you cannot read the contents of the Control register. If you read from the address of the Control register, you will access the Status register.** If you want to use a masking technique, you must maintain the Control code in memory. Here is an instruction sequence that will work:

```
LDA    CONTRL   LOAD CONTROL CODE FROM MEMORY
ANI    3FH      CLEAR TIMER BITS
(ORI   C0H      SET TIMER BITS)
OUT    C0H      OUTPUT CONTROL CODE TO 8155/8156
STA    CONTRL   SAVE CONTROL CODE IN MEMORY.
```

Your instruction sequence will include the ANI mask to clear timer bits, or the ORI mask to set timer bits, but obviously not both.

CONTRL is the label for some read/write memory byte which always holds the current 8155/8156 Control code.

# THE 8355 READ-ONLY MEMORY WITH I/O

**The 8355 provides 2048 bytes of read-only memory and two 8-bit I/O ports. The device has been designed to interface with the 8085A CPU.**

**Figure 5-23 illustrates that part of our general microcomputer system logic which has been implemented on the 8355 device.**

**The 8355 is packaged as a 40-pin DIP. It uses a single +5V power supply. All inputs and outputs are TTL-compatible. The device is implemented using N-channel MOS technology.**

**Figure 5-24 functionally illustrates logic of the 8355 device. A simple 8085A-8155/8156-8355 configuration is illustrated in Figure 5-26.**

**There are many similarities between the 8155/8156, which we have already described, and the 8355. Where appropriate we will refer back to the 8155/8156 discussion for clarification of concepts.**

## 8355 DEVICE PINS AND SIGNALS

**8355 pins and signals are illustrated in Figure 5-25.**

**The 8355-8085A interface differs somewhat from the 8155/8156-8085A interface in that the 8355 has more memory, fewer addressable I/O ports, plus the ability to address I/O ports within the memory space of the device.**

Having 2048 bytes of addressable read-only memory, **the 8355 requires eleven address pins. These are derived from AD0-AD7 and A8-A10.**

Having only four addressable I/O ports, the 8355 I/O address logic decodes AD0 and AD1 only. I/O ports are selected as follows:

| AD1 | AD0 | |
|---|---|---|
| 0 | 0 | I/O PORT A |
| 0 | 1 | I/O PORT B |
| 1 | 0 | DATA DIRECTION REGISTER A |
| 1 | 1 | DATA DIRECTION REGISTER B |

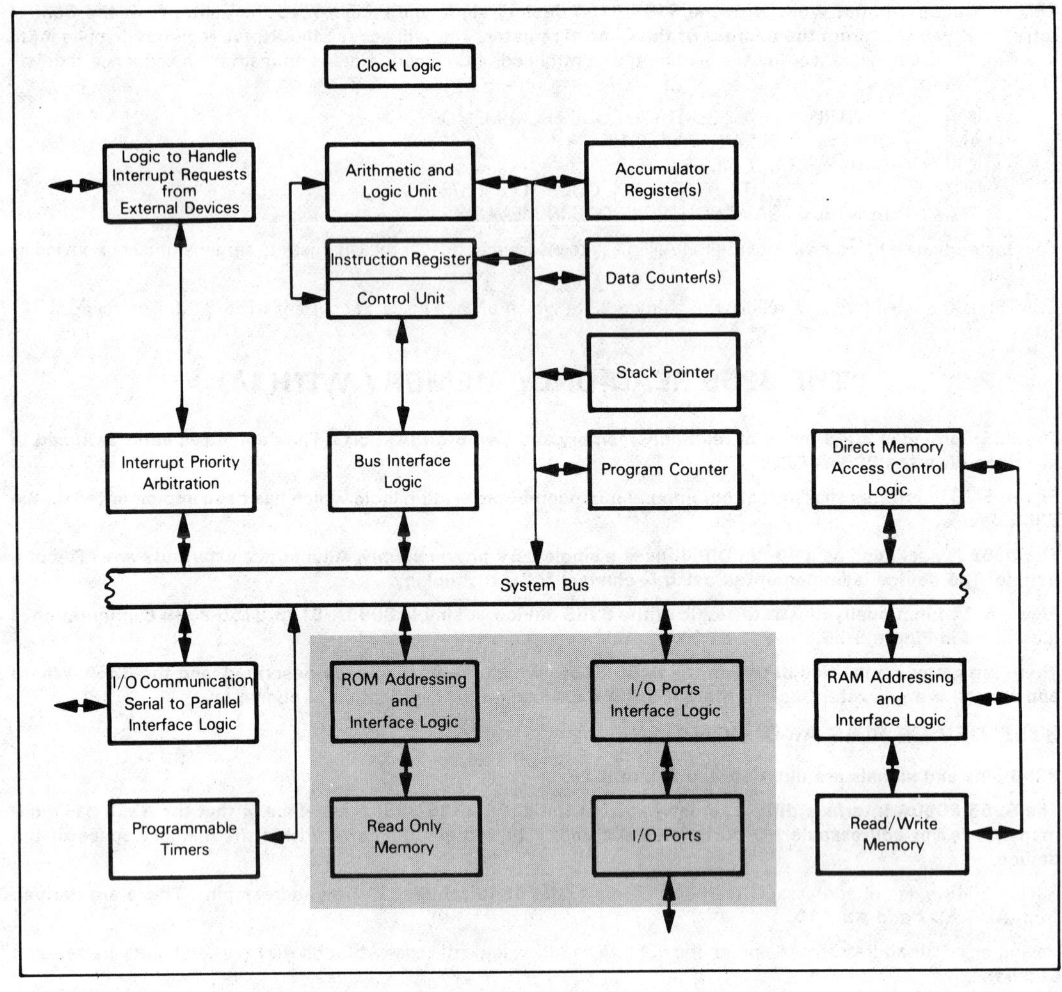


Figure 5-23. Logic of the 8355 and 8755 Multifunction Devices

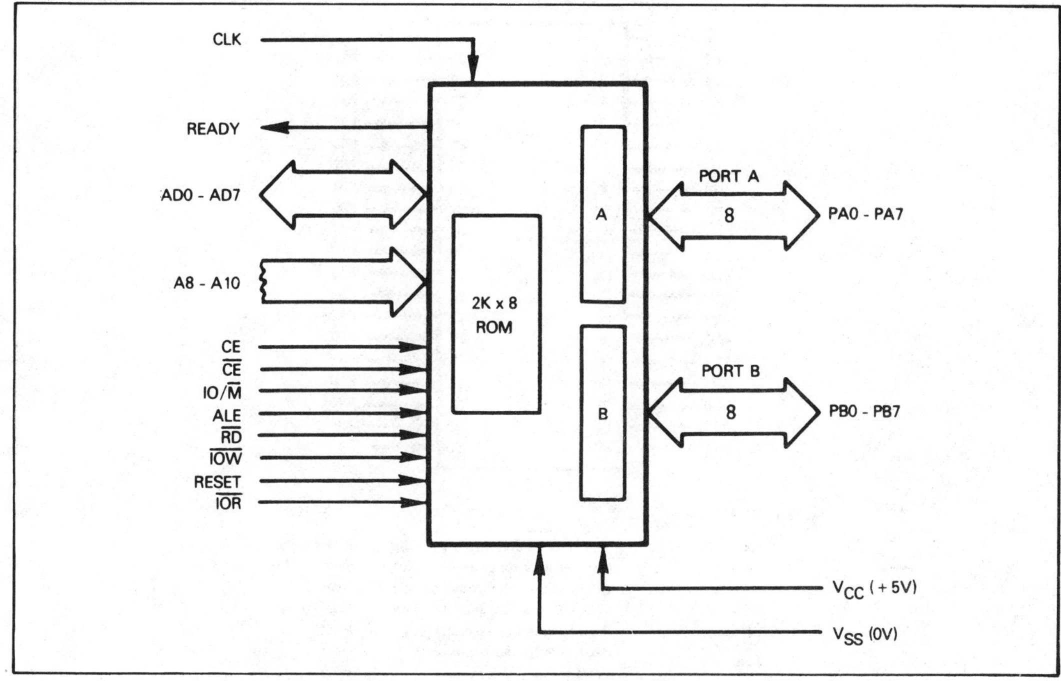


Figure 5-24. Logic Functions of the 8355 Device

**8355 device select logic must generate the chip enable signals $\overline{CE}$ and CE** from the five address lines A11-A15. The discussion of select logic given for the 8155/8156 device applies also to the 8355.

**If you select 8355 memory and I/O ports in their respective address spaces, the control signals ALE, $\overline{RD}$, and IO/$\overline{M}$ are used exactly as described for the 8155/8156 device.**

**But you can also access 8355 I/O ports within the 8355 memory space using control signals $\overline{IOW}$ and $\overline{IOR}$.**

$\overline{IOW}$ and $\overline{IOR}$ are control signals which override IO/$\overline{M}$ and $\overline{RD}$ when accessing I/O ports.

Providing CE and $\overline{CE}$ are true, a low input on $\overline{IOW}$ will cause data on the Data Bus to be written into the I/O port selected by AD0 and AD1, irrespective of the IO/$\overline{M}$ level. Similarly, $\overline{IOR}$ low will cause the contents of the I/O port selected by AD0 and AD1 to be output on the Data Bus.

You can connect $\overline{IOW}$ directly to the $\overline{WR}$ control signal, and thus write into the four I/O ports of the 8355 device as though they were the four low-order memory bytes. But connecting $\overline{IOR}$ to $\overline{RD}$ is not so straightforward. The 8355 device may receive a low input on $\overline{IOR}$, together with low inputs on $\overline{RD}$ and IO/$\overline{M}$; it will then attempt to read the contents of a read only memory byte and an I/O port at the same time. While elaborate schemes could be devised for generating separate selects that map the four I/O ports into a memory space of its own, **it is wisest to ignore the $\overline{IOR}$ signal if you are using 8355 memory and I/O logic. Use $\overline{IOR}$ only when the 8355 is configured as two I/O ports — and the 8355 memory is unused. $\overline{IOR}$ and $\overline{IOW}$ are used in 8048 microcomputer systems; that is the principal reason they were designed into the 8355 device.**

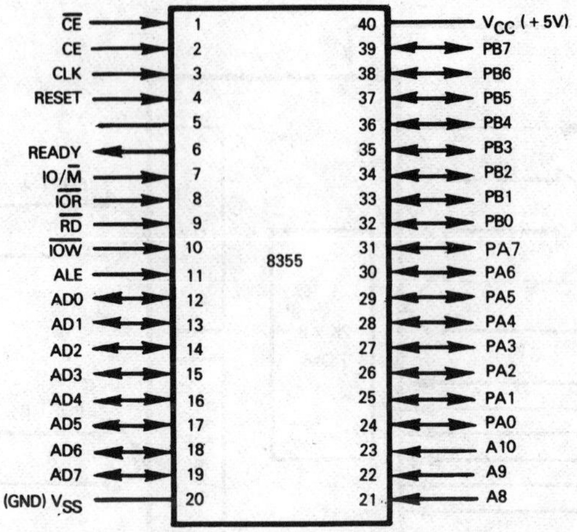

| Signal | Pin | | Pin | Signal |
|---|---|---|---|---|
| $\overline{CE}$ | 1 | 8355 | 40 | $V_{CC}$ (+5V) |
| CE | 2 | | 39 | PB7 |
| CLK | 3 | | 38 | PB6 |
| RESET | 4 | | 37 | PB5 |
| | 5 | | 36 | PB4 |
| READY | 6 | | 35 | PB3 |
| IO/$\overline{M}$ | 7 | | 34 | PB2 |
| $\overline{IOR}$ | 8 | | 33 | PB1 |
| $\overline{RD}$ | 9 | | 32 | PB0 |
| $\overline{IOW}$ | 10 | | 31 | PA7 |
| ALE | 11 | | 30 | PA6 |
| AD0 | 12 | | 29 | PA5 |
| AD1 | 13 | | 28 | PA4 |
| AD2 | 14 | | 27 | PA3 |
| AD3 | 15 | | 26 | PA2 |
| AD4 | 16 | | 25 | PA1 |
| AD5 | 17 | | 24 | PA0 |
| AD6 | 18 | | 23 | A10 |
| AD7 | 19 | | 22 | A9 |
| (GND) $V_{SS}$ | 20 | | 21 | A8 |

| PIN NAME | DESCRIPTION | TYPE |
|---|---|---|
| AD0 - AD7 | Multiplexed Address and Data Bus | Bidirectional |
| A8 - A10 | Memory Address Lines | Input |
| PA0 - PA7 | Eight I/O pins, designated as Port A | Bidirectional |
| PB0 - PB7 | Eight I/O pins, designated as Port B | Bidirectional |
| $\overline{RD}$ | Read from device control | Input |
| $\overline{IOR}$ | Read from I/O port control | Input |
| $\overline{IOW}$ | Write to I/O port control | Input |
| IO/$\overline{M}$ | I/O ports or memory select | Input |
| ALE | Address latch enable | Input |
| RESET | System reset | Input |
| CE, $\overline{CE}$ | Chip enables | Input |
| READY | Wait state request | Output, tristate |
| CLK | Timing for Wait state request | Input |
| $V_{SS}$, $V_{CC}$ | Ground, Power | |

Figure 5-25. 8355 Multifunction Device Signals and Pin Assignments

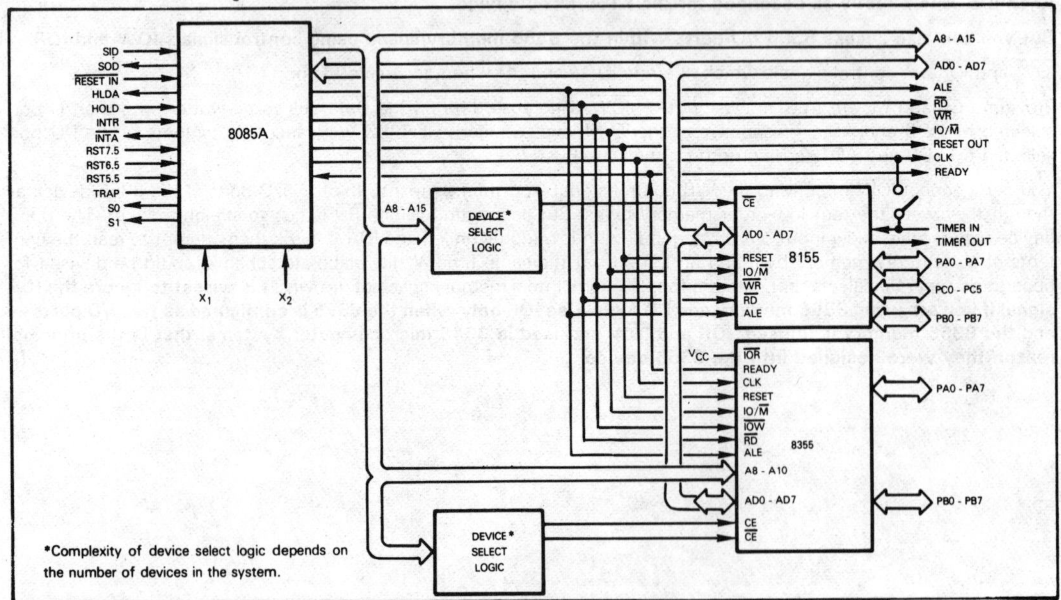


Figure 5-26. An 8085A-8155/8156-8355 Microcomputer System

## 8355 READY LOGIC

**The 8355 device has on-chip logic to create a READY signal that will insert one Wait state into the 8085A machine cycle that references the 8355 device.** 8355 READY signal timing may be illustrated as follows:

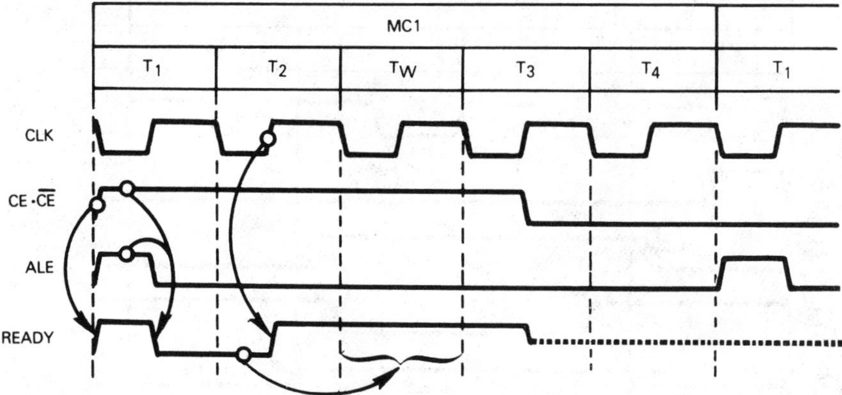


The READY output is floated by the 8355 device while CE•$\overline{CE}$ is false.

READY is forced low by the combination of Chip Enable true while ALE is high; READY stays low until the first low-to-high transition of CLK following the end of the ALE pulse. If you refer back to Figure 5-11, you will see that this READY logic creates a single Wait state.

The problem with the READY logic illustrated above is that in order to have Chip Enable true while ALE is high, chip enable logic must be tied directly to Address Bus lines. Refer to the timing diagram below and you will see that A0-A15 is stable while ALE is high.

But as we discussed earlier in this chapter, you can derive chip enable logic directly from A8-A15 only in small 8085 microcomputer systems. When a large number of support devices are connected to the System Bus, you must guarantee against spurious device selects by including control signals in the chip enable logic. Logic illustrated earlier in this chapter shows how to create a chip select signal that is true between the trailing edge of ALE and the low-to-high transition of $\overline{RD}$ or $\overline{WR}$. The following chip enable timing results:

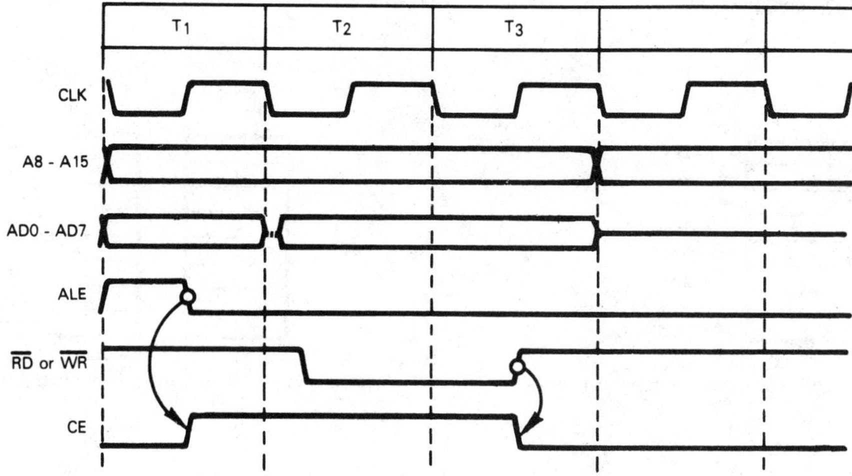

Timing illustrated above is theoretically the best guarantee against spurious selects; but it will not work if you want to create a single Wait state when using an 8355 device. If Chip Enable (CE) goes true on the trailing edge of ALE, READY will never be reset low:

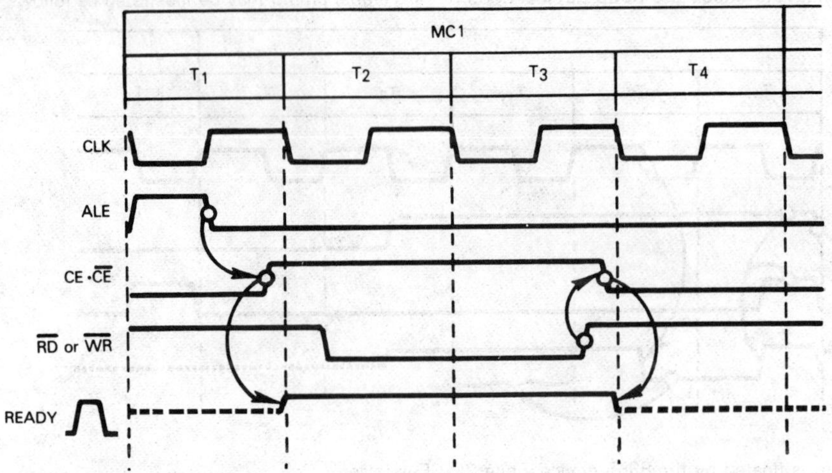


You can resolve this problem by simply inverting ALE as a clock input to the select logic flip-flop.

**But when do you need to induce a Wait state?**

8355 device timing is fast enough to respond to memory and I/O accesses without the inclusion of a Wait state, unless you have buffers on the System Bus and the buffers introduce unacceptably long response delays. Therefore, ignore the READY signal logic of the 8355 in small 8085A systems and derive chip enable logic directly from the high-order address lines A11-A15. In larger systems where buffers on the System Bus force the 8355 device to require a Wait state, use READY logic of the 8355 device.

## 8355 I/O LOGIC

**Let us now look at the I/O logic of the 8355 device. This device has two I/O ports whose pins can be individually assigned to input or output. This assignment is made by loading appropriate Control codes into a Data Direction register associated with each I/O port.** A 1 in any bit position of the Data Direction register defines the associated I/O port pin as an output pin. A 0 in any bit position defines the associated I/O port pin as an input pin. This may be illustrated as follows:

Observe that the 8355 has no I/O with handshaking. For I/O with handshaking you should use the 8155/8156 or the 8255 devices.

# THE 8755A ERASABLE PROGRAMMABLE READ-ONLY MEMORY WITH I/O

**The 8755A device provides 2048 bytes of erasable programmable read-only memory and two 8-bit I/O ports. The only difference between this device and the 8355, which we have just described, is the fact that the 8755A read-only memory is programmable and erasable. There are minor pin and signal variations supporting the EPROM. These differences are identified in Figure 5-27.**

**8755 AND 8755A**

**The 8755A is a new version of an earlier device, the 8755. The only difference between the two is the level of $V_{DD}$ during normal read operations: +5V on the current 8755A, but 0V on the earlier 8755.**

This discussion of the 8755A device is limited to describing how you program the read-only memory. In all other ways, the 8755A device is identical to the 8355.

There are two Chip Enable signals on the 8755A device; CE is the standard chip enable, which must be true when the 8755 device is being accessed for any purpose, either in normal operation or when programming the read-only memory. CE is a high true signal.

The second Chip Enable signal, $\overline{CE}$/PROG, is first held low, then is pulsed true only when you are programming the read-only memory. You must apply a +25V pulse lasting between 50 and 100 milliseconds, beginning with the leading edge of ALE. At this time, data will be written into the addressed read-only memory location. Timing may be illustrated as follows:

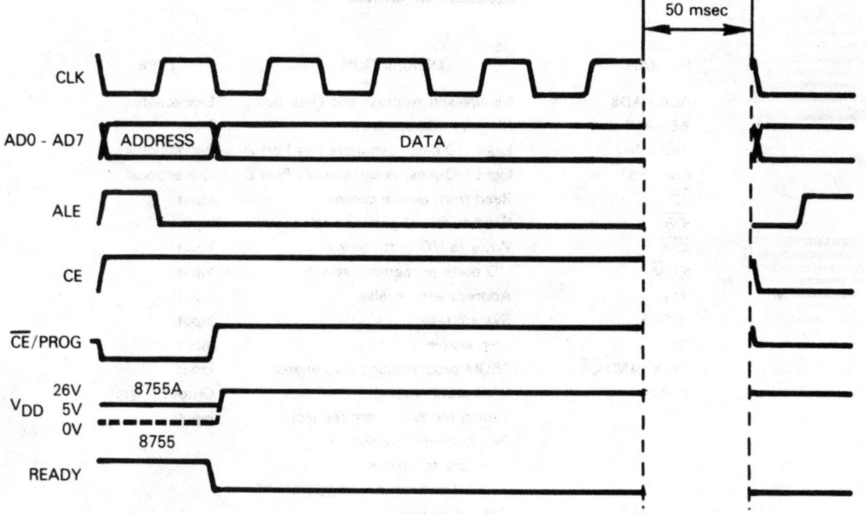


You erase the programmable read-only memory by exposing it to ultraviolet light for a minimum of twenty minutes.

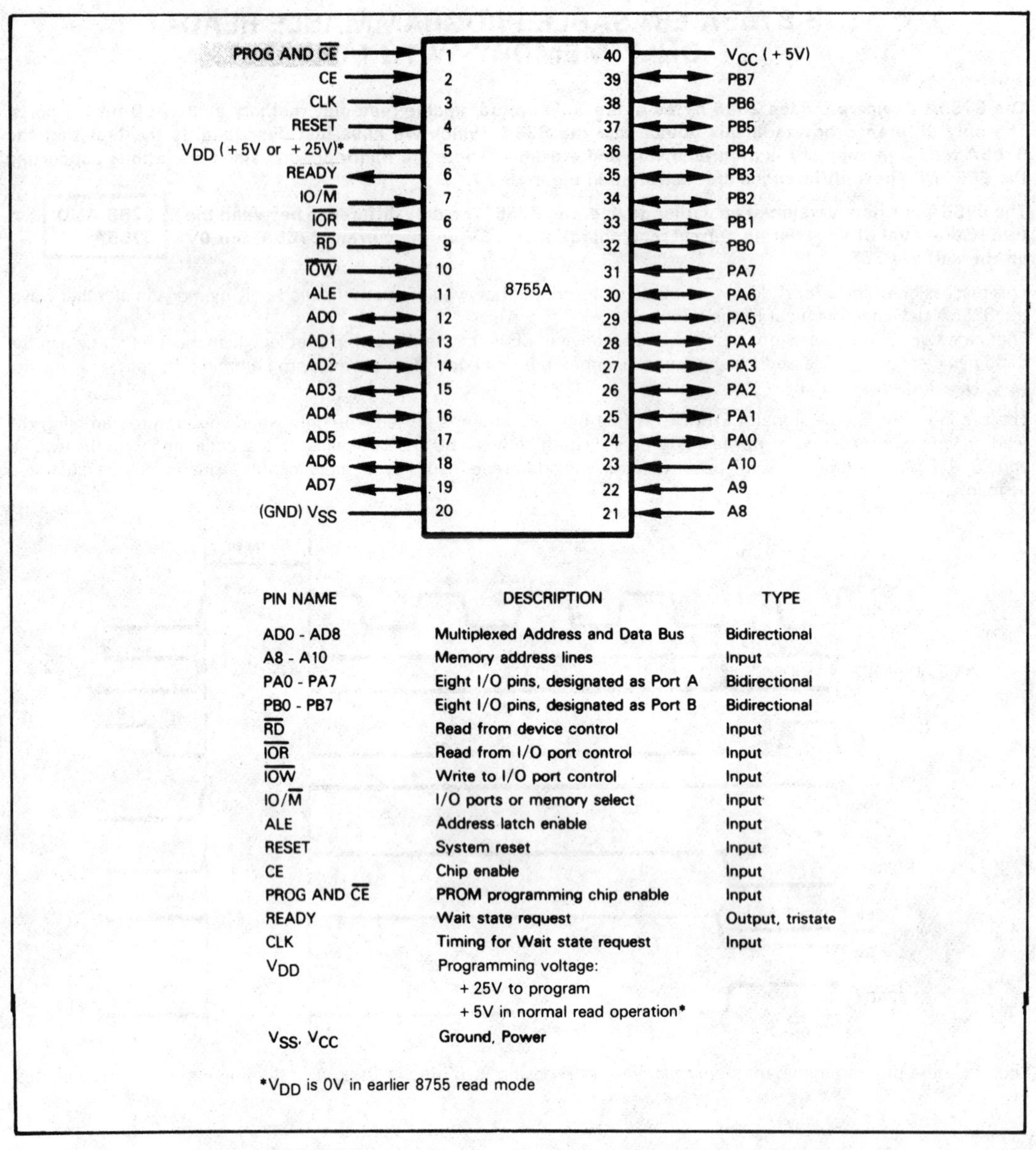


| PIN NAME | DESCRIPTION | TYPE |
|---|---|---|
| AD0 - AD8 | Multiplexed Address and Data Bus | Bidirectional |
| A8 - A10 | Memory address lines | Input |
| PA0 - PA7 | Eight I/O pins, designated as Port A | Bidirectional |
| PB0 - PB7 | Eight I/O pins, designated as Port B | Bidirectional |
| $\overline{RD}$ | Read from device control | Input |
| $\overline{IOR}$ | Read from I/O port control | Input |
| $\overline{IOW}$ | Write to I/O port control | Input |
| IO/$\overline{M}$ | I/O ports or memory select | Input |
| ALE | Address latch enable | Input |
| RESET | System reset | Input |
| CE | Chip enable | Input |
| PROG AND $\overline{CE}$ | PROM programming chip enable | Input |
| READY | Wait state request | Output, tristate |
| CLK | Timing for Wait state request | Input |
| $V_{DD}$ | Programming voltage: +25V to program; +5V in normal read operation* | |
| $V_{SS}$, $V_{CC}$ | Ground, Power | |

*$V_{DD}$ is 0V in earlier 8755 read mode

Figure 5-27. 8755A Multifunction Device Signals and Pin Assignments

# DATA SHEETS

This section contains specific electrical and timing data fro the following devices:

- 8085A/8085A-2 CPU
- 8155/8156 RAM-I/O
- 8355 ROM-I/O
- 8755 EPROM-I/O

**TABLE 4. ABSOLUTE MAXIMUM RATINGS***

Ambient Temperature Under Bias. . . . . . . . . 0°C to 70°C
Storage Temperature . . . . . . . . . . . . . . –65°C to +150°C
Voltage on Any Pin
With Respect to Ground . . . . . . . . . . . . –0.5V to +7V
Power Dissipation . . . . . . . . . . . . . . . . . . 1.5 Watt

*COMMENT
Stresses above those listed under "Absolute Maximum Ratings" may cause permanent damage to the device. This is a stress rating only and functional operation of the device at these or any other conditions above those indicated in the operational sections of this specification is not implied. Exposure to absolute maximum rating conditions for extended periods may affect device reliability.

**TABLE 5. D.C. CHARACTERISTICS**

($T_A$ = 0°C to 70°C; $V_{CC}$ = 5V ±5%; $V_{SS}$ = 0V; unless otherwise specified)

| Symbol | Parameter | Min. | Max. | Units | Test Conditions |
|---|---|---|---|---|---|
| $V_{IL}$ | Input Low Voltage | -0.5 | +0.8 | V | |
| $V_{IH}$ | Input High Voltage | 2.0 | $V_{CC}$+0.5 | V | |
| $V_{OL}$ | Output Low Voltage | | 0.45 | V | $I_{OL}$ = 2mA |
| $V_{OH}$ | Output High Voltage | 2.4 | | V | $I_{OH}$ = -400μA |
| $I_{CC}$ | Power Supply Current | | 170 | mA | |
| $I_{IL}$ | Input Leakage | | ±10 | μA | $V_{in} = V_{CC}$ |
| $I_{LO}$ | Output Leakage | | ±10 | μA | $0.45V \leq V_{out} \leq V_{CC}$ |
| $V_{ILR}$ | Input Low Level, RESET | -0.5 | +0.8 | V | |
| $V_{IHR}$ | Input High Level, RESET | 2.4 | $V_{CC}$ +0.5 | V | |
| $V_{HY}$ | Hysteresis, RESET | 0.25 | | V | |

**Data sheets on pages 5-D2 through 5-D20 are reprinted by permission of Intel Corporation.**

**TABLE 6. A.C. CHARACTERISTICS**
$T_A = 0°C$ to $70°C$; $V_{CC} = 5V \pm 5\%$; $V_{SS} = 0V$

| Symbol | Parameter | 8085A[2] | | 8085A-2[2] | | Units |
|---|---|---|---|---|---|---|
| | | Min. | Max. | Min. | Max. | |
| $t_{CYC}$ | CLK Cycle Period | 320 | 2000 | 200 | 2000 | ns |
| $t_1$ | CLK Low Time (Standard CLK Loading) | 80 | | 40 | | ns |
| $t_2$ | CLK High Time (Standard CLK Loading) | 120 | | 70 | | ns |
| $t_r, t_f$ | CLK Rise and Fall Time | | 30 | | 30 | ns |
| $t_{XKR}$ | $X_1$ Rising to CLK Rising | 30 | 120 | 30 | 100 | ns |
| $t_{XKF}$ | $X_1$ Rising to CLK Falling | 30 | 150 | 30 | 110 | ns |
| $t_{AC}$ | $A_{8-15}$ Valid to Leading Edge of Control[1] | 270 | | 115 | | ns |
| $t_{ACL}$ | $A_{0-7}$ Valid to Leading Edge of Control | 240 | | 115 | | ns |
| $t_{AD}$ | $A_{0-15}$ Valid to Valid Data In | | 575 | | 350 | ns |
| $t_{AFR}$ | Address Float After Leading Edge of $\overline{READ}$ ($\overline{INTA}$) | | 0 | | 0 | ns |
| $t_{AL}$ | $A_{8-15}$ Valid Before Trailing Edge of ALE[1] | 115 | | 50 | | ns |
| $t_{ALL}$ | $A_{0-7}$ Valid Before Trailing Edge of ALE | 90 | | 50 | | ns |
| $t_{ARY}$ | READY Valid from Address Valid | | 220 | | 100 | ns |
| $t_{CA}$ | Address ($A_{8-15}$) Valid After Control | 120 | | 60 | | ns |
| $t_{CC}$ | Width of Control Low ($\overline{RD}$, $\overline{WR}$, $\overline{INTA}$) Edge of ALE | 400 | | 230 | | ns |
| $t_{CL}$ | Trailing Edge of Control to Leading Edge of ALE | 50 | | 25 | | ns |
| $t_{DW}$ | Data Valid to Trailing Edge of $\overline{WRITE}$ | 420 | | 230 | | ns |
| $t_{HABE}$ | HLDA to Bus Enable | | 210 | | 150 | ns |
| $t_{HABF}$ | Bus Float After HLDA | | 210 | | 150 | ns |
| $t_{HACK}$ | HLDA Valid to Trailing Edge of CLK | 110 | | 40 | | ns |
| $t_{HDH}$ | HOLD Hold Time | 0 | | 0 | | ns |
| $t_{HDS}$ | HOLD Setup Time to Trailing Edge of CLK | 170 | | 120 | | ns |
| $t_{INH}$ | INTR Hold Time | 0 | | 0 | | ns |
| $t_{INS}$ | INTR, RST, and TRAP Setup Time to Falling Edge of CLK | 160 | | 150 | | ns |
| $t_{LA}$ | Address Hold Time After ALE | 100 | | 50 | | ns |
| $t_{LC}$ | Trailing Edge of ALE to Leading Edge of Control | 130 | | 60 | | ns |
| $t_{LCK}$ | ALE Low During CLK High | 100 | | 50 | | ns |
| $t_{LDR}$ | ALE to Valid Data During Read | | 460 | | 270 | ns |
| $t_{LDW}$ | ALE to Valid Data During Write | | 200 | | 120 | ns |
| $t_{LL}$ | ALE Width | 140 | | 80 | | ns |
| $t_{LRY}$ | ALE to READY Stable | | 110 | | 30 | ns |

**Table 6. A.C. Characteristics (Cont.)**

| Symbol | Parameter | 8085A[2] | | 8085A-2[2] | | Units |
|---|---|---|---|---|---|---|
| | | Min. | Max. | Min. | Max. | |
| $t_{RAE}$ | Trailing Edge of $\overline{READ}$ to Re-Enabling of Address | 150 | | 90 | | ns |
| $t_{RD}$ | $\overline{READ}$ (or $\overline{INTA}$) to Valid Data | | 300 | | 150 | ns |
| $t_{RV}$ | Control Trailing Edge to Leading Edge of Next Control | 400 | | 220 | | ns |
| $t_{RDH}$ | Data Hold Time After $\overline{READ}$ $\overline{INTA}$[7] | 0 | | 0 | | ns |
| $t_{RYH}$ | READY Hold Time | 0 | | 0 | | ns |
| $t_{RYS}$ | READY Setup Time to Leading Edge of CLK | 110 | | 100 | | ns |
| $t_{WD}$ | Data Valid After Trailing Edge of $\overline{WRITE}$ | 100 | | 60 | | ns |
| $t_{WDL}$ | LEADING Edge of WRITE to Data Valid | | 40 | | 20 | ns |

Notes:

1. $A_8$-$A_{15}$ address Specs apply to IO/$\overline{M}$, $S_0$, and $S_1$ except $A_8$-$A_{15}$ are undefined during $T_4$-$T_6$ of OF cycle whereas IO/$\overline{M}$, $S_0$. and$S_1$ are stable.
2. Test conditions: $t_{CYC}$ = 320 ns (8085A)/200 ns (8085A-2); $C_L$ = 150 pF.
3. For all output timing where $C_L$ = 150 pF use the following correction factors:
   25 pF $\leq C_L <$ 150 pF: −0.10 ns/pF
   150 pF $< C_L \leq$ 300 pF: +0.30 ns/pF
4. Output timings are measured with purely capacitive load.
5. All timings are measured at output votage $V_L$ = 0.8V, $V_H$ = 2.0V, and 1.5V with 20 ns rise and fall time on inputs.
6. To calculate timing specifications at other values of $t_{CYC}$ use Table 7.
7. Data hold time is guaranteed under all loading conditions.

**Input Waveform for A.C. Tests:**

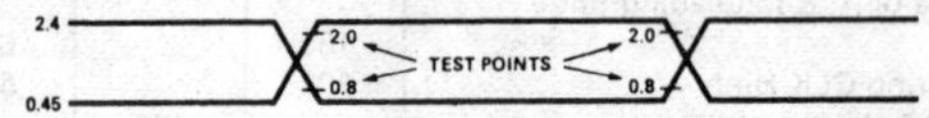

**TABLE 7. BUS TIMING SPECIFICATION AS A $T_{CYC}$ DEPENDENT**

8085A

| | | | |
|---|---|---|---|
| $t_{AL}$ | – | (1/2) T - 45 | MIN |
| $t_{LA}$ | – | (1/2) T - 60 | MIN |
| $t_{LL}$ | – | (1/2) T - 20 | MIN |
| $t_{LCK}$ | – | (1/2) T - 60 | MIN |
| $t_{LC}$ | – | (1/2) T - 30 | MIN |
| $t_{AD}$ | – | (5/2 + N) T - 225 | MAX |
| $t_{RD}$ | – | (3/2 + N) T - 180 | MAX |
| $t_{RAE}$ | – | (1/2) T - 10 | MIN |
| $t_{CA}$ | – | (1/2) T - 40 | MIN |
| $t_{DW}$ | – | (3/2 + N) T – 60 | MIN |
| $t_{WD}$ | – | (1/2) T - 60 | MIN |
| $t_{CC}$ | – | (3/2 + N) T - 80 | MIN |
| $t_{CL}$ | – | (1/2) T - 110 | MIN |
| $t_{ARY}$ | – | (3/2) T - 260 | MAX |
| $t_{HACK}$ | – | (1/2) T - 50 | MIN |
| $t_{HABF}$ | – | (1/2) T + 50 | MAX |
| $t_{HABE}$ | – | (1/2) T + 50 | MAX |
| $t_{AC}$ | – | (2/2) T - 50 | MIN |
| $t_1$ | – | (1/2) T - 80 | MIN |
| $t_2$ | – | (1/2) T - 40 | MIN |
| $t_{RV}$ | – | (3/2) T - 80 | MIN |
| $t_{LDR}$ | – | (4/2) T - 180 | MAX |

NOTE: N is equal to the total WAIT states.
$T = t_{CYC}$.

8085A-2

| | | | |
|---|---|---|---|
| $t_{AL}$ | – | (1/2) T - 50 | MIN |
| $t_{LA}$ | – | (1/2) T - 50 | MIN |
| $t_{LL}$ | – | (1/2) T - 20 | MIN |
| $t_{LCK}$ | – | (1/2) T - 50 | MIN |
| $t_{LC}$ | – | (1/2) T - 40 | MIN |
| $t_{AD}$ | – | (5/2 + N) T - 150 | MAX |
| $t_{RD}$ | – | (3/2 + N) T - 150 | MAX |
| $t_{RAE}$ | – | (1/2) T - 10 | MIN |
| $t_{CA}$ | – | (1/2) T - 40 | MIN |
| $t_{DW}$ | – | (3/2 + N) T – 70 | MIN |
| $t_{WD}$ | – | (1/2) T - 40 | MIN |
| $t_{CC}$ | – | (3/2 + N) T - 70 | MIN |
| $t_{CL}$ | – | (1/2) T - 75 | MIN |
| $t_{ARY}$ | – | (3/2) T - 200 | MAX |
| $t_{HACK}$ | – | (1/2) T - 60 | MIN |
| $t_{HABF}$ | – | (1/2) T + 50 | MAX |
| $t_{HABE}$ | – | (1/2) T + 50 | MAX |
| $t_{AC}$ | – | (2/2) T - 85 | MIN |
| $t_1$ | – | (1/2) T - 60 | MIN |
| $t_2$ | – | (1/2) T - 30 | MIN |
| $t_{RV}$ | – | (3/2) T - 80 | MIN |
| $t_{LDR}$ | – | (4/2) T - 130 | MAX |

NOTE: N is equal to the total WAIT states.
$T = t_{CYC}$.

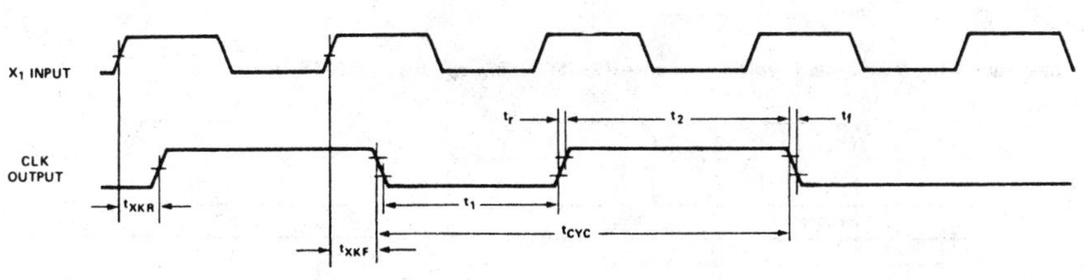


**Figure 10. Clock Timing Waveform**

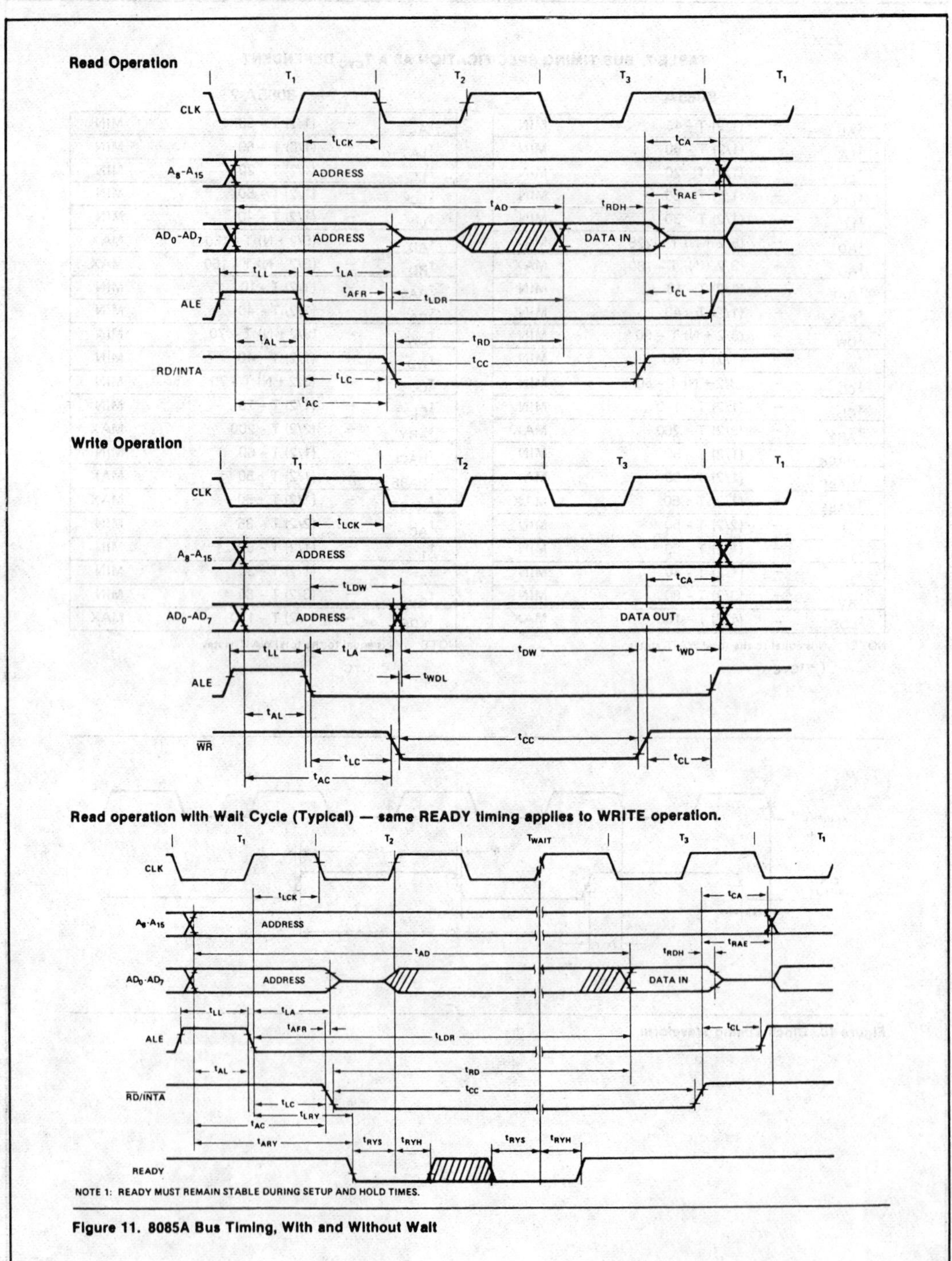


**Figure 11. 8085A Bus Timing, With and Without Wait**

**Hold Operation**

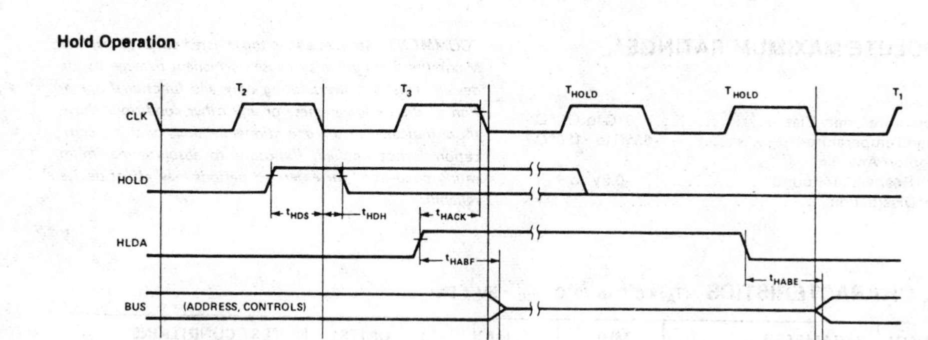


**Figure 12. 8085A Hold Timing.**

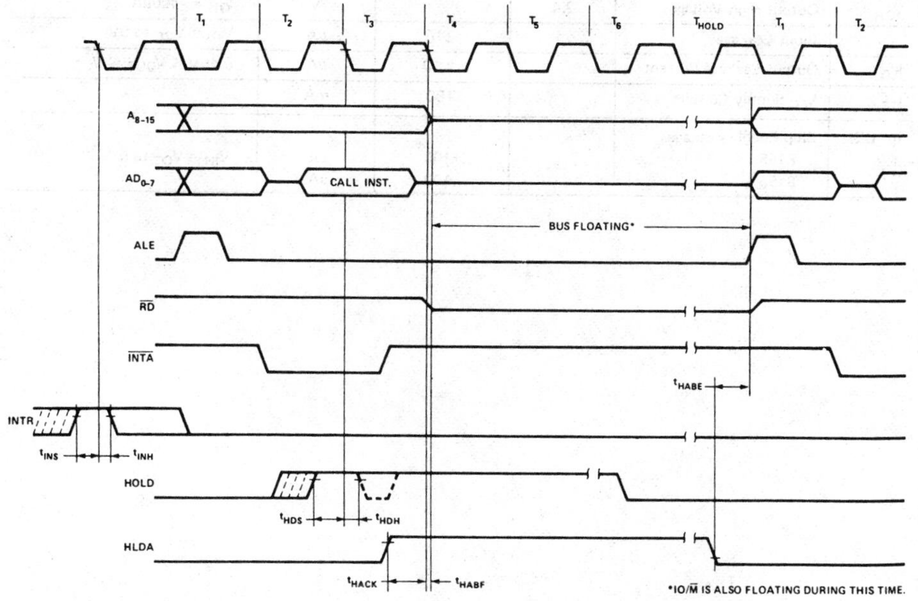


**Figure 13. 8085A Interrupt and Hold Timing**

## ABSOLUTE MAXIMUM RATINGS*

Temperature Under Bias ................ 0°C to +70°C
Storage Temperature ............... -65°C to +150°C
Voltage on Any Pin
With Respect to Ground ............... -0.5V to +7V
Power Dissipation ............................ 1.5W

**COMMENT: Stresses above those listed under "Absolute Maximum Ratings" may cause permanent damage to the device. This is a stress rating only and functional operation of the device at these or any other conditions above those indicated in the operational sections of this specification is not implied. Exposure to absolute maximum rating conditions for extended periods may affect device reliability.*

## D.C. CHARACTERISTICS ($T_A$ = 0°C to 70°C; $V_{CC}$ = 5V ± 5%)

| SYMBOL | PARAMETER | MIN. | MAX. | UNITS | TEST CONDITIONS |
|---|---|---|---|---|---|
| $V_{IL}$ | Input Low Voltage | -0.5 | 0.8 | V | |
| $V_{IH}$ | Input High Voltage | 2.0 | $V_{CC}$+0.5 | V | |
| $V_{OL}$ | Output Low Voltage | | 0.45 | V | $I_{OL}$ = 2mA |
| $V_{OH}$ | Output High Voltage | 2.4 | | V | $I_{OH}$ = -400μA |
| $I_{IL}$ | Input Leakage | | ±10 | μA | $V_{IN}$ = $V_{CC}$ to 0V |
| $I_{LO}$ | Output Leakage Current | | ± 10 | μA | 0.45V ⩽ $V_{OUT}$ ⩽ $V_{CC}$ |
| $I_{CC}$ | $V_{CC}$ Supply Current | | 180 | mA | |
| $I_{IL}$ (CE) | Chip Enable Leakage<br>8155<br>8156 | | <br>+100<br>−100 | <br>μA<br>μA | <br>$V_{IN}$ = $V_{CC}$ to 0V |

## A.C. CHARACTERISTICS ($T_A$ = 0°C to 70°C; $V_{CC}$ = 5V ± 5%)

| | | 8155/8156 | | 8155-2/8156-2 (Preliminary) | | |
|---|---|---|---|---|---|---|
| SYMBOL | PARAMETER | MIN. | MAX. | MIN. | MAX. | UNITS |
| $t_{AL}$ | Address to Latch Set Up Time | 50 | | 30 | | ns |
| $t_{LA}$ | Address Hold Time after Latch | 80 | | 30 | | ns |
| $t_{LC}$ | Latch to READ/WRITE Control | 100 | | 40 | | ns |
| $t_{RD}$ | Valid Data Out Delay from READ Control | | 170 | | 140 | ns |
| $t_{AD}$ | Address Stable to Data Out Valid | | 400 | | 330 | ns |
| $t_{LL}$ | Latch Enable Width | 100 | | 70 | | ns |
| $t_{RDF}$ | Data Bus Float After READ | 0 | 100 | 0 | 80 | ns |
| $t_{CL}$ | READ/WRITE Control to Latch Enable | 20 | | 10 | | ns |
| $t_{CC}$ | READ/WRITE Control Width | 250 | | 200 | | ns |
| $t_{DW}$ | Data In to WRITE Set Up Time | 150 | | 100 | | ns |
| $t_{WD}$ | Data In Hold Time After WRITE | 0 | | 0 | | ns |
| $t_{RV}$ | Recovery Time Between Controls | 300 | | 200 | | ns |
| $t_{WP}$ | WRITE to Port Output | | 400 | | 300 | ns |
| $t_{PR}$ | Port Input Setup Time | 70 | | 50 | | ns |
| $t_{RP}$ | Port Input Hold Time | 50 | | 10 | | ns |
| $t_{SBF}$ | Strobe to Buffer Full | | 400 | | 300 | ns |
| $t_{SS}$ | Strobe Width | 200 | | 150 | | ns |
| $t_{RBE}$ | READ to Buffer Empty | | 400 | | 300 | ns |
| $t_{SI}$ | Strobe to INTR On | | 400 | | 300 | ns |
| $t_{RDI}$ | READ to INTR Off | | 400 | | 300 | ns |
| $t_{PSS}$ | Port Setup Time to Strobe Strobe | 50 | | 0 | | ns |
| $t_{PHS}$ | Port Hold Time After Strobe | 120 | | 100 | | ns |
| $t_{SBE}$ | Strobe to Buffer Empty | | 400 | | 300 | ns |
| $t_{WBF}$ | WRITE to Buffer Full | | 400 | | 300 | ns |
| $t_{WI}$ | WRITE to INTR Off | | 400 | | 300 | ns |
| $t_{TL}$ | TIMER-IN to $\overline{\text{TIMER-OUT}}$ Low | | 400 | | 300 | ns |
| $t_{TH}$ | TIMER-IN to $\overline{\text{TIMER-OUT}}$ High | | 400 | | 300 | ns |
| $t_{RDE}$ | Data Bus Enable from READ Control | 10 | | 10 | | ns |
| $t_1$ | TIMER-IN Low Time | 80 | | 40 | | ns |
| $t_2$ | TIMER-IN High Time | 120 | | 70 | | ns |

**Input Waveform for A.C. Tests:**

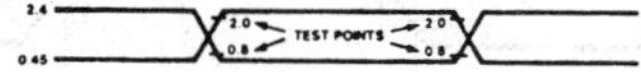

## WAVEFORMS

**a. Read Cycle**

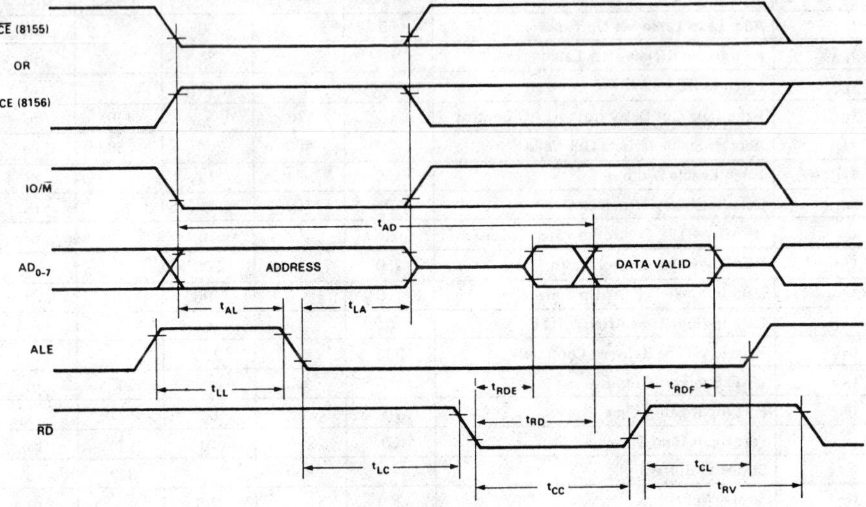


**b. Write Cycle**

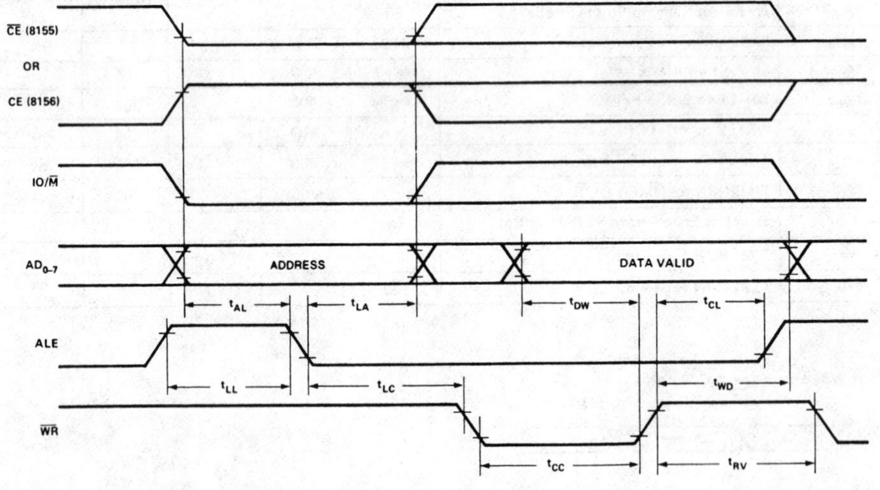


**Figure 12. 8155/8156 Read/Write Timing Diagrams**

a. Strobed Input Mode

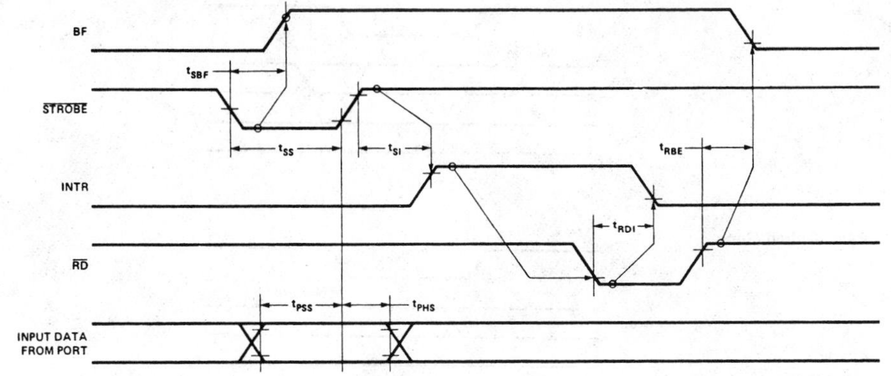


b. Strobed Output Mode

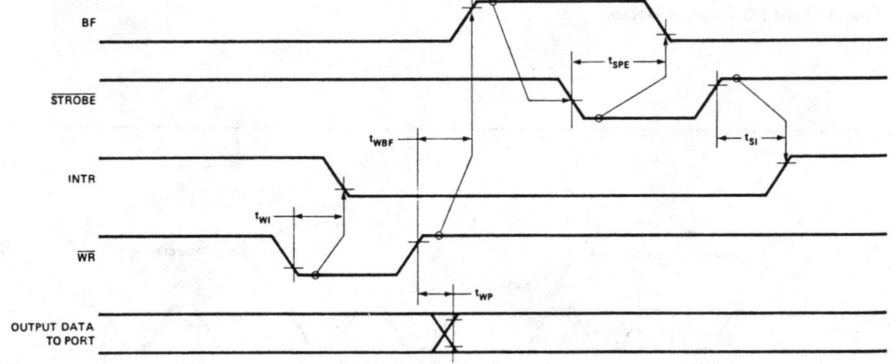


Figure 13. Strobed I/O Timing

a. Basic Input Mode

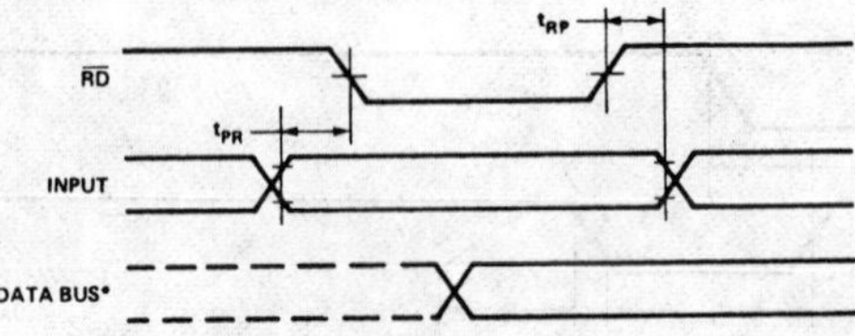


b. Basic Output Mode

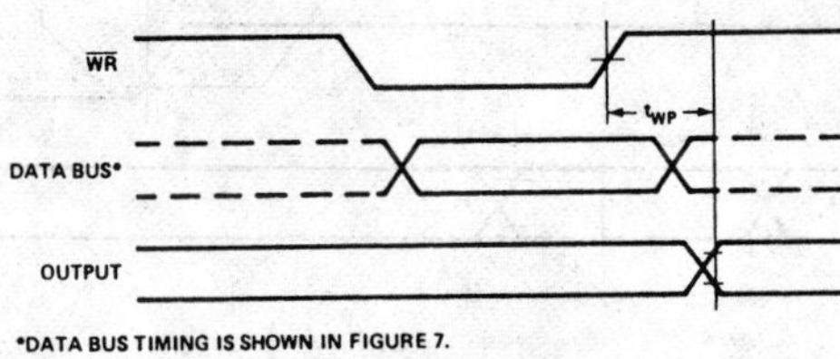


*DATA BUS TIMING IS SHOWN IN FIGURE 7.

Figure 14. Basic I/O Timing Waveform

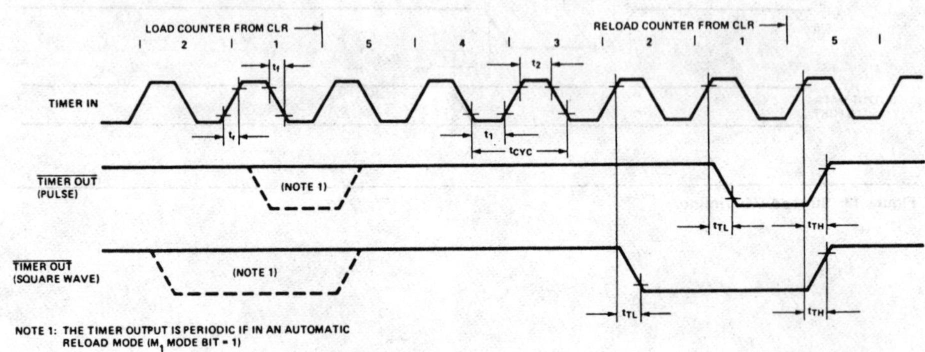


NOTE 1: THE TIMER OUTPUT IS PERIODIC IF IN AN AUTOMATIC RELOAD MODE ($M_1$ MODE BIT = 1)

Figure 15. Timer Output Waveform Countdown from 5 to 1

## ABSOLUTE MAXIMUM RATINGS*

Temperature Under Bias ................ 0°C to +70°C
Storage Temperature ............... -65°C to +150°C
Voltage on Any Pin
With Respect to Ground ............... -0.5V to +7V
Power Dissipation ............................ 1.5W

**COMMENT: Stresses above those listed under "Absolute Maximum Ratings" may cause permanent damage to the device. This is a stress rating only and functional operation of the device at these or any other conditions above those indicated in the operational sections of this specification is not implied. Exposure to absolute maximum rating conditions for extended periods may affect device reliability.*

## D.C. CHARACTERISTICS ($T_A$ = 0°C to 70°C; $V_{CC}$ = 5V ± 5%)

| SYMBOL | PARAMETER | MIN. | MAX. | UNITS | TEST CONDITIONS |
|---|---|---|---|---|---|
| $V_{IL}$ | Input Low Voltage | -0.5 | 0.8 | V | $V_{CC}$ = 5.0V |
| $V_{IH}$ | Input High Voltage | 2.0 | $V_{CC}$+0.5 | V | $V_{CC}$ = 5.0V |
| $V_{OL}$ | Output Low Voltage | | 0.45 | V | $I_{OL}$ = 2mA |
| $V_{OH}$ | Output High Voltage | 2.4 | | V | $I_{OH}$ = -400μA |
| $I_{IL}$ | Input Leakage | | 10 | μA | $V_{IN}$ = $V_{CC}$ to 0V |
| $I_{LO}$ | Output Leakage Current | | ±10 | μA | 0.45V ≤$V_{OUT}$ ≤$V_{CC}$ |
| $I_{CC}$ | $V_{CC}$ Supply Current | | 180 | mA | |

## A.C. CHARACTERISTICS ($T_A$ = 0°C to 70°C; $V_{CC}$ = 5V ± 5%)

| Symbol | Parameter | 8355 | | 8355-2 | | |
|---|---|---|---|---|---|---|
| | | Min. | Max. | Min. | Max. | Units |
| $t_{CYC}$ | Clock Cycle Time | 320 | | 200 | | ns |
| $T_1$ | CLK Pulse Width | 80 | | 40 | | ns |
| $T_2$ | CLK Pulse Width | 120 | | 70 | | ns |
| $t_f, t_r$ | CLK Rise and Fall Time | | 30 | | 30 | ns |
| $t_{AL}$ | Address to Latch Set Up Time | 50 | | 30 | | ns |
| $t_{LA}$ | Address Hold Time after Latch | 80 | | 30 | | ns |
| $t_{LC}$ | Latch to READ/WRITE Control | 100 | | 40 | | ns |
| $t_{RD}$ | Valid Data Out Delay from READ Control | | 170 | | 140 | ns |
| $t_{AD}$ | Address Stable to Data Out Valid | | 400 | | 330 | ns |
| $t_{LL}$ | Latch Enable Width | 100 | | 70 | | ns |
| $t_{RDF}$ | Data Bus Float after READ | 0 | 100 | 0 | 85 | ns |
| $t_{CL}$ | READ/WRITE Control to Latch Enable | 20 | | 10 | | ns |
| $t_{CC}$ | READ/WRITE Control Width | 250 | | 200 | | ns |
| $t_{DW}$ | Data In to Write Set Up Time | 150 | | 150 | | ns |
| $t_{WD}$ | Data In Hold Time After WRITE | 10 | | 10 | | ns |
| $t_{WP}$ | WRITE to Port Output | | 400 | | 400 | ns |
| $t_{PR}$ | Port Input Set Up Time | 50 | | 50 | | ns |
| $t_{RP}$ | Port Input Hold Time | 50 | | 50 | | ns |
| $t_{RYH}$ | READY HOLD Time | 0 | 160 | 0 | 160 | ns |
| $t_{ARY}$ | ADDRESS (CE) to READY | | 160 | | 160 | ns |
| $t_{RV}$ | Recovery Time Between Controls | 300 | | 200 | | ns |
| $t_{RDE}$ | READ Control to Data Bus Enable | 10 | | 10 | | ns |

Note: $C_{LOAD}$ = 150pF

**Input Waveform for A.C. Tests:**

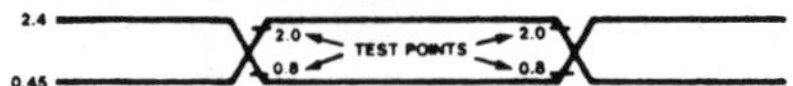

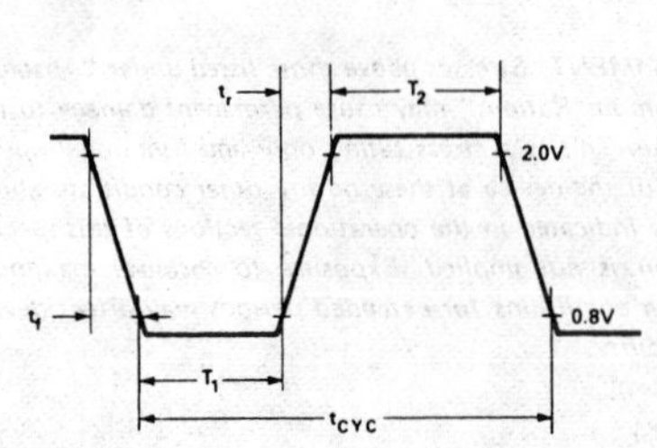


Figure 3. Clock Specification for 8355

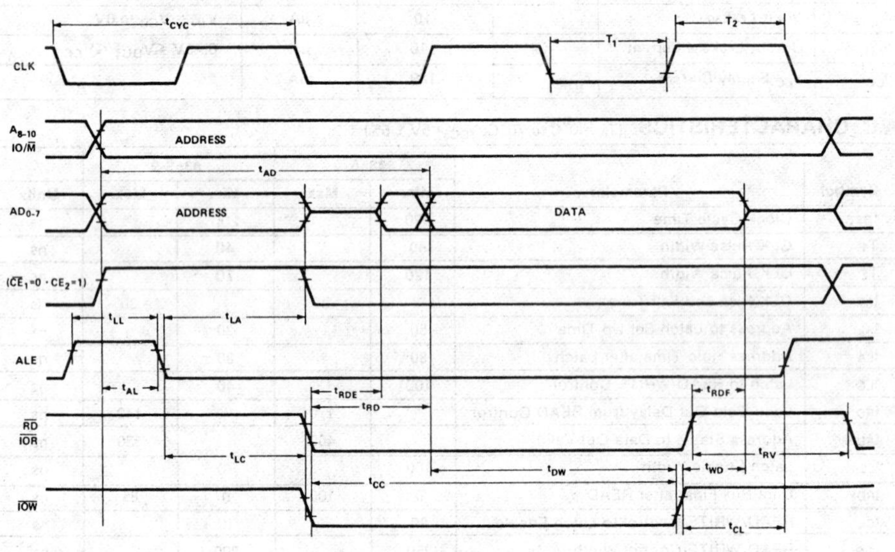


Figure 4. ROM Read and I/O Read and Write

a. Input Mode

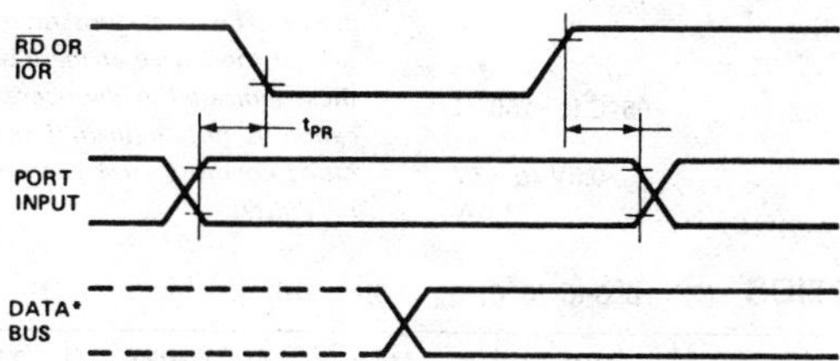


b. Output Mode

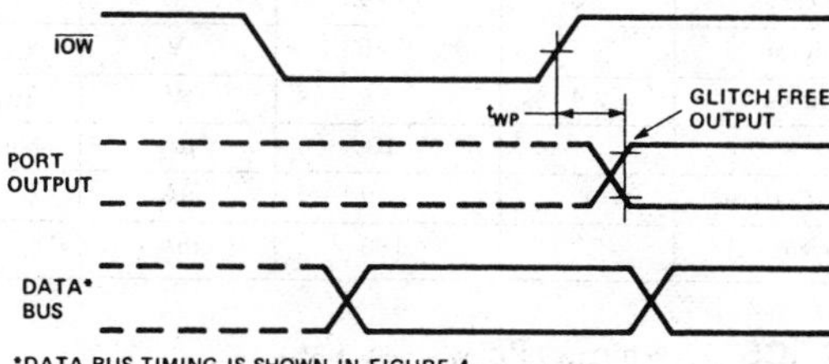


*DATA BUS TIMING IS SHOWN IN FIGURE 4.

**Figure 5. I/O Port Timing**

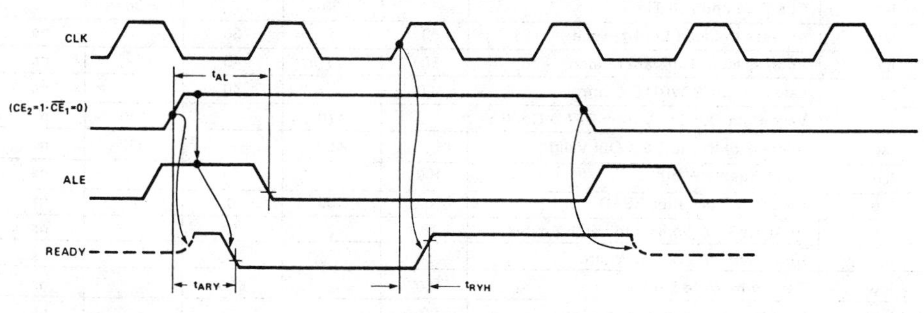


**Figure 6. Wait State Timing (Ready = 0)**

## ABSOLUTE MAXIMUM RATINGS*

Temperature Under Bias ................ 0°C to +70°C
Storage Temperature ............... -65°C to +150°C
Voltage on Any Pin
  With Respect to Ground ............... -0.5V to +7V
Power Dissipation ............................. 1.5W

*COMMENT: Stresses above those listed under "Absolute Maximum Ratings" may cause permanent damage to the device. This is a stress rating only and functional operation of the device at these or any other conditions above those indicated in the operational sections of this specification is not implied. Exposure to absolute maximum rating conditions for extended periods may affect device reliability.*

## D.C. CHARACTERISTICS ($T_A$ = 0°C to 70°C; $V_{CC}$ = 5V ± 5%)

| SYMBOL | PARAMETER | MIN. | MAX. | UNITS | TEST CONDITIONS |
|---|---|---|---|---|---|
| $V_{IL}$ | Input Low Voltage | -0.5 | 0.8 | V | $V_{CC}$ = 5.0V |
| $V_{IH}$ | Input High Voltage | 2.0 | $V_{CC}$+0.5 | V | $V_{CC}$ = 5.0V |
| $V_{OL}$ | Output Low Voltage | | 0.45 | V | $I_{OL}$ = 2mA |
| $V_{OH}$ | Output High Voltage | 2.4 | | V | $I_{OH}$ = -400μA |
| $I_{IL}$ | Input Leakage | | 10 | μA | $V_{IN}$ = $V_{CC}$ to 0V |
| $I_{LO}$ | Output Leakage Current | | ±10 | μA | 0.45V ≤$V_{OUT}$ ≤$V_{CC}$ |
| $I_{CC}$ | $V_{CC}$ Supply Current | | 180 | mA | |

## A.C. CHARACTERISTICS ($T_A$ = 0°C to 70°C; $V_{CC}$ = 5V ± 5%)

| Symbol | Parameter | 8755A | | 8755A-2 (Preliminary) | | |
|---|---|---|---|---|---|---|
| | | Min. | Max. | Min. | Max. | Units |
| $t_{CYC}$ | Clock Cycle Time | 320 | | 200 | | ns |
| $T_1$ | CLK Pulse Width | 80 | | 40 | | ns |
| $T_2$ | CLK Pulse Width | 120 | | 70 | | ns |
| $t_f, t_r$ | CLK Rise and Fall Time | | 30 | | 30 | ns |
| $t_{AL}$ | Address to Latch Set Up Time | 50 | | 30 | | ns |
| $t_{LA}$ | Address Hold Time after Latch | 80 | | 45 | | ns |
| $t_{LC}$ | Latch to READ/WRITE Control | 100 | | 40 | | ns |
| $t_{RD}$ | Valid Data Out Delay from READ Control | | 170 | | 140 | ns |
| $t_{AD}$ | Address Stable to Data Out Valid | | 450 | | 330 | ns |
| $t_{LL}$ | Latch Enable Width | 100 | | 70 | | ns |
| $t_{RDF}$ | Data Bus Float after READ | 0 | 100 | 0 | 85 | ns |
| $t_{CL}$ | READ/WRITE Control to Latch Enable | 20 | | 10 | | ns |
| $t_{CC}$ | READ/WRITE Control Width | 250 | | 200 | | ns |
| $t_{DW}$ | Data In to Write Set Up Time | 150 | | 150 | | ns |
| $t_{WD}$ | Data In Hold Time After WRITE | 30 | | 10 | | ns |
| $t_{WP}$ | WRITE to Port Output | | 400 | | 400 | ns |
| $t_{PR}$ | Port Input Set Up Time | 50 | | 50 | | ns |
| $t_{RP}$ | Port Input Hold Time | 50 | | 50 | | ns |
| $t_{RYH}$ | READY HOLD Time | 0 | 160 | 0 | 160 | ns |
| $t_{ARY}$ | ADDRESS (CE) to READY | | 160 | | 160 | ns |
| $t_{RV}$ | Recovery Time Between Controls | 300 | | 200 | | ns |
| $t_{RDE}$ | READ Control to Data Bus Enable | 10 | | 10 | | ns |
| $t_{LD}$ | **ALE to Data Out Valid** | | 350 | | 270 | ns |

Note $C_{LOAD}$ = 150pF

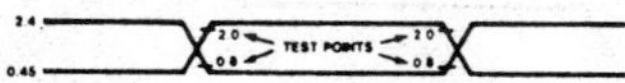


## WAVEFORMS

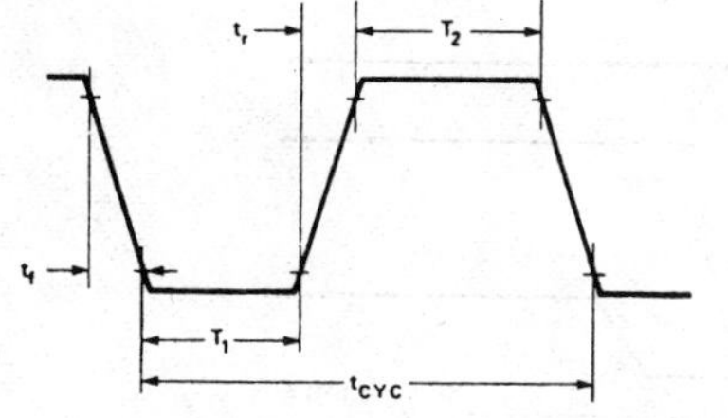


**Figure 3. Clock Specification for 8755A**

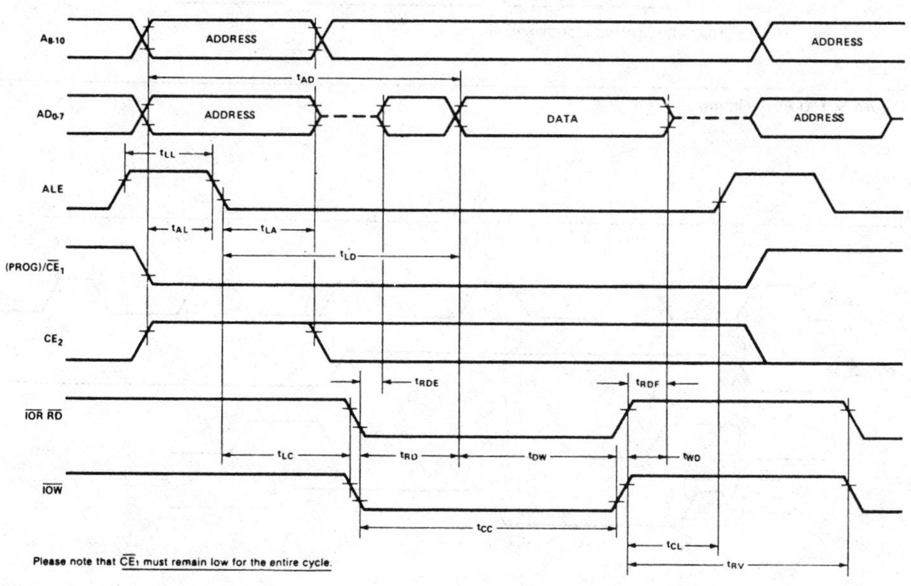


**Figure 4. PROM Read, I/O Read and Write Timing**

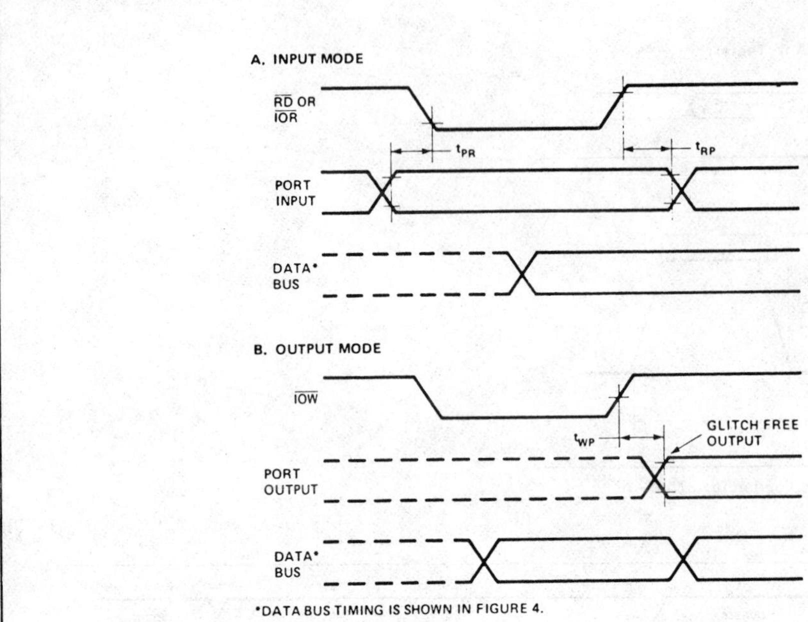


**Figure 5. I/O Port Timing**

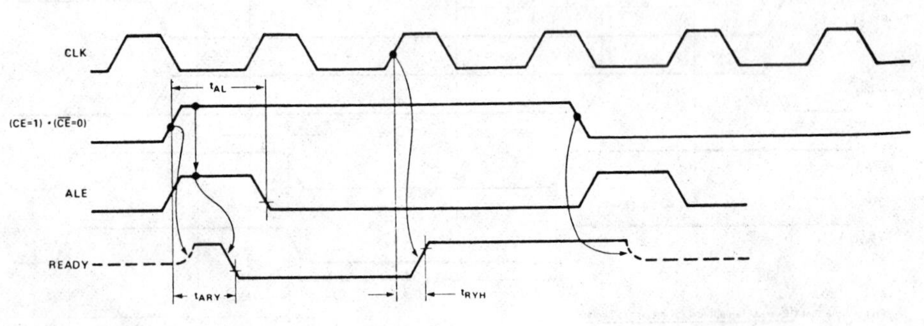


**Figure 6. Wait State Timing (READY = 0)**

## D.C. SPECIFICATION PROGRAMMING

($T_A$ = 0°C to 70°C; $V_{CC}$ = 5V ± 5%; $V_{SS}$ = 0V)

| Symbol | Parameter | Min. | Typ. | Max. | Unit |
|---|---|---|---|---|---|
| $V_{DD}$ | Programming Voltage (during Write to EPROM) | 24 | 25 | 26 | V |
| $I_{DD}$ | Prog Supply Current | | 15 | 30 | mA |

## A.C. SPECIFICATION FOR PROGRAMMING

($T_A$ = 0°C to 70°C; $V_{CC}$ = 5V ± 5%; $V_{SS}$ = 0V)

| Symbol | Parameter | Min. | Typ. | Max. | Unit |
|---|---|---|---|---|---|
| $t_{PS}$ | Data Setup Time | 10 | | | ns |
| $t_{PD}$ | Data Hold Time | 0 | | | ns |
| $t_S$ | Prog Pulse Setup Time | 2 | | | μs |
| $t_H$ | Prog Pulse Hold Time | 2 | | | μs |
| $t_{PR}$ | Prog Pulse Rise Time | 0.01 | 2 | | μs |
| $t_{PF}$ | Prog Pulse Fall Time | 0.01 | 2 | | μs |
| $t_{PRG}$ | Prog Pulse Width | 45 | 50 | | msec |

## WAVEFORMS

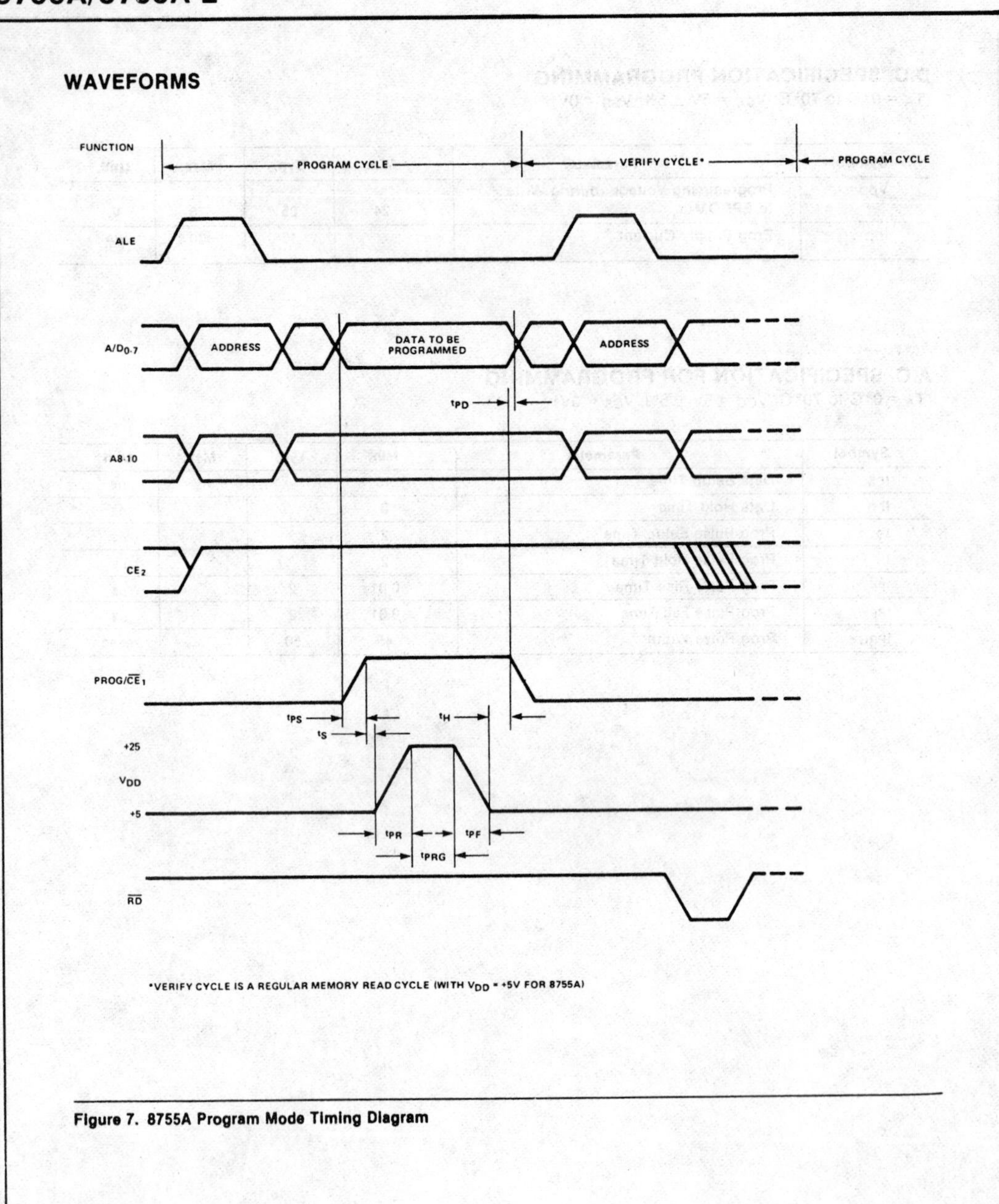


**Figure 7. 8755A Program Mode Timing Diagram**

# Chapter 6
# THE 8048 MICROCOMPUTER DEVICES

**The 8048 series microcomputers are single-chip 8-bit devices which have been developed by Intel to compete in the market for low-cost, high-volume applications. This is a market where the 8080A, with its high chip counts, does not do well. One version of the 8048, the 8748, is also likely to do exceptionally well in low-volume, custom applications because it is very easy to use.**

**The 8048 looks like a one-chip 8080A with heavy F8 influence. The F8 was the first 8-bit microprocessor to bring the economics of low chip counts to the attention of the semiconductor industry. It is therefore not surprising to find an F8 influence in the 8048. (The F8 has now been superceded by the 3870; both parts are described in Chapter 2.)**

**It is intriguing to note that, in terms of general architectural organization, there are striking similarities between the 8048 and the MCS6530 (which is described in Chapter 10).**

**The 8041, 8021 and 8022 are slave microcomputers of the 8048 family. On simple inspection the principal difference between the 8048 and the 8041/8021/8022 would appear to be that the 8041/8021/8022 cannot generate external System Busses. In fact, there are non-obvious differences between the 8048 and the 8041/8021/8022; there are further significant differences between the 8041 and the 8021/8022 and between the 8021 and 8022.**

The 8048 is a simple, single-chip microcomputer that may be a stand-alone device, or part of a multi-microprocessor configuration. As a stand-alone device, the 8048 may or may not have external additional logic. Thus, **the 8048 is a straightforward, low-end, low-cost microprocessor** with less versatility than a device such as the 8085.

If you continue the philosophical progression from the 8085 to the 8048, you reach **the 8021/8022.** These **are single-chip microcomputers with no expansion capabilities,** and very low-cost. The 8021/8022 do not have external bus logic, no RAM or ROM expansion capability is provided. However I/O port expansion is possible via an 8243 I/O expander.

The 8041, in sharp contrast, is a slave microprocessor that assumes the presence of a master microprocessor on one side and external logic on the other side. The 8041 thus becomes an interface and control part — which is how the 8041 should be considered. But you will observe that a large number of microprocessor support parts also act as interfaces between a microprocessor, assumed to exist on one side, and some other logic, assumed to exist on the other side. This is a very accurate parallel to draw. The 8041 is, in fact, a universal interface device, limited only by the speed of the part and the amount of programmed logic that can be included in it. The 8041 can serve a wide variety of interface logic functions. Thus, **whenever you consider using a complex interface controller part, you should also consider using the 8041 as an alternative.** Because the 8041 is programmable, you can tailor it to meet, exactly, the requirements of the specific microprocessor on one side and specific logic on the other side. This is something you cannot do with dedicated controller parts such as floppy disk and CRT controllers, which must look generically, rather than specifically, upon the CPU on one side and the device being controlled on the other side.

**There is also an erasable programmable read-only memory version of the 8041; it is the 8741.**

**8048 series microcomputers are summarized in Table 6-1.**

**The only support device described in this chapter is the 8243 I/O Expander. In addition, the 8155, the 8355, and the 8755 multifunction devices (which have been described in Chapter 5) can be used with 8048 family microcomputers.**

The prime source for the 8048 series microcomputers is:

INTEL CORPORATION
3065 Bowers Avenue
Santa Clara, California 95051

Second sources for the 8048 include:

ADVANCED MICRO DEVICES
901 Thompson Place
Sunnyvale, California 94086

SIGNETICS
811 East Arques Avenue
Sunnyvale, California 94043

Intersil produces a CMOS version of the 8048.

The 8048 series microcomputers use a single +5V power supply. There are two versions of each microcomputer; one uses a 2.5 microsecond clock while the other uses a 5 microsecond clock. 8048 instructions execute in either one or two clock periods. The 8021 uses a 10 microsecond clock. A new version of the 8049 uses a 1.4 μsec clock.

All 8048, 8049, 8041 and 8022 devices are packaged as 40-pin DIPs and have TTL-compatible signals. 8021 devices are packaged as 28-pin DIPs and have TTL-compatible signals.

Table 6-1. A Summary of 8048 Series Microcomputers

| | ON CHIP MEMORY | | CYCLE TIME | I/O PORTS | EXTERNAL INTERRUPTS | TIMER | PACKAGE PINS | EXPANDABLE | ANALOG TO DIGITAL CONVERTER |
|---|---|---|---|---|---|---|---|---|---|
| | ROM/EPROM | RAM | | | | | | | |
| 8048 | 1024 ROM | 64 | 2.5 μsec | 3x8 bits | 1 | Yes | 40 | Yes | No |
| 8035 | 0 | 64 | 2.5 μsec | 3x8 bits | 1 | Yes | 40 | Yes | No |
| 8035-8 | 0 | 64 | 5.0 μsec | 3x8 bits | 1 | Yes | 40 | Yes | No |
| 8039 | 0 | 128 | 1.4 μsec | 3x8 bits | 1 | Yes | 40 | Yes | No |
| 8748 | 1024 EPROM | 64 | 2.5 μsec | 3x8 bits | 1 | Yes | 40 | Yes | No |
| 8748-8 | 1024 EPROM | 64 | 5.0 μsec | 3x8 bits | 1 | Yes | 40 | Yes | No |
| 8049 | 2048 ROM | 64 | 1.4 μsec | 3x8 bits | 1 | Yes | 40 | Yes | No |
| 8041 | 1024 ROM | 64 | 2.5 μsec | 3x8 bits | 0 | Yes | 40 | No | No |
| 8741 | 1024 EPROM | 64 | 2.5 μsec | 3x8 bits | 0 | Yes | 40 | No | No |
| 8021 | 1024 ROM | 64 | 10 μsec | 2x8 bits<br>1x4 bits | 0 | Yes | 28 | No | No |
| 8022 | 2048 ROM | 64 | 10 μsec | 3x8 bits | 1 | Yes | 40 | No | Yes |

## THE 8048, 8748, 8049, 8749, 8035 AND 8039 MICROCOMPUTERS

**For a description of an 8048, 8748, 8049, 8749, 8035 or 8039 device, read the following text; where ambiguities may arise in your mind, remember these overriding rules:**

1) The 8049 is an 8048 with twice as much on-chip program memory, and, in newer models, higher execution speed. There are no other differences between these two parts.
2) An 8035 is an 8048 with no on-chip program memory. There are no other differences between these two parts.
3) An 8039 is an 8049 with no on-chip program memory. There are no other differences between these two parts.

**For a description of an 8041, 8741, 8021 or 8022 device, read the following text, then read the specific device discussion that appears later in this chapter.**

**Functions implemented on the three versions of the 8048 microcomputer are illustrated in Figure 6-1. With the exception of the 8035, you will see that complete microcomputer logic is provided within a single package.** But remember, just because a function is present in Figure 6-1, that does not mean to say it will be sufficient for your application. For example, read/write memory is shown as present, yet there are only 64 bytes of read/write memory on any 8048 series microcomputer chip.

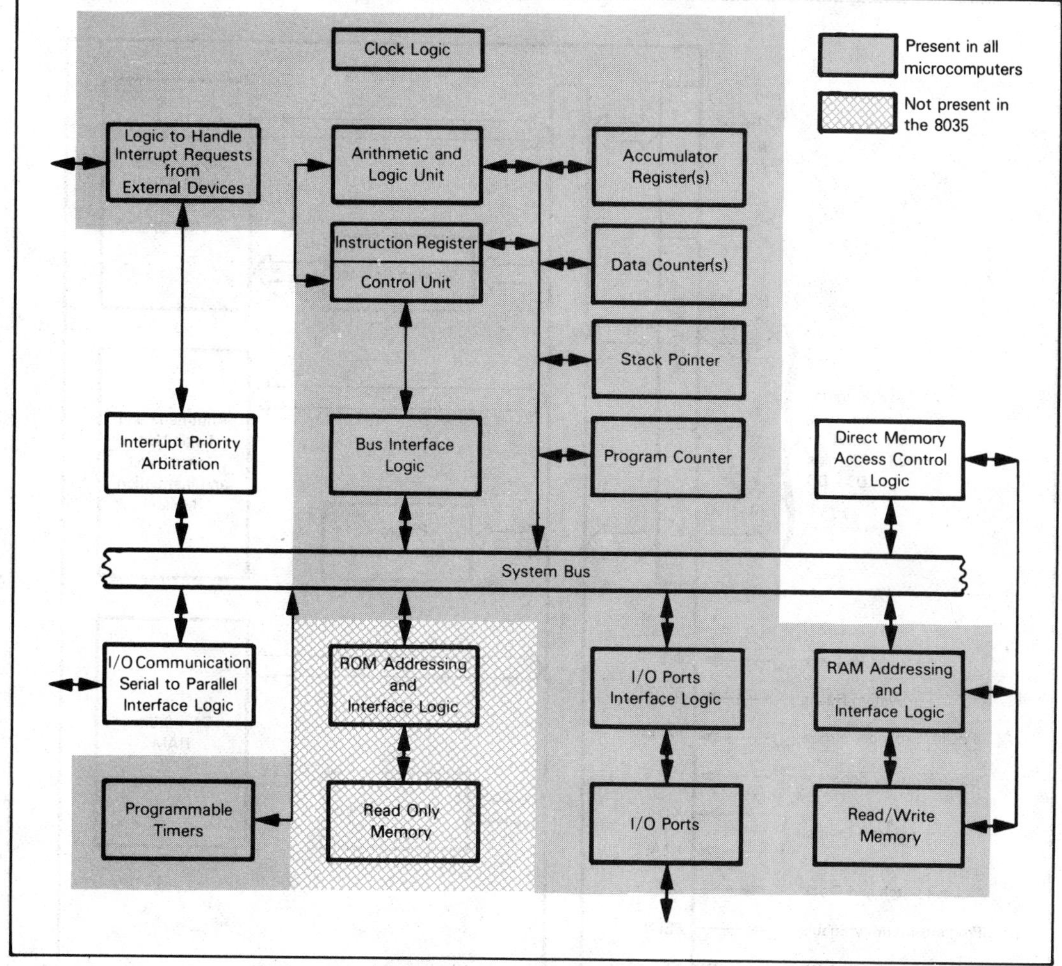


Figure 6-1. Logic of the 8048 Series Microcomputers

**8049 SERIES MICROCOMPUTERS**

The only differences between 8048 series and 8049 series microcomputers are in the on-chip read-only memory and execution speed; 8049 series microcomputers have twice as much on-chip read-only memory as 8048 series microcomputers, and execute instructions 80% faster.

## AN 8048 AND 8049 FUNCTIONAL OVERVIEW

**Logic of the 8048 and 8049 series microcomputers is illustrated functionally in Figure 6-2.**

The Arithmetic and Logic Unit, the Control Unit and the Instruction register are all inaccessible to you as a user; therefore we will ignore this portion of the microcomputer.

1024 bytes of program memory are provided by the 8048 and 8748 microcomputers; the 8035 has no program memory. The 8049 has 2048 bytes of program memory. The 8048 and 8049 have Read Only Memory (ROM), while the 8748 has Erasable Programmable Read Only Memory (EPROM); this is the only difference between the 8048/8049 and the 8748.

There is a 12-bit Program Counter which allows the 8048 series microcomputers to access 4096 bytes of program memory. Since the 8048 and 8748 microcomputers have only 1024 bytes of program memory on the computer chip, the additional 3072 bytes must be external if you are going to expand program memory to the maximum addressable space. All 8035 microcomputer program memory is external. Only 2048 bytes of external program memory can be added to an 8049.

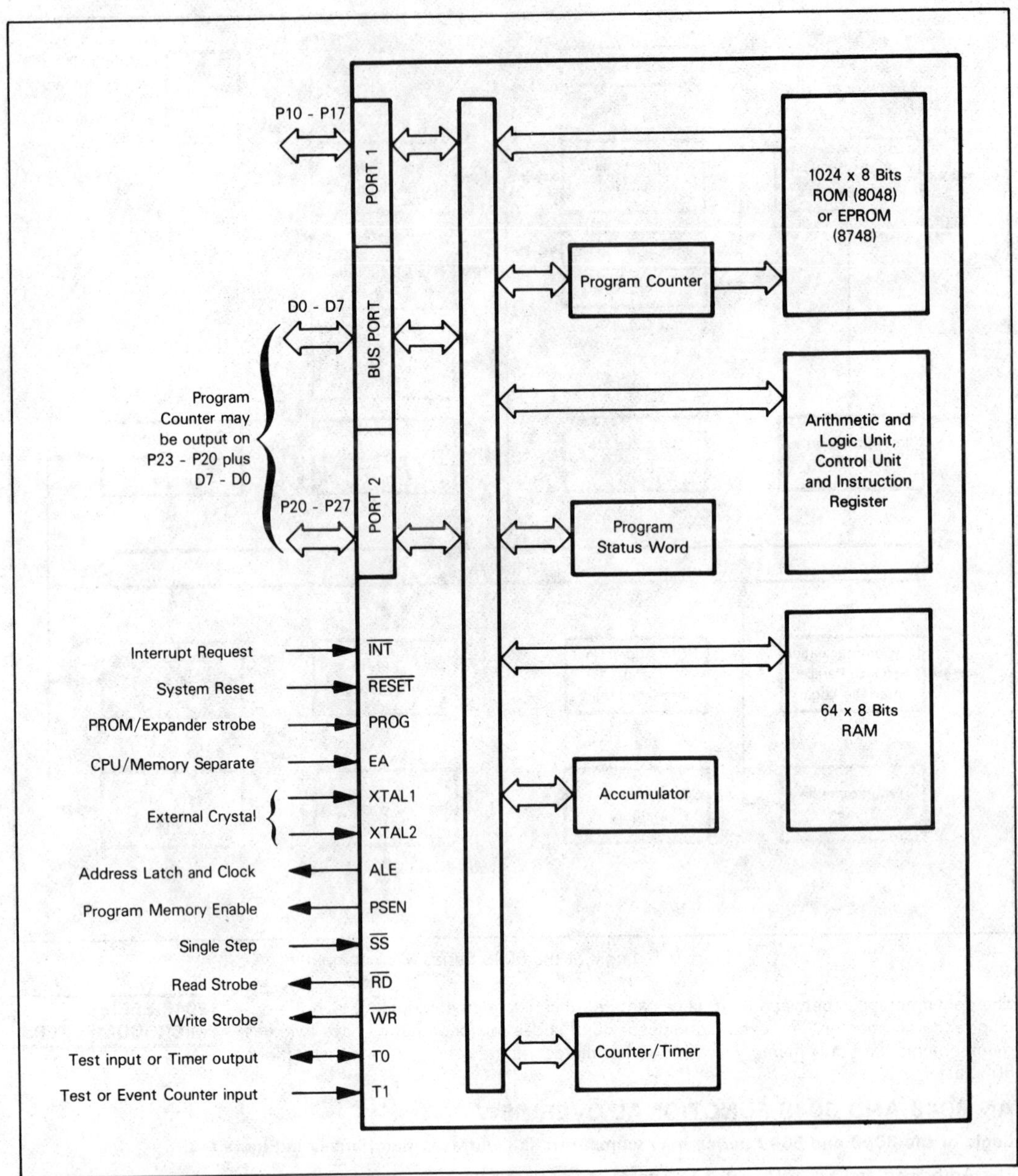


Figure 6-2. Functional Logic of the 8048, 8049, 8748, 8749 and 8035 Microcomputers

**8048 SERIES I/O PORTS**

**All 8048 series microcomputers (with the exception of the 8021) have three 8-bit I/O ports. For the 8048 series and 8049 series microcomputers, one of these ports, the Bus Port, is a truly bidirectional I/O port with input and output strobes.** Outputs can be statically latched, while inputs are nonlatching. This means that external logic must hold input data true at Bus Port pins until the data has been read. All eight pins of the Bus Port must be assigned either to input or output; you cannot mix input and output on the Bus Port.

Bus Port is used as the primary I/O port in a single-chip microcomputer system. In multiple-chip microcomputer systems Bus Port serves as a multiplexed Address and Data Bus.

**I/O Ports 1 and 2 are secondary I/O ports with characteristics that differ significantly from Bus Port.** If you output parallel data to I/O Port 1 or 2, it is latched and maintained at the I/O port until you next write data. But the only way external logic can input data to I/O Port 1 or 2 is by pulling individual pins from a high to a low level. Thus when a high level is being output at any pin of I/O Port 1 or 2, external logic can pull this level low — and subsequently if the CPU reads back data from the I/O port it will read a 0 bit value. This may be illustrated as follows:

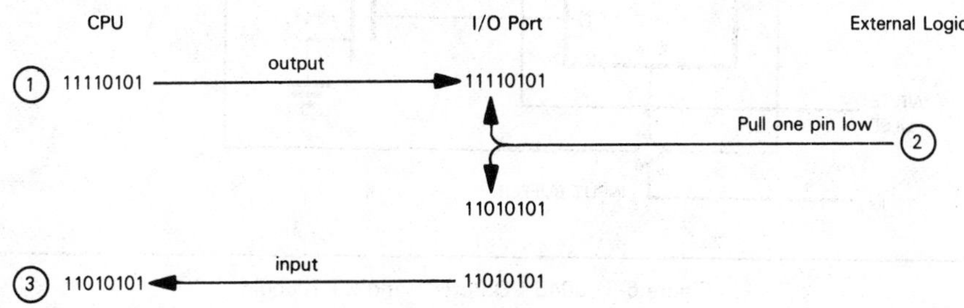


External logic cannot create a high level at any pin of I/O Port 1 or 2 which is outputting a low level.

**Here is a summary of I/O Port 1 and 2 capabilities:**

1) You can at any time output parallel data to I/O Port 1 or 2. The data will be latched and held until the next output.
2) Individual pins of I/O Ports 1 and 2 can serve as input or output pins. When you output data to I/O Port 1 or 2, you must output a 1 bit to any input pin. This may be illustrated as follows:

Data Output → X 1 1 X X 1 X 1 (X = 0 or 1)

| 7 | 6 | 5 | 4 | 3 | 2 | 1 | 0 | ← Bit No. |
|---|---|---|---|---|---|---|---|---|
| O | I | I | O | O | I | O | I | ← I/O Port 1 or 2 (O = Output, I = Input) |

3) External logic writes to input pins of I/O Ports 1 and 2 by leaving low levels alone, and by pulling high levels low.

**8048 SERIES I/O PORT PIN LOGIC**

**Figure 6-3 illustrates logic associated with each pin of I/O Ports 1 and 2** in all 8048 series microcomputers.

Output data is latched by a D-type flip-flop.

The Q and $\overline{Q}$ outputs of the D-type flip-flop control a pair of gates on either side of the pin connection. To provide fast switching times in 0-to-1 transitions, a relatively low impedance (~5K ohms) is switched in for approximately 500 nanoseconds whenever a 1 is output.

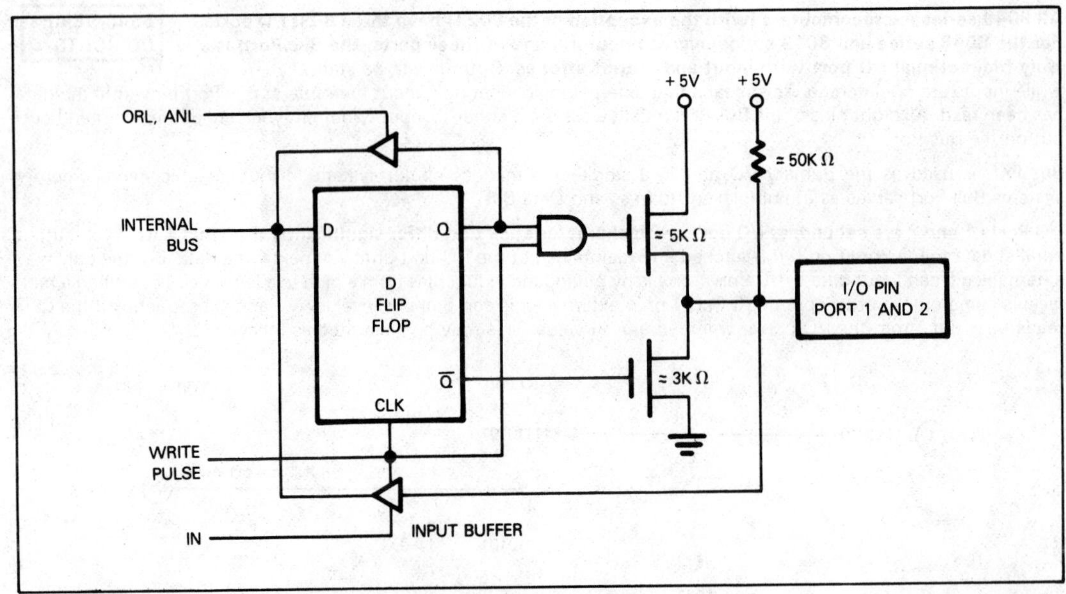


Figure 6-3. 8048 I/O Ports 1 and 2 Pin Logic

Pins are continuously pulled up to +5V through a relatively high impedance (~50K ohms). When a 0 is output to the D-type flip-flop, a low impedance (~3K ohms) overcomes the pull-up and provides TTL current sinking capability.

When a pin of I/O Port 1 or 2 is at a high level, external logic can sink the 50KΩ pull-up. But when the pin is at a low level, external logic cannot overcome the low impedance to ground; thus it cannot pull the pin up to a high level.

By placing an input buffer between the pin and the switching gates, pin logic allows the CPU to read current levels induced by external logic — but only while external logic is connected to the pin.

The buffer connecting the Q output of the D-type flip-flop to the D input is present to enable 8048 instructions that mask I/O port data.

Later in this chapter we will look at I/O ports in more detail, showing programming and design examples.

## 8048, 8049, 8748, 8749, 8035 AND 8039 MICROCOMPUTER PROGRAMMABLE REGISTERS

**The 8048 series microcomputers have an 8-bit Accumulator, a 12-bit Program Counter and 64 bytes of scratchpad memory. Scratchpad memory may be visualized either as read/write memory or as general purpose registers.**

**The Accumulator, Program Counter and scratchpad memory may be illustrated as follows:**

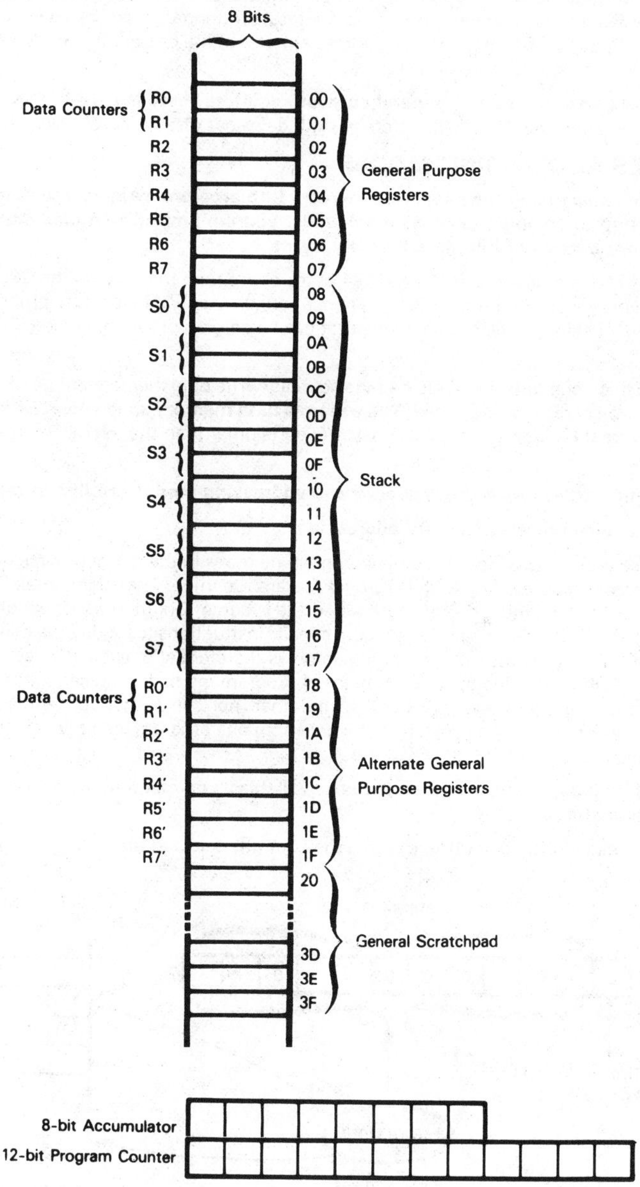

Beware of the fact that both sets of general purpose registers as well as the Stack are implemented in the scratchpad area. Thus, if both the registers and the Stack are fully utilized, 32 bytes of RAM are no longer available for program use. In an 8048 system this cuts your usable RAM area by one half.

**The Accumulator is the principal conduit for all data transfers. The Accumulator is always one source and the destination for Arithmetic or Boolean operations involving memory or registers.**

**Two sets of eight scratchpad bytes serve as secondary registers.** At any time one set of general purpose registers is selected while the other set of general purpose registers is not selected.

**The first two general purpose registers of each set, R0 and R1, act as Data Counters** to address scratchpad memory and external data memory. Thus you address scratchpad memory using implied memory addressing via general purpose Register R0 or R1; you can address any one of the 64 scratchpad bytes, including the general purpose registers, or even the Data Counter register itself.

**In between the two sets of eight general purpose registers there is a 16-byte stack.** The Stack Pointer is maintained in the Program Status Word; therefore we will defer our discussion of stack operations until we look at status.

## 8048 SERIES ADDRESSING MODES

**8048 SERIES MEMORY SPACES**

**The 8048 series microcomputers separate memory into program memory and data memory. Without resorting to complex expansion schemes, you are limited to a maximum of 4096 program memory bytes and 320 data memory bytes.**

The 8048 and 8748 microcomputers have 1024 bytes of program memory on the CPU chip. The 8049 microcomputer has 2048 bytes of program memory on the CPU chip. More program memory, if present, must be external to the CPU chip. The 8035 microcomputer has no on-chip program memory; it requires all program memory to be external.

All 8048 series microcomputers provide 64 bytes of read/write data memory on the CPU chip. In addition, 256 bytes of external data memory may be addressed. **The external data memory space must be shared by external data memory and any external I/O ports** — that is to say, I/O ports other than the microcomputer's own three I/O ports or 8243 Expander ports.

**8048 series microcomputer address spaces and addressing modes are illustrated in Figure 6-4.**

**Let us first examine program memory addressing.**

**8048 SERIES PROGRAM MEMORY ADDRESSING**

A single address space is used to access all of program memory. In the normal course of events program memory is addressed via the 12-bit Program Counter. The high order Program Counter bit is isolated in Figure 6-4 because when the Program Counter is incremented only bits 0 through 10 are affected. You must execute special instructions to modify the contents of the high order Program Counter bit. Program memory is therefore effectively divided into two memory banks, each containing up to 2048 bytes of program memory. You cannot branch, via Jump-on-Condition instructions, from one program memory bank to the other, nor can instructions stored in one program memory bank directly access the other. You can switch completely from one program memory bank to the other by preceding a JMP, CALL or RET instruction with a SEL MB instruction.

**Two types of program memory addressing are available: you can read data from program memory and you can execute Jump instructions.**

You can unconditionally jump anywhere within the currently selected program memory bank; this may be illustrated as follows:

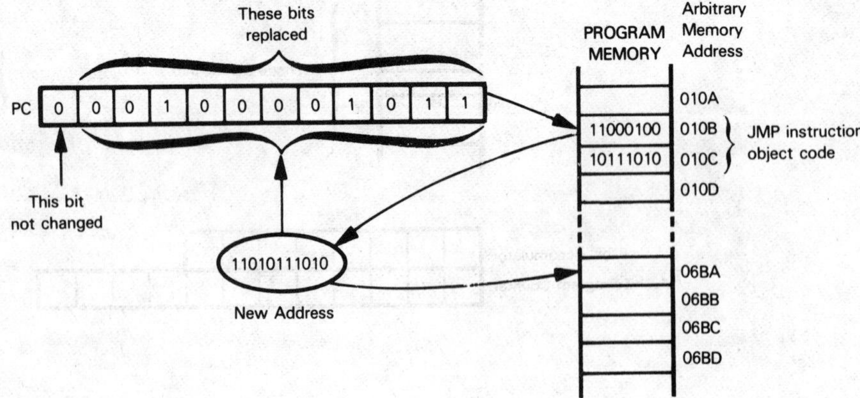

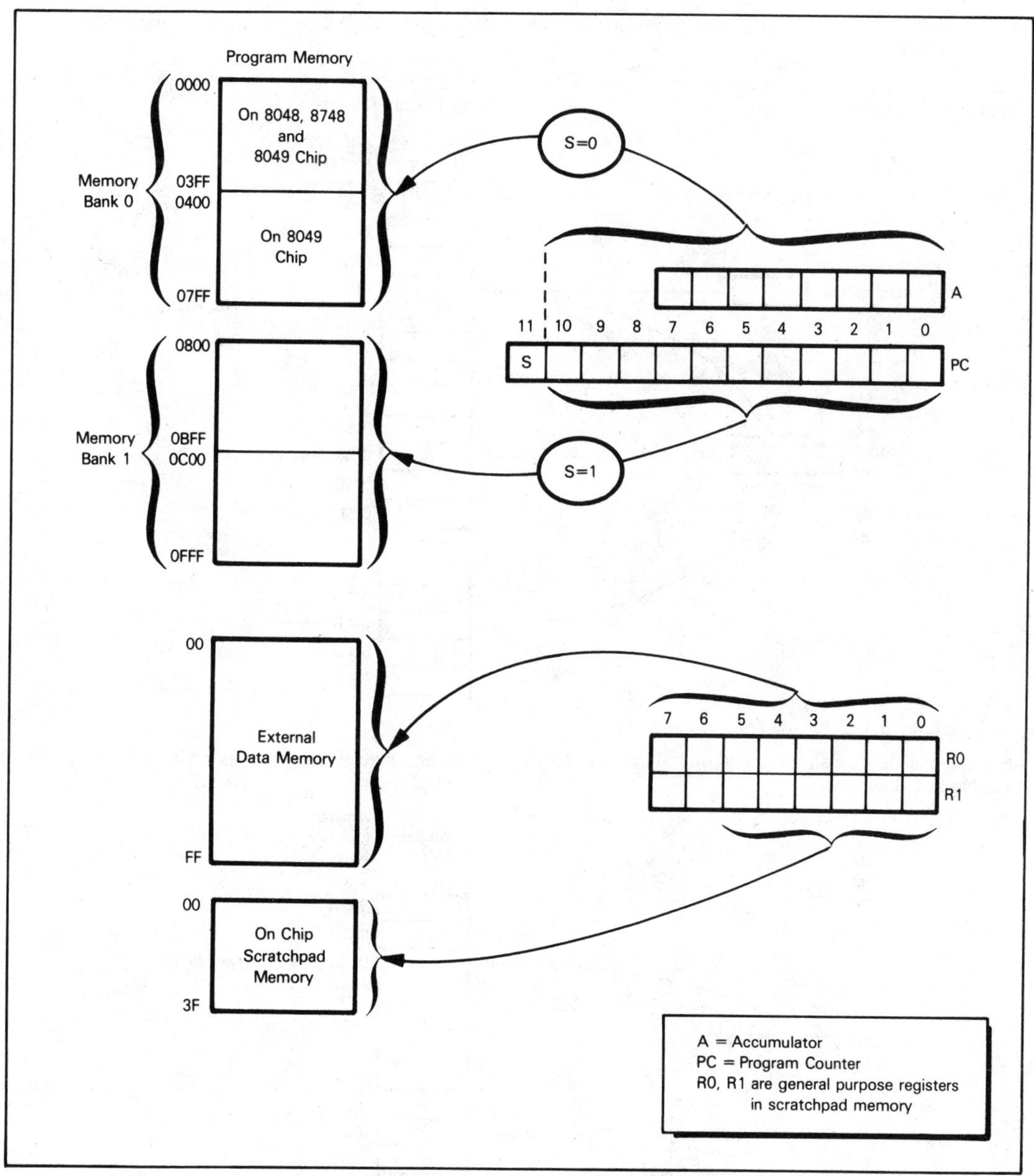


Figure 6-4. 8048 Series Microcomputers' Memory Addressing

Thus the JMP instruction stored in program memory bytes $010B_{16}$ and $010C_{16}$ causes program execution to jump to location $06BA_{16}$.

You can also jump using a form of paged, indirect addressing, where the Accumulator points to an indirect address stored in the current page of program memory. This may be illustrated as follows:

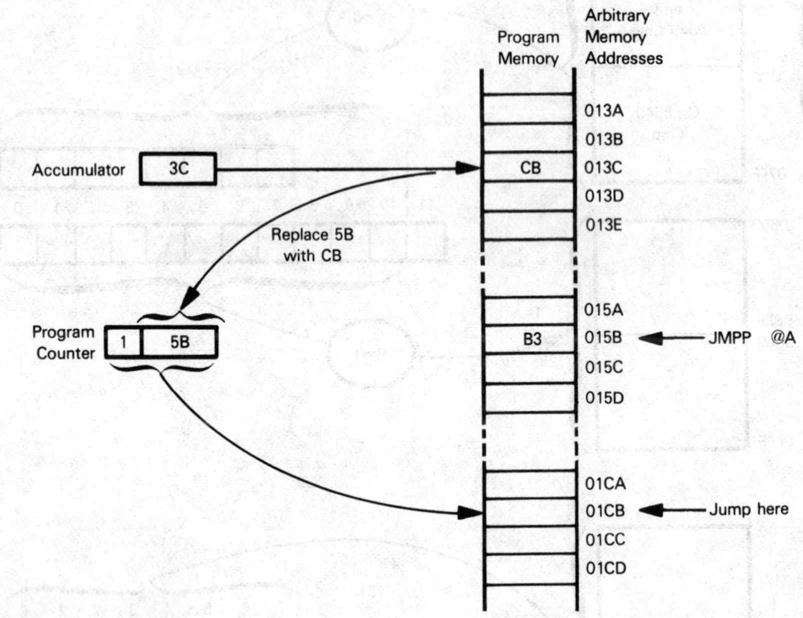


All conditional Jump instructions allow you to branch within the current page of program memory only. This may be illustrated as follows:

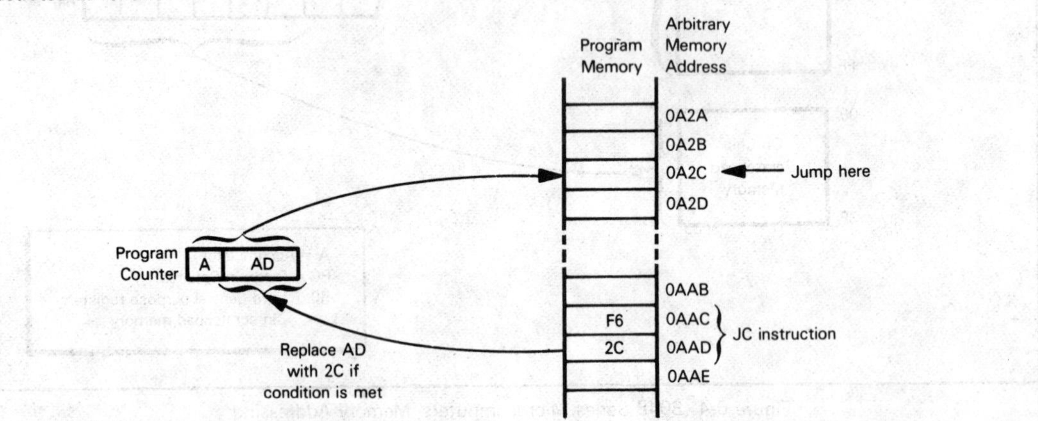

**You can read data from program memory, but there are no instructions which allow you to write data to program memory. Instructions (other than immediate instructions) that read data from program memory use paged, implied addressing.** There are two forms of paged, implied programming memory addressing; they may be illustrated as follows:

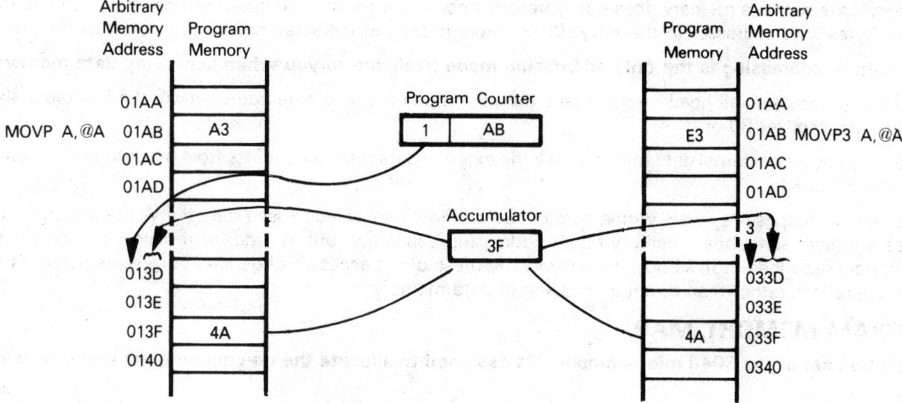


The illustration above compares execution of the MOVP and MOVP3 instructions. These are the two instructions which allow you to read a byte of data from program memory into the Accumulator. Both instructions load 4A into the Accumulator, as illustrated above.

When the MOVP instruction is executed, the program memory address is formed by concatenating the high-order four bits of the Program Counter with the contents of the Accumulator:

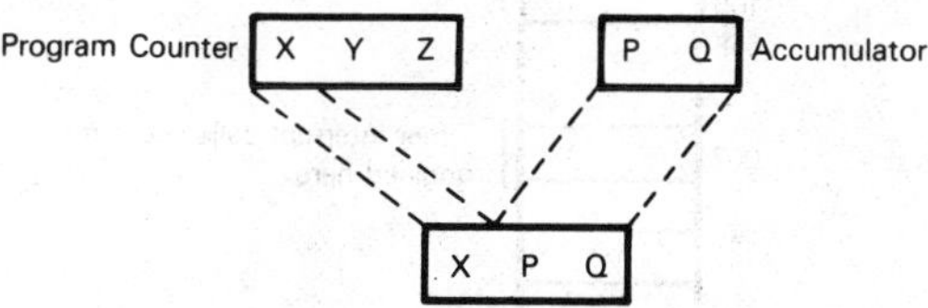


When the MOVP3 instruction is executed, the program memory address is computed by appending the Accumulator contents to 0011:

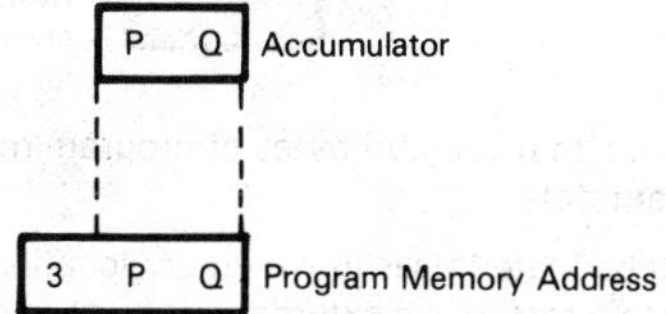


Thus the MOVP instruction loads into the Accumulator the contents of a program memory byte within the current program page. The MOVP3 instruction loads into the Accumulator the contents of a byte from program memory page 3.

**Note carefully that paged addressing of program memory carries with it the usual page boundary problems.** The program memory addressing modes which replace the low-order eight Program Counter bits keep the four high-order Program Counter bits — after the Program Counter has been incremented.

Refer back to the JMPP @A instruction. This instruction is illustrated as being stored in program memory location $015B_{16}$. But suppose this instruction were stored in memory location $01FF_{16}$; then after the JMPP instruction is fetched, the Program Counter will no longer contain $01FF_{16}$, it will contain $0200_{16}$. Now instead of jumping to program memory location $01CB_{16}$, you would jump to program memory location $02CB_{16}$.

This page boundary problem is common to all microcomputers that use absolute paged addressing. For a complete discussion of this problem refer to Volume 1 — Basic Concepts, Chapter 6.

**Note that the 8048 has no instructions which write into program memory. If you want to write into program memory you must have external logic which overlaps external program and data memory.**

**Let us now look at data memory addressing.** First of all, notice that scratchpad memory and external data memory have overlapping address spaces. Separate and distinct instructions access scratchpad memory as against external data memory. External data memory does not represent a continuation of scratchpad memory. For example, there will be memory bytes with addresses in the range $00_{16}$ through $3F_{16}$ in the scratchpad and in external data memory.

**Implied memory addressing is the only addressing mode available to you when accessing data memory.**

Instructions that access scratchpad memory take the scratchpad memory byte address from the low-order six bits of General Purpose Register R0 or R1.

Instructions that access external data memory take the external data memory address from all eight bits of General Purpose Register R0 or R1.

The eight general purpose registers within scratchpad memory can be addressed directly. We could argue that this constitutes a limited scratchpad memory direct addressing capability; but in order to remain consistent with other microcomputers described in this book, we will classify these direct accesses of general purpose registers as register-to-register operations rather than direct addressing of data memory.

## A PROGRAM MEMORY MAP

**The instruction set of the 8048 microcomputer is designed to allocate the on-chip program memory as follows:**

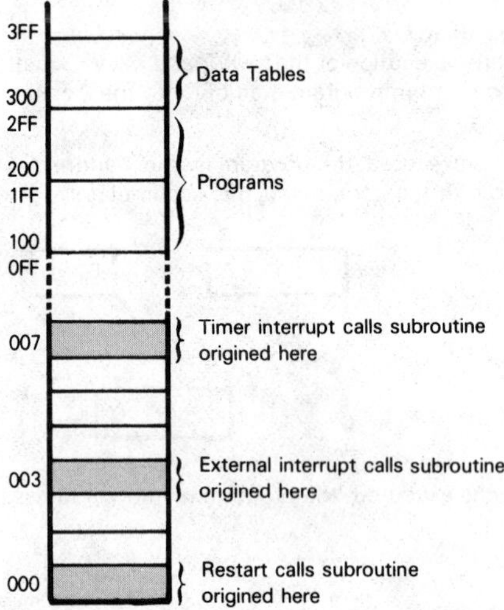


The MOVP3 instructions assume that the 256 bytes of program memory with addresses $300_{16}$ - $3FF_{16}$ have been set aside to hold tables of constant data.

Interrupt logic (which is described later) uses low memory locations 0, 3 and 7 to origin interrupt service routines that will be executed in response to a restart, an external interrupt or a timer interrupt. Jump instructions will normally be located in these low program memory locations.

## 8048 SERIES STATUS

**8048 series microcomputers have an 8-bit Program Status Word which may be illustrated as follows:**

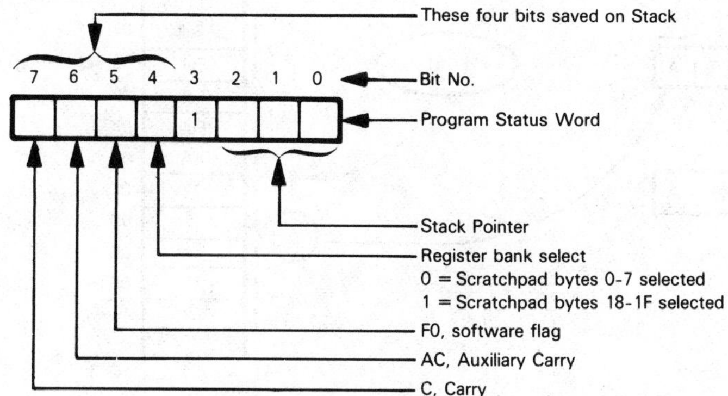


**C and AC are the standard Carry and Auxiliary Carry statuses as defined in Volume I and used throughout this book.**

**F0 is a flag which you set or reset using appropriate Status instructions.** A conditional Jump instruction tests the level of F0. F0 is not connected to external logic and cannot be modified or tested by external logic.

**BS identifies which set of general purpose registers is currently selected.** If BS is 0, then scratchpad bytes 0 through 7 are serving as general purpose registers. If BS is 1, then scratchpad bytes $18_{16}$ through $1F_{16}$ are serving as general purpose registers.

**The low-order three Program Status Word bits serve as a Stack Pointer.** The 16 Stack bytes are treated as eight 16-bit registers, with the current top of Stack identified by the three low-order Program Status Word bits.

**A subroutine Call instruction pushes the Program Counter contents and the four high-order Program Status Word bits onto the Stack as follows:**

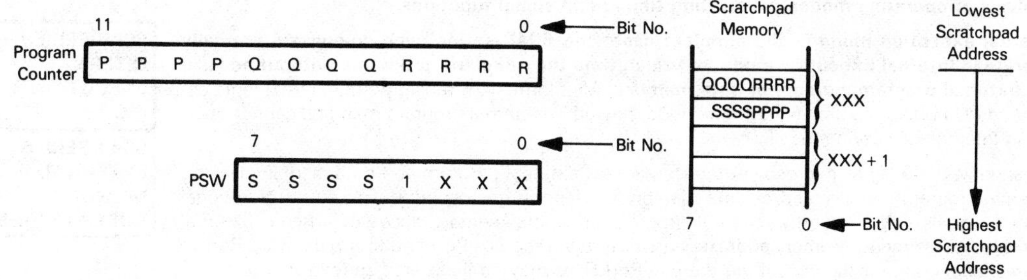


In the illustration above, P, Q, R, S and X represent any binary digits.

Observe that the beginning of the Stack has the lowest scratchpad address. The order in which Program Status Word and Program Counter contents are pushed onto the Stack is illustrated above. Here is a specific case:

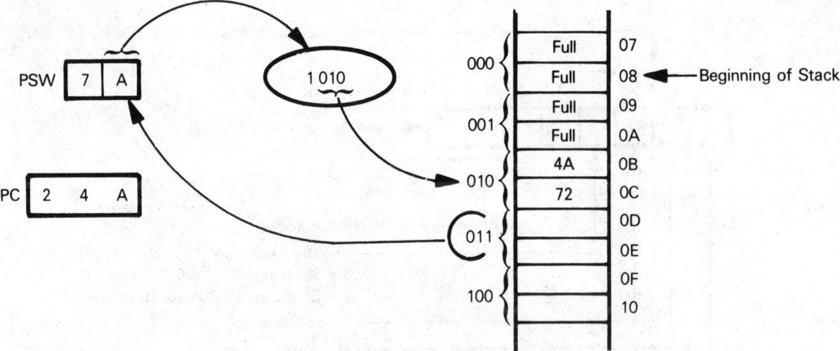


You need to know the exact order in which data is stored on the Stack since the Stack is also accessible as general scratchpad memory.

There are two Return-from-Subroutine instructions; one restores Program Counter contents only, the other restores Program Counter and Program Status Word contents.

Since the Stack has eight 16-bit registers, subroutines may be nested eight deep. If you are using interrupts, then the combined total of subroutine nesting levels on either side of the interrupt must sum to 7 or less. For example, if the interrupt service routine nests subroutines to a maximum level of 3, then non-interrupt programs cannot nest subroutines to a level greater than 4. The interrupt itself requires one Stack location.

## 8048 SERIES MICROCOMPUTER OPERATING MODES

**8048 series microcomputers can operate in a variety of modes. Many signals serve more than one function, depending on the operating mode.**

**In order to clarify this potentially confusing subject, we will summarize 8048 series operating modes in the paragraphs below, then we will summarize device signals; these two summaries are followed by an in-depth analysis of operating modes, illustrating timing and signal functions.**

**8048 SERIES INTERNAL EXECUTION MODE**

**Internal execution mode is the simplest case; the 8048 series microcomputers normally operate in Internal Execution mode, at which time they execute programs without accessing external program memory or data memory.** All information transfer with external logic occurs via I/O ports or control signals. The 8035, having no internal program memory, cannot operate in Internal Execution mode.

**8048 SERIES EXTERNAL MEMORY ACCESS MODE**

Expandable 8048 series microcomputers can access external program and data memory. Having external program memory and/or data memory causes the microcomputer to output additional control signals which identify external program and data memory accesses. This is External Memory Access mode. Memory addresses are output via the Bus Port and four pins of I/O Port 2; bidirectional data transfers occur via the Bus Port. This may be illustrated as follows:

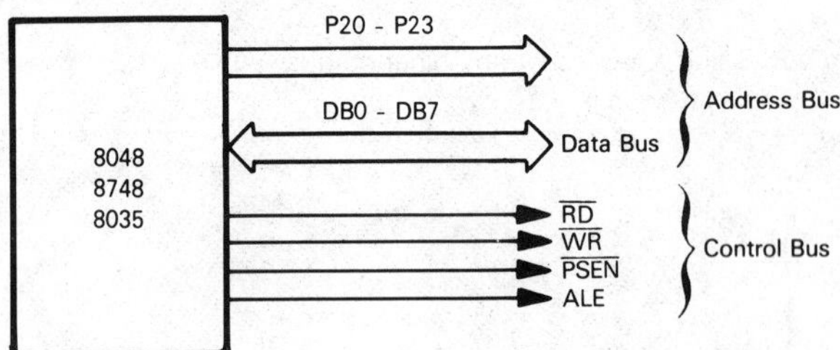

External Memory Access mode represents the simplest case for the 8035 microcomputer, which has no on-chip program memory.

The 8048 series microcomputers can be operated in Debug mode. **In Debug mode the CPU is disconnected from its internal program memory.** All program memory accesses are deflected to external program memory. This may be illustrated as follows:

**8048 AND 8748 DEBUG MODE**

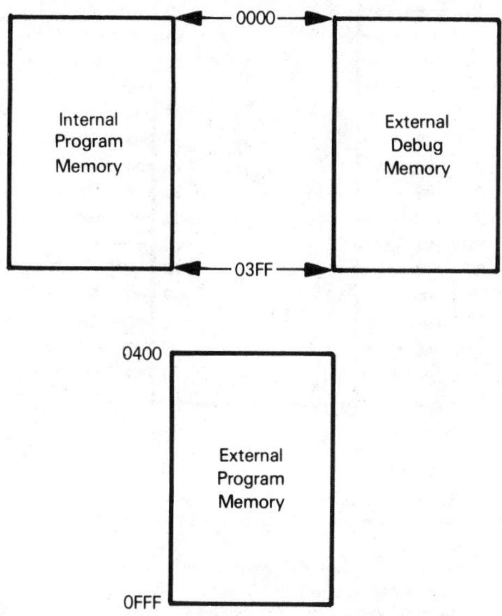


0400

External Program Memory

0FFF

Since the 8035 has no internal program memory, it is always in "Debug mode."

You will use Debug mode to test microcomputer systems built around an 8048 series microcomputer. Typically, special purpose test and verify programs will be maintained in external debug memory.

**Single stepping is not really a mode, but is worth mentioning in connection with Debug mode since it is a powerful debugging tool.** In any of the operating modes you can apply a Single Step signal ($\overline{SS}$) which halts instruction execution following the next instruction fetch. This allows you to execute programs one instruction at a time in order to locate errors or gain a better understanding of event sequences.

**8048 SERIES SINGLE STEPPING**

The 8748 microcomputer contains Erasable Programmable Read Only Memory (EPROM). **In Programming mode you can program the EPROM.**

**8748 PROGRAMMING MODE**

Finally, there is a Verify mode. **In Verify mode you can read the contents of internal or external program memory as data.** Verify mode is used in conjunction with Programming mode to test data written into EPROMs. Verify mode can also be used on its own to examine the contents of program memory for any 8048 series microcomputer.

**8048 SERIES VERIFY MODE**

## 8048 SERIES MICROCOMPUTER PINS AND SIGNALS

**Figure 6-5 illustrates pins and signals for the 8048 series microcomputers. We will briefly summarize functions performed by signals before discussing how signals are used in different modes.**

**DB0 - DB7 serves both as a bidirectional I/O port and as a multiplexed Address and Data Bus.** When no external data or program memory accesses are occurring, DB0 - DB7 serves as a simple bidirectional I/O port or latch. During external program or data memory accesses, DB0 - DB7 serves as a bidirectional Data Bus as well as outputting the low-order eight bits of all memory addresses. Data inputs are not latched in bidirectional mode. External logic must hold input signal levels until the CPU has read input data.

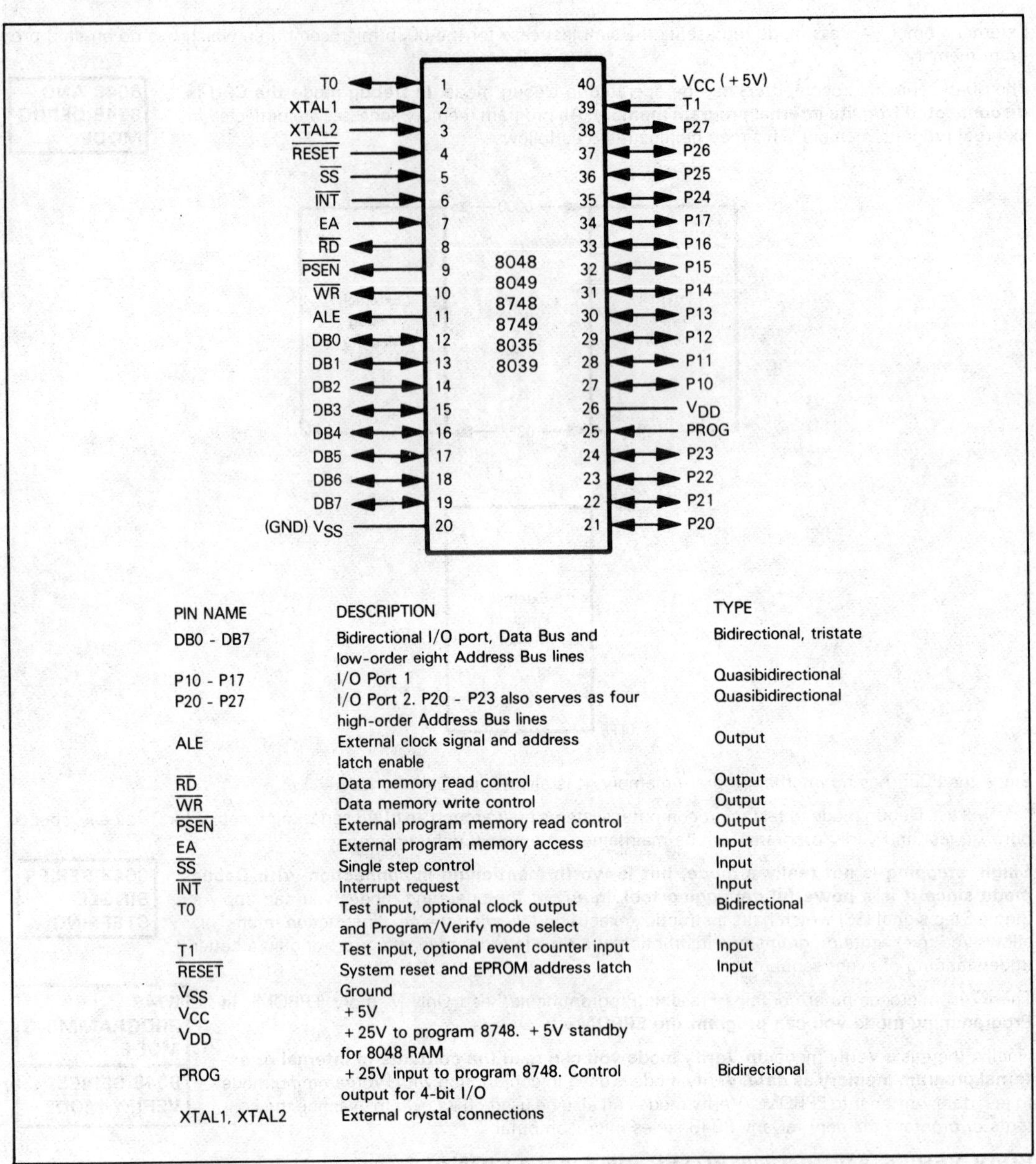


| PIN NAME | DESCRIPTION | TYPE |
|---|---|---|
| DB0 - DB7 | Bidirectional I/O port, Data Bus and low-order eight Address Bus lines | Bidirectional, tristate |
| P10 - P17 | I/O Port 1 | Quasibidirectional |
| P20 - P27 | I/O Port 2. P20 - P23 also serves as four high-order Address Bus lines | Quasibidirectional |
| ALE | External clock signal and address latch enable | Output |
| $\overline{RD}$ | Data memory read control | Output |
| $\overline{WR}$ | Data memory write control | Output |
| $\overline{PSEN}$ | External program memory read control | Output |
| EA | External program memory access | Input |
| $\overline{SS}$ | Single step control | Input |
| $\overline{INT}$ | Interrupt request | Input |
| T0 | Test input, optional clock output and Program/Verify mode select | Bidirectional |
| T1 | Test input, optional event counter input | Input |
| $\overline{RESET}$ | System reset and EPROM address latch | Input |
| $V_{SS}$ | Ground | |
| $V_{CC}$ | +5V | |
| $V_{DD}$ | +25V to program 8748. +5V standby for 8048 RAM | |
| PROG | +25V input to program 8748. Control output for 4-bit I/O | Bidirectional |
| XTAL1, XTAL2 | External crystal connections | |

Figure 6-5. 8048/49, 8748/49 and 8035/39 Microcomputer Pins and Signals

**P10 - P17 and P20 - P27 support I/O Ports 1 and 2, respectively.** We described the characteristics of these two I/O ports earlier in this chapter. During external accesses of program memory the four high-order address lines are output via P20 - P23.

**ALE is a control signal which is pulsed high at the beginning of every instruction execution machine cycle.** This signal may be used as a clock by external logic. During external memory accesses, the trailing edge of ALE strobes memory addresses being output.

**$\overline{\text{RD}}$ is** a control signal which is **pulsed low to strobe data** from external data memory **onto the Data Bus.**

**$\overline{\text{WR}}$ is** a control signal which is **strobed low** when external data memory is **to read data off the Data Bus.**

**$\overline{\text{PSEN}}$ is** a control signal which is **strobed low** when external program memory is **to place data on the Data Bus.**

**External logic inputs EA high** in order to separate the CPU from internal program memory and force the microcomputer into **Debug mode.**

**$\overline{\text{SS}}$ is input low** in order to stop instruction execution following an instruction fetch; this allows you **to single step through a program.**

**$\overline{\text{INT}}$ is the input for external interrupt requests.** If the interrupt is enabled, a low input at $\overline{\text{INT}}$ causes a subroutine call to program memory location 3 when the current instruction finishes execution.

**T0 is a test input** which may be sampled by a conditional Jump instruction. **T0 is also used while selecting External Program mode and Verify mode. The internal CPU clock signal can be output via T0.**

**T1 is a test input** which can be sampled by a Jump-on-Condition instruction. **T1 can also be used to input a signal to Counter/Timer logic** when it is serving as an event counter.

**8048, 8049**
**8748, 8749**
**8035 AND 8039**
**RESET**

**$\overline{\text{RESET}}$ is a standard system reset input signal.** The normal $\overline{\text{RESET}}$ signal should be output from an open collector or active pull-up:

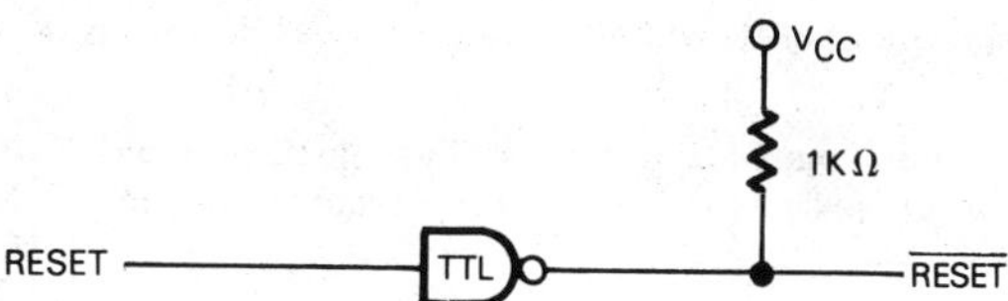


The power-on RESET should be generated as follows:

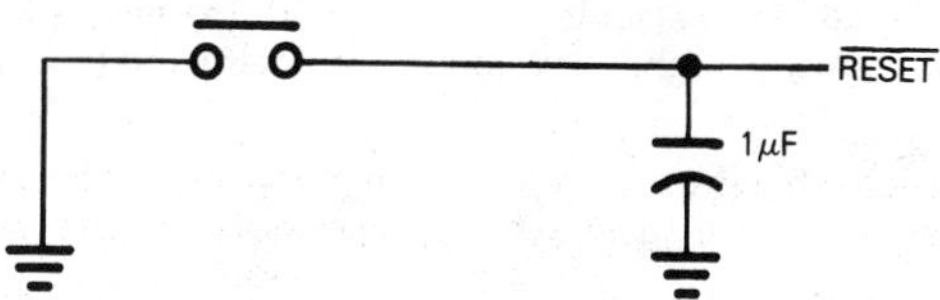


There is an internal pull-up resistor which, in combination with an external 1μF capacitor, generates an adequate internal RESET pulse. If the RESET pulse is generated externally, then it must be held below 0.5V for at least 50 milliseconds.

**This is what happens when you reset an 8048 series microcomputer:**

1) The Program Counter and the Program Status Word are cleared. This selects register bank 0 and program memory bank 0. Also, the first instruction executed following a Reset will be fetched from program memory location 0.
2) The Bus Port is floated.
3) I/O Ports 1 and 2 are set to Input mode.
4) External interrupts are disabled.
5) The counter/timer is stopped and T0 is disconnected from the timer.
6) The timer flag and internal flags F1 and F0 are cleared.

**An external crystal,** if present, **is connected across XTAL1 and XTAL2.** Typically a 6 MHz crystal will be used. **You can input a clock signal directly to XTAL1.** If you do, the input clock signal should have a frequency in the range of 1 MHz to 6 MHz, or 11 MHz for the 8049.

**The 8048 series microcomputers use power supplies in a number of interesting ways.**

$V_{CC}$ is the standard +5V power supply. $V_{SS}$ is the standard ground connection.

**$V_{DD}$ is an additional +5V standby power supply. This standby power supply will maintain the contents of scratchpad memory when all other power has been removed.** Typically $V_{DD}$ will be connected to a battery so that when the system is powered down data can be preserved in scratchpad memory (8048, 8035L and 8049 only).

**The 8748 and 8749 microcomputers use $V_{DD}$ and PROG in order to program the EPROM.** While programming the EPROM, a voltage of +25V is input at $V_{DD}$. +25V pulses lasting 50 milliseconds are input at PROG. A single byte of program memory will be written during a single PROG +25V pulse.

**PROG serves as a control strobe output to the 8243 Input/Output Expander** during the execution of instructions that reference the Expander ports. This function of PROG is described in more detail later in this chapter, when we describe the 8243 I/O Expander.

# 8048 SERIES TIMING AND INSTRUCTION EXECUTION

**Let us begin our detailed analysis of 8048 series microcomputer operations by looking at basic instruction timing.**

**A master clock signal must be input via XTAL1, or the clock signal may be generated internally** by connecting a crystal across XTAL1 or XTAL2. A 6 MHz crystal is recommended. **This clock signal is divided by 3 to generate a master synchronizing 2 MHz signal** which is used throughout the microcomputer system. **You can output this 2 MHz clock signal via the T0 pin.**

**All -8 versions of 8048 series microcomputers operate at half speed;** they use 3 MHz crystals and generate a 1 MHz master synchronizing signal.

**8048 SERIES MACHINE CYCLES AND CLOCK PERIODS**

**Instructions execute in machine cycles. Every machine cycle has five clock periods.** Using a 2 MHz clock signal, therefore, each machine cycle will last 2.5 microseconds. Instructions execute in either one or two machine cycles.

## INTERNAL EXECUTION MODE

**Figure 6-6 illustrates timing for** the simplest case — **execution of a** single machine cycle **instruction accessing internal program or data memory only.** The only signal change seen beyond the microcomputer chip itself is the ALE pulse — and the CLK signal, if you elect to output it via T0. The events which occur during each clock period are illustrated in Figure 6-6; but remember, these operations are internal to the microcomputer. They are beyond your access or control.

Figure 6-6 also illustrates timing for instructions that execute in two machine cycles, but access only program and/or data memory internal to the microcomputer chip. Once again external logic sees ALE, and optionally CLK.

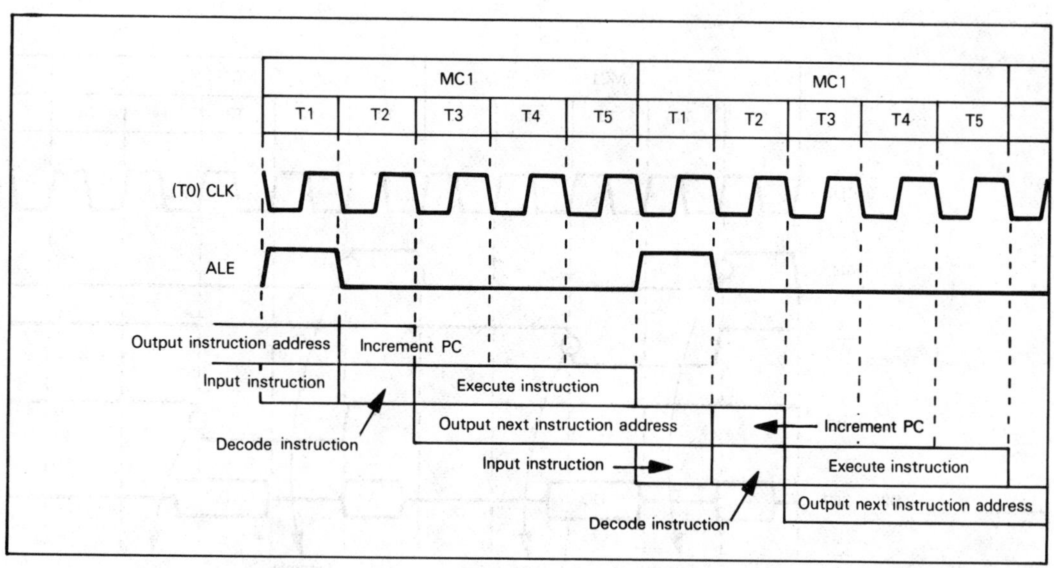


Figure 6-6. Execution of 8048 Single Machine Cycle Instructions without any External Access

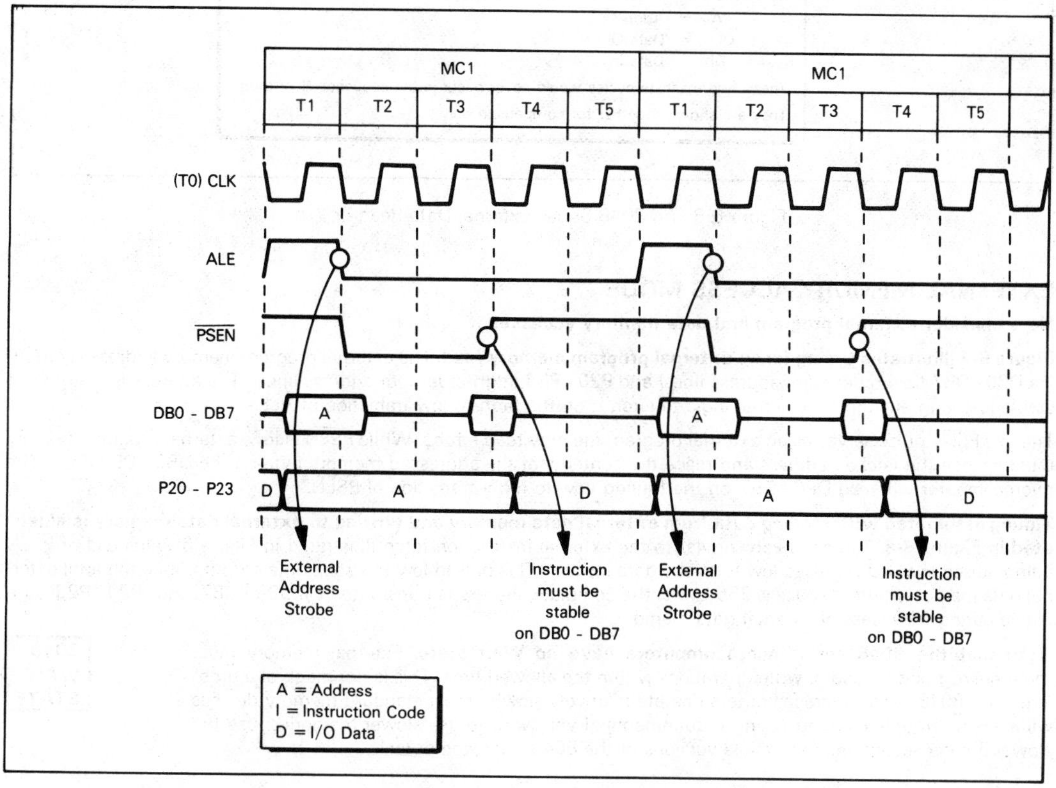

MC1
MC1
T1 T2 T3 T4 T5 T1 T2 T3 T4 T5
(T0) CLK
ALE
$\overline{\text{PSEN}}$
DB0 - DB7
P20 - P23
External Address Strobe
Instruction must be stable on DB0 - DB7
External Address Strobe
Instruction must be stable on DB0 - DB7

A = Address
I = Instruction Code
D = I/O Data

Figure 6-7. An 8048 Series External Instruction Fetch

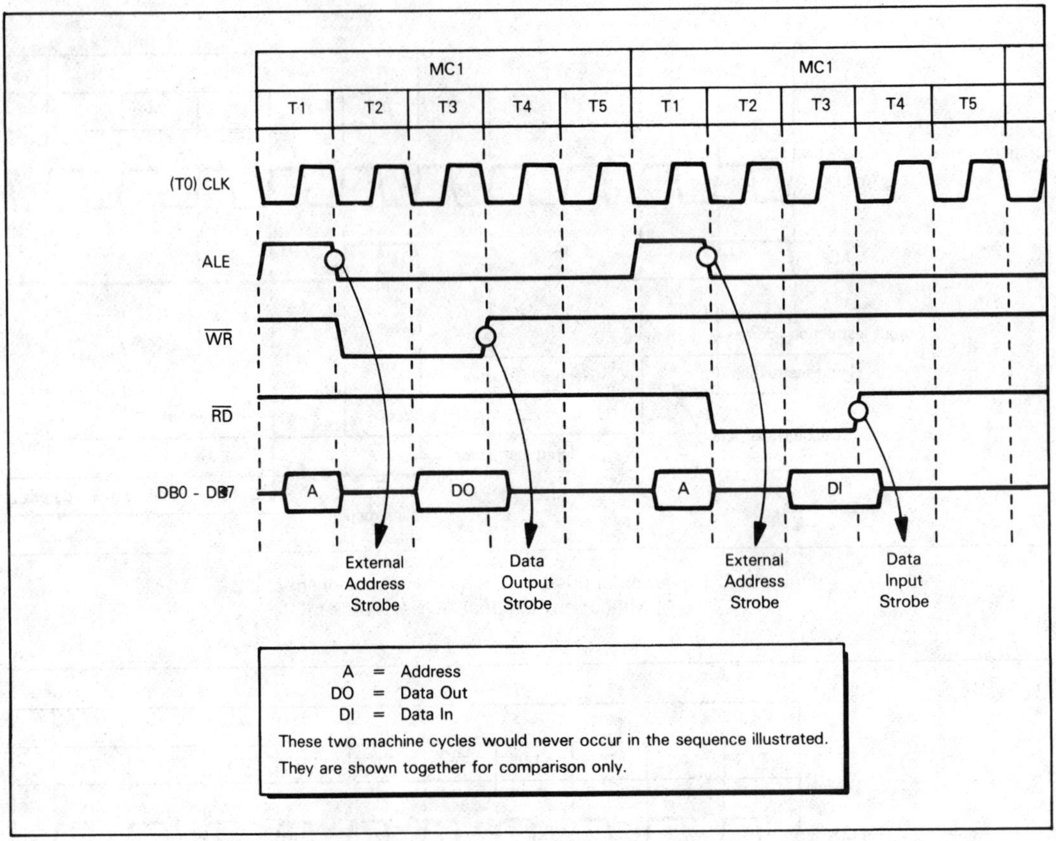

A = Address
DO = Data Out
DI = Data In

These two machine cycles would never occur in the sequence illustrated. They are shown together for comparison only.

Figure 6-8. An 8048 Series External Data Read or Write

## EXTERNAL MEMORY ACCESS MODE

**Now consider external program and data memory accesses.**

**Figure 6-7 illustrates timing for an external program memory read.** The external program memory address is output via DB0 - DB7 (low-order eight address lines) and P20 - P23 (high-order four address lines). The address is maintained stable just long enough for external logic to latch it on the high-to-low transition of ALE.

The low $\overline{PSEN}$ pulse serves as an external program memory read strobe. While $\overline{PSEN}$ is low, external program memory must decode the latched address and place the contents of the addressed memory byte on the DB0 - DB7 lines. The microcomputer will read DB0 - DB7 on the trailing (low-to-high) transition of $\overline{PSEN}$.

**Timing associated with reading data from external data memory and writing to external data memory is illustrated in Figure 6-8.** Timing is very similar to the external instruction fetch illustrated in Figure 6-7. Instead of $\overline{PSEN}$ being pulsed low, $\overline{RD}$ is pulsed low to strobe data input; $\overline{WR}$ is pulsed low to strobe data output. Since the total external data memory address space is 256 bytes, the complete address is transmitted via DB0 - DB7; thus P20 - P23 is inactive during an access of external data memory.

**Note that the 8048 series microcomputers have no Wait state.** External memory must therefore respond to read or write operations within the allowed time. This is not much of a problem since 8048 series microcomputers operate relatively slowly; most standard memory devices will have no trouble meeting timing requirements. If you want to use slower memories, use the slower 5 microsecond machine cycle versions of the 8048 microcomputers.

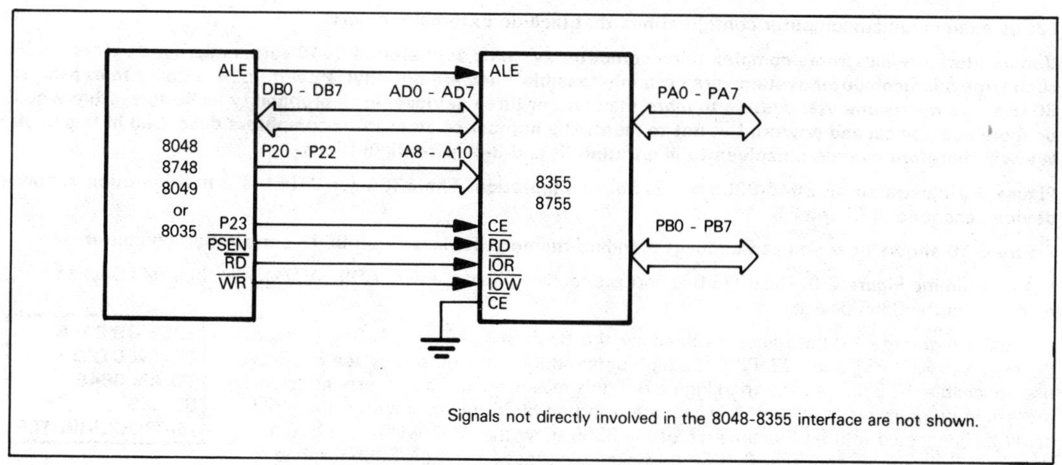


Figure 6-9. An 8048-8355 Configuration

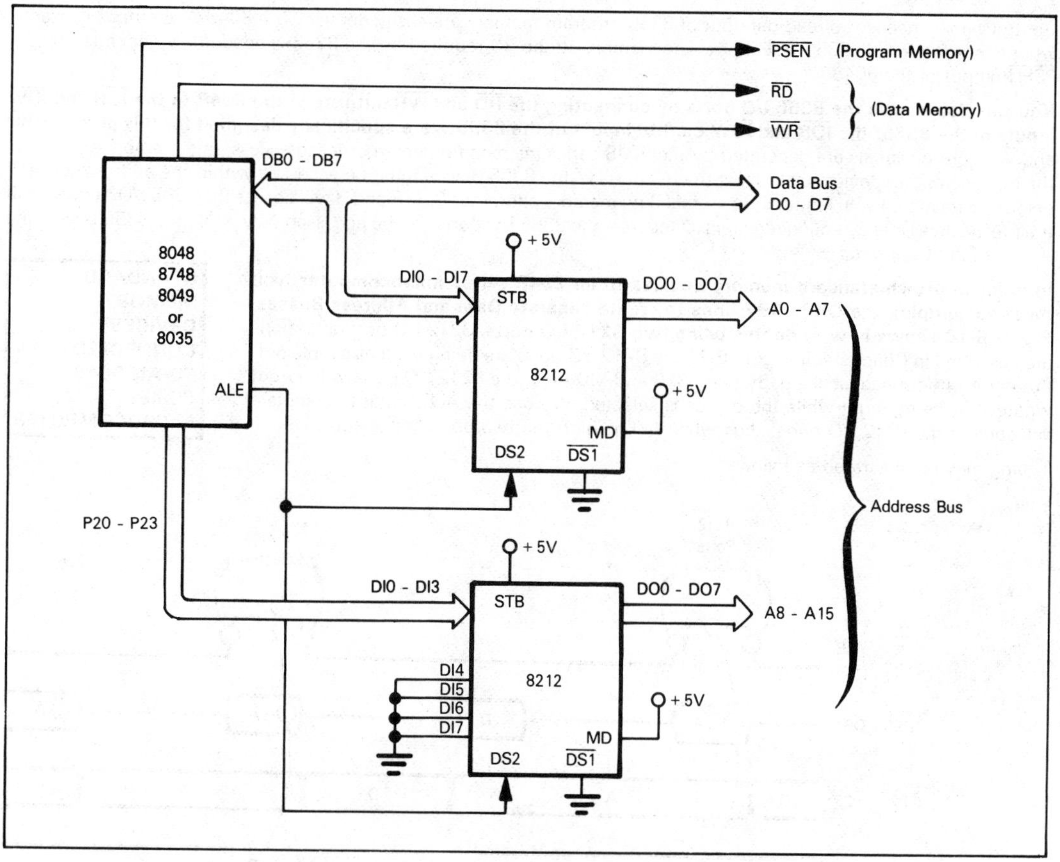

Figure 6-10. Demultiplexing DB0 - DB7 to Create Separate Address and Data Busses

**Let us examine microcomputer configurations that include external memory.**

**Vendor literature illustrates complex microcomputer systems built around 8048 series microcomputers; while such large microcomputer systems are certainly feasible, they are not advisable. If you are going to expand an 8048 series microcomputer system to more than two or three devices, in all probability an 8085 system would be more economical and powerful — not to mention a number of other microcomputers described in this book. We will therefore confine ourselves to illustrating 2- and 3-chip configurations.**

**Figure 6-9 illustrates an 8048-8355 (or 8755) configuration. The 8355 (or 8755) is a multifunction support device described in Chapter 5.**

**Figure 6-10 shows how you can connect standard memory devices to an 8048 series microcomputer.**

**Let us examine Figure 6-9.** The 8048 Bus Port is directly compatible with AD0 - AD7, the multiplexed Data and Address Bus of the 8355 device.

**8355 OR 8755 CONNECTED TO AN 8048 SERIES MICROCOMPUTER**

The three high-order address lines required by the 8355, A8, A9 and A10, are taken directly from P20, P21 and P22. P23, the high-order address line output by the 8048, is used to enable the 8355. As shown in Figure 6-9, this means the 8355 will respond to addresses in program memory bank 1. If you are using an 8035 microcomputer, then P23 could be connected to the $\overline{\text{CE}}$ enable pin of the 8355; now the 8355 will respond to addresses in program memory bank 0. It would make little sense having the 8355 respond to addresses in program memory bank 0 when using an 8048 or 8748, because the first 1024 bytes of program memory are internal to these microcomputers; that means the first 1024 bytes of 8355 memory would never be accessed. The 8049 microcomputer has 2048 bytes of on-chip program memory, so you would access no 8355 memory.

Control signals needed to read data out of 8355 program memory are easily derived. The 8048 ALE output is exactly what is needed for the 8355 ALE input. The memory strobe $\overline{\text{RD}}$ required by the 8355 is adequately generated by the $\overline{\text{PSEN}}$ output of the 8048.

**You can also access the 8355 I/O ports by connecting the $\overline{\text{RD}}$ and $\overline{\text{WR}}$ outputs of the 8048 to the $\overline{\text{IOR}}$ and $\overline{\text{IOW}}$ inputs of the 8355; the $\overline{\text{IOR}}$ and $\overline{\text{IOW}}$ control inputs of the 8355 were specifically designed for this purpose.** $\overline{\text{RD}}$ and $\overline{\text{WR}}$ control signals are generated by the 8048 series microcomputers in order to access data memory external to the microcomputer device itself. Thus the I/O ports of the 8355 device must be accessed within the address space of external data memory. In Figure 6-9 external data memory addresses 0, 1, 2 and 3 will access the 8355 I/O ports — and their respective Data Direction registers. Of course, the 8355 I/O ports can be accessed only while the 8355 is selected — via a high CE input.

**STANDARD MEMORY DEVICES CONNECTED TO AN 8048 SERIES MICROCOMPUTER**

**In order to attach standard memory devices to an 8048 series microcomputer, you must demultiplex the DB0 - DB7 lines to create separate Data and Address Busses. Figure 6-10 shows how to do this using two 8212 I/O ports.** 8212 I/O port operations are described in Chapter 4. In Figure 6-10 the 8212 I/O ports are being used as simple output ports without handshaking. By tying STB and MD high, the 8212 I/O ports will output whatever is being input while the device is selected. We use the ALE signal to complete selection of the 8212 I/O ports; thus while ALE is high the two ports are selected.

Timing may be illustrated as follows:

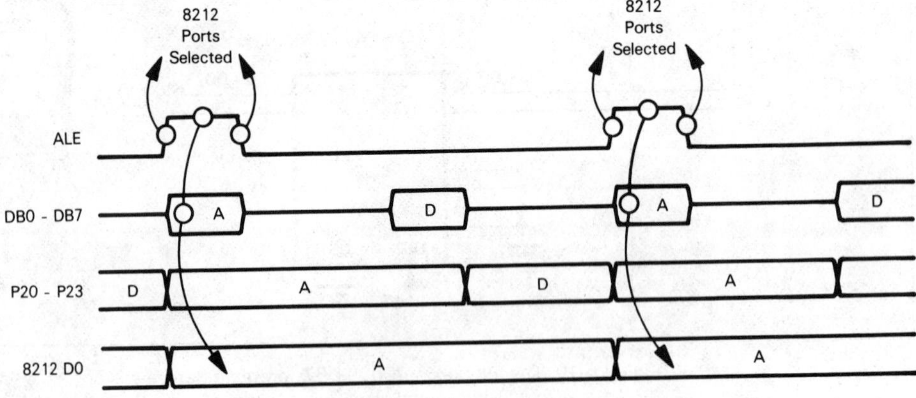

Thus the 8212 ports output DB0 - DB7 or P20 - P23 levels latched while ALE is high. Once ALE goes low, 8212 port outputs remain constant.

**But there are a few subtleties associated with Figure 6-10.**

When an 8048 series microcomputer is accessing external program memory, a 12-bit address is output via DB0 - DB7 and P20 - P23; therefore the entire Address Bus is needed as illustrated. A low $\overline{\text{PSEN}}$ pulse serves as the external memory read strobe.

When 8048 series microcomputers access external data memory, however, only DB0 - DB7 is affected. Thus the second 8212 I/O port creates address lines A8 - A15, which will carry the most recent data output to I/O Port 2 — for example, you may set all I/O Port 2 pins to 0 during initialization. If I/O Port 2 is undefined, spurious selection of program memory will occur in configurations that include external program and data memory. At the time ALE is output as a high pulse no other signals indicate whether the subsequent memory access will involve program memory or data memory. It is only the separate control strobes — $\overline{\text{PSEN}}$ for program memory, $\overline{\text{WR}}$ and $\overline{\text{RD}}$ for data memory — that insure the correct memory module will be accessed. If your 8048 program uses I/O Port 2 for data output as well as for external memory addressing, you should buffer the System Bus; make sure, in this case, that the System Bus has sufficient capacity to handle two selected memory devices simultaneously.

Even though two memory devices may be selected simultaneously, you will not run into memory access contentions since program memory is strobed by $\overline{\text{PSEN}}$ while data memory is strobed by $\overline{\text{RD}}$ and $\overline{\text{WR}}$. Only one of these signals will be active at any time.

## DEBUG MODE

**You can bypass program memory internal to the 8048 series microcomputer by inputting a high signal at EA. While EA is high, timing for all program memory accesses will conform to external program memory accesses as illustrated in Figure 6-7. You may change the level of EA only when $\overline{\text{RESET}}$ is low;** that is, you cannot switch between internal and external memory during program execution.

Here is one of the ways in which you may use Debug mode:

In user end products an external memory device may contain test and verify programs. A service representative will execute these test and verify programs by applying a high input at EA. For example, you could connect an 8355 multifunction device to the 8048, selecting it via program memory bank 0. If EA is taken out to a switch, a serviceman will be able to execute programs out of the first 1024 bytes of 8355 program memory, instead of internal microcomputer memory.

**EA is also used by programming and verification modes. This use of EA, however, has nothing to do with Debug mode.**

## SINGLE STEPPING

If you input a low signal at $\overline{\text{SS}}$, then when ALE next pulses high, it will stay high until $\overline{\text{SS}}$ returns high. While ALE is high, instruction execution ceases and the current Program Counter contents are output via DB0 - DB7 and P20 - P23. Timing may be illustrated as follows:

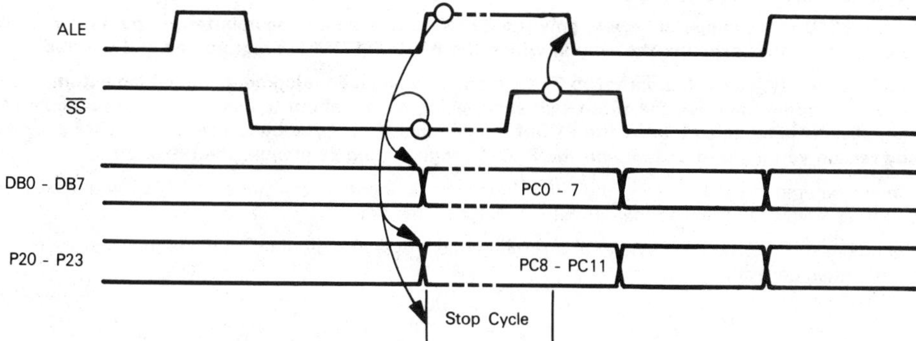


The CPU only tests $\overline{\text{SS}}$ level while ALE is high. At other times $\overline{\text{SS}}$ level is irrelevant.

**Single stepping is an 8048 series microcomputer program debugging aid. Intel literature suggests the circuit illustrated in Figure 6-11 to create an $\overline{\text{SS}}$ signal that is initiated by an ALE pulse and terminated by a pushbutton.**

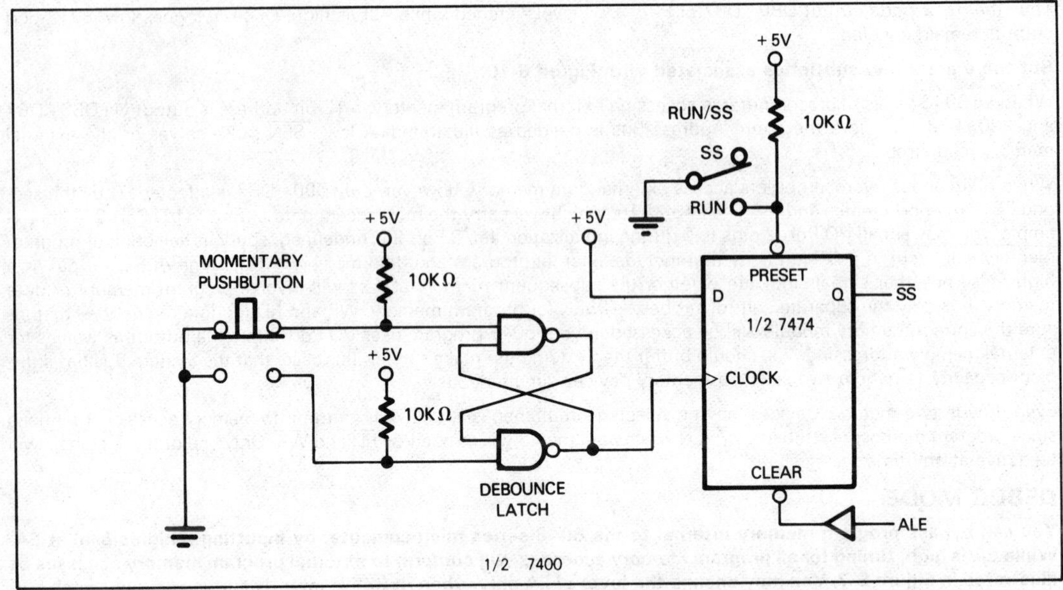


Figure 6-11. An 8048 Single Step Circuit

If you do not wish to single step, then connecting the Single Step switch in the Run position will hold PRESET at ground, which forces the Q output high; instructions will execute normally. With the Single Step switch in the Single Step position, PRESET is held high; now the $\overline{ALE}$ input to CLEAR becomes active. As soon as ALE goes low the Q output is also driven low; thus $\overline{SS}$ is low. The low $\overline{SS}$ is detected on the next high ALE pulse, at which time ALE remains high and the cycle is stopped. This condition persists until the pushbutton is depressed. Depressing the pushbutton creates a low-to-high clock transition which forces $\overline{SS}$ high — thus terminating the stopped condition. **You, as a user, will see a program advance one instruction every time you press the pushbutton.**

**While an 8048 series microcomputer is stopped in a single step, the current Program Counter contents are output via the Bus Port (DB0 - DB7) and P20 - P23.** The Bus Port output presents no problem since you would expect to see address information output at this time. But if I/O Port 2 is being used as a regular I/O port, then prior data present on lines P20 - P23 will not be available during the address output. **Thus if you wish to view I/O data output while single stepping, you must latch I/O Port 2 data externally.**

## PROGRAMMING MODE

**Of the 8048 microcomputer series, only the 87XX numbered microcomputer program memory can be written into. We will now examine the way in which the 8748 EPROM is programmed and verified.**

**In all probability, you will program an 87XX memory using a development tool which automates the entire process. That being the case, the event sequence which we are about to describe is not particularly interesting to you, since it is taken care of by the PROM programmer. But if you build your own PROM programmer, or if for any reason you need to understand the PROM programming sequence, then read on.**

While programming and verifying the EPROM, you should input a clock signal at XTAL1 with a frequency between 1 and 6 MHz; you can also use the on-chip oscillator at this time.

Operations now proceed one byte at a time; you write a byte into program memory, then you verify that the data has been written correctly.

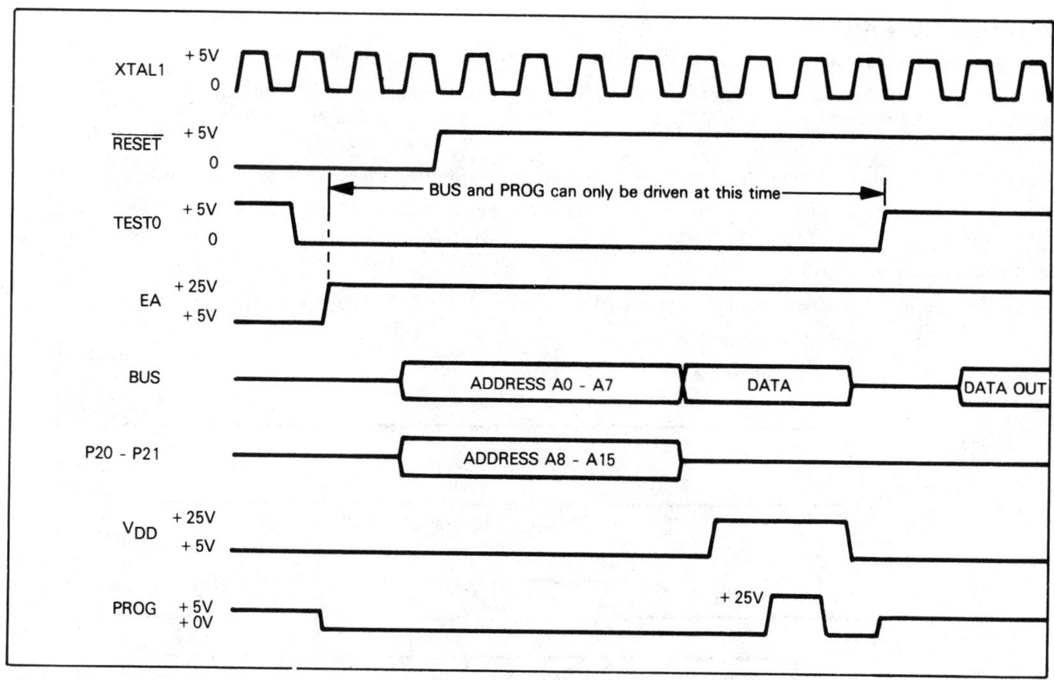


Figure 6-12. 8748 EPROM Programming and Verification Timing

In the discussion which follows, refer to Figure 6-12, which illustrates timing for the program/verify sequence.

Step 1) Initially +5V is input at $V_{DD}$, T0 and EA. $\overline{RESET}$ is held at ground. Under these conditions you insert the 8748 into the programming socket. **You must make certain to insert the 8748 correctly. If you insert the 8748 incorrectly you will destroy it.**

Step 2) T0 is pulled to ground; this selects Programming mode.

Step 3) +25V is applied to EA. This activates Programming mode.

Step 4) A 10-bit memory address is applied via DB0 - DB7 and P20 - P23. Remember, there are 1024 bytes of program memory on the 8748 device. The low-order eight address bits are input via DB0 - DB7 while the two high-order address bits are input via P20 and P21.

Step 5) +5V is applied at $\overline{RESET}$. This latches the address.

Step 6) The data to be written into the addressed programmed memory byte is input at DB0 - DB7.

Step 7) In order to write the data into the addressed program memory byte apply +25V to $V_{DD}$, then ground PROG, then apply a +25V pulse at PROG; the +25V pulse at PROG must last at least 50 milliseconds.

Step 8) Now reduce $V_{DD}$ to +5V. Programming is complete and verification is about to begin.

Step 9) In order to verify the data just written, apply +5V to the T0 input. This selects Verify mode.

Step 10) As soon as Verify mode has been selected, the data just written is output on DB0 - DB7. You must read and verify this data using appropriate external circuitry. Verification is now complete.

In order to write into the next memory byte, select Programming mode again by connecting T0 and $\overline{RESET}$ to ground; then return to Step 3.

Repeat the program/verify sequence, byte-by-byte, until the entire program memory has been written into.

**In order to erase the EPROM expose it to ultraviolet light for a minimum of 20 minutes.**

## VERIFICATION MODE

**You can verify the contents of an 8048 series microcomputer program memory at any time.**

When verifying program memory contents for an 8048 series microcomputer with EPROM, you enter the Verify mode by applying +25V to the EA pin and +5V to the T0 pin. $\overline{\text{RESET}}$ must be held at ground while you apply +5V to the T0 pin.

Using an 8048 series microcomputer with ROM, you enter the Verify mode by applying +12V to the EA pin.

Once in the Verify mode, place the address of the program memory location which is to be read at DB0 - DB7 (low-order byte) and P20 - P21 (high-order four bits).

Latch this address by applying +5V to $\overline{\text{RESET}}$.

While $\overline{\text{RESET}}$ is high, the contents of the addressed program memory location are output via DB0 - DB7.

You may repeat the verification process, byte-by-byte.

Verification timing is illustrated as follows:

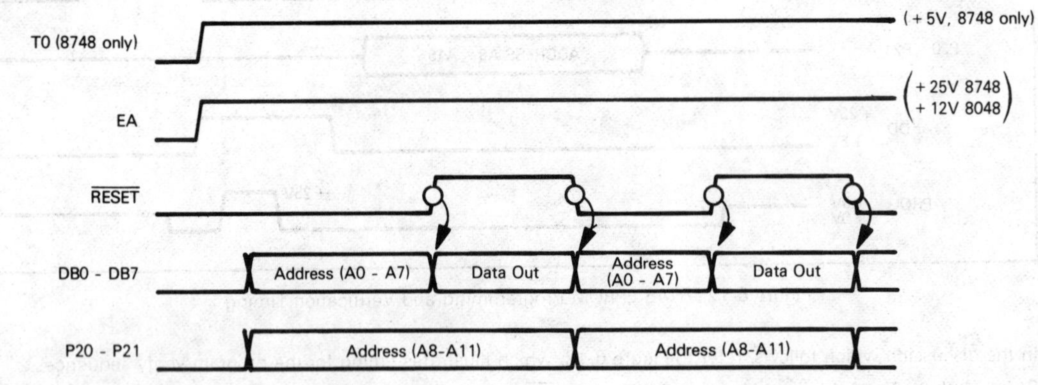


## INPUT/OUTPUT PROGRAMMING

**8048 series microcomputers (with the exception of the 8021) have three I/O ports,** the physical characteristics of which we have already described. **Instructions allow you to input or output Accumulator data** via any one of the three I/O ports. **You can also directly mask data** resident at an I/O port using an AND mask or an OR mask.

**There are two types of input/output beyond the 8048 series microcomputer chip itself.**

**The low-order four bits of I/O Port 2 may be connected to the 8243 Input/Output Expander** which has four individually addressable 4-bit I/O ports. The 8243 Input/Output Expander is described later in this chapter.

**You can also implement I/O ports within the external data memory address space for the expandable microcomputers of the 8048 series.** We have already seen how you do this using an 8355 multifunction device connected to an 8048 series microcomputer. In this particular case the two I/O ports of the 8355 device are addressed as external data memory locations 0 and 1. Any other implementation of external I/O ports is allowed; however, in every case the I/O ports must be addressed as external data memory bytes using external data memory access instructions.

## HOLD STATE

**There is no Hold state that external logic can induce in an 8048 series microcomputer. This is not unreasonable, since the purpose of the Hold state is to enable direct memory access operations — which would make little sense in a microcomputer system as small as an 8048, which has a maximum of 256 external data memory bytes.**

# COUNTER/TIMER OPERATIONS

**All 8048 series microcomputers have an internal counter/timer. Counter/timer logic may be illustrated as follows:**

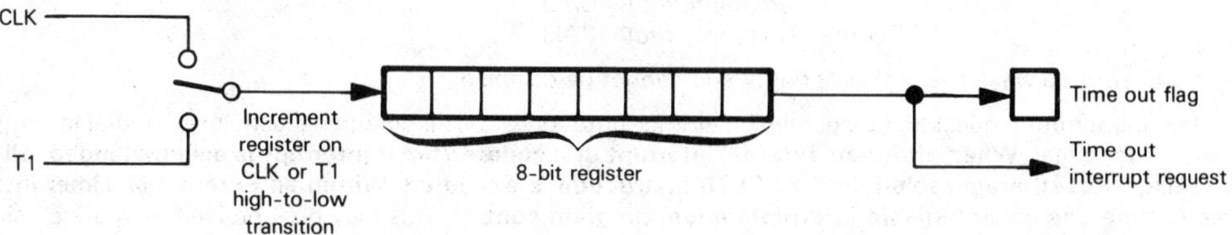


The Counter/Timer register is eight bits wide; it is accessed via Accumulator instructions, which move Accumulator contents to the Counter/Timer register or move Counter/Timer register contents to the Accumulator.

**Generally stated, this is how the counter/timer works:**

You begin by loading an initial value into the Counter/Timer register. Next, you start the counter/timer by executing the STRT T or STRT CNT instruction. The counter/timer will increment continuously until stopped by a Stop Counter/Timer instruction.

Whenever the counter/timer increments from $FF_{16}$ to $00_{16}$, it activates a counter/timer interrupt request and sets a time-out flag. If the counter/timer interrupt has been enabled, then program execution will branch to the appropriate interrupt service routine. If the counter/timer interrupt has been enabled, then you must test for a time-out by executing the JT0 Branch-on-Condition instruction.

**You can operate the counter/timer as a counter or as a timer.** The STRT T instruction operates the counter/timer as a timer, in which case **the internal system clock increments the Timer register once every 480 crystal oscillations (80 microseconds, assuming a 6 MHz crystal).**

You operate the counter/timer as a counter by executing the STRT CNT instruction. **Now high-to-low transitions of a signal input at T1 increment the counter.** The minimum time interval between high-to-low T1 transitions is 45 crystal oscillations (7.5 microseconds, assuming a 6 MHz crystal). There is no maximum delay between T1 high-to-low transitions. Once T1 goes high it must remain high for at least 3 crystal oscillations (500 nanoseconds, assuming a 6 MHz crystal).

You execute the STOP TCNT instruction to stop the counter/timer, whether it is operating as a counter or as a timer.

**Here is an instruction sequence which initiates the counter/timer operating as a timer with interrupts enabled:**

```
MOV    A,#TSTART   ;LOAD INITIAL COUNTER/TIMER CONSTANT
MOV    T,A
EN     TCNTI       ;ENABLE TIMER INTERRUPT
STRT   T           ;START THE TIMER
```

The following instruction sequence operates the counter/timer as a counter with interrupts disabled:

```
DIS    TCNTI       ;DISABLE COUNTER INTERRUPT EARLY IN PROGRAM
-
-
-
MOV    A,#TSTART   ;LOAD INITIAL COUNTER/TIMER CONSTANT
MOV    T,A
STRT   CNT         ;START COUNTER
```

## INTERNAL AND EXTERNAL INTERRUPTS

**The 8048 series microcomputers have a simple interrupt scheme that is effective and adequate for small microcomputers. Interrupts can originate from one of three sources:**

1) A Reset. This is a non-maskable interrupt.
2) An external interrupt induced by setting $\overline{INT}$ low. (This is not available on the 8041 and 8021 series microcomputers.)
3) A counter/timer interrupt which is automatically requested every time the Counter/Timer register increments from $FF_{16}$ to $00_{16}$.

External interrupts and counter/timer interrupts can be enabled and disabled individually.

**When any one of the three interrupt requests is acknowledged, the microcomputer executes a Call instruction to one of these three locations:**

| | |
|---:|:---|
| Reset: | CALL 0 |
| External interrupt: | CALL 3 |
| Counter/Timer interrupt: | CALL 7 |

The Reset interrupt always has highest priority and cannot be disabled.

If an external interrupt request and a counter/timer interrupt request occur simultaneously, the external interrupt will be acknowledged first. **When either an external interrupt or a counter/timer interrupt is acknowledged, all interrupts (except Reset) are disabled until an RETR instruction is executed. Within an External or Timer interrupt service routine you cannot enable interrupts under program control.** This may be a problem if you are using the timer and external interrupts in timer sensitive applications. If execution time for an external interrupt's service routine extends over more than one counter/timer time out, then you will fail to detect one or more time outs. The simplest way of resolving this problem is to make sure that your External interrupt service routines are very short — executing in 75% of the counter/timer interval, or less. If this is not feasible, then you must monitor the counter/timer by testing its time out flag rather than by using counter/timer interrupt logic. You can execute the JTF conditional Jump instruction at frequent intervals within the main program and interrupt service routines, thus catching time outs irrespective of when they occur.

**You can re-enable interrupts within an interrupt service routine by executing a dummy RETR instruction.** Here is an appropriate instruction sequence:

```
START OF INTERRUPT SERVICE ROUTINE
        -
        -
        -
        CALL    ENAB            ;RE-ENABLE INTERRUPTS
        EN      I
        EN      TCNTI
        -
        -
        -
END OF INTERRUPT SERVICE ROUTINE
ENAB    RETR
```

**Enabling interrupts within a service routine, as illustrated above, is not recommended** in an 8048 microcomputer system.

**Two problems need to be resolved when using external interrupts in an 8048 series microcomputer system: an interrupt acknowledge must be created, and in multiple interrupt configurations we must be able to identify the interrupting source.**

8048 series microcomputers have no interrupt acknowledge signal. An interrupt acknowledge signal must be created; otherwise external logic does not know when to remove its interrupt request. And if the interrupt request remains after an RETR instruction executes, the interrupt will be reacknowledged. **The only straightforward way of acknowledging an interrupt is to assign one of the I/O port pins to serve as an interrupt acknowledge signal.** The external interrupt service routine will begin by outputting an appropriate low pin signal. **Here is one possibility:**

```
        ANL     P1,#7FH         ;RESET PIN 7 OF I/O PORT 1 LOW
        ORL     P1,#80H         ;SET PIN 7 OF I/O PORT 1 HIGH
```

Here, the output at pin 7 of I/O Port 1 is a low pulse with a duration of two machine cycles (5.0 microseconds).

But remember, if you use an I/O port pin as an interrupt acknowledge, you cannot use the same pin to perform standard I/O operations.

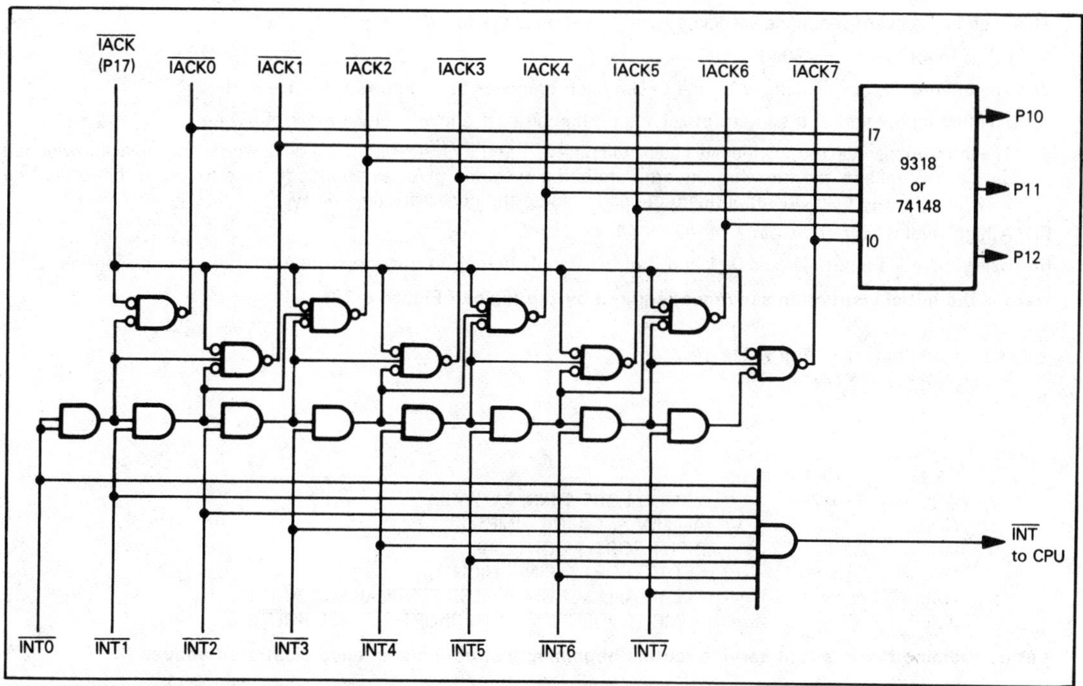


Figure 6-13. An Eight-Device Daisy Chained Interrupt Request/Acknowledge Scheme

If there are many external devices which can request interrupt service, then the most effective way of handling multiple interrupts is via a daisy chain. Daisy chain logic has been discussed in Volume 1 — Basic Concepts. The acknowledged device in the daisy chain must create a device code that is input to an I/O port. **Figure 6-13 illustrates a scheme whereby eight devices in a daisy chain may request interrupt service, and upon being acknowledged, the selected device will input a unique code to I/O Port 1.** The high-order bit of I/O Port 1 serves as an interrupt acknowledge. I/O Port 1 bits 0, 1 and 2 receive as inputs a 3-bit code identifying the acknowledged device.

The daisy chain logic in Figure 6-13 is created using a chain of eight AND gates and eight NAND gates. The AND gates are chained in order of priority, with $\overline{INT0}$ having the highest priority and $\overline{INT7}$ having the lowest priority. The first NAND gate receives as its inputs $\overline{INT0}$ and the acknowledge signal output via pin 7 of I/O Port 1. Subsequent NAND gates receive as their inputs an interrupt request signal, the acknowledge signal and the output of the previous AND gate. The output of each NAND gate becomes an interrupt acknowledge signal which is low-true. Thus in Figure 6-13 there are eight low-true interrupt requests, represented by signals $\overline{INT0}$ through $\overline{INT7}$, and there are eight low-true interrupt acknowledges, represented by $\overline{IACK0}$ through $\overline{IACK7}$. Each external device capable of requesting an interrupt must output a low-true $\overline{INTn}$ which it removes upon receiving a low-true $\overline{IACKn}$. For device 3 this may be illustrated as follows:

The eight interrupt request signals $\overline{INT0}$ through $\overline{INT7}$ are input to an AND gate. The AND gate generates a master low-true interrupt request, $\overline{INT}$. If any one or more of the $\overline{INTn}$ signals are low, then the AND gate will output a low $\overline{INT}$.

The eight interrupt acknowledge signals $\overline{IACK0}$ - $\overline{IACK7}$ are input to an 8-to-3 Decoder. The 8-to-3 Decoder will receive seven high signals and one low signal. The one low signal will be identified by the decoder 3-bit output which is transmitted to pins 0, 1 and 2 of I/O Port 1.

This then is the event sequence associated with an interrupt request:

1) $\overline{INT}$ is input low to the 8048.
2) The interrupt is acknowledged by the CPU, which branches to an interrupt service routine.
3) The first instruction of the interrupt service routine outputs a low level via pin 7 of I/O Port 1.
4) The interrupt service routine receives back, via pins 0, 1 and 2 of I/O Port 1, the device code for the acknowledged device. You must make sure that the program being executed gives external logic time to return this code. You may have to insert No Operation instructions to create the necessary time delay.
5) A high level is output via pin 7 of I/O Port 1.
6) Using the code input via pins 0, 1 and 2 of I/O Port 1, branch to the appropriate interrupt service routine.

**Here is the initial instruction sequence required by the logic of Figure 6-13:**

```
        ORG     3
;START OF INTERRUPT SERVICE ROUTINE
        JMP     EXTINT
        -
        -
        -
        ORG     EXTINT
        ANL     P1,#7FH         ;SET I/O PORT 1 PIN 7 LOW
        NOP                     ;ALLOW SETTLING TIME
        IN      A,P1            ;INPUT PORT 1 CONTENTS
        ORL     P1,#80H         ;SET I/O PORT 1 PIN 7 HIGH
        ANL     A,#7            ;CLEAR ALL ACCUMULATOR BITS BAR 0, 1 AND 2
        JMPP    @A              ;JUMP TO IDENTIFIED INTERRUPT SERVICE ROUTINE
```

**Let us examine the interrupt service routine beginning instruction sequence illustrated above.**

When an 8048 series microcomputer is initially reset, all I/O port pins output high levels. Thus you do not have to initialize pin 7 of I/O Port 1 to a high level.

We actually identify one of eight device interrupt service routines by creating a 3-bit code in bits 1, 2 and 3 of the Accumulator. We then perform an indirect Jump. This Jump instruction will branch to a location on the current page of program memory; the address is fetched from the location in the current page addressed by the Accumulator contents. We illustrated this addressing technique earlier in the chapter.

Given the instruction sequence illustrated above, the first eight program memory locations on the same page as the JMPP instruction must be set aside for eight addresses; these are the starting addresses for the interrupt service routines. This may be illustrated as follows:

```
        ORG     #0300H
        DB      IS0             ;ADDRESS OF INTERRUPT SERVICE ROUTINE 0
        DB      IS1             ;ADDRESS OF INTERRUPT SERVICE ROUTINE 1
        DB      IS2             ;ADDRESS OF INTERRUPT SERVICE ROUTINE 2
        DB      IS3             ;ADDRESS OF INTERRUPT SERVICE ROUTINE 3
        DB      IS4             ;ADDRESS OF INTERRUPT SERVICE ROUTINE 4
        DB      IS5             ;ADDRESS OF INTERRUPT SERVICE ROUTINE 5
        DB      IS6             ;ADDRESS OF INTERRUPT SERVICE ROUTINE 6
        DB      IS7             ;ADDRESS OF INTERRUPT SERVICE ROUTINE 7
EXTINT  ANL     #7FH            ;SET I/O PORT 1 PIN 7 LOW
        -
        -
        -
```

**The daisy chained interrupt scheme discussed above can also be implemented using the circuit in Figure 6-14. The advantage of this circuit is that it requires fewer chips than the circuit of Figure 6-13. As far as the 8048 program is concerned, however, the two circuits are identical.**

The $\overline{INT}$ and device code inputs are generated in exactly the same way. However, an eight-line-to-three-line priority encoder (9318 or 74148) replaces the network of AND gates. As the function table for the encoder shows, the device code output on lines A2, A1 and A0 is that of the highest priority request. The CPU enables the code outputs by sending the acknowledge signal.

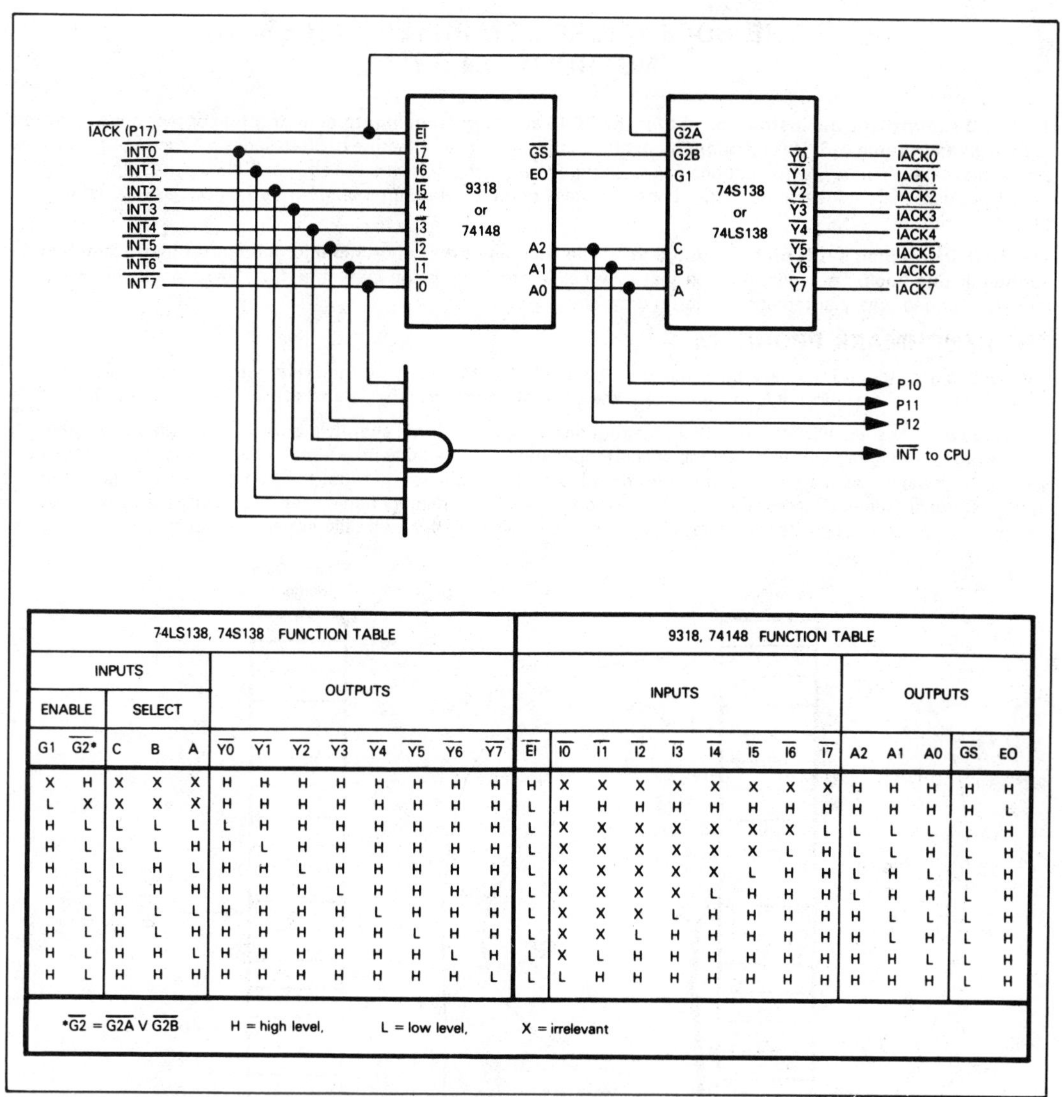


**74LS138, 74S138 FUNCTION TABLE**

| INPUTS | | | | | OUTPUTS | | | | | | | |
|---|---|---|---|---|---|---|---|---|---|---|---|---|
| ENABLE | | SELECT | | | | | | | | | | |
| G1 | $\overline{\text{G2}}$* | C | B | A | $\overline{\text{Y0}}$ | $\overline{\text{Y1}}$ | $\overline{\text{Y2}}$ | $\overline{\text{Y3}}$ | $\overline{\text{Y4}}$ | $\overline{\text{Y5}}$ | $\overline{\text{Y6}}$ | $\overline{\text{Y7}}$ |
| X | H | X | X | X | H | H | H | H | H | H | H | H |
| L | X | X | X | X | H | H | H | H | H | H | H | H |
| H | L | L | L | L | L | H | H | H | H | H | H | H |
| H | L | L | L | H | H | L | H | H | H | H | H | H |
| H | L | L | H | L | H | H | L | H | H | H | H | H |
| H | L | L | H | H | H | H | H | L | H | H | H | H |
| H | L | H | L | L | H | H | H | H | L | H | H | H |
| H | L | H | L | H | H | H | H | H | H | L | H | H |
| H | L | H | H | L | H | H | H | H | H | H | L | H |
| H | L | H | H | H | H | H | H | H | H | H | H | L |

**9318, 74148 FUNCTION TABLE**

| INPUTS | | | | | | | | | OUTPUTS | | | | |
|---|---|---|---|---|---|---|---|---|---|---|---|---|---|
| $\overline{\text{EI}}$ | $\overline{\text{I0}}$ | $\overline{\text{I1}}$ | $\overline{\text{I2}}$ | $\overline{\text{I3}}$ | $\overline{\text{I4}}$ | $\overline{\text{I5}}$ | $\overline{\text{I6}}$ | $\overline{\text{I7}}$ | A2 | A1 | A0 | $\overline{\text{GS}}$ | EO |
| H | X | X | X | X | X | X | X | X | H | H | H | H | H |
| L | H | H | H | H | H | H | H | H | H | H | H | H | L |
| L | X | X | X | X | X | X | X | L | L | L | L | L | H |
| L | X | X | X | X | X | X | L | H | L | L | H | L | H |
| L | X | X | X | X | X | L | H | H | L | H | L | L | H |
| L | X | X | X | X | L | H | H | H | L | H | H | L | H |
| L | X | X | X | L | H | H | H | H | H | L | L | L | H |
| L | X | X | L | H | H | H | H | H | H | L | H | L | H |
| L | X | L | H | H | H | H | H | H | H | H | L | L | H |
| L | L | H | H | H | H | H | H | H | H | H | H | L | H |

*$\overline{\text{G2}}$ = $\overline{\text{G2A}}$ V $\overline{\text{G2B}}$ H = high level, L = low level, X = irrelevant

Figure 6-14. A Low Chip Count Implementation of an Eight-Device Daisy Chained Interrupt Request/Acknowledge Scheme

In Figure 6-13, a network of NAND gates generated the low-true interrupt acknowledge signal to inform the appropriate device that its interrupt was being serviced. In Figure 6-14, a three-line-to-eight-line decoder (74S138 or 74LS138) translates the device code output by the encoder and sets the corresponding acknowledge line low, as is shown in the function table for the decoder.

Connecting the enable inputs as shown prevents spurious acknowledgements or phantom device codes, provided that the CPU gives the external devices time for response and propagation delay.

# THE 8048 MICROCOMPUTER SERIES INSTRUCTION SET

**Table 6-2 summarizes the instruction set for the 8048 series microcomputers. Instruction object codes and timing are given in Table 6-3.** This instruction set reflects the specific architecture of 8048 series microcomputers. For example, there are separate I/O instructions to access the three on-chip I/O ports, as against 8243 Input/Output Expander I/O ports. Also, there are separate instructions to access on-chip scratchpad read/write memory, as against external data memory.

**The 8048 instruction set is probably more versatile than any other one-chip microcomputer instruction set described in this book.** The only omission that may cause problems is the lack of an Overflow status; this will make multibyte signed binary arithmetic harder to program.

## THE BENCHMARK PROGRAM

The benchmark program we have been using in this book is not realistic for the 8048 with its limited data memory. Using the 8048 you would not load data into some general depository, then transfer it to a specific data table.

In order to provide some illustration of 8048 instructions, however, we will slightly modify the benchmark program and move a number of data bytes from the top of scratchpad memory to a table in external data memory. Since the data in scratchpad memory must have been input from an I/O port, we will assume that the number of scratchpad memory bytes is stored in General Purpose Register R7. The table in external memory begins at a known location and the first table byte addresses the first free table location. Operations performed may be illustrated as follows:

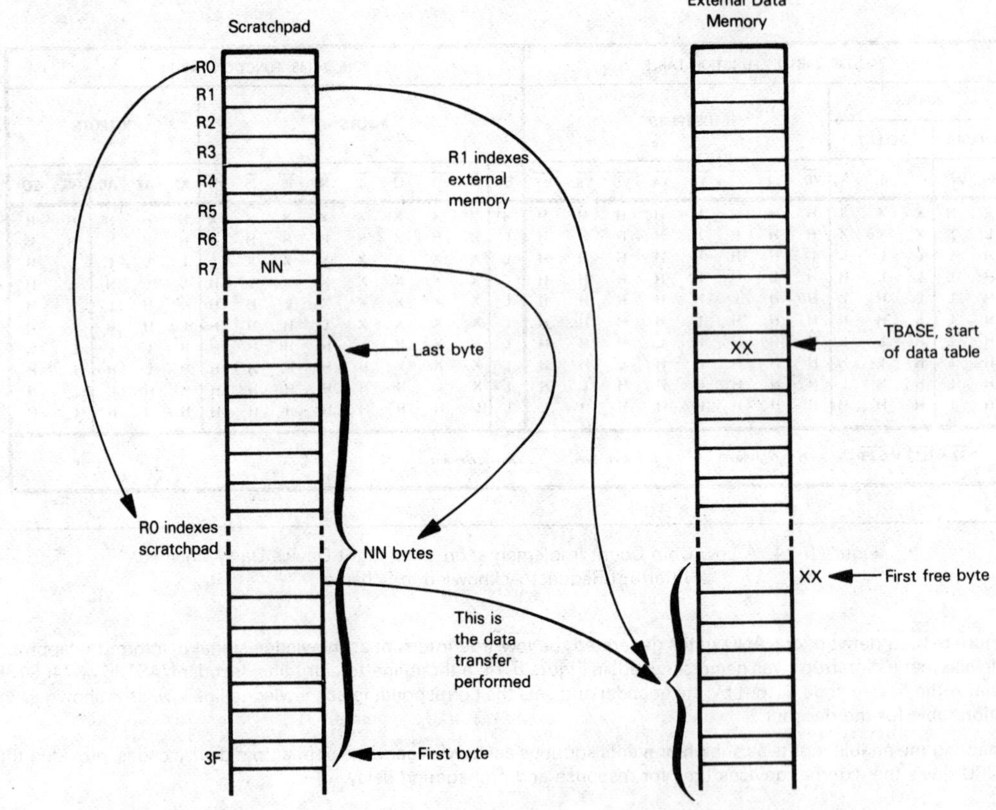

```
        MOV     R0,#TBASE     ;LOAD EXTERNAL TABLE BASE ADDRESS INTO R0
        MOVX    A,@R0         ;LOAD ADDRESS OF FIRST FREE BYTE INTO A
        MOV     R1,A          ;SAVE IN R1
        ADD     A,R7          ;ADD NEW BYTE COUNT TO A
        MOVX    @R0,A         ;RESTORE IN FIRST FREE BYTE OF EXTERNAL TABLE
        MOV     R0,#3FH       ;LOAD SCRATCHPAD ADDRESS INTO R0
LOOP    MOV     A,@R0         ;MOVE DATA FROM SCRATCHPAD TO A
        MOVX    @R1,A         ;STORE IN EXTERNAL DATA TABLE
        DEC     R0            ;DECREMENT R0
        INC     R1            ;INCREMENT R1
        DJNZ    R7,LOOP       ;DECREMENT R7, SKIP IF NOT ZERO
```

**These are the abbreviations used in Table 6-2:**

| | |
|---|---|
| A | The Accumulator |
| A03 | Accumulator bits 0-3 |
| R | Register R0 or R1 |
| REG | Accumulator, R0, R1, R2, R3, R4, R5, R6 or R7 |
| RN | Register R0, R1, R2, R3, R4, R5, R6 or R7 |
| T | Timer/Counter |
| C | Carry status |
| AC | Auxiliary Carry status |
| MB0 | Program memory bank 0 |
| MB1 | Program memory bank 1 |
| MBN | MB0 or MB1 |
| I | The Instruction register |
| I2 | Second object code byte |
| PC | The Program Counter |
| PC10 | The Program Counter, bits 0-10 |
| PCL | The Program Counter, bits 0-7 |
| PCH | The Program Counter, bits 8-11 |
| SP | Stack Pointer: PSW bits 0, 1 and 2 |
| PSW | The Program Status Word which has bits assigned to status flags as follows: |

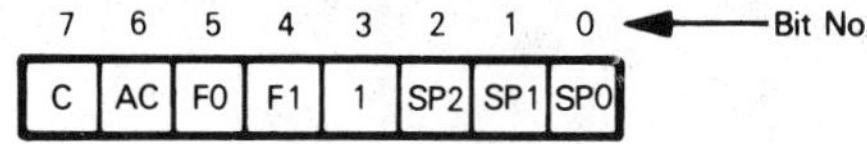


| | |
|---|---|
| S | F0 or F1 |
| DATA | 8-bit immediate data |
| DEV | An I/O device |
| PORT | I/O Port P1, P2 |
| ADDR | An 11-bit address, specifying a data memory byte |
| ADDR8 | The low-order eight bits of a memory address |
| [ ] | Contents of location identified within brackets |
| [[ ]] | Scratchpad memory byte addressed by location identified within brackets |
| {[ ]} | External memory byte addressed by location identified within brackets |
| ([ ]) | Program memory byte addressed by location identified within brackets |

| | |
|---|---|
| ← | Move data in direction of arrow |
| ←→ | Exchange contents of locations on either side of arrow |
| + | Add |
| - | Subtract |
| Λ | AND |
| V | OR |
| ⊻ | Exclusive-OR |
| BUS | Bus I/O port |
| P1 | I/O Port 1 |
| P2 | I/O Port 2 |
| EP | 8243 Expander Port P4, P5, P6 or P7 |
| PN | P1 or P2 |

Table 6-2. A Summary of 8048 Microcomputer Instruction Set

| TYPE | MNEMONIC | OPERAND(S) | 8021 | 8022 | 8041 | 8048 8049 | BYTES | STATUS C | STATUS AC | OPERATION PERFORMED |
|---|---|---|---|---|---|---|---|---|---|---|
| I/O | ANL | PORT,#DATA | | | X | X | 2 | | | [PORT]←[PORT] ∧ DATA<br>AND immediate data with I/O Port P1, P2 or BUS |
| | ANL | BUS,#DATA | | | | X | 2 | | | [BUS] ← [BUS] ∧ DATA<br>AND immediate data with BUS Port |
| | ANLD | EP,A | X | X | X | X | 1 | | | [EP]←[A03] ∧ [EP]<br>AND expander port P4, P5, P6 or P7 with Accumulator bits 0 - 3 |
| | IN | A,PN | X | X | X | X | 1 | | | [A]←[PN]<br>Input I/O Port P1 or P2 to Accumulator |
| | IN | A,DBB | | | X | | 1 | | | [A]←[BUS]<br>Input to Accumulator from Data Bus buffer |
| | INS | A,BUS | | | | X | 1 | | | [A]←[BUS]<br>Input BUS to Accumulator with strobe |
| | MOVD | A,EP | X | X | X | X | 1 | | | [A03]←[EP]<br>Input expander port P4, P5, P6 or P7 to Accumulator bits 0 - 3 |
| | MOVD | EP,A | X | | X | X | 1 | | | [EP]←[A03]<br>Output Accumulator bits 0 - 3 to expander port P4, P5, P6 or P7 |
| | ORL | PORT,#DATA | | | X | X | 2 | | | [PORT]←[PORT] V DATA<br>OR immediate data with I/O Port P1, P2 or BUS |
| | ORL | BUS,#DATA | | | | X | 2 | | | [BUS] ← [BUS] V DATA<br>OR immediate data with BUS Port |
| | ORLD | EP,A | X | X | X | X | 1 | | | [EP]←[A03] V [EP]<br>OR Accumulator bits 0 - 3 with expander port P4, P5, P6 or P7 |
| | OUT | DBB,A | | | X | | 1 | | | [BUS]←[A]<br>Output from Accumulator to Data Bus buffer |
| | OUTL | PORT,A | X | X | X | X | 1 | | | [PORT]←[A]<br>Output Accumulator contents to I/O Port P1, P2 (or BUS 8048, 8049 only) |
| | OUTL | BUS,A | | | | X | 2 | | | [BUS] ← [A] |
| | RAD | A | | X | | | 1 | | | [A] ← [A/D register] |
| | SEL | AN0 | | X | | | 1 | | | Select analog input 0 |
| | SEL | AN1 | | X | | | 1 | | | Select analog input 1 |
| PRIMARY MEMORY REFERENCE | MOV | A,@R | X | X | X | X | 1 | | | [A]←[[R]]<br>Load contents of scratchpad byte addressed by R0 or R1 into Accumulator |
| | MOV | @R,A | X | X | X | X | 1 | | | [[R]]←[A]<br>Store Accumulator contents in scratchpad byte addressed by R0 or R1 |
| | MOVP | A,@A | X | X | X | X | 1 | | | [A]←([PCH] [A])<br>Load into the Accumulator the contents of the program memory byte addressed by the Accumulator and Program Counter bits 8 - 11. |
| | MOVP3 | A,@A | | | X | X | 1 | | | [A]←(3 [A])<br>Load into the Accumulator the contents of the program memory byte with binary address 0011XXXXXXXX where XXXXXXXX represents initial Accumulator contents. |
| | MOVX | A,@R | | | | X | 1 | | | [A]←¦[R]¦<br>Load contents of external data memory byte addressed by R0 or R1 into Accumulator |
| | MOVX | @R,A | | | | X | 1 | | | ¦[R]¦ ← [A]<br>Store Accumulator contents in external data memory byte addressed by R0 or R1 |
| | XCH | A,@R | X | X | X | X | 1 | | | [A] ←→ [[R]]<br>Exchange contents of Accumulator and scratchpad memory byte addressed by R0 or R1 |
| | XCHD | A,@R | X | X | X | X | 1 | | | [A03] ←→ [[R]03]<br>Exchange contents of Accumulator bits 0 - 3 with bits 0 - 3 of scratchpad memory byte addressed by R0 or R1 |

Table 6-2. A Summary of 8048 Microcomputer Instruction Set (Continued)

| TYPE | MNEMONIC | OPERAND(S) | 8021 | 8022 | 8041 | 8048 8049 | BYTES | STATUS C | STATUS AC | OPERATION PERFORMED |
|---|---|---|---|---|---|---|---|---|---|---|
| SECONDARY MEMORY REFERENCE (MEMORY OPERATE) | ADD | A,@R | X | X | X | X | 1 | X | X | [A]←[A] + [[R]]<br>Add contents of scratchpad byte addressed by R0 or R1 to Accumulator |
| | ADDC | A,@R | X | X | X | X | 1 | X | X | [A]←[A] + [[R]] + [C]<br>Add contents of scratchpad byte addressed by R0 or R1, plus Carry, to Accumulator |
| | ANL | A,@R | X | X | X | X | 1 | | | [A]←[A] ∧ [[R]]<br>AND contents of scratchpad byte addressed by R0 or R1 with Accumulator |
| | ORL | A,@R | X | X | X | X | 1 | | | [A]←[A] ∨ [[R]]<br>OR contents of scratchpad byte addressed by R0 or R1 with Accumulator |
| | XRL | A,@R | X | X | X | X | 1 | | | [A]←[A] ⊻ [[R]]<br>Exclusive OR contents of scratchpad byte addressed by R0 or R1 with Accumulator |
| | INC | A,@R | | | X | X | 1 | | | [[R]]←[[R]] + 1<br>Increment the contents of the scratchpad byte addressed by R0 or R1 |
| IMMEDIATE | MOV | REG,#DATA | X | X | X | X | 2 | | | [REG]←DATA<br>Load immediate data into Accumulator, or Register R0, R1, R2, R3, R4, R5, R6 or R7 |
| | MOV | @R,#DATA | X | X | X | X | 2 | | | [[R]]←DATA<br>Load immediate data into scratchpad byte addressed by R0 or R1 |
| JUMP | JMP | ADDR | X | X | X | X | 2 | | | [PC10]←ADDR<br>Jump to instruction in current 2K block having label ADDR |
| | JMPP | @A | X | X | X | X | 1 | | | [PC]←[PCH][A], [PCL]←([PCH][A])<br>Load into the eight low order Program Counter bits the contents of the program memory byte addressed by the Accumulator and the four hgih order Program Counter bits. |
| | SEL | MB0 | | | | X | 1 | | | With the next JMP or CALL instruction, reset the high order bit of PC to 0, thus selecting first 2K program memory bytes. |
| | SEL | MB1 | | | | X | 1 | | | With the next JMP or CALL instruction, set high order bit of PC to 1, thus selecting second 2K program memory bytes. |
| SUBROUTINE CALL AND RETURN | CALL | ADDR | X | X | X | X | 2 | | | STACK ← STATUS + [PC], [SP]←[SP] + 1, [PC]←ADDR<br>Call subroutine at specified address. |
| | RET | | X | X | X | X | 1 | | | [PC]←STACK, [SP]←[SP]-1<br>Return from subroutine without restoring status |
| | RETR | | | X | X | X | 1 | X | X | [PC] + STATUS ← STACK, [SP]←[SP]-1<br>Return from subroutine and restore status. Mnemonic is RETI on 8022. |

Table 6-2. A Summary of 8048 Microcomputer Instruction Set (Continued)

| TYPE | MNEMONIC | OPERAND(S) | 8021 | 8022 | 8041 | 8048 8049 | BYTES | STATUS C | STATUS AC | OPERATION PERFORMED |
|---|---|---|---|---|---|---|---|---|---|---|
| IMMEDIATE OPERATE | ADD | A, #DATA | X | X | X | X | 2 | X | X | [A]←[A] + DATA<br>Add immediate data to Accumulator |
| | ADDC | A, #DATA | X | X | X | X | 2 | X | X | [A]←[A] + DATA + [C]<br>Add immediate data plus Carry to Accumulator |
| | ANL | A, #DATA | X | X | X | X | 2 | | | [A]←[A] ∧ DATA<br>AND immediate data with Accumulator contents |
| | ORL | A, #DATA | X | X | X | X | 2 | | | [A]←[A] V DATA<br>OR immediate data with Accumulator contents |
| | XRL | A, #DATA | X | X | X | X | 2 | | | [A]←[A] ⊻ DATA<br>Exclusive OR immediate data with Accumulator contents |
| JUMP ON CONDITION | DJNZ | RN,ADDR8 | X | X | X | X | 2 | | | [RN]←[RN]-1. If [RN] ≠ 0, [PCL]← ADDR8<br>Decrement Register R0, R1, R2, R3, R4, R5, R6 or R7. If the result is not 0, branch to ADDR8 on the current program memory page. |
| | JBb | ADDR8 | | | X | X | 2 | | | [PCL]← ADDR8<br>Jump on current page if Accumulator bit b is 1. b must be 0, 1, 2, 3, 4, 5, 6 or 7 |
| | JC | ADDR8 | X | X | X | X | 2 | | | [PCL]← ADDR8<br>Jump on current page if Carry is 1 |
| | JF0 | ADDR8 | | | X | X | 2 | | | [PCL]← ADDR8<br>Jump on current page if flag F0 is 1 |
| | JF1 | ADDR8 | | | X | X | 2 | | | [PCL]← ADDR8<br>Jump on current page if flag F1 is 1 |
| | JNC | ADDR8 | X | X | X | X | 2 | | | [PCL]← ADDR8<br>Jump on current page if Carry is 0 |
| | JNI | ADDR8 | | | | X | 2 | | | [PCL]← ADDR8<br>Jump on current page if interrupt request input is 0 |
| | JNIBF | ADDR8 | | | X | | 2 | | | [PCL]←ADDR8<br>Jump if IBF flag is 0 |
| | JNT0 | ADDR8 | | | X | X | 2 | | | [PCL]← ADDR8<br>Jump on current page if T0 input is 0 |
| | JNT1 | ADDR8 | | | X | X | 2 | | | [PCL]← ADDR8<br>Jump on current page if T1 input is 0 |
| | JNZ | ADDR8 | X | X | X | X | 2 | | | [PCL]← ADDR8<br>Jump on current page if Accumulator contents is nonzero |
| | JOBF | ADDR8 | | | | X | 2 | | | [PCL]←ADDR8<br>Jump if OBF flag is 1 |
| | JTF | ADDR8 | X | X | X | X | 2 | | | [PCL]← ADDR8<br>Jump on current page if timer has timed out, that is, if timer flag is 1. The timer flag is reset to 0 by this instruction. |
| | JT0 | ADDR8 | | | X | X | 2 | | | [PCL]← ADDR8<br>Jump on current page if T0 input is 1 |
| | JT1 | ADDR8 | X | X | X | X | 2 | | | [PCL]← ADDR8<br>Jump on current page if T1 input is 1 |
| | JZ | ADDR8 | X | X | X | X | 2 | | | [PCL]← ADDR8<br>Jump on current page if Accumulator contents are zero |

Table 6-2. A Summary of 8048 Microcomputer Instruction Set (Continued)

| TYPE | MNEMONIC | OPERAND(S) | 8021 | 8022 | 8041 | 8048 8049 | BYTES | STATUS C | STATUS AC | OPERATION PERFORMED |
|---|---|---|---|---|---|---|---|---|---|---|
| REGISTER-REGISTER MOVE | MOV | A,RN | X | X | X | X | 1 | | | [A]←[RN]<br>Move the contents of a general purpose register to the Accumulator |
| | MOV | RN,A | X | X | X | X | 1 | | | [RN]←[A]<br>Move the Accumulator contents to a general purpose register |
| | XCH | A,RN | X | X | X | X | 1 | | | [A]←→[RN]<br>Exchange the Accumulator contents with the contents of a general purpose register |
| REGISTER-REGISTER OPERATE | ADD | A,RN | X | X | X | X | 1 | X | X | [A]←[A] + [RN]<br>Add the contents of a general purpose register to the Accumulator |
| | ADDC | A,RN | X | X | X | X | 1 | X | X | [A]←[A] + [RN] + [C]<br>Add the contents of a general purpose register, plus Carry, to the Accumulator |
| | ANL | A,RN | X | X | X | X | 1 | | | [A]←[A] ∧ [RN]<br>AND the contents of a general purpose register with the Accumulator |
| | ORL | A,RN | X | X | X | X | 1 | | | [A]←[A] V [RN]<br>OR the contents of a general purpose register with the Accumulator |
| | XRL | A,RN | X | X | X | X | 1 | | | [A]←[A] ∀ [RN]<br>Exclusive-OR the contents of a general purpose register with the Accumulator |
| REGISTER OPERATE | CLR | A | X | X | X | X | 1 | | | [A]←0<br>Zero the Accumulator |
| | CPL | A | X | X | X | X | 1 | | | $[A]\leftarrow\overline{[A]}$<br>Complement the Accumulator |
| | DAA | A | X | X | X | X | 1 | | | Decimal adjust Accumulator contents |
| | DEC | RN | | | X | X | 1 | | | [RN] ← [RN] - 1<br>Decrement the contents of the general purpose register. |
| | DEC | A | X | X | X | X | 1 | | | [A] ← [A] - 1<br>Decrement the contents of the Accumulator |
| | INC | REG | X | X | X | X | | | | [REG]←[REG] + 1<br>Increment the contents of the Accumulator or general purpose register |
| | RL | A | X | X | X | X | 1 | | | Rotate Accumulator left<br>[A] |
| | RLC | A | X | X | X | X | 1 | X | | Rotate Accumulator left through Carry<br>[C] [A] |
| | RR | A | X | X | X | X | 1 | | | Rotate Accumulator right |

Table 6-2. A Summary of 8048 Microcomputer Instruction Set (Continued)

| TYPE | MNEMONIC | OPERAND(S) | 8021 | 8022 | 8041 | 8048 8049 | BYTES | STATUS C | STATUS AC | OPERATION PERFORMED |
|---|---|---|---|---|---|---|---|---|---|---|
| REGISTER OPERATE (CONTINUED) | RRC | A | X | X | X | X | 1 | X | | Rotate Accumulator right through Carry |
| | | | | | | | | | | [C] |
| | SEL | RB0 | | | | X | 1 | | | Select register bank 0 |
| | SEL | RB1 | | | | X | 1 | | | Select register bank 1 |
| | SWAP | A | X | X | X | X | 1 | | | Swap Accumulator nibbles |
| | | | | | | | | | | [A] |
| | DIS | TCNTI | | X | X | X | 1 | | | Disable timer interrupt |
| | EN | TCNTI | | X | X | X | 1 | | | Enable timer interrupt |
| | DIS | I | | X | X | X | 1 | | | Disable external interrupt |
| | EN | I | | X | X | X | 1 | | | Enable external interrupts |
| | ENT0 | CLK | | | | X | 1 | | | Enable timer output on T0 until next system reset |
| | MOV | A,T | X | X | X | X | 1 | | | [A]←[T] Read timer/counter |
| | MOV | T,A | X | X | X | X | 1 | | | [T]←[A] Load timer/counter |
| | STOP | TCNT | X | X | X | X | 1 | | | Stop timer/counter |
| | STRT | CNT | X | X | X | X | 1 | | | Start counter |
| | STRT | T | X | X | X | X | 1 | | | Start timer |
| | CLR | S | | | X | X | 1 | | | Clear F0 or F1. |
| | CLR | C | X | X | X | X | 1 | 0 | | Clear PSW bit C |
| | CPL | S | | | X | X | 1 | | | Complement F0 or F1. |
| | CPL | C | X | X | X | X | | X | | Complement PSW bit C |
| | MOV | A,PSW | | | X | X | 1 | | | [A]←[PSW] Move Program Status Word contents to the Accumulator |
| | MOV | PSW,A | | | X | X | | X | X | [PSW]←[A] Move Accumulator contents to the Program Status Word |
| | NOP | | X | | X | X | 1 | | | No Operation |

The following symbols are used in Table 6-3:

bbb Three bits designating which bit of the Accumulator is to be tested.

ee Two bits designating an 8243 Expander port:

00 - P4
01 - P5
10 - P6
11 - P7

k One bit selecting a memory or register bank:

0 MB0 or RB0
1 MB1 or RB1

MM Eight bits of immediate data

nnn Three bits designating one of the eight general purpose registers

pp Two bits designating one of the on-chip I/O ports:

00 - BUS
01 - P1
10 - P2

qq Two bits designating either I/O Port 1 or I/O Port 2:

01 - P1
10 - P2

r One bit selecting a pointer register:

0 - R0
1 - R1

xxx The high-order three bits of a program memory address

XX The low-order eight bits of a program memory address

Table 6-3. 8048 Series Instruction Set Object Codes

| INSTRUCTION | | OBJECT CODE | BYTES | MACHINE CYCLES |
|---|---|---|---|---|
| ADD | A,RN | 01101nnn | 1 | 1 |
| ADD | A,@R | 0110000r | 1 | 1 |
| ADD | A,#DATA | 03 MM | 2 | 2 |
| ADDC | A,RN | 01111nnn | 1 | 1 |
| ADDC | A,@R | 0111000r | 1 | 1 |
| ADDC | A,#DATA | 13 MM | 2 | 2 |
| ANL | A,RN | 01011nnn | 1 | 1 |
| ANL | A,@R | 0101000r | 1 | 1 |
| ANL | A,#DATA | 53 MM | 2 | 2 |
| ANL | PORT,#DATA | 100110pp | 2 | 2 |
| | | MM | | |
| ANLD | EP,A | 100111ee | 1 | 2 |
| CALL | ADDR | xxx10100 | 2 | 2 |
| | | XX | | |
| CLR | A | 27 | 1 | 1 |
| CLR | C | 97 | 1 | 1 |
| CLR | F1 | A5 | 1 | 1 |
| CLR | F0 | 85 | 1 | 1 |
| CPL | A | 37 | 1 | 1 |
| CPL | C | A7 | 1 | 1 |
| CPL | F0 | 95 | 1 | 1 |
| CPL | F1 | B5 | 1 | 1 |
| DA | A | 57 | 1 | 1 |
| DEC | A | 07 | 1 | 1 |
| DEC | RN | 11001nnn | 1 | 1 |
| DIS | I | 15 | 1 | 1 |
| DIS | TCNTI | 35 | 1 | 1 |
| DJNZ | RN,ADDR8 | 11101rrr | 2 | 2 |
| | | XX | | |
| EN | I | 05 | 1 | 1 |
| EN | TCNTI | 25 | 1 | 1 |
| ENT0 | CLK | 75 | 1 | 1 |
| IN | A,PN | 000010qq | 1 | 2 |
| IN | A,DBB | 22 | 1 | 1 |
| INC | A | 17 | 1 | 1 |
| INC | RN | 00011nnn | 1 | 1 |
| INC | @R | 0001000r | 1 | 1 |
| INS | A,BUS | 08 | 1 | 2 |
| JBb | ADDR8 | bbb10010 | 2 | 2 |
| | | XX | | |
| JC | ADDR8 | F6 XX | 2 | 2 |
| JF0 | ADDR8 | B6 XX | 2 | 2 |
| JF1 | ADDR8 | 76 XX | 2 | 2 |
| JMP | ADDR | xxx00100 | 2 | 2 |
| | | XX | | |
| JMPP | @A | B3 | 1 | 2 |
| JNC | ADDR8 | E6 XX | 2 | 2 |
| JNI | ADDR8 | 86 XX | 2 | 2 |
| JNIBF | ADDR8 | D6 XX | 2 | 2 |
| JNT0 | ADDR8 | 26 XX | 2 | 2 |
| JNT1 | ADDR8 | 46 XX | 2 | 2 |
| JNZ | ADDR8 | 96 XX | 2 | 2 |

| INSTRUCTION | | OBJECT CODE | BYTES | MACHINE CYCLES |
|---|---|---|---|---|
| JOBF | ADDR8 | 86 XX | 2 | 2 |
| JTF | ADDR8 | 16 XX | 2 | 2 |
| JT0 | ADDR8 | 36 XX | 2 | 2 |
| JT1 | ADDR8 | 56 XX | 2 | 2 |
| JZ | ADDR8 | C6 XX | 2 | 2 |
| MOV | A,#DATA | 23 MM | 2 | 2 |
| MOV | A,PSW | C7 | 1 | 1 |
| MOV | A,RN | 11111nnn | 1 | 1 |
| MOV | A,@R | 1111000r | 1 | 1 |
| MOV | A,T | 42 | 1 | 1 |
| MOV | PSW,A | D7 | 1 | 1 |
| MOV | RN,A | 10101nnn | 1 | 1 |
| MOV | RN,#DATA | 10111nn | 2 | 2 |
| | | MM | | |
| MOV | @R,A | 1010000r | 1 | 1 |
| MOV | @R,#DATA | 1011000r | 2 | 2 |
| | | MM | | |
| MOV | T,A | 62 | 1 | 1 |
| MOVD | A,EP | 000011ee | 1 | 2 |
| MOVD | EP,A | 001111ee | 1 | 2 |
| MOVP | A,@A | A3 | 1 | 2 |
| MOVP3 | A,@A | E3 | 1 | 2 |
| MOVX | A,@R | 1000000r | 1 | 2 |
| MOVX | @R,A | 1001000r | 1 | 2 |
| NOP | | 00 | 1 | 1 |
| ORL | A,RN | 01001nnn | 1 | 1 |
| ORL | A,@R | 0100000r | 1 | 1 |
| ORL | A,#DATA | 43 MM | 2 | 2 |
| ORL | PORT,#DATA | 100010pp | 2 | 2 |
| | | MM | | |
| ORLD | EP,A | 100011ee | 1 | 2 |
| OUT | DBB,A | 02 | 1 | 1 |
| OUTL | BUS,A | 02 | 1 | 2 |
| OUTL | PN,A | 001110qq | 1 | 2 |
| RET | | 83 | 1 | 2 |
| RETR | | 93 | 1 | 2 |
| RL | A | E7 | 1 | 1 |
| RLC | A | F7 | 1 | 1 |
| RR | A | 77 | 1 | 1 |
| RRC | A | 67 | 1 | 1 |
| SEL | MBk | 111k0101 | 1 | 1 |
| SEL | RBk | 110k0101 | 1 | 1 |
| STOP | TCNT | 65 | 1 | 1 |
| STRT | CNT | 45 | 1 | 1 |
| STRT | T | 55 | 1 | 1 |
| SWAP | A | 47 | 1 | 1 |
| XCH | A,RN | 00101nnn | 1 | 1 |
| XCH | A,@R | 0010000r | 1 | 1 |
| XCHD | A,@R | 0011000r | 1 | 1 |
| XRL | A,RN | 11011nnn | 1 | 1 |
| XRL | A,@R | 1101000r | 1 | 1 |
| XRL | A,#DATA | D3 MM | 2 | 2 |

# THE 8041 SLAVE MICROCOMPUTER

**This device is also referred to in Intel literature as a Universal Programmable Interface (UPI); it represents a simple variation of the 8048 microcomputer.**

**The 8741 is a slave variation of the 8748 microcomputer.**

**This discussion of the 8041 and 8741 slave microcomputers explains differences as compared to the 8048 and 8748; you should therefore read the following pages after reading the 8048 and 8748 descriptions.**

## AN 8041 FUNCTIONAL OVERVIEW

**The principal difference between the 8048 and the 8041 is the fact that the 8041 Data Bus and I/O Port 0 are used exclusively to communicate with a master microprocessor. The 8041 generates no external Address or Data Bus,** so on-chip 8041 program memory and scratchpad data memory cannot be expanded.

**External interrupt logic, which is available on the 8048, is not available on an 8041; the 8041 uses this logic as a handshaking interrupt for data input from the master microprocessor.**

**8048 and 8041 logic are compared functionally in Figure 6-15.**

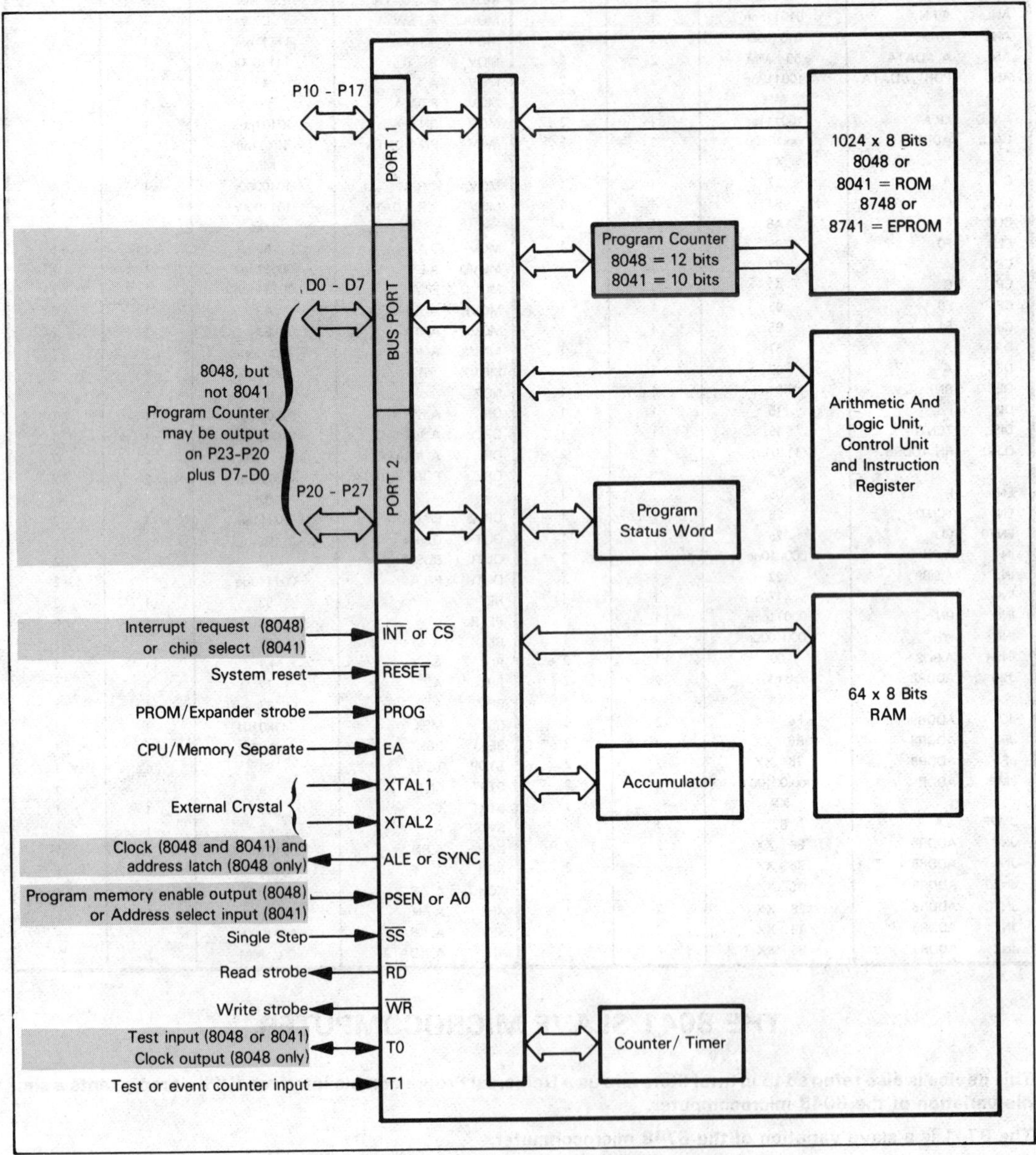


Figure 6-15. A Comparison of 8048 and 8041 Functional Logic

**Communications between an 8041 and a master microprocessor are very limited.** Data must be transferred byte-by-byte under program control, with nearly all handshaking protocol being implemented via program logic. You must therefore define the protocol within the logic of your 8041 and master microprocessor programs. **A rigid protocol is absolutely necessary, since the 8041 offers no protection against data transfer contentions.**

## 8041 DATA BUS LOGIC

**8041 Data Bus logic may be illustrated conceptually as follows:**

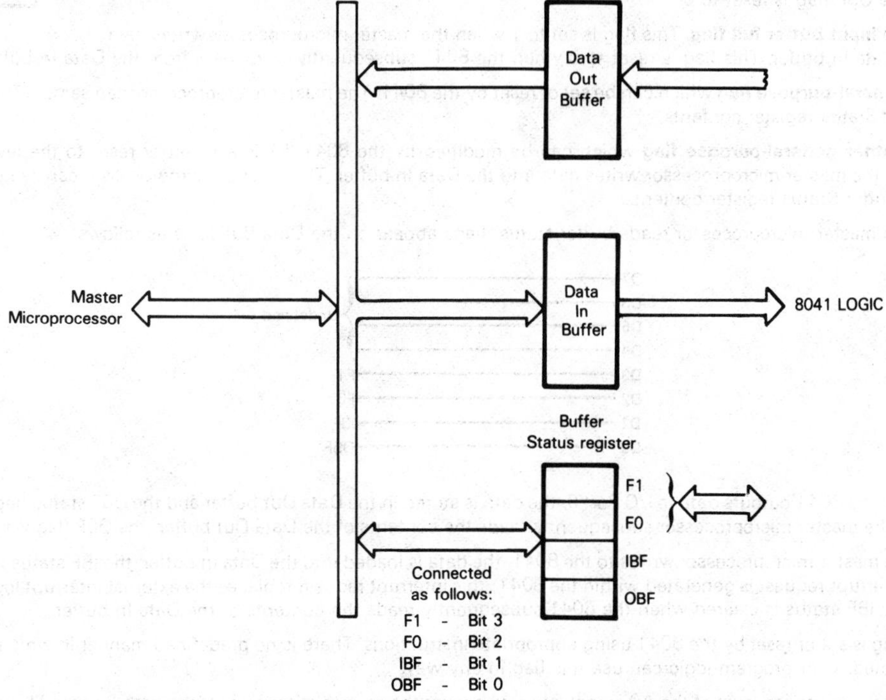


**In reality, the Data Out buffer and the Data In buffer are a single piece of logic; however, operations occur (to some extent) as though there were two separate buffers.**

**A master microprocessor will access an 8041 as two I/O ports or two memory locations.** These locations are identified via chip select ($\overline{CS}$) and address (A0) input signals as follows:

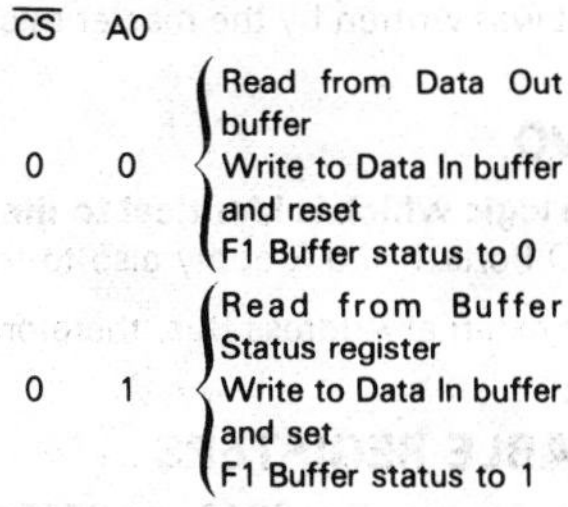

$\overline{CS}$ A0
0 0 Read from Data Out buffer
Write to Data In buffer and reset F1 Buffer status to 0
0 1 Read from Buffer Status register
Write to Data In buffer and set F1 Buffer status to 1

"Read" and "Write" above refer to master microprocessor operations.

**The 8041 accesses the Data Bus buffer register as I/O Port 0.** The Status register is inaccessible to the 8041 as an addressable I/O port; however, there are specific 8041 instructions that access the F0 and F1 Buffer Status bits.

**8041 BUFFER STATUS REGISTER**

**The four Buffer Status register bits may be defined as follows:**

**OBF is the output buffer full flag.** This flag is automatically set to 1 when the 8041 outputs data to the Data Out buffer. When the master microprocessor reads the contents of the Data Out buffer, the OBF flag is reset to 0.

**IBF is the input buffer full flag.** This flag is set to 1 when the master microprocessor writes data into the Data In buffer. This flag is reset to 0 when the 8041 subsequently reads data from the Data In buffer.

**F0 is a general-purpose flag** which can be set or reset by the 8041. The master microprocessor can sample F0 by reading Buffer Status register contents.

**F1 is another general-purpose flag** which can be modified by the 8041. F1 is also set or reset to the level of A0 whenever the master microprocessor writes data into the Data In buffer. The master microprocessor can sample F1 by reading Buffer Status register contents.

When the master microprocessor reads buffer status, flags appear on the Data Bus lines as follows:

Whenever the 8041 outputs data to I/O Port 0, the data is stored in the Data Out buffer and the OBF status flag is set to 1; when the master microprocessor subsequently reads the contents of the Data Out buffer, the OBF flag is reset to 0.

When the master microprocessor writes to the 8041, the data is loaded into the Data In buffer, the IBF status is set to 1 and an interrupt request is generated within the 8041; this interrupt request replaces the external interrupt logic of the 8048. The IBF status is cleared when the 8041 subsequently reads the contents of the Data In buffer.

The F0 flag is set or reset by the 8041 using appropriate instructions. There is no predefined manner in which this flag is interpreted; your program logic can use this flag in any way.

The F1 flag is set to the level of the A0 signal input whenever the master microprocessor writes a control byte into the Data In buffer. In reality, there is no difference between a control byte and a data byte; that is to say, there is no predefined way in which the 8041 will interpret the contents of the Data In buffer based on the F1 flag level.

The master microprocessor reads data which has been output by the 8041; the master microprocessor cannot read back data which it wrote to the 8041.

The 8041 inputs from I/O Port 0 data that was written by the master microprocessor; the 8041 cannot read back data which it previously output to I/O Port 0.

## 8041 I/O PORTS ONE AND TWO

**Physically, 8041 I/O Ports 1 and 2 have logic which is identical to the 8048.** Thus the pseudo-bidirectional I/O port characteristics described for the 8048 I/O Ports 1 and 2 apply also to the 8041 I/O Ports 1 and 2.

Note that the 8041 does not generate an external Address Bus, therefore I/O Port 2 pins P20 - P23 never output address information.

## 8041 AND 8741 PROGRAMMABLE REGISTERS

The 8041 and 8741 have a 10-bit Program Counter. The 8048 and 8748 have a 12-bit Program Counter. These are the only differences between the 8041 series and 8048 series programmable registers.

## 8041 AND 8741 ADDRESSING MODES

The 8041 and 8741 can address only on-chip memory. This includes the 1024 bytes of on-chip program memory and 64 bytes of on-chip scratchpad data memory. **8041 and 8741 addressing modes are identical to the 8048 and 8748 on-chip memory addressing modes.** Of course, the 8048 and 8748 external memory addressing modes will not apply to the 8041 or the 8741.

## 8041 AND 8741 STATUS

**The 8041 and 8741 slave microcomputers have two Status registers. First, there is the Buffer Status register, which is part of the Data Bus logic. We have already described this 4-bit Status register. The 8041 and 8741 also have the 8-bit Program Status Word described for the 8048 series microcomputers. 8041 and 8048 Program Status Words are identical.**

## 8041 AND 8741 SLAVE MICROCOMPUTER OPERATING MODES

**The 8041 and 8741 can be operated in Internal Execution mode and Debug mode; in addition, the 8741 can be operated in Single Stepping mode, Programming mode and Verification mode. Neither the 8041 nor the 8741 can be operated in External Memory Access mode.**

## 8041 AND 8741 PINS AND SIGNALS

**There are a few differences between 8041 and 8741 pins and signals, as compared to the 8048 and 8748. Figure 6-16 defines 8041 and 8741 pins and signals; the four changed signals are shaded.**

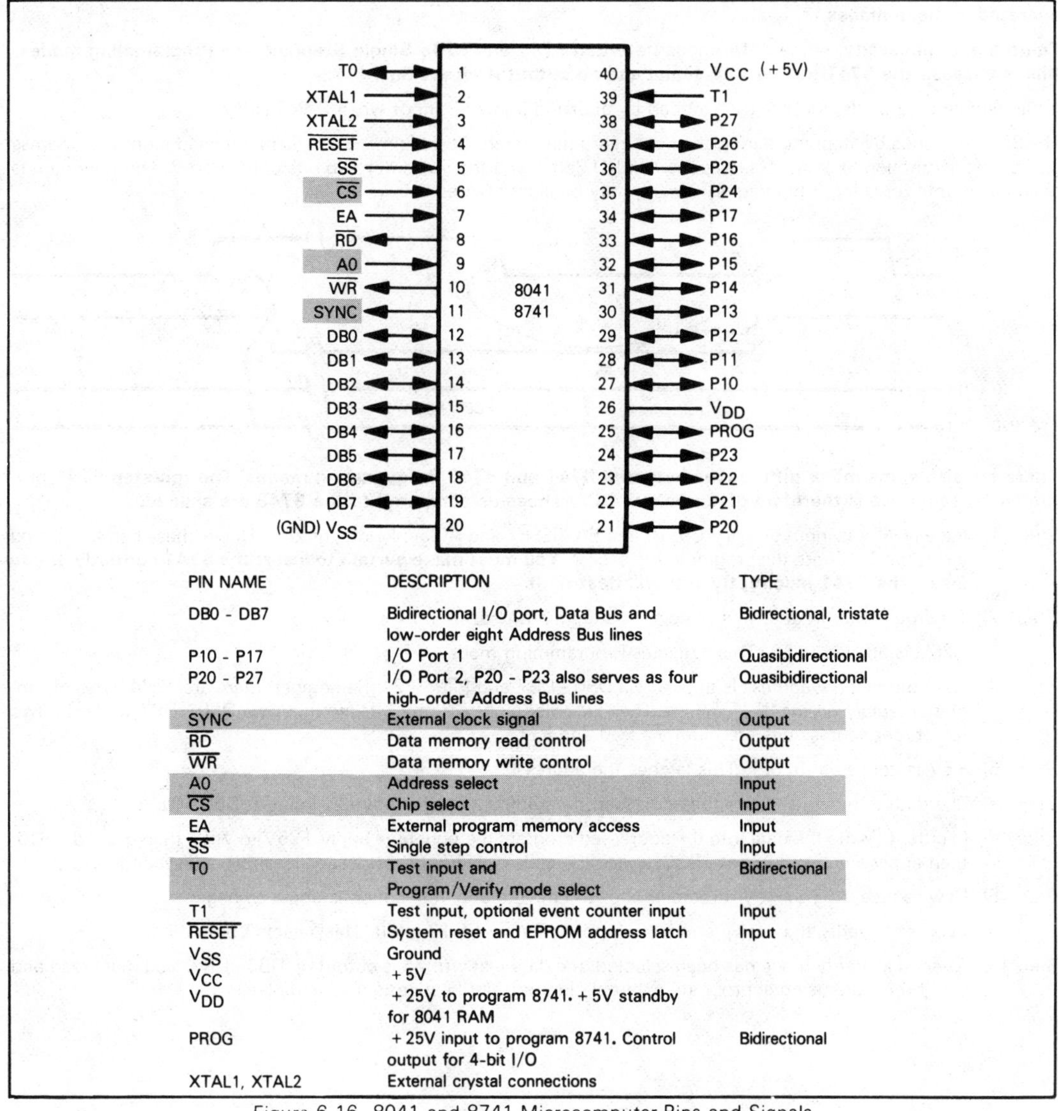


| PIN NAME | DESCRIPTION | TYPE |
|---|---|---|
| DB0 - DB7 | Bidirectional I/O port, Data Bus and low-order eight Address Bus lines | Bidirectional, tristate |
| P10 - P17 | I/O Port 1 | Quasibidirectional |
| P20 - P27 | I/O Port 2, P20 - P23 also serves as four high-order Address Bus lines | Quasibidirectional |
| SYNC | External clock signal | Output |
| RD | Data memory read control | Output |
| WR | Data memory write control | Output |
| A0 | Address select | Input |
| CS | Chip select | Input |
| EA | External program memory access | Input |
| SS | Single step control | Input |
| T0 | Test input and Program/Verify mode select | Bidirectional |
| T1 | Test input, optional event counter input | Input |
| RESET | System reset and EPROM address latch | Input |
| $V_{SS}$ | Ground | |
| $V_{CC}$ | + 5V | |
| $V_{DD}$ | + 25V to program 8741. + 5V standby for 8041 RAM | |
| PROG | + 25V input to program 8741. Control output for 4-bit I/O | Bidirectional |
| XTAL1, XTAL2 | External crystal connections | |

Figure 6-16. 8041 and 8741 Microcomputer Pins and Signals

**$\overline{CS}$ and A0 are the device select inputs** which we have already described.

**SYNC is an external synchronizing signal** which is output once per machine cycle.

**T0 cannot be connected to the internal system clock; other uses of T0 are the same for the 8041/8741 and the 8048/8748.**

All other signals are identical to the 8048 and 8748 as previously described. Note, however, that no addresses are output on the DB0 - DB7 pins or the P20 - P23 pins.

## 8041 SERIES TIMING AND INSTRUCTION EXECUTION

The 8041/8741 clock signals and instruction execution timing logic is identical to the 8048/8748. Of course, the 8041 and 8741 have no external memory reference instructions, therefore timing associated with these instructions will not apply.

## 8741 SINGLE STEPPING AND PROGRAMMING MODE

**Single Stepping and Programming modes of operation are available only with the 8741; the 8041 cannot be operated in these modes.**

**There are, of necessity, some differences between 8741 and 8748 Single Stepping and Programming modes; this is because the 8741 has no ALE signal and no output Address Bus.**

In Single Stepping mode, the 8741 is stopped by applying a low $\overline{SS}$ input when SYNC is low.

The 8741 responds by stopping during the next instruction fetch. At this time, SYNC is maintained high. The address of the next instruction to be accessed appears at I/O Port 1 and the low-order two bits of I/O Port 2. This condition is maintained until $\overline{SS}$ is input high again. Timing may be illustrated as follows:

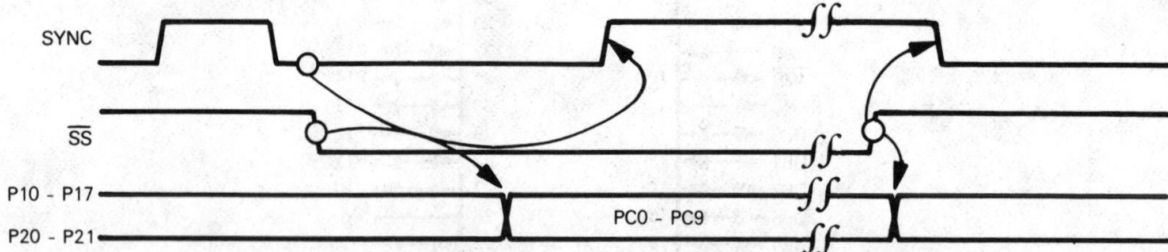


**There are also some minor differences between 8741 and 8748 Programming modes. The ten-step 8741 programming sequence is therefore given below. Differences as compared to the 8748 are shaded.**

Step 1) Initially +5V is input at $V_{DD}$, $\overline{CS}$, T0 and EA. $\overline{RESET}$ and A0 are held at ground. Under these conditions you insert the 8741 into the programming socket. **You must make certain to insert the 8741 correctly. If you insert the 8741 incorrectly you will destroy it.**

Step 2) T0 is pulled to ground; this selects Programming mode.

Step 3) +25V is applied to EA. This activates Programming mode.

Step 4) A 10-bit memory address is applied via DB0 - DB7 and P20 - P21. Remember, there are 1024 bytes of program memory on the 8741 device. The low-order eight address bits are input via DB0 - DB7 while the two high-order address bits are input via P20 and P21.

Step 5) +5V is applied at $\overline{RESET}$. This latches the address.

Step 6) The data to be written into the addressed programmed memory byte is input at DB0 - DB7.

Step 7) In order to write the data into the addressed program memory byte apply +25V to $V_{DD}$, then ground PROG, then apply a +25V pulse at PROG; the +25V pulse at PROG must last at least 50 milliseconds.

Step 8) Now reduce $V_{DD}$ to +5V. Programming is complete and verification is about to begin.

Step 9) In order to verify the data just written, apply +5V to the T0 input. This selects Verify mode.

Step 10) As soon as Verify mode has been selected, the data just written is output on DB0 - DB7. You must read and verify this data using appropriate external circuitry. Verification is now complete.

## 8041 INPUT/OUTPUT PROGRAMMING

**The only differences between 8041/8741 and 8048/8748 input/output programming are those which result from the unique 8041 I/O Port 0 logic — which we have described.**

## 8041 COUNTER/TIMER OPERATIONS

**8041 series and 8048 series counter/timer operations are identical.**

## 8041 INTERRUPT LOGIC

**The entire external interrupt logic of the 8048 has been converted in the 8041/8741 Data Bus handshaking interrupt logic. This interrupt request occurs every time a master microprocessor writes to either of the 8041/8741 addressable locations.**

In order to generate external interrupt logic at an 8041 or 8741 you must use the counter/timer. By loading the counter/timer with an initial value of $FF_{16}$ and operating the counter/timer in Counter mode, the first high-to-low input transition on T1 will generate a Timer interrupt request. Of course, if you are using the counter/timer in this way, you cannot use it for any of its normal functions.

## PROGRAMMING 8048-8041 DATA TRANSFERS

**The only complexity associated with programming an 8041 involves data transfers between the 8041 and a master microcomputer. Programming these data transfers is not straightforward.**

We described earlier how there are separate data paths for data entering or leaving the 8041 via the Data Bus buffer. Nevertheless, **if a master microcomputer attempts to write to the 8041/8741 while the 8041/8741 is simultaneously outputting to I/O Port 0, then there will be an undefined result.** This is unfortunate, since there are no signals or indicators of any kind allowing the master microcomputer to lock out the 8041/8741; nor can the 8041/8741 lock out the master microcomputer. **Lock out logic must be implemented by you, via your program logic.** Program logic must also make sure that data written by a master microcomputer has been read by the 8041/8741 before the master microcomputer writes any new data; similarly, the 8041/8741 must make sure that any data it has output to I/O Port 0 has been read by the master microcomputer before the 8041/8741 attempts to output new data to I/O Port 0.

**Let us look at the programming steps required for error free data transfers between the 8041/8741 and a master microcomputer.** Programming examples assume an 8048 is the master microprocessor because the 8048 is described in this chapter and has an instruction set that is similar to the 8041. In reality, the master microprocessor is likely to be an 8085-type device.

The master microcomputer can make sure that it does not overwrite data by testing both the IBF and the OBF flags; that is to say, the master microcomputer will not attempt to write data to the 8041/8741 if prior data it wrote is waiting to be read by the 8041/8741, or if data output by the 8041/8741 is waiting to be read by the master microcomputer. The following master microcomputer output instruction sequence will suffice:

```
MOV     0,ADDR+1   ;LOAD 8041 ADDRESS INTO 8048 REGISTER R0
-
-
-
MOVX    A,@0       ;LOAD STATUS
RRC     A          ;TEST LOW ORDER (OBF) FLAG
JC      NEXT       ;IF IT IS 1, DO NOT WRITE NEW DATA
RRC     A          ;TEST NEXT BIT (IBF) FLAG
JC      READ       ;IF IT IS 1, DATA IS WAITING TO BE READ
DEC     0          ;OK TO OUTPUT
-
-
-
```

But this scheme does not prevent the master microcomputer and the 8041/8741 from simultaneously accessing the Data Bus buffer. This must be guaranteed by 8041/8741 lock out logic. The 8041/8741 can use programming logic or interrupt logic to lock out the master microcomputer. Using programming logic, the 8041/8741 will use the F0 flag to identify those time intervals when the master microcomputer is free to access the Data Bus buffer. Now any 8048 master microcomputer instruction sequence that accesses the 8041/8741 will first read 8041/8741 status and test the F0 flag. If this flag is "false", no data transfer must occur. Continuing our master microprocessor instruction sequence, this may be illustrated as follows:

```
        MOV     0,ADDR+1    ;LOAD 8041 ADDRESS INTO 8048 REGISTER R0
        -
        -
        -
TEST    MOVX    A,@0        ;LOAD STATUS
        RRC     A           ;TEST LOW ORDER (OBF) FLAG
        JC      NEXT        ;IF IT IS 1, DO NOT WRITE NEW DATA
        RRC     A           ;TEST NEXT BIT (IBF) FLAG
        JC      READ        ;IF IT IS 1, DATA IS WAITING TO BE READ
        RRC     A           ;TEST F0 FLAG
        JNC     TEST        ;IF F0 IS 0, MASTER IS LOCKED OUT
        DEC     0           ;F0 IS 1 SO IT IS OK TO OUTPUT DATA
        MOV     A,@1        ;LOAD DATA TO BE OUTPUT INTO ACCUMULATOR
        MOVX    @0,A        ;OUTPUT DATA TO 8041
        JMP     OUT
READ    RRC     A           ;TEST F0 FLAG
        JNC     TEST        ;IF F0 IS 0, MASTER IS LOCKED OUT
        DEC     0           ;F0 IS 1 SO IT IS OK TO READ DATA
        MOVX    A,@0        ;INPUT DATA
        MOV     @1,A        ;STORE IN SCRATCHPAD
        JMP     OUT
```

The instructions above assume that scratchpad register R1 addresses the scratchpad byte out of which written data is fetched, or into which read data is stored.

If there is heavy traffic between an 8041/8741 and a master microcomputer, then the 8041/8741 should use interrupt logic to identify times when a master microcomputer can either output data to the 8041/8741 or input data from the 8041/8741. To do this, one or two 8041/8741 I/O port pins must be set aside as interrupt request generation lines. Now the master microcomputer will not access the 8041/8741 except within an interrupt service routine which is initiated by an interrupt request arising from one of the two dedicated 8041/8741 I/O port pins.

Data transfers from the 8041/8741 to the master microcomputer are easy to program. When the 8041/8741 writes to I/O Port 0, the OBF flag is set to 1; this flag is reset to 0 when a master microcomputer reads data. Thus, the 8041/8741 simply tests the OBF status before outputting data; here are appropriate instructions:

```
        CLR     F0          ;ZERO F0 TO LOCK OUT THE MASTER MICROPROCESSOR
        JOBF    NEXT        ;TEST OBF FLAG
        OUT     DBB,A       ;IF IT IS ZERO, OUTPUT NEXT DATA BYTE
        CPL     F0          ;SET F0 TO ALLOW MASTER MICROPROCESSOR ACCESS
        -
        -
        -
NEXT
```

The 8041/8741 can respond to data arriving from the master microcomputer by using polling logic or interrupt logic. If polling logic is used, then the 8041/8741 must test the IBF flag before reading any data that the master microcomputer has output. In order to determine whether the master microprocessor has output data or a control code, the 8041/8741 must also check the F1 flag. Here is an appropriate instruction sequence:

```
        CLR     F0      ;ZERO F0 TO LOCK OUT THE MASTER MICROPROCESSOR
        JNIBF   NEXT    ;TEST FOR DATA WAITING TO BE READ
        JF1     CONT    ;DATA IS READY TO BE READ. TEST
                        ;FOR DATA BYTE OR CONTROL BYTE
        IN      A,DBB   ;READ DATA
        CPL     F0      ;SET F0 TO ALLOW MASTER MICROPROCESSOR ACCESS
        -
        -
        -
CONT    IN      A,DBB   ;READ CONTROL CODE
        CPL     F0      ;SET F0 TO ALLOW MASTER MICROPROCESSOR ACCESS
        -
        -
        -
NEXT
```

If 8041/8741 data input logic is interrupt driven, then external interrupts must be left enabled. Now as soon as the master microcomputer outputs data to the 8041/8741, an interrupt request will occur, followed by a Call 3 instruction being executed. Beginning at memory location 3, the following instruction sequence will initiate the data input interrupt service routine within the 8041/8741:

```
        ORG     3
        JMP     DTIN    ;JUMP TO DATA INPUT ROUTINE
        -
        -
        -
DTIN    CLR     F0      ;ZERO F0 TO LOCK OUT MASTER MICROPROCESSOR
        JF1     CONT    ;TEST FOR DATA TYPE
        IN      A,DBB   ;READ DATA
        -
        -
        -
CONT    IN      A,DBB   ;READ CONTROL CODE
        -
        -
        -
        CPL     F0      ;SET F0 TO ALLOW MASTER MICROPROCESSOR ACCESS
        RET             ;RETURN FROM INTERRUPT SERVICE ROUTINE
```

The master microprocessor must not write to the 8041/8741 while data that the 8041/8741 has output is waiting to be read; similarly, the 8041/8741 cannot output data to the master microprocessor while data from the master microprocessor is waiting to be read by the 8041/8741. In each case, prior data will be overwritten and lost. In order to prevent this from happening, you must have appropriate lock out logic. F0 is used for this purpose above.

## THE 8041/8741 INSTRUCTION SET

**The 8041/8741 instruction set differs from the 8048/8748 in minor ways only. Tables 6-2 and 6-3 therefore summarize the instruction set for both the 8048 series and 8041 series microcomputers.**

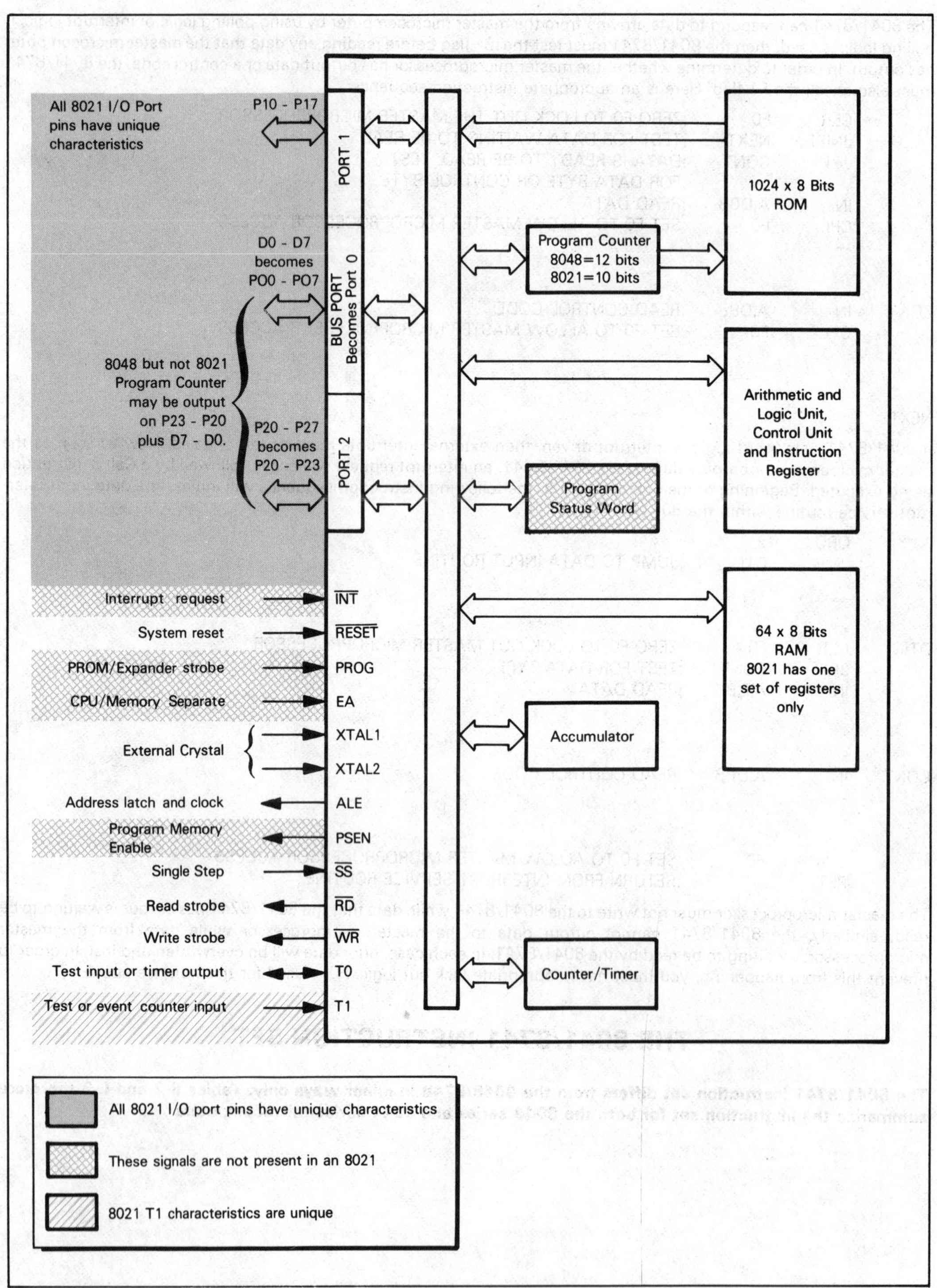

All 8021 I/O Port pins have unique characteristics
P10 - P17
PORT 1
1024 x 8 Bits ROM
D0 - D7 becomes P00 - P07
BUS PORT Becomes Port 0
Program Counter 8048=12 bits 8021=10 bits
8048 but not 8021 Program Counter may be output on P23 - P20 plus D7 - D0.
Arithmetic and Logic Unit, Control Unit and Instruction Register
P20 - P27 becomes P20 - P23
PORT 2
Program Status Word
Interrupt request
INT
System reset
RESET
64 x 8 Bits RAM 8021 has one set of registers only
PROM/Expander strobe
PROG
CPU/Memory Separate
EA
External Crystal
XTAL1
XTAL2
Accumulator
Address latch and clock
ALE
Program Memory Enable
PSEN
Single Step
SS
Read strobe
RD
Write strobe
WR
Test input or timer output
T0
Counter/Timer
Test or event counter input
T1
All 8021 I/O port pins have unique characteristics
These signals are not present in an 8021
8021 T1 characteristics are unique

Figure 6-17. A Comparison of 8048 and 8021 Functional Logic

# THE 8021/8022 SINGLE-CHIP MICROCOMPUTERS

**The 8021/8022 are low-cost subsets of the 8048 single-chip microcomputer family. Unlike the 8041, the 8021/8022 are not designed to operate as a slave microcomputer. The 8021/8022 are intended for high-volume, low-cost applications with limited microcomputer logic requirements.** The only easy way in which an 8021/8022 microcomputer can be expanded is by adding an 8243 Input/Output Expander. There is no simple way to increase either 8021/8022 program memory or data memory, over and above that which is internal to it.

**This discussion of the 8021/8022 single-chip microcomputers explains differences as compared to the 8048 and 8748; you should therefore read the following pages after reading the 8048 and 8748 descriptions.**

**In the following discussion all references to 8021 microcomputers are assumed to also apply to 8022 microcomputers unless otherwise noted. The 8022 is described in detail in a later section.**

## AN 8021 FUNCTIONAL OVERVIEW

**The principal difference between the 8048 and the 8021 is the fact that the 8021 has no Data Bus, and I/O Port 0 is simply another I/O port.** Thus, the only way in which an 8021 can communicate with logic beyond the chip itself is via its I/O ports, which have no accompanying handshaking control signals. In contrast, the 8041 has I/O Port 0 logic designed for two-way communication between the 8041 and a master microprocessor. The 8021 cannot distinguish between a master microprocessor or any other external logic.

The 8021 has no external interrupt logic and only one Test input.

Only two control signals are output by the 8021: a synchronizing clock signal and an 8243 Input/Output Expander control strobe.

With these reduced capabilities, **the 8021 is packaged as a 28-pin DIP,** in contrast to other members of the 8048 series including the 8022, which are packaged as 40-pin DIPs.

**The 8021 can be driven by a crystal oscillator with a maximum 3 MHz frequency.** This is half the maximum frequency of the 8048 and 8041, but equivalent to the maximum frequency of the -8 parts. This 3 MHz crystal generates 10-microsecond machine cycles. Thus, all 8021 instructions execute in either 10 or 20 microseconds.

**Functionally, 8048 and 8021 logic are compared in Figure 6-17. 8021 pins and signals are illustrated in Figure 6-18.**

## 8021 I/O PORT PINS

**8021 I/O port pins are referred to as quasi-bidirectional, a term we also use to describe 8048 I/O port pins. 8048 and 8021 I/O port pin logic is identical.**

## THE T1 PIN

**The T1 pin on the 8021 microcomputer can be used as a test input which can be sampled by a Jump-on-Condition instruction, and it can also be used to input a signal to Counter/Timer logic when it is serving as an event counter.** These are the same functions that the T1 pin performs on the 8048 microcomputer. **The electrical characteristics of the T1 pin on the 8021, however, differ from those of the 8048.** On the 8021, the T1 pin has a special bias input that allows zero crossover sensing of slowly changing AC signals. The following circuit could be used to detect when the input to T1 crosses zero within ±5%

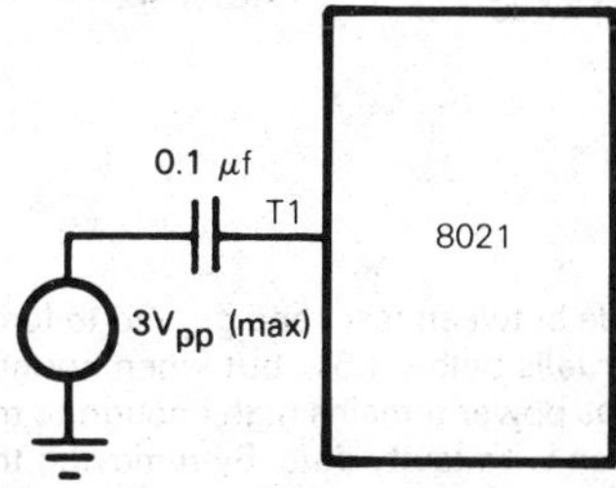


**As a ROM mask option, you can specify an internal pullup resistor for the T1 input.** This option would be useful if you are using a switch contact or standard TTL as the input to T1.

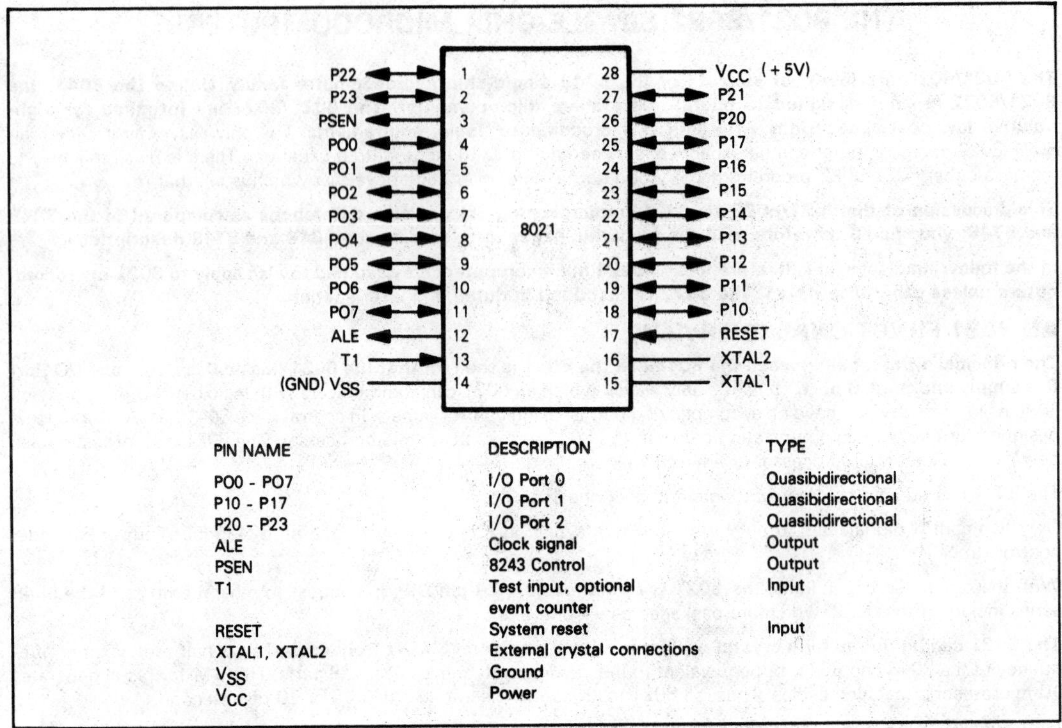


| PIN NAME | DESCRIPTION | TYPE |
|---|---|---|
| PO0 - PO7 | I/O Port 0 | Quasibidirectional |
| P10 - P17 | I/O Port 1 | Quasibidirectional |
| P20 - P23 | I/O Port 2 | Quasibidirectional |
| ALE | Clock signal | Output |
| PSEN | 8243 Control | Output |
| T1 | Test input, optional event counter | Input |
| RESET | System reset | Input |
| XTAL1, XTAL2 | External crystal connections | |
| $V_{SS}$ | Ground | |
| $V_{CC}$ | Power | |

Figure 6-18. 8021 Microcomputer Pins and Signals

## THE 8021 RESET INPUT

**When the 8021 is reset, the same internal operations occur as described for the 8048;** the Program Counter and Program Status Word are cleared and 1 is output to I/O port pins. **However, 8021 reset logic has been modified so that the 8021 can operate with noisy power supplies.** You have one of two options, which may be illustrated as follows:

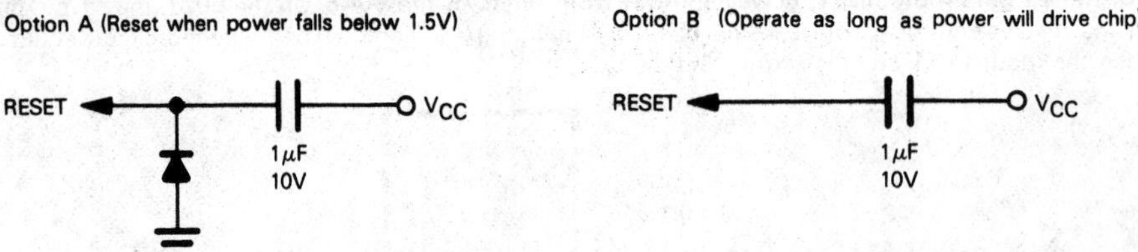


In the case of Option A, you connect the diode between reset and ground to force a reset whenever power drops below 1.5V. Thus, operations will stop while power falls below 1.5V, but when normal power returns operations will restart. Since chip operations continue only as long as power remains high enough to maintain the contents of chip read/write locations, this circuit guards against execution with faulty data. By removing the diode, as illustrated in Option B, this reset feature is eliminated and the 8021 will operate as long as power is sufficient to drive logic internal to the chip.

## THE 8021 CLOCK INPUTS

**A crystal Resistor/Capacitor or inductor circuit can be connected to the XTL1 and XTL2 pins to provide the needed internal clock signal.** The maximum external crystal frequency allowed is 3 MHz. This generates 10-microsecond machine cycles. All instructions execute in 1 or 2 machine cycles.

## THE 8021 TIMER/COUNTER

**Logic associated with the 8021 timer/counter is identical to that which we have described for the 8048.** The contents of the Accumulator can be moved to the Counter/Timer register, which is subsequently incremented once every 32 crystal oscillations in Timer mode, or once every high-to-low transition of a T1 input in Counter mode. However, **there is no interrupt logic on the 8021,** which means that a time-out will not cause an interrupt request to occur. You must therefore test for a time-out under program control using the JTF (Branch-on-Timer Flag) instruction.

## 8021 SCRATCHPAD MEMORY AND PROGRAMMING

**In addition to the lack of interrupt logic, the 8021 has no Status register and data memory is simplified.**

Instead of having a Status register, the 8021 has a 3-bit Stack Pointer and a single Carry status flag.

Data memory consists of eight general purpose registers in scratchpad bytes 0-7, plus a 16-byte Stack which uses scratchpad bytes 8-$17_{16}$. This stack allows subroutines to be nested to a level of 8. The 8021 does not have the second set of eight registers located in scratchpad bytes $18_{16}$ - $1F_{16}$, as is available on the 8048 and the 8041.

# THE 8021 INSTRUCTION SET

The 8021 instruction set is a subset of the 8048 instruction set. In Table 6-1, 8021 instructions are identified.

# THE 8022 SINGLE-CHIP MICROCOMPUTER

**The 8022 is an upgraded 8021. That is to say, the 8022 is a low-end, non-expandable microcomputer like the 8021. These two microcomputers are virtually identical. Their differences can be summarized as follows:**

**8022 MICROCOMPUTER**

1) **ROM capacity has been expanded from 1K for the 8021 to 2K for the 8022.**
2) **An 8-bit on-chip A/D converter has been added.**
3) **Port 0 has a mask option that allows it to be used as a capacitive touch panel input port.**
4) **Port 2 has eight bits instead of four.**
5) **The T0 test pin, which was omitted on the 8021, is present on the 8022.**
6) **The 8022 is packaged as a 40-pin DIP rather than a 28-pin DIP.**
7) **There are some minor differences between the instruction set of the 8021 and that of the 8022. Table 6-1 identifies the 8022 instructions.**

**In all other respects, the 8021 and the 8022 are identical.** These modifications and additions make the 8022 a much more useful microcomputer than the 8021. The ability to perform on-chip A/D conversion is quite powerful. It can be used to provide a wide variety of analog inputs to the microcomputer. Data such as temperatures, voltages, and rates of flow can all be input directly to the 8022 system without the need for external A/D logic. The additional 1K of program memory allows for more complex programs than would be possible with the 8021. Chip count is greatly reduced by both the on-board A/D converter and the touch panel input circuitry.

## 8022 A/D CONVERTER

**The on-board A/D is implemented using a resistor ladder network. A block diagram is shown in Figure 6-18a.** The Successive Approximation register drives the resistor ladder network. This selects a voltage to be compared with an unknown analog input. **Note that two analog inputs are provided. They are selected via the SEL AN0 and SEL AN1 instructions.** The comparison proceeds from most significant to least significant bit. **It takes eight comparisons to perform an entire conversion. Two comparisons are performed during each instruction cycle, therefore it takes four instruction cycles to perform an A/D conversion. The contents of the Conversion Result register can be read via the RAD (Read A/D) instruction. Since the Conversion Result register is latched, a RAD instruction can be executed at any time, although the Conversion Result register is updated only once every four instruction cycles.** The relatively fast ($\approx$40 $\mu$s) conversion makes it possible to multiplex many analog inputs. The 8022, as stated above, can multiplex two analog inputs. Additional analog inputs can be multiplexed via external logic accessed through the I/O ports.

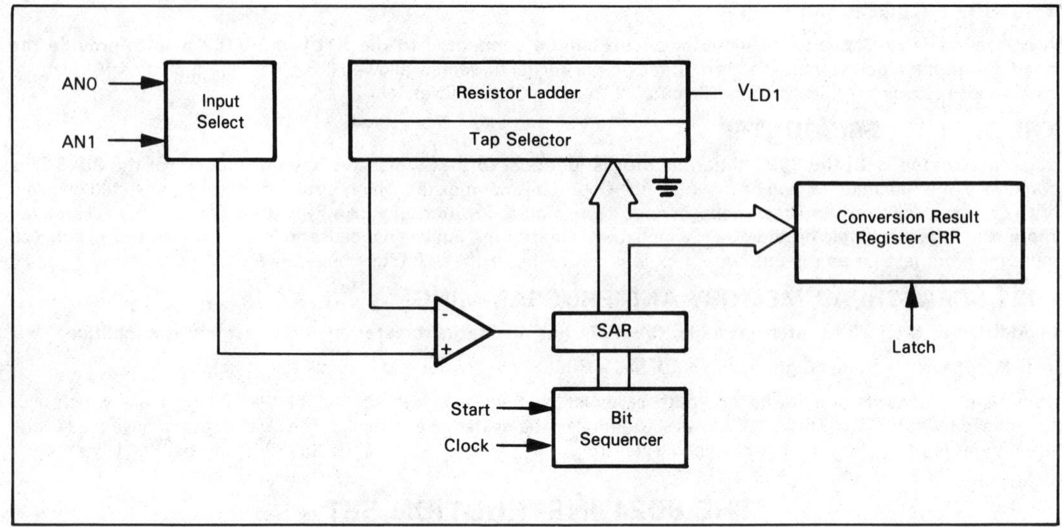


Figure 6-18a. 8022 Analog-to-Digital Converter

## 8022 PORT 0 TOUCH PANEL INPUT

**Capacitive touch panels are becoming widely used as input devices to microcomputers. The basic principle behind the touch panel is that a human finger is placed across two plates of a capacitor, causing the capacitor to be discharged to ground.** Two capacitors in series form the touch panel switch. One lead is attached to a high-voltage driver and the other lead is attached to one of the Port 0 input pins. The voltage spike produced by the capacitor's discharge is used to signal that a "key" has been pressed. **The input circuitry on Port 0 has a voltage comparator on each input line. Each comparator compares the voltage present on its associated input line with that of a common threshold reference. the voltage gain of each comparator is sufficient to sense a 100 mV input differential.** Pull-up resistors may be placed on any or all of the pins of Port 0 as a mask option. In order for the touch panel to operate correctly, the Port 0 outputs are open drain. Port 0 line transceiver circuitry is shown below:

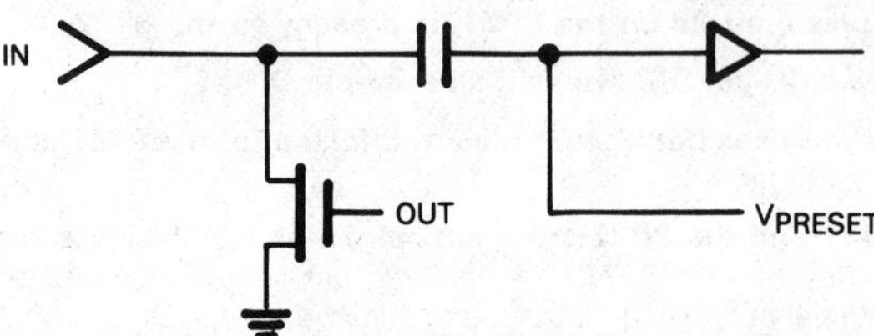


**When programming the touch panel, the Port 0 pins must first be set to all 0s to set the capacitors at ground level. Then the Port 0 pins should be set to 1s to float the pins so they can be pulled low by the comparators.** Slow moving noise, such as AC ripple, is rejected by initializing the capacitors each time Port 0 is accessed.

## 8022 PINS AND SIGNALS

**8022 PINS AND SIGNALS**

**This section will discuss only those signals which are unique to the 8022.** These pins are related to the A/D and touch panel capabilities of the 8022. Figure 6-18b illustrates the pinouts of the 8022.

$V_{TH}$ is the threshold voltage to which all pins of Port 0 are compared.

SUBSTRATE is a pin to which a substrate bypass capacitor is connected.

$AV_{SS}$ is the A/D ground potential pin. This allows ground for the A/D converter to be at a different potential from that of the 8022 ground.

$AV_{CC}$ is the supply voltage to the A/D converter. It is nominally +5V.

**$V_{LD1}$ is the resistor ladder reference voltage.** This is usually a regulated +5V.

**AN0 and AN1 are the two analog inputs to the A/D converter.** They are selected by the SEL AN0 and SEL AN1 instructions.

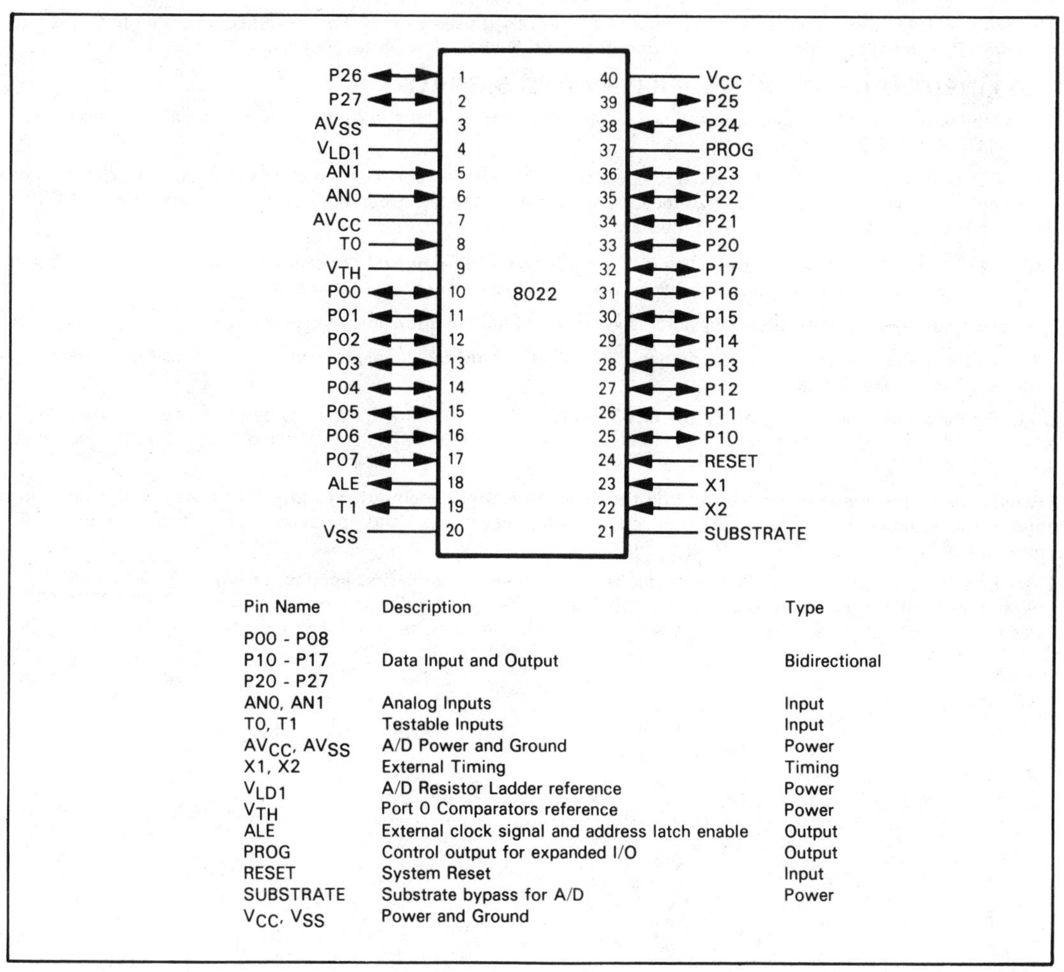


| Pin Name | Description | Type |
|---|---|---|
| P00 - P08<br>P10 - P17<br>P20 - P27 | Data Input and Output | Bidirectional |
| AN0, AN1 | Analog Inputs | Input |
| T0, T1 | Testable Inputs | Input |
| $AV_{CC}$, $AV_{SS}$ | A/D Power and Ground | Power |
| X1, X2 | External Timing | Timing |
| $V_{LD1}$ | A/D Resistor Ladder reference | Power |
| $V_{TH}$ | Port 0 Comparators reference | Power |
| ALE | External clock signal and address latch enable | Output |
| PROG | Control output for expanded I/O | Output |
| RESET | System Reset | Input |
| SUBSTRATE | Substrate bypass for A/D | Power |
| $V_{CC}$, $V_{SS}$ | Power and Ground | |

Figure 6-18b. 8022 Signals and Pin Assignments

# THE 8243 INPUT/OUTPUT EXPANDER

This support device expands I/O Port 2 of an 8041 or 8048 series microcomputer to four individually addressable 4-bit I/O ports. The 8243 Input/Output Expander is particularly useful in numerical applications where data is transferred in 4-bit nibbles.

Figure 6-19 illustrates that part of our general microcomputer system logic which has been implemented on the 8243 Input/Output Expander.

The 8243 Input/Output Expander is packaged as a 24-pin DIP. It uses a single +5V power supply. All inputs and outputs are TTL-compatible. The device is implemented using N-channel MOS technology.

## 8243 INPUT/OUTPUT EXPANDER PINS AND SIGNALS

The 8243 Input/Output Expander pins and signals are illustrated in Figure 6-20. Functional internal architecture is illustrated in Figure 6-21.

P20 - P23 represent the 4-bit bidirectional I/O port or bus connection between the 8243 Input/Output Expander and the 8048 series microcomputer. P20 - P23 must be connected to the low-order four pins of the microcomputer I/O Port 2. Figure 6-22 illustrates the 8243-8048 interface.

**P40 - P43, P50 - P53, P60 - P63 and P70 - P73 provide four bidirectional I/O ports,** referred to as Ports 4, 5, 6 and 7, respectively. These are 4-bit ports via which data is transferred to or from external logic.

Data being output via one of these four ports is latched and held in a low impedance state.

Data input is buffered. During a read operation 8243 I/O port pins are sampled — while the read is being executed; then I/O port pins are floated.

**$\overline{CS}$ is the single chip select signal for the 8243 device.** $\overline{CS}$ must be low for the device to be selected. There is no specifically defined manner in which $\overline{CS}$ has to be created; in Figure 6-22 it is shown being decoded off the four high-order pins of I/O Port 2.

**PROG is the single control strobe output by the 8048 series microcomputer to time 8243 events.** On the falling edge of PROG, data input via P20 - P23 is decoded as an I/O port select and operation specification. Resulting 8243 operations are strobed by the rising edge of PROG.

**8243 RESET**

There is no Reset input to the 8243. **The device is reset when power is first applied, or when power input at the $V_{CC}$ pin drops below +1 volt.** Following Reset, Port 2 is in Input mode while Ports 4, 5, 6 and 7 are floated. The 8243 device will exit the Reset mode on the first high-to-low transition of PROG.

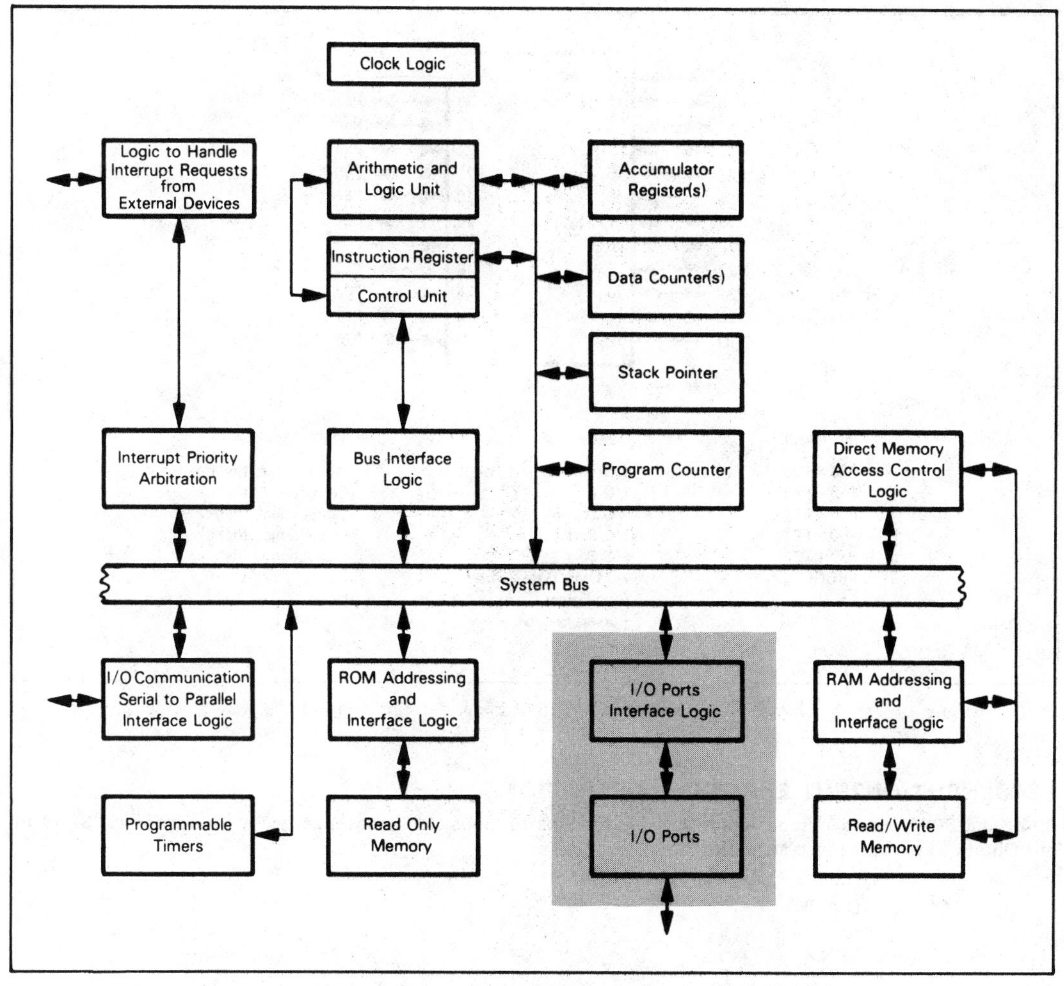


Figure 6-19. Logic of the 8243 Input/Output Expander

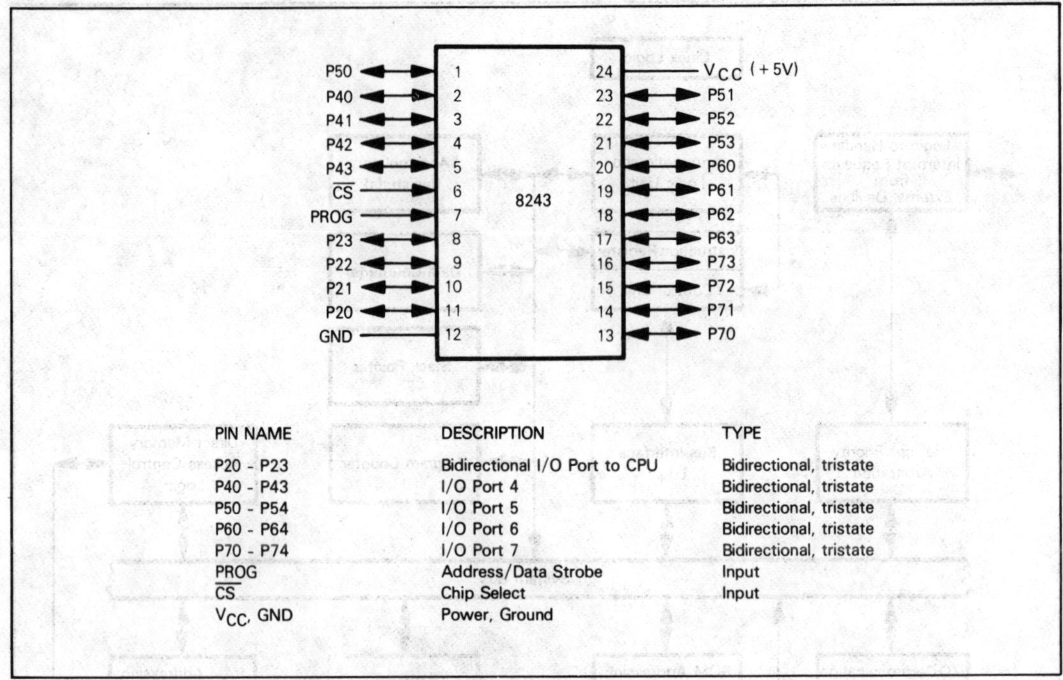


| PIN NAME | DESCRIPTION | TYPE |
|---|---|---|
| P20 - P23 | Bidirectional I/O Port to CPU | Bidirectional, tristate |
| P40 - P43 | I/O Port 4 | Bidirectional, tristate |
| P50 - P54 | I/O Port 5 | Bidirectional, tristate |
| P60 - P64 | I/O Port 6 | Bidirectional, tristate |
| P70 - P74 | I/O Port 7 | Bidirectional, tristate |
| $\overline{PROG}$ | Address/Data Strobe | Input |
| $\overline{CS}$ | Chip Select | Input |
| $V_{CC}$, GND | Power, Ground | |

Figure 6-20. 8243 Input/Output Expander Pins and Signals

## 8243 INPUT/OUTPUT EXPANDER OPERATIONS

**8048 and 8041 series microcomputers have four instructions designed specifically to access an 8243 Input/Output Expander.** These instructions are:

```
MOVD PN,A
MOVD A,PN
ORLD PN,A
ANLD PN,A
```

**These are the operations performed:**

1) **You can output the low-order four Accumulator bits** to I/O Expander Port 4, 5, 6 or 7. Following a write operation the four port lines are held in a low impedance state. External logic does not receive any type of "data ready" signal after data has been output; however, as illustrated in Figure 6-22, you can easily create such a signal by combining PROG and device select logic.

2) **You can input data from Port 4, 5, 6 or 7** of the 8243 device to the four low-order Accumulator bits. Again Figure 6-22 shows how you can create a strobe signal which tells external logic when to apply data to an I/O port of the 8243 device.

3) **You can** output data from the low-order four Accumulator bits to one of the four 8243 device ports, but instead of simply writing to the port, you can **AND or OR with data already in the port output latch.** That is to say, you perform a Boolean operation between the four low-order Accumulator bits and the data most recently output to the 8243 port.

**You cannot perform a Boolean operation between the low-order four Accumulator bits and data input to an 8243 port;** the input data is buffered, not latched. You must read the input data to the Accumulator and mask it there.

**8243 device Ports 4, 5, 6 and 7 have been designed to operate continuously as input ports or output ports. If you switch a port from input to output, or from output to input, then the first 4-bit data unit written or read will be erroneous and should be discarded.**

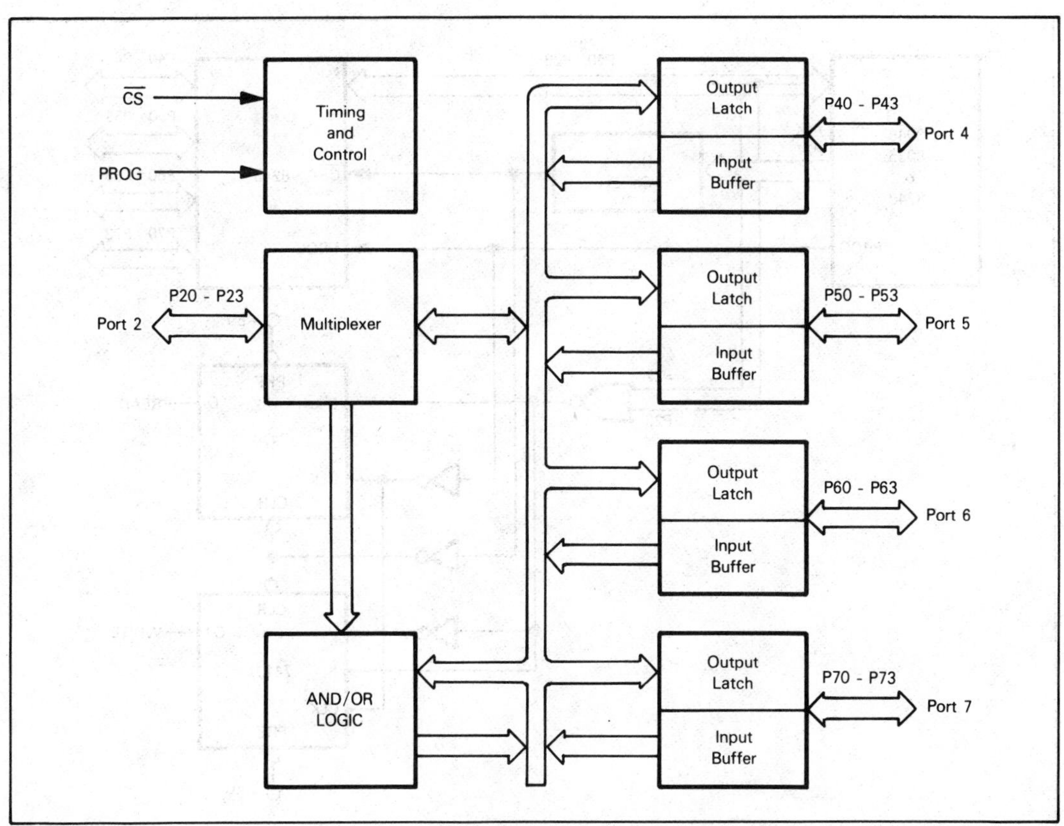


Figure 6-21. Functional Diagram of the 8243 Input/Output Expander

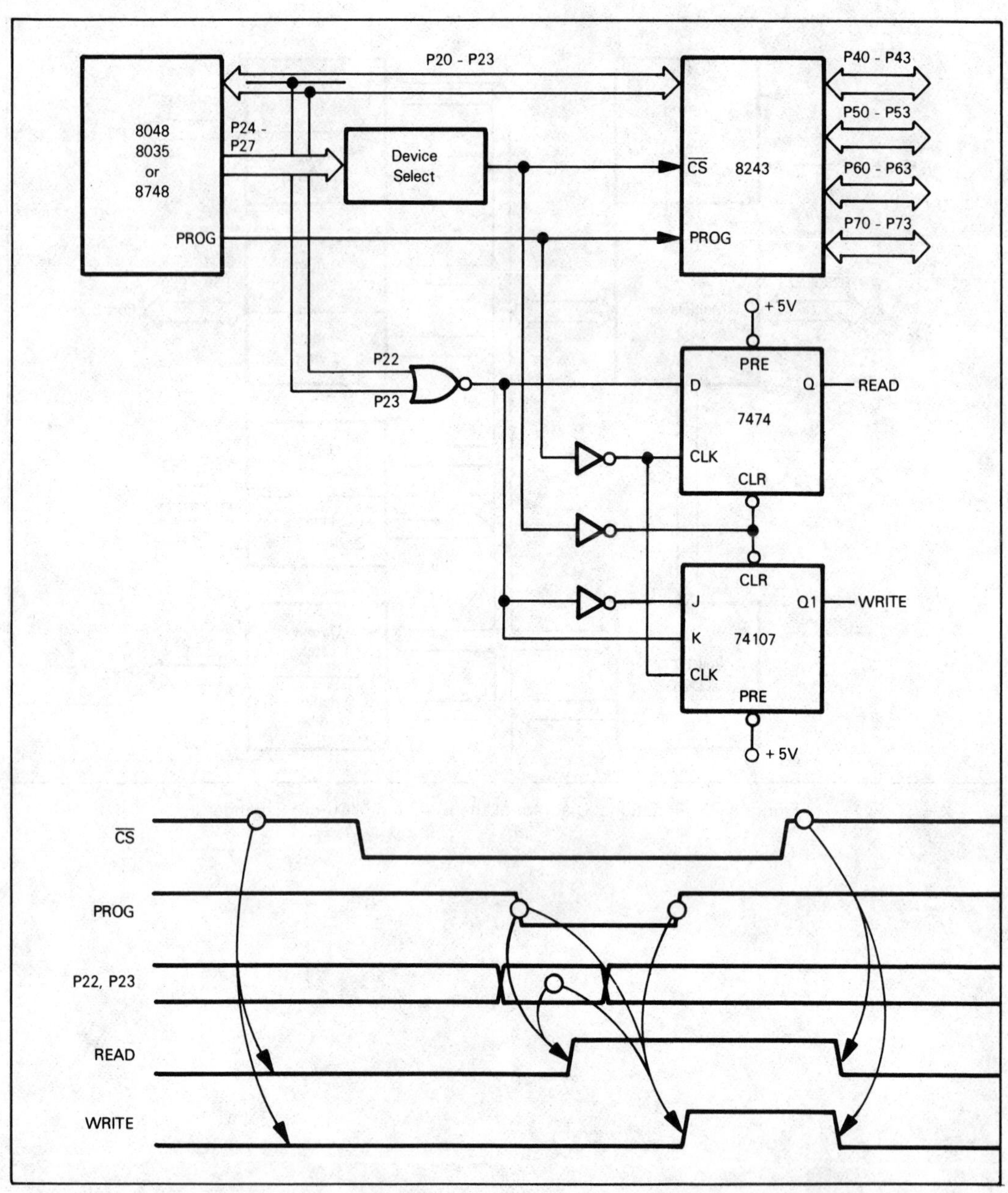


Figure 6-22. An 8243/8048 Configuration with External Logic Read and Write Strobes

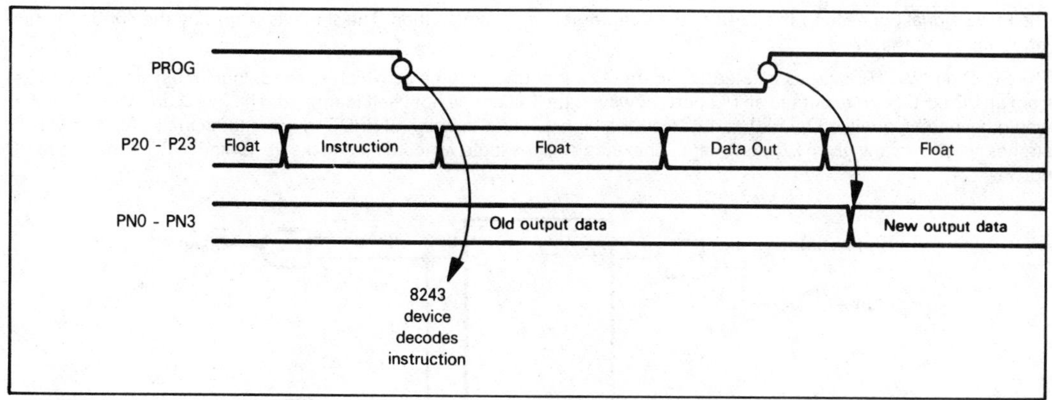


Figure 6-23. Timing for Data Output to an 8243 Port Via an MOVD, ORLD or ANLD Instruction

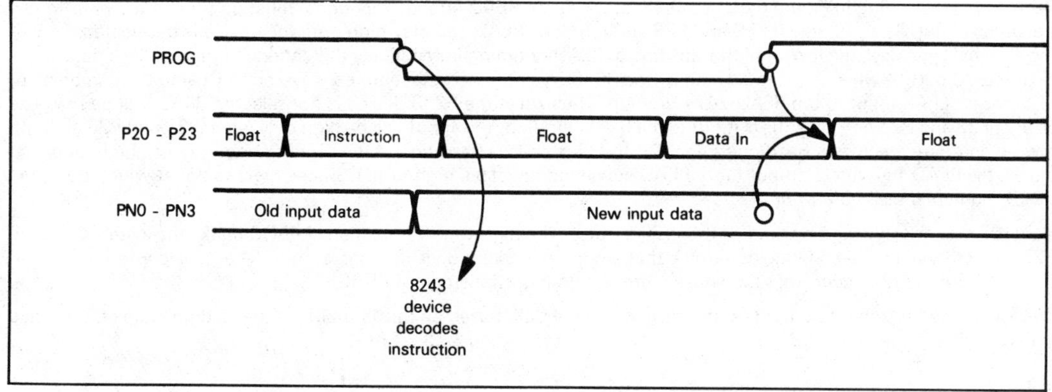


Figure 6-24. Timing for Data Input from an 8243 Port

**Timing for 8243 port accesses is illustrated in Figures 6-23 and 6-24.**

**In each case an instruction is output via P20 - P23 of the 8048 microcomputer on the high-to-low transition of PROG. The instruction is decoded as follows:**

| P20 | P21 | 8243 Port Selected | P22 | P23 | Function Defined |
|---|---|---|---|---|---|
| 0 | 0 | Port 4 | 0 | 0 | Read from Port |
| 0 | 1 | Port 5 | 0 | 1 | Write to Port |
| 1 | 0 | Port 6 | 1 | 0 | OR with Port |
| 1 | 1 | Port 7 | 1 | 1 | AND with Port |

**The actual I/O operation within the 8243 device is strobed by the subsequent low-to-high transition of PROG.**

Observe that external logic must transmit data to an 8243 I/O port on the high-to-low transition of PROG. External logic must read data output after the low-to-high transition of PROG. These **signals to external logic are shown in Figure 6-22. Let us take a more careful look at this figure.**

The 8243 device select $\overline{CS}$ is derived in some fashion from the four high-order lines of the 8048 I/O Port 2. The manner in which we decode $\overline{CS}$ from these four lines is not relevant; however, the fact that we are generating $\overline{CS}$ in this fashion means that any 8243 access instruction must be bracketed by instructions that select and then deselect the 8243 device.

It is not a good idea to leave the 8243 device selected when you are not accessing it; therefore do not leave high-order bits of I/O Port 2 in a condition that would select the 8243 device while the device is supposed to be idle.

The PROG signal connecting the 8048 to the 8243 requires no explanation. The signal is output by the 8048 with timing required by the 8243.

The READ and WRITE strobes created in Figure 6-22 identify the time at which external logic must either read data from an I/O port, or write data to an I/O port; however, the I/O port is not itself identified. The READ and WRITE strobes would have to be qualified by P20 and P21 on the high-to-low transition of PROG in order to create READ and WRITE strobes specific to any given I/O port. Here, for example, is the logic which would make READ and WRITE specific to I/O Port 5:

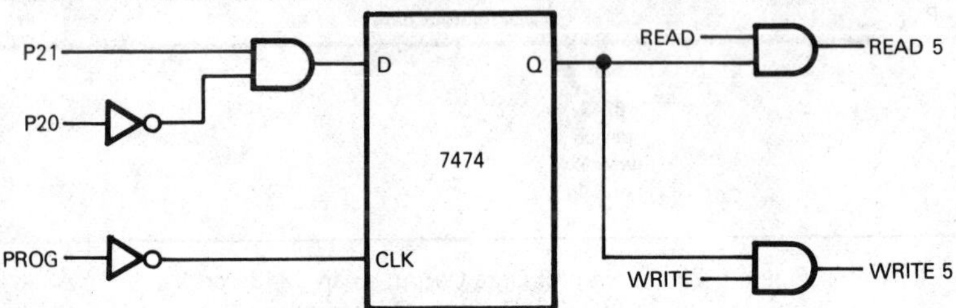


Referring to the timing in Figure 6-22, let us first look at the READ strobe. This signal must go true on the high-to-low transition of PROG — but only if P22 and P23 are both low. READ can stay high until the device is deselected, providing external logic uses the low-to-high transition of READ or timing immediately thereafter, in order to place data at the required I/O port — whence it can be read by the 8048. We obtained the required waveform by using the complement of $\overline{\text{CS}}$ as a CLEAR input to the READ 7474 flip-flop. Thus while the 8243 device is not selected READ will be low. The NOR of P22 and P23 becomes the D input to the READ flip-flop; this input will be high only when P22 and P23 are both low — and that specifies a Read operation. On the high-to-low transition of PROG, $\overline{\text{PROG}}$ goes low-to-high, and that clocks the READ flip-flop Q output high. READ subsequently stays high until $\overline{\text{CS}}$ goes high again, at which point the READ flip-flop is cleared and READ goes low.

A 74107 master-slave flip-flop creates the WRITE pulse. The high-to-low transition of PROG marks the instant at which P22 and P23 must be decoded to determine that a non-read operation is in progress, but the actual low-to-high transition WRITE must not occur until the subsequent low-to-high transition of PROG.

The 74107 modifies the Q1 output on the trailing edge of CLK, based on the JK inputs at the leading edge of CLK; thus WRITE logic requirements are met.

# DATA SHEETS

This section contains specific electrical and timing data for the following devices:

- 8048/8748/8035 } One-Chip Microcomputers
- 8049/8039 } One-Chip Microcomputers
- 8041A/8641A/8741A } One-Chip Microcomputers
- 8021/8022 } One-Chip Microcomputers
- 8243 I/O Expander

## ABSOLUTE MAXIMUM RATINGS*

Ambient Temperature Under Bias ........... 0°C to 70°C
Storage Temperature .................... -65°C to + 125°C
Voltage On Any Pin With Respect
to Ground ............................. -0.5V to +7V
Power Dissipation .............................. 1.5 Watt

*COMMENT: *Stresses above those listed under "Absolute Maximum Ratings" may cause permanent damage to the device. This is a stress rating only and functional operation of the device at these or any other conditions above those indicated in the operational sections of this specification is not implied.*

## D.C. AND OPERATING CHARACTERISTICS ($T_A$ = 0°C to 55°C for 8748-6)

| Symbol | Parameter | Limits | | | Unit | Test Conditions |
|---|---|---|---|---|---|---|
| | | Min. | Typ. | Max. | | |
| $V_{IL}$ | Input Low Voltage (All Except $\overline{RESET}$, X1, X2) | −.5 | | .8 | V | |
| $V_{IL1}$ | Input Low Voltage ($\overline{RESET}$, X1, X2) | −.5 | | .6 | V | |
| $V_{IH}$ | Input High Voltage (All Except XTAL1, XTAL 2, $\overline{RESET}$) | 2.0 | | $V_{CC}$ | V | |
| $V_{IH1}$ | Input High Voltage (X1, X2, $\overline{RESET}$) | 3.8 | | $V_{CC}$ | V | |
| $V_{OL}$ | Output Low Voltage (BUS) | | | .45 | V | $V_{OL}$ = 2.0 mA |
| $V_{OL1}$ | Output Low Voltage ($\overline{RD}$, $\overline{WR}$, $\overline{PSEN}$, ALE) | | | .45 | V | $I_{OL}$ = 1.8 mA |
| $V_{OL2}$ | Output Low Voltage (PROG) | | | .45 | V | $I_{OL}$ = 1.0 mA |
| $V_{OL3}$ | Output Low Voltage (All Other Outputs) | | | .45 | V | $I_{OL}$ = 1.6 mA |
| $V_{OH}$ | Output High Voltage (BUS) | 2.4 | | | V | $I_{OH}$ = −400 μA |
| $V_{OH1}$ | Output High Voltage ($\overline{RD}$, $\overline{WR}$, $\overline{PSEN}$, ALE) | 2.4 | | | V | $I_{OH}$ = −100 μA |
| $V_{OH2}$ | Output High Voltage (All Other Outputs) | 2.4 | | | V | $I_{OH}$ = −40 μA |
| $I_{LI}$ | Input Leakage Current (T1, $\overline{INT}$) | | | ±10 | μA | $V_{SS} \leq V_{IN} \leq V_{CC}$ |
| $I_{LI1}$ | Input Leakage Current (P10-P17, P20-P27, EA, $\overline{SS}$) | | | −500 | μA | $V_{SS} + .45 \leq V_{IN} \leq V_{CC}$ |
| $I_{LO}$ | Output Leakage Current (BUS, TO) (High Impedance State) | | | ±10 | μA | $V_{SS} + .45 \leq V_{IN} \leq V_{CC}$ |
| $I_{DD}$ | $V_{DD}$ Supply Current | | 5 | 15 | mA | |
| $I_{DD} + I_{CC}$ | Total Supply Current | | 60 | 135 | mA | |

**BUS**

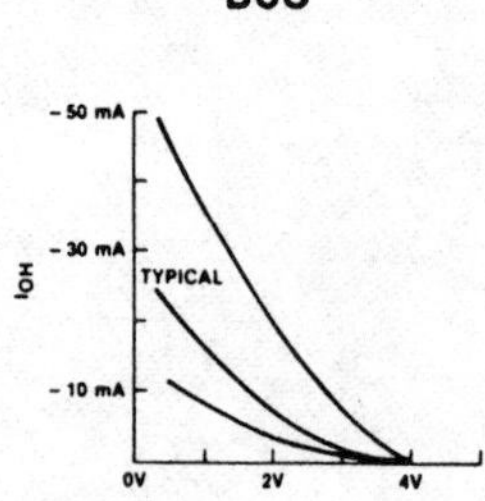


**P1, P2**

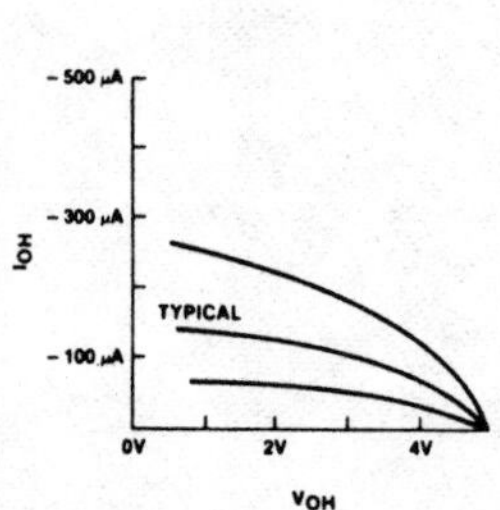


**BUS, P1, P2**

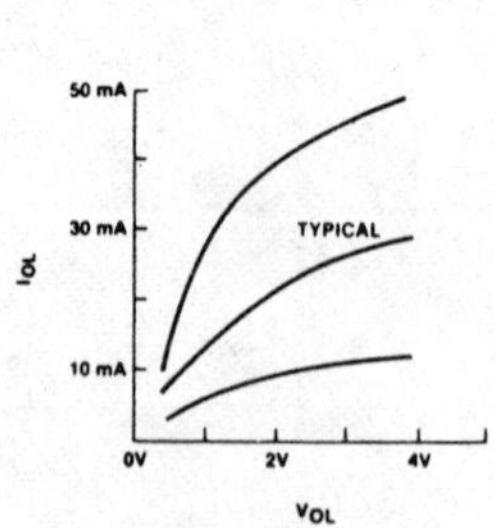


**Data sheets on pages 6-D2 through 6-D22 are reprinted by permission of Intel Corporation.**

## WAVEFORMS

**Instruction Fetch From External Program Memory**

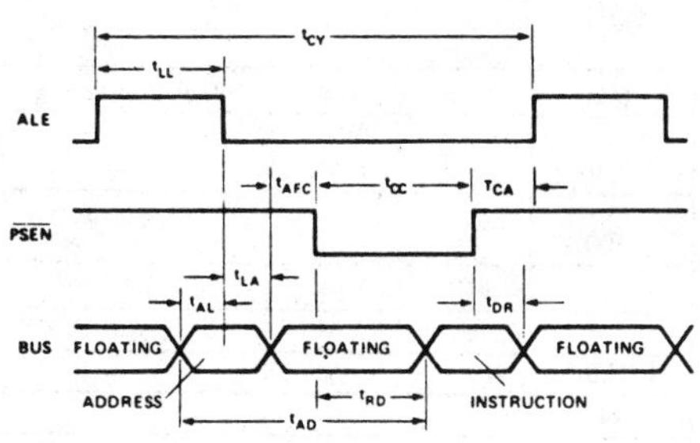


**Read From External Data Memory**

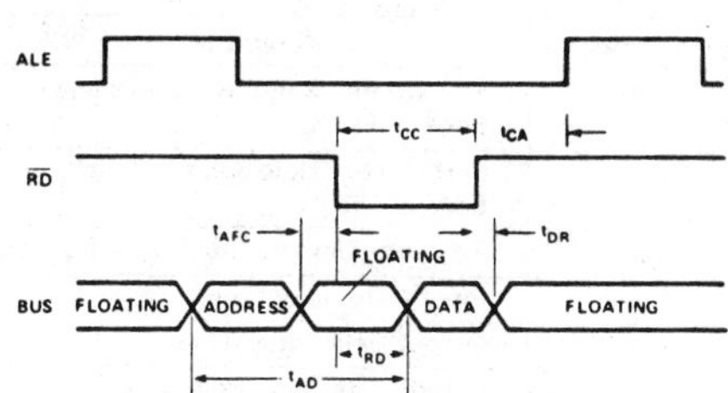


**Write to External Data Memory**

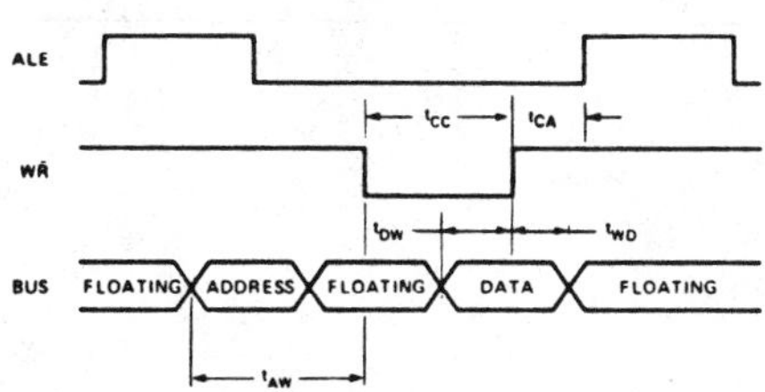


**Input and Output Waveforms for A.C. Tests**

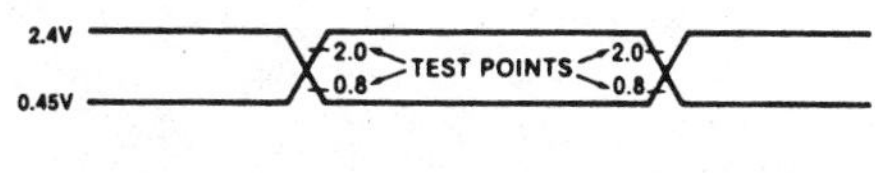


## A.C. CHARACTERISTICS $T_A = 0°C$ to $70°C^*$, $V_{CC} = V_{DD} = +5V \pm 10\%$, $V_{SS} = 0V$

| Symbol | Parameter | 8048 8748-6 8748/8035/8035L | | 8748-8** 8035-8 | | Unit | Conditions (Note 1) |
|---|---|---|---|---|---|---|---|
| | | Min. | Max. | Min. | Max. | | |
| $t_{LL}$ | ALE Pulse Width | 400 | | 600 | | ns | |
| $t_{AL}$ | Address Setup to ALE | 120 | | 150 | | ns | |
| $t_{LA}$ | Address Hold from ALE | 80 | | 80 | | ns | |
| $t_{CC}$ | Control Pulse Width ($\overline{PSEN}$, $\overline{RD}$, $\overline{WR}$) | 700 | | 1500 | | ns | |
| $t_{DW}$ | Data Setup before $\overline{WR}$ | 500 | | 640 | | ns | |
| $t_{WD}$ | Data Hold After $\overline{WR}$ | 120 | | 120 | | ns | $C_L = 20pF$ |
| $t_{CY}$ | Cycle Time | 2.5 | 15.0 | 4.17 | 15.0 | μs | 6 MHz XTAL = 2.5 (3.6 MHz XTAL for −8) |
| $t_{DR}$ | Data Hold | 0 | 200 | 0 | 200 | ns | |
| $t_{RD}$ | $\overline{PSEN}$, $\overline{RD}$ to Data In | | 500 | | 750 | ns | |
| $t_{AW}$ | Address Setup to $\overline{WR}$ | 230 | | 260 | | ns | |
| $t_{AD}$ | Address Setup to Data In | | 950 | | 1450 | ns | |
| $t_{AFC}$ | Address Float to $\overline{RD}$, $\overline{PSEN}$ | 0 | | 0 | | ns | |
| $t_{CA}$ | Control Pulse to ALE | 10 | | 20 | | ns | |

Note 1: Control outputs: $C_L = 80$ pF $t_{CY} = 2.5$ μs for standard parts
BUS Outputs: $C_L = 150$ pF $= 4.17$ μs for -8 parts

*$T_A = 0°C$ to $55°C$ for 8748-6
**$V_{CC}$ and $V_{DD}$ for 8748-8 and 8035-8 are ±5%

## A.C. CHARACTERISTICS (PORT 2 TIMING)

$T_A = 0°C$ to $70°C$, $V_{CC} = 5V \pm 10\%$, $V_{SS} = 0V$
($T_A = 0°C$ to $55°C$ for 8748-6)

| Symbol | Parameter | Min. | Max. | Unit | Test Conditions |
|---|---|---|---|---|---|
| $t_{CP}$ | Port Control Setup Before Falling Edge of PROG | 110 | | ns | |
| $t_{PC}$ | Port Control Hold After Falling Edge of PROG | 100 | | ns | |
| $t_{PR}$ | PROG to Time P2 Input Must Be Valid | | 810 | ns | |
| $t_{PF}$ | Input Data Hold Time | 0 | 150 | ns | |
| $t_{DP}$ | Output Data Setup Time | 250 | | ns | |
| $t_{PD}$ | Output Data Hold Time | 65 | | ns | |
| $t_{PP}$ | PROG Pulse Width | 1200 | | ns | |
| $t_{PL}$ | Port 2 I/O Data Setup | 350 | | ns | |
| $t_{LP}$ | Port 2 I/O Data Hold | 150 | | ns | |

**PORT 2 TIMING**

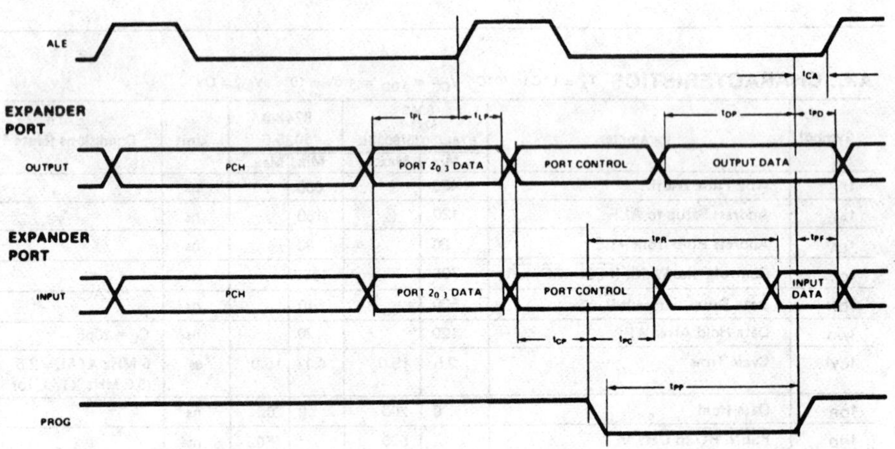

## AC TIMING SPECIFICATION FOR PROGRAMMING

$T_A = 25°C \pm 5°C$, $V_{CC} = 5V \pm 5\%$, $V_{DD} = 25V \pm 1V$

| Symbol | Parameter | Min. | Max. | Unit | Test Conditions |
|---|---|---|---|---|---|
| $t_{AW}$ | Address Setup Time to $\overline{RESET}$ ↑ | $4t_{CY}$ | | | |
| $t_{WA}$ | Address Hold Time After $\overline{RESET}$ ↑ | $4t_{CY}$ | | | |
| $t_{DW}$ | Data in Setup Time to PROG ↑ | $4t_{CY}$ | | | |
| $t_{WD}$ | Data in Hold Time After PROG ↓ | $4t_{CY}$ | | | |
| $t_{PH}$ | $\overline{RESET}$ Hold Time to Verify | $4t_{CY}$ | | | |
| $t_{VDDW}$ | $V_{DD}$ | $4t_{CY}$ | | | |
| $t_{VDDH}$ | $V_{DD}$ Hold Time After PROG ↓ | 0 | | | |
| $t_{PW}$ | Program Pulse Width | 50 | 60 | mS | |
| $t_{TW}$ | Test 0 Setup Time for Program Mode | $4t_{CY}$ | | | |
| $t_{WT}$ | Test 0 Hold Time After Program Mode | $4t_{CY}$ | | | |
| $t_{DO}$ | Test 0 to Data Out Delay | | $4t_{CY}$ | | |
| $t_{WW}$ | $\overline{RESET}$ Pulse Width to Latch Address | $4t_{CY}$ | | | |
| $t_r$, $t_f$ | $V_{DD}$ and PROG Rise and Fall Times | 0.5 | 2.0 | $\mu s$ | |
| $t_{CY}$ | CPU Operation Cycle Time | 5.0 | | $\mu s$ | |
| $t_{RE}$ | $\overline{RESET}$ Setup Time Before EA ↑. | $4t_{CY}$ | | | |

Note: If Test 0 is high $t_{DO}$ can be triggered by $\overline{RESET}$ ↑.

## DC SPECIFICATION FOR PROGRAMMING

$T_A = 25°C \pm 5°C$, $V_{CC} = 5V \pm 5\%$, $V_{DD} = 25V \pm 1V$

| Symbol | Parameter | Min. | Max. | Unit | Test Conditions |
|---|---|---|---|---|---|
| $V_{DOH}$ | $V_{DD}$ Program Voltage High Level | 24.0 | 26.0 | V | |
| $V_{DDL}$ | $V_{DD}$ Voltage Low Level | 4.75 | 5.25 | V | |
| $V_{PH}$ | PROG Program Voltage High Level | 21.5 | 24.5 | V | |
| $V_{PL}$ | PROG Voltage Low Level | | 0.2 | V | |
| $V_{EAH}$ | EA Program or Verify Voltage High Level | 21.5 | 24.5 | V | 8748 |
| $V_{EAH1}$ | EA1 Verify Voltage High Level | 11.4 | 12.6 | V | 8048 |
| $V_{EAL}$ | EA Voltage Low Level | | 5.25 | V | |
| $I_{DD}$ | $V_{DD}$ High Voltage Supply Current | | 30.0 | mA | |
| $I_{PROG}$ | PROG High Voltage Supply Current | | 16.0 | mA | |
| $I_{EA}$ | EA High Voltage Supply Current | | 1.0 | mA | |

## WAVEFORMS FOR PROGRAMMING

COMBINATION PROGRAM/VERIFY MODE (EPROM'S ONLY)

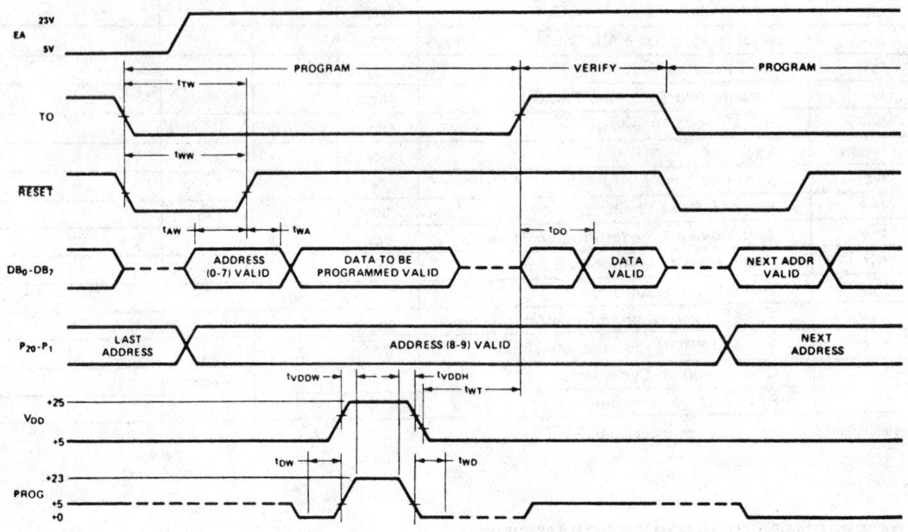


VERIFY MODE (ROM/EPROM)

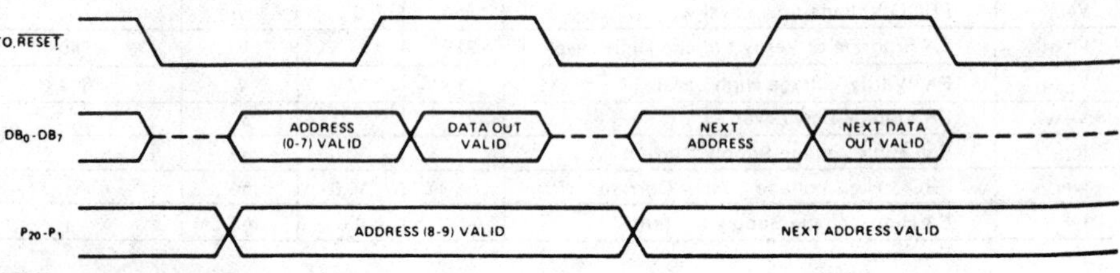


NOTES:

1. PROG MUST FLOAT IF EA IS LOW (i.e., ≠23V), OR IF T0 = 5V FOR THE 8748. FOR THE 8048 PROG MUST ALWAYS FLOAT.
2. $X_1$ AND $X_2$ DRIVEN BY 3 MHz CLOCK WILL GIVE 5μsec $t_{CY}$. THIS IS ACCEPTABLE FOR -8 PARTS AS WELL AS STANDARD PARTS.

The 8748 EPROM can be programmed by either of two Intel products:

1. PROMPT-48 Microcomputer Design Aid, or
2. Universal PROM Programmer (UPP series) peripheral of the Intellec® Development System with a UPP-848 Personality Card.

Note: See the ROM/PROM section for 8048 ROM ordering procedures. To minimize turnaround time on the first 25 pieces 8648 may be specified on the ROM order

## ABSOLUTE MAXIMUM RATINGS*

Ambient Temperature Under Bias ........ 0°C to 70°C
Storage Temperature ............... -65°C to +150°C
Voltage on Any Pin With
Respect to Ground ...................... -0.5V to +7V
Power Dissipation .......................... 1.5 Watt

**COMMENT:* *Stresses above those listed under "Absolute Maximum Ratings" may cause permanent damage to the device. This is a stress rating only and functional operation of the device at these or any other conditions above those indicated in the operational sections of this specification is not implied. Exposure to absolute maximum rating conditions for extended periods may affect device reliability.*

## D.C. AND OPERATING CHARACTERISTICS $T_A$ = 0°C to 70°C, $V_{CC}$ = $V_{DD}$ = +5V ±10%, $V_{SS}$ = 0V

| Symbol | Parameter | Limits Min. | Limits Typ. | Limits Max. | Unit | Test Conditions |
|---|---|---|---|---|---|---|
| $V_{IL}$ | Input Low Voltage | -0.5 | | 0.8 | V | |
| $V_{IH}$ | Input High Voltage (All Except XTAL1, XTAL2, $\overline{RESET}$) | 2.0 | | $V_{CC}$ | V | |
| $V_{IH1}$ | Input High Voltage ($\overline{RESET}$, X1, X2) | 3.8 | | $V_{CC}$ | V | |
| $V_{OL}$ | Output Low Voltage (BUS, $\overline{RD}$, $\overline{WR}$, $\overline{PSEN}$, ALE) | | | 0.45 | V | $I_{OL}$ = 2.0mA |
| $V_{OL1}$ | Output Low Voltage (All Other Outputs Except PROG) | | | 0.45 | V | $I_{OL}$ = 1.6mA |
| $V_{OL2}$ | Output Low Voltage (PROG) | | | 0.45 | V | $I_{OL}$ = 1.0mA |
| $V_{OH}$ | Output High Voltage (BUS, $\overline{RD}$, $\overline{WR}$, $\overline{PSEN}$, ALE) | 2.4 | | | V | $I_{OH}$ = -100μA |
| $V_{OH1}$ | Output High Voltage (All Other Outputs) | 2.4 | | | V | $I_{OH}$ = -50μA |
| $I_{IL}$ | Input Leakage Current (T1, $\overline{INT}$) | | | ±10 | μA | $V_{SS} \leq V_{IN} \leq V_{CC}$ |
| $I_{OL}$ | Output Leakage Current (Bus, T0) (High Impedance State) | | | ±10 | μA | $V_{SS} + 0.45 \leq V_{IN} \leq V_{CC}$ |
| $I_{DD}$ | Power Down Supply Current | | 25 | 50 | mA | $T_A$ = 25°C |
| $I_{DD}+I_{CC}$ | Total Supply Current | | 100 | 170 | mA | $T_A$ = 25°C |

## A.C. CHARACTERISTICS $T_A$ = 0°C to 70°C, $V_{CC}$ = $V_{DD}$ = +5V ±10%, $V_{SS}$ = 0V

| Symbol | Parameter | 8049/8039 (Note 1) Min. | 8049/8039 (Note 1) Max. | 8039-6 Min. | 8039-6 Max. | Unit | Conditions (Note 2) |
|---|---|---|---|---|---|---|---|
| $t_{LL}$ | ALE Pulse Width | 150 | | 400 | | ns | |
| $t_{AL}$ | Address Setup to ALE | 70 | | 150 | | ns | |
| $t_{LA}$ | Address Hold from ALE | 50 | | 80 | | ns | |
| $t_{CC}$ | Control Pulse Width (PSEN, RD, WR) | 300 | | 700 | | ns | |
| $t_{DW}$ | Data Set-Up Before WR | 250 | | 500 | | ns | |
| $t_{WD}$ | Data Hold After WR | 40 | | 120 | | ns | $C_L$ = 20pF |
| $t_{CY}$ | Cycle Time | 1.36 | 15.0 | 2.5 | 15.0 | μs | 11MHz XTAL (6MHz XTAL for -6) |
| $t_{DR}$ | Data Hold | 0 | 100 | 0 | 200 | ns | |
| $t_{RD}$ | PSEN, RD to Data In | | 200 | | 500 | ns | |
| $t_{AW}$ | Address Setup to WR | 200 | | 230 | | ns | |
| $t_{AD}$ | Address Setup to Data In | | 400 | | 950 | ns | |
| $t_{AFC}$ | Address Float to RD, PSEN | -10 | | 0 | | ns | |

**Notes:** 1. 8039-6 specifications are also valid for 8049/8039 operating at 6MHz.
2. Control Outputs: $C_L$ = 80pF
BUS Outputs: $C_L$ = 150pF

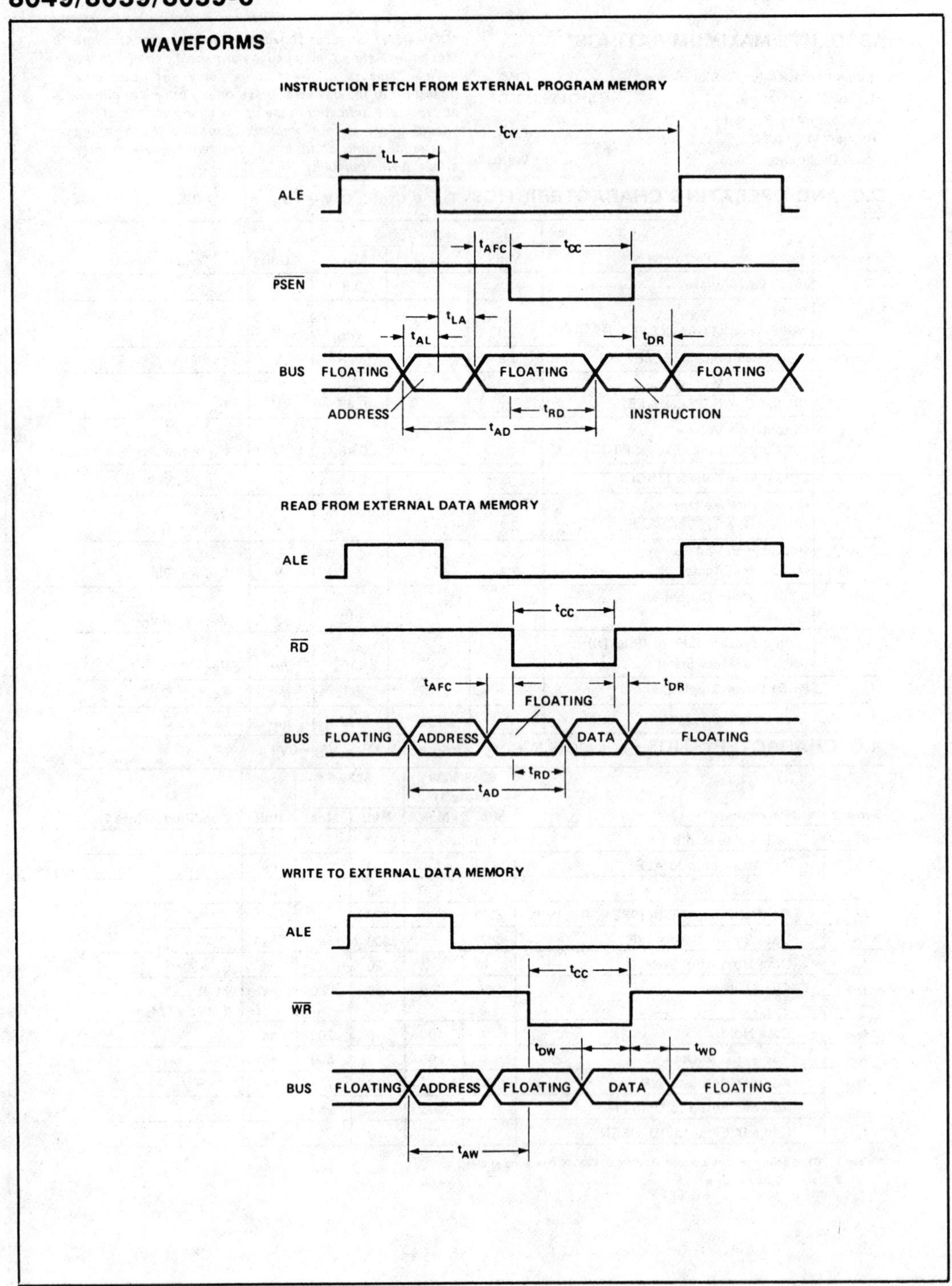
WAVEFORMS
INSTRUCTION FETCH FROM EXTERNAL PROGRAM MEMORY
tCY
tLL
ALE
tAFC
tCC
PSEN
tLA
tAL
tDR
BUS
FLOATING
FLOATING
FLOATING
ADDRESS
tRD
INSTRUCTION
tAD
READ FROM EXTERNAL DATA MEMORY
ALE
tCC
RD
tAFC
tDR
FLOATING
BUS
FLOATING
ADDRESS
DATA
FLOATING
tRD
tAD
WRITE TO EXTERNAL DATA MEMORY
ALE
tCC
WR
tDW
tWD
BUS
FLOATING
ADDRESS
FLOATING
DATA
FLOATING
tAW

## A.C. CHARACTERISTICS

$T_A = 0°C$ to $70°C$, $V_{CC} = 5V \pm 10\%$

| Symbol | Parameter | 8049/8039 Min. | 8049/8039 Max. | 8039-6 Min. | 8039-6 Max. | Unit | Conditions (Note 2) |
|---|---|---|---|---|---|---|---|
| $t_{CP}$ | Port Control Setup Before Falling Edge of PROG | 100 | | 110 | | ns | |
| $t_{PC}$ | Port Control Hold After Falling Edge of PROG | 60 | | 130 | | ns | |
| $t_{PR}$ | PROG to Time P2 Input Must Be Valid | | 650 | | 810 | ns | |
| $t_{DP}$ | Output Data Setup Time | 200 | | 220 | | ns | |
| $t_{PD}$ | Output Data Hold Time | 20 | | 65 | | ns | |
| $t_{PF}$ | Input Data Hold Time | 0 | 150 | 0 | 150 | ns | |
| $t_{PP}$ | PROG Pulse Width | 700 | | 1510 | | ns | |
| $t_{PL}$ | Port 2 I/O Data Setup | 300 | | 600 | | ns | |
| $t_{LP}$ | Port 2 I/O Data Hold | 120 | | 150 | | ns | |

## WAVEFORMS

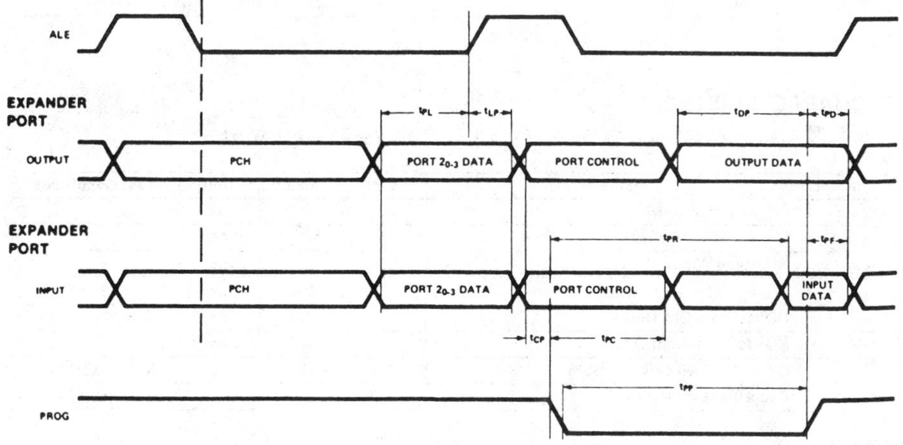

## ABSOLUTE MAXIMUM RATINGS*

Ambient Temperature Under Bias ..........0°C to 70°C
Storage Temperature ............... −65°C to +150°C
Voltage on Any Pin With Respect to Ground ............................0.5V to +7V
Power Dissipation ..........................1.5 Watt

*COMMENT: Stresses above those listed under "Absolute Maximum Ratings" may cause permanent damage to the device. This is a stress rating only and functional operation of the device at these or any other conditions above those indicated in the operational sections of this specification is not implied. Exposure to absolute maximum rating conditions for extended periods may affect device reliability.

## D.C. AND OPERATING CHARACTERISTICS

$T_A = 0°C$ to $70°C$, $V_{SS} = 0V$, 8041A: $V_{CC} = +5V \pm 10\%$, 8741A: $V_{CC} = +5V \pm 5\%$

| Symbol | Parameter | Min. | Max. | Unit | Test Conditions |
|---|---|---|---|---|---|
| $V_{IL}$ | Input Low Voltage (Except XTAL1, XTAL2, $\overline{RESET}$) | −0.5 | 0.8 | V | |
| $V_{IL1}$ | Input Low Voltage (XTAL1, XTAL2, $\overline{RESET}$) | −0.5 | 0.6 | V | |
| $V_{IH}$ | Input High Voltage (Except XTAL1, XTAL2, $\overline{RESET}$) | 2.2 | $V_{CC}$ | | |
| $V_{IH1}$ | Input High Voltage (XTAL1, XTAL2, $\overline{RESET}$) | 3.8 | $V_{CC}$ | V | |
| $V_{OL}$ | Output Low Voltage ($D_0$–$D_7$) | | 0.45 | V | $I_{OL} = 2.0$ mA |
| $V_{OL1}$ | Output Low Voltage ($P_{10}P_{17}$, $P_{20}P_{27}$, Sync) | | 0.45 | V | $I_{OL} = 1.6$ mA |
| $V_{OL2}$ | Output Low Voltage (Prog) | | 0.45 | V | $I_{OL} = 1.0$ mA |
| $V_{OH}$ | Output High Voltage ($D_0$–$D_7$) | 2.4 | | V | $I_{OH} = -400\ \mu A$ |
| $V_{OH1}$ | Output High Voltage (All Other Outputs) | 2.4 | | V | $I_{OH} = -50\ \mu A$ |
| $I_{IL}$ | Input Leakage Current ($T_0$, $T_1$, $\overline{RD}$, $\overline{WR}$, $\overline{CS}$, $A_0$, EA) | | ±10 | μA | $V_{SS} \leq V_{IN} \leq V_{CC}$ |
| $I_{OZ}$ | Output Leakage Current ($D_0$–$D_7$, High Z State) | | ±10 | μA | $V_{SS} + 0.45 \leq V_{IN} \leq V_{CC}$ |
| $I_{LI}$ | Low Input Load Current ($P_{10}P_{17}$, $P_{20}P_{27}$) | | 0.5 | mA | $V_{IL} = 0.8V$ |
| $I_{LI1}$ | Low Input Load Current ($\overline{RESET}$, $\overline{SS}$) | | 0.2 | mA | $V_{IL} = 0.8V$ |
| $I_{DD}$ | $V_{DD}$ Supply Current | | 15 | mA | Typical = 5 mA |
| $I_{CC} + I_{DD}$ | Total Supply Current | | 125 | mA | Typical = 60 mA |

## A.C. CHARACTERISTICS

$T_A = 0°C$ to $70°C$, $V_{SS} = 0V$, 8041A: $V_{CC} = V_{DD} = +5V \pm 10\%$, 8741A: $V_{CC} = V_{DD} = +5V \pm 5\%$

**DBB READ**

| Symbol | Parameter | Min. | Max. | Unit | Test Conditions |
|---|---|---|---|---|---|
| $t_{AR}$ | $\overline{CS}$, $A_0$ Setup to $\overline{RD}$↓ | 0 | | ns | |
| $t_{RA}$ | $\overline{CS}$, $A_0$ Hold After $\overline{RD}$↑ | 0 | | ns | |
| $t_{RR}$ | $\overline{RD}$ Pulse Width | 250 | | ns | |
| $t_{AD}$ | $\overline{CS}$, $A_0$ to Data Out Delay | | 225 | ns | $C_L = 150$ pF |
| $t_{RD}$ | $\overline{RD}$↓ to Data Out Delay | | 225 | ns | $C_L = 150$ pF |
| $t_{DF}$ | $\overline{RD}$↑ to Data Float Delay | | 100 | ns | |
| $t_{CY}$ | Cycle Time (Except 8741A-8) | 2.5 | 15 | μs | 6.0 MHz XTAL |
| $t_{CY}$ | Cycle Time (8741A-8) | 4.17 | 15 | μs | 3.6 MHz XTAL |

**DBB WRITE**

| Symbol | Parameter | Min. | Max. | Unit | Test Conditions |
|---|---|---|---|---|---|
| $t_{AW}$ | $\overline{CS}$, $A_0$ Setup to $\overline{WR}$↓ | 0 | | ns | |
| $t_{WA}$ | $\overline{CS}$, $A_0$ Hold After $\overline{WR}$↑ | 0 | | ns | |
| $t_{WW}$ | $\overline{WR}$ Pulse Width | 250 | | ns | |
| $t_{DW}$ | Data Setup to $\overline{WR}$↑ | 150 | | ns | |
| $t_{WD}$ | Data Hold After $\overline{WR}$↑ | 0 | | ns | |

## INPUT AND OUTPUT WAVEFORMS FOR A.C. TESTS

$C_L = 150$ pF

## WAVEFORMS

### 1. READ OPERATION—DATA BUS BUFFER REGISTER.

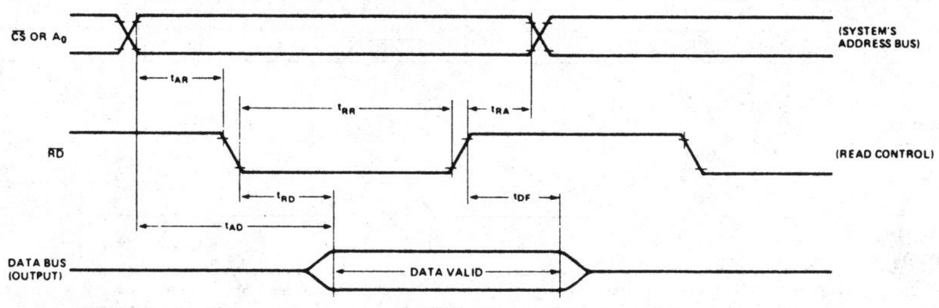


### 2. WRITE OPERATION—DATA BUS BUFFER REGISTER.

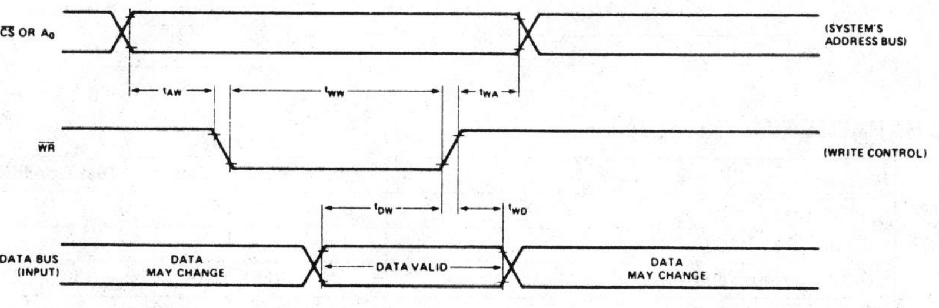


## TYPICAL 8041/8741A CURRENT

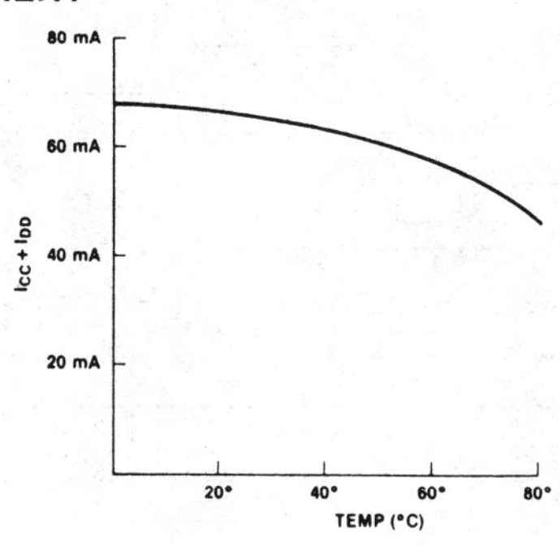

## A.C. CHARACTERISTICS—PORT 2

$T_A = 0°C$ to $70°C$, 8041A: $V_{CC} = +5V \pm 10\%$, 8741A: $V_{CC} = +5V \pm 5\%$

| Symbol | Parameter | Min. | Max. | Unit | Test Conditions |
|---|---|---|---|---|---|
| $t_{CP}$ | Port Control Setup Before Falling Edge of PROG | 110 | | ns | |
| $t_{PC}$ | Port Control Hold After Falling Edge of PROG | 100 | | ns | |
| $t_{PR}$ | PROG to Time P2 Input Must Be Valid | | 810 | ns | |
| $t_{PF}$ | Input Data Hold Time | 0 | 150 | ns | |
| $t_{DP}$ | Output Data Setup Time | 250 | | ns | |
| $t_{PD}$ | Output Data Hold Time | 65 | | ns | |
| $t_{PP}$ | PROG Pulse Width | 1200 | | ns | |

**PORT 2 TIMING**

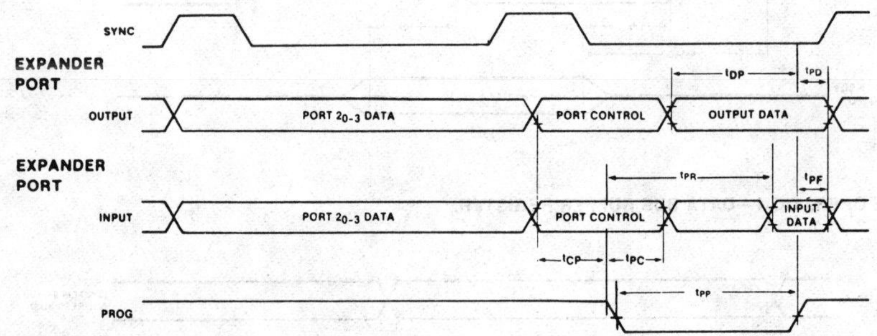


## A.C. CHARACTERISTICS—DMA

| Symbol | Parameter | Min. | Max. | Unit | Test Conditions |
|---|---|---|---|---|---|
| $t_{ACC}$ | $\overline{DACK}$ to $\overline{WR}$ or $\overline{RD}$ | 0 | | ns | |
| $t_{CAC}$ | $\overline{RD}$ or $\overline{WR}$ to $\overline{DACK}$ | 0 | | ns | |
| $t_{ACD}$ | $\overline{DACK}$ to Data Valid | | 225 | ns | $C_L = 150$ pF |
| $t_{CRQ}$ | $\overline{RD}$ or $\overline{WR}$ to DRQ Cleared | | 200 | ns | |

## WAVEFORMS—DMA

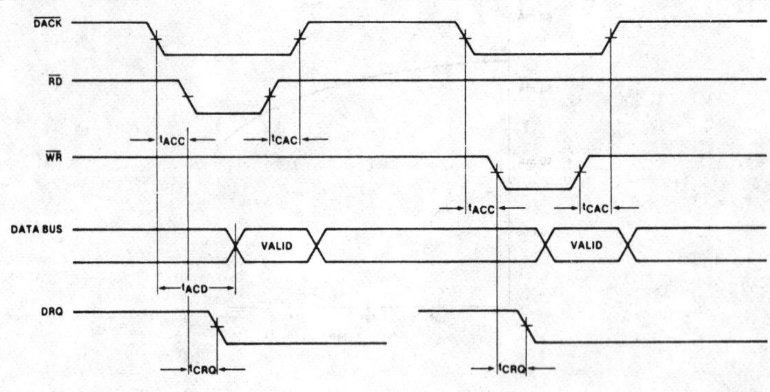

**8741A Erasure Characteristics**

The erasure characteristics of the 8741A are such that erasure begins to occur when exposed to light with wavelengths shorter than approximately 4000 Angstroms (Å). It should be noted that sunlight and certain types of fluorescent lamps have wavelengths in the 3000–4000Å range. Data show that constant exposure to room level fluorescent lighting could erase the typical 8741A in approximately 3 years while it would take approximately one week to cause erasure when exposed to direct sunlight. If the 8741A is to be exposed to these types of lighting conditions for extended periods of time, opaque labels are available from Intel which should be placed over the 8741A window to prevent unintentional erasure.

The recommended erasure procedure for the 8741A is exposure to shortwave ultraviolet light which has a wavelength of 2537Å. The integrated dose (i.e., UV intensity x exposure time) for erasure should be a minimum of 15 w-sec/cm$^2$. The erasure time with this dosage is approximately 15 to 20 minutes using an ultraviolet lamp with a 12,000 $\mu$W/cm$^2$ power rating. The 8741A should be placed within one inch of the lamp tubes during erasure. Some lamps have a filter on their tubes which should be removed before erasure.

## A.C. TIMING SPECIFICATION FOR PROGRAMMING

$T_A = 25°C \pm 5°C$, $V_{CC} = 5V \pm 5\%$, $V_{DD} = 25V \pm 1V$

| Symbol | Parameter | Min. | Max. | Unit | Test Conditions |
|---|---|---|---|---|---|
| $t_{AW}$ | Address Setup Time to $\overline{RESET}$ ↑ | $4t_{CY}$ | | | |
| $t_{WA}$ | Address Hold Time After $\overline{RESET}$ ↑ | $4t_{CY}$ | | | |
| $t_{DW}$ | Data in Setup Time to PROG ↑ | $4t_{CY}$ | | | |
| $t_{WD}$ | Data in Hold Time After PROG ↓ | $4t_{CY}$ | | | |
| $t_{PH}$ | $\overline{RESET}$ Hold Time to Verify | $4t_{CY}$ | | | |
| $t_{VDDW}$ | $V_{DD}$ Setup Time to PROG ↑ | $4t_{CY}$ | | | |
| $t_{VDDH}$ | $V_{DD}$ Hold Time After PROG ↓ | 0 | | | |
| $t_{PW}$ | Program Pulse Width | 50 | 60 | mS | |
| $t_{TW}$ | Test 0 Setup Time for Program Mode | $4t_{CY}$ | | | |
| $t_{WT}$ | Test 0 Hold Time After Program Mode | $4t_{CY}$ | | | |
| $t_{DO}$ | Test 0 to Data Out Delay | | $4t_{CY}$ | | |
| $t_{WW}$ | $\overline{RESET}$ Pulse Width to Latch Address | $4t_{CY}$ | | | |
| $t_r$, $t_f$ | $V_{DD}$ and PROG Rise and Fall Times | 0.5 | 2.0 | $\mu$s | |
| $t_{CY}$ | CPU Operation Cycle Time | 5.0 | | $\mu$s | |
| $t_{RE}$ | $\overline{RESET}$ Setup Time Before EA ↑. | $4t_{CY}$ | | | |

**Note:** If TEST 0 is high, $t_{DO}$ can be triggered by $\overline{RESET}$ ↑.

## D.C. SPECIFICATION FOR PROGRAMMING

$T_A = 25°C \pm 5°C$, $V_{CC} = 5V \pm 5\%$, $V_{DD} = 25V \pm 1V$

| Symbol | Parameter | Min. | Max. | Unit | Test Conditions |
|---|---|---|---|---|---|
| $V_{DDH}$ | $V_{DD}$ Program Voltage High Level | 24.0 | 26.0 | V | |
| $V_{DDL}$ | $V_{DD}$ Voltage Low Level | 4.75 | 5.25 | V | |
| $V_{PH}$ | PROG Program Voltage High Level | 21.5 | 24.5 | V | |
| $V_{PL}$ | PROG Voltage Low Level | | 0.2 | V | |
| $V_{EAH}$ | EA Program or Verify Voltage High Level | 21.5 | 24.5 | V | |
| $V_{EAL}$ | EA Voltage Low Level | | 5.25 | V | |
| $I_{DD}$ | $V_{DD}$ High Voltage Supply Current | | 30.0 | mA | |
| $I_{PROG}$ | PROG High Voltage Supply Current | | 16.0 | mA | |
| $I_{EA}$ | EA High Voltage Supply Current | | 1.0 | mA | |

## WAVEFORMS FOR PROGRAMMING

COMBINATION PROGRAM/VERIFY MODE (EPROM'S ONLY)

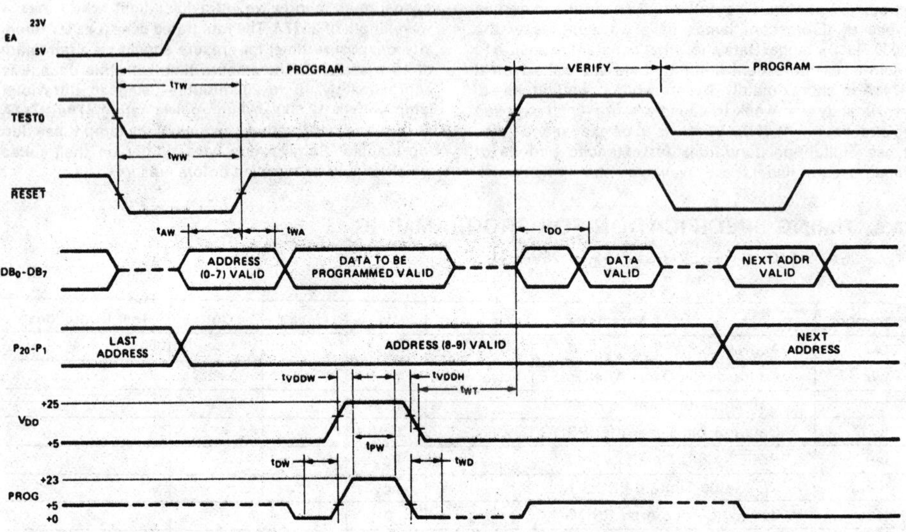


VERIFY MODE (ROM/EPROM)

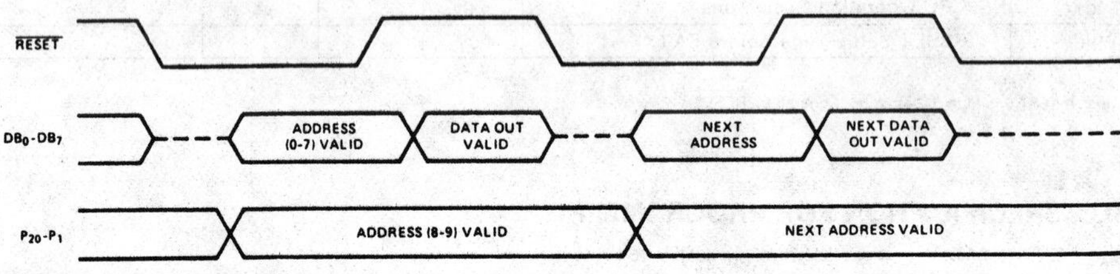


NOTES:
1. PROG MUST FLOAT IF EA IS LOW (i.e., ≠23V), OR IF T0 = 5V FOR THE 8741A. FOR THE 8041A PROG MUST ALWAYS FLOAT.
2. XTAL1 AND XTAL 2 DRIVEN BY 3.6 MHz CLOCK WILL GIVE 4.17 μsec $t_{CY}$. THIS IS ACCEPTABLE FOR 8741A-8 PARTS AS WELL AS STANDARD PARTS.
3. AO MUST BE HELD LOW (i.e., = 0V) DURING PROGRAM/VERIFY MODES.

The 8741A EPROM can be programmed by either of two Intel products:

1. PROMPT-48 Microcomputer Design Aid, or
2. Universal PROM Programmer (UPP series) peripheral of the Intellec® Development System with a UPP-848 Personality Card.

## ABSOLUTE MAXIMUM RATINGS*

Ambient Temperature Under Bias .......0°C to 70°C

Storage Temperature ...........−65°C to +150°C

Voltage on Any Pin with
Respect to Ground ...............−0.5V to + 7V

Power Dissipation ............................1 W

*COMMENT: Stresses above those listed under "Absolute Maximum Ratings" may cause permanent damage to the device. This is a stress rating only and functional operation of the device at these or any other conditions above those indicated in the operational sections of this specification is not implied. Exposure to absolute maximum rating conditions for extended periods may affect device reliability.

## D.C. AND OPERATING CHARACTERISTICS

$T_A$ = 0°C to 70°C, $V_{CC}$ = 5.5V ± 1V, $V_{SS}$ = 0V

| Symbol | Parameter | Limits | | | Unit | Test Conditions |
|---|---|---|---|---|---|---|
| | | Min. | Typ. | Max. | | |
| $V_{IL}$ | Input Low Voltage | −0.5 | | 0.8 | V | |
| $V_{IH}$ | Input High Voltage (All except XTAL 1 & 2, T1 RESET) | 3.0 | | $V_{CC}$ | V | |
| $V_{IH_1}$ | Input High Voltage (XTAL 1 & 2, T1 RESET) | 3.8 | | $V_{CC}$ | V | |
| $V_{IH(10\%)}$ | Input high voltage (all except XTAL 1 & 2, T1, RESET) | 2.0 | | $V_{CC}$ | V | $V_{CC}$ = 5.0V ± 10% |
| $V_{IH_1(10\%)}$ | Input high voltage (XTAL 1 & 2, T1, RESET) | 3.5 | | $V_{CC}$ | V | $V_{CC}$ = 5.0V ± 10% |
| $V_{OL}$ | Output Low Voltage | | | 0.45 | V | $I_{OL}$ = 1.6 mA |
| $V_{OL_1}$ | Output Low Voltage (P10, P11) | | | 2.5 | V | $I_{OL}$ = 7 mA |
| $V_{OH}$ | Output High Voltage (All unless Open Drain) | 2.4 | | | V | $I_{OH}$ = 40 μA |
| $I_{LO}$ | Output Leakage Current (Open Drain Option—Port 0) | | | ± 10 | μA | $V_{SS}+0.45 \leq V_{IN} \leq V_{CC}$ |
| $I_{CC}$ | $V_{CC}$ Supply Current | | 40 | 75 | mA | |

## T1 ZERO CROSS CHARACTERISTICS

$T_A$ = 0°C to 70°C, $V_{CC}$ = 5.5V ± 1V, $V_{SS}$ = 0V, $C_L$ = $80_pF$

| Symbol | Parameter | Min. | Max. | Unit | Test Conditions |
|---|---|---|---|---|---|
| $V_{ZX}$ | Zero-Cross Detection Input (T1) | 1 | 3 | $V_{PP}$ | AC Coupled, C = .2μF |
| $A_{ZX}$ | Zero-Cross Accuracy | | ± 135 | mV | 60 Hz Sine Wave |
| $F_{ZX}$ | Zero-Cross Detection Input Frequency (T1) | 0.05 | 1 | kHZ | |

## A.C. CHARACTERISTICS

$T_A = 0°C$ to $70°C$, $V_{CC} = 5.5V \pm 1V$, $V_{SS} = 0V$ Test Conditions: $C_L = 80\ pF$, $t_{CY} = 8.38\ \mu s$

| | Symbol | Parameter | Min. | Max. | Unit | Test Conditions |
|---|---|---|---|---|---|---|
| Normal Operation | $t_{CY}$ | Cycle Time | 8.38 | 50.0 | μs | 3.58 MHz XTAL |
| | $t_{PRL}$ | ALE to Time P± Input Must Be Valid (input setup) | | 4.0 | μs | |
| | $t_{PL}$ | Output Data Setup Time | o.6 | | μs | |
| | $t_{LP}$ | Output Data Hold Time | 0.6 | | μs | |
| | $t_{PFL}$ | Input Data Hold Time | 0 | | μs | |
| | $t_{LL}$ | ALE Pulse Width | 0.8 | | μs | |
| | $t_R$ | Reset High | 3 | | $t_{CY}$ | |
| | $R_{XTAL}$ | Resistor Across XTAL | .5 | 1 | | |
| Expander Operation | $t_{CP}$ | Port Control Setup Before Falling Edgle of PROG | 0.3 | | μs | |
| | $t_{CP}$ | Port Control Hold After Falling Edge of PROG | 0.8 | | μs | |
| | $t_{PR}$ | PROG to Time P± Input Must Be Valid | 2.0 | 4.0 | μs | |
| | $t_{DP}$ | Output Data Setup Time | 1.0 | | μs | |
| | $t_{PD}$ | Output Data Hold Time | 0.6 | | μs | |
| | $t_{PF}$ | Input Data Hold Time | 0 | .15 | μs | |
| | $t_{PP}$ | PROG Pulse Width | 6.0 | | μs | |

### PORT 2 TIMING

NORMAL OPERATION

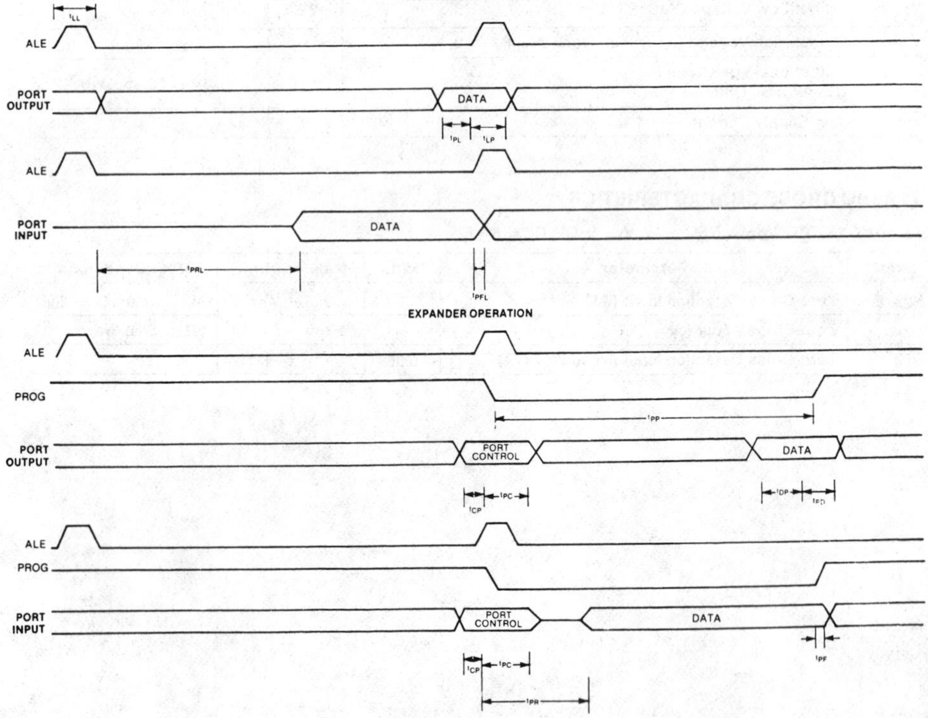

ALE, PORT OUTPUT, DATA, $t_{LL}$, $t_{PL}$, $t_{LP}$

ALE, PORT INPUT, DATA, $t_{PRL}$, $t_{PFL}$

EXPANDER OPERATION

ALE, PROG, PORT OUTPUT, PORT CONTROL, DATA, $t_{PP}$, $t_{CP}$, $t_{PC}$, $t_{DP}$, $t_{PD}$

ALE, PROG, PORT INPUT, PORT CONTROL, DATA, $t_{CP}$, $t_{PC}$, $t_{PR}$, $t_{PF}$

## ABSOLUTE MAXIMUM RATINGS*

Ambient Temperature Under Bias .......0°C to 70°C
Storage Temperature ...........−65°C to +180°C
Voltage on Any Pin with
Respect to Ground .................−0.5V to +7V
Power Dissipation ........................1 Watt

*COMMENT: Stresses above those listed under "Absolute Maximum Ratings" may cuase permanent damage to the device. This is a stress rating only and functional operation of the device at these or any other conditions above those indicated in the operational sections of this specification is not implied. Exposure to absolute maximum rating conditions for extended periods may affect device reliability.

## D.C. AND OPERATING CHARACTERISTICS

$T_A$=0°C to 70°C, $V_{CC}$=5.5V ± 1V, $V_{SS}$=0V

| Symbol | Parameter | Limits | | | Unit | Test Conditions |
|---|---|---|---|---|---|---|
| | | Min. | Typ. | Max. | | |
| $V_{IL}$ | Input Low Voltage | −0.5 | | 0.8 | V | $V_{TH}$ Floating |
| $V_{IL1}$ | Input Low Voltage (Port 0) | −0.5 | | $V_{TH}$−0.1 | V | |
| $V_{IH}$ | High Voltage (All except XTAL 1, RESET) | 2.0 | | $V_{CC}$ | V | $V_{CC}$ = 5.0V ± 10% $V_{TH}$ Floating |
| $V_{IH1}$ | Input High Voltage (All except XTAL 1, RESET) | 3.0 | | $V_{CC}$ | V | $V_{CC}$ = 5.5V ± 1V $V_{TH}$ Floating |
| $V_{IH2}$ | Input High Voltage (Port 0) | $V_{TH}$+0.1 | | $V_{CC}$ | V | |
| $V_{IH3}$ | Input High Voltage (RESET, XTAL 1) | 3.0 | | $V_{CC}$ | V | $V_{CC}$ = 5.0V ± 10% |
| $V_{TH}$ | Port 0 Threshold Reference Voltage | 0 | | .4$V_{CC}$ | V | |
| $V_{OL}$ | Output Low Voltage | | | 0.45 | V | $I_{OL}$ = 1.6 mA |
| $V_{OL1}$ | Output Low Voltage (P10, P11) | | | 2.5 | V | $I_{OL}$ = 7 mA |
| $V_{OH}$ | Output High Voltage (All unless Open Drain Option—Port 0) | 2.4 | | | V | $I_{OH}$ = 50 μA |
| $I_{LI}$ | Input Current (T1) | | | ±200 | μA | $V_{CC} \geq V_{IN} \geq V_{SS}$+.45V |
| $I_{LO}$ | Output Leakage Current (Open Drain Option—Port 0) | | | ±10 | μA | $V_{CC} \geq V_{IN} \geq V_{SS}$+0.45V |
| $I_{CC}$ | $V_{CC}$ Supply Current | | 50 | 100 | mA | |

## A.C. CHARACTERISTICS

$T_A$=0°C to 70°C, $V_{CC}$=5.5V ± 1V, $V_{SS}$=0V

| Symbol | Parameter | Min. | Max. | Unit | Test Conditions |
|---|---|---|---|---|---|
| $t_{CY}$ | Cycle Time | 8.38 | 50.0 | μs | 3 MHz XTAL = 10 μs $t_{CY}$ |
| $V_{ZX}$ | Zero-Cross Detection Input (T1) | 1 | 3 | VACpp | AC Coupled |
| $A_{ZX}$ | Zero-Cross Accuracy | | ±135 | mV | 60 Hz Sine Wave |
| $F_{ZX}$ | Zero-Cross Detection Input Frequency (T1) | 0.05 | 1 | kHz | |

## A.C. CHARACTERISTICS

$T_A$=0°C to 70°C, $V_{CC}$=5.5V ± 1V, $V_{SS}$=0V    Test Conditions: $C_L$=80 pF   $t_{CY}$=8.38 μs

| | Symbol | Parameter | Min. | Max. | Unit | Notes |
|---|---|---|---|---|---|---|
| Expander Operation | $t_{CP}$ | Port Control Setup Before Falling Edge of PROG | 0.5 | | μs | |
| | $t_{PC}$ | Port Control Hold After Falling Edge of PROG | 0.8 | | μs | |
| | $t_{PR}$ | PROG to Time P2 Input Must Be Valid | | 1.0 | μs | |
| | $t_{DP}$ | Output Data Setup Time | 7.0 | | μs | |
| | $t_{PD}$ | Output Data Hold Time | 8.3 | | μs | |
| | $t_{PF}$ | Input Data Hold Time | 0 | .150 | μs | |
| | $t_{PP}$ | PROG Pulse Width | 8.3 | | μs | |
| Normal Operation | $t_{PRL}$ | ALE to Time P2 Input Must Be Valid | | 3.6 | μs | |
| | $t_{PL}$ | Output Data Setup Time | 0.8 | | μs | |
| | $t_{LP}$ | Output Data Hold Time | 1.6 | | μs | |
| | $t_{PFL}$ | Input Data Hold Time | 0 | | μs | |
| | $t_{LL}$ | ALE Pulse Width | 3.9 | 23.0 | μs | $t_{CY}$=8.38 μs for min |

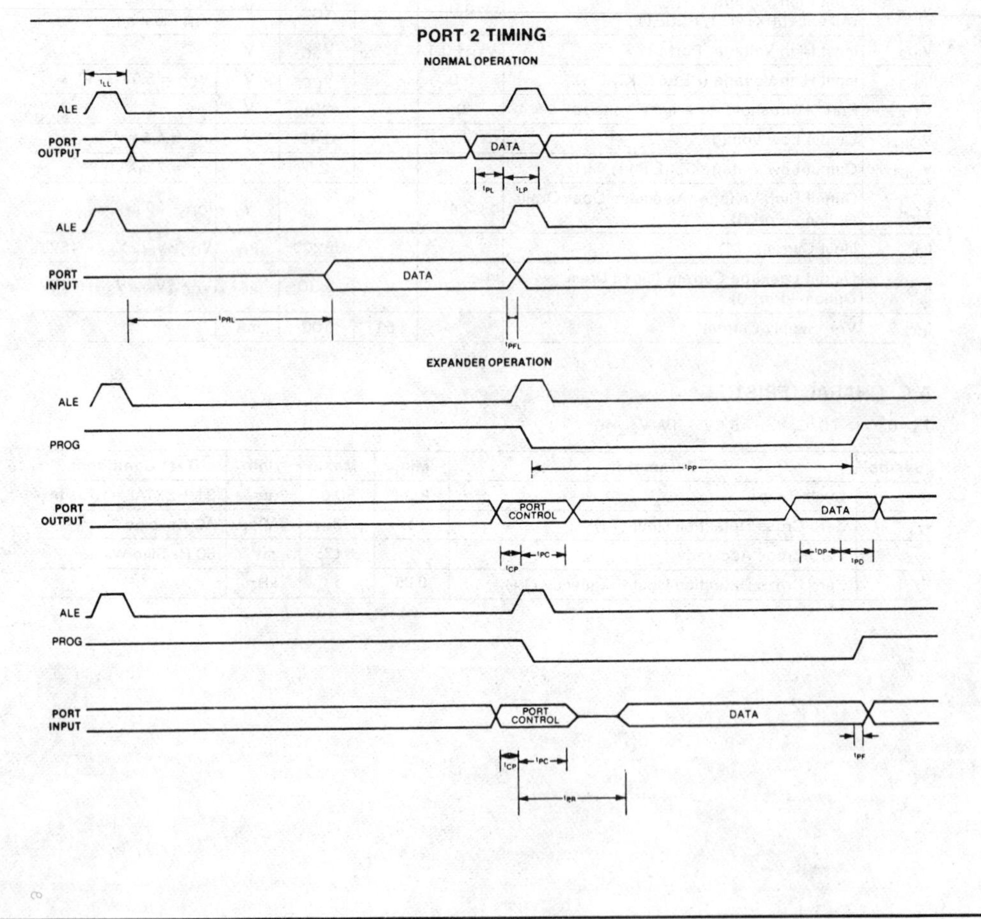

## A/D CONVERTER CHARACTERISTICS

$T_A = 0°C$ to $70°C$, $V_{CC} = 5.5V \pm 1V$, $V_{SS} = 0V$, $AV_{CC} = 5.5V \pm 1V$, $AV_{SS} = 0V$, $AV_{CC}/2 \leq V_{AREF} \leq AV_{CC}$

| Parameter | Min. | Typ. | Max. | Unit | Comments |
|---|---|---|---|---|---|
| Resolution | 8 | | | Bits | |
| Absolute Accuracy | | | .8% FSR ± ½ LSB | LSB | (Note 1) |
| Sample Setup Before Falling Edge of ALE ($t_{SS}$) | | 0.20 | | $t_{CY}$ | |
| Sample Hold After Falling Edge of ALE ($t_{SH}$) | | 0.10 | | $t_{CY}$ | |
| Input Capacitance (AN0, AN1) | | 1 | | pF | |
| Conversion Time | 4 | | 4 | $t_{CY}$ | |

### ANALOG INPUT TIMING

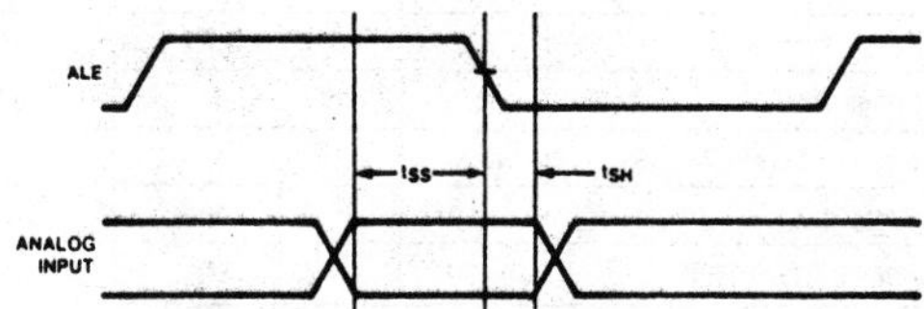


NOTE:

1. The analog input must be maintained at a constant voltage during the sample time ($t_{SS} + t_{SH}$).

## ABSOLUTE MAXIMUM RATINGS*

Ambient Temperature Under Bias . . . . . . . . . . 0°C to 70°C
Storage Temperature . . . . . . . . . . . . . . . . . −65°C to +150°C
Voltage on Any Pin
With Respect to Ground . . . . . . . . . . . . . −0.5V to +7V
Power Dissipation . . . . . . . . . . . . . . . . . . . . . . 1 Watt

**COMMENT*: *Stresses above those listed under "Absolute Maximum Ratings" may cause permanent damage to the device. This is a stress rating only and functional operation of the device at these or any other conditions above those indicated in the operational sections of this specification is not implied. Exposure to absolute maximum rating conditions for extended periods may affect device reliability.*

## D.C. AND OPERATING CHARACTERISTICS

$T_A$ = 0°C to 70°C, $V_{CC}$ = 5V ±10%

| SYMBOL | PARAMETER | MIN. | TYP. | MAX. | UNITS | TEST CONDITIONS |
|---|---|---|---|---|---|---|
| $V_{IL}$ | Input Low Voltage | -0.5 | | 0.8 | V | |
| $V_{IH}$ | Input High Voltage | 2.0 | | $V_{CC}$+0.5 | V | |
| $V_{OL1}$ | Output Low Voltage Ports 4-7 | | | 0.45 | V | $I_{OL}$ = 5 mA* |
| $V_{OL2}$ | Output Low Voltage Port 7 | | | 1 | V | $I_{OL}$ = 20 mA |
| $V_{OH1}$ | Output High Voltage Ports 4-7 | 2.4 | | | V | $I_{OH}$ = 240μA |
| $I_{IL1}$ | Input Leakage Ports 4-7 | -10 | | 20 | μA | $V_{in}$ = $V_{CC}$ to 0V |
| $I_{IL2}$ | Input Leakage Port 2, CS, PROG | -10 | | 10 | μA | $V_{in}$ = $V_{CC}$ to 0V |
| $V_{OL3}$ | Output Low Voltage Port 2 | | | .45 | V | $I_{OL}$ = 0.6 mA |
| $I_{CC}$ | $V_{CC}$ Supply Current | | 10 | 20 | mA | |
| $V_{OH2}$ | Output Voltage Port 2 | 2.4 | | | | $I_{OH}$ = 100μA |
| $I_{OL}$ | Sum of all $IO_L$ from 16 Outputs | | | 80 | mA | 5 mA Each Pin |

*See following graph for additional sink current capability

## A.C. CHARACTERISTICS

$T_A$ = 0°C to 70°C, $V_{CC}$ = 5V ±10%

| SYMBOL | PARAMETER | MIN. | MAX. | UNITS | TEST CONDITIONS |
|---|---|---|---|---|---|
| $t_A$ | Code Valid Before PROG | 100 | | ns | 80 pF Load |
| $t_B$ | Code Valid After PROG | 60 | | ns | 20 pF Load |
| $t_C$ | Data Valid Before PROG | 200 | | ns | 80 pF Load |
| $t_D$ | Data Valid After PROG | 20 | | ns | 20 pF Load |
| $t_H$ | Floating After PROG | 0 | 150 | ns | 20 pF Load |
| $t_K$ | PROG Negative Pulse Width | 700 | | ns | |
| $t_{CS}$ | CS Valid Before/After PROG | 50 | | ns | |
| $t_{PO}$ | Ports 4-7 Valid After PROG | | 700 | ns | 100 pF Load |
| $t_{LP1}$ | Ports 4-7 Valid Before/After PROG | 100 | | ns | |
| $t_{ACC}$ | Port 2 Valid After PROG | | 650 | ns | 80 pF Load |

## WAVEFORMS

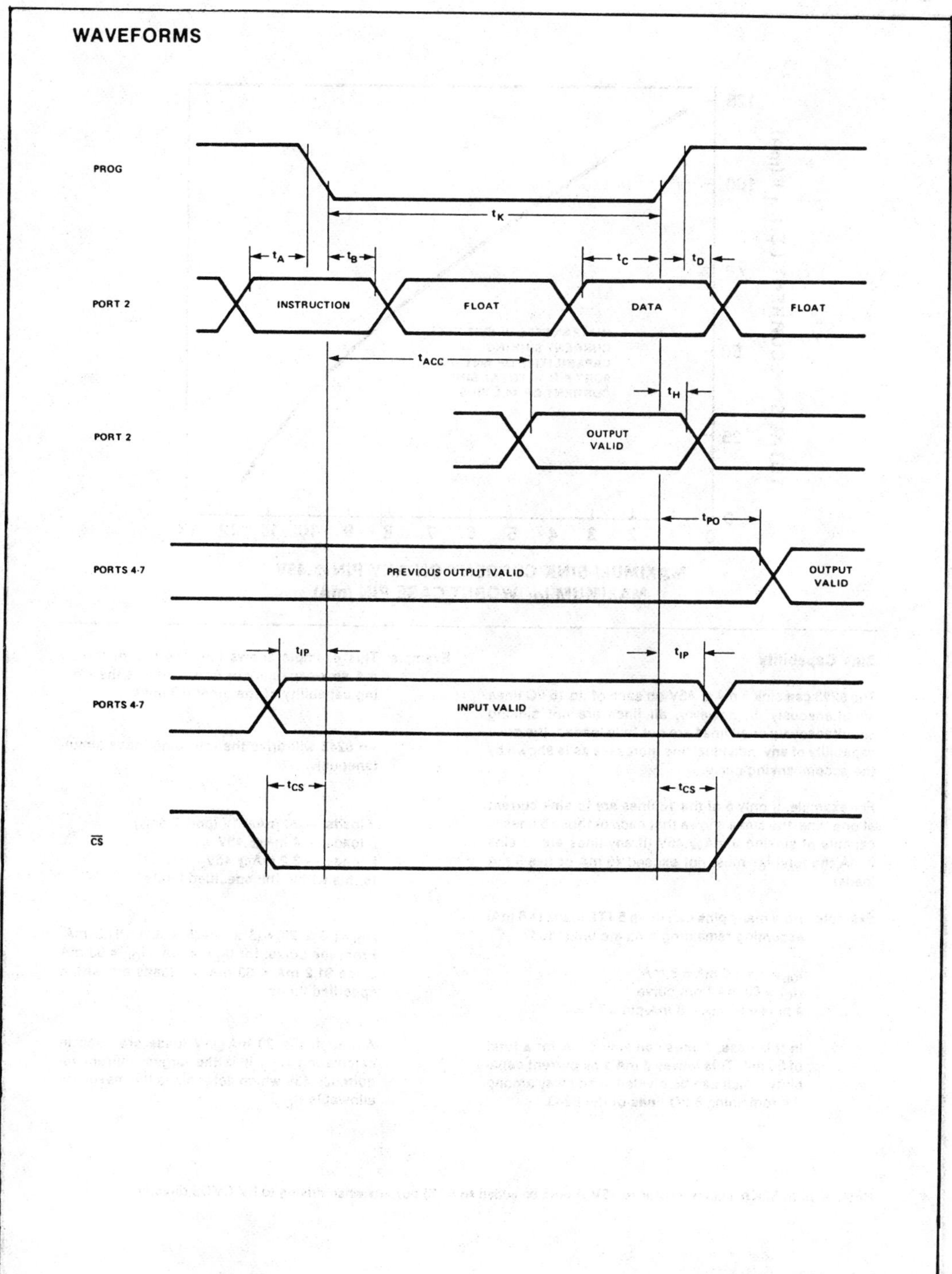
PROG
$t_K$
$t_A$
$t_B$
$t_C$
$t_D$
PORT 2
INSTRUCTION
FLOAT
DATA
FLOAT
$t_{ACC}$
$t_H$
PORT 2
OUTPUT VALID
$t_{PO}$
PORTS 4-7
PREVIOUS OUTPUT VALID
OUTPUT VALID
$t_{IP}$
$t_{IP}$
PORTS 4-7
INPUT VALID
$t_{CS}$
$t_{CS}$
$\overline{CS}$

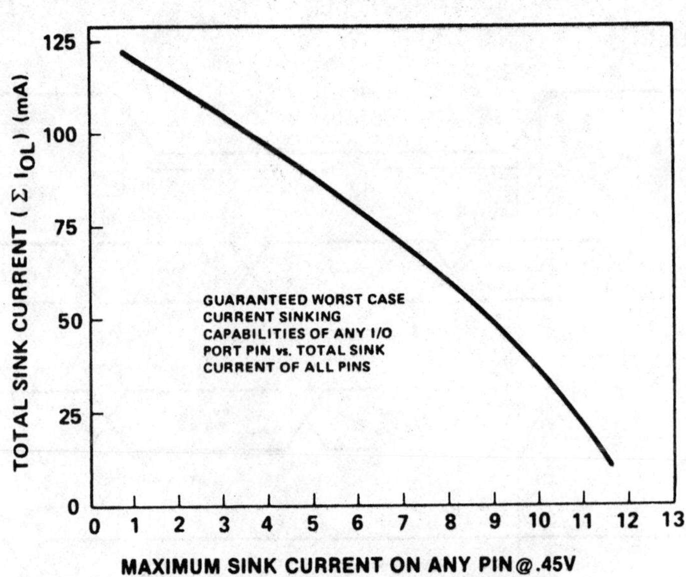


**Sink Capability**

The 8243 can sink 5 mA@.45V on each of its 16 I/O lines simultaneously. If, however, all lines are not sinking simultaneously or all lines are not fully loaded, the drive capability of any individual line increases as is shown by the accompanying curve.

For example, if only 5 of the 16 lines are to sink current at one time, the curve shows that each of those 5 lines is capable of sinking 9 mA@.45V (if any lines are to sink 9 mA the total $I_{OL}$ must not exceed 45 mA or five 9 mA loads).

Example: How many pins can drive 5 TTL loads (1.6 mA) assuming remaining pins are unloaded?

$I_{OL} = 5 \times 1.6$ mA = 8 mA
$\epsilon I_{OL} = 60$ mA from curve
\# pins = 60 mA ÷ 8 mA/pin = 7.5 = 7

In this case, 7 lines can sink 8 mA for a total of 56 mA. This leaves 4 mA sink current capability which can be divided in any way among the remaining 8 I/O lines of the 8243.

Example: This example shows how the use of the 20 mA sink capability of Port 7 affects the sinking capability of the other I/O lines.

An 8243 will drive the following loads simultaneously.

2 loads — 20 mA@1V (port 7 only)
8 loads — 4 mA@.45V
6 loads — 3.2 mA@.45V
Is this within the specified limits?

$\epsilon I_{OL} = (2 \times 20) + (8 \times 4) + (6 \times 3.2) = 91.2$ mA.
From the curve: for $I_{OL} = 4$ mA, $\epsilon I_{OL} \approx 93$ mA since 91.2 mA < 93 mA the loads are within specified limits.

Although the 20 mA@1V loads are used in calculating $\epsilon I_{OL}$, it is the largest current required@.45V which determines the maximum allowable $\epsilon I_{OL}$.

Note: A 10 to 50KΩ pullup resistor to +5V should be added to 8243 outputs when driving to 5V CMOS directly.

# Chapter 7
# ZILOG Z80

**Zilog Z80 microcomputer devices have been designed as 8080A enhancements. In fact, the same individuals responsible for designing the 8080A CPU at Intel designed the Z80 devices at Zilog. The 8085, described in Chapter 5, is Intel's 8080A enhancement.**

**The Z80 instruction set includes all 8080A instructions as a subset. In deference to rational necessity, however, neither the Z80 CPU, nor any of its support devices attempt to maintain pin-for-pin compatibility with 8080A counterparts. Compatibility is limited to instruction sets and general functional capabilities. A program that has been written to drive an 8080A microcomputer system will also drive the Z80 system — within certain limits; for example, a ROM device that has been created to implement object programs for an 8080A microcomputer system can be physically removed and used in a Z80 system.**

**But Z80-8080A compatibility does extend somewhat further, since most support devices that have been designed for the 8080A CPU will also work with a Z80 CPU; therefore in many cases you will be able to upgrade an 8080A microcomputer system to a Z80, confining hardware modifications to the CPU and its immediate interface only.**

**It is interesting to note that the Z80 pins and signal interface is far closer than the 8085 to the three-chip 8080A configuration illustrated in 8080A chapter.** Also, whereas the Z80 instruction set is greatly expanded as compared to the 8080A, the 8085 instruction set contains just two new instructions. However, both the Z80 and the 8085 have resolved the two most distressing problems associated with the 8080A — the three-chip 8080A CPU has in both cases been reduced to one chip, and the three 8080A power supplies have in both cases been reduced to a single +5V power supply.

ZILOG, INC., manufacturers of the Z80, are located at:

10460 Bubb Road
Cupertino, California 95014

The official second source for Zilog products is:

MOSTEK, INC.
1215 West Crosby Road
Carrollton, Texas 75006

**N-Channel MOS technology is used for all Z80 devices.**

**Z80 LSI TECHNOLOGY**

## THE Z80 CPU

**Functions implemented on the Z80 CPU are illustrated in Figure 7-1. They represent "typical" CPU logic, equivalent to the three devices: 8080A CPU, 8224 Clock and 8228 System Controller.**

### A SUMMARY OF Z80/8080A DIFFERENCES

**We are going to summarize Z80/8080A differences before describing differences in detail. If you know the 8080A well, read on; if you do not, come back to this summary after reading the rest of the Z80 CPU description. We will also contrast the Z80 and the 8085, where relevant.**

**For the programmer, the Z80 provides more registers and addressing modes than the 8080A, plus a much larger instruction set.**

**Significant hardware features are a single power supply (+5V), a single system clock signal, an additional interrupt, and logic to refresh dynamic memories.**

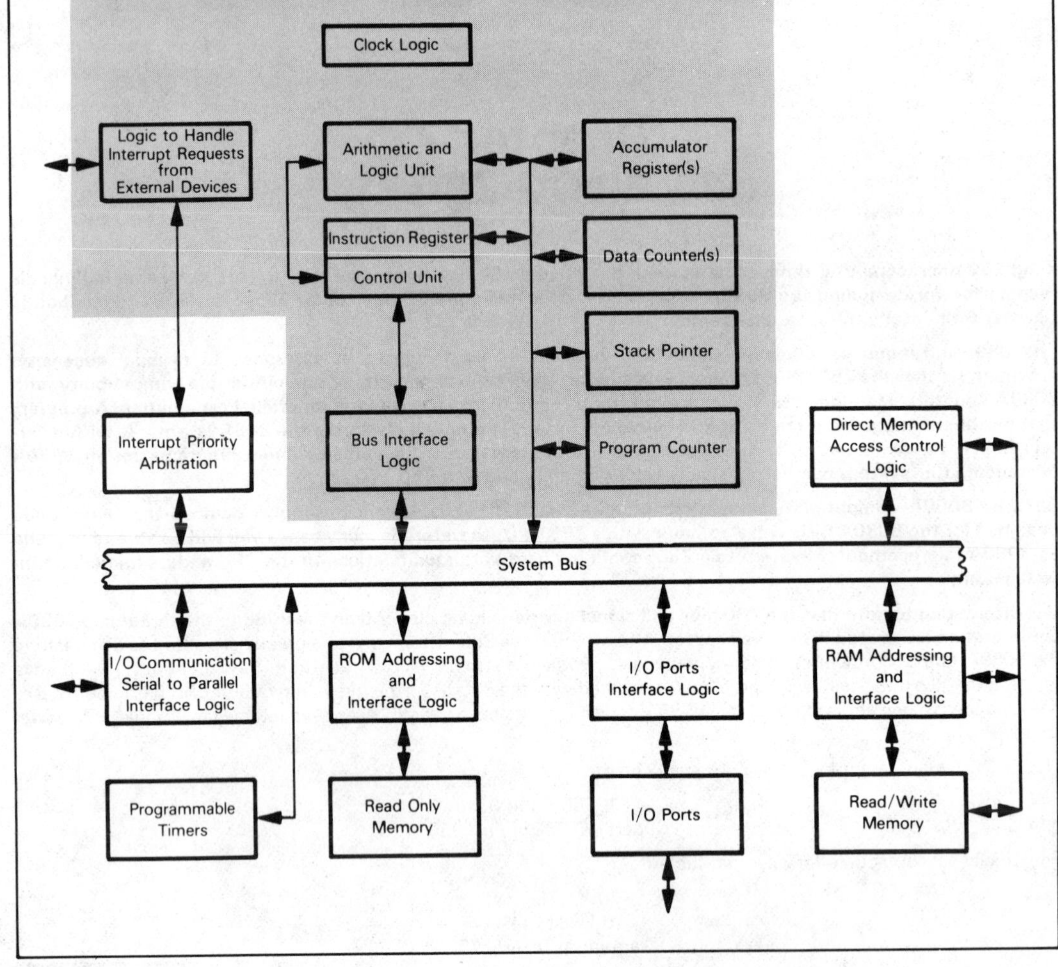


Figure 7-1. Logic Functions of the Z80 CPU

The 8085 also has a single power supply and a single system clock signal. The 8085 has three additional interrupts, but lacks logic to refresh dynamic memories.

**Is the Z80 CPU indeed the logical next 8080A evolution?**

**Hardware aspects of the 8080A represent its weakest features, as compared to principal current competitors.** Specifically, the fact that the 8080A is really a three-chip CPU is its biggest single problem; three chips are always going to cost more than one. Next, the fact that the 8080A requires three power supplies (+5V, -5V and +12V) is a very negative feature for many users and the desirability of going to a single power supply is self-evident; the Z80 requires a single +5V power supply. This is also true of the 8085.

The problems associated with condensing logic from three chips onto one chip are not so straightforward. Figure 7-2 illustrates the standard three-chip 8080A CPU. Let us assume that the three devices are to be condensed into a single chip. Asterisks (*) have been placed by the signals which must be maintained if the single chip is to be hardware compatible with the three chips it replaces. Forty-three signals are asterisked, therefore the standard 40-pin DIP cannot be used. The problem is compounded by the fact that not all 8080A systems use an 8228 System Controller. Some 8080A systems use an 8212 bidirectional I/O port to create control signals. A few of the earliest 8080 systems use neither the 8228 System Controller, nor an 8212 I/O port; rather external logic decodes the Data Bus when SYNC is true in order to generate control signals; for example, that is how the TMS5501 works. We must therefore conclude that any attempt to reduce three chips to one will create a product that is not pin compatible with the 8080A; and, indeed, the Z80 is not pin compatible. What Zilog has done is include as many hardware enhancements as possible within the confines of a 40-pin DIP that must be philosophically similar to the 8080A, without attempting any form of pin compatibility. Figure 7-2 identifies the correlation between Z80 signals and 8080A signals. Notice that there is a significant similarity.

Figure 5-3 is equivalent to Figure 7-2, comparing 8085 and 8080A signals. Z80 signals are far closer to the 8080A three-chip set than the 8085.

**Here is a summary of the hardware differences:**

1) The Z80 has reduced three power supplies to a single +5V power supply.

2) Clock logic is entirely within the Z80.

3) The complex, two clock signals of the 8080A have been replaced by a single clock signal.

4) Automatic dynamic memory refresh logic has been included within the CPU.

5) Read and write control signal philosophy has changed. The 8080A uses separate memory read, memory write, I/O read and I/O write signals. The Z80 uses a general read and a general write, coupled with a memory select and an I/O select. This means that if a Z80 CPU is to replace an 8080A CPU then additional logic will be required beyond the Z80 CPU. You will either have to combine the four Z80 control signals to generate 8080A equivalents, or you will have to change the select and strobe logic for every I/O device. We will discuss this in more detail later.

6) Address and Data Bus float timing associated with DMA operations have changed. The 8080A floats these busses at the beginning of the third or fourth time period within the machine cycle during which a bus request occurs; this initiates a Hold state. The Z80 has a more straightforward scheme; a Bus Request input signal causes the Data and Address Busses to float at the beginning of the machine cycle; floating busses are acknowledged with a Bus Acknowledge output signal.

7) The Z80 has an additional interrupt request. In addition to the RESET and normal 8080A interrupt request, the Z80 has a nonmaskable interrupt which is typically used to execute a short program that prepares for power failure, once a power failure has been detected.

**Now consider internal organization of the Z80 in terms of instruction set compatibility and enhancement.**

As illustrated by Table 7-3 the 8080A instruction set is, indeed, a subset of the Z80 instruction set. Unfortunately, the Z80 uses completely new source program instruction mnemonics, therefore 8080A instructions cannot immediately be identified. Technical Design Labs, Inc., has an 8080-like Z80 assembly language.

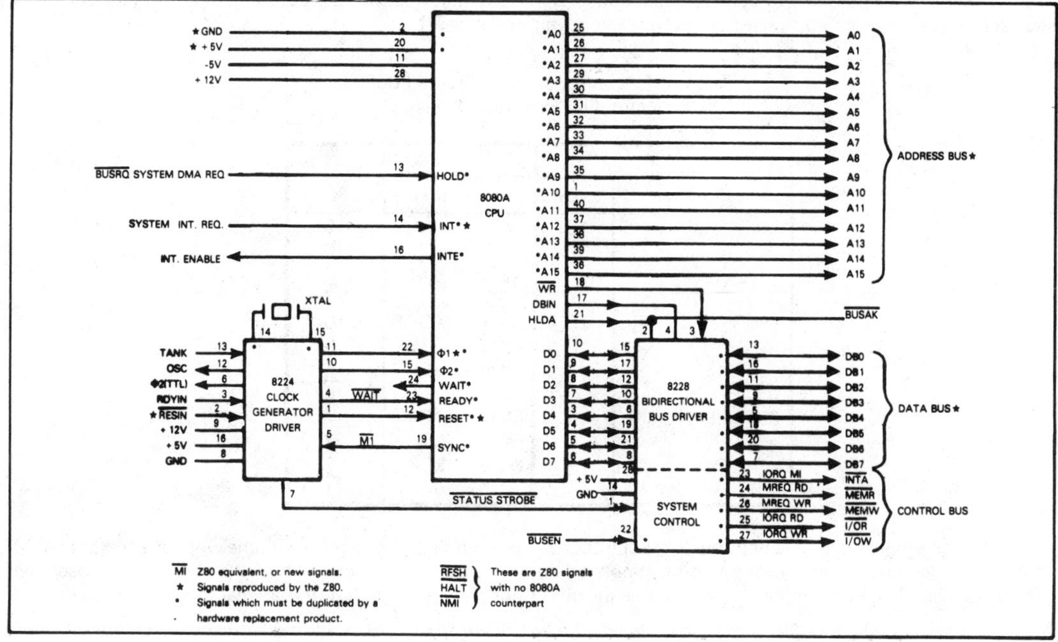


Figure 7-2. The Standard 8080A Three-Chip System and Z80 Signal Equivalents

There are very few unused object codes in the 8080A instruction set. The Z80 has therefore taken what few unused object codes there are, and used them to specify that an additional byte of object code follows:

```
11011101 ◄── Spare 8080A object code
         ◄── Specifies new Z80 object code follows
```

This results in most new Z80 instructions having 16-bit object codes; but simultaneously it means that a very large number of new instructions can be added.

Any enhancement of the 8080A can include major changes within the CPU; providing the 8080A registers and status flags remain as a subset of the new design, instruction compatibility remains. These are the principal enhancements made by the Z80:

1) The standard general purpose registers and status flags have been duplicated. This makes it very easy to handle single-level interrupts, since general purpose register and Accumulator contents no longer need to be saved on the Stack; instead, the program may simply switch to the alternate register set.

2) Two Index registers have been added. This means that additional Z80 instructions can use indexed memory addressing.

2) An Interrupt Vector register allows external logic the option of responding to an interrupt acknowledge by issuing the equivalent of a Call instruction — which vectors program execution to a memory address which is dedicated to the acknowledged external logic.

4) A single Block Move instruction allows the contents of any number of contiguous memory bytes to be moved from one area of memory to another, or between an area of memory and a single I/O port. You can also scan a block of memory for a defined value by executing a Block Compare instruction.

5) Instructions have been added to test or alter the condition of individual register and memory bits.

In contrast to the extensive enhancements of the Z80, the 8085 registers and status architecture are identical to the 8080A. There are only two additional instructions in the 8085 instruction set; however, the 8085, like the Z80, allows Call instructions to be used when acknowledging an interrupt — a particularly useful enhancement.

**While on the surface the Z80 instruction set appears to be very powerful, note that instruction sets are very subjective; right and wrong, good and bad are not easily defined. Let us look at some nonobvious features of the Z80 instruction set.**

First of all, the execution speed advantage that results from the new Z80 instructions is reduced by the fact that many of these instructions require two bytes of object code. Some examples of Z80 instructions and equivalent 8080A instruction sequences with equivalent cycle times are given in Table 7-1.

Table 7-1. Comparisons of Z80 and 8080A Instruction Execution Cycles

| Z80 | | | 8080A | | |
|---|---|---|---|---|---|
| Instructions | | Cycles | Instructions | | Cycles |
| LD | R,(IX + d) | 19 | LXI | H,d | 10 |
| | | | DAD | IX | 10 |
| | | | MOV | R,M | 7 |
| | | | | | 27 |
| LD | RP,ADDR | 20 | LHLD | ADDR | 16 |
| | | | MOV | C,L | 5 |
| | | | MOV | B,H | 5 |
| | | | | | 26 |
| SET | B,(HL) | 15 | MOV | A,M | 7 |
| | | | ORI | MASK | 7 |
| | | | MOV | M,A | 7 |
| | | | | | 21 |

Also, a novice programmer may find the Z80 instruction set bewilderingly complex. At a time when the majority of potential microcomputer users are terrified by simple assembly language instruction sets, it is possible that users will react negatively to an instruction set whose complexity (if not power) rivals that of many large minicomputers.

Many of the new Z80 instructions use direct, indexed memory addressing to perform operations which are otherwise identical to existing 8080A instructions. Now the Z80 has two new 16-bit Index registers whose contents are added to an 8-bit displacement provided by the instruction code; this is the scheme adopted by the Motorola MC6800. This scheme is inherently weaker than having a 16-bit, instruction-provided displacement, as implemented by the Signetics 2650. When the Index register is larger than the displacement, the Index register, in effect, becomes a base register. When the Index register has the same size, or is smaller than the displacement, it is truly an Index register as described in "Volume 1 — Basic Concepts". The Signetics 2650 implementation is more powerful.

## Z80 PROGRAMMABLE REGISTERS

**We will now start looking at the Z80 CPU in detail, beginning with its programmable registers.**

**The Z80 has two sets of 8-bit programmable registers, and two Program Status Words.** At any time one set of programmable registers and one Program Status Word will be active and accessible.

**In addition, the Z80 has a 16-bit Program Counter, a 16-bit Stack Pointer, two 16-bit Index registers, an 8-bit Interrupt Vector and an 8-bit Memory Refresh register.**

**Figure 7-3 illustrates the Z80 registers. Within this figure, the 8080A registers' subset is shaded.**

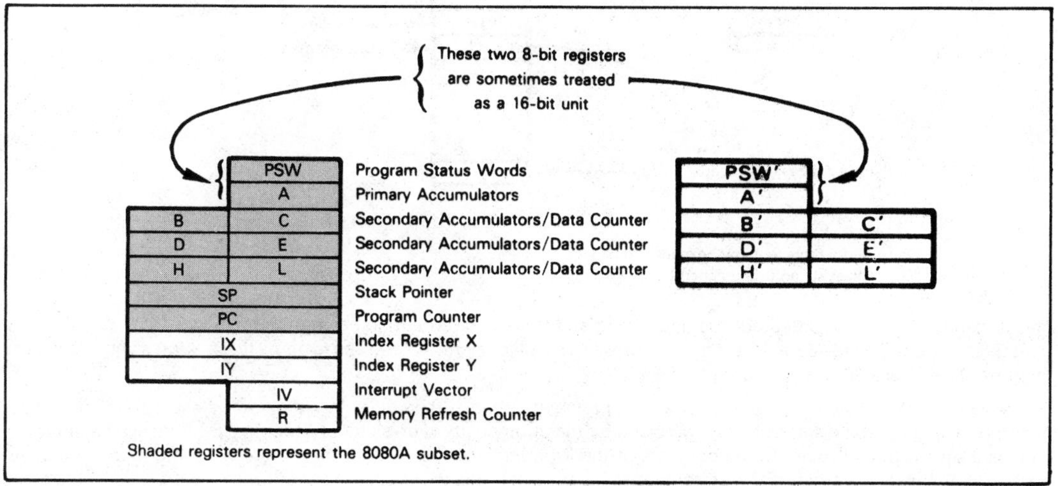


Figure 7-3. Z80 Programmable Registers

**The Z80 uses its Program Status Word, its A, B, C, D, E, H, and L registers, plus the Stack Pointer and the Program Counter exactly as the 8080A uses these locations; therefore no additional discussion of these registers is needed.**

**The Program Status Word, plus registers A, B, C, D, E, H and L are duplicated.** Single Z80 instructions allow you to switch access from one register set to another, or to exchange the contents of selected registers. At any time, one or the other set of registers, but not both, is accessible.

**There are two 16-bit Index registers, marked IX and IY.** These are more accurately looked upon as base registers, as will become apparent when we examine Z80 addressing modes.

**The Interrupt Vector register performs a function similar to the ICW2 byte of the 8259 PICU device (described in the 8080A chapter).** Z80 interrupt acknowledge logic gives you the option of initiating an interrupt service routine with a Call instruction, where the high order address byte for the call is provided by the Interrupt Vector register. The 8085 also provides this capability.

**The Memory Refresh Counter register represents a feature of microcomputer systems which has been overlooked by everyone except Fairchild and Zilog.** Dynamic memory devices will not hold their contents for very long, irrespective of whether power is off or on. A dynamic memory must therefore be accessed at millisecond intervals. Dynamic memory devices compensate for this short-coming by being very cheap — and dynamic refresh circuitry is very simple. Using a technique akin to direct memory access, dynamic refresh circuitry will periodically access dynamic memories, rewriting the contents of individual memory words on each access. About the only logic needed by dynamic refresh is a counter via which it keeps track of its progress through the dynamic memory; that is the purpose of the Z80 Memory Refresh Counter register. The Z80 also has a special DMA refresh control signal; therefore the Z80 provides much of the dynamic refresh logic needed by dynamic memory devices.

## Z80 ADDRESSING MODES

**Z80 instructions use all of the 8080A addressing modes; the Z80 also has these two enhancements:**

1) **A number of memory reference instructions use the IX and IY registers for indexed, or base relative addressing.**

2) **There are some two-byte program relative Jump instructions.**

**Z80 INDEXED ADDRESSING**

A memory reference instruction that uses the IX or IY register will include a single data displacement byte. The 8-bit value provided by the instruction object code is added to the 16-bit value provided by the identified Index register in order to compute the effective memory address:

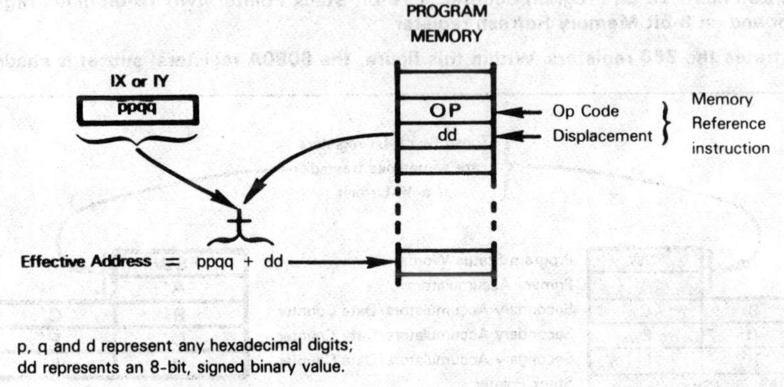


This is standard microcomputer indexed addressing and is less powerful than having the memory reference instruction provide a 16-bit base address or displacement; for a discussion of these addressing modes see "Volume 1 — Basic Concepts", Chapter 6.

The program relative, two-byte Jump instructions provided by the Z80 provide standard two-byte, program relative addressing. A single, 8-bit displacement is provided by the Jump instruction's object code; this 8-bit displacement is added, as a signed binary value, to the contents of the Program Counter — after the Program Counter has been incremented to point to the sequential instruction:

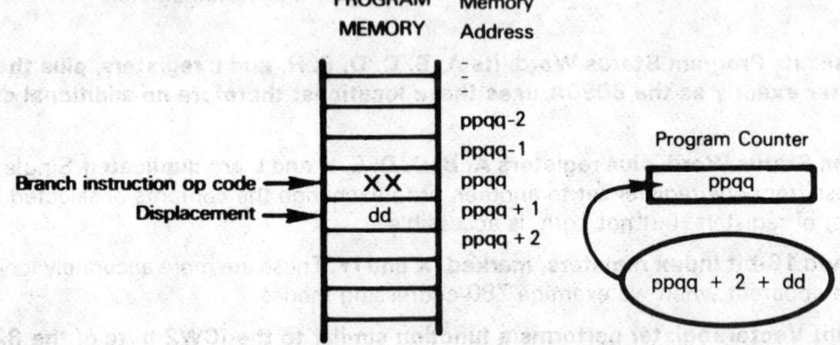


The next instruction object code will be fetched from memory location ppqq+2+dd. p, q, and d represent any hexadecimal digits. dd represents a signed binary, 8-bit value.

For a discussion of program relative addressing, see "Volume 1 - Basic Concepts".

**The Z80 addressing enhancements are of significant value when comparing the Z80 to the 8080A.**

The value of the Index register comes not so much from having an additional addressing option, but rather IX and IY allow an efficient programmer to husband his CPU register space more effectively. Look upon IX and IY as performing memory addressing tasks which the 8080A would have to perform using the BC and DE registers. By freeing up the BC and DE registers for data manipulation, you can significantly reduce the number of memory reference instructions executed by the Z80.

The two-byte program relative Jump instruction is useful because in most programs 80% of the Jump instructions branch to a memory location that is within 128 bytes of the Jump. That is the rationale for most microcomputers offering two-byte as well as three-byte Jump instructions.

## Z80 STATUS

**The Z80 and 8080A both use the Program Status Word in order to store status flags. These are the Z80 status flags:**

Carry (C)
Zero (Z)
Sign (S)
Parity/Overflow (P/O)
Auxiliary Carry ($A_C$)
Subtract (N)

Statuses are recorded in the Program Status Word by the Z80, as compared to the 8080A, as follows:

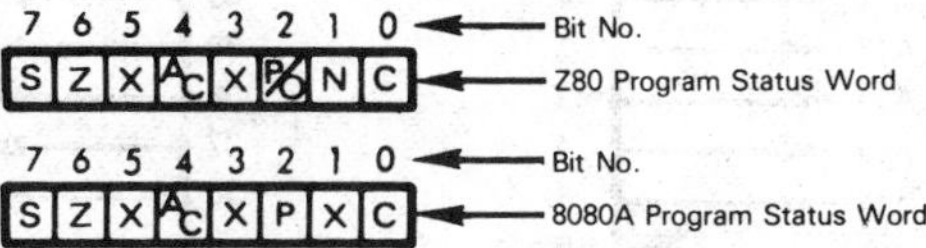


**The Parity/Overflow and Subtract statuses differ from the 8080A. All other statuses are the same. Note that the Z80, like the 8080A, uses borrow philosophy for the Carry status** when performing subtract operations. That is to say, during a subtract operation, the Carry status takes the reciprocal value of any Carry out of the high-order bit. For details see the 8080A Carry status descriptions given in the 8080A chapter.

The 8080A has a Parity status but no Overflow status. The Z80 uses a single status flag for both operations, which makes a lot of sense. The Z80 Overflow status is absolutely standard, therefore only has meaning when signed binary arithmetic is being performed — at which time the Parity status has no meaning. Within the Z80, therefore, this single status is used by arithmetic operations to record overflow and by other operations to record parity. For a complete discussion of the Overflow status see "Volume 1 — Basic Concepts".

The Subtract status is used by the DAA instruction for BCD operations, to differentiate between decimal addition or subtraction. The Subtract and Auxiliary Carry statuses cannot be used as conditions for program branching (conditional Jump, Call or Return instructions).

## Z80 CPU PINS AND SIGNALS

**The Z80 CPU pins and signals are illustrated in Figure 7-4. Figure 7-2 provides the direct comparison between Z80 CPU signals and the standard 8080A, 8228, 8224 three-chip systems.**

**Let us first look at the Data and Address Busses.**

**The 16 address lines A0 - A15 output memory and I/O device addresses.** The address lines are tristate; they may be floated by the Z80 CPU, giving external logic control of the Address Bus. **There is no difference between Z80 and 8080A Address Bus lines.**

**The Data Bus lines D0 - D7 transmit bidirectional data into or out of the Z80 CPU.** Like the Address Bus lines, the Data Bus lines are tristate. **The Z80 Data Bus lines do differ from the 8080A equivalent.** The 8080A Data Bus is multiplexed; status output on the Data Bus by the 8080A during the T2 clock period of very machine cycle is strobed by the SYNC pulse. The Z80 does not multiplex the Data Bus in this way. The Z80 Data Bus lines operate at normal TTL levels, whereas the 8080A Data Bus lines do not.

**Z80 SYSTEM CONTROL SIGNALS**

**Control signals are described next; these may be divided into system control, CPU control and Bus control. First we will describe the System control signals.**

**$\overline{\text{M1}}$ identifies the instruction fetch machine cycle of an instruction's execution. Its function is similar, but not identical to the 8080A SYNC pulse.** The Z80 PIO device uses the low $\overline{\text{M1}}$ pulse as a reset signal if it occurs without $\overline{\text{IORQ}}$ or $\overline{\text{RD}}$ simultaneously low.

**$\overline{\text{MREQ}}$ identifies any memory access operation in progress; it is a tristate control signal.**

**$\overline{\text{IORQ}}$ identifies any I/O operation in progress.** When $\overline{\text{IORQ}}$ is low, A0 - A7 contain a valid I/O port address. **$\overline{\text{IORQ}}$ is also used as an interrupt acknowledge; an interrupt is acknowledged by $\overline{\text{M1}}$ and $\overline{\text{IORQ}}$ being output low** — a unique combination, since $\overline{\text{M1}}$ is otherwise low only during an instruction fetch, which cannot address an I/O device.

**$\overline{\text{RD}}$ is a tristate signal which indicates that the CPU wishes to read data** from either memory or an I/O device, as identified $\overline{\text{MREQ}}$ or $\overline{\text{IORQ}}$.

**$\overline{\text{WR}}$ is a tristate control signal which indicates that the CPU wishes to write** data to memory or an I/O device as indicated by $\overline{\text{MREQ}}$ and $\overline{\text{IORQ}}$. Some Z80 I/O devices have no $\overline{\text{WR}}$ input. These devices assume a Write operation when $\overline{\text{IORQ}}$ is low and $\overline{\text{RD}}$ is high. $\overline{\text{RD}}$ low specifies a Read operation.

The various ways in which the three control signals, $\overline{\text{M1}}$, $\overline{\text{IORQ}}$, and $\overline{\text{RD}}$, may be interpreted are summarized in Table 7-5, which occurs in the description of the Z80 PIO device.

**$\overline{\text{RFSH}}$ is a control signal used to refresh dynamic memories.** When $\overline{\text{RFSH}}$ is output low, the current $\overline{\text{MREQ}}$ signal should be used to refresh dynamic memory, as addressed by the lower seven bits of the Address Bus, A0 - A6.

**Next we will describe CPU control signals.**

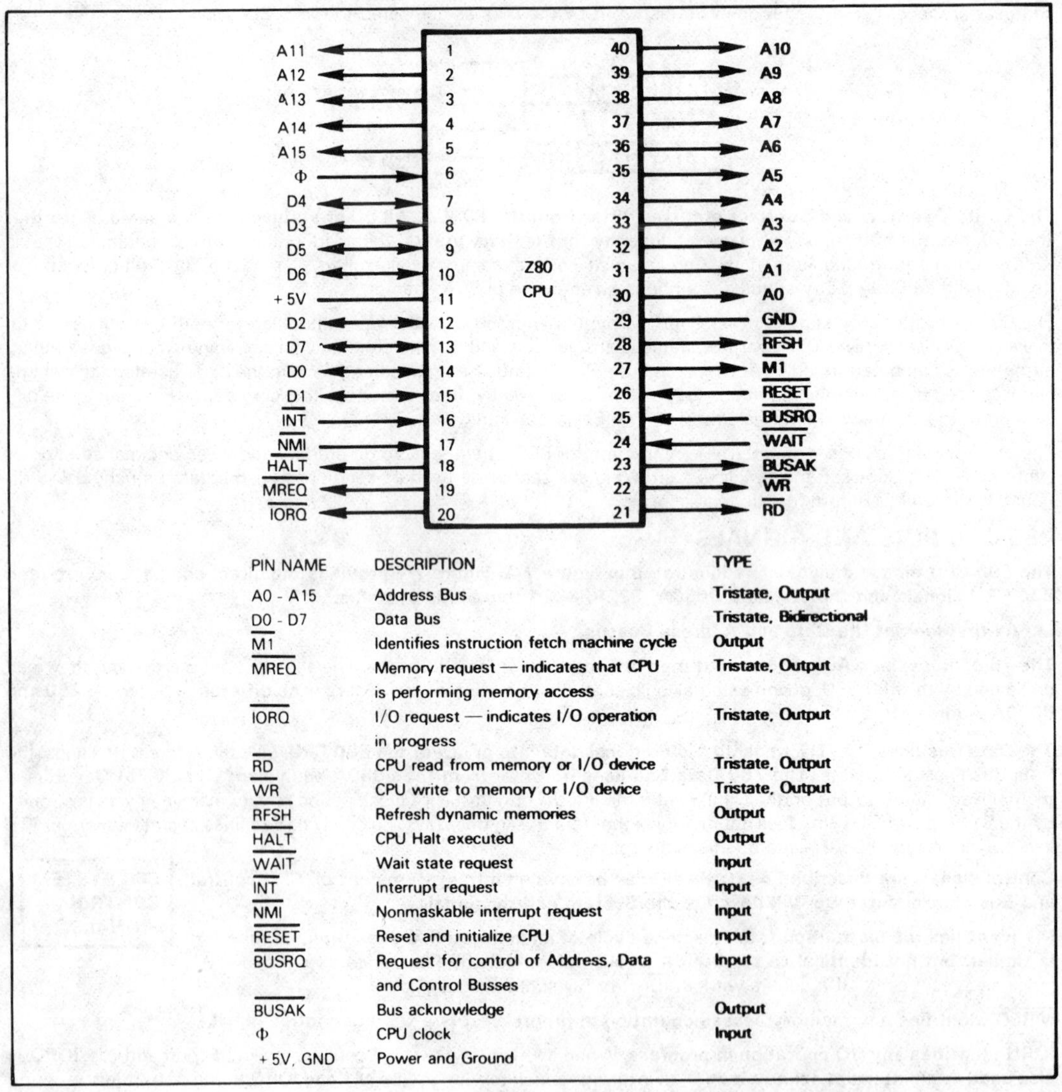


| PIN NAME | DESCRIPTION | TYPE |
|---|---|---|
| A0 - A15 | Address Bus | Tristate, Output |
| D0 - D7 | Data Bus | Tristate, Bidirectional |
| $\overline{\text{M1}}$ | Identifies instruction fetch machine cycle | Output |
| $\overline{\text{MREQ}}$ | Memory request — indicates that CPU is performing memory access | Tristate, Output |
| $\overline{\text{IORQ}}$ | I/O request — indicates I/O operation in progress | Tristate, Output |
| $\overline{\text{RD}}$ | CPU read from memory or I/O device | Tristate, Output |
| $\overline{\text{WR}}$ | CPU write to memory or I/O device | Tristate, Output |
| $\overline{\text{RFSH}}$ | Refresh dynamic memories | Output |
| $\overline{\text{HALT}}$ | CPU Halt executed | Output |
| $\overline{\text{WAIT}}$ | Wait state request | Input |
| $\overline{\text{INT}}$ | Interrupt request | Input |
| $\overline{\text{NMI}}$ | Nonmaskable interrupt request | Input |
| $\overline{\text{RESET}}$ | Reset and initialize CPU | Input |
| $\overline{\text{BUSRQ}}$ | Request for control of Address, Data and Control Busses | Input |
| $\overline{\text{BUSAK}}$ | Bus acknowledge | Output |
| Φ | CPU clock | Input |
| +5V, GND | Power and Ground | |

Figure 7-4. Z80 CPU Signals and Pin Assignments

**Z80 CPU CONTROL SIGNALS**

**HALT is output low following execution of a Halt instruction.** The CPU now enters a Halt state during which it continuously re-executes a NOP instruction in order to maintain memory refresh activity. A Halt can only be terminated with an interrupt.

**WAIT is equivalent to the 8080A READY input.** External logic which cannot respond to a CPU access request within the allowed time interval extends the time interval by pulling the WAIT input low. In response to WAIT low, the Z80 enters a Wait state during which the CPU inserts an integral number of clock periods; taken together, these clock periods constitute a Wait state.

**INT and NMI are two interrupt request inputs.** The difference between these two signals is that NMI has higher priority and cannot be disabled.

**Z80 BUS CONTROL SIGNALS**

**There are two Bus control signals.**

**RESET is a standard reset control input.** When the Z80 is reset, this is what happens:

The Program Counter, IV and R registers' contents are all set to zero.

Interrupt requests via INT are disabled.

All tristate bus signals are floated.

**BUSRQ and BUSAK are bus request and acknowledge signals.** In order to perform any kind of DMA operation, external logic must acquire control of the microcomputer System Bus. This is done by inputting BUSRQ low; at the conclusion of the current machine cycle, the Z80 CPU will float all tristate bus lines and will acknowledge the bus request by outputting BUSAK low.

## Z80 - 8080A SIGNAL COMPATIBILITY

**If you are designing a new product around the Z80 CPU, then questions of Z80 - 8080A signal compatibility are irrelevant; you will design for the CPU on hand.**

**If you are replacing an 8080A with a Z80, then it would be helpful to have some type of lookup table which directly relates 8080A signals to Z80 signals. Unfortunately, such a lookup table cannot easily be created.** The problem is that the Z80 is an implementation of three devices; the 8080A CPU, the 8224 Clock, and 8228 System Controller; but there are very many 8080A configurations that do not include an 8228 System Controller.

Possibly the most important conceptual difference between the Z80 and 8080A involves read and write control signals. **The 8228 System Controller develops four discrete control signals for memory read, memory write, I/O read and I/O write. The Z80 has a general read and a general write, coupled with an I/O select and a memory select.** By adding logic, it would be easy enough to generate the four discrete 8080A signals from the two Z80 signal pairs; here is one elementary possibility:

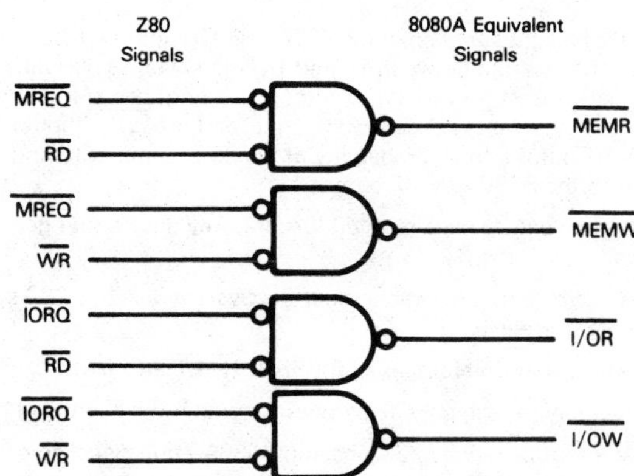

If your design allows it, however, it would be wiser to extend the Z80 philosophy to the various support devices surrounding the CPU. Recall from our discussion of 8080A support devices in Chapter 4 that every device requires separate device select and device access logic. For some arbitrary read operation, timing might be illustrated as follows:

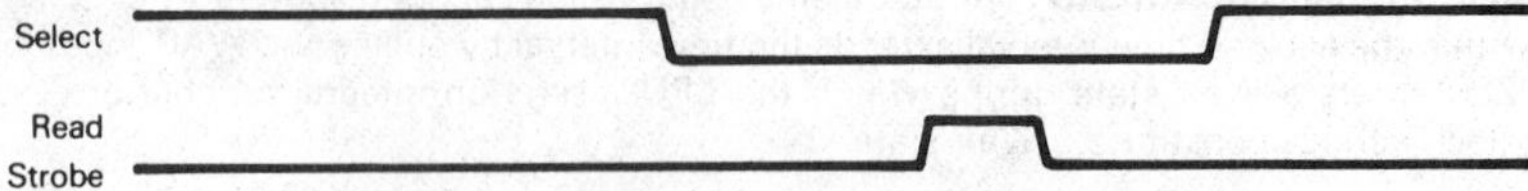


With an 8080A scheme, select logic is decoded from Address Bus lines, while strobe logic depends on one of the four control lines $\overline{I/OR}$, $\overline{I/OW}$, $\overline{MEMR}$ or $\overline{MEMW}$. Using the Z80 philosophy, the memory select ($\overline{MREQ}$) or I/O select ($\overline{IORQ}$) control lines become part of the device select logic, while the read ($\overline{RD}$) or write ($\overline{WR}$) controls generate the strobe.

**The Z80 has no interrupt acknowledge signal; rather it combines $\overline{IORQ}$ with $\overline{M1}$ as follows:**

Some Z80 support devices also check for a "Return-from-Interrupt" instruction object code appearing on the Data Bus during an instruction fetch (when $\overline{M1}$ and $\overline{RD}$ will both be low). This condition is used to reset interrupt priorities among Z80 support devices.

**The 8080A HOLD and HLDA signals are functionally reproduced by the Z80 $\overline{BUSRQ}$ and $\overline{BUSAK}$ signals.**

The 8080A SYNC pulse has no direct Z80 equivalent. $\overline{M1}$ is pulsed low during an instruction fetch, or an interrupt acknowledge, but it is not pulsed low during the initial time periods of an instruction's second or subsequent machine cycles. **Frequently the complement of $\overline{M1}$ can be used instead of SYNC** to drive those 8080A peripheral devices that require the SYNC pulse.

**The Z80 has no signals equivalent to 8080A INTE, WAIT or Φ2. There is also no signal equivalent to the 8228 $\overline{BUSEN}$.**

If for any reason external logic must know when interrupts have been disabled internally by the CPU, then the Z80 will be at a loss to provide any signal equivalent to the 8080A control signals. Remember INTE in an 8080A system tells external logic when the CPU has enabled or disabled all interrupts;since external logic can do nothing about interrupts being disabled, and requesting an interrupt at this time does neither good nor harm, knowing that the condition exists is generally irrelevant.

The single Z80 $\overline{WAIT}$ input serves the function of the 8080A READY input. Irrespective of when the WAIT is requested, a Wait clock period will only be inserted between $T_2$ and $T_3$; moreover, as we will see shortly, there are certain Z80 instructions which automatically insert a Wait state, without waiting for external demand. You would need relatively complex logic to decode instruction object codes, clock signal and the $\overline{WAIT}$ input if your Z80 system is to generate the equivalent of an 8080A WAIT output. In all probability, it would be simpler to find an alternative scheme that did not require a signal equivalent to the 8080A WAIT output.

The Z80 simply has no second clock equivalent to 8080A Φ2. Any device that needs clock signal Φ2 cannot easily be used in Z80 configurations.

The 8228 $\overline{BUSEN}$ input is used by external logic to float the System Bus. In a Z80 system, CPU logic floats the System Bus; therefore $\overline{BUSEN}$ becomes irrelevant.

**The 8080A CPU has no signals equivalent to Z80 $\overline{RFSH}$, $\overline{HALT}$ and $\overline{NMI}$.**

$\overline{RFSH}$ applies to dynamic memory refresh only; it is irrelevant within the context of a Z80 - 8080A signal comparison.

$\overline{NMI}$, being a nonmaskable interrupt request, also has no 8080A equivalent logic.

**The Z80 $\overline{HALT}$ output needs some discussion. One of the more confusing aspects of the 8080A is the interaction of Wait, Halt and Hold states. Let us look at these three states, comparing the Z80 and 8080A configurations and in the process we will see the purpose of the Z80 $\overline{HALT}$ output.**

The purpose of the Wait state is to elongate a memory reference machine cycle in deference to slow external memory or I/O devices. The Wait state consists of one or more Wait clock periods inserted between $T_2$ and $T_3$ of a machine cycle. The 8080A and the Z80 handle Wait states in exactly the same way, except for the fact that the Z80 has no Wait acknowledge output and under certain circumstances will automatically insert Wait clock periods.

The purpose of the Hold condition is to allow external logic to acquire control of the System Bus and perform Direct Memory Access operations. Again both the Z80 and the 8080A have very similar Hold states. The only significant difference is that the Z80 initiates a Hold state at the conclusion of a machine cycle, whereas the 8080A initiates the Hold state during time period $T_3$ or $T_4$. The 8228 System Controller also needs a high BUSEN input in order to float its Data and Control Busses while the Z80 has no equivalent need.

The big difference between the Z80 and the 8080A comes within the Halt state. When the 8080A executes a Halt instruction, it goes into a Halt state, which differs from a Hold state. There are some complex interactions between Hold, Halt, Wait and interrupts within 8080A systems. None of these complications exists in the Z80 system, since the Z80 has no Halt state. After executing a Halt instruction, the Z80 outputs HALT low, then proceeds to continuously execute a NOP instruction. This allows dynamic memory refresh logic to continue operating. **If you are replacing an 8080A with a Z80, you must give careful attention to the Halt state. This is one condition where unexpected incompatibilities can arise.**

## Z80 TIMING AND INSTRUCTION EXECUTION

**Z80 timing is conceptually similar to, but far simpler than 8080A timing. Like the 8080A, the Z80 divides its instructions into machine cycles and clock periods.** However, all Z80 machine cycles consist of either three or four clock periods. Some instructions always insert Wait clock periods, in which case five or six clock periods may be present in a machine cycle. Recall that 8080A machine cycles may have three, four or five clock periods.

The 8080A may require from one to five machine cycles in order to execute an instruction; Z80 instructions execute in one to six machine cycles. If we shade optional machine cycles and clock periods, Z80 and 8080A instruction time subdivisions may be compared and illustrated as follows:

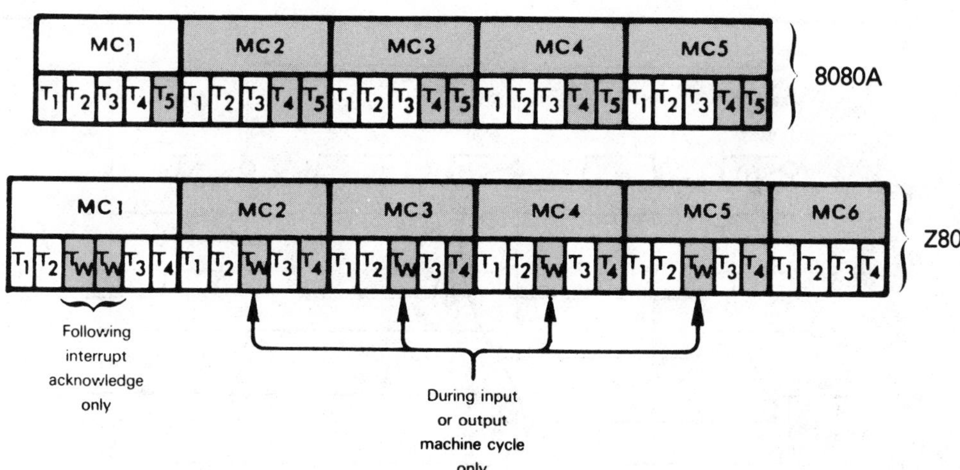

**Z80 clock signals are also far simpler than the 8080A equivalent.** Where the 8080A uses two clock signals the Z80 uses one. Clock logic may be compared as follows:

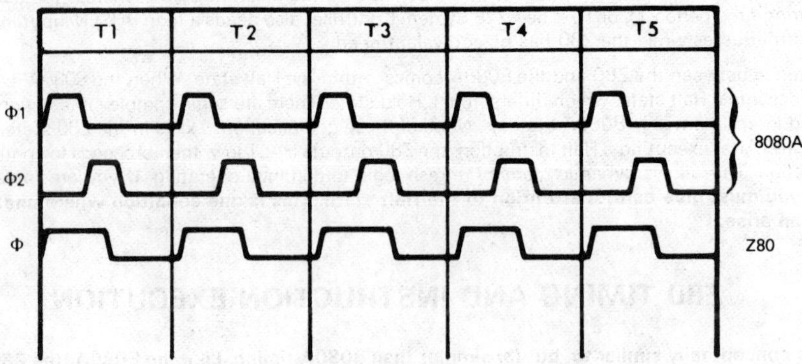


## INSTRUCTION FETCH EXECUTION SEQUENCES

**As compared to the 8080A, Z80 instruction timing is marvelously simple.** Gone is the SYNC pulse and the decoding of Data Bus for status. Every instruction's timing degenerates into an instruction fetch, optionally followed by memory or I/O read or write. Add to this a few variations for Wait state, interrupt acknowledge and bus floating and you are done.

**Let us begin by looking at an instruction fetch.** Timing is illustrated in Figure 7-5. Look at the instruction fetch timing in the 8080A chapter to obtain an immediate comparison of the Z80 and the 8080A.

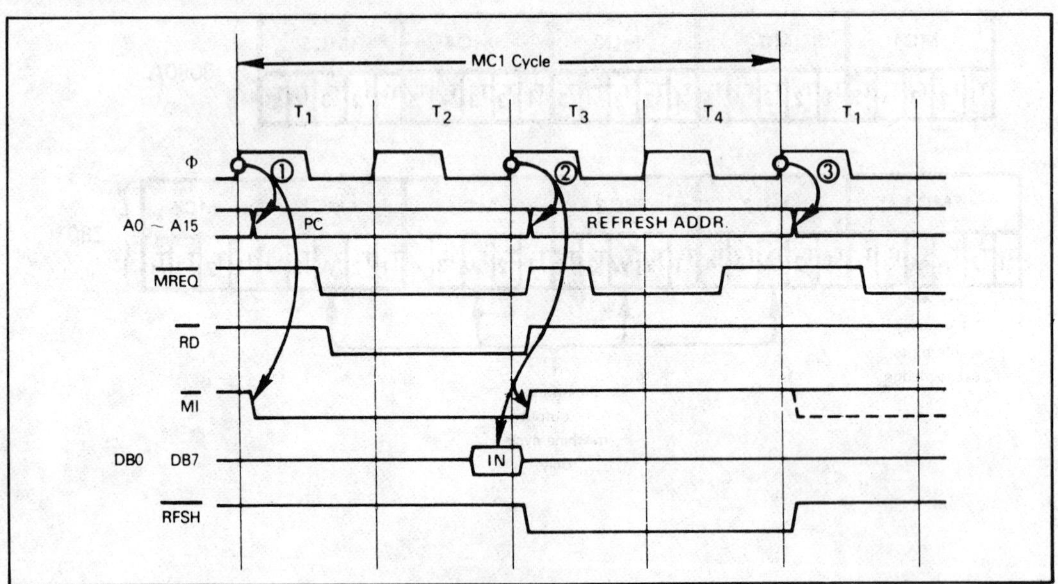


Figure 7-5. Z80 Instruction Fetch Sequence

Referring to Figure 7-5, note that the instruction fetch cycle is identified by $\overline{M1}$ output low during $T_1$ and $T_2$ (①). Since there is no status on the Data Bus to worry about, the Program Counter contents are output immediately on the Address Bus and stay stable for the duration of $T_1$ and $T_2$.

Since an instruction fetch is also a memory operation, $\overline{MREQ}$ and $\overline{RD}$ controls are both output low. This occurs half-way through $T_1$, at which time the Address Bus will stabilize. The falling edges of $\overline{MREQ}$ and $\overline{RD}$ can therefore be used to select a memory device and strobe data out. The CPU polls data on the Data Bus at the rising edge of the $T_3$ clock (②).

**Clock perods $T_3$ and $T_4$ of the instruction fetch machine cycle are used** by the Z80 CPU for internal operations. These clock periods are also used **to refresh dynamic memory.** As soon as the Program Counter contents are taken off the Address Bus (②), the refresh address from the Refresh register is output on lines A0 - A6 of the Address Bus. This address stays on the Address Bus until the conclusion of $T_4$ (③).

Since a memory refresh is a memory access operation, $\overline{MREQ}$ is again output low; however, it is accompanied by $\overline{RFSH}$ rather than $\overline{RD}$ low. Thus memory reference logic does not attempt to read data during a refresh cycle.

## A MEMORY READ OPERATION

**Memory interface logic responds to an instruction fetch and a memory read in exactly the same way. There are, however, a few differeces between memory read and instruction fetch timing.** Memory read timing is illustrated in Figure 7-6. The principal difference to note is that during a memory read operation, the data is sampled on the falling edge of the $T_3$ clock pulse, whereas during an instruction fetch it is sampled on the rising edge of this clock pulse. Also a normal memory read machine cycle will consist of three clock periods, while the normal instruction fetch consists of four clock periods. Remember also that the Z80 identifies an instruction fetch machine cycle by outputting $\overline{M1}$ low during the first two clock periods of the instruction fetch machine cycle.

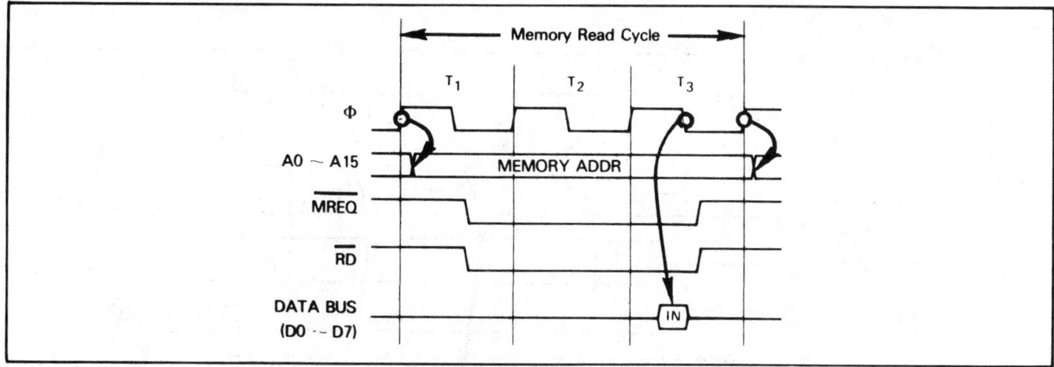


Figure 7-6. Z80 Memory Read Timing

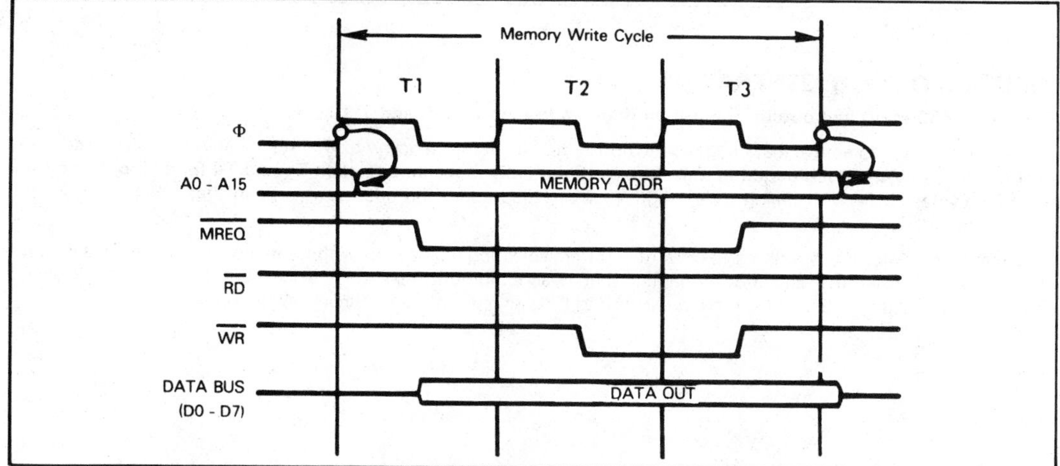


Figure 7-7. Z80 Memory Write Timing

## MEMORY WRITE OPERATION

**Figure 7-7 illustrates memory write timing for the Z80. The only differences between memory read and memory write timing are the obvious ones:** $\overline{WR}$ is pulsed low for a write, and can be used as a strobe by memory interface logic to read data off the Data Bus.

## THE WAIT STATE

Like the 8080A, **the Z80 allows a Wait state to occur between clock periods $T_2$ and $T_3$ of a machine cycle.** The Wait state frees external logic or memory from having to operate at CPU speed.

The Z80 CPU samples the $\overline{\text{WAIT}}$ input on the falling edge of $\Phi$ during $T_2$. Providing $\overline{\text{WAIT}}$ is low on the falling edge of $\Phi$ during $T_2$, Wait clock periods will be inserted. The number of Wait clock periods inserted depends strictly on how long the $\overline{\text{WAIT}}$ input is held low. As soon as the Z80 detects $\overline{\text{WAIT}}$ high on the falling edge of $\Phi$, it will initiate $T_3$ on the next rising edge of $\Phi$.

**Note that the single Z80 $\overline{\text{WAIT}}$ signal replaces the READY and $\overline{\text{WAIT}}$ 8080A signals.** As this would imply, no signal is output telling external logic the Z80 has entered the Wait state. **In the event that external logic needs to know whether or not a Wait state has been entered, these are the rules:**

1) The Z80 will sample $\overline{\text{WAIT}}$ on the falling edge of $\Phi$ in $T_2$.
2) If $\overline{\text{WAIT}}$ is low, then the Z80 will continue to sample the $\overline{\text{WAIT}}$ input for all subsequent Wait state clock periods.
3) The Z80 will not sample the $\overline{\text{WAIT}}$ input during any clock period other than $T_2$ or a Wait state.

Figure 7-8 illustrates Z80 Wait state timing.

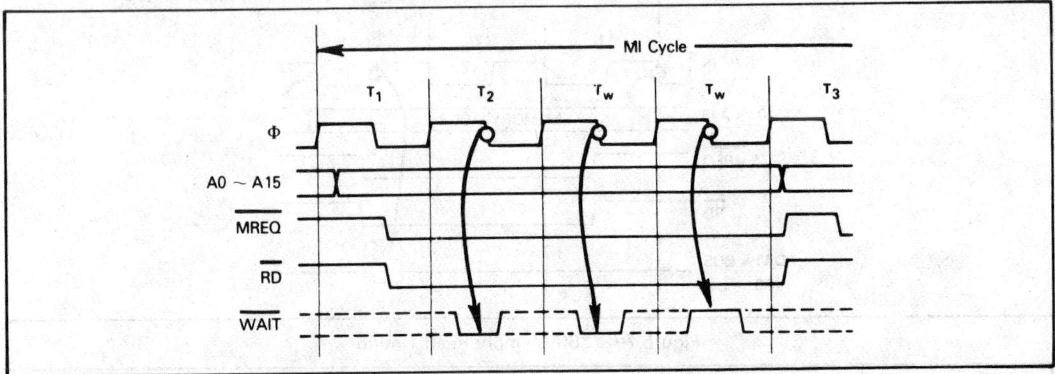


Figure 7-8. Z80 Wait State Timing

## INPUT OR OUTPUT GENERATION

**Timing for Z80 input and output generation is given in Figures 7-9 and 7-10.**

The important point to note is that Zilog has acknowledged the infrequency with which typical I/O logic can operate at CPU speed. **One Wait clock period is therefore automatically inserted between $T_2$ and $T_3$ for all input or output machine cycles.** Otherwise timing differs from memory read and write operations only in that $\overline{\text{IORQ}}$ is output low rather than $\overline{\text{MREQ}}$.

Note that there is absolutely nothing to prevent you from selecting I/O devices within the memory space. This is something we did consistently in the 8080A chapter when describing 8080A support devices. But if you adopt this design policy, remember that your I/O logic must execute at CPU speed, unless you insert Wait states.

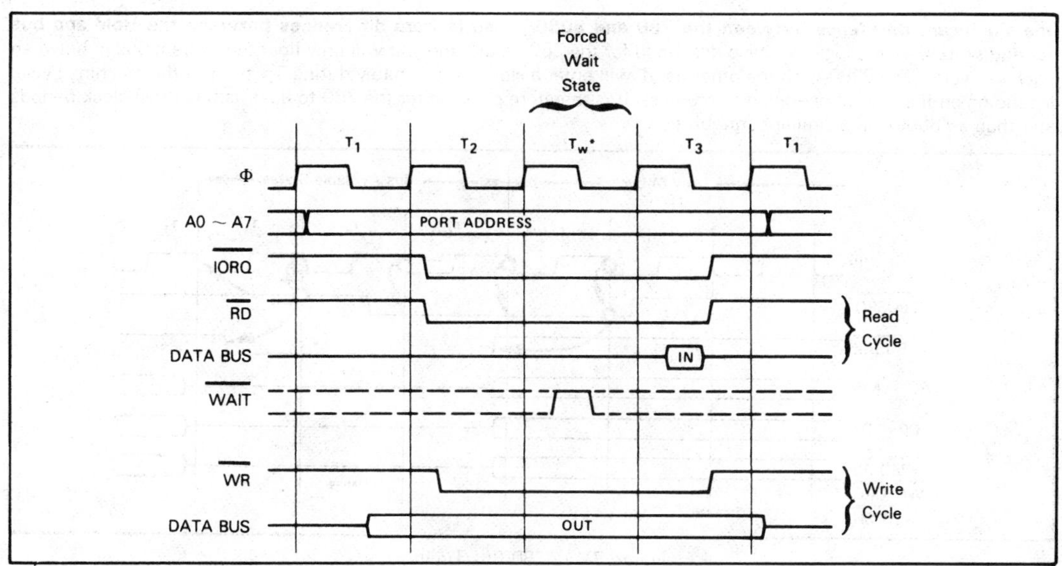


Figure 7-9. Z80 Input or Output Cycles

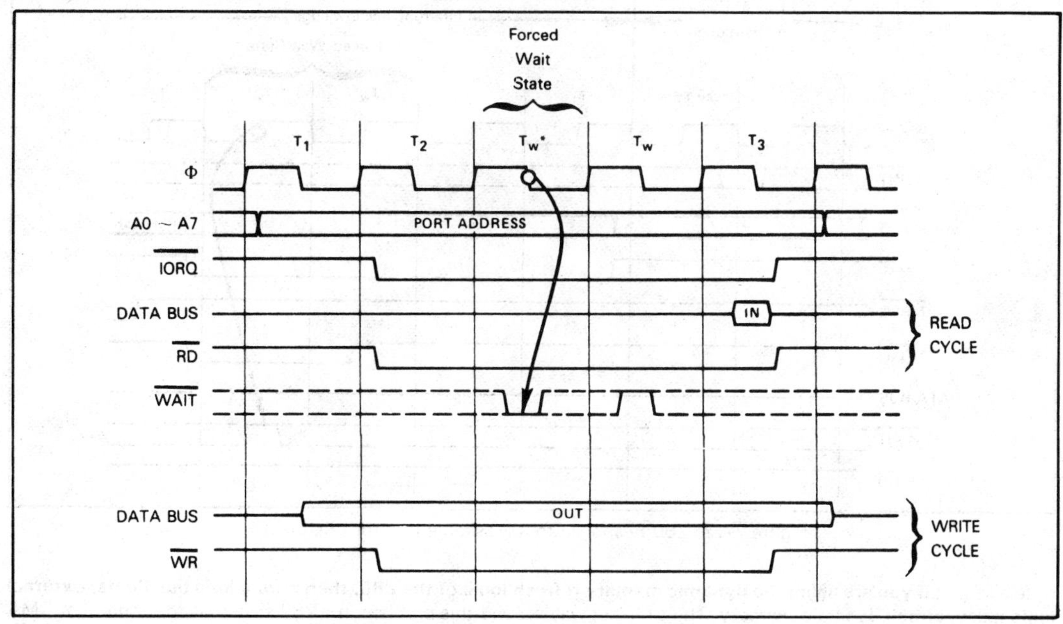


Figure 7-10. Z80 Input or Output Cycles with Wait States

## BUS REQUESTS

The Z80 does not have a Hold state as described for the 8080A, but Z80 bus request logic is equivalent. **The Z80 will float Address, Data and tristate Control Bus lines upon sensing a low BUSRQ signal.** BUSRQ is sampled by the Z80 CPU on the rising edge of the last clock pulse of any machine cycle. If BUSRQ is sampled low, then tristate lines are floated by the CPU, which also outputs BUSAK low. The Z80 CPU continues to sample BUSRQ on the rising edge of every clock pulse. As soon as BUSRQ is sensed high, floating will cease on the next clock pulse. This timing is illustrated in Figure 7-11.

**One significant difference between the Z80 and 8080A results from differences between the Hold and bus floating states.** As the logic we have described for the Z80 would imply, it will only float the System Bus in between machine cycles. The 8080A, on the other hand, will enter a Hold state variably during $T_3$ or $T_4$ of the machine cycle, depending on the type of operation in progress. It is therefore possible for the Z80 to float its bus three clock periods later than an 8080A in a similar configuration.

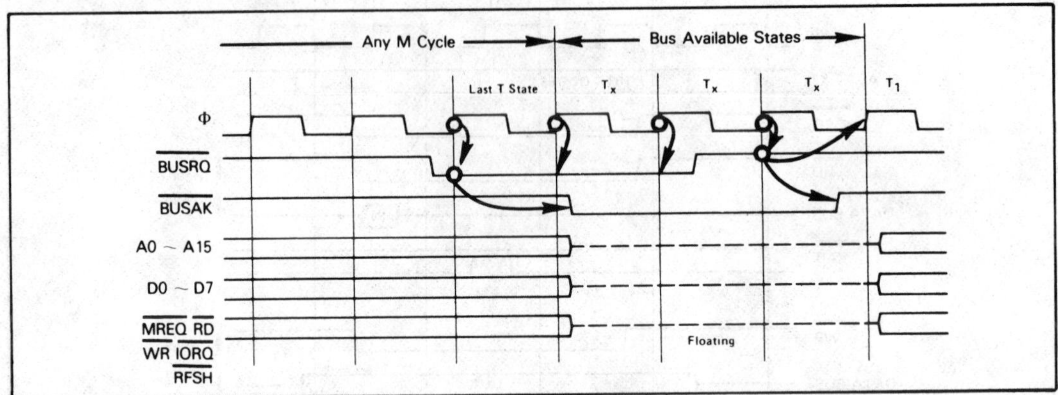


Figure 7-11. Z80 Bus Timing

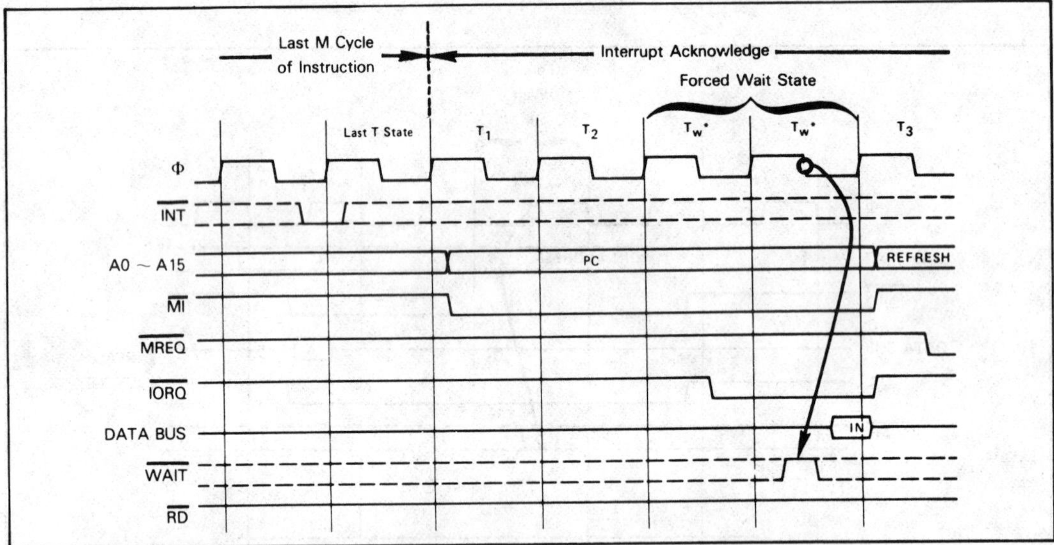


Figure 7-12. Z80 Response to a Maskable Interrupt Request

Note also that **if you are using the dynamic memory refresh logic of the Z80, then during long bus floats, external logic must refresh dynamic memory.** The simplest way around this problem in a Z80 system is to ensure that DMA operations acquire the System Bus for many short periods of time, rather than for a single long access.

## EXTERNAL INTERRUPTS

**The Z80 has two interrupt request input signals: $\overline{INT}$ and $\overline{NMI}$. The $\overline{NMI}$ (non-maskable interrupt) input cannot be disabled and has a higher priority than the $\overline{INT}$ interrupt input. There are three different operating or response modes for the $\overline{INT}$ input, while the response to $\overline{NMI}$ is simple and straightforward.** Let us therefore begin by describing the $\overline{INT}$ interrupt request.

**Timing for $\overline{INT}$ interrupt request and acknowledge sequence differs significantly from that of the 8080A interrupt request and is illustrated in Figure 7-12.**

**The interrupt request signal $\overline{INT}$ is sampled by the Z80 CPU on the rising edge of the last clock pulse of any instruction's execution.** Note that there is an exception to this statement: during execution of block search and transfer instructions, the interrupt request signal is sampled after each byte of data is transferred/compared.

An interrupt request will be denied if interrupts have been disabled under program control, or if the $\overline{BUSRQ}$ signal is also low. Thus a DMA access will have priority over maskable interrupts.

The Z80 CPU acknowledges an interrupt request by outputting $\overline{M1}$ and $\overline{IORQ}$ low. This occurs in a special interrupt acknowledge machine cycle, as illustrated in Figure 7-12. Note that this machine cycle has two Wait states inserted so that external logic will have time for any type of daisy chained priority interrupt scheme to be implemented.

**When $\overline{IORQ}$ is output low while $\overline{M1}$ is low, external logic must interpret this signal combination as requiring an interrupt vector to be placed on the Data Bus by the acknowledged external interrupt requesting source. This interrupt vector can take one of three forms;** the form depends on which of the three modes you have selected for the Z80 under program control.

In **Mode 0,** the interrupt vector will be interpreted as an object code, representing the first instruction to be executed following the interrupt acknowledge. If a multi-byte object code is supplied, then the bytes following the first must be supplied during subsequent machine cycles. This **is equivalent to the standard interrupt response of the 8080A.** Whenever you are replacing an 8080A with a Z80, therefore, the Z80 must operate in interrupt response Mode 0.

Z80 interrupt response logic in **Mode 1 automatically assumes that the first instruction executed following the interrupt response will be a Restart, branching to memory location $0038_{16}$.** If the Z80 is in Mode 1, no interrupt vector is needed.

Z80 Mode 2 interrupt response has no 8080A equivalent. When you operate the Z80 **in Mode 2, you must create a table of 16-bit interrupt address vectors,** which can reside anywhere in addressable memory. These 16-bit addresses identify the first executable instruction of interrupt service routines. When an interrupt is acknowledged by the CPU in Mode 2, **the acknowledged external logic must place an interrupt response vector on the Data Bus. The Z80 CPU will combine the IV register contents with the interrupt acknowledge vector to form a 16-bit address, which accesses the interrupt address vector table.** Since 16-bit addresses must lie at even memory address boundaries, only seven of the eight bits provided by the acknowledged external logic will be used to create the table address; the low order bit will be set to 0. Thus the table of 16-bit interrupt address vectors will be accessed as follows:

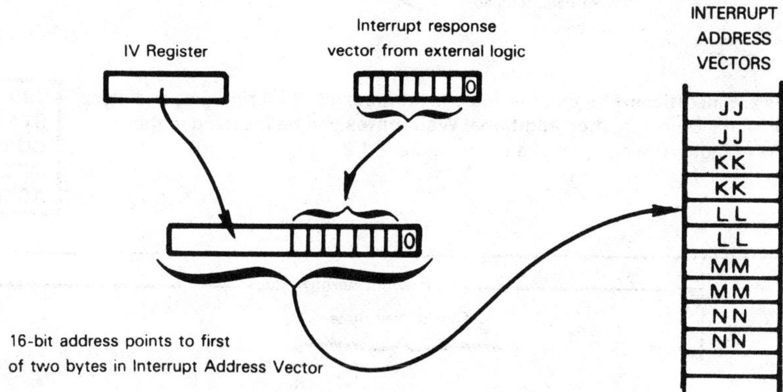


**The Z80 CPU will execute a Call to the memory location obtained from the interrupt address vector table.**

**Let us clarify this logic with a simple example.** Suppose that you have 64 possible external interrupts; each interrupt has its own interrupt service routine, therefore 64 starting addresses will be stored in 128 bytes of memory. Let us arbitrarily assume that these 128 bytes are stored in a table with memory addresses $0F00_{16}$ through $0F7F_{16}$. Now in order to use Mode 2, you must initially load the value $0F_{16}$ into the Z80 IV register. Subsequently an external interrupt request is acknowledged and the acknowledged external logic returns on the Data Bus the vector $2E_{16}$; this is what will happen:

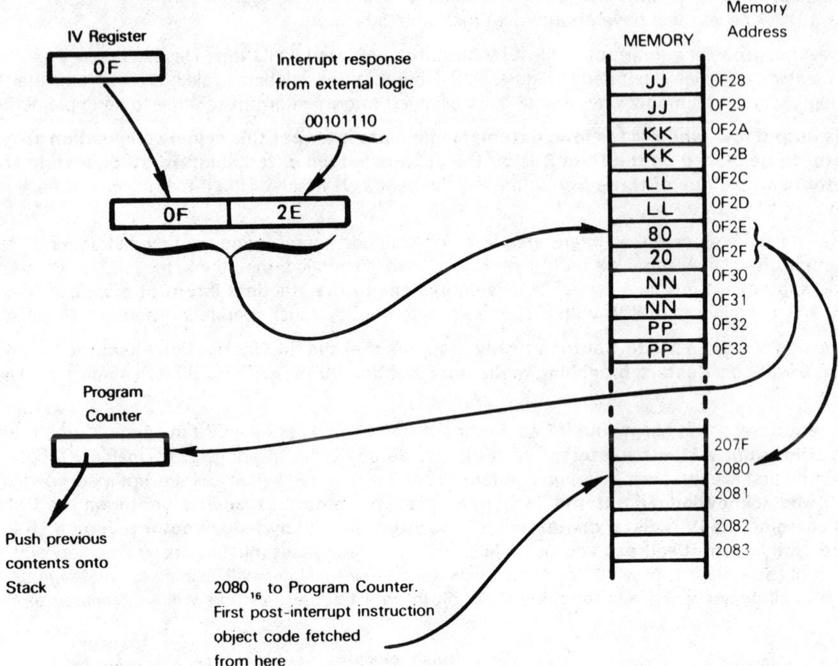


**Z80 WAIT STATES DURING INTERRUPT ACKNOWLEDGE**

**If two Wait states are insufficient** for external logic to arbitrate interrupt priorities and place the required vector on the Data Bus, **then additional Wait states can be inserted** in the usual way by inputting $\overline{WAIT}$ low. Timing is illustrated in Figure 7-13.

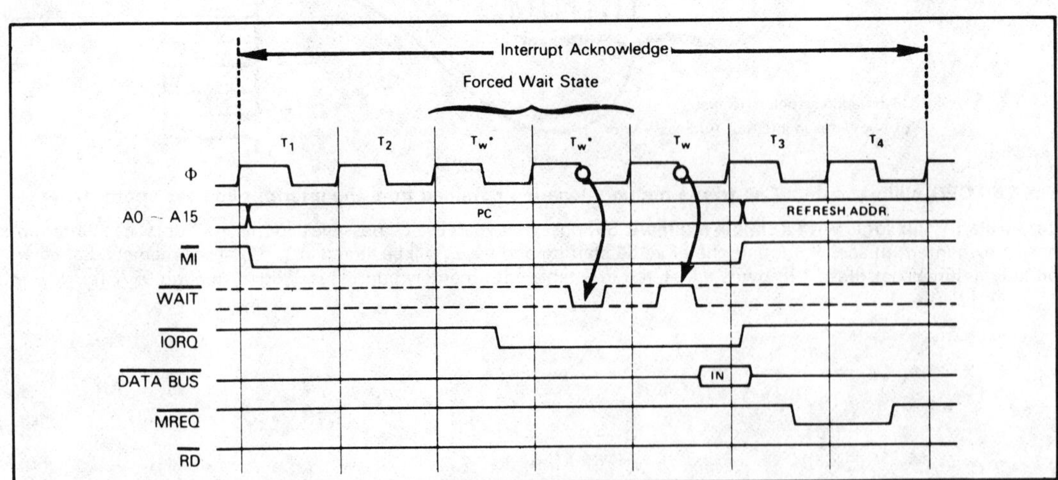


Figure 7-13. Wait States During Z80 Response to a Maskable Interrupt Request

**Z80 NON-MASKABLE INTERRUPT**

The response of the Z80 CPU to the non-maskable interrupt ($\overline{NMI}$) is quite similar to Mode 1 interrupt operation. There are a number of significant differences, however. First of all, the $\overline{NMI}$ interrupt cannot be disabled and has priority over the $\overline{INT}$ interrupt. (Remember that $\overline{BUSRQ}$ has priority over both interrupt inputs.)

Next, the non-maskable interrupt is an edge-sensitive (negative edge triggered) input. The Z80 reacts only to the edge of a pulse on the $\overline{NMI}$ line, rather than to a low level as is the case with the $\overline{INT}$ input. The negative edge of the $\overline{NMI}$ input causes an internal flip-flop to be set in the Z80, and this flip-flop is checked during the last cycle of an instruction execution. The CPU response to this interrupt is similar to a normal memory read operation except that the Data Bus is ignored on the next $\overline{M1}$ cycle. Timing for the interrupt response to the non-maskable interrupt request is illustrated in Figure 7-14.

The Z80 pushes the contents of the Program Counter onto the external stack and then automatically executes a Restart instruction to memory location $0066_{16}$. Thus, this response is the same as the response to an $\overline{INT}$ interrupt in Mode 1 except that the Restart call is to a different memory location.

While the Z80 CPU is responding to the non-maskable interrupt, the internal flip-flop (IFF1) used to enable maskable interrupts is reset to prevent interrupts during the $\overline{NMI}$ service routine. Upon completion of the service routine, you do not simply want to once again set the IFF1 flip-flop, since maskable interrupts may not have been enabled prior to $\overline{NMI}$. This quandary is solved by using a second internal flip-flop (IFF2) for temporary storage. As the CPU begins its response to the $\overline{NMI}$ interrupt, it saves the state of the interrupt enable flip-flop (IFF1) by copying it into IFF2. At the end of the $\overline{NMI}$ service routine, you must execute a Return from Non-Maskable Interrupt (RETN) instruction which will copy the contents of IFF2 back into IFF1, thus automatically restoring the correction status for the maskable interrupt enable.

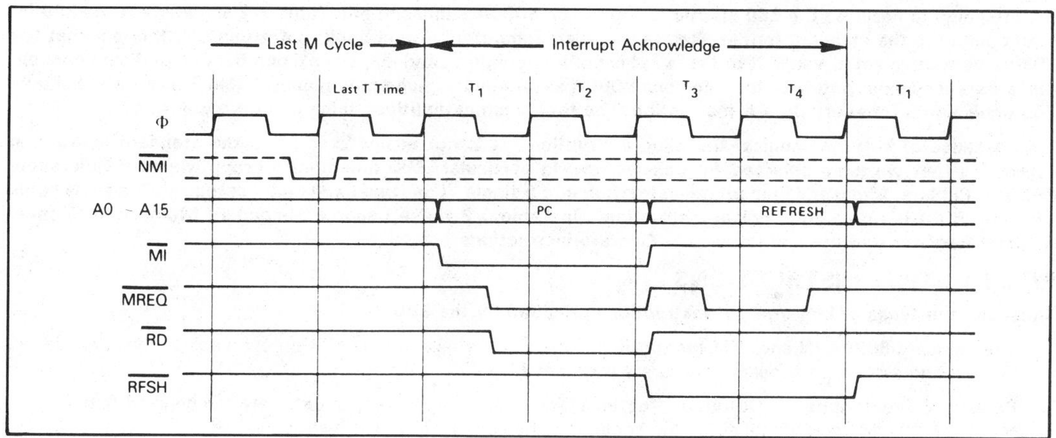


Figure 7-14. Z80 Response to a Nonmaskable Interrupt Request

## THE HALT INSTRUCTION

When a Halt instruction is executed by the Z80 CPU, a sequence of NOP instructions is executed until an interrupt request is received. Both maskable and nonmaskable interrupt request lines are sampled on the rising edge of $\Phi$ during $T_4$ of every NOP instruction's machine cycle.

The Halt state will terminate when any interrupt request is detected, at which time the appropriate interrupt acknowledge sequence will be initiated, as illustrated in Figures 7-13 and 7-14.

Note that the Z80 executes the sequence of NOP instructions during a Halt so that it can continue to generate dynamic memory refresh signals.

Halt instruction timing is illustrated in Figure 7-15.

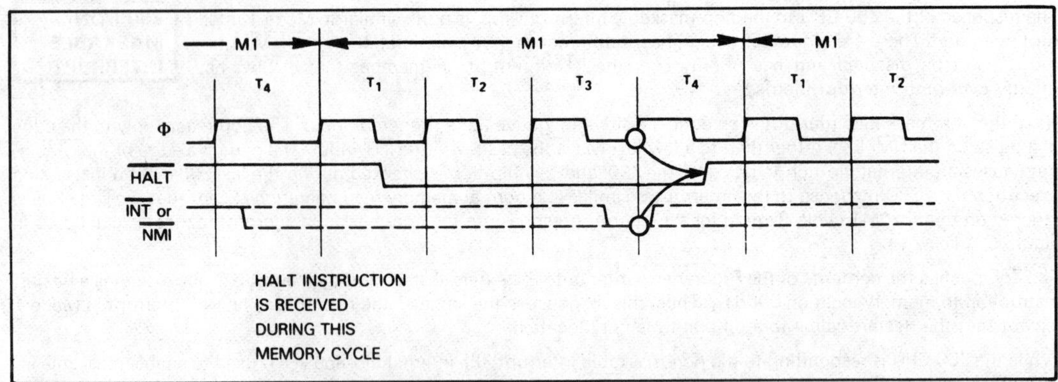


Figure 7-15. Z80 Halt Instruction Timing

# THE Z80 INSTRUCTION SET

**We are going to describe the Z80 instruction set as an 8080A enhancement. Table 7-2 summarizes the Z80 instruction set in the standard format used for all microcomputers in this book; unfortunately, the fact that the 8080A instruction set is a subset of Table 7-2 is not immediately obvious, since a number of significant conceptual differences exist between the Zilog and 8080A assembly language mnemonics. Table 7-3 therefore shows Z80 equivalents for every 8080A instruction. The few incompatibilities which exist are identified.**

**Also because of Z80 mnemonics, the Zilog instruction set is not easily forced into the standard instruction categories that we have selected for consistency. In particular, Z80 mnemonics group Memory Reference, Register-Register Move and Immediate instruction into a single "Load and Exchange" category. The same holds true for Z80 Arithmetic and Logical instructions; in Table 7-2 these become Secondary Memory Reference, Register-Register Operate and Immediate Operate instructions.**

## INPUT/OUTPUT INSTRUCTIONS

**These are the types of input/output instructions provided by the Z80:**

1) **The standard 8080A IN and OUT instructions,** whereby the second byte of instruction object code provides an I/O port address, which appears on Address Bus lines A0 - A7.

2) **Register indirect Input and Output instructions.** These instructions transfer data between Register A, B, C, D, E, H or L, and the I/O port identified by the contents of Register C. Thus the instruction:

```
LD      C,PORTN     ;LOAD PORT NUMBER INTO REGISTER C
-
-
-
IN      D,(C)       ;INPUT DATA FROM PORTN TO REGISTER D
```

is equivalent to:

```
IN      A,(PORTN)
LD      D,A
```

The I/O port address, now the contents of Register C, is output on A0 - A7 in the usual way.

3) **Block Transfer I/O instructions.** These instructions move a block of data between the I/O port identified by Register C and a memory location addressed by the H and L register pair. Register B is used as a block byte counter. After each byte of data within the block is transferred, the contents of Register B are decremented; you can specify block transfer I/O instructions that will either increment or decrement the memory address in Registers H and L. Here is a programming example with the 8080A equivalent:

```
        Z80                          8080A
LD      B,COUNT              MVI     B,COUNT
LD      C,PORTN              LXI     H,START
LD      HL,START     LOOP:   IN      PORTN
```

```
INIR                            MOV     M,A
                                INX     H
                                DCR     B
                                JNZ     LOOP
```

These instruction sequences input COUNT bytes from I/O port PORTN, and store the data in a memory buffer whose beginning address is START. COUNT and PORTN are symbols representing 8-bit numbers. START is an address label. The block transfer I/O instruction will continue executing until the B register has decremented to 0.

4) **Single Step Block Transfer I/O instructions.** These are identical to the block transfer I/O instructions described in category 3 above, except that instruction execution ceases after one iterative step. Referring to the INIR instruction example, if the INIR instruction were replaced by an INI instruction, a single byte of data would be transferred from PORTN to the memory location addressed by START. The address START would be incremented, Register B contents would be decremented, then instruction execution would cease.

When a block transfer or single step, block transfer I/O instruction is executed, C register contents, which identify the I/O port, are output on the lower eight Address Bus lines in the usual way; however, B register contents are output on the higher eight address lines A15 - A8. Therefore external logic can, if it wishes, determine the extent of the transfer.

**Let us now look at the advantages gained by having the new Z80 I/O instructions.**

**The value of the Register Indirect I/O instructions is that programs stored in ROM can access any I/O port.** If I/O port assignments change, then all you need to do is modify that small portion of program which loads the I/O port address into the C register.

**The Block Transfer I/O instructions must be approached with an element of caution.** In response to the execution of a single instruction's object code, up to 256 bytes of data may be transferred between memory and an I/O port. This data transfer occurs at CPU speed — which means external logic must input or output data at the same speed. If external logic cannot operate fast enough, it can insert Wait states in order to slow the CPU, but that takes additional logic; and one might argue that the traditional methods of polling on status to effect block I/O transfers is cheaper than adding extra Wait state logic.

Note that all Z80 enhanced I/O instructions require two bytes of object code.

## PRIMARY MEMORY REFERENCE INSTRUCTIONS

Instructions that we classify as Primary Memory Reference constitute a subset of the Load instructions, as classifed by Zilog. **Within the Primary Memory Reference instructions category, as we define it, Zilog offers a single enhancement: base relative addressing.** Instructions that move data between a register and memory may specify the memory address as the contents of an Index register; plus an 8-bit displacement provided by the instruction object code. Here is a programming example of Zilog base relative addressing and the 8080A equivalent:

```
          Z80                    8080A
LD        IX,BASE          LXI       H,BASE
LD        C,(IX + DISP)    LXI       D,DISP
                           DAD       D
                           MOV       C,M
```

Observe that the two Z80 instructions do not use any CPU registers — other than the IX Index register. The 8080A uses the DE and HL registers. Here is an example of the true value that results from having Index registers. The Z80 can use the DE and HL registers to store temporary data, which the 8080A cannot do; the 8080A would have to store such temporary data in external read/write memory.

The biggest single advantage that accrues to the Z80 from having indexed addressing is the fact that well written Z80 programs will contain far fewer memory reference instructions than equivalent 8080A programs; therefore Z80 programs will execute faster.

Other primary memory reference instructions provided by the Z80, and not present in the 8080A, include instructions which load data into the Index registers and store Index registers' contents in memory. Since the 8080A does not have Index registers, it cannot have memory reference instructions for them. The Z80 also has instructions which transfer 16-bit data between directly addressed memory and any register pair, except AF. Recall that in the 8080A, HL is the only register pair which stores to memory and loads from memory using direct addressing.

## BLOCK TRANSFER AND SEARCH INSTRUCTIONS

**We classify the Zilog Block Transfer and Search instructions in a separate category, since our hypothetical computer, as described in Volume I, had no equivalent instructions.**

**A Block Transfer instruction allows you to move up to 65,536 bytes of data between two memory buffers which may be anywhere in memory.** The H and L registers address the source buffer, the D and E registers address the destination buffer, and the B and C registers hold the byte count.

After every byte of data is transferred, the B and C registers' contents are decremented; instruction execution ceases after the B and C registers decrement to zero. You have the option of incrementing or decrementing the source and destination addresses following the transfer of each data byte. Thus you can transfer data from low to high memory, or from high to low memory. Here is a programming example of the Z80 Block Move instruction, along with the 8080A equivalent:

```
        Z80                         8080A
   LD    BC,COUNT               LXI    B,COUNT
   LD    DE,DEST                LXI    D,DEST
   LD    HL,SRCE                LXI    H,SRCE
   LDIR                 LOOP:   MOV    A,M
                                STAX   D
                                INX    H
                                INX    D
                                DCX    B
                                MOV    A,B
                                ORA    C
                                JNZ    LOOP
```

The two instruction sequences illustrated above move a block of data, COUNT bytes long, from a buffer whose starting address is SRCE to another buffer whose starting address is DEST. SRCE and DEST are 16-bit address labels. COUNT is a symbol representing a 16-bit data value.

The Z80 - 8080A comparison above is one that makes the 8080A look particularly bad. This is because it emphasizes 8080A weaknesses; the 8080A requires memory addresses to be incremented as separate steps. Also, after decrementing the counter in Registers B and C, status is not set, therefore BC contents are tested by loading B into A and ORing with C.

**You can use Block Move instructions in Z80 configurations that include dynamic memory.** While the Block Move is being executed, dynamic memory is refreshed.

**The Block Search instruction will search a block of data in memory, looking for a match with the Accumulator contents.** The H and L registers address memory, while the B and C registers again act as a byte counter. When a match between Accumulator contents and a memory location is found, the Search instruction ceases executing. After every Compare, the B and C registers' contents are decremented; once again you have the option of either incrementing or decrementing H and L registers' contents. Thus you can search a block of memory from high address down, or from low address up.

The results of every step in a Block Search are reported in the Z and P/O statuses. If a match is found between Accumulator and memory contents, then Z is set to 1; otherwise Z will equal 0. When the B and C registers count out to zero, the P/O status will be reset to 0; otherwise the P/O status will equal 1.

Here is an example of a program using the Z80 Block Search instruction, along with 8080A program equivalent:

```
        Z80                         8080A
   LD    A,REFC                 LXI    BC,COUNT
   LD    BC,COUNT               LXI    HL,SRCE
   LD    HL,SRCE        LOOP:   MVI    A,REFC
   CPDR                         CMP    M
   JR    Z,FOUND                JZ     FOUND
;NO MATCH FOUND                  DCX    H
   -                            DCX    B
   -                            MOV    A,B
;MATCH FOUND                    ORA    C
FOUND:                          JNZ    LOOP
   -                    ;NO MATCH FOUND
   -                            -
   -                            -
                                -
                        ;MATCH FOUND
                        FOUND:  -
                                -
                                -
```

Each of the above instruction sequences tries to match a character represented by the symbol REFC with the contents of bytes in a memory buffer. The memory buffer is origined at SRCE and is COUNT bytes long.

In the example illustrated above, SRCE is the highest memory address for the buffer, which is searched towards the low memory address. FOUND is the label for the first instruction in the sequence which is executed if a match is found. If no match is found, that is, the BC registers count out to 0, program execution continues with the next sequential instruction.

**The Z80 Block Search instruction is particularly useful when searching a large memory buffer for a byte that may frequently occur.** Suppose you have an ASCII text in which Control codes have been imbedded. For the sake of argument, let us assume that all Control codes are two bytes long, where the first byte has the hexadecimal value 02 and the second byte identifies the Control code. You can use one set of registers in order to search the text buffer for Control codes, while using the second set of registers to process the text buffer after each Control code has been located.

All you need to do in the Block Search instruction sequence illustrated above is follow the CPDR instruction with an EXX instruction; after executing the instruction sequence following MATCH FOUND, again execute an EXX instruction before returning to search for the next Control code.

**Each of the Block Move and Block Search instructions has a single step equivalent.** The single step instruction moves one byte of data, or compares the Accumulator contents with the next byte in a data buffer; addresses and counters are incremented and decremented as for the Block Move and Search instructions, however execution ceases after a single step has been completed.

## SECONDARY MEMORY REFERENCE (MEMORY OPERATE) INSTRUCTIONS

Instructions that we classify as Secondary Memory Reference, or Memory Operate, constitute a portion of the arithmetic and logical instructions, as defined by the Z80. **Within the Memory Operate group of instructions, the single enhancement offered by the Z80 is a duplicate set of instructions that uses base relative addressing.** We have already discussed this enhancement in connection with Primary Memory Reference instructions. Here is a programming example with the 8080A equivalent:

```
          Z80                  8080A
LD        IX,BASE         LXI      H,BASE
ADD       (IX + DISP)     LXI      D,DISP
                          DAD      D
                          ADD      M
```

The same comments we made regarding the use of indexed addressing in the Primary Memory Reference example apply to the instruction sequences above.

## IMMEDIATE INSTRUCTIONS

**Within the group of instructions that we classify as Immediate, the Z80 offers two enhancements:**

1) Instructions are provided to load immediate data into the additional Z80 registers.
2) You can use base relative addressing to load a byte of data immediately into read/write memory.

## JUMP INSTRUCTIONS

**In addition to the standard Jump instruction offered by the 8080A, the Z80 has a two-byte, unconditional Branch instruction, and two instructions which allow you to jump to the memory location specified by an Index register.**

The two indexed Jump instructions transfer the contents of the identified Index register to the Program Counter.

The two-byte Jump instruction interprets the second object code byte as an 8-bit signed binary number, which is added to the Program Counter, after the Program Counter has been incremented to point to the next instruction. This is a standard program relative branch, as described in Volume I.

Note that the Z80 uses many of the spare 8080A object codes to implement the two-byte Branch and Branch-on-Condition instructions. This makes sense; it would certainly not make much sense to have two bytes of object code followed by a single branch byte, since that would create a three-byte Branch instruction — offering no advantage over the three-byte Jump instructions which already exist.

## SUBROUTINE CALL AND RETURN INSTRUCTIONS

**The Z80 instructions in this group are identical to 8080A equivalents.**

## IMMEDIATE OPERATE INSTRUCTIONS

**Z80 Immediate Operate instructions, as we define them, are identical to those in the 8080A instruction set.**

## JUMP-ON-CONDITION INSTRUCTION

**The Z80 offers two significant Jump-on-Condition instruction enhancements over the 8080A:**

1) **There are two-byte equivalents for four of the more commonly used Jump-on-Condition instructions.** The two-byte Jump-on-Condition instructions execute exactly as described for the two-byte Jump instruction.

2) **There is a decrement and Jump-on-Nonzero instruction** which is particularly useful in any kind of iterative loop. When this instruction is executed, the B register contents are decremented; if the B register contents, after being decremented, equal zero, the next sequential instruction is executed. If after being decremented the B register contents are not zero, then a Jump occurs. This is a two-byte instruction, where the Jump is specified by a single 8-bit signed binary value.

Here is an example of how the DJNZ instruction may be used along with the 8080A equivalent:

```
               Z80                          8080A
        AND    A                     ANA    A
        LD     IX,VALA               LXI    D,VALA
        LD     IY,VALB               LXI    H,VALB
        LD     B,CNT                 MVI    B,CNT
LOOP:   LD     A,(IX)        LOOP:   LDAX   D
        ADC    A,(IY)                ADC    M
        LD     (IX),A                STAX   D
        INC    IX                    INX    D
        INC    IY                    INX    H
        DJNZ   LOOP                  DCR    B
                                     JNZ    LOOP
```

The two instruction sequences illustrated above perform simple multibyte binary addition. The contents of two buffers, origined at VALA and VALB, are summed; the results are stored in buffer VALA.

The first instruction in each sequence is executed in order to clear the Carry status. Like the 8080A, the Z80 does not have an instruction which sets the Carry status to 0, while performing no other operation.

## REGISTER-REGISTER MOVE INSTRUCTIONS

Register-Register Move instructions, as we defined them in this book, constitute a subset of the Z80 Load instructions. All Z80 Exchange instructions, except those that exchange with the top of the Stack, are also classified as Register-Register Move instructions.

**The Z80 enhancements within this instruction group apply strictly to the additional registers implemented within the Z80.** That is to say, because the Z80 has registers which the 8080A does not have, the Z80 must also have instructions to move data in and out of these additional registers.

The instructions which exchange data between registers and their alternates need comment. Note that you can swap the entire set of duplicated registers, or you can swap selected register pairs. If you use these instructions following an interrupt acknowledge, you do not have to save the contents of the registers on the Stack. Of course, this will only work for a single interrupt level. There are also occasions when the alternate set of registers can be used effectively in normal programming logic, as we illustrated when describing the Block Search instruction.

## REGISTER-REGISTER OPERATE INSTRUCTIONS

**There are a few new Z80 Register-Register Operate instructions which do the following:**

1) Add without Carry the contents of a register pair to an Index register.

2) Add with Carry to HL the contents of a register pair.

3) Subtract with Carry from HL the contents of a register pair.

## REGISTER OPERATE INSTRUCTIONS

**Within this category, the Z80 has two enhancements:**

1) You can increment or decrement the contents of an Index register.

2) A rich variety of Shift and Rotate instructions have been added. These instructions are illustrated in Table 7-2. In particular, note the RLD and RRD instructions, which are very useful when performing multidigit BCD left and right shifts.

## BIT MANIPULATION INSTRUCTIONS

**The 8080A has no equivalent for this set of Z80 instructions.** We give these instructions a separate category in Table 7-2 because of their extreme importance in microprocessor applications.

Bit manipulation instructions are particularly important for signal processing. A single signal is a binary entity; it is not part of an 8-bit unit. One of the great oversights among microprocessor designers has been to ignore bit manipulation instructions. **The Z80 has instructions that set to 1 (SET), reset to 0 (RES) or test (BIT) individual bits in memory or any general purpose register.** The result of a bit test is reported in the Zero status.

Here are some Z80 instructions with 8080A equivalents:

```
        Z80                   8080A
BIT      4,A            MOV     B,A
                        ANI     10H
                        MOV     A,B
```

The 8080A tests Accumulator bits destructively — all untested bits are cleared; Accumulator contents must therefore be saved before testing. We can also contrive an example to emphasize the strengths of the Z80 bit instructions:

```
         Z80                     8080A
LD       IY,BASE            LXI      H,BASE
SET      2,(IY + DISP)      LXI      D,DISP
                            DAD      D
                            MVI      A,4
                            ORA      M
```

Once again, note that the 8080A needs to use the D, E, H and L registers.

Note that all Z80 Bit instructions operate on memory or CPU registers. But in most microcomputer applications individual pins at I/O ports will most frequently be set, reset or tested. The Z80 has no I/O Bit instructions. If you wish, you can interface I/O devices so that they are addressed as memory locations; however, in that case, you cannot use Block I/O instructions.

The 8080A can do anything that a Z80 Bit Manipulation instruction can do but an additional Mask instruction is needed and the Accumulator is involved. On the surface these seem to be small penalties; but it is the frequency with which Bit Manipulation instructions are needed that escalates small penalties into major aggravations.

## STACK INSTRUCTIONS

**Additional Stack instructions provided by the Z80 allow the Z80 Index registers to be pushed onto the Stack, popped from the Stack, or exchanged with the top of the Stack.**

## INTERRUPT INSTRUCTIONS

In addition to the 8080A Interrupt instructions, the Z80 has two Return-from-Interrupt instructions. **RETI and RETN are used to return from maskable and nonmaskable interrupt service routines, respectively.**

RETI and RETN are two-byte instructions. **Within the CPU these instructions enable interrupts, but otherwise execute exactly as a Return-from-Subroutine (RET) instruction. However, devices designed by Zilog to support the Z80 CPU use the RETI and RETN instructions in a unique way.** Any support device that has logic to request an interrupt also includes logic which tests the Data Bus contents during the low $\overline{M1}$ pulse. Upon detecting the second byte of an RETI or RETN instruction's object code, a device which has had an interrupt request acknowledged determines that the interrupt has been serviced.

Why does a support device need to know that an interrupt service routine has completed execution? The reason is that Zilog extends interrupt priority arbitration logic beyond the interrupt acknowledge process to the entire interrupt service routine.

This is the scheme adopted by the 8259 PICU. After reading the next paragraph, if you are still unclear on concepts, refer to the 8259 PICU discussion in the 8080A chapter.

Consider the typical daisy chain scheme used to set interrupt priorities in a multiple interrupt microcomputer system. Daisy chaining has been described in good detail in Volume 1. When more than one device is requesting an interrupt, an acknowledge ripples down the daisy chain until trapped by the interrupt requesting device electrically closest to the CPU. As soon as the interrupt acknowledge process has ceased, an interrupt service routine is executed for the acknowledged interrupt; acknowledged external logic will now remove its interrupt request. Unless the CPU disables further interrupts, a lower priority device can immediately interrupt the service routine of a higher priority device. With the Zilog system, that is not the case. A device which has its interrupt request acknowledged continues to suppress interrupt requests from all lower priority devices in a daisy chain, until the second object code byte for an RETI or RETN instruction is detected on the Data Bus. The acknowledged device responds to an RETI or RETN instruction's object code by re-enabling interrupts for devices with lower priority in the daisy chain.

Providing a Zilog microcomputer system has been designed to make correct use of the RETI and RETN instructions, interrupt priority arbitration logic will allow an interrupt service routine to be interrupted only by a high priority interrupt request.

Here is an illustration of the Zilog interrupt priority arbitration scheme:

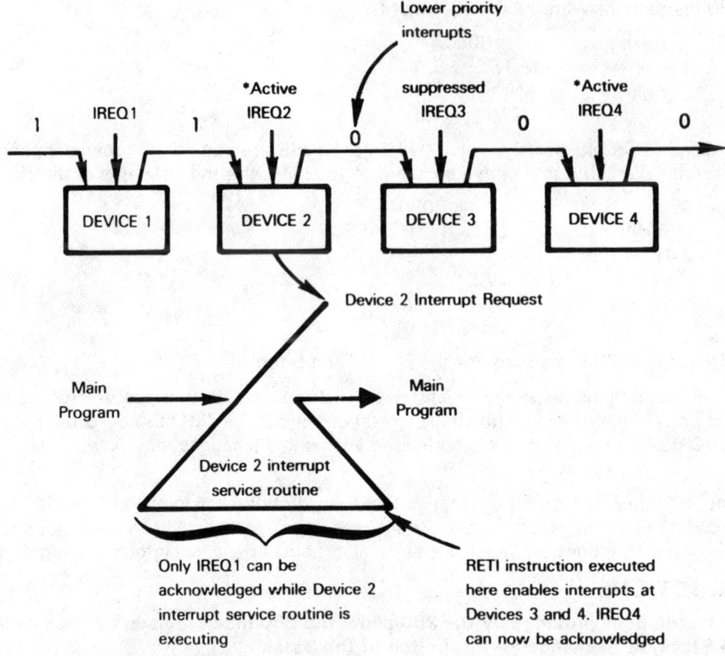


**The three IM instructions allow you to specify that the CPU will respond to maskable interrupts in Mode 0, 1 or 2.** These three interrupt response modes have already been described.

## STATUS AND MISCELLANEOUS INSTRUCTIONS

Z80 and 8080A instructions in these categories are identical.

## THE BENCHMARK PROGRAM

Our benchmark program is coded for the Z80 as follows:

```
LD      BC,LENGTH      ;LOAD IO BUFFER LENGTH INTO BC
LD      DE,(TABLE)     ;LOAD ADDRESS OF FIRST FREE TABLE BYTE OUT OF FIRST TWO TABLE
                       ;BYTES
LD      HL,IOBUF       ;LOAD SOURCE ADDRESS INTO HL
LDIR                   ;EXECUTE BLOCK MOVE
```

The program above makes absolutely no assumptions. Both source and destination tables may have any length and may be located anywhere in memory.

Notice that there is no instruction execution loop, since the LDIR block move will not stop executing until the entire block of data has been moved.

The following abbreviations are used in this chapter:

| | |
|---|---|
| A,F,B,C,D,E,H,L | The 8-bit registers. A is the Accumulator and F is the Program Status Word. |
| AF',BC',DE',HL' | The alternative register pairs |
| addr | A 16-bit memory address |
| x(b) | Bit b of 8-bit register or memory location x |
| cond | Condition for program branching. Conditions are:<br>NZ - Non-Zero (Z=0)<br>Z - Zero (Z=1)<br>NC - Non-carry (C=0)<br>C - Carry (C=1)<br>PO - Parity Odd (P=0)<br>PE - Parity Even (P=1)<br>P - Sign Positive (S=0)<br>M - Sign Negative (S=1) |
| data | An 8-bit binary data unit |
| data16 | A 16-bit binary data unit |
| disp | An 8-bit signed binary address displacement |
| xx(HI) | The high-order 8 bits of a 16-bit quantity xx |
| IV | Interrupt vector register (8 bits) |
| IX,IY | The Index registers (16 bits each) |
| xy | Either one of the Index registers (IX or IY) |
| LSB | Least Significant Bit (Bit 0) |
| label | A 16-bit instruction memory address |
| xx(LO) | The low-order 8 bits of a 16-bit quantity xx |
| MSB | Most Significant Bit (Bit 7) |
| PC | Program Counter |
| port | An 8-bit I/O port address |
| pr | Any of the following register pairs:<br>BC<br>DE<br>HL<br>AF |
| R | The Refresh register (8 bits) |
| reg | Any of the following registers:<br>A<br>B<br>C<br>D<br>E<br>H<br>L |
| rp | Any of the following register pairs:<br>BC<br>DE<br>HL<br>SP |
| SP | Stack Pointer (16 bits) |

| | |
|---|---|
| Statuses | The Z80 has the following status flags:<br>C - Carry status<br>Z - Zero status<br>S - Sign status<br>P/O - Parity/Overflow status<br>$A_C$ - Auxiliary Carry status<br>N - Subtract status<br>The following symbols are used in the status columns:<br>X - flag is affected by operation<br>(blank) - flag is not affected by operation<br>1 - flag is set by operation<br>0 - flag is reset by operation<br>? - flag is unknown after operation<br>P - flag shows parity status<br>O - flag shows overflow status<br>I - flag shows interrupt enabled/disabled status |
| [ ] | Contents of location enclosed within brackets. If a register designation is enclosed within the brackets, then the designated register's contents are specified. If an I/O port number is enclosed within the brackets, then the I/O port contents are specified. If a memory address is enclosed within the brackets, then the contents of the addressed memory location are specified. |
| [[ ]] | Implied memory addressing; the contents of the memory location designated by the contents of a register. |
| ∧ | Logical AND |
| ∨ | Logical OR |
| ∀ | Logical Exclusive-OR |
| ← | Data is transferred in the direction of the arrow |
| ←→ | Data is exchanged between the two locations designated on either side of the arrow. |

**The fixed part of an assembly language instruction is shown in UPPER CASE.**

**The variable part (immediate data, I/O device number, register name, label or address) is shown in lower case.**

## Table 7-2. A Summary of the Z80 Instruction Set

| TYPE | MNEMONIC | OPERAND(S) | BYTES | STATUS C | Z | S | P/O | $A_C$ | N | OPERATION PERFORMED |
|---|---|---|---|---|---|---|---|---|---|---|
| I/O | IN | A,port | 2 | | | | | | | [A]←[port]<br>Input to Accumulator from directly addressed I/O port.<br>Address Bus: A0-A7: port<br>A8-A15: [A] |
| | IN | reg,(C) | 2 | | X | X | P | X | 0 | [reg]←[[C]]<br>Input to register from I/O port addressed by the contents of C.*<br>If second byte is $70_{16}$ only the flags will be affected. |
| | INIR | | 2 | | 1 | ? | ? | ? | 1 | Repeat until [B]=0:<br>[[HL]]←[[C]]<br>[B]←[B] - 1<br>[HL]←[HL] + 1<br>Transfer a block of data from I/O port addressed by contents of C to memory location addressed by contents of HL, going from low addresses to high. Contents of B serve as a count of bytes remaining to be transferred.* |
| | INDR | | 2 | | 1 | ? | ? | ? | 1 | Repeat until [B]=0:<br>[[HL]]←[[C]]<br>[B]←[B] - 1<br>[HL]←[HL] - 1<br>Transfer a block of data from I/O port addressed by contents of C to memory location addressed by contents of HL, going from high addresses to low. Contents of B serve as a count of bytes remaining to be transferred.* |
| | INI | | 2 | | X | ? | ? | ? | 1 | [[HL]]←[[C]]<br>[B]←[B] - 1<br>[HL]←[HL] + 1<br>Transfer a byte of data from I/O port addressed by contents of C to memory location addressed by contents of HL. Decrement byte count and increment destination address.* |
| | IND | | 2 | | X | ? | ? | ? | 1 | [[HL]]←[[C]]<br>[B]←[B] - 1<br>[HL]←[HL] - 1<br>Transfer a byte of data from I/O port addressed by contents of C to memory location addressed by contents of HL. Decrement both byte count and destination address.* |
| | OUT | port,A | 2 | | | | | | | [port]←[A]<br>Output from Accumulator to directly addressed I/O port.<br>Address Bus: A0-A7: port<br>A8-A15: [A] |
| | OUT | (C),reg | 2 | | | | | | | [[C]]←[reg]<br>Output from register to I/O port addressed by the contents of C.* |
| | OTIR | | 2 | | 1 | ? | ? | ? | 1 | Repeat until [B]=0:<br>[[C]]←[[HL]]<br>[B]←[B] - 1<br>[HL]←[HL] + 1<br>Transfer a block of data from memory location addressed by contents of HL to I/O port addressed by contents of C, going from low memory to high. Contents of B serve as a count of bytes remaining to be transferred.* |

*Address Bus: A0-A7: [C]
A8-A15: [B]

Table 7-2. A Summary of the Z80 Instruction Set (Continued)

| TYPE | MNEMONIC | OPERAND(S) | BYTES | C | Z | S | P/O | $A_C$ | N | OPERATION PERFORMED |
|---|---|---|---|---|---|---|---|---|---|---|
| I/O (Continued) | OTDR | | 2 | | 1 | ? | ? | ? | 1 | Repeat until [B]=0:<br>[[C]]←[[HL]]<br>[B]←[B] - 1<br>[HL]←[HL] - 1<br>Transfer a block of data from memory location addressed by contents of HL to I/O port addressed by contents of C, going from high memory to low. Contents of B serve as a count of bytes remaining to be transferred.* |
| | OUTI | | 2 | | X | ? | ? | ? | 1 | [[C]]←[[HL]]<br>[B]←[B] - 1<br>[HL]←[HL] + 1<br>Transfer a byte of data from memory location addressed by contents of HL to I/O port addressed by contents of C. Decrement byte count and increment source address.* |
| | OUTD | | 2 | | X | ? | ? | ? | 1 | [[C]]←[[HL]]<br>[B]←[B] - 1<br>[HL]←[HL] - 1<br>Transfer a byte of data from memory location addressed by contents of HL to I/O port addressed by contents of C. Decrement both byte count and source address.* |
| PRIMARY MEMORY REFERENCE | LD | A,(addr) | 3 | | | | | | | [A]←[addr]<br>Load Accumulator from directly addressed memory location. |
| | LD | HL,(addr) | 3 | | | | | | | [H]←[addr + 1], [L]←[addr]<br>Load HL from directly addressed memory. |
| | LD | rp,(addr)<br>xy,(addr) | 4 | | | | | | | [rp(HI)]←[addr + 1], [rp(LO)]←[addr] or<br>[xy(HI)]←[addr + 1], [xy(LO)]←[addr]<br>Load register pair or Index register from directly addressed memory. |
| | LD | (addr),A | 3 | | | | | | | [addr]←[A]<br>Store Accumulator contents in directly addressed memory location. |
| | LD | (addr),HL | 3 | | | | | | | [addr + 1]←[H], [addr]←[L]<br>Store contents of HL to directly addressed memory location. |
| | LD | (addr),rp<br>(addr),xy | 4 | | | | | | | [addr + 1]←[rp(HI)], [addr]←[rp(LO)] or<br>[addr + 1]←[xy(HI)], [addr]←[xy(LO)]<br>Store contents of register pair or Index register to directly addressed memory. |
| | LD | A,(BC)<br>A,(DE) | 1 | | | | | | | [A]←[[BC]] or [A]←[[DE]]<br>Load Accumulator from memory location addressed by the contents of the specified register pair. |
| | LD | reg,(HL) | 1 | | | | | | | [reg]←[[HL]]<br>Load register from memory location addressed by contents of HL. |
| | LD | (BC),A<br>(DE),A | 1 | | | | | | | [[BC]]←[A] or [[DE]]←[A]<br>Store Accumulator to memory location addressed by the contents of the specified register pair. |
| | LD | (HL),reg | 1 | | | | | | | [[HL]]←[reg]<br>Store register contents to memory location addressed by the contents of HL. |
| | LD | reg,(xy + disp) | 3 | | | | | | | [reg]←[[xy] + disp]<br>Load register from memory location using base relative addressing. |
| | LD | (xy + disp),reg | 3 | | | | | | | [[xy] + disp]←[reg]<br>Store register to memory location addressed relative to contents of Index register. |

*Address Bus: A0-A7: [C]
A8-A15: [B]

Table 7-2. A Summary of the Z80 Instruction Set (Continued)

| TYPE | MNEMONIC | OPERAND(S) | BYTES | STATUS | | | | | | OPERATION PERFORMED |
|---|---|---|---|---|---|---|---|---|---|---|
| | | | | C | Z | S | P/O | $A_C$ | N | |
| BLOCK TRANSFER AND SEARCH | LDIR | | 2 | | | | 0 | 0 | 0 | Repeat until [BC]=0:<br>[[DE]]←[[HL]]<br>[DE]←[DE] + 1<br>[HL]←[HL] + 1<br>[BC]←[BC] - 1<br>Transfer a block of data from the memory location addressed by the contents of HL to the memory location addressed by the contents of DE, going from low addresses to high. Contents of BC serve as a count of bytes to be transferred. |
| | LDDR | | 2 | | | | 0 | 0 | 0 | Repeat until [BC]=0:<br>[[DE]]←[[HL]]<br>[DE]←[DE] - 1<br>[HL]←[HL] - 1<br>[BC]←[BC] - 1<br>Transfer a block of data from the memory location addressed by the contents of HL to the memory location addressed by the contents of DE, going from high addresses to low. Contents of BC serve as a count of bytes to be transferred. |
| | LDI | | 2 | | | | X | 0 | 0 | [[DE]]←[[HL]]<br>[DE]←[DE] + 1<br>[HL]←[HL] + 1<br>[BC]←[BC] - 1<br>Transfer one byte of data from the memory location addressed by the contents of HL to the memory location addressed by the contents of DE. Increment source and destination addresses and decrement byte count. |
| | LDD | | 2 | | | | X | 0 | 0 | [[DE]]←[[HL]]<br>[DE]←[DE] - 1<br>[HL]←[HL] - 1<br>[BC]←[BC] - 1<br>Transfer one byte of data from the memory location addressed by the contents of HL to the memory location addressed by the contents of DE. Decrement source and destination addresses and byte count. |
| | CPIR | | 2 | | X | X | X | X | 1 | Repeat until [A]=[[HL]] or [BC]=0:<br>[A] - [[HL]] (only flags are affected)<br>[HL]←[HL] + 1<br>[BC]←[BC] - 1<br>Compare contents of Accumulator with those of memory block addressed by contents of HL, going from low addresses to high. Stop when a match is found or when the byte count becomes zero. |
| | CPDR | | 2 | | X | X | X | X | 1 | Repeat until [A]=[[HL]] or [BC]=0:<br>[A] - [[HL]] (only flags are affected)<br>[HL]←[HL] - 1<br>[BC]←[BC] - 1<br>Compare contents of Accumulator with those of memory block addressed by contents of HL, going from high addresses to low. Stop when a match is found or when the byte count becomes zero. |

Table 7-2. A Summary of the Z80 Instruction Set (Continued)

| TYPE | MNEMONIC | OPERAND(S) | BYTES | STATUS C | Z | S | P/O | $A_C$ | N | OPERATION PERFORMED |
|---|---|---|---|---|---|---|---|---|---|---|
| BLOCK TRANSFER AND SEARCH (Continued) | CPI | | 2 | | X | X | X | X | 1 | [A] - [[HL]] (only flags are affected)<br>[HL]←[HL] + 1<br>[BC]←[BC] - 1<br>Compare contents of Accumulator with those of memory location addressed by contents of HL. Increment address and decrement byte count. |
| | CPD | | 2 | | X | X | X | X | 1 | [A] - [[HL]] (only flags are affected)<br>[HL]←[HL] - 1<br>[BC]←[BC] - 1<br>Compare contents of Accumulator with those of memory location addressed by contents of HL. Decrement address and byte count. |
| SECONDARY MEMORY REFERENCE | ADD | (HL)<br>(xy + disp) | 1<br>3 | X | X | X | O | X | 0 | [A]←[A] + [[HL]] or [A]←[A] + [[xy] + disp]<br>Add to Accumulator using implied addressing or base relative addressing. |
| | ADC | (HL)<br>(xy + disp) | 1<br>3 | X | X | X | O | X | 0 | [A]←[A] + [[HL]] + C or [A]←[A] + [[xy] + disp] + C<br>Add with Carry using implied addressing or base relative addressing. |
| | SUB | (HL)<br>(xy + disp) | 1<br>3 | X | X | X | O | X | 1 | [A]←[A] - [[HL]] or [A]←[A] - [[xy] + disp]<br>Subtract from Accumulator using implied addressing or base relative addressing. |
| | SBC | (HL)<br>(xy + disp) | 1<br>3 | X | X | X | O | X | 1 | [A]←[A] - [[HL] - C or [A]←[A] - [[xy] + disp] - C<br>Subtract with Carry using implied addressing or base relative addressing. |
| | AND | (HL)<br>(xy + disp) | 1<br>3 | 0 | X | X | P | 1 | 0 | [A]←[A] Λ [[HL]] or [A]←[A] Λ [[xy] + disp]<br>AND with Accumulator using implied addressing or base relative addressing |
| | OR | (HL)<br>(xy + disp) | 1<br>3 | 0 | X | X | P | 1 | 0 | [A]←[A] V [[HL]] or [A]←[A] V [[xy] + disp]<br>OR with Accumulator using implied addressing or base relative addressing. |
| | XOR | (HL)<br>(xy + disp) | 1<br>3 | 0 | X | X | P | 1 | 0 | [A]←[A]⊻ [[HL]] or [A]←[A]⊻ [[xy] + disp]<br>Exclusive-OR with Accumulator using implied addressing or base relative addressing. |
| | CP | (HL)<br>(xy + disp) | 1<br>3 | X | X | X | O | X | 1 | [A] - [[HL]] or [A] - [[xy] + disp]<br>Compare with Accumulator using implied addressing or base relative addressing. Only the flags are affected. |
| | INC | (HL)<br>(xy + disp) | 1<br>3 | | X | X | O | X | 0 | [[HL]]←[[HL]] + 1 or [[xy] + disp]←[[xy] + disp] + 1<br>Increment using implied addressing or base relative addressing. |
| | DEC | (HL)<br>(xy + disp) | 1<br>3 | | X | X | O | X | 1 | [[HL]]←[[HL]] - 1 or [[xy] + disp]←[[xy] + disp] - 1<br>Decrement using implied addressing or base relative addressing. |

Table 7-2. A Summary of the Z80 Instruction Set (Continued)

| TYPE | MNEMONIC | OPERAND(S) | BYTES | STATUS C | Z | S | P/O | $A_C$ | N | OPERATION PERFORMED |
|---|---|---|---|---|---|---|---|---|---|---|
| MEMORY SHIFT AND ROTATE | RLC | (HL)<br>(xy + disp) | 2<br>4 | X | X | X | P | 0 | 0 | 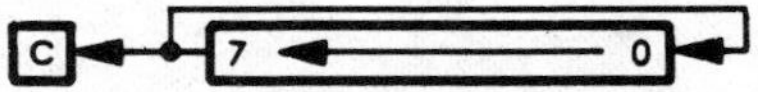 [[HL]] or [[xy] + disp]<br>Rotate contents of memory location (implied or base relative addressing) left with branch Carry. |
| | RL | (HL)<br>(xy + disp) | 2<br>4 | X | X | X | P | 0 | 0 | 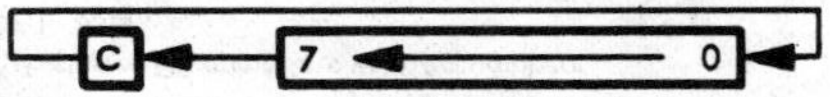 [[HL]] or [[xy] + disp]<br>Rotate contents of memory location left through Carry. |
| | RRC | (HL)<br>(xy + disp) | 2<br>4 | X | X | X | P | 0 | 0 | 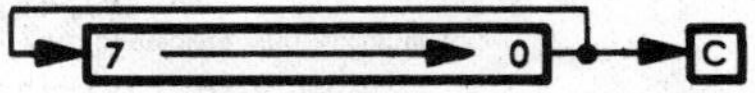 [[HL]] or [[xy] + disp]<br>Rotate contents of memory location right with branch Carry. |
| | RR | (HL)<br>(xy + disp) | 2<br>4 | X | X | X | P | 0 | 0 | 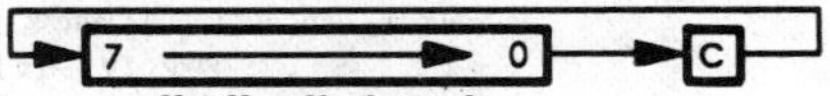 [[HL]] or [[xy] + disp]<br>Rotate contents of memory location right through Carry. |
| | SLA | (HL)<br>(xy + disp) | 2<br>4 | X | X | X | P | 0 | 0 | [[HL]] or [[xy] + disp]<br>Shift contents of memory location left and clear LSB (Arithmetic Shift). |
| | SRA | (HL)<br>(xy + disp) | 2<br>4 | X | X | X | P | 0 | 0 | 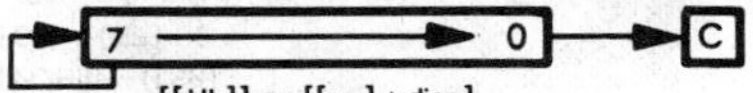 [[HL]] or [[xy] + disp]<br>Shift contents of memory location right and preserve MSB (Arithmetic Shift). |
| | SRL | (HL)<br>(xy + disp) | 2<br>4 | X | X | X | P | 0 | 0 | 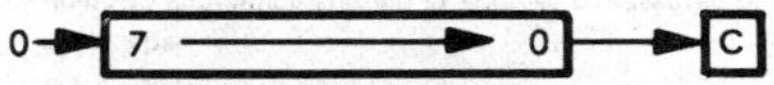 [[HL]] or [[xy] + disp]<br>Shift contents of memory location right and clear MSB (Logical Shift). |
| IMMEDIATE | LD | reg,data | 2 | | | | | | | [reg] ← data<br>Load immediate into register. |
| | LD | rp,data16<br>xy,data16 | 3<br>4 | | | | | | | [rp] ← data16 or [xy] ← data16<br>Load 16 bits of immediate data into register pair or Index register. |
| | LD | (HL),data<br>(xy + disp),data | 2<br>4 | | | | | | | [[HL]] ← data or [[xy] + disp] ← data<br>Load immediate into memory location using implied or base relative addressing. |

Table 7-2. A Summary of the Z80 Instruction Set (Continued)

| TYPE | MNEMONIC | OPERAND(S) | BYTES | STATUS C | STATUS Z | STATUS S | STATUS P/O | STATUS $A_C$ | STATUS N | OPERATION PERFORMED |
|---|---|---|---|---|---|---|---|---|---|---|
| JUMP | JP | label | 3 | | | | | | | [PC]←label<br>Jump to instruction at address represented by label. |
| | JR | disp | 2 | | | | | | | [PC]←[PC] + 2 + disp<br>Jump relative to present contents of Program Counter. |
| | JP | (HL)<br>(xy) | 1<br>2 | | | | | | | [PC]←[HL] or [PC]←[xy]<br>Jump to address contained in HL or Index register. |
| SUBROUTINE CALL AND RETURN | CALL | label | 3 | | | | | | | [[SP]-1]←[PC(HI)]<br>[[SP]-2]←[PC(LO)]<br>[SP]←[SP]-2<br>[PC]←label<br>Jump to subroutine starting at address represented by label. |
| | CALL | cond,label | 3 | | | | | | | Jump to subroutine if condition is satisfied; otherwise, continue in sequence. |
| | RET | | 1 | | | | | | | [PC(LO)]←[[SP]]<br>[PC(HI)]←[[SP] + 1]<br>[SP]←[SP] + 2<br>Return from subroutine. |
| | RET | cond | 1 | | | | | | | Return from subroutine if condition is satisfied; otherwise, continue in sequence. |
| IMMEDIATE OPERATE | ADD | data | 2 | X | X | X | O | X | 0 | [A]←[A] + data<br>Add immediate to Accumulator. |
| | ADC | data | 2 | X | X | X | O | X | 0 | [A]←[A] + data + C<br>Add immediate with Carry. |
| | SUB | data | 2 | X | X | X | O | X | 1 | [A]←[A] - data<br>Subtract immediate from Accumulator. |
| | SBC | data | 2 | X | X | X | O | X | 1 | [A]←[A] - data - C<br>Subtract immediate with Carry. |
| | AND | data | 2 | 0 | X | X | P | 1 | 0 | [A]←[A] Λ data<br>AND immediate with Accumulator. |
| | OR | data | 2 | 0 | X | X | P | 1 | 0 | [A]←[A] V data<br>OR immediate with Accumulator. |
| | XOR | data | 2 | 0 | X | X | P | 1 | 0 | [A]←[A] ⊻ data<br>Exclusive-OR immediate with Accumulator. |
| | CP | data | 2 | X | X | X | O | X | 1 | [A] - data<br>Compare immediate data with Accumulator contents; only the flags are affected. |

Table 7-2. A Summary of the Z80 Instruction Set (Continued)

| TYPE | MNEMONIC | OPERAND(S) | BYTES | STATUS | | | | | | OPERATION PERFORMED |
|---|---|---|---|---|---|---|---|---|---|---|
| | | | | C | Z | S | P/O | $A_C$ | N | |
| JUMP ON CONDITION | JP | cond,label | 3 | | | | | | | If cond, then [PC]←label<br>Jump to instruction at address represented by label if the condition is true. |
| | JR | C,disp | 2 | | | | | | | If C=1, then [PC]←[PC] + 2 + disp<br>Jump relative to contents of Program Counter if Carry flag is set. |
| | JR | NC,disp | 2 | | | | | | | If C=0, then [PC]←[PC] + 2 + disp<br>Jump relative to contents of Program Counter if Carry flag is reset. |
| | JR | Z,disp | 2 | | | | | | | If Z=1, then [PC]←[PC] + 2 + disp<br>Jump relative to contents of Program Counter if Zero flag is set. |
| | JR | NZ,disp | 2 | | | | | | | If Z=0, then [PC]←[PC] + 2 + disp<br>Jump relative to contents of Program Counter if Zero flag is reset. |
| | DJNZ | disp | 2 | | | | | | | [B]←[B] - 1<br>If [B] ≠ 0, then [PC]←[PC] + 2 + disp<br>Decrement contents of B and Jump relative to contents of Program Counter if result is not 0. |
| REGISTER-REGISTER MOVE | LD | dst,src | 1 | | | | | | | [dst]←[src]<br>Move contents of source register to destination register. Register designations src and dst may each be A, B, C, D, E, H or L. |
| | LD | A,IV | 2 | | X | X | I | 0 | 0 | [A]←[IV]<br>Move contents of Interrupt Vector register to Accumulator. |
| | LD | A,R | 2 | | X | X | I | 0 | 0 | [A]←[R]<br>Move contents of Refresh register to Accumulator. |
| | LD | IV,A | 2 | | | | | | | [IV]←[A]<br>Load Interrupt Vector register from Accumulator. |
| | LD | R,A | 2 | | | | | | | [R]←[A]<br>Load Refresh register from Accumulator. |
| | LD | SP,HL | 1 | | | | | | | [SP]←[HL]<br>Move contents of HL to Stack Pointer. |
| | LD | SP,xy | 2 | | | | | | | [SP]←[xy]<br>Move contents of Index register to Stack Pointer. |
| | EX | DE,HL | 1 | | | | | | | [DE]←→[HL]<br>Exchange contents of DE and HL. |
| | EX | AF,AF' | 1 | | | | | | | [AF]←→[AF']<br>Exchange program status and alternate program status. |
| | EXX | | 1 | | | | | | | ([BC] [DE] [HL]) ←→ ([BC'] [DE'] [HL'])<br>Exchange register pairs and alternate register pairs. |

Table 7-2. A Summary of the Z80 Instruction Set (Continued)

| TYPE | MNEMONIC | OPERAND(S) | BYTES | STATUS C | STATUS Z | STATUS S | STATUS P/O | STATUS $A_C$ | STATUS N | OPERATION PERFORMED |
|---|---|---|---|---|---|---|---|---|---|---|
| REGISTER-REGISTER OPERATE | ADD | reg | 1 | X | X | X | O | X | 0 | [A]←[A] + [reg]<br>Add contents of register to Accumulator. |
| | ADC | reg | 1 | X | X | X | O | X | 0 | [A]←[A] + [reg] + C<br>Add contents of register and Carry to Accumulator. |
| | SUB | reg | 1 | X | X | X | O | X | 1 | [A]←[A] - [reg]<br>Subtract contents of register from Accumulator. |
| | SBC | reg | 1 | X | X | X | O | X | 1 | [A]←[A] - [reg] - C<br>Subtract contents of register and Carry from Accumulator. |
| | AND | reg | 1 | 0 | X | X | P | 1 | 0 | [A]←[A] ∧ [reg]<br>AND contents of register with contents of Accumulator. |
| | OR | reg | 1 | 0 | X | X | P | 1 | 0 | [A]←[A] ∨ [reg]<br>OR contents of register with contents of Accumulator. |
| | XOR | reg | 1 | 0 | X | X | P | 1 | 0 | [A]←[A] ⊻ [reg]<br>Exclusive-OR contents of register with contents of Accumulator. |
| | CP | reg | 1 | X | X | X | O | X | 1 | [A] - [reg]<br>Compare contents of register with contents of Accumulator. Only the flags are affected. |
| | ADD | HL,rp | 1 | X | | | | ? | 0 | [HL]←[HL] + [rp]<br>16-bit add register pair contents to contents of HL. |
| | ADC | HL,rp | 2 | X | X | X | O | ? | 0 | [HL]←[HL] + [rp] + C<br>16-bit add with Carry register pair contents to contents of HL. |
| | SBC | HL,rp | 2 | X | X | X | O | ? | 1 | [HL]←[HL] - [rp] - C<br>16-bit subtract with Carry register pair contents from contents of HL. |
| | ADD | IX,pp | 2 | X | | | | ? | 0 | [IX]←[IX] + [pp]<br>16-bit add register pair contents to contents of Index register IX (pp=BC, DE, IX, SP) |
| | ADD | IY,rr | 2 | X | | | | ? | 0 | [IY]←[IY] + [rr]<br>16-bit add register pair contents to contents of Index register IY (rr=BC, DE, IY, SP). |
| REGISTER OPERATE | DAA | | 1 | X | X | X | P | X | | Decimal adjust Accumulator, assuming that Accumulator contents are the sum or difference of BCD operands. |
| | CPL | | 1 | | | | | 1 | 1 | [A]←[$\overline{A}$]<br>Complement Accumulator (ones complement). |
| | NEG | | 2 | X | X | X | O | X | 1 | [A]←[$\overline{A}$] + 1<br>Negate Accumulator (twos complement). |
| | INC | reg | 1 | | X | X | O | X | 0 | [reg]←[reg] + 1<br>Increment register contents. |
| | INC | rp<br>xy | 1 | | | | | | | [rp]←[rp] + 1 or [xy]←[xy] + 1<br>Increment contents of register pair or Index register. |
| | DEC | reg | 2 | | X | X | O | X | 1 | [reg]←[reg] - 1<br>Decrement register contents. |
| | DEC | rp<br>xy | 1<br>2 | | | | | | | [rp]←[rp] - 1 or [xy]←[xy] - 1<br>Decrement contents of register pair or Index register. |

Table 7-2. A Summary of the Z80 Instruction Set (Continued)

| TYPE | MNEMONIC | OPERAND(S) | BYTES | STATUS C | STATUS Z | STATUS S | STATUS P/O | STATUS $A_C$ | STATUS N | OPERATION PERFORMED |
|---|---|---|---|---|---|---|---|---|---|---|
| REGISTER SHIFT AND ROTATE | RLCA | | 1 | X | | | | 0 | 0 |  [A] Rotate Accumulator left with branch Carry. |
| | RLA | | 1 | X | | | | 0 | 0 |  [A] Rotate Accumulator left through Carry. |
| | RRCA | | 1 | X | | | | 0 | 0 |  [A] Rotate Accumulator right with branch Carry. |
| | RRA | | 1 | X | | | | 0 | 0 |  [A] Rotate Accumulator right through Carry. |
| | RLC | reg | 2 | X | X | X | P | 0 | 0 |  [reg] Rotate contents of register left with branch Carry. |
| | RL | reg | 2 | X | X | X | P | 0 | 0 |  [reg] Rotate contents of register left through Carry. |
| | RRC | reg | 2 | X | X | X | P | 0 | 0 |  [reg] Rotate contents of register right with branch Carry. |
| | RR | reg | 2 | X | X | X | P | 0 | 0 |  [reg] Rotate contents of register right through Carry. |
| | SLA | reg | 2 | X | X | X | P | 0 | 0 |  [reg] Shift contents of register left and clear LSB (Arithmetic Shift). |
| | SRA | reg | 2 | X | X | X | P | 0 | 0 |  [reg] Shift contents of register right and preserve MSB (Arithmetic Shift). |

Table 7-2. A Summary of the Z80 Instruction Set (Continued)

| TYPE | MNEMONIC | OPERAND(S) | BYTES | STATUS C | Z | S | P/O | $A_C$ | N | OPERATION PERFORMED |
|---|---|---|---|---|---|---|---|---|---|---|
| REGISTER SHIFT AND ROTATE (Continued) | SRL | | 2 | X | X | X | P | 0 | 0 | 0→ [7 → 0] → C<br>[reg]<br>Shift contents of register right and clear MSB (Logical Shift). |
| | RLD | | 2 | | X | X | P | 0 | 0 | [7 4\|3 0] [7 4\|3 0]<br>[A] [[HL]]<br>Rotate one BCD digit left between the Accumulator and memory location (implied addressing).<br>Contents of the upper half of the Accumulator are not affected. |
| | RRD | reg | 2 | | X | X | P | 0 | 0 | [7 4\|3 0] [7 4\|3 0]<br>[A] [[HL]]<br>Rotate one BCD digit right between the Accumulator and memory location (implied addressing).<br>Contents of the upper half of the Accumulator are not affected. |
| BIT MANIPULATION | BIT | b,reg | 2 | | X | ? | ? | 1 | 0 | Z←$\overline{\text{reg(b)}}$<br>Zero flag contains complement of the selected register bit. |
| | BIT | b,(HL)<br>b,(xy + disp) | 2<br>4 | | X | ? | ? | 1 | 0 | Z← $\overline{\text{[[HL]](b)}}$ or Z← $\overline{\text{[[xy] + disp](b)}}$<br>Zero flag contains complement of selected bit of the memory location (implied addressing or base relative addressing). |
| | SET | b,reg | 2 | | | | | | | reg(b)←1<br>Set indicated register bit. |
| | SET | b,(HL)<br>b,(xy + disp) | 2<br>4 | | | | | | | [[HL]](b)←1 or [[xy] + disp](b)←1<br>Set indicated bit of memory location (implied addressing or base relative addressing). |
| | RES | b,reg | 2 | | | | | | | reg(b)←0<br>Reset indicated register bit. |
| | RES | b,(HL)<br>b,(xy + disp) | 2<br>4 | | | | | | | [[HL]](b)←0 or [[xy] + disp](b)←0<br>Reset indicated bit in memory location (implied addressing or base relative addressing). |
| STACK | PUSH | pr<br>xy | 1<br>2 | | | | | | | [[SP]-1]←[pr(HI)]<br>[[SP]-2]←[pr(LO)]<br>[SP]←[SP]-2<br>Put contents of register pair or Index register on top of Stack and decrement Stack Pointer. |
| | POP | pr<br>xy | 1<br>2 | | | | | | | [pr(LO)]←[[SP]]<br>[pr(HI)]←[[SP] + 1]<br>[SP]←[SP] + 2<br>Put contents of top of Stack in register pair or Index register and increment Stack Pointer. |
| | EX | (SP),HL<br>(SP),xy | 1<br>2 | | | | | | | [H]←[[SP] + 1]<br>[L]←[[SP]]<br>Exchange contents of HL or Index register and top of Stack. |

Table 7-2. A Summary of the Z80 Instruction Set (Continued)

| TYPE | MNEMONIC | OPERAND(S) | BYTES | STATUS C | STATUS Z | STATUS S | STATUS P/O | STATUS $A_C$ | STATUS N | OPERATION PERFORMED |
|---|---|---|---|---|---|---|---|---|---|---|
| INTERRUPT | DI | | 1 | | | | | | | Disable interrupts. |
| | EI | | 1 | | | | | | | Enable interrupts. |
| | RST | n | 1 | | | | | | | [[SP]-1]←[PC(HI)]<br>[[SP]-2]←[PC(LO)]<br>[SP]←[SP]-2<br>[PC]←$(8 \cdot n)_{16}$<br>Restart at designated location. |
| | RETI | | 2 | | | | | | | Return from interrupt. |
| | RETN | | 2 | | | | | | | Return from nonmaskable interrupt. |
| | IM | 0<br>1<br>2 | 2 | | | | | | | Set interrupt mode 0, 1, or 2. |
| STATUS | SCF | | 1 | 1 | | | | 0 | 0 | C←1<br>Set Carry flag. |
| | CCF | | 1 | X | | | | ? | 0 | C←$\overline{C}$<br>Complement Carry flag. |
| | NOP | | 1 | | | | | | | No operation — volatile memories are refreshed. |
| | HALT | | 1 | | | | | | | CPU halts, executes NOPs to refresh volatile memories. |

Table 7-3. A Summary of Instruction Object Codes and Execution Cycles with 8080A Mnemonics for Identical Instructions

| INSTRUCTION | OBJECT CODE | BYTES | CLOCK PERIODS | 8080A MNEMONIC | 8080A CLOCK PERIODS |
|---|---|---|---|---|---|
| ADC data | CE yy | 2 | 7 | ACI data | 7 |
| ADC (HL) | 8E | 1 | 7 | ADC M | 7 |
| ADC HL,rp | ED 01xx1010 | 2 | 15 | | |
| ADC (IX + disp) | DD 8E yy | 3 | 19 | | |
| ADC (IY + disp) | FD 8E yy | 3 | 19 | | |
| ADC reg | 10001xxx | 1 | 4 | ADC reg | 4 |
| ADD data | C6 yy | 2 | 7 | ADI data | 7 |
| ADD (HL) | 86 | 1 | 7 | ADD M | 7 |
| ADD HL,rp | 00xx1001 | 1 | 11 | DAD rp | 10 |
| ADD (IX + disp) | DD 86 yy | 3 | 19 | | |
| ADD IX,pp | DD 00xx1001 | 2 | 15 | | |
| ADD (IY + disp) | FD 86 yy | 3 | 19 | | |
| ADD IY,rr | FD 00xx1001 | 2 | 15 | | |
| ADD reg | 10000xxx | 1 | 4 | ADD reg | 4 |
| AND data | E6 yy | 2 | 7 | ANI data | 7 |
| AND (HL) | A6 | 1 | 7 | ANA M | 7 |
| AND (IX + disp) | DD A6 yy | 3 | 19 | | |
| AND (IY + disp) | FD A6 yy | 3 | 19 | | |
| AND reg | 10100xxx | 1 | 4 | ANA reg | 4 |
| BIT b,(HL) | CB<br>01bbb110 | 2 | 12 | | |
| BIT b,(IX + disp) | DD CB yy<br>01bbb110 | 4 | 20 | | |
| BIT b,(IY + disp) | FD CB yy<br>01bbb110 | 4 | 20 | | |
| BIT b,reg | CB<br>01bbbxxx | 2 | 8 | | |
| CALL label | CD ppqq | 3 | 17 | CALL label | 17 |
| CALL C,label | DC ppqq | 3 | 10/17 | CC label | 11/17 |
| CALL M,label | FC ppqq | 3 | 10/17 | CM label | 11/17 |
| CALL NC,label | D4 ppqq | 3 | 10/17 | CNC label | 11/17 |
| CALL NZ,label | C4 ppqq | 3 | 10/17 | CNZ label | 11/17 |
| CALL P,label | F4 ppqq | 3 | 10/17 | CP label | 11/17 |
| CALL PE,label | EC ppqq | 3 | 10/17 | CPE label | 11/17 |
| CALL PO,label | E4 ppqq | 3 | 10/17 | CPO label | 11/17 |
| CALL Z,label | CC ppqq | 3 | 10/17 | CZ label | 11/17 |
| CCF | 3F | 1 | 4 | CMC | 4 |
| CP data | FE yy | 2 | 7 | CPI data | 7 |
| CP (HL) | BE | 1 | 7 | CMP M | 7 |
| CP (IX + disp) | DD BE yy | 3 | 19 | | |
| CP (IY + disp) | FD BE yy | 3 | 19 | CMP reg | 19 |
| CP reg | 10111xxx | 1 | 4 | | |
| CPD | ED A9 | 2 | 16 | | |
| CPDR | ED B9 | 2 | 21/16* | | * |
| CPI | ED A1 | 2 | 16 | | |
| CPIR | ED B1 | 2 | 21/16* | | * |
| CPL | 2F | 1 | 4 | CMA | 4 |
| DAA | 27 | 1 | 4 | DAA | 4 |
| DEC (HL) | 35 | 1 | 11 | DCR M | 10 |
| DEC IX | DD 2B | 2 | 10 | | |
| DEC (IX + disp) | DD 35 yy | 3 | 23 | | |
| DEC IY | FD 2B | 2 | 10 | | |
| DEC (IY + disp) | FD 35 yy | 3 | 23 | | |
| DEC rp | 00xx1011 | 1 | 6 | DCX rp | 5 |
| DEC reg | 00xxx101 | 1 | 4 | DCR reg | 5 |
| DI | F3 | 1 | 4 | DI | 4 |
| DJNZ disp | 10 yy | 2 | 8/13 | | |
| EI | FB | 1 | 4 | EI | 4 |
| EX AF,AF' | 08 | 1 | 4 | | |
| EX DE,HL | EB | 1 | 4 | XCHG | 4 |
| EX (SP),HL | E3 | 1 | 19 | XTHL | 18 |
| EX (SP),IX | DD E3 | 2 | 23 | | |

Table 7-3. A Summary of Instruction Object Codes and Execution Cycles with 8080A Mnemonics for Identical Instructions (Continued)

| INSTRUCTION | | OBJECT CODE | BYTES | CLOCK PERIODS | 8080A MNEMONIC | | 8080A CLOCK PERIODS |
|---|---|---|---|---|---|---|---|
| EX | (SP),IY | FD E3 | 2 | 23 | | | |
| EXX | | D9 | 1 | 4 | | | |
| HALT | | 76 | 1 | 4 | HLT | | 4 |
| IM | 0 | ED 46 | 2 | 8 | | | |
| IM | 1 | ED 56 | 2 | 8 | | | |
| IM | 2 | ED 5E | 2 | 8 | | | |
| IN | A,port | DB yy | 2 | 10 | IN | port | 10 |
| IN | reg,(C) | ED 01ddd000 | 2 | 11 | | | |
| INC | (HL) | 34 | 1 | 11 | INR | M | 10 |
| INC | IX | DD 23 | 2 | 10 | | | |
| INC | (IX + disp) | DD 34 yy | 3 | 23 | | | |
| INC | IY | FD 23 | 2 | 10 | | | |
| INC | (IY + disp) | FD 34 yy | 3 | 23 | | | |
| INC | rp | 00xx0011 | 1 | 6 | INX | rp | 5 |
| INC | reg | 00xxx100 | 1 | 4 | INR | reg | 5 |
| IND | | ED AA | 2 | 15 | | | * |
| INDR | | ED BA | 2 | 20/15 | | | |
| INI | | ED A2 | 2 | 15 | | | |
| INIR | | ED B2 | 2 | 20/15 | | | |
| JP | label | C3 ppqq | 3 | 10 | JMP | label | 10 |
| JP | C,label | DA ppqq | 3 | 10 | JC | label | 10 |
| JP | (HL) | E9 | 1 | 4 | PCHL | | 5 |
| JP | (IX) | DD E9 | 2 | 8 | | | |
| JP | (IY) | FD E9 | 2 | 8 | | | |
| JP | M,label | FA ppqq | 3 | 10 | JM | label | 10 |
| JP | NC,label | D2 ppqq | 3 | 10 | JNC | label | 10 |
| JP | NZ,label | C2 ppqq | 3 | 10 | JNZ | label | 10 |
| JP | P,label | F2 ppqq | 3 | 10 | JP | label | 10 |
| JP | PE,label | EA ppqq | 3 | 10 | JPE | label | 10 |
| JP | PO,label | E2 ppqq | 3 | 10 | JPO | label | 10 |
| JP | Z,label | CA ppqq | 3 | 10 | JZ | label | 10 |
| JR | C,disp | 38 yy | 2 | 7/12 | | | |
| JR | disp | 18 yy | 2 | 12 | | | |
| JR | NC,disp | 30 yy | 2 | 7/12 | | | |
| JR | NZ,disp | 20 yy | 2 | 7/12 | | | |
| JR | Z,disp | 28 yy | 2 | 7/12 | | | |
| LD | A,(addr) | 3A ppqq | 3 | 13 | LDA | addr | 13 |
| LD | A,(BC) | 0A | 1 | 7 | LDAX | B | 7 |
| LD | A,(DE) | 1A | 1 | 7 | LDAX | D | 7 |
| LD | A,I | ED 57 | 2 | 9 | | | |
| LD | A,R | ED 5F | 2 | 9 | | | |
| LD | (addr),A | 32 ppqq | 3 | 13 | STA | addr | 13 |
| LD | (addr),BC | ED 43 ppqq | 4 | 20 | | | |
| LD | (addr),DE | ED 53 ppqq | 4 | 20 | | | |
| LD | (addr),HL | 22 ppqq | 3 | 16 | SHLD | addr | 16 |
| LD | (addr),IX | DD 22 ppqq | 4 | 20 | | | |
| LD | (addr),IY | FD 22 ppqq | 4 | 20 | | | |
| LD | (addr),SP | ED 73 ppqq | 4 | 20 | | | |
| LD | (BC),A | 02 | 1 | 7 | STAX | B | 7 |
| LD | (DE),A | 12 | 1 | 7 | STAX | D | 7 |
| LD | HL,(addr) | 2A ppqq | 3 | 16 | LHLD | addr | 16 |
| LD | (HL),data | 36 yy | 2 | 10 | MVI | M,data | 10 |
| LD | (HL),reg | 01110sss | 1 | 7 | MOV | M,reg | 7 |
| LD | I,A | ED 47 | 2 | 9 | | | |
| LD | IX,(addr) | DD 2A ppqq | 4 | 20 | | | |
| LD | IX,data16 | DD 21 yyyy | 4 | 14 | | | |
| LD | (IX + disp),data | DD 36 yy yy | 4 | 19 | | | |
| LD | (IX + disp),reg | DD 01110sss yy | 3 | 19 | | | |
| LD | IY,(addr) | FD 2A ppqq | 4 | 20 | | | |
| LD | IY,data16 | FD 21 yyyy | 4 | 14 | | | |

Table 7-3. A Summary of Instruction Object Codes and Execution Cycles with 8080A Mnemonics for Identical Instructions (Continued)

| INSTRUCTION | OBJECT CODE | BYTES | CLOCK PERIODS | 8080A MNEMONIC | 8080A CLOCK PERIODS |
|---|---|---|---|---|---|
| LD (IY + disp),data | FD 36 yyyy | 4 | 19 | | |
| LD (IY + disp),reg | FD 01110sss<br>yy | 3 | 19 | | |
| LD R,A | ED 4F | 2 | 9 | | |
| LD reg,data | 00ddd110<br>yy | 2 | 7 | MVI reg,data | 7 |
| LD reg,(HL) | 01ddd110 | 1 | 7 | MOV reg,M | 7 |
| LD reg,(IX + disp) | DD<br>01ddd110<br>yy | 3 | 19 | | |
| LD reg,(IY + disp) | FD<br>01dddd110<br>yy | 3 | 19 | | |
| LD reg,reg | 01dddsss | 1 | 4 | MOV reg,reg | 5 |
| LD rp,(addr) | ED 01xx1011<br>ppqq | 4 | 20 | | |
| LD rp,data16 | 00xx0001<br>yyyy | 3 | 10 | LXI rp,data16 | 10 |
| LD SP,HL | F9 | 1 | 6 | SPHL | 5 |
| LD SP,IX | DD F9 | 2 | 10 | | |
| LD SP,IY | FD F9 | 2 | 10 | | |
| LDD | ED A8 | 2 | 16 | | |
| LDDR | ED B8 | 2 | 21/16* | | * |
| LDI | ED A0 | 2 | 16 | | |
| LDIR | ED B0 | 2 | 21/16* | | * |
| NEG | ED 44 | 2 | 8 | | |
| NOP | 00 | 1 | 4 | NOP | 4 |
| OR data | F6 yy | 2 | 7 | ORI data | 7 |
| OR (HL) | B6 | 1 | 7 | ORA M | 7 |
| OR (IX + disp) | DD B6 yy | 3 | 19 | | |
| OR (IY + disp) | FD B6 yy | 3 | 19 | | |
| OR reg | 10110xxx | 1 | 4 | ORA reg | 5 |
| OTDR | ED BB | 2 | 20/15* | | * |
| OTIR | ED B3 | 2 | 20/15* | | * |
| OUT (C),reg | ED 01sss001 | 2 | 12 | | |
| OUT port,A | D3 yy | 2 | 11 | OUT port | 10 |
| OUTD | ED AB | 2 | 15 | | |
| OUTI | ED A3 | 2 | 15 | | |
| POP IX | DD E1 | 2 | 14 | | |
| POP IY | FD E1 | 2 | 14 | | |
| POP pr | 11xx0001 | 1 | 10 | POP rp | 10 |
| PUSH IX | DD E5 | 2 | 15 | | |
| PUSH IY | FD E5 | 2 | 15 | | |
| PUSH pr | 11xx0101 | 1 | 11 | PUSH rp | 11 |
| RES b,(HL) | CB<br>10bbb110 | 2 | 15 | | |
| RES b,(IX + disp) | DD CB yy<br>10bbb110 | 4 | 23 | | |
| RES b,(IY + disp) | FD CB yy<br>10bbb110 | 4 | 23 | | |
| RES b,reg | CB<br>10bbbxxx | 2 | 8 | | |
| RET | C9 | 1 | 10 | RET | 10 |
| RET C | D8 | 1 | 5/11 | RC | 5/11 |
| RET M | F8 | 1 | 5/11 | RM | 5/11 |
| RET NC | D0 | 1 | 5/11 | RNC | 5/11 |
| RET NZ | C0 | 1 | 5/11 | RNZ | 5/11 |
| RET P | F0 | 1 | 5/11 | RP | 5/11 |
| RET PE | E8 | 1 | 5/11 | RPE | 5/11 |
| RET PO | E0 | 1 | 5/11 | RPO | 5/11 |
| RET Z | C8 | 1 | 5/11 | RZ | 5/11 |
| RETI | ED 4D | 2 | 14 | | |

Table 7-3. A Summary of Instruction Object Codes and Execution Cycles with 8080A Mnemonics for Identical Instructions (Continued)

| INSTRUCTION | OBJECT CODE | BYTES | CLOCK PERIODS | 8080A MNEMONIC | 8080A CLOCK PERIODS |
|---|---|---|---|---|---|
| RETN | ED 45 | 2 | 14 | | |
| RL (HL) | CB 16 | 2 | 15 | | |
| RL (IX + disp) | DD CB yy 16 | 4 | 23 | | |
| RL (IY + disp) | FD CB yy 16 | 4 | 23 | | |
| RL reg | CB<br>00010xxx | 2 | 8 | | |
| RLA | 17 | 1 | 4 | RAL | 4 |
| RLC (HL) | CB 06 | 2 | 15 | | |
| RLC (IX + disp) | DD CB yy 06 | 4 | 23 | | |
| RLC (IY + disp) | FD CB yy 06 | 4 | 23 | | |
| RLC reg | CB<br>00000xxx | 2 | 8 | | |
| RLCA | 07 | 1 | 4 | RLC | 4 |
| RLD | ED 6F | 2 | 18 | | |
| RR (HL) | CB 1E | 2 | 15 | | |
| RR (IX + disp) | DD CB yy 1E | 4 | 23 | | |
| RR (IY + disp) | FD CB yy 1E | 4 | 23 | | |
| RR reg | CB<br>00011xxx | 2 | 8 | | |
| RRA | 1F | 1 | 4 | RAR | 4 |
| RRC (HL) | CB 0E | 2 | 15 | | |
| RRC (IX + disp) | DD CB yy 0E | 4 | 23 | | |
| RRC (IY + disp) | FD CB yy 0E | 4 | 23 | | |
| RRC reg | CB<br>00001xxx | 2 | 8 | | |
| RRCA | 0F | 1 | 4 | RRC | 4 |
| RRD | ED 67 | 2 | 18 | | |
| RST n | 11xxx111 | 1 | 11 | RST n | 11 |
| SBC data | DE yy | 2 | 7 | SBI data | 7 |
| SBC (HL) | 9E | 1 | 7 | SBB m | 7 |
| SBC HL,rp | ED 01xx0010 | 2 | 15 | | |
| SBC (IX + disp) | DD 9E yy | 3 | 19 | | |
| SBC (IY + disp) | FD 9E yy | 3 | 19 | | |
| SBC reg | 10011xxx | 1 | 4 | SBB reg | 4 |
| SCF | 37 | 1 | 4 | STC | 4 |
| SET b,(HL) | CB<br>11bbb110 | 2 | 15 | | |
| SET b,(IX + disp) | DD CB yy<br>11bbb110 | 4 | 23 | | |
| SET b,(IY + disp) | FD CB yy<br>11bbb110 | 4 | 23 | | |
| SET b,reg | CB<br>11bbbxxx | 2 | 8 | | |
| SLA (HL) | CB 26 | 2 | 15 | | |
| SLA (IX + disp) | DD CB yy 26 | 4 | 23 | | |
| SLA (IY + disp) | FD CB yy 26 | 4 | 23 | | |
| SLA reg | CB 00100xxx | 2 | 8 | | |
| SRA (HL) | CB 2E | 2 | 15 | | |
| SRA (IX + disp) | DD CB yy 2E | 4 | 23 | | |
| SRA (IY + disp) | FD CB yy 2E | 4 | 23 | | |
| SRA reg | CB 00101xxx | 2 | 8 | | |
| SRL (HL) | CB 3E | 2 | 15 | | |
| SRL (IX + disp) | DD CB yy 3E | 4 | 23 | | |
| SRL (IY + disp) | FD CB yy 3E | 4 | 23 | | |
| SRL reg | CB 00111xxx | 2 | 8 | | |
| SUB data | D6 yy | 2 | 7 | SUI data | 7 |
| SUB (HL) | 96 | 1 | 7 | SUB M | 7 |
| SUB (IX + disp) | DD 96 yy | 3 | 19 | | |
| SUB (IY + disp) | FD 96 yy | 3 | 19 | | |
| SUB reg | 10010xxx | 1 | 4 | SUB reg | 4 |
| XOR data | EE yy | 2 | 7 | XRI data | 7 |
| XOR (HL) | AE | 1 | 7 | XRA M | 7 |

Table 7-3. A Summary of Instruction Object Codes and Execution Cycles with 8080A Mnemonics for Identical Instructions (Continued)

| INSTRUCTION | | OBJECT CODE | BYTES | CLOCK PERIODS | 8080A MNEMONIC | | 8080A CLOCK PERIODS |
|---|---|---|---|---|---|---|---|
| XOR | (IX + disp) | DD AE yy | 3 | 19 | | | |
| XOR | (IY + disp) | FD AE yy | 3 | 19 | | | |
| XOR | reg | 10101xxx | 1 | 4 | XRA | reg | 4 |

x represents an optional binary digit.

bbb represents optional binary digits identifying a bit location in a register or memory byte. (000 = LSB, 111 = MSB)

ddd represents optional binary digits identifying a destination register.
111 = A
000 = B
001 = C
010 = D
011 = E
100 = H
101 = L

sss represents optional binary digits identifying a source register — same coding as ddd.

ppqq represents a four hexadecimal digit memory address.

yy represents two hexadecimal data digits.

yyyy represents four hexadecimal data digits.

When two possible execution times are shown (i.e., 5/11), it indicates that the number of clock periods depends on condition flags.

*Execution time shown is for one iteration.

# SUPPORT DEVICES THAT MAY BE USED WITH THE Z80

The Z80 signal interface is very close to that of the 8080A. When looking at Z80 signals we saw how they may be combined to generate 8080A equivalents. Thus **8080A support devices may be used with the Z80 CPU. Exceptions are the 8259 Priority Interrupt Control Unit and the TMS5501 multifunction device.**

The 8259 Priority Interrupt Control Unit should not be used with the Z80 CPU because the Z80 CPU provides essentially the same capabilities within the CPU chip itself. So far as signal interface is concerned, you could use an 8259 with a Z80, but it would make no sense.

The TMS5501 cannot be used with a Z80 because it assumes status on the Data Bus — as output by the 8080A without an 8228 System Controller.

**The 8085 support devices** — the 8155, the 8355 and the 8755 — **are difficult to use with the Z80;** you have to multiplex the low order eight Z80 address lines and the Z80 8-bit Data Bus to simulate the 8085 multiplexed bus lines. Logic needed to perform this bus multiplexing would likely be more expensive than discrete packages that implement individual functions provided by the 8155 and 8355 multifunction devices.

**Using MC6800 support devices with the Z80 is not practical.** MC6800 support devices all require a synchronizing clock signal whose characteristics cannot be generated simply from the Z80 clock signal.

**With the exception of the Z80 DMA device, Z80 support devices (which we are about to describe) are not general-purpose devices.** The Z80 PIO, SIO, and CTC devices decode the $\overline{M1}$, $\overline{IORQ}$, and $\overline{RD}$ control signals to identify a number of functions. Table 7-4 defines the manner in which these signals are decoded. Were you to use the Z80 PIO, SIO, or CTC with any other microprocessor, you would have to multiplex the other microprocessor's control signals in order to create equivalents of $\overline{M1}$, $\overline{IORQ}$, and $\overline{RD}$; this may not be straightforward.

Table 7-4. Z80 PIO Interpretation of Control Signals

| SIGNALS | | | FUNCTIONAL INTERPRETATION * |
|---|---|---|---|
| $\overline{M1}$ | $\overline{IORQ}$ | $\overline{RD}$ | |
| 0 | 0 | 0 | No function |
| 0 | 0 | 1 | Interrupt acknowledge |
| 0 | 1 | 0 | Check for end of interrupt service routine |
| 0 | 1 | 1 | Reset |
| 1 | 0 | 0 | Read from PIO to CPU |
| 1 | 0 | 1 | Write from CPU to PIO |
| 1 | 1 | 0 | No function |
| 1 | 1 | 1 | No function |

* These interpretations only apply if the device has been selected

Z80 support devices also rely on exact Z80 CPU characteristics for interrupt processing. Specifically, Z80 support devices detect every instruction fetch, as identified by $\overline{M1}$ and $\overline{RD}$ simultaneously low; if a return from interrupt object code is fetched, then Z80 support devices respond to this object code by resetting internal interrupt priority logic. Accounting for this end of interrupt logic in a non-Z80 system could be difficult.

**Because of the unique characteristics of the Z80 support devices, the Z80 PIO and CTC devices are described in this chapter. The Z80 DMA device is described in Volume 3,** however, because this device is easily used in non-Z80 configurations; moreover, its unique capabilities make it a highly desirable part to include in any microcomputer system that has to move text or data strings. **The Z80 SIO device is also described in Volume 3** because it is an exceptionally powerful device; in many cases the power of the Z80 SIO device will compensate for the additional logic it will demand in a non-Z80 microcomputer system.

## THE Z80 PARALLEL I/O INTERFACE (PIO)

**The Z80 PIO is Zilog's parallel interface device; it may be looked upon as a replacement for the 8255 PPI, but it is equivalent to the PPI at a functional level only. No attempt has been made to make the Z80 PIO an upward compatible replacement for the 8255 PPI.**

**The Z80 PIO has 16 I/O pins, divided into two 8-bit I/O ports. Each I/O port has two associated control lines. This makes the Z80 PIO more like the Motorola MC6820 than the 8255 PPI.**

**The two Z80 PIO I/O ports may be separately specified as input, output or control ports. When specified as a control port, pins may be individually assigned to input or output. Port A may be used as a bidirectional I/O port.**

**The Z80 PIO also provides a significant interrupt handling capability. This includes:**

- **The ability to define conditions which will initiate an interrupt.**
- **Interrupt priority arbitration**
- **Vectored response to an interrupt acknowledge**

**Figure 7-16 illustrates that part of our general microcomputer system logic which has been implemented on the Z80 PIO.**

**The Z80 PIO is packaged as a 40-pin DIP. It uses a single +5V power supply. All inputs and outputs are TTL-level compatible. The device is fabricated using N-channel silicon gate depletion load technology.**

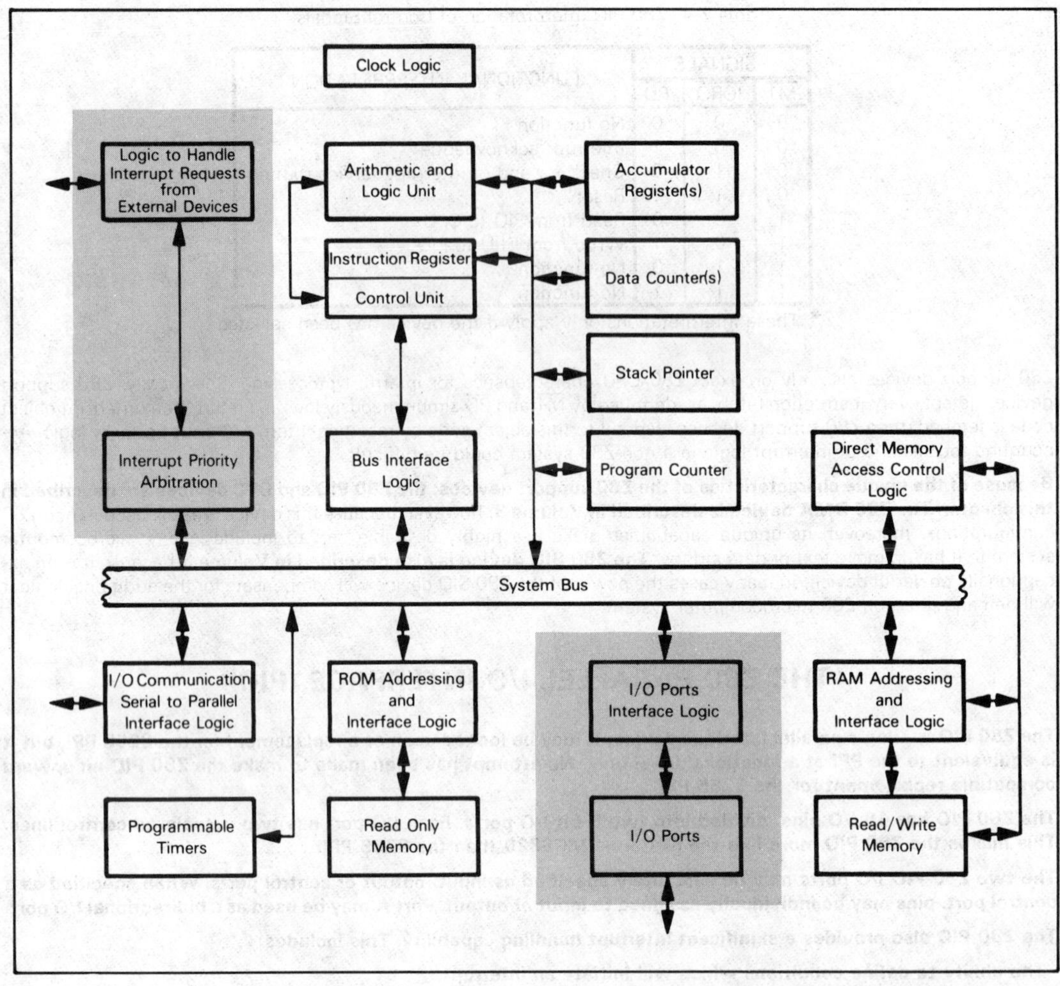


Figure 7-16. Logic Functions of the Z80 PIO

## Z80 PIO PINS AND SIGNALS

**Z80 PIO pins and signals are illustrated in Figure 7-17.** Signals are very straightforward; therefore their functions will be summarized before we discuss device characteristics and operation.

**Let us first consider the PIO CPU interface.**

**All data transfers between the PIO and the CPU occur via the Data Bus, which connects to pins D0 - D7.**

**For the PIO to be selected, a low input must be present at $\overline{CE}$.** There are two additional address lines. **B/$\overline{A}$ SEL selects Port A if low and Port B if high. For the selected I/O port, C/$\overline{D}$ SEL selects a data buffer when low and a control buffer when high.** Device select logic is summarized in Table 7-5.

Table 7-5. Z80 PIO Select Logic

| SIGNAL | | | SELECTED LOCATION |
|---|---|---|---|
| $\overline{CE}$ | B/$\overline{A}$ SEL | C/$\overline{D}$ SEL | |
| 0 | 0 | 0 | Port A data buffer |
| 0 | 0 | 1 | Port A control buffer |
| 0 | 1 | 0 | Port B data buffer |
| 0 | 1 | 1 | Port B control buffer |
| 1 | X | X | Device not selected |

Z80 PIO device control logic is not straightforward. Of the control signals output by the Z80 CPU, three are input to the PIO: $\overline{M1}$, $\overline{IORQ}$, and $\overline{RD}$. $\overline{WR}$ is not input to the PIO. **Table 7-5 illustrates the way in which Z80 PIO interprets $\overline{M1}$, $\overline{IORQ}$ and $\overline{RD}$.** Observe that $\overline{RD}$ is being treated as a signal with two active states: low $\overline{RD}$ specifies a read operation, whereas high $\overline{RD}$ specifies a write operation. This does not conform to the CPU, which treats $\overline{RD}$ and $\overline{WR}$ as signals with a low active state only.

**Let us now look at the PIO external logic interface.**

**A0 - A7 represent the eight bidirectional I/O Port A lines; I/O Port A is supported by two control signals, A RDY and $\overline{A\ STB}$.**

**Similarly, I/O Port B is implemented via the eight bidirectional lines B0 - B7 and the two associated control lines B RDY and $\overline{B\ STB}$.**

**The I/O Port A and B control lines provide handshaking logic which we will describe shortly.**

**Now consider interrupt control signals.**

**IEI and IEO are standard daisy chain interrupt priority signals.** When more than one PIO is present in a system, the highest priority PIO will have IEI tied to +5V and will connect its IEO to the IEI for the next highest priority PIO in the daisy chain:

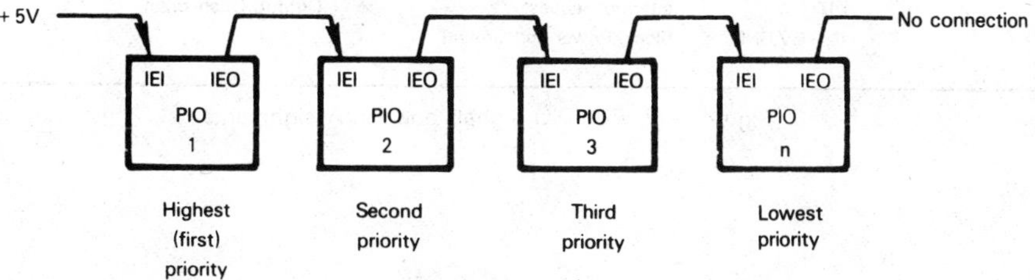


If you are unsure of daisy chain priority networks, refer to Volume 1 for clarification.

**$\overline{INT}$ is a standard interrupt request signal** which is output by the Z80 PIO and must be connected as an input to the Z80 CPU interrupt request. Observe that there is no interrupt acknowledge line, since $\overline{M1}$ and $\overline{IORQ}$ simultaneously low constitute an interrupt acknowledge and will thus be decoded by the Z80 PIO.

**Clock, power, and ground signals are absolutely standard.** The same clock signal is used by the PIO and the Z80 CPU.

**Observe that there is no Reset signal to the PIO.** $\overline{M1}$ low with both $\overline{RD}$ and $\overline{IORQ}$ high constitutes a reset. We will describe the effect of a Z80 PIO reset after discussing operating modes.

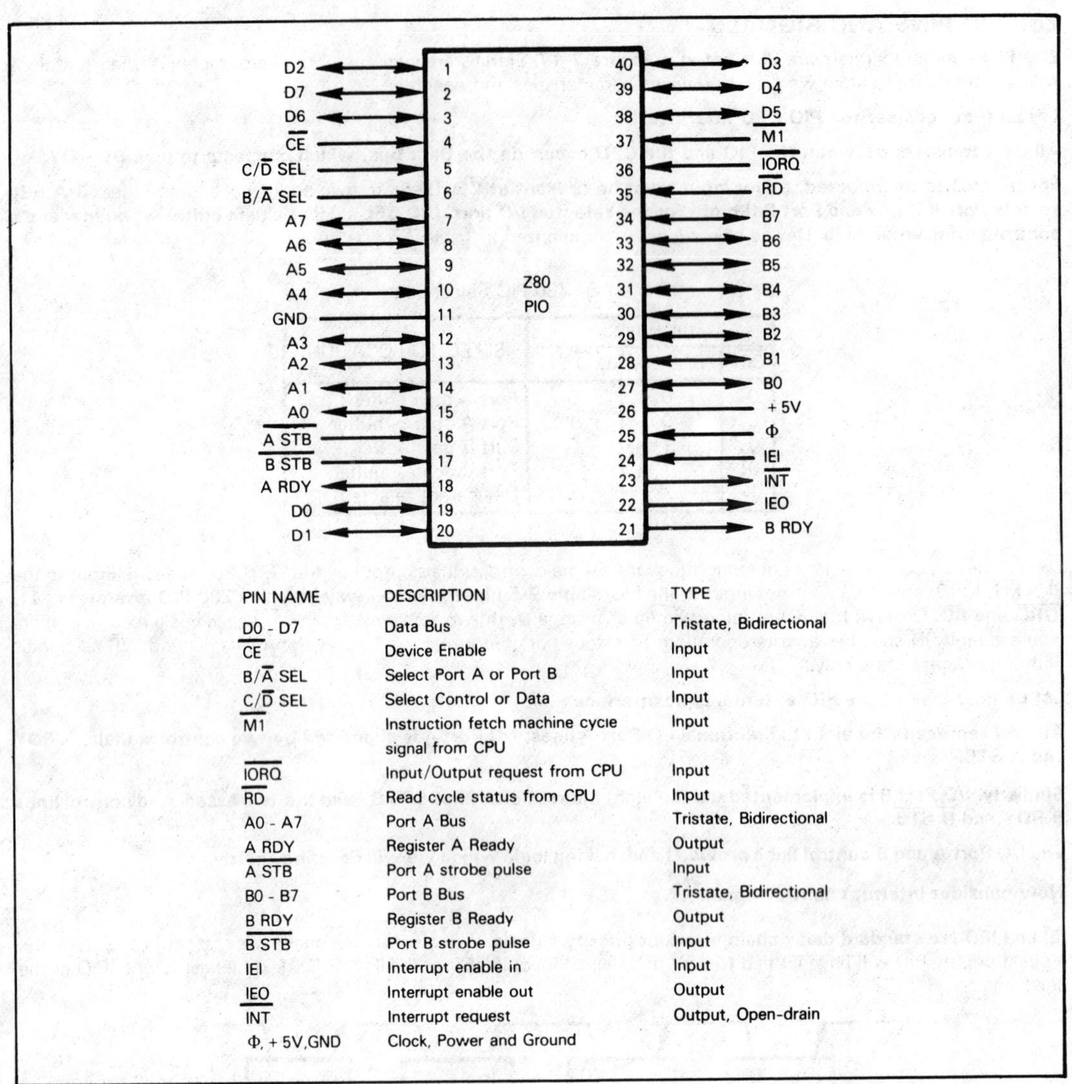


| PIN NAME | DESCRIPTION | TYPE |
|---|---|---|
| D0 - D7 | Data Bus | Tristate, Bidirectional |
| $\overline{CE}$ | Device Enable | Input |
| B/$\overline{A}$ SEL | Select Port A or Port B | Input |
| C/$\overline{D}$ SEL | Select Control or Data | Input |
| $\overline{M1}$ | Instruction fetch machine cycle signal from CPU | Input |
| $\overline{IORQ}$ | Input/Output request from CPU | Input |
| $\overline{RD}$ | Read cycle status from CPU | Input |
| A0 - A7 | Port A Bus | Tristate, Bidirectional |
| A RDY | Register A Ready | Output |
| $\overline{A\ STB}$ | Port A strobe pulse | Input |
| B0 - B7 | Port B Bus | Tristate, Bidirectional |
| B RDY | Register B Ready | Output |
| $\overline{B\ STB}$ | Port B strobe pulse | Input |
| IEI | Interrupt enable in | Input |
| IEO | Interrupt enable out | Output |
| $\overline{INT}$ | Interrupt request | Output, Open-drain |
| Φ, + 5V,GND | Clock, Power and Ground | |

Figure 7-17. Z80 PIO Signals and Pin Assignments

## Z80 PIO OPERATING MODES

**To the programmer, a Z80 PIO will be accessed as four addressable locations:**

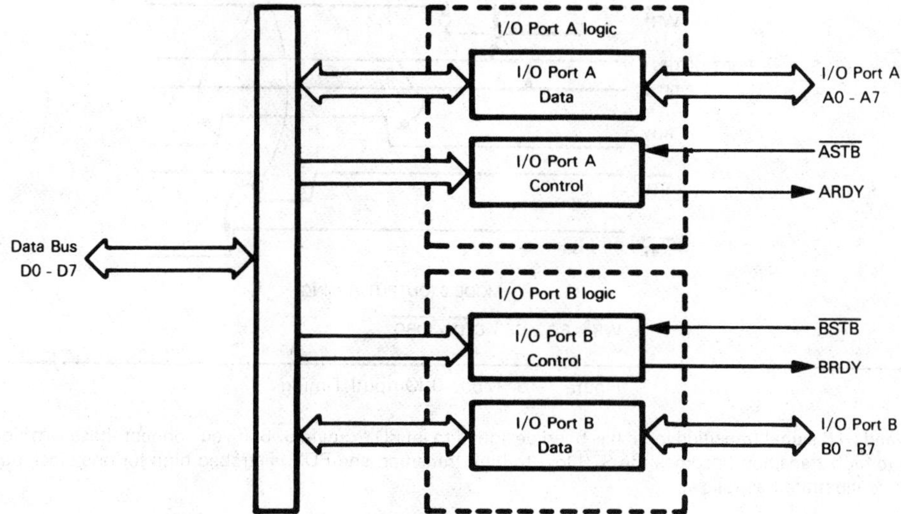


**By loading appropriate information into the Control register you determine the mode in which the I/O port is to operate.**

**The Z80 PIO has operating modes which are equivalent to those of the 8255 PPI, plus an additional mode which the 8255 PPI does not have.** However, 8255 PPI Mode 0 provides 24 I/O lines, as against a maximum of 16 I/O lines available with the Z80 PIO.

Zilog literature uses Mode 0, Mode 1, Mode 2, and Mode 3 to describe the ways in which the Z80 PIO can operate; in order to avoid confusion between mode designations as used by the Z80 PIO and the 8255 PPI, mode equivalences are given in Table 7-6.

Table 7-6. Z80 PIO And 8255 Mode Equivalences

| Z80 PIO | 8255 PPI | INTERPRETATION |
|---|---|---|
| Mode 3* | Mode 0 | Simple input or output |
| Mode 0 | Mode 1 | Output with handshaking |
| Mode 1 | Mode 1 | Input with handshaking |
| Mode 2 | Mode 2 | Bidirectional I/O with handshaking |
| Mode 3 | None | Port pins individually assigned as controls |

*Special case of Mode 3

**Let us now look at the Z80 PIO modes in more detail.**

**Output mode (Mode 0) allows Port A and/or Port B to be used as a conduit for transferring data to external logic. Figure 7-18 illustrates timing for Mode 0.** An output cycle is initiated when the CPU executes any Output instruction accessing the I/O port. The Z80 PIO does not receive the $\overline{WR}$ pulse from the CPU, therefore it derives an equivalent signal by ANDing RD • $\overline{CE}$ • $\overline{C/D}$ • $\overline{IORQ}$.

This pseudo write pulse ($\overline{WR}$* in Figure 7-18) is used to strobe data off the Data Bus and into the addressed I/O port's Output register. After the pseudo write pulse goes high, on the next high-to-low transition of the clock pulse $\Phi$, the RDY control signal is output high to external logic. RDY remains high until external logic returns a low pulse on the $\overline{STB}$ acknowledge. On the following high-to-low clock pulse $\Phi$ transition, RDY returns low. The low-to-high $\overline{STB}$ transition also generates an interrupt request.

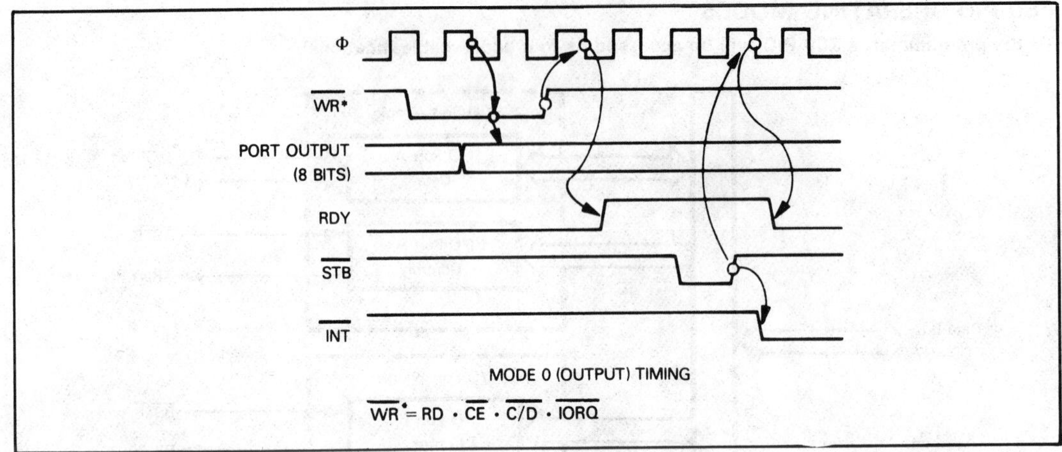


Figure 7-18. Mode 0 (Output) Timing

The RDY and $\overline{STB}$ signal transition logic has been designed to let RDY create $\overline{STB}$. If you connect these two signals, the RDY low-to-high transition becomes the $\overline{STB}$ low-to-high transition and RDY is strobed high for one clock pulse only. This may be illustrated as follows:

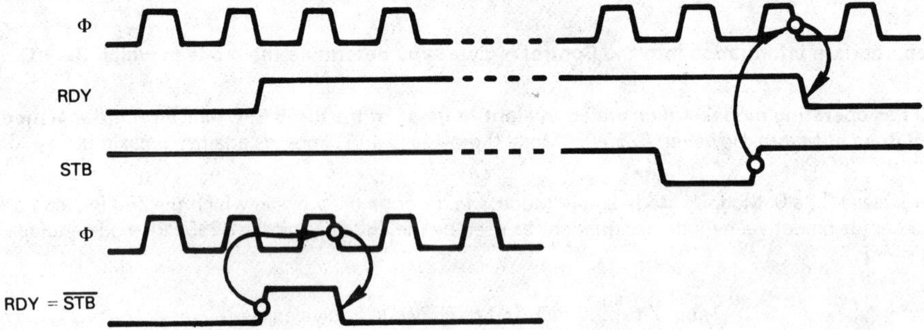


**Timing for input mode (Mode 1) is illustrated in Figure 7-19.** External logic initiates an input cycle by pulsing $\overline{STB}$ low. This low pulse causes the Z80 PIO to load data from the I/O port pins into the port Input register. On the rising edge of the $\overline{STB}$ pulse an interrupt request will be triggered.

On the falling edge of the Φ clock pulse which follows $\overline{STB}$ input high, RDY will be output low informing external logic that its data has been received but has not yet been read. RDY will remain low until the CPU has read the data, at which time RDY will be returned high.

**It is up to external logic to ensure that data is not input to the Z80 PIO while RDY is low.** If external logic does input data to the Z80 PIO while RDY is low, then the previous data will be overwritten and lost — and no error status will be reported.

**In bidirectional mode (Mode 2), the control lines supporting I/O Ports A and B are both applied to bidirectional data being transferred via Port A; Port B must be set to bit control (Mode 3).**

Figure 7-20 illustrates timing for bidirectional data transfers. This figure is simply a combination of Figures 7-18 and 7-19 where the A control lines apply to data output while the B control lines apply to data input. The only unique feature of Figure 7-20 is that bidirectional data being output via Port A is stable only for the duration of the $\overline{A\ STB}$ low pulse. This is necessary in bidirectional mode since the Port A pins must be ready to receive input data as soon as the output operation has been completed.

Once again, it is up to external logic to make sure that it conforms with the timing requirements of bidirectional mode operation. External logic must read output data while $\overline{A\ STB}$ is low. If external logic does not read data at this time, the data will not be read and the Z80 PIO will not report an error status to the CPU; there is no signal that external logic sends back to the Z80 PIO following a successful read.

Also, it is up to external logic to make sure that it transmits data to Port A only while B RDY is high and A RDY is low. If external logic tries to input data while the Z80 PIO is outputting data, input data will not be accepted. If external logic tries to input data before previously input data has been read, the previously input data will be lost and no error status will be reported.

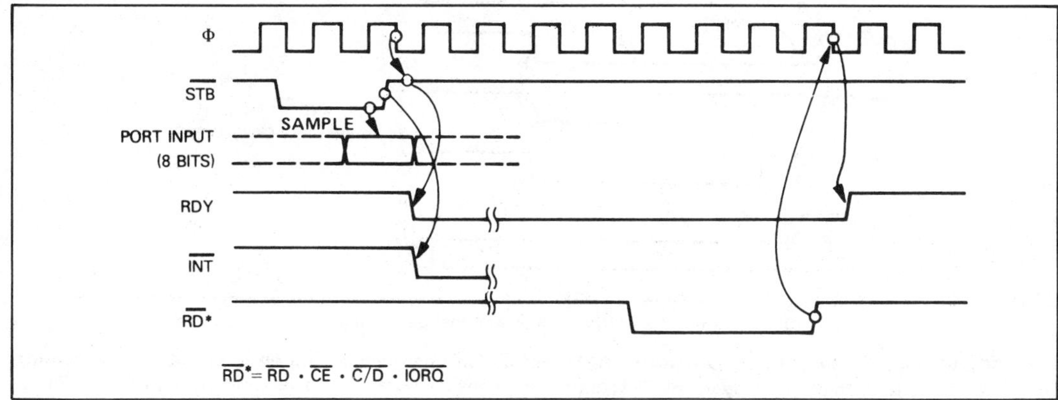


Figure 7-19. Mode 1 (Input) Timing

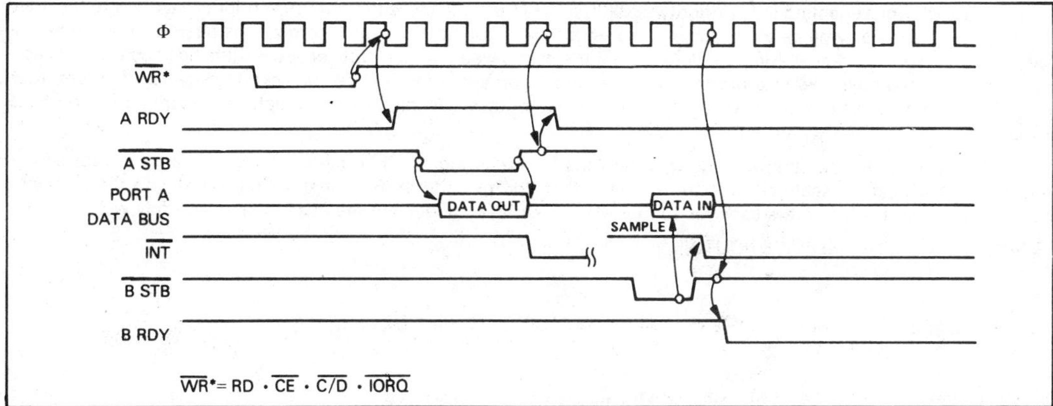


Figure 7-20. Port A, Mode 2 (Bidirectional) Timing

**Control mode (Mode 3) does not use control signals. You must define every pin of an I/O port in Mode 3 as an input or an output pin.** The section on programming the Z80 PIO explains how to do this. Timing associated with the actual transfer of data at a single pin is as illustrated in Figures 7-18 and 7-19, ignoring the RDY and STB signals. If all the pins of a single port are defined in the same direction, then that port can be used for simple parallel input or output (without handshaking).

## Z80 PIO INTERRUPT SERVICING

The Z80 PIO has a single interrupt request line via which it transmits interrupt requests to the CPU.

**An interrupt request can originate from I/O Port A logic, or from I/O Port B logic. In the case of simultaneous interrupt requests, I/O Port A logic has higher priority.**

An interrupt request may be created in one of two ways. We have already seen in our discussion of Modes 0, 1 and 2 that appropriate control signal transitions will activate the interrupt request line; that is the first way in which an interrupt request may occur. In Mode 3 you can program either I/O port to generate an interrupt request based on the status of signals at individual I/O port pins; you can specify which I/O port pins will contribute to interrupt request logic and what the pin states must be for the interrupt request to occur. In a microcomputer system that has more than one Z80 PIO, interrupt priorities are arbitrated using daisy chain logic as we have already described. But there is a significant difference between priority arbitration within a Z80 system as compared to typical priority arbitration. Figure 7-21 illustrates interrupt acknowledge timing.

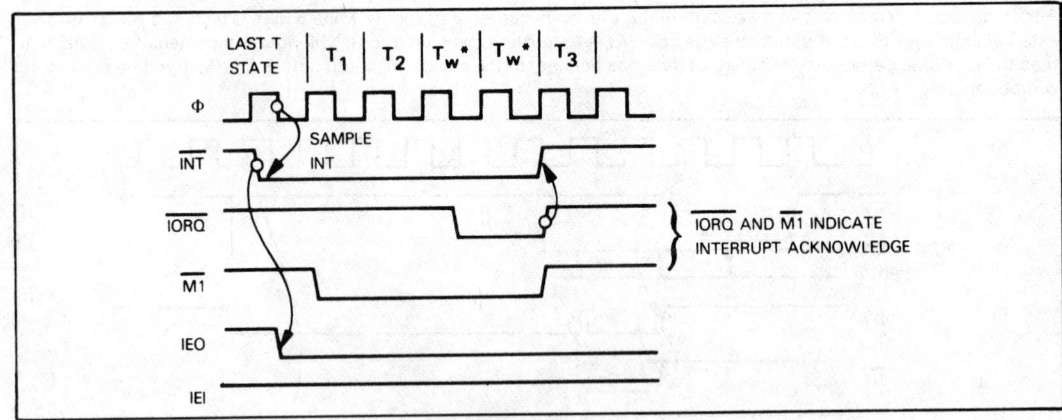


Figure 7-21. Interrupt Acknowledge Timing

**The Z80 PIO requires the CPU to execute an RETI instruction upon concluding an interrupt service routine.** Following an interrupt, an acknowledged Z80 PIO continously scans the Data Bus whenever $\overline{M1}$ is pulsed low. Until an RETI instruction's object code is detected, the acknowledged Z80 PIO will continuously output IEO low, thus disabling all lower priority Z80 PIOs. As soon as an RETI instruction's object code is detected on the Data Bus, the Z80 PIO will output IEO high, thus enabling lower priority Z80 PIOs. What this means is that interrupt priorities extend to the interrupt service routine as well as the interrupt request arbitration logic. Once an interrupt has been acknowledged, all lower priority interrupt requests will be denied until the acknowledged interrupt service routine has completed execution and has executed an RETI instruction. However, higher priority interrupts can be acknowledged and in turn interrupt an executing service routine. This is identical to the priority arbitration logic which we described for the 8259 PICU.

You can, if you wish, enable lower priority interrupts by executing an RETI instruction before an interrupt service routine has completed execution. But this requires that you execute an RETI instruction in order to return from a subroutine within the interrupted service routine. This instruction sequence may be illustrated as follows:

```
;START OF INTERRUPT SERVICE ROUTINE
        -
        -
        -
        CALL    ENABLE      ;ENABLE ALL INTERRUPTS AT PIO DEVICES
        -
        -
        -
        RET                 ;END OF INTERRUPT SERVICE ROUTINE
ENABLE  RETI
```

If you simply executed an RETI instruction shortly after entering an interrupt service routine, you would make a hasty exit from the routine — before completing the tasks that have to be performed in response to the acknowledged interrupt.

## PROGRAMMING THE Z80 PIO

**You program the Z80 PIO by outputting a series of commands.**

**Let us start by identifying command format.**

**If the 0 bit of a command is low, then the receiving I/O port logic will interpret the command as an interrupt vector,** with which it must respond to an interrupt acknowledge, assuming that the CPU is operating in interrupt Mode 2:

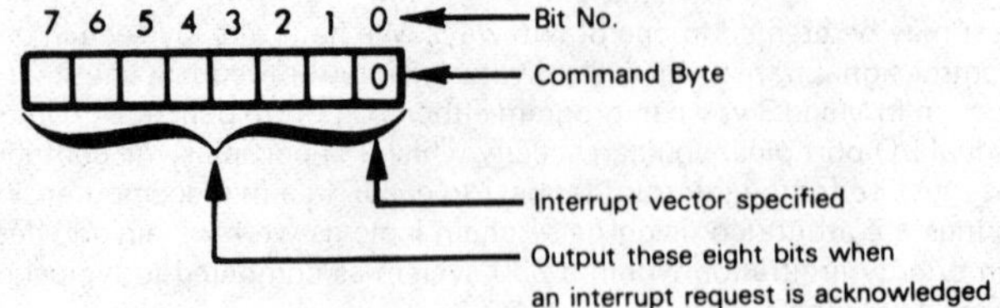

Do not confuse CPU interrupt modes with I/O port modes; they have nothing in common.

**In order to define an I/O port's mode you must output a Control code to the I/O port's Control buffer. This is the Control code format:**

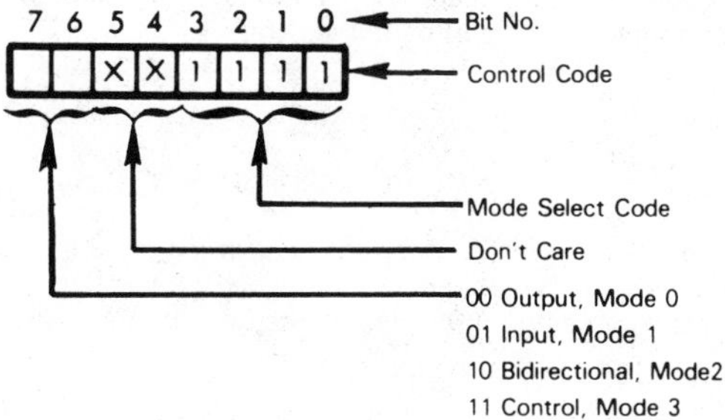


Observe that the same address, the I/O Port A or B Control buffer address, is used when outputting a Control code, an interrupt vector, or a mode select. The low-order four bits of the Control code determine the way in which the Control code will be interpreted. **The following Control code will enable or disable interrupts:**

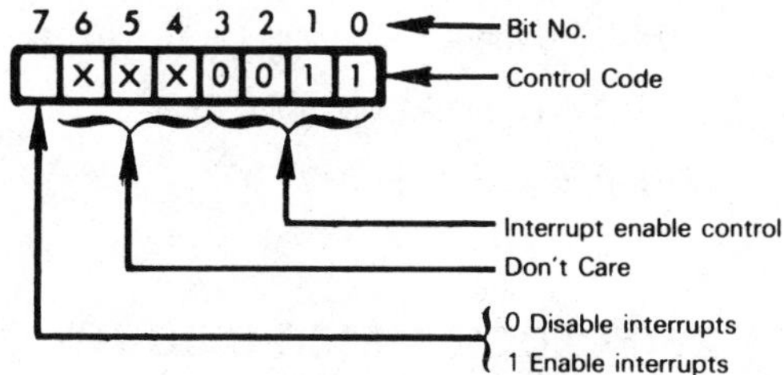


**If a Mode Select Control code is output specifying that an I/O port will operate in Mode 3, then the next byte output is assumed to be a pin direction mask.** 1 identifies an input pin, whereas 0 identifies an output pin. Here is a sample instruction sequence:

```
LD      C,(PORTAC)    ;LOAD PORT A CONTROL ADDRESS INTO REGISTER C
LD      A,0CFH        ;LOAD MODE 3 SELECT INTO ACCUMULATOR
OUT     (C),A         ;OUTPUT TO PORT A CONTROL REGISTER
LD      A,3AH         ;DEFINE PINS 5, 4, 3 AND 1 AS INPUTS,
OUT     (C),A         ;PINS 7, 6, 2 AND 0 AS OUTPUTS
```

**If you set an I/O port to Mode 3, then you can define the conditions which will cause an interrupt request; you do this by outputting the following interrupt Control code:**

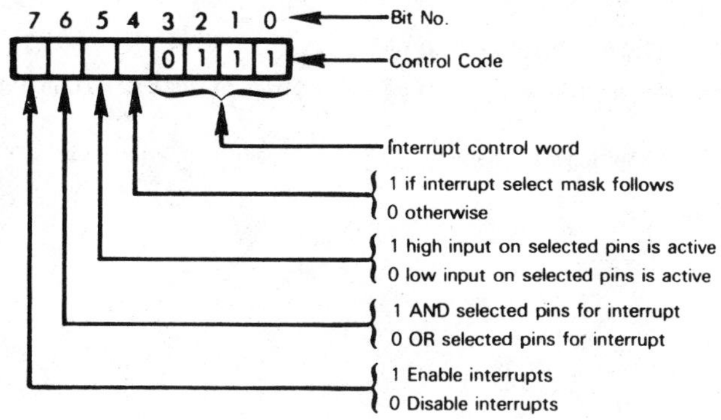

When you output an interrupt Control code, as illustrated above, if bit 4 is 1, Z80 PIO logic will assume that the next Control code output is an interrupt mask. An interrupt mask selects the pins that will contribute to interrupt request logic. A 0 bit selects a pin, while a 1 bit deselects the pin.

Combining the various Control codes that have been described we can now illustrate a typical sequence of instructions for accessing a Z80 PIO. Assume that PIO I/O port addresses are:

| | |
|---|---|
| Port A data | 4 |
| Port A command | 5 |
| Port B data | 6 |
| Port B command | 7 |

We are going to set I/O Port B to Mode 3, with an interrupt request triggered by either pin 6, 3 or 2 high. Pins 6, 3, 2 and 1 will be input pins, while pins 7, 5, 4 and 0 are outputs. The Port B interrupt vector will be 04. Port A will be a bidirectional I/O port with an interrupt vector of 02. Here is the initialization instruction sequence:

```
LD      A,8FH       ;SET PORT A TO MODE 2
OUT     (5),A
LD      A,2         ;OUTPUT INTERRUPT VECTOR
OUT     (5),A
LD      C,7         ;SET PORT B ADDRESS IN C
LD      A,0CFH      ;SET PORT B TO MODE 3
OUT     (C),A
LD      A,4EH       ;OUTPUT PIN DIRECTION MASK
OUT     (C),A
LD      A,4         ;OUTPUT INTERRUPT VECTOR
OUT     (C),A
LD      A,0B7H      ;OUTPUT INTERRUPT CONTROL WORD
OUT     (C),A
LD      A,0B3H      ;OUTPUT INTERRUPT MASK
OUT     (C),A
```

# THE Z80 CLOCK TIMER CIRCUIT (CTC)

**The Z80 Clock Timer Circuit is a programmable device which contains four sets of timing logic. Each set of timing logic can be programmed independently as an interval timer or an external event counter.**

The master Z80 system clock is used by interval timer logic. A time out may be identified by an interrupt request.

An external signal is used to trigger decrement logic when the timer is functioning as an event counter. An interrupt may be requested when the predetermined number of events count out.

**If you compare the Z80 CTC with the 8253 Counter/Timer** described in Volume 3, **you will see that the Z80 CTC has four sets of counter/timer logic as compared to the three sets of the 8253;** however, the 8253 has more programmable options. In addition to functioning as an event counter or an interval timer, the 8253 can be programmed to generate a variety of square waves and pulse output signals.

**The Z80 CTC is fabricated using N-channel depletion load technology. It is packaged as a 28-pin DIP. All pins are TTL-level compatible.**

## Z80 CTC FUNCTIONAL ORGANIZATION

**Before we examine pins, signals, and operating charactercs of the Z80 CTC in detail, let us take an overall look at device logic.**

There are four counter/timer logic elements in a Z80 CTC; each is referred to as a "channel".

**Each of the four counter/timer channels may be visualized as consisting of three 8-bit registers and two control signals.** This may be illustrated as follows:

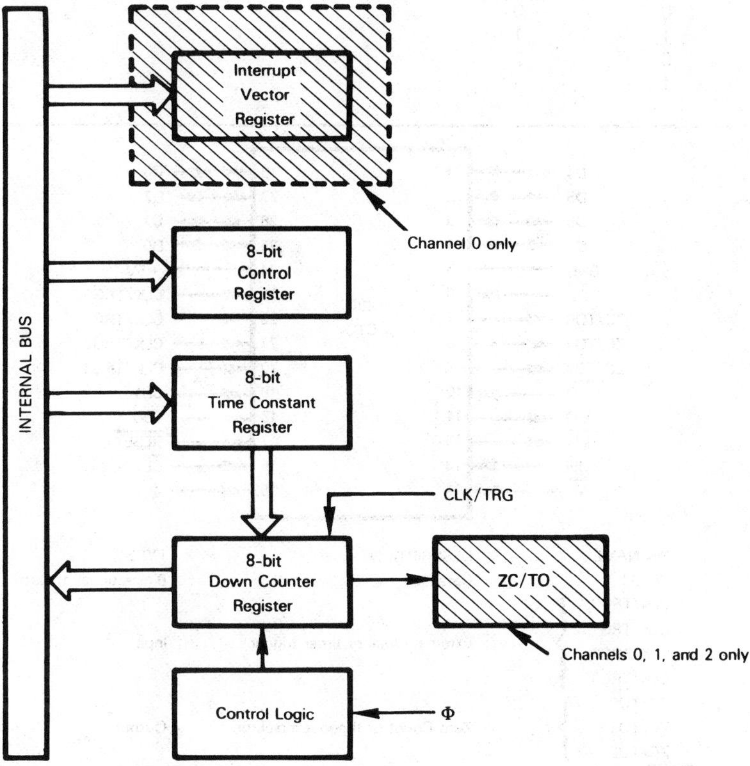


**An initial counter or timer constant is loaded into the Time Constant register.** The value in the Time Constant register is maintained unaltered until you write a new value into this register.

**The initial Timer Constant is loaded into the Down Counter register at the beginning of a counter or timer operation;** the contents of the Down Counter register are decremented. You can at any time read the contents of the Down Counter register in order to determine how far a time interval or event counting sequence has progressed.

**The Channel Control register contains a Control code which defines the channel's programmable options.** There are four Control registers, one for each of the four channels. Thus one channel's operations in no way influence operations for any other channel.

**There is an Interrupt Vector register which is addressed as though it were part of channel 0 logic. This register contains the address which is transmitted by the Z80 CTC upon receiving an interrupt acknowledge.** The Z80 CTC assumes that the Z80 CPU is operating in Interrupt mode 2 — in which mode the device requesting an interrupt responds to an acknowledge by providing the second byte of a subroutine address which the CPU will Call. For details refer to our earlier discussion of the Z80 CPU.

## Z80 CTC PINS AND SIGNALS

**Z80 CTC pins and signals are illustrated in Figure 7-22.**

**D0 - D7 is the bidirectional Data Bus** via which parallel data is transferred between the CPU and any register of the Z80 CTC.

**$\overline{\text{CE}}$ is the master chip select** signal for the Z80 CTC. This signal must be low for the device to be selected.

While $\overline{CE}$ is low, **CS0 and CS1 are used to select one of the four counter/timer logic channels** as follows:

| CS1 | CS0 | Channel |
|---|---|---|
| 0 | 0 | 0 |
| 0 | 1 | 1 |
| 1 | 0 | 2 |
| 1 | 1 | 3 |

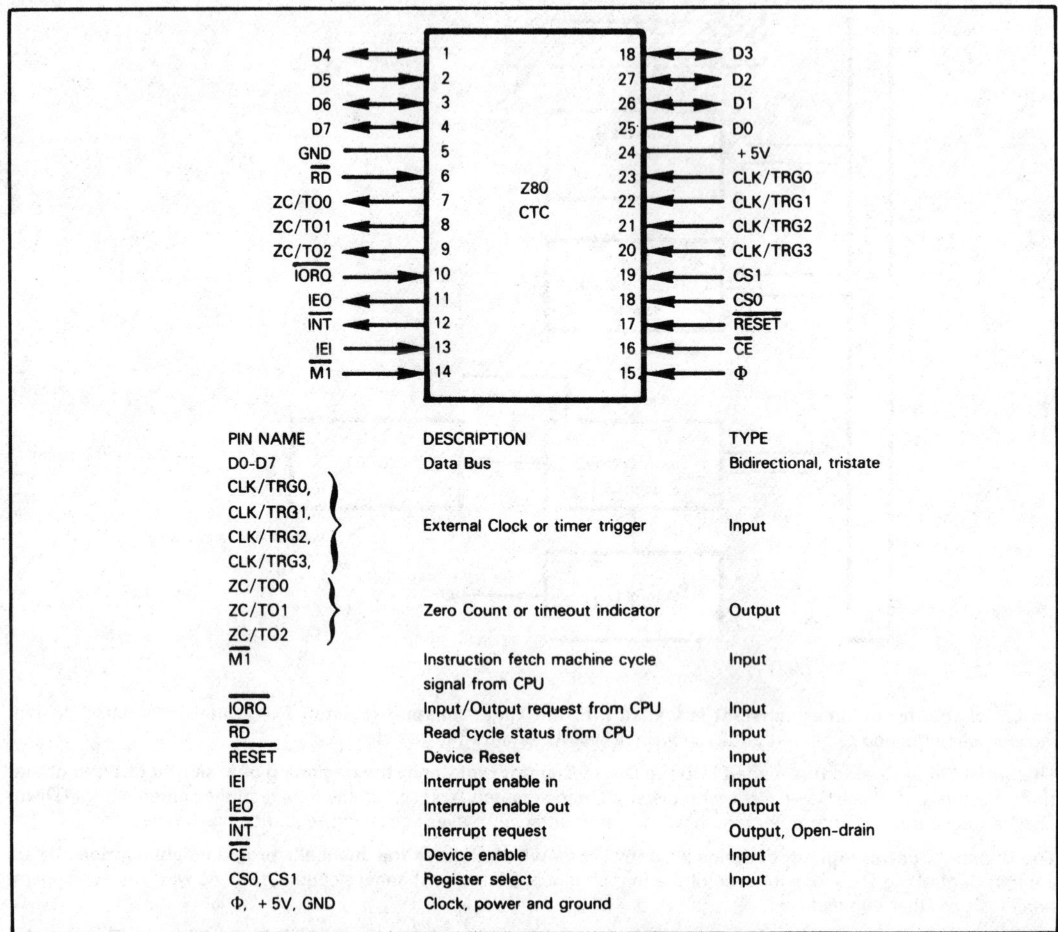


| PIN NAME | DESCRIPTION | TYPE |
|---|---|---|
| D0-D7 | Data Bus | Bidirectional, tristate |
| CLK/TRG0, CLK/TRG1, CLK/TRG2, CLK/TRG3, | External Clock or timer trigger | Input |
| ZC/TO0 ZC/TO1 ZC/TO2 | Zero Count or timeout indicator | Output |
| $\overline{M1}$ | Instruction fetch machine cycle signal from CPU | Input |
| $\overline{IORQ}$ | Input/Output request from CPU | Input |
| $\overline{RD}$ | Read cycle status from CPU | Input |
| $\overline{RESET}$ | Device Reset | Input |
| IEI | Interrupt enable in | Input |
| IEO | Interrupt enable out | Output |
| $\overline{INT}$ | Interrupt request | Output, Open-drain |
| $\overline{CE}$ | Device enable | Input |
| CS0, CS1 | Register select | Input |
| Φ, +5V, GND | Clock, power and ground | |

Figure 7-22. Z80-CTC Signals and Pin Assignments

CS0 and CS1 select registers associated with counter/timer logic, to be accessed by read and write operations. The actual register which will be accessed is determined as follows:

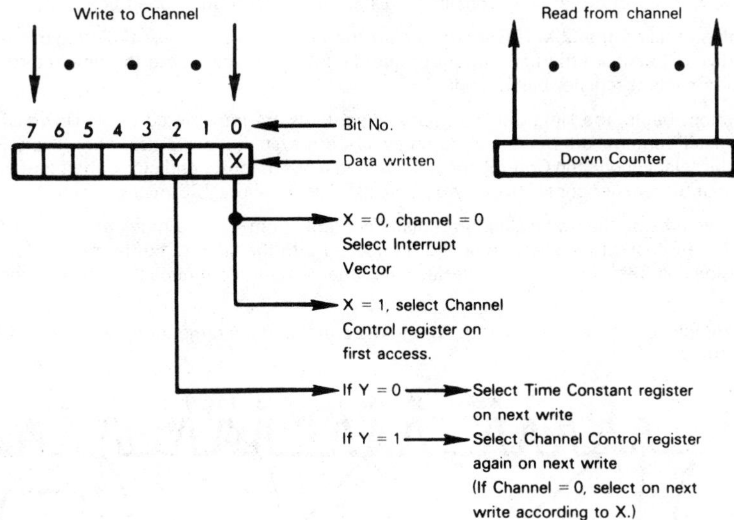


As the illustration above would imply, the Down Counter register is the only location of any channel whose contents can be read. All other registers are write only locations.

When you write to a channel, bits 0 and 2 of the data byte being written determine the data destination as follows:

1) If bit 0 is 0 and you are selecting channel 0, then the data is written to the Interrupt Vector register.
2) If bit 0 is 0 and you select channel 1, 2 or 3, the data destination is undefined.
3) If bit 0 is 1, then on the first access of any channel the data will be written to the Channel Control register.
4) If within the data byte written to a Channel Control register bit 0 is 1 and bit 2 is 0, then the next data byte written to this channel will be loaded into the Time Constant register, irrespective of whether bit 0 is 0 or 1. The data written will be interpreted as a time constant; select logic will immediately revert to selecting the Channel Control register or the Interrupt Vector register on the next write, depending on the condition of bit 0 of the next data byte.

**$\overline{\text{M1}}$, $\overline{\text{IORQ}}$ and $\overline{\text{RD}}$** are three control signals input to the Z80 CTC. Combinations of these three control signals **control logic within the Z80 CTC, as described for the Z80 PIO. An exception is the device Reset.** The Z80 CTC has its own $\overline{\text{RESET}}$ input. The PIO decodes a Reset when $\overline{\text{M1}}$ is low while $\overline{\text{IORQ}}$ and $\overline{\text{RD}}$ are high. With the exception of the RESET function, Table 7-4 defines the manner in which the Z80 CTC interprets $\overline{\text{M1}}$, $\overline{\text{IORQ}}$, and $\overline{\text{RD}}$ signals.

**Interrupt logic has three associated signals: IEI, IEO and $\overline{\text{INT}}$.** These signals operate exactly as described for the Z80 PIO.

The Z80 CTC requests an interrupt with a low $\overline{\text{INT}}$ output.

IEI and IEO are used to implement daisy chain priority interrupt logic as described for the PIO.

**Each of the four counter/timer channels has a CLK/TRG input control.** This signal can be used to trigger timer logic; it is also used as a decrement control by counter logic.

Counter/timer logic channels 0, 1 and 2 have a ZC/TO output. This signal is pulsed high on a time out or a count out.

**When a low input is applied to the $\overline{\text{RESET}}$ pin, the Z80 CTC is reset.** At this time all counter/timer logic is stopped, $\overline{\text{INT}}$ is output high, IEO is output at the IEI level and the Data Bus is floated. Register contents are not cleared during a reset.

## Z80 CTC OPERATING MODES

**The Z80 CTC is accessed by the CPU as four I/O ports or four memory locations. Timing for any CTC access conforms to descriptions given earlier in this chapter for the CPU.**

**Let us begin by looking at a counter/timer operating as a timer.**

Using an appropriate Control code (described later) you select Timer mode for the channel and specify that an initial time constant is to follow.

You load an initial constant into the Time Constant register, after which timer operations begin.

You have the option of using the CLK/TRG input to start the timer, in which case timer logic is initiated by external logic. The alternative is to initiate the timer under program control, in which case the timer starts on the clock pulse following the Time Constant register being loaded.

When timer operations begin, the Time Constant register contents are transmitted to the Down Counter register. The Down Counter register contents are decremented on every 16th system clock pulse, or on every 256th system clock pulse. You make the selection via the Control code. Assuming a 500 nanosecond clock, therefore, the timer will decrement the Down Counter register contents every 8 microseconds, or every 128 microseconds.

When timer logic decrements the Down Counter register contents from 1 to 0 a time out occurs. At this time ZC/TO is pulsed high, the Time Constant register contents are reloaded into the Down Counter register and timer logic starts again. Thus timer logic is free running; once started, the timer will run continuously until stopped by an appropriate Control code.

Here is a timing example for a timer started under program control and decrementing the Down Counter register on every 16th clock pulse:

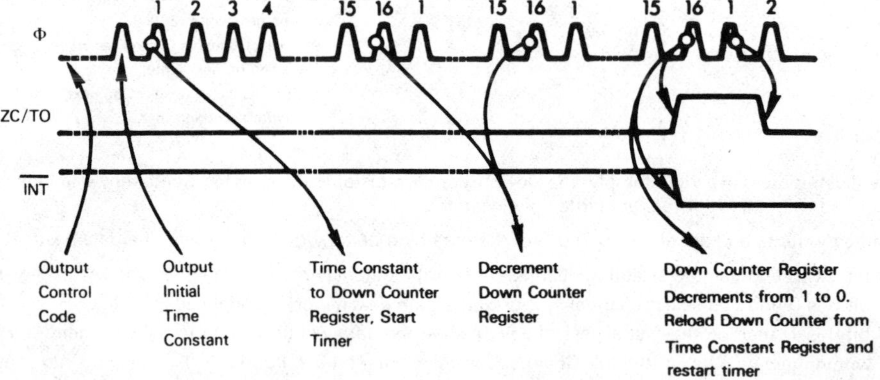


Here is a timing example for a timer whose operations are initiated by CLK/TRG, where the Down Counter register contents are decremented on every 256th clock pulse:

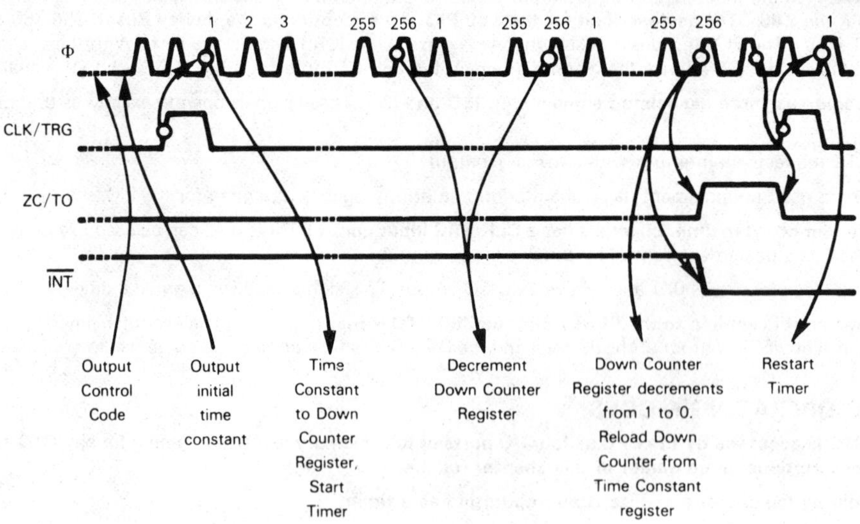

Observe that every time out is marked by a ZC/TO high pulse. $\overline{INT}$ is also output low providing interrupt logic is enabled at the channel.

In the illustration above CLK/TRG is shown as a high true signal. You can specify CLK/TRG as a low true signal via the Channel Control code; the timer will be initiated as follows:

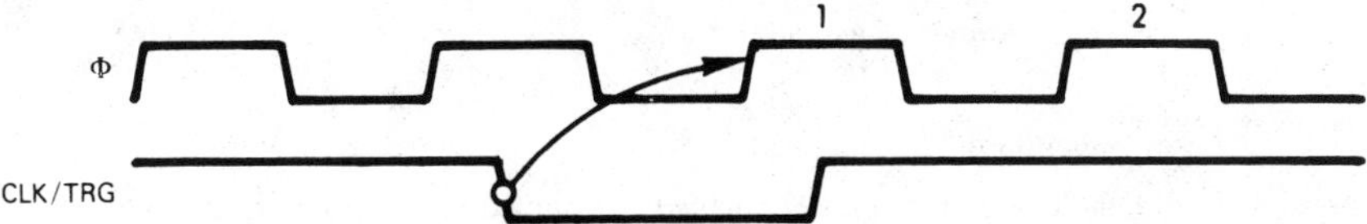


For exact timing requirements see the data sheets at the end of this chapter.

You can at any time write new data into the Time Constant register. If you do this while the timer is running, nothing happens until the next time out; at that time the new Time Constant register contents will be transferred to the Down Counter register and subsequent time intervals will be computed based on the new Time Constant register contents.

If you are unfortunate enough to output data to the Time Constant register while a time out is in progress and the Time Constant register contents are being transferred to the Down Counter register, then an undefined value will be loaded into the Down Counter register; however, following the next time out the new value in the Time Constant register will apply; that is to say, there will only be one undefined time interval.

**Let us now look at a counter/timer operating as a counter.**

Using an appropriate Control code (described later) you select Counter mode for the channel and specify that an initial time constant is to follow.

You load an initial constant into the Time Constant register, after which counter operations begin.

When counter operations begin, the Time Constant register contents are transmitted to the Down Counter register. The Down Counter register contents are decremented every time the CLK/TRG input makes an active transition. Counter logic begins on the first active transition of CLK/TRG following data being loaded into the Time Constant register. The active transition of CLK/TRG may be selected under program control as low-to-high or high-to-low.

When counter logic decrements the Down Counter register contents from 1 to 0, a count out occurs. At this time the ZC/TO signal is pulsed high; an interrupt request occurs, providing the channel's interrupt logic has been enabled. The Time Constant register contents are reloaded into the Down Counter register and counter operations begin again. That is to say, counter logic is free running and will continue to re-execute until specifically stopped by an appropriate Control code. Counter logic timing may be illustrated as follows:

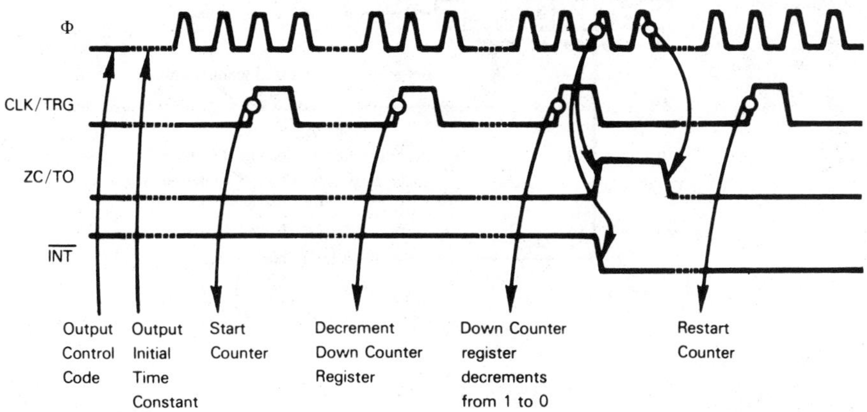

## Z80 CTC INTERRUPT LOGIC

**Every Z80 CTC channel has its own interrupt logic. A channel's interrupt logic generates an interrupt request when the channel counts out or times out. All interrupt requests are transmitted to the CPU via the $\overline{INT}$ output. This is true if one, or more than one channel is requesting an interrupt. If more than one channel is requesting an interrupt, then priorities are arbitrated as follows:**

| | |
|---|---|
| Highest Priority | Channel 0 |
| | Channel 1 |
| | Channel 2 |
| Lowest Priority | Channel 3 |

Every channel's interrupt logic can be individually enabled or disabled under program control.

**The Z80 CTC device's overall interrupt logic is identical to that which we have already described for the Z80 PIO.**

The interrupt request is transmitted to the CPU via a low $\overline{INT}$ signal.

The CPU acknowledges the interrupt by outputting $\overline{M1}$ and $\overline{IORQ}$ low as illustrated in the data sheets at the end of this chapter.

The device requesting an interrupt which is highest in the daisy chain acknowledges the interrupt. Presuming this is a Z80 CTC, the CTC places its interrupt vector on the Data Bus; it is assumed that the CPU is operating in Interrupt mode 2. The Z80 CTC immediately outputs IEO low, disabling all devices below it in the daisy chain.

When an RETI instruction is executed, Z80 CTC logic sets IEO high again.

For more information on Z80 interrupt logic refer to discussions of this subject given earlier in the chapter for the Z80 CPU and the PIO.

## PROGRAMMING THE Z80 CTC

**These are the steps required to program a Z80 CTC:**

1) **Output an interrupt vector once, when initializing the Z80 CTC.**
2) **For each active counter/timer channel, output one or more Control codes. Control codes are used initially to set counter/timer operating conditions and to load the Time Constant register. Subsequently Control codes are used to start and stop the counter/timer, or to change the initial time constant.**

The interrupt vector is written to a counter/timer by outputting a byte of data to counter/timer channel 0 with a 0 in the low order bit. The interrupt vector may be illustrated as follows:

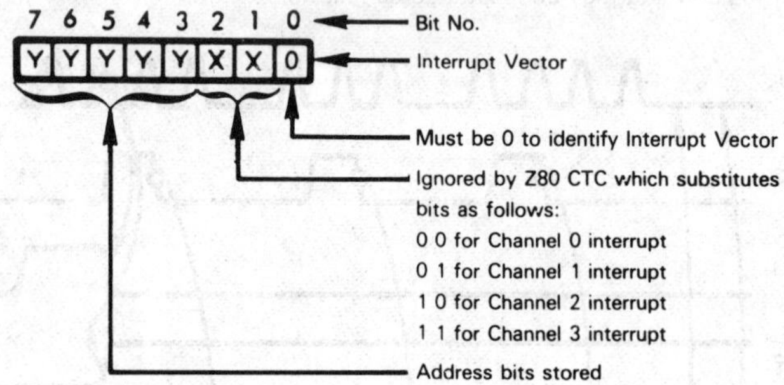

**The Control code which must be output to each active channel will be interpreted as illustrated in Figure 7-23.**

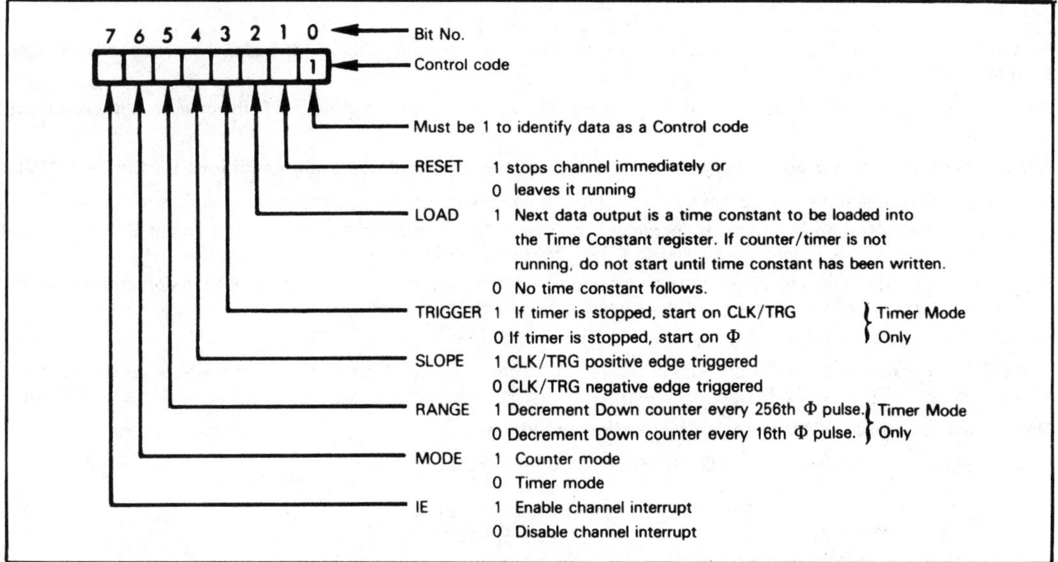


Figure 7-23. Z80 CTC Control Code Interpretation

Bit 0 must be 1 to identify the data as a Control code. If bit 0 is 0, then the data is interpreted as an interrupt vector — providing Channel 0 is addressed; the data is undefined otherwise.

Bit 1 is used to stop the channel when it is running. If bit 1 is 0, then every time the channel times out the Down Counter register is immediately reloaded from the Time Constant register contents and channel operations restart according to current options. If bit 1 is 1, the channel stops immediately; the ZC/TO output is inactive and channel interrupt logic is disabled. The channel must be restarted by outputting a new Control code.

Bit 2 is used to output time constants. If bit 2 is 1, then the next data output to the channel will be interpreted as a time constant. If bit 2 is 0, then the next data output to the channel will be interpreted as another Control code, or an interrupt vector, depending on the bit 0 value.

Bit 3 applies to Timer mode only; assuming that the timer is not running, it determines whether timer operations will be initiated by the system clock signal Φ, or by CLK/TRG.

If bit 3 is 0 then timer operations are initiated by system clock signal Φ; the timer will start on the next leading edge of Φ, unless the current Control code specifies (via bit 2) that a new time constant is to be output, in which case the timer will start on the rising edge of Φ which immediately follows output of the time constant. Timing for these two cases has been illustrated earlier.

If bit 3 is 1, then the active transition of the CLK/TRG signal initiates the timer. Once again, if bit 2 of the current Control code specifies that a new time constant is to be output then timer logic cannot be started until this new time constant has been output. Timing has been illustrated earlier.

Bit 4 determines whether the low-to-high or the high-to-low transition of CLK/TRG is active. Assuming that bit 6 has specified Timer mode and bit 3 has specified the timer will be triggered externally by CLK/TRG, the active transition of CLK/TRG starts the timer. If bit 6 is not 0 or bit 3 is not 1, then the active transition of CLK/TRG decrements the counter.

If bit 4 specifies that a low-to-high transition of CLK/TRG will be active then CLK/TRG may be illustrated as follows:

If bit 4 specifies that the high-to-low transition of CLK/TRG will be active then CLK/TRG may be illustrated as follows:

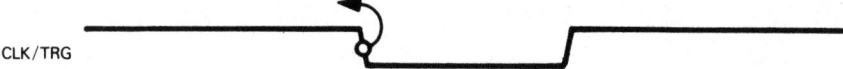

Bit 5 applies to Timer mode only. If bit 5 is 0, Down Counter register contents will be decremented every 16th system clock pulse (Φ). If bit 5 is 1, the Down Counter register contents will be decremented every 256th system clock pulse (Φ).

Bit 6 determines whether the channel will be operated as a counter or a timer. If bit 6 is 0, Timer mode is selected; Counter mode is selected if bit 6 is 1.

Bit 7 is an interrupt enable/disable flag. If 0, the channel's interrupt logic is disabled; if 1, the channel's interrupt logic is enabled.

**Let us now look at the programming example. Here are the assumed operating conditions for the Z80 CTC:**

1) Channel 0 is operating as a counter with an initial time constant of $80_{16}$ and interrupt logic enabled.
2) Channel 1 is operating as a timer. It decrements on every 16th system clock pulse and has an initial time constant of $40_{16}$; its interrupts are disabled and CLK/TRG starts the timer on its low-to-high transition.
3) Channel 2 is operating as a timer. It decrements every 256th system clock pulse and has an initial time constant of $C8_{16}$; its interrupts are enabled and the system clock starts the timer.
4) Channel 3 is inactive.

The CPU is operating with interrupt logic in Mode 2. CTC interrupt service routine starting addresses are stored at memory locations $2C40_{16}$, $2C42_{16}$ and $2C44_{16}$. The CTC is accessed as I/O ports $B8_{16}$, $B9_{16}$, $BA_{16}$, and $BB_{16}$.

**Here is the appropriate CTC initiation instruction sequence:**

```
        LD      A,2CH       ;LOAD INTERRUPT VECTOR REGISTER OF CPU
        LD      I,A
        IM      2           ;SELECT CPU INTERRUPT MODE 2
        LD      A,40H       ;OUTPUT INTERRUPT VECTOR TO
        OUT     (0B8H),A    ;CHANNEL 0
;START CHANNEL 0
        LD      A,0C5H      ;OUTPUT THE CONTROL CODE TO CHANNEL 0
        OUT     (0B8H),A
        LD      A,80H       ;OUTPUT THE INITIAL COUNT TO CHANNEL 0
        OUT     (0B8H),A    ;CHANNEL 0 BEGINS OPERATING.
;START CHANNEL1
        LD      A,1DH       ;OUTPUT THE CONTROL CODE TO CHANNEL 1
        OUT     (0B9H),A
        LD      A,40H       ;OUTPUT THE INITIAL TIMER CONSTANT TO CHANNEL1
        OUT     (0B9H),A    ;CHANNEL 1 BEGINS OPERATING. (IF TRANSITION OCCURS)
;START CHANNEL 2
        LD      A,0A5H      ;OUTPUT THE CONTROL CODE TO CHANNEL 2
        OUT     (0BAH),A
        LD      A,0C8H      ;OUTPUT THE INITIAL TIMER CONSTANT TO CHANNEL 2
        OUT     (0BAH),A    ;CHANNEL 2 BEGINS OPERATING
```

# DATA SHEETS

This section contains specific electrical and timing data for the following devices:

Z80 and Z80A CPU
Z80 and Z80A PIO
Z80 and Z80A CTC

## Z80-CPU
# Absolute Maximum Ratings

| | |
|---|---|
| Temperature Under Bias | Specified operating range. |
| Storage Temperature | -65°C to +150°C |
| Voltage On Any Pin with Respect to Ground | -0.3V to +7V |
| Power Dissipation | 1.5W |

*Comment

Stresses above those listed under "Absolute Maximum Rating" may cause permanent damage to the device. This is a stress rating only and functional operation of the device at these or any other condition above those indicated in the operational sections of this specification is not implied. Exposure to absolute maximum rating conditions for extended periods may affect device reliability.

Note: For Z80-CPU all AC and DC characteristics remain the same for the military grade parts except $I_{cc}$.

$I_{cc}$ = 200 mA

# Z80-CPU D.C. Characteristics

$T_A$ = 0°C to 70°C, $V_{cc}$ = 5V ± 5% unless otherwise specified

| Symbol | Parameter | Min. | Typ. | Max. | Unit | Test Condition |
|---|---|---|---|---|---|---|
| $V_{ILC}$ | Clock Input Low Voltage | -0.3 | | 0.45 | V | |
| $V_{IHC}$ | Clock Input High Voltage | $V_{cc}$ -.6 | | $V_{cc}$+.3 | V | |
| $V_{IL}$ | Input Low Voltage | -0.3 | | 0.8 | V | |
| $V_{IH}$ | Input High Voltage | 2.0 | | $V_{cc}$ | V | |
| $V_{OL}$ | Output Low Voltage | | | 0.4 | V | $I_{OL}$=1.8mA |
| $V_{OH}$ | Output High Voltage | 2.4 | | | V | $I_{OH}$ = -250μA |
| $I_{CC}$ | Power Supply Current | | | 150 | mA | |
| $I_{LI}$ | Input Leakage Current | | | 10 | μA | $V_{IN}$=0 to $V_{cc}$ |
| $I_{LOH}$ | Tri-State Output Leakage Current in Float | | | 10 | μA | $V_{OUT}$=2.4 to $V_{cc}$ |
| $I_{LOL}$ | Tri-State Output Leakage Current in Float | | | -10 | μA | $V_{OUT}$=0.4V |
| $I_{LD}$ | Data Bus Leakage Current in Input Mode | | | ±10 | μA | $0 \leq V_{IN} \leq V_{cc}$ |

# Capacitance

$T_A$ = 25°C, f = 1 MHz,
unmeasured pins returned to ground

| Symbol | Parameter | Max. | Unit |
|---|---|---|---|
| $C_\Phi$ | Clock Capacitance | 35 | pF |
| $C_{IN}$ | Input Capacitance | 5 | pF |
| $C_{OUT}$ | Output Capacitance | 10 | pF |

# Z80-CPU Ordering Information

C – Ceramic
P – Plastic
S – Standard 5V ±5% 0° to 70°C
E – Extended 5V ±5% -40° to 85°C
M – Military 5V ±10% -55° to 125°C

# Z80A-CPU D.C. Characteristics

$T_A$ = 0°C to 70°C, $V_{cc}$ = 5V ± 5% unless otherwise specified

| Symbol | Parameter | Min. | Typ. | Max. | Unit | Test Condition |
|---|---|---|---|---|---|---|
| $V_{ILC}$ | Clock Input Low Voltage | -0.3 | | 0.45 | V | |
| $V_{IHC}$ | Clock Input High Voltage | $V_{cc}$ -.6 | | $V_{cc}$+.3 | V | |
| $V_{IL}$ | Input Low Voltage | -0.3 | | 0.8 | V | |
| $V_{IH}$ | Input High Voltage | 2.0 | | $V_{cc}$ | V | |
| $V_{OL}$ | Output Low Voltage | | | 0.4 | V | $I_{OL}$=1.8mA |
| $V_{OH}$ | Output High Voltage | 2.4 | | | V | $I_{OH}$ = -250μA |
| $I_{CC}$ | Power Supply Current | | 90 | 200 | mA | |
| $I_{LI}$ | Input Leakage Current | | | 10 | μA | $V_{IN}$=0 to $V_{cc}$ |
| $I_{LOH}$ | Tri-State Output Leakage Current in Float | | | 10 | μA | $V_{OUT}$=2.4 to $V_{cc}$ |
| $I_{LOL}$ | Tri-State Output Leakage Current in Float | | | -10 | μA | $V_{OUT}$=0.4V |
| $I_{LD}$ | Data Bus Leakage Current in Input Mode | | | ±10 | μA | $0 \leq V_{IN} \leq V_{cc}$ |

# Capacitance

$T_A$ = 25°C, f = 1 MHz,
unmeasured pins returned to ground

| Symbol | Parameter | Max. | Unit |
|---|---|---|---|
| $C_\Phi$ | Clock Capacitance | 35 | pF |
| $C_{IN}$ | Input Capacitance | 5 | pF |
| $C_{OUT}$ | Output Capacitance | 10 | pF |

# Z80A-CPU Ordering Information

C – Ceramic
P – Plastic
S – Standard 5V ±5% 0° to 70°C

**We reprint data sheets on pages 7-D2 through 7-D13 by permission of Zilog, Incorporated.**

# Z80-CPU

## A.C. Characteristics

$T_A$ = 0°C to 70°C, Vcc = +5V ± 5%, Unless Otherwise Noted.

| Signal | Symbol | Parameter | Min | Max | Unit | Test Condition |
|---|---|---|---|---|---|---|
| Φ | $t_c$ | Clock Period | .4 | [12] | μsec | |
| | $t_w(ΦH)$ | Clock Pulse Width, Clock High | 180 | [E] | nsec | |
| | $t_w(ΦL)$ | Clock Pulse Width, Clock Low | 180 | 2000 | nsec | |
| | $t_{r,f}$ | Clock Rise and Fall Time | | 30 | nsec | |
| $A_{0-15}$ | $t_{D(AD)}$ | Address Output Delay | | 145 | nsec | $C_L$ = 50pF |
| | $t_{F(AD)}$ | Delay to Float | | 110 | nsec | |
| | $t_{acm}$ | Address Stable Prior to $\overline{MREQ}$ (Memory Cycle) | [1] | | nsec | |
| | $t_{aci}$ | Address Stable Prior to $\overline{IORQ}$, $\overline{RD}$ or $\overline{WR}$ (I/O Cycle) | [2] | | nsec | |
| | $t_{ca}$ | Address Stable from $\overline{RD}$, $\overline{WR}$, $\overline{IORQ}$ or $\overline{MREQ}$ | [3] | | nsec | |
| | $t_{caf}$ | Address Stable From $\overline{RD}$ or $\overline{WR}$ During Float | [4] | | nsec | |
| $D_{0-7}$ | $t_{D(D)}$ | Data Output Delay | | 230 | nsec | $C_L$ = 50pF |
| | $t_{F(D)}$ | Delay to Float During Write Cycle | | 90 | nsec | |
| | $t_{SΦ(D)}$ | Data Setup Time to Rising Edge of Clock During M1 Cycle | 50 | | nsec | |
| | $t_{S\overline{Φ}(D)}$ | Data Setup Time to Falling Edge of Clock During M2 to M5 | 60 | | nsec | |
| | $t_{dcm}$ | Data Stable Prior to $\overline{WR}$ (Memory Cycle) | [5] | | nsec | |
| | $t_{dci}$ | Data Stable Prior to $\overline{WR}$ (I/O Cycle) | [6] | | nsec | |
| | $t_{cdf}$ | Data Stable From $\overline{WR}$ | [7] | | | |
| | $t_H$ | Any Hold Time for Setup Time | 0 | | nsec | |
| $\overline{MREQ}$ | $t_{DL\overline{Φ}(MR)}$ | $\overline{MREQ}$ Delay From Falling Edge of Clock, $\overline{MREQ}$ Low | | 100 | nsec | $C_L$ = 50pF |
| | $t_{DHΦ(MR)}$ | $\overline{MREQ}$ Delay From Rising Edge of Clock, $\overline{MREQ}$ High | | 100 | nsec | |
| | $t_{DH\overline{Φ}(MR)}$ | $\overline{MREQ}$ Delay From Falling Edge of Clock, $\overline{MREQ}$ High | | 100 | nsec | |
| | $t_{w(\overline{MRL})}$ | Pulse Width, $\overline{MREQ}$ Low | [8] | | nsec | |
| | $t_{w(\overline{MRH})}$ | Pulse Width, $\overline{MREQ}$ High | [9] | | nsec | |
| $\overline{IORQ}$ | $t_{DLΦ(IR)}$ | $\overline{IORQ}$ Delay From Rising Edge of Clock, $\overline{IORQ}$ Low | | 90 | nsec | $C_L$ = 50pF |
| | $t_{DL\overline{Φ}(IR)}$ | $\overline{IORQ}$ Delay From Falling Edge of Clock, $\overline{IORQ}$ Low | | 110 | nsec | |
| | $t_{DHΦ(IR)}$ | $\overline{IORQ}$ Delay From Rising Edge of Clock, $\overline{IORQ}$ High | | 100 | nsec | |
| | $t_{DH\overline{Φ}(IR)}$ | $\overline{IORQ}$ Delay From Falling Edge of Clock, $\overline{IORQ}$ High | | 110 | nsec | |
| $\overline{RD}$ | $t_{DLΦ(RD)}$ | $\overline{RD}$ Delay From Rising Edge of Clock, $\overline{RD}$ Low | | 100 | nsec | $C_L$ = 50pF |
| | $t_{DL\overline{Φ}(RD)}$ | $\overline{RD}$ Delay From Falling Edge of Clock, $\overline{RD}$ Low | | 130 | nsec | |
| | $t_{DHΦ(RD)}$ | $\overline{RD}$ Delay From Rising Edge of Clock, $\overline{RD}$ High | | 100 | nsec | |
| | $t_{DH\overline{Φ}(RD)}$ | $\overline{RD}$ Delay From Falling Edge of Clock, $\overline{RD}$ High | | 110 | nsec | |
| $\overline{WR}$ | $t_{DLΦ(WR)}$ | $\overline{WR}$ Delay From Rising Edge of Clock, $\overline{WR}$ Low | | 80 | nsec | $C_L$ = 50pF |
| | $t_{DL\overline{Φ}(WR)}$ | $\overline{WR}$ Delay From Falling Edge of Clock, $\overline{WR}$ Low | | 90 | nsec | |
| | $t_{DH\overline{Φ}(WR)}$ | $\overline{WR}$ Delay From Falling Edge of Clock, $\overline{WR}$ High | | 100 | nsec | |
| | $t_{w(\overline{WRL})}$ | Pulse Width, $\overline{WR}$ Low | [10] | | nsec | |
| $\overline{M1}$ | $t_{DL(M1)}$ | $\overline{M1}$ Delay From Rising Edge of Clock, $\overline{M1}$ Low | | 130 | nsec | $C_L$ = 50pF |
| | $t_{DH(M1)}$ | $\overline{M1}$ Delay From Rising Edge of Clock, $\overline{M1}$ High | | 130 | nsec | |
| $\overline{RFSH}$ | $t_{DL(RF)}$ | $\overline{RFSH}$ Delay From Rising Edge of Clock, $\overline{RFSH}$ Low | | 180 | nsec | $C_L$ = 50pF |
| | $t_{DH(RF)}$ | $\overline{RFSH}$ Delay From Rising Edge of Clock, $\overline{RFSH}$ High | | 150 | nsec | |
| $\overline{WAIT}$ | $t_{s(WT)}$ | $\overline{WAIT}$ Setup Time to Falling Edge of Clock | 70 | | nsec | |
| $\overline{HALT}$ | $t_{D(HT)}$ | $\overline{HALT}$ Delay Time From Falling Edge of Clock | | 300 | nsec | $C_L$ = 50pF |
| $\overline{INT}$ | $t_{s(IT)}$ | $\overline{INT}$ Setup Time to Rising Edge of Clock | 80 | | nsec | |
| $\overline{NMI}$ | $t_{w(\overline{NML})}$ | Pulse Width, $\overline{NMI}$ Low | 80 | | nsec | |
| $\overline{BUSRQ}$ | $t_{s(BQ)}$ | $\overline{BUSRQ}$ Setup Time to Rising Edge of Clock | 80 | | nsec | |
| $\overline{BUSAK}$ | $t_{DL(BA)}$ | $\overline{BUSAK}$ Delay From Rising Edge of Clock, $\overline{BUSAK}$ Low | | 120 | nsec | $C_L$ = 50pF |
| | $t_{DH(BA)}$ | $\overline{BUSAK}$ Delay From Falling Edge of Clock, $\overline{BUSAK}$ High | | 110 | nsec | |
| $\overline{RESET}$ | $t_{s(RS)}$ | $\overline{RESET}$ Setup Time to Rising Edge of Clock | 90 | | nsec | |
| | $t_{F(C)}$ | Delay to Float ($\overline{MREQ}$, $\overline{IORQ}$, $\overline{RD}$ and $\overline{WR}$) | | 100 | nsec | |
| | $t_{mr}$ | $\overline{M1}$ Stable Prior to $\overline{IORQ}$ (Interrupt Ack.) | [11] | | nsec | |

[12] $t_c = t_{w(ΦH)} + t_{w(ΦL)} + t_r + t_f$

[1] $t_{acm} = t_{w(ΦH)} + t_f - 75$

[2] $t_{aci} = t_c - 80$

[3] $t_{ca} = t_{w(ΦL)} + t_r - 40$

[4] $t_{caf} = t_{w(ΦL)} + t_r - 60$

[5] $t_{dcm} = t_c - 210$

[6] $t_{dci} = t_{w(ΦL)} + t_r - 210$

[7] $t_{cdf} = t_{w(ΦL)} + t_r - 80$

[8] $t_{w(MRL)} = t_c - 40$

[9] $t_{w(MRH)} = t_{w(ΦH)} + t_f - 30$

[10] $t_{w(\overline{WRL})} = t_c - 40$

[11] $t_{mr} = 2t_c + t_{w(ΦH)} + t_f - 80$

NOTES:

A. Data should be enabled onto the CPU data bus when $\overline{RD}$ is active. During interrupt acknowledge data should be enabled when $\overline{M1}$ and $\overline{IORQ}$ are both active.

B. All control signals are internally synchronized, so they may be totally asynchronous with respect to the clock.

C. The $\overline{RESET}$ signal must be active for a minimum of 3 clock cycles.

D. Output Delay vs. Loaded Capacitance

TA = 70°C Vcc = +5V ±5%

**Add 10nsec delay for each 50pf increase in load up to a maximum of 200pf for the data bus & 100pf for address & control lines**

E. Although static by design, testing guarantees $t_{w(ΦH)}$ of 200 μsec maximum

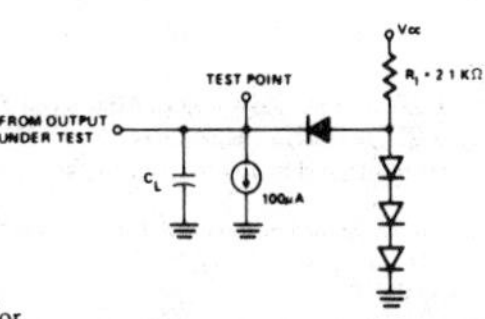


Load circuit for Output

# Z80A-CPU
## A.C. Characteristics

$T_A = 0°C$ to $70°C$, $V_{cc} = +5V \pm 5\%$, Unless Otherwise Noted.

| Signal | Symbol | Parameter | Min | Max | Unit | Test Condition |
|---|---|---|---|---|---|---|
| $\Phi$ | $t_c$ | Clock Period | .25 | [12] | μsec | |
| | $t_w(\Phi H)$ | Clock Pulse Width, Clock High | 110 | [E] | nsec | |
| | $t_w(\Phi L)$ | Clock Pulse Width, Clock Low | 110 | 2000 | nsec | |
| | $t_{r,f}$ | Clock Rise and Fall Time | | 30 | nsec | |
| $A_{0-15}$ | $t_{D(AD)}$ | Address Output Delay | | 110 | nsec | $C_L = 50pF$ |
| | $t_{F(AD)}$ | Delay to Float | | 90 | nsec | |
| | $t_{acm}$ | Address Stable Prior to $\overline{MREQ}$ (Memory Cycle) | [1] | | nsec | |
| | $t_{aci}$ | Address Stable Prior to $\overline{IORQ}$, $\overline{RD}$ or $\overline{WR}$ (I/O Cycle) | [2] | | nsec | |
| | $t_{ca}$ | Address Stable from $\overline{RD}$, $\overline{WR}$, $\overline{IORQ}$ or $\overline{MREQ}$ | [3] | | nsec | |
| | $t_{caf}$ | Address Stable From $\overline{RD}$ or $\overline{WR}$ During Float | [4] | | nsec | |
| $D_{0-7}$ | $t_{D(D)}$ | Data Output Delay | | 150 | nsec | $C_L = 50pF$ |
| | $t_{F(D)}$ | Delay to Float During Write Cycle | | 90 | nsec | |
| | $t_{S\Phi(D)}$ | Data Setup Time to Rising Edge of Clock During M1 Cycle | 35 | | nsec | |
| | $t_{S\overline{\Phi}(D)}$ | Data Setup Time to Falling Edge of Clock During M2 to M5 | 50 | | nsec | |
| | $t_{dcm}$ | Data Stable Prior to $\overline{WR}$ (Memory Cycle) | [5] | | nsec | |
| | $t_{dci}$ | Data Stable Prior to $\overline{WR}$ (I/O Cycle) | [6] | | nsec | |
| | $t_{cdf}$ | Data Stable From $\overline{WR}$ | [7] | | | |
| | $t_H$ | Any Hold Time for Setup Time | | 0 | nsec | |
| $\overline{MREQ}$ | $t_{DL\overline{\Phi}(MR)}$ | $\overline{MREQ}$ Delay From Falling Edge of Clock, $\overline{MREQ}$ Low | | 85 | nsec | $C_L = 50pF$ |
| | $t_{DH\Phi(MR)}$ | $\overline{MREQ}$ Delay From Rising Edge of Clock, $\overline{MREQ}$ High | | 85 | nsec | |
| | $t_{DH\overline{\Phi}(MR)}$ | $\overline{MREQ}$ Delay From Falling Edge of Clock, $\overline{MREQ}$ High | | 85 | nsec | |
| | $t_{w(\overline{MRL})}$ | Pulse Width, $\overline{MREQ}$ Low | [8] | | nsec | |
| | $t_{w(\overline{MRH})}$ | Pulse Width, $\overline{MREQ}$ High | [9] | | nsec | |
| $\overline{IORQ}$ | $t_{DL\Phi(IR)}$ | $\overline{IORQ}$ Delay From Rising Edge of Clock, $\overline{IORQ}$ Low | | 75 | nsec | $C_L = 50pF$ |
| | $t_{DL\overline{\Phi}(IR)}$ | $\overline{IORQ}$ Delay From Falling Edge of Clock, $\overline{IORQ}$ Low | | 85 | nsec | |
| | $t_{DH\Phi(IR)}$ | $\overline{IORQ}$ Delay From Rising Edge of Clock, $\overline{IORQ}$ High | | 85 | nsec | |
| | $t_{DH\overline{\Phi}(IR)}$ | $\overline{IORQ}$ Delay From Falling Edge of Clock, $\overline{IORQ}$ High | | 85 | nsec | |
| $\overline{RD}$ | $t_{DL\Phi(RD)}$ | $\overline{RD}$ Delay From Rising Edge of Clock, $\overline{RD}$ Low | | 85 | nsec | $C_L = 50pF$ |
| | $t_{DL\overline{\Phi}(RD)}$ | $\overline{RD}$ Delay From Falling Edge of Clock, $\overline{RD}$ Low | | 95 | nsec | |
| | $t_{DH\Phi(RD)}$ | $\overline{RD}$ Delay From Rising Edge of Clock, $\overline{RD}$ High | | 85 | nsec | |
| | $t_{DH\overline{\Phi}(RD)}$ | $\overline{RD}$ Delay From Falling Edge of Clock, $\overline{RD}$ High | | 85 | nsec | |
| $\overline{WR}$ | $t_{DL\Phi(WR)}$ | $\overline{WR}$ Delay From Rising Edge of Clock, $\overline{WR}$ Low | | 65 | nsec | $C_L = 50pF$ |
| | $t_{DL\overline{\Phi}(WR)}$ | $\overline{WR}$ Delay From Falling Edge of Clock, $\overline{WR}$ Low | | 80 | nsec | |
| | $t_{DH\overline{\Phi}(WR)}$ | $\overline{WR}$ Delay From Falling Edge of Clock, $\overline{WR}$ High | | 80 | nsec | |
| | $t_{w(\overline{WRL})}$ | Pulse Width, $\overline{WR}$ Low | [10] | | nsec | |
| $\overline{M1}$ | $t_{DL(M1)}$ | $\overline{M1}$ Delay From Rising Edge of Clock, $\overline{M1}$ Low | | 100 | nsec | $C_L = 50pF$ |
| | $t_{DH(M1)}$ | $\overline{M1}$ Delay From Rising Edge of Clock, $\overline{M1}$ High | | 100 | nsec | |
| $\overline{RFSH}$ | $t_{DL(RF)}$ | $\overline{RFSH}$ Delay From Rising Edge of Clock, $\overline{RFSH}$ Low | | 130 | nsec | $C_L = 50pF$ |
| | $t_{DH(RF)}$ | $\overline{RFSH}$ Delay From Rising Edge of Clock, $\overline{RFSH}$ High | | 120 | nsec | |
| $\overline{WAIT}$ | $t_{s(WT)}$ | $\overline{WAIT}$ Setup Time to Falling Edge of Clock | 70 | | nsec | |
| $\overline{HALT}$ | $t_{D(HT)}$ | $\overline{HALT}$ Delay Time From Falling Edge of Clock | | 300 | nsec | $C_L = 50pF$ |
| $\overline{INT}$ | $t_{s(IT)}$ | $\overline{INT}$ Setup Time to Rising Edge of Clock | 80 | | nsec | |
| $\overline{NMI}$ | $t_{w(\overline{NML})}$ | Pulse Width, $\overline{NMI}$ Low | 80 | | nsec | |
| $\overline{BUSRQ}$ | $t_{s(BQ)}$ | $\overline{BUSRQ}$ Setup Time to Rising Edge of Clock | 50 | | nsec | |
| $\overline{BUSAK}$ | $t_{DL(BA)}$ | $\overline{BUSAK}$ Delay From Rising Edge of Clock, $\overline{BUSAK}$ Low | | 100 | nsec | $C_L = 50pF$ |
| | $t_{DH(BA)}$ | $\overline{BUSAK}$ Delay From Falling Edge of Clock, $\overline{BUSAK}$ High | | 100 | nsec | |
| $\overline{RESET}$ | $t_{s(RS)}$ | $\overline{RESET}$ Setup Time to Rising Edge of Clock | 60 | | nsec | |
| | $t_{F(C)}$ | Delay to Float ($\overline{MREQ}$, $\overline{IORQ}$, $\overline{RD}$ and $\overline{WR}$) | | 80 | nsec | |
| | $t_{mr}$ | M1 Stable Prior to IORQ (Interrupt Ack.) | [11] | | nsec | |

[12] $t_c = t_{w(\Phi H)} + t_{w(\Phi L)} + t_r + t_f$

[1] $t_{acm} = t_{w(\Phi H)} + t_f - 65$

[2] $t_{aci} = t_c - 70$

[3] $t_{ca} = t_{w(\Phi L)} + t_r - 50$

[4] $t_{caf} = t_{w(\Phi L)} + t_r - 45$

[5] $t_{dcm} = t_c - 170$

[6] $t_{dci} = t_{w(\Phi L)} + t_r - 170$

[7] $t_{cdf} = t_{w(\Phi L)} + t_r - 70$

[8] $t_{w(\overline{MRL})} = t_c - 30$

[9] $t_{w(\overline{MRH})} = t_{w(\Phi H)} + t_f - 20$

[10] $t_{w(\overline{WRL})} = t_c - 30$

[11] $t_{mr} = 2t_c + t_{w(\Phi H)} + t_f - 65$

NOTES:

A. Data should be enabled onto the CPU data bus when $\overline{RD}$ is active. During interrupt acknowledge data should be enabled when $\overline{M1}$ and $\overline{IORQ}$ are both active.

B. All control signals are internally synchronized, so they may be totally asynchronous with respect to the clock.

C. The $\overline{RESET}$ signal must be active for a minimum of 3 clock cycles.

D. Output Delay vs. Loaded Capacitance
TA = 70°C   Vcc = +5V ±5%
Add 10nsec delay for each 50pf increase in load up to maximum of 200pf for data bus and 100pf for address & control lines.

E. Although static by design, testing guarantees $t_{w(\Phi H)}$ of 200 μsec maximum

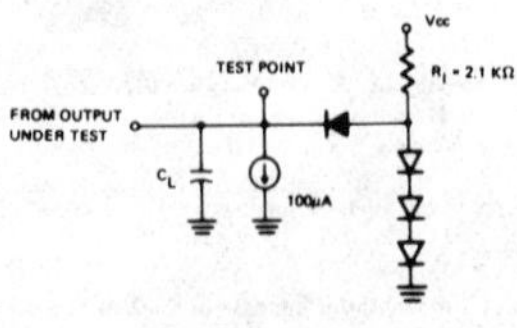


Load circuit for Output

# A.C. Timing Diagram

Timing measurements are made at the following voltages, unless otherwise specified:

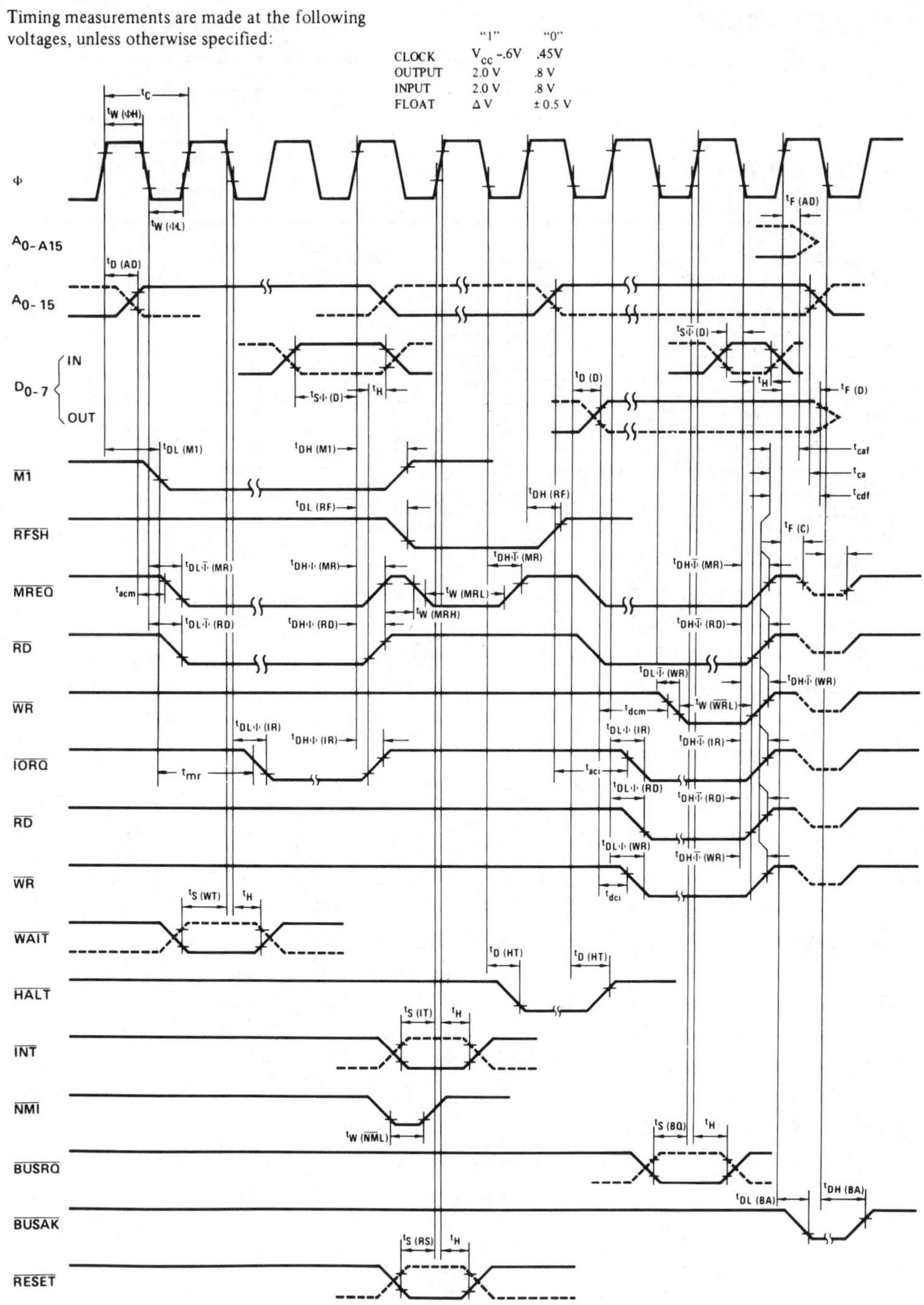

## Absolute Maximum Ratings

| | |
|---|---|
| Temperature Under Bias | Specified operating range. |
| Storage Temperature | -65° C to +150° C |
| Voltage On Any Pin With Respect To Ground | -0.3 V to +7 V |
| Power Dissipation | .6 W |

***Comment**
Stresses above those listed under "Absolute Maximum Rating" may cause permanent damage to the device. This is a stress rating only and functional operation of the device at these or any other condition above those indicated in the operational sections of this specification is not implied. Exposure to absolute maximum rating conditions for extended periods may affect device reliability.

Note: **All AC and DC characteristics remain the same for the military grade parts except $I_{cc}$.**

$I_{cc}$ = 130 mA.

## Z80-PIO and Z80A-PIO D.C. Characteristics

TA = 0° C to 70° C, Vcc = 5 V ± 5% unless otherwise specified

| Symbol | Parameter | Min. | Max. | Unit | Test Condition |
|---|---|---|---|---|---|
| $V_{ILC}$ | Clock Input Low Voltage | -0.3 | .45 | V | |
| $V_{IHC}$ | Clock Input High Voltage | Vcc-.6 | Vcc+.3 | V | |
| $V_{IL}$ | Input Low Voltage | -0.3 | 0.8 | V | |
| $V_{IH}$ | Input High Voltage | 2.0 | Vcc | V | |
| $V_{OL}$ | Output Low Voltage | | 0.4 | V | $I_{OL}$ = 2.0 mA |
| $V_{OH}$ | Output High Voltage | 2.4 | | V | $I_{OH}$ = -250 μA |
| $I_{CC}$ | Power Supply Current | | 70 | mA | |
| $I_{LI}$ | Input Leakage Current | | 10 | μA | $V_{IN}$ = 0 to Vcc |
| $I_{LOH}$ | Tri-State Output Leakage Current in Float | | 10 | μA | $V_{OUT}$ = 2.4 to Vcc |
| $I_{LOL}$ | Tri-State Output Leakage Current in Float | | -10 | μA | $V_{OUT}$ = 0.4 V |
| $I_{LD}$ | Data Bus Leakage Current in Input Mode | | ±10 | μA | $0 \leq V_{IN} \leq Vcc$ |
| $I_{OHD}$ | Darlington Drive Current | -1.5 | 3.8 | mA | $V_{OH}$ = 1.5 V<br>$R_{EXT}$ = 390 Ω<br>Port B Only |

# Z80-PIO
# A.C. Characteristics

TA = 0° C to 70° C, Vcc = +5 V ± 5%, unless otherwise noted

| SIGNAL | SYMBOL | PARAMETER | MIN | MAX | UNIT | COMMENTS |
|---|---|---|---|---|---|---|
| $\Phi$ | $t_c$ | Clock Period | 400 | [1] | nsec | |
| | $t_W(\Phi H)$ | Clock Pulse Width, Clock High | 170 | 2000 | nsec | |
| | $t_W(\Phi L)$ | Clock Pulse Width, Clock Low | 170 | 2000 | nsec | |
| | $t_r, t_f$ | Clock Rise and Fall Times | | 30 | nsec | |
| | $t_H$ | Any Hold Time for Specified Set-Up Time | 0 | | nsec | |
| CS, $\overline{CE}$ ETC. | $t_{S\Phi}(CS)$ | Control Signal Set-Up Time to Rising Edge of $\Phi$ During Read or Write Cycle | 280 | | nsec | |
| $D_0$-$D_7$ | $t_{DR}(D)$ | Data Output Delay from Falling Edge of $\overline{RD}$ | | 430 | nsec | [2] |
| | $t_{S\Phi}(D)$ | Data Set-Up Time to Rising Edge of $\Phi$ During Write or $\overline{M1}$ Cycle | 50 | | nsec | $C_L$ = 50 pF |
| | $t_{DI}(D)$ | Data Output Delay from Falling Edge of $\overline{IORQ}$ During INTA Cycle. | | 340 | nsec | [3] |
| | $t_F(D)$ | Delay to Floating Bus (Output Buffer Disable Time) | | 160 | nsec | |
| IEI | $t_S(IEI)$ | IEI Set-Up Time to Falling Edge of $\overline{IORQ}$ During INTA Cycle | 140 | | nsec | |
| IEO | $t_{DH}(IO)$ | IEO Delay Time from Rising Edge of IEI | | 210 | nsec | [5] |
| | $t_{DL}(IO)$ | IEO Delay Time from Falling Edge of IEI | | 190 | nsec | [5] $C_L$ = 50 pF |
| | $t_{DM}(IO)$ | IEO Delay from Falling Edge of $\overline{M1}$ (Interrupt Occurring Just Prior to $\overline{M1}$) See Note A. | | 300 | nsec | [5] |
| $\overline{IORQ}$ | $t_{S\Phi}(IR)$ | $\overline{IORQ}$ Set-Up Time to Rising Edge of $\Phi$ During Read or Write Cycle | 250 | | nsec | |
| $\overline{M1}$ | $t_{S\Phi}(M1)$ | $\overline{M1}$ Set-Up Time to Rising Edge of $\Phi$ During INTA or $\overline{M1}$ Cycle. See Note B. | 210 | | nsec | |
| $\overline{RD}$ | $t_{S\Phi}(RD)$ | $\overline{RD}$ Set-Up Time to Rising Edge of $\Phi$ During Read or $\overline{M1}$ Cycle | 240 | | nsec | |
| $A_0$-$A_7$, $B_0$-$B_7$ | $t_S(PD)$ | Port Data Set-Up Time to Rising Edge of $\overline{STROBE}$ (Mode 1) | 260 | | nsec | |
| | $t_{DS}(PD)$ | Port Data Output Delay from Falling Edge of $\overline{STROBE}$ (Mode 2) | | 230 | nsec | [5] |
| | $t_F(PD)$ | Delay to Floating Port Data Bus from Rising Edge of $\overline{STROBE}$ (Mode 2) | | 200 | nsec | $C_L$ = 50 pF |
| | $t_{DI}(PD)$ | Port Data Stable from Rising Edge of $\overline{IORQ}$ During WR Cycle (Mode 0) | | 200 | nsec | [5] |
| $\overline{ASTB}$, $\overline{BSTB}$ | $t_W(ST)$ | Pulse Width, $\overline{STROBE}$ | 150<br>[4] | | nsec<br>nsec | |
| $\overline{INT}$ | $t_D(IT)$ | $\overline{INT}$ Delay Time from Rising Edge of $\overline{STROBE}$ | | 490 | nsec | |
| | $t_D(IT3)$ | $\overline{INT}$ Delay Time from Data Match During Mode 3 Operation | | 420 | nsec | |
| ARDY, BRDY | $t_{DH}(RY)$ | Ready Response Time from Rising Edge of $\overline{IORQ}$ | | $t_c$+ 460 | nsec | [5] $C_L$ = 50 pF |
| | $t_{DL}(RY)$ | Ready Response Time from Rising Edge of $\overline{STROBE}$ | | $t_c$+ 400 | nsec | [5] |

NOTES:

A. $2.5\ t_c > (N-2)\ t_{DL}(IO) + t_{DM}(IO) + t_S(IEI)$ + TTL Buffer Delay, if any

B. $\overline{M1}$ must be active for a minimum of 2 clock periods to reset the PIO.

[1] $t_c = t_W(\Phi H) + t_W(\Phi L) + t_r + t_f$

[2] Increase $t_{DR}(D)$ by 10 nsec for each 50 pF increase in loading up to 200 pF max.

[3] Increase $t_{DI}(D)$ by 10 nsec for each 50 pF increase in loading up to 200 pF max.

[4] For Mode 2: $t_W(ST) > t_S(PD)$

[5] Increase these values by 2 nsec for each 10 pF increase in loading up to 100 pF max.

**Output load circuit.**

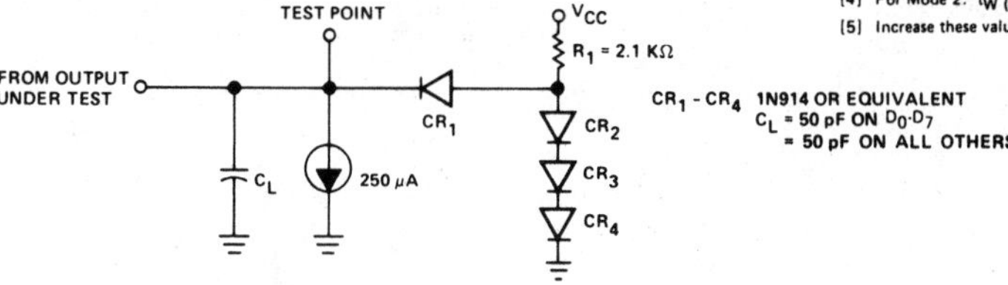


# Capacitance

TA = 25° C, f = 1 MHz

| Symbol | Parameter | Max. | Unit | Test Condition |
|---|---|---|---|---|
| $C_\Phi$ | Clock Capacitance | 10 | pF | Unmeasured Pins |
| $C_{IN}$ | Input Capacitance | 5 | pF | Returned to Ground |
| $C_{OUT}$ | Output Capacitance | 10 | pF | |

# Z80A-PIO

## A.C. Characteristics

TA = 0° C to 70° C, Vcc = +5 V ± 5%, unless otherwise noted

| SIGNAL | SYMBOL | PARAMETER | MIN | MAX | UNIT | COMMENTS |
|---|---|---|---|---|---|---|
| Φ | $t_c$ | Clock Period | 250 | [1] | nsec | |
| | $t_{W(\Phi H)}$ | Clock Pulse Width, Clock High | 105 | 2000 | nsec | |
| | $t_{W(\Phi L)}$ | Clock Pulse Width, Clock Low | 105 | 2000 | nsec | |
| | $t_r, t_f$ | Clock Rise and Fall Times | | 30 | nsec | |
| | $t_h$ | Any Hold Time for Specified Set-Up Time | 0 | | nsec | |
| CS, $\overline{CE}$ ETC. | $t_{S\Phi}$ (CS) | Control Signal Set-Up Time to Rising Edge of Φ During Read or Write Cycle | 145 | | nsec | |
| $D_0$-$D_7$ | $t_{DR}$ (D) | Data Output Delay From Falling Edge of $\overline{RD}$ | | 380 | nsec | [2] |
| | $t_{S\Phi}$ (D) | Data Set-Up Time to Rising Edge of Φ During Write or $\overline{M1}$ Cycle | 50 | | nsec | $C_L$ = 50 pF |
| | $t_{DI}$ (D) | Data Output Delay from Falling Edge of $\overline{IORQ}$ During INTA Cycle | | 250 | nsec | [3] |
| | $t_F$ (D) | Delay to Floating Bus (Output Buffer Disable Time) | | 110 | nsec | |
| IEI | $t_S$ (IEI) | IEI Set-Up Time to Falling edge of $\overline{IORQ}$ During INTA Cycle | 140 | | nsec | |
| IEO | $t_{DH}$ (IO) | IEO Delay Time from Rising Edge of IEI | | 160 | nsec | [5] |
| | $t_{DL}$ (IO) | IEO Delay Time from Falling Edge of IEI | | 130 | nsec | [5] $C_L$ = 50 pF |
| | $t_{DM}$ (IO) | IEO Delay from Falling Edge of $\overline{M1}$ (Interrupt Occurring Just Prior to $\overline{M1}$) See Note A. | | 190 | nsec | [5] |
| $\overline{IORQ}$ | $t_{S\Phi}$ (IR) | $\overline{IORQ}$ Set-Up Time to Rising Edge of Φ During Read or Write Cycle. | 115 | | nsec | |
| $\overline{M1}$ | $t_{S\Phi}$ (M1) | $\overline{M1}$ Set-Up Time to Rising Edge of Φ During INTA or $\overline{M1}$ Cycle See Note B | 90 | | nsec | |
| $\overline{RD}$ | $t_{S\Phi}$ (RD) | $\overline{RD}$ Set-Up Time to Rising Edge of Φ During Read or $\overline{M1}$ Cycle | 115 | | nsec | |
| $A_0$-$A_7$, $B_0$-$B_7$ | $t_S$ (PD) | Port Data Set-Up Time to Rising Edge of $\overline{STROBE}$ (Mode 1) | 230 | | nsec | |
| | $t_{DS}$ (PD) | Port Data Ourput Delay from Falling Edge of $\overline{STROBE}$ (Mode 2) | | 210 | nsec | [5] |
| | $t_F$ (PD) | Delay to Floating Port Data Bus from Rising Edge of $\overline{STROBE}$ (Mode 2) | | 180 | nsec | $C_L$ = 50 pF |
| | $t_{DI}$ (PD) | Port Data Stable from Rising Edge of $\overline{IORQ}$ During WR Cycle (Mode 0) | | 180 | nsec | [5] |
| $\overline{ASTB}$, $\overline{BSTB}$ | $t_W$ (ST) | Pulse Width, $\overline{STROBE}$ | 150<br>[4] | | nsec<br>nsec | |
| $\overline{INT}$ | $t_D$ (IT) | $\overline{INT}$ Delay time from Rising Edge of $\overline{STROBE}$ | | 440 | nsec | |
| | $t_D$ (IT3) | $\overline{INT}$ Delay Time from Data Match During Mode 3 Operation | | 380 | nsec | |
| ARDY, BRDY | $t_{DH}$ (RY) | Ready Response Time from Rising Edge of $\overline{IORQ}$ | | $t_c$+ 410 | nsec | [5] $C_L$ = 50 pF |
| | $t_{DL}$ (RY) | Ready Response Time from Rising Edge of $\overline{STROBE}$ | | $t_c$+ 360 | nsec | [5] |



NOTES:

A. $2.5\ t_c > (N-2)\ t_{DL}(IO) + t_{DM}(IO) + t_S(IEI)$ + TTL Buffer Delay, if any

B. $\overline{M1}$ must be active for a minimum of 2 clock periods to reset the PIO.

[1] $t_c = t_{W(\Phi H)} + t_{W(\Phi L)} + t_r + t_f$

[2] Increase $t_{DR}$ (D) by 10 nsec for each 50 pF increase in loading up to 200 pF max.

[3] Increase $t_{DI}$ (D) by 10 nsec for each 50 pF increase in loading up to 200 pF max.

[4] For Mode 2. $t_W(ST) > t_S(PD)$

[5] Increase these values by 2 nsec for each 10 pF increase in loading up to 100 pF max.

# Z80-PIO

## A.C. Timing Diagram

Timing measurements are made at the following voltages, unless otherwise specified:

| | "1" | "0" |
|---|---|---|
| CLOCK | $V_{cc}-.6$ | .45V |
| OUTPUT | 2.0V | 0.8V |
| INPUT | 2.0V | 0.8V |
| FLOAT | $\Delta V$ | = +0.5V |

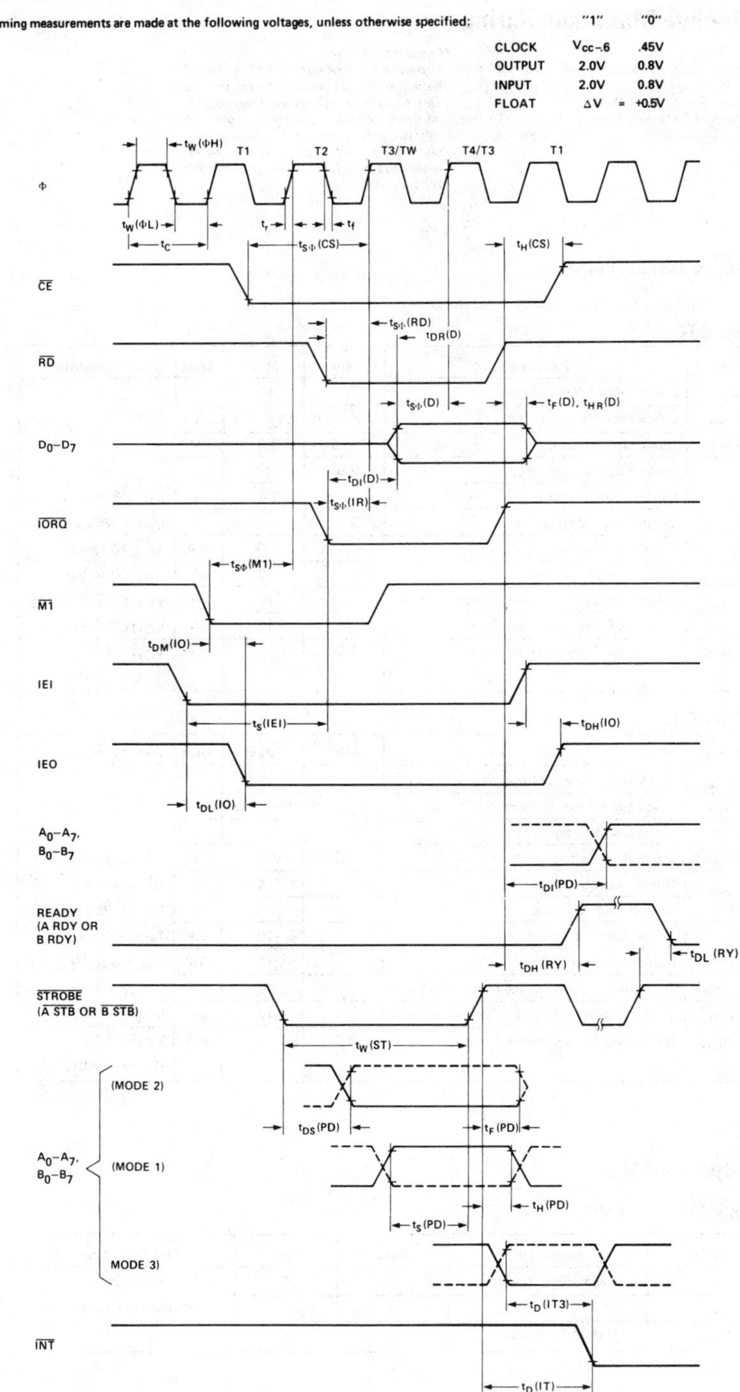

## Z80-CTC

# Absolute Maximum Ratings

| | |
|---|---|
| Temperature Under Bias | 0° C to 70° C |
| Storage Temperature | -65° C to +150° C |
| Voltage On Any Pin With Respect To Ground | -0.3 V to +7 V |
| Power Dissipation | 0.8W |

***Comment**
Stresses above those listed under "Absolute Maximum Rating" may cause permanent damage to the device. This is a stress rating only and functional operation of the device at these or any other condition above those indicated in the operational sections of this specification is not implied. Exposure to absolute maximum rating conditions for extended periods may affect device reliability.

# D.C. Characteristics

TA = 0° C to 70° C, Vcc = 5 V ± 5% unless otherwise specified

### Z80-CTC

| Symbol | Parameter | Min | Max | Unit | Test Condition |
|---|---|---|---|---|---|
| $V_{ILC}$ | Clock Input Low Voltage | -0.3 | .45 | V | |
| $V_{IHC}$ | Clock Input High Voltage [1] | $V_{CC}$ - .6 | $V_{CC}$ + .3 | V | |
| $V_{IL}$ | Input Low Voltage | -0.3 | 0.8 | V | |
| $V_{IH}$ | Input High Voltage | 2.0 | $V_{CC}$ | V | |
| $V_{OL}$ | Output Low Voltage | | 0.4 | V | $I_{OL}$ = 2 mA |
| $V_{OH}$ | Output High Voltage | 2.4 | | V | $I_{OH}$ = -250 μA |
| $I_{CC}$ | Power Supply Current | | 120 | mA | $T_C$ = 400 nsec |
| $I_{LI}$ | Input Leakage Current | | 10 | μA | $V_{IN}$ = 0 to $V_{CC}$ |
| $I_{LOH}$ | Tri-State Output Leakage Current in Float | | 10 | μA | $V_{OUT}$ = 2.4 to $V_{CC}$ |
| $I_{LOL}$ | Tri-State Output Leakage Current in Float | | -10 | μA | $V_{OUT}$ = 0.4V |
| $I_{OHD}$ | Darlington Drive Current | -1.5 | | mA | $V_{OH}$ = 1.5V<br>$R_{EXT}$ = 390Ω |

### Z80A-CTC

| Symbol | Parameter | Min | Max | Unit | Test Condition |
|---|---|---|---|---|---|
| $V_{ILC}$ | Clock Input Low Voltage | -0.3 | .45 | V | |
| $V_{IHC}$ | Clock Input High Voltage [1] | $V_{CC}$ - .6 | $V_{CC}$ + .3 | V | |
| $V_{IL}$ | Input Low Voltage | -0.3 | 0.8 | V | |
| $V_{IH}$ | Input High Voltage | 2.0 | $V_{CC}$ | V | |
| $V_{OL}$ | Output Low Voltage | | 0.4 | V | $I_{OL}$ = 2 mA |
| $V_{OH}$ | Output High Voltage | 2.4 | | V | $I_{OH}$ = -250 μA |
| $I_{CC}$ | Power Supply Current | | 120 | mA | $T_C$ = 250 nsec |
| $I_{LI}$ | Input Leakage Current | | 10 | μA | $V_{IN}$ = 0 to $V_{CC}$ |
| $I_{LOH}$ | Tri-State Output Leakage Current in Float | | 10 | μA | $V_{OUT}$ = 2.4 to $V_{CC}$ |
| $I_{LOL}$ | Tri-State Output Leakage Current in Float | | -10 | μA | $V_{OUT}$ = 0.4V |
| $I_{OHD}$ | Darlington Drive Current | -1.5 | | mA | $V_{OH}$ = 1.5V<br>$R_{EXT}$ = 390Ω |

# Capacitance

TA = 25° C, f = 1 MHz

| Symbol | Parameter | Max. | Unit | Test Condition |
|---|---|---|---|---|
| $C_{\Phi}$ | Clock Capacitance | 20 | pF | Unmeasured Pins |
| $C_{IN}$ | Input Capacitance | 5 | pF | Returned to Ground |
| $C_{OUT}$ | Output Capacitance | 10 | pF | |

# Z80-CTC
# A.C. Characteristics

TA = 0° C to 70° C, Vcc = +5 V ± 5%, unless otherwise noted

| Signal | Symbol | Parameter | Min | Max | Unit | Comments |
|---|---|---|---|---|---|---|
| Φ | $t_C$ | Clock Period | 400 | [1] | ns | |
| | $t_W(\Phi H)$ | Clock Pulse Width, Clock High | 170 | 2000 | ns | |
| | $t_W(\Phi L)$ | Clock Pulse Width, Clock Low | 170 | 2000 | ns | |
| | $t_r, t_f$ | Clock Rise and Fall Times | | 30 | ns | |
| | $t_H$ | Any Hold Time for Specified Setup Time | 0 | | ns | |
| CS, $\overline{CE}$, etc. | $t_{S\Phi}(CS)$ | Control Signal Setup Time to Rising Edge of Φ During Read or Write Cycle | 160 | | ns | |
| $D_0-D_7$ | $t_{DR}(D)$ | Data Output Delay from Rising Edge of $\overline{RD}$ During Read Cycle | | 480 | ns | [2] |
| | $t_{S\Phi}(D)$ | Data Setup Time to Rising Edge of Φ During Write or M1 Cycle | 60 | | ns | |
| | $t_{DI}(D)$ | Data Output Delay from Falling Edge of IORQ During INTA Cycle | | 340 | ns | [2] |
| | $t_F(D)$ | Delay to Floating Bus (Output Buffer Disable Time) | | 230 | ns | |
| IEI | $t_S(IEI)$ | IEI Setup Time to Falling Edge of $\overline{IORQ}$ During INTA Cycle | 200 | | ns | |
| IEO | $t_{DH}(IO)$ | IEO Delay Time from Rising Edge of IEI | | 220 | ns | [3] |
| | $t_{DL}(IO)$ | IEO Delay Time from Falling Edge of IEI | | 190 | ns | [3] |
| | $t_{DM}(IO)$ | IEO Delay from Falling Edge of $\overline{M1}$ (Interrupt Occurring just Prior to $\overline{M1}$) | | 300 | ns | [3] |
| $\overline{IORQ}$ | $t_{S\Phi}(IR)$ | $\overline{IORQ}$ Setup Time to Rising Edge of Φ During Read or Write Cycle | 250 | | ns | |
| $\overline{M1}$ | $t_{S\Phi}(M1)$ | $\overline{M1}$ Setup Time to Rising Edge of Φ During INTA or M1 Cycle | 210 | | ns | |
| $\overline{RD}$ | $t_{S\Phi}(RD)$ | $\overline{RD}$ Setup Time to Rising Edge of Φ During Read or M1 Cycle | 240 | | ns | |
| $\overline{INT}$ | $t_{DCK}(IT)$ | $\overline{INT}$ Delay Time from Rising Edge of CLK/TRG | | $2t_C(\Phi) + 200$ | | Counter Mode |
| | $t_{D\Phi}(IT)$ | $\overline{INT}$ Delay Time from Rising Edge of Φ | | $t_C(\Phi) + 200$ | | Timer Mode |
| $CLK/TRG_{0-3}$ | $t_C(CK)$ | Clock Period | $2t_C(\Phi)$ | | | Counter Mode |
| | $t_r, t_f$ | Clock and Trigger Rise and Fall Times | | 50 | | |
| | $t_S(CK)$ | Clock Setup Time to Rising Edge of Φ for Immediate Count | 210 | | | Counter Mode |
| | $t_S(TR)$ | Trigger Setup Time to Rising Edge of Φ for Enabling of Prescaler on Following Rising Edge of Φ | 210 | | | Timer Mode |
| | $t_W(CTH)$ | Clock and Trigger High Pulse Width | 200 | | | Counter and Timer Modes |
| | $t_W(CTL)$ | Clock and Trigger Low Pulse Width | 200 | | | Counter and Timer Modes |
| $ZC/TO_{0-2}$ | $t_{DH}(ZC)$ | ZC/TO Delay Time from Rising Edge of Φ, ZC/TO High | | 190 | | Counter and Timer Modes |
| | $t_{DL}(ZC)$ | ZC/TO Delay Time from Falling Edge of Φ, ZC/TO Low | | 190 | | Counter and Timer Modes |

**Notes:** [1] $t_C = t_W(\Phi H) + t_W(\Phi L) + t_r + t_f$.
[2] Increase delay by 10 nsec for each 50 pF increase in loading, 200 pF maximum for data lines and 100 pF for control lines.
[3] Increase delay by 2 nsec for each 10 pF increase in loading, 100 pF maximum
[4] $\overline{RESET}$ must be active for a minimum of 3 clock cycles.

## OUTPUT LOAD CIRCUIT

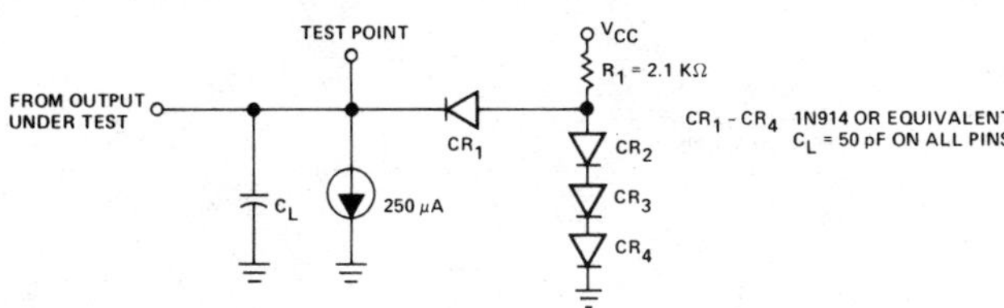

# Z80A-CTC
## A.C. Characteristics

TA = 0° C to 70° C, Vcc = +5 V ± 5%, unless otherwise noted

| Signal | Symbol | Parameter | Min | Max | Unit | Comments |
|---|---|---|---|---|---|---|
| Φ | $t_C$ | Clock Period | 250 | [1] | ns | |
| | $t_W(\Phi H)$ | Clock Pulse Width, Clock High | 105 | 2000 | ns | |
| | $t_W(\Phi L)$ | Clock Pulse Width, Clock Low | 105 | 2000 | ns | |
| | $t_r, t_f$ | Clock Rise and Fall Times | | 30 | ns | |
| | $t_H$ | Any Hold Time for Specified Setup Time | 0 | | ns | |
| CS, $\overline{\text{CE}}$, etc | $t_{S\Phi}(CS)$ | Control Signal Setup Time to Rising Edge of Φ During Read or Write Cycle | 60 | | ns | |
| $D_0$–$D_7$ | $t_{DR}(D)$ | Data Output Delay from Falling Edge of $\overline{\text{RD}}$ During Read Cycle | | 380 | ns | [2] |
| | $t_{S\Phi}(D)$ | Data Setup Time to Rising Edge of Φ During Write or M1 Cycle | 50 | | ns | |
| | $t_{DI}(D)$ | Data Output Delay from Falling Edge of IORG During INTA Cycle | | 160 | ns | [2] |
| | $t_F(D)$ | Delay to Floating Bus (Output Buffer Disable Time) | | 110 | ns | |
| IEI | $t_S(IEI)$ | IEI Setup Time to Falling Edge of $\overline{\text{IORQ}}$ During INTA Cycle | 140 | | ns | |
| IEO | $t_{DH}(IO)$ | IEO Delay Time from Rising Edge of IEI | | 160 | ns | [3] |
| | $t_{DL}(IO)$ | IEO Delay Time from Falling Edge of IEI | | 130 | ns | [3] |
| | $t_{DM}(IO)$ | IEO Delay from Falling Edge of $\overline{\text{M1}}$ (Interrupt Occurring just Prior to $\overline{\text{M1}}$) | | 190 | ns | [3] |
| $\overline{\text{IORQ}}$ | $t_{S\Phi}(IR)$ | $\overline{\text{IORQ}}$ Setup Time to Rising Edge of Φ During Read or Write Cycle | 115 | | ns | |
| $\overline{\text{M1}}$ | $t_{S\Phi}(M1)$ | $\overline{\text{M1}}$ Setup Time to Rising Edge of Φ During INTA or M1 Cycle | 90 | | ns | |
| $\overline{\text{RD}}$ | $t_{S\Phi}(RD)$ | $\overline{\text{RD}}$ Setup Time to Rising Edge of Φ During Read or M1 Cycle | 115 | | ns | |
| $\overline{\text{INT}}$ | $t_{DCK}(IT)$ | $\overline{\text{INT}}$ Delay Time from Rising Edge of CLK/TRG | | $2t_C(\Phi) + 140$ | | Counter Mode |
| | $t_{D\Phi}(IT)$ | $\overline{\text{INT}}$ Delay Time from Rising Edge of Φ | | $t_C(\Phi) + 140$ | | Timer Mode |
| CLK/TRG$_{0-3}$ | $t_C(CK)$ | Clock Period | $2t_C(\Phi)$ | | | Counter Mode |
| | $t_r, t_f$ | Clock and Trigger Rise and Fall Times | | 30 | | |
| | $t_S(CK)$ | Clock Setup Time to Rising Edge of Φ for Immediate Count | 130 | | | Counter Mode |
| | $t_S(TR)$ | Trigger Setup Time to Rising Edge of Φ for enabling of Prescaler on Following Rising Edge of Φ | 130 | | | Timer Mode |
| | $t_W(CTH)$ | Clock and Trigger High Pulse Width | 120 | | | Counter and Timer Modes |
| | $t_W(CTL)$ | Clock and Trigger Low Pulse Width | 120 | | | Counter and Timer Modes |
| ZC/TO$_{0-2}$ | $t_{DH}(ZC)$ | ZC/TO Delay Time from Rising Edge of Φ, ZC/TO High | | 120 | | Counter and Timer Modes |
| | $t_{DL}(ZC)$ | ZC/TO Delay Time from Rising Edge of Φ, ZC/TO Low | | 120 | | Counter and Timer Modes |

**Notes:** [1] $t_C = t_W(\Phi H) + t_W(\Phi L) + t_r + t_f$.
[2] Increase delay by 10 nsec for each 50 pF increase in loading, 200 pF maximum for data lines and 100 pF for control lines.
[3] Increase delay by 2 nsec for each 10 pF increase in loading, 100 pF maximum.
[4] $\overline{\text{RESET}}$ must be active for a minimum of 3 clock cycles.

## OUTPUT LOAD CIRCUIT

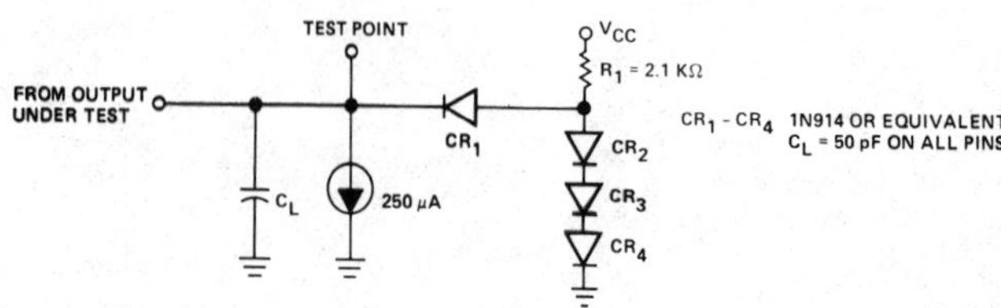

# Z80-CTC
## A.C. Timing Diagram

Timing measurements are made at the following voltages, unless otherwise specified:

| | "1" | "0" |
|---|---|---|
| CLOCK | $V_{CC}$ - .6V | .45V |
| OUTPUT | 2.0V | .8V |
| INPUT | 2.0V | .8V |
| FLOAT | ΔV | ±0.5V |

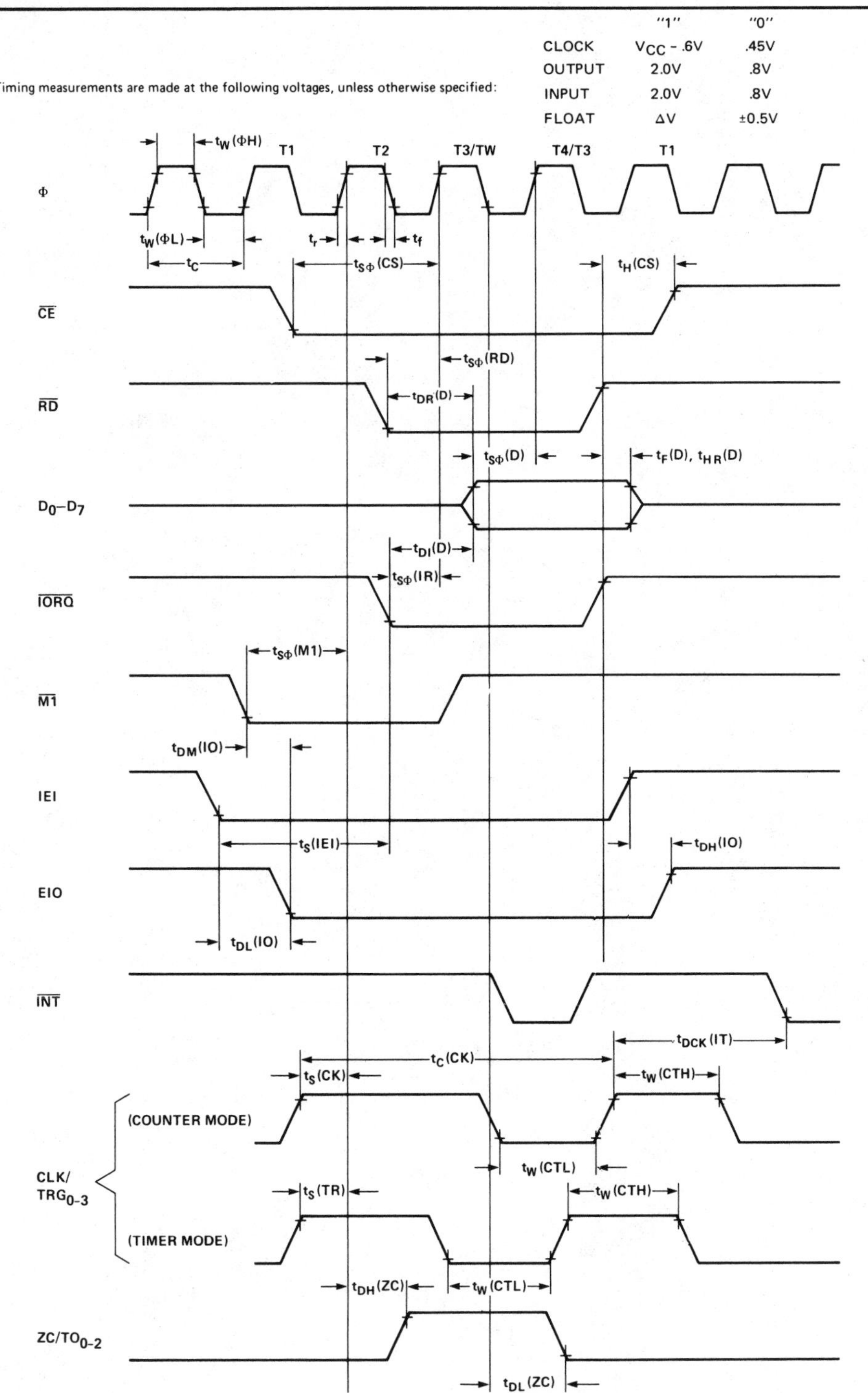

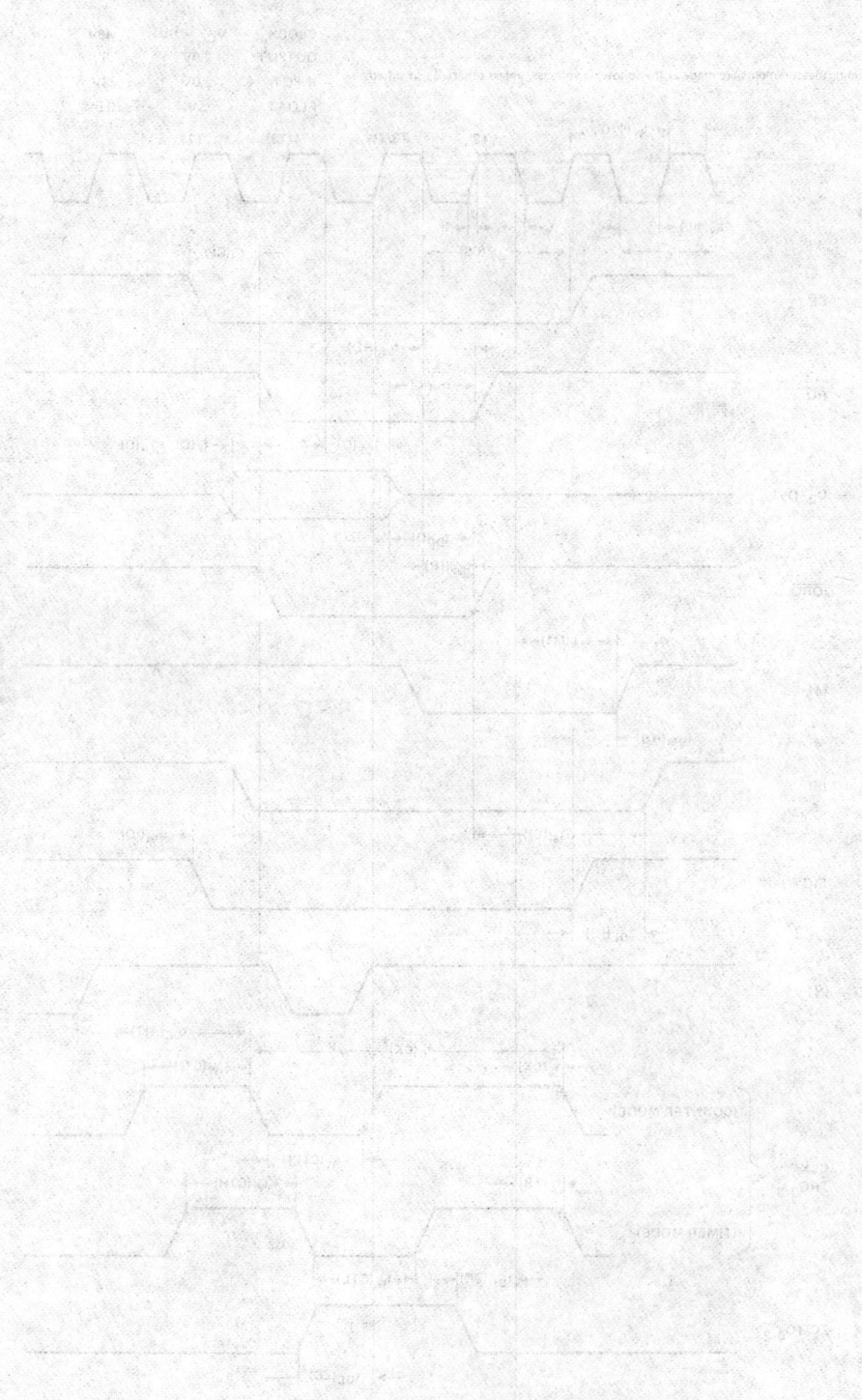

# Chapter 8
# THE ZILOG Z8

**The Z8 is Zilog's first one-chip microcomputer: it is a late entry, but the Z8 and Motorola's 6801 are clearly the most powerful and versatile of the one-chip microcomputers available in early 1979.**

**The Z8 can be configured in numerous ways; to operate as a one-chip microcomputer, as the Central Processing Unit for a large microcomputer system, as a secondary microprocessor in multiple-CPU configuration, or in a variety of mixed roles.**

**The most noteworthy Z8 characteristic is the fact that its many configuration options are selected under program control, and may be changed dynamically under program control. Other one-chip microcomputers nearly always require configuration options to be specified at the mask level. You should look carefully at the advantages which accrue from being able to reconfigure the Z8 dynamically under program control.**

The one deficiency of the Z8 is the fact that no EPROM version is currently available, or planned in the near future.

The Z8 is manufactured by:

ZILOG INC.
10460 Bubb Road
Cupertino, California 95014

Currently there is no second source for the Z8 and it is unclear whether Advanced Micro Devices or MOS Technology will become the official second source.

## THE Z8 CPU

**There are two versions of the Z8: a 40-pin version for use in commercial products, and a 64-pin version provided for Z8 product development.**

The Z8 uses a single +5 V power supply.

Using an 8 MHz clock, instruction execution times range between 1.5 and 2.5 microseconds.

Z8 signals are all TTL-level compatible.

**Figure 8-1 represents that part of our general microcomputer system logic which is provided by the Z8, whereas Figure 8-2 represents the logic of the Z8 in block diagram form.**

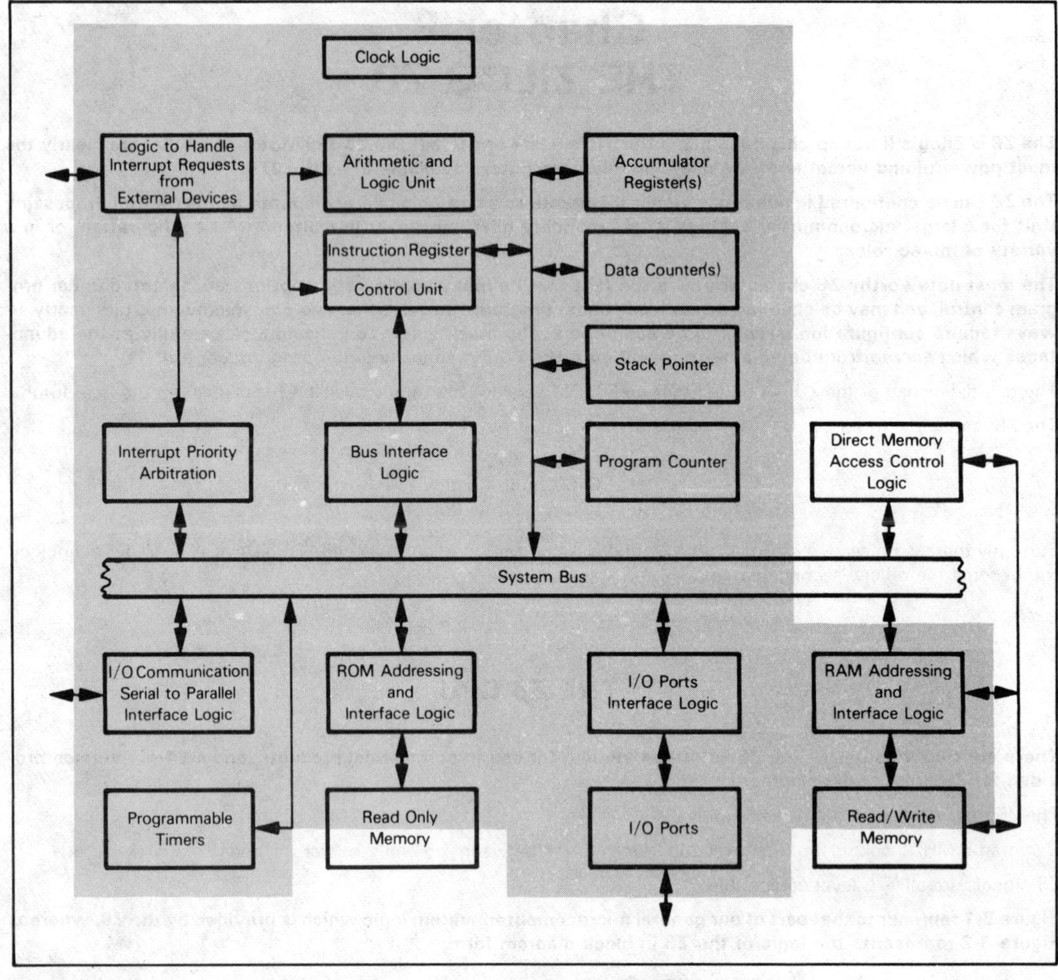


Figure 8-1. Functional Logic Included in the Z8 Microcomputer

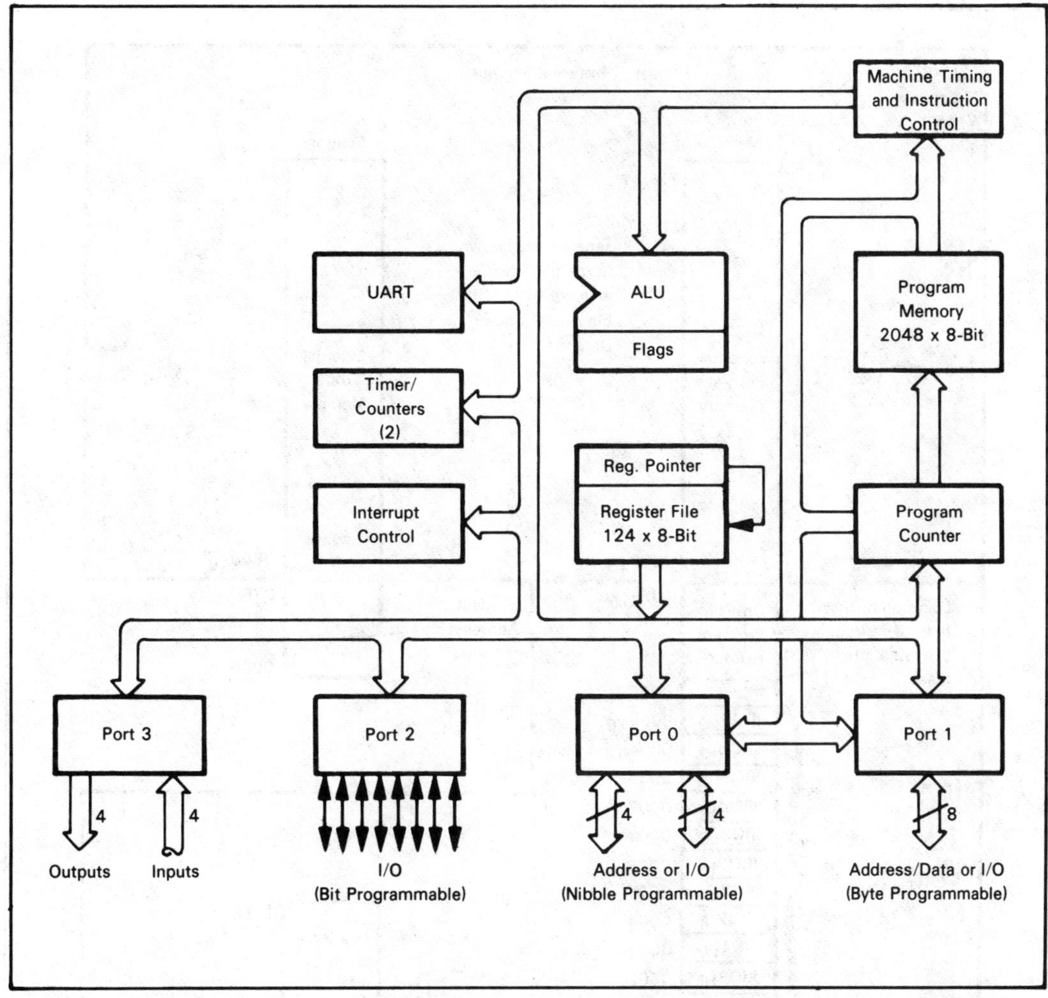


Figure 8-2. Z8 Microcomputer Block Diagram

## Z8 PROGRAMMABLE REGISTERS, MEMORY SPACES, AND ADDRESSING MODES

**When the Z8 is configured as a one-chip microcomputer, its registers also serve as its data memory. We will therefore include a discussion of Z8 programmable registers with an overall description of Z8 address spaces and addressing modes.**

**Figure 8-3 summarizes microcomputer address spaces.**

**Z8 ONE-CHIP MICROCOMPUTER CONFIGURATION MEMORY SPACES**

**In its one-chip microcomputer configuration, the Z8 offers 2048 bytes of on-chip read-only program memory and 144 bytes of on-chip read/write data memory.**

**The first 12 bytes of on-chip program memory serve dedicated functions.**

Six 16-bit interrupt vector addresses are stored in the first 12 bytes of program memory. We will describe these interrupt vector addresses in more detail later, when discussing Z8 interrupt logic in general.

Following a system reset, program execution begins at address $000C_{16}$.

**Z8 EXTERNAL PROGRAM MEMORY**

**The 2048 bytes of on-chip program memory can be extended with 63,488 bytes of external program memory.**

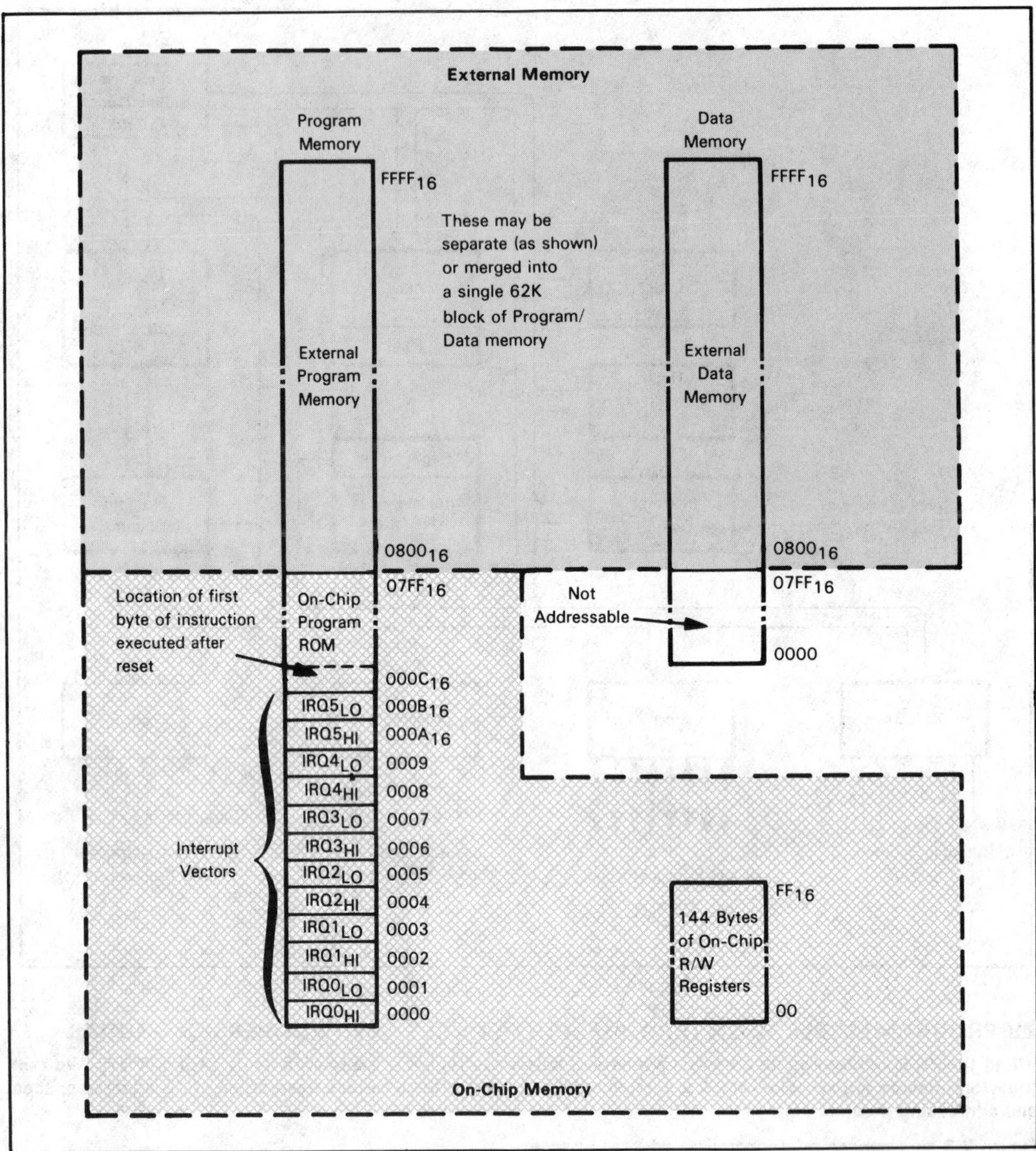


Figure 8-3. Z8 Microcomputer Address Spaces

**Up to 63,488 bytes of external data memory can also be added.**

**Z8 EXTERNAL DATA MEMORY**

Program memory may be looked upon as a continuum; that is to say, external program memory is a logical extension of on-chip program memory. Instructions that reference program memory do not distinguish between on-chip program memory and external program memory. Such is not the case for data memory. You can access on-chip data memory using a wealth of instructions and addressing modes, none of which access external data memory. The Z8 assumes that external data memory will be used exclusively as a depository for data. A limited number of well thought out instructions move data between internal registers and external data memory. No instructions that operate on data allow external data memory to be specified as a data source or destination.

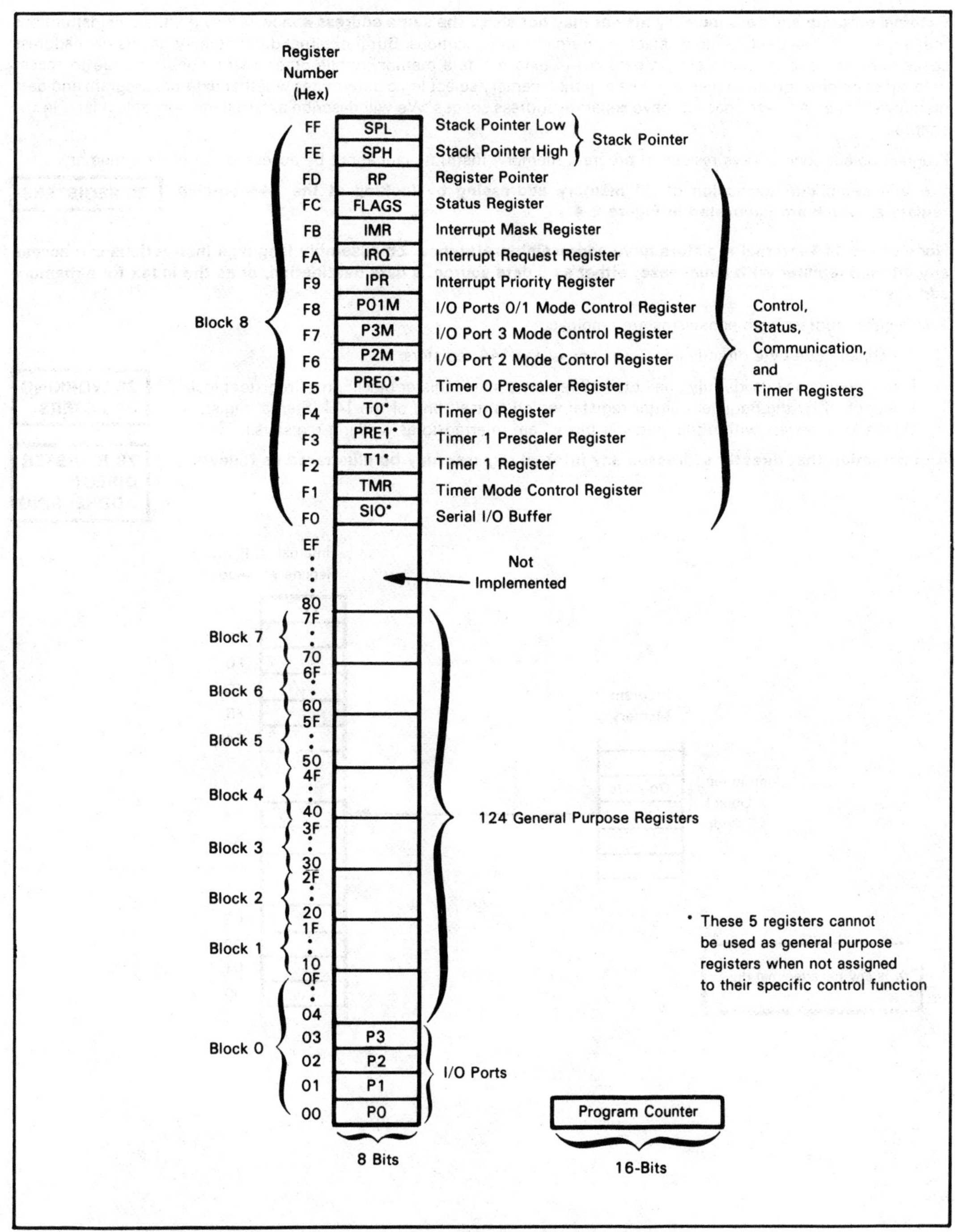


Figure 8-4. Z8 Microcomputer Internal Registers

**External program and data memory may or may not share the same address space.** If they do, then all instructions that access external data memory select program memory locations. But if external data memory has its own address space, then some instructions access data out of external data memory, while other instructions continue to access data out of external program memory. The external memory select logic determines whether external program and data memory share an address space or have separate address spaces. We will describe external memory select later in the chapter.

Program object code always resides in program memory. Instructions cannot be accessed out of data memory.

**Z8 REGISTERS**

**We will begin our discussion of Z8 memory addressing by looking at the 144 on-chip registers, which are illustrated in Figure 8-4.**

**None of the 144 internal registers have addressing preference. Z8 assembly language instructions can access any internal register with equal ease, either as a data source, a data destination, or as the index for a memory address.**

Two register addressing mechanisms are employed:

1) An object code byte directly addresses one of the 144 registers.

**Z8 WORKING REGISTERS**

2) Four object code bits identify one of the 16 registers in a "register block"; the "register block" is identified by the Register Pointer register, which is itself one of the 144 internal registers. (These 16 registers within the "register block" are referred to as working registers.)

**Z8 REGISTER DIRECT ADDRESSING**

**An instruction that directly addresses any internal register may be illustrated as follows:**

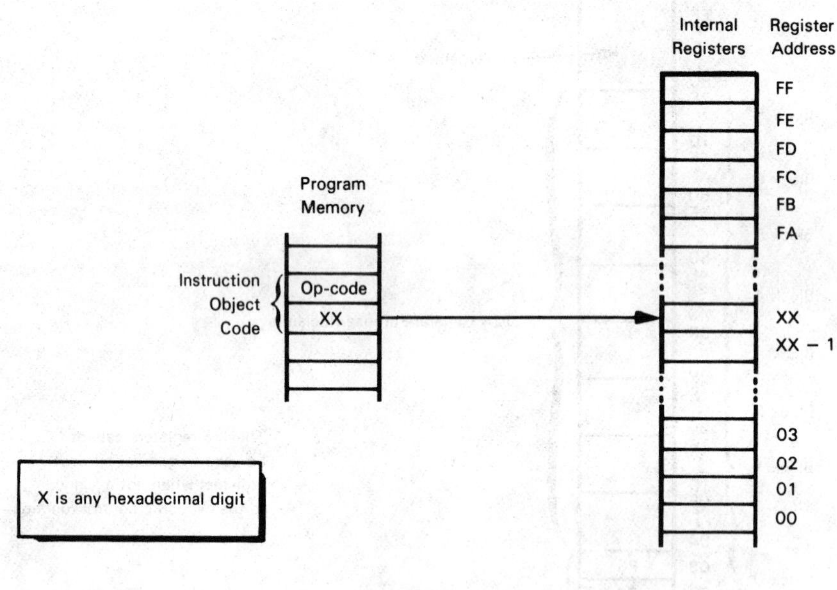

Instructions that address one register within a 16-register block may be used as follows:

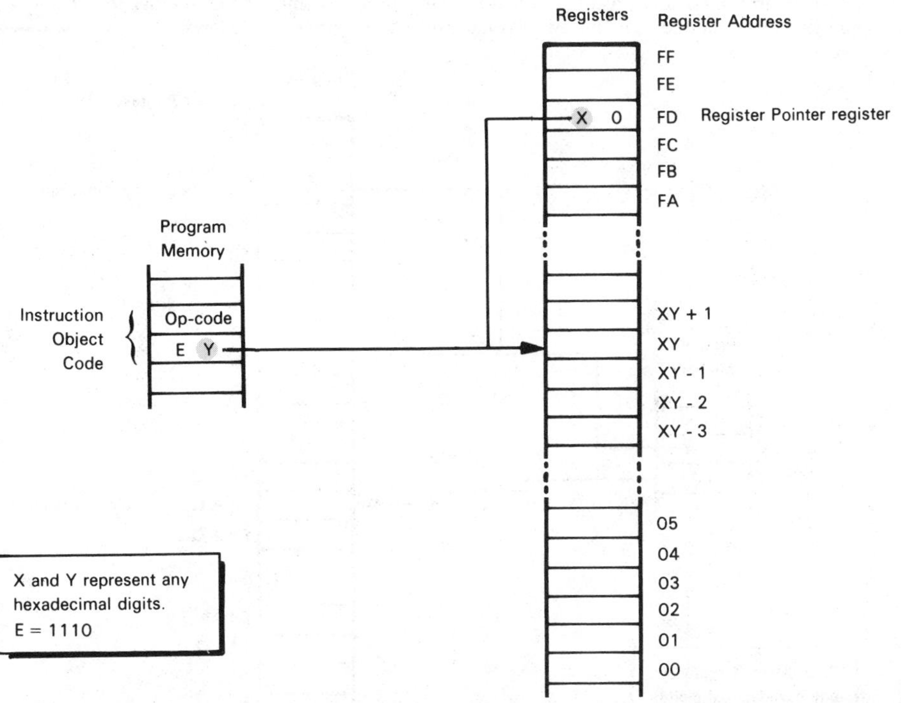


**As illustrated above, the Register Pointer register provides the four high-order bits for the selected register address, and thus identifies the selected register block. The RP register can be written with any value; however, since the lower four bits are not used, they are always forced to zero.**

Thus, to select a particular register, the four bits supplied by the object code are concatenated with the four high-order bits of RP to form the actual 8-bit register address.

To allow all instructions access to the working register block in this manner, additional logic has been included. When a direct register address falls within the range of E0 through EF (which are non-implemented register addresses), the high-order four bits (1110) are replaced with the high-order four bits of the contents of RP. This may be illustrated as follows:

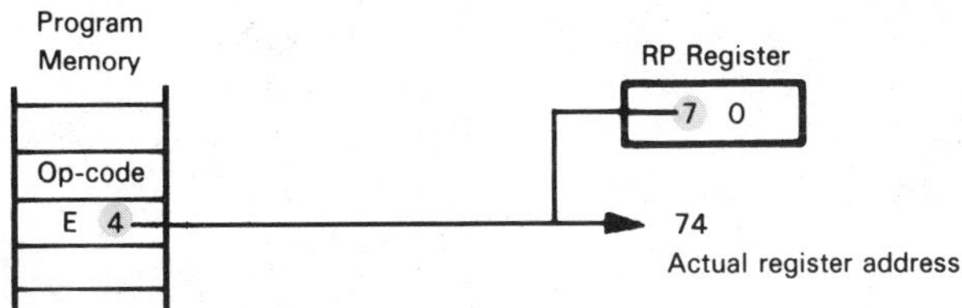


**Note that there are 256 register addresses, even though there are only 144 actual registers. Addresses $80_{16}$ through $EF_{16}$ are unused.**

**A single instruction (LD) uses indexed addressing to access one of the on-chip registers.** In this addressing mode, the Index register is one of 16 working registers. The contents of the Index register are added to an 8-bit displacement provided by the instruction object code in order to compute the effective register address. This address logic may be illustrated as follows:

**Z8 REGISTER INDEXED ADDRESSING**

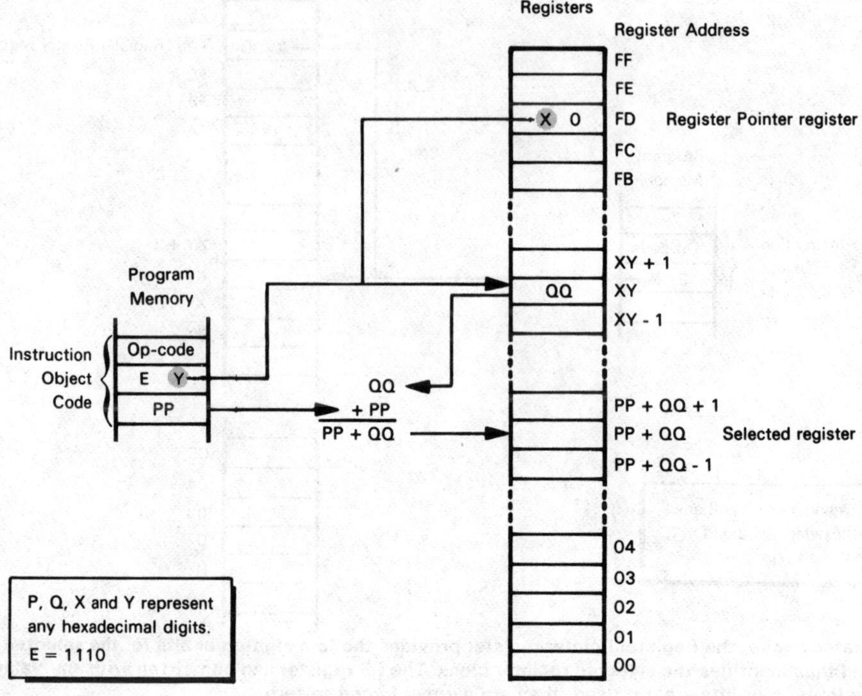

**Z8 REGISTER INDIRECT ADDRESSING**

**You can also address registers indirectly.** Either a working register or any register can provide the effective register address.

First **consider indirect addressing via any register;** this may be illustrated as follows:

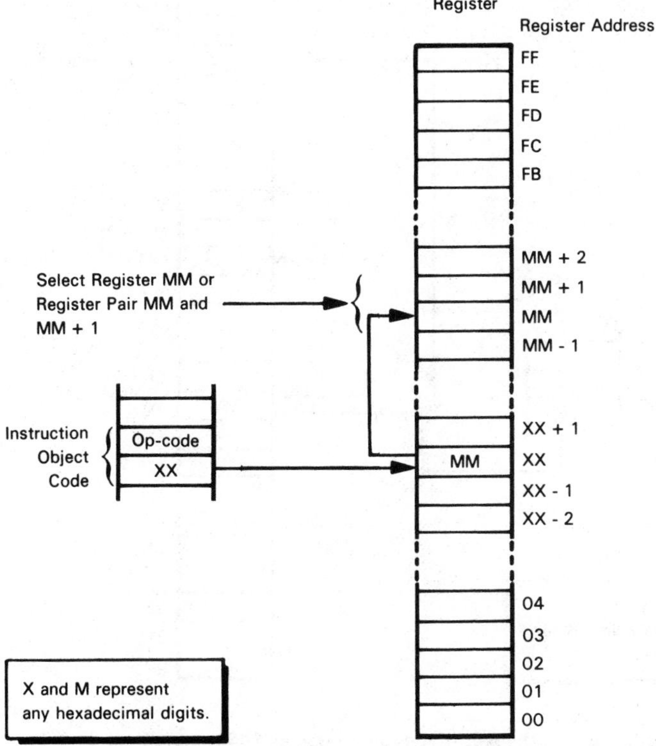


**Z8 WORD ADDRESSING**

Some instructions use indirect addressing, via any register, or, in some cases, via a working register only, in order to select 16-bit words which are subsequently used as addresses. For these instructions, the effective register address (MM in the illustration above) must be even, and must select the high-order byte of the addressed word or register pair. This may be illustrated as follows:

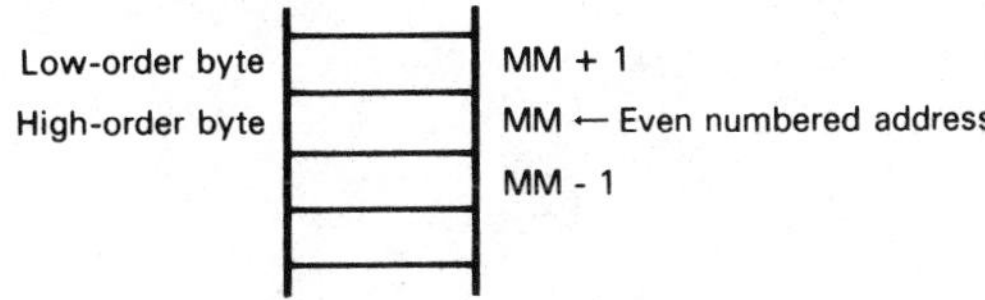

**Here is an illustration of indirect addressing via a working register:**

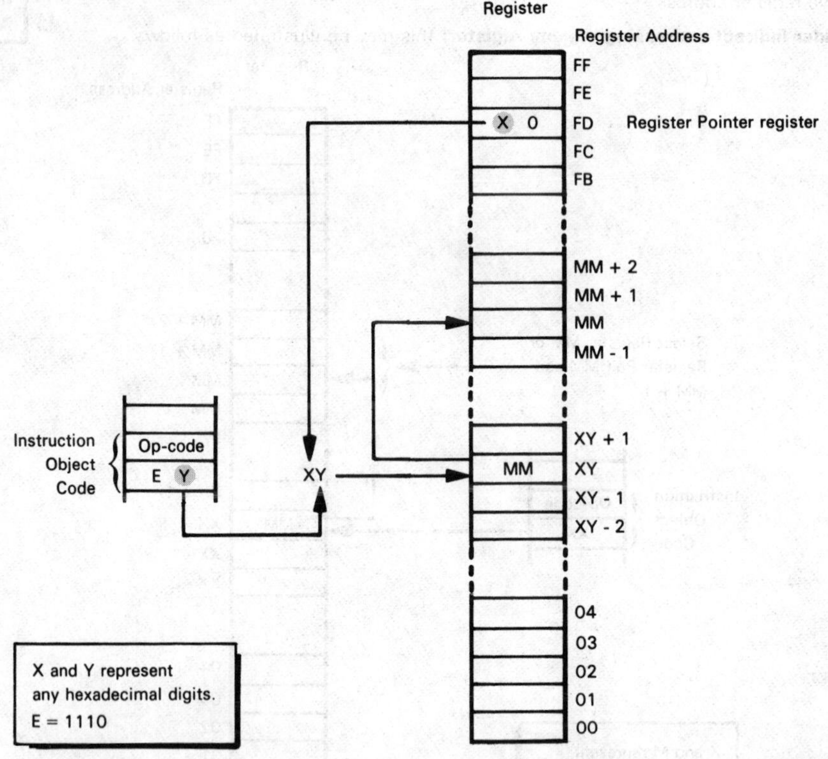


**Z8 REGISTER ASSIGNMENTS**

**The key to Z8 general utilization is the fact that even though all 144 registers can be addressed with equal ease, 20 of the registers have special assignments.** Registers 0 through 3 access four I/O ports, while registers $F0_{16}$ through $FF_{16}$ implement Stack Pointer, Control, and Status registers, together with special registers required by timer and serial logic.

We will now examine external data memory addressing.

**Z8 EXTERNAL DATA MEMORY ADDRESSING**

**All external data memory is addressed indirectly via a working register pair.**

**Here is an illustration of indirect data memory addressing via any register pair:**

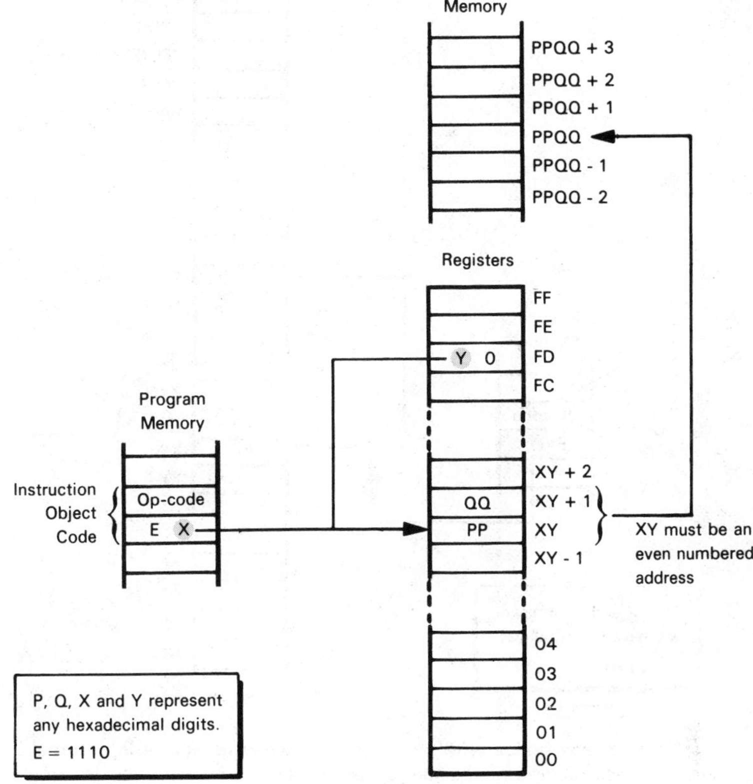


The indirect address is held in a pair of registers, since a 16-bit address must be generated in order to access any addressable memory location. In the illustration above, this 16-bit memory address is represented by the label PPQQ. Note carefully that the instruction object code must contain an even register address, illustrated above as XY; this register holds the high-order byte of the effective 16-bit memory address.

If the indirect address PPQQ is $07FF_{16}$ or less, then one of the on-chip 2048 bytes of program memory will be selected.

If the indirect address PPQQ is $0800_{16}$ or more, then an external memory location will be selected. If external program and data memory share an address space, then PPQQ can only address one memory location. But if external program and data memory have separate address spaces, then two memory locations may have the address PPQQ. In order to distinguish between these two memory locations, the special control signal $\overline{DM}$ is output low during execution of instructions that specifically access external data memory. $\overline{DM}$ remains high during execution of all other instructions. We will describe this control signal, together with associated memory select logic, later in the chapter.

**An indirect address held in a working register pair may address external memory as follows:**

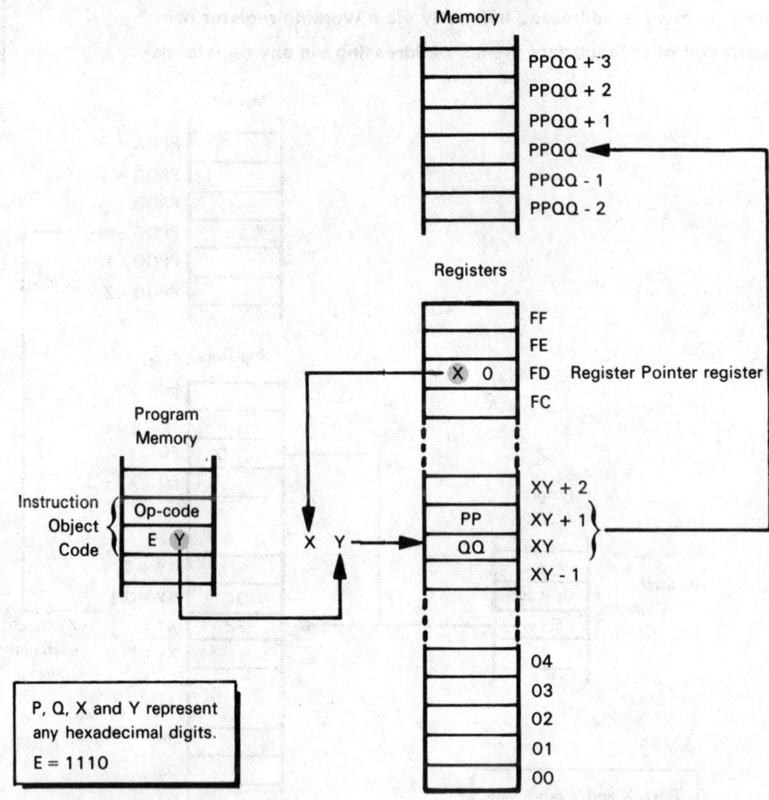


**Z8 STACK**

**The Z8 uses a Stack which may reside within general purpose registers, or in external memory.** You select the Stack location via the control code which you load into the Port 0/1 Control register. If you select an on-chip stack, then Register $FF_{16}$ serves as the Stack Pointer. Any number of contiguous general purpose registers can function as a stack.

If you select an external Stack, then Registers $FE_{16}$ and $FF_{16}$ function as a Stack Pointer. $FF_{16}$ holds the low-order byte of the Stack address, while $FE_{16}$ holds the high-order byte of the Stack address. Now the Stack can occupy any contiguous block of external memory locations, but it cannot reside in the general purpose registers.

We now turn to Z8 program memory addressing modes.

**Z8 PROGRAM MEMORY ADDRESSING**

**Z8 program memory addressing is very straightforward. Conditional jump and subroutine call instructions directly address any program memory location using a 16-bit direct memory address** which is provided by the instruction object code.

The Decrement-and-Jump and the Jump Relative instructions both use program relative, direct addressing. An 8-bit displacement provided by the instruction object code is added, as a signed binary number, to the Program Counter contents following a "true" condition.

Z8 program memory addressing options are absolutely standard. For a discussion of these addressing modes, see Volume 1, Chapter 6.

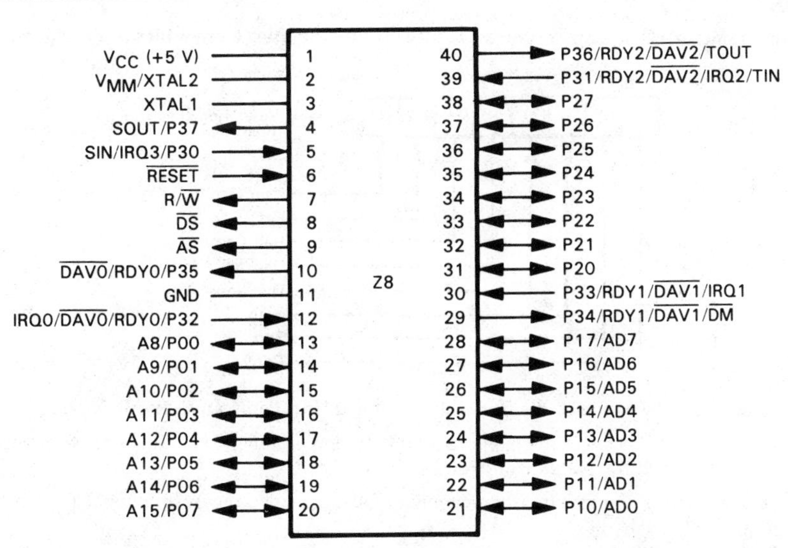


| Pin Name | Description | Type |
|---|---|---|
| P00-P07 | I/O Port 0 | Bidirectional, Tristate |
| P10-P17 | I/O Port 1 | Bidirectional, Tristate |
| P20-P27 | I/O Port 2 | Bidirectional, Open Drain Option |
| P30-P33 | I/O Port 3 | Input |
| P34-P37 | I/O Port 3 | Ouput |
| AD0-AD7 | Data/Address Bus | Bidirectional |
| A8-A15 | Address Bus | Output |
| RDY0, $\overline{\text{DAV0}}$ | I/O Port 0 Handshaking Controls | Input or Output |
| RDY1, $\overline{\text{DAV1}}$ | I/O Port 1 Handshaking Controls | Input or Output |
| RDY2, $\overline{\text{DAV2}}$ | I/O Port 2 Handshaking Controls | Input or Output |
| R/$\overline{\text{W}}$ | Read/Write Control | Output, Tristate |
| $\overline{\text{DS}}$ | Data Strobe | Output, Tristate |
| $\overline{\text{AS}}$ | Address Strobe | Output, Tristate |
| $\overline{\text{DM}}$ | Data Memory Select | Output |
| IRQ0-IRQ3 | Interrupt Requests | Input |
| SIN | Serial Data Input | Input |
| SOUT | Serial Data Output | Output |
| TIN | Timer Input | Input |
| TOUT | Timer Output | Output |
| $\overline{\text{RESET}}$ | System Reset | Input |
| XTAL1, XTAL2 | Crystal/Clock Connections | |
| $V_{MM}$ | Standby Power Supply | |
| $V_{CC}$, GND | Power, Ground | |

Figure 8-5. Z8 Microcomputer Signals and Pin Assignments

## Z8 STATUS

**General purpose register $FC_{16}$ also serves as the Z8 Status register. Status bits are assigned as follows:**

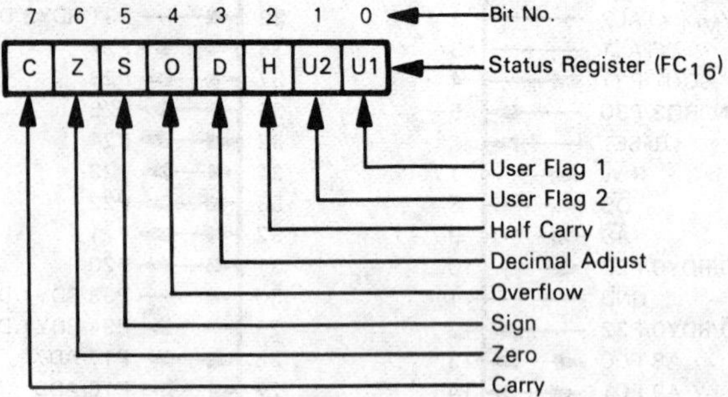


**Z8 Status flags** (with the exception of the Decimal Adjust and User flag status) are all standard.

**The Carry status** reports carries out of the high-order bit following arithmetic operations as described in Chapter 4 for the 8080A; it is also modified by rotate instructions.

**The Overflow status** reports carries out of the magnitude bits for signed binary arithmetic. For a discussion of Overflow status logic see Volume 1.

**The Zero status** is set to 1 when the result of an arithmetical or logical operation generates a 0 result; the Zero status is set to 0 otherwise.

**The Sign status** is set to the value of the high-order result bit following an arithmetic or logic operation.

**The Half-carry status** represents any carry from bit 3 to bit 4 following an add or subtract operation.

The Z8 uses its **Decimal Adjust status** in a fashion that differs slightly from other microprocessors. Like many other microprocessors, the Z8 uses a Decimal Adjust instruction, following binary addition or subtraction, in order to handle binary coded decimal arithmetic. But (as explained in Volume 1) different decimal adjust steps are needed following binary addition, as opposed to subtraction. The Z8 Decimal Adjust status is therefore set to 1 following binary subtraction, and it is reset to 0 following binary addition. Subsequently, the Decimal Adjust instruction uses this status to make the correct decimal adjustment to the result of a binary arithmetic operation.

**You set and reset the two user flags under program control.** Conditional Jump instructions can subsequently interrogate these two flags.

## Z8 MICROCOMPUTER PINS AND SIGNALS

**Z8 microcomputer pins and signals are illustrated in Figure 8-5. This figure shows all Z8 signals, including those which can optionally occur at various Z8 pins.**

Note carefully that mask options are never needed when assigning a multifunction pin to one function or another; **all choices are made under program control, by loading appropriate codes into control registers.** These codes and control registers are described later in the chapter.

**The Z8 has four 8-bit I/O ports, represented by P00 - P07, P10 - P17, P20 - P27, and P30 - P37.** Following our usual convention, pin 7 is the high-order pin and pin 0 is the low-order pin.

**Z8 I/O PORT DIRECTION ASSIGNMENTS**

I/O Ports 0, 1, and 2 are bidirectional but they have different signal assignment capabilities.

The low-order four bits and high-order four bits of I/O Port 0 are each assigned to input or output as a group.

All eight pins of I/O Port 1 must simultaneously be assigned to input or to output.

Pins of I/O Port 2 can be assigned individually to input or output.

Pins of I/O Port 3 are permanently assigned. The four low-order pins are always assigned to input, while the four high-order pins are always assigned to output.

Thus, we can summarize Z8 I/O port pin direction assignment options as follows:

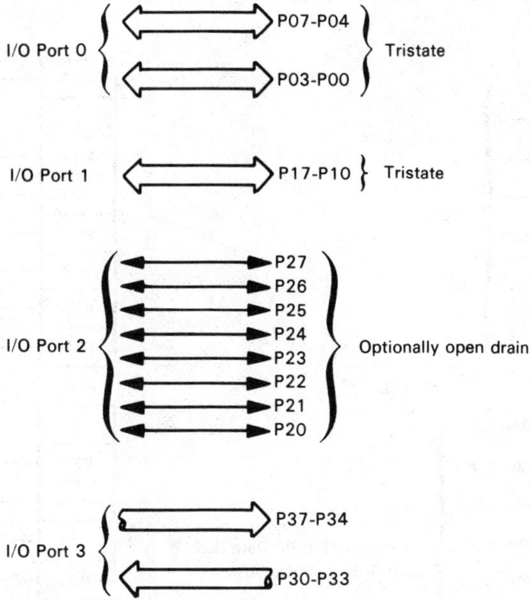


As illustrated above, **I/O Port 2 outputs can optionally be open drain.** No other I/O port outputs can be open drain. You select the open drain option for I/O Port 2 under program control, by loading the appropriate code into the I/O Port 2 Control register.

As we will see in the course of this chapter, Z8 I/O ports can be programmed to function in a variety of ways. But when functioning as I/O ports, Ports 0, 1, and 2 can operate with or without handshaking control signals. **All handshaking control signals are I/O Port 3 pin options. They are shown in Figure 8-5 as RDY0 and $\overline{\text{DAV0}}$, RDY1 and $\overline{\text{DAV1}}$, and RDY2 and $\overline{\text{DAV2}}$.** Each signal occurs twice, once as an input and once as an output. We will describe these signals in detail later when looking at parallel I/O logic in general.

**I/O Ports 0 and 1 serve optionally as Data and Address Busses connecting the Z8 with external memory; output signals from these two I/O ports can be floated.**

**You can create external Data and Address Busses in three increments. For very small memory increments, you can create an 8-bit multiplexed Data and Address Bus at I/O Port 1.** This may be illustrated as follows:

**Z8 DATA AND ADDRESS BUSSES**

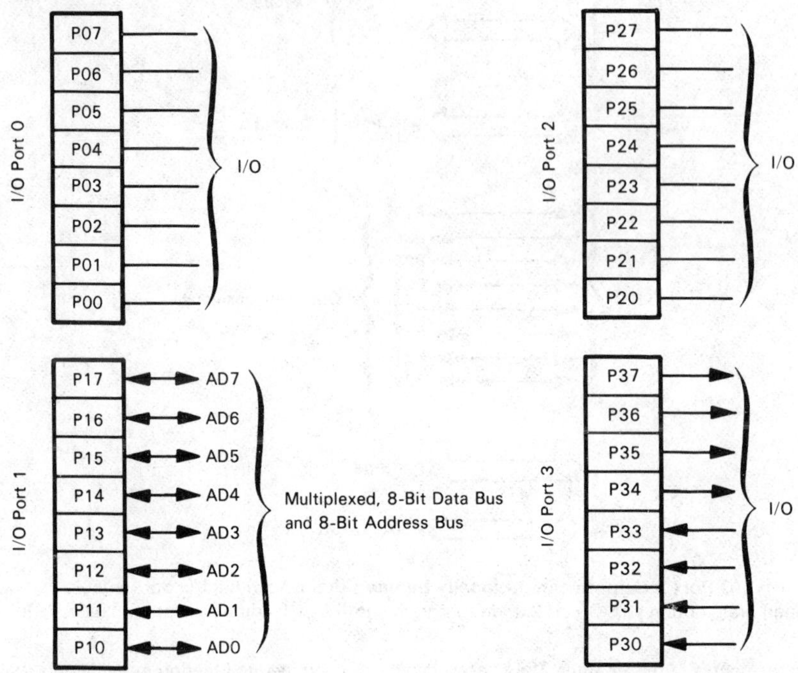


This minimum expansion actually allows the Z8 to communicate with up to 256 bytes of external memory, or 512 bytes of external memory if external program and data memory have separate address spaces. Logic internal to I/O Port 1 switches pin assignments between input and output at the proper time, so that I/O Port 1 can support a bidirectional Data Bus.

If 256 bytes of external memory is insufficient, **the first level of expansion allows I/O Port 0 pins 0 through 3 to add four Address Bus lines, thus generating a 12-bit Address Bus** whose eight low-order bits are multiplexed with the Data Bus. This configuration allows for a total of 6K of program memory and 4K of external data memory, for a total of 10K of addressable memory using only 12 address lines. The address spaces would be as follows:

| Program Memory Address | Data Memory Address | Physical Address on Ports 0 and 1 | A11 | $\overline{DS}$ and R/$\overline{W}$ |
|---|---|---|---|---|
| 0000 - 07FF | ---- | 000 - 7FF | 0 | Inactive |
| 0800 - 0FFF | 0800 - 0FFF | 800 - FFF | 1 | Active |
| 1000 - 17FF | 1000 - 17FF | 000 - 7FF | 1 | Active |

This addressing configuration may be illustrated as follows:

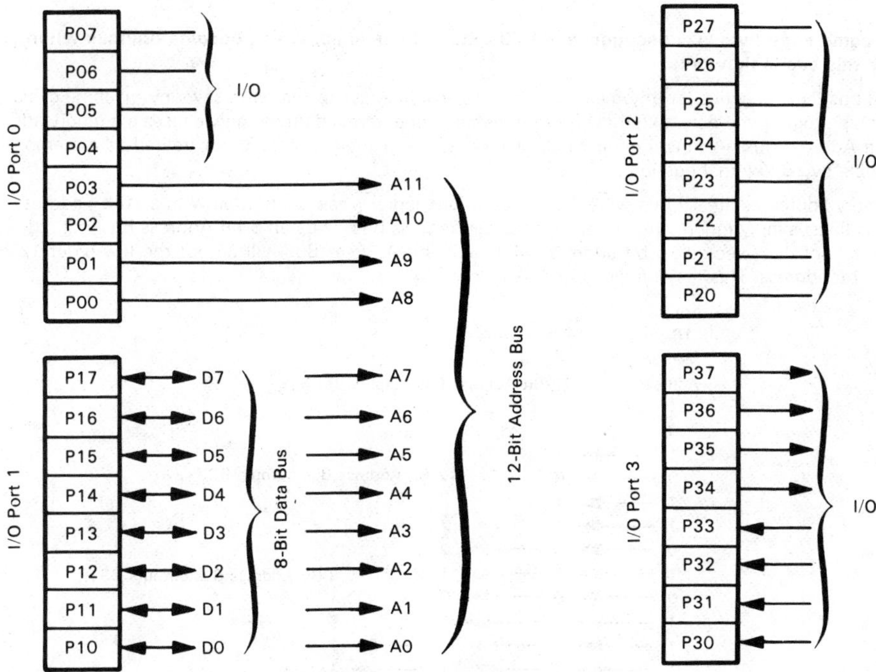


**You can generate a 16-bit Address Bus** by outputting the high-order eight Address Bus lines via I/O Port 0 as follows:

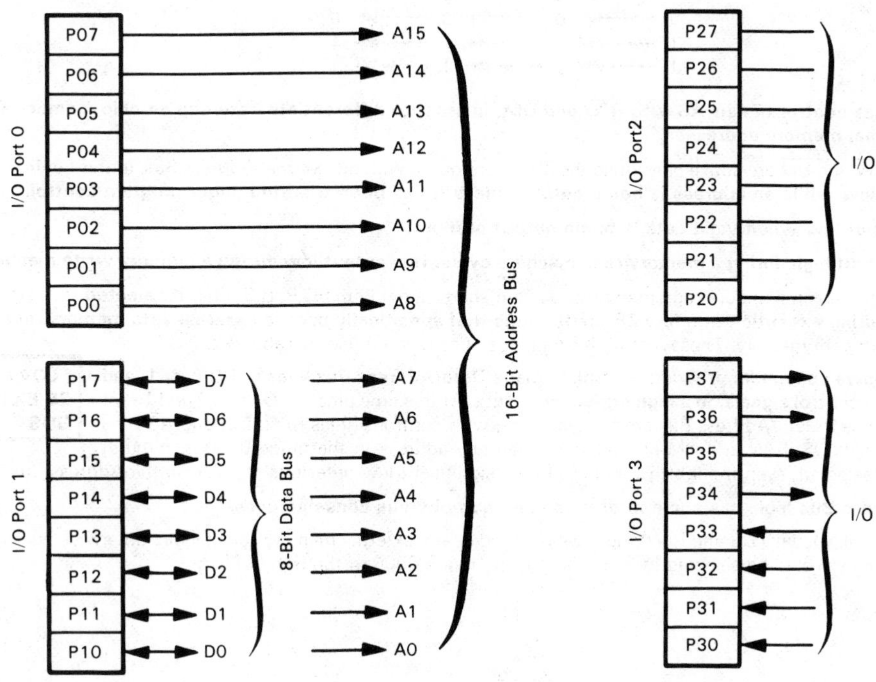

As illustrated above, the Z8 now generates a 16-bit Address Bus whose low-order eight bits are multiplexed with the Data Bus.

**There are some non-obvious consequences of Z8 external bus logic, which become obvious when you understand how this bus logic works.**

Z8 external bus logic is active for any memory reference machine cycle; that is to say, any machine cycle which accesses on-chip program memory, external program memory, or external data memory causes a memory address to appear on the Address Bus. (An instruction which accesses one of the registers is not treated as a memory reference machine cycle by Z8 external bus logic.)

All Z8 memory addresses are 16 bits wide. But external bus logic, when confronted with a 16-bit address and fewer Address Bus lines, simply ignores the excess high-order address bits. Thus an 8-bit Address Bus will output the low-order eight bits of the selected 16-bit address, while a 12-bit Address Bus will output the low-order 12 bits of the selected 16-bit address. This may be illustrated as follows:

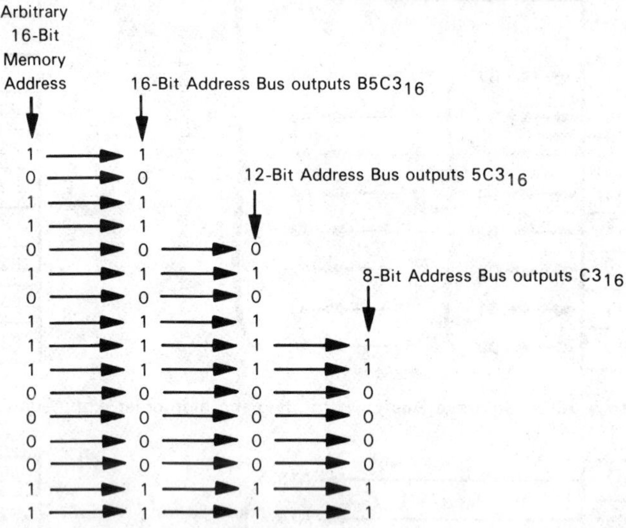


**The Z8 uses control signals $\overline{AS}$, $\overline{DS}$, R/$\overline{W}$ and $\overline{DM}$, in order to differentiate between on-chip memory addresses and external memory addresses.**

$\overline{AS}$, $\overline{DS}$, R/$\overline{W}$ and $\overline{DM}$ are active only while the Z8 is configured with an external Address Bus. In this configuration, **$\overline{AS}$ is pulsed low while an address is being output unless it has been tristated under program control.**

**$\overline{DS}$ is output low when valid data is being output or input.**

**R/$\overline{W}$ is output high during a memory read machine cycle; it is output low during a memory write machine cycle.**

**$\overline{DM}$** must be selected under program control, since it shares a pin with I/O Port 3 bit 4. **If selected,** this signal **is output low during execution of a few Z8 instructions that specifically access external data memory,** in contrast to external program memory. These instructions are specifically identified in Table 8-7.

**FLOATING THE Z8 EXTERNAL BUS**

**The Z8 allows you, under program control, to place Data/Address Bus lines of I/O Port 1, and companion control signals, in a high impedance state.** At this time pins of I/O Ports 0 and 1 that are serving as a Data/Address Bus are floated, along with control signals R/$\overline{W}$, $\overline{DS}$, and $\overline{AS}$. The control signals $\overline{DS}$, R/$\overline{W}$ and $\overline{DM}$ are inactive when any address in the range $0000_{16}$ through $07FF_{16}$ is selected, even though this address (or its significant low-order bits) appear on the Address Bus.

**This Address Bus logic has some interesting and non-obvious consequences.**

Control signals (usually $\overline{DS}$ and R/$\overline{W}$) must be included in any external memory select logic, otherwise internal and external memory would be selected by addresses in the range $0000_{16}$ through $07FF_{16}$.

**A 16-bit Address Bus can, in consequence, select only 63,488 bytes of external memory. However, you can use $\overline{AS}$ to select program memory, and $\overline{DM}$ to select data memory having the same addresses, thus doubling the amount of externally addressable memory,** as illustrated in Figure 8-3.

**Z8 counter/timer logic uses the TIN and TOUT optional signals, which occur at I/O Port 3 pins 1 and 6, respectively.** An external clock input may be received via TIN. Various square wave outputs may be generated at TOUT. For a detailed discussion of these two signals, see the description of Z8 counter/timer logic which is given later in this chapter.

**The Z8 has four optional interrupt request inputs: $\overline{IRQ0}$, $\overline{IRQ1}$, $\overline{IRQ2}$, and $\overline{IRQ3}$.** These four interrupt request inputs share pins with I/O Port 3 bits 2, 3, 1, and 0, respectively. You assign pins of I/O Port 3 to their various possible functions by loading the appropriate code into the I/O Port 3 Control register.

**Z8 serial I/O logic uses I/O Port 3 pins 0 and 7 to accept serial data input (SIN, via P30) and to output serial data (SOUT, via P37).** Once again, these are shared pins and you use the appropriate I/O Port 3 control code to assign these two pins to service serial data input and output logic.

**There are two signals associated with Z8 reset logic: $\overline{RESET}$ and $V_{MM}$.** These signals are described later in this chapter, together with a general discussion of Z8 reset logic.

**XTAL1 and XTAL2 provide the Z8 with its clock logic.** You can connect an external crystal or an LC circuit across these pins; you can also input a clock signal directly via XTAL1. Since **the standby power supply $V_{MM}$ shares a pin with XTAL2,** you must use an external clock signal if you are using a standby power supply.

## Z8 EXTERNAL MEMORY SELECT LOGIC

**Because of the various external memory options provided by the Z8, it is worth summarizing memory select logic associated with various implementations.**

**You can ignore the internal registers when designing external memory select logic, since internal Z8 register addressing logic is separate and distinct in all respects from logic which addresses program memory or external memory.**

When you configure a Z8 with external memory, memory select logic will decode addresses off the Address Bus, but companion control signals must contribute to memory select logic; this is because an Address Bus once configured, will be active when on-chip program memory is being addressed (but not when on-chip registers are being selected). In the simplest case, you use the low $\overline{DS}$ strobe as an external memory enable, since this signal is output low only when external memory is being addressed. This logic may be illustrated as follows:

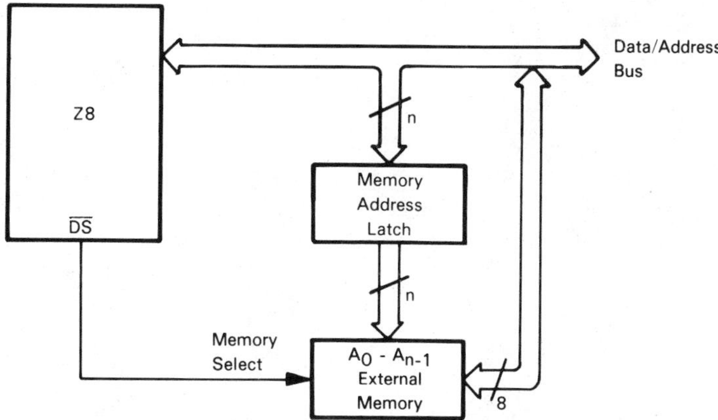


When configuring a Z8 with 8-bit or 12-bit Address Busses, you cannot discriminate between on-chip and external memory via the address alone. This is a consequence of Z8 Address Bus logic, which we described earlier in this chapter. But if the Z8 is configured with a 16-bit Address Bus, you can differentiate between on-chip program memory and external memory via the address alone, in which case you no longer need the $\overline{DS}$ control signal as an external memory enable.

If you have separate external program and data memories, then you must use $\overline{DM}$ as the separate data memory select. There are two configurations in which you may wish to discriminate between external program and data memory. If your Z8 is configured with a 16-bit Address Bus, then separating external program and data memory allows the Z8 to address 124K bytes of external memory. This may be illustrated as follows:

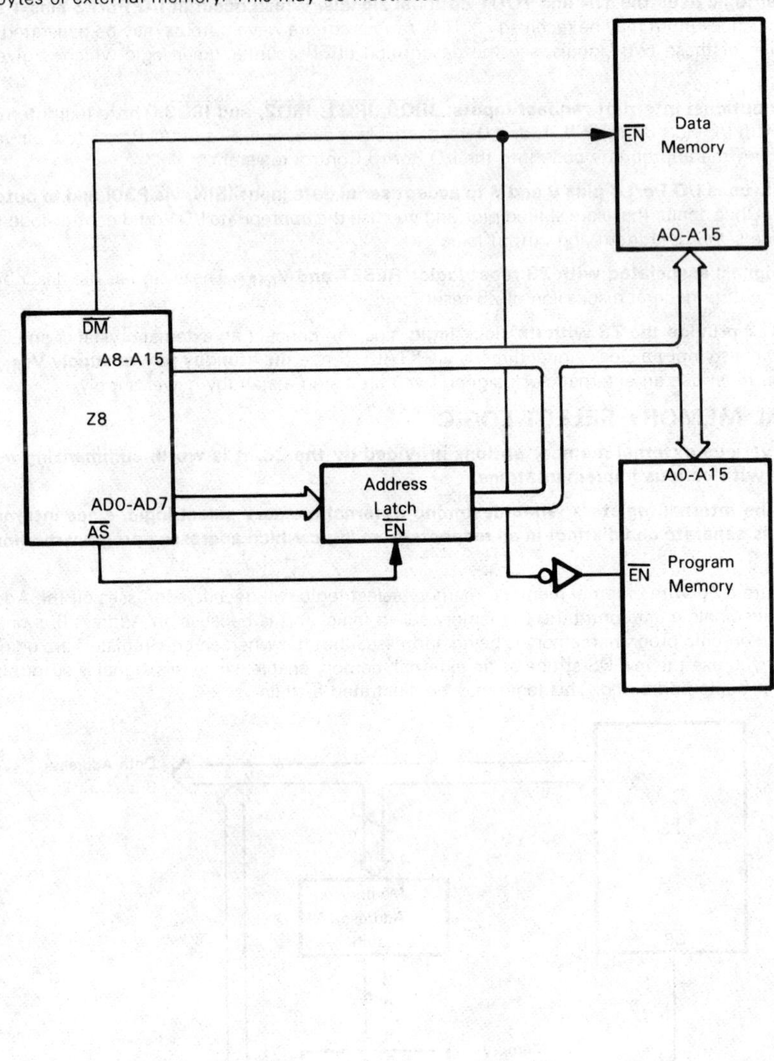

# Z8 TIMING AND INSTRUCTION EXECUTION

**Z8 MACHINE CYCLE**

**The Z8 executes instructions as a series of machine cycles, each of which contains three internal clock periods.** The internal clock which times clock periods runs at half the clock frequency input via XTAL1 (or generated by an external crystal). In the discussion that follows, when the clock signal is referenced, it is assumed to be the internal clock.

With the exception of special circumstances, such as a Reset and Interrupt Acknowledge sequence, **the Z8 combines three types of machine cycles in order to execute any of its instructions; these are: a memory read, a memory write and an internal operation. Timing for memory read and write machine cycles is illustrated in Figures 8-6 and 8-7.** Timing for the internal operation machine cycle is not shown, since there is no external bus activity. Thus, to external logic an internal operation machine cycle would be equivalent to a three-clock-period delay (of six external clock periods).

**Timing is identical for machine cycles that reference on-chip program memory or external memory.**

**Z8 EXTENDED MACHINE CYCLE**

**You can, under program control, add a fourth internal clock period to each external memory read/write machine cycle.** You select this option by loading an appropriate code into the I/O Ports 0/1 Control register, which is described later in conjunction with our discussion of I/O Ports 0 and 1. **The additional clock period occurs between T2 and T3.** Signal levels shown for T2 are propagated through T3.

Z8 memory read and write machine cycle timing is very straightforward. We will first examine the memory read/instruction fetch machine cycle illustrated in Figure 8-6.

**Z8 MEMORY READ MACHINE CYCLE**

We described earlier in this chapter how the Z8 Address Bus, if selected, may vary from eight lines occurring at I/O Port 1 only, up to 16 lines occurring at I/O Ports 1 and 0. In Figure 8-5, P00 - P07 is shown in parentheses, since these lines are optional.

The address output via P10 - P17 is stable for the first clock period of the machine cycle only; these lines are turned around during the second clock period, so that data can be input on the same lines during the third clock period.

Any address output via I/O Port 0 remains stable for the entire machine cycle.

$\overline{\text{AS}}$ is pulsed low for half of the first clock period within the first machine cycle. Memory select logic should use the trailing low-to-high transition of $\overline{\text{AS}}$ as an address stable strobe. The low-order byte of the address output via P10 - P17 must be latched, since it disappears at the end of the first clock period. The high-order byte of the address need not be latched, since it remains stable for the entire machine cycle.

$\overline{\text{DS}}$ goes low at the end of the first clock period. External logic must place data from the addressed memory location at P10 - P17 by the low-to-high transition of $\overline{\text{DS}}$; this low-to-high transition of $\overline{\text{DS}}$ is used as a data-in strobe.

R/$\overline{\text{W}}$ will remain high for the duration of a memory read machine cycle.

$\overline{\text{DM}}$, if selected, will be output low for the duration of a memory read machine cycle executed in response to an instruction that explicitly selects data memory.

**Z8 MEMORY WRITE MACHINE CYCLE**

**Turning now to a Z8 memory write machine cycle, timing illustrated in Figure 8-7 does not differ significantly from Figure 8-6.** Address logic remains the same. Once again $\overline{\text{AS}}$ is pulsed low for the first half of the first clock period; on the trailing edge of $\overline{\text{AS}}$, the low-order address byte occurring at P10 - P17 must be latched, but any address output via P00- P07 need not be latched since it remains stable for the entire machine cycle.

No turnaround time is needed at P10 - P17, since data is to be output. Data out is valid at the leading edge of DS and remains valid throughout $\overline{\text{DS}}$ active low.

R/$\overline{\text{W}}$ is output low for the duration of the memory write machine cycle.

$\overline{\text{DM}}$, if selected, will be output low for the duration of a memory write machine cycle executed in response to an instruction that explicitly selects data memory.

**Z8 instructions execute in six or more machine cycles, and the way in which machine cycles are concatenated is very important.**

Every instruction's execution begins with an instruction fetch which may require one or more machine cycles.

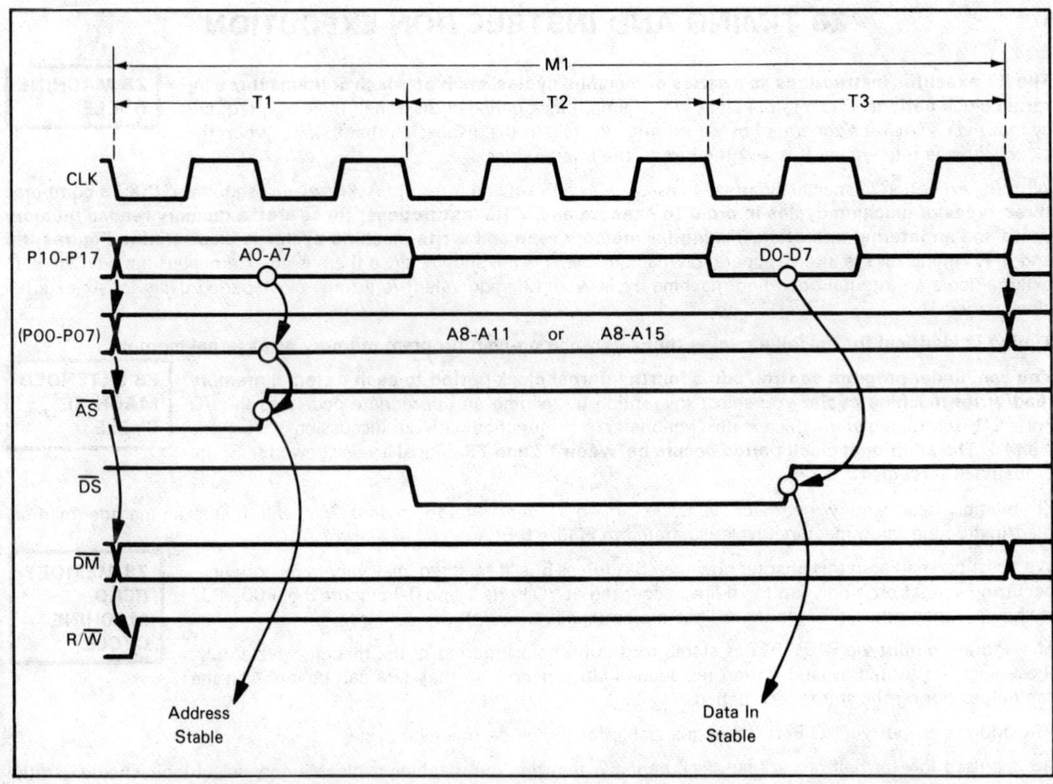


Figure 8-6. A Z8 Memory Read or Instruction Fetch Machine Cycle

**Z8 INSTRUCTION PIPELINING**

**For many Z8 instructions, instruction execution terminates with one or more internal operation machine cycles. The Z8 will use these machine cycles to fetch the next instruction.** This has the effect of reducing an instruction's execution time by the number of trailing machine cycles which get utilized as instruction fetch machine cycles for the next instruction. This may be illustrated as follows:

| | M | M | M | |
|---|---|---|---|---|
| Instruction n | I | I | | |
| | F | F | | Instruction n + 1 |

M = A machine cycle

I = An internal execute machine cycle

F = An instruction fetch memory read machine cycle

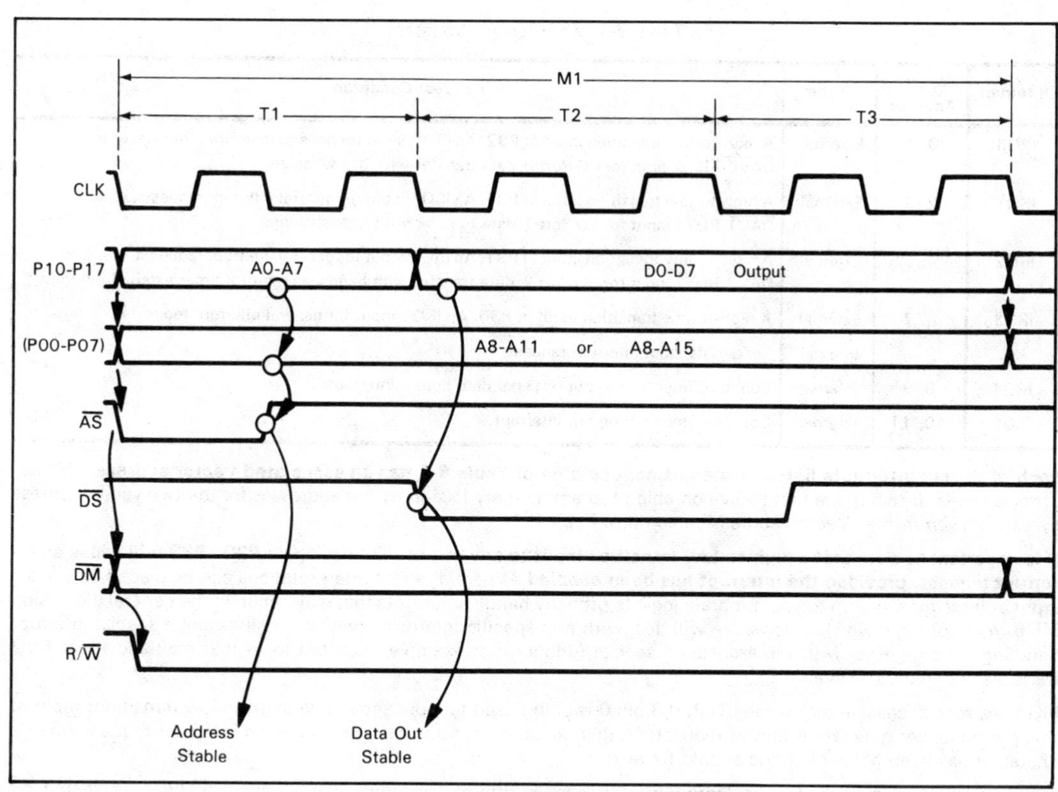


Figure 8-7. A Z8 Memory Write Machine Cycle

**We use the name "pipeline" machine cycles to describe an instruction's trailing internal operation machine cycles that get used to fetch the next instruction's object code.** Not all instructions have trailing pipeline machine cycles; those which do have two. In Table 8-8, the number of internal clock periods pipelined to complete the instruction's execution is identified. Z8 instructions have one, two, or three bytes of object code, requiring one, two, or three instruction fetch machine cycles.

## INTERRUPT LOGIC

**The Z8 can respond to internal and external interrupt requests. Four internal and four external interrupt requests are supported; they combine to generate six separately identifiable vectored interrupts, as summarized in Table 8-1.**

Table 8-1. Z8 Interrupt Sources

| Interrupt | Vector Address | Type | Request Condition |
|---|---|---|---|
| IRQ0 | 0, 1 | External | A high-to-low transition input at P32. An IRQ0 input for general interrupt requests, or a $\overline{\text{DAV0}}$/RDY0 input for I/O Port 0 data transfer with handshaking. |
| IRQ1 | 2, 3 | External | A high-to-low transition input at P33. An IRQ1 input for general interrupt requests, or a $\overline{\text{DAV1}}$/RDY1 input for I/O Port 1 data transfer with handshaking. |
| IRQ2 | 4, 5 | External | A high-to-low transition input at P31. An IRQ2 input for general interrupt requests, or a $\overline{\text{DAV2}}$/RDY2 input for I/O Port 2 data transfer with handshaking, or a timer external interrupt. |
| IRQ3 | 6, 7 | External | A high-to-low transition input at P30. An IRQ3 input for general interrupt requests. |
| | | Internal | Serial data input interrupt request. |
| IRQ4 | 8, 9 | Internal | Counter/Timer 0 time out or serial data output interrupt. |
| IRQ5 | 10, 11 | Internal | Counter/Timer 1 time out interrupt. |

**Each of the six interrupts listed in the leftmost column of Table 8-1 has an associated vector address.** This address is stored in two of the first twelve on-chip program memory locations; the addresses for the two vector address bytes are given in the "Vector Address" column of Table 8-1.

**It is important to note that a high-to-low transition input to any one of I/O Port 3 pins P30 - P33 will cause an interrupt request, provided the interrupt has been enabled.** Where different interpretations can be placed on signals input at these pins, it is up to your program logic to properly handle interrupts that may occur. In the general discussion of Z8 interrupt logic which follows, we will deal with non-specific interrupts only. We will describe special interrupt handling logic together with the associated special function (for example, interrupt logic that may accompany I/O transfers with handshaking).

IRQ3 is a special case, in that when I/O Port 3 pin 0 is being used to input serial data, high-to-low transitions input at this pin no longer generate interrupt requests; rather, serial data input logic generates an interrupt request when a character has been assembled and should be read.

Interrupts IRQ4 and IRQ5 are generated in response to internal interrupt conditions only. IRQ4 is shared by Counter/Timer 0 and serial data output, since these two sets of logic are mutually exclusive — as described later in this chapter.

**Z8 INTERRUPT MASK REGISTER**

**Z8 interrupts are enabled and disabled using the Interrupt Mask register ($FB_{16}$). Register bits are assigned as follows:**

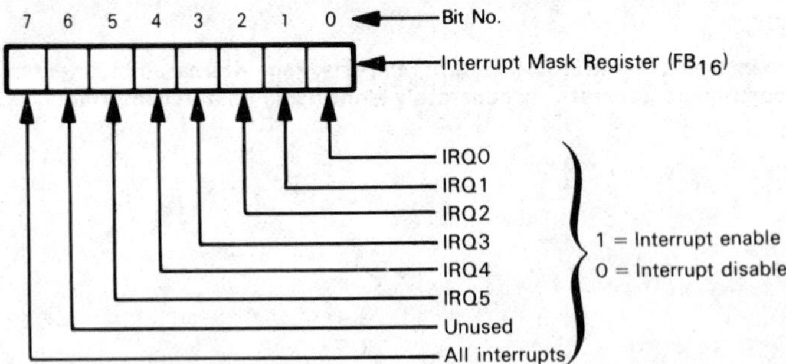


Bit 7 is used to globally enable and disable interrupts: with bit 7 reset to zero, all interrupts are disabled; with bit 7 set to one, all interrupts which have their corresponding interrupt mask bit (bits 0 through 5) set are enabled.

**You define interrupt priorities via the Interrupt Priority register ($F9_{16}$).** Interrupt Priority register bits are assigned as follows:

**Z8 INTERRUPT PRIORITY REGISTER**

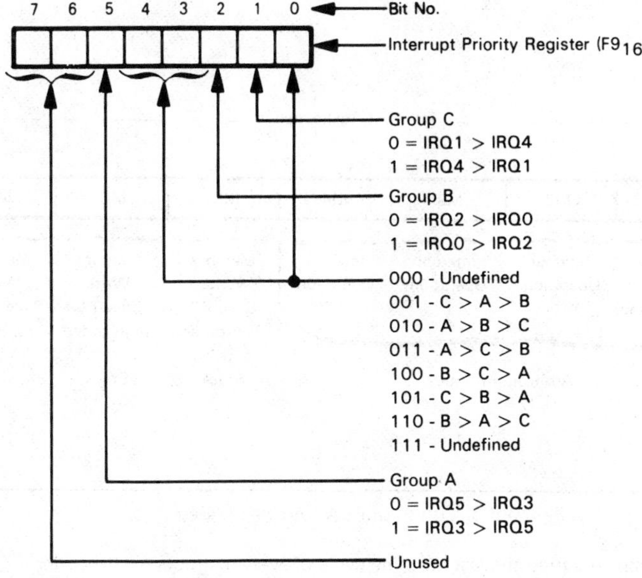


The logic illustrated above pairs internal and external interrupts; you define a priority within each of three pairs, then you define an overall priority for the three sets of pairs.

**You can dynamically modify the Interrupt Mask register and the Interrupt Priority register;** however, you should not write to either of these registers without first disabling all interrupts by executing a Disable Interrupts instruction (DI).

The Interrupt Request register ($FA_{16}$) reports active interrupt requests as follows:

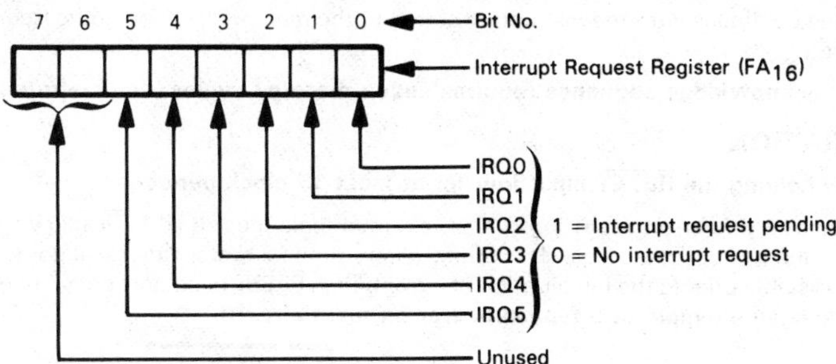


**You will not normally use the Interrupt Request register,** since interrupt priority arbitration is handled automatically, as specified by the Interrupt Priority register, and the highest priority interrupt is serviced via its vector address. You use the Interrupt Request register with polling logic when all interrupts are disabled.

You can force an interrupt by writing to this register; however, interrupts should be disabled (by executing a DI instruction) first.

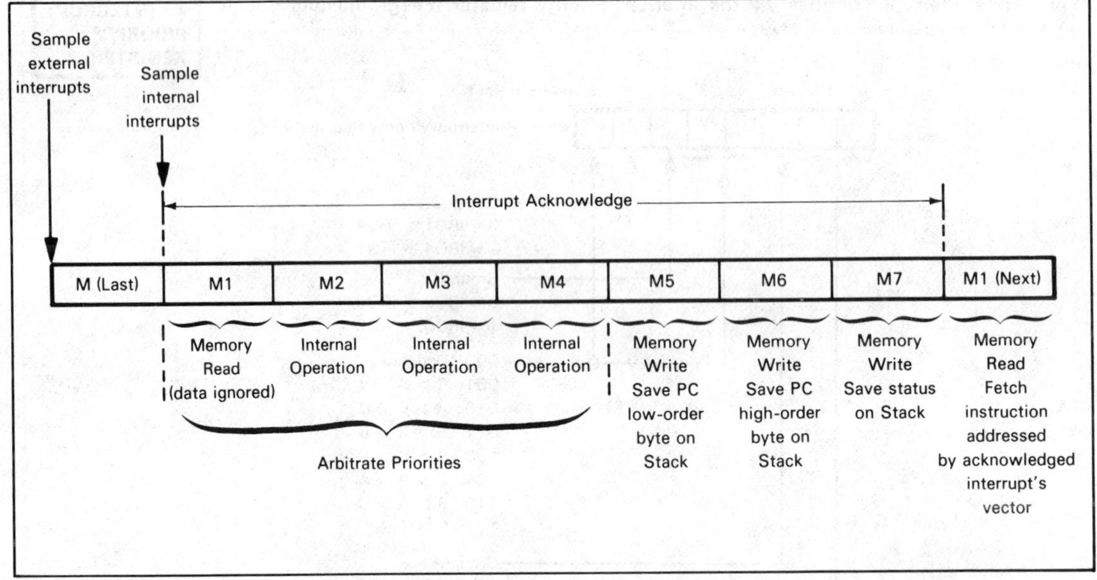


Figure 8-8. Z8 Interrupt Acknowledge Sequence

**Z8 INTERRUPT ACKNOWLEDGE TIMING**

Interrupt requests are sampled during the last machine cycle of every instruction's execution. External interrupt requests are sampled during the first clock period of this machine cycle; internal interrupt requests are sampled during the last clock period of this machine cycle. If an interrupt request is acknowledged, the following steps occur:

1) The low-order byte of the Program Counter is pushed onto the Stack.
2) The high-order byte of the Program Counter is pushed onto the Stack.
3) The Status register (the contents of register $FC_{16}$) is pushed onto the Stack.
4) Program execution continues with the instruction stored in the memory location addressed by the acknowledged interrupt's vector.

**The entire interrupt acknowledge sequence requires seven machine cycles, as illustrated in Figure 8-8.**

## Z8 RESET OPERATION

**You reset the Z8 by holding the $\overline{\text{RESET}}$ input low for at least 18 clock periods.**

**The Z8 has no automatic power-on reset logic.** Your external logic must hold $\overline{\text{RESET}}$ low for at least 50 ms after power has been input and has become stable. This 50 ms allows time for the crystal oscillator to stabilize and reset internal logic. If power is stable prior to the initialization of a reset, then $\overline{\text{RESET}}$ need only be held low for 18 external clock cycles. **The following is an example of a typical power-on reset circuit:**

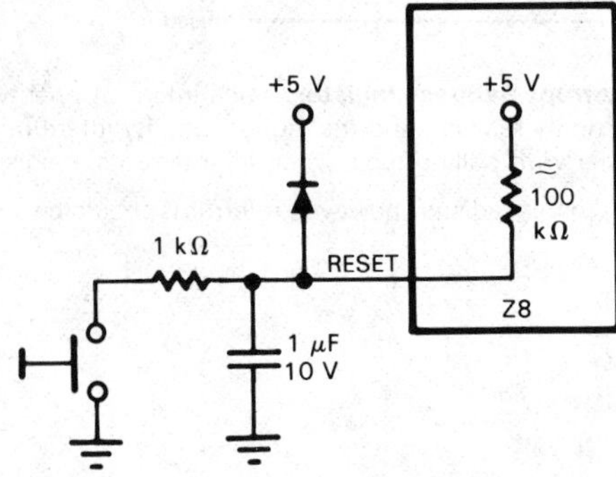

Table 8-2. Z8 Control Register Contents Following a Reset

| Register Number | Register Name | Contents After Reset 76543210 |
|---|---|---|
| FF | Stack Pointer, high-order byte | XXXXXXXX |
| FE | Stack Pointer, low-order byte | XXXXXXXX |
| FD | Register Pointer register | XXXX0000 |
| FC | Status register | XXXXXXXX |
| FB | Interrupt Mask register - Disable all interrupts | 0XXXXXXX |
| FA | Interrupt Request register - No interrupts pending | XX000000 |
| F9 | Interrupt Priority register | XXXXXXXX |
| F8 | Ports 0/1 Control register - Ports defined as inputs, normal memory cycles, internal Stack | 01001101 |
| F7 | Ports 2/3 Control register - Port 2 open drain. Port 3 simple I/O | 000000X0 |
| F6 | Port 2 Data Direction register - Port 2 lines all input | 11111111 |
| F5 | Timer 0 Prescaler register - Single count mode, internal clock source | XXXXXXX0 |
| F4 | Timer 0 register | XXXXXXXX |
| F3 | Timer 1 Prescaler register - Single count mode, internal clock source | XXXXXX00 |
| F2 | Timer 1 register | XXXXXXXX |
| F1 | Timer Control register - Timers stopped | 00000000 |
| F0 | Serial I/O register | XXXXXXXX |

X - bit undefined

While $\overline{RESET}$ is low, $\overline{AS}$ is output at the internal clock rate (which is half of the applied external clock rate). $\overline{DS}$ is held low, $R/\overline{W}$ is high. All lines of I/O Ports 0, 1, and 2 are assigned to input.

When $\overline{RESET}$ subsequently goes high, program execution begins with the instruction stored in on-chip memory location $000C_{16}$.

Only during a $\overline{RESET}$ operation can $\overline{AS}$ and $\overline{DS}$ simultaneously be low. Zilog literature suggests that you can use this condition to generate a reset pulse for external logic connected to the Z8.

**Table 8-2 summarizes Control register contents following a reset.**

## Z8 POWER-DOWN AND STANDBY POWER SUPPLY

**If you input an external clock signal to the Z8 via XTAL1, then you can use the XTAL2 pin to input a standby power supply. Zilog literature recommends the following circuit:**

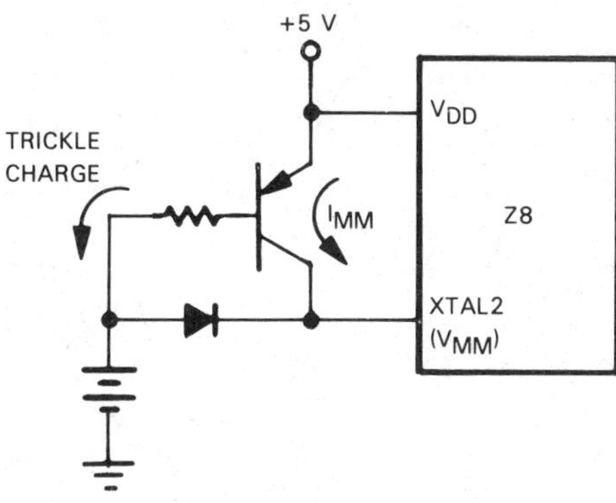

Following a general power-down, the circuit illustrated above will provide standby power to Registers $04_{16}$ through $7F_{16}$, and to Z8 reset logic. But **in order to use the standby power supply, external logic must monitor the power supply input to its transformer, and detect incipient power failure sufficiently in advance of actual power failure to allow time for a Power Fail interrupt service routine.** This may be illustrated as follows:

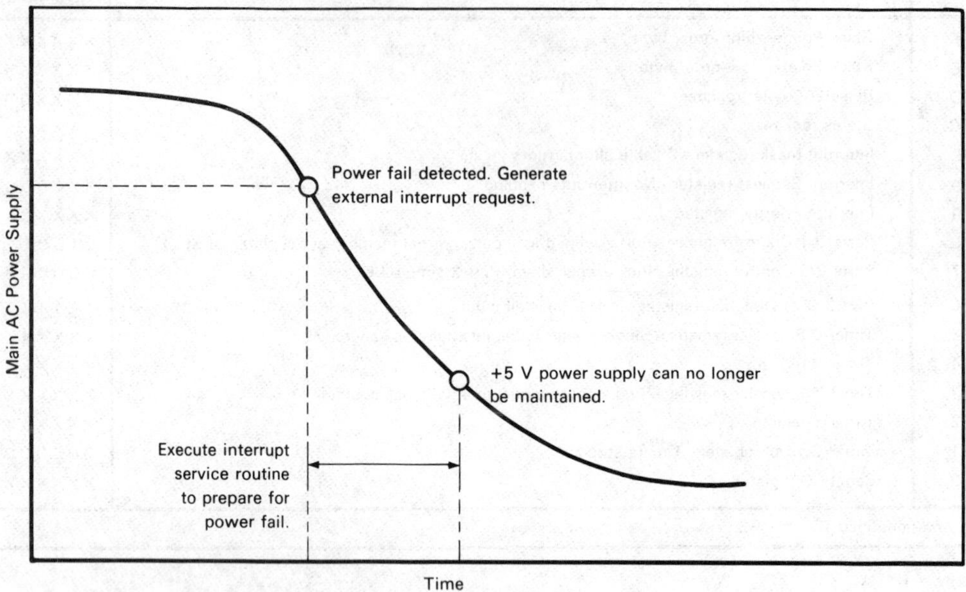


An external interrupt request will typically be generated at the point where power failure is detected. You now have a few milliseconds until external power falls to the point where +5 V cannot be maintained. During these few milliseconds you should execute a preparatory interrupt service routine. This interrupt service routine should load that data which must be preserved into the protected registers.

Once the Reset interrupt service routine has completed execution, the $\overline{\text{RESET}}$ input should be pulled low and held low until the subsequent power-up has gone to completion.

## Z8 I/O PORTS AND I/O DATA TRANSFERS

**From our previous discussion of Z8 pins and signal assignments, it will be apparent that Z8 I/O ports can function in a variety of ways. We will now describe the actual logic associated with Z8 I/O ports. Tables 8-3 and 8-4 summarize programmable options that are described in the discussion that follows.**

Table 8-3. Z8 I/O Port Data Transfers with Handshaking

| I/O Port | Bits | Direction | Control Signals | Comment |
|---|---|---|---|---|
| 0 | 4 (P04-P07) or 8 (P00-P07) | IN | $\overline{\text{DAV0}}$ input at P32<br>RDY0 output at P35 | Data directions can be specified separately for P00-P03 and for P04-P07.<br>The P04-P07 specification selects IN or OUT control signals. |
| | | OUT | RDY0 input at P32<br>$\overline{\text{DAV0}}$ output at P35 | |
| 1 | 8 (P10-P17) | IN | $\overline{\text{DAV1}}$ input at P33<br>RDY1 output at P34 | Data direction assignment must be the same for all lines of I/O Port 1. |
| | | OUT | RDY1 input at P33<br>$\overline{\text{DAV1}}$ output at P34 | |
| 2 | 8 (P20-P27) | IN | $\overline{\text{DAV2}}$ input at P31<br>RDY2 output at P36 | Pin directions are individually assigned. P27 direction specification selects IN or OUT control signals.<br>Open drain OUT can function as pseudo-bidirectional. |
| | | OUT | RDY2 input at P31<br>$\overline{\text{DAV2}}$ output at P36 | |
| | | Pseudo-bidirectional | | |

I/O Ports 0, 1, and 2 have logic which may be illustrated as follows:

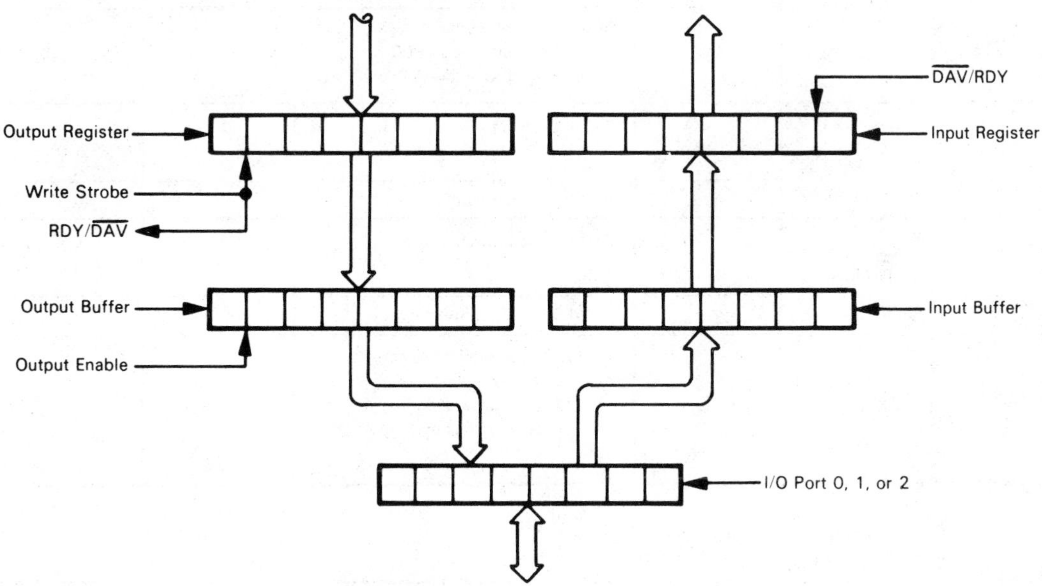

Table 8-4. Z8 I/O Ports 0, 1, and 2 Options Summary

| I/O Port | Direction | Handshaking | Comment | Register F8 | | | | | | | | Register F7 | | | | | | | |
|---|---|---|---|---|---|---|---|---|---|---|---|---|---|---|---|---|---|---|---|
| | | | | 7 | 6 | 5 | 4 | 3 | 2 | 1 | 0 | 7 | 6 | 5 | 4 | 3 | 2 | 1 | 0 |
| 0 | Input | No | P00-P07, 8-bit input | 0 | 1 | | | | | 0 | 1 | | | | | | 0 | | |
| | | | P04-P07, 4-bit input, P00-P03 functioning as Address Bus | 0 | 1 | | | | | 1 | | | | | | | 0 | | |
| | | Yes | P00-P07, 8-bit input | 0 | 1 | | | | | 0 | 1 | | | | | | 1 | | |
| | | | P04-P07, 4-bit input, P00-P03 functioning as Address Bus | 0 | 1 | | | | | 1 | | | | | | | 1 | | |
| | Bidirectional | No | P00-P03 input, P04-P07 output | 0 | 0 | | | | | 0 | 1 | | | | | | 0 | | |
| | | | P00-P03 output, P04-P07 input | 0 | 1 | | | | | 0 | 0 | | | | | | 0 | | |
| | | Yes | P00-P03 input without handshaking P04-P07 output with handshaking | 0 | 0 | | | | | 0 | 1 | | | | | | 1 | | |
| | | | P00-P03 output without handshaking P04-P07 input with handshaking | 0 | 1 | | | | | 0 | 0 | | | | | | 1 | | |
| | Output | No | P00-P07, 8-bit output | 0 | 0 | | | | | 0 | 0 | | | | | | 0 | | |
| | | | P04-P07, 4-bit output, P00-P03 functioning as Address Bus | 0 | 0 | | | | | 1 | | | | | | | 0 | | |
| | | Yes | P00-P07, 8-bit output | 0 | 0 | | | | | 0 | 0 | | | | | | 1 | | |
| | | | P04-P07, 4-bit output, P00-P03 functioning as Address Bus | 0 | 0 | | | | | 1 | | | | | | | 1 | | |
| 1 | Input | No | P10-P17, 8-bit input | | | | 0 | 1 | | | | | | | 0 | X | | | |
| | | | | | | | | | | | | | | | 1 | 0 | | | |
| | | Yes | P10-P17, 8-bit input | | | | 0 | 1 | | | | | | | 1 | 1 | | | |
| | Output | No | P10-P17, 8-bit output | | | | 0 | 0 | | | | | | | 0 | X | | | |
| | | | | | | | | | | | | | | | 1 | 0 | | | |
| | | Yes | P10-P17, 8-bit output | | | | 0 | 0 | | | | | | | 1 | 1 | | | |
| 2 | I/O | | Data Direction register selects direction for individual bits of I/O Port 2. Bit 7 direction determines handshaking logic | | | | | | | | | | | | | | | | |

X - This bit can be 0 or 1
P - 0 makes I/O Port 2 outputs open drain
1 makes I/O Port 2 outputs function with pull-ups

**Z8 I/O DATA TRANSFER WITHOUT HANDSHAKING**

**Let us begin by looking at simple data input and output, without handshaking, for I/O Ports 0, 1, or 2.**

You write data to an output port by writing to its associated register. Output data flows through the Output register to the Output buffer, and thence to any I/O port pins which have been assigned to output. Output data also flows to Input buffer and Input register bits that correspond to I/O port pins which have been assigned to output. Writing to an I/O port has no effect on pins that have been assigned to input, nor does it affect Input buffer or Input register bits corresponding to pins that have been assigned to input. Here is one example of data output to I/O Port 2:

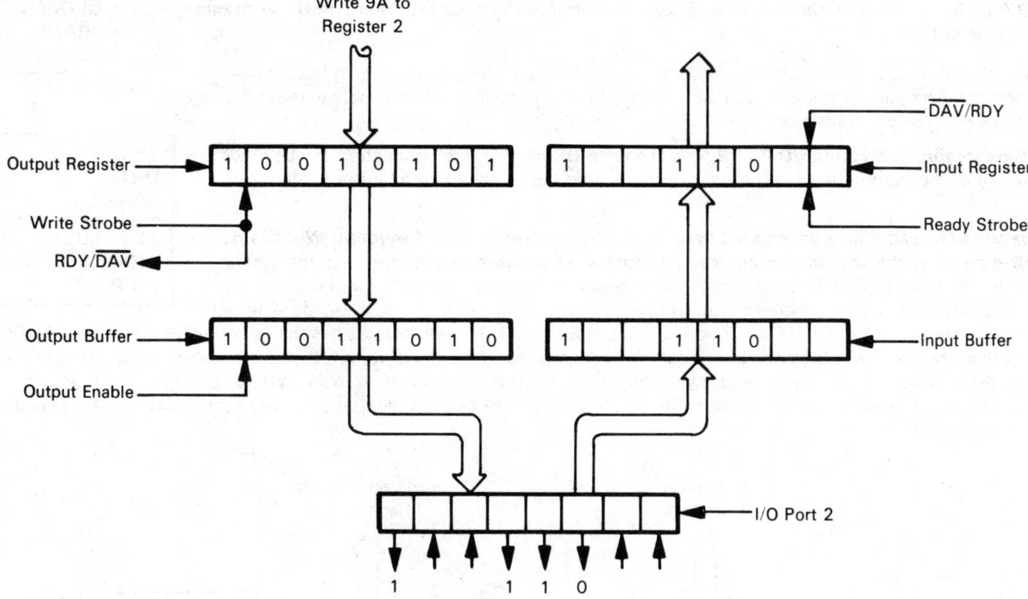


While the illustration above identifies I/O Port 2, only the individually assigned I/O port bits are unique to I/O Port 2. I/O port logic and concepts, as illustrated, apply also to I/O Ports 0 and 1.

When external logic transmits data to pins of I/O Ports 0, 1, or 2, then bit positions corresponding to input lines are immediately modified within the Input buffer and Input register. If you read from an I/O Port, then bit positions corresponding to output pins return data held in the Output register and buffer. Continuing the example above, this may be illustrated as follows:

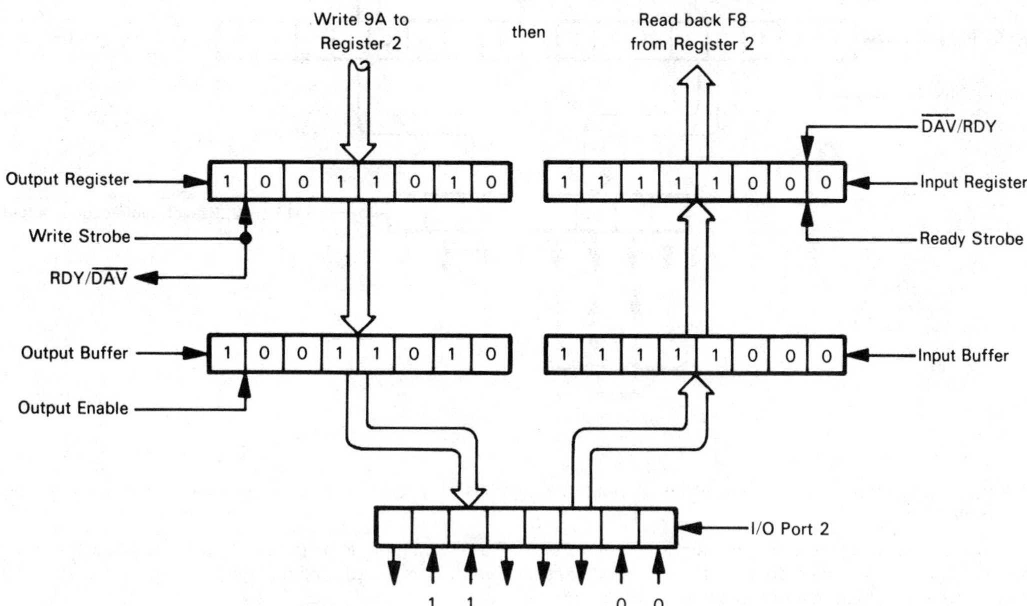

Again, the illustration above is specific to I/O Port 2 only insofar as pins have been individually assigned to input and output. The illustrated concepts apply also to I/O Ports 0 and 1.

**Z8 OPEN DRAIN OUTPUTS**

**I/O Port 2, but not I/O Ports 0, 1, or 3, can be configured under program control with open drain output pins.**

If an I/O Port 2 open drain output is high, then external logic can pull this signal low. The reverse is not true. An open drain low output cannot be pulled high by any external logic without damage to the Port 2 output transistor.

**Z8 OPEN DRAIN WIRE OR**

If **two or more open drain I/O Port 2 pins are wire-ORed,** then the connection will be low if one or more of the outputs is low. The connection will be high only when all outputs are high.

**Z8 PSEUDO-BIDIRECTIONAL I/O PORT**

**The wire-OR capability associated with open drain outputs is self-evident. What is not self-evident is the fact that open drain outputs are pseudo-bidirectional** — in the manner described for the 8048 microcomputer. This is because you will read back a 0 in any bit position corresponding to an open drain output which was high and got pulled low by external logic. If you write a 1 to an I/O Port 2 open drain output pin, then external logic has the option of leaving a 1 at the pin, or pulling the pin low, thus changing it to a 0. From a programmer's viewpoint, this is equivalent to saying that you must prepare I/O Port 2 pins for input by writing 1s to all bit positions with associated input pins. But if you write 0 to any bit position, then you block input to the associated pin. Here is an illustration of I/O Port 2 serving as a pseudo-bidirectional I/O port:

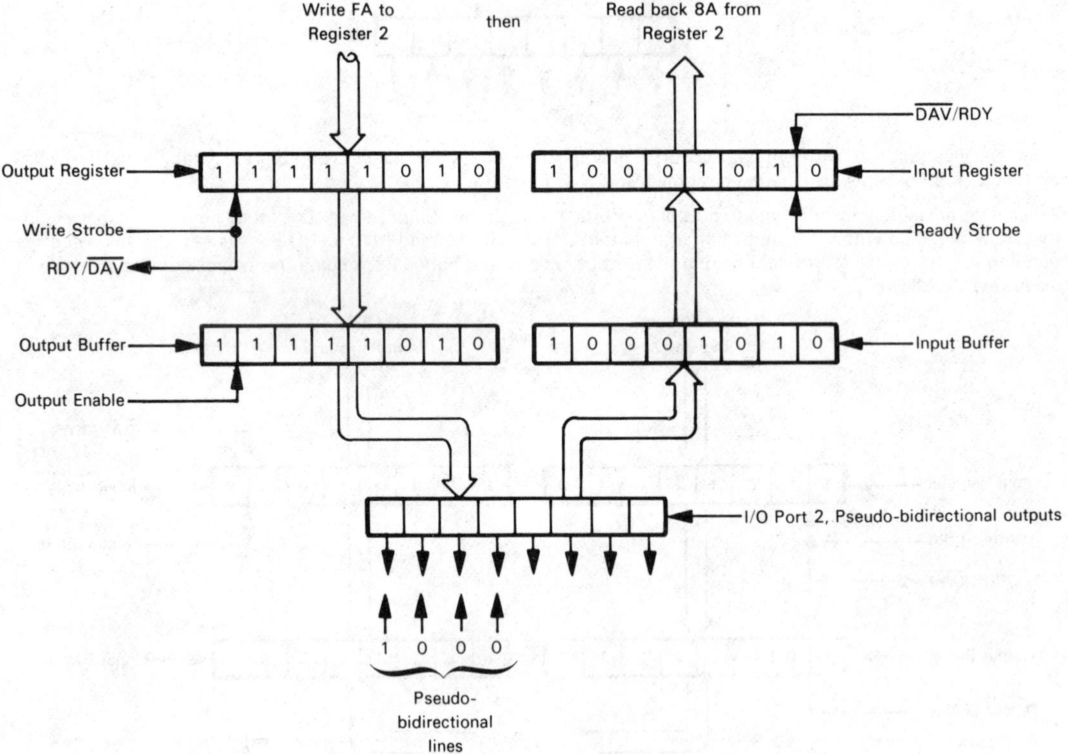


Note that the illustration above, unlike the previous two, applies only to I/O Port 2, since only I/O Port 2 can output open drain signals.

The illustration above shows the four high-order lines of I/O Port 2 functioning as pseudo-bidirectional lines; but this choice is arbitrary. Any open drain I/O Port 2 output lines can function as pseudo-bidirectional lines, provided you write 1s to those lines which must be capable of receiving input.

**If I/O Ports 0 and 1 are functioning as a Data/Address Bus, then you can no longer write to Registers 0 or 1;** if you do, the instruction is ignored. If you read from Register 0 or 1, you will read whatever transient data happens to be on associated internal bus lines at the point in time when the instruction execution reads the register.

**I/O Port 0 can be configured with the four low-order bits functioning as part of the Address Bus, while the four high-order bits function as a 4-bit I/O port.** In this configuration, you continue to access I/O Port 0 via Register 0, but only the four high-order bits of Register 0 are significant.

From the programmer's viewpoint, when I/O Port 0 is split between I/O and address functions, you continue to access I/O Port 0 via Register 0, but you ignore its four low-order bits. Anything you write to these bits will be lost, while anything you read back from these bits will be indeterminate.

**I/O Port 3 has simpler logic than I/O Ports 0, 1, and 2. I/O Port 3 logic may be illustrated as follows:**

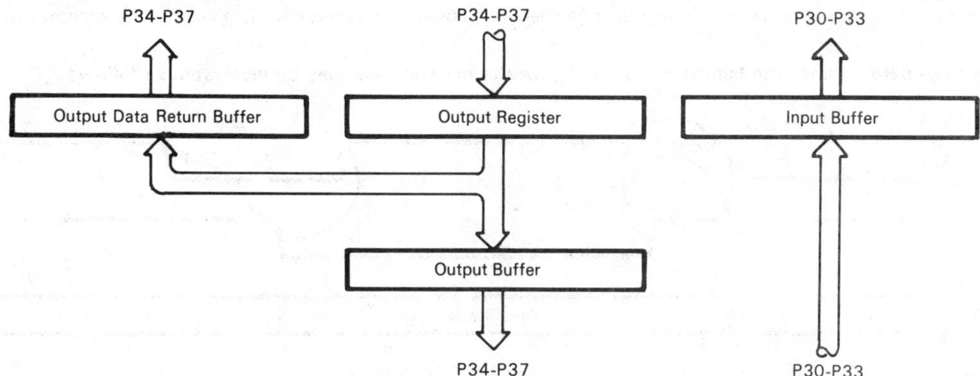


As illustrated above, the four low-order bits of I/O Port 3 can function only as inputs, while the four high-order bits of I/O Port 3 can function only as outputs.

You output to I/O Port 3 by writing to Register 3. You input from I/O Port 3 by reading from Register 3. When you write to I/O Port 3, the four low-order bits are lost; the four high-order bits are held in the Output Data Return buffer, as well as being output via connected pins. When you read from I/O Port 3, data input to P30-P33 is returned in the four low-order bits, while previously output data is returned in the four high-order bits.

As we saw when describing Z8 pins and signal assignments, I/O Port 3 pins can serve a variety of control functions. You cannot write to any bit position of I/O Port 3 if its associated pin is functioning as a special control signal; and if you read from the bit position, you will get indeterminate data.

**Z8 I/O WITH HANDSHAKING**

**I/O Ports 0, 1, and 2 can function as input or output ports with handshaking. Table 8-3 summarizes Z8 I/O capabilities with handshaking.**

**In the general case we can illustrate input handshaking logic as follows:**

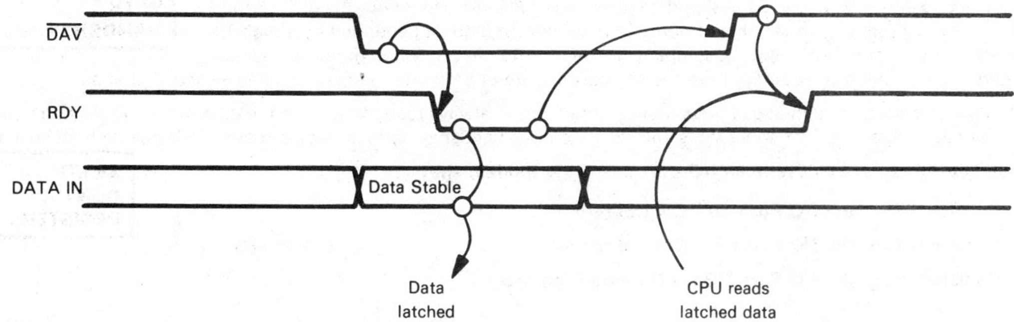

Initially, RDY will be output high and $\overline{DAV}$ will be input high at appropriate pins of I/O Port 3. When external logic inputs new data, it simultaneously inputs $\overline{DAV}$ low.

The low $\overline{DAV}$ input causes I/O port logic to latch the input data into the Input register, provided the Input register is not holding data that is waiting to be read. External logic cannot overwrite data in the Input register.

The high-to-low transition of $\overline{DAV}$, since it occurs at pin 1, 2, or 3 of I/O Port 3, will cause an interrupt request —assuming that interrupts have been appropriately enabled. If interrupts have not been enabled, the Z8 can use polling software to detect data input. Recall that the Interrupt Request register bit corresponding to the interrupt request will be set. You could also read Port 3 to determine which signal line caused the interrupt.

The Z8 may read the contents of the Input register at any time, since external logic cannot overwrite this data.

External logic will normally wait for RDY to go low, then raise $\overline{DAV}$ high. I/O port logic will output RDY high after $\overline{DAV}$ is input high and the contents of the Input register have been read by the CPU. External logic should use RDY high as an indicator that its previously transmitted data has been read by the CPU, and new data will now be accepted by the input port.

**Turning to data output with handshaking, timing for the general case may be illustrated as follows:**

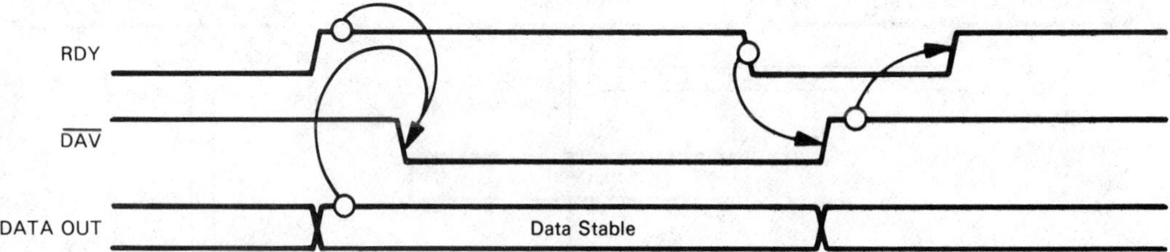


Initially, external logic will input RDY low, while the Z8 outputs $\overline{DAV}$ high.

When external logic is ready to receive data, it must input RDY high. A program executed by the Z8 may output data to the I/O port at any time; however, I/O port logic will not output $\overline{DAV}$ low until data has been written to the I/O port by the CPU, and the RDY input has been driven high by external logic.

Once external logic has input RDY high, it should wait for a low $\overline{DAV}$ output as its signal that fresh output data is available. Having read this data, external logic should input RDY low again. This will cause I/O port logic to output $\overline{DAV}$ high; the high-to-low transition of the RDY input will also generate an interrupt request, if interrupts have been enabled, and set the appropriate Interrupt Request register bit. The Z8 program controlling data output should wait for this interrupt request, or test its associated Interrupt Request register bit, before outputting any more data to the I/O port. This is the only protection offered by the Z8 against a program's writing premature data to an I/O port, and thus overwriting previously output data before external logic is able to process it.

As soon as I/O port logic outputs $\overline{DAV}$ high, external logic is free to input RDY high again — assuming that it is ready to receive fresh data.

**Z8 HIGH-SPEED I/O WITH HANDSHAKING**

**High-speed I/O data transfer with handshaking control signals will make the assumption that the receiving station is always ready for transmitted data.** If the Z8 is the receiving station and external logic is transmitting data, then external logic can ignore the RDY output. The Z8, however, must give very high priority to the interrupt request generated by a high-to-low transition of the $\overline{DAV}$ input accompanying fresh data. A very short interrupt service routine will load the received data from the I/O port into an appropriate memory location — and that is all.

If the Z8 is transmitting high-speed data, and external logic is always ready to receive the data, then you may turn the $\overline{DAV}$ output back as the RDY input. This will satisfy output handshaking logic requirements and provide high speed.

**Z8 I/O CONTROL REGISTERS**

**Three control registers determine I/O port operating modes; they are:**

1) **Register $F8_{16}$, the I/O Ports 0/1 Control register.**
2) **Register $F7_{16}$, the I/O Ports 2/3 Control register.**
3) **Register $F6_{16}$, the I/O Port 2 Data Direction register.**

**Bits of Register $F8_{16}$, the I/O Ports 0/1 Control register, are interpreted as follows:**

**Z8 I/O PORTS 0/1 CONTROL REGISTER**

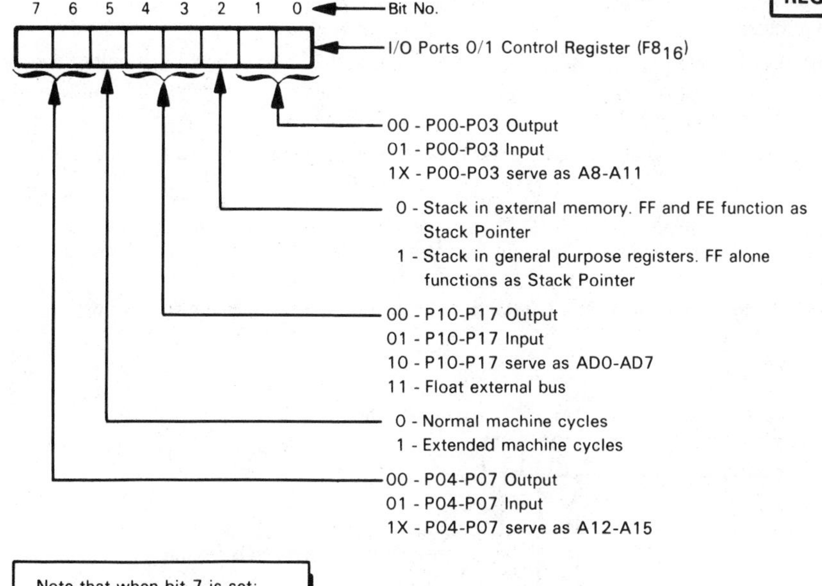


Note that when bit 7 is set:
P04-P07 serve as A12-A15
P00-P03 serve as A8-A11

In addition to defining options for I/O Ports 0 and 1, Register $F8_{16}$ also controls machine cycle timing and Stack location.

**Z8 STACK LOCATION SELECT**

Bit 2 of Register $F8_{16}$ determines whether the Stack will reside in external memory or within the on-chip general purpose registers. If you select external memory, then Registers $FE_{16}$ and $FF_{16}$ combine to function as a 16-bit Stack Pointer, and all instructions that reference the Stack generate external memory reference machine cycles in order to access the Stack. If you select an on-chip Stack, then instructions which reference the Stack generate register access machine cycles, using Register $FF_{16}$ as the Stack Pointer.

**Z8 STACK POINTER**

Registers $FE_{16}$ and $FF_{16}$ have combined 16-bit increment logic; this is an obvious necessity if the two registers are to function as a 16-bit Stack Pointer. But this increment logic remains active when you select an on-chip Stack within the local registers. Under normal circumstances, Stack Pointer 16-bit increment logic is irrelevant, since it becomes active only when the low-order byte of the Stack increments from $FF_{16}$ to 00. Since an on-chip Stack should reside entirely within the unassigned general purpose registers (which have a ceiling address of $80_{16}$), no problems should arise. For Register $FF_{16}$ to increment from $FF_{16}$ to 00, the Stack would have to overwrite the top 20 control registers and the Stack Pointer itself. If for any reason an error condition should occur which resulted in Register $FF_{16}$ contents being incremented from $FF_{16}$ to 00, then Register $FE_{16}$ contents would also increment. So long as you avoid this problem, you are free to use Register $FE_{16}$ as an unassigned data register when an on-chip Stack has been specified.

**Z8 MEMORY REFERENCE MACHINE CYCLE SELECT**

**I/O Ports 0/1 Control register bit 5 determines whether there will be three or four clock periods within memory reference machine cycles.** If you select four clock periods, then the additional clock period occurs between T3 and T4; T2 signal levels persist through the extra clock period. Figures 8-6 and 8-7 illustrate Z8 machine cycle timing.

You cannot specify four clock periods within a non-memory reference machine cycle.

**Z8 extended machine cycle logic differs sharply from that of most other microcomputers;** commonly an external READY signal triggers extended machine cycles, and allows any number of additional clock periods to be inserted within an extended machine cycle.

**Bits 0, 1, 6, and 7 of Register F8$_{16}$ control I/O Port 0 operations.** Bits 0 and 1 control the low-order four bits of I/O Port 0, while bits 6 and 7 control the four high-order bits of I/O Port 0. Your choice in each case is to assign the associated four bits of I/O Port 0 to data input, data output, or high-order Address Bus lines.

**Z8 I/O PORT 0 OPTIONS SELECT**

As an I/O port, Port 0 can function as an input port, an output port, or a combined input/output port. (See Table 8-4.)

All or half of I/O Port 0 may function as part of the Address Bus. If half of I/O Port 0 is functioning as part of the Address Bus, then it will be the low-order half — P00-P03.

**I/O Ports 0/1 Control Register bits 3 and 4 determine I/O Port 1 operations.** You have the choice of assigning I/O Port 1 to parallel data input or parallel data output, or it can serve as a multiplexed Data/Address Bus. You can also put I/O Port 1 lines in a high impedance state; in addition to I/O Port 1, this floats any lines of I/O Port 0 that are functioning as Address Bus lines, along with control signals $\overline{AS}$, $\overline{DS}$, and R/$\overline{W}$. In other words, the entire external bus is floated, irrespective of which Address Bus option you have selected.

**Z8 I/O PORT 1 OPTIONS SELECT**

**Register F7$_{16}$, which functions as the I/O Ports 2/3 Control register, has the following bit assignments:**

**Z8 I/O PORTS 2/3 CONTROL REGISTER**

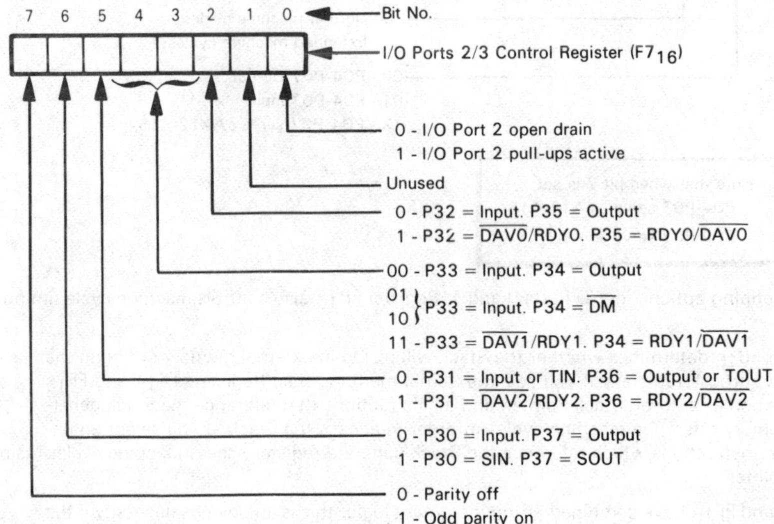


**Bit 0 alone applies to I/O Port 2; this bit determines whether I/O Port 2 outputs are open drain, or whether pull-ups are active.**

**Z8 I/O PORT 2 OPTIONS SELECT**

Bit 1 is unused.

Bit 2 of Register F7$_{16}$ determines whether I/O Port 3 pins 2 and 5 serve as data inputs and outputs, respectively, or whether they provide I/O Port 0 with handshaking control signals. The data direction specified for P04-P07 determines whether input or output handshaking controls are selected.

**Z8 I/O PORT 3 OPTIONS SELECT**

Bits 3 and 4, likewise, determine whether I/O Port 3 pins 3 and 4 function as data input and output lines, or whether they provide I/O Port 1 with handshaking control signals. **You also have the option of assigning I/O Port 3 pin 4 to function as $\overline{DM}$, the data memory select control signal.** If you select handshaking controls, then the data direction you select for P10-P17 determines whether input or output handshaking controls are selected.

**Z8 I/O WITH HANDSHAKING SELECT**

**Z8 DATA MEMORY SELECT**

Bit 5 determines whether I/O Port 3 pins 1 and 6 function as data input and data output lines, or whether they provide I/O Port 2 with handshaking control signals. I/O Port 3 pins 1 and 6 must be assigned to data input and data output if counter/timer logic is going to use these signals. Therefore, **you cannot use I/O Port 2 with handshaking if counter/timer logic uses external clock and square wave output options.** The data direction selected for P27 determines whether input or output handshaking controls are selected.

Note that when you assign any I/O Port 3 pins to function as handshaking control signals, the tacit assumption is made that the associated port is correctly configured to transfer parallel data. But there is nothing to stop you from assigning I/O Port 3 pins as handshaking control signals, even though the associated I/O Port may have been separately assigned to function as a Data/Address Bus. However, the results of such an assignment would be unpredictable.

Table 8-4 summarizes Registers $F7_{16}$ and $F8_{16}$ bit settings that give you the legitimate Z8 parallel I/O options.

**Z8 SERIAL I/O SELECT**

**Z8 PARITY OPTION**

**I/O Ports 2/3 Control Register bits 7 and 6 apply to serial I/O logic.** If bit 6 is 0, then serial I/O logic is disabled and I/O Port 3 pins 0 and 7 function as data input and output lines, respectively. But if bit 6 is 1, then I/O Port 3 bit 0 receives serial data input, while bit 7 transmits serial data output; under these circumstances, I/O Port 2/3 Control Register bit 7 enables or disables parity logic associated with serial I/O. **If parity is selected, then odd parity is assumed** for transmitted and received serial data.

**Z8 I/O PORT 2 DATA DIRECTION REGISTER**

**Register $F6_{16}$ specifies the data direction for I/O Port 2 pins as follows:**

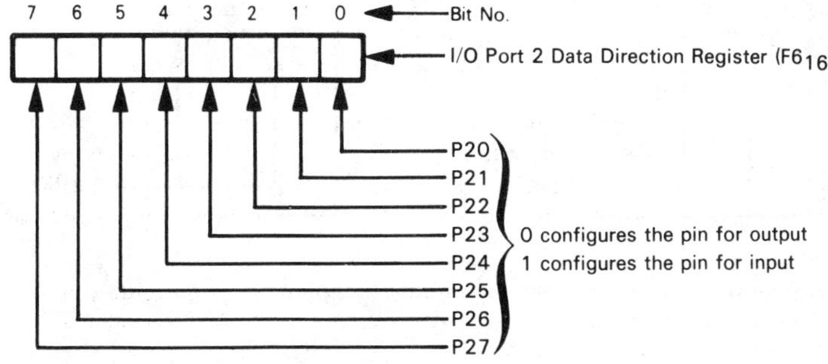


## Z8 SERIAL INPUT/OUTPUT

**The Z8 has a relatively primitive serial input/output capability; its logic may be illustrated as follows:**

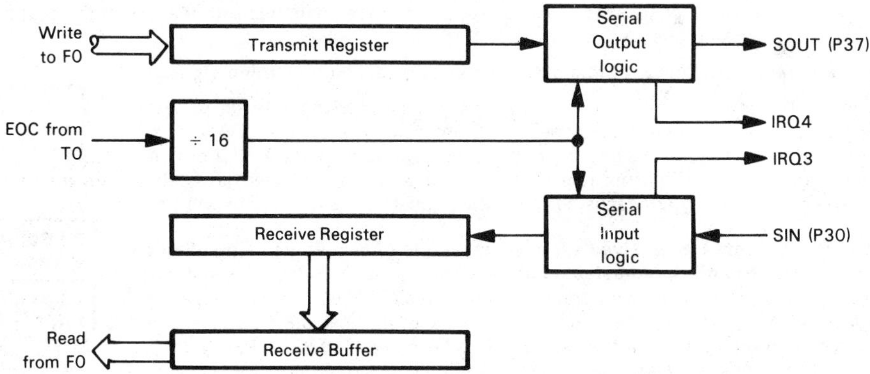


**Z8 serial I/O logic uses Counter/Timer 0 in order to generate the serial bit rate clock. Therefore, if you use the Z8 serial I/O capability, you cannot use Counter/Timer 0;** conversely, if you need Counter/Timer 0, you cannot use the serial I/O capability. For details, see the Counter/Timer 0 description.

**Z8 SERIAL I/O PARITY LOGIC**

**The only programmable serial I/O option is to select odd parity or no parity. Bits 7 and 6 of the I/O Ports 2/3 Control register ($F7_{16}$) control Z8 serial I/O logic. We have already described this Control register.**

**Z8 SERIAL I/O CHARACTER FORMAT**

Without parity, transmitted and received characters have the following formats:

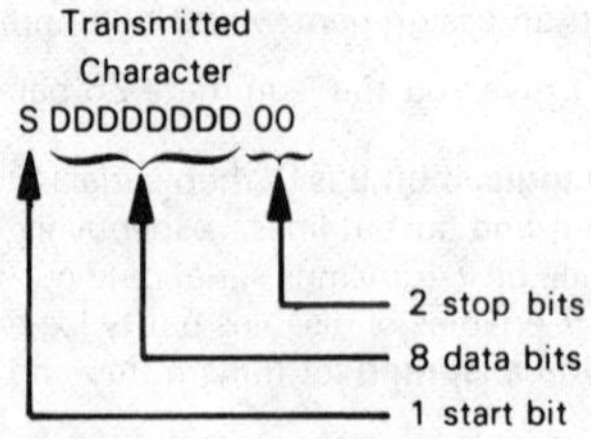


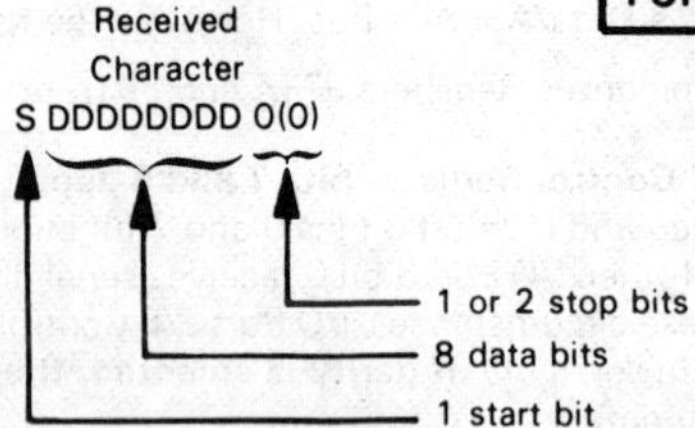


With the parity option, transmitted and received characters have the following formats:

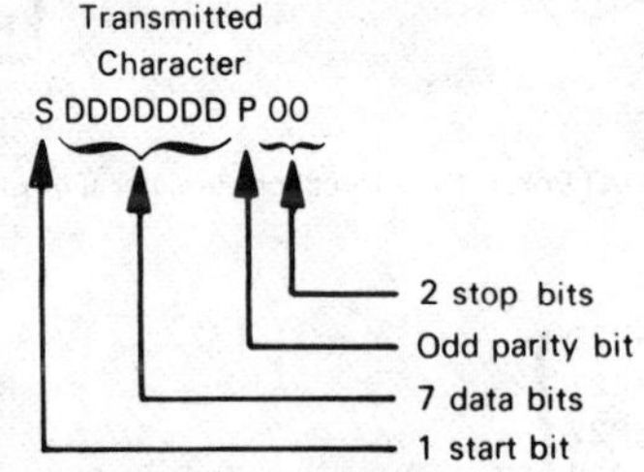


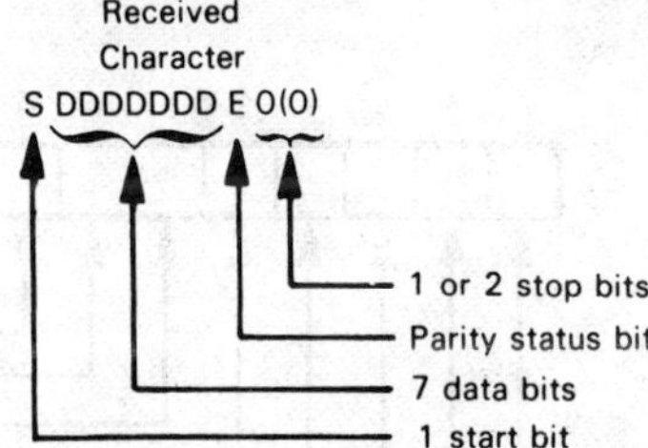


**Address $F0_{16}$ accesses separate read-only and write-only locations.** (This prevents you from using Register $F0_{16}$ as a general purpose register when you are not using Z8 serial I/O logic, since you cannot read back what you write out.)

**Z8 SERIAL I/O TRANSMIT LOGIC**

**You transmit characters by writing to Register $F0_{16}$.** The character is held in the Transmit register. If parity is not selected, then the eight data bits of the Transmit register are output, least significant bit first, with a single leading start bit and two trailing stop bits. If parity has been selected, then seven data bits are taken from the Transmit register; the high-order bit is ignored. The transmitted character consists of a leading start bit, seven data bits with the least significant bit leading, an odd parity bit, and two stop bits.

**In between characters, serial output logic outputs a continuous high marking signal.**

**Z8 SERIAL I/O OVERRUN**

Since there is no Transmit buffer, there will always be some marking interval between transmitted characters. Serial output logic generates an interrupt request via IRQ4, which a supervisory program should use as a signal to transmit the next data character. If a program writes another character to the Transmit register before the previous character has been output, then the previous character will be overwritten, an erroneous output will be generated, and no error will be reported!

**Z8 SERIAL I/O RECEIVE LOGIC**

**Z8 SERIAL I/O PARITY ERROR**

**Serial input logic interprets the received serial signal in one of two ways, depending on whether parity has or has not been selected.** If parity has not been selected, serial input logic assumes one start bit, eight data bits, and at least one stop bit. The eight data bits are assembled in the Receive register, with the assumption that the least significant bit was received first. **If parity has been selected, then the eighth data bit is converted into a Parity Status bit.** If the eight bits occurring between a leading start and trailing stop bit have odd parity, then a 0 is returned for the Parity Status bit. But if even parity is detected, then a 1 is returned for the Parity Status bit. **The high-order bit of the character assembled in the Receive register will be the Parity Status bit. A supervisory program must examine this bit in order to detect status errors.**

**Z8 SERIAL I/O OVERFLOW ERROR**

**Serial input logic has a Receive buffer.** As soon as a character has been assembled in the Receive register, it is transmitted to the Receive buffer, and an interrupt request is generated via IRQ3. **A monitoring program has one character time within which to read the contents of the Receive buffer.** If the Receive buffer contents are not read in time, the Receive register contents will overwrite the Receive buffer, but no overrun error will be reported!

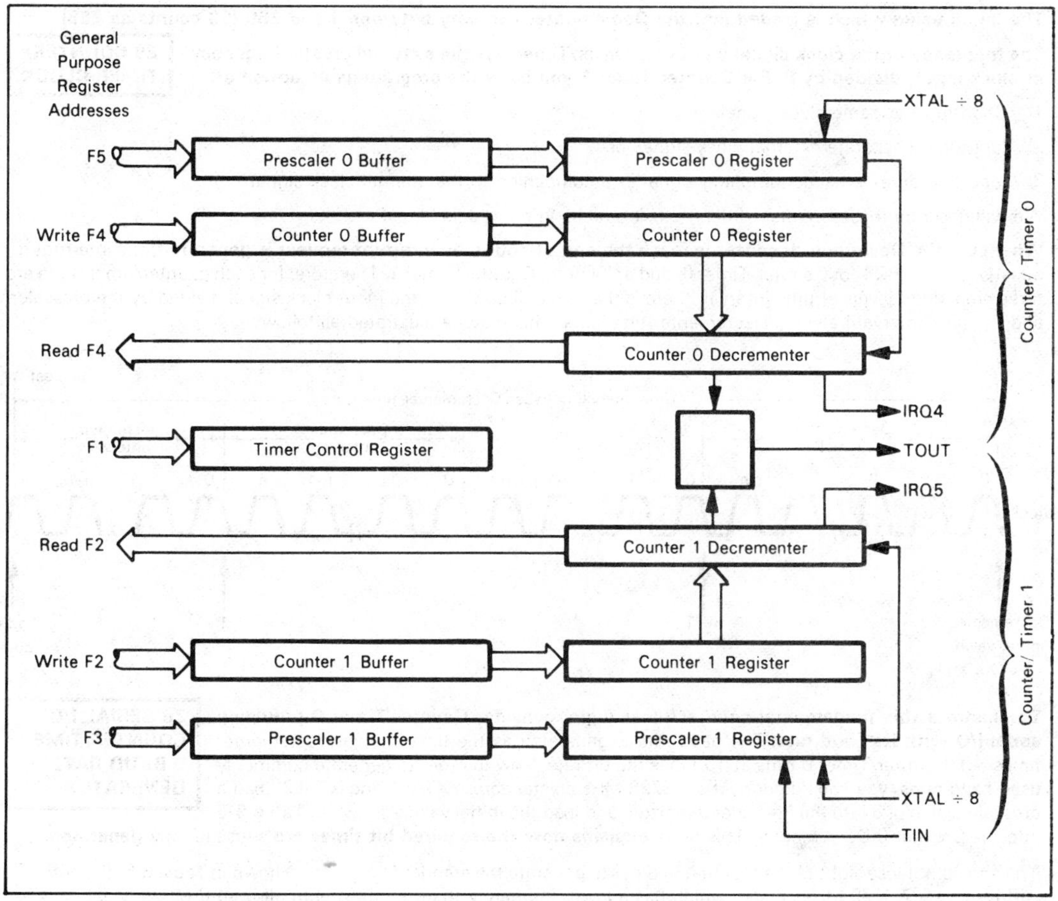

Figure 8-9. Z8 Counter/Timer Logic

## Z8 COUNTER/TIMER LOGIC

**The Z8 has extensive counter/timer logic, centered around two counter/timers, as illustrated in Figure 8-9.**

**Counter/Timer 0 has fewer programmable options than Counter/Timer 1. Also, Counter/Timer 0 functions as the baud rate generator for Z8 serial I/O operations. Therefore, you should use Counter/Timer 1 in preference to Counter/Timer 0, and remember that Counter/Timer 0 will become unavailable whenever serial I/O is enabled.**

**Both counter/timers are based on very elementary logic.** Each counter/timer receives a clock signal which is divided by a prescaler. The prescaler value, which is held in the Prescaler register, can vary between 1 and 64. The input clock frequency divided by the prescaler value becomes the decrement time interval. The Counter Decrementer contents are decremented once each decrement time interval. **This logic may be illustrated as follows:**

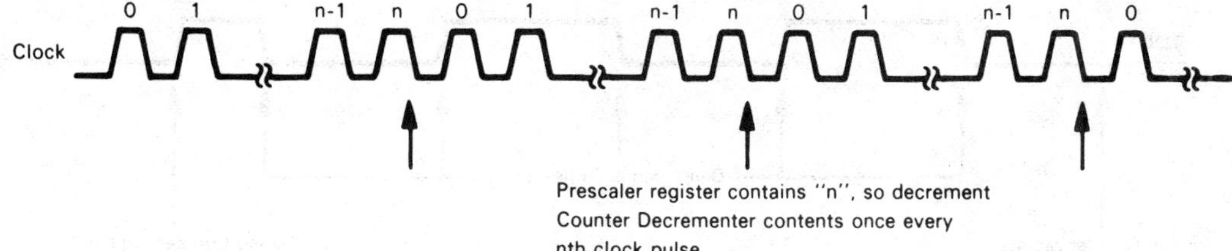

**The initial value which is loaded into the Decrementer can vary between 1 and 256 (00 counts as 256).**

**Z8 COUNTER/ TIMER CLOCK**

**The frequency of the clock signal input to Counter/Timer 0 is the external crystal frequency or clock input, divided by 8. For Counter/Timer 1 you have the programmable option of:**

1) Choosing this same clock signal, or
2) Inputting a separate external clock signal, or
3) Inputting an external conditioning signal as a companion to the internal clock signal.

We will describe these Counter/Timer 1 clock options in more detail later.

**Whenever the Decrementer contents reach the end-of-count, an interrupt request is generated;** the interrupt request occurs at IRQ4 for Counter/Timer 0, and at IRQ5 for Counter/Timer 1. Therefore, for each counter/timer there are three embedded levels of time interval; there is the input clock signal, the input clock signal divided by the prescaler, and the time interval between Decrementer time-outs. This may be illustrated as follows:

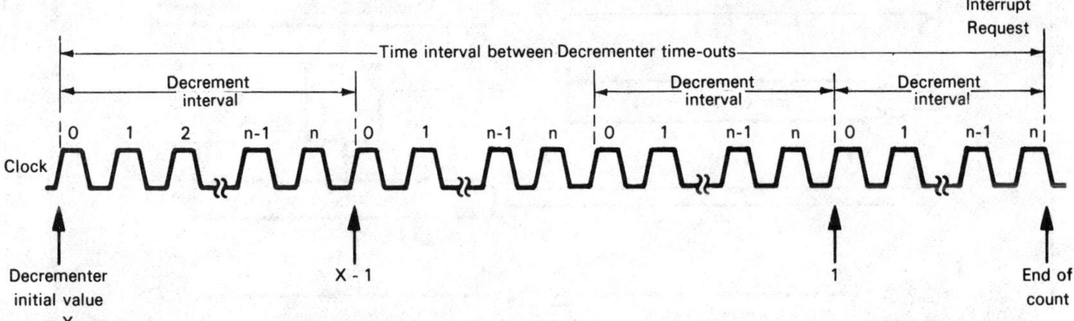


**Z8 SERIAL I/O COUNTER/TIMER 0 BAUD RATE GENERATOR**

**To illustrate this fundamental counter/timer logic, consider Counter/Timer 0 providing serial I/O with its baud rate.** The baud rate is generated as the time interval Decrementer times out. Counter/Timer 0 runs at 16 times the bit rate. Now in order to generate commonly used baud rates, you should connect a 7.3728 MHz crystal across XTAL1 and XTAL2, load a prescaler value of 3 into the Prescaler 0 register, and load the initial values shown in **Table 8-5** into the Counter 0 Decrementer. This table **explains how the required bit times are** subsequently **generated.**

You should not lose sight of the fact that in order to generate the standard baud rates shown in Table 8-5, the entire Z8 is driven by a 7.3728 MHz crystal, which has a lower frequency than the maximum allowed 8 MHz crystal.

A few simple options are available with Counter/Timer 0 or 1.

**Z8 COUNTER/ TIMER OPTIONS**

**Both counter/timers may be free running or one-shot.** If free running, then every time the Decrementer decrements to end-of-count it is reloaded with an initial value, which is preserved in the Counter register; then decrementing continues. In one-shot mode, Counter 0 stops when the Counter 0 Decrementer decrements to 0.

**When the Decrementer decrements to end-of-count, an interrupt request occurs** at IRQ4 for Counter/Timer 0, and at IRQ5 for Counter/Timer 1. You have the option of enabling or disabling these interrupt requests.

**Z8 COUNTER/ TIMER SQUARE WAVE OUTPUT**

**Counter/Timer 0 or 1 can drive the TOUT output** (which is an optional use for I/O Port 3 pin 6). TOUT is output low when you write to either counter register. Subsequently it switches level whenever the Decrementer decrements to end-of-count. Thus TOUT generates a square wave output, which may be illustrated as follows:

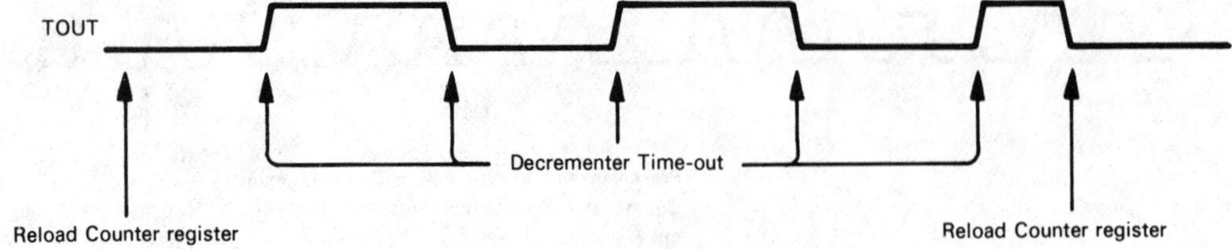

Table 8-5. Counter/Timer 0 Baud Rate Generation

| A<br>Crystal<br>Frequency<br>(MHz) | B<br>Counter 0<br>Clock<br>= A/8<br>(kHz) | C<br>Time Interval<br>from Prescaler *<br>= 3/B<br>($\mu$sec) | D<br>Decrementer<br>Present | E<br>Decrementer<br>Time Out<br>Interval<br>= C x D ($\mu$sec) | F<br>Bit Rate<br>= $10^6/(16E)$<br>(Bits/Sec) |
|---|---|---|---|---|---|
| | | | 1 | 3.255 | 19200 |
| | | | 2 | 6.510 | 9600 |
| | | | 4 | 13.021 | 4800 |
| | | | 8 | 26.042 | 2400 |
| 7.3728 | 921.6 | 3.2552 | 16 | 52.083 | 1200 |
| | | | 32 | 104.167 | 600 |
| | | | 64 | 208.333 | 300 |
| | | | 128 | 416.667 | 150 |
| | | | 175 ** | 569.661 | 110 ** |

* Prescaler register contains 3
** Error = 0.26%

Counter/Timer 1 has a number of powerful options that are not available with Counter/Timer 0.

**TIN can provide Counter/Timer 1 with its internal clock.** The clock input at TIN is not divided before being processed by the prescaler; therefore, it can have a maximum frequency of 1 MHz — equivalent to the maximum frequency that internal clock logic can derive. There is no minimum frequency for a clock signal input via TIN.

**Z8 EVENT COUNTER**

**TIN may also receive an input with random transitions, in which case Counter/Timer 1 will function as an event counter.** You should load a prescaler value of 1 at this time, otherwise Counter/Timer 1 will divide the TIN input by the prescaler value and report some fraction of the active transitions.

**TIN may be programmed to function as an enabling signal, capable of starting and stopping the internal counter/timer clock.** When gating the clock in this fashion, TIN stops Counter/Timer 1 when low, and allows it to run when high. This may be illustrated as follows:

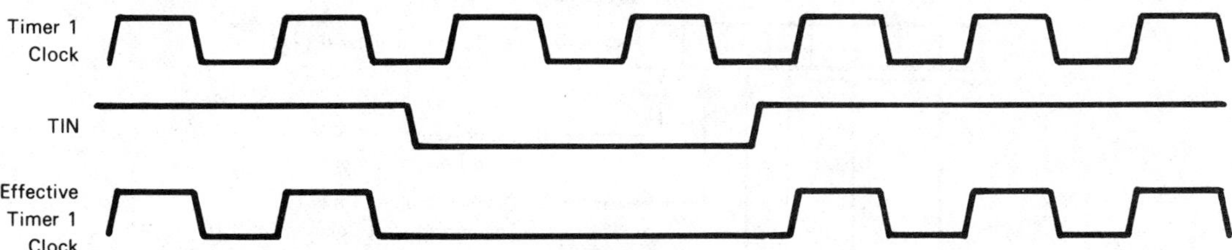


**TIN may also function as a retriggerable or non-retriggerable trigger input to Counter/Timer 1.** As a trigger input, a high-to-low transition of TIN downloads the contents of the Counter 1 register to the Counter 1 Decrementer and starts Counter/Timer 1. If the retriggerable option is selected, then on each subsequent occasion that TIN makes a high-to-low transition, Counter/Timer 1 logic will be restarted, irrespective of its status when the retrigger occurs.

If the non-retriggerable option is selected, then subsequent transitions of TIN are ignored.

**Z8 COUNTER/ TIMER PROGRAMMING**

**Z8 counter/timer logic is accessed via the five register addresses $F1_{16}$, $F2_{16}$, $F3_{16}$, $F4_{16}$, and $F5_{16}$.**

Register addresses $F4_{16}$ and $F5_{16}$ access Counter/Timer 0. Register addresses $F2_{16}$ and $F3_{16}$ access Counter/Timer 1. When you write to $F2_{16}$ and $F4_{16}$, data is loaded into the Counter 1 and Counter 0 buffers, respectively. When you write to $F3_{16}$ and $F5_{16}$, data is loaded into the Prescaler 1 and 0 buffers, respectively. You subsequently load appropriate codes into the Timer Control register to move the contents of buffers to their respective registers, and to start the counter/timers. When you read from Registers $F2_{16}$ and $F4_{16}$, you read the contents of the Counter 1 and Counter 0 Decrementers, respectively. Thus you can monitor a counter or timer operation by reading the Decrementer contents on the fly. You cannot read the contents of the Prescaler buffer or register.

**Prescaler register contents for Counter/Timers 0 and 1 are interpreted as follows:**

**Z8 COUNTER/ TIMER PRESCALER REGISTER**

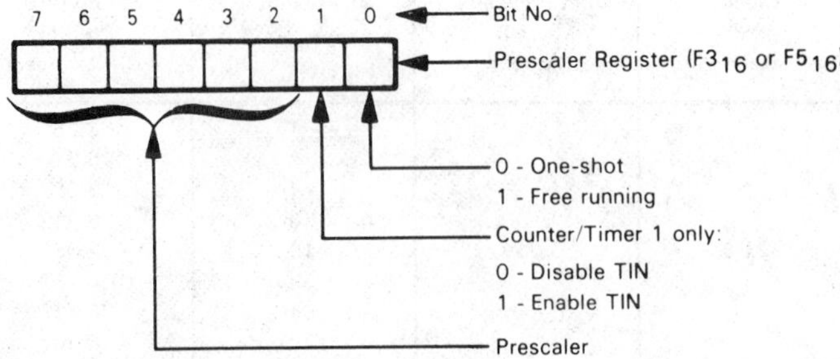


**Bit 0 determines whether the counter/timer will be free running or one-shot.** In free running mode, whenever the Decrementer decrements to end-of-count, Counter register contents are downloaded into the Decrementer, which continues operating uninterrupted. But in the one-shot mode, counter/timer logic stops following a Decrementer time-out.

**Prescaler register bit 1** applies only to Counter/Timer 1. This bit **must be set to 1 in order to enable TIN.** If this bit is 0, then any TIN options selected via the Counter/Timer Control register will be ignored.

The six high-order bits of the Prescaler registers provide the prescaler values used by each set of counter/timer logic. A value of 00 is interpreted as $40_{16}$; therefore, the prescaler will always report a value ranging between 1 and 64.

**You can write to any counter/timer register at any time. But you can only read the contents of the two Decrementers. This allows a program controlling counter/timers to read the Decrementer on the fly. A program can also modify Prescaler and/or Counter register contents at any time; before starting a counter/timer, or while the counter/timer is running.**

**You write to Register $F1_{16}$ in order to access the Timer Control register, whose bits are interpreted as follows:**

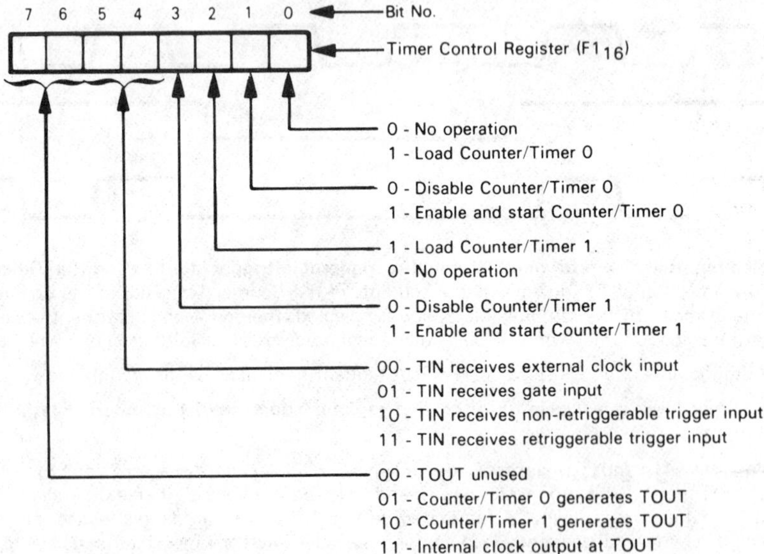

**Control register bits 0, 1, 2, and 3 enable and start the counter/timers.**

Bit 0, when set to 1, moves the Prescaler 0 buffer contents to the Prescaler 0 register, and the Counter 0 buffer contents to the Counter 0 register. Bit 2, when set to 1, performs the same operation for Counter/Timer 1.

Bit 1, when set to 1, starts Counter/Timer 0. Bit 3, when set to 1, starts Counter/Timer 1.

If you write to Control register bit 0 or 2 then the 1 is reset to 0 as soon as the specified operation has been performed.

**Control register bits 4 and 5 specify the way in which Counter/Timer 1 uses TIN.** These two bits depend on bit 1 of the Prescaler 1 register, which enables or disables TIN. In other words, Counter/Timer 1 logic ignores Control register bits 4 and 5 if the Prescaler 1 register holds a 0 in bit 1.

**We have already described the four TIN options available at Counter/Timer 1.**

**Control register bits 7 and 6 select TOUT logic.**

If Counter/Timer 0 or 1 generates TOUT, then a square wave output will occur, with a transition occurring at every Decrementer time-out, as we have already described.

**If the internal clock is output via TOUT, then the clock signal used by the Z8 is output, not the clock signal used by counter/timer logic.** In other words, TOUT will output a signal whose frequency is half of the crystal frequency connected across XTAL1 and XTAL2.

# THE Z8 INSTRUCTION SET

**Table 8-7 summarizes the Z8 instruction set. Table 8-8 provides a listing of instructions by their object codes in numerical order.**

Table 8-7 treats Z8 registers as registers, rather than as data memory. Accordingly, Table 8-7 shows relatively few memory reference instructions, and no memory operate instructions. On the other hand, there are a large number of register-register operate and register operate instructions.

When the Z8 is used in a one-chip microcomputer configuration, then the net effect of its instruction set is to give you excellent access to data memory, plus great data manipulation flexibility.

When the Z8 is configured with external data memory, then you should use the external data memory as a simple data depository. All programs must be broken into modules that load data into registers, operate on this data, then return data to external data memory when it is no longer needed.

## THE Z8 BENCHMARK PROGRAM

Since we are dealing with a one-chip microcomputer, we will modify our benchmark program for the Z8, showing how a block of data may be moved from registers to external data memory. The beginning external data memory address, the beginning register address, and the number of bytes to be moved are held in four contiguous registers within a register block as follows:

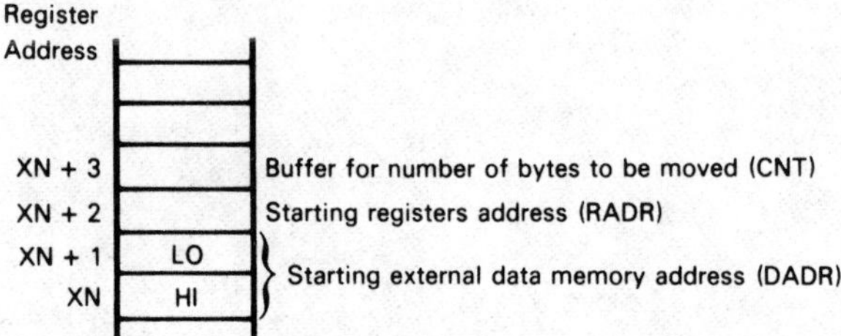


We will assume that the external data memory address DADR can be left unaltered, since data from registers must be moved into the external data memory buffer, beginning with the first free buffer location — which will be the residual address following the previous data movement. The starting register address RADR must be reinitialized after every block of data is moved, since the same register space will be reused as each sequential data block is written out to data memory. Similarly, the number of data bytes to be moved must be held permanently in some appropriate memory location and must be moved to a buffer where it can be decremented during the subroutine's execution. This may be illustrated as follows:

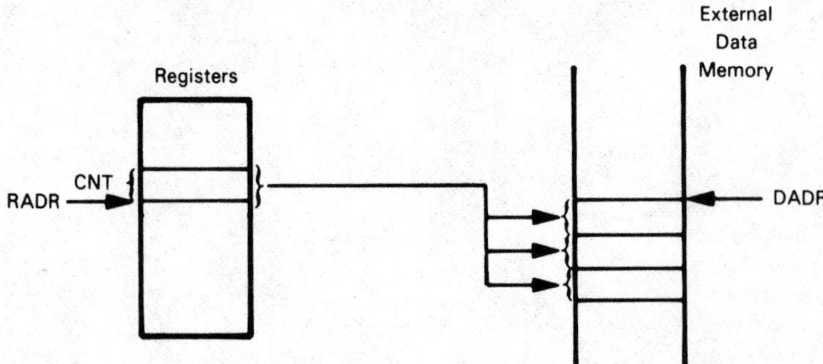


**The Z8 benchmark program appears as follows:**

```
        SRP     X               ;SELECT REGISTER BLOCK
        LD      CNT,CNTP        ;LOAD BYTE COUNT INTO BUFFER REGISTER
LOOP    LDEI    (DADR), (RADR)  ;MOVE NEXT DATA BYTE
        DJNZ    CNT, LOOP       ;DECREMENT COUNT, RETURN FOR MORE
        SUB     RADR, CNTP      ;RESTORE REGISTER'S STARTING ADDRESS
```

Table 8-6. Mnemonics, Object Code Bits and Interpretation for Z8 Condition Codes

| Condition Code | Mnemonic | Object Code Bits | Status | Comment |
|---|---|---|---|---|
| 0 | | 0000 | None | Never true |
| 1 | LT | 0001 | $S \oplus O = 1$ | Less than |
| 2 | LE | 0010 | $Z+(S \oplus O) = 1$ | Less than or equal |
| 3 | ULE | 0011 | C+Z = 1 | Unsigned less than |
| 4 | OV | 0100 | O = 1 | Overflow |
| 5 | MI | 0101 | S = 1 | Minus |
| 6 | Z | 0110 | Z = 1 | Zero |
| 7 | ULT | 0111 | C = 1 | Unsigned less than |
| 8 | | 1000 | None | Always true |
| 9 | GE | 1001 | $S \oplus O = 0$ | Greater than or equal |
| 10 | GT | 1010 | $Z+(S \oplus O) = 0$ | Greater than |
| 11 | UGT | 1011 | C+Z = 0 | Unsigned greater than |
| 12 | NOV | 1100 | O = 0 | No overflow |
| 13 | PL | 1101 | S = 0 | Plus |
| 14 | NZ | 1110 | Z = 0 | Not zero |
| 15 | NC | 1111 | C = 0 | Not carry |

This program is very short because the Z8 architecture is well suited to the particular benchmark program selected in this book.

A single instruction moves data to external data memory, from a register, using indirect addressing to identify source and destination locations. This instruction, LDEI, also increments the indirect addresses. RADR is the label assigned to the register address, and DADR is the label assigned to the external data memory address. These labels identify appropriate registers within the selected block is illustrated previously.

The DJNZ instruction then increments the Byte Counter; LDEI is re-executed if the byte count is not 0.

The following abbreviations apply to Tables 8-7 and 8-8:

| | |
|---|---|
| C | The Carry status |
| cc | A Condition Code (see Table 8-6) |
| DA | A 16-bit unsigned binary Direct Address |
| $DA_{HI}$ | The High-order byte of a Direct Address |
| $DA_{LO}$ | The Low-order byte of a Direct Address |
| Disp | An 8-bit signed binary address Displacement |
| IM | Immediate data |
| IR | Any Indirect Register (or indirect working register) address |
| Ir | An Indirect working register address |
| IRR | Any Indirect Register (or indirect working register) pair address |
| Irr | An Indirect working register pair address |
| IX | An Indexed address |
| r | Any Register (or working register) address |
| R | A working register address |
| RA | A Relative Address (for which a Disp is generated) |
| RR | Any Register (or working register) pair address |
| SR | The Status Register |
| U | An Undefined status bit setting |
| X | A status bit that is modified during the instruction's execution |
| @ | Indirect Address prefix |

Table 8-7. A Summary of the Z8 Microcomputer Instruction Set

| TYPE | MNEMONIC | OPERAND | OBJECT CODE | BYTES | CLOCK CYCLES | STATUS C | Z | S | O | D | H | OPERATION PERFORMED |
|---|---|---|---|---|---|---|---|---|---|---|---|---|
| Primary Memory Reference | LDC | @rr,r | D2 rlrr | 2 | 12,0 | | | | | | | [[rr]] ← [r]<br>Transfer the contents of the selected working-register to the external memory location addressed by the contents of the working-register pair. |
| | LDC | r,@rr | C2 lrrr | 2 | 12,0 | | | | | | | [r] ← [[rr]]<br>Transfer the contents of the external memory location addressed by the contents of the working-register pair to the selected working-register. |
| | LDCI | @rr,@r | D3 Irrlr | 2 | 18,0 | | | | | | | [[rr]] ← [[r]], [r] ← [r] + 1, [rr] ← [rr] + 1<br>Transfer the contents of the indirectly addressed register to the external memory location addressed by the working-register pair. Increment the memory address and the working-register address. |
| | LDCI | @r,@rr | C3 Irlrr | 2 | 18,0 | | | | | | | [[r]] ← [[rr]], [r] ← [r] + 1, [rr] ← [rr] + 1<br>Transfer the contents of the external memory location addressed by the working-register pair to the indirectly addressed register. Increment the memory address and the working-register address. |
| | LDE | @rr,r | 92 rlrr | 2 | 12,0 | | | | | | | As LDC, but with $\overline{DM}$ active low to indicate data memory. |
| | LDE | r,@rr | 82 lrrr | 2 | 12,0 | | | | | | | |
| | LDEI | @rr,@r | 93 Irrlr | 2 | 18,0 | | | | | | | As LDCI, but with $\overline{DM}$ active low to indicate data memory. |
| | LDEI | @r,@rr | 83 Irlrr | 2 | 18,0 | | | | | | | |
| Immediate | LD | R,IM | E6 R IM | 3 | 10,5 | | | | | | | [R] ← IM<br>Transfer the immediate data to the selected register. |
| | LD | @R,IM | E7 IR IM | 3 | 10,5 | | | | | | | [[R]] ← IM<br>Transfer the immediate data to the indirectly addressed register. |
| | LD | r,IM | rC IM | 2 | 6,5 | | | | | | | [r] ← IM<br>Transfer the immediate data to the selected working-register. |
| | SRP | IM | 31 | 2 | 6,1 | | | | | | | $[FD_{16}]$ ← IM<br>Transfer the immediate data to the Register Pointer register. |

Table 8-7. A Summary of the Z8 Microcomputer Instruction Set (Continued)

| TYPE | MNEMONIC | OPERAND | OBJECT CODE | BYTES | CLOCK CYCLES | STATUS C | Z | S | O | D | H | OPERATION PERFORMED |
|---|---|---|---|---|---|---|---|---|---|---|---|---|
| Jump | DJNZ | r,RA | rA Disp | 2 | 12/10, 3/5 | | | | | | | [r] ← [r] − 1, if [r] ≠ 0 then [PC] ← [PC] + Disp<br>Decrement the contents of the selected working-register. If it is not then zero, execute a program relative jump. |
| | JP | cc,DA | ccD $DA_{HI}$ $DA_{LO}$ | 3 | 12/10,0 | | | | | | | If cc is "true" then [PC] ← DA<br>Jump to the Directly Addressed memory location if cc is true. |
| | JP | @RR | 30 IRR | 2 | 8,0 | | | | | | | [PC] ← [RR]<br>Jump to the memory location whose address is the contents of the register pair. |
| | JR | cc,RA | ccB Disp | 2 | 12/10,3 | | | | | | | If cc is "true" then [PC] ← [PC] + Disp<br>Execute a program relative jump if cc is true. |
| Subroutine Call and Return | CALL | DA | D6 $DA_{HI}$ $DA_{LO}$ | 3 | 20,0 | | | | | | | [SP] ← [SP] − 2, [[SP]] ← [PC], [PC] ← DA<br>Jump to the directly addressed subroutine. |
| | CALL | @RR | D4 IRR | 2 | 20,0 | | | | | | | [SP] ← [SP] − 2, [[SP]] ← [PC], [PC] ← [RR]<br>Jump to the subroutine whose address is contained in the register pair. |
| | RET | | AF | 1 | 14,0 | | | | | | | [PC] ← [[SP]], [SP] ← [SP] + 2<br>Return from subroutine. |
| Immediate Operate | ADC | R,IM | 16 R IM | 3 | 10,5 | X | X | X | X | 0 | X | [R] ← [R] + IM + C<br>Add immediate data with carry to the contents of the selected register. |
| | ADC | @R,IM | 17 IR IM | 3 | 10,5 | X | X | X | X | 0 | X | [[R]] ← [[R]] + IM + C<br>Add immediate data with carry to the contents of the indirectly addressed register. |
| | ADD | R,IM | 06 R IM | 3 | 10,5 | X | X | X | X | 0 | X | [R] ← [R] + IM } As ADC but without carry added. |
| | ADD | @R,IM | 07 IR IM | 3 | 10,5 | X | X | X | X | 0 | X | [[R]] ← [[R]] + IM } |
| | AND | R,IM | 56 R IM | 3 | 10,5 | | X | X | 0 | | | [R] ← [R] Λ IM } As ADC but a logical AND operation is performed. |
| | AND | @R,IM | 57 IR IM | 3 | 10,5 | | X | X | 0 | | | [[R]] ← [[R]] Λ IM } |
| | CP | R,IM | A6 R IM | 3 | 10,5 | X | X | X | X | | | [R] − IM } As ADC but this operation only affects the state of the flags. |
| | CP | @R,IM | A7 IR IM | 3 | 10,5 | X | X | X | X | | | [[R]] − IM } |
| | OR | R,IM | 46 R IM | 3 | 10,5 | | X | X | 0 | | | [R] ← [R] V IM } As ADC but a logical OR operation is performed. |
| | OR | @R,IM | 47 IR IM | 3 | 10,5 | | X | X | 0 | | | [[R]] ← [[R]] V IM } |
| | SBC | R,IM | 36 R IM | 3 | 10,5 | X | X | X | X | 1 | X | [R] ← [R] − IM − C } As ADC but a subtract with borrow operation is performed. |
| | SBC | @R,IM | 37 IR IM | 3 | 10,5 | X | X | X | X | 1 | X | [[R]] ← [[R]] − IM − C } |
| | SUB | R,IM | 26 R IM | 3 | 10,5 | X | X | X | X | 1 | X | [R] ← [R] − IM } As ADC but a subtract operation is performed. |
| | SUB | @R,IM | 27 IR IM | 3 | 10,5 | X | X | X | X | 1 | X | [[R]] ← [[R]] − IM } |

Table 8-7. A Summary of the Z8 Microcomputer Instruction Set (Continued)

| TYPE | MNEMONIC | OPERAND | OBJECT CODE | BYTES | CLOCK CYCLES | STATUS C | Z | S | O | D | H | OPERATION PERFORMED |
|---|---|---|---|---|---|---|---|---|---|---|---|---|
| Immediate Operate (Continued) | TCM | R,IM | 66 R IM | 3 | 10,5 | | X | X | 0 | | | $[R] \wedge \overline{IM}$ } As ADC but this operation only affects the state of the flags. |
| | TCM | @R,IM | 67 IR IM | 3 | 10,5 | | X | X | 0 | | | $[[R]] \wedge \overline{IM}$ } |
| | TM | R,IM | 76 R IM | 3 | 10,5 | | X | X | 0 | | | $[R] \wedge IM$ } As ADC but this operation only affects the state of the flags. |
| | TM | @R,IM | 77 IR IM | 3 | 10,5 | | X | X | 0 | | | $[[R]] \wedge IM$ } |
| | XOR | R,IM | B6 R IM | 3 | 10,5 | | X | X | 0 | | | $[R] \leftarrow [R] \oplus IM$ } As ADC but a logical exclusive-OR operation is performed. |
| | XOR | @R,IM | B7 IR IM | 3 | 10,5 | | X | X | 0 | | | $[[R]] \leftarrow [[R]] \oplus IM$ } |
| Register-Register Move and I/O | LD | r,R | r8 R | 2 | 6,5 | | | | | | | $[r] \leftarrow [R]$ Transfer the contents from the selected register to the selected working-register. |
| | LD | R,r | r9 R | 2 | 6,5 | | | | | | | $[R] \leftarrow [r]$ Transfer the contents from the selected working-register to the selected register. |
| | LD | $R_x,R_y$ | E4 $R_x$ $R_y$ | 3 | 10,5 | | | | | | | $[R_x] \leftarrow [R_y]$ Transfer the contents from the selected register ($R_y$) to the selected register ($R_x$). |
| | LD | $R_x$,@$R_y$ | E5 $R_x$ $IR_y$ | 3 | 10,5 | | | | | | | $[R_x] \leftarrow [[R_y]]$ |
| | LD | @$R_x,R_y$ | F5 $IR_x$ $R_y$ | 3 | 10,5 | | | | | | | $[[R_x]] \leftarrow [R_y]$ Transfer data between a selected register and an indirectly addressed register. |
| | LD | r,IX,R | C7 rIX R | | | | | | | | | $[r] \leftarrow [R + [IX]]$ |
| | LD | R,IX,r | D7 rIX R | | | | | | | | | $[R + [IX]] \leftarrow [r]$ Transfer data between a selected working-register and a register addressed using indexed addressing. |
| Register-Register Operate | ADC | $r_x,r_y$ | 12 $r_xr_y$ | 2 | 6,5 | X | X | X | X | 0 | X | $[r_x] \leftarrow [r_x] + [r_y] + C$ Add the contents of the selected source working-register with carry to the contents of the selected destination working-register. |
| | ADC | $r_x$,@$r_y$ | 13 $r_xIr_y$ | 2 | 6,5 | X | X | X | X | 0 | X | $[r_x] \leftarrow [r_x] + [[Ir_y]] + C$ Add the contents of the selected indirectly addressed source working-register with carry to the contents of the selected destination working-register. |
| | ADC | $R_x,R_y$ | 14 $R_x$ $R_y$ | 3 | 10,5 | X | X | X | X | 0 | X | $[R_x] \leftarrow [R_x] + [R_y] + C$ Add the contents of the selected source register with carry to the contents of the selected destination register. |

Table 8-7. A Summary of the Z8 Microcomputer Instruction Set (Continued)

| TYPE | MNEMONIC | OPERAND | OBJECT CODE | BYTES | CLOCK CYCLES | STATUS C | Z | S | O | D | H | OPERATION PERFORMED |
|---|---|---|---|---|---|---|---|---|---|---|---|---|
| Register-Register Operate (Continued) | ADC | $R_x,@R_y$ | 15 $R_x$ $IR_y$ | 3 | 10,5 | X | X | X | X | 0 | X | $[R_x] \leftarrow [R_x] + [[R_y]] + C$ |
| | | | | | | | | | | | | Add the contents of the selected indirectly addressed source register with carry to the contents of the selected destination register. |
| | ADD | $r_x,r_y$ | 02 $r_xr_y$ | 2 | 6,5 | X | X | X | X | 0 | X | $[r_x] \leftarrow [r_x] + [r_y]$ |
| | ADD | $r_x,@r_y$ | 03 $r_xIr_y$ | 2 | 6,5 | X | X | X | X | 0 | X | $[r_x] \leftarrow [r_x] + [[r_y]]$ |
| | ADD | $R_x,R_y$ | 04 $R_x$ $R_y$ | 3 | 10,5 | X | X | X | X | 0 | X | $[R_x] \leftarrow [R_x] + [R_y]$ |
| | ADD | $R_x,@R_y$ | 05 $R_x$ $IR_y$ | 3 | 10,5 | X | X | X | X | 0 | X | $[R_x] \leftarrow [R_x] + [[R_y]]$ |
| | | | | | | | | | | | | Add the contents of the source register to that of the destination register using one of the addressing options described for ADC. |
| | AND | $r_x,r_y$ | 52 $r_xr_y$ | 2 | 6,5 | | X | X | X | | | $[r_x] \leftarrow [r_x] \wedge [r_y]$ |
| | AND | $r_x,@r_y$ | 53 $r_xIr_y$ | 2 | 6,5 | | X | X | X | | | $[r_x] \leftarrow [r_x] \wedge [[r_y]]$ |
| | AND | $R_x,R_y$ | 54 $R_x$ $R_y$ | 3 | 10,5 | | X | X | X | | | $[R_x] \leftarrow [R_x] \wedge [R_y]$ |
| | AND | $R_x,@R_y$ | 55 $R_x$ $IR_y$ | 3 | 10,5 | | X | X | X | | | $[R_x] \leftarrow [Rx] \wedge [[R_y]]$ |
| | | | | | | | | | | | | Logical AND the source register with the destination register using one of the addressing options described for ADC. |
| | CP | $r_x,r_y$ | A2 $r_xr_y$ | 2 | 6,5 | X | X | X | X | | | $[r_x] - [r_y]$ |
| | CP | $r_x@r_y$ | A3 $r_xIr_y$ | 2 | 6,5 | X | X | X | X | | | $[r_x] - [[r_y]]$ |
| | CP | $R_x,R_y$ | A4 $R_x$ $R_y$ | 3 | 10,5 | X | X | X | X | | | $[R_x] - [R_y]$ |
| | CP | $R_x,@R_y$ | A5 $R_x$ $IR_y$ | 3 | 10,5 | X | X | X | X | | | $[R_x] - [[R_y]]$ |
| | | | | | | | | | | | | Compare the source register to the destination register using one of the addressing options described for ADC. |
| | OR | $r_x,r_y$ | 42 $r_xr_y$ | 2 | 6,5 | | X | X | X | | | $[r_x] \leftarrow [r_x] \vee [r_y]$ |
| | OR | $r_x,@r_y$ | 43 $r_xIr_y$ | 2 | 6,5 | | X | X | X | | | $[r_x] \leftarrow [r_x] \vee [[r_y]]$ |
| | OR | $R_x,R_y$ | 44 $R_x$ $R_y$ | 3 | 10,5 | | X | X | X | | | $[R_x] \leftarrow [R_x] \vee [R_y]$ |
| | OR | $R_x,@R_y$ | 45 $R_x$ $IR_y$ | 3 | 10,5 | | X | X | X | | | $[R_x] \leftarrow [R_x] \vee [[R_y]]$ |
| | | | | | | | | | | | | Logical OR the source register with the destination register using one of the addressing options described for ADC. |
| | SBC | $r_x,r_y$ | 32 $r_xr_y$ | 2 | 6,5 | X | X | X | X | 1 | X | $[r_x] \leftarrow [r_x] - [r_y] - C$ |
| | SBC | $r_x,@r_y$ | 33 $r_xIr_y$ | 2 | 6,5 | X | X | X | X | 1 | X | $[r_x] \leftarrow [r_x] - [[r_y]] - C$ |
| | SBC | $R_x,R_y$ | 34 $R_x$ $R_y$ | 3 | 10,5 | X | X | X | X | 1 | X | $[R_x] \leftarrow [R_x] - [R_y] - C$ |
| | SBC | $R_x,@R_y$ | 35 $R_x$ $IR_y$ | 3 | 10,5 | X | X | X | X | 1 | X | $[R_x] \leftarrow [R_x] - [[R_y]] - C$ |
| | | | | | | | | | | | | Subtract with carry the source register from the destination register using one of the addressing options described for ADC. |
| | SUB | $r_x,r_y$ | 22 $r_xr_y$ | 2 | 6,5 | X | X | X | X | 1 | X | $[r_x] \leftarrow [r_x] - [r_y]$ |
| | SUB | $r_x,@r_y$ | 23 $r_xIr_y$ | 2 | 6,5 | X | X | X | X | 1 | X | $[r_x] \leftarrow [r_x] - [[r_y]]$ |
| | SUB | $R_x,R_y$ | 24 $R_x$ $R_y$ | 3 | 10,5 | X | X | X | X | 1 | X | $[R_x] \leftarrow [R_x] - [R_y]$ |
| | SUB | $R_x,@R_y$ | 25 $R_x$ $IR_y$ | 3 | 10,5 | X | X | X | X | 1 | X | $[R_x] \leftarrow [R_x] - [[R_y]]$ |
| | | | | | | | | | | | | Subtract the source register from the destination register using one of the addressing options described for ADC. |

Table 8-7. A Summary of the Z8 Microcomputer Instruction Set (Continued)

| TYPE | MNEMONIC | OPERAND | OBJECT CODE | BYTES | CLOCK CYCLES | STATUS C | Z | S | O | D | H | OPERATION PERFORMED |
|---|---|---|---|---|---|---|---|---|---|---|---|---|
| Register-Register Operate (Continued) | TCM | $r_x,r_y$ | 62 $r_xr_y$ | 2 | 6,5 | | X | X | 0 | | | $[r_x] \land \overline{[r_y]}$ |
| | TCM | $r_x,@r_y$ | 63 $r_xIr_y$ | 2 | 6,5 | | X | X | 0 | | | $[r_x] \land \overline{[[r_y]]}$ |
| | TCM | $R_x,R_y$ | 64 $R_x$ $R_y$ | 3 | 10,5 | | X | X | 0 | | | $[R_x] \land \overline{[R_y]}$ |
| | TCM | $R_x,@R_y$ | 65 $R_x$ $IR_y$ | 3 | 10,5 | | X | X | 0 | | | $[R_x] \land \overline{[[R_y]]}$ |
| | | | | | | | | | | | | Logical AND the contents of the first register with the complement of the contents of the second register using one of the addressing options described for ADC. |
| | TM | $r_x,r_y$ | 72 $r_xr_y$ | 2 | 6,5 | | X | X | 0 | | | $[r_x] \land [r_y]$ |
| | TM | $r_x,@r_y$ | 73 $r_xIr_y$ | 2 | 6,5 | | X | X | 0 | | | $[r_x] \land [[r_y]]$ |
| | TM | $R_x,R_y$ | 74 $R_x$ $R_y$ | 3 | 10,5 | | X | X | 0 | | | $[R_x] \land [R_y]$ |
| | TM | $R_x,@R_y$ | 75 $R_x$ $IR_y$ | 3 | 10,5 | | X | X | 0 | | | $[R_x] \land [[R_y]]$ |
| | | | | | | | | | | | | Logical AND the contents of the first register with the contents of the second register using one of the addressing options described for ADC. |
| | XOR | $r_x,r_y$ | B2 $r_xr_y$ | 2 | 6,5 | | X | X | 0 | | | $[r_x] \leftarrow [r_x] \oplus [r_y]$ |
| | XOR | $r_x,@r_y$ | B3 $r_xIr_y$ | 2 | 6,5 | | X | X | 0 | | | $[r_x] \leftarrow [r_x] \oplus [[r_y]]$ |
| | XOR | $R_x,R_y$ | B4 $R_x$ $R_y$ | 3 | 10,5 | | X | X | 0 | | | $[R_x] \leftarrow [R_x] \oplus [R_y]$ |
| | XOR | $R_x,@R_y$ | B5 $R_xIR_y$ | 3 | 10,5 | | X | X | 0 | | | $[R_x] \leftarrow [R_x] \oplus [[R_y]]$ |
| | | | | | | | | | | | | Logical Exclusive-OR the source register with the destination register using one of the addressing options described for ADC. |
| Register Operate | CLR | R | B0 R | 2 | 6,5 | | | | | | | $[R] \leftarrow 0$ Clear the selected register. |
| | CLR | @R | B1 IR | 2 | 6,5 | | | | | | | $[[R]] \leftarrow 0$ Clear the indirectly addressed register. |
| | COM | R | 60 R | 2 | 6,5 | | X | X | 0 | | | $[R] \leftarrow \overline{[R]}$ Complement the contents of the selected register. |
| | COM | @R | 61 IR | 2 | 6,5 | | X | X | 0 | | | $[[R]] \leftarrow \overline{[[R]]}$ Complement the contents of the indirectly addressed register. |
| | DA | R | 40 R | 2 | 8,5 | X | X | X | u | | | Decimal Adjust the contents of the selected register. |
| | DA | @R | 41 IR | 2 | 8,5 | X | X | X | u | | | Decimal Adjust the contents of the indirectly addressed register. |
| | DEC | R | 00 R | 2 | 6,5 | | X | X | X | | | $[R] \leftarrow [R] - 1$ Decrement the contents of the selected register. |
| | DEC | @R | 01 IR | 2 | 6,5 | | X | X | X | | | $[[R]] \leftarrow [[R]] - 1$ Decrement the contents of the indirectly addressed register. |
| | DECW | RR | 80 RR | 2 | 10,5 | | X | X | X | | | $[RR] \leftarrow [RR] - 1$ Decrement the contents of the selected register pair. |
| | DECW | @RR | 81 IRR | 2 | 10,5 | | X | X | X | | | $[[RR]] \leftarrow [[RR]] - 1$ Decrement the contents of the indirectly addressed register pair. |

Table 8-7. A Summary of the Z8 Microcomputer Instruction Set (Continued)

| TYPE | MNEMONIC | OPERAND | OBJECT CODE | BYTES | CLOCK CYCLES | STATUS C | STATUS Z | STATUS S | STATUS O | STATUS D | STATUS H | OPERATION PERFORMED |
|---|---|---|---|---|---|---|---|---|---|---|---|---|
| Register Operate (Continued) | INC | r | rE | 1 | 6,5 | | X | X | X | | | [r] ← [r] + 1<br>Increment the contents of the selected working-register. |
| | INC | R | 20 R | 2 | 6,5 | | X | X | X | | | [R] ← [R] + 1<br>Increment the contents of the selected register. |
| | INC | @R | 21 IR | 2 | 6,5 | | X | X | X | | | [[R]] ← [[R]] + 1<br>Increment the contents of the indirectly addressed register. |
| | INCW | RR | A0 RR | 2 | 10,5 | | X | X | X | | | [RR] ← [RR] + 1<br>Increment the contents of the selected register pair. |
| | INCW | @RR | A1 IRR | 2 | 10,5 | | X | X | X | | | [[RR]] ← [[RR]] + 1<br>Increment the contents of the indirectly addressed register pair. |
| | RL<br>RL | R<br>@R | 90 R<br>91 IR | 2<br>2 | 6,5<br>6,5 | X<br>X | X<br>X | X<br>X | X<br>X | | | Perform a left rotate with carry on a selected register or indirectly addressed register as follows: |
| | RLC<br>RLC | R<br>@R | 10 R<br>11 IR | 2<br>2 | 6,5<br>6,5 | X<br>X | X<br>X | X<br>X | X<br>X | | | Perform a left rotate through carry on a selected register or indirectly addressed register as follows: |
| | RR<br>RR | R<br>@R | E0 R<br>E1 IR | 2<br>2 | 6,5<br>6,5 | X<br>X | X<br>X | X<br>X | X<br>X | | | Perform a right rotate with carry on a selected register or indirectly addressed register as follows: |
| | RRC<br>RRC | R<br>@R | 10 R<br>11 IR | 2<br>2 | 6,5<br>6,5 | X<br>X | X<br>X | X<br>X | X<br>X | | | Perform a right rotate through carry on a selected register or indirectly addressed register as follows: |

Table 8-7. A Summary of the Z8 Microcomputer Instruction Set (Continued)

| TYPE | MNEMONIC | OPERAND | OBJECT CODE | BYTES | CLOCK CYCLES | STATUS C | Z | S | O | D | H | OPERATION PERFORMED |
|---|---|---|---|---|---|---|---|---|---|---|---|---|
| Register Operate (Continued) | SRA<br>SRA | R<br>@R | D0 R<br>D1 IR | 2<br>2 | 6,5<br>6,5 | X<br>X | X<br>X | X<br>X | 0<br>0 | | | Perform a right arithmetic shift with carry on a selected register or indirectly addressed register as follows: (C; 7 → 0; register) |
| | SWAP<br>SWAP | R<br>@R | F0 R<br>F1 IR | 2<br>2 | 8,5<br>8,5 | X<br>X | X<br>X | X<br>X | X<br>X | | | Swap nibbles of a selected register or indirectly addressed register as follows: (register) |
| Stack | POP<br>POP | R<br>@R | 50 R<br>51 IR | 2<br>2 | 10,5<br>10,5 | | | | | | | [R] ← [[SP]], [SP] ← [SP] + 1<br>[[R]] ← [[SP]], [SP] ← [SP] + 1<br>Pop the Stack to a directly or indirectly addressed register. |
| | PUSH<br>PUSH | R<br>@R | 70 R<br>71 IR | 2<br>2 | 10/12,1<br>12/14,1 | | | | | | | [SP] ← [SP] − 1, [[SP]] ← [R]<br>[SP] ← [SP] − 1, [[SP]] ← [[R]]<br>Push the contents of the directly or indirectly addressed register onto the Stack. |
| Interrupt | DI<br>EI<br>IRET | | 8F<br>9F<br>BF | 1<br>1<br>1 | 6,1<br>6,1<br>16,0 | | | | | | | Disable Interrupts: $[FB_{16}] \leftarrow [FB_{16}] \wedge 7F_{16}$<br>Enable Interrupts: $[FB_{16}] \leftarrow [FB_{16}] \vee 80_{16}$<br>$[PC] \leftarrow [[SP]], [SP] \leftarrow [SP] + 2, [FB_{16}] \leftarrow [FB_{16}] \vee 80_{16}$<br>Return from (interrupt service) subroutine and enable interrupts. |
| Status | CCF | | EF | 1 | 6,5 | X | | | | | | $[C] \leftarrow [\overline{C}]$<br>Complement the Carry status. |
| | RCF | | CF | 1 | 6,5 | 0 | | | | | | [C] ← 0<br>Reset the Carry status to zero. |
| | SCF | | DF | 1 | 6,5 | 1 | | | | | | [C] ← 1<br>Set the Carry status to one. |
| | NOP | | FF | 1 | 6,0 | | | | | | | No operation. |

# THE Z8/64 DEVELOPMENT MICROCOMPUTER

**The Z8/64 is a 64-pin version of the Z8; it has been designed as a Z8 development device. The Z8/64 has no on-chip program memory. You use external memory to simulate Z8 on-chip program memory. Address and Data Bus lines are provided by the Z8/64 specifically to service this substitute, external program memory. Also, the Z8/64 has no standby power or associated logic.**

**Figure 8-10 illustrates Z8/64 pins and signal assignments. The following Z8/64 signals differ from those which we have already described for the Z8:**

SA0-SA10 is a Program Memory Address Bus used to select the first 2048 bytes of program memory, that is to say, the program memory which will ultimately become on-chip Z8 program memory.

SA11 is a special Address Bus line whose function is not specified by Zilog; it is described as a reversed pin.

SD0-SD7 serves as the Data Bus when the first 2048 bytes of program memory are being addressed.

Note carefully that SA0-SA10 and SD0-SD7 do not substitute for the external Data/Address Bus configured out of Z8 I/O ports. The Z8/64 will generate external Data/Address Busses out of its I/O ports exactly as described for the Z8. SA0-SA10 and SD0-SD7 are present solely to access 2048 bytes of external memory which are substituting for the eventual on-chip program memory.

$\overline{\text{MDS}}$ is a program memory data strobe that is output low during the instruction fetch machine cycle for any instruction that accesses the first 2048 bytes of program memory.

$\overline{\text{SYNC}}$ is a synchronization strobe that is output low during the clock period that directly precedes the beginning of a new instruction fetch.

SCLK outputs the internal clock. SCLK has a frequency that is half of the external crystal frequency.

IACK is an interrupt acknowledge signal that is output high during the interrupt acknowledge sequence.

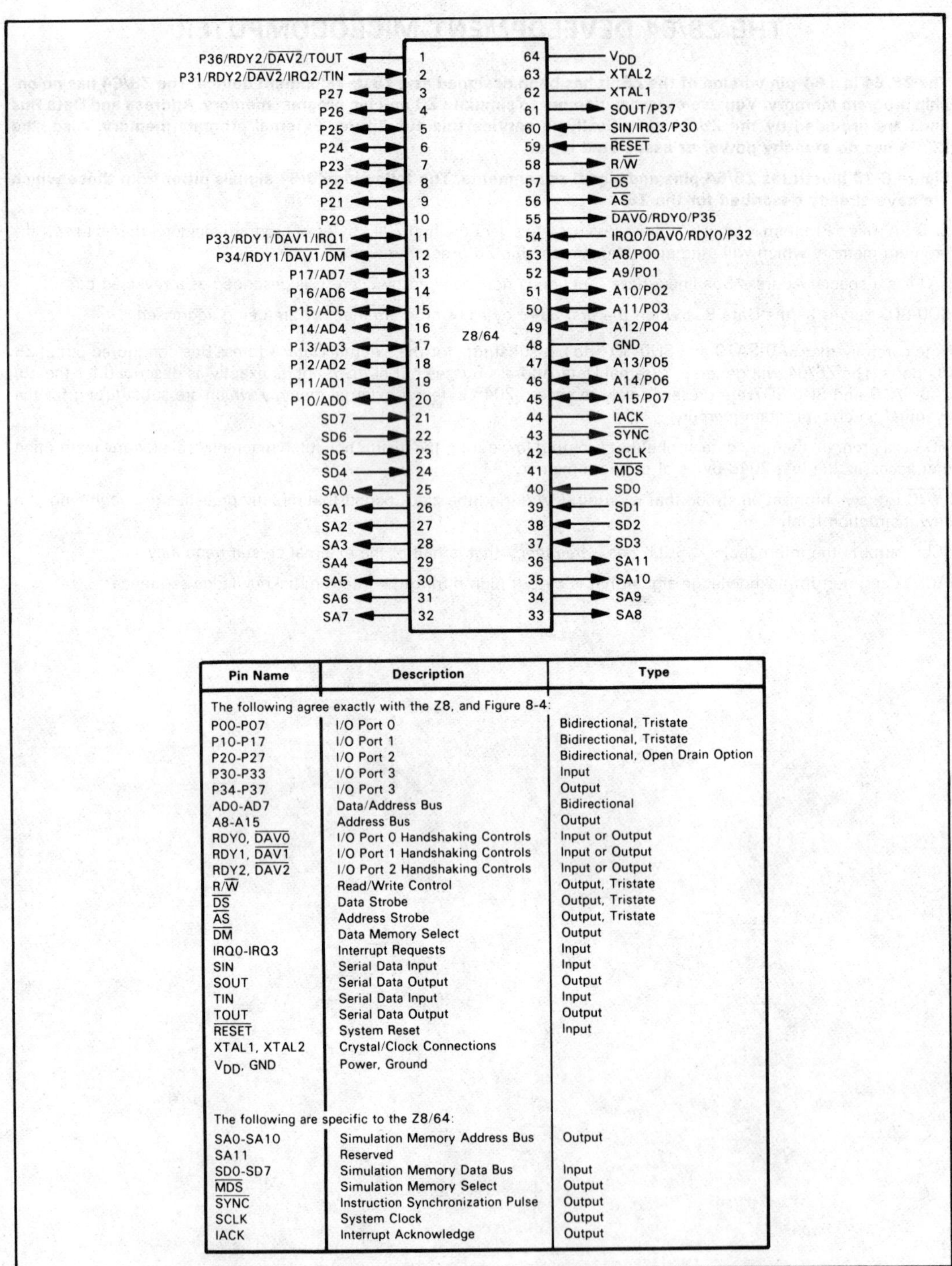


| Pin Name | Description | Type |
|---|---|---|
| The following agree exactly with the Z8, and Figure 8-4: | | |
| P00-P07 | I/O Port 0 | Bidirectional, Tristate |
| P10-P17 | I/O Port 1 | Bidirectional, Tristate |
| P20-P27 | I/O Port 2 | Bidirectional, Open Drain Option |
| P30-P33 | I/O Port 3 | Input |
| P34-P37 | I/O Port 3 | Output |
| AD0-AD7 | Data/Address Bus | Bidirectional |
| A8-A15 | Address Bus | Output |
| RDY0, DAV0 | I/O Port 0 Handshaking Controls | Input or Output |
| RDY1, DAV1 | I/O Port 1 Handshaking Controls | Input or Output |
| RDY2, DAV2 | I/O Port 2 Handshaking Controls | Input or Output |
| R/W | Read/Write Control | Output, Tristate |
| DS | Data Strobe | Output, Tristate |
| AS | Address Strobe | Output, Tristate |
| DM | Data Memory Select | Output |
| IRQ0-IRQ3 | Interrupt Requests | Input |
| SIN | Serial Data Input | Input |
| SOUT | Serial Data Output | Output |
| TIN | Serial Data Input | Input |
| TOUT | Serial Data Output | Output |
| RESET | System Reset | Input |
| XTAL1, XTAL2 | Crystal/Clock Connections | |
| $V_{DD}$, GND | Power, Ground | |
| The following are specific to the Z8/64: | | |
| SA0-SA10 | Simulation Memory Address Bus | Output |
| SA11 | Reserved | |
| SD0-SD7 | Simulation Memory Data Bus | Input |
| MDS | Simulation Memory Select | Output |
| SYNC | Instruction Synchronization Pulse | Output |
| SCLK | System Clock | Output |
| IACK | Interrupt Acknowledge | Output |

Figure 8-10. Z8/64 Microcomputer Development Device Signals and Pin Assignments

Table 8-8. Z8 Instructions Listed by Op-code

| HEX OP-CODE | | | INSTRUCTION | |
|---|---|---|---|---|
| **00** | R | | **DEC** | R |
| **01** | IR | | **DEC** | @R |
| **02** | $r_xr_y$ | | **ADD** | $r_x,r_y$ |
| **03** | rlr | | **ADD** | r,@r |
| **04** | $R_X$ | $R_Y$ | **ADD** | $R_X,R_Y$ |
| **05** | R | IR | **ADD** | R,@R |
| **06** | R | IM | **ADD** | R,IM |
| **07** | IR | IM | **ADD** | @R,IM |
| **08** | R | | **LD** | r0,R |
| **09** | R | | **LD** | R,r0 |
| **0A** | RA | | **DJNZ** | r0,Addr |
| **0B** | RA | | **JR** | cc0,Addr |
| **0C** | IM | | **LD** | r0,IM |
| **0D** | $DA_{HI}$ | $DA_{LO}$ | **JP** | cc0,Addr |
| **0E** | | | **INC** | r0 |
| **0F** | | | — | |
| **10** | R | | **RLC** | R |
| **11** | IR | | **RLC** | @R |
| **12** | $r_xr_y$ | | **ADC** | $r_x,r_y$ |
| **13** | rlr | | **ADC** | r,@r |
| **14** | $R_X$ | $R_Y$ | **ADC** | $R_X,R_Y$ |
| **15** | R | IR | **ADC** | R,@R |
| **16** | R | IM | **ADC** | R,IM |
| **17** | IR | IM | **ADC** | @R,IM |
| **18** | R | | **LD** | r1,R |
| **19** | R | | **LD** | R,r1 |
| **1A** | RA | | **DJNZ** | r1,Addr |
| **1B** | RA | | **JR** | cc1,Addr |
| **1C** | IM | | **LD** | r1,IM |
| **1D** | $DA_{HI}$ | $DA_{LO}$ | **JP** | cc1,Addr |
| **1E** | | | **INC** | r1 |
| **1F** | | | — | |
| **20** | R | | **INC** | R |
| **21** | IR | | **INC** | @R |
| **22** | $r_xr_y$ | | **SUB** | $r_x,r_y$ |
| **23** | rlr | | **SUB** | r,@r |
| **24** | $R_X$ | $R_Y$ | **SUB** | $R_X,R_Y$ |
| **25** | R | IR | **SUB** | R,@R |
| **26** | R | IM | **SUB** | R,IM |
| **27** | IR | IM | **SUB** | @R,IM |
| **28** | R | | **LD** | r2,R |
| **29** | R | | **LD** | R,r2 |
| **2A** | RA | | **DJNZ** | r2,Addr |
| **2B** | RA | | **JR** | cc2,Addr |
| **2C** | IM | | **LD** | r2,IM |
| **2D** | $DA_{HI}$ | $DA_{LO}$ | **JP** | cc2,Addr |
| **2E** | | | **INC** | r2 |
| **2F** | | | — | |
| **30** | IRR | | **JP** | @RR |
| **31** | IM | | **SRP** | IM |
| **32** | $r_xr_y$ | | **SBC** | $r_x,r_y$ |
| **33** | rlr | | **SBC** | r,@r |
| **34** | $R_X$ | $R_Y$ | **SBC** | $R_X,R_Y$ |
| **35** | R | IR | **SBC** | R,@R |
| **36** | R | IM | **SBC** | R,IM |
| **37** | IR | IM | **SBC** | @R,IM |
| **38** | R | | **LD** | r3,R |
| **39** | R | | **LD** | R,r3 |
| **3A** | RA | | **DJNZ** | r3,Addr |
| **3B** | RA | | **JR** | cc3,Addr |
| **3C** | IM | | **LD** | r3,IM |
| **3D** | $DA_{HI}$ | $DA_{LO}$ | **JP** | cc3,Addr |
| **3E** | | | **INC** | r3 |
| **3F** | | | — | |

| HEX OP-CODE | | | INSTRUCTION | |
|---|---|---|---|---|
| **40** | R | | **DA** | R |
| **41** | IR | | **DA** | @R |
| **42** | $r_xr_y$ | | **OR** | $r_x,r_y$ |
| **43** | rlr | | **OR** | r,@r |
| **44** | $R_X$ | $R_Y$ | **OR** | $R_X,R_Y$ |
| **45** | R | IR | **OR** | R,@R |
| **46** | R | IM | **OR** | R,IM |
| **47** | IR | IM | **OR** | @R,IM |
| **48** | R | | **LD** | r4,R |
| **49** | R | | **LD** | R,r4 |
| **4A** | RA | | **DJNZ** | r4,Addr |
| **4B** | RA | | **JR** | cc4,Addr |
| **4C** | IM | | **LD** | r4,IM |
| **4D** | $DA_{HI}$ | $DA_{LO}$ | **JP** | cc4,Addr |
| **4E** | | | **INC** | r4 |
| **4F** | | | — | |
| **50** | R | | **POP** | R |
| **51** | IR | | **POP** | @R |
| **52** | $r_xr_y$ | | **AND** | $r_x,r_y$ |
| **53** | rlr | | **AND** | r,@r |
| **54** | $R_X$ | $R_Y$ | **AND** | $R_X,R_Y$ |
| **55** | R | IR | **AND** | R,@R |
| **56** | R | IM | **AND** | R,IM |
| **57** | IR | IM | **AND** | @R,IM |
| **58** | R | | **LD** | r5,R |
| **59** | R | | **LD** | R,r5 |
| **5A** | RA | | **DJNZ** | r5,Addr |
| **5B** | RA | | **JR** | cc5,Addr |
| **5C** | IM | | **LD** | r5,IM |
| **5D** | $DA_{HI}$ | $DA_{LO}$ | **JP** | cc5,Addr |
| **5E** | | | **INC** | r5 |
| **5F** | | | — | |
| **60** | R | | **COM** | R |
| **61** | IR | | **COM** | @R |
| **62** | $r_xr_y$ | | **TCM** | $r_x,r_y$ |
| **63** | rlr | | **TCM** | r,@r |
| **64** | $R_X$ | $R_Y$ | **TCM** | $R_X,R_Y$ |
| **65** | R | IR | **TCM** | R,@R |
| **66** | R | IM | **TCM** | R,IM |
| **67** | IR | IM | **TCM** | @R,IM |
| **68** | R | | **LD** | r6,R |
| **69** | R | | **LD** | R,r6 |
| **6A** | RA | | **DJNZ** | r6,Addr |
| **6B** | RA | | **JR** | cc6,Addr |
| **6C** | IM | | **LD** | r6,IM |
| **6D** | $DA_{HI}$ | $DA_{LO}$ | **JP** | cc6,Addr |
| **6E** | | | **INC** | r6 |
| **6F** | | | — | |
| **70** | R | | **PUSH** | R |
| **71** | IR | | **PUSH** | @R |
| **72** | $r_xr_y$ | | **TM** | $r_x,r_y$ |
| **73** | rlr | | **TM** | r,@r |
| **74** | $R_X$ | $R_Y$ | **TM** | $R_X,R_Y$ |
| **75** | R | IR | **TM** | R,@R |
| **76** | R | IM | **TM** | R,IM |
| **77** | IR | IM | **TM** | @R,IM |
| **78** | R | | **LD** | r7,R |
| **79** | R | | **LD** | R,r7 |
| **7A** | RA | | **DJNZ** | r7,Addr |
| **7B** | RA | | **JR** | cc7,Addr |
| **7C** | IM | | **LD** | r7,IM |
| **7D** | $DA_{HI}$ | $DA_{LO}$ | **JP** | cc7,Addr |
| **7E** | | | **INC** | r7 |
| **7F** | | | — | |

Table 8-8. Z8 Instructions Listed by Op-code (Continued)

| HEX OP-CODE | | | INSTRUCTION | |
|---|---|---|---|---|
| **80** | RR | | **DECW** | RR |
| **81** | IRR | | **DECW** | @RR |
| **82** | rIrr | | **LDE** | r,@rr |
| **83** | IrIrr | | **LDEI** | @r,@rr |
| **84** | | | — | |
| **85** | | | — | |
| **86** | | | — | |
| **87** | | | — | |
| **88** | R | | **LD** | r8,R |
| **89** | R | | **LD** | R,r8 |
| **8A** | RA | | **DJNZ** | r8,Addr |
| **8B** | RA | | **JR** | cc8,Addr |
| **8C** | IM | | **LD** | r8,IM |
| **8D** | $DA_{HI}$ | $DA_{LO}$ | **JP** | cc8,Addr |
| **8E** | | | **INC** | r8 |
| **8F** | | | **DI** | |
| **90** | R | | **RL** | R |
| **91** | IR | | **RL** | @R |
| **92** | Irrr | | **LDE** | @rr,r |
| **93** | IrrIr | | **LDEI** | @rr,@r |
| **94** | | | — | |
| **95** | | | — | |
| **96** | | | — | |
| **97** | | | — | |
| **98** | R | | **LD** | r9,R |
| **99** | R | | **LD** | R,r9 |
| **9A** | RA | | **DJNZ** | r9,Addr |
| **9B** | RA | | **JR** | cc9,Addr |
| **9C** | IM | | **LD** | r9,IM |
| **9D** | $DA_{HI}$ | $DA_{LO}$ | **JP** | cc9,Addr |
| **9E** | | | **INC** | r9 |
| **9F** | | | **EI** | |
| **A0** | RR | | **INCW** | RR |
| **A1** | IRR | | **INCW** | @RR |
| **A2** | $r_xr_y$ | | **CP** | $r_x,r_y$ |
| **A3** | rIr | | **CP** | r,@r |
| **A4** | $R_X$ | $R_Y$ | **CP** | $R_X,R_Y$ |
| **A5** | R | IR | **CP** | R,@R |
| **A6** | R | IM | **CP** | R,IM |
| **A7** | IR | IM | **CP** | @R,IM |
| **A8** | R | | **LD** | r10,R |
| **A9** | R | | **LD** | R,r10 |
| **AA** | RA | | **DJNZ** | r10,Addr |
| **AB** | RA | | **JR** | cc10,Addr |
| **AC** | IM | | **LD** | r10,IM |
| **AD** | $DA_{HI}$ | $DA_{LO}$ | **JP** | cc10,Addr |
| **AE** | | | **INC** | r10 |
| **AF** | | | **RET** | |
| **B0** | R | | **CLR** | R |
| **B1** | IR | | **CLR** | @R |
| **B2** | $r_xr_y$ | | **XOR** | $r_x,r_y$ |
| **B3** | rIr | | **XOR** | r,@R |
| **B4** | $R_X$ | $R_Y$ | **XOR** | $R_X,R_Y$ |
| **B5** | R | IR | **XOR** | R,@R |
| **B6** | R | IM | **XOR** | R,IM |
| **B7** | IR | IM | **XOR** | @R,IM |
| **B8** | R | | **LD** | r11,R |
| **B9** | R | | **LD** | R,r11 |
| **BA** | RA | | **DJNZ** | r11,Addr |
| **BB** | RA | | **JR** | cc11,Addr |
| **BC** | IM | | **LD** | r11,IM |
| **BD** | $DA_{HI}$ | $DA_{LO}$ | **JP** | cc11,Addr |
| **BE** | | | **INC** | r11 |
| **BF** | | | **IRET** | |
| **C0** | R | | **RRC** | R |
| **C1** | IR | | **RRC** | @R |
| **C2** | rIrr | | **LDC** | r,@rr |
| **C3** | IrIrr | | **LDCI** | @r,@rr |
| **C4** | | | — | |
| **C5** | | | — | |
| **C6** | | | — | |
| **C7** | rx | R | **LD** | r,x,R |
| **C8** | R | | **LD** | r12,R |
| **C9** | R | | **LD** | R,r12 |
| **CA** | RA | | **DJNZ** | r12,Addr |
| **CB** | RA | | **JR** | cc12,Addr |
| **CC** | IM | | **LD** | r12,IM |
| **CD** | $DA_{HI}$ | $DA_{LO}$ | **JP** | cc12,Addr |
| **CE** | | | **INC** | r12 |
| **CF** | | | **RCF** | |
| **D0** | R | | **SRA** | R |
| **D1** | IR | | **SRA** | @R |
| **D2** | rIrr | | **LDC** | r,@rr |
| **D3** | Irrr | | **LDCI** | @rr,r |
| **D4** | IRR | | **CALL** | @RR |
| **D5** | | | — | |
| **D6** | $DA_{HI}$ | $DA_{LO}$ | **CALL** | Addr |
| **D7** | rx | R | **LD** | R,r,x |
| **D8** | R | | **LD** | r13,R |
| **D9** | R | | **LD** | R,r13 |
| **DA** | RA | | **DJRZ** | r13,Addr |
| **DB** | RA | | **JR** | cc13,Addr |
| **DC** | IM | | **LD** | r13,IM |
| **DD** | $DA_{HI}$ | $DA_{LO}$ | **JP** | cc13,Addr |
| **DE** | | | **INC** | r13 |
| **DF** | | | **SCF** | |
| **E0** | R | | **RR** | R |
| **E1** | IR | | **RR** | @R |
| **E2** | | | — | |
| **E3** | rIr | | **LD** | r,@r |
| **E4** | $R_X$ | $R_Y$ | **LD** | $R_X,R_Y$ |
| **E5** | $R_X$ | $IR_Y$ | **LD** | $R_X,@R_Y$ |
| **E6** | R | IM | **LD** | R,IM |
| **E7** | IR | IM | **LD** | @R,IM |
| **E8** | R | | **LD** | r14,R |
| **E9** | RA | | **LD** | R,r14 |
| **EA** | RA | | **DJRZ** | r14,Addr |
| **EB** | IM | | **JR** | cc14,Addr |
| **EC** | $DA_{HI}$ | $DA_{LO}$ | **LD** | r14,IM |
| **ED** | | | **JP** | cc14,Addr |
| **EE** | | | **INC** | r14 |
| **EF** | | | **CCF** | |
| **F0** | R | | **SWAP** | R |
| **F1** | IR | | **SWAP** | @R |
| **F2** | | | — | |
| **F3** | $Ir_xr_y$ | | **LD** | $@r_x,r_y$ |
| **F4** | | | — | |
| **F5** | $IR_X$ | $R_Y$ | **LD** | $@R_X,R_Y$ |
| **F6** | | | — | |
| **F7** | | | — | |
| **F8** | R | | **LD** | r15,R |
| **F9** | R | | **LD** | R,r15 |
| **FA** | RA | | **DJNZ** | r15,Addr |
| **FB** | RA | | **JR** | cc15,Addr |
| **FC** | IM | | **LD** | r15,IM |
| **FD** | $DA_{HI}$ | $DA_{LO}$ | **JP** | cc15,Addr |
| **EE** | | | **INC** | r15 |
| **FF** | | | **NOP** | |

# DATA SHEETS

This section contains specific electrical and timing data for the Z8 Microcomputer.

# Electrical Parameters

**1 Absolute Maximum Ratings**

Voltages on all inputs and outputs with respect to GND . . . . . . . -0.3V to +7.0V

Operating Ambient Temperature . . . . . . . . . . . . . . 0 °C to +70 °C

Storage Temperature . . . . -65 °C to +150 °C

Stresses greater than those listed under "Absolute Maximum Ratings" may cause permanent damage to the device. This is a stress rating only; operation of the device at any condition above those indicated in the operational sections of these specifications is not implied. Exposure to absolute maximum rating conditions for extended periods may affect device reliability.

**2 Standard Test Conditions**

The characteristics below apply for the following standard test conditions, unless otherwise noted. All voltages are referenced to GND. Positive current flows into the reference pin. Standard conditions are as follows: $+4.75V \le V_{CC} \le +5.25V$, GND = 0V, $0°C \le T_A \le +70°C$.

**3 DC Characteristics**

| Symbol | Parameter | Min | Max | Unit | Condition | Notes |
|---|---|---|---|---|---|---|
| $V_{CH}$ | Clock Input High Voltage | | | V | Driven by External Clock Generator | |
| $V_{CL}$ | Clock Input Low Voltage | | | V | Driven by External Clock Generator | |
| $V_{IH}$ | Input High Voltage | 2.0 | $V_{CC}$ | V | | |
| $V_{IL}$ | Input Low Voltage | -0.3 | 0.8 | V | | |
| $V_{RH}$ | Reset Input High Voltage | | | V | | |
| $V_{RL}$ | Reset Input Low Voltage | | | V | | |
| $V_{OH}$ | Output High Voltage | 2.4 | | V | $I_{OH} = -250\ \mu A$ | 1 |
| $V_{OL}$ | Output Low Voltage | | 0.4 | V | $I_{OL} = +2.0$ mA | 1 |
| $I_{IL}$ | Input Leakage | | | $\mu A$ | $0 \le V_{IN} \le +5.25V$ | |
| $I_{OL}$ | Output Leakage | | | $\mu A$ | $0 \le V_{IN} \le +5.25V$ | |
| $I_{IR}$ | Reset Input Current | | | $\mu A$ | $V_{RL} = 0V$, $V_{CC} = +5.25V$ | |
| $I_{DD}$ | $V_{DD}$ Supply Current | | | mA | | |
| $I_{MM}$ | $V_{MM}$ Supply Current | | | mA | | |

1. For $A_0$-$A_{11}$, $\overline{MDS}$, $\overline{SYNC}$, SCLK and IACK on the Z8/64 pin version, $I_{OH} = -100\ \mu A$ and $I_{OL} = 1.0$ mA.

## 4 External Instruction Fetch, I/O or Memory Read Timing

| Symbol | Parameter | Min | Max | Unit | Condition | Notes |
|---|---|---|---|---|---|---|
| TdA(AS) | Address Valid to Address Strobe Delay Time | 30 | | ns | Test Load 1 | 1 |
| TdAS(A) | Address Strobe to Address Float Delay Time | 60 | | ns | Test Load 1 | 1 |
| TdAS(DI) | Address Strobe to Data In Valid Delay Time | | 280 | ns | Test Load 1 | 3 |
| TwAS | Address Strobe Width | 60 | | ns | Test Load 1 | 1 |
| TdA(DS) | Address Float to Data Strobe Delay Time | 0 | | ns | Test Load 1 | |
| TwDS | Data Strobe Width | 230 | | ns | Test Load 1 | 2 |
| TdDS(DI) | Data Strobe to Data In Valid Delay Time | | 160 | ns | Test Load 1 | 3 |
| ThDS(DI) | Data In Hold Time | 0 | | ns | | |
| TdDS(A) | Data Strobe to Address Change Delay Time | 60 | | ns | Test Load 1 | 1 |
| TdDS(AS) | Data Strobe to Address Strobe Delay Time | 50 | | ns | Test Load 1 | 1 |
| TdR(AS) | Read Valid to Address Strobe Delay Time | 30 | | ns | Test Load 1 | 1 |
| TdDS(R) | Data Strobe to Read Change Delay | 60 | | ns | Test Load 1 | 1 |

1. Delay times given are for an 8 MHz crystal input frequency. For lower frequencies, the change in clock period must be added to the delay time.
2. Data Strobe Width is given for an 8 MHz crystal input frequency. For lower frequencies the change in three clock periods must be added to obtain the minimum width. The Data Strobe Width varies according to the instruction being executed. Refer to Figures 1-9 and 1-10.
3. Address Strobe and Data Strobe to Data In Valid delay times represent memory system access times and are given for an 8 MHz crystal input frequency. For lower frequencies; the change in four clock periods must be added to TdAS(DI) and the change in three clock periods added to TdDS(DI).
4. All timing references assume 2.0V for a logic "1" and 0.8V for a logic "0."

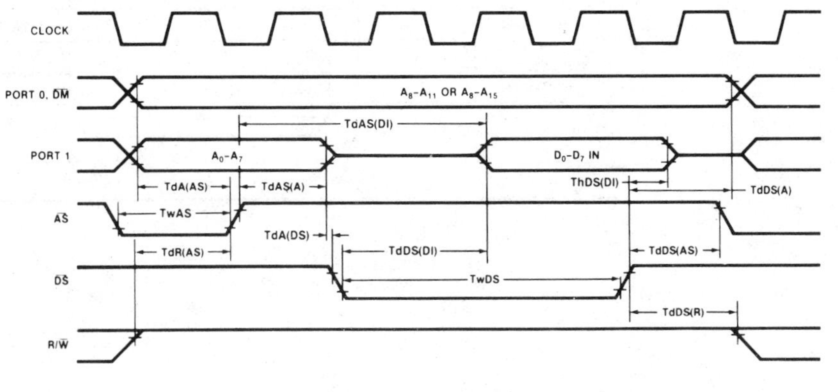

**5**
**External I/O or Memory Write Timing**

| Symbol | Parameter | Min | Max | Unit | Condition | Notes |
|---|---|---|---|---|---|---|
| TdA(AS) | Address Valid to Address Strobe Delay Time | 30 | | ns | Test Load 1 | 1 |
| TdAS(A) | Address Strobe to Address Change Delay Time | 60 | | ns | Test Load 1 | 1 |
| TwAS | Address Strobe Width | 60 | | ns | Test Load 1 | 1 |
| TdDO(DS) | Data Out Valid to Data Strobe Delay Time | 30 | | ns | Test Load 1 | 1 |
| TwDS | Data Strobe Width | 150 | | ns | Test Load 1 | 2 |
| TdDS(A) | Data Strobe to Address Change Delay Time | 60 | | ns | Test Load 1 | 1 |
| TdDS(DO) | Data Strobe to Data Out Change Delay Time | 60 | | ns | Test Load 1 | 1 |
| TdDS(AS) | Data Strobe to Address Strobe Delay Time | 50 | | ns | Test Load 1 | 1 |
| TdW(AS) | Write Valid to Address Strobe Delay Time | 30 | | ns | Test Load 1 | 1 |
| TdDS(W) | Data Strobe to Write Change Delay Time | 60 | | ns | Test Load 1 | 1 |

1. Delay times given are for an 8 MHz crystal input frequency. For lower frequencies, the change in clock period must be added to the delay time.
2. Data Strobe Width is given for an 8 MHz crystal input frequency. For lower frequencies the change in three clock periods must be added to obtain the minimum width. The Data Strobe Width varies according to the instruction being executed. Refer to Figures 1-9 and 1-10.
3. All timing references assume 2.0V for a logic "1" and 0.8V for a logic "0."

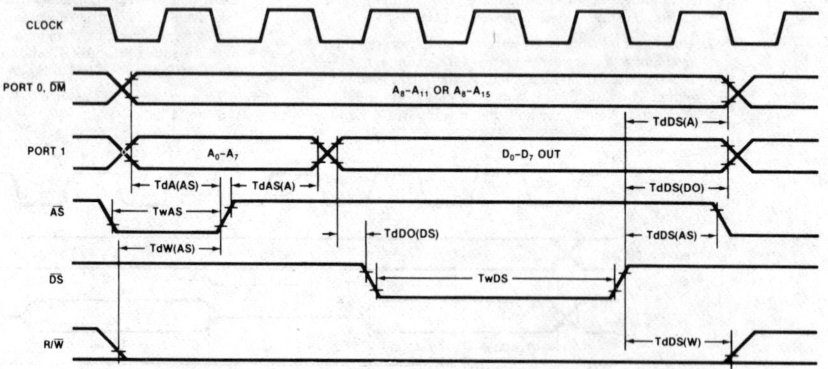

**6**
**Memory Port (Z8/64) Timing**

| Symbol | Parameter | Min | Max | Unit | Condition | Notes |
|---|---|---|---|---|---|---|
| TdA(AS) | Address Valid to Address Strobe Delay Time | 30 | | ns | Test Load 2 | 1 |
| TdAS(DI) | Address Strobe to Data In Valid Delay Time | | 280 | ns | Test Load 2 | 3 |
| TwAS | Address Strobe Width | 60 | | ns | Test Load 2 | 1 |
| TdAS(MD) | Address Strobe to Memory Data Strobe Delay Time | 60 | | ns | Test Load 2 | 1 |
| TwMD | Memory Data Strobe Width | 230 | | ns | Test Load 2 | 2 |
| TdMD(DI) | Memory Data Strobe to Data In Valid Delay Time | | 160 | ns | Test Load 2 | 1 |
| ThMD(DI) | Data In Hold Time | 0 | | ns | | |
| TdMD(A) | Memory Data Strobe to Address Change Delay Time | 60 | | ns | Test Load 2 | 1 |
| TdMD(AS) | Memory Data Strobe to Address Strobe Delay Time | 50 | | ns | Test Load 2 | 1 |

1. Delay times given are for an 8 MHz crystal input frequency. For lower frequencies, the change in clock period must be added to the delay time.
2. Memory Data Strobe Width is given for an 8 MHz crystal input frequency. For lower frequencies the change in three clock periods must be added to obtain the minimum width. The Memory Data Strobe Width varies according to the instruction being executed. Refer to Figures 1-9 and 1-10.
3. Address Strobe and Memory Data Strobe to Data In Valid delay times represent memory system access times and are given at an 8 MHz crystal input frequency. For lower frequencies the change in four clock periods must be added to TdAS(DI) and the change in three clock periods added to TdMS(DI).
4. All timing references assume 2.0V for a logic "1" and 0.8V for a logic "0."

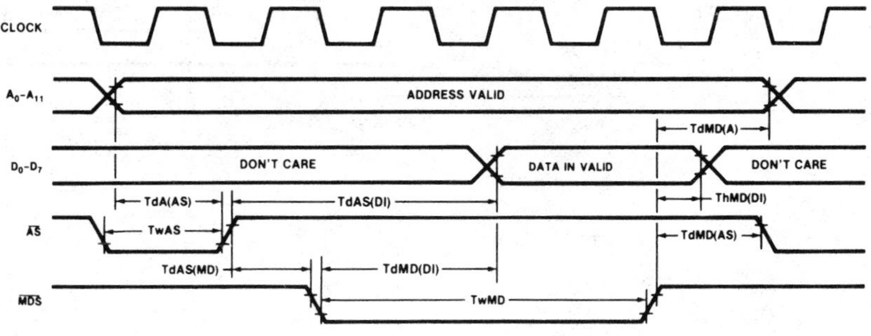

## 7 Additional Timing

| Symbol | Parameter | Min | Max | Unit | Condition | Notes |
|---|---|---|---|---|---|---|
| TpC | Input Clock Period | 125 | | ns | | |
| TrC, TfC | Input Clock Rise and Fall Times | | | ns | From External Clock Generator | |
| TwC | Input Clock Width | | | ns | From External Clock Generator | |
| TdSC(AS) | System Clock Out to Address Strobe Delay Time | | | ns | | 1 |
| TdSY(DS) | Instruction Sync Out to Data Strobe Delay Time | | | ns | | 1, 2 |
| TwSY | Instruction Sync Out Width | | | ns | | 1, 2 |

1. Test Conditions use Test Load 1 for SCLK and $\overline{\text{SYNC}}$ when output through their respective Port 3 pins and Test Load 2 on the SCLK and $\overline{\text{SYNC}}$ direct outputs on the 64 pin version.
2. Times given assume an 8 MHz crystal input frequency. For lower frequencies, the change in two clock periods must be added.
3. All timing references assume 2.0V for a logic "1" and 0.8V for a logic "0."

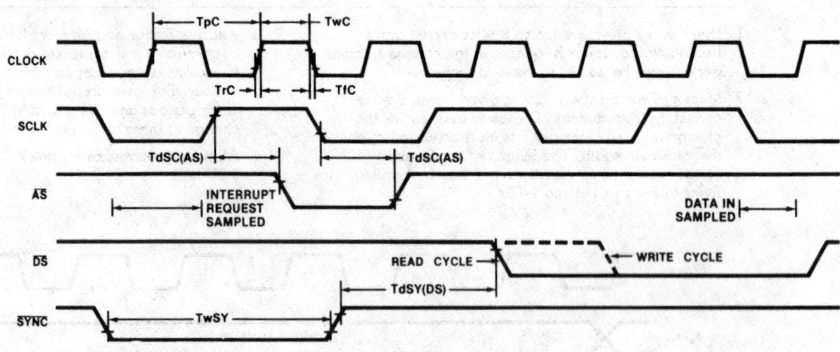

**8 Handshake Timing**

| Symbol | Parameter | Min | Max | Unit | Condition |
|---|---|---|---|---|---|
| TsDI(DA) | Data In Setup Time | 0 | | ns | |
| ThDA(DI) | Data In Hold Time | 190 | | ns | |
| TwDA | Data Available Width | | | ns | Input Handshake Test Load 1 |
| TdDAL(RY) | Data Available Low to Ready Delay Time | | | ns | Input Handshake Test Load 1 |
| | | 0 | | ns | Output Handshake Test Load 1 |
| TdDAH(RY) | Data Available High to Ready Delay Time | | | ns | Input Handshake Test Load 1 |
| | | 0 | | ns | Output Handshake Test Load 1 |
| TdDO(DA) | Data Out to Data Available Delay Time | | | ns | Test Load 1 |
| TdRY(DA) | Ready to Data Available Delay Time | | | ns | Test Load 1 |

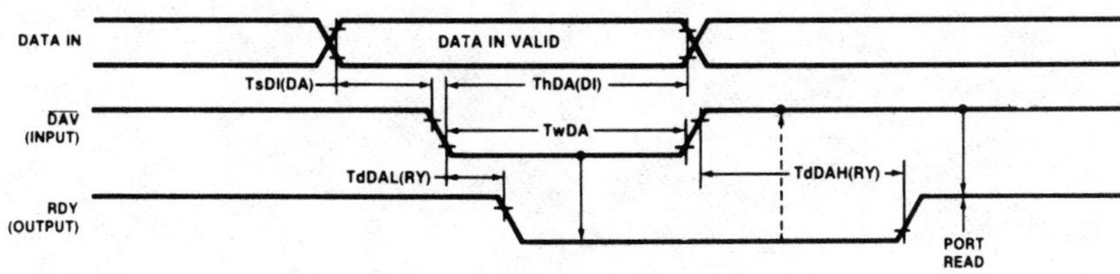


**Input Handshake**

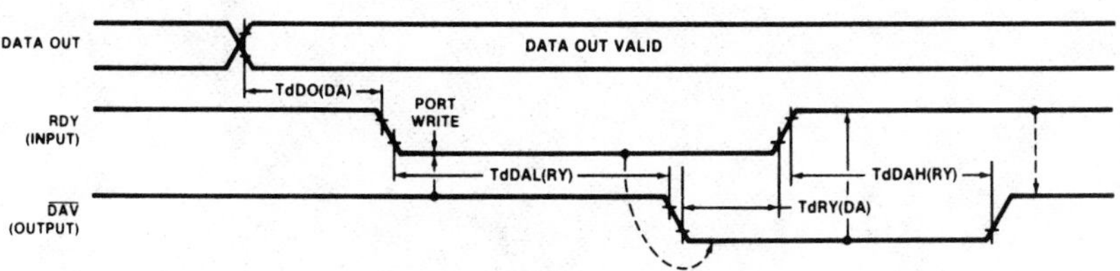


**Output Handshake**

## 9 Test Load Circuits

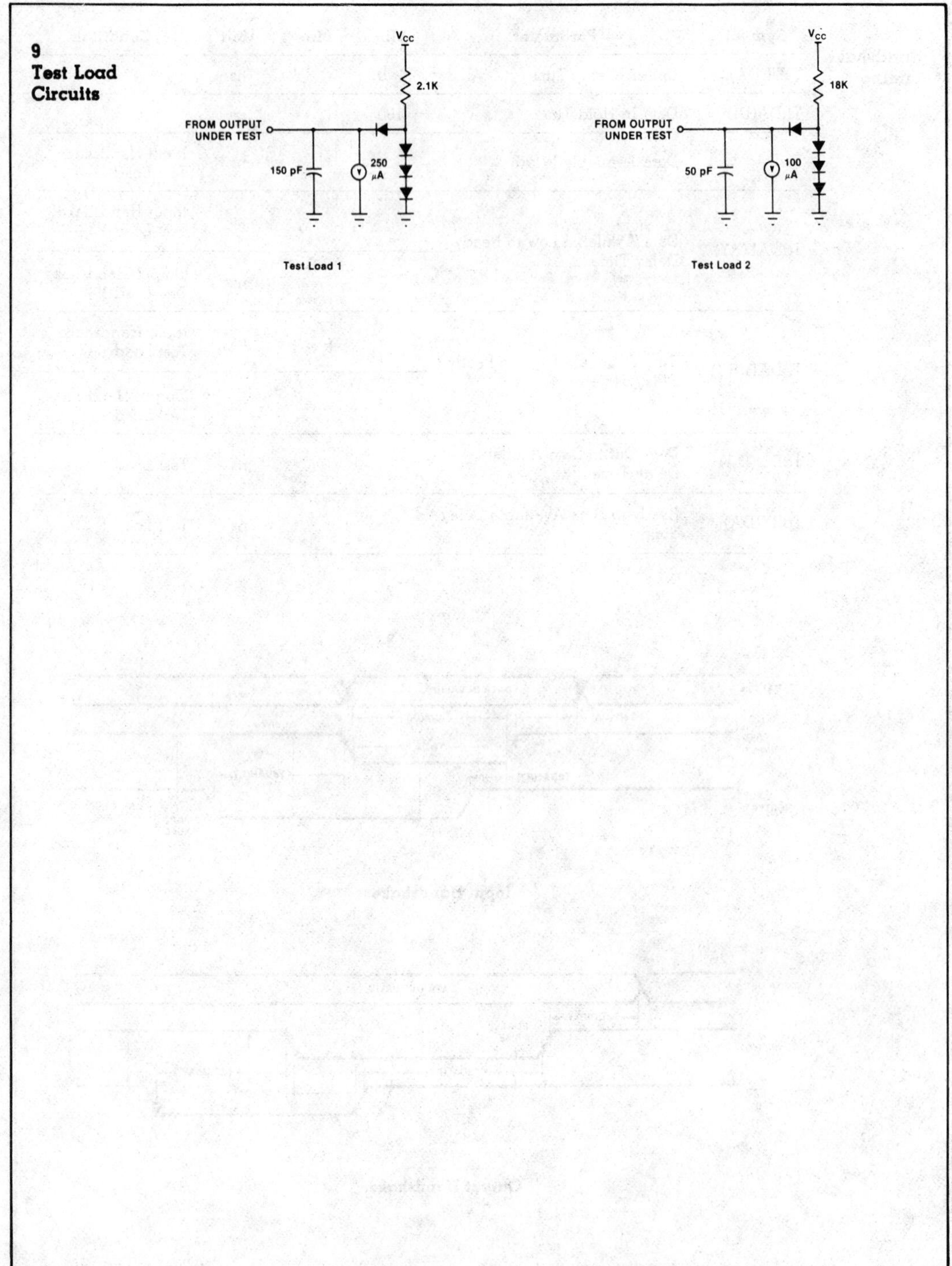

# Chapter 9
# THE MOTOROLA MC6800

**The MC6800 was developed by Motorola as an enhancement of the Intel 8008, at the same time that Intel was developing the 8080A, also as an enhancement of the 8008.**

**When comparing the MC6800 to the 8080A, the most important feature of the MC6800 is its relative simplicity. Here are a few superficial, but illustrative comparisons between the two products:**

1) As compared to the 8080A, MC6800 timing is very simple. MC6800 instructions execute in two or more machine cycles, all of which are identical in length. In contrast to the 8080A, which we described in Chapter 4, note that an MC6800 machine cycle and clock period are one and the same thing — each MC6800 machine cycle has a single clock period.
2) Whereas the 8080A has separate I/O instructions, the MC6800 includes memory and I/O within a single address space. Thus all I/O devices are accessed as memory locations.
3) The MC6800 has a simpler set of control signals, therefore it does not multiplex the Data Bus — and does not need any device equivalent to the 8228 System Controller.
4) Whereas the 8080A requires three levels of power supply, the MC6800 uses just one — +5V.
5) The instruction set of the MC6800 is much easier to comprehend than that of the 8080A. The MC6800 has fewer basic instruction types, with more memory addressing options; the 8080A, by way of contrast, has a large number of special, one-of-a-kind instructions.

**It is very informative to extend the five comparisons above with the enhancements that Intel has made to the 8080A in order to come up with the 8085.** Let us take the five points one at a time.

1) 8085 instruction execution timing is far simpler than the 8080A. But MC6800 timing is still far simpler than the 8085.
2) The 8085 retains the separate memory and I/O spaces of the 8080A.
3) The 8085 has separate control signals which do not need to be demultiplexed off the Data Bus, as required by the 8080A. The price paid by the 8085 is a multiplexed Data and Address Bus. Neither the MC6800 nor the 8085 need any device equivalent to the 8228 System Controller; however, the 8085 will need a bus demultiplexer in configurations that do not use the standard 8085 support devices.
4) The 8085, like the MC6800, has gone to a single +5V power supply.
5) The 8085 instruction set is almost identical to that of the 8080A.

An additional point worth noting is that the 8085 includes clock logic on the CPU chip. The MC6800 requires a separate clock logic chip.

**Looking at the 8085, there are grounds for arguing that Intel has acknowledged that the MC6800 has some desirable characteristics not present in the 8080A. In order to compete with the 8085, therefore, Motorola will not be required to make MC6800 enhancements of the same magnitude as Intel made going from the 8080A to the 8085. Specifically, these are the MC6800 characteristics which remain to be addressed by any MC6800 enhancement:**

1) Clock logic must be moved on to the CPU chip.
2) Multifunction CPU and support devices must be developed so that Motorola can offer low chip count microcomputers.

**Additional weaknesses of the MC6800 that have manifested themselves include:**

1) An instruction set that makes excessive use of memory as a result of too few Index registers and a lack of data mobility between registers of the CPU. This is a weakness that was identified in the first version of this book.
2) The synchronizing E signal, required by support devices of the MC6800, render these support devices useless in any microcomputer system other than the MC6800. In contrast, 8080A support devices can be used widely in microcomputer systems not based on the 8080A CPU.

Future Motorola plans address many of the points raised above. The MC6802 and 6801 described in this chapter are the first steps towards reducing chip counts in MC6800-based microcomputer systems. The MC6809 is the new enhanced MC6800 and competes with the 8085. The MC6809 provides additional Index registers, plus instructions that move data between Accumulators and Index registers. The MC6809 has clock logic on the CPU chip.

MC6800 and MCS6500 support devices are interchangeable; that is to say, you can use MC6800 support devices (described in this chapter) with the MCS6500 microprocessor (described in Chapter 10) and you can use MCS6500 support devices (described in Chapter 10) with the MC6800 CPU.

**These are the devices described in this chapter:**

- **The MC6800 CPU**
- **The MC6802 CPU with RAM**
- **The MC6870 series Clocks**
- **The MC6820 Peripheral Interface Adapter (PIA)**
- **The MC6850 Asynchronous Communications Interface Adapter (ACIA)**
- **The XC6852 Synchronous Serial Data Adapter (SSDA)**
- **The MC6828 Priority Interrupt Controller (PIC)**
- **The MC6840 Programmable Counter/Timer**
- **The MC6844 Direct Memory Access Controller**
- **The MC6846 Multifunction device - the second part in an MC6802-based two-chip microcomputer.**
- **The MC6801 Single-Chip Microcomputer**
- **The MC6809 Microprocessor**

**MOTOROLA A AND B SERIES PARTS**

**Two new series of MC6800 parts offer higher speeds.** Standard MC6800 parts use a 1 MHz clock signal. "A" parts use a 1.5 MHz clock signal, while "B" parts use a 2 MHz clock signal. There is, in addition, an MC6821 PIA which is identical to the MC6820 in operating characteristics, but has different physical characteristics.

The principal MC6800 manufacturer is:

MOTOROLA INCORPORATED
Semiconductor Products Division
3501 Ed Bluestein Boulevard
Austin, TX 78721

The second sources are:

AMERICAN MICROSYSTEMS
3800 Homestead Road
Santa Clara, California 95051

FAIRCHILD SEMICONDUCTOR
464 Ellis Street
Mountain View, California 94040

HITACHI
Semiconductors And Integrated
Circuits Division of Hitachi LTD
1450 Josuihan-Cho-Kodaira-Shi
Tokyo, Japan

SESCOSEM
Thompson CSF
173 Haussmann Blvd.
Paris, France 75008

**The MC6800 devices use a single +5V power supply. Using a one microsecond clock, instruction execution times range from 2 to 12 microseconds. A one microsecond clock is the standard for MC6800 microcomputer systems. 667 nanosecond clocks are standard for the 68A00 series while 500 nanosecond clocks are standard for the 68B00 series.**

**All MC6800 devices have TTL compatible signals.**

**N-channel silicon gate, depletion load MOS technology is used for the MC6800.**

# THE MC6800 CPU

**Functions implemented on the MC6800 CPU are illustrated in Figure 9-1;** they represent typical CPU logic. As compared to other microprocessors described in this book, the MC6800 might be considered deficient in requiring external clock logic; however, its principal competitor, the 8080A, requires external clock logic and Data Bus demultiplexing logic.

The need for external clock logic simply reflects the fact that the MC6800 is one of the earlier microprocessors.

## THE MC6800 PROGRAMMABLE REGISTERS

**The MC6800 has two Accumulators, a Status register, an Index register, a Stack Pointer and a Program Counter. These may be illustrated as follows:**

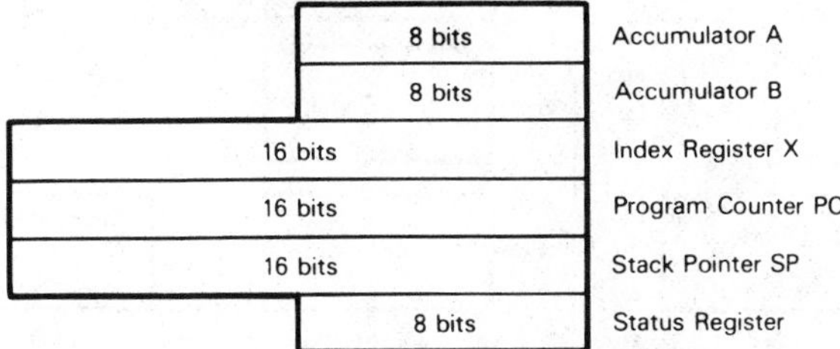


**The two Accumulators, A and B, are both primary Accumulators.** The only instructions which apply to one Accumulator, but not the other, are the instructions which move statuses between Accumulator A and the Status register and the DAA (Decimal Adjust) instruction.

**The Index register is a typical microcomputer Index register, as described in Volume 1.**

**The MC6800 has a Stack implemented in memory and indexed by the Stack Pointer, as described in Volume 1.** Because of the nature of the MC6800 instruction set, it is more realistic to look upon the MC6800 Stack Pointer as a cross between a Stack Pointer and a Data Counter. Memory reference instructions make it very easy to store the contents of either the Stack Pointer or the Index register in read/write memory; by maintaining a number of base page memory locations as storage for these two Address registers, each can be put to multiple use.

**The Program Counter is a typical Program Counter, as described in Volume 1.**

## MC6800 MEMORY ADDRESSING MODES

**MC6800 memory reference instructions use direct addressing and indexed addressing.**

**The MC6800 has an unusually large variety of three-byte memory referencing instructions; a 16-bit direct address is provided by the second and third bytes of the instruction. Therefore, 65,536 bytes of memory can be directly addressed. The commonly used memory reference instructions also have a base page, direct addressing option; this is a two-byte instruction, with a one-byte address which can directly address any one of the first 256 bytes of memory.**

**All memory reference instructions are available with indexed addressing.** Indexed addressing on the MC6800 differs from indexed addressing as described in Volume 1, in that the one-byte displacement provided by the memory reference instruction is added to the Index register as an unsigned 8-bit value:

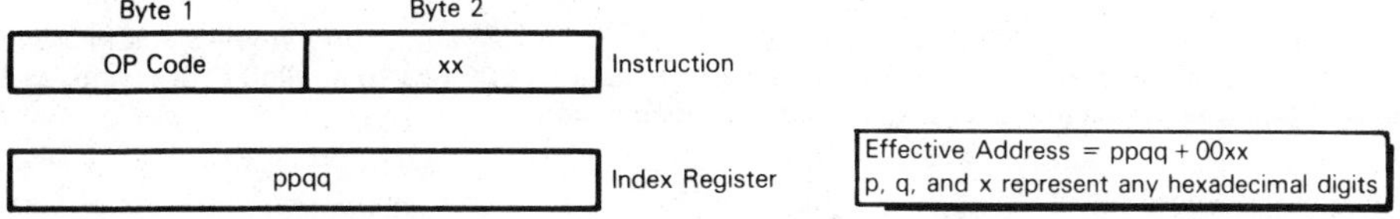


MC6800 programs can use the Stack Pointer as an Address register, but two bytes of read/write memory must be reserved for the current top of Stack address and interrupts must be disabled while the Stack Pointer is being used to address data memory. A single instruction allows an address to be loaded into the Stack Pointer; another single instruction allows the Stack Pointer contents to be stored in read/write memory. This use of the Stack Pointer is not recommended, however, since you cannot disable the non-maskable interrupt ($\overline{NMI}$). Additionally, you would not be able to use the software interrupt instruction (SWI) as a program debugging tool if the program were using the Stack Pointer as an Address register.

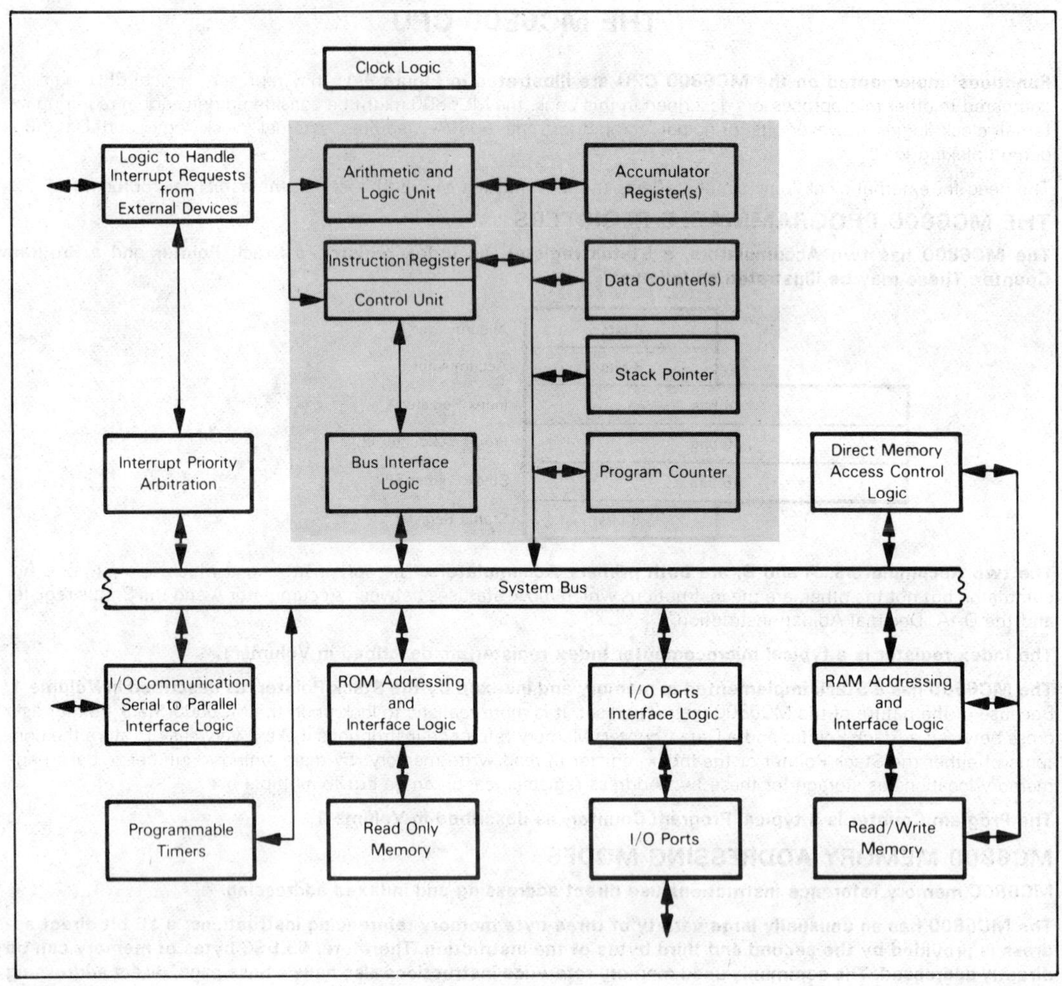


Figure 9-1. Logic of the MC6800 CPU Device

**Branch and Branch-on-Condition instructions use program relative, direct addressing;** a single byte displacement is treated as a signed binary number which is added to the Program Counter, after Program Counter contents have been incremented to address the next sequential instruction. This allows displacements in the range +129 to -126 bytes.

One note of caution: Motorola's MC6800 literature uses the term "implied addressing" to describe instructions that identify one of the programmable registers. **The closest thing the MC6800 has to implied addressing, as the term is used in this book, is indexed addressing with a zero displacement.**

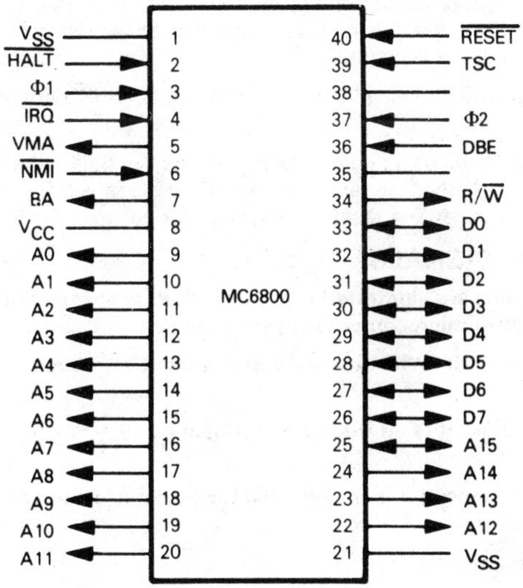

| Signal | Pin | Pin | Signal |
|---|---|---|---|
| $V_{SS}$ | 1 | 40 | $\overline{RESET}$ |
| $\overline{HALT}$ | 2 | 39 | TSC |
| Φ1 | 3 | 38 | |
| $\overline{IRQ}$ | 4 | 37 | Φ2 |
| VMA | 5 | 36 | DBE |
| $\overline{NMI}$ | 6 | 35 | |
| BA | 7 | 34 | R/$\overline{W}$ |
| $V_{CC}$ | 8 | 33 | D0 |
| A0 | 9 | 32 | D1 |
| A1 | 10 | 31 | D2 |
| A2 | 11 | 30 | D3 |
| A3 | 12 | 29 | D4 |
| A4 | 13 | 28 | D5 |
| A5 | 14 | 27 | D6 |
| A6 | 15 | 26 | D7 |
| A7 | 16 | 25 | A15 |
| A8 | 17 | 24 | A14 |
| A9 | 18 | 23 | A13 |
| A10 | 19 | 22 | A12 |
| A11 | 20 | 21 | $V_{SS}$ |

MC6800

| PIN NAME | DESCRIPTION | TYPE |
|---|---|---|
| *A0 - A15 | Address Lines | Tristate, Output |
| *D0 - D7 | Data Bus Lines | Tristate, Bidirectional |
| *$\overline{HALT}$ | Halt | Input |
| *TSC | Three State Control | Input |
| *R/$\overline{W}$ | Read/Write | Tristate, Output |
| *VMA | Valid Memory Address | Output |
| *DBE | Data Bus Enable | Input |
| *BA | Bus Available | Output |
| *$\overline{IRQ}$ | Interrupt Request | Input |
| $\overline{RESET}$ | Reset | Input |
| $\overline{NMI}$ | Non-Maskable Interrupt | Input |
| Φ1, Φ2 | Clock Signals | Input |
| $V_{SS}$, $V_{CC}$ | Power | |

*These signals connect to the System Bus.

Figure 9-2. MC6800 CPU Signals and Pin Assignments

## MC6800 STATUS FLAGS

**The MC6800 has a Status register which maintains five status flags and an interrupt control bit. These are the five status flags:**

Carry (C)
Overflow (O)
Sign (S)
Zero (Z)
Auxiliary Carry ($A_C$)

Statuses are assigned bit positions within the Status register as follows:

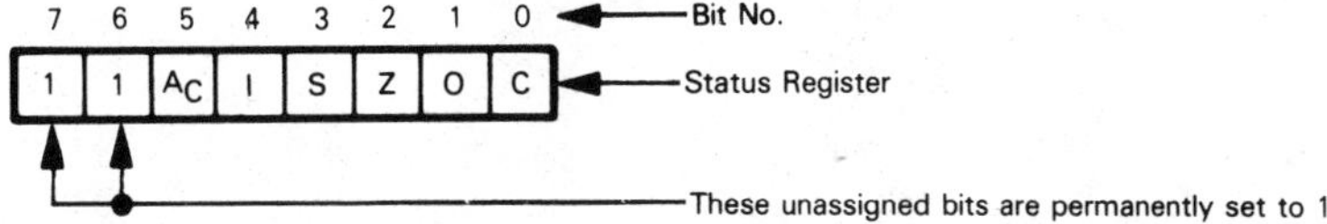

The Carry status is standard for all additions and shift operations; however, Borrow logic sets the Carry status to 1 when there is no carry out of the high-order bit during a subtract operation, while the carry status is reset to 0 if there is a carry out of the high-order bit during a subtract operation. For a discussion of Carry status logic during subtract operations, see the Status flag section of Chapter 4.

I is the external interrupt enable/disable flag. When it is 1, interrupts via $\overline{\text{IRQ}}$ are disabled; when it is 0, interrupts via $\overline{\text{IRQ}}$ are enabled.

MC6800 literature refers to the Sign bit as a negative bit, given the symbol N; the Overflow bit is given the symbol V. The Intermediate Carry bit represents the standard Carry out of bit 3 and is referred to as the Half Carry bit, given the symbol H. Statuses are nevertheless set and reset as described for our hypothetical microcomputer in Volume 1.

## MC6800 CPU PINS AND SIGNALS

**The MC6800 CPU pins and signals are illustrated in Figure 9-2. A description of these signals is useful as a guide to the way in which the MC6800 microcomputer system works.**

**The Address Bus is a tristate bus; it is 16 bits wide and is used to address all types of memory and external devices.**

**The Data Bus is also a tristate bus; it is an 8-bit bidirectional bus** via which data is transmitted between memory and all MC6800 microcomputer system devices.

**Control signals on the MC6800 Control Bus may be divided into bus state controls, bus data identification, and interrupt processing.**

**MC6800 BUS STATE CONTROLS**

**These are the bus state control signals:**

**Three State Control (TSC).** This input is used to float the Address Bus and the read/write control output.

**Data Bus Enable (DBE).** This signal is input low in order to float the Data Bus. When the Data Bus, the Address Bus and the read/write control output have all been floated, Direct Memory Access operations may be performed by external logic. DBE is frequently tied to the Φ2 clock input, in which case Φ2 and DBE are identical signals.

**$\overline{\text{HALT}}$.** When this signal is input low, the CPU ceases execution at the end of the present instruction execution and floats the entire System Bus.

**Bus Available (BA).** This line is output high when the Data and Address Busses have been floated following a $\overline{\text{HALT}}$ input only. **When BA is low, the CPU is controlling the Data and Address Busses; information on these busses is identified by the following two control signals:**

**Read/Write (R/$\overline{\text{W}}$).** When high, this signal indicates that the CPU wishes to read data off the Data Bus; when low, this signal indicates that the CPU is outputting data on the Data Bus. The normal standby state for this signal is "read" (high).

**Valid Memory Address (VMA).** This signal is output high whenever a valid address has been output on the Address Bus.

**There are three interrupt processing signals as follows:**

**$\overline{\text{IRQ}}$. This signal is used to request an interrupt.** If interrupts have been enabled and the CPU is not in the Halt state, then it will acknowledge the interrupt at the end of the currently executing instruction.

**Non-Maskable Interrupt ($\overline{\text{NMI}}$).** This signal differs from $\overline{\text{IRQ}}$ in that it cannot be inhibited. Typically, this input is used for catastrophic interrupts such as power fail.

**$\overline{\text{RESET}}$.** This is a typical reset signal.

Note that a number of control signals output by the MC6800 are only capable of driving one standard TTL load. Some form of signal buffering and amplification will therefore be required in most systems.

# MC6800 TIMING AND INSTRUCTION EXECUTION

**The MC6800 uses a relatively simple combination of two clock signals** to time events within the microprocessor CPU and the microcomputer system in general. **These two clock signals may be illustrated as follows:**

**MC6800 CLOCK SIGNALS**

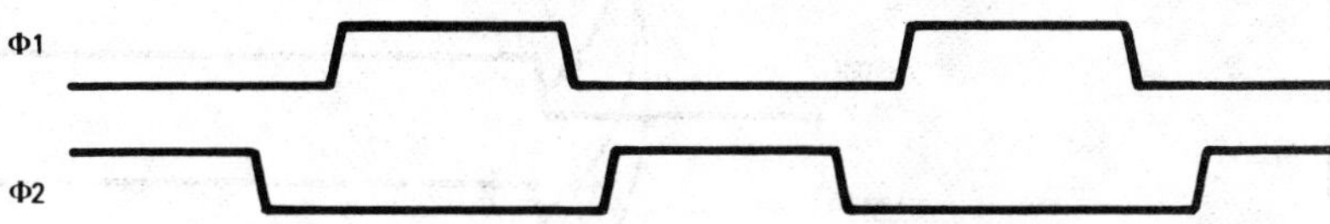


Observe that clock signals Φ1 and Φ2 both have high pulses which occur within the width of the other clock signal's low pulse.

**A further timing signal, given the symbol E, is used by support devices within an MC6800 microcomputer system. Φ1, Φ2 and E timing signals are generated by the clock logic devices described later in this chapter.**

**Each repeating pattern of Φ1 and Φ2 signals constitutes a single machine cycle:**

**MC6800 MACHINE CYCLE**

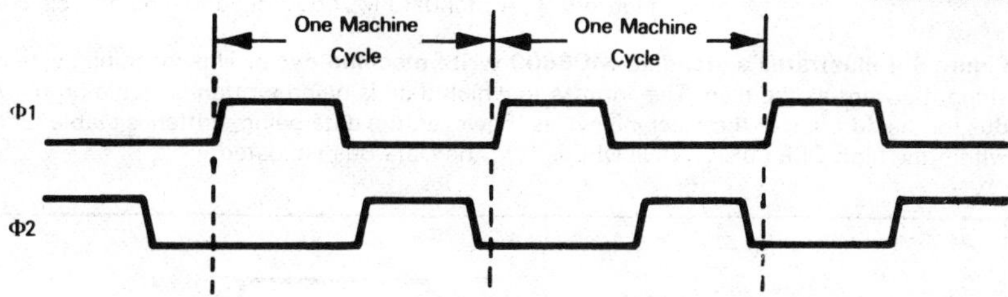


MC6800 instructions require between two and eight machine cycles to execute. Interrupt instructions are an exception, requiring longer instruction execution times.

**So far as external logic is concerned, there are only three types of machine cycles which can occur during an instruction's execution:**

**MC6800 MACHINE CYCLE TYPES**

1) **A read operation** during which a byte of data must be input to the CPU.
2) **A write operation** during which a byte of data is output by the CPU.
3) **An internal operation** during which no activity occurs on the System Bus.

**All MC6800 instructions have timing which is a simple concatenation of the three basic machine cycle types.**

**Let us therefore begin by looking at these three basic machine cycles.**

**Figure 9-3 illustrates timing for a standard read machine cycle.** Observe that in the normal course of events, neither the Address nor the Data Busses are available for DMA operations. The address output is stable for most of the machine cycle. Data needs to be stable for a short interval of time late in the machine cycle. Exact timing is given in MC6800 data sheets at the end of this chapter.

**MC6800 READ MACHINE CYCLE**

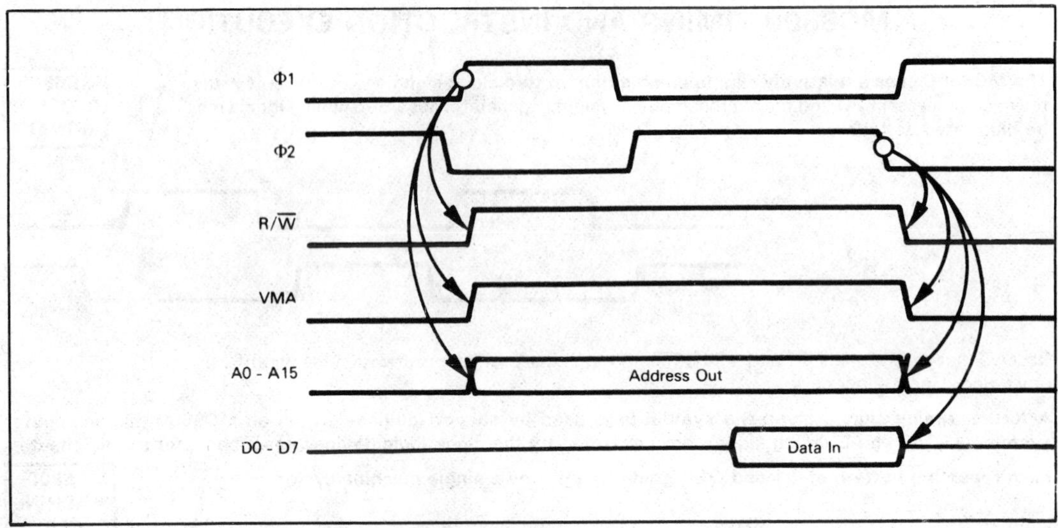


Figure 9-3. A Standard MC6800 Read Machine Cycle

**MC6800 WRITE MACHINE CYCLE**

**Figure 9-4 illustrates a standard MC6800 write machine cycle.** This machine cycle is not as straightforward as the read. The address to which data is being written is stable on the Address Bus for the duration of the machine cycles; however, the data being written is stable for a period within the high DBE pulse. While DBE is low, the Data Bus is floated.

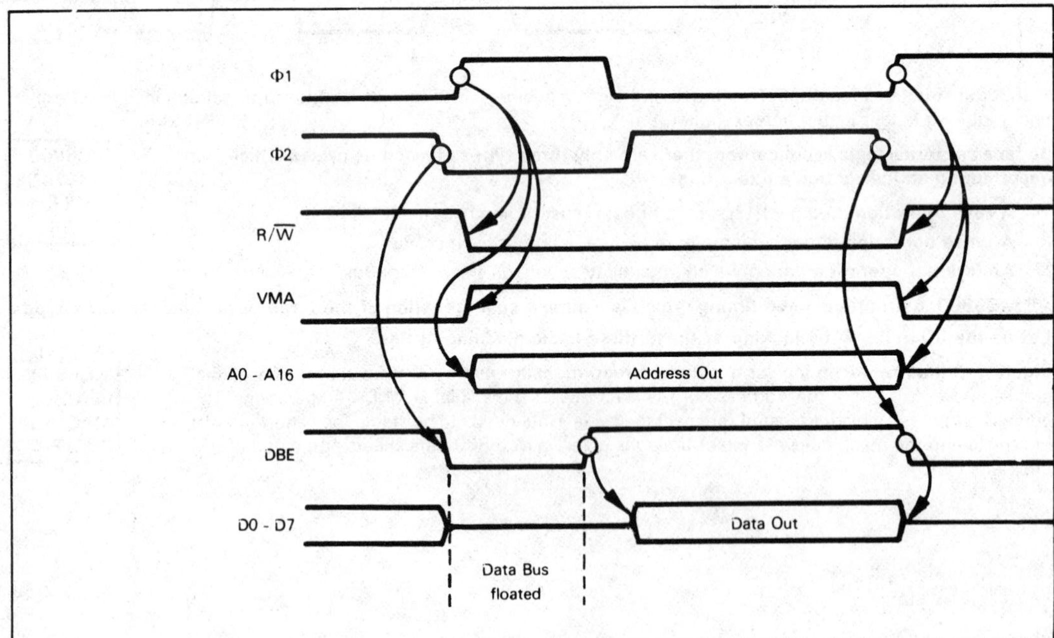


Figure 9-4. A Standard MC6800 Write Machine Cycle

**Under normal circumstances, DBE is identical to Φ2:**

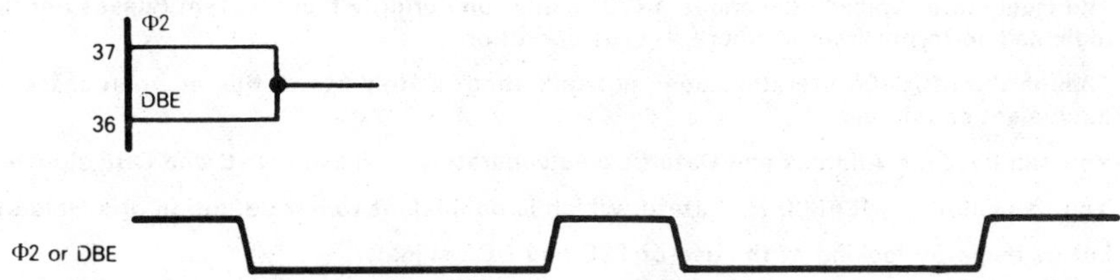


**If the high Φ2 pulse is too short for external logic to respond to the write, the slow external logic can be accommodated in two ways. You can input a DBE signal to the CPU that has a shorter low pulse and a longer high pulse.** DBE and Φ2 are no longer identical signals:

**MC6800 WAIT STATE WITH SLOW MEMORY**

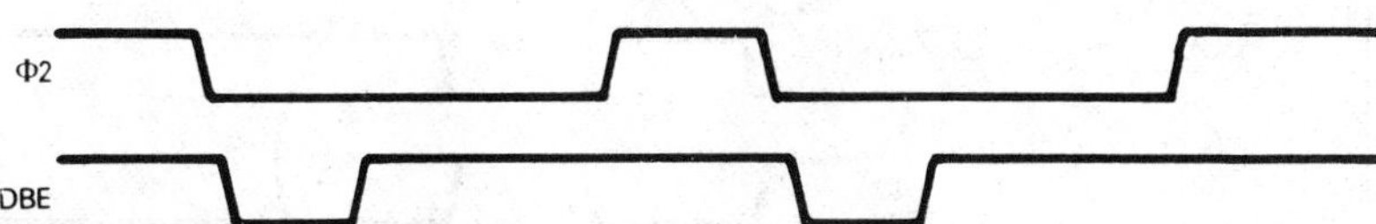


There is some minimum time during which DBE must be low, since the CPU itself requires time to perform internal operations. This minimum time is given in the MC6800 data sheets at the end of this chapter.

**You can also accommodate slow memories by stretching the system clocks; this may be illustrated as follows:**

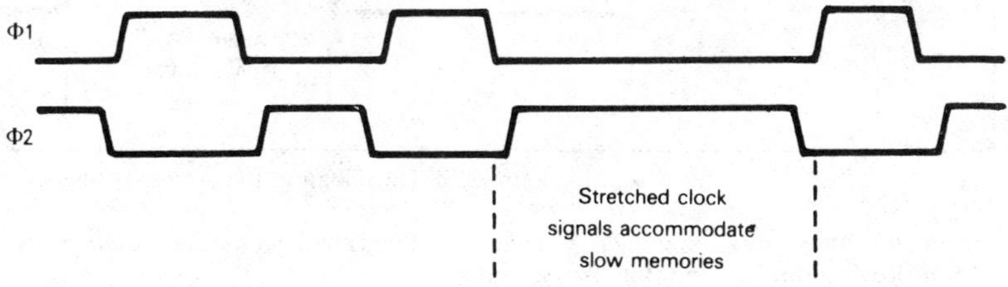


The standard clock devices, described later in this chapter, provide clock stretching logic. During a clock stretch, Φ1 and Φ2 cannot be held constant for more than 9.5 μsec; the MC6800 is a dynamic device, and longer static clock periods can result in loss of internal data.

**During an internal operation's machine cycle, there is no activity on the System Bus.** R/$\overline{W}$ is in its normal high state and VMA is low.

**MC6800 INTERNAL OPERATIONS MACHINE CYCLE**

**Table 9-2 defines the way in which individual MC6800 instructions concatenate machine cycles and use the System Bus during the course of instruction execution.**

**The VMA and DBE signals require special mention, because their significance can easily be missed.** External logic uses VMA as a signal identifying the address on the Address Bus as having been placed there by the CPU. DBE similarly identifies that portion of a machine cycle when the CPU is active at one end of the Data Bus, either transmitting or receiving data. And this is why these signals are so important: MC6800 microcomputer systems rely heavily on clock signal manipulation as a means of accommodating slow memories, implementing Direct Memory Access, or refreshing dynamic memory. On the next few pages we are going to see examples of how this is done. So long as you understand that the VMA and DBE signals identify the unmanipulated portions of a standard machine cycle, you will have no trouble locating the time slices within which special operations such as Direct Memory Access or dynamic memory refresh are occurring.

## THE HOLD STATE, THE HALT STATE AND DIRECT MEMORY ACCESS

**The Hold state typically describes a CPU condition during which System Busses are floated, so that external logic can perform Direct Memory Access operations.**

**Though the MC6800 literature does not talk about a Hold state, this microprocessor does indeed have two equivalent conditions.**

**You can float the Address and Data Busses separately, using the TSC and DBE signals.**

**You can enter an MC6800 Halt state, which is equivalent to our definition of a Hold state.**

**Let us begin by looking at the use of TSC and DBE signals.**

The Three State Control signal (TSC), if input high, will float the Address Bus and R/$\overline{W}$ line. VMA and BA are forced low. The unusual feature of the Three State Control input is that when this signal is input high, you must simultaneously stop the clock by holding Φ1 high and Φ2 low. Timing is illustrated in Figure 9-5. Now the MC6800, being a dynamic device, will lose its data contents if the clock is stopped for more than 9.5 μsec. You must therefore float the Address Bus just long enough to perform a single Direct Memory Access.

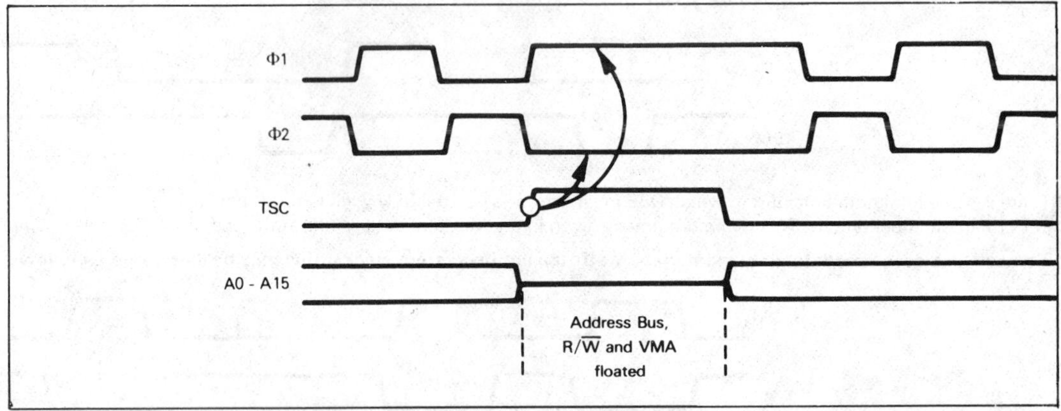


Figure 9-5. TSC Floating the Address Bus

Just as the Three State Control input floats the Address Bus, so the Data Bus Enable input (DBE) floats the Data Bus. When DBE is input low, the Data Bus is floated.

The clock devices, which are described later in this chapter, provide all necessary clock stretching logic.

There are two very important points to note regarding the use of Three State Control (TSC) and Data Bus Enable (DBE) signals.

First of all, note carefully that the Bus Available (BA) signal is held low when the busses are floated by the Three State Control (TSC) and Data Bus Enable (DBE) signals. The purpose of the Bus Available signal is to indicate that the System Bus is available during a Halt or Wait state, both of which we have yet to describe.

The second important feature of the Three State Control (TSC) and Data Bus Enable (DBE) signals is that they do indeed float the System Bus in two halves. Now in many MC6800 systems Φ2 and DBE are the same signal; in such a configuration you will automatically float the Data Bus whenever you float the Address Bus, as illustrated in Figure 9-6.

**Now consider the MC6800 Halt state.**

**The Halt state of the MC6800 is equivalent to the Hold state of the 8080A.** If a low $\overline{\text{HALT}}$ is input to the MC6800, then upon conclusion of the current instruction's execution, the System Bus is floated. Timing is illustrated in Figure 9-7. Observe that the Bus Available signal, BA, is output high; VMA is output low. The Address and Data Busses, and the R/$\overline{W}$ control are floated.

**In summary, the MC6800 provides two means of performing Direct Memory Access operations. You can use the TSC and DBE inputs to gain control of the System Bus for as long as it takes to perform a single DMA access, or you can use the $\overline{\text{HALT}}$ input, following which external logic can gain control of the System Bus for as long as you wish.**

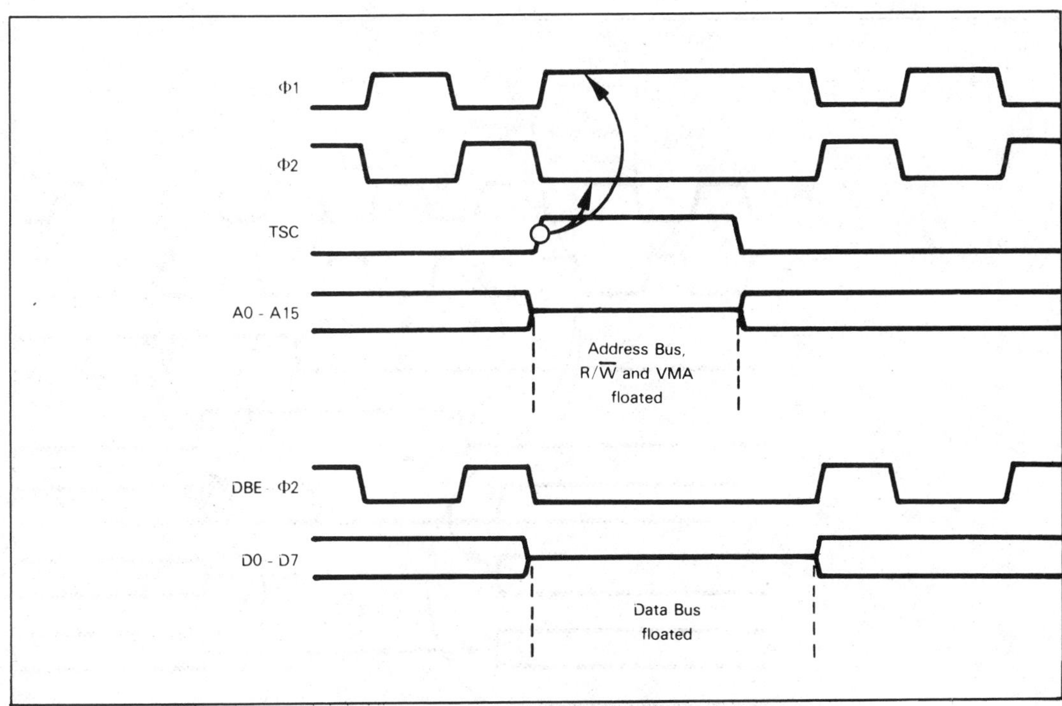


Figure 9-6. TSC Floating the Address and Data Busses When DBE Is Tied to Φ2

Conceptually, the MC6800 scheme for implementing Direct Memory Access or dynamic memory refresh, is very elegant. **If you stretch the Φ1 and Φ2 clock signals, then you can transfer the normal CPU generated address, and an extraneous address within one machine cycle. VMA identifies the CPU generated address. Within the one machine cycle can perform two Data Bus transfers; the first is in response to the external address, while the second is in response to the CPU address. Now DBE identifies the CPU response.** This scheme may be illustrated as follows:

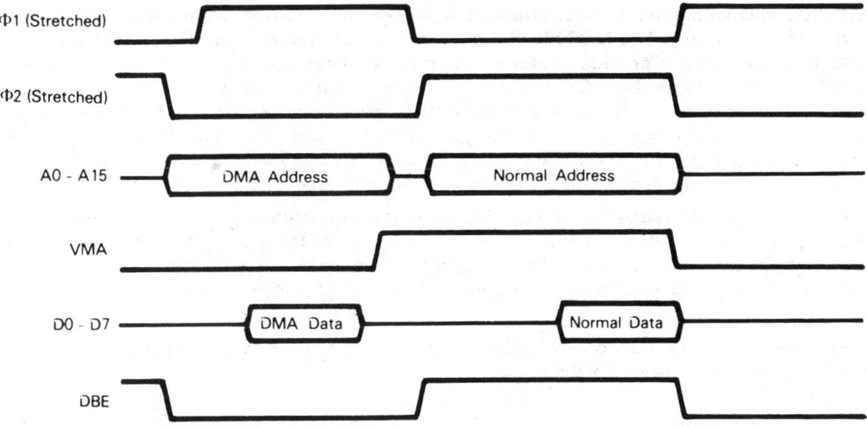


**From this conceptually elegant beginning, some very complex design considerations can arise. Complexities disappear, however, when standard 6800 support devices are used to implement direct memory access logic. Specifically, you should use the MC6875 clock device in conjunction with the 6844 Direct Memory Access controller.**

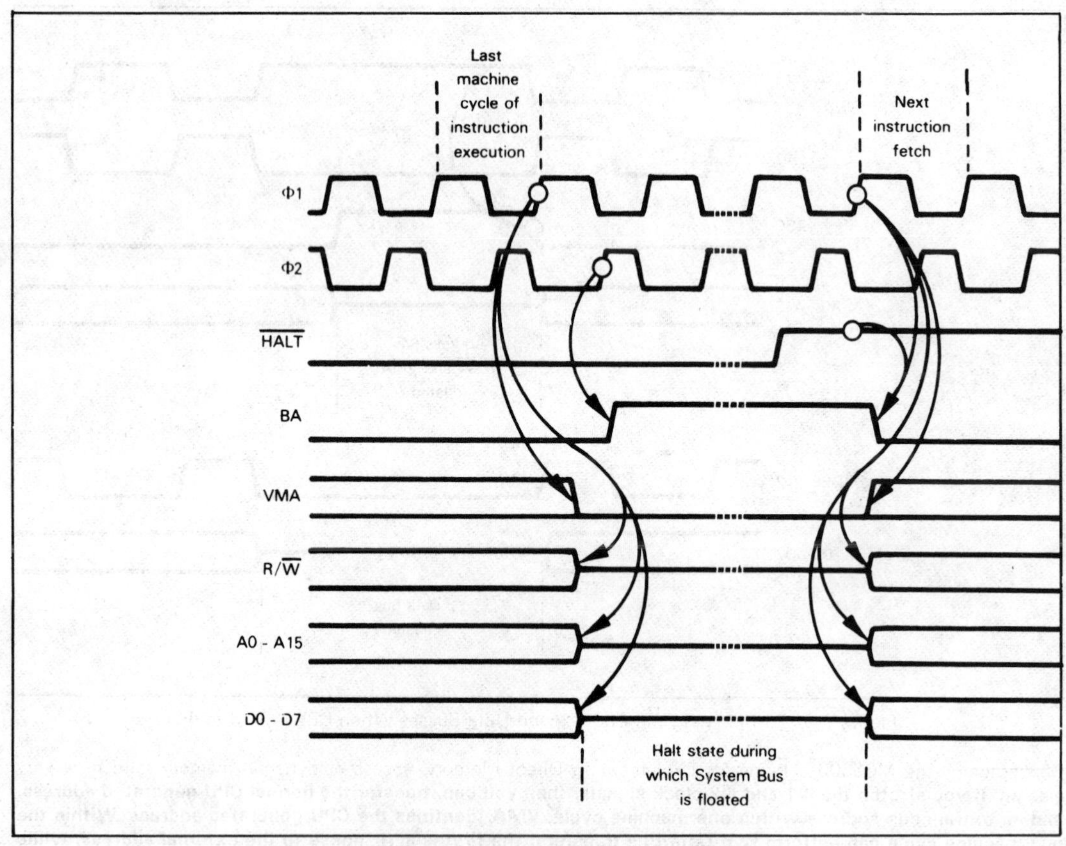


Figure 9-7. System Bus Floating During the Halt State

## INTERRUPT PROCESSING, RESET AND THE WAIT STATE

**MC6800 microcomputer system interrupt logic, as implemented within the 6800 CPU, is based on polling rather than vectoring. The MC6828 Priority Interrupt Control device, described later in this chapter, extends CPU interrupt logic to provide vectored interrupt response.** All normal interrupt requests, when acknowledged, result in an indirect addressing Call through a single high memory address. If more than one device can request an interrupt, then the basic assumption made is that the interrupt service routine will initially read the Status register contents of every device that might be requesting an interrupt; and by testing appropriate status bits, the interrupt service routine will determine which interrupt requests are active. If more than one interrupt request is active, interrupt service routine logic must decide the order in which interrupt requests will be acknowledged.

**But be warned: this type of polling quickly becomes untenable** as a means of controlling microcomputer systems with multiple random interrupts. If you have more than two or three competing external interrupts, the time taken to read Status register contents and arbitrate priority will become excessive. If your application demands numerous external interrupts, then you must resort to external hardware which implements interrupt vectoring. We will describe ways in which this can be done.

If you casually look at a description of MC6800 interrupt logic, you may at first believe that some level of interrupt vectoring is provided. In reality, that is not the case.

**The MC6800 sets aside the eight highest addressable memory locations for interrupt processing purposes. Four 16-bit addresses are stored in these eight memory locations, identifying the interrupt service routine's starting address for the four possible sources of interrupt. This is how the eight memory locations are used:**

| | |
|---|---|
| FFF8 and FFF9 | Normal external interrupt |
| FFFA and FFFB | Software interrupt |
| FFFC and FFFD | Non-maskable interrupt |
| FFFE and FFFF | Reset (or restart) |

The lower address (FFF8, FFFA, FFFC, FFFE) holds the high order byte of the starting address.

**MC6800 INTERRUPT PRIORITIES**

In the event of simultaneous interrupt requests, **this is the priority sequence** during the acknowledge process:

| | | |
|---|---|---|
| Highest | (1) | Restart |
| | (2) | Non-maskable interrupt |
| | (3) | Software interrupt |
| Lowest | (4) | Normal external interrupt |

Only the lowest priority interrupt is normally used by the typical support device that is capable of requesting interrupt service. The three higher priority interrupt levels represent special conditions and cannot be accessed by the standard external interrupt request.

**We will begin our discussion of MC6800 interrupt processing by describing the four interrupts.**

**MC6800 NORMAL EXTERNAL INTERRUPTS**

**The normal external interrupt request is the standard interrupt present on all microprocessors that support interrupts;** it is equivalent to the 8080A INT input. In very simple systems, the addresses $FFF8_{16}$ and $FFF9_{16}$ may indeed access real memory locations; in the multiple interrupt MC6800 microcomputer systems, $FFF9_{16}$ is more likely to select an 8-bit buffer within which an address vector is stored identifying the interrupting source. This is essentially how the MC6828 Priority Interrupt Controller (PIC) works.

**MC6800 SOFTWARE INTERRUPT**

**MC6800 SWI INSTRUCTION**

**A software interrupt is initiated by the execution of the SWI instruction.** What the SWI instruction does is cause the MC6800 to go through the complete logic of an interrupt request and acknowledge, even though the interrupting source is within the CPU. Software interrupts are typically used as a response to fatal errors occurring within program logic. Whenever your program logic encounters a situation that must not, or should not exist, the error condition may be trapped by executing an SWI instruction; this causes a call to some general purpose, error recovery program.

**MC6800 NON-MASKABLE INTERRUPT**

**The non-maskable interrupt cannot be disabled.** Otherwise it is identical to the normal external interrupt request. Note that the 8080A has no non-maskable interrupt; however, the Zilog Z80 and the 8085 have incorporated this feature.

**MC6800 RESET**

A Reset is treated as the highest priority interrupt in an MC6800. How does the Reset differ from the non-maskable interrupt? Conceptually, the non-maskable interrupt is going to be triggered by a termination condition such as power failure, while the **Reset is going to be triggered by an initiating condition such as power being turned on.**

**There are some differences between the MC6800's response to a Reset as compared to any other interrupt request.**

To contrast the two, we will look at the normal interrupt acknowledge sequence, and then we will look at a reset. Figure 9-8 illustrates **MC6800 response to a normal external interrupt, a software interrupt, or a non-maskable interrupt.** In each case, the interrupt request will be acknowledged upon completion of an instruction's execution. A normal external interrupt will only be acknowledged providing interrupts have been enabled.

If more than one interrupt request exists, then the highest priority interrupt will be acknowledged.

Following the interrupt acknowledge, normal interrupts are disabled by the CPU, which then pushes onto the Stack the contents of all internal registers. This process is illustrated in Figure 9-8. The Program Counter is then loaded with the appropriate interrupt service routine starting address, which will be fetched from memory locations $FFF8_{16}$ and $FFF9_{16}$, $FFFA_{16}$ and $FFFB_{16}$ or $FFFC_{16}$ and $FFFD_{16}$.

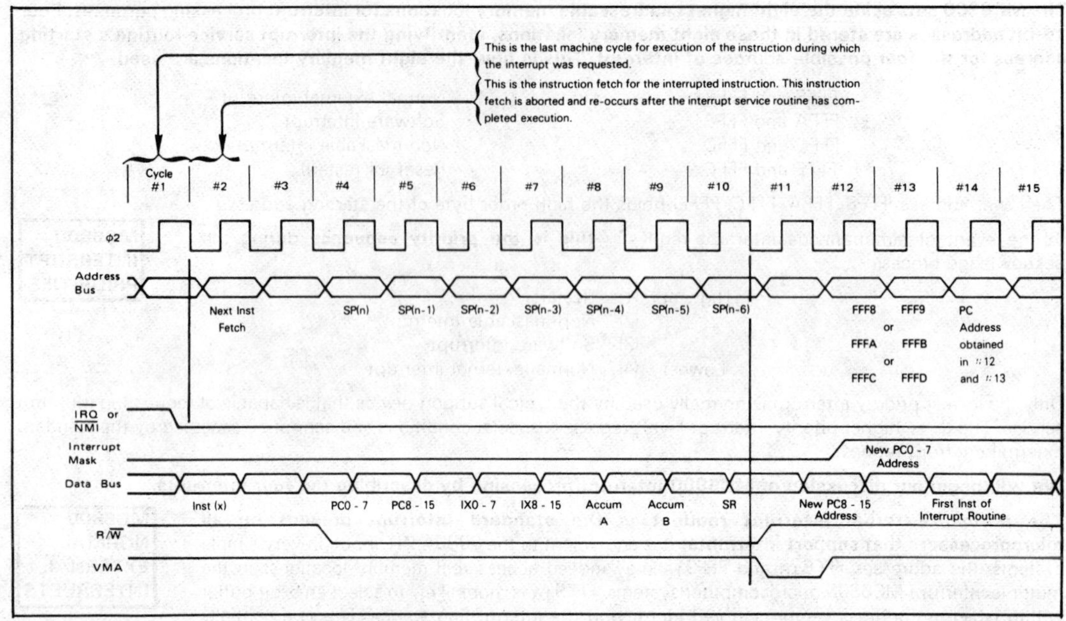


Figure 9-8. MC6800 Interrupt Acknowledge Sequence

Referring to Figure 9-8, note that an interrupt is acknowledged following the last machine cycle for the instruction during which the interrupt request occurred. During the first two machine cycles following the interrupt acknowledge, an instruction fetch is executed, as it would have been had the interrupt not occurred. This instruction fetch is aborted and will reoccur after the interrupt service routine has completed execution. Two machine cycles are expended performing this aborted instruction fetch.

Following the aborted instruction fetch, CPU registers' contents are pushed onto the Stack in the following order:

- Lower half of Program Counter
- Upper half of Program Counter
- Lower half of Index register
- Upper half of Index register
- Accumulator A
- Accumulator B
- Status register

When the 8080A acknowledges an interrupt, if CPU registers' contents are going to be saved on the Stack, you must execute individual instructions to perform the operations which the MC6800 performs automatically. The advantage of the MC6800's scheme is that it saves instruction execution time. The disadvantage of this scheme is that there are occasions when you do not need to bother saving registers' contents.

After all CPU registers' contents have been saved on the Stack, the next two machine cycles are used to fetch an address from the appropriate two high memory bytes. This address is loaded into the Program Counter, causing a branch to the appropriate interrupt service routine.

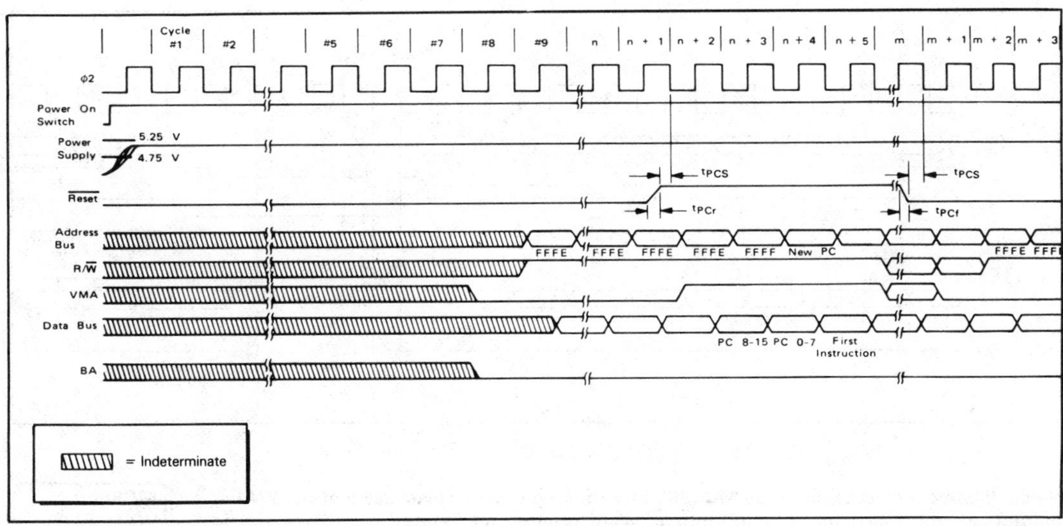


Figure 9-9. The Reset Sequence

**The MC6800 RESET OPERATION**

**We will now examine the MC6800 Reset operation.**

**Figure 9-9 illustrates Reset timing.** First of all, note that $\overline{\text{RESET}}$ must be held low for at least eight machine cycles to give the CPU sufficient response time. On the high-to-low transition of $\overline{\text{RESET}}$ the CPU outputs VMA and BA low and R/$\overline{\text{W}}$ is high. On the subsequent low-to-high transition of $\overline{\text{RESET}}$, maskable interrupts are disabled, then the contents of memory locations FFFE$_{16}$ and FFFF$_{16}$ are fetched and loaded into the Program Counter. If $\overline{\text{RESET}}$ is not held low for a minimum of eight machine cycles, then when $\overline{\text{RESET}}$ is input high again, indeterminate program execution may follow.

**It is absolutely vital that the $\overline{\text{RESET}}$ rise time is less than 100 nanoseconds on the low-to-high transition of $\overline{\text{RESET}}$.**

Additionally, you must provide external logic to hold $\overline{\text{IRQ}}$ and $\overline{\text{NMI}}$ high (inactive) while $\overline{\text{RESET}}$ is active (low). If an interrupt input becomes active while $\overline{\text{RESET}}$ is active, indeterminate program execution will result when $\overline{\text{RESET}}$ goes high.

We stated that the difference between a Reset and a non-maskable interrupt is that the Reset represents initiation conditions. This is illustrated in Figure 9-9, which includes the power supply level. When power is first turned on, the MC6800 will automatically trigger a Reset when power increases above +4.75 volts; this is in response to the normal powering up sequence. The fact that Reset represents initiation conditions also explains why no CPU registers' contents are saved, as occurs with any other interrupt. Clearly, if we are initiating operations, there can be no prior registers' contents to be saved. Therefore pushing registers' contents on the Stack would be pointless and impossible: it would be pointless because there is nothing to save; it would be impossible because when powering up, we have no idea what the Stack Pointer contains.

**MC6800 RESET DURING POWER UP**

**Powering up an MC6800 microcomputer system represents a special Reset case.** Those MC6800 microcomputer system devices that have an external Reset input control, expect this control to be held low while power is being turned on for the first eight clock cycles following power-up. When designing Reset logic be sure to keep this in mind.

MC6800 configurations using 8080A support devices are easy to design and commonly seen. Necessary system bus logic is described later in this chapter. But if you have such a mixed configuration, be sure to satisfy the separate and distinct Reset requirements of the MC6800 CPU as against the 8080A support devices.

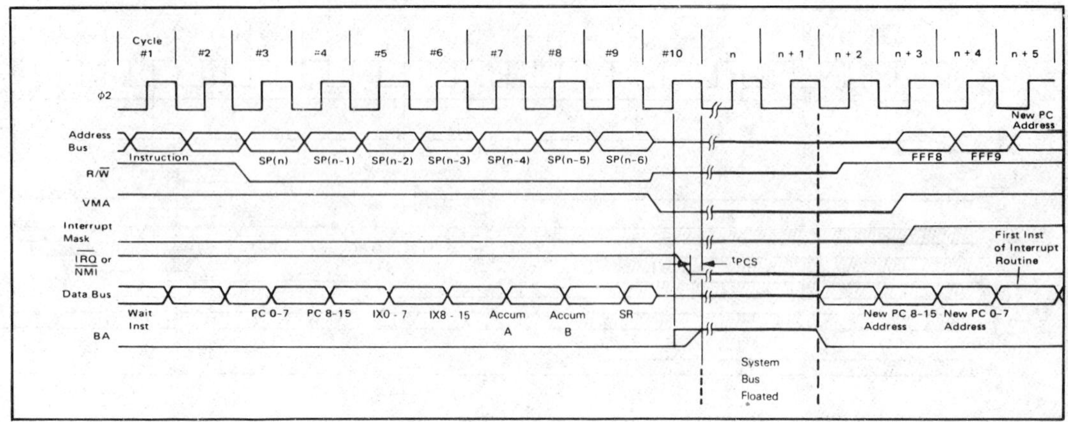


Figure 9-10. MC6800 Wait Instruction Execution Sequence

**MC6800 WAIT STATE**

**We complete our discussion of the MC6800 interrupt logic with a discussion of the WAI instruction, which puts the MC6800 into a "Wait-for-interrupt" state.**

**MC6800 WAI INSTRUCTION**

**A WAI instruction is executed when the CPU has nothing to do except wait for an interrupt.** Rather than pushing registers' contents onto the Stack following the interrupt acknowledge, as illustrated in Figure 9-8, the WAI instruction pushes registers' contents onto the Stack while waiting for the interrupt, as illustrated in Figure 9-10. Thus some execution time is saved.

Once all registers' contents have been pushed onto the Stack, the MC6800 floats the System Bus in the Wait state.

**This gives rise to another frequent use of the WAI instruction: block data transfers under DMA control.**

**MC6800 USE OF WAIT FOR DMA**

Consider again the sequence of events which follows the WAI instruction execution:

1) All registers' contents are pushed onto the Stack.
2) The System Bus is floated.

This is very convenient if you are going to transfer a large block of data via DMA, because you will announce the end of the DMA transfer with an interrupt request. This method of handling block DMA transfers has been discussed in Volume 1. Now when using an MC6800 microcomputer system, all you need to do is initiate the actual DMA transfer by executing a WAI instruction; knowing that once the DMA transfer has been completed, an interrupt will be requested and program execution can continue.

## THE MC6800 INSTRUCTION SET

**Table 9-1 summarizes the MC6800 instruction set;** this instruction set is characterized by a heavy use of read/write memory and a rich variety of instructions that are able to manipulate the contents of memory locations as though they were programmable registers. Whereas the primary memory reference instructions offer base page direct addressing, extended direct addressing or indexed addressing, secondary memory reference instructions offer extended direct addressing and indexed addressing only. This simply means that secondary memory reference instructions use three-byte direct addressing even when a base page byte must be accessed.

**Of the microcomputers described in this book, the MC6800 has one of the largest varieties of Branch-on-Condition instructions.** Note that these and the unconditional Branch instructions are the only MC6800 instructions which use program relative direct addressing.

**When comparing the MC6800 and 8080A instruction sets,** the conclusion we must draw is that the MC6800 is going to have to rely on a large number of memory reference instructions. You are going to have to set up programs with this in mind. As a result, relatively simple programs will make the MC6800 look better than the 8080A, because the MC6800 has such a diverse variety of memory reference instructions. The moment a program starts to become complicated, the large number of 8080A registers is quickly going to become an advantage, since the MC6800 will be forced to execute memory reference instructions where the 8080A can use register-register instructions.

**The SWI and WAI instructions within the interrupt instruction group are relatively unusual within microcomputer systems.**

The SWI instruction initiates a normal interrupt sequence, taking the interrupt service routine's starting address from memory locations $FFFA_{16}$ and $FFFB_{16}$.

The WAI instruction prepares for an interrupt by saving the contents of all registers and status on the Stack; the System Bus is then floated while the CPU waits for an interrupt request to occur.

**We have described both the SWI and WAI instructions in some detail earlier in this chapter.**

The one set of instructions which are missing, and which would greatly enhance the MC6800 instruction set, are instructions that move data between the Accumulator and the Index register, or allow Accumulator contents to be added to the Index register.

## THE BENCHMARK PROGRAM

**The benchmark program is coded for the MC6800 as follows:**

```
        STS    SSP      SAVE STACK POINTER CONTENTS IN MEMORY
        LDX    #TABLE   LOAD TABLE BASE ADDRESS INTO INDEX REGISTER
        LDX    0,X      LOAD ADDRESS OF FIRST FREE TABLE BYTE
        LDS    #IOBUF   LOAD I/O BUFFER STARTING ADDRESS
LOOP    PULL   A        LOAD NEXT BYTE INTO A
        STAA   0,X      STORE IN NEXT FREE TABLE BYTE
        INX             INCREMENT INDEX REGISTER
        DEC    IOCNT    DECREMENT I/O BYTE COUNT IN MEMORY
        BNE    LOOP     RETURN FOR MORE BYTES
        STX    TABLE    STORE NEW ADDRESS FOR FIRST FREE TABLE BYTE
        LDS    SSP      RELOAD STACK POINTER
```

The memory initialization for the MC6800 interpretation of the benchmark program is identical to the memory initialization for the 8080A benchmark program. The MC6800 assumes that there is some memory location in which the current real Stack address can be stored, so that the Stack Pointer may be used as a Data Counter.

In Table 9-1, symbols are used as follows:

ACX    Either Accumulator A or Accumulator B

The registers:

- A,B  Accumulator
- X  Index register
- PC  Program Counter
- SP  Stack Pointer
- SR  Status register

Statuses shown:

- C  Carry status
- Z  Zero status
- S  Sign status
- O  Overflow status
- I  Interrupt status
- $A_C$  Auxiliary Carry status

Symbols in the STATUSES column:

- (blank)  operation does not affect status
- X  operation affects status
- 0  flag is cleared by the operation
- 1  flag is set by the operation

| | |
|---|---|
| ADR8 | An 8-bit (1-byte) quantity which may be used to directly address the first 256 locations in memory, or may be an 8-bit unsigned displacement to be added to the Index register. |
| ADR16 | A 16-bit memory address |
| B2 | Instruction Byte 2 |
| B3 | Instruction Byte 3 |
| DATA | An 8-bit binary data unit |
| DATA16 | A 16-bit binary data unit |
| DISP | An 8-bit signed binary address displacement |
| xx(HI) | The high order 8 bits of the 16-bit quantity xx; for example, SP(HI) means bits 15 - 8 of the Stack Pointer. |
| xx(LO) | The low order 8 bits of the 16-bit quantity xx; for example, PC(LO) means bits 7 - 0 of the Program Counter. |
| [ ] | Contents of location enclosed within brackets. |
| [[ ]] | Implied memory addressing; the contents of the memory location designated by the contents of a register. |
| [MEM] | Symbol for memory location indicated by base page direct, extended direct, or indexed addressing. That is:<br>[MEM] = [ADR8]<br>or<br>[ADR16]<br>or<br>[[X]+ADR8] |
| [M] | Symbol for memory location indicated by extended direct or indexed addressing. That is:<br>[M]=[ADR16]<br>or<br>[[X]+ADR8] |
| ∧ | Logical AND |
| ∨ | Logical OR |
| ⊻ | Logical Exclusive-OR |
| ← | Data is transferred in the direction of the arrow. |

Table 9-1. A Summary of the MC6800 Instruction Set

| TYPE | MNEMONIC | OPERAND(S) | BYTES | STATUS | | | | | | OPERATION PERFORMED |
|---|---|---|---|---|---|---|---|---|---|---|
| | | | | C | Z | S | O | $A_C$ | I | |
| PRIMARY MEMORY REFERENCE AND I/O | LDA | ACX,ADR8<br>ACX,ADR16 | 2<br>3 | | X | X | 0 | | | [ACX]←[MEM]<br>Load A or B using base page direct, extended direct, or indexed addressing. |
| | STA | ACX,ADR8<br>ACX,ADR16 | 2<br>3 | | X | X | 0 | | | [MEM]←[ACX]<br>Store A or B using direct, extended, or indexed addressing. |
| | LDX | ADR8<br>ADR16 | 2<br>3 | | X | X | 0 | | | [X(HI)]←[MEM], [X(LO)]←[MEM + 1]<br>Load Index register using direct, extended, or indexed addressing. Sign status reflects Index register bit 15. |
| | STX | ADR8<br>ADR16 | 2<br>3 | | X | X | 0 | | | [MEM]←[X(HI)], [MEM + 1]←[X(LO)]<br>Store contents of Index register using direct, extended, or indexed addressing. Sign status reflects Index register bit 15. |
| | LDS | ADR8<br>ADR16 | 2<br>3 | | X | X | 0 | | | [SP(HI)]←[MEM], [SP(LO)]←[MEM + 1]<br>Load Stack Pointer using direct, extended, or indexed addressing. Sign status reflects Stack Pointer bit 15. |
| | STS | ADR8<br>ADR16 | 2<br>3 | | X | X | 0 | | | [MEM]←[SP(HI)], [MEM + 1]←[SP(LO)]<br>Store contents of Stack Pointer using direct, extended, or indexed addressing. Sign status reflects Stack Pointer bit 15. |
| SECONDARY MEMORY REFERENCE (MEMORY OPERATE) | ADD | ACX,ADR8<br>ACX,ADR16 | 2<br>3 | X | X | X | X | X | | [ACX]←[ACX] + [MEM]<br>Add to Accumulator A or B using base page direct, extended direct, or indexed addressing. |
| | ADC | ACX,ADR8<br>ACX,ADR16 | 2<br>3 | X | X | X | X | X | | [ACX]←[ACX] + [MEM] + C<br>Add with carry to Accumulator A or B using direct, extended, or indexed addressing. |
| | AND | ACX,ADR8<br>ACX,ADR16 | 2<br>3 | | X | X | 0 | | | [ACX]←[ACX] $\wedge$ [MEM]<br>AND with Accumulator A or B using direct, extended, or indexed addressing. |
| | BIT | ACX,ADR8<br>ACX,ADR16 | 2<br>3 | | X | X | 0 | | | [ACX] $\wedge$ [MEM]<br>AND with Accumulator A or B, but only Status register is affected. |
| | CMP | ACX,ADR8<br>ACX,ADR16 | 2<br>3 | X | X | X | X | | | [ACX] - [MEM]<br>Compare with Accumulator A or B (only Status register is affected). |
| | EOR | ACX,ADR8<br>ACX,ADR16 | 2<br>3 | | X | X | 0 | | | [ACX]←[ACX] $\forall$ [MEM]<br>Exclusive-OR with Accumulator A or B using direct, extended, or indexed addressing. |
| | ORA | ACX,ADR8<br>ACX,ADR16 | 2<br>3 | | X | X | 0 | | | [ACX]←[ACX] V [MEM]<br>OR with Accumulator A or B using direct, extended, or indexed addressing. |
| | SUB | ACX,ADR8<br>ACX,ADR16 | 2<br>3 | X | X | X | X | | | [ACX]←[ACX] - [MEM]<br>Subtract from Accumulator A or B using direct, extended, or indexed addressing. |
| | SBC | ACX,ADR8<br>ACX,ADR16 | 2<br>3 | X | X | X | X | | | [ACX]←[ACX] - [MEM] - C<br>Subtract with carry from Accumulator A or B using direct, extended, or indexed addressing. |
| | CPX | ADR8<br>ADR16 | 2<br>3 | | X | X | X | | | [X(HI)] - [MEM], [X(LO)] - [MEM + 1]<br>Compare with contents of Index register (only Status register is affected). Sign and Overflow statuses reflect result on most significant byte. |
| | CLR | ADR8<br>ADR16 | 2<br>3 | 0 | 1 | 0 | 0 | | | [M] ← $00_{16}$<br>Clear memory location using extended or indexed addressing. |
| | COM | ADR8<br>ADR16 | 2<br>3 | 1 | X | X | 0 | | | [M]←$\overline{[M]}$<br>Complement contents of memory location (ones complement). |
| | NEG | ADR8<br>ADR16 | 2<br>3 | X | X | X | X | | | [M] ← $00_{16}$ - [M]<br>Negate contents of memory location (twos complement). Carry status is set if result is $00_{16}$ and reset otherwise. Overflow status is set if result is $80_{16}$ and reset otherwise. |

| TYPE | MNEMONIC | OPERAND(S) | BYTES | STATUS C | Z | S | O | $A_C$ | I | OPERATION PERFORMED |
|---|---|---|---|---|---|---|---|---|---|---|
| SECONDARY MEMORY REFERENCE (MEMORY OPERATE) CONTINUED | DEC | ADR8<br>ADR16 | 2<br>3 | | X | X | X | | | [M]←[M] - 1<br>Decrement contents of memory location, using extended or indexed addressing. Overflow status is set if operand was $80_{16}$ before execution, and cleared otherwise. |
| | INC | ADR8<br>ADR16 | 2<br>3 | | X | X | X | | | [M]←[M] + 1<br>Increment contents of memory location, using extended or indexed addressing. Overflow status is set if operand was $7F_{16}$ before execution, and cleared otherwise. |
| | ROL | ADR8<br>ADR16 | 2<br>3 | X | X | X | X | | | C ← 7 ← 0 [M], O ← S ∀ C<br>Rotate contents of memory location left through carry. |
| | ROR | ADR8<br>ADR16 | 2<br>3 | X | X | X | X | | | C → 7 → 0 [M], O ← S ∀ C<br>Rotate contents of memory location right through carry. |
| | ASL | ADR8<br>ADR16 | 2<br>3 | X | X | X | X | | | C ← 7 ← 0 [M] ← 0, O ← S ∀ C<br>Arithmetic shift left. Bit 0 is set to 0. |
| | ASR | ADR8<br>ADR16 | 2<br>3 | X | X | X | X | | | 7 → 0 [M] → C, O ← S ∀ C<br>Arithmetic shift right. Bit 7 stays the same. |
| | LSR | ADR8<br>ADR16 | 2<br>3 | X | X | 0 | X | | | 0 → 7 → 0 → C, O ← S ∀ C<br>Logical shift right. Bit 7 is set to 0. |
| | TST | ADR8<br>ADR16 | 2<br>3 | 0 | X | X | 0 | | | [M] - $00_{16}$<br>Test contents of memory location for zero or negative value. |
| IMMEDIATE | LDA | ACX,DATA | 2 | | X | X | 0 | | | [ACX]←DATA<br>Load A or B immediate. |
| | LDX | DATA16 | 3 | | X | X | 0 | | | [X(HI)]←[B2], [X(LO)]←[B3]<br>Load Index register immediate. Sign status reflects Index register bit 15. |
| | LDS | DATA16 | 3 | | X | X | 0 | | | [SP(HI)]←[B2], [X(LO)]←[B3]<br>Load Stack Pointer immediate. Sign status reflects Stack Pointer bit 15. |
| IMMEDIATE OPERATE | ADD | ACX,DATA | 2 | X | X | X | X | X | | [ACX]←[ACX] + DATA<br>Add immediate to Accumulator A or B. |
| | ADC | ACX,DATA | 2 | X | X | X | X | X | | [ACX]←[ACX] + DATA + C<br>Add immediate with carry to Accumulator A or B. |
| | AND | ACX,DATA | 2 | | X | X | 0 | | | [ACX]←[ACX] ∧ DATA<br>AND immediate with Accumulator A or B. |

Table 9-1. A Summary of the MC6800 Instruction Set (Continued)

| TYPE | MNEMONIC | OPERAND(S) | BYTES | STATUS | | | | | | OPERATION PERFORMED |
|---|---|---|---|---|---|---|---|---|---|---|
| | | | | C | Z | S | O | $A_C$ | I | |
| IMMEDIATE OPERATE (CONTINUED) | BIT | ACX,DATA | 2 | | X | X | 0 | | | [ACX] Λ DATA<br>AND immediate with Accumulator A or B, but only the Status register is affected. |
| | CMP | ACX,DATA | 2 | X | X | X | X | | | [ACX] - DATA<br>Compare immediate with Accumulator A or B (only the Status register is affected). |
| | EOR | ACX,DATA | 2 | | X | X | 0 | | | [ACX]←[ACX]⊻DATA<br>Exclusive-OR immediate with Accumulator A or B. |
| | ORA | ACX,DATA | 2 | | X | X | 0 | | | [ACX]←[ACX] V DATA<br>OR immediate with Accumulator A or B. |
| | SUB | ACX,DATA | 2 | X | X | X | X | | | [ACX]←[ACX] - DATA<br>Subtract immediate from Accumulator A or B. |
| | SBC | ACX,DATA | 2 | X | X | X | X | | | [ACX]←[ACX] - DATA - C<br>Subtract immediate with carry from Accumulator A or B. |
| | CPX | DATA16 | 3 | | X | X | X | | | [X(HI)] - [B2], [X(LO)] - [B3]<br>Compare immediate with contents of Index register (only the Status register is affected). Sign and Overflow status reflect result on most significant byte. |
| JUMP | JMP | ADR8<br>ADR16 | 2<br>3 | | | | | | | [PC]←[X] + ADR8 or<br>[PC(HI)]←[B2], [PC(LO)]←[B3]<br>Jump to indexed or extended address. |
| | JSR | ADR8<br>ADR16 | 2<br>3 | | | | | | | [[SP]]←[PC(LO)], [[SP]-1]←[PC(HI)], [SP]←[SP]-2<br>[PC]←[X] + ADR8 or<br>[PC(HI)]←[B2], [PC(LO)]←[B3]<br>Jump to subroutine (indexed or extended addressing). |
| | BRA | DISP | 2 | | | | | | | [PC]←[PC] + DISP + 2<br>Unconditional branch relative to present Program Counter contents. |
| | BSR | DISP | 2 | | | | | | | [[SP]]←[PC(LO)], [[SP]-1]←[PC(HI)], [SP]←[SP]-2,<br>[PC]←[PC] + DISP + 2<br>Unconditional branch to subroutine located relative to present Program Counter contents. |
| BRANCH ON CONDITION | BCC | DISP | 2 | | | | | | | [PC]←[PC] + DISP + 2 if the given condition is true:<br>C = 0 (Branch if carry clear) |
| | BCS | DISP | 2 | | | | | | | C = 1 (Branch if carry set) |
| | BEQ | DISP | 2 | | | | | | | Z = 1 (Branch if equal to zero) |
| | BGE | DISP | 2 | | | | | | | S ⊻ O = 0 (Branch if greater than or equal to zero) |
| | BGT | DISP | 2 | | | | | | | Z V (S ⊻ O) = 0 (Branch if greater than zero) |
| | BHI | DISP | 2 | | | | | | | C V Z = 0 (Branch if Accumulator contents higher than comparand) |
| | BLE | DISP | 2 | | | | | | | Z V (S ⊻ O) = 1 (Branch if less than or equal to zero) |
| | BLS | DISP | 2 | | | | | | | C V Z = 1 (Branch if Accumulator contents less than or same as comparand) |
| | BLT | DISP | 2 | | | | | | | S ⊻ O = 1 (Branch if less than zero) |
| | BMI | DISP | 2 | | | | | | | S = 1 (Branch if minus) |
| | BNE | DISP | 2 | | | | | | | Z = 0 (Branch if not equal to zero) |
| | BVC | DISP | 2 | | | | | | | O = 0 (Branch if overflow clear) |
| | BVS | DISP | 2 | | | | | | | O = 1 (Branch if overflow set) |
| | BPL | DISP | 2 | | | | | | | S = 0 (Branch if plus) |

Table 9-1. A Summary of the MC6800 Instruction Set (Continued)

| TYPE | MNEMONIC | OPERAND(S) | BYTES | STATUS C | Z | S | O | $A_C$ | I | OPERATION PERFORMED |
|---|---|---|---|---|---|---|---|---|---|---|
| REGISTER-REGISTER MOVE | TAB | | 1 | | X | X | 0 | | | [B]←[A] Move Accumulator A contents to Accumulator B. |
| | TBA | | 1 | | X | X | 0 | | | [A]←[B] Move Accumulator B contents to Accumulator A. |
| | TXS | | 1 | | | | | | | [SP]←[X]-1 Move Index register contents to Stack Pointer and decrement. |
| | TSX | | 1 | | | | | | | [X]←[SP]+1 Move Stack Pointer contents to Index register and increment. |
| REGISTER REGISTER OPERATE | ABA | | 1 | X | X | X | X | X | | [A]←[A]+[B] Add contents of Accumulators A and B. |
| | CBA | | 1 | X | X | X | X | | | [A] - [B] Compare contents of Accumulators A and B. Only the Status register is affected. |
| | SBA | | 1 | X | X | X | X | | | [A]←[A] - [B] Subtract contents of Accumulator B from those of Accumulator A. |
| REGISTER OPERATE | CLR | ACX | 1 | 0 | 1 | 0 | 0 | | | [ACX]←$00_{16}$ Clear Accumulator A or B. |
| | COM | ACX | 1 | 1 | X | X | 0 | | | [ACX]←$\overline{[ACX]}$ Complement contents of Accumulator A or B (ones complement). |
| | NEG | ACX | 1 | X | X | X | X | | | [ACX]←$00_{16}$ - [ACX] Negate contents of Accumulator A or B (twos complement). Carry status is set if result is $00_{16}$ and reset otherwise. Overflow status is set if result is $80_{16}$ and reset otherwise. |
| | DAA | | 1 | X | X | X | X | | | Decimal adjust A. Convert contents of A (the binary sum of BCD operands) to BCD format. Carry status is set if value of upper four bits is greater than 9, but not cleared if previously set. |
| | DEC | ACX | 1 | | X | X | X | | | [ACX]←[ACX] - 1 Decrement contents of Accumulator A or B. Overflow status is set if operand was $80_{16}$ before execution, and cleared otherwise. |
| | DEX | | 1 | | X | | | | | [X]←[X] - 1 Decrement contents of Index register. |
| | DES | | 1 | | | | | | | [SP]←[SP] - 1 Decrement contents of Stack Pointer. |
| | INC | ACX | 1 | | X | X | X | | | [ACX]←[ACX] + 1 Increment contents of Accumulator A or B. Overflow status is set if operand was $7F_{16}$ before execution, and cleared otherwise. |
| | INX | | 1 | | X | | | | | [X]←[X] + 1 Increment contents of Index register. |
| | INS | | 1 | | | | | | | [SP]←[SP] + 1 Increment contents of Stack Pointer. |
| | ROL | ACX | 1 | X | X | X | X | | | C ← 7 ← 0 [ACX] O←S⊻C Rotate Accumulator A or B left through carry. |

Table 9-1. A Summary of the MC6800 Instruction Set (Continued)

| TYPE | MNEMONIC | OPERAND(S) | BYTES | STATUS C | STATUS Z | STATUS S | STATUS O | STATUS $A_C$ | STATUS I | OPERATION PERFORMED |
|---|---|---|---|---|---|---|---|---|---|---|
| REGISTER OPERATE (CONTINUED) | ROR | ACX | 1 | X | X | X | X | | | C → [7 → 0] → C<br>[ACX]<br>O ← S ⊻ C<br>Rotate Accumulator A or B right through carry. |
| | ASL | ACX | 1 | X | X | X | X | | | C ← [7 ← 0] ← 0,<br>[ACX]<br>O ← S ⊻ C<br>Arithmetic shift left. Bit 0 is set to 0. |
| | ASR | ACX | 1 | X | X | X | X | | | [7 → 0] → C (bit 7 fed back)<br>[ACX]<br>O ← S ⊻ C<br>Arithmetic shift right. Bit 7 stays the same. |
| | LSR | ACX | 1 | X | X | 0 | X | | | 0 → [7 → 0] → C<br>O ← S ⊻ C<br>Logical shift right. Bit 7 is set to 0. |
| | TST | ACX | 1 | 0 | X | X | 0 | | | [ACX] - $00_{16}$<br>Test contents of Accumulator A or B for zero or negative value. |
| STACK | PSH | ACX | 1 | | | | | | | [[SP]] ← [ACX]<br>[SP] ← [SP] - 1<br>Push contents of Accumulator A or B onto top of Stack and decrement Stack Pointer. |
| | PUL | ACX | 1 | | | | | | | [SP] ← [SP] + 1<br>[ACX] ← [[SP]]<br>Increment Stack Pointer and pull Accumulator A or B from top of Stack. |
| | RTS | | 1 | | | | | | | [PC(HI)] ← [[SP] + 1], [PC(LO)] ← [[SP] + 2], [SP] ← [SP] + 2<br>Return from subroutine. Pull PC from top of Stack and increment Stack Pointer. |
| INTERRUPT | CLI | | 1 | | | | | | 0 | I ← 0<br>Clear interrupt mask to enable interrupts. |
| | SEI | | 1 | | | | | | 1 | I ← 1<br>Set interrupt mask to disable interrupts. |
| | RTI | | 1 | X | X | X | X | X | X | [SR] ← [[SP] + 1],<br>[B] ← [[SP] + 2],<br>[A] ← [[SP] + 3],<br>[X(HI)] ← [[SP] + 4],<br>[X(LO)] ← [[SP] + 5],<br>[PC(HI)] ← [[SP] + 6],<br>[PC(LO)] ← [[SP] + 7],<br>[SP] ← [SP] + 7<br>Return from interrupt. Pull registers from Stack and increment Stack Pointer. |

Table 9-1. A Summary of the MC6800 Instruction Set (Continued)

| TYPE | MNEMONIC | OPERAND(S) | BYTES | STATUS | | | | | | OPERATION PERFORMED |
|---|---|---|---|---|---|---|---|---|---|---|
| | | | | C | Z | S | O | $A_C$ | I | |
| INTERRUPT (CONTINUED) | SWI | | 1 | | | | | | 1 | [[SP]]←[PC(LO)],<br>[[SP]-1]←[PC(HI)],<br>[[SP]-2]←[X(LO)],<br>[[SP]-3]←[X(HI)],<br>[[SP]-4]←[A],<br>[[SP]-5]←[B],<br>[[SP]-6]←[SR],<br>[SP]←[SP]-7,<br>[PC(HI)]←[$FFFA_{16}$]<br>[PC(LO)]←[$FFFB_{16}$]<br>Software Interrupt: push registers onto Stack, decrement Stack Pointer, and jump to interrupt subroutine. |
| | WAI | | 1 | | | | | | 1 | [[SP]]←[PC(LO)],<br>[[SP]-1]←[PC(HI)],<br>[[SP]-2]←[X(LO)],<br>[[SP]-3]←[X(HI)],<br>[[SP]-4]←[A],<br>[[SP]-5]←[B],<br>[[SP]-6]←[SR],<br>[SP]←[SP]-7<br>Push registers onto Stack, decrement Stack Pointer, and wiat for interrupt. If [I]=1 when WAI is executed, a non-maskable interrupt is required to exit the Wait state. Otherwise, [I]←1 when the interrupt occurs. |
| STATUS | CLC | | 1 | 0 | | | | | | C←0<br>Clear carry |
| | SEC | | 1 | 1 | | | | | | C←1<br>Set carry |
| | CLV | | 1 | | | | 0 | | | O←0<br>Clear overflow status bit |
| | SEV | | 1 | | | | 1 | | | O←1<br>Set overflow status bit |
| | TAP | | 1 | X | X | X | X | X | X | [SR]←[A]<br>Transfer contents of Accumulator A to Status register. |
| | TPA | | 1 | | | | | | | [A]←[SR]<br>Transfer contents of Status register to Accumulator A. |
| | NOP | | 1 | | | | | | | No Operation |

## MC6800 SUMMARY OF CYCLE BY CYCLE OPERATION

This table provides a detailed description of the information present on the Address Bus, Data Bus, Valid Memory Address line (VMA), and the Read/Write line (R/W) during each cycle for each instruction.

This information is useful in comparing actual with expected results during debug of both software and hardware as the control program is executed. The information is categorized in groups according to Addressing Mode and Number of Cycles per instruction. (In general, instructions with the same Addressing Mode and Number of Cycles execute in the same manner; exceptions are indicated in the table.)

Table 9-2. Operation Summary

| | ADDRESS MODE AND INSTRUCTIONS | CYCLES | CYCLE NO. | VMA LINE | ADDRESS BUS | R/W LINE | DATA BUS |
|---|---|---|---|---|---|---|---|
| IMMEDIATE | ADC EOR<br>ADD LDA<br>AND ORA<br>BIT SBC<br>CMP SUB | 2 | 1 | 1 | Op Code Address | 1 | Op Code |
| | | | 2 | 1 | Op Code Address + 1 | 1 | Operand Data |
| | CPX<br>LDS<br>LDX | 3 | 1 | 1 | Op Code Address | 1 | Op Code |
| | | | 2 | 1 | Op Code Address + 1 | 1 | Operand Data (High Order Byte) |
| | | | 3 | 1 | Op Code Address + 2 | 1 | Operand Data (Low Order Byte) |
| DIRECT | ADC EOR<br>ADD LDA<br>AND ORA<br>BIT SBC<br>CMP SUB | 3 | 1 | 1 | Op Code Address | 1 | Op Code |
| | | | 2 | 1 | Op Code Address + 1 | 1 | Address of Operand |
| | | | 3 | 1 | Address of Operand | 1 | Operand Data |
| | CPX<br>LDS<br>LDX | 4 | 1 | 1 | Op Code Address | 1 | Op Code |
| | | | 2 | 1 | Op Code Address + 1 | 1 | Address of Operand |
| | | | 3 | 1 | Address of Operand | 1 | Operand Data (High Order Byte) |
| | | | 4 | 1 | Operand Address + 1 | 1 | Operand Data (Low Order Byte) |
| | STA | 4 | 1 | 1 | Op Code Address | 1 | Op Code |
| | | | 2 | 1 | Op Code Address + 1 | 1 | Destination Address |
| | | | 3 | 0 | Destination Address | 1 | Irrelevant Data (Note 1) |
| | | | 4 | 1 | Destination Address | 0 | Data from Accumulator |
| | STS<br>STX | 5 | 1 | 1 | Op Code Address | 1 | Op Code |
| | | | 2 | 1 | Op Code Address + 1 | 1 | Address of Operand |
| | | | 3 | 0 | Address of Operand | 1 | Irrelevant Data (Note 1) |
| | | | 4 | 1 | Address of Operand | 0 | Register Data (High Order Byte) |
| | | | 5 | 1 | Address of Operand + 1 | 0 | Register Data (Low Order Byte) |
| INDEXED | JMP | 4 | 1 | 1 | Op Code Address | 1 | Op Code |
| | | | 2 | 1 | Op Code Address + 1 | 1 | Offset |
| | | | 3 | 0 | Index Register | 1 | Irrelevant Data (Note 1) |
| | | | 4 | 0 | Index Register Plus Offset (w/o Carry) | 1 | Irrelevant Data (Note 1) |
| | ADC EOR<br>ADD LDA<br>AND ORA<br>BIT SBC<br>CMP SUB | 5 | 1 | 1 | Op Code Address | 1 | Op Code |
| | | | 2 | 1 | Op Code Address + 1 | 1 | Offset |
| | | | 3 | 0 | Index Register | 1 | Irrelevant Data (Note 1) |
| | | | 4 | 0 | Index Register Plus Offset (w/o Carry) | 1 | Irrelevant Data (Note 1) |
| | | | 5 | 1 | Index Register Plus Offset | 1 | Operand Data |
| | CPX<br>LDS<br>LDX | 6 | 1 | 1 | Op Code Address | 1 | Op Code |
| | | | 2 | 1 | Op Code Address + 1 | 1 | Offset |
| | | | 3 | 0 | Index Register | 1 | Irrelevant Data (Note 1) |
| | | | 4 | 0 | Index Register Plus Offset (w/o Carry) | 1 | Irrelevant Data (Note 1) |
| | | | 5 | 1 | Index Register Plus Offset | 1 | Operand Data (High Order Byte) |
| | | | 6 | 1 | Index Register Plus Offset + 1 | 1 | Operand Data (Low Order Byte) |
| | STA | 6 | 1 | 1 | Op Code Address | 1 | Op Code |
| | | | 2 | 1 | Op Code Address + 1 | 1 | Offset |
| | | | 3 | 0 | Index Register | 1 | Irrelevant Data (Note 1) |
| | | | 4 | 0 | Index Register Plus Offset (w/o Carry) | 1 | Irrelevant Data (Note 1) |
| | | | 5 | 0 | Index Register Plus Offset | 1 | Irrelevant Data (Note 1) |
| | | | 6 | 1 | Index Register Plus Offset | 0 | Operand Data |
| | ASL LSR<br>ASR NEG<br>CLR ROL<br>COM ROR<br>DEC TST<br>INC | 7 | 1 | 1 | Op Code Address | 1 | Op Code |
| | | | 2 | 1 | Op Code Address + 1 | 1 | Offset |
| | | | 3 | 0 | Index Register | 1 | Irrelevant Data (Note 1) |
| | | | 4 | 0 | Index Register Plus Offset (w/o Carry) | 1 | Irrelevant Data (Note 1) |
| | | | 5 | 1 | Index Register Plus Offset | 1 | Current Operand Data |
| | | | 6 | 0 | Index Register Plus Offset | 1 | Irrelevant Data (Note 1) |
| | | | 7 | 1/0 (Note 3) | Index Register Plus Offset | 0 | New Operand Data (Note 3) |
| | STS<br>STX | 7 | 1 | 1 | Op Code Address | 1 | Op Code |
| | | | 2 | 1 | Op Code Address + 1 | 1 | Offset |
| | | | 3 | 0 | Index Register | 1 | Irrelevant Data (Note 1) |
| | | | 4 | 0 | Index Register Plus Offset (w/o Carry) | 1 | Irrelevant Data (Note 1) |
| | | | 5 | 0 | Index Register Plus Offset | 1 | Irrelevant Data (Note 1) |
| | | | 6 | 1 | Index Register Plus Offset | 0 | Operand Data (High Order Byte) |
| | | | 7 | 1 | Index Register Plus Offset + 1 | 0 | Operand Data (Low Order Byte) |
| | JSR | 8 | 1 | 1 | Op Code Address | 1 | Op Code |
| | | | 2 | 1 | Op Code Address + 1 | 1 | Offset |
| | | | 3 | 0 | Index Register | 1 | Irrelevant Data (Note 1) |
| | | | 4 | 1 | Stack Pointer | 0 | Return Address (Low Order Byte) |
| | | | 5 | 1 | Stack Pointer – 1 | 0 | Return Address (High Order Byte) |
| | | | 6 | 0 | Stack Pointer – 2 | 1 | Irrelevant Data (Note 1) |
| | | | 7 | 0 | Index Register | 1 | Irrelevant Data (Note 1) |
| | | | 8 | 0 | Index Register Plus Offset (w/o Carry) | 1 | Irrelevant Data (Note 1) |

Table 9-2. Operation Summary (Continued)

| | ADDRESS MODE AND INSTRUCTIONS | CYCLES | CYCLE NO. | VMA LINE | ADDRESS BUS | R/W LINE | DATA BUS |
|---|---|---|---|---|---|---|---|
| EXTENDED | JMP | 3 | 1 | 1 | Op Code Address | 1 | Op Code |
| | | | 2 | 1 | Op Code Address + 1 | 1 | Jump Address (High Order Byte) |
| | | | 3 | 1 | Op Code Address + 2 | 1 | Jump Address (Low Order Byte) |
| | ADC EOR<br>ADD LDA<br>AND ORA<br>BIT SBC<br>CMP SUB | 4 | 1 | 1 | Op Code Address | 1 | Op Code |
| | | | 2 | 1 | Op Code Address + 1 | 1 | Address of Operand (High Order Byte) |
| | | | 3 | 1 | Op Code Address + 2 | 1 | Address of Operand (Low Order Byte) |
| | | | 4 | 1 | Address of Operand | 1 | Operand Data |
| | CPX<br>LDS<br>LDX | 5 | 1 | 1 | Op Code Address | 1 | Op Code |
| | | | 2 | 1 | Op Code Address + 1 | 1 | Address of Operand (High Order Byte) |
| | | | 3 | 1 | Op Code Address + 2 | 1 | Address of Operand (Low Order Byte) |
| | | | 4 | 1 | Address of Operand | 1 | Operand Data (High Order Byte) |
| | | | 5 | 1 | Address of Operand + 1 | 1 | Operand Data (Low Order Byte) |
| | STA A<br>STA B | 5 | 1 | 1 | Op Code Address | 1 | Op Code |
| | | | 2 | 1 | Op Code Address + 1 | 1 | Destination Address (High Order Byte) |
| | | | 3 | 1 | Op Code Address + 2 | 1 | Destination Address (Low Order Byte) |
| | | | 4 | 0 | Operand Destination Address | 1 | Irrelevant Data (Note 1) |
| | | | 5 | 1 | Operand Destination Address | 0 | Data from Accumulator |
| | ASL LSR<br>ASR NEG<br>CLR ROL<br>COM ROR<br>DEC TST<br>INC | 6 | 1 | 1 | Op Code Address | 1 | Op Code |
| | | | 2 | 1 | Op Code Address + 1 | 1 | Address of Operand (High Order Byte) |
| | | | 3 | 1 | Op Code Address + 2 | 1 | Address of Operand (Low Order Byte) |
| | | | 4 | 1 | Address of Operand | 1 | Current Operand Data |
| | | | 5 | 0 | Address of Operand | 1 | Irrelevant Data (Note 1) |
| | | | 6 | 1/0 (Note 3) | Address of Operand | 0 | New Operand Data (Note 3) |
| | STS<br>STX | 6 | 1 | 1 | Op Code Address | 1 | Op Code |
| | | | 2 | 1 | Op Code Address + 1 | 1 | Address of Operand (High Order Byte) |
| | | | 3 | 1 | Op Code Address + 2 | 1 | Address of Operand (Low Order Byte) |
| | | | 4 | 0 | Address of Operand | 1 | Irrelevant Data (Note 1) |
| | | | 5 | 1 | Address of Operand | 0 | Operand Data (High Order Byte) |
| | | | 6 | 1 | Address of Operand + 1 | 0 | Operand Data (Low Order Byte) |
| | JSR | 9 | 1 | 1 | Op Code Address | 1 | Op Code |
| | | | 2 | 1 | Op Code Address + 1 | 1 | Address of Subroutine (High Order Byte) |
| | | | 3 | 1 | Op Code Address + 2 | 1 | Address of Subroutine (Low Order Byte) |
| | | | 4 | 1 | Subroutine Starting Address | 1 | Op Code of Next Instruction |
| | | | 5 | 1 | Stack Pointer | 0 | Return Address (Low Order Byte) |
| | | | 6 | 1 | Stack Pointer – 1 | 0 | Return Address (High Order Byte) |
| | | | 7 | 0 | Stack Pointer – 2 | 1 | Irrelevant Data (Note 1) |
| | | | 8 | 0 | Op Code Address + 2 | 1 | Irrelevant Data (Note 1) |
| | | | 9 | 1 | Op Code Address + 2 | 1 | Address of Subroutine (Low Order Byte) |
| REGISTER-REGISTER | ABA DAA SEC<br>ASL DEC SEI<br>ASR INC SEV<br>CBA LSR TAB<br>CLC NEG TAP<br>CLI NOP TBA<br>CLR ROL TPA<br>CLV ROR TST<br>COM SBA | 2 | 1 | 1 | Op Code Address | 1 | Op Code |
| | | | 2 | 1 | Op Code Address + 1 | 1 | Op Code of Next Instruction |
| | DES<br>DEX<br>INS<br>INX | 4 | 1 | 1 | Op Code Address | 1 | Op Code |
| | | | 2 | 1 | Op Code Address + 1 | 1 | Op Code of Next Instruction |
| | | | 3 | 0 | Previous Register Contents | 1 | Irrelevant Data (Note 1) |
| | | | 4 | 0 | New Register Contents | 1 | Irrelevant Data (Note 1) |
| | PSH | 4 | 1 | 1 | Op Code Address | 1 | Op Code |
| | | | 2 | 1 | Op Code Address + 1 | 1 | Op Code of Next Instruction |
| | | | 3 | 1 | Stack Pointer | 0 | Accumulator Data |
| | | | 4 | 0 | Stack Pointer – 1 | 1 | Accumulator Data |
| | PUL | 4 | 1 | 1 | Op Code Address | 1 | Op Code |
| | | | 2 | 1 | Op Code Address + 1 | 1 | Op Code of Next Instruction |
| | | | 3 | 0 | Stack Pointer | 1 | Irrelevant Data (Note 1) |
| | | | 4 | 1 | Stack Pointer + 1 | 1 | Operand Data from Stack |
| | TSX | 4 | 1 | 1 | Op Code Address | 1 | Op Code |
| | | | 2 | 1 | Op Code Address + 1 | 1 | Op Code of Next Instruction |
| | | | 3 | 0 | Stack Pointer | 1 | Irrelevant Data (Note 1) |
| | | | 4 | 0 | New Index Register | 1 | Irrelevant Data (Note 1) |
| | TXS | 4 | 1 | 1 | Op Code Address | 1 | Op Code |
| | | | 2 | 1 | Op Code Address + 1 | 1 | Op Code of Next Instruction |
| | | | 3 | 0 | Index Register | 1 | Irrelevant Data |
| | | | 4 | 0 | New Stack Pointer | 1 | Irrelevant Data |

Table 9-2. Operation Summary (Continued)

| | ADDRESS MODE AND INSTRUCTIONS | CYCLES | CYCLE NO. | VMA LINE | ADDRESS BUS | R/W LINE | DATA BUS |
|---|---|---|---|---|---|---|---|
| REGISTER-REGISTER (CONTINUED) | RTS | 5 | 1 | 1 | Op Code Address | 1 | Op Code |
| | | | 2 | 1 | Op Code Address + 1 | 1 | Irrelevant Data (Note 2) |
| | | | 3 | 0 | Stack Pointer | 1 | Irrelevant Data (Note 1) |
| | | | 4 | 1 | Stack Pointer + 1 | 1 | Address of Next Instruction (High Order Byte) |
| | | | 5 | 1 | Stack Pointer + 2 | 1 | Address of Next Instruction (Low Order Byte) |
| | WAI | 9 | 1 | 1 | Op Code Address | 1 | Op Code |
| | | | 2 | 1 | Op Code Address + 1 | 1 | Op Code of Next Instruction |
| | | | 3 | 1 | Stack Pointer | 0 | Return Address (Low Order Byte) |
| | | | 4 | 1 | Stack Pointer – 1 | 0 | Return Address (High Order Byte) |
| | | | 5 | 1 | Stack Pointer – 2 | 0 | Index Register (Low Order Byte) |
| | | | 6 | 1 | Stack Pointer – 3 | 0 | Index Register (High Order Byte) |
| | | | 7 | 1 | Stack Pointer – 4 | 0 | Contents of Accumulator A |
| | | | 8 | 1 | Stack Pointer – 5 | 0 | Contents of Accumulator B |
| | | | 9 | 1 | Stack Pointer – 6 (Note 4) | 1 | Contents of Cond. Code Register |
| | RTI | 10 | 1 | 1 | Op Code Address | 1 | Op Code |
| | | | 2 | 1 | Op Code Address + 1 | 1 | Irrelevant Data (Note 2) |
| | | | 3 | 0 | Stack Pointer | 1 | Irrelevant Data (Note 1) |
| | | | 4 | 1 | Stack Pointer + 1 | 1 | Contents of Cond. Code Register from Stack |
| | | | 5 | 1 | Stack Pointer + 2 | 1 | Contents of Accumulator B from Stack |
| | | | 6 | 1 | Stack Pointer + 3 | 1 | Contents of Accumulator A from Stack |
| | | | 7 | 1 | Stack Pointer + 4 | 1 | Index Register from Stack (High Order Byte) |
| | | | 8 | 1 | Stack Pointer + 5 | 1 | Index Register from Stack (Low Order Byte) |
| | | | 9 | 1 | Stack Pointer + 6 | 1 | Next Instruction Address from Stack (High Order Byte) |
| | | | 10 | 1 | Stack Pointer + 7 | 1 | Next Instruction Address from Stack (Low Order Byte) |
| | SWI | 12 | 1 | 1 | Op Code Address | 1 | Op Code |
| | | | 2 | 1 | Op Code Address + 1 | 1 | Irrelevant Data (Note 1) |
| | | | 3 | 1 | Stack Pointer | 0 | Return Address (Low Order Byte) |
| | | | 4 | 1 | Stack Pointer – 1 | 0 | Return Address (High Order Byte) |
| | | | 5 | 1 | Stack Pointer – 2 | 0 | Index Register (Low Order Byte) |
| | | | 6 | 1 | Stack Pointer – 3 | 0 | Index Register (High Order Byte) |
| | | | 7 | 1 | Stack Pointer – 4 | 0 | Contents of Accumulator A |
| | | | 8 | 1 | Stack Pointer – 5 | 0 | Contents of Accumulator B |
| | | | 9 | 1 | Stack Pointer – 6 | 0 | Contents of Cond. Code Register |
| | | | 10 | 0 | Stack Pointer – 7 | 1 | Irrelevant Data (Note 1) |
| | | | 11 | 1 | Vector Address FFFA (Hex) | 1 | Address of Subroutine (High Order Byte) |
| | | | 12 | 1 | Vector Address FFFB (Hex) | 1 | Address of Subroutine (Low Order Byte) |
| RELATIVE | BCC BHI BNE<br>BCS BLE BPL<br>BEQ BLS BRA<br>BGE BLT BVC<br>BGT BMI BVS | 4 | 1 | 1 | Op Code Address | 1 | Op Code |
| | | | 2 | 1 | Op Code Address + 1 | 1 | Branch Offset |
| | | | 3 | 0 | Op Code Address + 2 | 1 | Irrelevant Data (Note 1) |
| | | | 4 | 0 | Branch Address | 1 | Irrelevant Data (Note 1) |
| | BSR | 8 | 1 | 1 | Op Code Address | 1 | Op Code |
| | | | 2 | 1 | Op Code Address + 1 | 1 | Branch Offset |
| | | | 3 | 0 | Return Address of Main Program | 1 | Irrelevant Data (Note 1) |
| | | | 4 | 1 | Stack Pointer | 0 | Return Address (Low Order Byte) |
| | | | 5 | 1 | Stack Pointer – 1 | 0 | Return Address (High Order Byte) |
| | | | 6 | 0 | Stack Pointer – 2 | 1 | Irrelevant Data (Note 1) |
| | | | 7 | 0 | Return Address of Main Program | 1 | Irrelevant Data (Note 1) |
| | | | 8 | 0 | Subroutine Address | 1 | Irrelevant Data (Note 1) |

Note 1. If device which is addressed during this cycle uses VMA, then the Data Bus will go to the high impedance three-state condition. Depending on bus capacitance, data from the previous cycle may be retained on the Data Bus.

Note 2. Data is ignored by the MPU.

Note 3. For TST, VMA = 0 and Operand data does not change.

Note 4. While the MPU is waiting for the interrupt, Bus Available will go high indicating the following states of the control lines: VMA is low; Address Bus, R/W, and Data Bus are all in the high impedance state.

The following codes are used in Table 9-3:

aa two bits choosing the address mode:
- 00 immediate data
- 01 base page direct addressing
- 10 indexed addressing
- 11 extended direct addressing

pp the second byte of a two- or three-byte instruction.

qq the third byte of a three-byte instruction.

x one bit choosing the Accumulator:
- 0 Accumulator A
- 1 Accumulator B

yy two bits choosing the address mode:
- 00 (inherent addressing) Accumulator A
- 01 (inherent addressing) Accumulator B
- 10 indexed addressing
- 11 extended direct addressing

y one bit choosing the address mode:
- 0 indexed addressing
- 1 extended direct addressing

Two numbers in the "Machine Cycles" column (for example, 2 - 5) indicate that execution time depends on the addressing mode.

Table 9-3. MC6800 Instruction Set Object Codes

| MNEMONIC | OPERAND(S) | OBJECT CODE | BYTE | MACHINE CYCLES |
|---|---|---|---|---|
| ABA | | 1B | 1 | 2 |
| ADC | ACX, | 1xaa1001 | | |
| | ADR8 or DATA | pp | 2 | 2-5 |
| | ADR16 | qq | 3 | 4 |
| ADD | ACX, | 1xaa1011 | | |
| | ADR8 or DATA | pp | 2 | 2-5 |
| | ADR16 | qq | 3 | 4 |
| AND | ACX, | 1xaa0100 | | |
| | ADR8 or DATA | pp | 2 | 2-5 |
| | ADR16 | qq | 3 | 4 |
| ASL | ACX | 01yy1000 | 1 | 2 |
| | ADR8 | pp | 2 | 7 |
| | ADR16 | qq | 3 | 6 |
| ASR | ACX | 01yy0111 | 1 | 2 |
| | ADR8 | pp | 2 | 7 |
| | ADR16 | qq | 3 | 6 |
| BCC | DISP | 24 pp | 2 | 4 |
| BCS | DISP | 25 pp | 2 | 4 |
| BEQ | DISP | 27 pp | 2 | 4 |
| BGE | DISP | 2C pp | 2 | 4 |
| BGT | DISP | 2E pp | 2 | 4 |
| BHI | DISP | 22 pp | 2 | 4 |
| BIT | ACX, | 1xaa0101 | | |
| | ADR8 or DATA | pp | 2 | 2-5 |
| | ADR16 | qq | 3 | 4 |
| BLE | DISP | 2F pp | 2 | 4 |
| BLS | DISP | 23 pp | 2 | 4 |
| BLT | DISP | 2D pp | 2 | 4 |
| BMI | DISP | 2B pp | 2 | 4 |
| BNE | DISP | 26 pp | 2 | 4 |
| BPL | DISP | 2A pp | 2 | 4 |
| BRA | DISP | 20 pp | 2 | 4 |
| BSR | DISP | 8D pp | 2 | 8 |
| BVC | DISP | 28 pp | 2 | 4 |
| BVS | DISP | 29 pp | 2 | 4 |
| CBA | | 11 | 1 | 2 |
| CLC | | 0C | 1 | 2 |
| CLI | | 0E | 1 | 2 |
| CLR | ACX | 01yy1111 | 1 | 2 |
| | ADR8 | pp | 2 | 7 |
| | ADR16 | qq | 3 | 6 |
| CLV | | 0A | 1 | 2 |
| CMP | ACX, | 1xaa0001 | | |
| | ADR8 or DATA | pp | 2 | 2-5 |
| | ADR16 | qq | 3 | 4 |
| COM | ACX | 01yy0011 | 1 | 2 |
| | ADR8 | pp | 2 | 7 |
| | ADR16 | qq | 3 | 6 |
| CPX | | 10aa1100 | | |
| | ADR8 | pp | 2 | 4-6 |
| | ADR16 or DATA16 | qq | 3 | 3-5 |
| DAA | | 19 | 1 | 2 |
| DEC | ACX | 01yy1010 | 1 | 2 |
| | ADR8 | pp | 2 | 7 |
| | ADR16 | qq | 3 | 6 |
| DES | | 34 | 1 | 4 |
| DEX | | 09 | 1 | 4 |
| EOR | ACX, | 1xaa1000 | | |
| | ADR8 or DATA | pp | 2 | 2-5 |
| | ADR16 | qq | 3 | 4 |
| INC | ACX | 01yy1100 | 1 | 2 |
| | ADR8 | pp | 2 | 7 |
| | ADR16 | qq | 3 | 6 |
| INS | | 31 | 1 | 4 |
| INX | | 08 | 1 | 4 |

| MNEMONIC | OPERAND(S) | OBJECT CODE | BYTE | MACHINE CYCLES |
|---|---|---|---|---|
| JMP | | 011y1110 | | |
| | ADR8 | pp | 2 | 4 |
| | ADR16 | qq | 3 | 3 |
| JSR | | 101y1101 | | |
| | ADR8 | pp | 2 | 8 |
| | ADR16 | qq | 3 | 9 |
| LDA | ACX, | 1xaa0110 | | |
| | ADR8 or DATA | pp | 2 | 2-5 |
| | ADR16 | qq | 3 | 4 |
| LDS | | 10aa1110 | | |
| | ADR8 | pp | 2 | 3-5 |
| | ADR16 or DATA16 | qq | 3 | 4-6 |
| LDX | | 11aa1110 | | |
| | ADR8 | pp | 2 | 3-5 |
| | ADR16 or DATA16 | qq | 3 | 4-6 |
| LSR | ACX | 01yy0100 | 1 | 2 |
| | ADR8 | pp | 2 | 7 |
| | ADR16 | qq | 3 | 6 |
| NEG | ACX | 01yy0000 | 1 | 2 |
| | ADR8 | pp | 2 | 7 |
| | ADR16 | qq | 3 | 6 |
| NOP | | 01 | 1 | 2 |
| ORA | ACX, | 1xaa1010 | | |
| | ADR8 or DATA | pp | 2 | 2-5 |
| | ADR16 | qq | 3 | 4 |
| PSH | ACX | 0011011x | 1 | 4 |
| PUL | ACX | 0011001x | 1 | 4 |
| ROL | ACX | 01yy1001 | 1 | 2 |
| | ADR8 | pp | 2 | 7 |
| | ADR16 | qq | 3 | 6 |
| ROR | ACX | 01yy0110 | 1 | 2 |
| | ADR8 | pp | 2 | 7 |
| | ADR16 | qq | 3 | 6 |
| RTI | | 3B | 1 | 10 |
| RTS | | 39 | 1 | 5 |
| SBA | | 10 | 1 | 2 |
| SBC | ACX, | 1xaa0010 | | |
| | ADR8 or DATA | pp | 2 | 2-5 |
| | ADR16 | qq | 3 | 4 |
| SEC | | 0D | 1 | 2 |
| SEI | | 0F | 1 | 2 |
| SEV | | 0B | 1 | 2 |
| STA | ACX, | 1xaa0111 | * | |
| | ADR8 | pp | 2 | 4-6 |
| | ADR16 | qq | 3 | 5 |
| STS | | 10aa1111 | * | |
| | ADR8 | pp | 2 | 5-7 |
| | ADR16 | qq | 3 | 6 |
| STX | | 11aa1111 | * | |
| | ADR8 | pp | 2 | 5-7 |
| | ADR16 | qq | 3 | 6 |
| SUB | ACX, | 1xaa0000 | | |
| | ADR8 or DATA | pp | 2 | 2-5 |
| | ADR16 | qq | 3 | 4 |
| SWI | | 3F | 1 | 12 |
| TAB | | 16 | 1 | 2 |
| TAP | | 06 | 1 | 2 |
| TBA | | 17 | 1 | 2 |
| TPA | | 07 | 1 | 2 |
| TST | ACX | 01yy1101 | 1 | 2 |
| | ADR8 | pp | 2 | 7 |
| | ADR16 | qq | 3 | 6 |
| TSX | | 30 | 1 | 4 |
| TXS | | 35 | 1 | 4 |
| WAI | | 3E | 1 | 9 |

*aa = 00 is not permitted.

## SUPPORT DEVICES THAT MAY BE USED WITH THE MC6800

**Using 8080A support devices with the MC6800 is very straightforward in terms of control signals generated. You must break out the single MC6800 R/W̄ control signal into separate R̄D̄ and W̄R̄ control signals. Other signal interconnections are self-evident. Here is appropriate logic:**

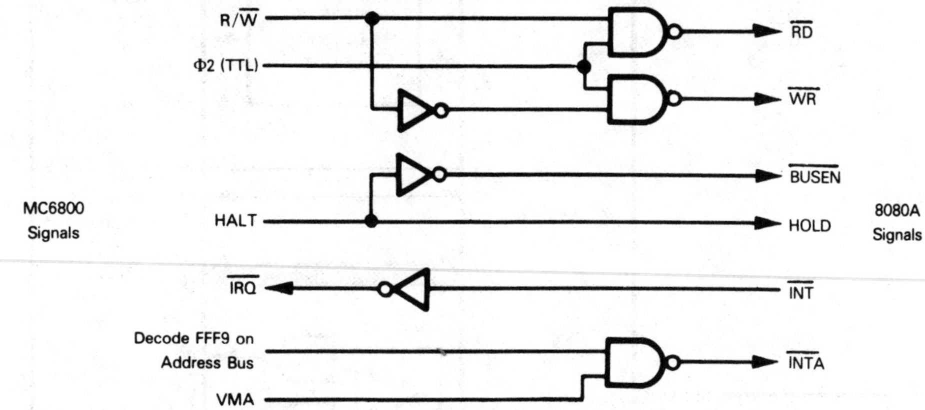


Signals illustrated above apply to communications between the MC6800 CPU and 8080A support devices. External memory will communicate with the MC6800 CPU using standard MC6800 timing.

There are some limitations imposed on communications between the MC6800 CPU and 8080A support devices.

As illustrated above, you must create an interrupt acknowledge control signal by decoding the second interrupt acknowledge address, $FFF9_{16}$, appearing on the Address Bus. Similarly, if you wish to create specific I/O read and write control signals, then you must decode off the Address Bus those memory addresses which you have assigned to I/O devices.

If you wish to extend instruction execution cycles for slow 8080A support devices, then you must use the MC6800 clock stretching logic for this purpose. Clearly the 8080A support devices cannot use Wait state logic since the MC6800 has no such logic.

**You can generate an 8080A compatible system clock from the Φ2 (TTL) 6870 series clock as follows:**

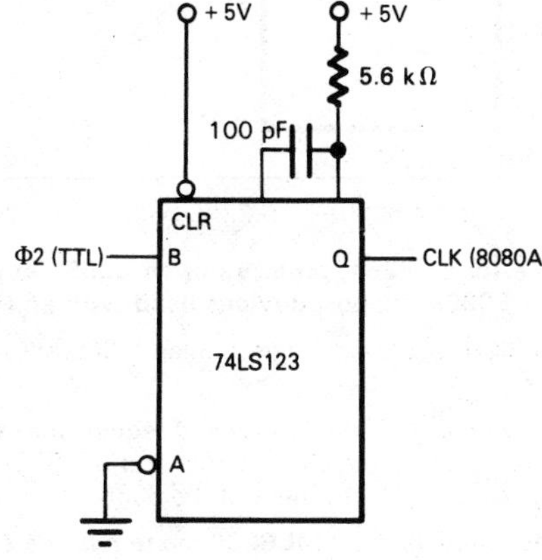

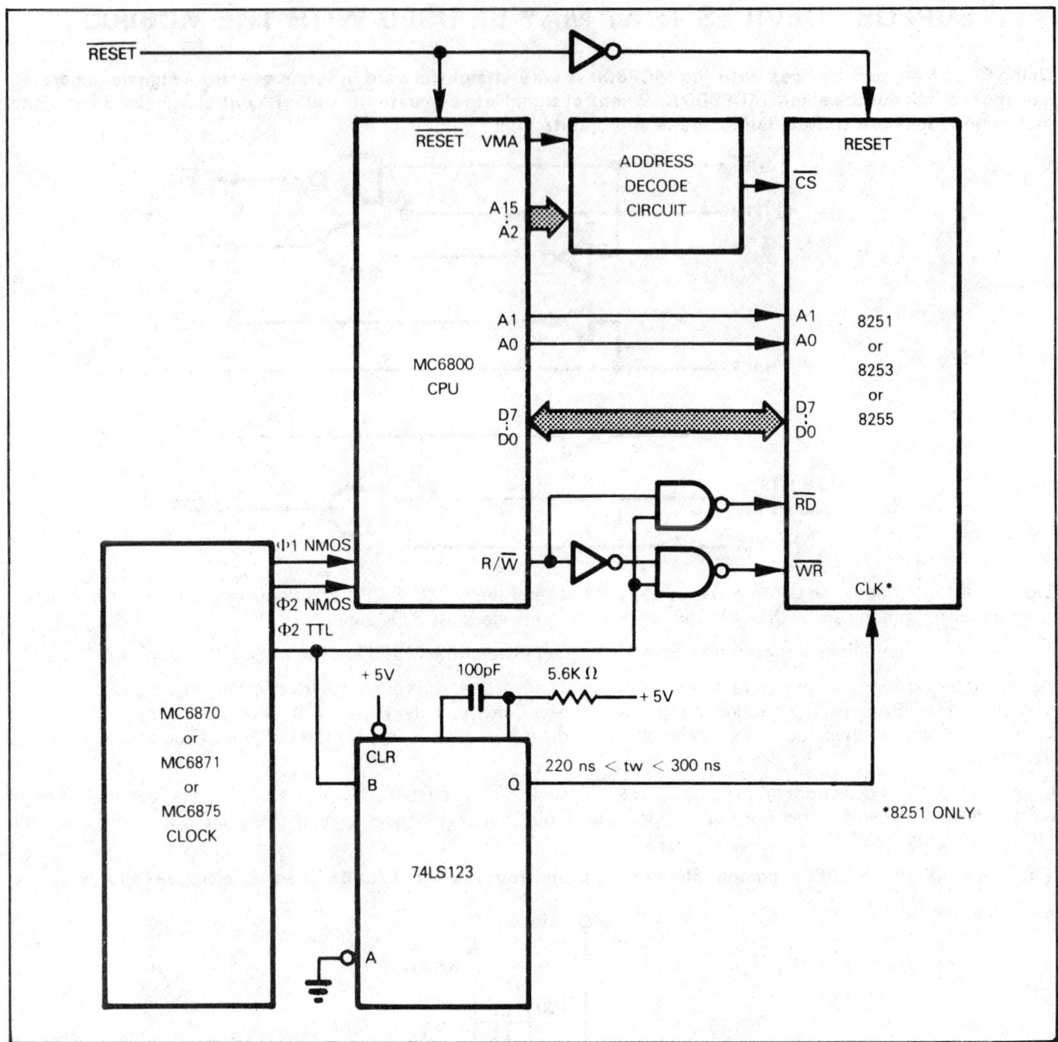


Figure 9-11. Use of 8080A Support Devices With MC6800 CPU

**Figure 9-11 illustrates the interface for an 8251, an 8253 or an 8255 device connected to an MC6800 CPU. Figure 9-12 provides the timing for 8080A support devices used with an MC6800 CPU.**

The 8257 DMA device and the 8259 PICU should not be used in an MC6800 since MC6800 DMA and interrupt logic are not compatible with these devices.

**8085 support devices** could be used with an MC6800 but **would require that you multiplex the Data Bus and low order eight Address Bus lines,** as required by the 8155, 8355, and 8755. Extra logic needed to perform this bus multiplexing would probably destroy the cost effectiveness of the 8085 support devices in an MC6800 system.

**The only Z80 support device that is practical in an MC6800 system is the Z80 DMA device.** This is because the other Z80 support devices decode a Write state from a combination of the $\overline{\text{M1}}$, $\overline{\text{INT}}$, and $\overline{\text{RD}}$ control signals. The Z80 DMA device uses separate read and write control inputs; therefore it may be used with an MC6800 CPU. The logic needed to create Z80 DMA control inputs from MC6800 control signals is identical to the 8080A control signal logic illustrated above. The Z80 SIO device will probabl, not be effective in an MC6800 system; in preference, use specific MC6800 serial I/O devices.

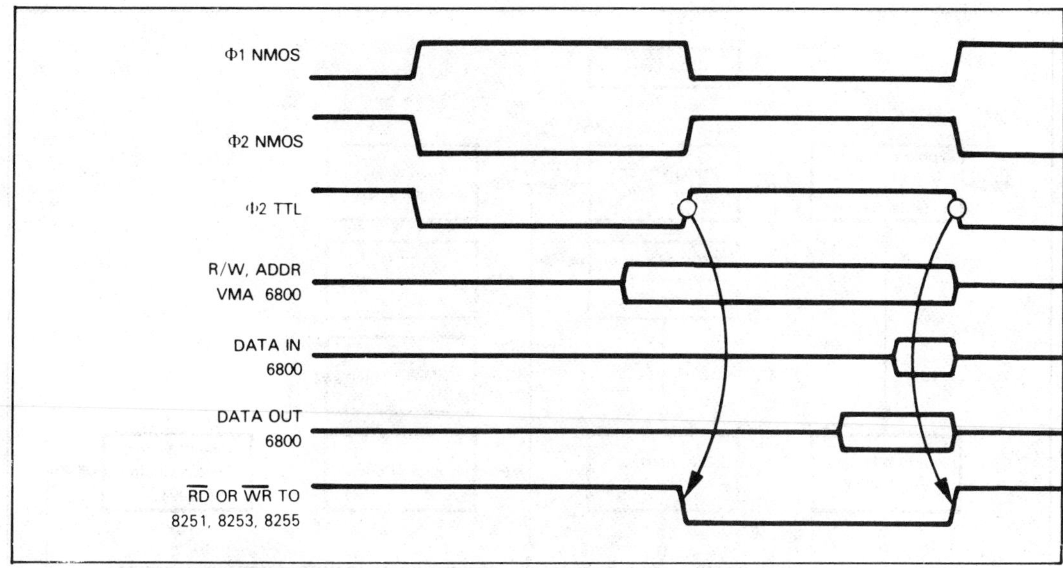


Figure 9-12. Timing for 8080A Support Devices Used With an MC6800 CPU

**When using non-MC6800 support devices with the MC6800 CPU, remember that there is a particularly pernicious problem associated with MC6800 Reset logic on power-up.** As discussed earlier in this chapter, the MC6800 does not internally disable interrupt requests until the trailing low-to-high transition of the RESET signal. Thus external devices capable of requesting an interrupt may randomly do so during the power on Reset sequence; and this may result in an interrupt being acknowledged following the initial system Reset, rather than the expected system initialization program getting executed. You must make certain that all support devices capable of requesting an interrupt are disabled by the leading high-to-low transition of RESET during the power-up sequence.

# THE MC6802 CPU WITH READ/WRITE MEMORY

**The MC6802 is a combination of the MC6800 CPU, clock logic, and 128 bytes of read/write memory. Figure 9-13 illustrates logic of the MC6802 CPU device.**

The actual CPU architecture and the instruction set of the MC6802 are identical to the MC6800 which we have already described.

The 128 bytes of read/write memory which are present on the MC6802 chip are accessed by memory addresses $0000_{16}$ through $007F_{16}$. The first 32 bytes of this read/write memory may be protected during power down by a special low power standby input.

**MC6802 CPU pins and signals are illustrated in Figure 9-14. Pins and signals which differ from the MC6800 illustrated in Figure 9-2 are shaded. We will examine these new signals only.**

Since clock logic is on the MC6802 chip, three pins are needed for this specific purpose. Normally **a crystal will be connected across XTAL1 and XTAL2.** A 4 MHz crystal should be used since the MC6802 has internal divide-by-four logic to create a 1 MHz system clock signal. (An inexpensive 3.58 MHz color burst crystal may also be used.) **A TTL level system clock signal is output via Φ2 (TTL).**

You can, if you wish, drive the MC6802 using **an external clock signal;** this signal **is input via XTAL2;** it must not be faster than 4 MHz. XTAL1 should be left unconnected in this mode.

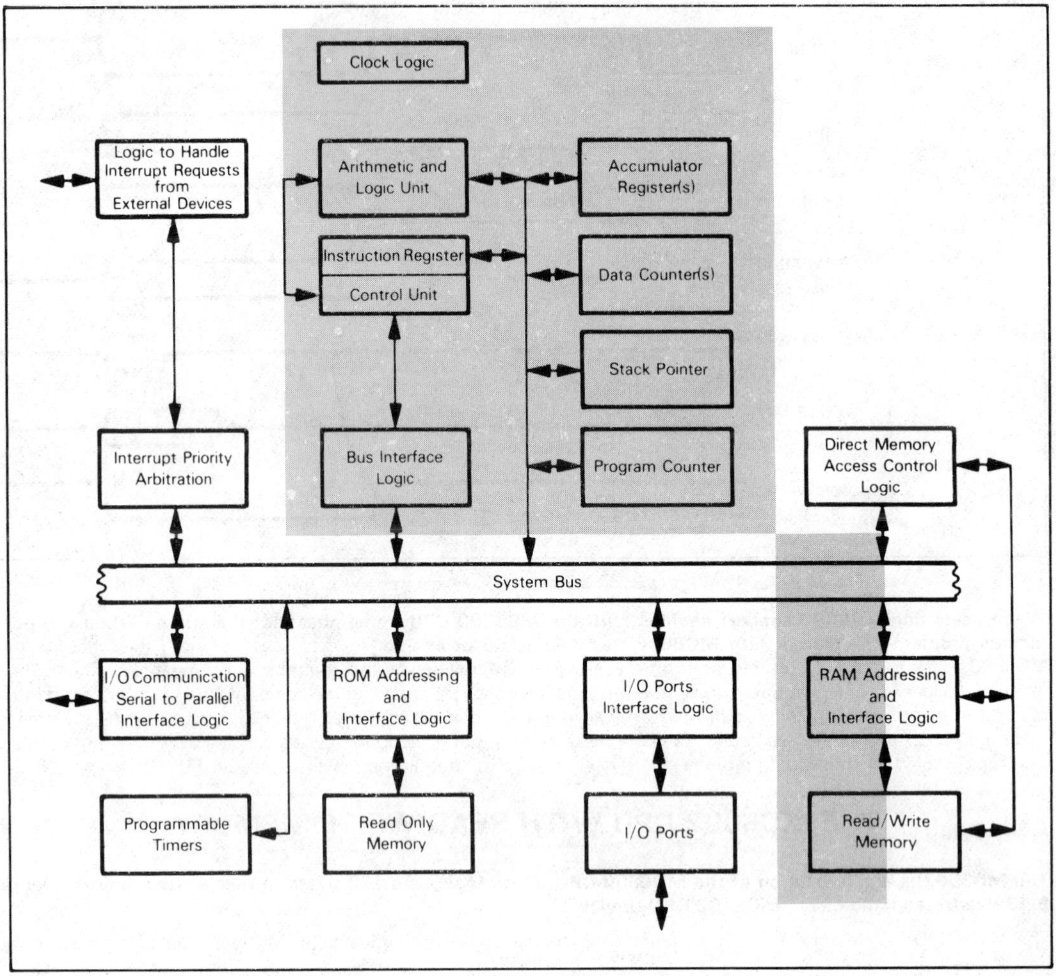

Figure 9-13. Logic of the MC6802 CPU Device

**In order to provide the clock stretching logic** that is a standard part of MC6800 microcomputer system, **a Memory Ready (MR) signal is present.** MR is normally high. In order to stretch Φ2, MR must make a high-to-low transition while Φ2 is high; Φ2 then remains high until MR makes a low-to-high transition. Timing may be illustrated as follows:

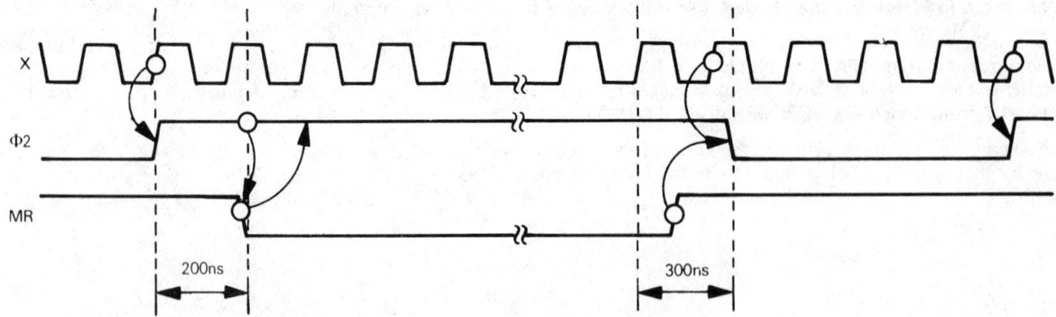

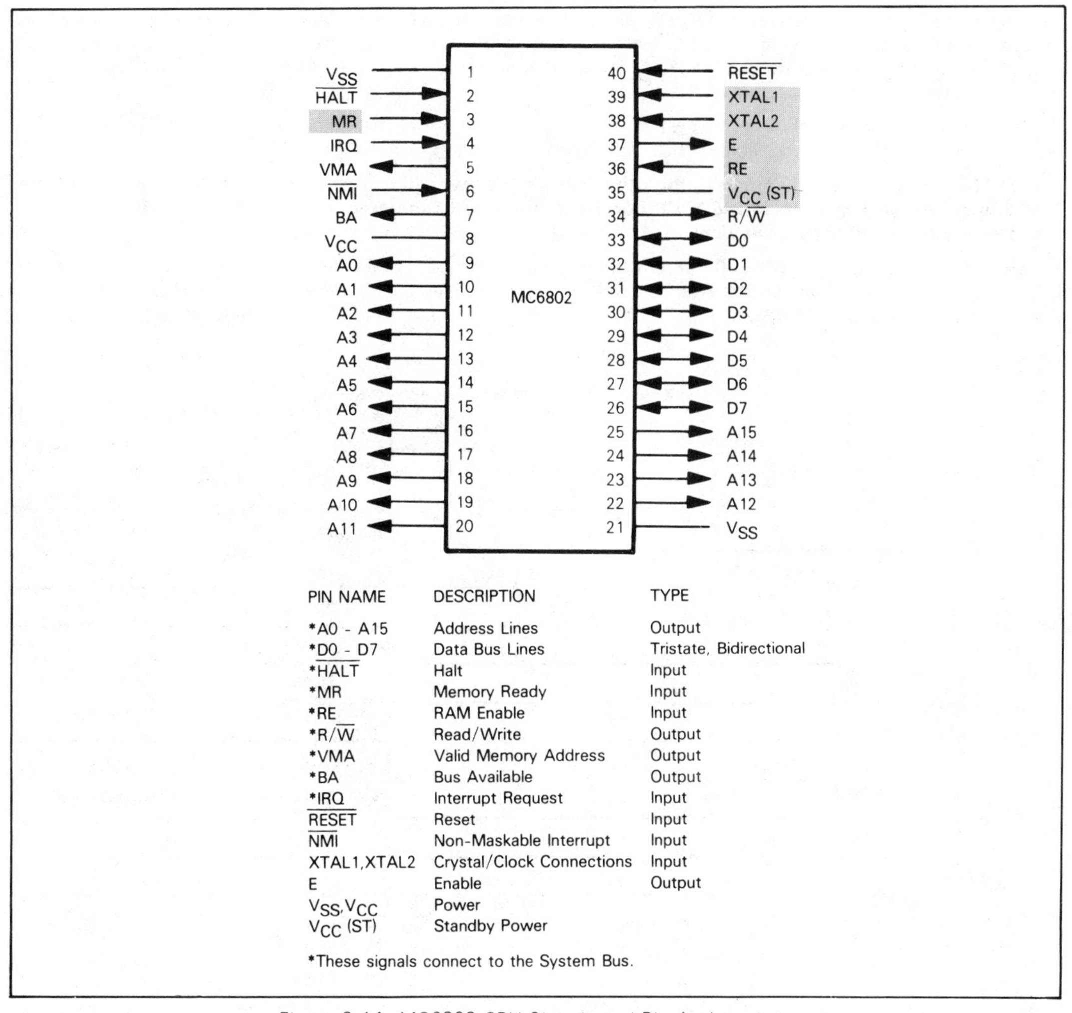


| PIN NAME | DESCRIPTION | TYPE |
|---|---|---|
| *A0 - A15 | Address Lines | Output |
| *D0 - D7 | Data Bus Lines | Tristate, Bidirectional |
| *HALT | Halt | Input |
| *MR | Memory Ready | Input |
| *RE | RAM Enable | Input |
| *R/W | Read/Write | Output |
| *VMA | Valid Memory Address | Output |
| *BA | Bus Available | Output |
| *IRQ | Interrupt Request | Input |
| RESET | Reset | Input |
| NMI | Non-Maskable Interrupt | Input |
| XTAL1,XTAL2 | Crystal/Clock Connections | Input |
| E | Enable | Output |
| $V_{SS}$, $V_{CC}$ | Power | |
| $V_{CC}$ (ST) | Standby Power | |

*These signals connect to the System Bus.

Figure 9-14. MC6802 CPU Signals and Pin Assignments

Two signals have been added to support the on-chip read/write memroy. **RE is an enable signal for the on-chip memory.** RE must be input high for the on-chip memory to be accessed. If RE is low, on-chip memory cannot be written into or read. While on-chip memory is disabled its address space is also disabled, and addresses in the range $0000_{16}$ through $007F_{16}$ are deflected to external memory. Thus **the address space $0000_{16}$ through $007F_{16}$ is duplicated;** it accesses on-chip RAM when RE is high, but it accesses external RAM when RE is low.

The first 32 on-chip read/write memory bytes (with addresses 0000 through 001F) can have the contents preserved by applying +5V at the $V_{CC}$ standby pin when power is down on the MC6802. But to be of any value, we must guarantee that the contents of these 32 read/write memory locations are not destroyed during any power down sequence; in other words, we must anticipate any power down. In order to preserve the contents of the 32 low-order read/write memory bytes, RE must be input low at least three clock periods before power drops below +4.75V. This is easy enough to do for a scheduled power down; however, it is impossible during a non-scheduled power down — such as might occur as the result of a power failure — unless power-down-interrupt circuitry is provided.

**MC6800 signals which have been removed,** going to the MC6802, **include the clock inputs Φ1 and Φ2,** plus the bus control signals **TSC and DBE.**

Obviously, the clock inputs must be removed since clock logic is now on the CPU chip.

Removal of the System Bus control signals TSC and DBE reflects the fact that if you are going to need direct memory access, you are not going to use the MC6802. Only larger microcomputer systems need direct memory access; for such systems the MC6800 is available. The MC6802 is intended as half of a two-chip 6800 configuration, within which direct memory access would be meaningless.

If DMA is necessary with a 6802-based system, then the use of external tristate bus drivers will be necessary. Bus Available (BA) and HALT are available on the 6802 for this purpose.

**The MC6846 multi-function device is the other half of the two-chip microcomputer system. However, the MC6846 can be used with the MC6800 CPU or the MC6802 CPU; therefore it is described later in this chapter along with other 6800 support devices.**

**When HALT is input low, the MC6802 enters the Halt state** at the end of the current instruction's execution. In the Halt state the Data Bus is floated, Bus Available (BA) is output high, and valid memory address (VMA) is output low. The Address Bus outputs the address of the instruction which will be executed when the halt condition ends. Timing may be illustrated as follows:

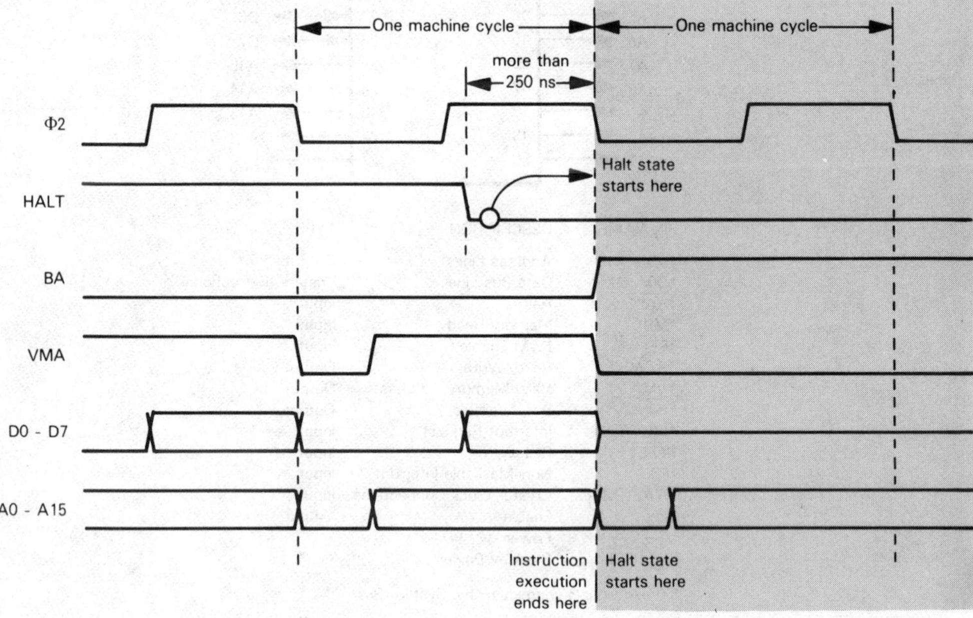


The HALT input signal is level sensitive. The level of HALT is sensed 250 nanoseconds before the end of a machine cycle. If HALT is low at this time, then the low level is detected. If HALT makes a high-to-low transition within the last 250 nanoseconds of a machine cycle, then it may not be detected. This may be illustrated as follows:

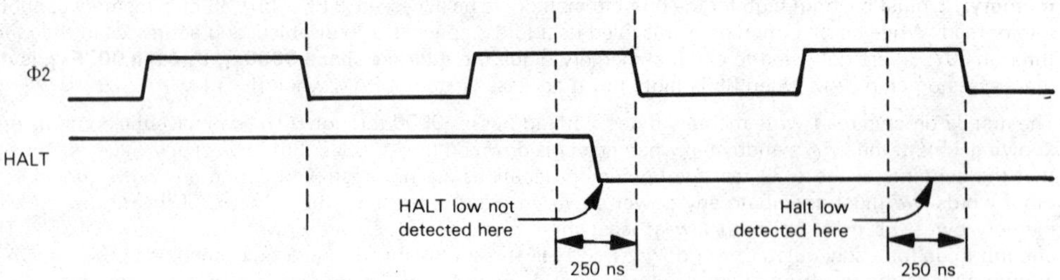

Once a Halt has been detected, the current instruction completes execution before the Halt condition starts. In the simplest case this may be illustrated as follows:

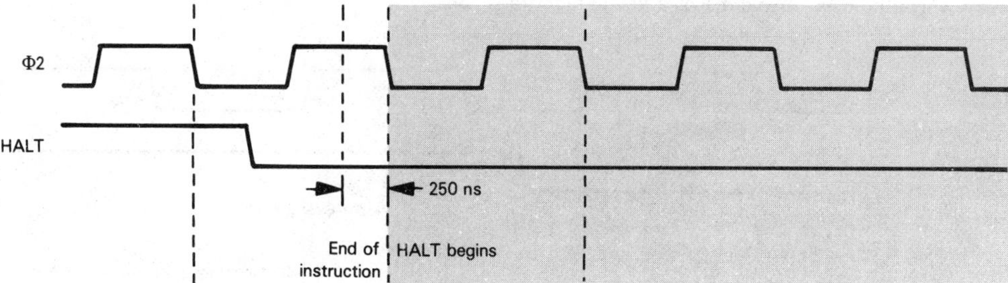


If a Halt transition occurs within the last 250 nanoseconds of a machine cycle, then the HALT will probably not be detected until the next machine cycle. Assuming that the next machine cycle terminates an instruction's exeuction, the Halt condition will begin as follows:

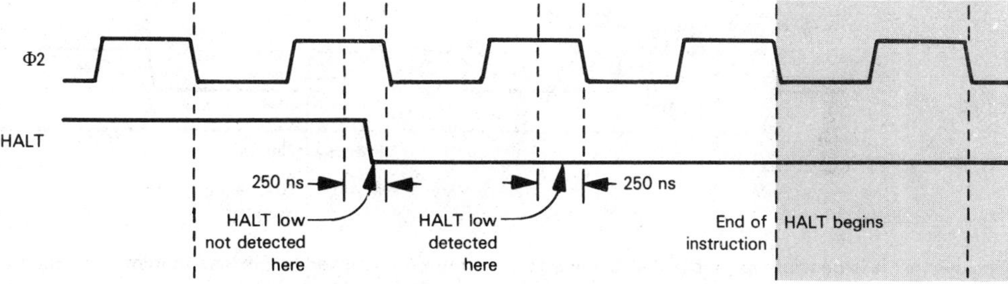


The next machine cycle could be the first of a multi-machine cycle instruction. Now the Halt condition will begin as follows:

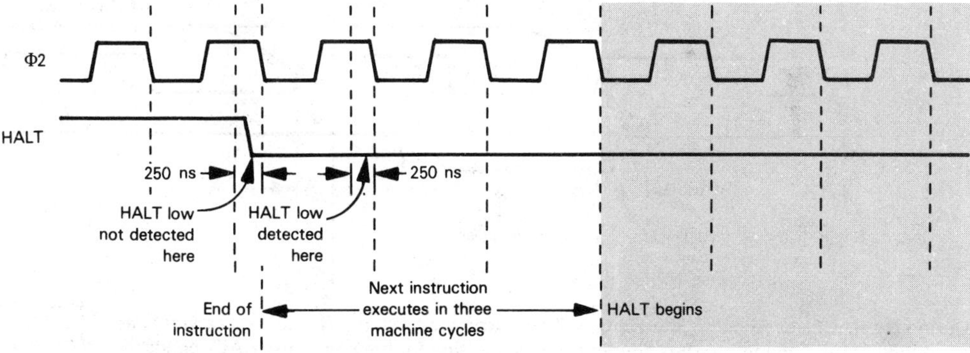


Note that if the HALT transition had occurred a little earlier, the HALT condition would have begun a whole instruction exeuction time sooner — three machine cycles sooner in the illustration above.

The HALT condition terminates on the machine cycle that follows HALT going high again. Once again the HALT signal is sampled 250 nanoseconds before the end of the machine cycle. Thus the HALT may terminate within the machine cycle where the HALT signal makes a low-to-high transition:

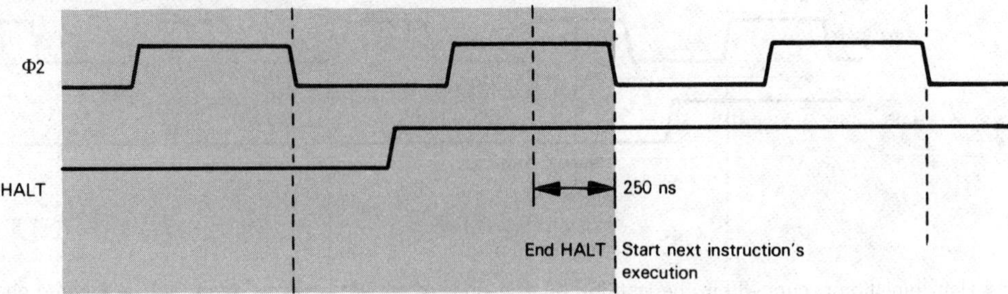


But the HALT condition may terminate one machine cycle later if the HALT signal makes its low-to-high transition within the last 250 nanoseconds of a machine cycle. This may be illustrated as follows:

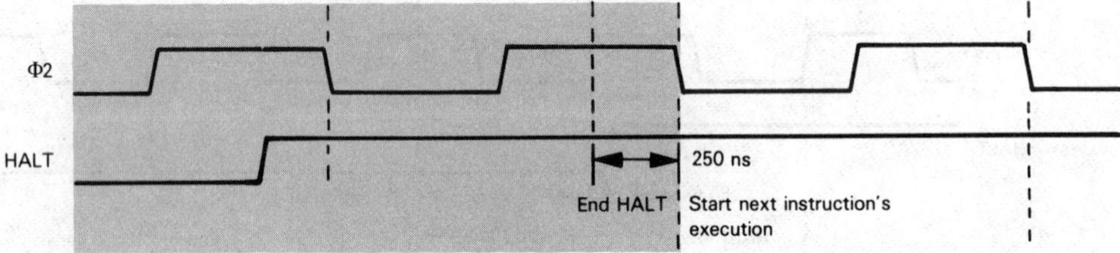


Observe that **it is possible for a low HALT pulse to be completely missed if it is less than one machine cycle long and transitions are not properly synchronized.** If, for example, the high-to-low transition occurs within the last 250 nanoseconds of a machine cycle and the subsequent low-to-high transition occurs correctly in the next machine cycle, the HALT pulse will be completely missed. This may be illustrated as follows:

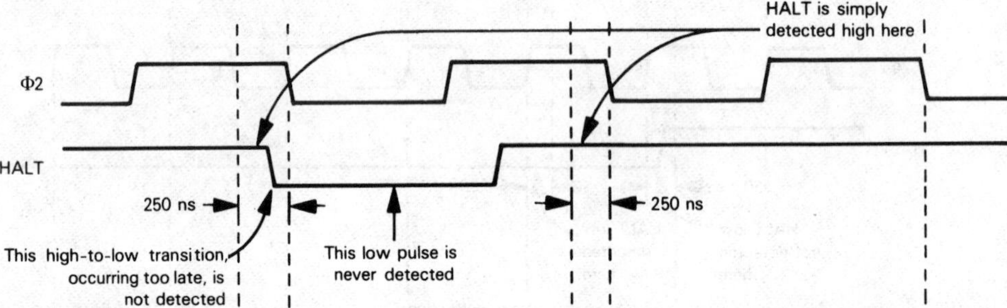


**INTERRUPTS DURING AN MC6802 HALT**

**During the HALT condition no interrupts will be acknowledged. If any interrupt requests occur during a HALT condition, they simply stack up waiting for the end of the HALT condition.**

**There are also some differences in MC6802 interrupt and reset logic as compared to the MC6800.**

Motorola literature recommends that interrupt request inputs $\overline{IRQ}$ and $\overline{MNI}$ have a 3K ohm external resistor to $V_{CC}$. This may be illustrated as follows:

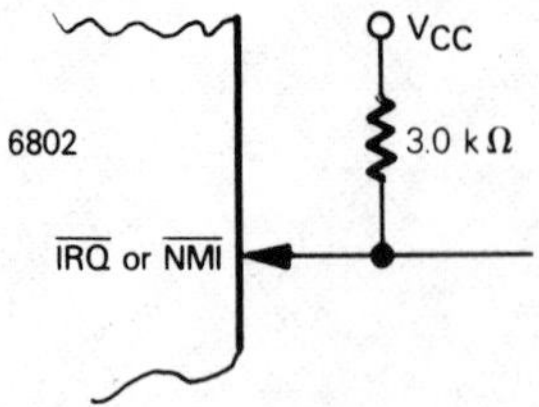

The MC6802 $\overline{RESET}$ input may be a stand-alone input or it may be tied to the RAM enable input (RE). Timing for the RESET signal rise and fall differs in the two cases, as defined in the data sheets at the end of this chapter. Note that by tying $\overline{RESET}$ to RE you cause the on-chip RAM to be enabled whenever the MC6802 is receiving power.

**The MC6802, like the MC6800, does not disable interrupts until close to the end of the reset sequence.** Thus, if you have non-6800 support devices connected to an MC6802, you must make certain that you have included logic that prevents these support devices from requesting an interrupt until after the reset operation has gone to completion. If you do not take this precaution, then following RESET you may vector to a support device's interrupt service routine rather than executing the intended system initialization program.

## THE MC6870 TWO PHASE CLOCKS

**Four clock logic devices supporting the MC6800 CPU are described. The MC6802 does not need any external clock logic device.**

**The MC6870A is a very elementary device providing minimum clock signals needed with an MC6800 microcomputer system. Its pin assignments are illustrated in Figure 9-15.**

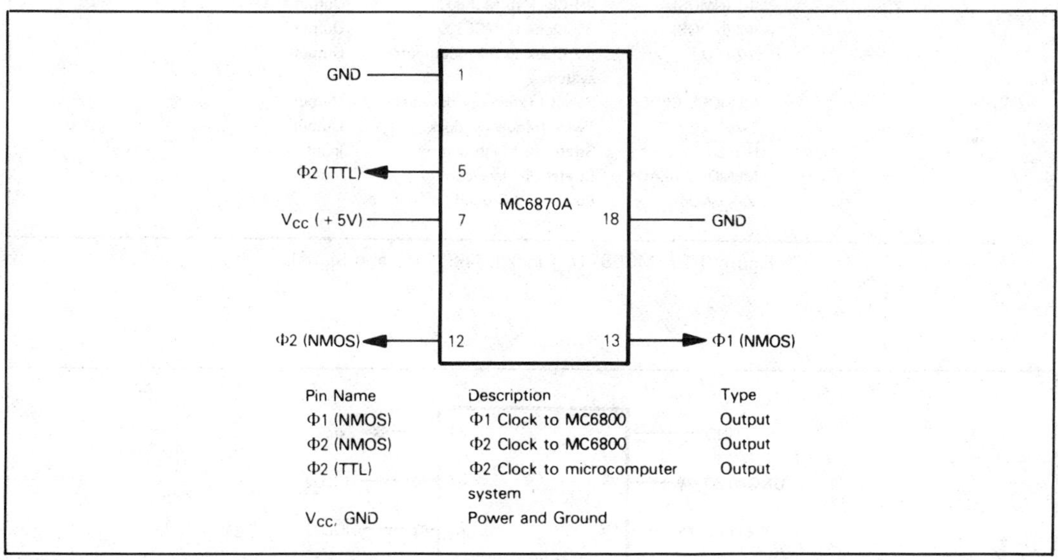


| Pin Name | Description | Type |
|---|---|---|
| Φ1 (NMOS) | Φ1 Clock to MC6800 | Output |
| Φ2 (NMOS) | Φ2 Clock to MC6800 | Output |
| Φ2 (TTL) | Φ2 Clock to microcomputer system | Output |
| $V_{CC}$, GND | Power and Ground | |

Figure 9-15. MC6870A Clock Device Pins and Signals

**The first enhancement is provided by the MC6871A, illustrated in Figure 9-16, which adds clock signal stretching capabilities and a twice frequency clock output.**

**The MC6871B, illustrated in Figure 9-17, is a variation of the MC6871A.**

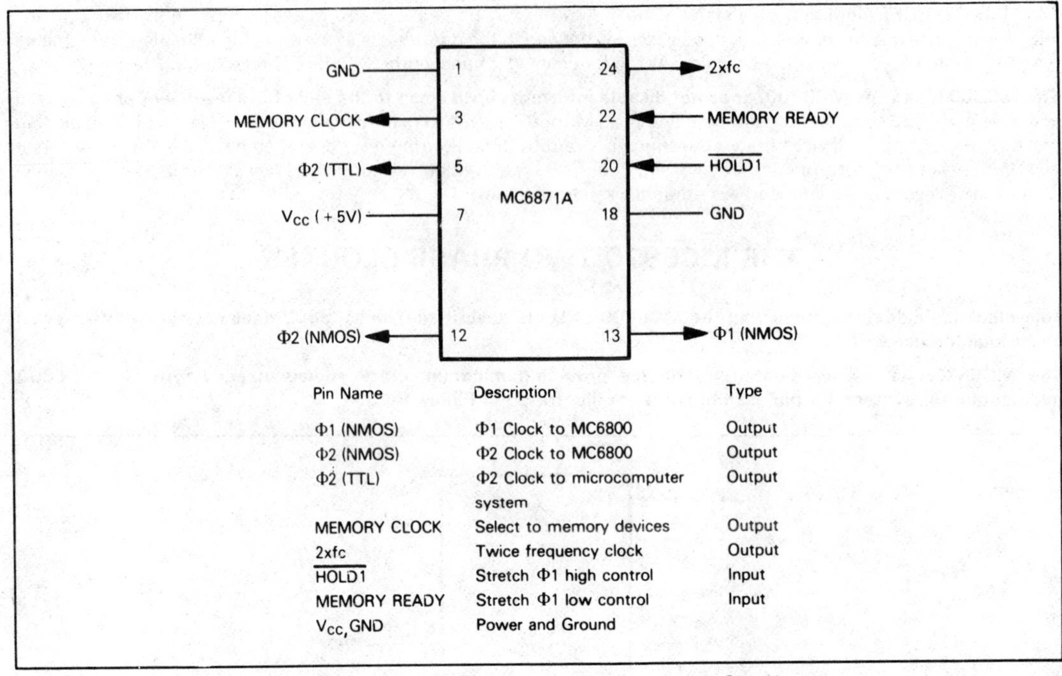


| Pin Name | Description | Type |
|---|---|---|
| Φ1 (NMOS) | Φ1 Clock to MC6800 | Output |
| Φ2 (NMOS) | Φ2 Clock to MC6800 | Output |
| Φ2 (TTL) | Φ2 Clock to microcomputer system | Output |
| MEMORY CLOCK | Select to memory devices | Output |
| 2xfc | Twice frequency clock | Output |
| $\overline{\text{HOLD1}}$ | Stretch Φ1 high control | Input |
| MEMORY READY | Stretch Φ1 low control | Input |
| $V_{CC}$, GND | Power and Ground | |

Figure 9-16. MC6871A Clock Device Pins and Signals

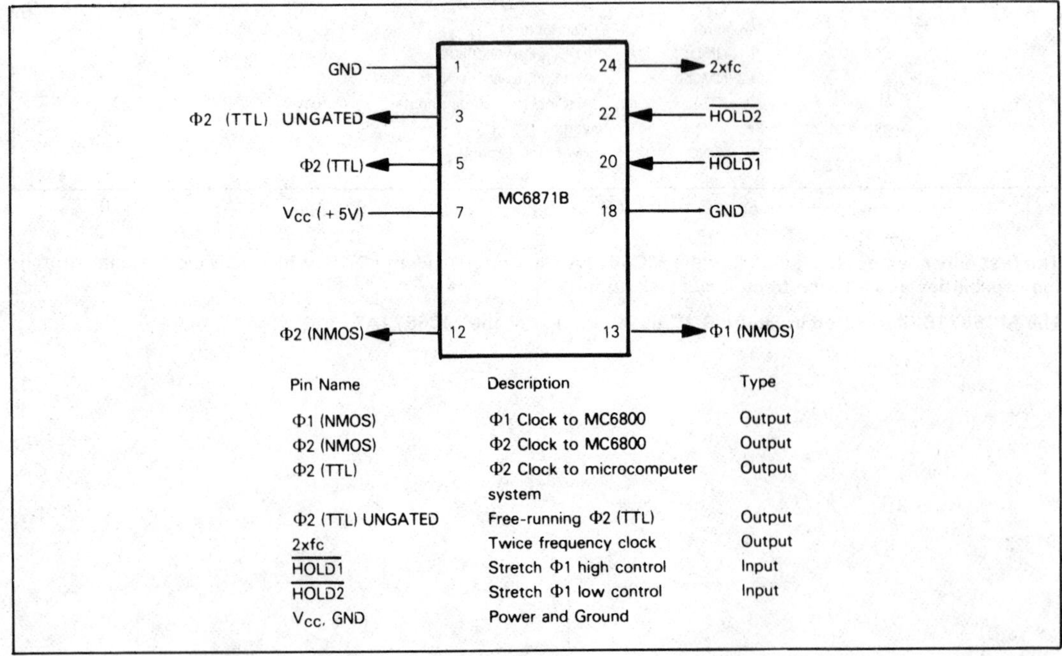


| Pin Name | Description | Type |
|---|---|---|
| Φ1 (NMOS) | Φ1 Clock to MC6800 | Output |
| Φ2 (NMOS) | Φ2 Clock to MC6800 | Output |
| Φ2 (TTL) | Φ2 Clock to microcomputer system | Output |
| Φ2 (TTL) UNGATED | Free-running Φ2 (TTL) | Output |
| 2xfc | Twice frequency clock | Output |
| $\overline{\text{HOLD1}}$ | Stretch Φ1 high control | Input |
| $\overline{\text{HOLD2}}$ | Stretch Φ1 low control | Input |
| $V_{CC}$, GND | Power and Ground | |

Figure 9-17. MC6871B Clock Device Pins and Signals

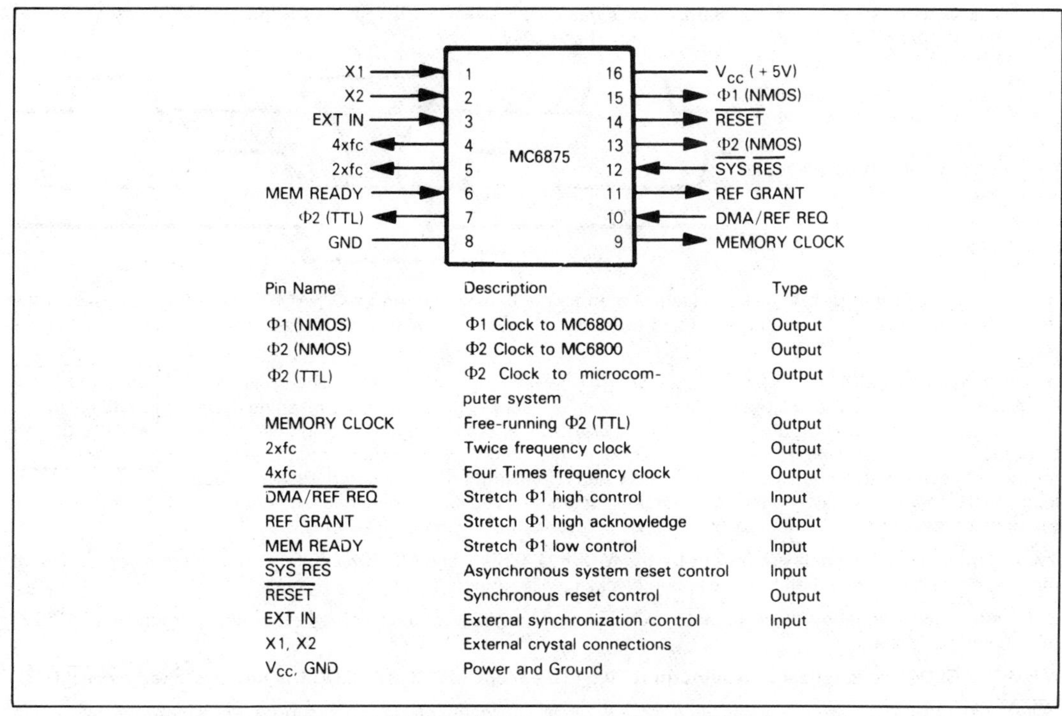


| Pin Name | Description | Type |
|---|---|---|
| Φ1 (NMOS) | Φ1 Clock to MC6800 | Output |
| Φ2 (NMOS) | Φ2 Clock to MC6800 | Output |
| Φ2 (TTL) | Φ2 Clock to microcomputer system | Output |
| MEMORY CLOCK | Free-running Φ2 (TTL) | Output |
| 2xfc | Twice frequency clock | Output |
| 4xfc | Four Times frequency clock | Output |
| $\overline{\text{DMA/REF REQ}}$ | Stretch Φ1 high control | Input |
| REF GRANT | Stretch Φ1 high acknowledge | Output |
| $\overline{\text{MEM READY}}$ | Stretch Φ1 low control | Input |
| $\overline{\text{SYS RES}}$ | Asynchronous system reset control | Input |
| $\overline{\text{RESET}}$ | Synchronous reset control | Output |
| EXT IN | External synchronization control | Input |
| X1, X2 | External crystal connections | |
| $V_{CC}$, GND | Power and Ground | |

Figure 9-18. MC6875 Clock Device Pins and Signals

**The MC6875 is the most versatile of the clock devices provided for the MC6800. It is illustrated in Figure 9-18.**

**Since these various clock logic devices represent essentially the same capabilities, but with increasing enhancements, we will describe logic and capabilities in the order of the device illustrations.**

**Much of the clock device logic we are going to describe stretches the Φ1 (NMOS) and Φ2 (NMOS) clock signals. But recall that stretching Φ1 (NMOS) and Φ2 (NMOS), in itself, is only half of the logic needed to stretch the entire System Bus. Additionally, the MC6800 needs a high TSC input to float the Address and R/W Bus lines while Φ1 (NMOS) is high. DBE must be input low in order to float the Data Bus lines while the clock is being stretched with Φ1 (NMOS) low.**

## THE MC6870A CLOCK DEVICE

**This is a minimum clock device; it outputs Φ1 (NMOS) and Φ2 (NMOS), the two clock signals required by an MC6800 CPU.**

**Φ2 (TTL) is also generated. Φ2 (TTL) is used to synchronize support devices; it has sufficient load capacity to drive five devices without signal buffering.**

The MC6870A contains an internal crystal and oscillator; in its standard form clock signals with a 1 MHz frequency are generated. A variety of other clock frequencies can also be ordered.

## THE MC6871A CLOCK DEVICE

In addition to the standard signals output by the MC6870A, the MC6871A provides two additional TTL output clock signals and externally controlled pulse stretching capabilities.

**HOLD1 is used to stretch the standard clock signals: Φ1 (NMOS), Φ2 (NMOS) and Φ2 (TTL),** which we described for the MC6870A. Timing may be illustrated as follows:

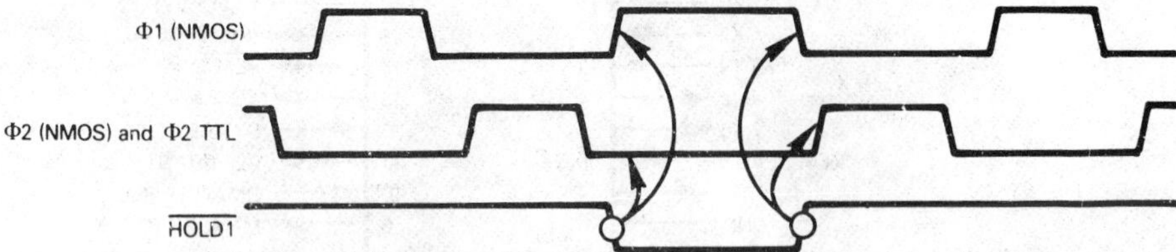


It is very important that HOLD1 makes its active high-to-low transition during a Φ1 (NMOS) high state. Subsequently, Φ1 (NMOS), Φ2 TTL clocks will be stretched until HOLD1 makes a low-to-high transition within the contraints described below.

**MC6800 STRETCHING ADDRESS TIMING**

As illustrated above, HOLD1 stretches clocks with Φ1 (NMOS) high. If you refer back to our discussion of the MC6800, you will see that these clock levels identify the portion of a machine cycle when an address is being output. Typically, the clock will be stretched so that two addresses can be output: the first for a Direct Memory Access or dynamic memory refresh operation; the second for the normal address output which is required when any instruction is executed. Device select logic must discriminate between the two addresses being output; DMA or dynamic memory refresh logic must receive the first address only, while memory or I/O devices receive the second address only.

**Two additional clock signals are output by the MC6871A:** 2xfc and MEMORY CLOCK; they are not part of normal memory addressing logic, therefore these two clock signals are not stretched by HOLD1.

**2xfc is a twice frequency clock signal** which can be used for various synchronization logic around an MC6800 microcomputer system.

**MEMORY CLOCK is identical in waveform to Φ2 TTL except MEMORY CLOCK is not stretched by HOLD1.**

HOLD1 must make its high-to-low transition while Φ1 (NMOS) is high. HOLD1 must subsequently make its low-to-high transition while Φ1 (NMOS) would have been high, had it not been stretched. **An asynchronous HOLD1 request must** therefore **be synchronized** with Φ1 (NMOS) in order to generate a valid HOLD1 clock input. This is a simple logic operation; here is one possibility:

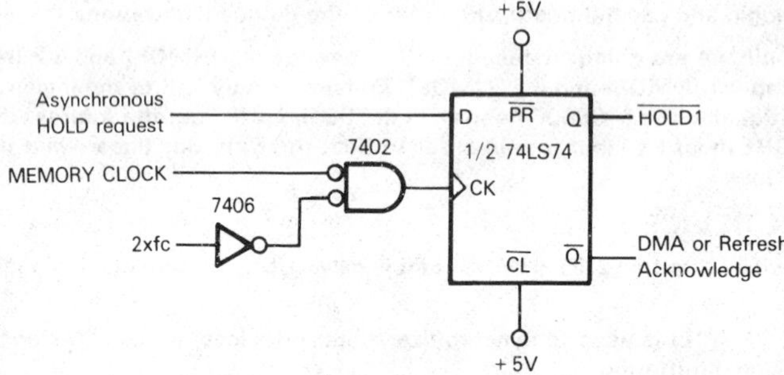

This circuit synchronizes the high-to-low and the low-to-high transition of $\overline{HOLD1}$. The low-to-high clock transition occurs only during Φ1 (NMOS) high time:

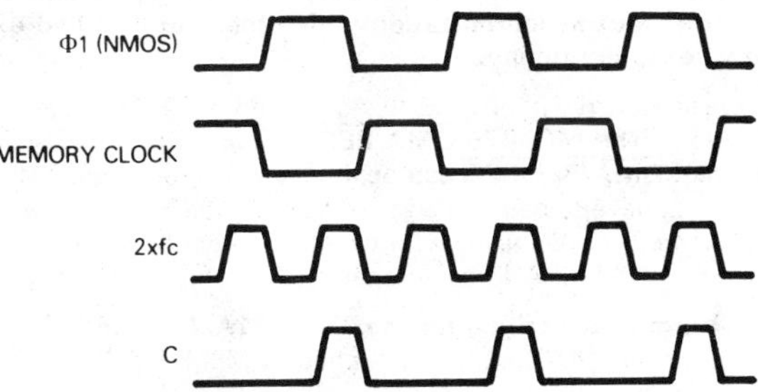


Observe that synchronization logic can create a time delay of up to one half clock cycle between the unsynchronized and the synchronized HOLD signals changing state.

**MEMORY READY also stretches clock signals.** Timing may be illustrated as follows:

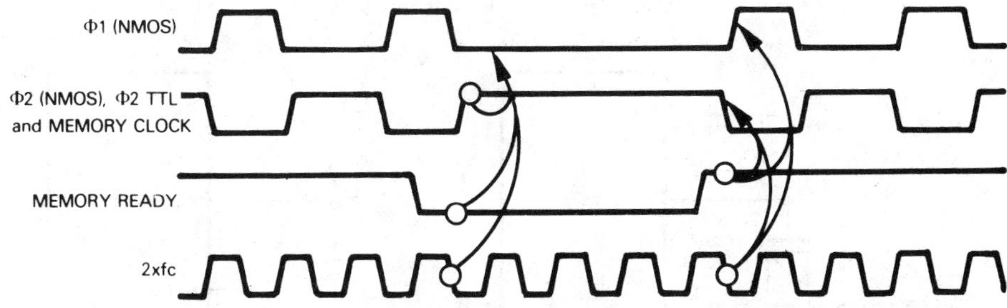


Clock signal stretching begins with Φ2 (NMOS) high following the MEMORY READY high-to-low transition. Clock stretching ends with the falling edge of 2xfc following the MEMORY READY low-to-high transition. Observe that MEMORY READY stretches MEMORY CLOCK, which $\overline{HOLD1}$ does not do. 2xfc, however, is not stretched, either by $\overline{HOLD1}$ or by MEMORY READY. Also note that MEMORY READY does not require input synchronization, as does $\overline{HOLD1}$.

If you refer back to the timing diagrams which illustrate MC6800 instructions' execution, you will see that MEMORY READY stretches clock signals during the data access portion of a machine cycle. This is the part of the machine cycle during which external memory has to respond to a CPU access; therefore, this is the portion of the machine cycle which must be stretched for slow memories — which is why MEMORY READY can be visualized as the signal which slow memories must input low in order to gain the access time they require.

**The MC6871A contains an internal crystal oscillator. In its standard form, clock signals with a 1 MHz frequency are generated. A variety of other clock frequencies can also be ordered.**

## THE MC6871B CLOCK DEVICE

**This device differs from the MC6871A in two ways. MEMORY READY is replaced by $\overline{HOLD2}$ and MEMORY CLOCK is replaced by Φ2 (TTL) UNGATED.** $\overline{HOLD2}$ stretches clock signals with Φ1 (NMOS) low, just as MEMORY READY did; however, like $\overline{HOLD1}$, $\overline{HOLD2}$ must have its active transitions synchronized with the clock output — in this case with Φ2 high. Φ2 (TTL) UNGATED, however, is not stretched. Timing may be illustrated as follows:

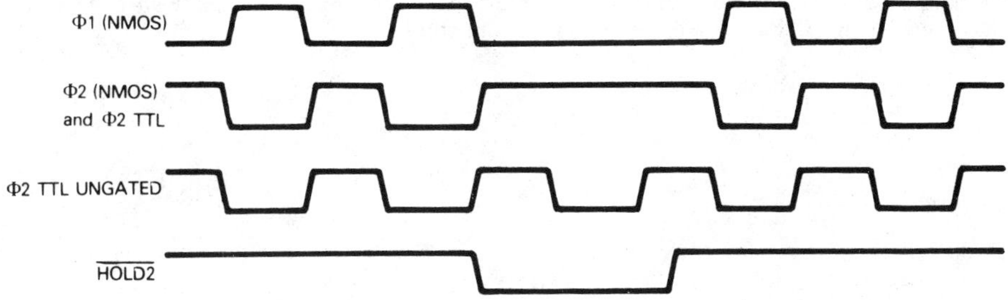

## THE MC6875 CLOCK DEVICE

**This is the most sophisticated of the clock devices offered with the MC6800 microcomputer system. Its principal features are that it performs control input synchronization which must be handled externally by other clock devices; also, the MC6875 allows external timing.**

As we have already stated, clock signals are stretched with Φ1 and Φ2 low in order to allow a Direct Memory Access or dynamic memory refresh address to be output. **The MC6875 $\overline{\text{DMA/REF REQ}}$ input performs this clock stretching operation, just as $\overline{\text{HOLD1}}$ does, except that $\overline{\text{DMA/REF REQ}}$ can be an asynchronous input.** MC6875 internal logic performs the synchronization operations which have to be handled externally for the MC6871A and MC6871B clocks. In addition, the MC6875 outputs REF GRANT high while the clocks are being stretched with Φ1 (NMOS) high. External DMA or dynamic memory refresh logic can use REF GRANT as an enable strobe.

**MEMORY READY and MEMORY CLOCK are as described for the MC6871A.** MEMORY READY stretches clocks with Φ1 (NMOS) low. MEMORY CLOCK follows Φ2 (NMOS) and is stretched by MEMORY READY but not by $\overline{\text{DMA/REF REQ}}$.

**The MC6875 clock signal outputs Φ1 (NMOS) and Φ2 (NMOS) have sufficient capacity to drive two MC6800 CPUs. 4xfc is an additional oscillator running at four times the Φ1 and Φ2 clock rates.**

**X1, X2 and EXT IN are three signals which allow MC6875 clock rates to be controlled externally.**

You can optionally attach a crystal oscillator or an RC network to X1, X2 as follows:

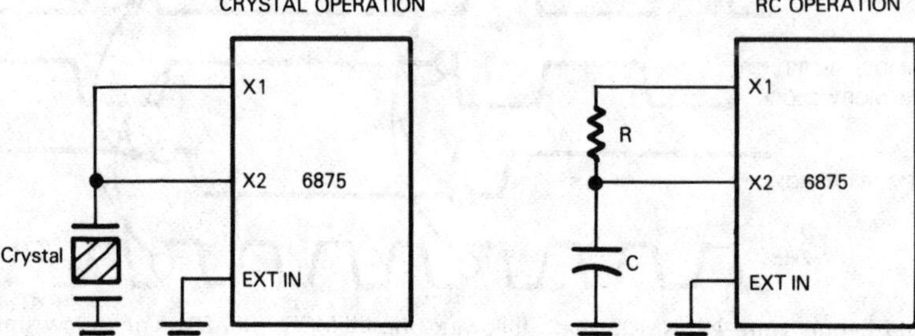


**You can also input an external clock signal to EXT IN, in which case the MC6875 will adopt the frequency of the external signal. The external clock frequency must be four times the Φ1 and Φ2 clock frequency.**

**The MC6875 is able to take an asynchronous SYSTEM RESET input and convert it into a synchronous RESET,** which may be used throughout an MC6800 microcomputer system. SYSTEM RESET can be any input signal which is processed through a Schmitt trigger to create a RESET output, as described for the 8224 clock device in Chapter 4.

## SOME STANDARD CLOCK SIGNAL INTERFACE LOGIC

**There are a number of very common ways in which MC6870 series clock signals are used within MC6800 microcomputer systems.**

**MC6800 ENABLE SIGNAL GENERATION**

**You will find that all of the support devices described in the rest of this chapter require an enable synchronizing signal, given the symbol "E". This signal is usually generated as the AND of the MC6800 VMA output and the Φ2 TTL clock output:**

The purpose of ANDing Φ2 with VMA is to make sure that devices receiving signal E are inhibited while VMA is low — at which time the CPU cannot be accessing the support device.

The $\overline{HALT}$ signal, which is used in MC6800 microcomputer systems to float the System Bus for extended periods, must be a synchronous input. **You can create a synchronous $\overline{HALT}$ from an asynchronous $\overline{HALT}$ using Φ2 TTL as follows:**

**MC6800 SYNCHRONOUS HALT GENERATION**

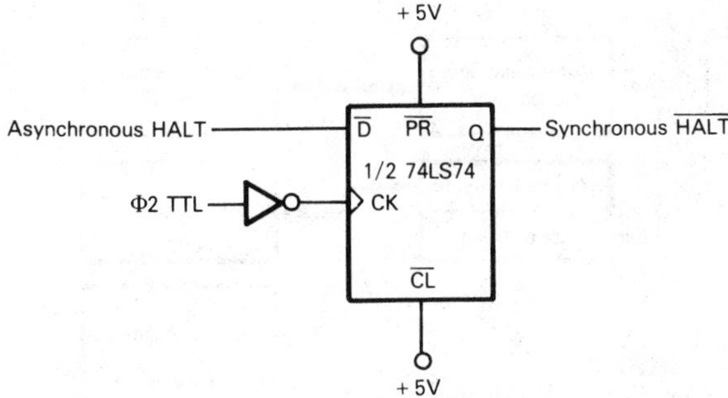


# THE MC6820 AND MCS6520 PERIPHERAL INTERFACE ADAPTER (PIA)

**This part is manufactured as the MC6820 by the companies listed at the beginning of this chapter. MOS Technology and its second source companies (whose products are described in Chapter 10) manufacture the same part, but call it the MCS6520.**

**The MC6820 PIA is a general purpose I/O device, designed for use within MC6800 microcomputer systems.**

**The MC6820 PIA provides 16 I/O pins, configured as two 8-bit I/O ports. We will refer to these as Port A and Port B. Individual pins of each I/O port may be used separately as inputs or outputs. Each I/O port has two associated control signals, one of which is input only, while the other is bidirectional. The only differences between I/O Ports A and B are in their electrical characteristics, and in their handshaking control capabilities.** But these are very significant differences, as we will explain shortly.

**Figure 9-19 illustrates that part of our general microcomputer system logic which has been implemented on the MC6820 PIA.**

**The MC6820 PIA is packaged as a 40-pin DIP. It uses a single +5V power supply. All inputs and outputs are TTL compatible.**

**The device is implemented using N-channel silicon gate MOS technology.**

## THE MC6820 PIA PINS AND SIGNALS

**The MC6820 pins and signals are illustrated in Figure 9-20. We will summarize signal functions before describing PIA operations.**

**Consider first the various Data Busses.**

**D0 - D7 represents the bidirectional Data Bus via which all communications between the CPU and the MC6820 occur.**

**PA0 - PA7 and PB0 - PB7 represent Data Busses connecting the two 8-bit I/O Ports A and B with external logic.** The 16 I/O port pins may be looked upon as 16 individual signal lines, or two 8-bit I/O busses. Each I/O port pin can be individually assigned to input or output, but an individual pin cannot support bidirectional data transfers.

**These are the differences between I/O Port A and B pins:**

1) Bits of I/O Port A may be set or reset at any time by voltage levels applied to associated pins. Irrespective of data that may be in a bit position following a Read or Write operation, an I/O Port A bit will be reset to zero any time a voltage of +0.8V or less is applied to a Port A pin. A 1 will be written into a Port A bit any time a voltage of +2V or more is applied to the Port A pin. I/O Port B bit contents are not affected by voltage levels at I/O Port B pins. For example, suppose that a 1 has been output to bit 2 of I/O Ports A and B. Subsequently suppose that pin 2 of I/O Ports A and B are drained excessively, so that voltage levels transiently drop to +0.5V. I/O Port A bit 2 will become 0, but I/O Port B bit 2 will retain a level of 1.
2) As outputs, I/O Port B pins may be used as a source of up to 1 mA at +1.5V, to directly drive the base of a transistor switch. This is not feasible using I/O Port A pins.

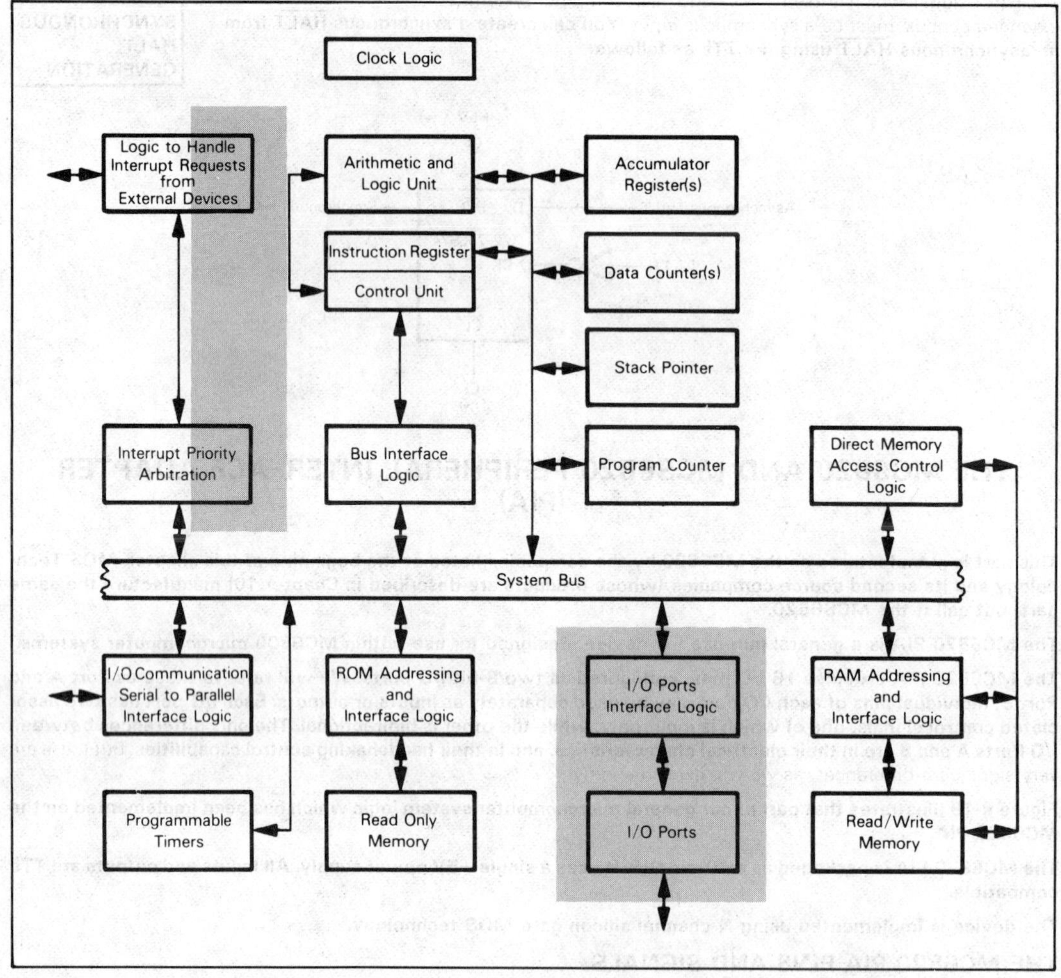


Figure 9-19. Logic of the MC6820 PIA

**There are five device select pins.**

**CS0, CS1 and $\overline{CS2}$ are three typical chip select signals.** For an MC6820 device to be selected, CS0 and CS1 must receive high inputs while $\overline{CS2}$ simultaneously receives a low input.

Providing CS0, CS1 and $\overline{CS2}$ have selected an MC6820 device, **RS0 and RS1 address one of four memory locations.** Thus an MC6820 device will appear to a programmer as four memory locations.

Any of the standard schemes described in Volume1 can be used to address an MC6820 PIA. There is nothing unusual about the select logic with which you will assign four unique memory addresses to an MC6820.

**There are four timing and control signals which interface an MC6820 with external logic.**

**CA1 and CA2 are control signals associated with I/O Port A.** CA1 is an input only signal and is usually used by external logic to request an interrupt. CA2 is a bidirectional control signal which is used to implement various types of handshaking logic.

**CB1 and CB2 are the control signals which support I/O Port B.** These two signals are analogous to CA1 and CA2, although there are some differences in the handshaking logic associated with CB2 as compared to CA2.

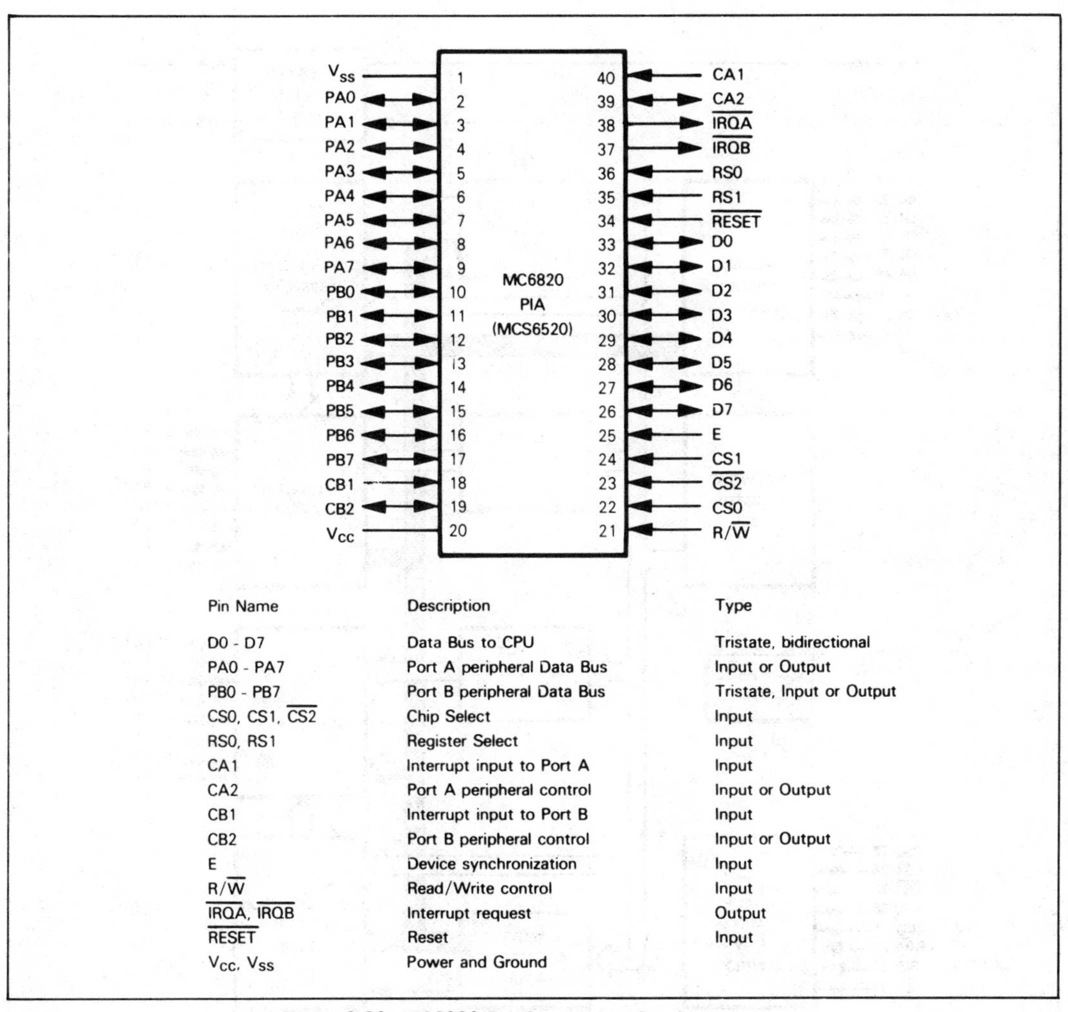


| Pin Name | Description | Type |
|---|---|---|
| D0 - D7 | Data Bus to CPU | Tristate, bidirectional |
| PA0 - PA7 | Port A peripheral Data Bus | Input or Output |
| PB0 - PB7 | Port B peripheral Data Bus | Tristate, Input or Output |
| CS0, CS1, $\overline{\text{CS2}}$ | Chip Select | Input |
| RS0, RS1 | Register Select | Input |
| CA1 | Interrupt input to Port A | Input |
| CA2 | Port A peripheral control | Input or Output |
| CB1 | Interrupt input to Port B | Input |
| CB2 | Port B peripheral control | Input or Output |
| E | Device synchronization | Input |
| R/$\overline{\text{W}}$ | Read/Write control | Input |
| $\overline{\text{IRQA}}$, $\overline{\text{IRQB}}$ | Interrupt request | Output |
| $\overline{\text{RESET}}$ | Reset | Input |
| $V_{CC}$, $V_{SS}$ | Power and Ground | |

Figure 9-20. MC6820 PIA Signals and Pin Assignments

**There are two control signals associated with the MC6820 CPU interface.**

**E is the standard synchronization signal generated by the various MC6870 series clock devices.** The trailing edge of E pulses synchronizes all logic and timing within the MC6820. Manufacturer literature refers to E as a device enable signal, but it is more accurately viewed as a device synchronization signal.

**R/$\overline{\text{W}}$ is the standard Read/Write control signal** output by the MC6800 CPU. When R/$\overline{\text{W}}$ is high, a Read operation is specified; that is, data transfer from the MC6820 PIA to the MC6800 CPU occurs. When R/$\overline{\text{W}}$ is low, a Write operation is specified; that is, data transfer from the CPU to the PIA occurs.

**There are two interrupt request signals, $\overline{\text{IRQA}}$ and $\overline{\text{IRQB}}$.** Under program control you can specify the conditions under which an interrupt request can originate at logic associated with I/O Port A or I/O Port B. The actual interrupt request is transmitted to the MC6800 CPU via signal $\overline{\text{IRQA}}$ for I/O Port A logic, and via $\overline{\text{IRQB}}$ for I/O Port B logic. Interrupt requests originating at either signal will connect to the MC6800 $\overline{\text{IRQ}}$ input.

**$\overline{\text{RESET}}$ is a standard Reset input.** When it is input low, the contents of all MC6820 registers will be set to zero.

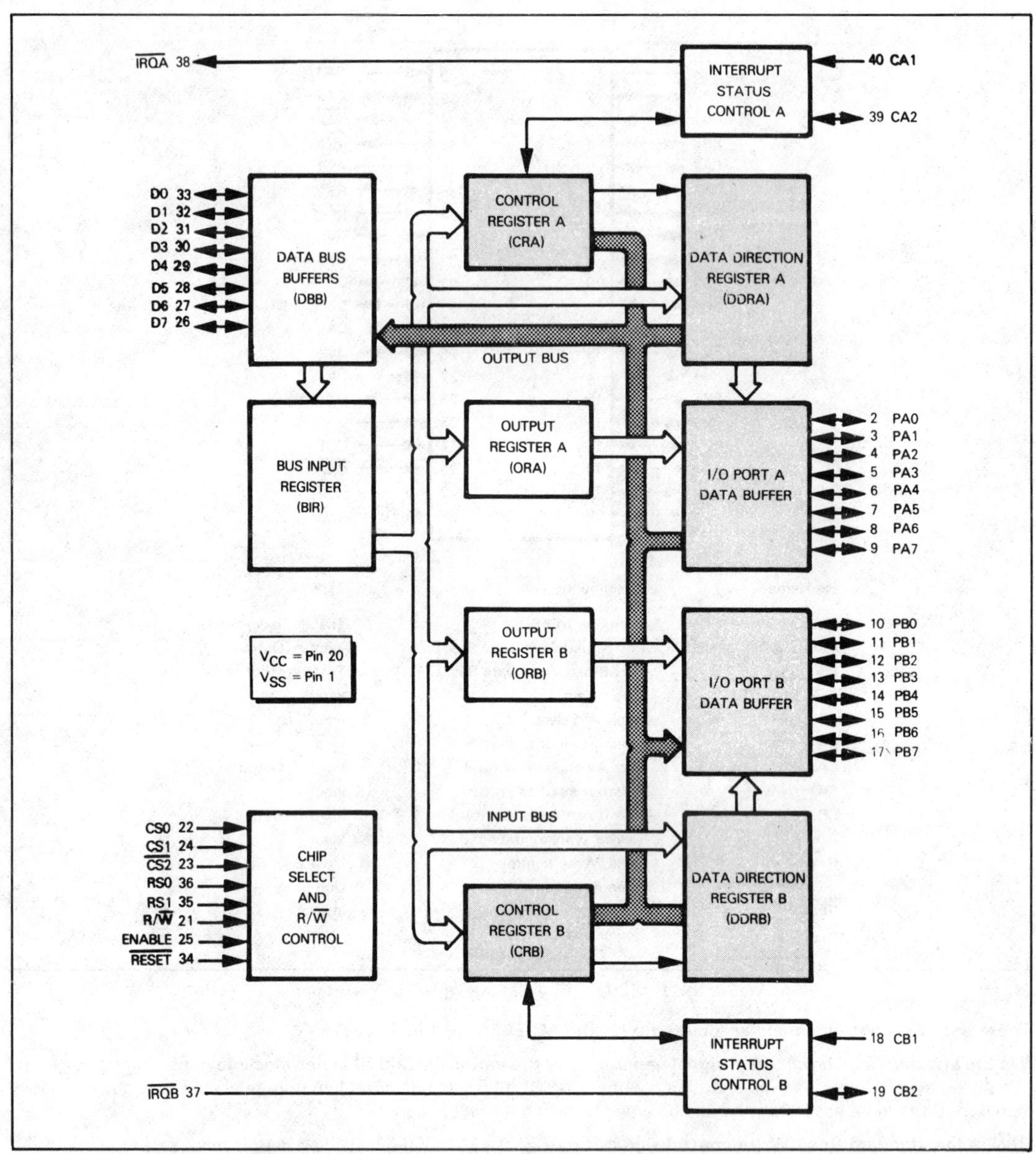


Figure 9-21. Functional Block Diagram for the MC6820 PIA

## MC6820 OPERATIONS

As compared to the 8255 PPI, the MC6820 PIA has less formalized operating modes. The MC6820-to-external logic interface consists of two I/O ports, each of which has two dedicated control lines. **You have the option of assigning individual I/O port lines to input or output; as a completely separate operation you can use the two control lines to perform a limited amount of handshaking and interrupt processing — or you can ignore the control lines, in which case the I/O port is supporting simple input and/or output. Bidirectional I/O, equivalent to 8255 Mode 2, is not available. Figure 9-21 generally represents MC6820 functional organization and Table 9-4 summarizes the available operating modes.**

Table 9-4. MC6820 Operating Modes

| OPERATING MODE | MC6800 AVAILABILITY |
|---|---|
| Simple input without handshaking | I/O Port A or B |
| Simple output without handshaking | I/O Port A or B |
| Bidirectional I/O without handshaking | Not available, but individual pins of either I/O port may be separately assigned to input or output |
| Input with handshaking | I/O Port A only |
| Output with handshaking | I/O Port B only |
| Bidirectional I/O with handshaking | Not Available |

Table 9-5. Addressing MC6820 Internal Registers

| SELECT LINES | | | ADDRESSED LOCATION |
|---|---|---|---|
| RS1 | RS0 | X | |
| 0 | 1 | | I/O Port A Control register (Bit No. 7 6 5 4 3 2 1 0; bit 2 = X) |
| 0 | 0 | 0 | I/O Port A Data Direction register |
| 0 | 0 | 1 | I/O Port A Data buffer |
| 1 | 1 | | I/O Port B Control register (Bit No. 7 6 5 4 3 2 1 0; bit 2 = X) |
| 1 | 0 | 0 | I/O Port B Data Direction register |
| 1 | 0 | 1 | I/O Port B Data buffer |

**MC6820 REGISTERS ADDRESSING**

**There are six addressable locations within an MC6820 PIA; they are shaded in Figure 9-21.** Since there are only two register select lines, RS0 and RS1, four unique addressable locations can be identified within the MC6820. Table 9-5 summarizes the manner in which the MC6820 uses four addresses to access six locations. Logic defined in Table 9-5 requires that you first output a Control code to each I/O port Control register; next you access either the I/O port Data Direction register, or the I/O port Data Buffer. You use the same memory address to access an I/O port Data Direction register and I/O port Data Buffer. Which location you access is determined by bit 2 of the I/O port's Control register.

You must precede any I/O port Data Direction register, or Data Buffer access with a Control code, written to the I/O port's Control register. Once you have written a Control code to an I/O port Control register, you do not have to write another Control code for addressing purposes until you wish to switch from accessing the I/O port Data Direction register to the Data Buffer, or from accessing the Data Buffer to the Data Direction register.

To illustrate MC6820 addressing, suppose the four addresses $C000_{16}$, $C001_{16}$, $C002_{16}$ and $C003_{16}$ select an MC6820. This is how addressable locations within the MC6820 would actually be selected if address line A0 were connected to RS0 and A1 to RS1:

| Address | Selected |
|---|---|
| $C000_{16}$ | I/O Port A Data Direction register, if $C001_{16CF1}$, bit 2 = 0 |
| | I/O Port A Data buffer, if $C001_{16}$, bit 2 = 1 |
| $C001_{16}$ | I/O Port A Control register |
| $C002_{16}$ | I/O Port B Data Direction register, if $C003_{16}$, bit 2 = 0 |
| | I/O Port B Data buffer, if $C003_{16}$, bit 2 = 1 |
| $C003_{16}$ | I/O Port B Control register |

If you read from an I/O port data buffer, you input from the I/O port to the CPU; if you write to an I/O port data buffer, you output from the CPU to the I/O port.

The Data Direction registers identify each pin of an I/O port as being dedicated to either input or output. These are write only registers. You must write a control word into each Data Direction register; a 0 in a bit position configures the corresponding I/O port pin as an input, while a 1 results in an output:

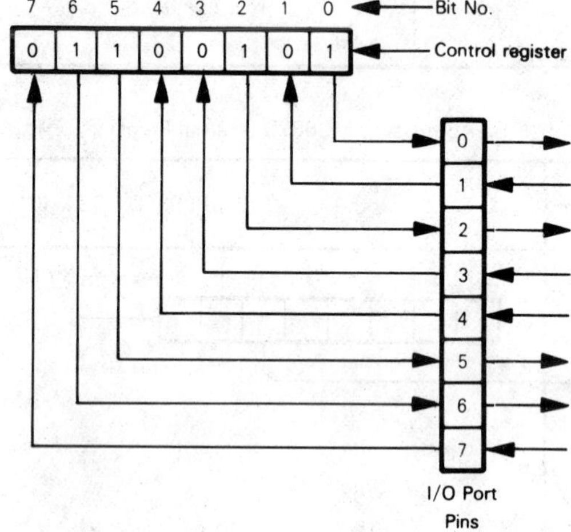


Observe that I/O Ports A and B will both be configured as 8-bit input ports when the MC6820 is reset, since $\overline{RESET}$ clears all internal registers.

**Control register interpretation is quite complex.**

The two high-order bits of each Control register are read only locations, which record the status of interrupt requests which may originate from either of two control lines associated with an I/O port:

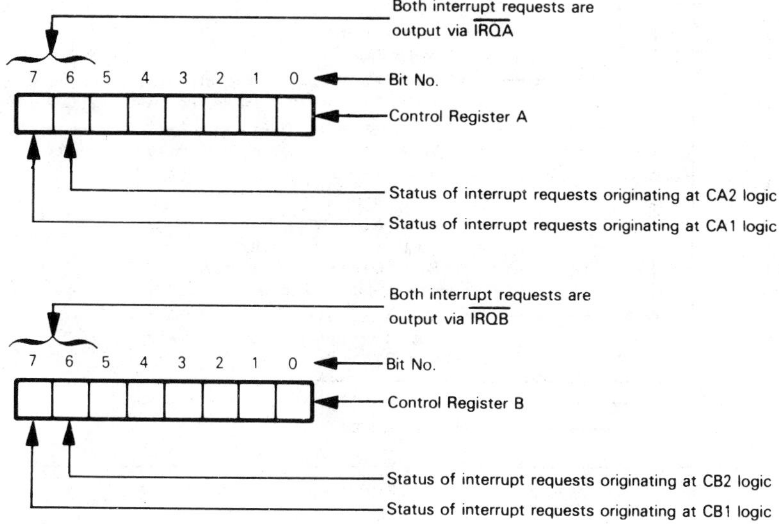


The remaining six control bits may be written into or read; they define the way in which the I/O port will operate.

Figures 9-22 and 9-23 describe the Control register interpretation for I/O Ports A and B respectively; since the two Control register interpretations are very similar, the points of difference are shaded so that they are easy to spot.

**Let us clarify the functions enabled by the two Control registers.**

**MC6820 INTERRUPT LOGIC**

Each I/O port has its own interrupt request signal: $\overline{IRQA}$ for I/O Port A and $\overline{IRQB}$ for I/O Port B. Each interrupt request signal has two separate sets of request logic, based on an interrupt request originating with a CA1/CB1 signal transition, or a CA2/CB2 signal transition.

Control register bit 0 enables or disables $\overline{IRQA}/\overline{IRQB}$, based on signal CA1/CB1 transitions only. Quite independently, Control register bit 3 enables or disables $\overline{IRQA}/\overline{IRQB}$ based on transitions of signal CA2/CB2. However, Control register bit 3 has an alternative interpretation; the one we have just described only applies if Control register bit 5 is 0.

Interrupt requests are triggered by the "active transitions" of a control signal. The active transitions of control signals may be a high-to-low, or a low-to-high transition. For CA1/CB1, the active transition is selected by Control register bit 1. For CA2/CB2, the active transition is selected by Control register bit 4, but only if Control register bit 5 is 0.

Irrespective of whether interrupt request signals $\overline{IRQA}$ and $\overline{IRQB}$ have been enabled or disabled, Control register bits 6 and 7 will report the interrupt request as a status, that is to say, if a condition exists where CA1/CB1 makes an interrupt requesting active transition, then Control register bit 7 will be set to 1. Similarly, if control signal CA2/CB2 makes an interrupt requesting transition, then Control register bit 6 will be set to 1. Once set, Control register bits 6 and 7 will remain set until a Read operation addresses the Control register; at that time Control register bits 6 and 7 will both be reset to 0, while other bits of the Control register are left unaltered.

If Control register bit 5 is 1, then Control register bits 4 and 3 take on a second interpretation. If Control register bits 5 and 4 are both 1, then control signal CA2/CB2 will be output at all times with the level of control bit 3.

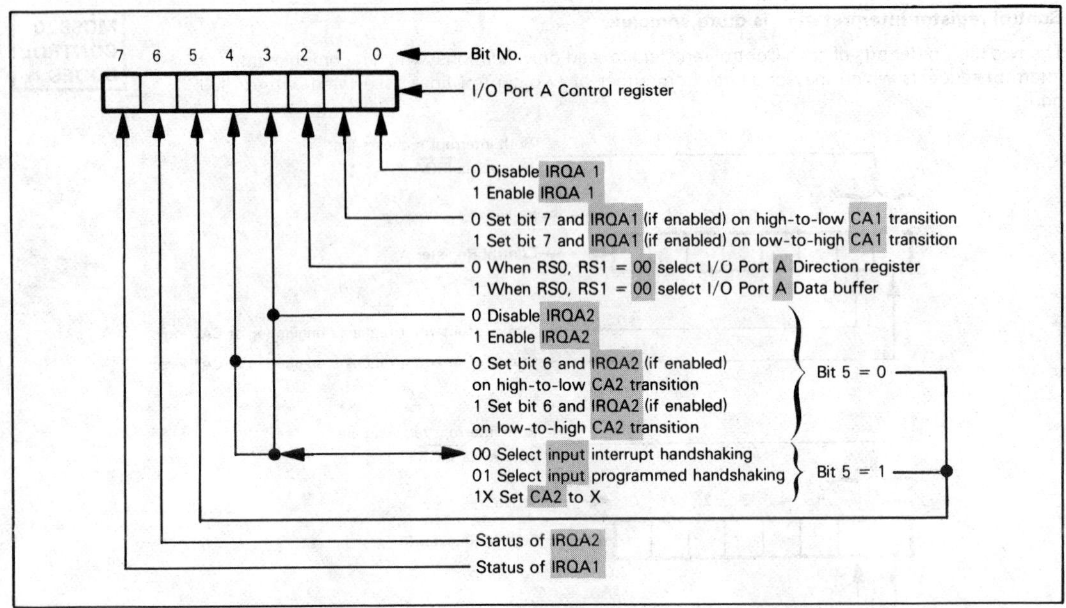

Figure 9-22. I/O Port A Control Register Interpretation

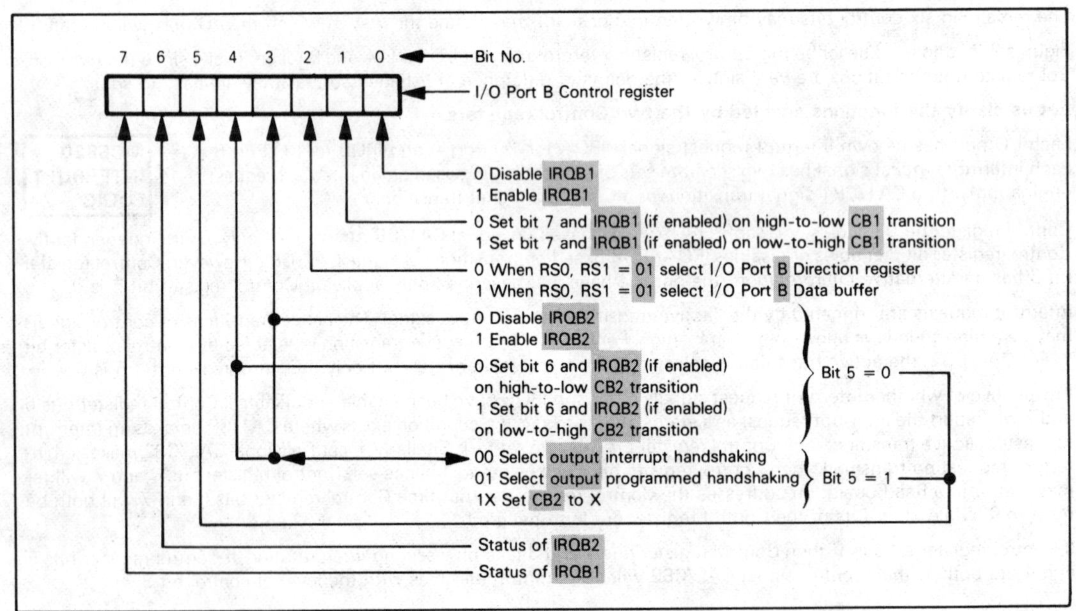

Figure 9-23. I/O Port B Control Register Interpretation

**If Control register bits 5 and 4 are 1 and 0 respectively, then Control register bit 3 specifies an automatic handshaking signal sequence. Let us describe these signal sequences.**

**MC6820 AUTOMATIC HANDSHAKING**

**Input interrupt handshaking applies to I/O Port A only, and may be illustrated as follows:**

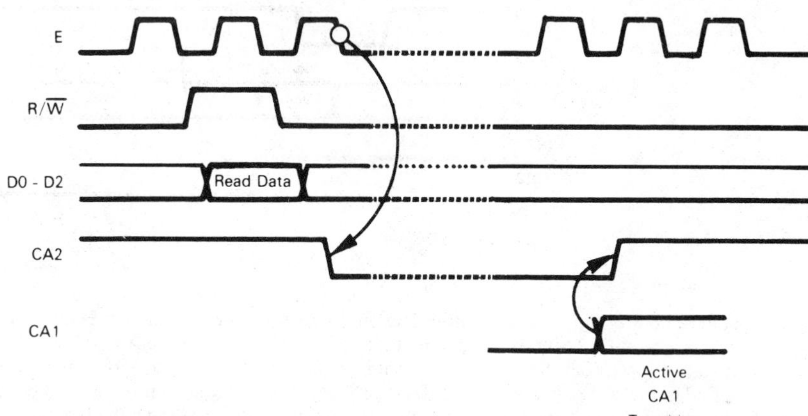


CA2 is output on the trailing edge of E, after the CPU has read the contents of the I/O Port A data buffer; this tells external logic that previously input data has been read and new data may now be input. External logic receives CA2 low, and upon transmitting new data to I/O Port A, must cause an active interrupt requesting transition of input control signal CA1. What constitutes an active transition will be determined by I/O Port A Control register bit 1. When external logic requests an interrupt via signal CA1, CA2 will be set high again.

**Input programmed handshaking applies only to I/O Port A, and may be illustrated as follows:**

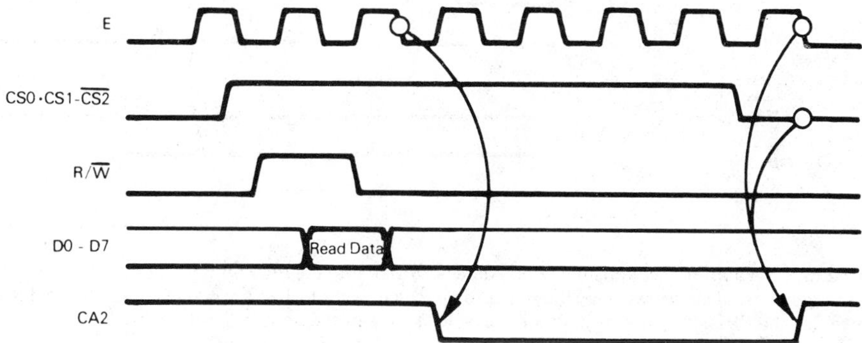


Once again control signal CA2 is output low when I/O Port A data buffer contents are read by the CPU. This tells external logic that previously input data has been read and new data may be input. External logic does not have to identify newly transmitted data with an interrupt request; rather, CA2 will be reset as soon as the MC6820 is deselected. Using programmed handshaking, external logic may use the CA2 low pulse as a Write strobe, causing new data to be input to I/O Port A.

**Output interrupt handshaking applies only to I/O Port B, and may be illustrated as follows:**

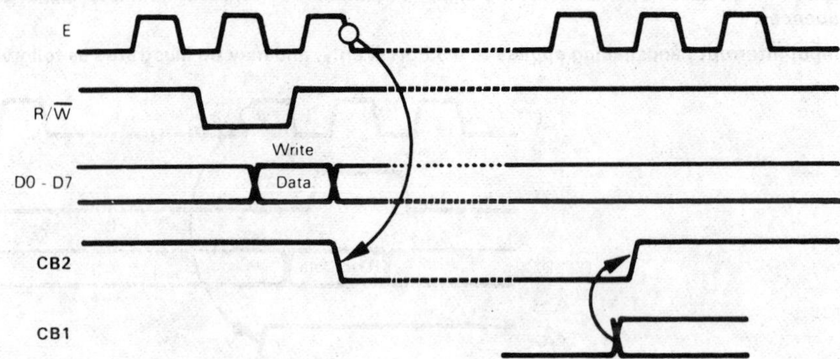


In this instance, control signal CB2 is output low on the high-to-low transition of E following a Write to I/O Port A Data buffer. In other words, CB2 tells external logic that new data has been output to I/O Port B and is ready to be read. External logic tells the MC6820 that I/O Port B contents have been read by making an interrupt requesting active transition of the CB1 signal. Once again, I/O Port B Control register bit 1 will determine what constitutes an active transition of the CB1 signal. Program logic can use an interrupt to branch to a program which outputs the next byte of data to I/O Port B.

**Output programmed handshaking applies only to I/O Port B, and may be illustrated as follows:**

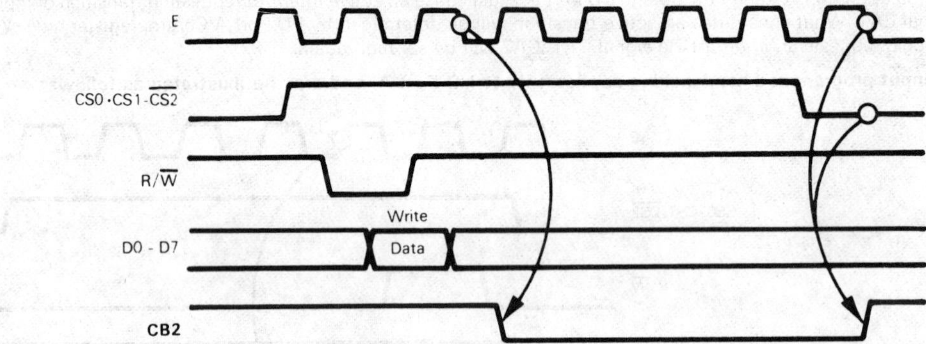


CB2 makes a high-to-low transition when data is written into the I/O Port B data buffer, just as occurred with output interrupt handshaking. However, CB2 will automatically be set to 1 as soon as the MC6820 is deselected. External logic can use the CB2 low pulse as a strobe, causing it to read the contents of I/O Port B.

**Many other handshaking protocols may be created under program control.** The four automatic protocols described above are simply four situations which can be specified, and which will subsequently occur without further program intervention. But remember, you can modify the level of control signal CA2/CB2 any time by outputting a Control code with bits 5 and 4 both set to 1; CA2/CB2 will then take the level of Control code bit 3. You can also determine the conditions which will cause an interrupt request as a result of any control signal transition.

# THE MC6850 ASYNCHRONOUS COMMUNICATIONS INTERFACE ADAPTER (ACIA)

**The MC6800 microcomputer system provides separate devices supporting synchronous and asynchronous serial I/O.** The MC6850, which we are about to describe, provides asynchronous serial I/O. The MC6852, which we will describe next, supports synchronous serial I/O.

**Taken together, the MC6850 and MC6852 devices are approximately equivalent to the 8251 USART.** The 8251 is a general purpose 8080 device that can be used with a variety of microcomputers. Refer to Volume 3 for a description of 8251's.

**Figure 9-24 illustrates that part of our general microcomputer system logic which is provided by the MC6850 and MC6852 devices.**

**Having separate synchronous and asynchronous serial I/O devices has advantages and disadvantages,** when compared to the 8251 USART which provides both sets of logic on a single device. In a microcomputer system that uses either asynchronous or synchronous serial I/O, but not both, separate devices are better, because they come in smaller packages and require less space on a PC card. If your microcomputer system uses both synchronous and asynchronous serial I/O, then a single device will be more economical.

**When comparing the MC6850 with the 8251, you will find that the 8251 offers more asynchronous serial I/O options, but it is harder to program.** In fact, you must program the 8251 defensively; 8251 statuses and control signals simply prompt your program logic, but actually do nothing within the 8251 USART itself. When using the MC6850 and MC6852, that is not the case; **these two devices are much easier to program.**

**The MC6850 ACIA is packaged as a 24-pin DIP. It is fabricated using N-channel silicon gate technology.**

A single +5V power supply is required.

In the discussion of the MC6850 that follows we will frequently refer to the 8251 USART description in Volume 3. **If you are unfamiliar with asynchronous serial I/O devices in general, see Chapter 5 of Volume 1, then read the description of the 8251 USART which is given in Volume 3.**

## THE MC6850 ACIA PINS AND SIGNALS

**MC6850 ACIA pins and signals are illustrated in Figure 9-25. Signals may be divided into the following four categories:**

1) CPU interface and control signals
2) Serial input
3) Serial output
4) Modem control

**We will first consider CPU interface and control signals.**

**D0 - D7 constitutes an 8-bit bidirectional Data Bus connecting the MC6850 with the CPU.**

When data is output to the MC6850 by the CPU, either a byte of parallel data or a Control code will be transmitted.

A byte of parallel data will be serialized and transmitted according to the protocol which has been selected under program control.

Either data or status may be input from the MC6850 ACIA to the CPU via the Data Bus. Data consists of an 8-bit parallel data unit extracted from the serial input data stream. Status consists of the contents of the ACIA Status register.

The Status register of the MC6850 ACIA is very important, because **the MC6850 uses status flags where the 8251 uses control signals to monitor serial data transfer logic.**

The MC6850 ACIA is accessed by the CPU as two memory locations. **MC6850 select logic consists of the three chip select signals CS0, CS1 and $\overline{CS2}$; manufacturers' literature also refers to the enable signal E as being part of the chip select logic;** however, E is more accurately visualized as an internal synchronization signal.

For the MC6850 ACIA to be selected, CS0 and CS1 must be input high while $\overline{CS2}$ is simultaneously input low. Once selected, **the register select signal RS determines which of the two addressable locations within the MC6850 ACIA will be accessed.** When RS is low, a Read will access the ACIA Status register, while a Write will access the ACIA Control register. When RS is high, ACIA data buffers will be addressed.

While the MC6850 ACIA is selected, internal logic is synchronized on the trailing edge of the E signal. E is a standard output of the various MC6870 clock devices used to synchronize support logic throughout an MC6800 microcomputer system.

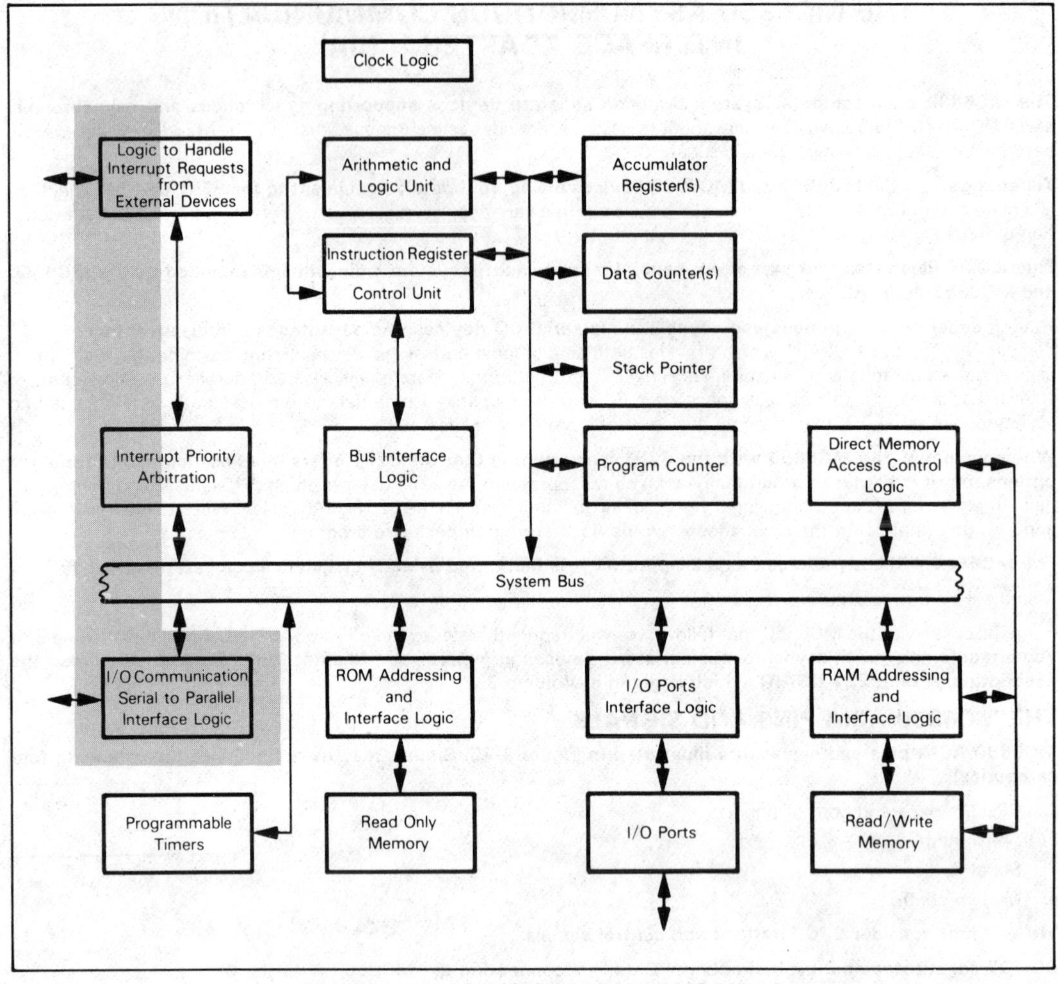


Figure 9-24. Logic of the MC6850 ACIA or MC6852 SSDA Devices

**R/$\overline{W}$ is the control input which determines whether a Read or Write operation is in progress.** When R/$\overline{W}$ is high, the CPU is reading data out of the MC6850. When R/$\overline{W}$ is low, the CPU is writing data to the MC6850.

**The MC6850 has no RESET input; a Control code is used as a master Reset.** When power is first detected within the MC6850, internal logic automatically initiates a Reset sequence. Subsequently, before initializing the MC6850 for serial data transfer you should again reset the device by inputting a Reset Control code.

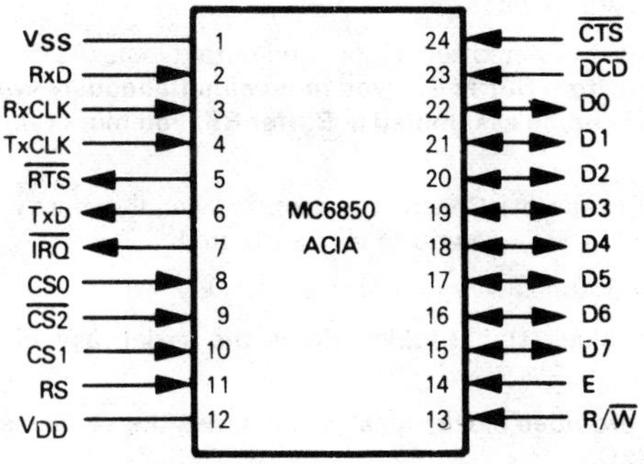

| Signal | Pin | | Pin | Signal |
|---|---|---|---|---|
| VSS | 1 | | 24 | $\overline{CTS}$ |
| RxD | 2 | | 23 | $\overline{DCD}$ |
| RxCLK | 3 | | 22 | D0 |
| TxCLK | 4 | | 21 | D1 |
| $\overline{RTS}$ | 5 | | 20 | D2 |
| TxD | 6 | MC6850 | 19 | D3 |
| $\overline{IRQ}$ | 7 | ACIA | 18 | D4 |
| CS0 | 8 | | 17 | D5 |
| $\overline{CS2}$ | 9 | | 16 | D6 |
| CS1 | 10 | | 15 | D7 |
| RS | 11 | | 14 | E |
| VDD | 12 | | 13 | R/$\overline{W}$ |

| Pin Name | Description | Type |
|---|---|---|
| D0 - D7 | Data Bus to CPU | Tristate, bidirectional |
| CS0, CS1, CS2 | Chip Select | Input |
| E | Internal synchronization | Input |
| RS | Register Select | Input |
| R/$\overline{W}$ | Read/Write control | Input |
| TxCLK | Transmit Clock | Input |
| TxD | Transmit Data | Output |
| RxCLK | Receive Clock | Input |
| RxD | Receive Data | Input |
| $\overline{CTS}$ | Clear To Send | Input |
| $\overline{RTS}$ | Request To Send | Output |
| $\overline{DCD}$ | Data Carrier Detect | Input |
| $\overline{IRQ}$ | Interrupt request | Output |
| VDD, VSS | Power and Ground | |

Figure 9-25. MC6850 ACIA Signals and Pin Assignments

## MC6850 DATA TRANSFER AND CONTROL OPERATIONS

**There are a number of buffers through which data flows in and out of the MC6850 ACIA. These data flows may be illustrated as follows:**

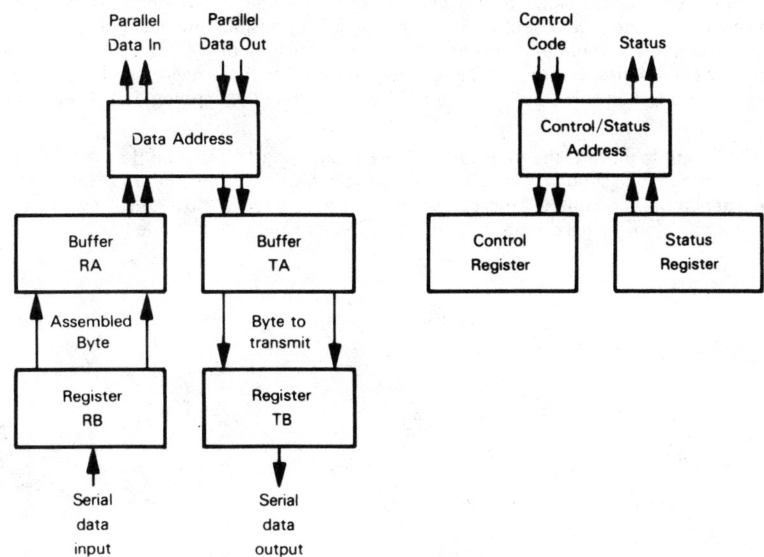

**Buffer names in the illustration above conform with terminology used for the 8251 in Volume 3; this will make it easier for you to compare the two devices.**

Like the 8251, the MC6850 has double buffered serial input and output logic. As described for the 8251, **while a data byte is being serialized and output from Buffer TB, you must simultaneously write the next data byte to Buffer TA. Also, while a serial data byte is being assembled in Buffer RB, you must read the previously assembled data byte out of Buffer RA.**

Unlike the 8251, **the MC6850 has a separate Control register.** You can therefore write Control codes and read status at any time without fear of scrambling data waiting to be transmitted.

**MC6850 SERIAL I/O DATA AND CONTROL SIGNALS**

As compared to the 8251, the MC6850 has very elementary serial I/O logic.

**TxCLK is an externally provided clock signal which times the serial, asynchronous data stream which is output via TxD.**

**Similarly, RxCLK is an externally provided clock signal which times the serial, asynchronous data stream which is input via RxD.**

**There are no control signals accompanying serial I/O data;** rather, a single interrupt request signal is shared by all transmit and receive conditions. You have to write an interrupt service routine which reads the contents of the MC6850 Status register, and thus determine which one of the many serial data transfer interrupt request conditions has occurred.

The fact that you must execute instructions to duplicate the logic which the 8251 provides with its TxRDY, RxRDY and TxE signals will certainly make an MC6800 microcomputer system less attractive in an application that makes heavy use of serial I/O. Conversely, the MC6800 system will appear more attractive in simple applications, since you have less interface circuitry to be concerned with.

**MC6850 MODEM CONTROL SIGNALS**

**Three modem control signals are provided: Clear To Send ($\overline{CTS}$), Request To Send ($\overline{RTS}$), and Data Carrier Detect ($\overline{DCD}$).** $\overline{CTS}$ and $\overline{RTS}$ are identical to the signals with the same names described in Volume 1, Chapter 5 for the general case, and in Volume 3 for the 8251.

$\overline{RTS}$ is output by the MC6850 under program control when the MC6850 is ready to transmit data. A full duplex line turns $\overline{RTS}$ around and sends it back as $\overline{CTS}$; a half duplex line returns $\overline{CTS}$ after line turnaround has occurred.

The MC6850 has no Data Set Ready ($\overline{DSR}$) signal; this is the signal which many serial I/O devices transmit to modems or any external receiving logic when ready to commence with serial data communications. When using an MC6850, $\overline{RTS}$ must serve double duty, additionally substituting for $\overline{DSR}$.

**Even though the MC6850 has only three of the normal four control signals, these signals work hard within the MC6850.**

The $\overline{DCD}$ input must be low for serial transmit logic within the MC6850 to be enabled. This is true also of the equivalent 8251 $\overline{DSR}$ signal; however, if the $\overline{DCD}$ signal makes a low-to-high transition, the MC6850 will generate an interrupt request, thus effectively halting serial data output. A low-to-high $\overline{DCD}$ transition implies that the modem has, for some reason, disconnected itself; any further data transfer will be lost. In the case of the 8251, if a modem disconnects itself and $\overline{DSR}$ goes high, this condition will be reflected in a Status register flag, but unless the CPU executes instructions to read the Status register and test for this condition, the 8251 will continue transmitting data — even though the receiving end is dead.

The MC6850 uses $\overline{CTS}$ high to prevent the Status register from reporting a "Transmit Register Empty" condition. The MC6800 CPU determines when to send another byte of data to the MC6850 by testing the Status register, and looking for a "Transmit Register Empty" condition. If this condition never gets reported, no data will ever be uselessly transmitted. Contrast this with 8251 logic, where a misprogrammed 8251 can and will continue to transmit data after $\overline{CTS}$ has gone high.

## MC6850 ACIA CONTROL CODES AND STATUS FLAGS

**Let us now examine the way in which the MC6850 Control and Status registers are interpreted.**

**Here is the Control register interpretation:**

**MC6850 CONTROL REGISTER**

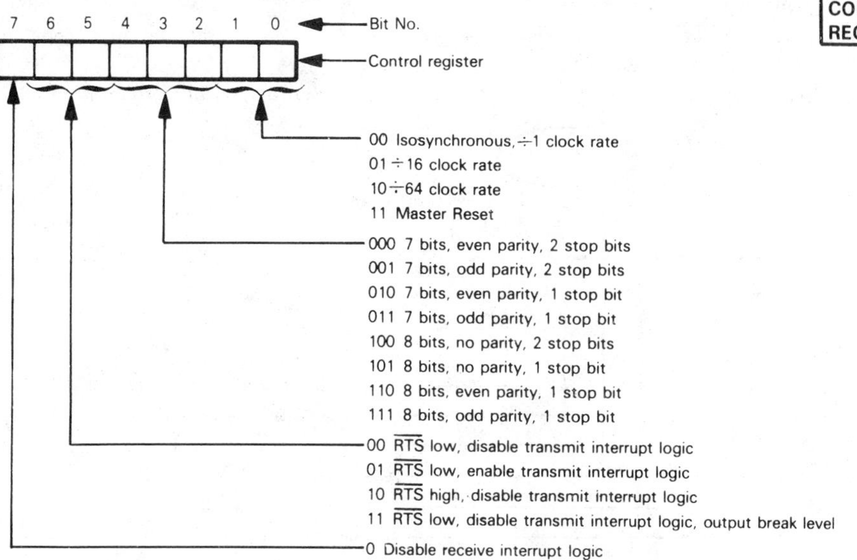


The CPU neither sends nor receives the parity bit. The MC6850 adds the parity bit to transmitted data and strips or resets the parity bit in received data before it goes to the CPU.

Control register bits 0 and 1 determine the data transfer clock rate. Recall that serial data is usually transmitted or received at 1/16th or 1/64th of the clock rate, TxCLK or RxCLK. Transferring serial data at the exact clock rate is referred to as isosynchronous data transfer.

**MC6850 SYSTEM RESET**

**The master reset Control code substitutes for the normal reset input signal, which the MC6850 lacks.** A master reset clears all MC6850 registers, with the exception of Status register bit 3, which is unaltered.

Control register bits 2, 3 and 4 identify data bit, stop bit and parity options. Compared to the 8251, MC6850 options are somewhat limited; five and six data bits are not provided and you cannot select 1.5 stop bits.

**MC6850 SERIAL I/O CONTROL LOGIC**

**Control register bits 5 and 6 are transmit logic control bits. Control register bit 7 is a receive logic control bit.**

Transmit logic consists of the $\overline{RTS}$ modem control and various transmit conditions that can cause an interrupt request.

Receive control logic consists of various receive conditions that can cause an interrupt request.

**MC6850 INTERRUPT LOGIC**

**Interrupt logic of the MC6850 is an integral part of status logic. Conditions that can result in an interrupt request are therefore summarized below along with a definition of Status register bits.** A "T" is placed in those bit positions that can result in an interrupt request from transmit logic. An "R" is placed in those bit positions that can result in an interrupt request from receive logic. Status register bit positions that have neither a "T" nor an "R" identify conditions that do not result in interrupt requests.

In those bit positions containing a "T" or an "R", a 1 causes an interrupt request to occur. $\overline{DCD}$ (bit 3) is an exception; here it is the transition from 0 to 1 that causes an interrupt request. In each case, the interrupt request will only occur if interrupt logic has been enabled. If you look back at the Control register, you will see that transmit and receive interrupt logic can be enabled and disabled separately. Control register bits 5 and 6 determine whether transmit interrupt logic is enabled, while Control register bit 7 determines whether receive interrupt logic is enabled. Note that the condition of Status register bit 3 can also disable a TDRE interrupt request.

When an interrupt request occurs, the requesting condition is cleared in various ways depending upon where the request originated.

An RDRF interrupt request will be cleared if the CPU reads data from the MC6850, or if a reset Control code is output.

A TDRE interrupt request will be cleared by writing data to the MC6850 or by issuing a reset Control code.

Interrupts requested by $\overline{\text{DCD}}$ or OVRN are cleared by reading the Status register after the error condition has occurred, and then reading the Data register. A Master Reset will also clear these interrupt requests.

Let us now take a closer look at the Status register itself. **This is how register bits are interpreted:**

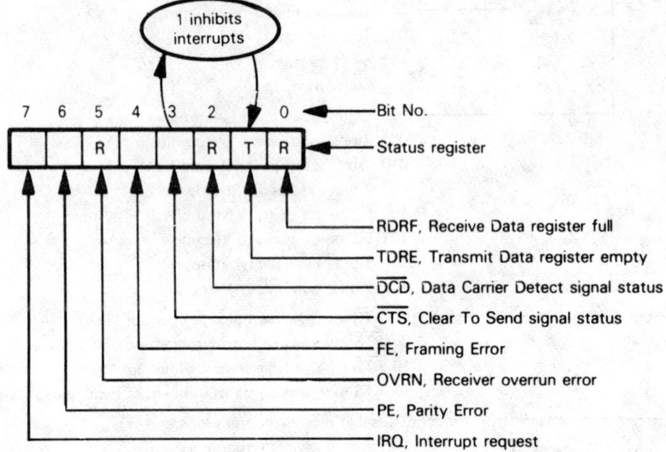


(1 in a bit position represents "true" condition for bits 7, 6, 5, 4, 1 and 0.)

**Status register bit 0, Receive Data Register Full,** goes to 1 when a byte of assembled data is transferred from Receive register RB to Receive register RA. Bit 0 is cleared as soon as the CPU reads the contents of Register RA. The $\overline{\text{DCD}}$ modem control signal, when high, forces Status register bit 0 to stay low so that the CPU will not attempt to read nonexistent data.

**Status register bit 1, Transmit Data Register Empty,** goes from 0 to 1 as soon as data is transferred from Register TA to Register TB. This bit is reset to 0 as soon as the CPU writes another bit of data into Register TA. Transmit Data Register Empty on the MC6850 is equivalent to Transmitter Ready on the 8251. The MC6850 has no status bit or pin equivalent to Transmitter Empty on the 8251.

**Status register bit 2, Data Carrier Detect,** is used by the MC6800 to determine the status of external logic communicating with the MC6850. When $\overline{\text{DCD}}$ makes a low-to-high transition, an interrupt request is generated and Status register bit 2 goes high. Bit 2 remains high until the Status register contents are read by the CPU after $\overline{\text{DCD}}$ has gone low again. A Reset will also set Status register bit 2 to 0. If the CPU reads the Status register while $\overline{\text{DCD}}$ is high, then subsequently Status register bit 2 will track the $\overline{\text{DCD}}$ level; however, another interrupt will not be requested. It is the actual low-to-high transition of the $\overline{\text{DCD}}$ signal which causes an interrupt request, not a high level of Status register bit 2.

**Status register bit 3, Clear To Send,** tracks the $\overline{\text{CTS}}$ modem control input. MC6850 logic uses Status register bit 3 to inhibit serial data transfer when external receiving logic is not ready to receive the serial data. When $\overline{\text{CTS}}$ is high, Status register bit 1 will be held low. A TDRE interrupt request cannot occur, and program logic which tests Status register bit 1 will not transmit another data byte to Register TA until it detects a 1 in Status register bit 1. Thus, for as long as $\overline{\text{CTS}}$ is high, serial transmit logic will be inhibited.

**Status register bits 4, 5 and 6 report framing, overrun and parity errors, respectively.** Recall that a framing error is reported when start and stop bits do not correctly frame a data character; a framing error refers to the data byte currently waiting to be read out of RA. An overrun error is reported if the CPU does not read Register RA contents before a byte of data is transferred from Register RB to Register RA. A parity error is reported if parity has been enabled by Control register bits 2, 3 and 4, but the wrong parity is detected.

A framing or parity error is automatically reset as soon as the erroneous data is read out of Register RA, or is overwritten.

An overrun error is cleared by reading data from the MC6850.

**Status register bit 7, Interrupt Request,** is 1 whenever there is an unacknowledged interrupt request pending at the MC6850 device. One method that an MC6800 will use to determine the source of an interrupt request is to read device Status registers. If the MC6850 has no other method of identifying itself to the CPU when requesting an interrupt, then the CPU determines whether the MC6850 was the requesting device by reading the contents of the MC6850 Status register and testing the condition of bit 7.

# THE MC6852 SYNCHRONOUS SERIAL DATA ADAPTER (SSDA)

**The MC6852 SSDA provides MC6800 microcomputer systems with synchronous serial I/O logic.**

**The MC6852 SSDA may be looked upon as a companion device to the MC6850 ACIA which we have just described. Taken together, these two devices provide MC6800 microcomputer systems with total serial I/O capability.**

**Figure 9-24 illustrates that part of our general microcomputer system logic which is provided by the MC6850 and MC6852 devices.**

**The most striking difference between the MC6850 and the MC6852 is their respective capabilities. Whereas the MC6850 offers fewer asynchronous serial I/O options than the 8251 USART (described in Volume 3), the MC6852 offers significantly more synchronous serial I/O options. Moreover, the MC6852 provides additional serial I/O options without the penalty of defensive programming which is demanded by the 8251 USART**

**The MC6852 SSDA is packaged as a 24-pin DIP. It is fabricated using N-channel silicon gate technology.**

**A single +5V power supply is required.**

**In the discussion of the MC6852 that follows, we will frequently refer to the 8251 USART description given in Volume 3. If you are unfamiliar with synchronous serial I/O devices in general, see Chapter 5 of Volume 1, then read the description of the 8251 USART which is given in Volume 3.**

## MC6852 SSDA PINS AND SIGNALS

**MC6852 SSDA pins and signals are illustrated in Figure 9-26. Most of these signals are identical to those illustrated in Figure 9-25 for the MC6850, therefore we will only describe four signals which differ.**

**The MC6852 has a master Reset input,** which, when input low, logically resets the MC6852. We will define how a Reset occurs after describing the MC6852 controls and status flags affected by a Reset.

**The Data Carrier Detect ($\overline{DCD}$) modem control input performs two functions.** The normal function of $\overline{DCD}$ is to serve as a control signal transmitted by an external data carrier which is ready to transmit serial data to the MC6852 SSDA. Both the high-to-low and the low-to-high transitions of $\overline{DCD}$ have additional significance. The high-to-low signal transition can optionally be used as an external synchronization indicator, while a subsequent low-to-high transition is an error indicator, signaling an unexpected disconnect:

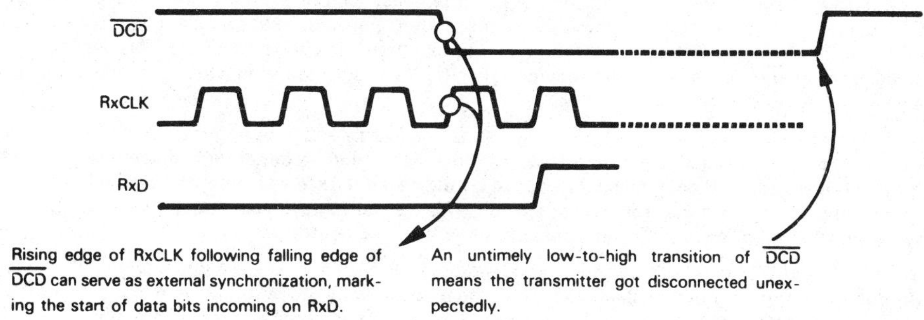

DCD
RxCLK
RxD
Rising edge of RxCLK following falling edge of DCD can serve as external synchronization, marking the start of data bits incoming on RxD.
An untimely low-to-high transition of DCD means the transmitter got disconnected unexpectedly.


Using the high-to-low $\overline{DCD}$ pulse for external synchronization is a programmable option. The error condition reported if $\overline{DCD}$ makes an unexpected low-to-high transition is not a programmable option; it is a permanent part of the MC6852 error detection logic.

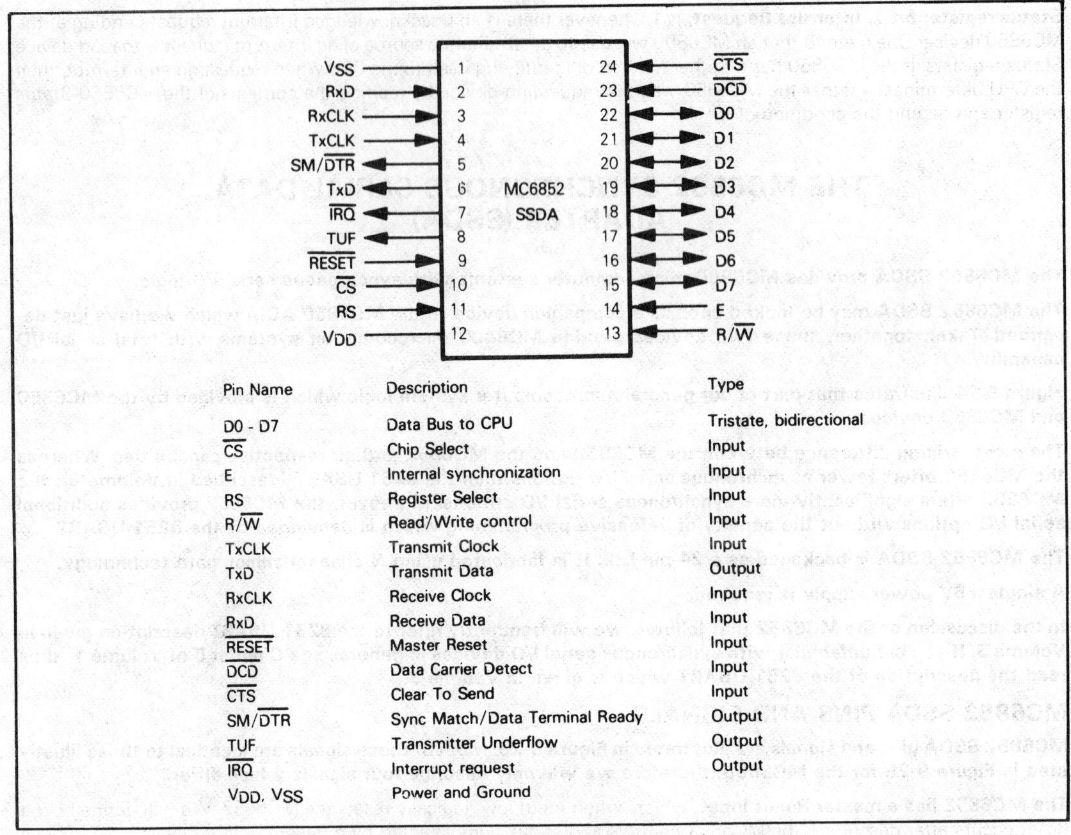


| Pin Name | Description | Type |
|---|---|---|
| D0 - D7 | Data Bus to CPU | Tristate, bidirectional |
| $\overline{CS}$ | Chip Select | Input |
| E | Internal synchronization | Input |
| RS | Register Select | Input |
| R/$\overline{W}$ | Read/Write control | Input |
| TxCLK | Transmit Clock | Input |
| TxD | Transmit Data | Output |
| RxCLK | Receive Clock | Input |
| RxD | Receive Data | Input |
| $\overline{RESET}$ | Master Reset | Input |
| $\overline{DCD}$ | Data Carrier Detect | Input |
| $\overline{CTS}$ | Clear To Send | Input |
| SM/$\overline{DTR}$ | Sync Match/Data Terminal Ready | Output |
| TUF | Transmitter Underflow | Output |
| $\overline{IRQ}$ | Interrupt request | Output |
| $V_{DD}$, $V_{SS}$ | Power and Ground | |

Figure 9-26. MC6852 SSDA Signals and Pin Assignments

**Clear To Send ($\overline{CTS}$)** is the modem control signal which is normally input by external receiving logic, indicating that the MC6852 may begin transmitting serial data. Like $\overline{DCD}$, the $\overline{CTS}$ high-to-low transition can be used to synchronize the beginning of data transmission; the low-to-high transition of $\overline{CTS}$ is an error indicator. Once again, using the high-to-low $\overline{CTS}$ pulse to provide external transmit synchronization is a programmable option. However, an untimely low-to-high transition of $\overline{CTS}$ is an error indicator only if internal synchronization is being used. Therefore, if the high-to-low $\overline{CTS}$ transition is active, then the low-to-high subsequent transition must be inactive; conversely, if the high-to-low $\overline{CTS}$ transition is inactive, then a subsequent low-to-high transition will be active. This is because the high-to-low transition, if active, means that external synchronization has been selected — in which case the disconnect error logic is inactive.

Note that whereas the $\overline{CTS}$ signal low-to-high transition is only active during internal synchronization operations, the $\overline{DCD}$ low-to-high transition is active at all times. This means that **external logic disconnecting itself during a serial transmit operation will only cause an error to be indicated if external synchronization has been selected. On the other hand, during a serial receive operation, if external logic disconnects itself, an error will be indicated whether internal or external synchronization has been selected.**

Since $\overline{DCD}$ and $\overline{CTS}$ can both be used for external synchronization, as we might expect, **$\overline{DTR}$ also serves a double function.** Under normal circumstances, $\overline{DTR}$ will be output low by the MC6852 when it is ready either to transmit, or to receive serial data. If the MC6852 has output $\overline{DTR}$ low before transmitting serial data, then the receiving data carrier will turn $\overline{DTR}$ around and send back a high-to-low $\overline{DCD}$ pulse as we illustrated. If you have selected external synchronization under program control, then you can additionally program $\overline{DTR}$ to output a single high pulse as soon as synchronization has been detected. This may be illustrated as follows:

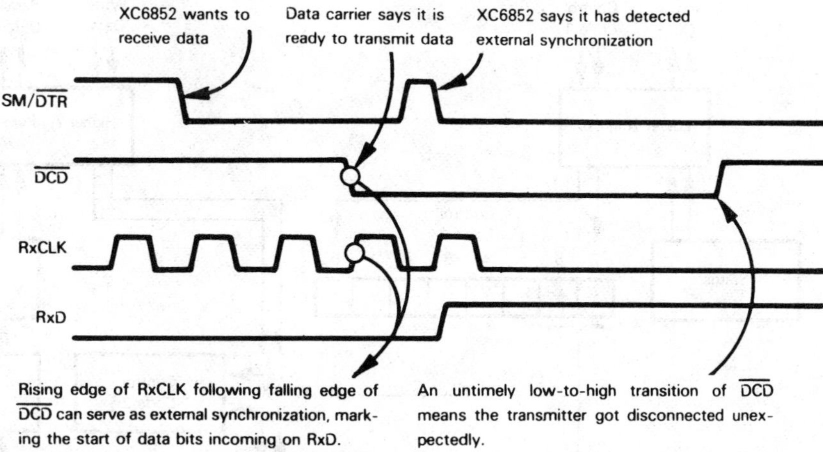
XC6852 wants to receive data
Data carrier says it is ready to transmit data
XC6852 says it has detected external synchronization
SM/$\overline{DTR}$
$\overline{DCD}$
RxCLK
RxD
Rising edge of RxCLK following falling edge of $\overline{DCD}$ can serve as external synchronization, marking the start of data bits incoming on RxD.
An untimely low-to-high transition of $\overline{DCD}$ means the transmitter got disconnected unexpectedly.

Because $\overline{DTR}$ also acts as a Sync Match acknowledge, it is referred to as SM/$\overline{DTR}$.

**MC6852 SERIALIZATION SEQUENCE**

**When the MC6852 transmits serial data, it transmits the least significant bit first. The MC6852 also expects to receive the least significant bit first when receiving serial data.**

**Transmitter Underflow (TUF) is the fourth unique MC6852 signal.** This signal is output when an underflow condition occurs during serial synchronous data transmission. Recall that during serial synchronous data transmission, if serial transmit logic finds no data ready to be output, then in order to maintain synchronization, a break character or a Sync character will be output. A break character is a continuous high level, equivalent to $FF_{16}$. A Sync character will have some predefined binary pattern. Providing you have programmed the MC6852 to output Sync characters when no valid data is ready for serial transmission, the MC6852 will precede each Sync character with a high TUF pulse. External receive logic can use a high TUF pulse as an indicator that the next received character is a Sync and can be discarded.

## MC6852 DATA TRANSFER AND CONTROL OPERATIONS

**Like the MC6850, the MC6852 SSDA is accessed via two memory addresses; however, these two memory addresses are shared by seven locations within the MC6852, which results in a complex set of data flows, as illustrated in Figure 9-27.**

These are the seven addressable locations of the MC6852:

1) Data input — a read only location.
2) Data output — a write only location.
3) Status register — a read only location.
4) Sync Code register — a write only location.
5, 6, and 7) Three Control registers — all are write only locations.

Data input and data output are self-evident; apart from being triple buffered — and we will discuss the implications of triple buffering shortly — there is nothing unusual about MC6852 data input or output.

The Status register is absolutely standard.

**The three 8-bit Control registers** provide the MC6852 with a substantial variety of control options, as compared to the MC6850, which was somewhat limited in this respect.

**The Sync Code register** stores the 8-bit synchronization character code; this is the character which must appear at the beginning of any synchronous serial data stream and may also be transmitted when data is unavailable during a normal transmit sequence.

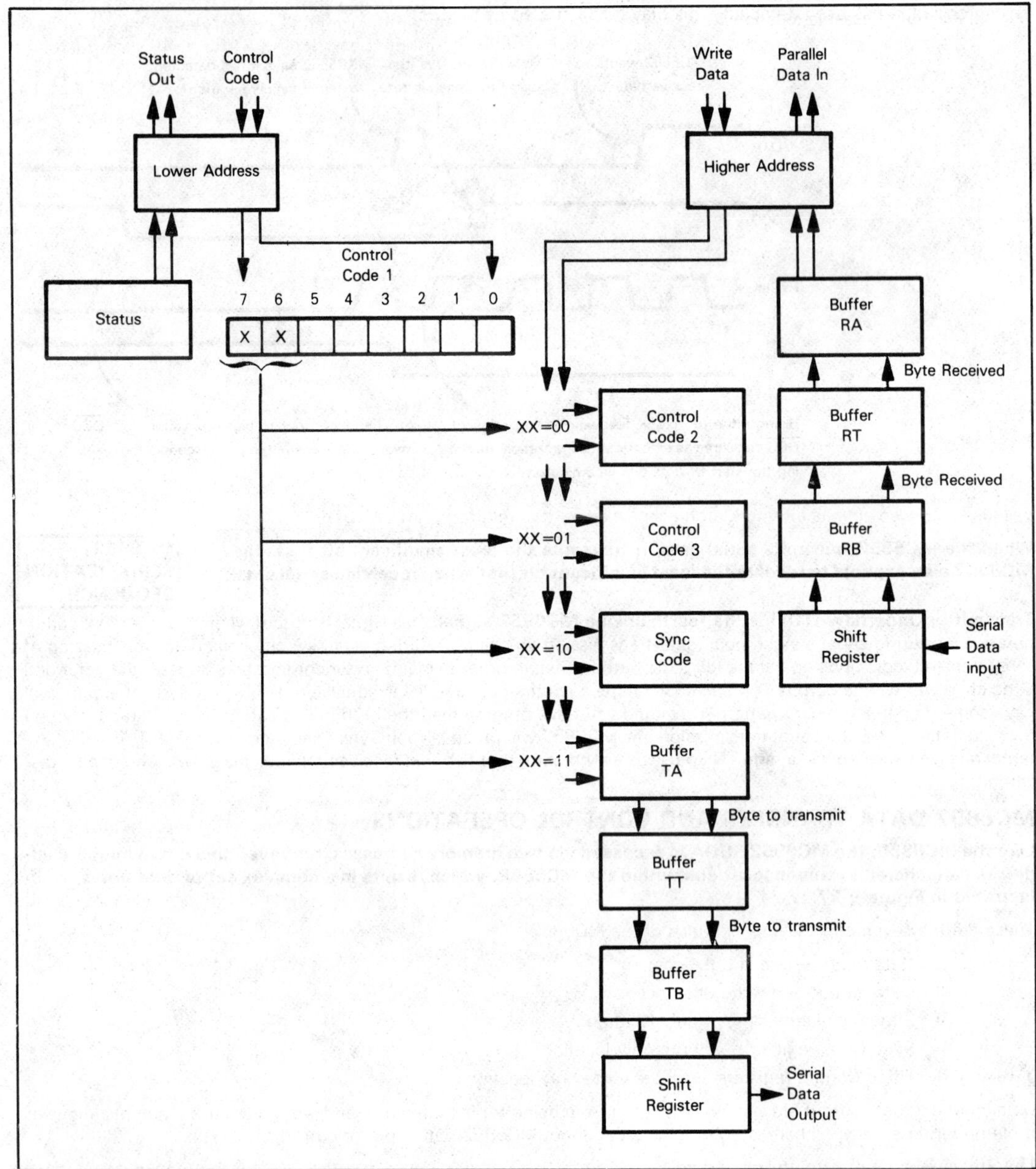


Figure 9-27. Data Flows Within an MC6852 SSDA

Of the seven addressable locations, two are read only, while five are write only. **Each memory address can access two locations, providing one is exclusively read only, while the other is exclusively write only.** Since there are just two read only locations, one is assigned to each memory address. Since there are five write only locations, one (Control Code 1) is assigned to the lower address, which leaves four assigned to the higher address; the two high-order bits of Control Code 1 are used to select one of the four write only locations assigned to the higher address. While this may look like a complex scheme, in reality it is not; all it means is that you have to observe a rigid programming sequence when using an MC6852. In fact, understanding the MC6852 depends completely on understanding the Control and Status registers; therefore we will describe these registers first, then look at data transfer sequences.

## MC6852 STATUS REGISTER

**The MC6852 Status register may be illustrated as follows:**

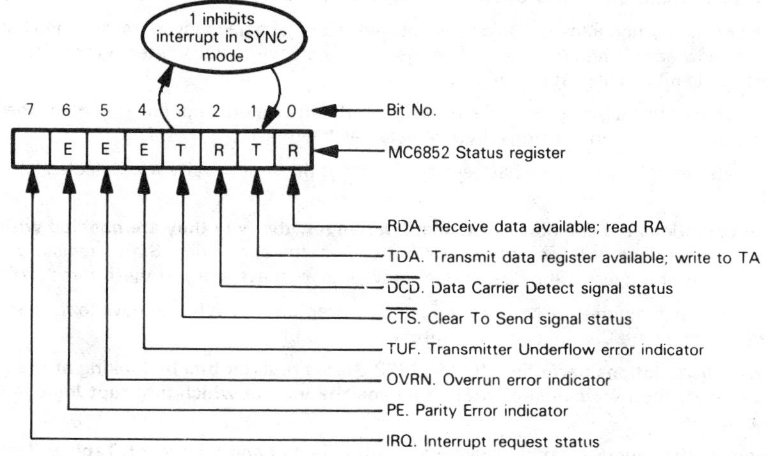


(1 in a bit position represents "true" condition for bits 7, 6, 5, 4, 1 and 0.)

**Conditions that may generate interrupts are marked with letters in appropriate Status register bit positions.** An interrupt request initiated by an error condition is represented by the letter E. Interrupt requests originating at transmit or receive logic are represented by the letters T and R, respectively.

**MC6852 TRIPLE DATA BUFFERS**

**Status register bit 0 (RDA) indicates when the MC6852 Status register has a byte of data ready to be read. Similarly Status register bit 1 (TDA) indicates when the MC6852 is ready to receive another byte of data** which will be output as a serial data stream.

As indicated in Figure 9-27, MC6852 transmit and receive logic is triple buffered. This differs from the MC6850 which uses double buffering.

**You can use the triple buffering of the MC6852 in one of two ways which you select using appropriate Control register codes.**

**You can select a single byte option,** in which case as soon as a single byte of data can be written to Buffer TA or read from Buffer RA, the appropriate status flag will be set —and if interrupts are enabled, an interrupt request will be made to the CPU. The program controlling MC6852 operation must respond by reading or writing a single byte of data. A byte of data written to Buffer TA will automatically be rippled through Buffer TT to Buffer TB, whence it will output as a serial data stream. Data arriving at Buffer RB will be rippled through Buffer RT to Buffer RA, whence it must be read by the CPU.

**If you select the two byte option under program control,** then no status flags will be set, nor will interrupt requests occur until two of the three 8-bit buffers are empty. Thus, status bit 0 will be set and a receive interrupt request will occur when Buffers RA and RT are both full. Under program control you must, at this time, read two bytes of data. So long as a single pulse of the timing E signal separates the two read commands, MC6852 logic will transfer Buffer RT contents to Buffer RA so that the second read accesses what had been in Buffer RT. In fact, you should read RA contents, then status, then RA contents again. If there are errors associated with the data byte in RT, they will not be reported until RT contents have been transferred to RA.

When using the two byte option with transmit logic. Status register bit 1 will not be set and the appropriate interrupt request will not occur until Buffers TA and TT are both empty. At this time the executing program must write two bytes of data to the higher MC6852 address. while Control code 1. bits 7 and 6 are both 1. The first byte of data written to the higher MC6852 address will store data in Buffer TA. The next pulse of the E clock will transfer the contents of Buffer TA to Buffer TT. The second write will again load Buffer TA whose previous contents are now in Buffer TT.

**Status register bits 2 and 3 are associated with signals $\overline{DCD}$ and $\overline{CTS}$, respectively.** If $\overline{DCD}$ or $\overline{CTS}$ makes a low-to-high transition. then its corresponding Status register bit will latch high — that is. it will maintain a level of 1 until it is reset by the CPU. Once bit 2 (or 3) has been reset. it will track $\overline{DCD}$ (or $\overline{CTS}$) until the next low-to-high transition.

**Note that in Sync mode, if Status register bit 3 is 1, then Status register bit 1 will be held at 0; this is how the MC6852 suppresses subsequent transmit logic.**

**Status register bits 4, 5 and 6 indicate Underflow, Overrun or Parity errors, respectively.**

**An Underflow error** occurs when transmit logic does not have a byte of data ready to transmit and has to insert a Sync character. The Underflow error is reported just before the Sync character is transmitted. When Status register bit 4 is set. the TUF signal is simultaneously pulsed high.

**An Overrun error** occurs when a byte of data is written into Buffer RA before prior buffer contents have been read. An Overrun error therefore indicates that a single byte of data has been lost.

**A Parity error** indicates that a Parity option has been selected. but the wrong Parity was detected for the data byte currently in Buffer RA.

**These three error conditions are completely standard; however, the way they are handled within the MC6852 is not standard.** When any one of these error conditions occurs. the appropriate Status register bit will be set and simultaneously an interrupt request will be generated. providing you have enabled these three error interrupts.

An error status is not cleared automatically. To clear Status register bits 4. 5 or 6. you have to read Status register contents. then issue an appropriate Control code to reset the selected bit.

**We can summarize the functions performed by MC6852 Status register bits by looking at the manner in which each bit is set or reset; then we can separately examine the way in which interrupt logic is associated with each status bit position.**

**Table 9-6 summarizes the conditions which cause each bit to be set and then reset. Table 9-7 summarizes interrupt requests associated with each status bit,** indicating the way the interrupt is enabled or disabled and the way in which an interrupt request occurs. You will find Table 9-7 following the three Control registers' description. because interrupt logic is equally dependent upon the Status register's contents and the three Control registers' contents.

## THE MC6852 CONTROL REGISTERS

**Now consider the three MC6852 Control registers.**

Control register 1 is normally the first to be accessed and has to be written into in order to select any other write only MC6852 location. **Control register 1 format may be illustrated as follows:**

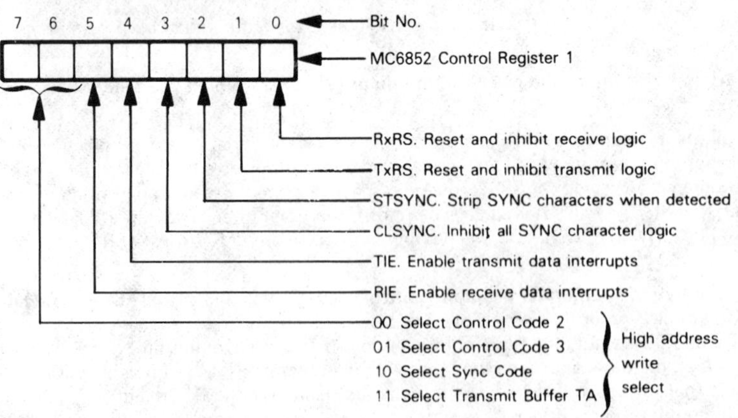


(1 in a bit position represents "true" condition for bits 5, 4, 3, 2, 1 and 0.)

**Control register 1, bits 0 and 1 reset and inhibit receive and transmit logic, respectively.** You use these two Control register bits in order to disable transmit and receive logic while modifying the contents of any Control register or the Sync register.

**Control register 1, bits 0 and 1 are very important. It is easy to miss the significance of these two control bits.** If you always inhibit transmit and receive logic before modifying the contents of Control or Sync registers, you can make sure that spurious data is never transmitted or received. The 8251 USART described in Volume 3, does not have any inhibit logic of this type; and as a result, you have to adopt elaborate precautions to avoid data transmission errors.

While transmit and receive logic is inhibited, Status register bits 2 and 3 will still track the $\overline{DCD}$ and $\overline{CTS}$ signals; however, no data transfers will occur and interrupts associated with the inhibited logic will be disabled.

Using Control register 1, bits 0 and 1 to inhibit transmit and/or receive logic also affects Status register bits and interrupt requests, as summarized in Tables 9-6 and 9-7.

Table 9-6. MC6852 Status Register Bit Set/Reset Conditions

| STATUS | SET | RESET |
|---|---|---|
| RDA - Bit 0 | 1) If Control register 2 bit 2 is 1, when Buffer RA is full.<br>2) If Control register 2 bit 2 is 0, when Buffers RA and RT are full. | 1) Write 1 in Control register 1 bit 0.<br>2) Read Buffer RA contents. |
| TDA - Bit 1 | 1) If Control register 2 bit 2 is 1 when Buffer TA is empty.<br>2) If Control register 2 bit 2 is 0 when Buffers TA and TT are empty. | 1) 1 occurs in Status register bit 5, together with 0 in Control register 3 bit 0.<br>2) Write 1 in Control register 1 bit 1.<br>3) Write into Buffer TA. |
| $\overline{DCD}$ - Bit 2 | A low-to-high $\overline{DCD}$ input transition when Control register 1 bit 0 is 0. | 1) Read Status register, then read Buffer RA. Status will subsequently go low when $\overline{DCD}$ input goes low.<br>2) Write 1 into Control register 1 bit 0. Status will subsequently go low when $\overline{DCD}$ input goes low. |
| $\overline{CTS}$ - Bit 3 | A low-to-high $\overline{CTS}$ input transition when Control register 1 bit 1 is 0. | 1) Write 1 to Control register 3 bit 2. Status will subsequently go low when $\overline{CTS}$ input goes low.<br>2) Write 1 into Control register bit 1. Status will subsequently go low when $\overline{CTS}$ input goes low. |
| TUF - Bit 4 | Underflow when Control register 3 bit 0 is 0 and Control register 2 bit 6 is 1. | 1) Write 1 into Control register 3 bit 3.<br>2) Write 1 into Control register 1 bit 1. |
| OVRN - Bit 5 | Buffer RT contents is transferred to Buffer RA before Buffer RA contents is read by CPU. | 1) Read Status register, then read Buffer RA.<br>2) Write 1 into Control register 1 bit 0. |
| PE - Bit 6 | Parity error for data in RA, providing Control register 2 bits 3, 4 and 5 identify a parity option. | 1) Read data out of Buffer RA.<br>2) Write 1 into Control register 1 bit 0. |
| IRQ - Bit 7 | Any interrupt request occurs. | No active interrupt requests exist. |

Table 9-7. MC6852 Interrupt Summary

| INTERRUPT | ENABLE | REQUEST |
|---|---|---|
| RDA — Read Buffer RA or Buffers RA and RT contents | Control register 1 bits 0 and 5 must be 0 and 1 respectively | Status register bit 0 = 1 |
| TDA — Write into Buffer TA or RA and TT | Control register 1 bits 1 and 4 must be 0 and 1 respectively. | Status register bit 1 = 1. This will not occur if Status register bit 3 = 1. |
| $\overline{DCD}$ — Transmitting data carrier disconnected | Control register 2 bit 7 must be 1 | On low-to-high transition of $\overline{DCD}$. |
| $\overline{CTS}$ — Receiving external logic disconnected | Control register 2 bit 7 must be 1. | On low-to-high transition of $\overline{CTS}$. |
| TUF — Transmit underflow has occurred | Control register 2 bit 7 must be 1. | Status register bit 4 = 1. |
| OVRN — Receive overrun error has occurred | Control register 2 bit 7 must be 1. | Status register bit 5 = 1. |
| PE — Parity Error | Control register 2 bit 7 must be 1 | Status register bit 6 = 1. |

**Control register 1, bit 5 allows you to enable or disable receive data interrupt logic. Control register 1, bit 4 allows you to enable or disable transmit data interrupt logic.**

There is no connection between Control register 1, bits 0 and 1, and Control register 1, bits 4 and 5. Obviously, if transmit or receive logic has been inhibited, then it makes no difference whether interrupt logic has been enabled or disabled; in either case an interrupt cannot occur. However, if transmit or receive logic is enabled, then interrupt logic may be separately enabled or disabled.

**Control register 1, bits 2 and 3 determine the way the Sync character will be handled.** If Control register 1 bit 2 is high, then all Sync characters in a serial receive data stream will be stripped, so that only non-Sync characters are read by the CPU. If Control register 1, bit 2 is low, then the entire data stream will be transmitted to the CPU, including data and Sync characters. Note that the initial Sync character is always stripped.

**Control register 1, bit 3 allows you to completely inhibit all Sync character logic.** Now the Sync character will be cleared, and the MC6852 must use external synchronization.

**Control register bits 6 and 7 determine which write only location will be accessed when the CPU writes to the higher memory location of the MC6852.**

**Now consider Control registers 2 and 3, which are best looked upon as a single 12-bit control unit. These two Control registers may be illustrated as follows:**

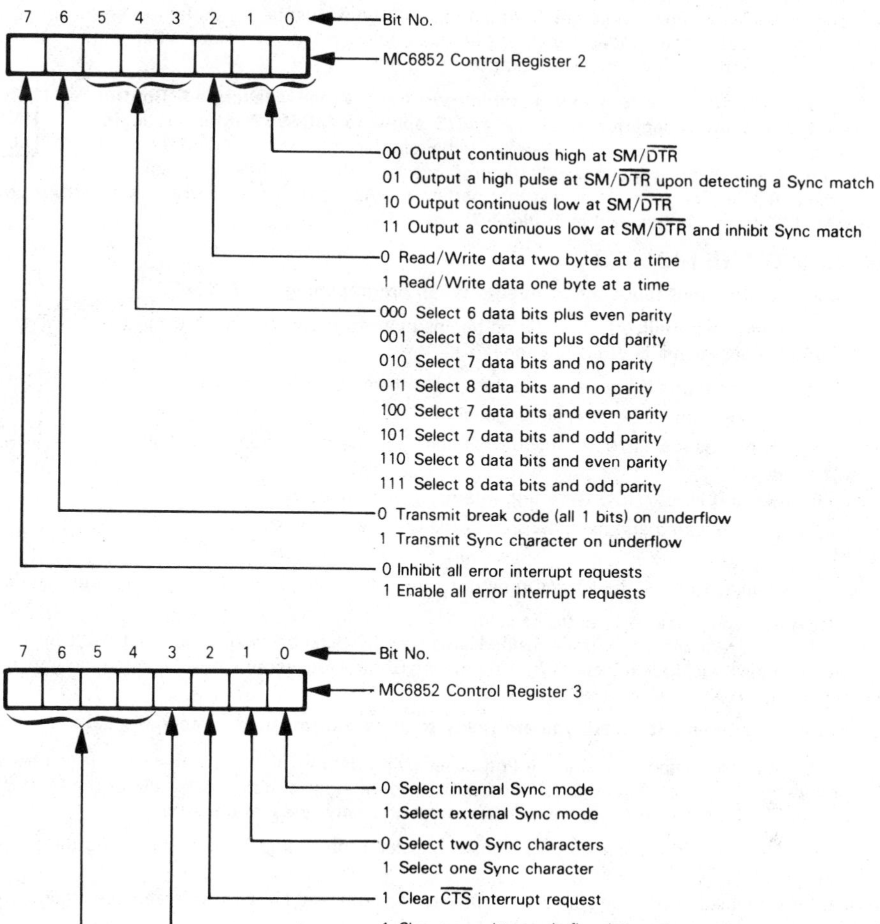


**Control register 2, bits 0 and 1, and Control register 3, bits 0, 1, 2 and 3 are used to define synchronization logic.**

Control register 3, bit 0 is used to determine whether internal or external synchronization will be employed. If internal synchronization is selected, then Control register 3, bit 1 determines whether one or two Sync characters must precede a serial data stream for initial synchronization to occur.

Control register 2, bits 0 and 1 must now be set so that SM/$\overline{DTR}$ logic conforms to the synchronization options selected by Control register 3, bits 0 and 1. You also use Control register 2, bits 0 and 1 to select the signal level that will be output for a standard DTR modem control.

**Control register 2, bits 2, 3, 4, 5 and 6 define the data transfer options.**

Recall that when the CPU reads received data, or writes data to be transmitted, data may be read and written one byte at a time, or two bytes at a time. We discussed this option when describing Status register bits 0 and 1. **You select the one byte or two byte mode via Control register 2, bit 2.**

**Control register 2, bits 3, 4 and 5 allow you to define the number of data bits per word, and parity options.** These are standard selections which have been described in detail in Volume 1, Chapter 5. Notice that the MC6852 provides a much wider variety of data and parity options than the MC6850.

Control register 2, bit 6 determines the response of MC6852 transmit logic when no data is ready to be transmitted. If Control register 2, bit 6 is 0, then a break code will be output on underflow; if this bit is 1, then a Sync character code will be output on underflow. Remember, an Underflow error will be reported in the Status register only if you transmit Sync character codes on Underflow. Therefore, Control register 2, bit 6 must be 1 if Underflow errors are to be reported in the Status register. Recall that an underflow error is reported before a Sync character is transmitted; also, the underflow error status is accompanied by a high TUF output signal pulse.

**MC6852 INTERRUPT LOGIC**

**Along with Control register 1, bits 4 and 5, which we have already described, Control register 2, bit 7 and Control register 3, bits 2 and 3 apply to MC6852 interrupt logic.** MC6852 interrupt logic is quite complex. There are a number of interrupt sources and no standard procedure for enabling, disabling, acknowledging or processing different interrupt requests. Rather than describing the Control register bits that pertain to interrupts, therefore, **various interrupt options provided by the MC6852 are summarized in Table 9-7.**

## PROGRAMMING THE MC6852

**Let us now look at the normal sequence of events when programming the MC6852.**

**MC6852 RESET OPERATION**

**First the MC6852 must be initialized.** Initialization begins by resetting the MC6852 using the $\overline{\text{RESET}}$ control input. **When the MC6852 is reset this is what happens:**

1) Control Register 1, bits 0 and 1 are set to 1, inhibiting transmit and receive logic.
2) Control register 2, bits 0 and 1 are reset to 0, causing SM/$\overline{\text{DTR}}$ to be output high.
3) Control register 2, bit 7 is reset to 0, disabling $\overline{\text{DCD}}$ and $\overline{\text{CTS}}$ interrupt requests, and all error interrupt requests.
4) Control register 3, bit 0 is reset to 0, selecting internal synchronous mode.
5) Status register bit 1 is cleared and held low so that the CPU never reads a status that requests data be written to the MC6852.

Control register bits affected by the $\overline{\text{RESET}}$ control input cannot be modified until $\overline{\text{RESET}}$ goes high again.

Following device Reset, you must load Control registers 1, 2 and 3 and the Sync Code register. The only caution concerns Control register 1; remember, Control register 1, bits 6 and 7 must be modified so that you can access Control registers 2 and 3 and the Sync Code register. When modifying Control register bits 6 and 7, be sure not to inadvertently modify the remaining six bits of Control register 1.

**Once the MC6852 has been initialized, you are ready to start transmitting or receiving data.**

The only complications associated with transmitting or receiving data involve the way in which you select the programmable options of this device. There is nothing intrinsically different or complicated about the MC6852, as compared to any other synchronous serial I/O device. **These are the only rules to observe:**

1) Always inhibit transmit and receive logic via Control register 1, bits 0 and 1 before modifying the contents of any Control register or the Sync register.
2) Unless you have enabled error interrupts, always precede any data read or write operation by reading the contents of the Status register and checking for errors.

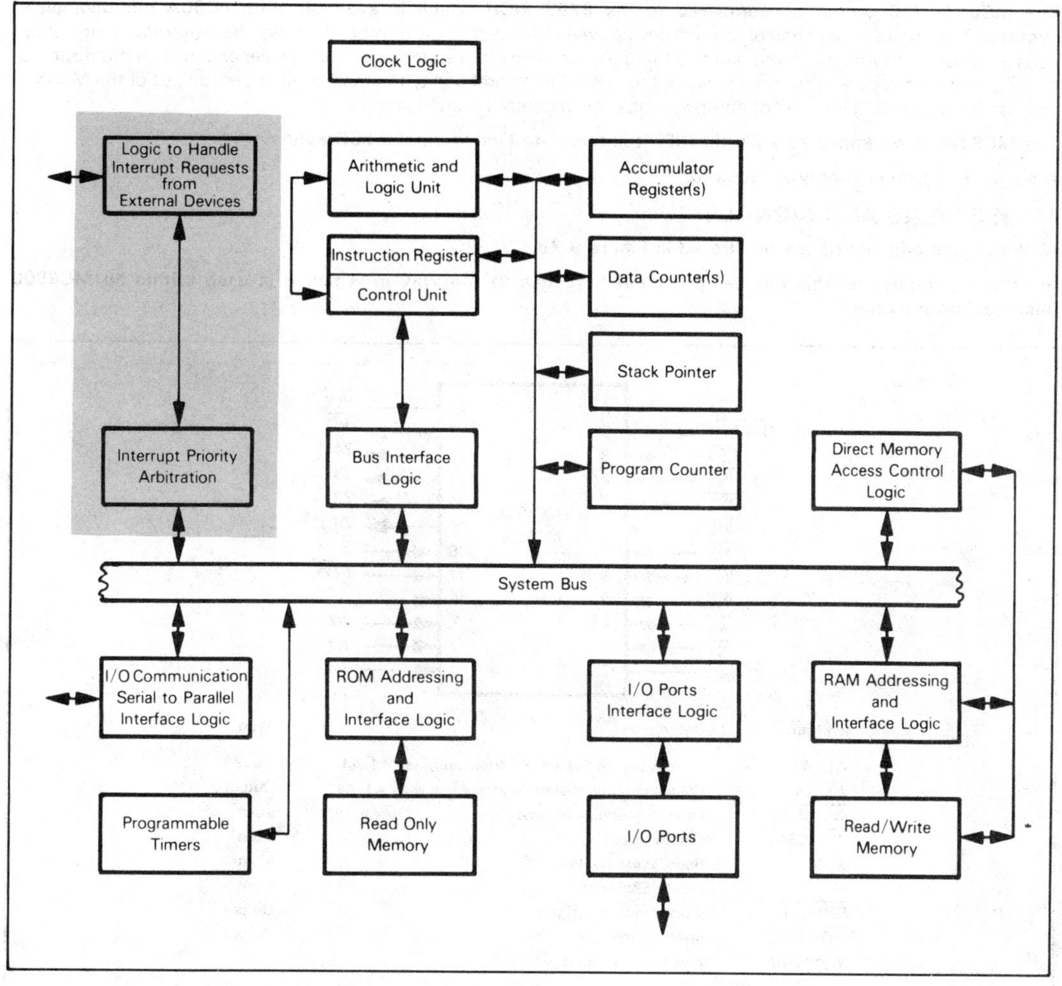


Figure 9-28. Logic of the MC6828 Priority Interrupt Controller

## THE MC8507 (OR MC6828) PRIORITY INTERRUPT CONTROLLER (PIC)

**This Priority Interrupt Controller has two part numbers, identifying the fact that it is a bipolar part, and also compatible with the NMOS family of the MC6800 microcomputer devices. We will use the part identification MC6828 in the discussion that follows.**

**The MC6828 Priority Interrupt Controller processes up to eight external interrupt requests, creating a vectored response to an interrupt acknowledge. Interrupt priorities are determined by pin connections, but under program control you can set a priority level below which all interrupts are inhibited.**

**Figure 9-28 illustrates that part of our general microcomputer system logic which is provided by the MC6828 PIC.**

**The MC6828 PIC cannot be compared to the 8259 PICU which is available with 8080A microcomputer systems.** The briefest inspection of the two devices will indicate that the 8259 offers a significantly wider range of options — which can be a good thing or a bad thing. As we have often stated, an excessive dependence on interrupt processing in microcomputer applications is hard to justify; in all probability the more limited capabilities of the MC6828 will adequately serve the needs of any reasonable microcomputer application.

**The MC6828 is packaged as a 24-pin DIP. It is fabricated using bipolar LSI technology.**

**A single +5V power supply is required.**

## MC6828 PINS AND SIGNALS

**MC6828 pins and signals are illustrated in Figure 9-29.**

**In order to understand this device, you must first look at the way in which it is used within an MC6800 microcomputer system.**

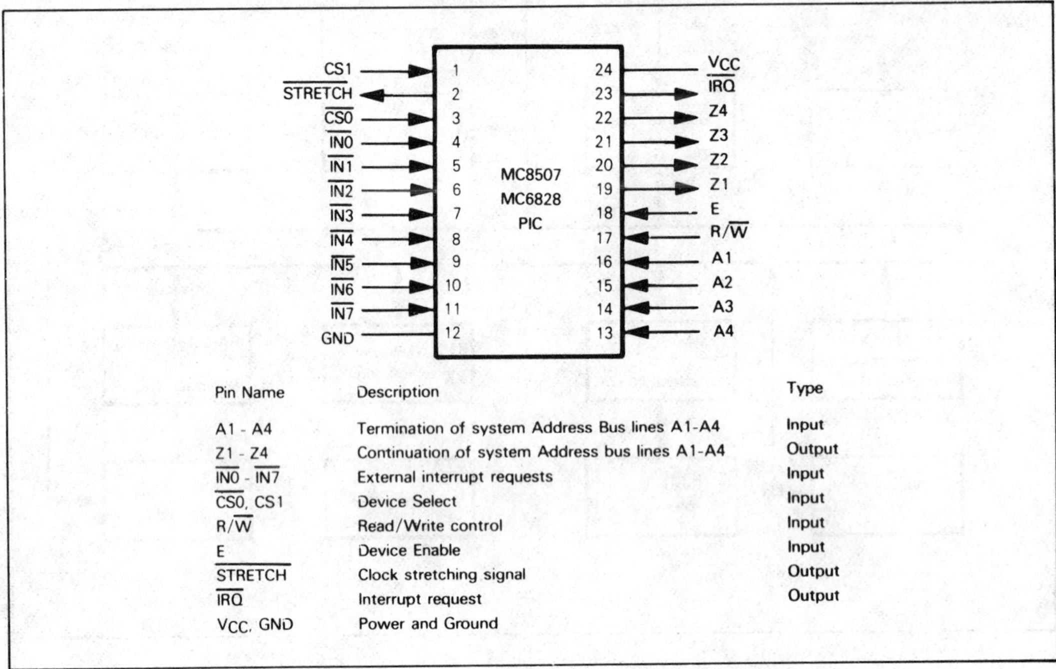


| Pin Name | Description | Type |
|---|---|---|
| A1 - A4 | Termination of system Address Bus lines A1-A4 | Input |
| Z1 - Z4 | Continuation of system Address bus lines A1-A4 | Output |
| $\overline{IN0}$ - $\overline{IN7}$ | External interrupt requests | Input |
| $\overline{CS0}$, CS1 | Device Select | Input |
| R/$\overline{W}$ | Read/Write control | Input |
| E | Device Enable | Input |
| $\overline{STRETCH}$ | Clock stretching signal | Output |
| $\overline{IRQ}$ | Interrupt request | Output |
| $V_{CC}$, GND | Power and Ground | |

Figure 9-29. MC6828 Signals and Pin Assignments

Recall that when any standard external interrupt is acknowledged by an MC6800 CPU, the CPU will fetch the starting address for the interrupt service routine from memory locations $FFF8_{16}$ and $FFF9_{16}$. These two addresses may be illustrated as follows:

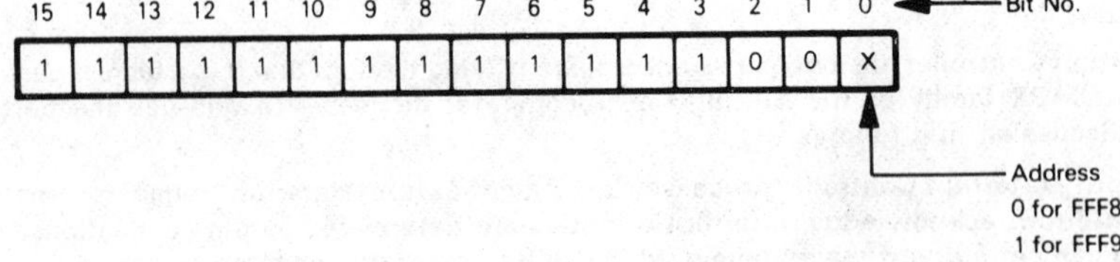

**The MC6828 PIC is positioned serially, preceding the external memory device which is to be selected by the addresses $FFF8_{16}$ and $FFF9_{16}$. Address lines A1, A2, A3 and A4 terminate at the MC6828. Logic within the MC6828 appropriately manipulates these four address lines and outputs some value which may differ from the input value. This may be illustrated as follows:**

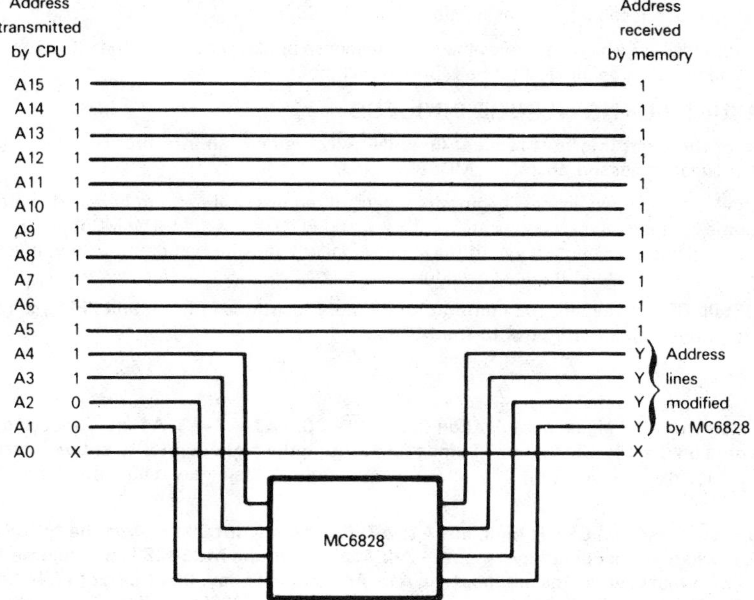


Thus, what the MC6828 does is extend the two addresses $FFF8_{16}$ and $FFF9_{16}$ into 16 addresses, $FFE8_{16}$ through $FFF7_{16}$.

The CPU knows nothing about the address manipulation which is taking place within the MC6828. So far as the CPU is concerned, upon acknowledging an external interrupt, it reads two bytes of data from memory locations $FFF8_{16}$ and $FFF9_{16}$; the fact that there are eight possible responses to these two addresses is of no concern to the CPU.

Conceptually, the MC6828 is acting as an 8-way switch. The CPU addresses the switch by its "stem", via a single address. The actual conduit for the transfer of two bytes of data depends on the switch position at the time the CPU accesses the switch stem; and the switch position is going to be determined by the highest priority active interrupt request. This may be illustrated as follows:

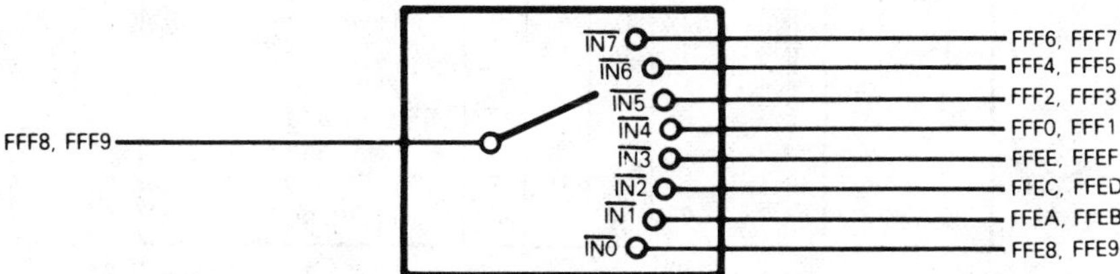


**Let us now look at the device pins and signals.**

**A1 - A4 represents the termination of System Address Bus lines A1 - A4** at the MC6828.

**The continuation of the four address lines is via pins Z1 - Z4.**

**The eight external interrupt requests are connected to $\overline{IN0}$ - $\overline{IN7}$. Interrupt priorities are in ascending level, from IN0 which has lowest priority through $\overline{IN7}$ which has highest priority.**

**Device select logic consists of $\overline{CS0}$ and CS1.** For this device to be selected, $\overline{CS0}$ must be low while CS1 is high. **There are additional select requirements** that depend on the operation being performed, as we will describe shortly.

**R/$\overline{W}$ is the read/write control output by the MC6800 CPU.**

**E is the standard enable signal required by all support devices of an MC6800 microcomputer system.** You can extend the response time available to the MC6828 by extending the E input.

**A $\overline{\text{STRETCH}}$ output is created** and can be connected directly to the clock device of the microcomputer system in order to provide as much response time as needed by the MC6828.

The actual interrupt request which generates the entire response process occurs via the $\overline{\text{IRQ}}$ output from the MC6828. This output will normally be connected to the MC6800 $\overline{\text{IRQ}}$ input.

## THE INTERRUPT ACKNOWLEDGE PROCESS

**When any one of the eight interrupt request lines $\overline{\text{IN0}}$ - $\overline{\text{IN7}}$ is low, an interrupt request is generated via $\overline{\text{IRQ}}$. This interrupt request is passed on to the MC6800 CPU.**

As is normal, the MC6800, upon acknowledging the interrupt request, will perform two read operations; during these read operations the contents of memory locations $FFF8_{16}$ and $FFF9_{16}$ are read. The MC6800 CPU interprets the contents of these two memory locations as a 16-bit address, identifying the beginning of the interrupt service routine which is to be executed following the acknowledge.

**When the MC6800 CPU is reading the contents of memory locations $FFF8_{16}$ and $FFF9_{16}$, these are the signal levels for the control and select inputs to the MC6828:**

| R/$\overline{W}$ | $\overline{\text{CS0}}$ | CS1 | A4 | A3 | A2 | A1 |
|---|---|---|---|---|---|---|
| 1 | 0 | 1 | 1 | 1 | 0 | 0 |

**The MC6828 interprets the signal combination R/W·$\overline{\text{CS0}}$·CS1·$\overline{\text{A1}}$·$\overline{\text{A2}}$·A3·A4, as a special select, causing it to output binary data on the Z1, Z2, Z3 and Z4 pins representing the highest priority active interrupt request** occurring on any of the interrupt request pins $\overline{\text{IN0}}$ - $\overline{\text{IN7}}$. Table 9-8 defines the binary data output corresponding to each interrupt level.

**If R/$\overline{W}$ is high, $\overline{\text{CS0}}$ is low and CS1 is high, but A1, A2, A3, A4 are not 0011, then the MC6828 will simply output, via Z1 - Z4, whatever is being input via A1 - A4. Also, when the MC6828 is not selected, A1 - A4 is simply output via Z1 - Z4, whatever values are input via A1 - A4; that is to say, 0011 input to A1 - A4 will be output via Z1 - Z4 if the MC6828 is not selected.** Thus, the presence of the MC6828 on the A1 - A4 address lines of the Address Bus will be transparent until either the address $FFF8_{16}$ or the address $FFF9_{16}$ appears on the Address Bus.

In order to guarantee that the MC6828 remains synchronized with the rest of the MC6800 microcomputer system, **logic internal to the MC6828 uses the E synchronization signal as part of internal enable logic.** The way in which the E synchronization signal is used is of no particular concern to you, as an MC6828 user. Providing the E synchronization signal which drives the rest of the MC6800 microcomputer system also drives the MC6828, problems will not arise.

Table 9-8. MC6828 Address Vectors Created for Eight Priority Interrupt Requests

| PRIORITY | PIN | Z4 | Z3 | Z2 | Z1 | EFFECTIVE ADDRESSES |
|---|---|---|---|---|---|---|
| Highest 7 | $\overline{\text{IN7}}$ | 1 | 0 | 1 | 1 | FFF6 and FFF7 |
| 6 | $\overline{\text{IN6}}$ | 1 | 0 | 1 | 0 | FFF4 and FFF5 |
| 5 | $\overline{\text{IN5}}$ | 1 | 0 | 0 | 1 | FFF2 and FFF3 |
| 4 | $\overline{\text{IN4}}$ | 1 | 0 | 0 | 0 | FFF0 and FFF1 |
| 3 | $\overline{\text{IN3}}$ | 0 | 1 | 1 | 1 | FFEE and FFEF |
| 2 | $\overline{\text{IN2}}$ | 0 | 1 | 1 | 0 | FFEC and FFED |
| 1 | $\overline{\text{IN1}}$ | 0 | 1 | 0 | 1 | FFEA and FFEB |
| Lowest 0 | $\overline{\text{IN0}}$ | 0 | 1 | 0 | 0 | FFE8 and FFE9 |

## INTERRUPT PRIORITIES

**Table 9-8 defines the priorities that will be applied to simultaneous interrupt requests occurring at pins $\overline{\text{IN0}}$ - $\overline{\text{IN7}}$. This table also indicates the exact memory addresses which will be created by the MC6828 in response to each of the interrupt requests.** In order to use the MC6828 PIC in an MC6800 microcomputer system, 16 bytes of PROM or ROM, selected by the addresses given in Table 9-8 must be connected to the MC6828. Within these 16 bytes of PROM or ROM, you must store the starting addresses for the eight interrupt service routines which are going to be executed following acknowledgement of each possible external interrupt request. For example, suppose that interrupt requests arriving at the $\overline{\text{IN5}}$ pin of the MC6828 must be serviced by an interrupt service routine whose first executable instruction is stored in memory location $2E00_{16}$. The value $2E00_{16}$ must then be stored in the two PROM or ROM bytes selected by memory addresses $FFF2_{16}$ and $FFF3_{16}$. Remember, the high-order byte of an address is always stored at the lower address. Thus $2E_{16}$ will be stored in memory location $FFF2_{16}$ while $00_{16}$ is stored in memory location $FFF3_{16}$.

**In simple configurations** the 16 bytes of PROM or ROM selected by **the MC6828** will be part of the MC6800 address space; the MC6828 simply **sits on the Address Bus.** Logic may be illustrated as follows:

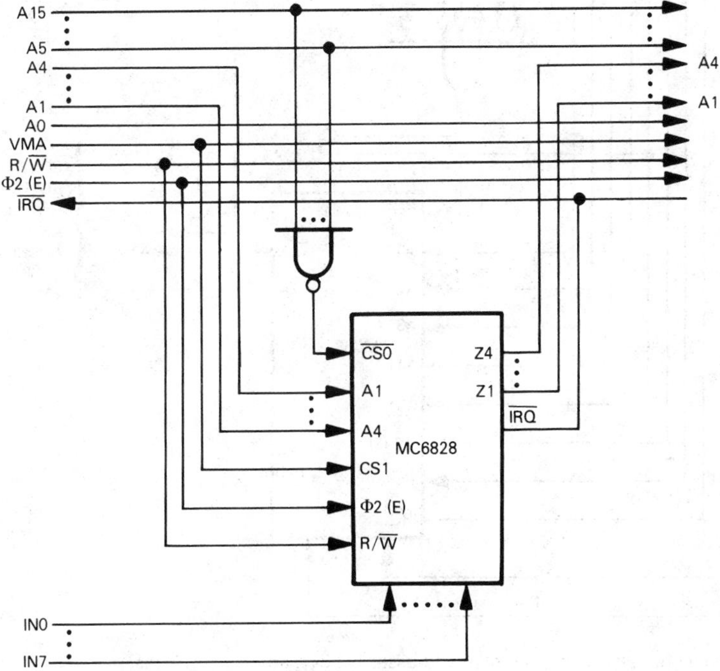


Chip select logic generates $\overline{\text{CS0}}$ as the NAND of address lines A5 through A15; thus, the MC6828 will be selected only when these address lines are all high. VMA is used to generate select line CS1. Since VMA is high only while a valid memory address is being output, valid select logic is completed. Address lines A4 through A1 physically terminate at the MC6828, which re-generates them via the Z4 through Z1 outputs. Z4 through Z1 will exactly reflect A4 through A1, unless the MC6828 is selected and A4 through A1 is 1100. Thus, the presence of the MC6828 will add a slight propagation delay on the Address Bus, but otherwise it will have no effect on addresses being transmitted until $FFF8_{16}$ or $FFF9_{16}$ appear.

**It is also possible to move the MC6828 PIC out of the main Address Bus path,** in which case its 16 bytes of PROM or ROM are not within the main microcomputer address space. This scheme may be illustrated as follows:

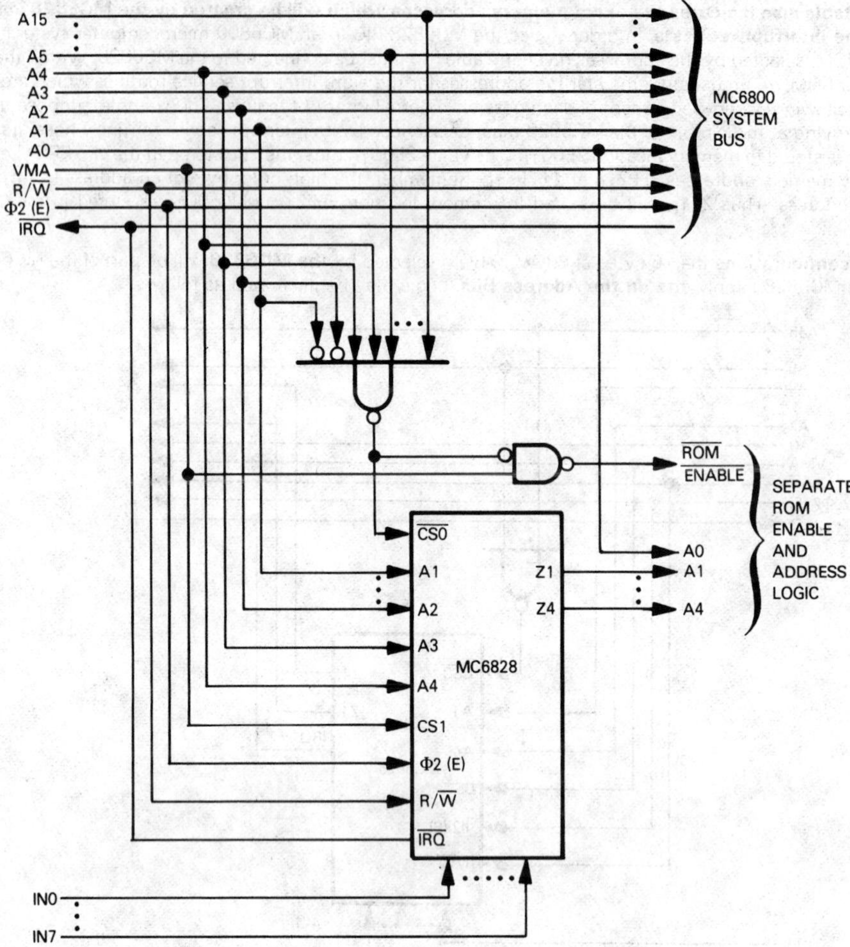


In the above scheme it is only necessary that memory addresses $FFF8_{16}$ and $FFF_{16}$ be reserved for the MC6828 PIC. This is because A4, A3, A2 and A1 contribute to $\overline{CS0}$ logic; they must be 1100 for $\overline{CS0}$ to be low. CS1 is generated by the high VMA pulse. Address Bus lines A1, A2, A3 and A4 now branch to form a new five-line Address Bus — A0 with Z1 through Z4. This five-line Address Bus is input to a separate ROM or PROM which is enabled by the same logic that enables the MC6828.

If you move the MC6828 PIC out of the main Address Bus, then you can have more than one MC6828 device within a single MC6800 microcomputer system. Each MC6828 device must have its own 32 bytes of PROM or ROM, and device priority must be established by conditioning lower priority MC6828 select logic with higher priority interrupt request logic. This may be illustrated as follows:

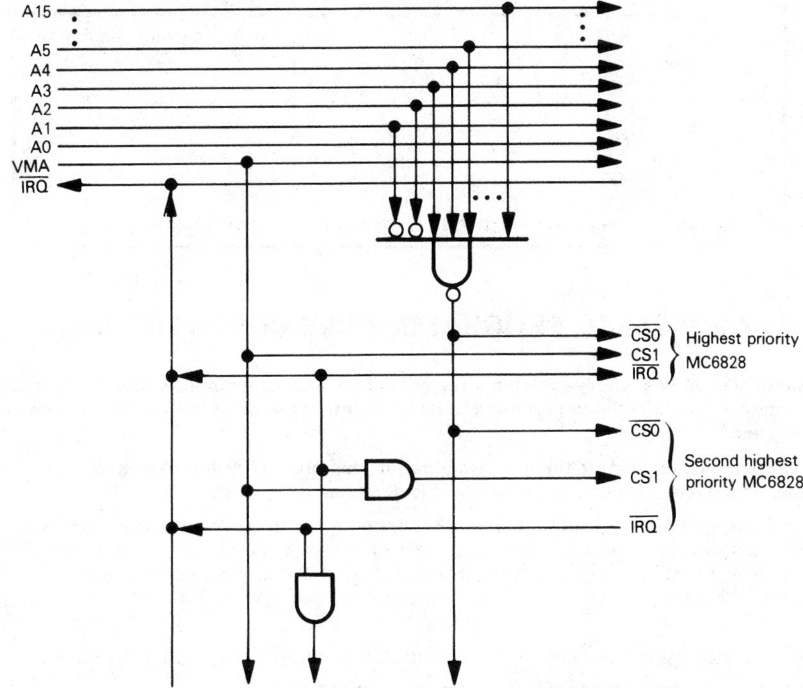


Any one interrupt request being true at a higher priority MC6828 PIC will suppress the high VMA pulse and automatically prevent a lower priority MC6828 PIC from being selected.

## INTERRUPT INHIBIT LOGIC

**The MC6828 provides a very elementary level of interrupt inhibit logic. You can output a mask to the MC6828 identifying a priority level below which all interrupts will be inhibited.**

Now the mask is written out to the MC6828 in a very unusual way.

Recall that the MC6828 requires memory addresses $FFE8_{16}$ through $FFF9_{16}$ to access PROM or ROM. Any attempt to write into these memory addresses will be ignored. The MC6828 takes advantage of this fact by trapping attempts to write into memory locations $FFE8_{16}$ through $FFF9_{16}$. That is to say, when R/$\overline{W}$ is low while $\overline{CS0}$ is low and CS1 is high, the MC6828 considers itself selected, but it interprets the four address lines A1, A2, A3, A4 as data, defining the mask level below which interrupts will be inhibited. **Table 9-9 defines the way in which the mask specified by address lines A1, A2, A3 and A4 will be interpreted.**

Table 9-9. MC6828 Interrupt Masks — Their Creation and Interpretation

| Write anything to this address: | and Address Bus lines A1-A4 will have this value: | Which will inhibit all interrupts, including and below: |
|---|---|---|
| FFE0 or FFE1 | 0000 | All interrupts enabled |
| FFE2 or FFE3 | 0001 | IN1 |
| FFE4 or FFE5 | 0010 | IN2 |
| FFE6 or FFE7 | 0011 | IN3 |
| FFE8 or FFE9 | 0100 | IN4 |
| FFEA or FFEB | 0101 | IN5 |
| FFEC or FFED | 0110 | IN6 |
| FFEE or FFEF | 0111 | IN7 |
| FFF0 through FFFF | 1000 through 1111 | All interrupts disabled |

# THE MC6840 PROGRAMMABLE COUNTER/TIMER

**This is a programmable device which contains three sets of counter/timer logic. Each set of counter/timer logic can be programmed independently to perform a variety of time interval, pulse width measurement and signal generation operations.**

**The MC6840 programmable counter/timer is described in this chapter rather than in Volume 3 because, like other 6800 support devices, it requires the enable clock signal as an input.**

**The MC6840 is somewhat more versatile than the 8253 programmable counter/timer,** which was first developed as an Intel 8080 support device; the 8253 counter/timer is described in Volume 3. Within an MC6800 or MCS6500 microcomputer system, the 8253 is probably preferable to the MC6840; this is because capabilities of the MC6840 are not sufficiently superior to the 8253 to compensate for the enable clock signal and its attendant synchronization problems.

The MC6840 is fabricated using N-channel silicon gate depletion load technology; it is packaged as a 28-pin DIP.

## THE MC6840 COUNTER/TIMER PINS AND SIGNALS

**MC6840 counter/timer pins and signals are illustrated in Figure 9-30. These pins and signals are described in conjunction with a general discussion of the MC6840 organization logic and capabilities.**

**Each of the three sets of timer logic has a 16-bit Counter, a 16-bit Latch and three control signals,** illustrated as follows:

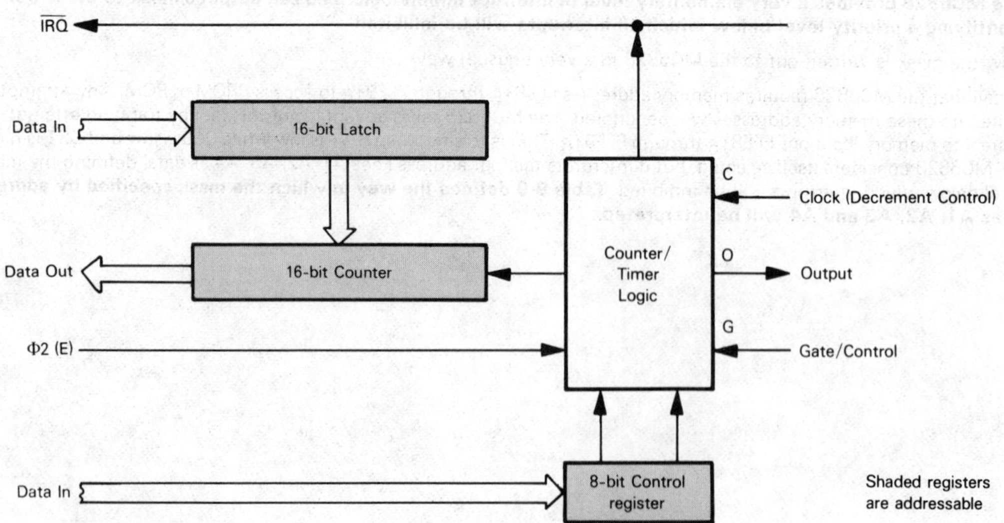

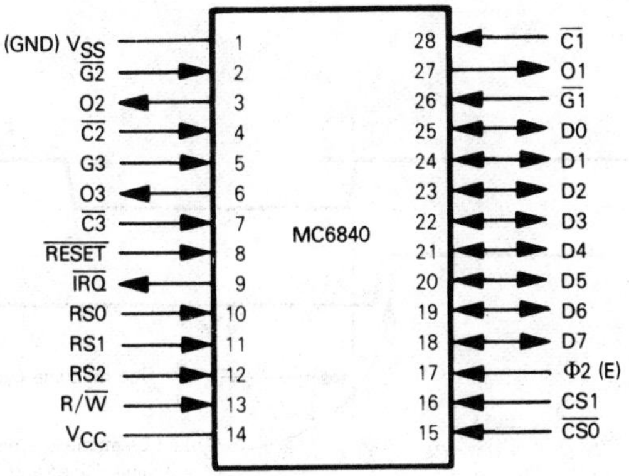

| | | | | |
|---|---|---|---|---|
| (GND) $V_{SS}$ | 1 | MC6840 | 28 | $\overline{C1}$ |
| $\overline{G2}$ | 2 | | 27 | O1 |
| O2 | 3 | | 26 | $\overline{G1}$ |
| $\overline{C2}$ | 4 | | 25 | D0 |
| G3 | 5 | | 24 | D1 |
| O3 | 6 | | 23 | D2 |
| $\overline{C3}$ | 7 | | 22 | D3 |
| $\overline{RESET}$ | 8 | | 21 | D4 |
| $\overline{IRQ}$ | 9 | | 20 | D5 |
| RS0 | 10 | | 19 | D6 |
| RS1 | 11 | | 18 | D7 |
| RS2 | 12 | | 17 | Φ2 (E) |
| R/$\overline{W}$ | 13 | | 16 | CS1 |
| $V_{CC}$ | 14 | | 15 | $\overline{CS0}$ |

| PIN NAME | DESCRIPTION | TYPE |
|---|---|---|
| D0 - D7 | Data Bus | Tristate, bidirectional |
| C1 | Timer 1 clock | Input |
| O1 | Timer 1 output | Output |
| G1 | Timer 1 gate | Input |
| C2 | Timer 2 clock | Input |
| O2 | Timer 2 output | Output |
| G2 | Timer 2 gate | Input |
| C3 | Timer 3 clock | Input |
| O3 | Timer 3 output | Output |
| G3 | Timer 3 gate | Input |
| RS0, RS1, RS2 | Register select | Input |
| CS0, CS1 | Chip select | Input |
| R/$\overline{W}$ | Read/Write control | Input |
| $\overline{RESET}$ | System reset | Input |
| $\overline{IRQ}$ | Interrupt request | Output |
| Φ2 (E) | Clock input | Input |
| $V_{CC}$, $V_{SS}$ | Power and Ground | |

Figure 9-30. MC6840 Counter/Timer Signals and Pin Assignments

**MC6840 COUNTER/TIMER INITIALIZATION**

**When any counter or timer operation is initialized, the 16-bit Latch contents are loaded into the associated 16-bit Counter.** The Counter is then decremented either on high-to-low transitions of the external clock signal (C), or on high-to-low transitions of the internal Φ2 clock signal; selecting one or the other is a programmable option. This may be illustrated as follows:

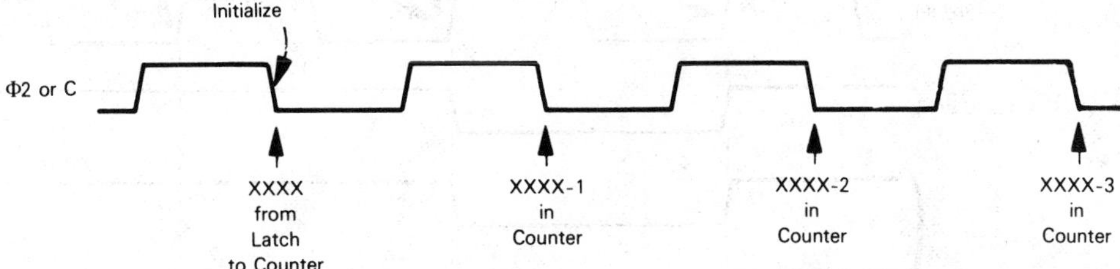


XXXX represents any initial 16-bit value.

**If the external clock signal is used to decrement the counter/timer, then it is being used as an event counter; if the internal synchronization clock is used to decrement the counter/timer, then it is being used as a timer.**

**The external signals $\overline{C}$ and $\overline{G}$ are sampled on the trailing edge of Φ2.** This has important synchronization consequences.

**Timing for external clock signal $\overline{C}$ or $\overline{G}$ may be illustrated as follows:**

**MC6840 EXTERNAL SIGNAL TIMING**

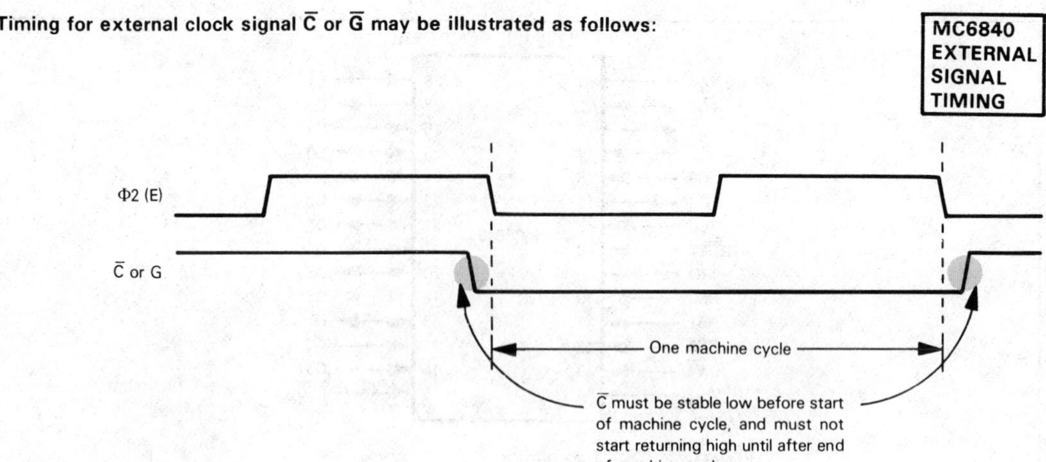


Thus, external clock signal frequencies may vary from 0 (DC) to somewhere less than half of the internal Φ2 clock frequency.

**It is very important that external signal timing conform to the illustration above.** If insufficient setup time is provided, MC6840 logic will possibly recognize the initial high-to-low signal transition twice: once assuming that the setup time just made it, and again assuming that it did not. this may be illustrated as follows:

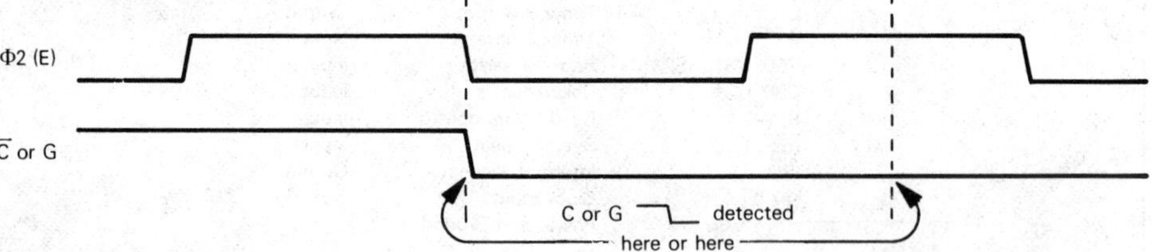


A similar problem may occur on the trailing edge of the external signal. This may result in clock pulses being missed. This may be illustrated as follows:

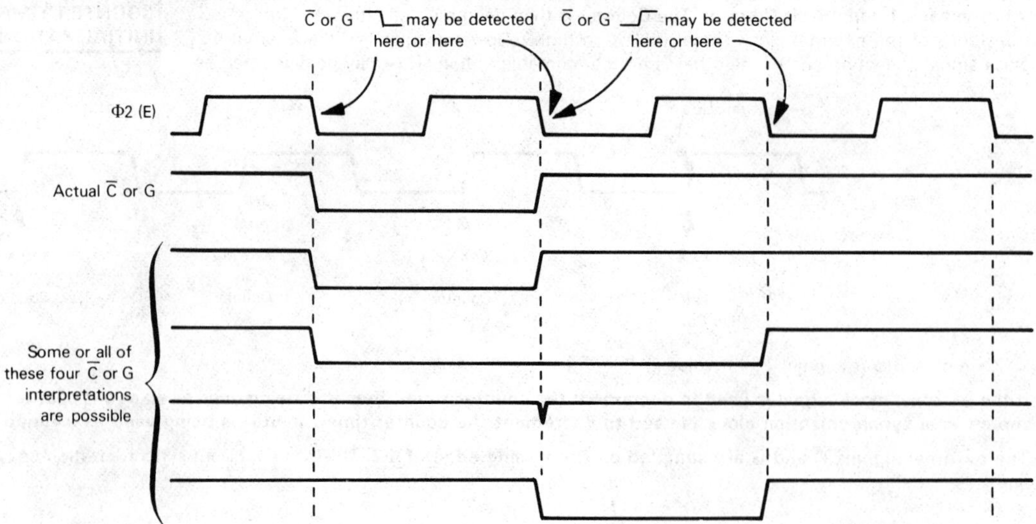

**Any transition of the $\overline{C}$ or G input signals is not recognized by internal MC6840 logic for four Φ2 clock periods.** This may be illustrated as follows:

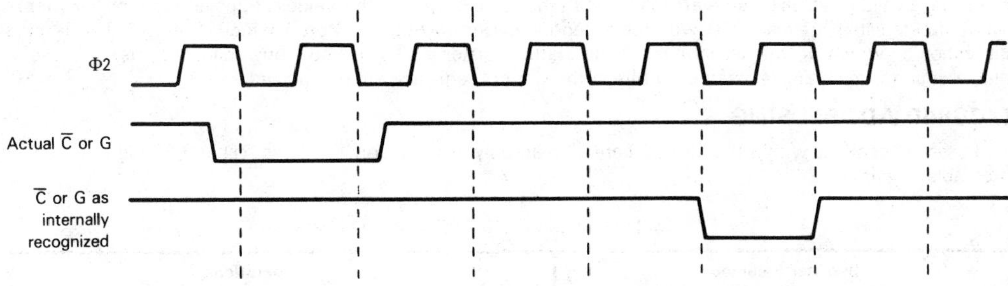


One point can cause confusion when you are using the external clock ($\overline{C}$) to decrement the counter/timer: it will still take four internal clock pulses (Φ2) to recognize each external clock pulse, as illustrated above. A common mistake, when using this part, is to assume that internal clock recognition is simply delayed four clock pulses; the delay is four internal clock pulses.

The only significance of this delay is that there is indeed a delay. This delay has no effect on external clock signal frequency or timing.

The gate input (G) is used variously to initiate or suspend timer operations.

Timer results can be output via the output signal O. A variety of continuous or one-shot wave forms may be generated via the O output signals.

The programmer accesses an MC6840 counter/timer as eight contiguous memory locations. A memory location is selected via two chip select inputs (CS0 and CS1) plus three register select inputs (RS0, RS1 and RS2).

As is standard for MC6800 support devices, chip select logic should be conditioned by the valid memory address (VMA) signal. Device select and addressing logic may be illustrated as follows:

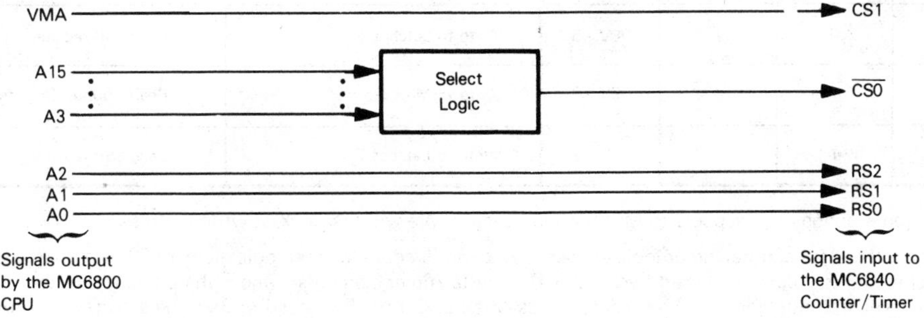


Once the MC6840 has been selected, **the level of the R/W signal determines whether a read (R/$\overline{W}$ high) or a write (R/$\overline{W}$ low) operation is to occur.** If R/$\overline{W}$ is low, the CPU will write into the selected MC6840 location; if R/$\overline{W}$ is high, the contents of the selected MC6840 location will be read.

**Any data transferred to or from the MC6840 is transferred via the Data Bus.** The MC6840 Data Bus connection is three-state; when a read or a write operation is not in progress, the MC6840 disconnects itself from the Data Bus.

**MC6840 RESET**

**The MC6840 is reset by applying a low input signal to the $\overline{RESET}$ pin. Necessary reset timing may be illustrated as follows:**

Φ2
$\overline{RESET}$
250 ns
RESET

$\overline{RESET}$ signal timing requirements are the same as the C and G requirements which we just described. The $\overline{RESET}$ is recognized by internal logic two clock pulses after a low level is detected.

Following a valid reset, all Latches are loaded with the value $FF_{16}$, and this value is transferred to the Counter registers. All Control registers are reset to 0, with the exception of Control Register 1 bit 0, which is set to 1. This is a system initialization bit which we will describe later. The Status register is also cleared. Thus, following a reset, those programmable options which are selected by 0 bits in the Control registers will be enabled.

## MC6840 ADDRESSING

Addressable locations within the MC6840 are all read-only or write-only locations. Table 9-10 identifies MC6840 addressable locations.

Table 9-10. MC6840 Addressable Locations

| **Register Selected** | | | | **Operations** | |
|---|---|---|---|---|---|
| **RS2** | **RS1** | **RS0** | **Label Address** | **R/$\overline{W}$=0 (Write)** | **R/$\overline{W}$=1 (Read)** |
| 0 | 0 | 0 | DEV | Write to Control Register 3 if Control Register 2, bit 0 is 0<br>Write to Control Register 1 if Control Register 2, bit 0 is 1 | No operation |
| 0 | 0 | 1 | DEV + 1 | Write to Control Register 2 | Read Status register |
| 0 | 1 | 0 | DEV + 2 | Write to MSB register | Read Counter Register 1 |
| 0 | 1 | 1 | DEV + 3 | Write to Latches 1 | Read LSB register |
| 1 | 0 | 0 | DEV + 4 | Write to MSB register | Read Counter Register 2 |
| 1 | 0 | 1 | DEV + 5 | Write to Latches 2 | Read LSB register |
| 1 | 1 | 0 | DEV + 6 | Write to MSB register | Read Counter Register 3 |
| 1 | 1 | 1 | DEV + 7 | Write to Latches 3 | Read LSB register |

There are some nonobvious aspects to MC6840 addressing. We will first look at write addresses.

If we number the three counter/timer logic elements 1, 2 and 3, counter/timer logic element 2 has a unique write-only address for its Control register. (It is address DEV+1). Counter/timer elements 1 and 3 share a single write-only address (DEV). The level of Control register 2 bit 0 determines whether Control Register 1 or 3 will be selected by address DEV. This may be illustrated as follows:

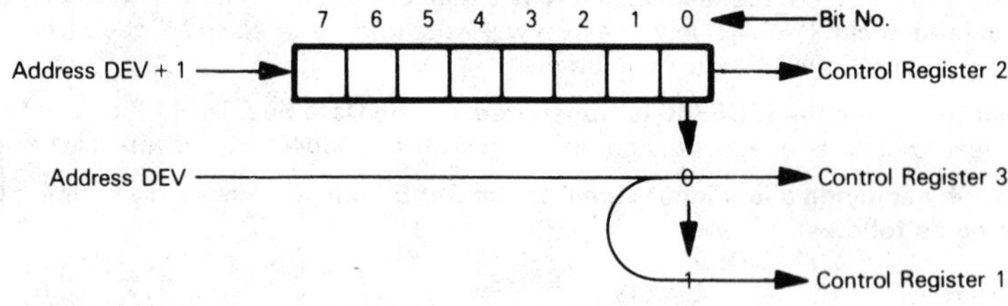

Following a device reset. Control Register 2. bit 0 will be 0. Therefore. initially Control Register 3 will be selected by address DEV. Thus. you will normally access Control registers in the sequence 3. 2. 1. as follows:

1) Select address DEV. access Control Register 3.

2) Select address DEV+1. access Control Register 2. Set Control Register 2. bit 0 to 1.

3) Select address DEV. access Control Register 1.

Three write addresses select an "MSB" register. All three write addresses select the same temporary "Most Significant Byte" buffer. This buffer allows 16 data bits to be written into any one of the three 16-bit latches when a single 8-bit write is executed. This may be illustrated as follows:

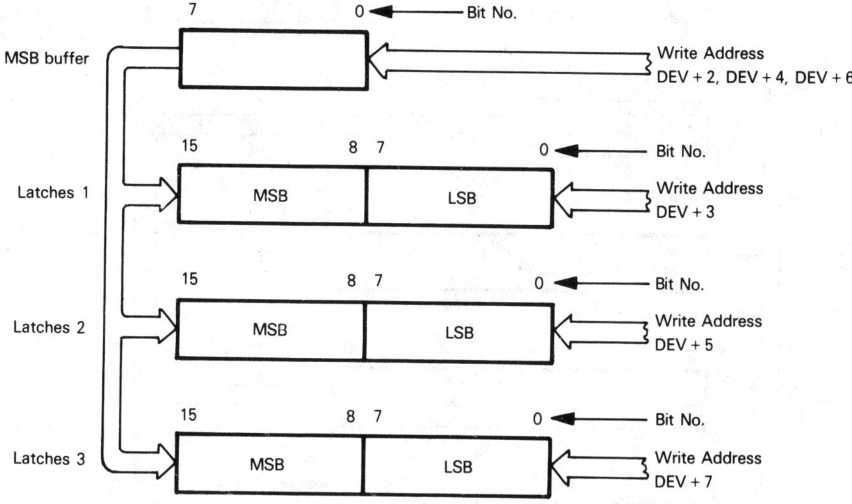


MSB means Most Significant Byte
LSB means Least Significant Byte

The Most Significant Byte (MSB) buffer allows the MC6840 to be accessed by MC6800 16-bit write instructions. You can, for example, use an STX or STS instruction to transfer the contents of the Index register or the Stack Pointer to the selected MC6840 location. There are three MC6840 locations which can receive a 16-bit data value; they are the three counter/timer latches illustrated above as Latches 1, Latches 2 and Latches 3. You address these counter/timer latches via their associated Most Significant Byte buffer address. Now when you output a 16-bit value (for example, from the Index register), first the high-order byte is transferred to the Most Significant Byte (MSB) buffer. For Latches 2 this may be illustrated as follows:

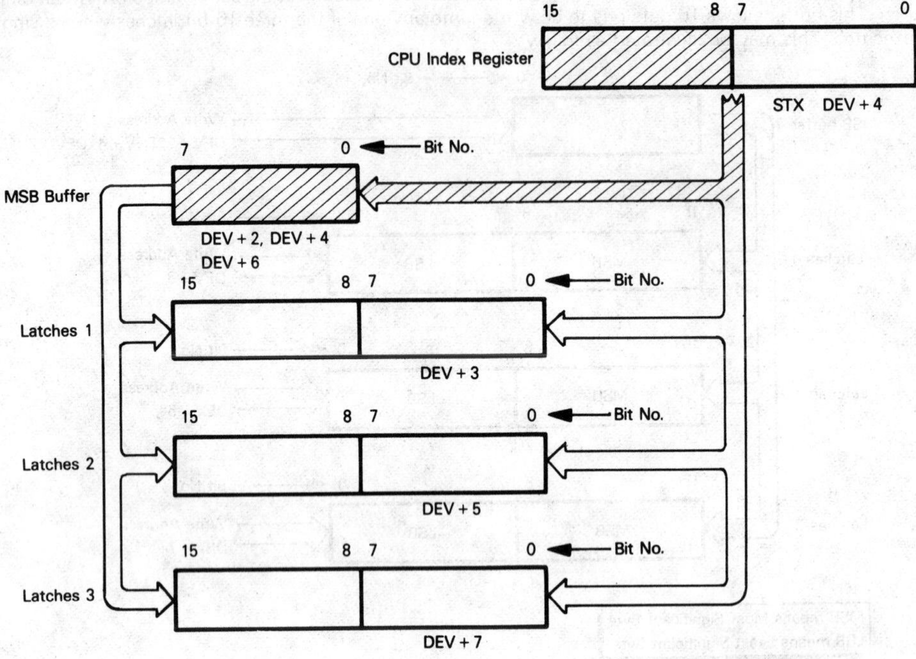

Then the low-order byte is transferred to the low-order byte of the addressed counter/timer latches, while simultaneously the Most Significant Byte (MSB) buffer contents are transferred to the high-order byte of the addressed counter/timer latches. This may be illustrated as follows:

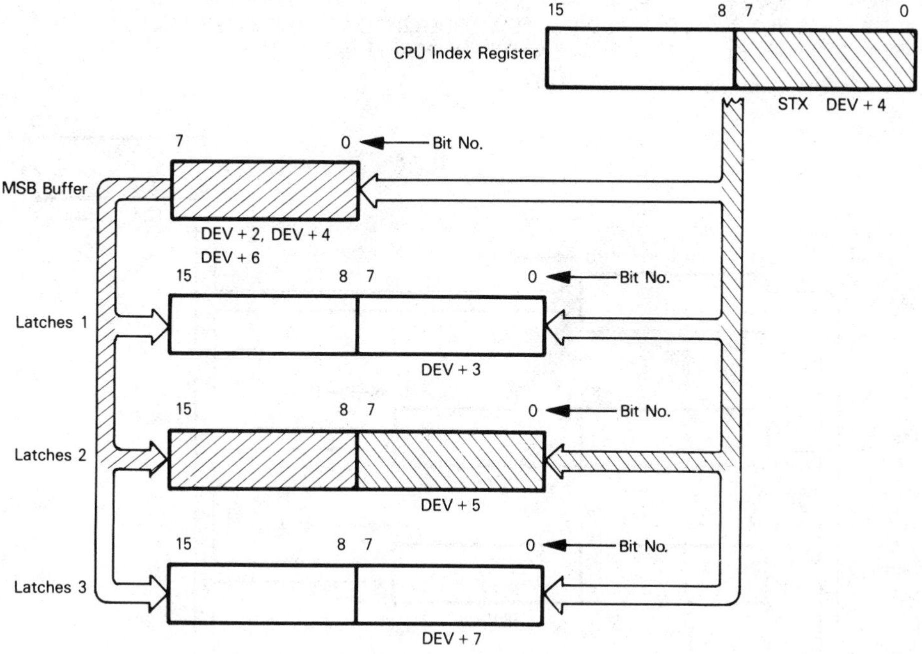

You can, of course, access counter/timer latches using single byte instructions. You could, for example, transfer a 16-bit value one byte at a time from Accumulator A, via the following instruction sequence:

```
LDA    A,#HI      LOAD ADDRESS HIGH-ORDER BYTE AS IMMEDIATE DATA
STA    A,DEV+4    STORE IN MSB BUFFER
LDA    A,#LO      LOAD ADDRESS LOW-ORDER BYTE AS IMMEDIATE DATA
STA    A,DEV+5    WRITE 11 DATA BITS TO LATCHES 2
```

This instruction sequence may be illustrated as follows:

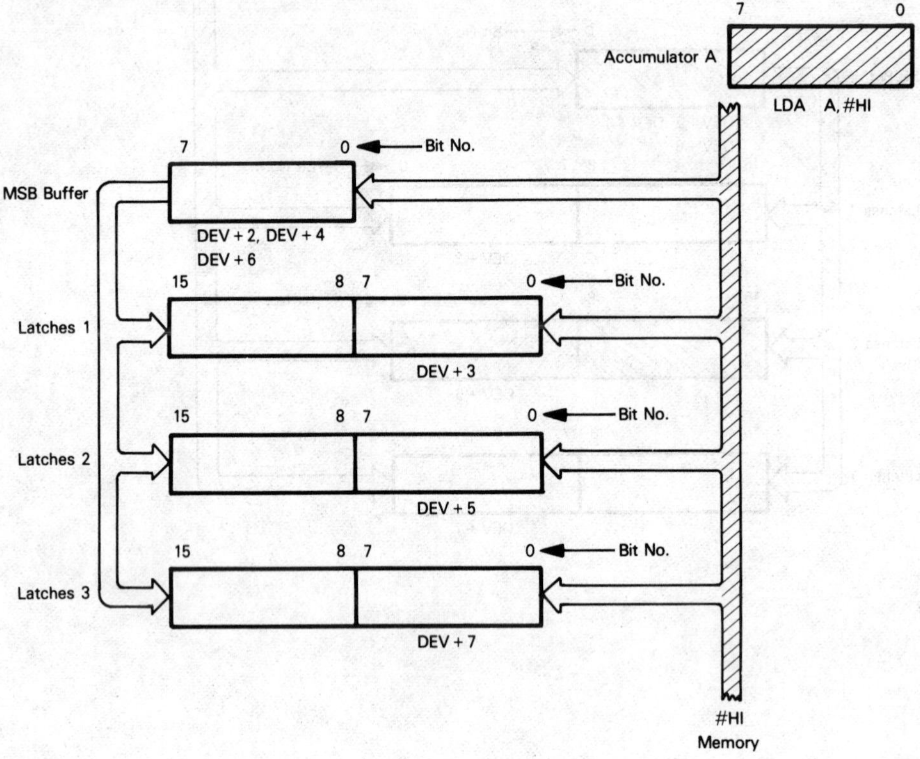

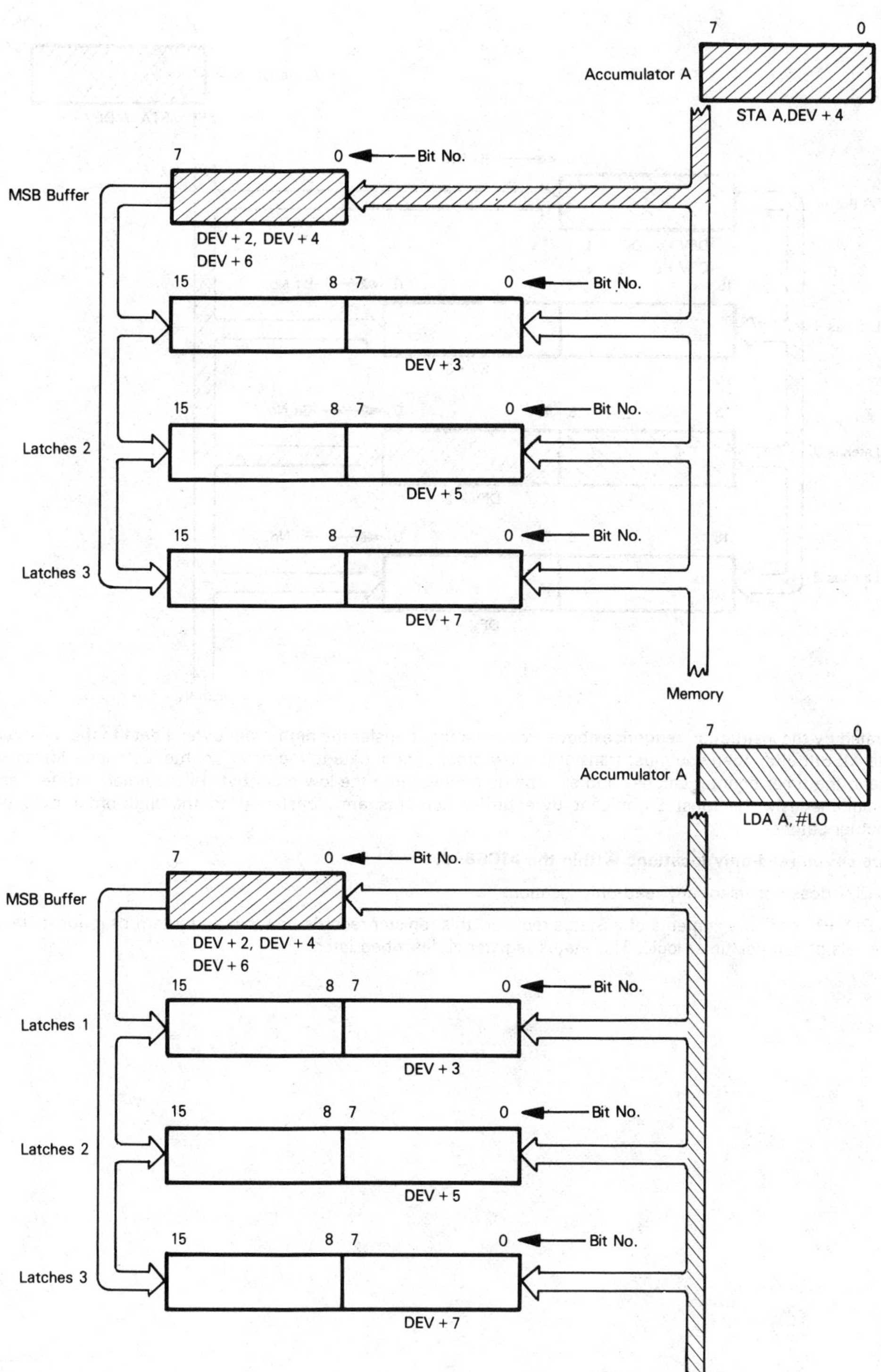

7
0
Accumulator A
STA A,DEV + 4
7
0
Bit No.
MSB Buffer
DEV + 2, DEV + 4
DEV + 6
15
8
7
0
Bit No.
DEV + 3
15
8
7
0
Bit No.
Latches 2
DEV + 5
15
8
7
0
Bit No.
Latches 3
DEV + 7
Memory
7
0
Accumulator A
LDA A, #LO
7
0
Bit No.
MSB Buffer
DEV + 2, DEV + 4
DEV + 6
15
8
7
0
Bit No.
Latches 1
DEV + 3
15
8
7
0
Bit No.
Latches 2
DEV + 5
15
8
7
0
Bit No.
Latches 3
DEV + 7
#LO Memory

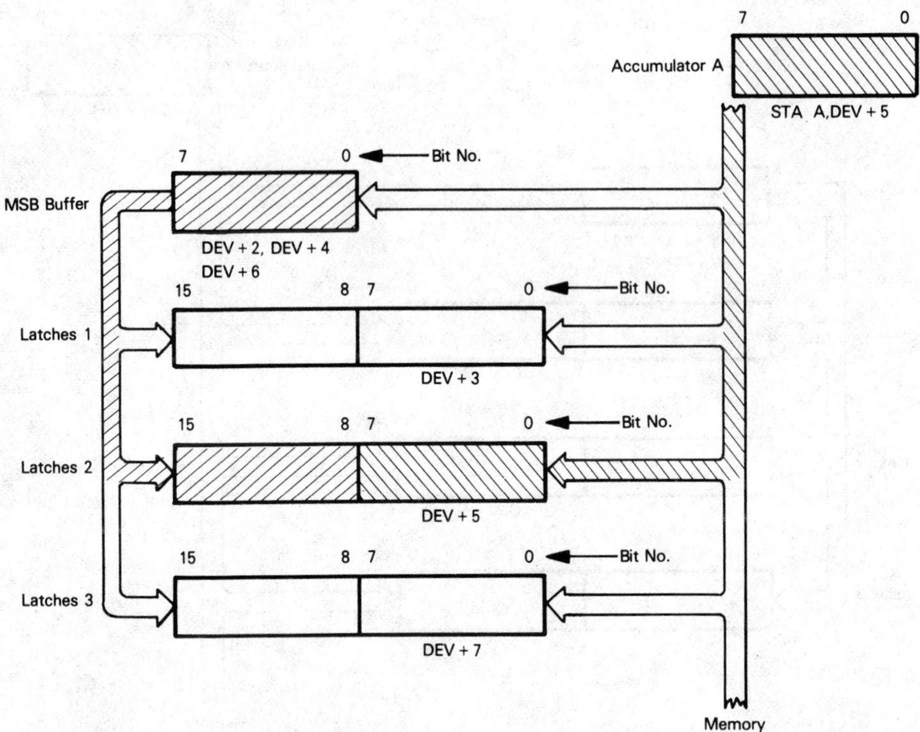


As illustrated by the instruction sequence above, you must first transfer the high-order byte of data to the Most Significant Byte (MSB) buffer, then you must transfer the low-order byte of data to the timer/counter Latches address; when you write to the timer/counter Latches address, the data moves into the low-order byte of the timer/counter Latches, while simultaneously the Most Significant Byte buffer contents are transferred to the high-order byte of the timer/counter Latches.

**There are seven read-only locations within the MC6840.**

Address DEV does not select any read-only location.

Address DEV+1 reads the contents of a Status register; this register records time out and interrupt request status for the three sets of counter/timer logic. The Status register is described later.

The remaining six read-only addresses are used to read the contents of the counter/timer counters in a manner that is analogous to the way in which you write into the counter/timer latches. This may be illustrated as follows:

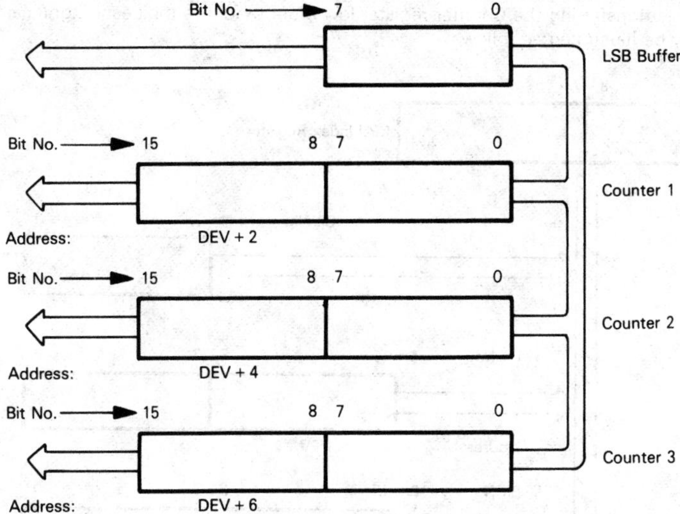

The three addresses which select the Least Significant Byte (LSB) buffer once again address the same location. Consider the LDX instruction which loads a 16-bit data value into the CPU Index register. When this instruction addresses an MC6840 counter/timer, you first read a Counter register high-order byte into the Index register high-order byte while simultaneously transferring the Counter register low-order byte into the Least Significant Byte (LSB) buffer. For Counter 2 this may be illustrated as follows:

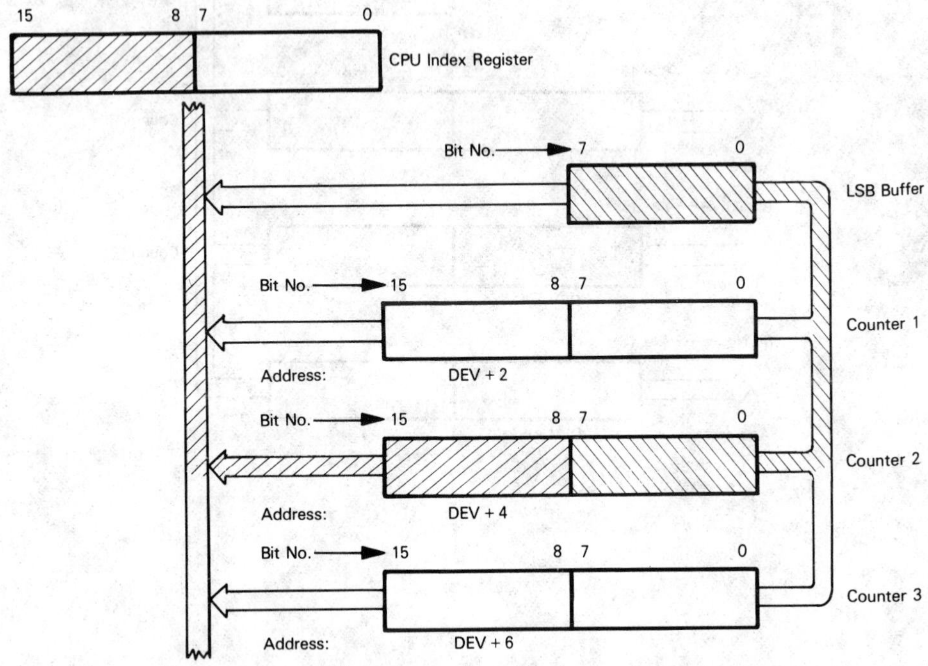

The Least Significant Byte (LSB) buffer contents are then transferred to the low-order Index register byte:

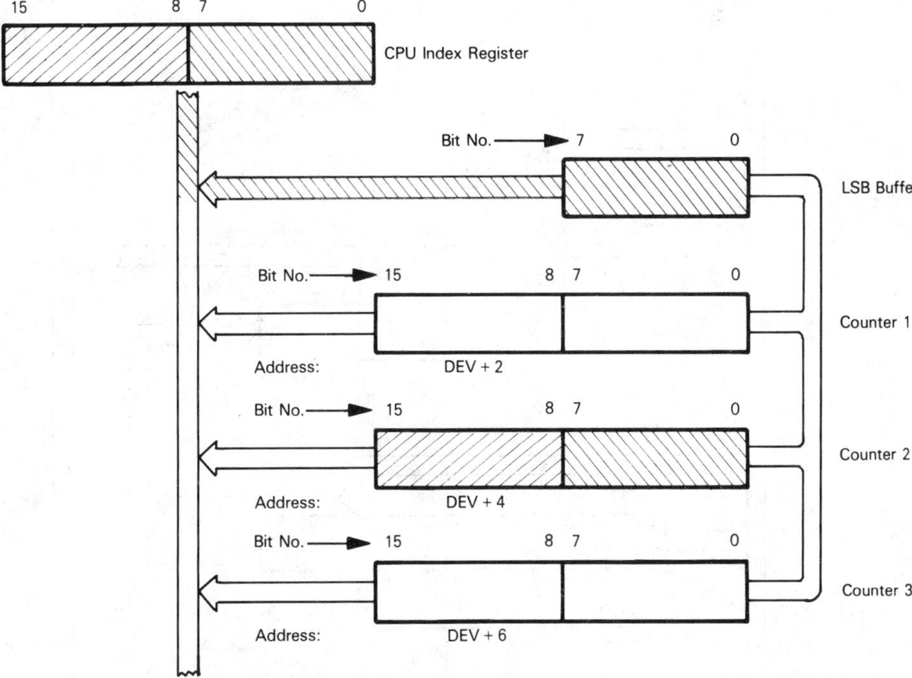


You can, of course, read Counter register contents one byte at a time, but you must make sure that you read the high-order byte first by addressing the counter itself; then you must read the low-order byte by addressing the next addressable location. This may be illustrated for Counter 2 by the following instruction sequence:

```
LDA     A,DEV+4     LOAD COUNTER HIGH-ORDER BYTE TO ACCUMULATOR A
LDA     B,DEV+5     LOAD COUNTER LOW-ORDER BYTE TO ACCUMULATOR B
```

**There are some ways of getting into trouble when accessing the MC6840.**

As illustrated for Counter read and Latch write operations, when reading or writing to the MC6840 you must first select an even address location, and then address the next sequential location. If you write first to an odd address, you will transfer into the selected latches eight bits of data plus whatever happens to be in the Most Significant Byte buffer.

If you read first from an odd address, you will read whatever happens to be in the Least Significant Byte (LSB) buffer. You must never access the MC6840 with an instruction that modifies the contents of a memory location; these instructions read the contents of the addressed memory location to the CPU, modify its contents, and then write the contents back to the same addressed memory location. For an increment memory instruction:

```
INC     DEV+4
```

this may be illustrated as follows:

Step 1

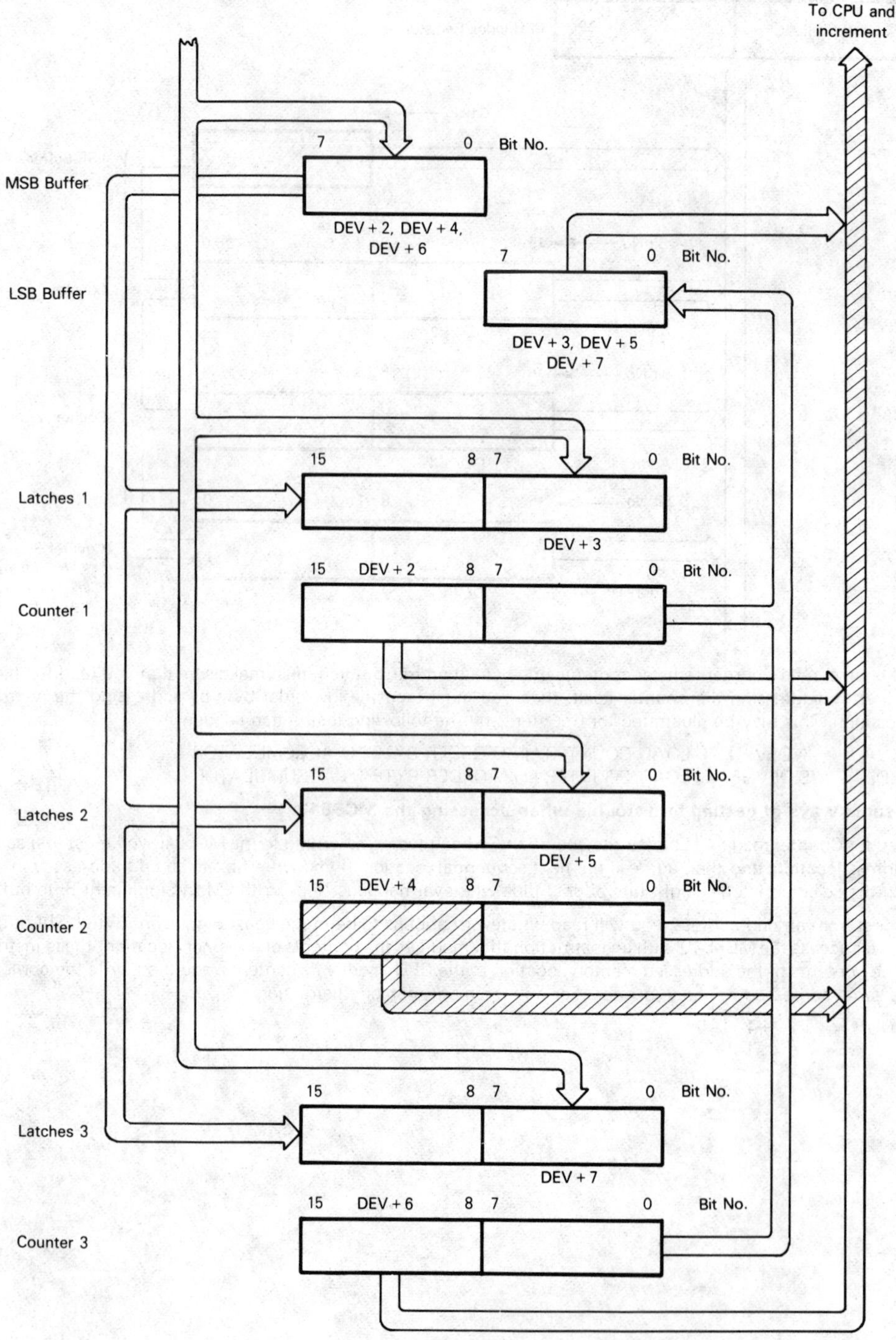

Step 2

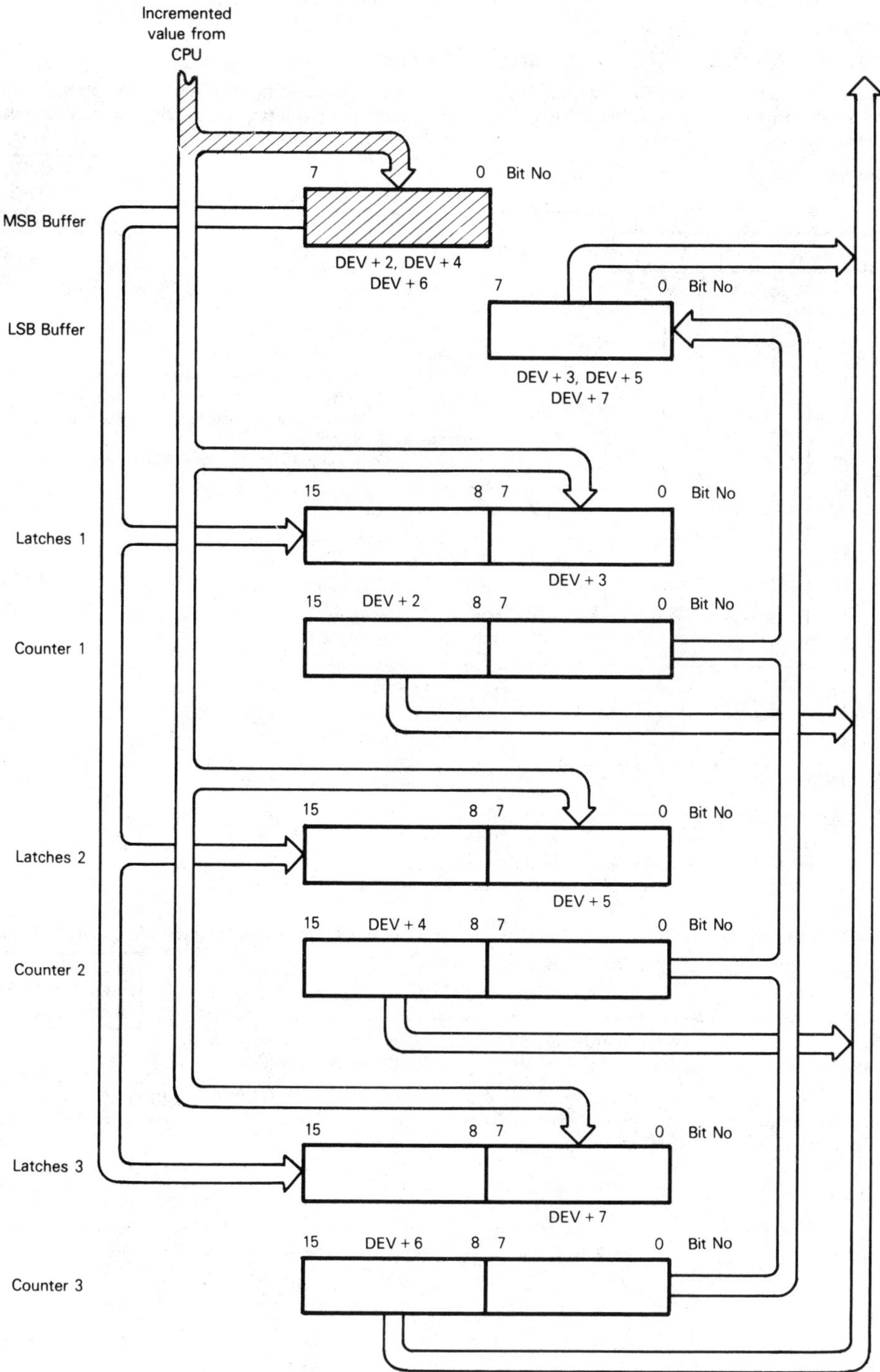

Incremented value from CPU
7
0
Bit No
MSB Buffer
DEV + 2, DEV + 4
DEV + 6
7
0
Bit No
LSB Buffer
DEV + 3, DEV + 5
DEV + 7
15
8
7
0
Bit No
Latches 1
DEV + 3
15
DEV + 2
8
7
0
Bit No
Counter 1
15
8
7
0
Bit No
Latches 2
DEV + 5
15
DEV + 4
8
7
0
Bit No
Counter 2
15
8
7
0
Bit No
Latches 3
DEV + 7
15
DEV + 6
8
7
0
Bit No
Counter 3

As illustrated above, the same address accesses different MC6840 locations on a read or write; you will read the contents of one location, modify them, and write them back to a totally different location. Therefore, when accessing the MC6840 under program control, you must be sure not to use instructions that modify memory; use only instructions that read from memory or write to memory.

## MC6840 COUNTER/TIMER PROGRAMMABLE OPTIONS

**We will begin our discussion of the MC6840 counter/timer options by describing the Control code which must be written into each Control register. Subsequently, the various operating modes will be discussed along with appropriate examples.**

**MC6840 CONTROL REGISTERS**

**This is the general format for the Control code:**

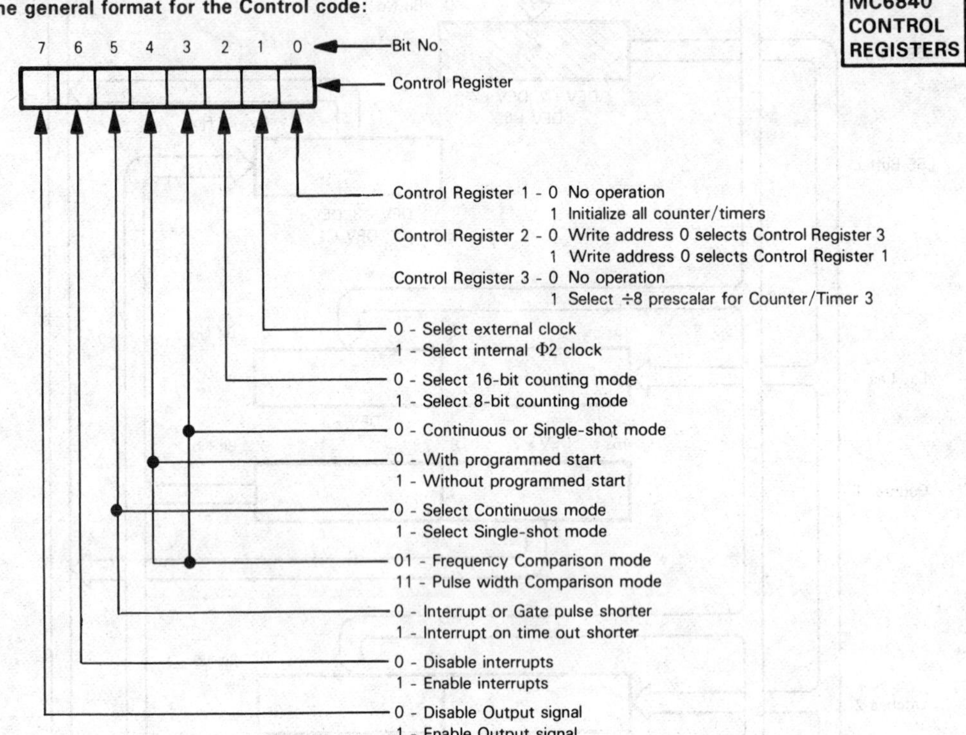


Bits 0 of the three Control registers are unusual in that they have different interpretations for the three Control registers.

**MC6840 PROGRAMMED INITIALIZATION**

Control Register 1, bit 0 is a system initialization bit. System initialization is identical to a system reset, with the exception that latches are not effective. Thus, as soon as a 1 is written to Control Register 1, bit 0, all three counter/timers are stopped, the contents of all three Latches are transferred to their associated Counter registers, the Status register is cleared, and all Control register bits (with the exception of Control Register 1 bit 0) are reset to 0.

Control Register 2, bit 0 is an addressing bit. When this bit is 0, a write to the lowest MC6840 address (DEV) will access Control Register 3; when this bit is 1, a write to address DEV will select Control Register 1. This was graphically illustrated in our earlier discussion of MC6840 addressing.

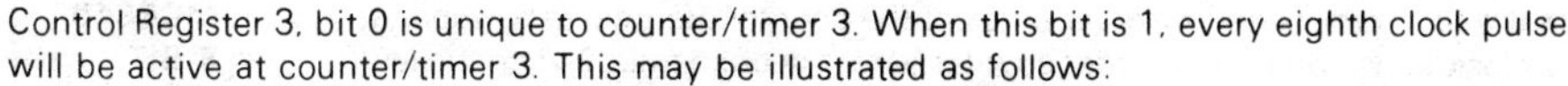

Control Register 3, bit 0 is unique to counter/timer 3. When this bit is 1, every eighth clock pulse will be active at counter/timer 3. This may be illustrated as follows:

**MC6840 DIVIDE-BY-EIGHT CLOCK**

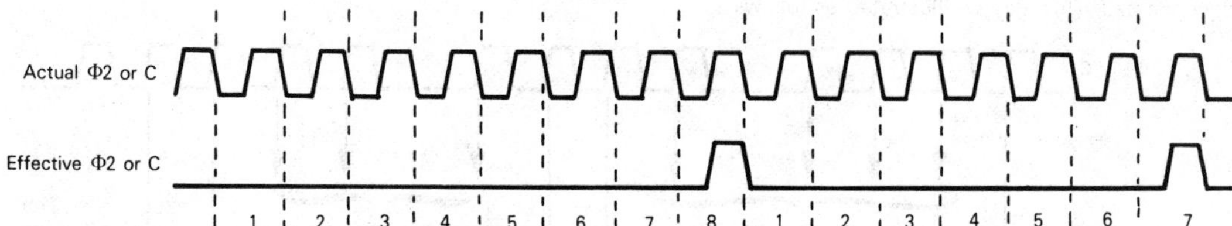


**Control register bits 1 through 7 serve identical functions, but apply only to one set of counter/timer logic. Each of the three counter/timer logic elements operates quite independently, and is in no way influenced by conditions at either of the other counter/timer elements.**

**Control register bit 1 determines whether Counter register contents will be decremented by external clock signal (C) transitions, or by the internal Φ2 clock.** In either case the counter will be decremented on high-to-low clock transitions.

**MC6840 16-BIT COUNTING MODE**

**Control register bit 2 determines the way in which the Counter register will decrement. There are two options: 16-bit counting mode and 8-bit counting mode.** In 16-bit counting mode, the 16-bit counter contents are treated as a single 16-bit entity. Once an initial value has been loaded into the counter, it decrements on each active clock transition. When the clock decrements to 0, a time out occurs. This may be illustrated as follows:

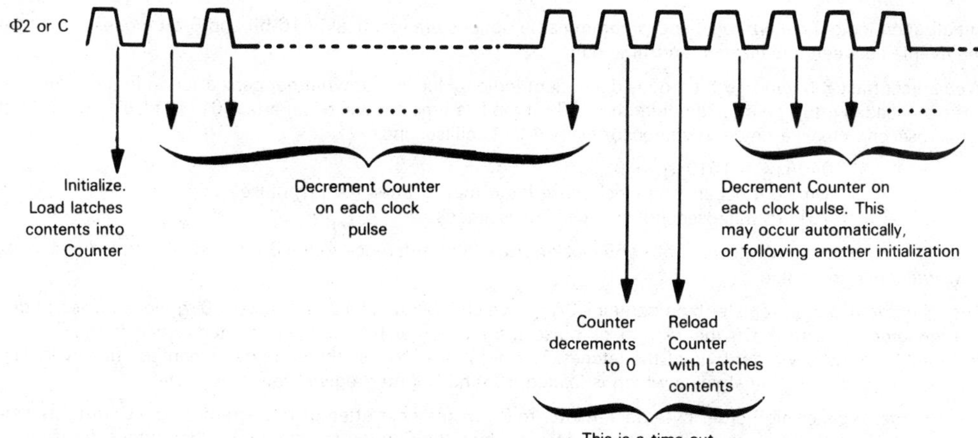


There are a variety of ways in which you initialize a counter/timer. These are programmable options which depend on the selected operating mode — which we will describe later.

A time out occurs after a Counter register decrements to 0. On the next clock pulse the Counter register is reloaded with the contents of the latches. Under program control you can determine whether a time out will be marked by an interrupt request, and whether the counter/timer will stop or run continuously.

In 8-bit counting mode the high-order and low-order bytes of the counter are treated as separate entities. On each active clock transition the low-order counter byte is decremented; when the low-order byte decrements from 1 to 0, nothing happens. On the next active transition of the clock, the low-order byte is reloaded from the low-order byte of the latch and the high-order byte is decremented. This may be illustrated as follows:

**MC6840 8-BIT COUNTING MODE**

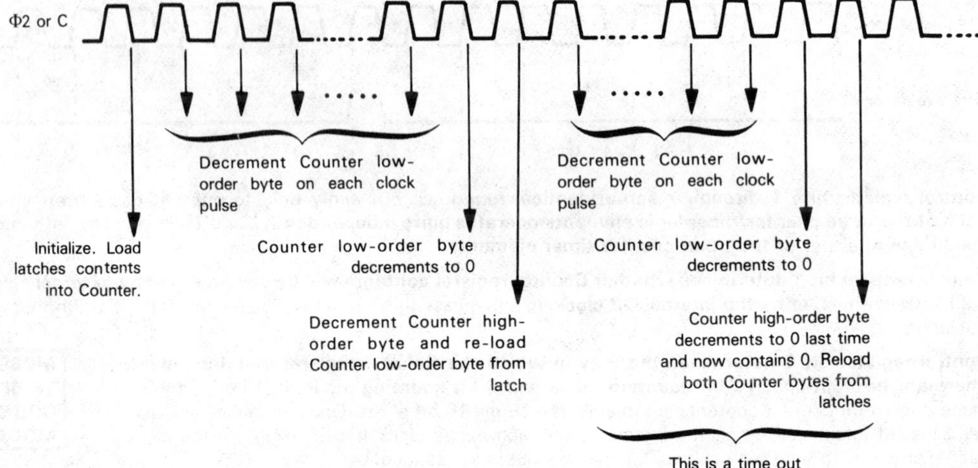


Initialization logic, time out logic and programmable options are identical in 16-bit and 8-bit modes. What differs are the events between initialization and time out.

We can contrast 8-bit and 16-bit modes decrement logic by looking at what happens after an initial value of $040A_{16}$ has been loaded into a counter/timer latch. In 16-bit mode a time out will occur after $1011_{10}$ clock pulses. Assuming a 1 microsecond clock, a time out will occur every 1.011 milliseconds:

$040A_{16} = 1010_{10}$
Time out occurs one clock pulse later, that is, after $1011_{10}$ pulses
$1011_{10}$ microseconds = 1.011 milliseconds

In 8-bit mode a time out will occur after 55 clock pulses. With reference to the 8-bit mode illustrated above, let us see how we derive this value.

The low-order Counter register byte contains $0A_{16}$, which is equal to $10_{10}$. It takes $10_{10}$ clock pulses to decrement the low-order byte to 0. On the 11th clock pulse the high-order byte is decremented, while the low-order byte is reloaded from the low-order byte of the latches. The high-order byte is therefore decremented once every N+1 clock pulses, where N is the initial value which is loaded into the Counter register low-order byte.

The Counter register high-order byte decrements to 0. On the next attempt to decrement the Counter register high-order byte, if it already contains 0, a time out occurs. Thus, the Counter register high-order byte is decremented M+1 times, where M is the initial Counter register high-order byte contents. Thus, you can compute the number of clock pulses until a time out occurs in 8-bit mode via the following equation:

$$(M+1) \cdot (N+1)$$

where M is the initial Counter register high-order byte contents and N is the initial Counter register low-order byte contents.

**For each counter/timer you can select one of eight operating methods via Control registers bits 3, 4 and 5.**

**For any MC6840 operating mode, interrupts and/or the output signal (O) may or may not be enabled.**

**MC6840 INTERRUPT ENABLE**

If interrupts have been enabled (via Control register bit 6), then on every time out (and for certain other special conditions) an interrupt request will be made to the CPU by outputting a low $\overline{IRQ}$ signal. Simultaneously, appropriate Status flags are set in a Status register. If interrupts are disabled, the Status register bit settings occur, but no interrupt request is output via $\overline{IRQ}$.

If the output signal (O) is enabled, then during Continuous and Single Shot operating modes an output signal is generated. The output signal (O) is not used in frequency comparison and pulse width comparison operating modes.

**MC6840 OUTPUT SIGNAL ENABLE**

**The Status register of the MC6840 reports time outs and interrupt request status. Status register bits are interpreted as follows:**

**STATUS REGISTER**

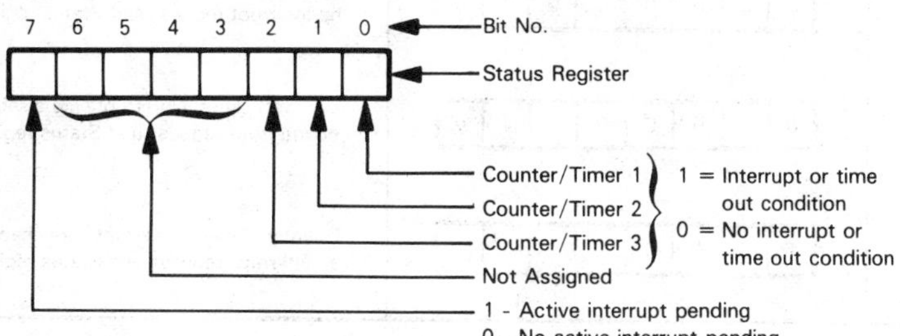


The MC6840 Status register is a read-only location accessed via the address DEV+1, as shown in Table 9-10.

**There are some nonobvious consequences of Status register organization. We will therefore describe the individual Status register bits and then the way in which they should be used.**

**Status register bits 0, 1 and 2 will be set to 1 if an interrupt condition exists at counter/timer 1, 2 or 3, respectively.** This will occur whether or not interrupts have been enabled. For example, if a time out occurs at counter/timer 2, then Status register bit 1 will be set, irrespective of whether counter/timer 2 interrupts have or have not been enabled via Control Register 2, bit 6. Thus, Status register bits 0, 1 and 2 do not report an interrupt pending from a counter/timer; rather, they report the existence of a condition capable of generating an interrupt request. **Status register bit 7 indicates the presence of a valid interrupt request.** Status register bit 7 will be set to 1 if a valid interrupt request has been generated by one or more of the counter/timers. That is to say, if Status register bit 0, 1 or 2 has been set to 1 while the associated Control register bit 6 is 1, then Status register bit 7 will be set to 1. This may be illustrated via the following logical equation:

$$S7 = (S0 \cdot C16) + (S1 \cdot C26) + (S2 \cdot C36)$$

In the equation above, S0, S1, S2 and S7 represent Status register bits 0, 1, 2 and 7, respectively. C16, C26 and C36 represent bit 6 of Control Registers 1, 2 and 3, respectively. • and + signs represent logical AND and OR operations, respectively.

Now, in an MC6800 microcomputer system that is using vectored interrupt acknowledge logic, Status register bit 7 is useless. This is because the vectoring logic associated with the interrupt acknowledge allows the executing program to branch directly to an interrupt service routine dedicated to this particular MC6840 device. For example, in an MC6800 microcomputer system that includes an MC6828 Priority Interrupt Controller (PIC), the interrupt request line from the MC6840 would terminate at one of the MC6828 interrupt request pins; the MC6840 interrupt service routine's start address would be fetched by the MC6828 PIC following an interrupt acknowledge.

Upon acknowledging the interrupt request, the MC6800 knows that this particular MC6840's interrupt has been acknowledged; therefore the high-order Status register bit contains no useful information. In MC6800 microcomputer systems that use polling logic following an interrupt acknowledge, the interrupt acknowledge process will begin with a general purpose interrupt service routine that reads the contents of every device Status register — checking for devices with an active interrupt request. Now Status register bit 7 of the MC6840 is useful. The initial general purpose interrupt service routine will read the contents of the MC6840 Status register and check bit 7. If this bit is 1, then an active interrupt request exists. Here is an appropriate instruction sequence:

```
LDA    A,DEV+1    READ STATUS REGISTER
BIT    A,#80H     TEST HIGH-ORDER BIT
BNE    MC6840     IF NOT 0, BRANCH TO SERVICE ROUTINE
LDA    A,NEXT     READ NEXT DEVICE'S STATUS REGISTER
```

**You cannot use the MC6800 Status register to create interrupt request priorities within the MC6840.** One or more counter/timer interrupts must be enabled via the Control register bit 6 for an interrupt request to be generated, but if more than one counter/timer can generate an interrupt request, you have no way of determining which counter/timer generated the interrupt request. Suppose, for example, that only counter/timer 1 has its interrupt request logic enabled via Control Register 1, bit 6. Now if a time out (or other condition capable of generating an interrupt request) occurs at counter/timer 2, and then at counter/timer 3, and then at counter/timer 1, this is how Status register bits will be set:

| Event | Status Register | Comment |
|---|---|---|
| Counter/Timer 2 times out | 0 0 0 0 0 0 1 0 | Counter/Timer 2 interrupts are disabled so there is no interrupt request and Status register bit 7 is 0. |
| Counter/Timer 3 times out | 0 0 0 0 0 1 1 0 | Counter/Timer 3 interrupts are disabled so there is no interrupt request and Status register bit 7 is 0. |
| Counter/Timer 1 times out | 1 0 0 0 0 1 1 1 | Counter/Timer 1 interrupts are enabled so there is an interrupt request and Status register bit 7 is 1. |

An interrupt request is generated only after counter/timer 1 encounters an interrupt condition, but there is no way of reading the Status register in order to find out what happened. All the Status register says is that all three counter/timers have active interrupt conditions and at least one of them has its interrupt request logic enabled. Program logic within the interrupt service routine must therefore take care of arbitrating priorities between the three counter/timer elements of an MC6840 counter/timer. Therefore, **use the MC6840 interrupt enable/disable logic to select the counter/timers that can cause an interrupt request to occur, but make sure that your MC6840 interrupt service routine uses program logic to arbitrate interrupt priorities between the three counter/timer elements.**

Status register bits are reset to 0 by a reset operation ($\overline{\text{RESET}}$ is input low) or by a general initialization (Control Register 1 bit 0 is 1). Logic that resets individual Status register bits has been carefully designed to avoid missing interrupt requests. In order to reset Status register bit 0, 1 or 2 to 0, you must read the Status register and then read the particular counter/timer's Counter register. This may be illustrated for counter/timer 2 as follows:

```
LDA    A,DEV+1    READ STATUS REGISTER CONTENTS
LDX    DEV+4      READ COUNTER 2 CONTENTS AND RESET STATUS REGISTER BIT 1 TO 0
```

By reading the contents of one particular Counter register, you also identify the Status register bit to be reset. If all Status register bits were reset when you read Status register contents, you might miss pending interrupts that you are not currently processing.

You can also reset individual Status register bits by writing to a counter/timer's counter latches, providing the counter/timer's Control register bit 4 is 0 — which results in the counter/timer being initialized when data is written to the counter/timer's latches.

**Let us now look at each of the operating modes in turn. Options are defined by the Control register, whose bits we have already described. Table 9-11 provides an options summary.**

**We will first examine Continuous mode.**

Table 9-11. A Summary of MC6840 Options and Control Register Settings

| Mode | Options | | | | | | | | | | |
|---|---|---|---|---|---|---|---|---|---|---|---|
| | Control Code Options | | | | | | | | | | Special Conditions |
| | Counter | | Initialize | | Output | | Interrupts | | Clock | | |
| | 16-Bit | 8-Bit | $\overline{G}\downarrow$ + R | $\overline{G}\downarrow$ + W + R | Enabled | Disabled | Enabled | Disabled | Internal | External | |
| Continuous | XX0X00XX | XX0X01XX | XX010XXX | XX000XXX | 1X0X0XXX | 0X0X0XXX | X10X0XXX | X00X0XXX | XX0X0X1X | XX0X0X0X | 8-bit counter with L=0 generates 16-bit waveform. N=0 generates square wave output with half clock frequency |
| One Shot | XX1X00XX | XX1X01XX | XX110XXX | XX100XXX | 1X1X0XXX | 0X1X0XXX | X11X0XXX | X01X0XXX | XX1X0X1X | XX1X0X0X | L and M=0 in 8-bit mode or N=0 in 16-bit mode disables output |
| Frequency Comparison | | | | | $\overline{G}$ pulse versus TO. | | | | | | Output signal is not significant in these modes. W is always part of initialization |
| | | | | | $\overline{G}$ less | $\overline{G}$ more | | | | | |
| | XXX010XX | XXX011XX | NA | NA | XX001XXX | XX101XXX | X1X01XXX | X0X01XXX | XXX01X1X | XXX01X0X | |
| Pulse Width Comparison | XXX110XX | XXX111XX | NA | NA | XX011XXX | XX111XXX | X1X11XXX | X0X11XXX | XXX11X1X | XXX11X0X | |

$\overline{G}\downarrow$ refers to ‾‾__ on G input

W refers to a write into counter/timer latches

N is the 16-bit value written into counter/timer latches; it has a high-order byte (M) and a low-order byte (L)

NA means not applicable

**MC6840 CONTINUOUS MODE**

In **Continuous Operating mode with 16-bit counting,** a time out will occur after N+1 active clock transitions; recall that you may select the internal Φ2 clock or the external clock (C). In each case the high-to-low transition of the selected clock is an active transition. If the output signal (O) is disabled, then Continuous Operating mode with 16-bit counting simply generates a time out every N+1 active clock transition. This may be illustrated as follows:

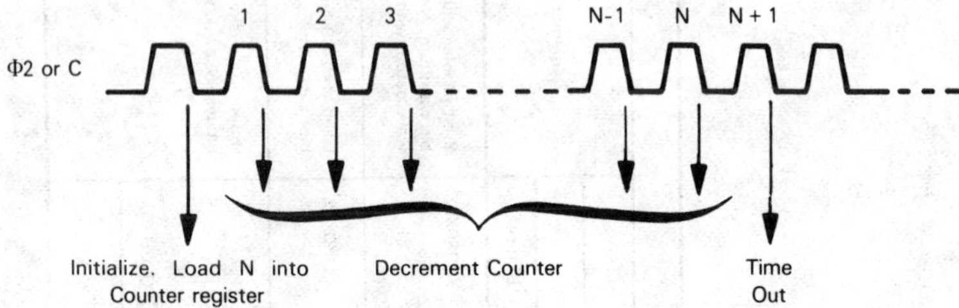


If interrupts are enabled for the counter/timer which times out, then the time out causes an interrupt request to be transmitted to the CPU and appropriate Status register bits are set. If interrupts are not enabled, then the appropriate Status register bit is set, but no interrupt request is transmitted to the CPU.

In Continuous Operating mode with 16-bit counting, if the output signal (O) is enabled, then this signal will change level on each time out, thus creating a square wave. Here is the exact waveform:

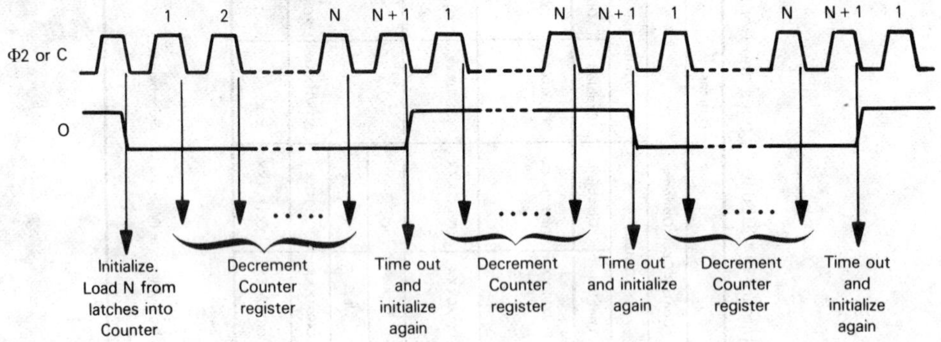


In Continuous mode, observe that following each time out the value held in the counter latches (N in the illustration above) is transferred to the Counter register. If the output signal O is enabled, therefore, the following square wave is generated:

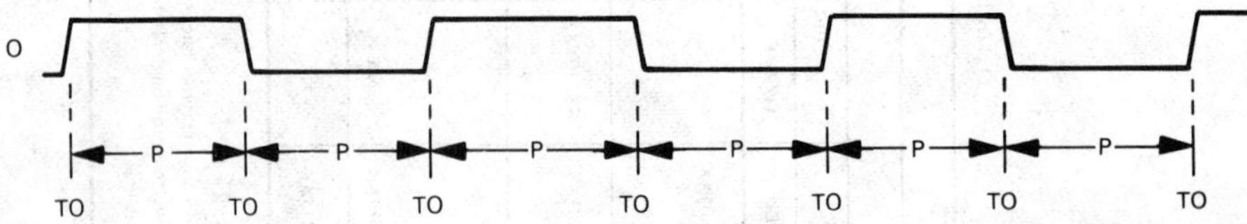


TO identifies a time out. P represents the time interval between time outs; it is equal to (N+1)*t where N is the initial 16-bit value loaded into the Counter register and t is the time interval between active transitions of the clock (Φ2 or C).

In **Continuous Operating mode with 8-bit counting,** the interval to time out is (N+1) * (M+1) clock transitions. where M is the initial Counter register byte and N is the initial low-order Counter register byte. We have already described this time out logic. If the output signal (O) is disabled. then a time out will occur after the appropriate number of active clock transitions. When the time out occurs. an interrupt will be requested via IRQ if interrupts are enabled for this counter/timer by setting its Control register bit 6 to 1. Simultaneously. appropriate Status register bits will be set. If interrupts are disabled. then a Status register bit will be set. but no interrupt request will occur. If the output signal (O) is enabled. then it generates pulses as follows:

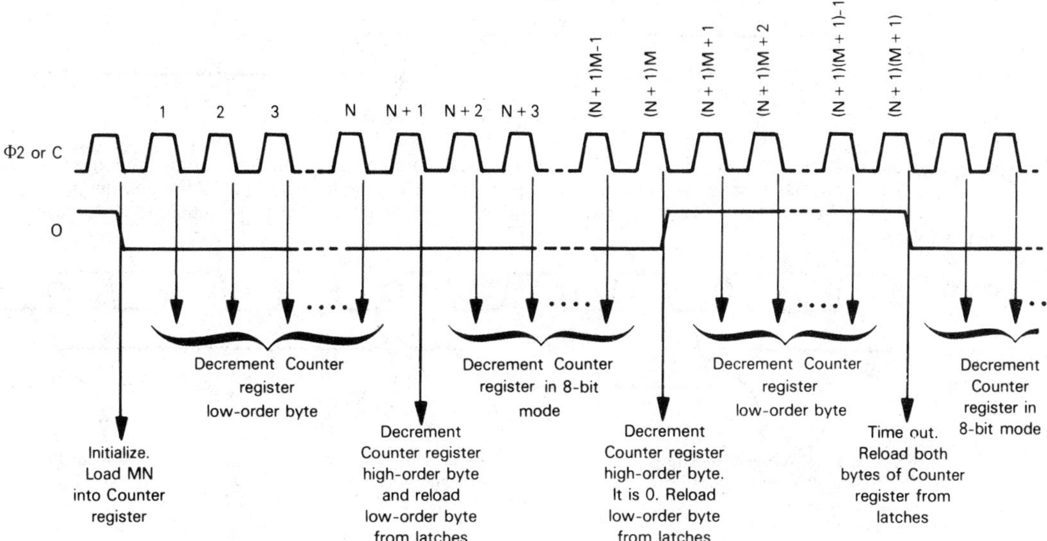


Thus. in 8-bit counting mode you use the low-order Counter register byte to define the pulse width. and you use the high-order Counter register byte to define the interval between pulses. This may be illustrated as follows:

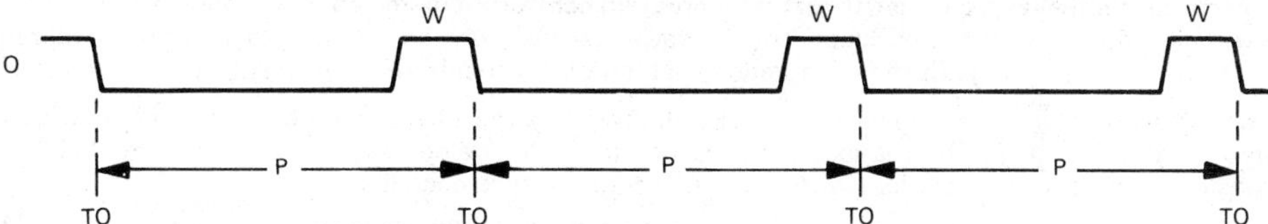


In the illustration above. TO identifies a time out. P represents the time interval between time outs. In 8-bit counting mode P is equal to (M+1) * (N+1) * t. where M is the initial value for the high-order byte of the Counter register. N is the initial value for the low-order byte of the Counter register. and t is the time interval between active transitions of the clock (Φ2 of C). W represents the time interval of the high O pulse. it is equal to N * T. Suppose. for example. $0A0C_{16}$ is the initial value loaded into the Counter register which is being operated in 8-bit counting mode. O will generate a pulse output where the high pulse is $12_{10}$ clock periods long and the frequency is $143_{10}$ clock periods:

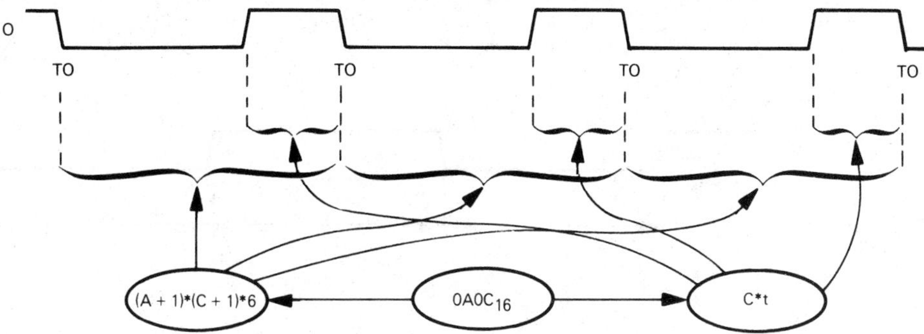

**There are some further options available to you when operating the MC6840 in Continuous mode.**

**MC6840 HARDWARE INITIALIZATION**

**Having loaded the counter latches by writing out data to the appropriate address, there are two ways in which you can initialize the counter.** A high-to-low transition of the Gate (G) input will always start the counter:

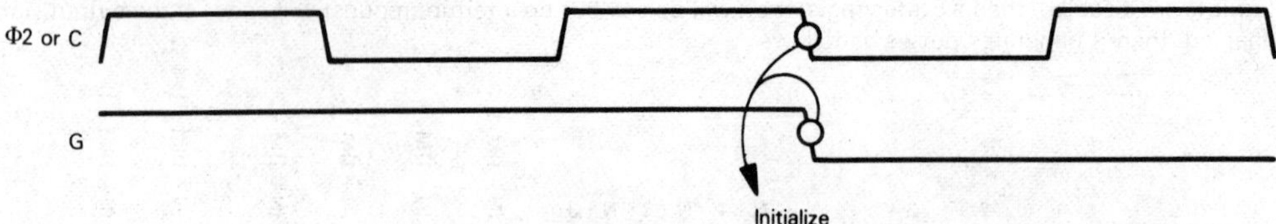


You can always initialize any counter/timer via its Gate input ($\overline{G}$) as illustrated above. Once a counter/timer has been initialized via its Gate input (G), G must remain low. If $\overline{G}$ goes high at any time this will stop the counter/timer immediately. When $\overline{G}$ subsequently makes a high-to-low transition, the counter/timer will be re-initialized. This may be illustrated as follows:

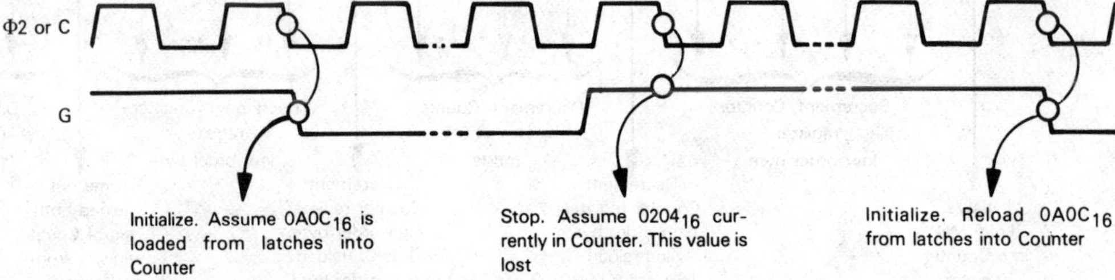


Note carefully that the Gate signal ($\overline{G}$) going high does not suspend counter/timer operations: it stops these operations, then restarts them with a re-initialization.

**You can also initialize a counter/timer under program control.** Programmed initialization is an option, whereas hardware initialization via the Gate input ($\overline{G}$) is always available, whether or not programmed initialization has been selected. You select programmed initialization via bit 4 of the counter/timer element's Control register.

If Control register bit 4 is 0, then the process of writing a 16-bit value to the counter/timer's latches will start the associated counter/timer logic. That is to say, as soon as the 16-bit value has been written to the latches, this value is transferred to the 16-bit Counter register and the counter begins operation.

**MC6840 DIVIDE BY 8 MODE**

**When using counter/timer 3 only, you can select a "divide by 8" mode;** this is done by setting Control Register 3, bit 0 to 1. Now every eighth active clock transition (of either the internal Φ2 clock or the external clock) will be considered active, as illustrated earlier. All other options remain available when operating counter/timer 3 in "divide-by-8" mode. The clock has effectively been slowed down by a factor of 8 — and that is all.

**MC6840 CONTINUOUS 8-BIT COUNTING SQUARE WAVE OPTION**

**When operating in Continuous mode with 8-bit counting, two special options that depend on the initial value loaded into the latches are available.** If the low-order byte of the initial counter value is 0, then, as we might expect, there is no high output signal (O) pulse (assuming that the output signal is enabled); however, on each time out the output signal changes levels to create a square wave that is similar to a 16-bit counting. This may be illustrated as follows:

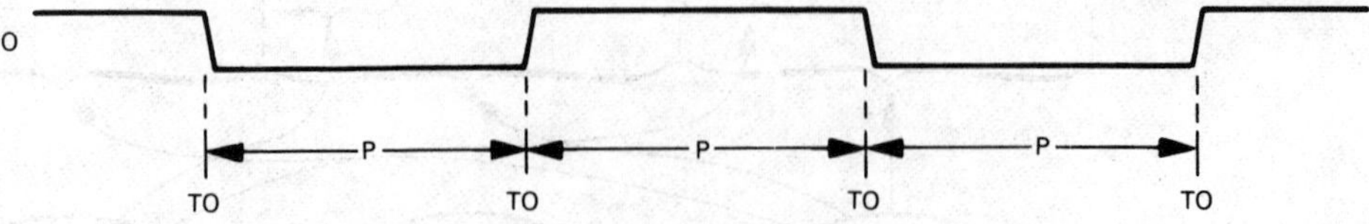

When operating in Continuous mode with either 8-bit or 16-bit counting, if the initial value loaded into the latches is 0, then Counter registers are not decremented and a square wave is output with half the clock frequency. This may be illustrated as follows:

**MC6840 CONTINUOUS MODE WITH 0 INITIAL VALUE**

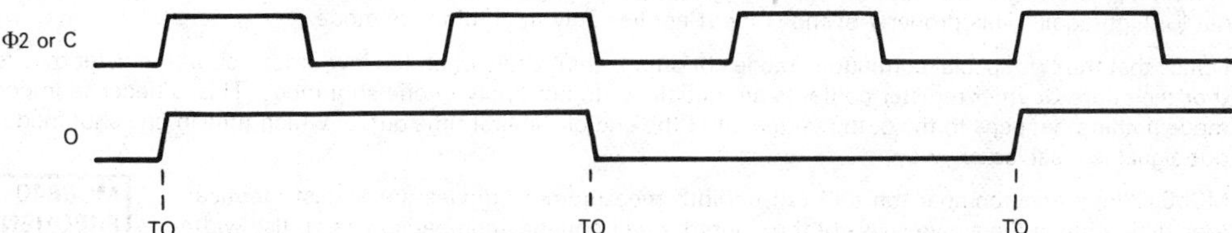


Time outs occur on every transition of O. Since interrupts could not possibly be serviced every other clock pulse, they should be disabled (by having 0 in Control Registers 1 to 6) for any counter/timer element operating in the form illustrated above.

**Note again that in any operating mode, continuous or otherwise, when the external clock (C) is selected, you are in fact counting events, not time.** Although all of our illustrations show a synchronous clock signal with all active transitions evenly spaced, in reality active transitions could be quite random. This may be illustrated as follows:

**MC6840 EVENT COUNTING**

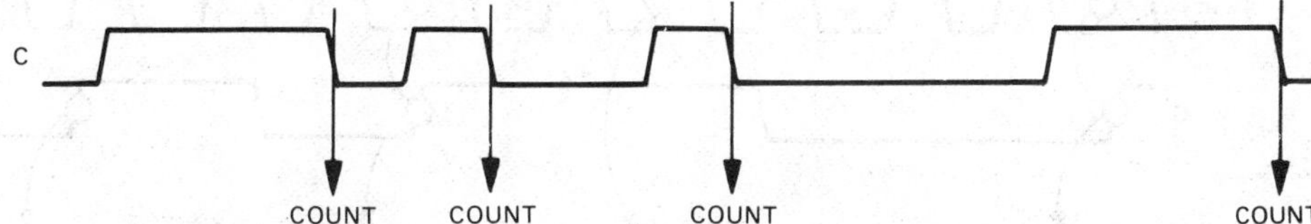


If random timing is present on the external clock (C), then wave forms, if output via the output signal (O), will not be uniform. This is something you may wish to use when counting external events. You could, for example, use continuous operating mode with 8-bit counting to count a fixed number of events, but to signal shortly before this fixed number of events has occurred.

Suppose you wish to count 100 events, with a signal identifying the 90th event. This could be done loading $0909_{16}$ as the initial Counter register value:

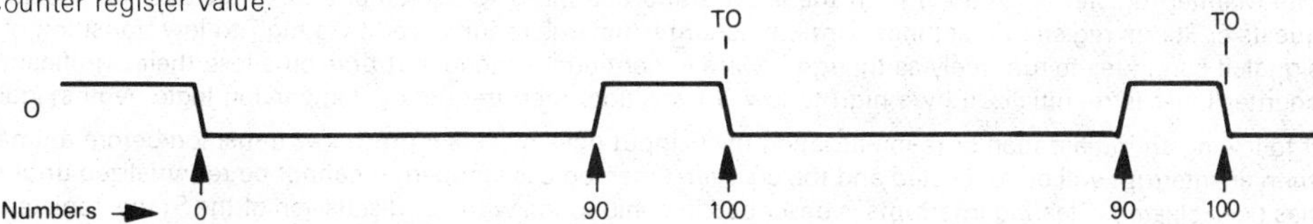


The low-to-high O signal transition must now be used to generate an interrupt request. Time Out (TO) interrupt requests may or may not be disabled.

**Note again that the three sets of counter/timer logic are totally independent of each other. The manner in which you operate one set of counter/timer logic has no bearing whatsoever on the manner in which you operate either of the other two sets of counter/timer logic.**

**The primary difference between one shot mode and continuous mode is that following the first time out the output signal (O), if enabled, is disabled.** In single shot, 16-bit counting mode, the output signal (O) does not make its low-to-high transition until he end of the first clock pulse. This may be illustrated as follows:

**MC6840 ONE SHOT MODE**

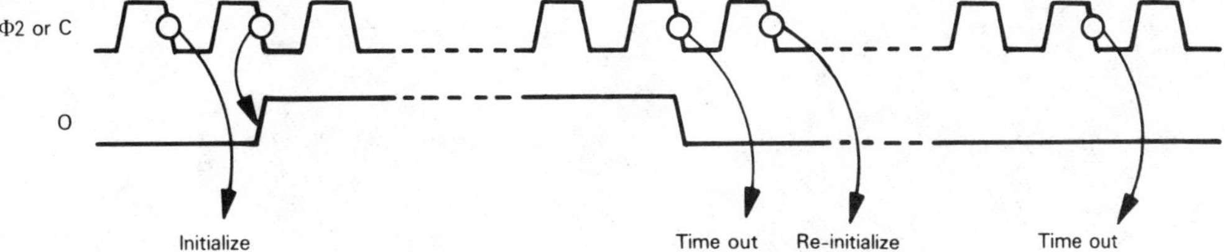

In single shot, 8-bit counting mode, the output signal is simply disabled after the first time out. The counter/timer continues to run and time outs continue to be generated, but the output signal (O) remains disabled until the counter/timer is re-initialized.

Another difference between one shot mode and continuous mode is that in one shot mode you do not stop the counter/timer by inputting the Gate signal ($\overline{G}$) high. Recall that in continuous mode, if the counter/timer has been initialized by inputting a high-to-low Gate ($\overline{G}$) pulse, you can stop the counter/timer at any time by inputting the Gate signal ($\overline{G}$) high again. This property of the $\overline{G}$ input applies only in continuous mode.

Notice that the two special continuous mode conditions that result when the low-order Counter register byte is initially 0 or the entire Counter register contents are initially 0 do not apply in one shot mode. This is because in continuous mode nothing happens to the output signal until the end of the first time out, at which time in one shot mode the output signal is disabled anyway.

**MC6840 FREQUENCY COMPARISON AND PULSE WIDTH MEASUREMENT MODE 5**

MC6840 frequency comparison and pulse width measurement modes are almost identical; they differ only in the active levels of the $\overline{G}$ input. The frequency comparison and pulse width measurement modes both compare the time interval of a pulse, input via the $\overline{G}$ signal, with the time interval to a time out. In frequency comparison mode a high $\overline{G}$ pulse is measured.

You can select frequency comparison mode with Gate pulse by having 001 in control register bits 5, 4, and 3 as described earlier; then an interrupt request will be generated if the G signal makes a high-to-low transition before a time out occurs. This may be illustrated as follows:

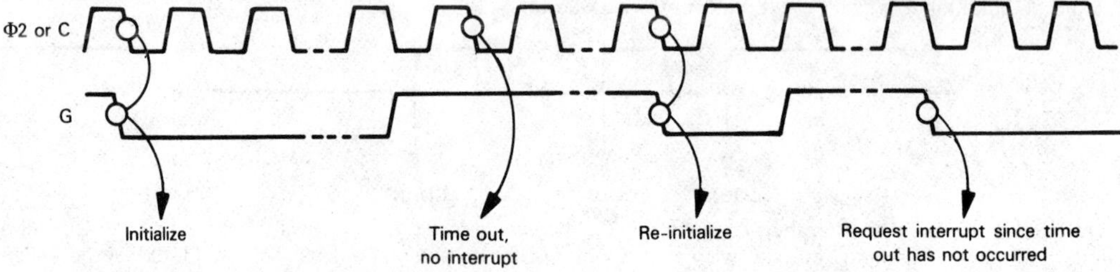


As illustrated above, if the G signal makes its high-to-low transition after the time out occurs, then no interrupt is requested.

The Counter register is reloaded from the latches and continues to decrement, but time outs do cause interrupt requests or Status register bit settings. Until the counter/timer is re-initialized by a high-to-low transition of the $\overline{G}$ input signal, it continues to run freely as though it were in continuous mode, but time outs lose their significance. Once the counter/timer is re-initialized by a high-to-low $\overline{G}$ transition, then frequency comparison logic begins again.

If following an initialization or re-initialization the $\overline{G}$ input does make a high-to-low transition before a time out occurs, then an interrupt will be requested and the counter/timer logic is stopped; it cannot be re-initialized until the interrupt has been cleared. Clearing interrupts is described in conjunction with our discussion of the Status register. Once an interrupt has been cleared, then on the next high-to-low transition of the gate input, counter/timer logic will be re-initialized.

In other words, between the time an interrupt request occurs and the interrupt is serviced, high-to-low transitions of the $\overline{G}$ input are ignored.

Observe that you can select either 8-bit or 16-bit counting modes in order to generate time outs when operating the MC6840 in frequency comparison or pulse width measurement modes.

**You select frequency comparison mode with time out shorter by loading 101 into bits 5, 4, and 3 of the Control register.** Now an interrupt request will occur if the $\overline{G}$ input makes its high-to-low transition after the time out has occurred. We can compare the previous illustration for frequency comparison mode with Gate pulse shorter, using the illustration below for frequency comparison mode with time out shorter:

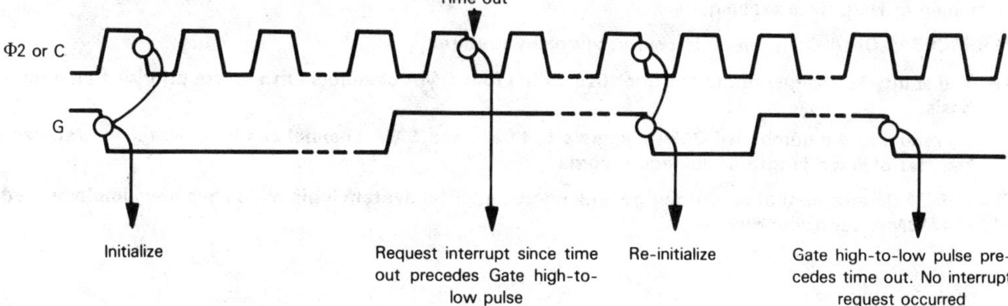


Once again, if an interrupt occurs the counter/timer will stop. It cannot be restarted until the interrupt is cleared and the $\overline{G}$ input makes a high-to-low transition.

**Pulse width comparison modes are identical to frequency comparison modes, with the exception that once a counter/timer is operating, low-to-high transitions of the gate input are active. The frequency comparison modes may therefore be reproduced for pulse width comparison equivalents, as follows.**

First, here is pulse width comparison mode with Gate pulse shorter:

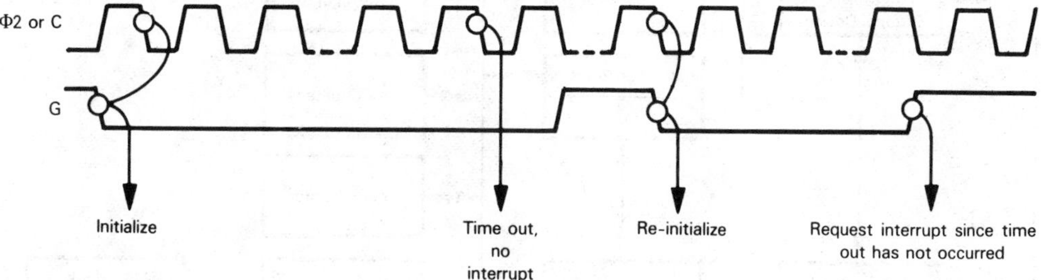


Next, here is pulse width comparison mode with time out shorter:

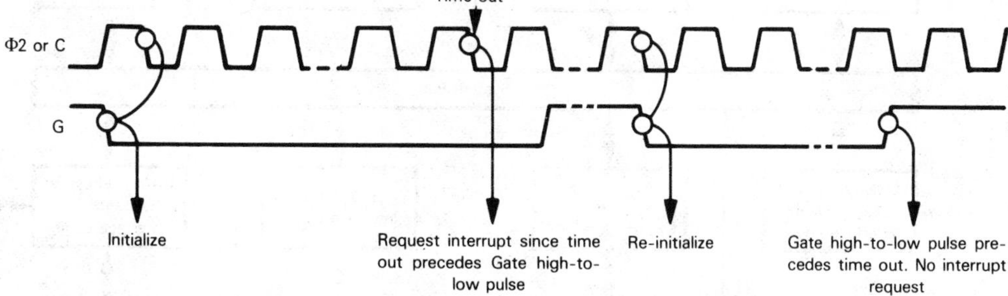


Notice that in pulse width comparison mode, initialization and re-initialization require a high-to-low $\overline{G}$ transition, although the end of the $\overline{G}$ pulse is marked by a low-to-high $\overline{G}$ transition.

# THE MC6844 DIRECT MEMORY ACCESS CONTROLLER

**The MC6844 Direct Memory Access controller provides MC6800-based microcomputer systems with logic to support four direct memory access channels. This device has been designed to work with the unique timing logic of MC6800 and MCS6500 microcomputer systems; it should therefore be used with MC6800 and MCS6500 microcomputer systems only. That is why the MC6844 is described in this chapter rather than in Volume 3.**

From our discussion of the MC6800 CPU, recall that this microprocessor allows its system clock to be stretched so that direct memory access operations may be intermingled with normal instruction execution. Alternatively, the MC6800 may be put into a Halt state during which the CPU disconnects itself from the system busses; external logic then accesses memory by mimicking CPU signals on the Address, Data and Control Busses. Logic of the MC6844 DMA controller allows you to perform Direct Memory Access operations using either clock stretching or Halt state techniques.

The MC6844 DMA Controller has two noteworthy features:

1) The ability to assign permanent priorities to the four DMA channels or to rotate priorities on a round-robin basis.

2) By reducing the number of DMA channels to three, one DMA channel can be used for the recursive DMA transfer of fixed length or chained records.

Figure 9-31 illustrates that part of our general microcomputer system logic which has been implemented on the MC6844 DMA controller device.

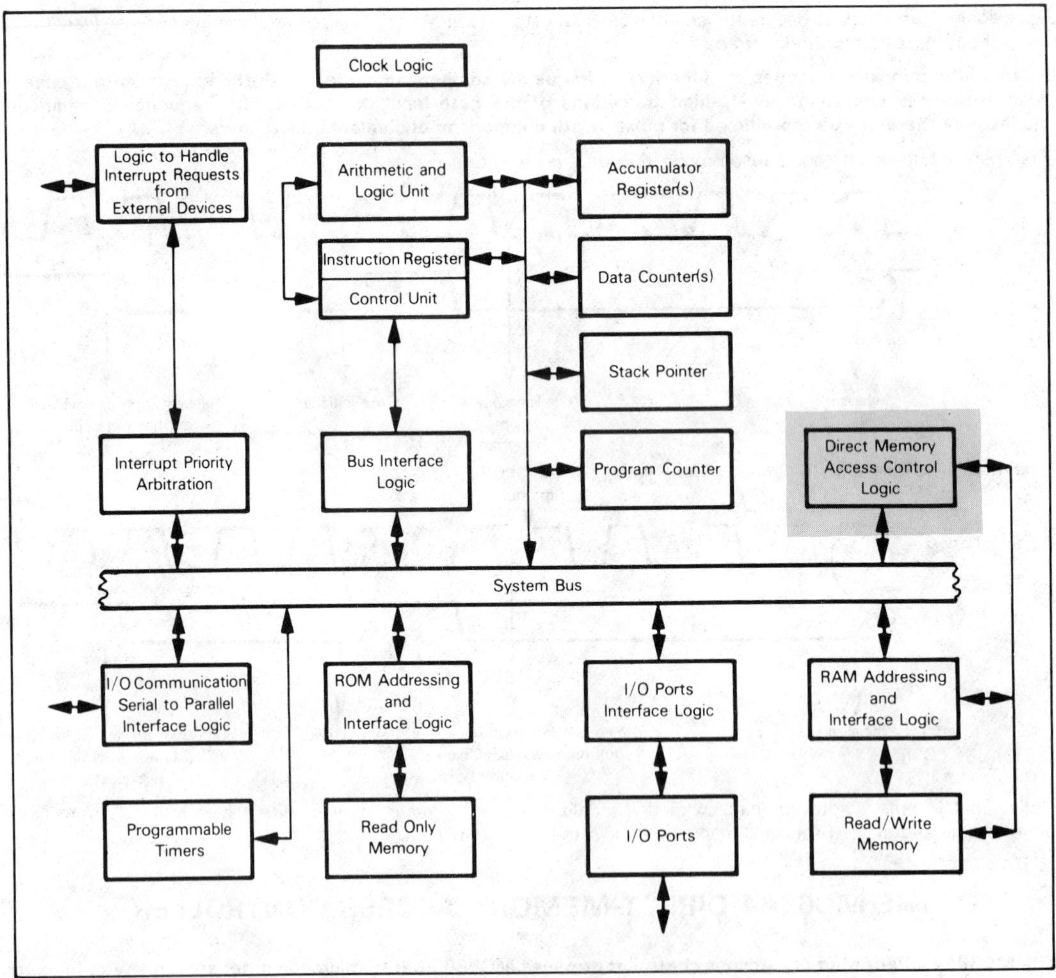


Figure 9-31. Logic of the MC6844 DMA Controller

The MC6844 DMA controller chip is fabricated using N-channel silicon gate MOS technology. It is packaged as a 40-pin ceramic or plastic DIP. All signals are TTL-compatible.

## MC6844 DMA CONTROLLER PINS AND SIGNALS

**Figure 9-32 summarizes MC6844 DMA pins and signals. Many of these signals have MC6800 counterparts; therefore we will describe them within the context of a general MC6844 device discussion.**

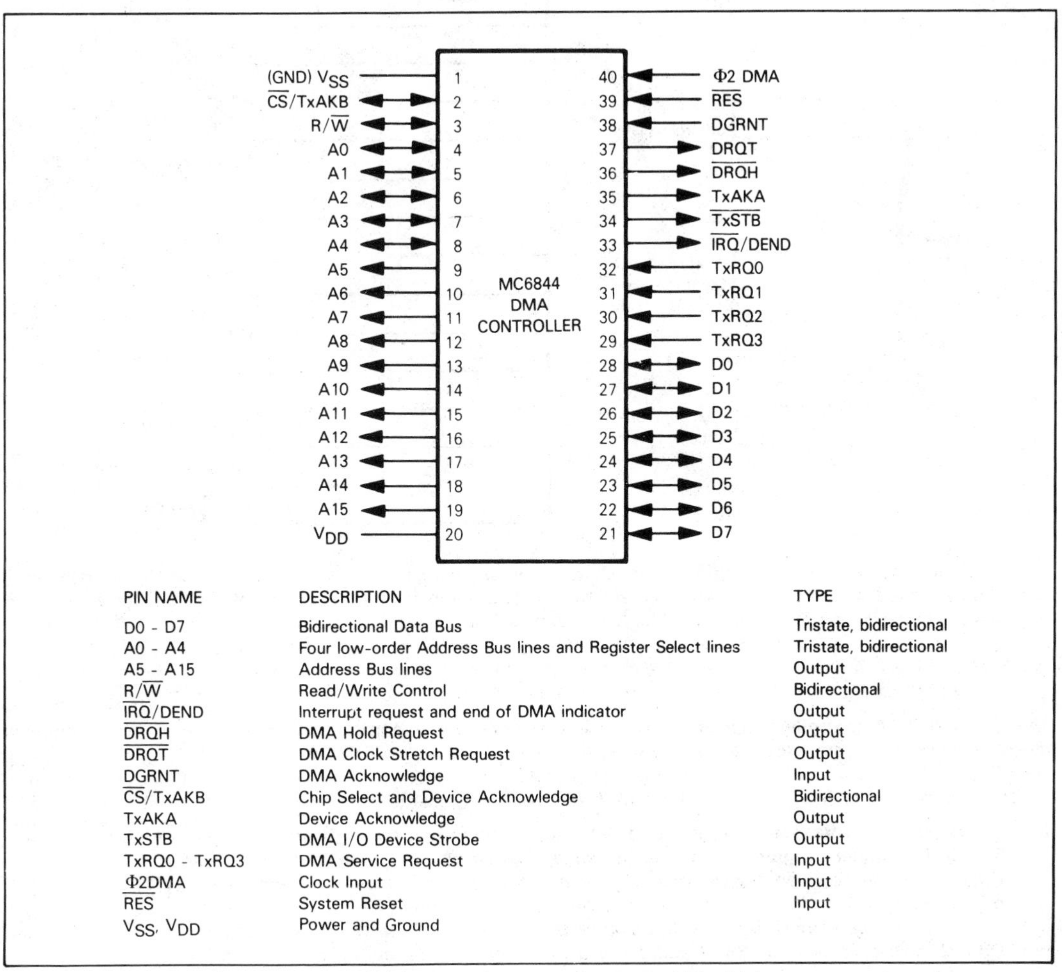


| PIN NAME | DESCRIPTION | TYPE |
|---|---|---|
| D0 - D7 | Bidirectional Data Bus | Tristate, bidirectional |
| A0 - A4 | Four low-order Address Bus lines and Register Select lines | Tristate, bidirectional |
| A5 - A15 | Address Bus lines | Output |
| R/$\overline{W}$ | Read/Write Control | Bidirectional |
| $\overline{IRQ}$/DEND | Interrupt request and end of DMA indicator | Output |
| $\overline{DRQH}$ | DMA Hold Request | Output |
| $\overline{DRQT}$ | DMA Clock Stretch Request | Output |
| DGRNT | DMA Acknowledge | Input |
| $\overline{CS}$/TxAKB | Chip Select and Device Acknowledge | Bidirectional |
| TxAKA | Device Acknowledge | Output |
| TxSTB | DMA I/O Device Strobe | Output |
| TxRQ0 - TxRQ3 | DMA Service Request | Input |
| Φ2DMA | Clock Input | Input |
| $\overline{RES}$ | System Reset | Input |
| $V_{SS}$, $V_{DD}$ | Power and Ground | |

Figure 9-32. MC6844 DMA Controller Signals and Pin Assignments

## MC6844 ADDRESSABLE REGISTERS

**Logic associated with each DMA channel consists of a 16-bit Address register, a 16-bit Byte Count register and an 8-bit Control register. There are three additional registers which are shared by the four DMA channels. These are a Priority Control register, an Interrupt Control register and a Data Chain Definition register.** These may be illustrated as follows:

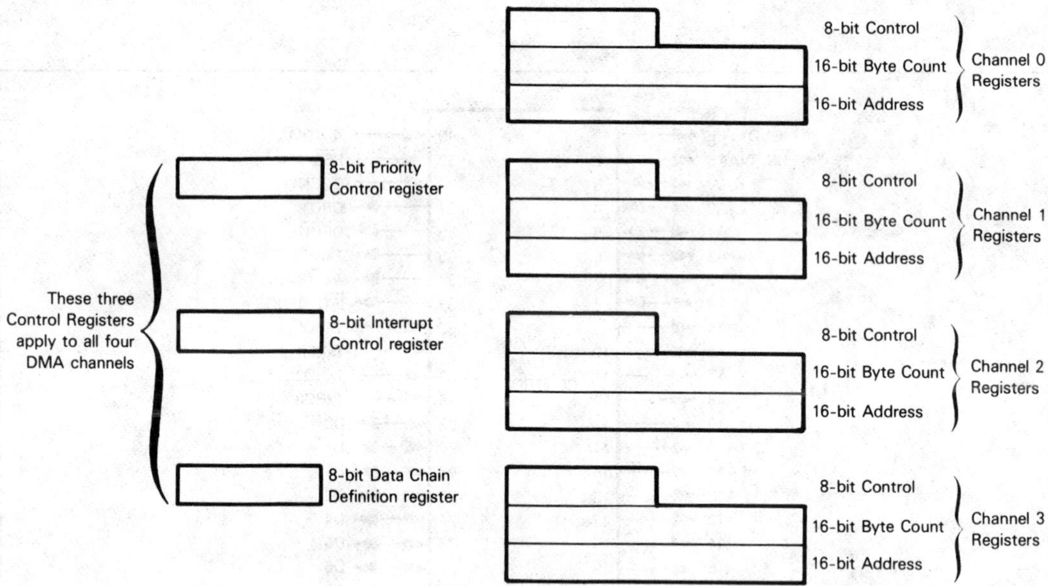


The transfer of any block of data via DMA begins with an initial memory address. byte count and DMA mode being specified via the registers illustrated above. As each byte of data is transferred. the method of data transfer is controlled by options selected via the Control register. The Address register identifies the memory location which will be accessed during the DMA transfer. Address register contents may either be incremented or decremented following each DMA transfer. The Byte Count register contents are always decremented following each data transfer. and the DMA operation ends when the Byte Count register contents reach 0.

**The MC6844 DMA controller is accessed by the CPU under program control as 23 memory locations. Individual memory locations are selected via address lines A0 - A4, as defined in Table 9-12.** When writing into or reading out of 16-bit registers. you will usually use the LDX and STX instruction: that is to say. the most efficient method of transferring 16-bit data between the CPU and MC6844 DMA controller is via the CPU Index register.

**MC6844 DMAC DATA BUS**

**MC6844 DMAC ADDRESS BUS**

**Note carefully that addresses given in Table 9-12 apply only when the CPU accesses the MC6844 DMAC under program control to initialize a DMA transfer or to monitor DMA operations.** These memory addresses have no significance to actual DMA logic. Furthermore. the Data Bus connection to the MC6844 DMA controller plays no part during a DMA operation. **Data is transferred between the CPU and the MC6844 DMAC via the Data Bus (D0 - D7) only while the CPU is accessing MC6844 addressable locations under program control.** Actual data transfers between an external device and memory occur via the microcomputer system Data Bus. completely bypassing the Data Bus connection to the MC6844 DMA device. However. during DMA data transfers. addresses and control signals are output from the MC6844 DMAC to the System Bus via the Address Bus lines A0 - A15 and appropriate control signal outputs. This is standard DMA logic. If you do not understand these DMA operations. see the discussion of direct memory access given in Volume 1 before proceeding further with this description of the MC6844 DMAC device.

**MC6844 DMAC DEVICE SELECT**

The CPU may access the MC6844 DMAC under program control at any time by simply executing an instruction which references one of the 23 memory addresses set aside for the MC6844 DMAC device. The MC6844 DMAC is selected by a low $\overline{CS}$ pulse. This low pulse must be generated by appropriately decoding Address Bus lines A5 through A15. together with VMA. VMA must contribute to MC6844 device select logic to guarantee that spurious selections do not occur during a DMA transfer or while the Address Bus is floated. In this context it is important that only a VMA signal output by the

MC6800 CPU be used by MC6844 device select logic. During a DMA operation, the MC6844 DMAC generates its own VMA equivalent via TxSTB. TxSTB must be excluded from MC6844 device select logic. Here is one possibility:

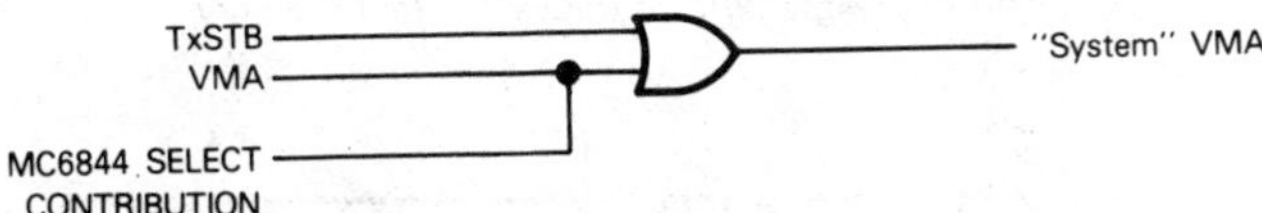


**Depending on the number of active MC6844 DMA channels, $\overline{CS}$ may become a bidirectional signal; TxAKB is output via the same pin as the $\overline{CS}$ input. In this case remember that $\overline{CS}$ must be generated as an open collector gate output.**

We will discuss the individual MC6844 addressable locations and the way in which you will program them after describing MC6844 operating modes.

Table 9-12. MC6844 DMAC Register Addresses

| Address | | | | | | Accessed Location |
|---|---|---|---|---|---|---|
| A4 | A3 | A2 | A1 | A0 | Label | |
| 0 | 0 | 0 | 0 | 0 | DEV | Channel 0 Address register, high-order byte |
| 0 | 0 | 0 | 0 | 1 | DEV + 1 | Channel 0 Address register, low-order byte |
| 0 | 0 | 0 | 1 | 0 | DEV + 2 | Channel 0 Byte Count register, high-order byte |
| 0 | 0 | 0 | 1 | 1 | DEV + 3 | Channel 0 Byte Count register, low-order byte |
| 0 | 0 | 1 | 0 | 0 | DEV + 4 | Channel 1 Address register, high-order byte |
| 0 | 0 | 1 | 0 | 1 | DEV + 5 | Channel 1 Address register, low-order byte |
| 0 | 0 | 1 | 1 | 0 | DEV + 6 | Channel 1 Byte Count register, high-order byte |
| 0 | 0 | 1 | 1 | 1 | DEV + 7 | Channel 1 Byte Count register, low-order byte |
| 0 | 1 | 0 | 0 | 0 | DEV + 8 | Channel 2 Address register, high-order byte |
| 0 | 1 | 0 | 0 | 1 | DEV + 9 | Channel 2 Address register, low-order byte |
| 0 | 1 | 0 | 1 | 0 | DEV + A | Channel 2 Byte Count register, high-order byte |
| 0 | 1 | 0 | 1 | 1 | DEV + B | Channel 2 Byte Count register, low-order byte |
| 0 | 1 | 1 | 0 | 0 | DEV + C | Channel 3 Address register, high-order byte |
| 0 | 1 | 1 | 0 | 1 | DEV + D | Channel 3 Address register, low-order byte |
| 0 | 1 | 1 | 1 | 0 | DEV + E | Channel 3 Byte Count register, high-order byte |
| 0 | 1 | 1 | 1 | 1 | DEV + F | Channel 3 Byte Count register, low-order byte |
| 1 | 0 | 0 | 0 | 0 | DEV + 10 | Channel 0 Control register |
| 1 | 0 | 0 | 0 | 1 | DEV + 11 | Channel 1 Control register |
| 1 | 0 | 0 | 1 | 0 | DEV + 12 | Channel 2 Control register |
| 1 | 0 | 0 | 1 | 1 | DEV + 13 | Channel 3 Control register |
| 1 | 0 | 1 | 0 | 0 | DEV + 14 | Priority Control register |
| 1 | 0 | 1 | 0 | 1 | DEV + 15 | Interrupt Control register |
| 1 | 0 | 1 | 1 | 0 | DEV + 16 | Data Chain Control register |

## MC6844 DMA TRANSFER MODES

**You can select, under program control, one of three modes via which DMA transfers will occur for each of the four MC6844 DMA channels. You can mix and match separate and distinct modes for each of the four channels in any way since each channel has its own Control register.**

We will begin our discussion of modes by looking at all three modes superficially before examining each one in detail.

**First there is Three-State Control, Cycle Stealing mode.** In this mode the MC6800 CPU clock is stretched with Φ2 low while the MC6844 device transfers a single byte of data via direct memory access. This may be illustrated as follows:

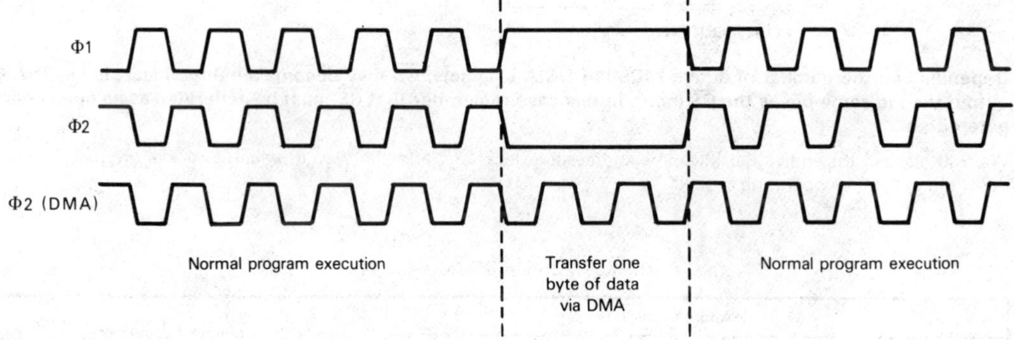


We have discussed clock stretching logic of the MC6800 microcomputer earlier in this chapter.

**The second and third MC6844 DMA transfer modes both force the MC6800 CPU into a Halt state** which floats the System Bus. **The Halt state may last long enough for a single byte of data to be transferred** via direct memory access, in which case **the mode is referred to as Halt, Steal mode.** This may be illustrated as follows:

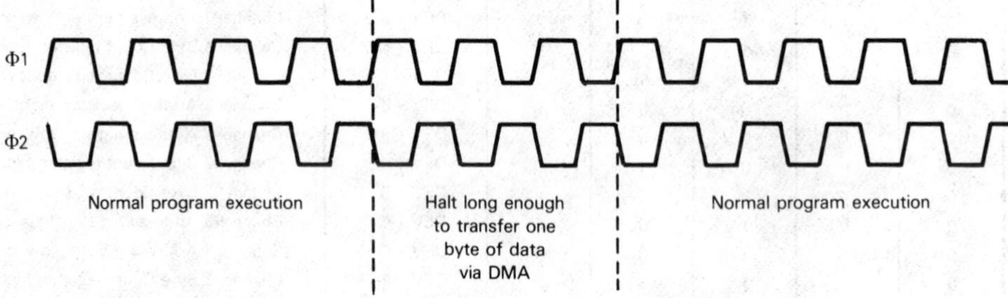


**The Halt state may be maintained** for as long as it takes to transfer an entire block of data, that is to say, **until a channel's Byte Count register decrements to 0. This is referred to as Halt Burst mode.**

## MC6844 DMAC THREE-STATE CONTROL, CYCLE STEALING MODE

**Let us now look at the different DMA modes in detail beginning with the three-state control cycle stealing mode. Timing for this mode is given in Figure 9-33 and appropriate pin connections are given in Figure 9-34.**

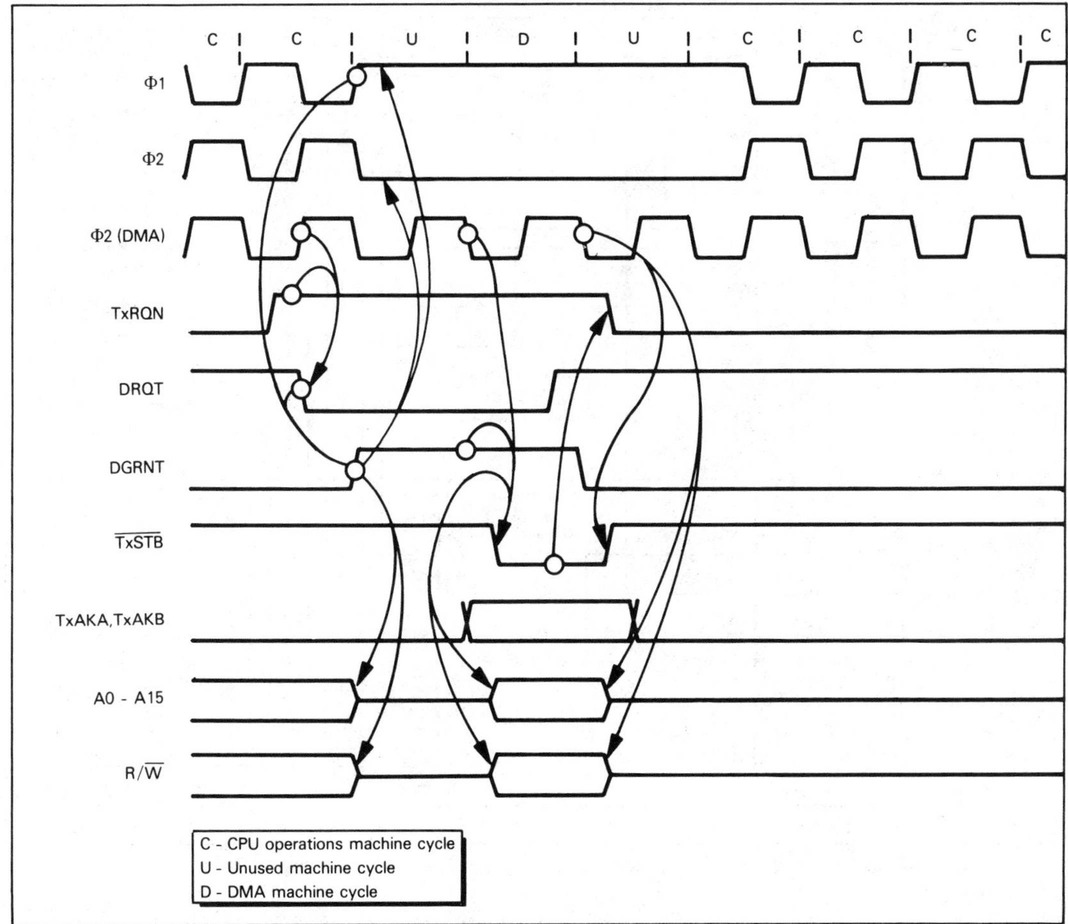


Figure 9-33. Timing for Three State Control, Cycle Stealing Direct Memory Access with the MC6844

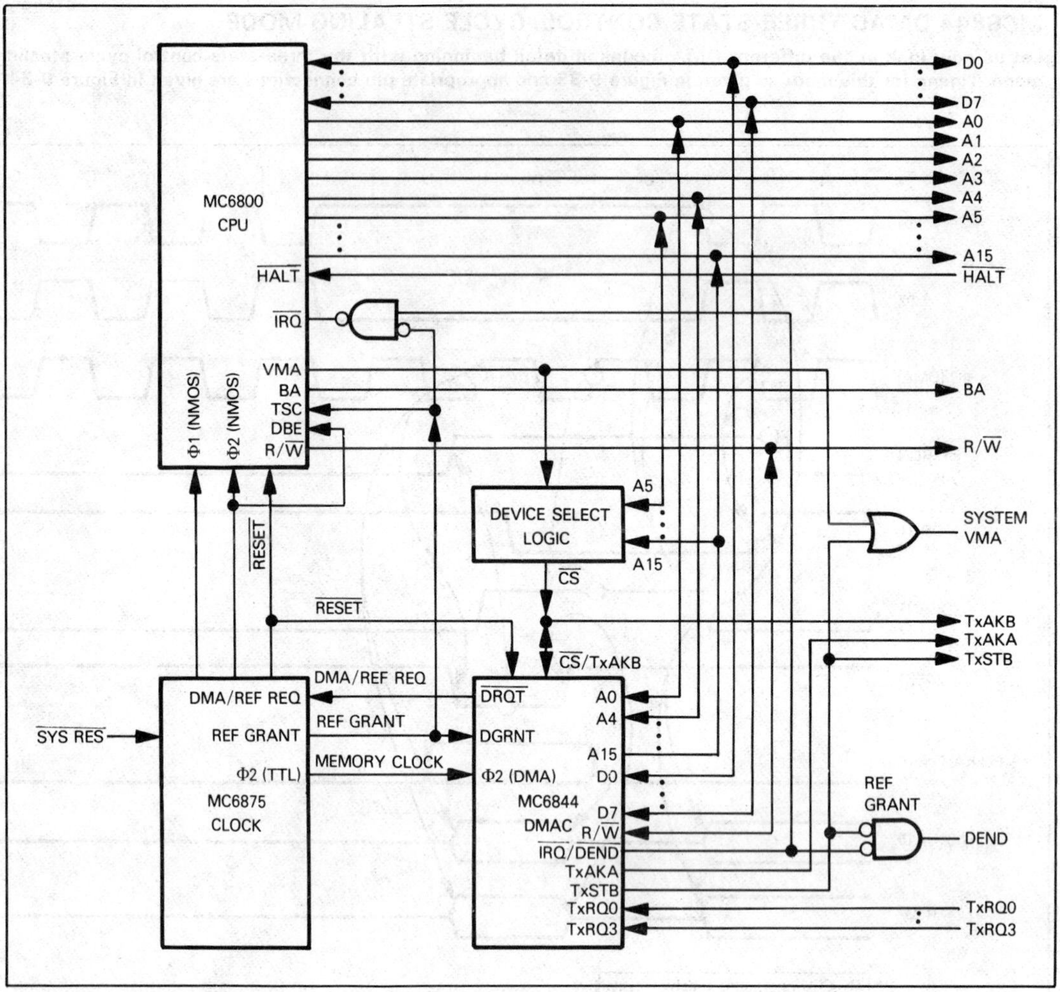

Figure 9-34. An MC6844 DMAC Connected for Three State Control, Cycle Stealing Direct Memory Access

**MC6844 DMAC TxRON, DQRT DGRNT SIGNALS**

**MC6844 DMAC Φ2 DMA CLOCK**

A DMA operation begins when an external device makes a DMA access request by inputting a high signal via one of the four inputs TxRQ0 through TxRQ3. This input to the MC6844 DMAC may be asynchronous. The MC6844 responds by outputting DRQT low. This low output must be connected to the MC6875 clock CMA/REF REQ input. This connection causes the MC6875 clock device to stretch the Φ1 and Φ2 clocks at the end of the next machine cycle — with Φ1 high and Φ2 low. The onset of the stretched clocks is identified by the MC6875 device outputting REF GRANT high. This signal must be input to the MC6844 DGRNT pin. The DMA data transfer now occurs, taking three machine cycles to transfer one byte of data. Machine cycles are timed by Φ2 DMA, which is the memory clock output of the MC6875 device. Recall that when the MC6875 clock device receives a low input via DMA/REF REQ it does not stretch the memory clock output. The MC6844 DMAC needs a Φ2 DMA input only while a DMA data transfer is in progress. Φ2 DMA is therefore frequently the AND of MEMORY CLOCK and REF GRANT:

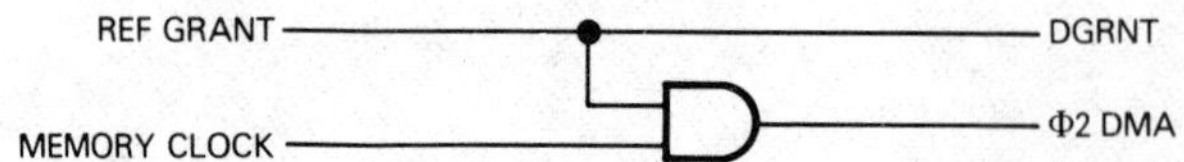

As soon as clock stretching begins, the MC6800 CPU must float the System Bus. This may be done by inputting the REF GRANT signal to the MC6800 TSC pin as well as to the MC6844 DGRNT pin. Now REF GRANT input to TSC will cause the MC6800 CPU to float its Address Bus and three-state control signals. If DBE is connected to $\Phi 2$, as is usually the case, then the low $\Phi 2$ signal will automatically cause the MC6800 CPU to float the Data Bus. Now as soon as REF GRANT goes high, the MC6800 CPU is disconnected from the System Bus and the MC6844 DMAC can become bus master.

**MC6844 DMAC TxAKA AND TxAKB SIGNALS**

The MC6844 DMAC takes control of the System Bus for three machine cycles, during which it transfers a single byte of data. The first and third machine cycles represent setup time. The actual DMA transfer occurs during the second machine cycle. For the memory end of the DMA transfer, the MC6844 DMAC outputs a memory address via the Address Bus. For the I/O device end of the DMA transfer, the DMAC identifies the direct memory access channel being acknowledged via the output signals TxAKA and TxAKB, as follows:

| TxAKB | TxAKA | Acknowledged |
|---|---|---|
| 0 | 0 | TxRQ0 |
| 0 | 1 | TxRQ1 |
| 1 | 0 | TxRQ2 |
| 1 | 1 | TxRQ3 |

Timing for signals output by the MC6844 DMAC conform to normal MC6800 System Bus timing for a memory read or memory write operation.

**MC6844 DMAC TxSTB SIGNAL**

The low $\overline{\text{TxSTB}}$ pulse substitutes for VMA at the memory and I/O device ends of the DMA transfer. The direction of the DMA transfer is defined by the level of the R/$\overline{\text{W}}$ signal; the interpretation of this signal conforms to normal memory read and write operations:

R/$\overline{\text{W}}$ low causes data to flow from the I/O device to memory.

R/$\overline{\text{W}}$ high causes data to flow from memory to the I/O device.

Data may flow freely across the Data Bus during the direct memory access operation, since both the MC6800 CPU and the MC6844 DMAC are disconnected from the Data Bus at this time.

**MC6844 DMAC $\overline{\text{IRQ}}$/$\overline{\text{DEND}}$ SIGNAL**

As each byte of data is transferred, the Byte Count register contents for the selected DMA channel are decremented; but the Address register contents may be either incremented or decremented, depending on the Control register option selected. When the Byte Count register contents decrement to 0, a low pulse is output via $\overline{\text{IRQ}}$/$\overline{\text{DEND}}$. This pulse can be used to generate an interrupt at the MC6800 CPU and/or it may be used to tell the external device that the current data transfer has gone to completion.

The interrupt request output $\overline{\text{IRQ}}$/$\overline{\text{DEND}}$ will pulse low when the Byte Count register decrements to 0 only if interrupts have been enabled for this DMA channel via its Interrupt Control register. If interrupts have been enabled, it is a good idea to guard against spurious interrupt requests by conditioning $\overline{\text{IRQ}}$/$\overline{\text{DEND}}$ with the DGRNT high pulse. The interrupt request input to the MC6800 CPU should be an open collector signal generated as follows:

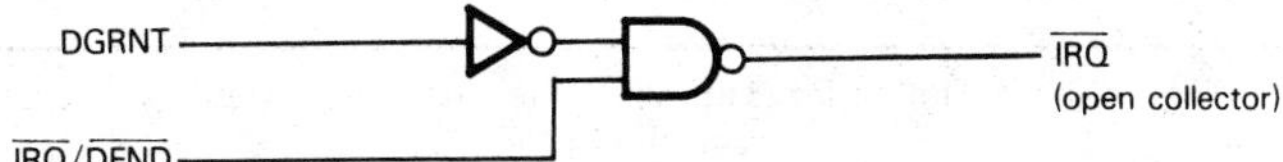


The $\overline{\text{DEND}}$ signal output to I/O devices may be ANDed with REF GRANT or with TxSTB. An AND with TxSTB is illustrated in Figure 9-34.

Assuming that the acknowledged DMA channel is transferring data at less than maximum speed, it must use the low TxSTB strobe to remove its TxRQN high request. If the channel keeps its TxRQN DMA request active, then the next DMA transfer will occur during the next machine cycle. Using Three-State Control, cycle stealing direct memory access, therefore, it is possible to transfer a byte of data during every machine cycle; however, each machine cycle will have its length increased by three machine cycles. Thus, any executing program will be reduced to executing at one quarter of its normal execution speed.

## MC6844 DMAC HALT MODES

**The next DMA operating mode we are going to look at is the Halt Cycle Stealing mode.** In this mode the CPU is halted for three machine cycles, during which a single byte of data is transferred. Timing is illustrated in Figure 9-35 and appropriate pin connections are illustrated in Figure 9-36.

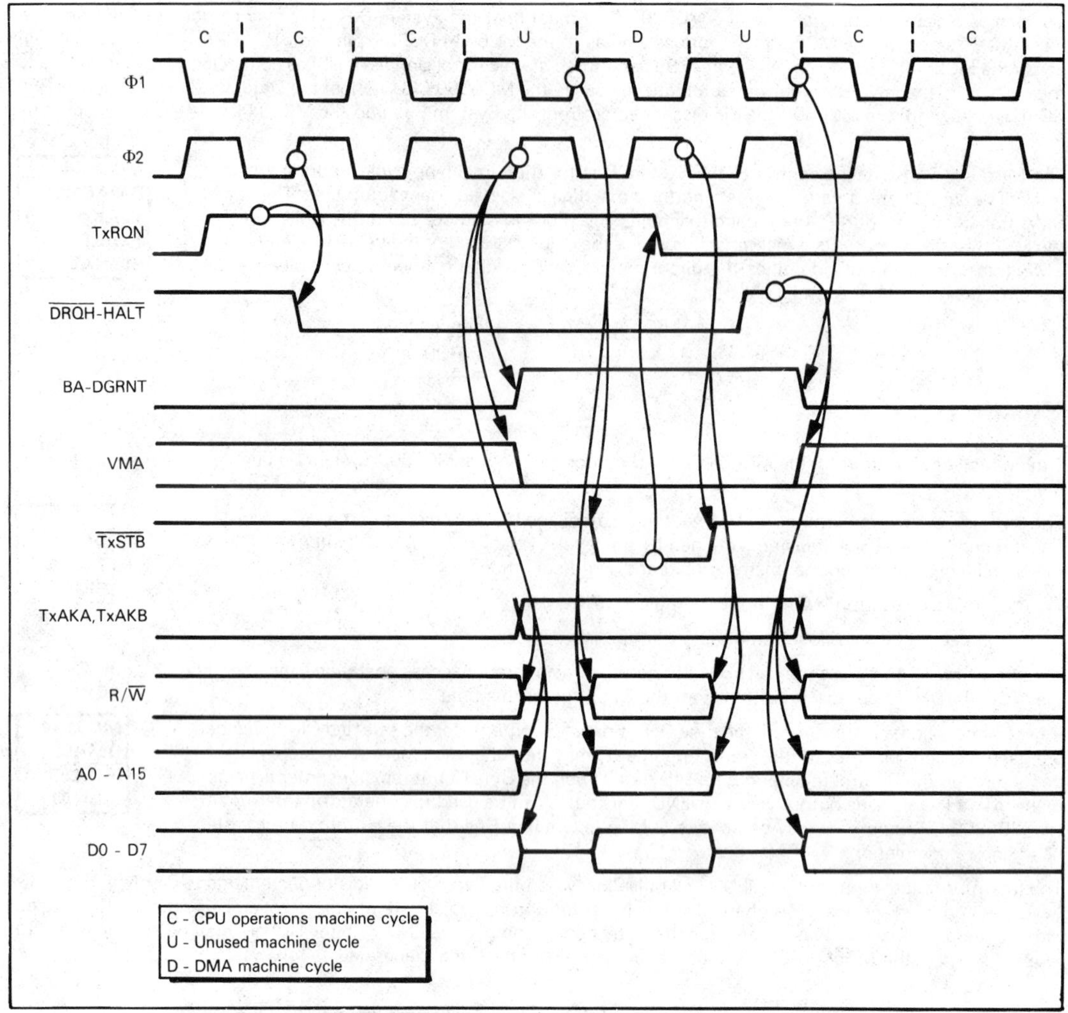


Figure 9-35. Timing for Halt, Cycle Stealing Direct Memory Access with the MC6844

**MC6844 DMAC TxR0 - TxR3 SIGNALS**

**MC6844 DMAC $\overline{DRQH}$ SIGNAL**

A DMA transfer is initiated by one of the four DMA request signals TxR0 through TxR3 going high. These signals are sampled on the rising edge of Φ2. The MC6844 responds to a high DMA transfer request by outputting $\overline{DRQH}$ low. In the Halt, Cycle Stealing mode, $\overline{DRQH}$ must be input as the MC6800 CPU halt request. As explained earlier in this chapter, when a low input occurs at HALT, the MC6800 CPU completes executing its current instruction, then enters a Halt state. During the Halt state, VMA is output low while the Address and Data Busses, along with the R/$\overline{W}$ control signal, are floated. In Figure 9-35 the Halt state is shown beginning one full machine cycle after $\overline{DRQH}$ goes low.

**MC6844 DMAC DGRNT, TxSTB, TxAKA AND TxAKB SIGNALS**

The MC6800 CPU indicates the onset of the Halt state by outputting BA high. This output becomes the DGRNT input to the MC6844. Once DGRNT goes high, the MC6844 assumes control of the System Bus. TxSTB is pulsed low as a substitute for the VMA signal. The address of the memory location to be accessed during the DMA transfer is output on the Address Bus along with the R/$\overline{W}$, which indicates the direction of the DMA data transfer (as described for three-state control cycle stealing mode). The DMA channel being acknowledged is identified via the TxAKA and TxAKB signals, which are decoded as described earlier.

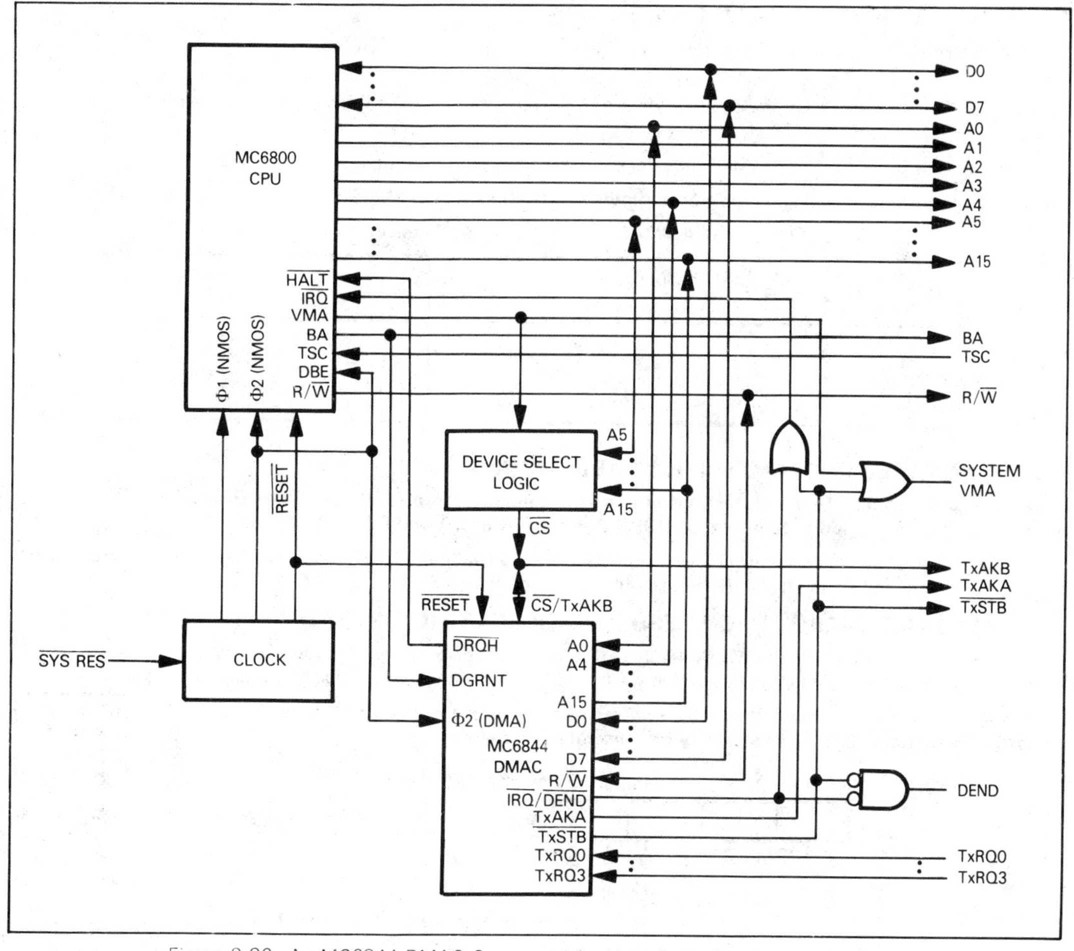


Figure 9-36. An MC6844 DMAC Connected for Halt, Cycle Stealing or Halt Burst Direct Memory Access

**MC6844 DMAC TxSTB SIGNAL**

The VMA signal used by the system must now be the OR of VMA and TxSTB. The external device whose DMA request has been acknowledged must detect the low TxSTB signal and use it to reset its DMA request. If the DMA request is still active after a single byte of data has been transferred via DMA, then a single instruction will be executed before the next byte of data is transferred via direct memory access. One instruction will be executed even if TxRQN remains high, because in Halt Cycle Stealing mode the MC6844 will return its DRQH signal high as soon as a single byte of data has been transferred via direct memory access. This will free the CPU to execute another instruction, and while this new instruction is being executed the whole timing process illustrated in Figure 9-35 will begin again.

When the Byte Count register contents decrement to 0, the IRQ/DEND signal will output low. As was the case for Three-State Control Cycle Stealing mode, this signal can be used to request an interrupt and/or to identify the end of a data transfer block to external logic. It is a good idea to condition interrupt requests and DEND outputs with TxSTB in order to avoid generating spurious signals.

**The third and last MC6844 DMA mode is the Halt Burst mode.** This differs from Halt Cycle Stealing mode in that once a Halt condition has been initiated, it is maintained while data is transferred via direct memory access until the Byte Count register has decremented to 0. Thus, Halt Burst mode timing will differ from Figure 9-35 only in that DRQH will remain low until the channel's Byte Count register decrements to 0. This will happen irrespective of the level on the DMA request line TxRQN. Note that, as illustrated in Figure 9-35, one byte of data will be transferred via direct memory access in three machine cycles, even when operating in Halt Burst mode. Pin connections for Halt Burst mode are as illustrated in Figure 9-36.

## COMPARING MC6844 DMAC MODES

You will use Three-State Control. Cycle Stealing mode when program execution time is critical but data transfer rates are not.

You will use Halt. Cycle Stealing mode when data transfer rates are not critical, program execution time is important and you do not have an MC6875 clock device.

You will use Halt Burst mode when data transfer rates are critical and program execution time is not.

Table 9-13 summarizes maximum data transfer rates for the three modes. A μsec machine cycle time is assumed.

Table 9-13. MC6844 DMAC Modes' Response Times and Transfer Rates

| Mode | Response Time (μsec) | Maximum Transfer Rate KHz |
|---|---|---|
| TSC Steal | 2.5 to 3.5 | 250 |
| Halt Steal | 3.5 to 15.5 | 200 - 67 |
| Halt Burst | 2.5 to 3.5 | 1000 |

## USING AN MC6844 DMAC WITH MIXED MODES

**If you are going to use Three-State Control and Halt modes with a single MC6844 DMAC device, the only special precaution needed is to generate DGRNT as the OR of BA and REF GRANT.**

The Three-State Control and Halt modes have separate DMA request lines. DRQT and DRQH, respectively; therefore no special logic is needed to handle DMA requests using mixed modes.

## THE MC6844 CONTROL REGISTERS AND OPERATING OPTIONS

As summarized in Table 9-12, **the MC6844 DMAC has a number of programmable Control registers,** which are used to select the DMA transfer modes which we have already described, plus additional operating options.

**MC6844 ENABLE/ PRIORITY CONTROL REGISTER**

The best place to begin a discussion of Control registers is with **the Enable/Priority Control register. Bit settings** for this register **may be illustrated as follows:**

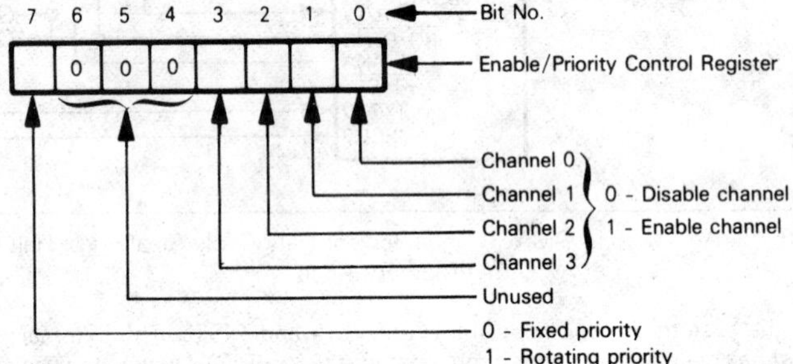


Each DMA channel that is to be active must have a 1 placed in its enable bit within the Enable/Priority Control register. A 0 in any channel's enable bit will disable the channel. It is important to understand that if a channel is disabled, this simply means that DMA requests arriving via the associated TxRQN input will be ignored. Disabling a DMA channel has no effect on your ability to write into the channel's registers or read from the channel's registers.

**MC6844 FIXED DMA PRIORITY ARBITRATION**

If more than one DMA channel is enabled, then two or more DMA requests can occur simultaneously. **You arbitrate priority in one of two ways.** If bit 7 of the Enable/Priority Control register is 0, the following fixed priorities will always be used:

Highest Priority: Channel 0
Channel 1
Channel 2
Lowest Priority: Channel 3

**MC6844 ROTATING DATA PRIORITY ARBITRATION**

Rotating priority may be selected by writing a 1 into bit 7 of the Enable/Priority Control register. Rotating priority initializes the four channels with the fixed priority illustrated above. As soon as any DMA channel has been serviced, however, it becomes the lowest priority channel — and associated channels are rotated in a round-robin fashion. In order to illustrate rotating priority mode, let us assume that DMA Channel 2 is serviced and then DMA Channel 0 is serviced. This is how priorities would be assigned:

Initial Priority:

| | |
|---|---|
| Highest Priority: | Channel 0 |
| | Channel 1 |
| | Channel 2 |
| Lowest Priority: | Channel 3 |

Channel 2 is serviced. These are the new priorities:

| | |
|---|---|
| Highest Priority: | Channel 3 |
| | Channel 0 |
| | Channel 1 |
| Lowest Priority: | Channel 2 |

Channel 0 is serviced. These are the new priorities:

| | |
|---|---|
| Highest Priority: | Channel 1 |
| | Channel 2 |
| | Channel 3 |
| Lowest Priority: | Channel 0 |

**MC6844 DATA CHAINING CONTROL REGISTER**

The next Control register we will look at is the Data Chaining Control register, because this also contributes to channel enable logic. **Data Chaining Control register bit assignments may be illustrated as follows:**

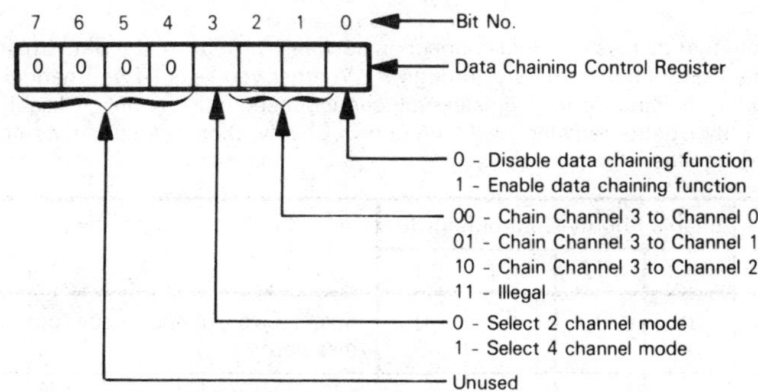


**MC6844 DMAC TWO-CHANNEL MODE**

Bit 3 of the Data Chaining Control register is, in fact, an enable/disable bit for the TxAKB output function associated with the $\overline{CS}$/TxAKB signal. TxAKB is disabled if the Data Chaining Control register bit 3 is 0. This is referred to as Two-Channel mode, because with only TxAKA enabled it is only possible to acknowledge DMA requests from channels 0 or 1. This may be illustrated as follows:

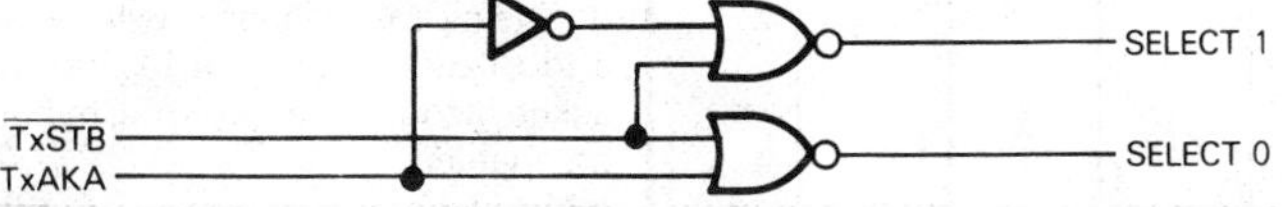

**If the Data Chaining Control register bit 3 is 1, then the TxAKB signal is active,** allowing any one of the four DMA channels to be acknowledged. **This is referred to as Four-Channel mode,** and may be illustrated as follows:

**MC6844 DMAC FOUR-CHANNEL MODE**

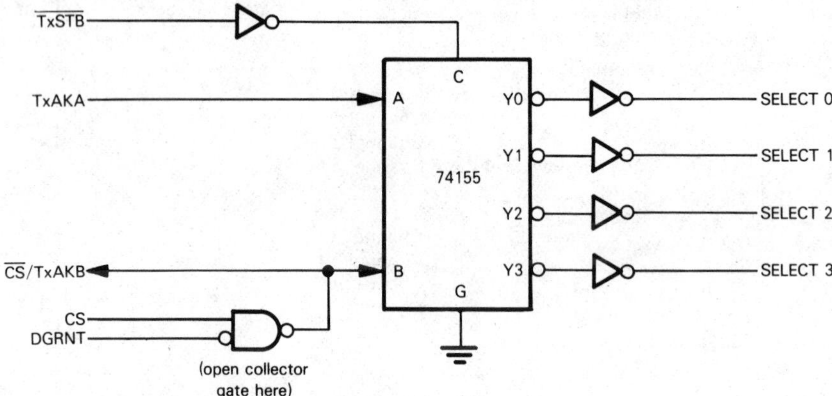


The logic above uses the $\overline{TxSTB}$ pulse as a strobe for a 2-to-4 decoder. The four decoder outputs become individual select lines for the four devices capable of requesting DMA access.

In order to rotate $\overline{CS}$/TxAKB requirements, chip select creation logic is shown. This logic has nothing to do with generation of the Select 0 through Select 3 lines; however, unless the chip select input portion of the $\overline{CS}$/TxAKB signal is correctly generated, TxAKB will either be held at ground or pulled to a level of 1, in which case the four-channel select logic will not work.

It is very important to note that there is no direct connection between the logic of the Data Chaining Control register bit 3 and the Enable/Priority Control register bits 0 through 3. Whether you select Two-Channel mode or Four-Channel mode via bit 3 of the Data Chaining Control register, you can independently enable or disable each of the individual channels via Enable/Priority Control register bits 0 through 3. Clearly, there are certain combinations which are not reasonable. Options may be illustrated as follows:

| Data Chaining Control Register Bit 3 | Enable/Priority Control Register | | | | |
|---|---|---|---|---|---|
| | Bit 3 | Bit 2 | Bit 1 | Bit 0 | |
| 0 | 0 | 0 | 0 | 0 | Select Two-Channel mode, but channels 0 and 1 are disabled. |
| 0<br>0 | 0<br>0 | 0<br>0 | 0<br>1 | 1<br>0 | Select Two-Channel mode, but only channel 0 or channel 1 is enabled. |
| 0 | 0 | 0 | 1 | 1 | Normal Two-Channel mode with both channels active. |
| 0<br>-<br>-<br>-<br>0 | 0<br><br><br><br>1 | 1<br><br><br><br>1 | X<br><br><br><br>X | X<br><br><br><br>X | In Two-Channel mode you can enable channels 2 and 3. Their DMA requests will be accepted via TxRQ2 and TxRQ3, but DMA requests will not be acknowledged via TxAKB. Channels 0 and/or 1 must be enabled. |
| 1 | 0 | 0 | X | X | Four-Channel mode with channels 2 and 3 disabled makes no sense. Use Two-Channel mode instead. |
| 1<br>-<br>-<br>-<br>1 | 0<br><br><br><br>1 | 1<br><br><br><br>1 | X<br><br><br><br>X | X<br><br><br><br>X | Four-Channel mode with channel 2 and/or 3 enabled, and any enable/disable combination for channels 0 and 1 is alright. |

**If you enable data chaining by writing a 1 into the Data Chaining Control register bit 0, then DMA operations at channel 0, 1 or 2 become continuous.** Via bits 1 and 2 of the Data Chaining Control register, you select channel 0, 1 or 2 to operate in Chained mode.

**MC6844 DATA CHAINING**

Chained mode simply means that as soon as the selected channel's Byte Count register decrements to 0, the selected channel's Byte Count and Address registers will be reloaded with values stored in the Channel 3 Byte Count and Address registers. Suppose, for example, you want to continuously transfer, via direct memory access, 256 bytes of data. The data is to flow via Channel 0 to memory, with the data being loaded in memory locations $0A00_{16}$ through $0AFF_{16}$. To perform this task you would store $00FF_{16}$ in the Channel 3 Byte Count register, and $0A00_{16}$ in the Channel 3 Address register. (We assume that the Address register is going to be incremented.) Every DMA transfer will begin with $00FF_{16}$ being loaded into the Channel 0 Byte Count register from the Channel 3 Byte Count register, while $0A00_{16}$ is loaded into the Channel 0 Address register from the Channel 3 Address register. This is an automatic operation which requires no program intervention once data chaining has been enabled. Thus, DMA transfer via Channel 0 will continue endlessly with the DMA transfer rate determined by the DMA mode selected.

It is important to note that a data chaining specification is to MC6844 DMAC logic an isolated event. The fact that data chaining has been enabled does not automatically disable DMA Channel 3 logic. You must do this by writing 0 into the Enable/Priority Control register bit 3. Also, if you specify chaining, you in no way affect the manner in which registers can be accessed. You can write into Channel 3 registers, or you can read the contents of Channel 3 registers. This can be very useful. If 256 bytes of data are continuously being read into memory locations $0A00_{16}$ through $0AFF_{16}$, it would take complex program logic to access all data that gets written into this buffer before the data gets overwritten on the next DMA pass.

A better way would be to have two buffers: for example, the first from $0A00_{16}$ through $0AFF_{16}$ and the second from $0B00_{16}$ through $0BFF_{16}$. Now, following each end of block interrupt, you would write the new address into the Channel 3 Address register. This is illustrated in Figure 9-37.

**There are some nonobvious aspects of Figure 9-37.**

Observe that when you are initializing the MC6844 operating in Chained mode, you must load initial addresses and byte counts in Channel 3 Address and Byte Count registers as well as in the Address and Byte Count register for the chained channel. The actual chaining operating does not occur until the chained channel's Byte Count register decrements to 0. When you start the chained channel, the first DMA operation uses initial Byte Count and Address values loaded into the chained channel's Byte Count and Address registers. After the first end-of-block interrupt, the byte count and address values loaded into the Channel 3 registers will be transferred to the chained channel registers for the next operation.

**Let us now consider the Channel Control register which is associated with each DMA channel. Channel Control register bit assignments may be illustrated as follows:**

**MC6844 CHANNEL CONTROL REGISTERS**

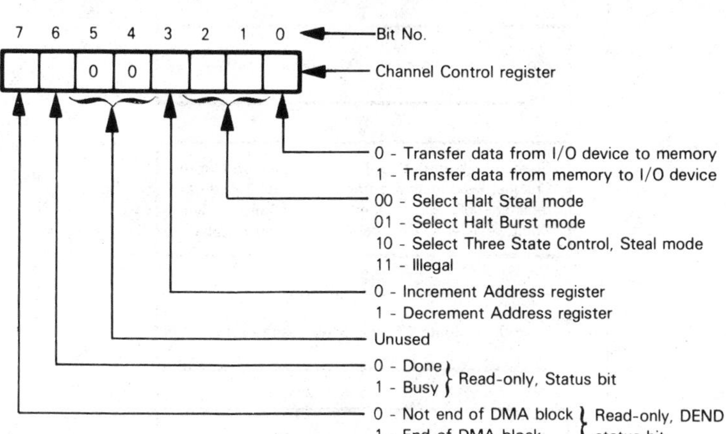


Channel Control register bit 0 simply reflects the level which will be output on the R/$\overline{W}$ pin during DMA operations — that is to say, while R/$\overline{W}$ is an output from the MC6844 DMAC. Channel Control register bit 0 has no effect on R/$\overline{W}$ while the MC6800 CPU is accessing the MC6844 DMAC under program control. The level of the R/$\overline{W}$ signal during a DMA operation determines whether data will be transferred from the I/O device to memory (R/$\overline{W}$ is low), or from memory to the I/O device (R/$\overline{W}$ is high). Since each DMA channel has its own Control register and therefore its own Control register bit 0, channels may be programmed independently to generate DMA transfers in either direction.

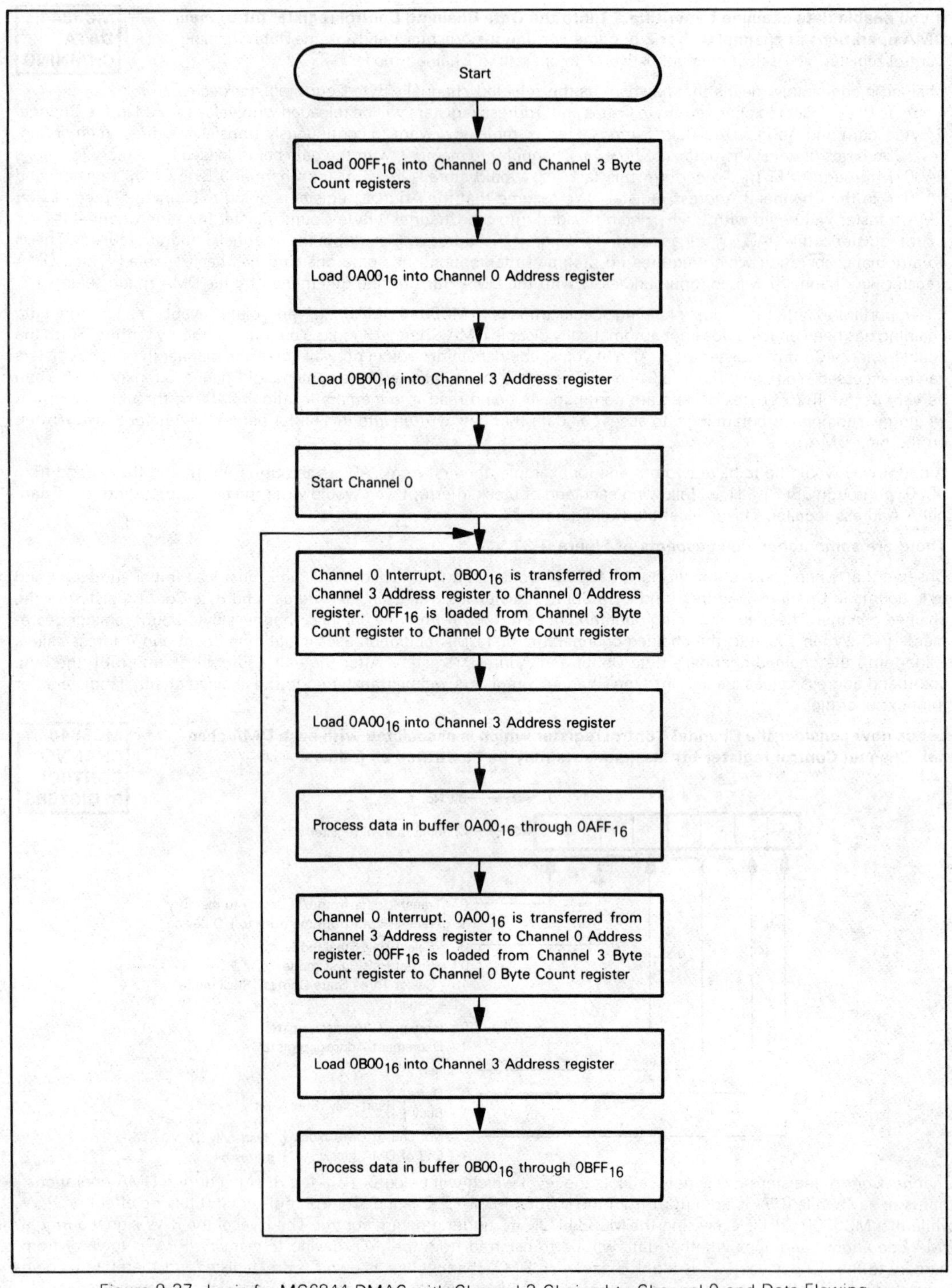


Figure 9-37. Logic for MC6844 DMAC with Channel 3 Chained to Channel 0 and Data Flowing into Alternate Memory Buffers

Channel Control register bits 1 and 2 are used to select one of the three DMA transfer modes which we have just described.

Channel Control register bit 3 determines whether the channel's Address register contents will be incremented or decremented following each DMA transfer. Thus you can perform a DMA operation specifying the highest address or the lowest address of a memory buffer as the starting address.

Channel Control register bits 4 and 5 are unassigned.

**MC6844 INTERRUPT CONTROL REGISTER**

Channel Control register bits 6 and 7 are read-only status bits which should be looked at in conjunction with the Interrupt Control register. **Interrupt Control register bits are assigned as follows:**

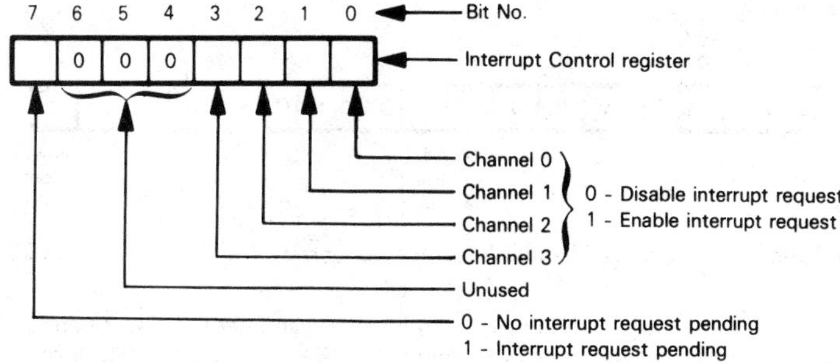


You can, at any time, examine a DMA channel to find out if it is "busy" or if it is "done". If "busy", the channel is in the middle of transferring a block of data. If "done", the channel is currently idle. You determine a channel's status by reading the contents of the Channel Control register and examining the level of bit 6.

When you reach the end of a data block, that is, a DMA channel's Byte Count register decrements to 0, the channel's Control register bit 7 will be set to 1. If the channel's interrupt logic has been enabled via bit 0, 1, 2 or 3 of the Interrupt Control register, then an interrupt request will occur via a low output at $\overline{IRQ}/\overline{DEND}$. This interrupt request will not occur if the channel's interrupt logic has been disabled within the Interrupt Control register.

If an interrupt request does occur, then bit 7 of the Interrupt Control register will be set to 1.

Irrespective of whether a channel's interrupt logic has or has not been disabled, the channel's Control register bit 7 will be set to 1 when the channel's Byte Count register decrements to 0.

Bit 7 of the Channel Control register remains set to 1 until the CPU reads the contents of the Channel Control register. The process of reading the Channel Control register contents automatically resets bit 7 to 0.

The Interrupt Control register bit 7 is reset to 0 as soon as the Channel Control register for the DMA channel requesting the interrupt is read by the CPU.

Suppose, for example, Channels 0 and 1 are active, with Channel 0 interrupts enabled and Channel 1 interrupts disabled. Here are appropriate Interrupt Control register settings:

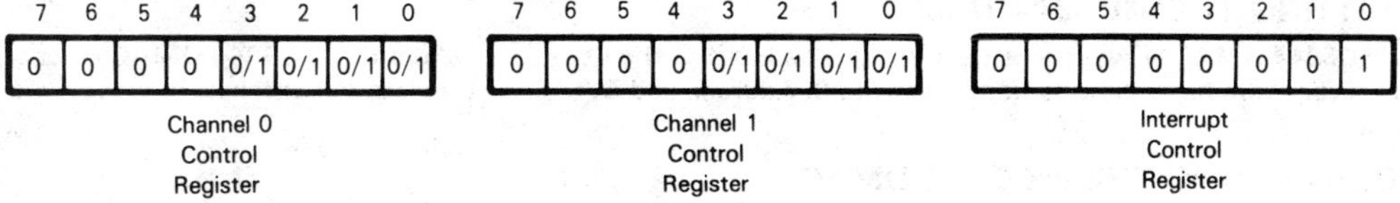


0/1 means the bit may be 0 or 1.

Now suppose Channel 1 becomes active. Its Control register Busy bit will be set:

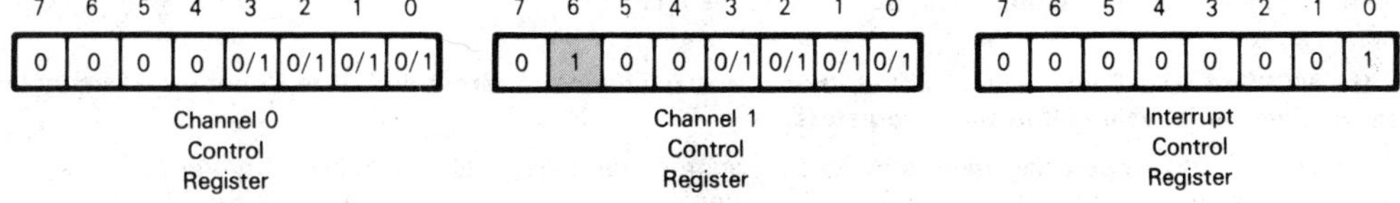

Next, suppose Channel 0 becomes active. The Channel 0 Busy bit will also be set:

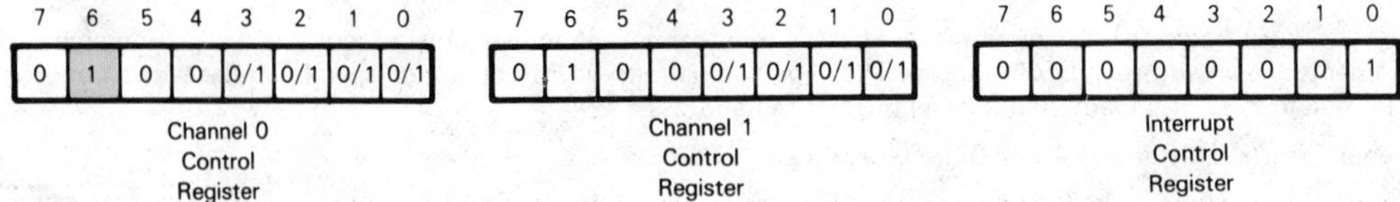


When the Channel 1 DMA operation ends, no interrupt request will occur, since the Channel 1 interrupt logic has been disabled. Thus, the Channel 1 Control register Busy bit will be reset to 0, the DEND bit will be set to 1 and the Interrupt Control register will not change:

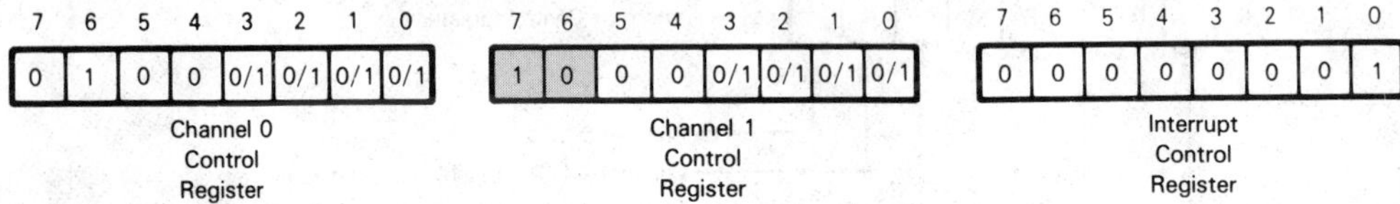


As soon as the CPU reads the contents of the Channel 1 Control register, the Channel 1 DEND bit (bit 7) will be reset to 0.

Suppose Channel 0 now reaches the end of a data block; it will request an interrupt. The Channel 0 Control register's Busy bit will be reset to 0, the DEND bit will be set to 1 and the active interrupt request bit of the Interrupt Control register will also be set to 1:

Reading the contents of the Channel 0 Control register will reset the Channel 0 DEND bit (bit 7). Reading the Channel 0 Control register contents will also reset the Interrupt Control register bit 7, since the Channel 0 interrupt request caused this bit to be set. Reading the Channel 1 Control register will have no effect on the Interrupt Control register bit 7, since Channel 1 did not cause the interrupt request to be generated.

If more than one active interrupt is present, then your program must arbitrate priorities by examining the DEND status of each channel's Control register. Also, bit 7 of the Interrupt Control register will be reset when you read the contents of the Control register for the first channel to request an interrupt. For example, suppose all channel interrupts have been enabled, and Channel 0, then Channel 2, then Channel 1 request interrupts— before the CPU acknowledges an interrupt. The CPU can determine which channels have requested interrupts by reading Control register contents for Channels 0, 1 and 2. But it is the act of reading Channel 0 Control register contents that will reset bit 7 of the Interrupt Control register.

## RESETTING THE MC6844 DMAC

**The MC6844 DMAC is reset when a low signal is input at the Reset pin. When the MC6844 DMAC is reset, all Control registers have their contents reset to 0. Address and Byte Count registers' contents, however, are not altered.**

## PROGRAMMING THE MC6844 DMAC

**Programming the MC6844 DMAC is quite straightforward.**

**The first step is initialization.** If you have reset the MC6844, then all Control registers' contents will be 0 — in which case all DMA requests and interrupt requests have been disabled. If you have not reset the MC6844 DMAC, then you should do so under program control by outputting 0 to the Enable/Priority Control register and the Interrupt Control register.

**Once the MC6844 DMAC has been disabled, then initialize channel Address and Byte Count registers by loading appropriate initial values into these registers.**

**Next, define the DMA operating modes** by loading appropriate codes into the channel Control registers for the enabled channels, and into the Data Chain Control register.

**Initialization is now complete.** You start DMA channels by outputting an appropriate code to the Interrupt Control register and then to the Enable/Priority Control register.

**Monitoring DMA operations while they are in progress is also quite straightforward.** Normally you will wait until the end of a DMA transfer is signaled by an interrupt request, at which time if more than one channel could have requested the interrupt, the interrupt service routine arbitrates priorities by reading all active channel Control registers' contents. The interrupt service routine must now respond to the active interrupt request according to the requirements of your program logic. This may or may not require restarting the same channel or another channel.

**You can monitor DMA operations while they are in progress by reading the contents of Address and Byte Count registers while a DMA operation is in progress. However, this is something you should only do while operating a DMA channel in one of the Halt modes. If you read register contents on the fly while operating in Three-State Control mode, you may read the wrong answer,** and determining what the right reading should be is not easy. This is because an instruction that reads 16 bits of data executes in two machine cycles. If this read operation occurs while a Three-State Control, Cycle Stealing DMA transfer is occurring, this is what happens:

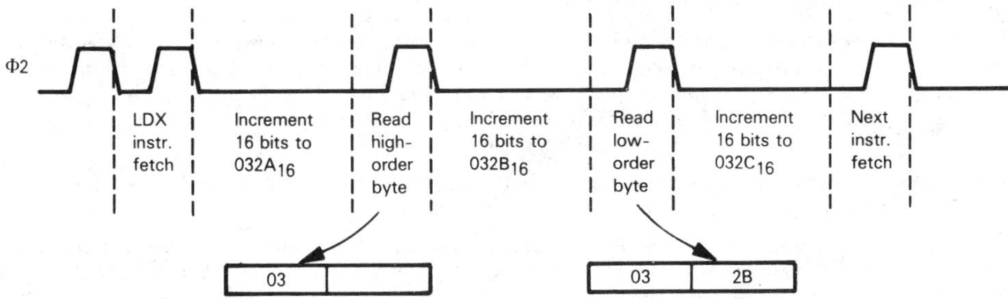


In the illustration above, an LDX instruction loads the contents of a 16-bit register (we will assume it is the Channel Address register) into the Index register of the CPU. First the high-order byte of the Address register (03) is transferred to the high-order byte of the Index register. At the end of this machine cycle, however, the Address register is incremented. Now, you may say that this is no problem since you have read the valid Address register contents as they were at the end of the LDX instruction's execution. But unfortunately there is a special case. Suppose the Address register contained $0200_{16}$ and was decrementing. Now you will read 02FF when 01FF was the correct value:

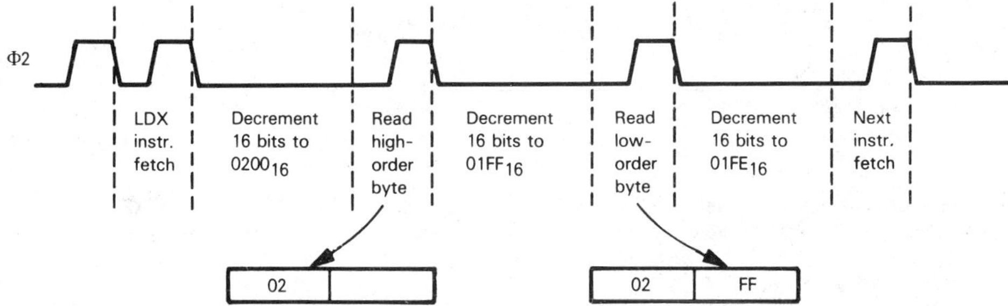


The error illustrated above cannot occur when operating DMA in a Halt mode, since the DMA transfer occurs in between instruction executions. Thus, the contents of any 16-bit registers within the MC6844 DMAC will not change while an LDX instruction is being executed, because no DMA transfer can occur until the LDX instruction has completed execution.

You can, if you wish, write into any MC6844 DMAC register at any time. For example, you can write into an Address or Byte Count register for a channel that is busy. Once again, you can get into trouble if you write into Address or Byte Count registers for a channel that is operating in Three-State Control, Cycle Stealing mode, since you will write the low-order byte, all 16 bits may be incremented or decremented, and then you will write the high-order byte; and who knows what the results will be. Writing into registers on the fly will not cause errors if you are operating in one of the Halt modes.

# THE MC6846 MULTIFUNCTION SUPPORT DEVICE

**The MC6846 multifunction support device is designed to work with the MC6802 as a two-chip microcomputer. However, the MC6846 can be used just as easily in any other MC6800 microcomputer system.**

**Figure 9-38 illustrates that part of our microcomputer system logic which is implemented on the MC6846 multifunction device. This device provides 2048 bytes of read-only memory, a single 8-bit parallel I/O port with handshaking control signals, and a counter/timer.**

**The MC6846 multifunction device is packaged as a 40-pin DIP. It uses a single +5V power supply. All inputs and outputs are TTL-compatible.**

**The device is implemented using N-channel silicon gate depletion load technology.**

## MC6846 MULTIFUNCTION DEVICE PINS AND SIGNALS

MC6846 pins and signals are illustrated in Figure 9-39.

**The device select lines CS0 and CS1 work in two ways: they activate the MC6846, and they select which function is in use — ROM or I/O and counter/timer. The user specifies as a mask option two active combinations of CS0 and CS1 levels: one to enable the ROM and one to enable the I/O and counter/timer.** For example, you might wish to enable ROM when CS1 is high and CS0 is low, and enable the I/O and counter/timer when both select lines are high. This combination would then disable the MC6846 when CS1 is low.

**When ROM is selected, the eleven lines A0 - A10 will address one of the 2048 bytes of read-only memory.** These 2048 memory bytes may be located anywhere in the memory space.

In addition to CS0 and CS1, **certain of the address lines are used to select the I/O and counter/timer functions.** Lines A5, A4, and A3 must be low to select the I/O and counter/timer operations. You select as a mask option what level at line A6 enables I/O and the counter/timer, and whether or not one of the lines A10, A9, A8, and A7 must be high to enable these functions. Here is how address lines are used to select I/O and the counter/timer:

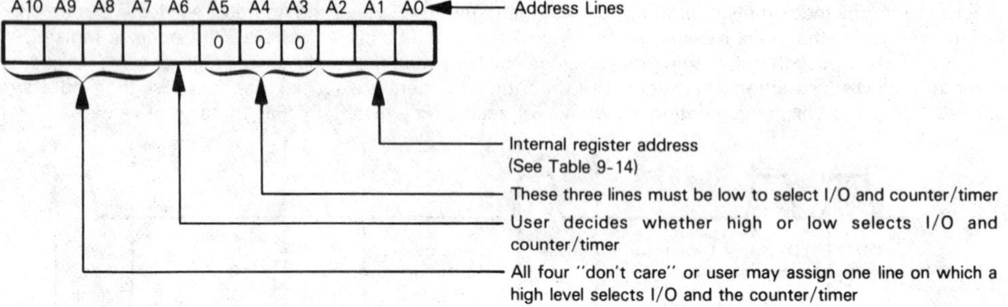


**Once an MC6846 has been selected as an I/O device, address lines A0, A1, and A2 select one of seven registers in eight I/O addressable locations.** Table 9-14 identifies the locations accessed with each address. Note that addresses 0 and 4 access the same location.

Table 9-14. MC6846 I/O Addressable Locations

| Address Line | | | Internal Register Selected |
|---|---|---|---|
| A2 | A1 | A0 | |
| 0 | 0 | 0 | Composite Status register |
| 0 | 0 | 1 | Peripheral Control register |
| 0 | 1 | 0 | Data Direction register |
| 0 | 1 | 1 | Peripheral Data register |
| 1 | 0 | 0 | Composite Status register |
| 1 | 0 | 1 | Timer Control register |
| 1 | 1 | 0 | Timer register (high-order byte) |
| 1 | 1 | 1 | Timer register (low-order byte) |

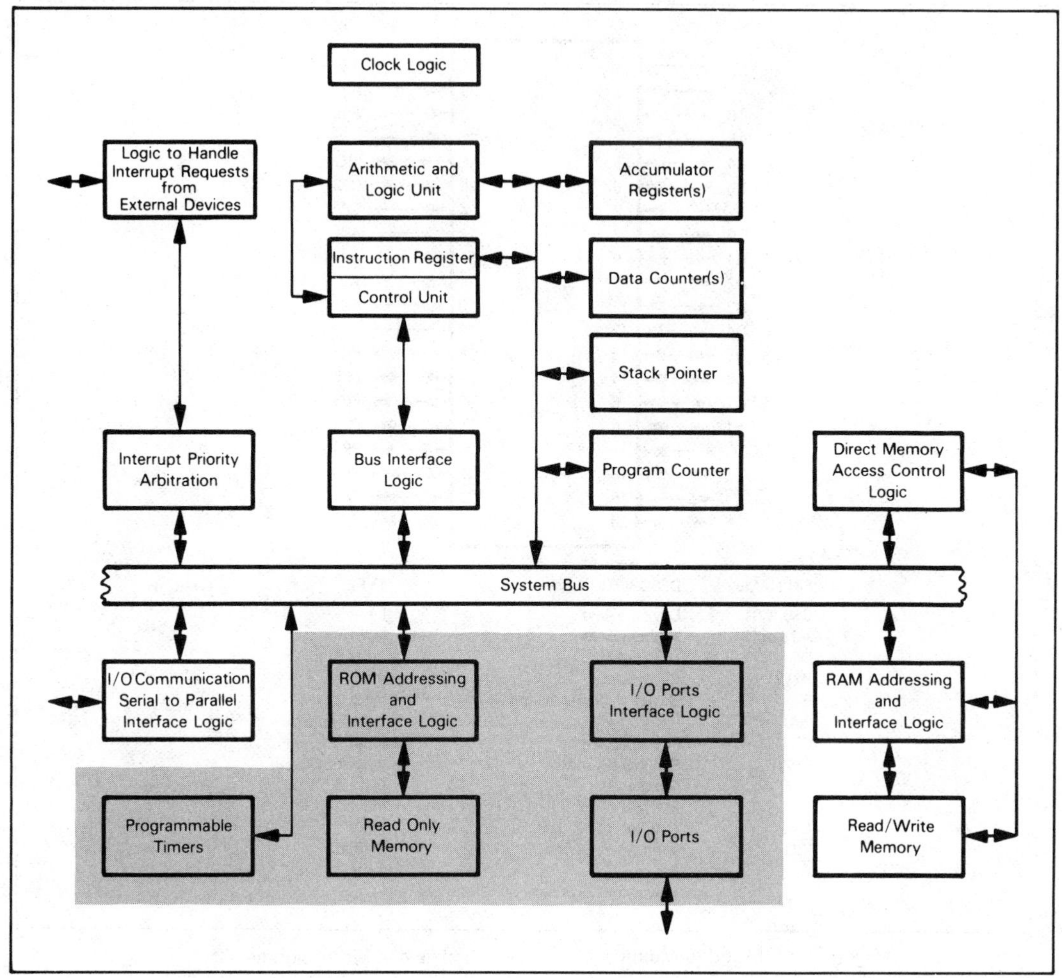


Figure 9-38. Logic of the MC6846 Multifunction Device

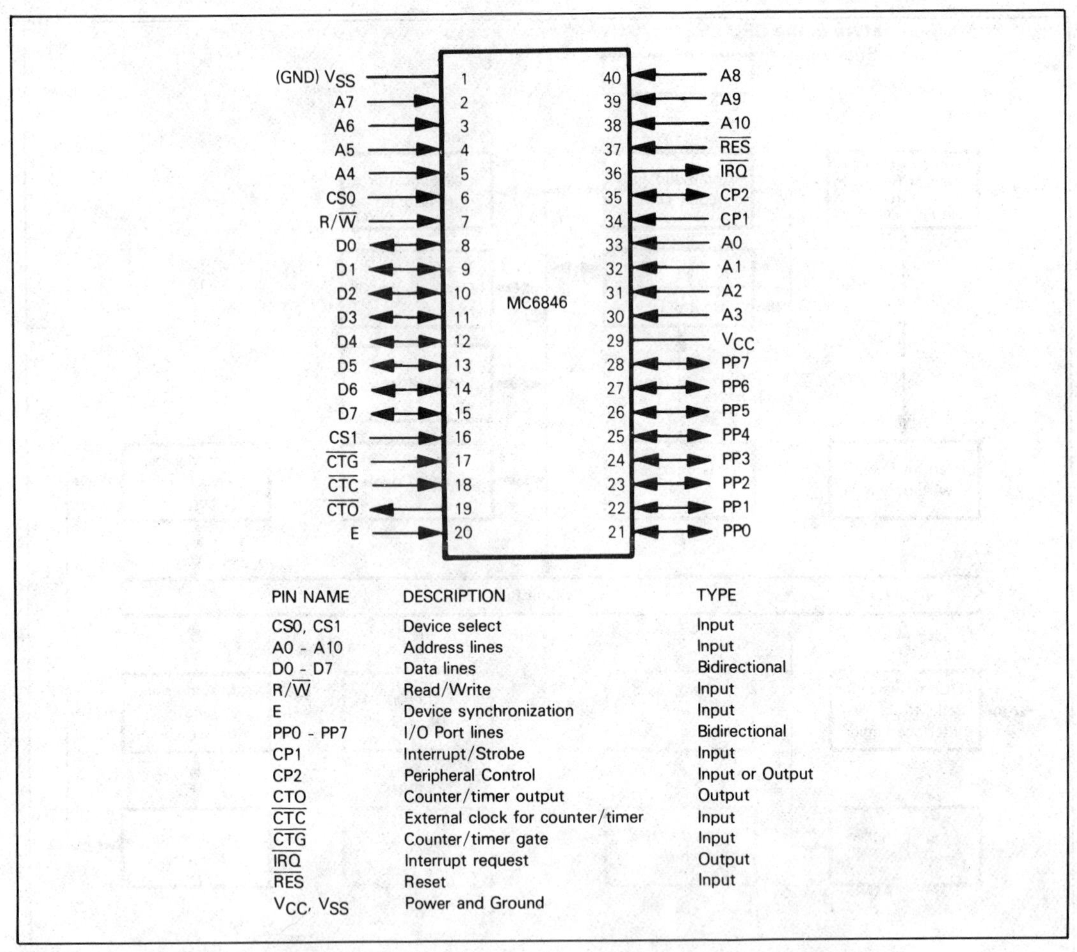


| PIN NAME | DESCRIPTION | TYPE |
|---|---|---|
| CS0, CS1 | Device select | Input |
| A0 - A10 | Address lines | Input |
| D0 - D7 | Data lines | Bidirectional |
| $R/\overline{W}$ | Read/Write | Input |
| E | Device synchronization | Input |
| PP0 - PP7 | I/O Port lines | Bidirectional |
| CP1 | Interrupt/Strobe | Input |
| CP2 | Peripheral Control | Input or Output |
| $\overline{CTO}$ | Counter/timer output | Output |
| $\overline{CTC}$ | External clock for counter/timer | Input |
| $\overline{CTG}$ | Counter/timer gate | Input |
| $\overline{IRQ}$ | Interrupt request | Output |
| $\overline{RES}$ | Reset | Input |
| $V_{CC}$, $V_{SS}$ | Power and Ground | |

Figure 9-39. MC6846 Multifunction Device Signals and Pin Assignments

**All data transfers between the CPU and the MC6846 device occur via the bidirectional Data Bus (D0 - D7).** This is a three-state Data Bus; when the device is not selected the MC6846 holds these lines in the high-impedance state.

**The R/W control determines whether data will flow into the MC6846 (a Write operation with R/W low) or from the MC6846 (a Read operation with R/W high).**

**E is the standard synchronizing clock signal used throughout an MC6800 microcomputer system.**

The 8-bit parallel I/O port of the MC6846 is very similar to I/O Port B of an MC6820 Peripheral Interface Adapter (PIA). Differences are described later. **Lines PP0 - PP7 constitute an 8-bit bidirectional parallel I/O port. Control lines CP1 and CP2 are the two handshaking and interrupt control signals associated with the parallel I/O port.**

**The counter/timer of the MC6846 is very similar to counter/timer 3 of the MC6840 counter/timer,** which has been described earlier in this chapter. **CTO is the output signal, CTC is the external clock and CTG is the gate input.**

**Interrupt requests originating from the parallel I/O logic of the counter/timer logic are output via IRQ.**

**The device is reset by inputting a low level at RES.** The actual operation of the reset logic is described after the registers which it affects have been discussed.

## MC6846 COUNTER/TIMER LOGIC

Before reading this section, you should be familiar with the MC6840 counter/timer device described earlier in this chapter. **We are only going to examine the differences between counter/timer logic of the MC6846 and channel 3 of the MC6840. Note that channel 3 of the MC6840, like the counter/timer logic of the MC6846, can be operated in divide-by-eight mode.**

**The MC6846 counter/timer has its own Control register, Most Significant Byte register, and Least Significant Byte register.** As illustrated in Table 9-13, these three registers are accessed via addresses DEV+5, DEV+6, and DEV+7 respectively. **The counter/timer logic does not have its own Status register; this is shared with I/O port logic.**

The counter/timer Control register address is not the same as any of the three addresses set aside for Control registers of the MC6840. The Most Significant Byte register and Least Significant Byte register addresses, however, are the same as two addresses allocated to these two registers by the MC6840.

Bits of the MC6846 counter/timer Control register are not assigned in the same way as they are for any MC6840 Control register. **Here are the counter/timer Control register bit assignments for the MC6846:**

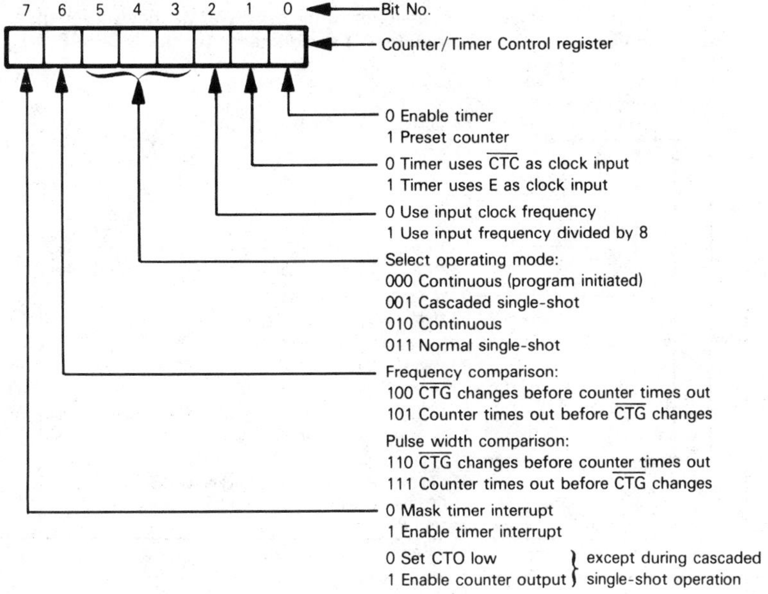

Bit 0 is the internal reset bit. This is the same as bit 0 of the Control register of MC6840 counter/timer logic 1.

Bit 1 determines whether the external clock ($\overline{CTC}$) or the system clock (Φ2, via E) will be the timing signal. This is the same as in MC6840 Control registers.

Bit 2 enables or disables the divide-by-eight prescaler; bit 0 of counter/timer 3's Control register performs the same task in the MC6840.

Bit 6 enables or disables interrupt logic, and bit 7 enables or disables the output signal for the counter/timer as described for the MC6840.

Control register bits 3, 4 and 5 determine the operating mode of the counter/timer. There is just one difference between the interpretation of these three bits in the MC6846 as compared to the interpretation of these three bits in the MC6840. The MC6846 has no program-initiated single-shot mode. Only a high-to-low transition of the gate input will initiate single-shot mode. This missing variation of single-shot mode is replaced by a cascade mode. In the cascade mode, Control register bit 7 is connected to the output signal CTO. When Control register bit 7 is 0, the output signal is set low on the next timeout; when Control register bit 7 is 1, the next timeout sets the output signal high. This is called a "cascade" mode because it allows you, under program control, to count timeouts which generate interrupt requests in the usual way and then, under program control, to change the level of the output based on the time interval computed via timeouts.

## MC6846 I/O PORT LOGIC

Before reading this section, you should be familiar with the MC6820 PIA described earlier in this chapter. **We are only going to examine the differences between I/O port logic of the MC6846 and I/O Port B of the MC6820.**

**The MC6846 I/O Port can provide programmed handshaking on either input or output.**

**Any of the data lines PP0 - PP7 can directly drive the base of a Darlington NPN transistor. The control line CP2 also has this capability.**

**The MC6846 I/O Port has its own Control register, Data Direction register, and Peripheral Data register.** As illustrated in Table 9-13, these three registers are accessed via addresses DEV+1, DEV+2, and DEV+3 respectively. **The I/O port logic does not have its own Status register; this is shared with the counter/timer logic.** We will describe the Composite Status register later on.

**In the MC6846, the Data Direction register and the Peripheral Data register have separate addresses.** Recall that in the MC6820 PIA these two registers share one address, and Bit 2 of the Control register determines which location is accessed by that address.

Bits of the MC6846 Peripheral Control register are not assigned in the same way as they are for either of the MC6820 Control registers. **Here are the Peripheral Control register bit assignments for the MC6846:**

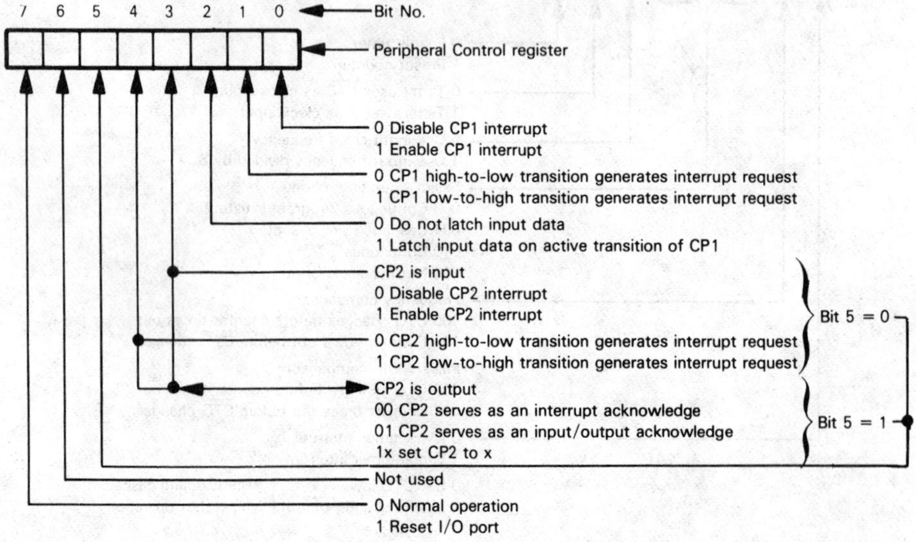

If Bit 0 is set to 1, then an active transition (as defined in Bit 1) at CP1 will set $\overline{IRQ}$ low. Bits 0 and 1 are used in the same way in the Control registers of the MC6820.

Bit 2 selects the input latch function. When bit 2 is set, an active transition at CP1 will latch data input on lines PP0 - PP7. The MC6820 does not provide an input latch function.

Bits 3, 4, and 5 control the CP2 line in the same way that MC6820 Control Register B bits 3, 4, and 5 control line CB2 of that device.

Bit 6 is not used in the MC6846.

Bit 7 serves as an internal reset for the I/O port. The CPU may set this bit by writing a 1 into it, but it will also be set automatically when the MC6846 receives a low level at the reset input, $\overline{RES}$. You clear bit 7 by writing a 0 to it during a CPU write to the Peripheral Control register.

**MC6846 COMPOSITE STATUS REGISTER**

**The interrupt flags for both the timer/counter and the I/O port appear in the Composite Status register,** which the CPU accesses via either of the addresses DEV or DEV+4. **This register is a read-only location.**

**Here are the bit assignments for the Composite Status register:**

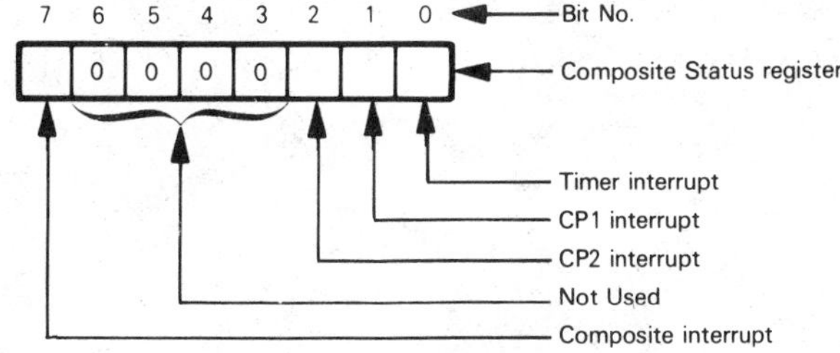


Note that interrupt conditions will appear in bits 0, 1, and 2 of the Composite Status register, whether or not interrupts are enabled in the corresponding Control register.

A counter/timer interrupt will set bit 0 of the Composite Status register. Any of the following actions will reset the counter/timer interrupt flag to 0:

- Timer reset via either Timer Control register bit 7 or $\overline{RES}$ input
- Initializing the counter
- Writing to the timer latches in Frequency Comparison mode or Pulse Width Comparison mode
- Reading the Timer register after reading the Composite Status register while the timer interrupt bit was set. That is, the following sequence resets bit 0 of the Composite Status register: bit 0 is set by the counter/timer interrupt; the CPU reads the Composite Status register (location DEV or DEV+4); then the CPU reads the Timer register (locations DEV+6 and DEV+7).

Interrupt transitions at CP1 and CP2 will set bits 1 and 2, respectively, of the Composite Status register. Each of these bits will be reset to 0 by a Read or Write to the Peripheral Data register (location DEV+3), but only if the flag was already set when the CPU last read the Composite Status register. This is analogous to the fourth counter/timer flag reset condition described above.

Bit 7 will be set to 1 only when $\overline{IRQ}$ is set low; that is, any one of the three interrupt bits described above will set bit 7, but only if that interrupt has been enabled in the appropriate Control register bit. Bit 7 will be 0 only when all three of bits 0, 1, and 2 are reset to 0.

Bits 3, 4, and 5 of the Composite Status register are not used.

**The Data Direction register and the Peripheral Data register work in the same way as those in the MC6820 do.**

## MC6846 DEVICE RESET

**When the MC6846 receives a low level on $\overline{RES}$, all the I/O and counter/timer logic enters the Reset state.** In addition, **the I/O port and the counter/timer can be reset individually via the internal reset bits of their respective Control registers** — bit 0 of the Timer Control register and bit 7 of the Peripheral Control register.

**These are the results of a counter/timer reset:**

- The counter latches take on the maximum count (65,536). This occurs only during external reset ($\overline{RES}$ low).
- The counter clock is disabled.
- Bits 1 through 6 of the Timer Control register are reset to 0, as are the output line CTO and the interrupt flag (bit 0 of the Composite Status register).

**The net effect is that the counter/timer becomes inactive until the CPU writes a 0 to bit 0 of the Timer Control register.**

**These are the results of an I/O port reset:**

- All bits of the Peripheral Data register and Data Direction register are reset to 0, as are the interrupt flags (bits 1 and 2 of the Composite Status register).
- Bits 6 through 0 of the Peripheral Control register are reset to 0.

**The net effect is that the port is in input mode, and its interrupts are disabled.**

## THE 6801 FAMILY OF SINGLE-CHIP MICROCOMPUTERS

**At the beginning of this chapter, we compared the MC6800 to the 8085 and noted that there were several enhancements required if the MC6800 microprocessors were to remain competitive. First, the clock logic must be moved onto the CPU chip and, second, a multifunction CPU should be developed so that low chip-count microcomputers could be designed with the 6800 family. The 6801 series of microcomputers address both of these shortcomings; all members of this family include an enhanced version of the basic 6800 CPU with an improved instruction set, on-chip memory, I/O ports, on-chip timer, and on-chip serial I/O logic. The primary version of the 6801 also includes an internal clock.**

**Members of the 6801 family include the NMOS devices — MC6801 and MC6803 — plus a CMOS version, the MC146805. All of these devices have on-chip clock oscillators. Versions using external clocking schemes are also available and are identified by having an E appended — thus, the MC6801E is the externally clocked version of the MC6801.**

**The primary version of the MC6801 provides on-chip ROM. Versions that provide EPROM are also available, and these devices are identified by the numerical 7 — thus, the MC68701 is the EPROM version of the MC6801.**

**The MC6801 is essentially an expandable, single-chip version of the MC6800, enhanced with additional features and capabilities. The MC6803 is a "ROM-less" version of the MC6801. Table 9-15 summarizes the general characteristics of the 6801 family members.**

Table 9-15. Summary of MC6801 Family Single-Chip Microcomputers

| Device | Description | Bytes of Memory | | | Input/Output | | Timer Functions (bits) |
|---|---|---|---|---|---|---|---|
| | | On Chip | | External | | | |
| | | ROM | RAM | | Parallel | Serial | |
| 6801 | Expandable to 3 modes<br>Internal clock | 2 K | 128 | 64 K | 31 | 3 | 3 x 16 |
| 6801E | Externally clocked | 2 K | 128 | 64 K | 31 | 3 | 3 x 16 |
| 68701 | EPROM version of 6801 | 2 K | 128 | 64 K | 31 | 3 | 3 x 16 |
| 68701E | EPROM version with external clock | 2 K | 128 | 64 K | 31 | 3 | 3 x 16 |
| 6803 | 6801 without ROM | 0 | 128 | 64 K | 13 | 3 | 3 x 16 |
| 6803E | 6803 with external clock | 0 | 128 | 64 K | 13 | 3 | 3 x 16 |

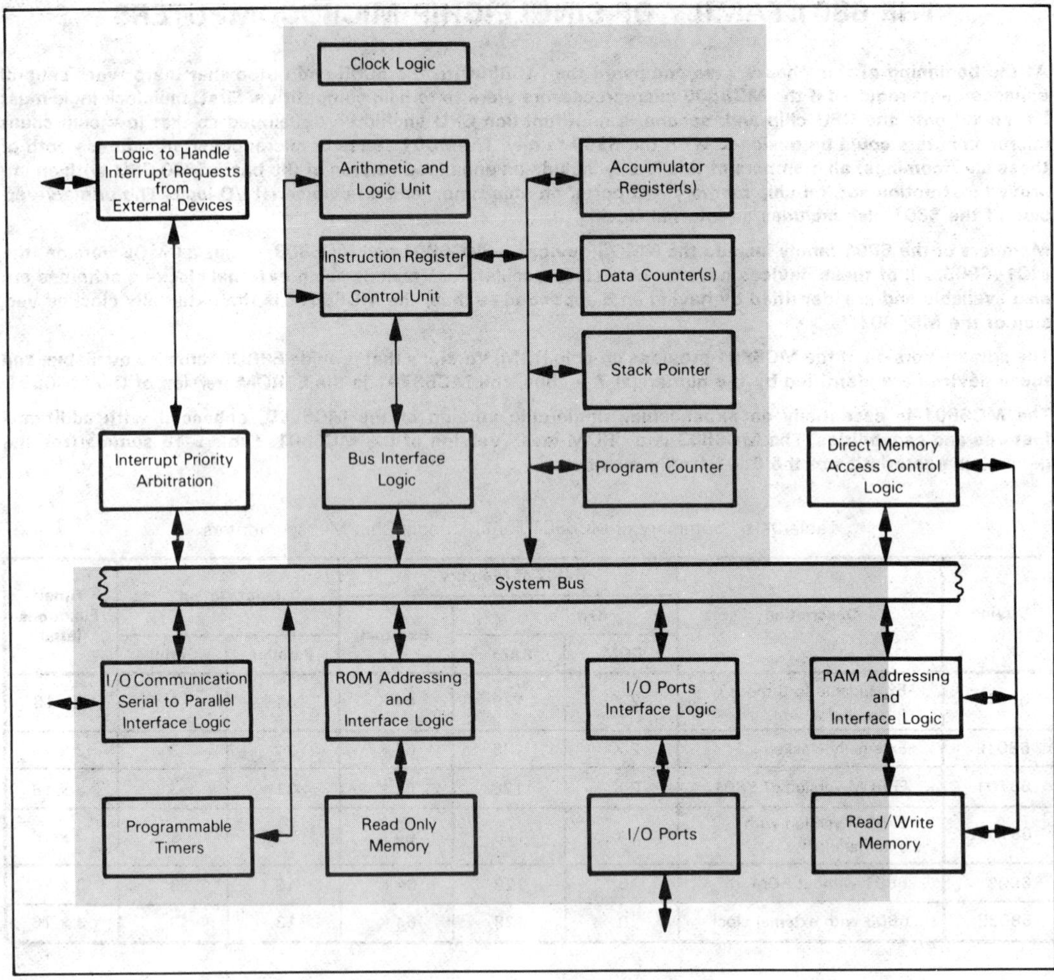


Figure 9-40. Logic of the MC6801 Microcomputer

## THE MC6801 SINGLE-CHIP MICROCOMPUTER

**The MC6801 is an expandable, single-chip, multi-mode microcomputer. It incorporates within a single package most of the functions of the following 6800 devices:**

- **6800 CPU**
- **6875 Clock**
- **6821 Peripheral Interface Adapter (PIA)**
- **6850 Asynchronous Communications Interface Adapter (ACIA) - partially**
- **6840 Programmable Counter/Timer**
- **68316 2K ROM**

**In short, this device is indeed a system. Figure 9-40 illustrates the functions provided by the MC6801.**

**In addition to an improved version of the basic 6800 CPU, the MC6801 provides 2K bytes of ROM, 128 bytes of read/write memory, clock circuitry, a programmable timer, a serial communication interface, and 31 parallel I/O lines.**

**Despite the fact that the MC6801 incorporates many of the capabilities of the standard 6800 support devices, the designers have wisely decided to make this family of devices as compatible as possible with the original family.** Therefore, even though the MC6801 includes a few new instructions, all of the 6800 instructions are object code compatible with those of the MC6801. The MC6801 is also hardware compatible with the basic 6800 system; therefore, this microcomputer can interact with all of the well-proven 6800 CPUs, memories, peripherals, and special purpose devices.

Because the primary version of the MC6801 incorporates a mask-programmed ROM one might assume that it is useful only in high volume applications where the cost of custom programming the ROM can be amortized over a large production run. Such is not the case, however. As will be shown later, the MC6801 can be configured with an external EPROM, permitting the user to reap the benefits of the MC6801 system architecture without having to pay the cost of a customized ROM. In addition, versions with on-chip EPROM have been announced.

## NEW INSTRUCTIONS FOR THE MC6801

**The full MC6800 instruction set is implemented on the MC6801 — thus current 6800 programs will run on the 6801 without modification. In addition, execution times of key instructions have been reduced to increase throughput.**

**Ten new instructions have been added, including six 16-bit (2-byte) operations and an 8 x 8 hardware multiply. Double precision operations are achieved by concatenating the A and B accumulators to form one 16-bit accumulator, as shown below:**

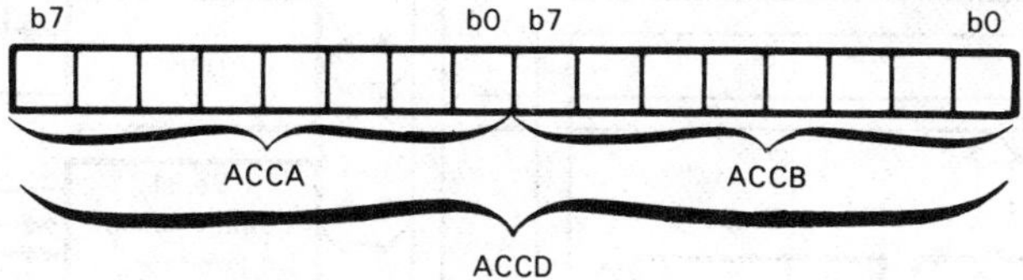


**This concatenated accumulator is denoted ACCAB, or simply ACCD.**

The 16-bit (double precision) instructions are: load the double accumulator, store the double accumulator, add a 16-bit number to the double accumulator, subtract a 16-bit number from the double accumulator, shift the double accumulator right, and shift the double accumulator left.

Three new Index register instructions have been added. They are: add the B accumulator to the Index register, push the Index register onto the Stack, and pull the Index register from the Stack. In addition, the existing instruction to compare the Index register has been changed so that the C bit of the Status register is properly conditioned when CPX is executed.

Finally, an 8 x 8 hardware multiply has been added. This instruction generates the unsigned 16-bit product of two 8-bit numbers in 10 microseconds (1 MHz clock), approximately twenty times faster than a software implementation.

The double precision instructions have been implemented with all the addressing modes available for single-accumulator instructions.

## MC6801 STATUS FLAGS, PROGRAMMABLE REGISTERS, AND ADDRESSING MODES

The status flags provided by the MC6801 are identical to those of the MC6800 as described at the beginning of this chapter. The programmable registers of the MC6801 CPU are also the same as those provided by the MC6800, with the one enhancement described in the preceding paragraph: Accumulators A and B can be concatenated to form one 16-bit accumulator — Accumulator D.

The addressing modes that can be used in MC6801 memory reference instructions are the same as those described for the MC6800.

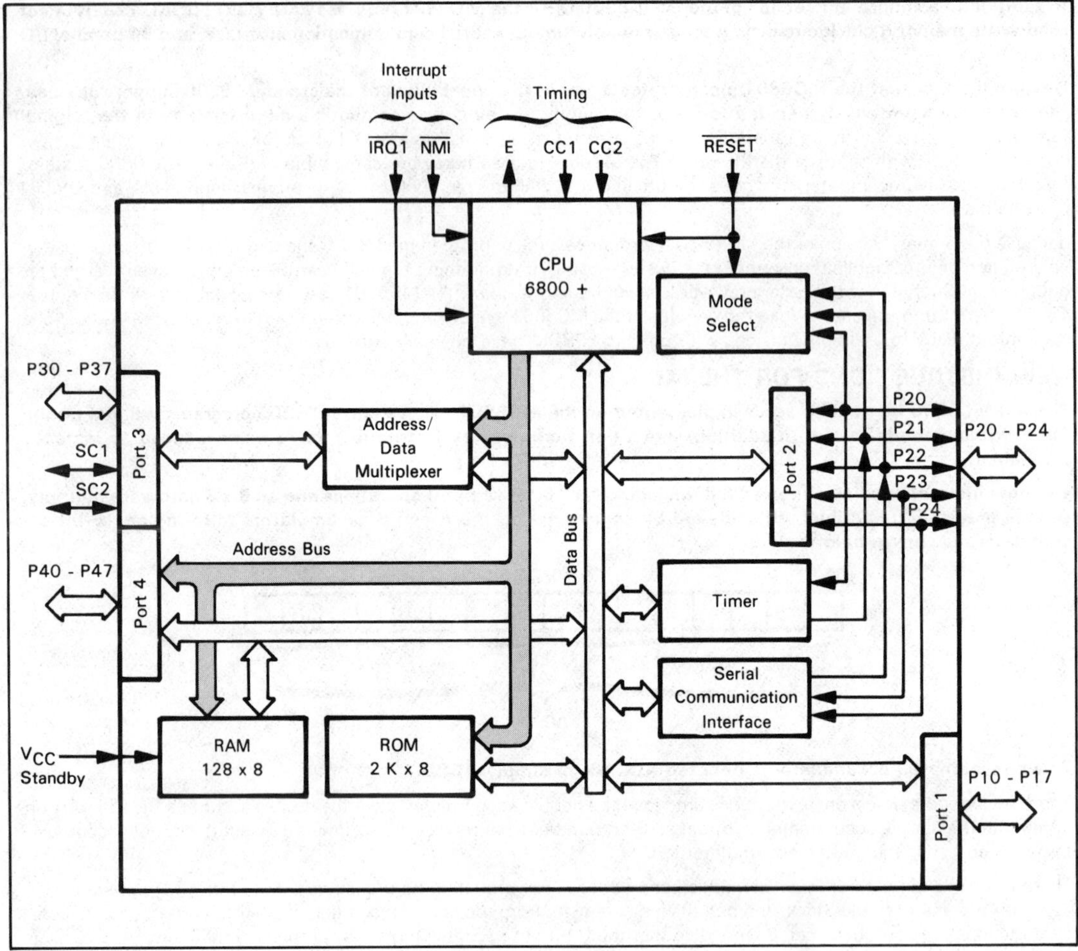


Figure 9-41. MC6801 Functional Block Diagram

## THE MC6801 OPERATING MODES AND FUNCTIONAL OVERVIEW

**There are three basic modes of operation for the MC6801:**

- **Single-chip mode**
- **Expanded multiplexed mode**
- **Expanded non-multiplexed mode**

**The operating modes control the definitions of the following 6801 resources:**

- **The configuration and use of I/O Ports 3 and 4**
- **The amount of memory address space available**
- **The physical location of interrupt vectors**

**Before we discuss the characteristics of each operating mode further, we must take a closer look at the resources provided by the MC6801. Figure 9-41 illustrates the functional logic of the MC6801.**

**In addition to the basic enhanced version of the 6800 CPU, the MC6801 includes four I/O ports, 128 bytes of RAM, 2K bytes of ROM, a programmable timer, and a serial communications interface.** We shall describe the operation of the timer and the serial communication interface later, since their operation is not mode dependent. The operating mode does have a slight impact on the way on-chip memory is addressed, but we shall defer that discussion until later in this chapter. Let us now concentrate on the four I/O ports and how they are configured for the various operating modes.

**MC6801 I/O PORT 1 FUNCTIONS**

**I/O Port 1** operates in a completely straightforward manner; it **is a simple I/O port that is always used for data input or output.** Each of its eight lines (P10-P17) can be individually programmed to act as an input or an output. The operation of I/O Port 1 is the same for all of the MC6801 operating modes.

**MC6801 I/O PORT 2 FUNCTIONS**

**I/O Port 2 is also unaffected by the MC6801 operating mode. You can see in Figure 9-41, however, that the lines to and from this port perform multiple functions.** This port has only five lines, and **all five may be used as simple parallel data inputs. Four of the five lines may also be used as simple data output lines,** but P21 can only be used to output information from the programmable timer. **Three of the lines are also used by serial communication interface logic whenever this function is enabled. During reset operations, the three low-order lines (P20, P21, P22) are used to select the MC6801 operating mode.** We shall describe this mode select function in detail when we discuss the reset operation.

You may have asked yourself why three lines are required to select the operating mode when we have stated that there are only a total of three different modes. The answer to that question is that there are several variations within each of the three primary operating modes, so that there is an actual total of seven different modes of operation. Thus, three lines or bits are required to select one of the seven modes. A detailed discussion of the nuances of each of these sub-modes is not necessary to the understanding of the three primary operating modes, and we shall therefore defer that discussion until we have completed our overview.

**MC6801 I/O PORT 3 FUNCTIONS**

**I/O Port 3 provides eight lines (P30-P37) that are used either for data input/output or address output, depending on the operating mode.** When the MC6801 is in the single-chip mode, P30-P37 simply function as parallel data inputs/outputs. In the expanded non-multiplexed mode of operation, I/O Port 3 becomes the bidirectional Data Bus for the 6800 CPU. In the expanded non-multiplexed mode, I/O Port 3 is used both as the Data Bus and as the Address Bus for the eight least significant address bits (A0-A7). This I/O port also has two strobe control signals (SCI, SC2) associated with it; these two signals are used as data input/output strobes in the single-chip mode, and as a read/write and I/O strobe signal in the expanded modes of operation.

**MC6801 I/O PORT 4 FUNCTIONS**

**I/O Port 4** operation also varies according to the MC6801 operating mode. **In single-chip mode,** this port **is a simple programmable parallel input/output port. In the expanded modes of operation, the lines from I/O Port 4 (P40-P47) are used as address outputs.**

Now that we are a bit more familiar with the resources of the MC6801, let us once again approach the topic of operating modes.

**MC6801 SINGLE-CHIP CONFIGURATION**

**The single-chip mode of operation for the MC6801 implies that the device will be used without external memory.** In this mode of operation, address information from the CPU is available only on the chip, since all of the I/O ports are used for transfer of data.

Obviously, if you cannot address external memory, then **during single-chip operation you are limited to the internal or on-chip memory provided by the MC6801,** and you therefore have 128 bytes of read/write memory and 2K bytes of ROM.

**MC6801 EXPANDED NON-MULTIPLEXED MODE**

**The expanded non-multiplexed mode of operation is intended to allow the MC6801 to be interfaced directly to the standard 6800 family of peripheral devices without additional external logic.** When you operate in this mode, I/O Port 3 is used as the standard 6800 system Data Bus and I/O Port 4 becomes a partial Address Bus (address lines A0-A7). These eight address lines allow the MC6801 to address up to 256 bytes of external memory in addition to the on-chip RAM and ROM. In this mode of operation, the two control signals (SC1, SC2) provided by Port 3 are used as the I/O Select (IOS) and Read/Write (R/$\overline{W}$) signals.

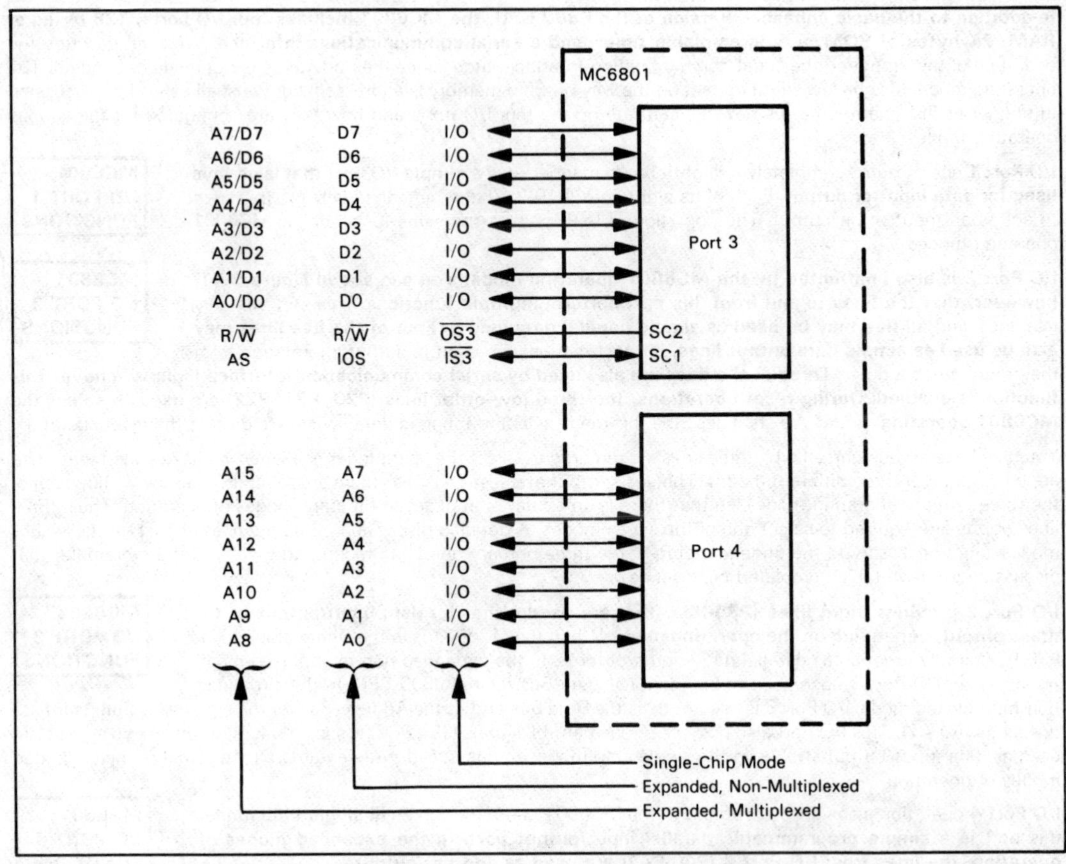


Figure 9-42. MC6801 Port 3 and Port 4 Usage

**MC6801 EXPANDED MULTIPLEXED MODE**

**The third primary mode of operation for the MC6801 is the expanded multiplexed mode. This mode allows the MC6801 to address a full 64K words of memory or I/O.** This addressing capability requires a total of 16 address lines and is achieved by devoting Port 4 to the eight high-order address lines (A8-A15), while Port 3 is used for both the low-order address lines (A0-A7) and the system Data Bus. Thus, the Port 3 lines are multiplexed: at the beginning of a read or write operation they are used to output address information and during the latter portion of a read/write cycle they are used to input or output data. The SC2 signal from Port 3 is used as the Read/Write (R/$\overline{W}$) signal, while the SC1 line from Port 3 is used as an address strobe (AS) signal. The address strobe can be used by external logic to demultiplex the address information from the Port 3 lines.

**Figure 9-42 illustrates the functions of each of the Port 3 and Port 4 lines for the three primary operating modes.**

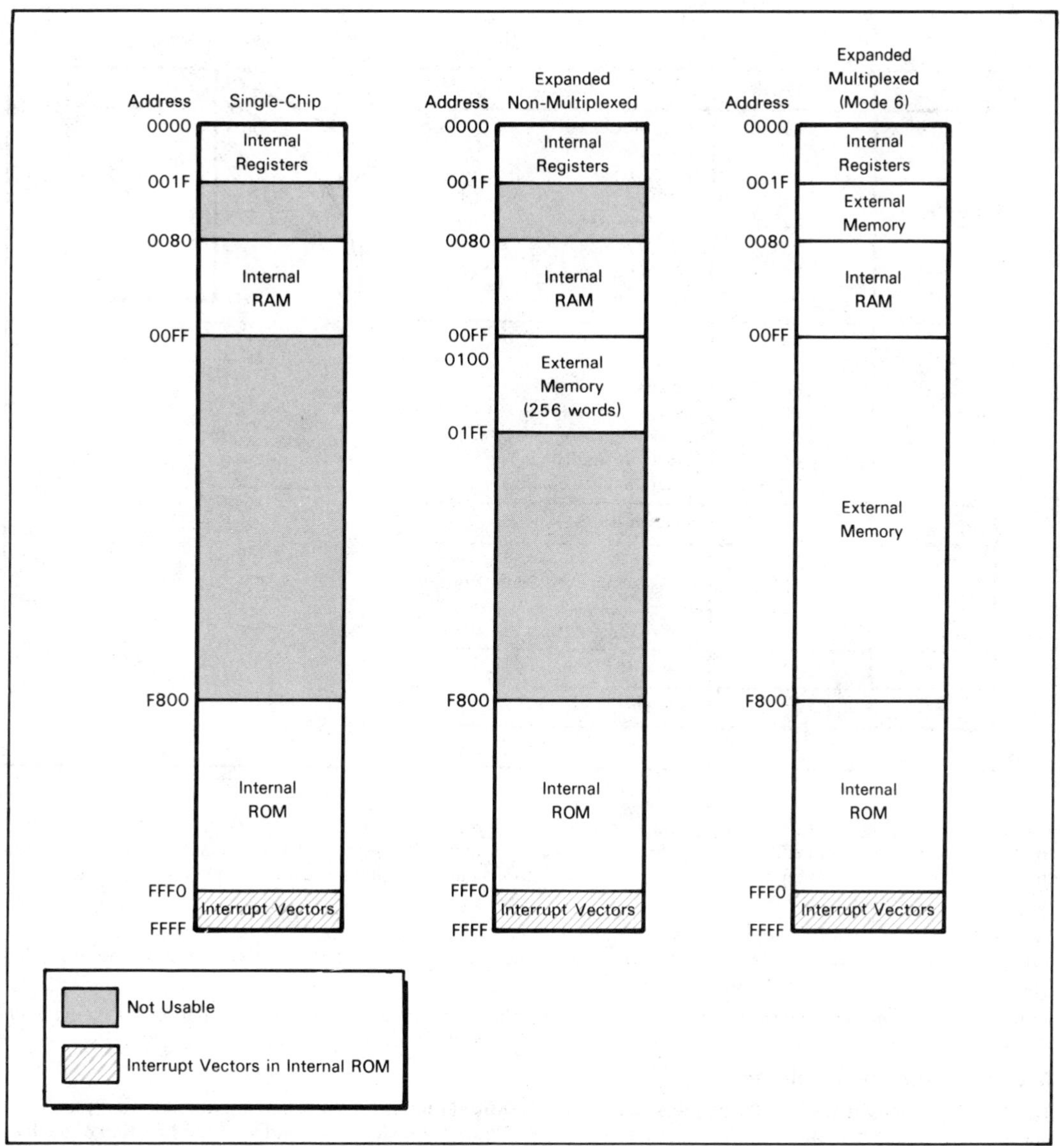


Figure 9-43. MC6801 Memory Map

## MC6801 MEMORY MAP

**The allocation of memory and/or I/O address space varies from mode to mode in the MC6801. Figure 9-43 illustrates the memory map for the three primary modes of operation.**

As we described in our discussions of each operating mode, **the amount of external memory address space available varies from 0 in the single-chip mode to 64K in the expanded multiplexed mode.** But as you can see in Figure 9-43, there are some constants that prevail in all modes. The address space from $0000_{16}$ to $001F_{16}$ is always devoted to internal registers. We will explain the purpose of these internal registers shortly. The 128 bytes of internal RAM are positioned in the address space from $0080_{16}$ to $00FF_{16}$. The 2K bytes of on-chip ROM are located in the address space F800 through FFFF, with the uppermost 16 bytes of this space reserved for interrupt vectors.

| | Hex Address | Register |
|---|---|---|
| I/O Ports | 00 | Data Direction 1 |
| | 01 | Data Direction 2 |
| | 02 | I/O Port 1 |
| | 03 | I/O Port 2 |
| | 04 | Data Direction 3 |
| | 05 | Data Direction 4 |
| | 06 | I/O Port 3 |
| | 07 | I/O Port 4 |
| Counter | 08 | TCSR |
| | 09 | Counter High Byte |
| | 0A | Counter Low Byte |
| | 0B | Output Compare High Byte |
| | 0C | Output Compare Low Byte |
| | 0D | Input Capture High Byte |
| | 0E | Input Capture Low Byte |
| Port 3 | 0F | I/O Port 3 C/S Register |
| Serial I/O | 10 | Serial Rate and Mode Register |
| | 11 | Serial Control and Status Register |
| | 12 | Serial Receiver Data Register |
| | 13 | Serial Transmit Data Register |
| | 14 | RAM/ROM Control Register |
| | 15-1F | Reserved |



Figure 9-44. MC6801 Internal Registers

For the single-chip mode, the internal memory is the only address space available. The expanded non-multiplexed mode makes an additional 256 memory address locations (from $0100_{16}$ to $01FF_{16}$) available. In the expanded multiplexed mode of operation, the entire 65K address locations can be addressed using both Ports 3 and 4 to output addresses to external devices.

We must note at this point that there are several other address map options that can be obtained or achieved in the expanded multiplexed mode of operation. We will discuss these additional options when we describe the expanded multiplexed mode of operation in further detail.

At this point, it is relevant to discuss the internal registers and interrupt vectors which occupy part of the memory address space, but which have not yet been referred to in our description of the MC6801.

## MC6801 Internal Registers

**The MC6801 reserves the first 32 address locations (0000-001F) for use as internal registers.** Currently, only the first 15 of these locations are assigned for specific functions. **Figure 9-44 illustrates and lists the function of each of the registers located in this address space.** As you can see in this figure, some of these registers are used to control and access the four I/O ports, while the others are used for the programmable timer and serial I/O functions of the MC6801. We shall describe how each of these registers is used when we describe the associated logic functions. At this point we shall merely point out that these address locations are not part of the internal RAM area. That is, although these internal registers might be considered read/write memory in the pure sense of that definition, any attempt to write to an address location in the memory space occupied by the internal registers will always result in a modification of the contents of these registers.

## MC6801 Low Power Standby Considerations

**This discussion may, at first glance, seem to have been incorrectly included within the section describing memory maps. But bear with us and you will see that the topic is indeed relevant at this point.**

**The first 64 bytes of internal RAM (locations 0080 to 00BF) have a low power standby mode. These locations are energized via a power pin separate from the power pin that supplies the rest of the MC6801.** This pin ($V_{CC}$ Standby) must be powered, regardless of whether or not the user intends to utilize the standby power feature. If the standby feature is not required, tie $V_{CC}$ Standby to $V_{CC}$. If the standby feature is required, the following circuit can be used:

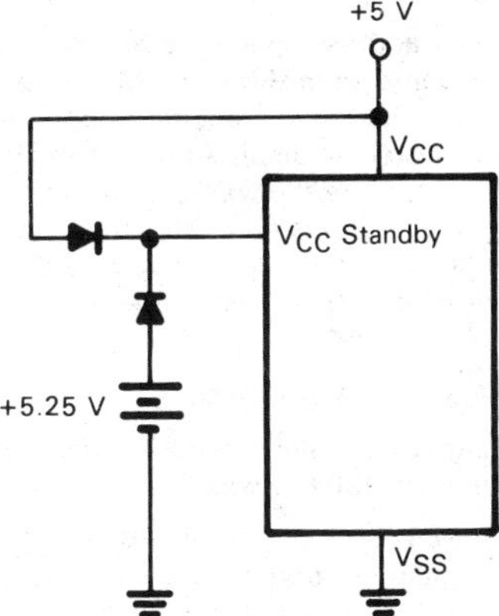


**To maintain the integrity of data in the standby memory, you must ensure that $V_{CC}$ Standby does not fall below the minimum specified value $V_{SBB}$ noted in the data sheets.**

**A RAM Control register is provided in the MC6801 internal registers (address 0014) to monitor and control the status of the standby RAM.** The following illustration shows the function of each bit in this register:

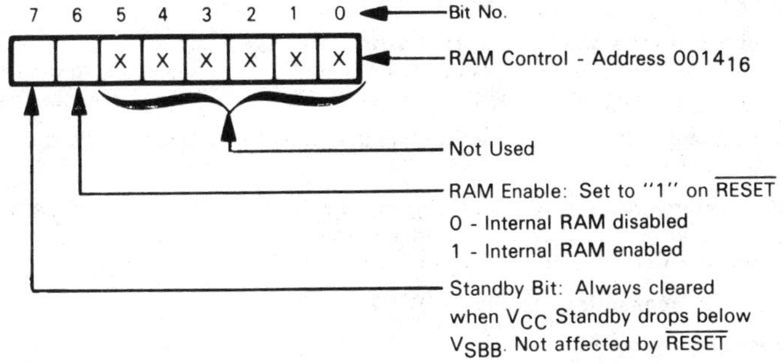


**RAME is the enable bit for on-chip RAM.** RAME must be "1" for the on-chip RAM to be accessed. If RAME is "0", on-chip RAM cannot be read from or written to. While on-chip RAM is disabled, its memory space is also disabled, and addresses in the range 0080 to 00FF are deflected to external memory. Thus, the address space $0080_{16}$ through $00FF_{16}$ is duplicated. When RAME = 0, external memory is accessed; when RAME = 1, internal RAM is accessed.

RAME is set to "1" during $\overline{\text{RESET}}$, provided that standby power is available on the positive edge of $\overline{\text{RESET}}$.

**For standby storage to be of any value, you must guarantee that the contents of the standby RAM are not destroyed by spurious writes as power-down occurs, and that the standby voltage has not dropped below the minimum $V_{SBB}$ required to maintain data integrity.** In the following discussion, it is assumed that the system has some sort of power-down interrupt circuitry.

As part of the power-down sequence, the software clears the RAME bit, removing the standby memory from the computer's address space. While this does not guarantee the integrity of data in the standby RAM (a "runaway" processor can still write a "1" to the RAME bit and subsequently alter the RAM), it greatly reduces the probability that this data will be altered. (By way of contrast, the MC6802 uses an external voltage source on its RE pin to enable or disable the internal standby RAM — thus, it cannot be accidentally restored to the computer's address space by a "runaway" processor).

**Bit 7 of the RAM Control register is used to monitor the standby source.** This bit is normally set to "1" by software during the power-down sequence. If the standby voltage drops below $V_{SBB}$ at any time (normal operation or during a power loss situation), this bit will be cleared by hardware. To determine whether the standby dropped too low, the state of bit 7 may be tested after powerup. If the bit is still set, $V_{CC}$ Standby did not drop below $V_{SBB}$. If the bit is cleared, the contents of the standby RAM should be suspect.

You can use bit 7 to test the standby voltage at any time by writing a "1" into it, then reading it back. If the result of this read is a "0", it means the standby voltage is below $V_{SBB}$.

## MC6801 Interrupt Vectors

**The uppermost 16 locations of the MC6801 address space are reserved for use as interrupt vectors. This use of address space for interrupt vectors is the same as in the basic MC6800 system, except that several additional interrupt options are provided.** We shall describe the operation of these interrupt vectors and the additional options available later when we discuss the interrupt system in detail. At this point we shall merely point out that in the memory map shown in Figure 9-43, the interrupt vectors are shown in internal ROM on the MC6801. This would be the most typical place for the interrupt vectors in a system that is mass produced. However, some of the variations available in the expanded multiplexed mode of operation allow the interrupt vectors to be located in external memory to provide additional flexibility in system configuration. We shall discuss these options in detail as we discuss each of the alternate modes.

## MC6801 MICROCOMPUTER PINS AND SIGNALS

**The MC6801 microcomputer pins and signals are illustrated in Figure 9-45. A description of these signals is useful as a guide to the way in which the MC6801 works.**

**P10-P17 serve as the Data Bus for I/O Port 1.** Each pin may be individually programmed for either input or output, and these pins perform only this function regardless of the mode operation.

**P20-P24 are multifunction pins.** These five pins serve I/O Port 2 and can be individually programmed for input or output. P20 and P21 also serve the programmable timer: P20 is the input to the timer and P21 is the output from the timer. P22, P23, and P24 serve the serial communication interface logic in addition to their I/O port function.

**P30-P37 serve I/O Port 3 and also serve as the Address Bus in expanded modes of operation.**

**P40-P47 serve I/O Port 4, and in the expanded multiplexed mode of operation serve as a partial Address Bus in conjunction with P30-P37.**

**SC1 and SC2 are strobe control signals associated with Port 3.** SC1 can be used as either an input or output handshaking signal in the single-chip mode and is the address strobe signal in expanded modes. SC2 is a data output strobe signal in the single-chip mode and is used as the Read/Write (R/$\overline{\text{W}}$) signal in expanded modes of operation.

**$\overline{\text{IRQ}}$ and $\overline{\text{NMI}}$ are the standard 6800 interrupt request inputs.** The $\overline{\text{IRQ}}$ input can be disabled under program control, while the $\overline{\text{NMI}}$ interrupt request cannot be inhibited.

**E is the standard 6800 system enabling synchronizing signal** which is output by the MC6801 to simplify interfacing to the 6800 family support devices. As we explained earlier in this chapter during our discussion of 6800 clock devices, E consists of the MC6800 VMA signal, ANDed with the symbol $\Phi$.

**CC1 and CC2 are the clock connections to the MC6801.**

**$\overline{\text{RESET}}$ is a typical reset signal.**

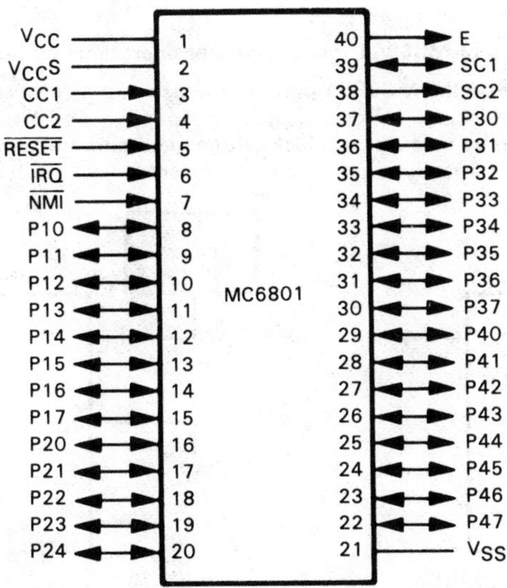


| Pin Name | Description | Type |
|---|---|---|
| P10 - P17 | Port 1 Data Bus | Input or Output |
| P20 - P24 | Port 2 Data Bus. P20, P21 also used by timer. P22 - P24 also used by Serial Communication Logic | Input or Output |
| P30 - P37 | Port 3 Data Bus. Also serves as Address Bus in Expanded Modes | Bidirectional, Tristate |
| P40 - P47 | Port 4 Data Bus. Also serves as partial Address Bus in Expanded Multiplexed Mode | Input or Output |
| SC1 | Strobe Control signal used with Port 3 as data or address strobe | Input or Output |
| SC2 | Strobe Control for Port 3 in Single-Chip Mode. $R/\overline{W}$ signal in Expanded Modes | Output |
| $\overline{IRQ}$ | Interrupt Request | Input |
| $\overline{NMI}$ | Non-Maskable Interrupt | Input |
| $\overline{RESET}$ | Reset | Input |
| E | Device Synchronization | Output |
| CC1, CC2 | Clock Connections | Input |
| $V_{CC}$, $V_{CC}S$, $V_{SS}$ | Power, Standby Power, and Ground | |

Figure 9-45. MC6801 Signals and Pin Assignments

# MC6801 TIMING AND INSTRUCTION EXECUTION

**Let us begin our detailed analysis of MC6801 microcomputer operations by looking at basic timing.**

**An internal divide-by-four circuit on the MC6801 permits the use of a 4 MHz crystal to achieve 1 MHz operation.** For applications where precise timing is not critical, an inexpensive 3.58 MHz color T.V. crystal may be used. **Alternatively, CC2 may be driven by an external clock with a maximum frequency of 4 MHz.** The divide-by-four circuitry is still used in this case. CC1 must be grounded if an external clock is used.

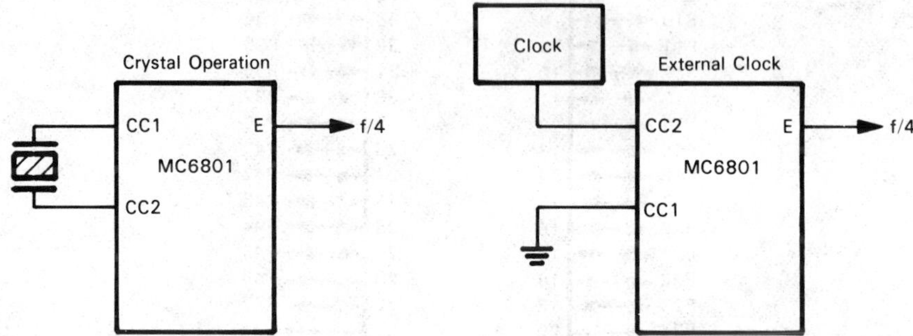


The clock on the MC6801 cannot be stretched — thus, dynamic memories which rely on this technique cannot be used. Memory must either be of the static type or use "hidden refresh" techniques.

**The Enable pin E distributes the synchronizing clock signal to the rest of the system.** It is a TTL-level signal derived from the processor clock, and provides data synchronization and clocking to other 6800 family devices.

There is a mask option of the MC6801 that requires an external clock. This mask option, the MC6801E, does not use an internal divide-by-four circuit, and thus the system functions at the frequency of the external source. There are several other differences between the standard MC6801 and the mask option MC6801E. These differences are relatively minor, and we shall describe all of them after we have completely described the basic MC6801.

## THE MC6801 RESET AND MODE SELECT OPERATIONS

**The reset operation for the MC6801 is basically the same as that described for the MC6800, with minor timing differences and one significant functional addition. To reset the MC6801, $\overline{\text{RESET}}$ must be asserted low for a minimum of three cycles to give the device sufficient response time.** On the subsequent low-to-high transition of $\overline{\text{RESET}}$, maskable interrupts are disabled, and then the contents of memory locations $FFFE_{16}$ and $FFFF_{16}$ are fetched and loaded into the Program Counter. This sequence is the same as for the basic MC6800 CPU.

**One additional function is accomplished during the reset operation: the mode in which the MC6801 is to be operated is established on the rising edge of $\overline{\text{RESET}}$. You specify the operating mode by applying the appropriate logic levels on pins P20, P21, and P22 of Port 2.** The levels present at these pins are sampled on the positive transition of $\overline{\text{RESET}}$. You will recall that P20, P21, and P22 also serve as the inputs and outputs for Port 2 and are used by both the programmable timer and serial communications interface logic. Therefore, you will usually not want to simply tie P20, P21, and P22 permanently to the required logic levels. A simple mode selection scheme that could be used is shown in Figure 9-46.

Isolation between peripheral devices and this initialization circuit may be required if those other devices require levels at initialization which differ from those required to program the operating mode of the MC6801. In this case, a bidirectional coupler, such as an MC14066B, may be used.

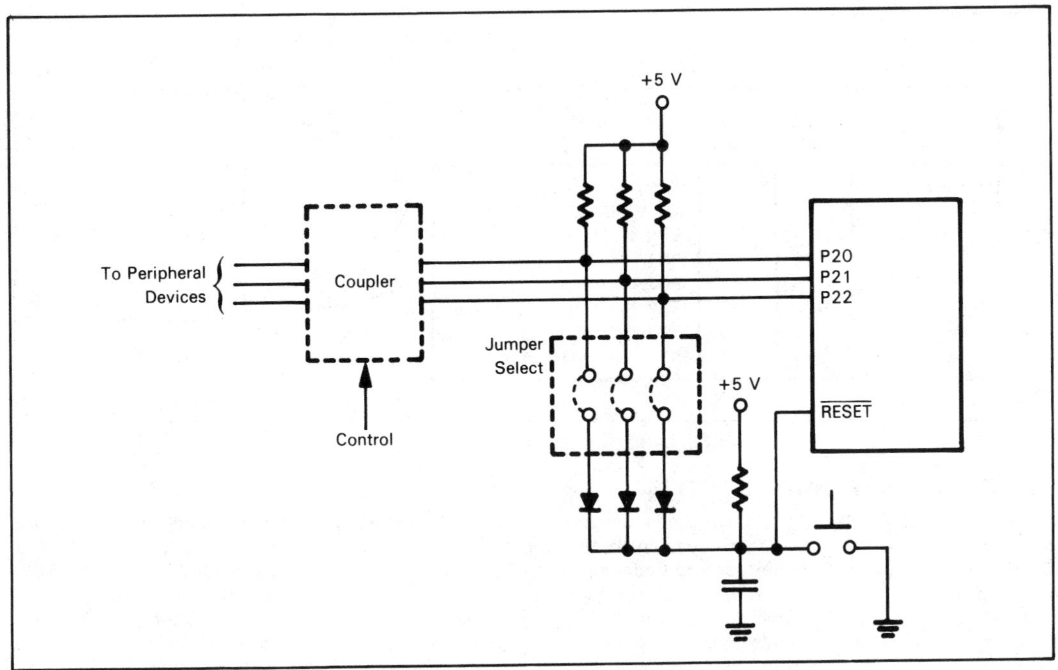


Figure 9-46. MC6801 Typical Mode Selection Circuit

**The following table summarizes the allocation of the MC6801 resources for the various operating modes. Modes 5, 6, and 7 are the three primary operating modes which we have already described. Modes 1,2, and 3 are variations of the expanded multiplexed mode (mode 6) and we shall describe these variations when we discuss that mode in detail. Mode 0 and mode 4 are special purpose test modes.**

| Mode | | P22 | P21 | P20 | ROM | RAM | Interrupt Vectors | Bus |
|---|---|---|---|---|---|---|---|---|
| 7 | Single-Chip | Hi | Hi | Hi | I | I | I | I |
| 6 | Expanded Multiplexed | Hi | Hi | Lo | I | I | I | Ep/M |
| 5 | Expanded Non-Multiplexed | Hi | Lo | Hi | I | I | I | Ep |
| 4 | Single-Chip Test | Hi | Lo | Lo | I(2) | I(1) | I | I |
| 3 | 64 K Address I/O | Lo | Hi | Hi | E | E | E | Ep/M |
| 2 | Ports 3 and 4 External | Lo | Hi | Lo | E | I | E | Ep/M |
| 1 | | Lo | Lo | Hi | I | I | E | Ep/M |
| 0 | Test Data Output from ROM and RAM to I/O Port 3 | Lo | Lo | Lo | I | I | I* | Ep/M |

E — External (all vectors are external)
I — Internal
Ep — Expanded
M — Multiplexed

*First two addresses read from external after reset
(1) Address for RAM XX80 - XXFF
(2) ROM disabled

**When the operating mode is established during the reset operation, the state of the P20, P21, and P22 lines is stored in the Data register for I/O Port 2.** (Data and Control registers for I/O ports will be described shortly.) Therefore, you can determine the current operating mode by reading the contents of I/O Port 2. These three bits in the I/O Port 2 Data register are read-only bits, with one exception — when the MC6801 is operating in mode 4 (the single-chip test mode) you can change the least significant mode bit to a 1 and thus go to mode 5 without having to reset the processor.

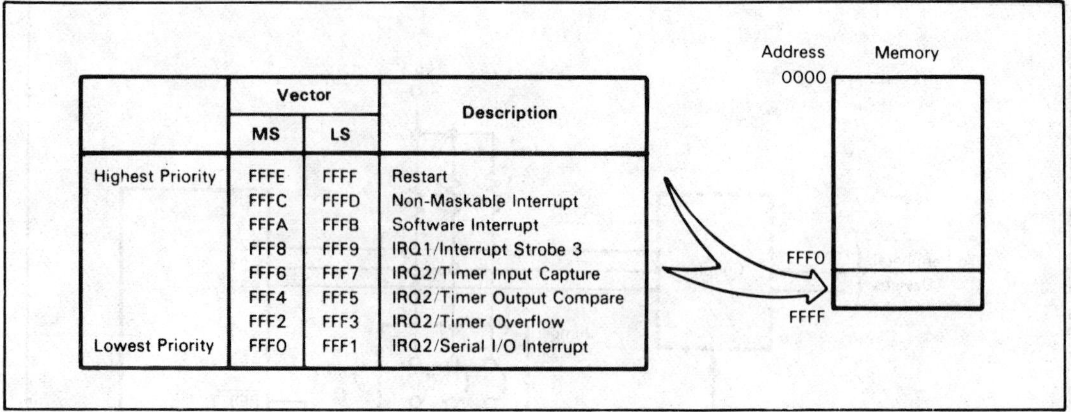

| | Vector MS | Vector LS | Description |
|---|---|---|---|
| Highest Priority | FFFE | FFFF | Restart |
| | FFFC | FFFD | Non-Maskable Interrupt |
| | FFFA | FFFB | Software Interrupt |
| | FFF8 | FFF9 | IRQ1/Interrupt Strobe 3 |
| | FFF6 | FFF7 | IRQ2/Timer Input Capture |
| | FFF4 | FFF5 | IRQ2/Timer Output Compare |
| | FFF2 | FFF3 | IRQ2/Timer Overflow |
| Lowest Priority | FFF0 | FFF1 | IRQ2/Serial I/O Interrupt |



Figure 9-47. MC6801 Interrupt Vectors

## THE MC6801 INTERRUPT SYSTEM

**The response of the MC6801 to interrupts is identical to that of the MC6800, and you should refer to the discussion of the MC6800 interrupt processing at the beginning of this chapter for detailed information. The MC6801, however, does include four additional sources of interrupts beyond those provided by the MC6800.** Figure 9-47 shows the memory map for the interrupt vectors. The sources of interrupts are listed in the order of their priority. The four lowest priority interrupts are the ones that have been added to the MC6801 and, as you can see, they are associated with the programmable timer and serial I/O functions provided by the MC6801. Since the response to these interrupts is identical to that of the MC6800, we shall not repeat a description of the interrupt response. We shall defer discussion of the usage of these new interrupts until later, when we describe the programmable timer and serial I/O functions provided by the MC6801.

## MC6801 I/O PORT OPERATIONS

**Each of the four MC6801 I/O ports has two registers associated with it: a Data Direction register and a Data register or buffer. All of these registers are internal (on the MC6801 chip) and occupy address locations $0000_{16}$ through $0007_{16}$ (as shown in Figure 9-44).**

**The Data Direction register for each port is used to specify which lines are to function as inputs and which as outputs. The Data register associated with each port is used to hold the data being transferred from the CPU to the I/O port (on output) or from the I/O port to the CPU (on input).** To specify that a line is to be an output, you write a "1" into the corresponding bit position of that port's Data Direction register. Those lines that are to be inputs must have a "0" written into the appropriate bit position of the Data Direction register. For example, addresses $0000_{16}$ and $0002_{16}$ are the Data Direction register and Data register, respectively, for Port 1. The following four-instruction sequence

```
LDA A #$FF
STA A $00
LDA A #$15
STA A $02
```

results in all eight of the Port 1 lines being defined as outputs, and causes the following logic levels to be output on pins P10-P17:

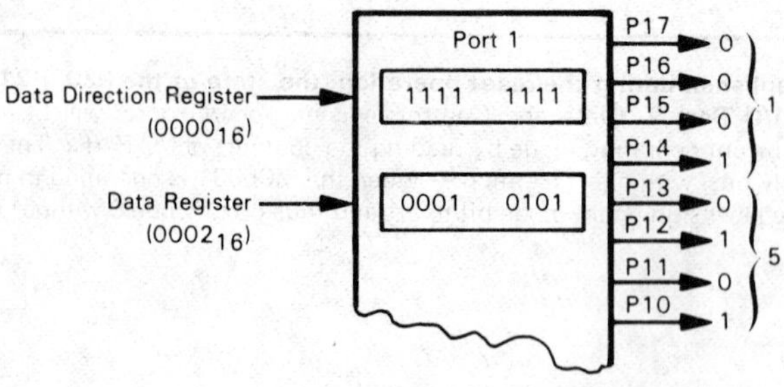

This aspect of the I/O ports is the same for all four when they are being used as simple I/O ports. As we have seen in our preceding discussion, however, Port 1 is the only port that always functions as a simple I/O port. Additionally, the electrical characteristics of all of the ports are not the same. Let us now consider each of the I/O ports and its characteristics.

**MC6801 PORT 1 OPERATING CHARACTERISTICS**

**Consider Port 1. This port is the most straightforward and always functions as a simple I/O port.** Its eight output buffers are tristate devices, permitting them to enter a high-impedance state when configured for input. As outputs, these lines are TTL-level compatible and may source up to one mA at 1.5 volts to drive a Darlington transistor. On $\overline{RESET}$, all of the Port 1 lines default to the input state.

**MC6801 PORT 2 OPERATING CHARACTERISTICS**

**Consider Port 2. This port provides only five lines, which are shared between the programmable timer, the serial communications interface, and the parallel I/O port.** While all five lines may be configured as parallel inputs, only lines P20, P22, P23, and P24 may be used as parallel outputs. When line P21 is configured as an output, it becomes the timer output. When the serial I/O logic utilizes lines P22, P23, and P24, this usage overrides any other use of these lines.

**The five output buffers for Port 2 have tristate capability, permitting them to enter a high-impedance state when configured for input.** As outputs, these lines have no internal pull-up resistors, but will drive TTL directly. External pull-up resistors are required for driving CMOS circuits. On $\overline{RESET}$, the Port 2 lines default to the input state.

**As we described in our earlier discussion of the reset operation, Port 2 is also used during initialization to establish the operating mode. Since Port 2 provides only five I/O lines, it uses only the five least significant bits in its Data register. The three most significant bits are then used to store the mode bits:**

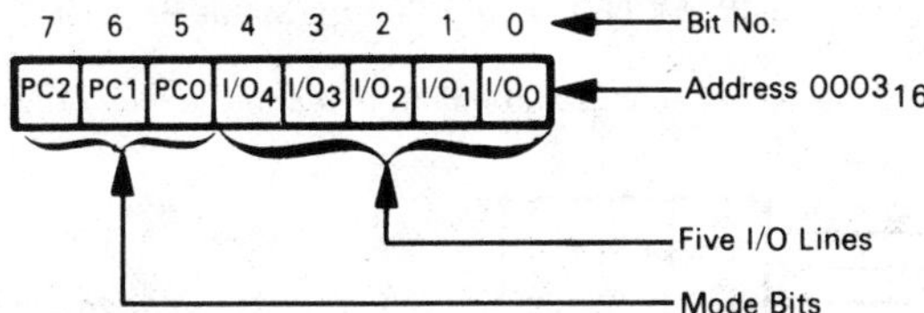


When $\overline{RESET}$ goes high, the operating mode (asserted on lines P20, P21, and P22) is latched into bits PC0, PC1, and PC2, respectively. You can then read the contents of these locations to determine the current operating mode. As we have mentioned previously, these bits are read-only bits with one exception — you can go from mode 4 to mode 5 by setting PC0 to a "1".

**MC6801 PORT 3 OPERATING CHARACTERISTICS**

**Let us now consider Port 3. First of all, the function of Port 3 depends on the operating mode of the MC6801. At this point we shall only consider the operation of Port 3 when the MC6801 is in the single-chip mode (mode 7).** We shall describe how Port 3 is used in the expanded modes of operation later when we discuss those modes in detail.

**In the single-chip mode of operation, Port 3 may be used in the following ways:**

- **As a simple I/O port**
- **As an I/O port with handshaking**
- **As an I/O port with latched inputs**

**When used as a simple I/O port, the operation of Port 3 is the same as Port 1, which we described earlier.**

**When Port 3 is used as an I/O port with handshaking or as an I/O port with latched inputs, the two strobe control signals (SC1 and SC2) associated with Port 3 are used. SC1 becomes an input strobe signal (referred to as $\overline{IS3}$) and SC2 becomes an output strobe signal (referred to as $\overline{OS3}$). The operation of Port 3 when it is used with handshaking or as a latched input port is supervised and controlled by the Port 3 Control/Status register.** The Port 3 Control/Status register is one of the internal registers and is at address $000F_{16}$. Figure 9-48 shows how each bit in this registeis used. The significance of each of these bits will become apparent as we proceed through our descriptions of the latched and handshaking I/O operations.

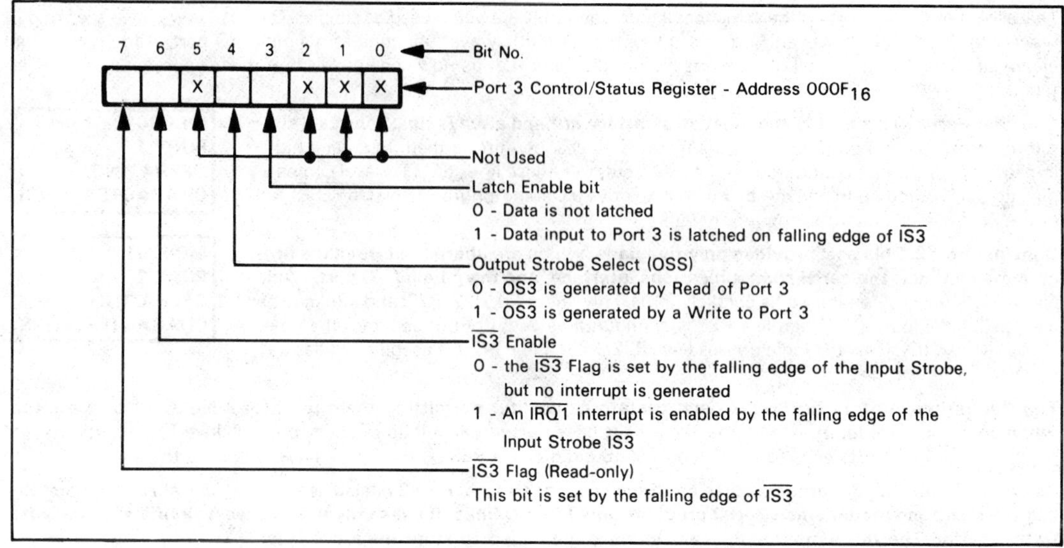


Figure 9-48. MC6801 Port 3 Control/Status Register

The following illustration shows the general connections and timing that apply when Port 3 is used as a latched input port:

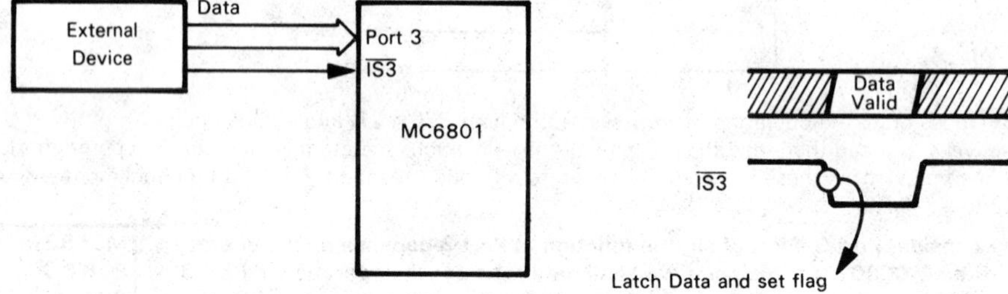


As illustrated above, data supplied to the CPU by the external device is latched into Port 3 on the falling edge of $\overline{IS3}$. A subsequent LDA instruction may be used to load the data into the CPU. A flag is also set by $\overline{IS3}$. This flag may be checked by software or it may initiate an interrupt, depending on the configuration of the Port 3 Control/Status register.

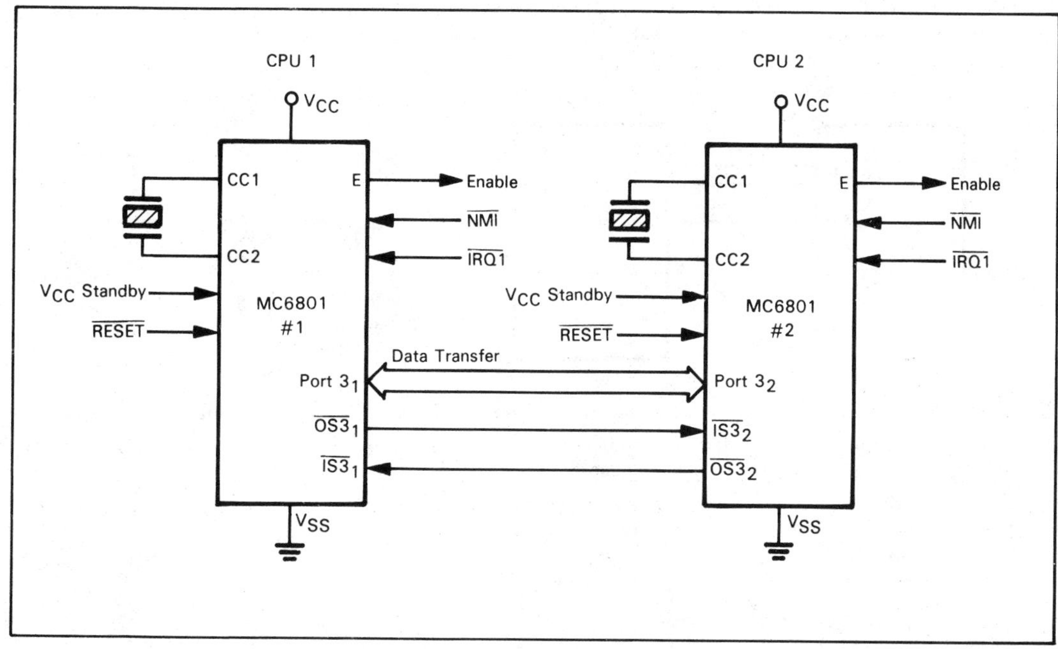


Figure 9-49. MC6801 Port 3 Used in Handshake Mode

**Timing for the input strobe is shown below.** Note that it is the external device which must meet these timing constraints, as it supplies the data and asserts $\overline{IS3}$ low to effect the transfer.

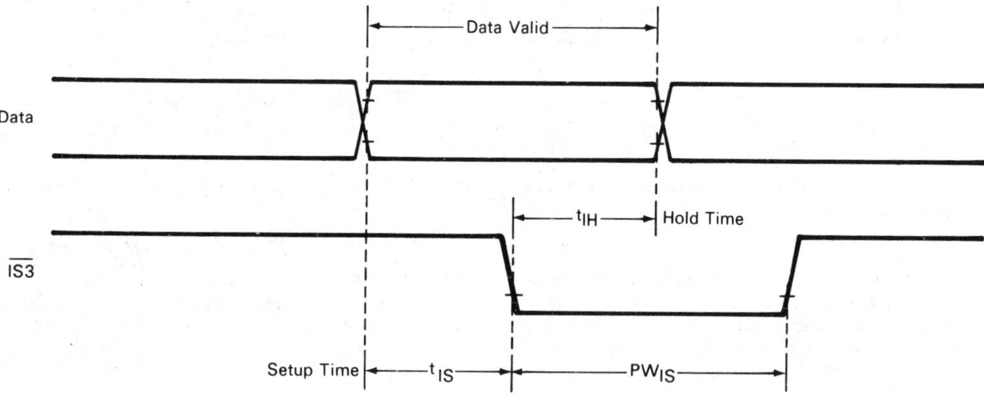


Consult the MC6801 data sheets at the end of this chapter for timing details.

**MC6801 PORT 3 HANDSHAKE MODE**

**Figure 9-49 illustrates a pair of MC6801 microcomputers communicating with one another by using Port 3 in the handshake mode.**

**In this case, strobe lines $\overline{IS3}$ (SC1) and $\overline{OS3}$ (SC2) are responsible for I/O management. Output strobe $\overline{OS3}$ is an active-low strobe generated by the MC6801.** Typical operation is as follows:

1) CPU 1 places data on its Port 3 output lines and asserts $\overline{OS3}_1$ low.

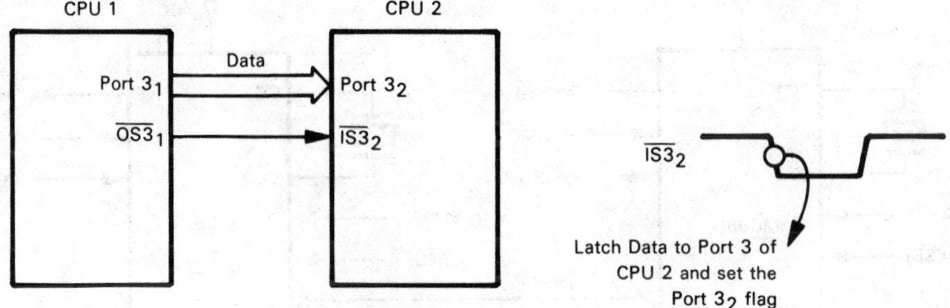


2) The low-going strobe $\overline{IS3}_2$ latches this data into Port 3 on CPU 2, setting a flag or generating an interrupt.

3) When CPU 2, determines that it has new data in Port 3 (either via an interrupt or by checking the flag), it loads it into an accumulator and manipulates it as necessary.

4) CPU 2 now acknowledges the receipt of the above-mentioned data by asserting $\overline{OS3}_2$ low. This may be a simple acknowledgement, or it may be used to return a word of data to CPU 2.

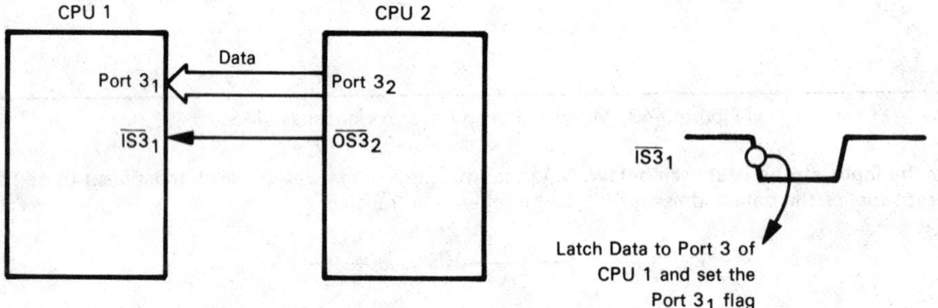


5) If CPU 2 is returning data to CPU 1, the low-going strobe on $\overline{IS3}_1$ latches this data into CPU 1 Port 3 and sets the flag (or asserts an interrupt). If CPU 2 is not returning data, the signal from $\overline{OS3}_2$ is simply treated as an acknowledgement that CPU 2 has received that data and is ready for more.

Since **Port 3 is the only port involved in the above transaction, the remaining 21 I/O lines may be used for other control functions.**

This illustration of handshaking is, of course, only one of the many variations that may be implemented.

**MC6801 PORT 4 OPERATING CHARACTERISTICS**

**Let us now consider Port 4. In the single-chip mode of operation, Port 4 functions as a simple I/O port** with its Data Direction register at $0005_{16}$ and its Data register at $0007_{16}$. **In the expanded, multiplexed mode of operation (mode 6), the Port 4 pins are used to output address information.** However, some of the Port 4 pins may still be available as input pins even in this mode of operation. We shall provide a further discussion of the Port 4 pins when we describe the expanded operating modes in detail.

## THE MC6801 OPERATING MODES

**As we have seen in the preceding discussion, there are three primary modes of operation for the MC6801: single-chip mode, expanded non-multiplexed mode, and expanded multiplexed mode. Figure 9-50 shows the signal definitions for the single-chip mode of operation.**

In the single-chip mode of operation the only memory available is the on-chip memory provided by the MC6801. We have already discussed how each of the I/O ports functions in this single-chip mode, and no further discussion is needed at this point.

**The expanded, non-multiplexed mode of operation (mode 5) is intended to allow the MC6801 to be interfaced directly to standard 6800 devices.** To operate in this mode, **Ports 3 and 4 must be functionally redefined as shown in Figure 9-51. Configuration of these ports occurs at $\overline{RESET}$ time. Ports 1 and 2 remain unchanged.**

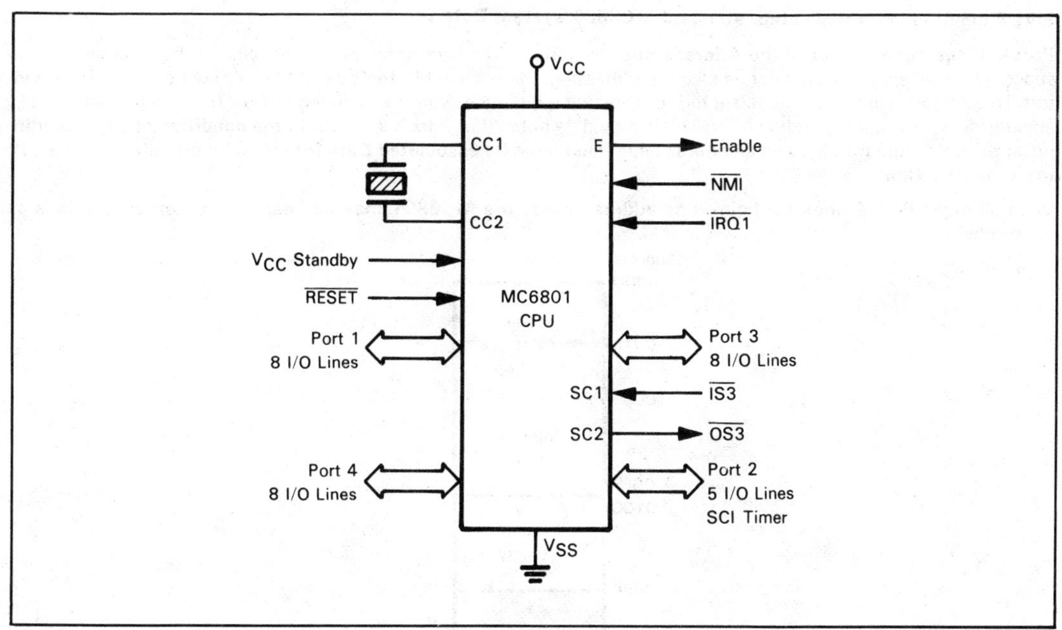


Figure 9-50. MC6801 Single-Chip Mode (Mode 7)

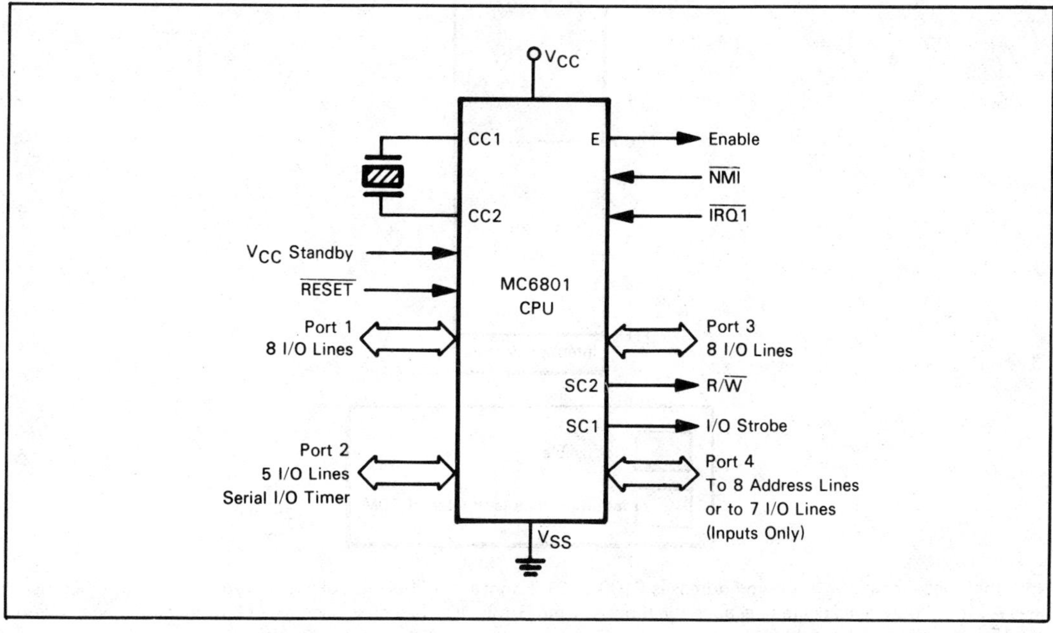


Figure 9-51. MC6801 Expanded, Non-Multiplexed Mode (Mode 5)

**Port 3 functions as a dedicated, standard MC6800 system Data Bus.**

**Port 4 brings out a subset of the Address Bus** (lines A0 to A7), permitting partial decoding of the external memory space. When all eight lines are not needed for addressing, the not used **("don't care") lines may be used for data input.** To configure a line as an input, set the corresponding bit in the Data Direction register to "0"; to configure a line as an address, set the corresponding bit to "1". It should be noted that **Port 4 defaults to the condition of eight user inputs; thus, any line that is to be an address line must have its associated Data Direction bit initialized to the "1" state by software.**

**With all eight Port 4 lines configured as address lines, the MC6801 may address 256 external locations as shown below.**

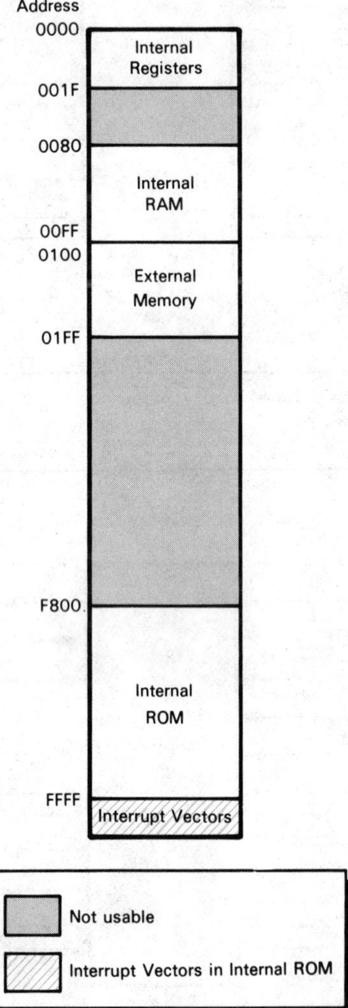


Note that these locations are from addresses 0100 to 01FF, not from 0000 to 00FF as one might expect when using lines A0 to A7 only. This occurs because the Input/Output Strobe $\overline{IOS}$ (which is used as a chip select) decodes bits A9 to A15 internally as 01 (hex).

Standard MC6800 parts can be interfaced to the system as illustrated in Figure 9-52.

**R/$\overline{W}$ and E play the same role in this interface as they do in the basic MC6800 scheme.**

**Figures 9-53 and 9-54 illustrate Read and Write timing for devices on the bus.** Exact timing is given in the MC6801 data sheets at the end of this chapter.

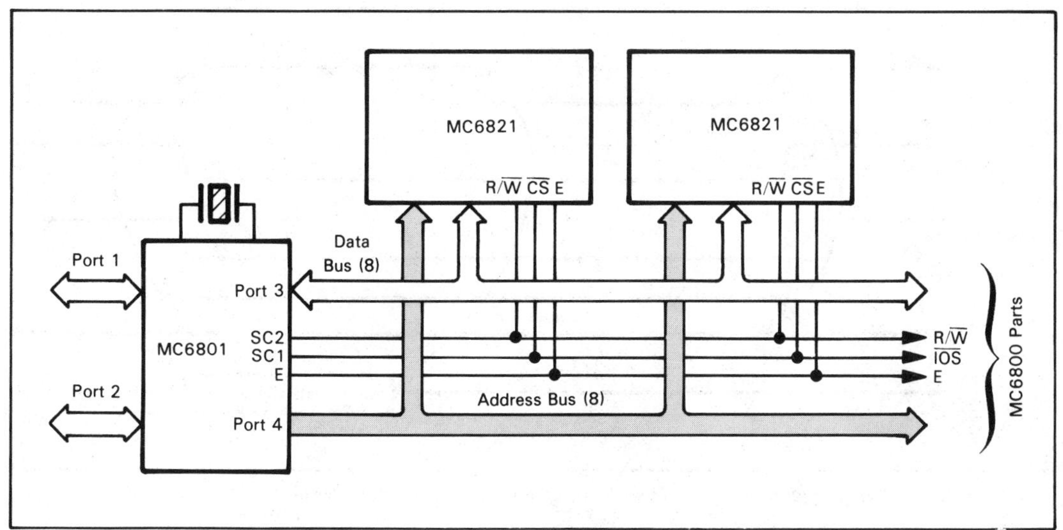


Figure 9-52. Interfacing Standard MC6800 Peripherals to the MC6801

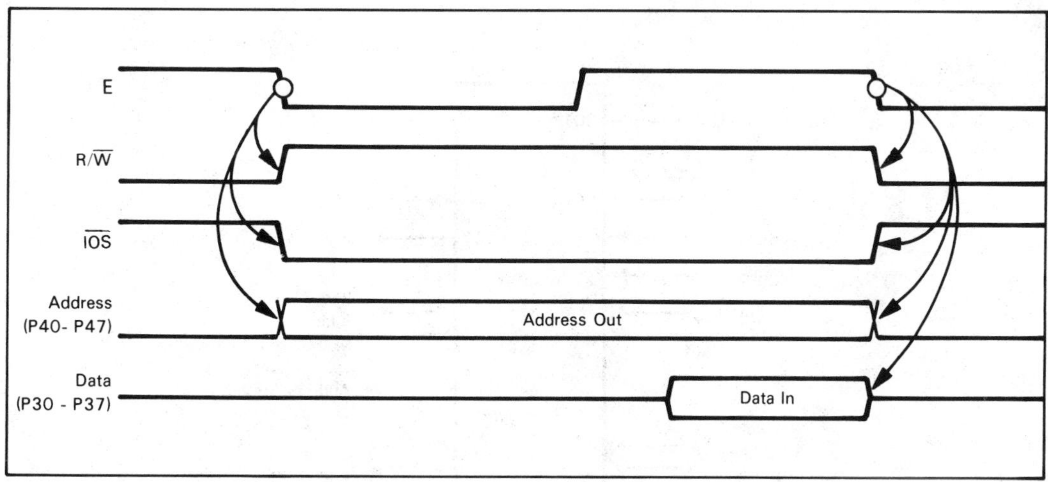


Figure 9-53. MC6801 Non-Multiplexed Bus Timing (Read Cycle)

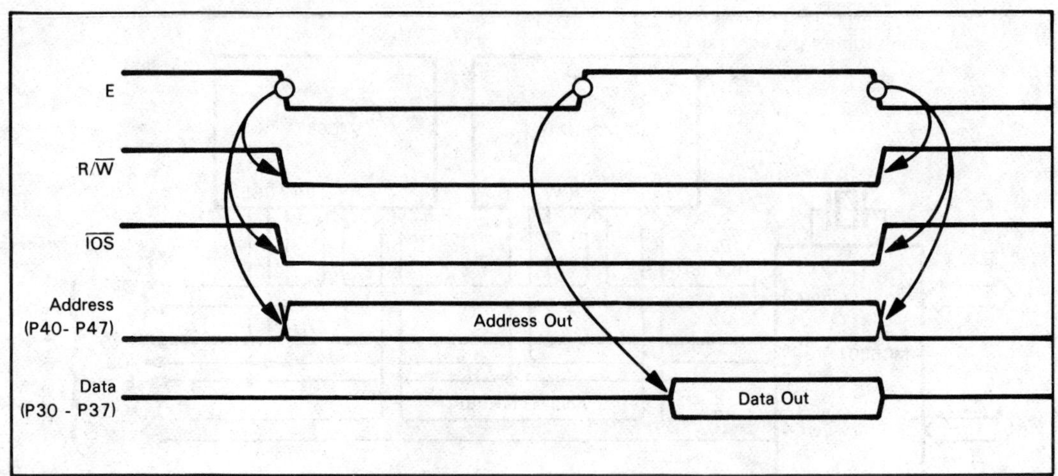


Figure 9-54. MC6801 Non-Multiplexed Bus Timing (Write Cycle)

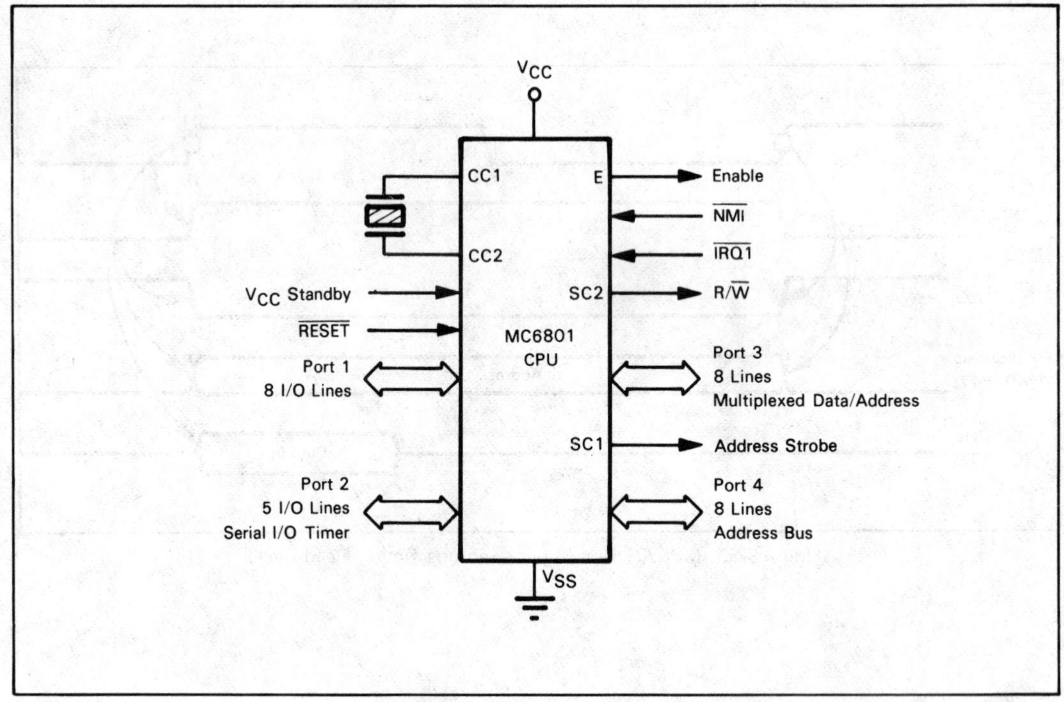


Figure 9-55. Expanded, Multiplexed Mode (Mode 6)

**Let us now consider the expanded, multiplexed modes of operation — modes 1, 2, 3, and 6.**

In these modes, **the MC6801 may be expanded to a full 64K of memory and I/O. This is achieved by multiplexing the Data Bus and low-order address lines on Port 3 and bringing the high-order address lines out on Port 4** as shown in Figure 9-55. It should be noted that any Port 4 lines not required for addressing may be used for inputs.

Since address lines A0 to A7 and data lines D0 to D7 share Port 3, an **external, 8-bit latch will typically be required to capture or demultiplex the address bits. The Address Strobe signal (AS)** can be used as the demultiplexing control signal, as shown in the following illustration:

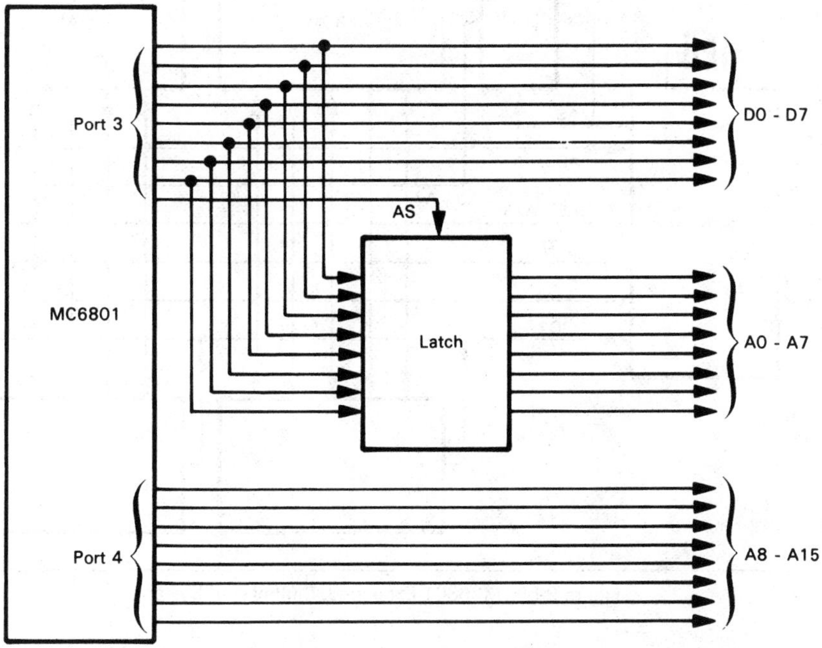


Figure 9-56 illustrates the general connections required to create an expanded system with external PROM, RAM, and I/O interfaces.

**The timing waveforms that result from this expanded, multiplexed mode of operation are illustrated in Figure 9-57.**

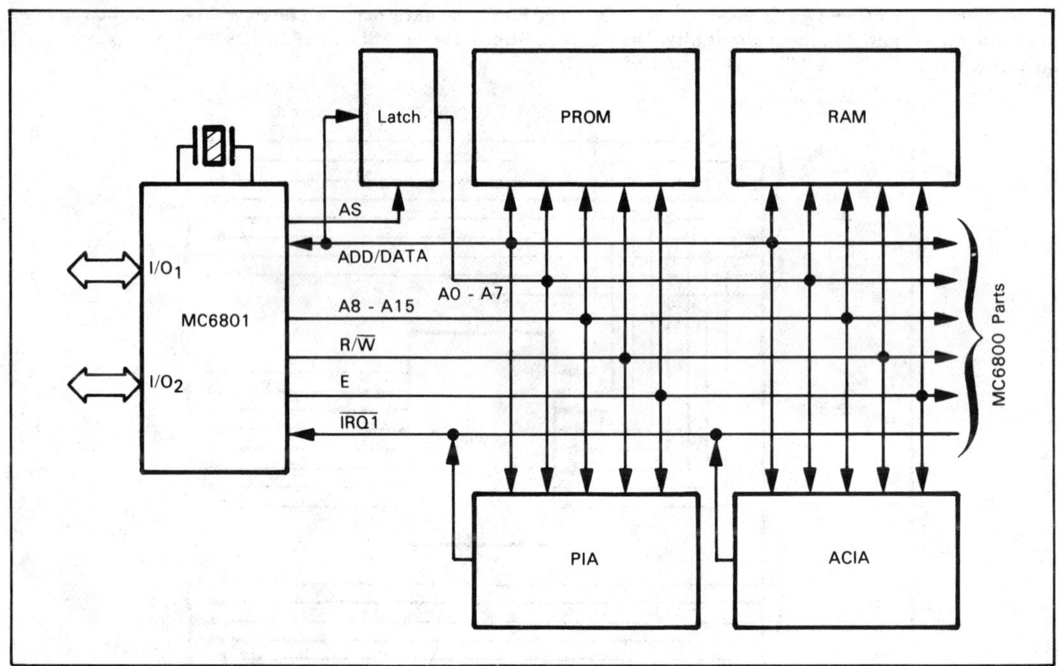


Figure 9-56. MC6801 Expanded, Multiplexed System

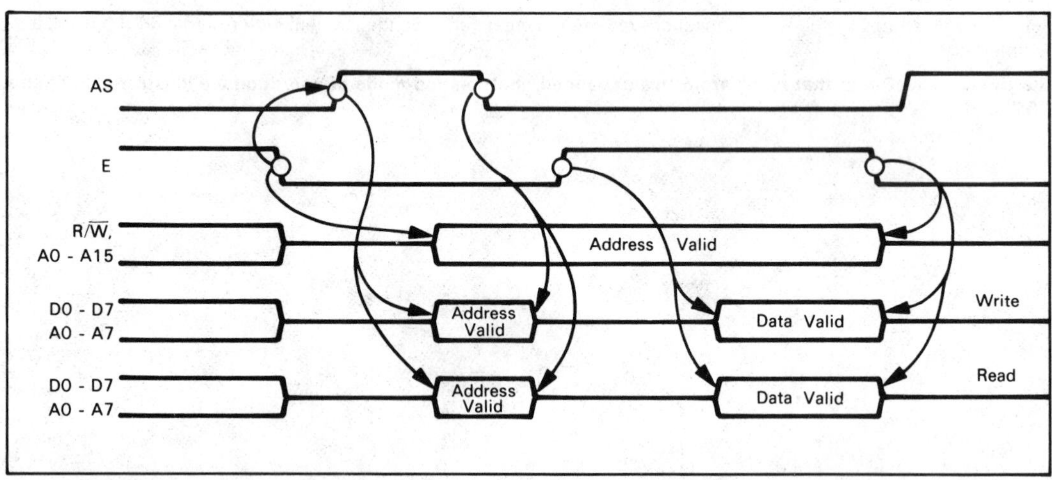


Figure 9-57. MC6801 Bus Timing for MUX Operation (Read and Write)

**Although the Read and Write waveforms are similar, data setup and hold times differ for the two cases.** Actual values are contained in the data sheets for the MC6801 at the end of this chapter.

**MC6801 MEMORY SPACE OPTIONS FOR EXPANDED, MULTIPLEXED MODES**

**The four different expanded, multiplexed modes (1, 2, 3, and 6) provide four memory space options, giving you the choice between internal RAM, ROM, and interrupt vectors. Memory maps for each of the four modes are shown in Figure 9-58.**

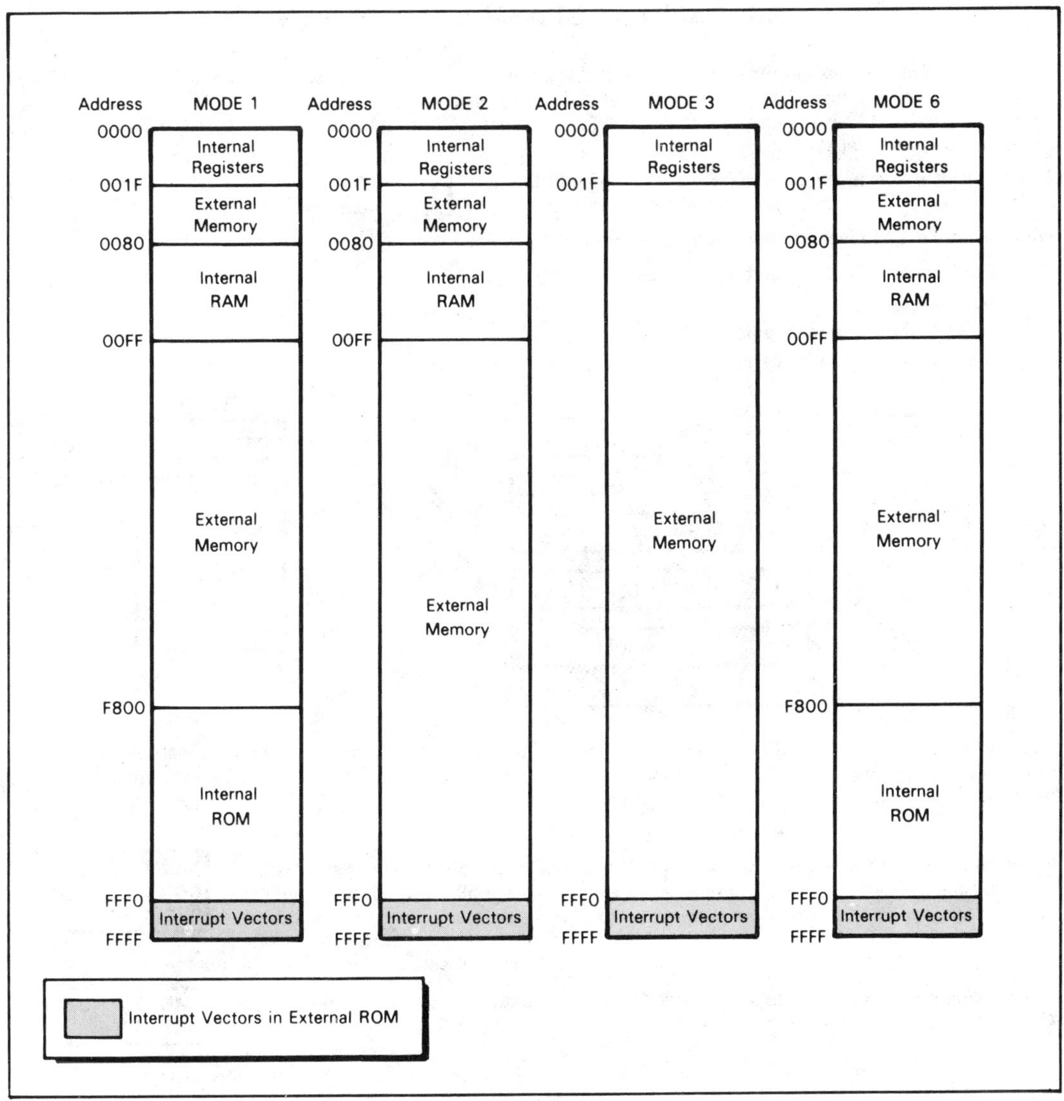


Figure 9-58. MC6801 Memory Maps for Multiplexed Operation

These options give you a great deal of flexibility. For example, consider mode 2. This is defined as an expanded, multiplexed mode, capable of expansion to 64K of memory and I/O. Normally, one would expect to use this mode to implement memory- and I/O-rich expanded systems. However, this mode can also be used to implement simple, low-end systems that consist essentially of an MC6801, an EPROM, and a latch. Such a system takes advantage of the fact that the total operating program (including interrupt and restart vectors) can be inserted into the external memory space via a standard, off-the-shelf EPROM. Such a minimal system provides an EPROM-based control program and 13 lines of I/O, including timer and serial communications capability.

# MC6801 PROGRAMMABLE TIMER

**Three timer functions are provided on the MC6801 — one controls outputs, one controls inputs, and the third serves as a timer overflow.** Together, they permit the user to make measurements on input waveforms and to generate output waveforms, all under software control. Pulse widths for both inputs and outputs may range from a few microseconds to several seconds.

**The timer interface to the outside world is via pins P20 and P21 of Port 2 as shown in Figure 9-41.** Bit 1 of the Port 2 Data Direction register must be set to "1" (output) to steer the timer output to P21.

**Four user-accessible internal hardware registers are** provided:

- **an 8-bit Control/Status register**
- **a 16-bit counter**
- **a 16-bit Output Compare register**
- **a 16-bit Input Capture register**

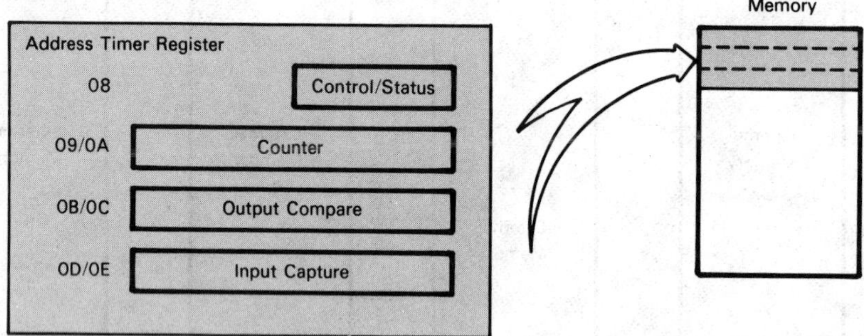


The 16-bit registers are formed by the concatenation of pairs of memory locations in the "internal register" area of MC6801 memory and are accessed by the low-order address of the pair. Thus, the contents of the counter may be read by the double-precision instruction:

LDD $09

**MC6801 TIMER CONTROL/STATUS REGISTER**

**Monitoring and control of the timer is via the 8-bit Timer Control/Status register** (TCS) located at address $0008_{16}$. Bit assignments are shown in Figure 9-59. Bits 5, 6, and 7 are read-only flag bits, set by certain hardware operations. Bits 2, 3, and 4 are Interrupt Enable bits — they enable interrupt $\overline{IRQ2}$ for the conditions specified. If the I-bit in the processor Condition Code register is clear (I = 0), a priority vectored interrupt will be effected, corresponding to the flag bits set.

**MC6801 TIMER'S COUNTER**

**The free-running counter at address 0009/000A is a 16-bit up-counter, clocked by the MC6801 CPU's internal clock signal, Φ2.** It is a read-only register with one exception — for test purposes, a user may write into address 0009, but such a write will always result in a present value of $FFF8_{16}$, regardless of the value involved in the write. You should also note that this 'test write' can disturb operation of the SCI. The counter is cleared to zero on $\overline{RESET}$.

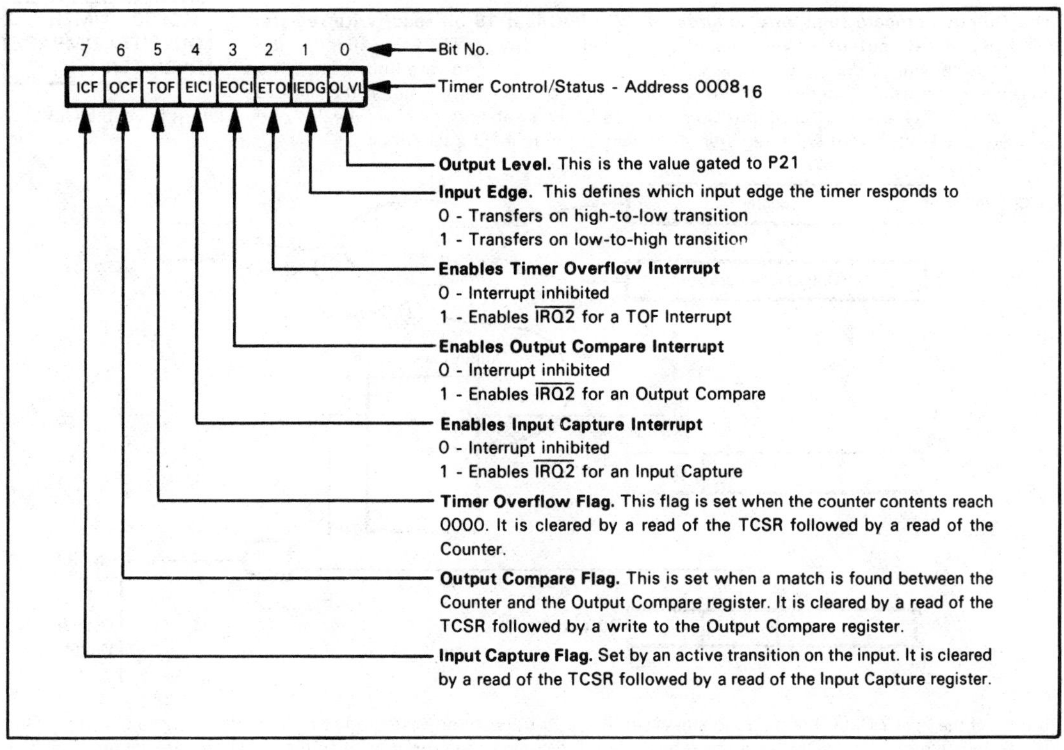


Figure 9-59. MC6801 Timer Control/Status Register (TCSR)

**MC6801 TIMER OUTPUT COMPARE REGISTER**

**The Output Compare register at address 000B/000C is a 16-bit read/write register used to generate output waveforms.** It is initialized by software. The value stored in this register is constantly compared to the value in the counter by hardware (this operation is invisible to the user). When the incremented contents of the counter match the number pre-stored in this register, the Output Compare flag (OCF) is set, and the current value of the Output Level bit (OLVL) is strobed to a 1-bit Output Level register, as shown in the following illustration:

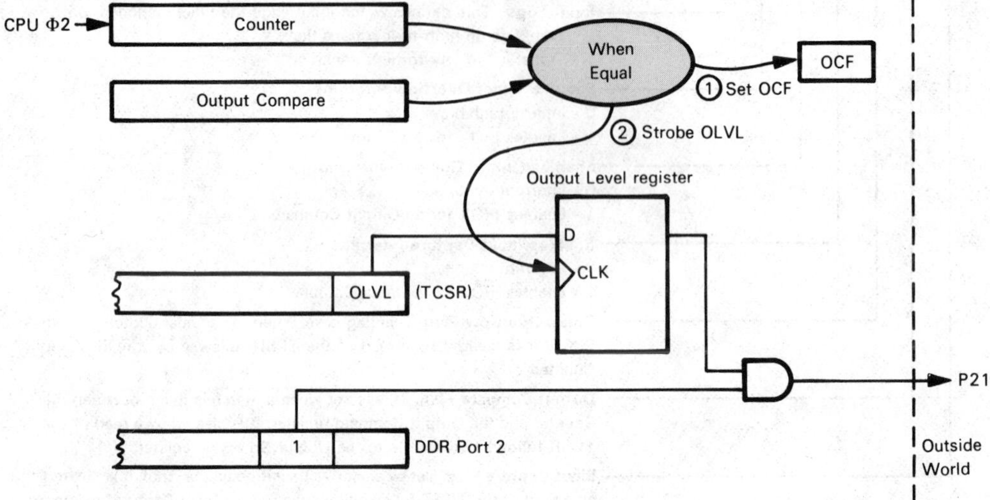


If bit 1 of the Port 2 Data Direction register is set, the Output Level bit is steered to port pin P21. The values in the Output Compare register and OLVL may now be updated to control the output level on the next compare value. On $\overline{\text{RESET}}$, the Output Compare register is initialized to FFFF.

To illustrate, let us generate a square wave.

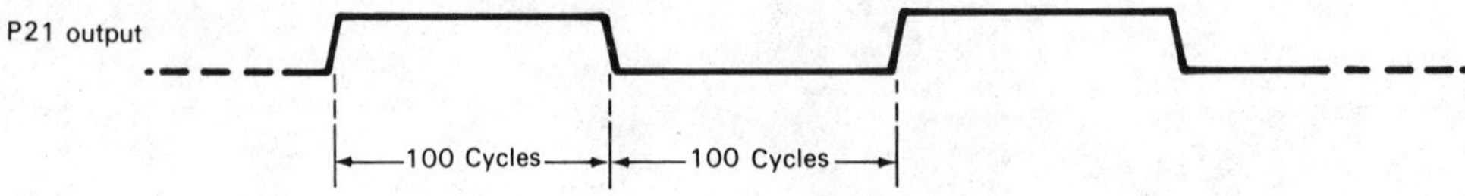

An appropriate instruction sequence is shown below.

Note:

1) P21 is configured for output by setting bit 1 of Data Direction Register 2 to 1.

2) The output level bit OLVL is complemented (using the exclusive-OR instruction) each time a match is found.

3) The Output Compare register is updated with the next compare value before the timer reaches the new value. Increment size is $64_{16}$ = 100.

```
START   LDA A #02         INITIALIZATION FOR TIMER OUTPUT
        STA A DDR2
*
LOOP    LDA A TCSR
        BIT A #$40        CHECK OUTPUT COMPARE FLAG OCF
        BEQ LOOP
*
*FOUND MATCH — CHANGE OUTPUT
        EOR A #01         TOGGLE OLVL BIT
*       STA A TCSR        UPDATE OLUL BIT
*UPDATE OUTPUT COMPARE REGISTER
        LDD OUTCMP        GET CURRENT REGISTER VALUE
        ADD D #$0064      ADD OFFSET
        STD OUTCMP        UPDATE OUTPUT COMPARE REGISTER
        BRA LOOP
```

**MC6801 TIMER INPUT CAPTURE REGISTER**

**The Input Capture register at address 000D/000E is a 16-bit read-only register. It is used to capture "on the fly" the current value of the free-running counter at the instant a defined edge transition occurs on input pin P20 of Port 2.** If bit 1 (IEDG) of the Timer Control/Status register is 0, capture occurs on a high-to-low transition, whereas, if IEDG is 1, capture occurs on the low-to-high transition.

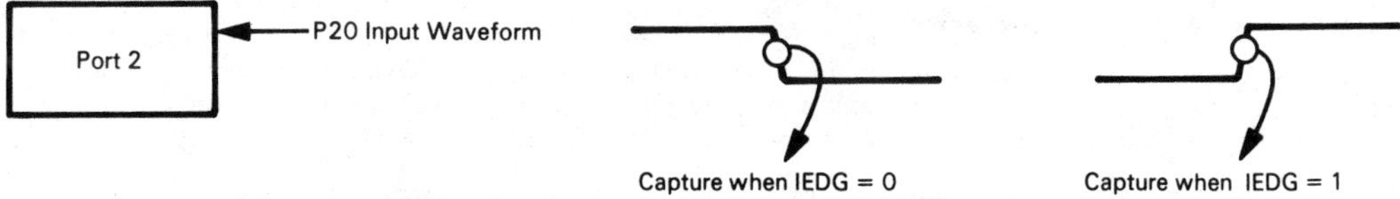


Note that the Input Capture Flag (ICF) in the Timer Control/Status register is also set by this transition.

Since IEDG is a read/write bit, it can be changed at any time under program control. Thus, you can measure pulse widths as shown below, redefining the active transition between captures.

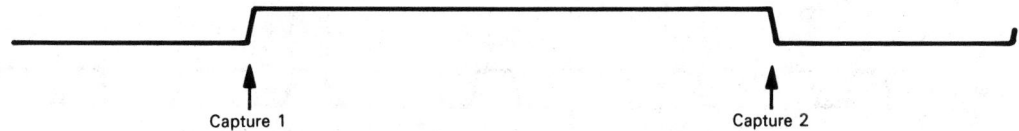


**If the above pulse width is less than 65,536 CPU cycles, it can be measured as follows:**

1) Define the active edge as a leading edge by setting IEDG = 1.

2) When the first capture occurs, store the counter value.

3) Set IEDG = 0 to redefine the active transition.

4) When the second capture occurs, read the new counter value.

5) The difference between the two values is the pulse width (in CPU cycles).

Obviously, the pulse width must be longer than the service time in order for this technique to work.

**When measuring pulses whose width exceeds 65,536 CPU cycles, the Timer Overflow Flag (TOF) may be used.** It is set by hardware when the counter contents roll over to 0000. By tallying these occurrences, you can determine how many times the counter has cycled through its complete range of 65,536 counts during the measurement interval. The tallying must be done by software.

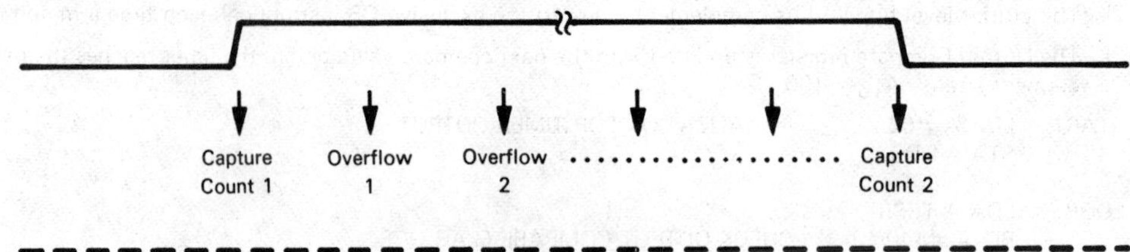


**With a 4 MHz crystal, the CPU clock rate is 1 MHz; thus, each CPU cycle is one microsecond long.**

## MC6801 SERIAL COMMUNICATION INTERFACE (SCI)

**The MC6801 incorporates an on-chip, Serial Communication Interface (SCI). This is a serial I/O port** which can be used to communicate with a variety of devices — these include simple serial I/O devices as shift registers, and standard computer terminals such as CRTs — or it can be used to link together a number of processors in a multiprocessing environment. A "wake-up" feature permits units in a multiprocessor scheme to respond only when accessed.

**The SCI is a full duplex, asynchronous interface. It is comprised of a transmitter and a receiver which operate independently of each other, but at the same data rate and using the same data format.** Clocking is obtained from the internal baud rate generator; or, optionally, clocking may be supplied from an external source.

The SCI interfaces to the outside world via pins P22, P23, and P24 of Port 2 as shown in Figure 9-41. **Two data formats are provided.** These are program selectable:

- **Standard Mark/Space (NRZ)**
- **Self Clocking Bi-Phase (Manchester)**

Standard Mark/Space is normally used with terminals (CRTs) and modems, while Bi-Phase is intended for interprocessor communications. (Bi-Phase provides a much larger tolerance to clock mismatch between the transmitter and receiver oscillators than does standard Mark/Space encoding.) Data formats are as follows:

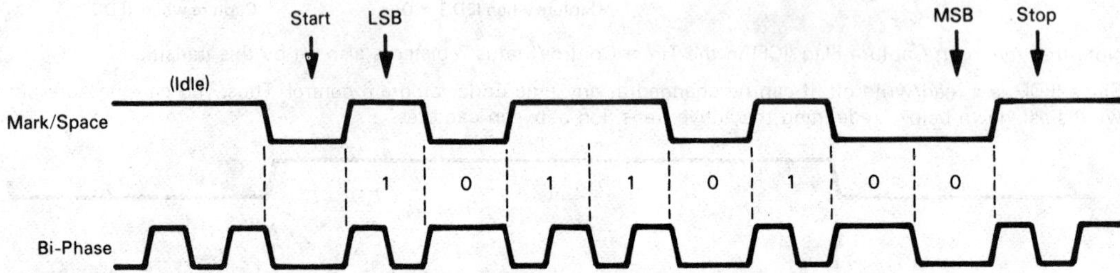


**Ten bits are used: a Start bit, eight data bits, and a Stop bit.**

For configurations using the on-chip oscillator, communication occurs at one of four program selectable sub-multiples of the CPU Φ2 clock. For systems using an external source, the clock must be eight times the desired baud rate.

**MC6801 SCI PROGRAMMING OPTIONS**

**The following options must be software configured:**

- **Data Format - Mark/Space or Bi-Phase**
- **Clock Source - Internal or external**
- **Baud Rate - Select one of four internal or the external x8 input**
- **Clock Output - Internal out or external in**
- **Wake-Up Feature - Enabled or disabled**
- **Interrupt Requests - Enabled or masked individually for transmitter and receiver**

In addition, since bits 3 and 4 (P23, P24) are shared among other Port 2 activities, you must appropriately configure the SCI to serve the serial I/O function.

## MC6801 SCI CONTROL

**Four user-accessible registers are provided:**

- **a 4-bit Rate/Mode Control register**
- **an 8-bit Control/Status register**
- **an 8-bit Receive Data register**
- **an 8-bit Transmit Data register**

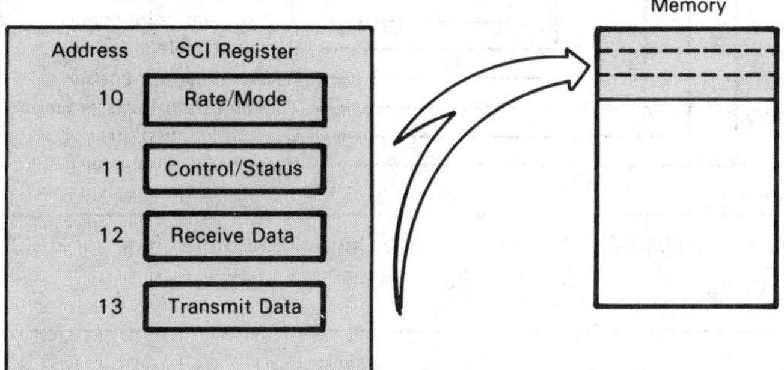


**MC6801 SCI TRANSMIT/RECEIVE CONTROL/STATUS REGISTER**

**Monitoring and control of the SCI is via the 8-bit Transmit/Receive Control/Status (TRCS) register** located in the MC6801 internal registers at address 0011. Bit assignments are as shown in Figure 9-60. Bits 5, 6, and 7 are read-only Flag bits set by hardware. Bits 1, 2, 3, and 4 are Enable bits, while WU is the wake-up bit — these are read/write bits set by the user to select the operations desired. Bits which enable $\overline{IRQ2}$ will cause an interrupt if the I-bit in the processor Condition Code register is clear (I = 0).

$\overline{RESET}$ initializes the TRCS register to $20_{16}$ (bit 5 set, all others cleared). This is in addition to the following techniques of setting and clearing bits.

Bit 0 **WU:** This bit must be set by software. It is cleared by hardware upon receipt of ten consecutive 1s.

Bit 1 **TE:** Must be set by software. Setting this bit produces a preamble of nine consecutive 1s and enables the transmitter output to Port 2 pin P24, regardless of the corresponding bit value in the Port 2 Data Direction register. When clear, the SCI has no effect on P24.

Bit 2 **TIE:** This bit is set or cleared by software. When set, it enables an $\overline{IRQ2}$ interrupt to occur when TDRE (bit 5) is set. When bit 2 is clear, TDRE cannot generate an interrupt.

Bit 3 **RE:** When set, this bit gates pin P23 of Port 2 to the Receiver, regardless of the corresponding bit value in the Port 2 Data Direction register. When this bit is clear, the SCI has no effect on P23.

Bit 4 **RIE:** Set or cleared by software. When set, it enables an $\overline{IRQ2}$ interrupt to occur when RDRF (bit 7) or ORFE (bit 6) is set. When clear, these bits cannot generate interrupts.

Bit 5 **TDRE:** This is a read-only bit which is set by the transmitter hardware when a transfer is made from the Transmit Data register to the Output Shift register. This bit is cleared by a programmed read of the TRCS register followed by a write of new data to the Transmit Data register. $\overline{RESET}$ initializes this bit to the 1 state, indicating the Transmit Data register is ready to receive a byte of data. No data will be transmitted if TDRE is not cleared.

Bit 6 **ORFE:** This is a read-only bit which is set by hardware when an overrun or a framing error occurs. It is cleared by performing a read of the TRCS register followed by a read of the Receive Data register. (An overrun is reported if the user does not read the data from the Receive Data register before a new byte is received. A framing error occurs if the data received is not properly framed by the Start and Stop bits.)

Bit 7 **RDRF:** This is a read-only bit, set by hardware when a transfer from the Input Shift register to the Receive Data register is made. To clear RDRF, read the Transmit/Receive Control/Status register (TRCS), then read the Receive Data register.

**MC6801 SCI RATE/MODE CONTROL REGISTER**

**Selection of data format, baud rate, clocking source and configuration of P22 is accomplished via bits set by software in the Rate/Mode Control register** (shown in Figure 9-61) at address $0010_{16}$. (These bits are all cleared on $\overline{RESET}$.)

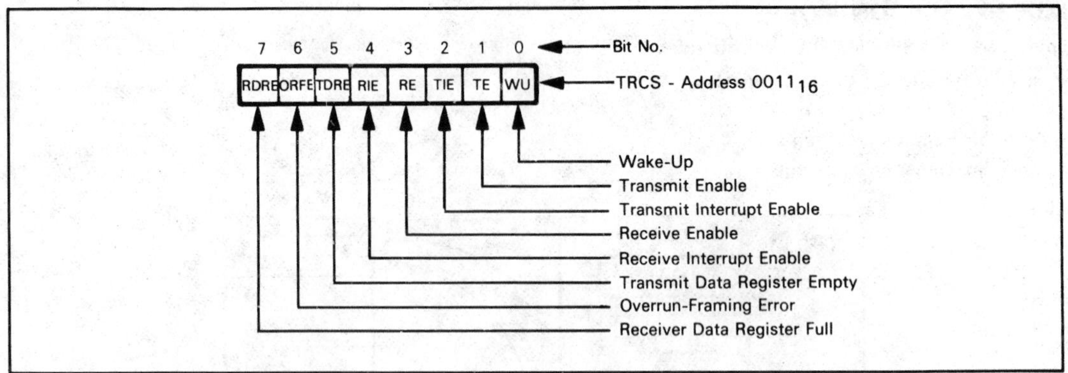


Figure 9-60. MC6801 Transmit/Receive Control and Status Register (TRCS)

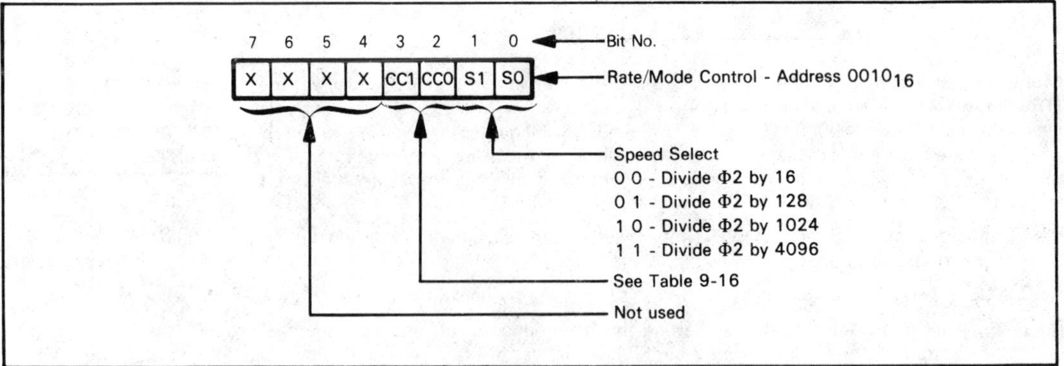


Figure 9-61. MC6801 SCI Rate/Mode Control Register

Table 9-16. MC6801 SCI Clock Control and Format Select

| CC1, CC0 | Format | Clock Source | Port 2 Bit 2 | Port 2 Bit 3 | Port 2 Bit 4 |
|---|---|---|---|---|---|
| 0 0 | Bi-Phase | Internal | Not Used | Note 1 | Note 2 |
| 0 1 | NRZ | Internal | Not Used | Note 1 | Note 2 |
| 1 0 | NRZ | Internal | Output | Serial Input | Serial Output |
| 1 1 | NRZ | External | Input | Serial Input | Serial Output |

Notes:

1) Serial data can be input on P23 for these cases only if RE = 1.

2) Serial output appears on P24 for these cases only if TE = 1.

**Bits S0 and S1 are speed select bits.** They select the baud rate as a function of the internal CPU Φ2 clock, but have no effect when external clocking of the SCI is used.

**Bits CC1 and CC0 select the data format and SCI clocking source,** as shown in Table 9-16.

## MC6801 SCI OPERATION

**The SCI must be software initialized by configuring the Transmit/Receive Control/Status register (TRCS) and the Rate/Mode Control register.**

**MC6801 SCI TRANSMIT OPERATIONS**

**Setting the Transmit Enable bit (TE) to 1 causes the output of the SCI to be gated to Port 2 pin 4 (P24)** regardless of the value in the corresponding bit position of the Port 2 Data Direction register. The following illustration shows the relationship between the TRCS register, transmitter logic, and the P24 pin:

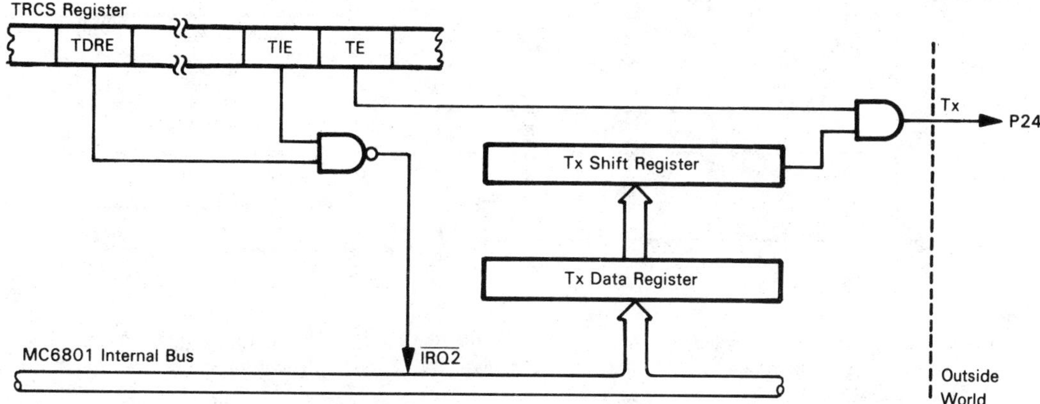


**In addition, setting TE to 1 initiates the transmission of a 10-bit preamble for synchronization purposes.** The preamble consists of a succession of ones, which sets the output line to the high (Mark) condition as required to mark the line idle condition. The line will remain in this Mark condition until a byte of data is ready for transmission.

**To transmit a byte of data, you must first check the status of the TDRE flag.** If TDRE is set (indicating that the Transmit Data register is empty), a byte of data may be loaded into it using an STA instruction. This clears the TDRE flag (TDRE = 0), indicating that the Transmit Data register is full. The following instruction sequence would perform the required steps we have described:

```
        LDA A #$20
LOOP    BIT A TRCS     CHECK TDRE FLAG
        BEQ LOOP
        LDA A CHAR     GET CHARACTER
        STA A TX       LOAD TO TRANSMITTER
```

The data written will remain in the Transmit Data register until the Shift register is empty; that is, until it has finished sending the previous byte. When the Shift register is empty, the byte will be transferred to the Shift register, and the TDRE flag will be set (automatically, by hardware), indicating that a new byte may be loaded into the Transmit Data register.

If a new byte is not available in the Transmit Data register when the previous one has been sent, the output will go to the idle state, and transmit a Mark condition.

Bi-phase operation is the same as that described above, except that a "1" output is represented by toggling at half bit times, instead of Marking, and a "0" is represented by toggling at full bit times, instead of as a Space.

If you wish to use interrupt programming, you must set TIE to 1. This permits an $\overline{IRQ2}$ interrupt to be generated when TDRE is set.

**MC6801 SCI RECEIVE OPERATIONS**

**Setting the Receive Enable bit (RE) to 1 steers the serial input applied to P23 (Port 2 pin 3) to the Receive Shift register.** The following illustration shows the relationship between the TRCS register, receiver logic, and the P23 pin.

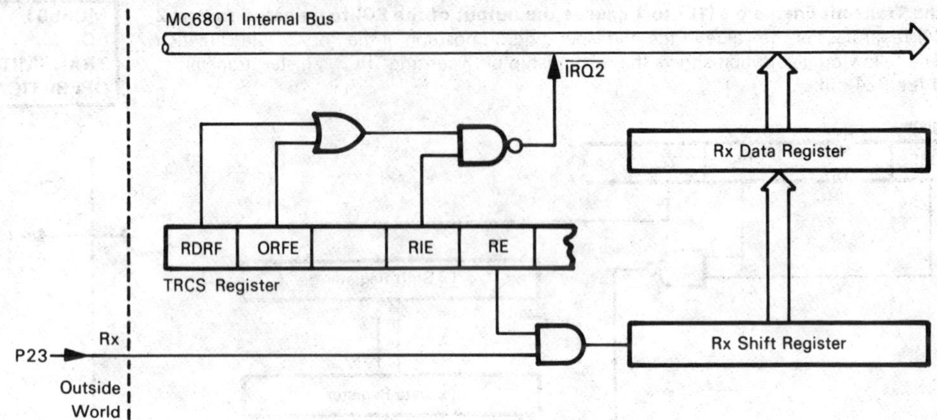


The incoming data stream is assembled into a parallel byte by the Shift register. When a full byte has been correctly received (no overrun, no framing error), it is transferred (automatically by the hardware) to the Receive Data register, and the RDRF flag bit is set.

**To determine whether a byte of data is available, the program must read the TRCS register and check the RDRF flag.** When a byte is available, it is read by an LDA instruction. This read also clears the RDRF flag.

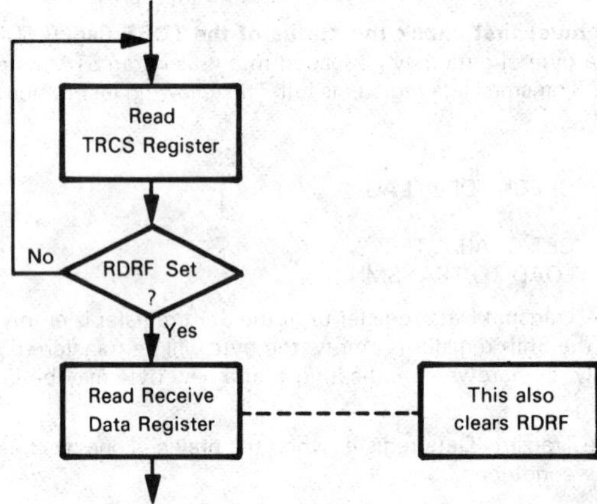


If the above read is **not performed by the time a new byte is assembled in the Shift register, an overrun is reported by setting the ORFE flag to 1.**

If you wish to use interrupt programming, you must set RIE to 1. This permits an $\overline{IRQ2}$ interrupt to be generated by RDRF or ORFE. There is only **one level of interrupt priority for the SCI.** Thus, **software polling is necessary to determine which of the flags — RDRF, ORFE, or TDRE — caused the interrupt.**

## MC6801 SCI CLOCKING OPTIONS

**Clocking for the SCI may be derived internally from Φ2 of the CPU, or alternatively, an external clock may be used.**

As noted in Table 9-16, if CC1 = 1 and CC0 = 0, the **internal clock is brought out on P22 (Port 2 pin 2).** This clocking signal is 1 times the bit rate and has its rising edge at mid-bit. The output data format is NRZ. This permits the MC6801 to communicate with standard shift register, providing a very low-cost serial interface.

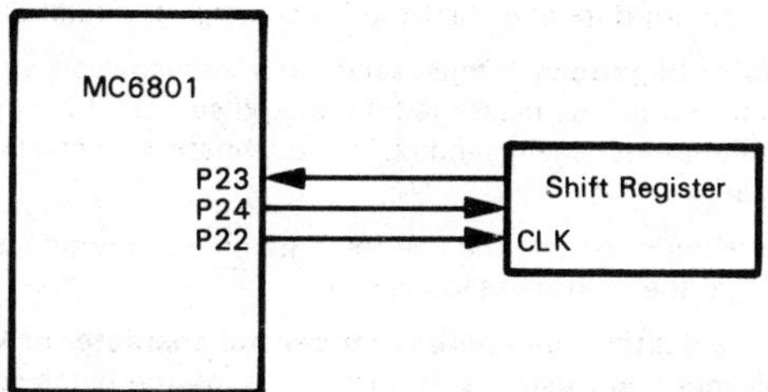


The clock output signal is available regardless of the settings of RE and TE; thus, this clock signal is made available to the outside world, even if pins 3 and 4 have been disabled for serial I/O. The maximum frequency is Φ2 divided by 16.

As an alternative, an externally supplied source may be used. In this case, Port 2 pin 2 (P22) brings the clock signal into the SCI. This clock frequency must be eight times (8x) the desired baud rate, with a maximum of E or Φ2. To use this option, CC0 and CC1 must be set to 11.

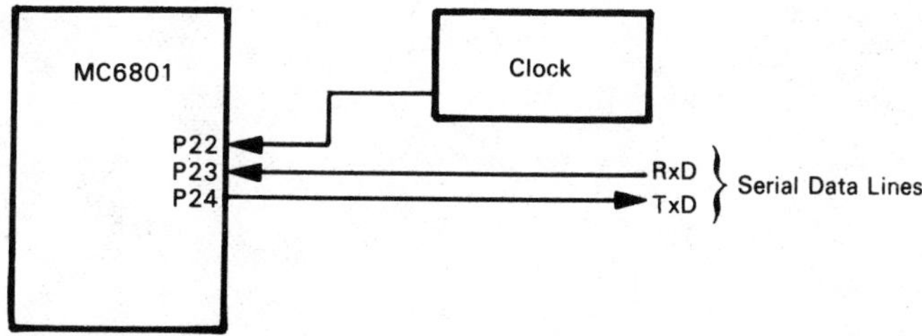


## MC6801 WAKE-UP OPERATION

The MC6801 contains a **"wake-up" feature that is useful in serially linked, multiprocessor applications. Any processor in the link can be programmed to respond only to messages directed to it, and ignore all others.** This is achieved by including a control word or destination address in the data stream that identifies the destination receiver. All processors for which the message is not intended simply ignore the remainder of the message, and carry on with whatever they are programmed to do.

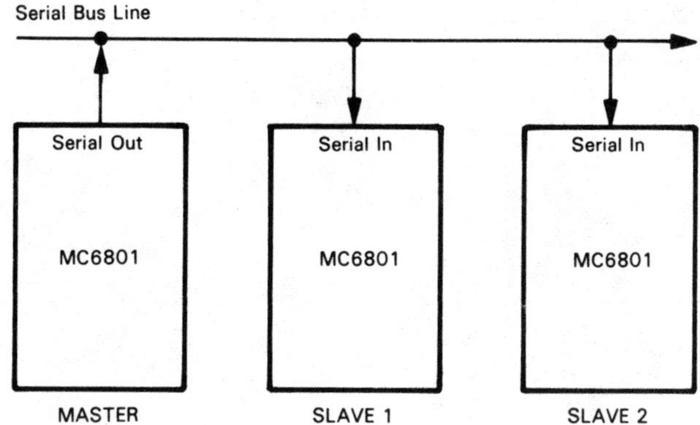

**The "wake-up" feature is enabled by bit WU in the Transmit/Receive Control and Status register (TRCS).** If WU = 0, the serial I/O channel functions normally; if WU = 1, the wake-up feature is invoked. With the wake-up feature operational, the receiver section of the SCI continues to assemble bytes of data in its Receive Shift register as they are received, but it does not set the RDRF flag bit to signal reception of a byte — thus the incoming data stream is effectively masked from the processor. This action is performed automatically by the hardware and is transparent to the software.

**The reception of ten consecutive 1s in the data stream (indicating an idle line) clears WU,** reestablishing normal flag operation in the SCI receiver. Note that both data and the Stop bit count in the total of ten 1s.

**The transmitter in this scheme has certain obligations.** It must send out a message as a string of characters in such a manner that it does not let the line go idle within the message for a period sufficient for the receivers to clear their "wake-up" bits. If this happens, the transmitter must again send out the destination receiver identification before continuing with the remainder of the message.

After the last byte of a message, the transmitter must idle the line for a minimum of ten consecutive 1s to permit the other receivers on the line to wake-up before the next message is sent.

**It is important to note that testing for the destination address (or central character or words, as the case may be) is carried out simultaneously by all receivers using software.** Thus, as the bytes specifying the destination receiver arrive, they are read by software from the respective Receive Data registers and compared with each receiver's preprogrammed code. If no match is found, the software sets the WU bit and ignores the remainder of the message.

# THE MC6801 INSTRUCTION SET

The MC6801 uses all MC6800 instructions plus ten new ones. Only the new instructions are summarized in Table 9-17. Symbology here follows that of Table 9-1, with the following additions:

: This symbol denotes concatenation.

ACCD is the double Accumulator formed by concatenating the A and B Accumulators.

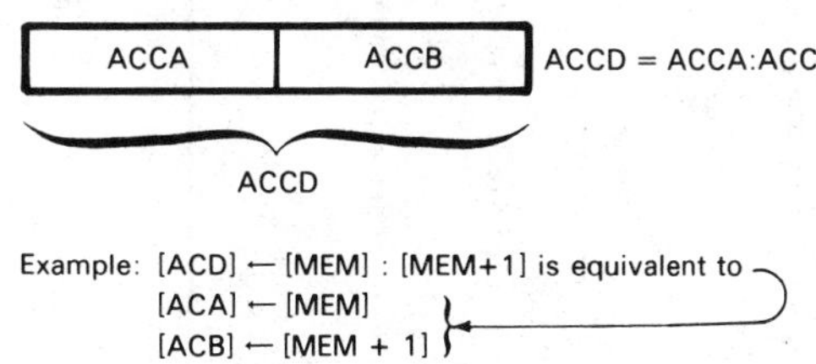

Table 9-17. Summary of New MC6801 Instructions

| TYPE | MNEMONIC | OPERAND(S) | BYTES | STATUS C | Z | S | O | $A_C$ | I | OPERATION PERFORMED |
|---|---|---|---|---|---|---|---|---|---|---|
| PRIMARY MEMORY REFERENCE | LDD | ADR8<br>ADR16 | 2<br>3 | | X | X | 0 | | | [ADC] ← [MEM]:[MEM]+1<br>Load D using base page direct, extended direct or indexed addressing. |
| | STD | ADR8<br>ADR16 | 2<br>3 | | X | X | 0 | | | [MEM]:[M+1] ← [ACD]<br>Store D using direct, extended or indexed addressing. |
| SECONDARY MEMORY REFERENCE (MEMORY OPERATE) | ADDD | ADR8<br>ADR16 | 2<br>3 | X | X | X | X | | | [ACD] ← [ACD] + [MEM]:[MEM]:[MEM+1]<br>Add to Accumulator D using base page direct, extended direct or indexed addressing. |
| | SUBD | ADR8<br>ADR16 | 2<br>3 | X | X | X | X | | | [ACD] ← [ACD] - [MEM]:[MEM+1]<br>Subtract from Accumulator D using direct, extended or indexed addressing. |
| IMMEDIATE | LDD | DATA16 | 3 | | X | X | 0 | | | [ACD] ← DATA16<br>Load Accumulator D immediate. |
| IMMEDIATE OPERATE | ADDD | DATA16 | 3 | X | X | X | X | | | [ACD] ← [ACD] + DATA16<br>Add immediate to Accumulator D. |
| | SUBD | DATA16 | 3 | X | X | X | X | | | [ACCD] ← [ACCD] - DATA16<br>Subtract immediate from D. |

Table 9-17. Summary of New MC6801 Instructions (Continued)

| TYPE | MNEMONIC | OPERAND(S) | BYTES | STATUS C | STATUS Z | STATUS S | STATUS O | STATUS $A_C$ | STATUS I | OPERATION PERFORMED |
|---|---|---|---|---|---|---|---|---|---|---|
| REGISTER-TO-REGISTER OPERATE | ABX | | 1 | | | | | | | [X] ← [X] + [B]<br>Add the contents of ACCB to the contents of the Index register. |
| | MUL | | 1 | X | | | | | | [ACD] ← [A] x [B] |
| REGISTER OPERATE | ASLD | | 1 | X | X | X | X | | | ACD: C ← 15 ← 0 ← 0<br>Arithmetic Shift Left. Bit 0 is set to 0. O = S ⊻ C. |
| | LSRD | | 1 | X | X | 0 | X | | | 0 → 15 → 0 → C<br>Logical Shift Right. Bit 15 is set to 0. O = S ⊻ C. |
| STACK | PSHX | | 1 | | | | | | | [[SP]] ← [X(LO)]<br>[SP] ← [SP] - 1<br>[[SP]] ← [X(HI)]<br>[SP] ← [SP] - 1<br>Push contents of Index register (2 bytes) onto top of Stack and decrement Stack Pointer by two. |
| | PULX | | 1 | | | | | | | [SR] ← [SP] + 1<br>[X(HI)] ← [[SP]]<br>[SP] ← [SP] + 1<br>[X(LO)] ← [[SP]]<br>Pull the top two bytes from the Stack and place them in the Index register. The Stack Pointer is incremented twice. |

## MC6801 SUMMARY OF CYCLE-BY-CYCLE OPERATION

Table 9-18 is similar to the one for the MC6800. However, the execution times of many instructions have been reduced to increase throughput, and ten new instructions have been added.

This table provides a detailed description of the information present on the Address Bus, Data Bus, and the Read/Write line (R/$\overline{W}$) during each cycle for each instruction.

This information is useful in comparing actual results with expected results during debugging of both software and hardware as the control program is executed. The information is categorized in groups according to addressing modes and number of cycles per instruction. (In general, instructions with the same addressing mode and number of cycles execute in the same manner; exceptions are indicated in the table.)

Table 9-18. MC6801 Cycle-by-Cycle Operation Summary

| | Address Mode and Instructions | Cycles | Cycle No. | Address Bus | R/$\overline{W}$ Line | Data Bus |
|---|---|---|---|---|---|---|
| Immediate | ADC EOR<br>ADD LDA<br>AND ORA<br>BIT SBC<br>CMP SUB | 2 | 1<br>2 | Op Code Address<br>Op Code Address + 1 | 1<br>1 | Op Code<br>Operand Data |
| | LDS<br>LDX | 3 | 1<br>2<br>3 | Op Code Address<br>Op Code Address + 1<br>Op Code Address + 2 | 1<br>1<br>1 | Op Code<br>Operand Data (High-order Byte)<br>Operand Data (Low-order Byte) |
| | CPX<br>SUBD<br>ADDD | 4 | 1<br>2<br>3<br>4 | Op Code Address<br>Op Code Address + 1<br>Op Code Address + 2<br>Address Bus FFFF | 1<br>1<br>1<br>1 | Op Code<br>Operand Data (High-order Byte)<br>Operand Data (Low-order Byte)<br>Low Byte of Restart Vector |
| Direct | ADC EOR<br>ADD LDA<br>AND ORA<br>BIT SBC<br>CMP SUB | 3 | 1<br>2<br>3 | Op Code Address<br>Op Code Address + 1<br>Address of Operand | 1<br>1<br>1 | Op Code<br>Address of Operand<br>Operand Data |
| | STA | 3 | 1<br>2<br>3 | Op Code Address<br>Op Code Address + 1<br>Destination Address | 1<br>1<br>0 | Op Code<br>Destination Address<br>Data from Accumulator |
| | LDS<br>LDX<br>LDD | 4 | 1<br>2<br>3<br>4 | Op Code Address<br>Op Code Address + 1<br>Address of Operand<br>Operand Address + 1 | 1<br>1<br>1<br>1 | Op Code<br>Address of Operand<br>Operand Data (High-order Byte)<br>Operand Data (Low-order Byte) |
| | STS<br>STX<br>STD | 4 | 1<br>2<br>3<br>4 | Op Code Address<br>Op Code Address + 1<br>Address of Operand<br>Address of Operand + 1 | 1<br>1<br>0<br>0 | Op Code<br>Address of Operand<br>Register Data (High-order Byte)<br>Register Data (Low-order Byte) |
| | CPX<br>SUBD<br>ADDD | 5 | 1<br>2<br>3<br>4<br>5 | Op Code Address<br>Op Code Address + 1<br>Operand Address<br>Operand Address + 1<br>Address Bus FFFF | 1<br>1<br>1<br>1<br>1 | Op Code<br>Address of Operand<br>Operand Data (High-order Byte)<br>Operand Data (Low-order Byte)<br>Low Byte of Restart Vector |
| | JSR | 5 | 1<br>2<br>3<br>4<br>5 | Op Code Address<br>Op Code Address + 1<br>Subroutine Address<br>Stack Pointer<br>Stack Pointer + 1 | 1<br>1<br>1<br>0<br>0 | Op Code<br>Irrelevant Data<br>First Subroutine Op Code<br>Return Address (Low-order Byte)<br>Return Address (High-order Byte) |

Table 9-18. MC6801 Cycle-by-Cycle Operation Summary (Continued)

| | Address Mode and Instructions | Cycles | Cycle No. | Address Bus | R/$\overline{W}$ Line | Data Bus |
|---|---|---|---|---|---|---|
| Indexed | JMP | 3 | 1 | Op Code Address | 1 | Op Code |
| | | | 2 | Op Code Address + 1 | 1 | Offset |
| | | | 3 | Address Bus FFFF | 1 | Low Byte of Restart Vector |
| | ADC EOR<br>ADD LDA<br>AND ORA<br>BIT SBC<br>CMP SUB | 4 | 1 | Op Code Address | 1 | Op Code |
| | | | 2 | Op Code Address + 1 | 1 | Offset |
| | | | 3 | Address Bus FFFF | 1 | Low Byte of Restart Vector |
| | | | 4 | Index Register Plus Offset | 1 | Operand Data |
| | STA | 4 | 1 | Op Code Address | 1 | Op Code |
| | | | 2 | Op Code Address + 1 | 1 | Offset |
| | | | 3 | Address Bus FFFF | 1 | Low Byte of Restart Vector |
| | | | 4 | Index Register Plus Offset | 0 | Operand Data |
| | LDS<br>LDX<br>LDD | 5 | 1 | Op Code Address | 1 | Op code |
| | | | 2 | Op Code Address + 1 | 1 | Offset |
| | | | 3 | Address Bus FFFF | 1 | Low Byte of Restart Vector |
| | | | 4 | Index Register Plus Offset | 1 | Operand Data (High-order Byte) |
| | | | 5 | Index Register Plus Offset + 1 | 1 | Operand Data (Low-order Byte) |
| | STS<br>STX<br>STD | 5 | 1 | Op Code Address | 1 | Op Code |
| | | | 2 | Op Code Address + 1 | 1 | Offset |
| | | | 3 | Address Bus FFFF | 1 | Low Byte of Restart Vector |
| | | | 4 | Index Register Plus Offset | 0 | Operand Data (High-order Byte) |
| | | | 5 | Index Register Plus Offset + 1 | 0 | Operand Data (Low-order Byte) |
| | ASL LSR<br>ASR NEG<br>CLR ROL<br>COM ROR<br>DEC TST (1)<br>INC | 6 | 1 | Op Code Address | 1 | Op Code |
| | | | 2 | Op Code Address + 1 | 1 | Offset |
| | | | 3 | Address Bus FFFF | 1 | Low Byte of Restart Vector |
| | | | 4 | Index Register Plus Offset | 1 | Current Operand Data |
| | | | 5 | Address Bus FFFF | 1 | Low Byte of Restart Vector |
| | | | 6 | Index Register Plus Offset | 0 | New Operand Data |
| | CPX<br>SUBD<br>ADDD | 6 | 1 | Op Code Address | 1 | Op code |
| | | | 2 | Op Code Address + 1 | 1 | Offset |
| | | | 3 | Address Bus FFFF | 1 | Low Byte of Restart Vector |
| | | | 4 | Index Register + Offset | 1 | Operand Data (High-order Byte) |
| | | | 5 | Index Register + Offset + 1 | 1 | Operand Data (Low-order Byte) |
| | | | 6 | Address Bus FFFF | | Low Byte of Restart Vector |
| | JSR | 6 | 1 | Op Code Address | 1 | Op Code |
| | | | 2 | Op Code Address + 1 | 1 | Offset |
| | | | 3 | Address Bus FFFF | 1 | Low Byte of Restart Vector |
| | | | 4 | Index Register + Offset | 1 | First Subroutine Op Code |
| | | | 5 | Stack Pointer | 0 | Return Address (Low-order Byte) |
| | | | 6 | Stack Pointer - 1 | 0 | Return Address (High-order Byte) |
| Inherent | ABA DAA SEC<br>ASL DEC SEI<br>ASR INC SEV<br>CBA LSR TAB<br>CLC NEG TAP<br>CLI NOP TBA<br>CLR ROL TPA<br>CLV ROR TST<br>COM SBA | 2 | 1 | Op Code Address | 1 | Op Code |
| | | | 2 | Op Code Address + 1 | 1 | Op Code of Next Instruction |

Table 9-18. MC6801 Cycle-by-Cycle Operation Summary (Continued)

| | Address Mode and Instructions | Cycles | Cycle No. | Address Bus | R/$\overline{W}$ Line | Data Bus |
|---|---|---|---|---|---|---|
| Inherent (Continued) | ABX | 3 | 1<br>2<br>3 | Op Code Address<br>Op Code Address + 1<br>Address Bus FFFF | 1<br>1<br>1 | Op Code<br>Irrelevant Data<br>Low Byte of Restart Vector |
| | ASLD<br>LSRD | 3 | 1<br>2<br>3 | Op Code Address<br>Op Code Address + 1<br>Address Bus FFFF | 1<br>1<br>1 | Op Code<br>Irrelevant Data<br>Low Byte of Restart Vector |
| | DES<br>INS | 3 | 1<br>2<br>3 | Op Code Address<br>Op Code Address + 1<br>Previous Register Contents | 1<br>1<br>1 | Op Code<br>Op Code of Next Instruction<br>Irrelevant Data |
| | INX<br>DEX | 3 | 1<br>2<br>3 | Op Code Address<br>Op Code Address + 1<br>Address Bus FFFF | 1<br>1<br>1 | Op Code<br>Op Code of Next Instruction<br>Low Byte of Restart Vector |
| | PSHA<br>PSHB | 3 | 1<br>2<br>3 | Op Code Address<br>Op Code Address + 1<br>Stack Pointer | 1<br>1<br>0 | Op Code<br>Op Code of Next Instruction<br>Accumulator Data |
| | ISX | 3 | 1<br>2<br>3 | Op Code Address<br>Op Code Address + 1<br>Stack Pointer | 1<br>1<br>1 | Op Code<br>Op Code of Next Instruction<br>Irrelevant Data |
| | TXS | 3 | 1<br>2<br>3 | Op Code Address<br>Op Code Address + 1<br>Address Bus FFFF | 1<br>1<br>1 | Op Code<br>Op Code of Next Instruction<br>Low Byte of Restart Vector |
| | PULA<br>PULB | 4 | 1<br>2<br>3<br>4 | Op Code Address<br>Op Code Address + 1<br>Stack Pointer<br>Stack Pointer + 1 | 1<br>1<br>1<br>1 | Op Code<br>Op Code of Next Instruction<br>Irrelevant Data |
| | PSHX | 4 | 1<br>2<br>3<br>4 | Op Code Address<br>Op Code Address + 1<br>Stack Pointer<br>Stack Pointer - 1 | 1<br>1<br>0<br>0 | Op Code<br>Irrelevant Data<br>Index Register (Low-order Byte)<br>Index Register (High-order Byte) |
| | PULX | 5 | 1<br>2<br>3<br>4<br>5 | Op Code Address<br>Op Code Address + 1<br>Stack Pointer<br>Stack Pointer + 1<br>Stack Pointer + 2 | 1<br>1<br>1<br>1<br>1 | Op Code<br>Irrelevant Data<br>Irrelevant Data<br>Index Register (High-order Byte)<br>Index Register (Low-order Byte) |
| | BCC BHT BNE<br>BCS BLE BPL<br>BEQ BLS BRA<br>BGE BLT BVC<br>BGT BMT BVS | 3 | 1<br>2<br>3 | Op Code Address<br>Op Code Address + 1<br>Address Bus FFFF | 1<br>1<br>1 | Op Code<br>Branch Offset<br>Low Byte of Restart Vector |
| | BSR | 6 | 1<br>2<br>3<br>4<br>5<br>6 | Op Code Address<br>Op Code Address + 1<br>Address Bus FFFF<br>Subroutine Starting Address<br>Stack Pointer<br>Stack Pointer - 1 | 1<br>1<br>1<br>1<br>0<br>0 | Op Code<br>Branch Offset<br>Low Byte of Restart Vector<br>Op Code of Next Instruction<br>Return Address (Low-order Byte)<br>Return Address (High-order Byte) |

Table 9-18. MC6801 Cycle-by-Cycle Operation Summary (Continued)

| | Address Mode and Instructions | Cycles | Cycle No. | Address Bus | R/$\overline{W}$ Line | Data Bus |
|---|---|---|---|---|---|---|
| Extended | JMP | 3 | 1 | Op Code Address | 1 | Op Code |
| | | | 2 | Op Code Address + 1 | 1 | Jump Address (High-order Byte) |
| | | | 3 | Op Code Address + 2 | 1 | Jump Address (Low-order Byte) |
| | ADC EOR<br>ADD LDA<br>AND ORA | 4 | 1 | Op Code Address | 1 | Op Code |
| | | | 2 | Op Code Address + 1 | 1 | Address of Operand |
| | | | 3 | Op Code Address + 2 | 1 | Address of Operand (Low-order Byte) |
| | BIT SBC<br>CMP SUB | | 4 | Address of Operand | 1 | Operand Data |
| | STA A<br>STA B | 4 | 1 | Op Code Address | 1 | Op Code |
| | | | 2 | Op Code Address + 1 | 1 | Destination Address (High-order Byte) |
| | | | 3 | Op Code Address + 2 | 1 | Destination Address (Low-order Byte) |
| | | | 4 | Operand Destination Address | 0 | Data from Accumulator |
| | LDS<br>LDX | 5 | 1 | Op Code Address | 1 | Op Code |
| | | | 2 | Op Code Address + 1 | 1 | Address of Operand (High-order Byte) |
| | LDD | | 3 | Op Code Address + 2 | 1 | Address of Operand (Low-order Byte) |
| | | | 4 | Address of Operand | 1 | Operand Data (High-order Byte) |
| | | | 5 | Address of Operand + 1 | 1 | Operand Data (Low-order Byte) |
| | STS<br>STX | 5 | 1 | Op Code Address | 1 | Op Code |
| | | | 2 | Op Code Address + 1 | 1 | Address of Operand (High-order Byte) |
| | STD | | 3 | Op Code Address + 2 | 1 | Address of Operand (Low-order Byte) |
| | | | 4 | Address of Operand | 0 | Operand Data (High-order Byte) |
| | | | 5 | Address of Operand + 1 | 0 | Operand Data (Low-order Byte) |
| | ASL LSR<br>ASR NEG | 6 | 1 | Op Code Address | 1 | Op Code |
| | | | 2 | Op Code Address + 1 | 1 | Address of Operand (High-order Byte) |
| | CLR ROL | | 3 | Op Code Address + 2 | 1 | Address of Operand (Low-order Byte) |
| | COM ROR | | 4 | Address of Operand | 1 | Current Operand Data |
| | DEC TST (1) | | 5 | Address Bus FFFF | 1 | Low Byte of Restart Vector |
| | INC | | 6 | Address of Operand | 0 | New Operand Data |
| | CPX<br>SUBD | 6 | 1 | Op Code Address | 1 | Op Code |
| | | | 2 | Op Code Address + 1 | 1 | Operand Address (High-order Byte) |
| | ADDD | | 3 | Op Code Address + 2 | 1 | Operand (Low-order Byte) |
| | | | 4 | Operand Address | 1 | Operand Data (High-order Byte) |
| | | | 5 | Operand Address + 1 | 1 | Operand Data (Low-order Byte) |
| | | | 6 | Address Bus FFFF | 1 | Low Byte of Restart Vector |
| | JSR | 6 | 1 | Op Code Address | 1 | Op Code |
| | | | 2 | Op Code Address + 1 | 1 | Address of Subroutine (High-order Byte) |
| | | | 3 | Op Code Address + 2 | 1 | Address of Subroutine (Low-order Byte) |
| | | | 4 | Subroutine Starting Address | 1 | Op Code of Next Instruction |
| | | | 5 | Stack Pointer | 0 | Return Address (Low-order Byte) |
| | | | 6 | Stack Pointer - 1 | 0 | Address of Operand (High-order Byte) |

# THE MC6809 MICROPROCESSOR

**The MC6809 is an advanced processor within the 6800 family. It is a high performance machine, both faster and more powerful than its predecessor (the MC6800), yet it retains hardware and software compatibility (at the source code level) with existing MC6800 parts.**

**The MC6809** has been developed with particular attention to the software needs of the user. Because it **provides powerful new addressing modes and an extended register complement,** the MC6809 is capable of supporting modern software techniques, such as modular programming, position independent (self-relative) coding, recursive programming, reentrancy, and high level language generation.

The MC6809 instruction set contains fewer instructions than the MC6800; some existing 6800 instructions have been combined into more general and powerful ones, leaving room for some new ones. Many of these new MC6809 instructions perform 16-bit manipulations.

**The MC6809 retains all the MC6800 addressing modes and adds some new ones. These modes include long relative branches, sixteen variations of indexed addressing, Program Counter relative modes, and extended indirect modes.** This extension of existing modes retains the ease and familiarity of the 6800 language, but adds high performance capability where needed.

**Hardware improvements have also been implemented on the MC6809. On-chip clock facilities have been added, an internal Schmitt trigger circuit has been incorporated to permit the use of an RC Reset Circuit, and the bus timing specifications have been improved to make the system easier to use. Some bus signals have been redefined, and new ones have been added, to permit the CPU to function in multiprocessor applications while still retaining compatibility with existing parts.** In all, these enhancements, combined with the software enhancements, simplify the use, increase the throughput, and make the CPU tremendously more capable than its predecessor.

Motorola has clearly aimed the MC6809 at the vast consumer markets yet to come, as well as at existing markets that have already been penetrated by the MC6800. With the MC6809, Motorola has maximized the performance of its mid-range 6800 family, and now offers an updated product line that spans the range from the low-end single-chip MC6805 series through the expandable single-chip MC6801 and the mid-range MC6809, up to the newly introduced 16-bit processor, the MC68000.

The principal manufacturer is Motorola. The primary second source is AMI, and other firms that second source the MC6800 may also second source the MC6809.

**The MC6809 family is fabricated using N-channel, silicon gate, ion-implanted depletion load technology. It has TTL-level compatible inputs and outputs and operates from a single +5 volt power supply. All outputs are able to drive 130 pf (typically eight MOS devices) plus one standard TTL load (or four Low Power Schottky loads) at full rated bus speed.**

## THE MC6809 CPU

**Figure 9-62 illustrates that part of our general microcomputer system that is implemented on the MC6809.** Enhancements over the MC6800 include an on-chip clock, control logic for cycle-stealing DMA, and interrupt-priority arbitration. Not evident in this illustration is the enhanced register complement provided by the MC6809.

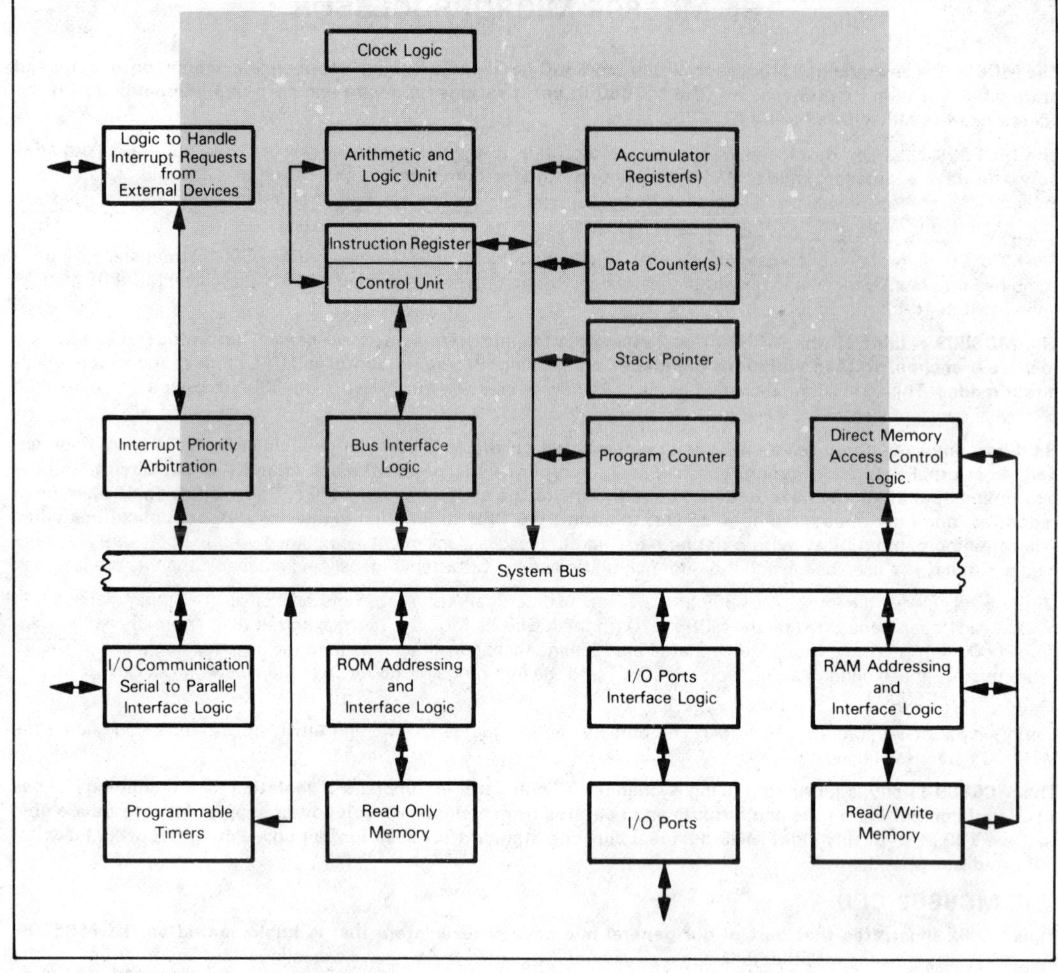


Figure 9-62. Logic of the MC6809 Microprocessor

## THE MC6809 PROGRAMMABLE REGISTERS

**The MC6809 has an enriched set of registers as compared to the basic MC6800. The register complement consists of two Accumulators, a Status register, two Index registers, two stack Pointers, a Program Counter and a Direct Page register. The mobility of data between the registers has been improved by the introduction of a "Transfer Registers" instruction (TFR).** This instruction, and the indexing capability of four of the MC6809 registers, overcomes most of the weaknesses of the 6800 CPU identified at the beginning of this chapter.

The following illustration shows the programmable registers provided by the MC6809. The registers that have been added beyond the basic 6800 CPU complement are shown shaded.

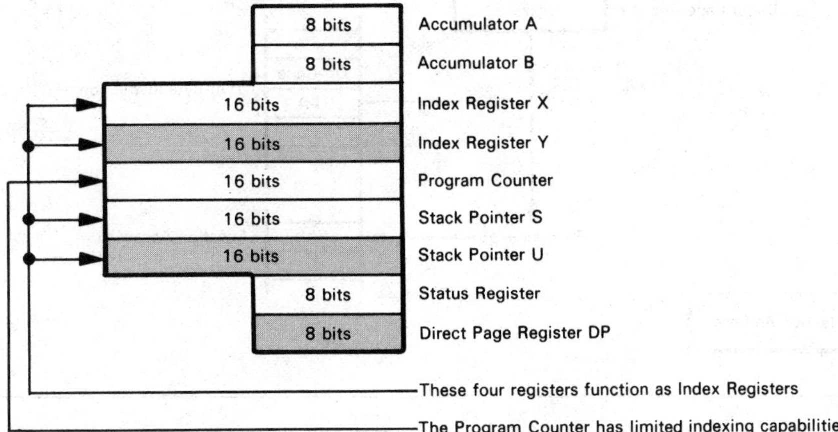


**Sixteen-bit operations are implemented by concatenating the A and B Accumulators to form one double-precision Accumulator D as follows:**

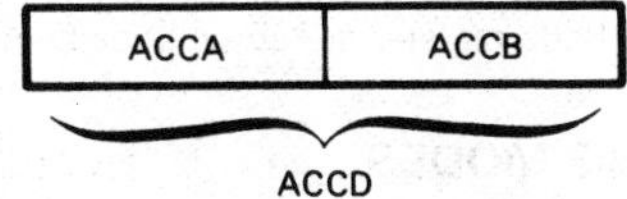


This concatenated Accumulator is referred to as ACCD.

**Four registers (X, Y, S, and U) provide indexing capability.** They permit a 16-bit Effective Address (EA) to be formed by the addition of an optional offset to the pre-loaded contents of the specified register. **There are some differences in the ways in which these registers operate and can be used.**

**Registers X and Y have been designated the Index registers.** Both are capable of performing the same indexing functions as were implemented on the basic MC6800, plus a great deal more. Full details are included below, in the memory addessing section.

**Two Stack Pointers have been provided, permitting the implementation of two independent Stacks.** These Stacks are implemented in read/write memory at the locations pointed to by their respective Stack Pointers. These Stacks function on a "Last-In, First-Out" (LIFO) basis.

**Stack Pointer S is a hardware stack pointer used by the processor to automatically save machine status and active register contents during subroutines and interrupts** in a manner similar to that of the MC6800. With the MC6809, however, the user has the option to save a subset only, or the entire register complement.

**Stack Pointer U is a User's Stack Pointer, controlled exclusively by the user's software.** It facilitates the passage of arguments to and from subroutines.

The Stack Pointers U and S feature the same indexing capabilities as the X and Y registers; thus, **S and U are essentially enhanced index registers.** (There are some differences when using the "Load Effective Address" (LEA) instructions. This will be discussed later.)

The Program Counter points to the next instruction to be executed. Its capability has been enhanced such that **Program Counter relative addressing is now provided.** This capability effectively permits the Program Counter to be used as an index register with limited capabilities.

**The Direct Page register (DPR) permits enhanced direct addressing by allowing a page (in addition to the base page) to be software relocated anywhere in memory during program execution.** By way of contrast, the MC6800 does not have a Direct Page register. All MC6800 instructions using the direct mode have their high-order address bytes fixed at 00 by hardware. This limits direct addressing in the MC6800 to the first 256 memory locations (0000 to 00FF).

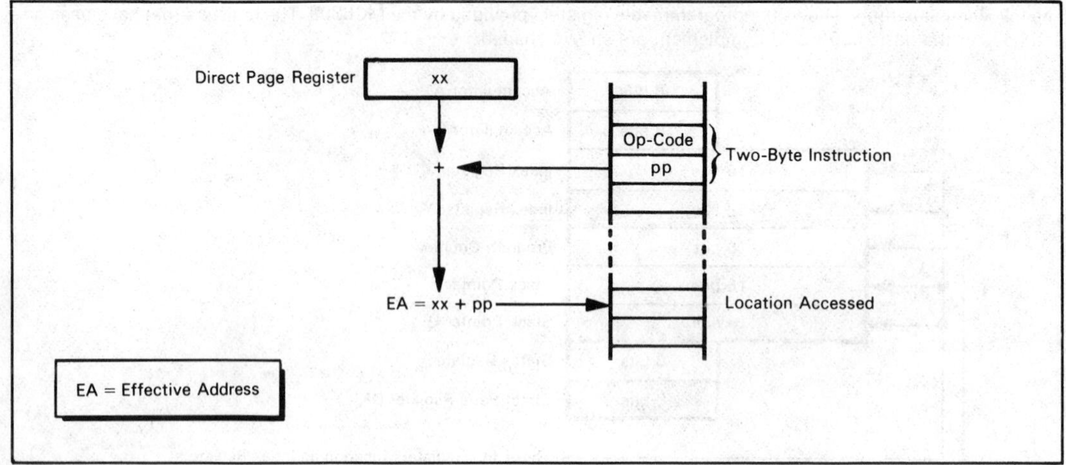


Figure 9-63. MC6809 Direct Page Addressing Scheme

To enforce compatibility with the MC6800, the contents of the Direct Page register on the MC6809 are automatically cleared on Reset. To move the page to some other location, the user must software relocate it by loading the high-order address bytes into the Direct Page register during program execution. When an instruction using Direct Page addressing is executed, the contents of the Direct Page register are automatically concatenated with the usual 8-bit address byte contained in a direct instruction.

## MC6809 MEMORY ADDRESSING MODES

**Let us now look at the addressing enhancements provided by the MC6809.**

**MC6809 DIRECT PAGE ADDRESSING**

**With the incorporation of a Direct Page register, direct addressing has been extended throughout all memory.** Direct page addressing uses a two-byte instruction format in which the second byte specifies the address to be added to the Direct Page register contents. This scheme is illustrated in Figure 9-63. The Direct Page register contains the most significant byte of the 16-bit address to be accessed, while the second byte of the instruction contains the least significant byte.

Since the contents of the Direct Page register are software defined, this page can be dynamically relocated within the read/write memory as desired during program execution.

**MC6809 POST BYTE**

**Many of the new addressing modes require a byte immediately following the operation code to further define the interpretation of the instruction. This is called a Post Byte.**

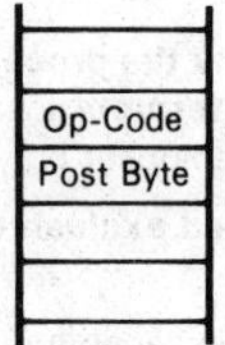


While this added byte may at first seem wasteful of memory space, the extra power and flexibility provided far outweigh the small additional amount of memory required. It should also be noted that many programs will be composed primarily of familiar 6800-type instructions and that the amount of additional memory space consumed by those instructions requiring Post Bytes will usually constitute a relatively small percentage of the total memory used.

**The meaning ascribed to the various bits in the Post Byte depends on the addressing mode — see Table 9-19.**

**MC6809 INDEXED ADDRESSING**

The four registers X, Y, S, and U are indexable. The Post Byte in this case defines the options according to the scheme shown in Figure 9-64.

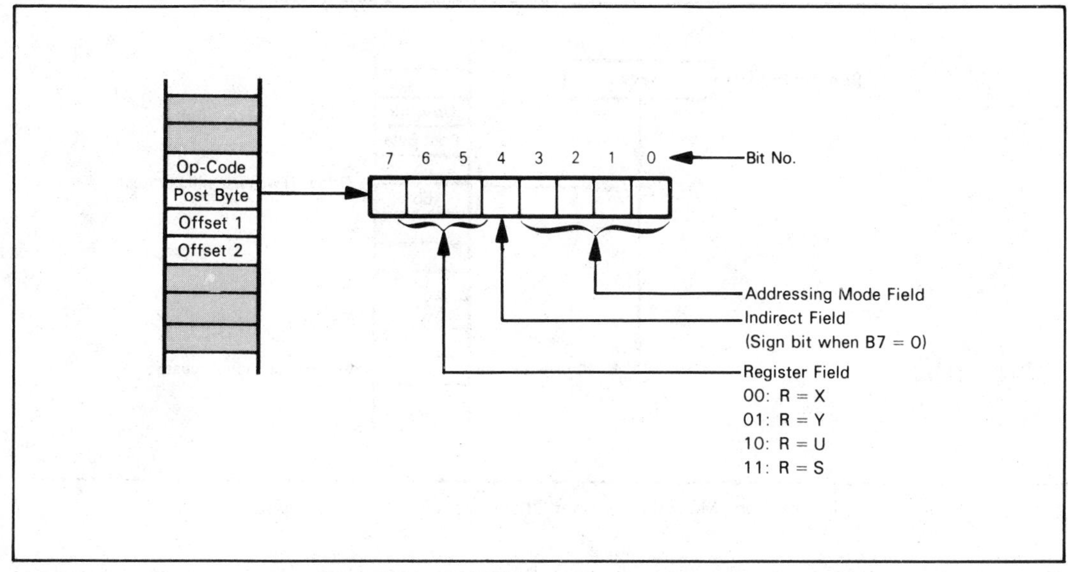


Figure 9-64. MC6809 Post Byte Bit Assignments

Table 9-19. MC6809 Indexed Addressing Post Byte Register Bit Assignments

| Bit Number | | | | | | | | Addressing Mode | Line |
|---|---|---|---|---|---|---|---|---|---|
| 7 | 6 | 5 | 4 | 3 | 2 | 1 | 0 | | |
| 0 | R | R | X | X | X | X | X | 5-Bit Offset | 1 |
| 1 | R | R | 0 | 0 | 0 | 0 | 0 | Auto Increment by One | 2 |
| 1 | R | R | 1 | 0 | 0 | 0 | 1 | Auto Increment by Two | 3 |
| 1 | R | R | 0 | 0 | 0 | 1 | 0 | Auto Decrement by One | 4 |
| 1 | R | R | 1 | 0 | 0 | 1 | 1 | Auto Decrement by Two | 5 |
| 1 | R | R | 1 | 0 | 1 | 0 | 0 | Zero Offset | 6 |
| 1 | R | R | 1 | 0 | 1 | 0 | 1 | Accumulator B Offset | 7 |
| 1 | R | R | 1 | 0 | 1 | 1 | 0 | Accumulator A Offset | 8 |
| 1 | R | R | 1 | 1 | 0 | 0 | 0 | 8-Bit Offset | 9 |
| 1 | R | R | 1 | 1 | 0 | 0 | 1 | 16-Bit Offset | 10 |
| 1 | R | R | 1 | 1 | 0 | 1 | 1 | Accumulator D Offset | 11 |
| 1 | X | X | 1 | 1 | 1 | 0 | 0 | Program Counter 8-Bit Offset | 12 |
| 1 | X | X | 1 | 1 | 1 | 0 | 1 | Program Counter 16-Bit Offset | 13 |
| 1 | X | X | 1 | 1 | 1 | 1 | 1 | Indirect | 14 |

Addressing Mode Field
Indirect Field
(Sign bit when B7 = 0)
Register Field
00: R = X
01: R = Y
10: R = U
11: R = S

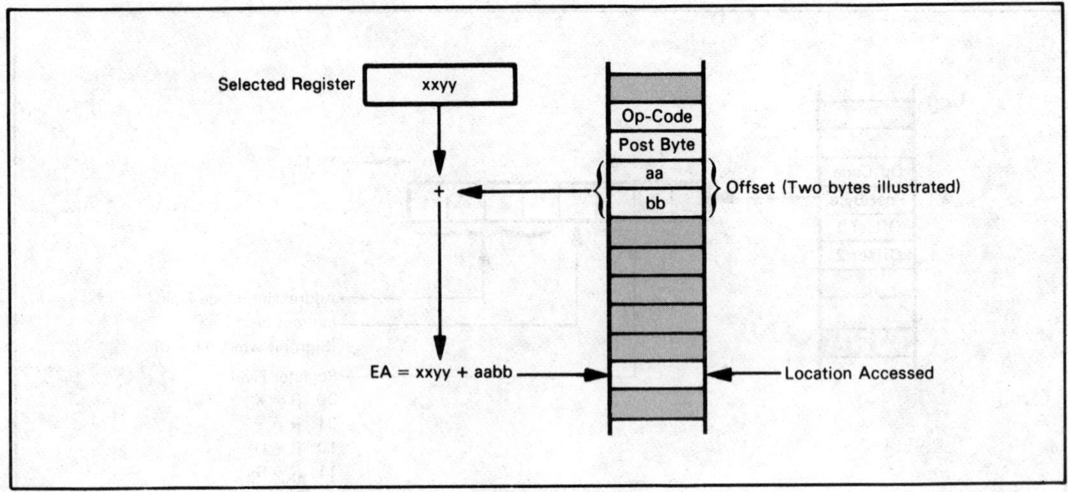


Figure 9-65. MC6809 Constant Offset (Indexed Mode) Addressing

**Many options are provided — they are constant offset, accumulator offset (using Accumulator A, Accumulator B, or Accumulator D), auto increment or decrement (by one or two) and indirection.**

Figure 9-65 illustrates a two-byte offset. However, some options do not require any offset, while others require one and still others require two. Thus, depending on the option chosen, the indexed mode may require two, three, or four bytes.

**Note: Most MC6800 indexed instructions map into an equivalent two bytes on the MC6809.**

**MC6809 CONSTANT OFFSET INDEXING ADDRESSING**

**In the constant offset mode, the offset is temporarily added to the value contained in the specified register to form an Effective Address (EA).** Note that these offsets may be positive or negative. In contrast, the MC6800 permits only positive offsets.

**Several variations of constant offset indexing are provided.** One of the variations uses bit space in the Post Byte itself to specify the offset. In this case, the offset is limited to that which may be specified by four bits. The instruction thus consists of the op-code and the Post Byte — no additional offset bytes are used. The offset is specified by the bit pattern contained in bit positions 0 through 3. Bit position 4 contains the sign of the displacement. this can be illustrated as follows:

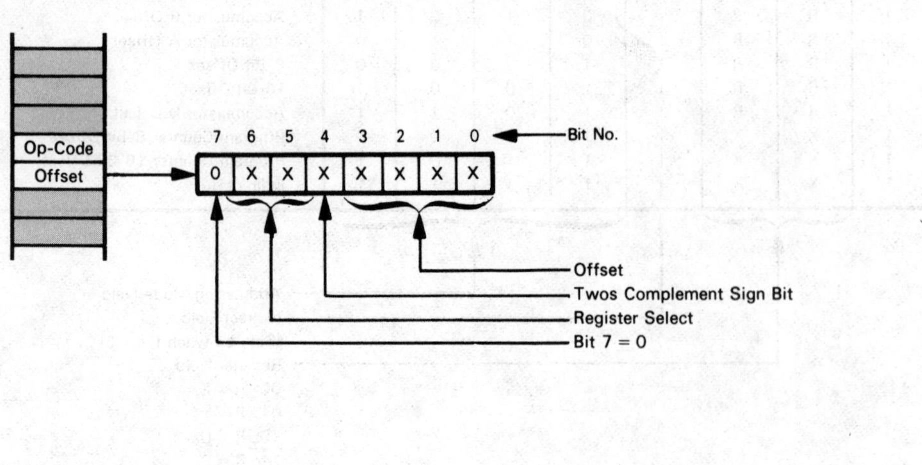

The second constant offset mode is a three-byte instruction, consisting of an op-code, a Post Byte, and a 7-bit twos complement offset. This mode can be illustrated as follows:

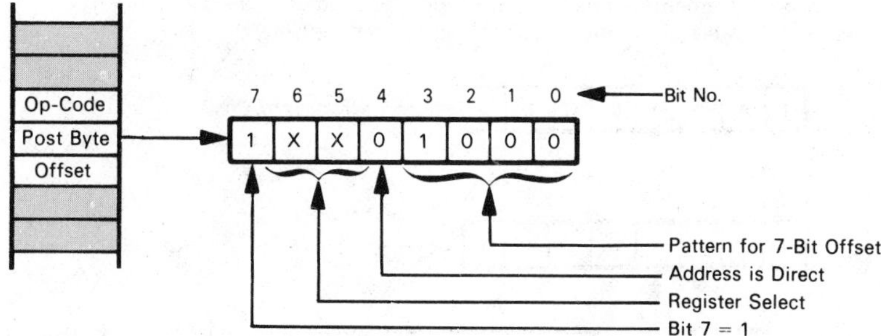


To achieve longer offsets than provided above, two offset bytes are used; a four-byte instruction results. The offset is specified in twos complement form. The applicable Post Byte is shown as line 10 in Table 9-19.

**MC6809 ACCUMULATOR OFFSET ADDRESSING**

**Accumulator offset is implemented as a two-byte instruction. There are three variations, one for each of the Accumulators A, B, and D** (see lines 8, 7, and 11 of Table 9-19). The contents of the specified accumulator are treated by the instruction as a twos complement offset. Since this is rather complex, let us illustrate with an example. Suppose Accumulator D contains $1107_{16}$ and Index Register X contains $1032_{16}$. The Post Byte, shown here,

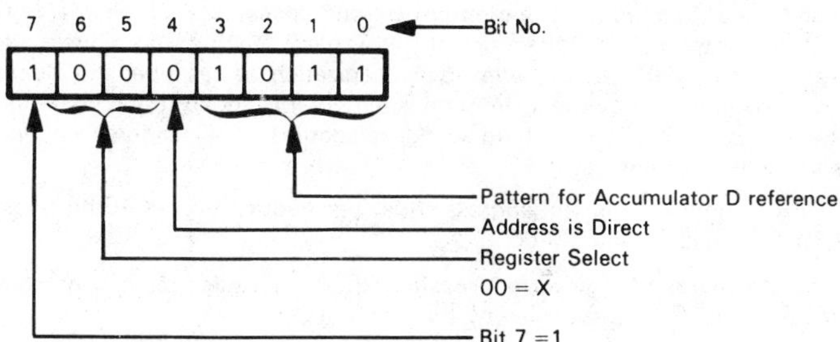


specifies that the contents of Accumulator D are to be added to the contents of the X register to form an Effective Address (EA):

$$EA = 1107_{16} + 1032_{16} = 2139_{16}$$

This is the address to be accessed by the instruction.

**MC6809 ZERO OFFSET ADDRESSING**

**A zero offset addressing option is also defined in which the selected pointer register (X, Y, S, or U) contains the effective address of the data to be used by the instruction.** This is a two-byte instruction which may incorporate an automatic increment or automatic decrement of the addressing register's contents as part of the addressing mode mechanization.

**When auto increment is employed, the address in the designated register (X, Y, U, or S) is used to access the desired memory location, then the contents of the register are automatically incremented.** Incrementation is by one or two, depending on the bit configuration of the Post Byte — see Table 9-19, lines 2 and 3 (reproduced below).

**MC6809 AUTO INCREMENT ADDRESSING**

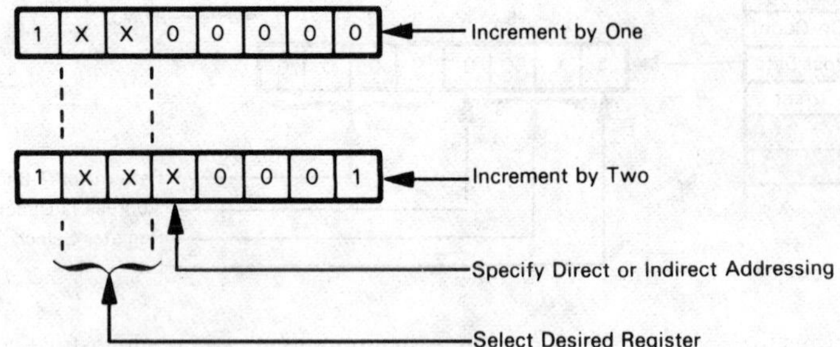


**When auto decrement is employed, the address in the designated register (X, Y, U, or S) is decremented, then the updated address is used to access the desired memory location.** Decrementation is by one or two, depending on the bit configuration of the Post Byte — see Table 9-19, lines 4 and 5.

**MC6809 AUTO DECREMENT ADDRESSING**

**Indexed indirect addressing is also provided for all indexed options except the 5-bit offset case and the auto increment/decrement-by-one cases.** Bit 4 of the Post Byte is used to define whether the instruction is indirect or not (see Table 9-19). Indexed indirect addressing as implemented on the MC6809 is a pre-indexed mechanization, as described in Volume 1, Chapter 6. The offset value referenced by the instruction is temporarily added to the contents of the designated pointer register (X, Y, U, or S) to form an indexed address. The memory location pointed to by this indexed address contains the actual address desired.

**MC6809 INDEXED INDIRECT ADDRESSING**

The offset for indexed indirect addressing is specified as 8-bit or 16-bit twos complement offset following the Post Byte, as illustrated in Figure 9-66.

**Accumulator indexed indirect addressing** obtains the offset as a twos complement number from one of the Accumulators A, B, or D as specified by the instruction.

**Indirect addressing for the auto increment/decrement cases is implemented only for the increment by two and decrement by two cases** — thus indirect increment and indirect decrement by one are not permitted.

**For the case of auto increment indirect, the address in the designated pointer register (X, Y, U, or SP) is used to recover an address from memory. This recovered address is the address of the location to be accessed (the Effective Address). Following this transaction, the contents of the Pointer register are incremented by two.** Post Byte bit definitions are indicated in Table 9-19.

**Auto decrement indirect is similar to auto increment indirect. In this case, however, the specified register contents are decremented twice before the indirect address is abstracted from the register.** Post Byte bit definitions are indicated in Table 9-19.

**Limited indexed mode addressing is also permitted with the Program Counter.** This is detailed in Table 9-19 (lines 12 and 13). Note that 8-bit and 16-bit offsets only are provided.

**Relative addressing in the MC6809 has been greatly enhanced over that provided in the basic MC6800. First, it is no longer limited to branch instructions and, second, the relative range has been extended through the use of a 16-bit twos complement offset.**

**MC6809 RELATIVE ADDRESSING**

Relative addressing is an important ingredient in position-independent coding, and the enhanced scheme provided on the MC6809 greatly facilitates this method of program structuring.

All branch instructions have been implemented in the traditional MC6800 form (referred to as the short form) and in a long form. The short form takes a one-byte op-code with a one-byte offset, while the long form takes a one- or two-byte op-code with a two-byte offset. For the long branch case, the actual address is formed by adding the two bytes following the op-code as a twos complement number to the Program Counter. (Remember, the Program Counter points to the next instruction — thus, it has already stepped over the offset bytes.)

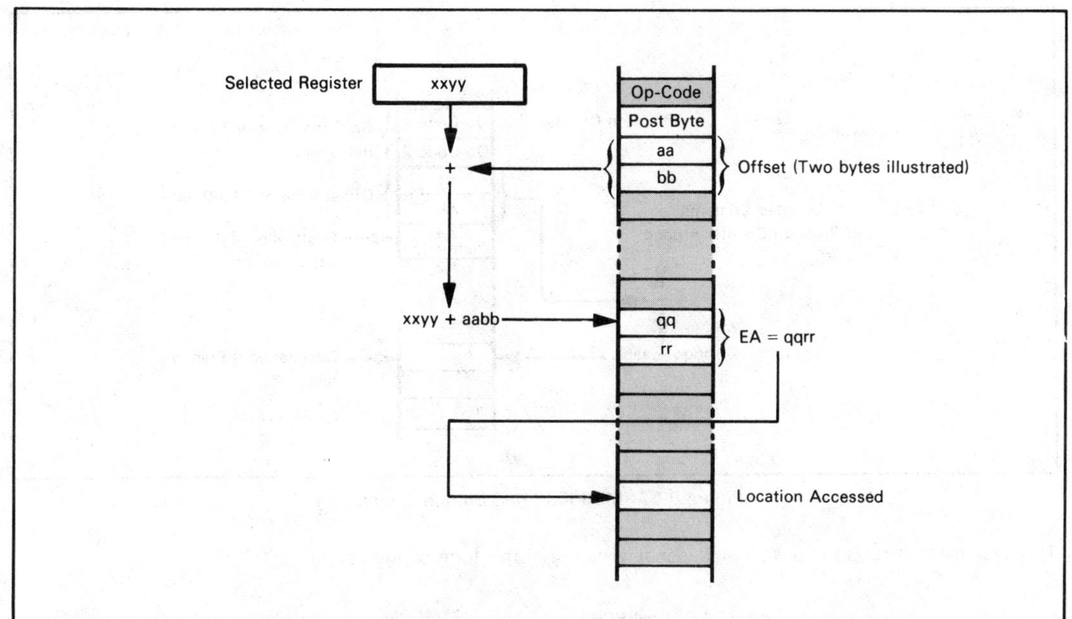


Figure 9-66. MC6809 Constant Offset Indexed Indirect Addressing

**Relative addressing has been extended to include all memory reference instructions. It has been implemented as Program Counter relative indexed addressing.** Two variations are permitted; one uses an 8-bit twos complement offset (for short reaches), and the other uses a 16-bit twos complement offset (long reaches). Table 9-19 defines the Post Bytes for these two cases (lines 12 and 13). The general address formation scheme is similar to that of Figure 9-67. This is illustrated below for a long relative transfer.

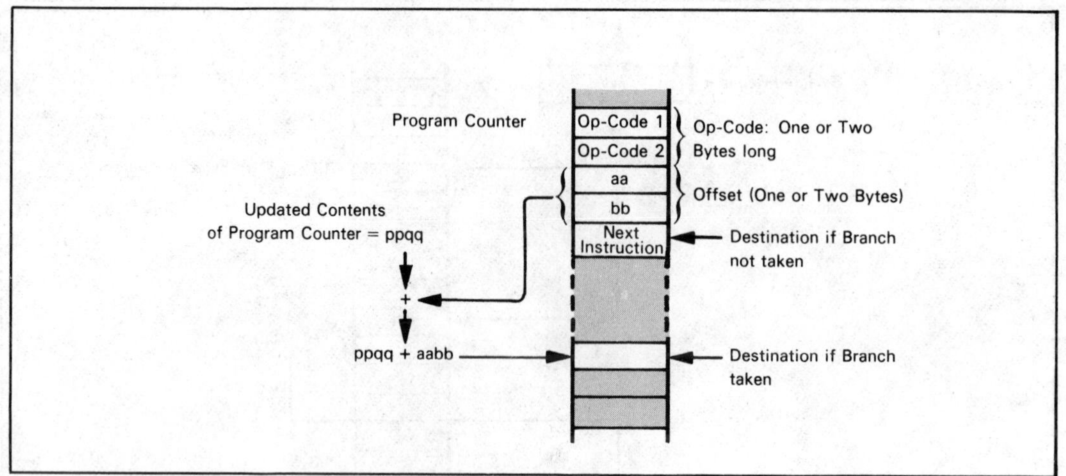


Figure 9-67. MC6809 Long Branch Addressing

This example illustrates the position-independent nature of this form of addressing:

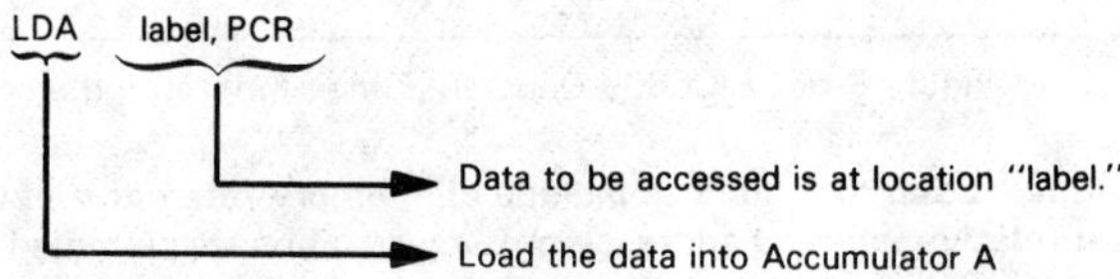


The MC6809 assembler requires that you use the mnemonic "PCR" for Program Counter relative addressing. The assembler then automatically computes the distance or offset from the "present" Program Counter value to the specified location.

From Table 9-21, we determine that the hex code for LDA (indexed) is A6. From Table 9-19, line 12, we get the Post Byte for an 8-bit offset:

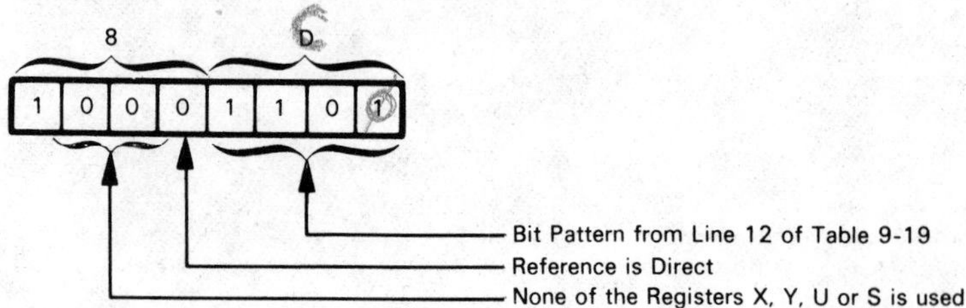

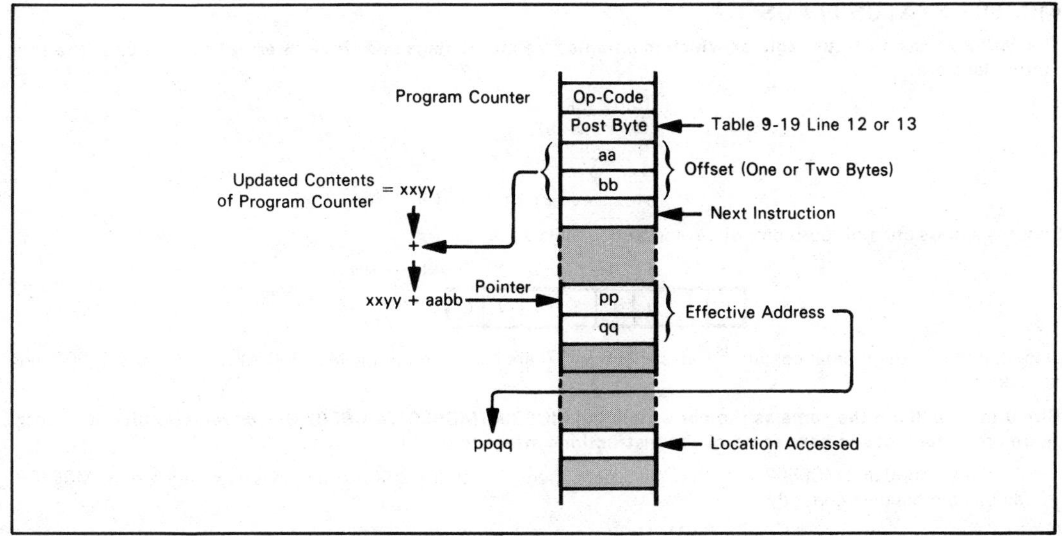


Figure 9-68. MC6809 Relative Indirect Addressing

Assume the program segment starts at address $1000_{16}$, and that "label" represents location $104A_{16}$.

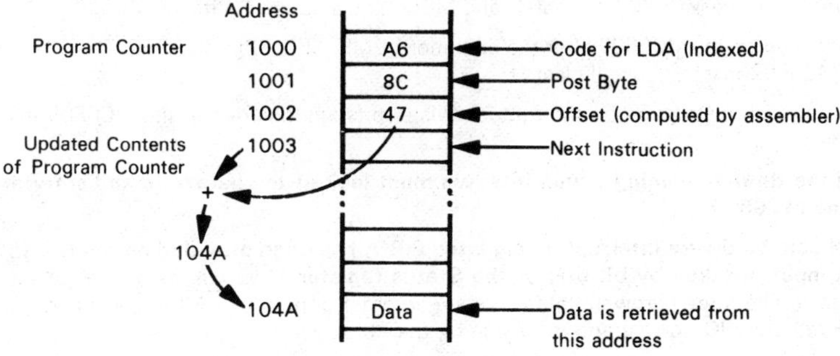


During execution, the updated Program Counter value is added to the offset; thus, if the program is relocated, it still functions correctly since the location referenced remains the same relative distance away.

Long reaches are similar to the above, except that the Post Byte is $8D_{16}$ (line 13 of Table 9-19), and two bytes are required for the twos complement offset.

**MC6809 RELATIVE INDIRECT ADDRESSING**

**Relative indirect addressing is an extension of relative addressing. The Program Counter is used again as an indexed register. The general scheme is illustrated in Figure 9-68.**

The offset (one or two bytes, twos complement) is added to the updated contents of the Program Counter to form a pointer to a pair of memory locations which contain the actual address to be accessed. For a one-byte offset, the Post Byte is $9C_{16}$; for a two-byte offset, the Post Byte is $9D_{16}$ — see Table 9-19, lines 12 and 13.

**Instructions that use extended indirect addressing require four bytes of object code: an op-code, a Post Byte and two bytes which specify a 16-bit address. These last two bytes are a pointer to a location that contains the actual address to be referenced.** This approach to indirect addressing differs from that of Volume 1, Chapter 6 only in that a Post Byte is used. The Post Byte has a value of 10011111 ($9F_{16}$) as defined by line 14 of Table 9-19. (This mode is shown in Table 9-19, since it is actually implemented as an indexed, indirect instruction, relative to the Program Counter.)

## MC6809 STATUS FLAGS

**The MC6809 has a Status register which maintains five status flags and three interrupt control bits. The five status flags are:**

Carry (C)
Overflow (V)
Sign (S)
Zero (Z)
Auxiliary or Half-Carry (H)

Statuses are assigned bit positions within the Status register as follows:

| 7 | 6 | 5 | 4 | 3 | 2 | 1 | 0 ← Bit No. |
|---|---|---|---|---|---|---|---|
| E | F | H | I | S | Z | V | C |

Note that the two high-order condition codes (bits 6 and 7) are used here; in the MC6800, MC6801, and MC6802 they are permanently set to 1.

**Bits 0 through 5 are the same as the corresponding MC6800/MC6801/MC6802 Status register bits; however, there are differences in how some of the instructions affect these bits:**

1) On the MC6800 and MC6802, only the Z bit is set correctly when the CPX instruction is executed. On the MC6809, all bits are handled correctly.
2) The multiply instruction (MUL) on the MC6809 sets the Z bit (if appropriate). The MUL instruction of the MC6801 does not.
3) On the MC6800, MC6801, and MC6802, the right shift instructions (ASR, LSR, and ROR) set the overflow bit (V) if applicable; the corresponding instructions on the MC6809 do not affect Overflow status.
4) The TST instruction on the MC6800, MC6801, and MC6802 clears the C bit; the MC6809 TST does not affect it.
5) The H bit is undefined on the MC6809 after the operations CMP, NEG, SBC, and SUB. The corresponding MC6800, MC6801, and MC6802 instructions all clear H.

Details of the effect of each instruction on the Status register bits are included in the MC6809 Instruction Set Summary — Table 9-22.

**Before describing the three remaining status bits, we must look at the hardware and software interrupts that are provided on the MC6809.**

**An additional maskable hardware interrupt, designated $\overline{\text{FIRQ}}$, has been provided on the MC6809. This is a Fast Interrupt Request input, masked by bit 6(F) of the Status register.** $\overline{\text{FIRQ}}$ causes only a subset of registers to be pushed onto the Stack. The three hardware interrupts are, in order of priority, $\overline{\text{NMI}}$ (highest and non-maskable), $\overline{\text{FIRQ}}$ (maskable by the F bit) and $\overline{\text{IRQ}}$ (lowest and maskable by the I bit).

**Three software interrupts are provided. They are SWI, SWI2 and SWI3.**

**Let us now return to the three status bits I, F, and E.**

**I is the external interrupt disable flag associated with hardware interrupt input $\overline{\text{IRQ}}$.** When I = 1, interrupts via $\overline{\text{IRQ}}$ are disabled; when I = 0, interrupts via $\overline{\text{IRQ}}$ are enabled. $\overline{\text{NMI}}$, $\overline{\text{FIRQ}}$, $\overline{\text{IRQ}}$, $\overline{\text{RESET}}$ and SWI all set I to 1. SWI2 and SWI3 have no effect on I.

**F is the external interrupt disable flag associated with hardware interrupt input $\overline{\text{FIRQ}}$.** When F = 1, interrupts via $\overline{\text{FIRQ}}$ are disabled; when F = 0, interrupts via $\overline{\text{FIRQ}}$ are enabled. $\overline{\text{NMI}}$, $\overline{\text{FIRQ}}$, SWI and $\overline{\text{RESET}}$ all set F to 1; $\overline{\text{IRQ}}$, SWI2 and SWI3 have no effect on F.

**E is the Entire flag bit.** The occurrence of $\overline{\text{NMI}}$, $\overline{\text{IRQ}}$, SWI, SWI2 or SWI3 sets E and stacks the entire machine register complement, while $\overline{\text{FIRQ}}$ clears E and stacks only the Program Counter and the Status register. Note that only the E bit in the saved or Stack Status register has any significance.

**E is used at the end of interrupt processing to determine how much to unstack.** When the RTI instruction is executed at the end of an interrupt, the processor checks the E bit from the recovered Status register. If E = 1, the full complement of registers is restored from the Stack, whereas, if E = 0, only the subset consisting of the Program Counter and Status register is retrieved.

## MC6809 CPU PINS AND SIGNALS

**The MC6809 CPU pins and signals are illustrated in Figure 9-69. A description of these signals is useful as a guide to the way in which the MC6809 works and to the ways in which it differs from the MC6800.**

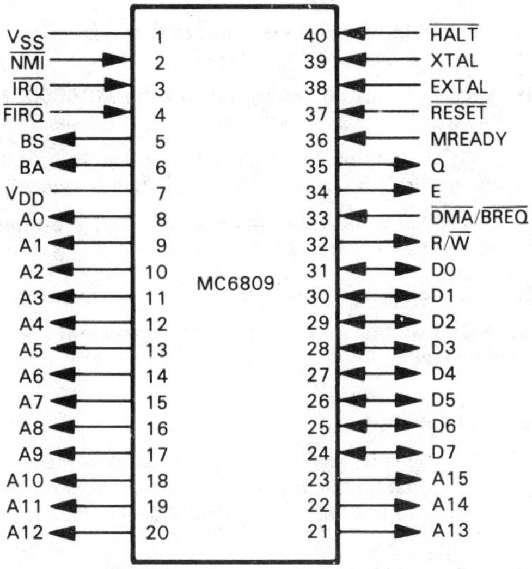

| Signal | Pin | Pin | Signal |
|---|---|---|---|
| $V_{SS}$ | 1 | 40 | $\overline{HALT}$ |
| $\overline{NMI}$ | 2 | 39 | XTAL |
| $\overline{IRQ}$ | 3 | 38 | EXTAL |
| $\overline{FIRQ}$ | 4 | 37 | $\overline{RESET}$ |
| BS | 5 | 36 | MREADY |
| BA | 6 | 35 | Q |
| $V_{DD}$ | 7 | 34 | E |
| A0 | 8 | 33 | $\overline{DMA/BREQ}$ |
| A1 | 9 | 32 | R/$\overline{W}$ |
| A2 | 10 | 31 | D0 |
| A3 | 11 | 30 | D1 |
| A4 | 12 | 29 | D2 |
| A5 | 13 | 28 | D3 |
| A6 | 14 | 27 | D4 |
| A7 | 15 | 26 | D5 |
| A8 | 16 | 25 | D6 |
| A9 | 17 | 24 | D7 |
| A10 | 18 | 23 | A15 |
| A11 | 19 | 22 | A14 |
| A12 | 20 | 21 | A13 |

MC6809

| Pin Name | Description | Type |
|---|---|---|
| *A0-A15 | Address Lines | Tristate, Output |
| *D0-D7 | Data Bus Lines | Tristate, Bidirectional |
| *E, Q | Clock Signals | Output |
| *R/$\overline{W}$ | Read/Write | Tristate, Output |
| *BA | Bus Available | Output |
| *BS | Bus State | Output |
| EXTAL, XTAL | Crystal | Input |
| *MRDY | Memory Ready | Input |
| *$\overline{DMA/BREQ}$ | DMA/Bus Request | Input |
| *$\overline{HALT}$ | Halt | Input |
| *$\overline{RESET}$ | Reset | Input |
| $\overline{NMI}$ | Non-Maskable Interrupt | Input |
| *$\overline{FIRQ}$ | Fast Interrupt Request | Input |
| *$\overline{IRQ}$ | Interrupt Request | Input |
| $V_{DD}$, $V_{SS}$ | Power and Ground | |

*These signals connect to the System Bus.

Figure 9-69. MC6809 CPU Signals and Pin Assignments

The $\overline{RESET}$ input is used to initialize the CPU. To reset it, the $\overline{RESET}$ line must be asserted low for at least one bus cycle. This aborts the current operation. An internal Schmitt Trigger circuit on the $\overline{RESET}$ input permits the use of a simple RC network to reset the entire system.

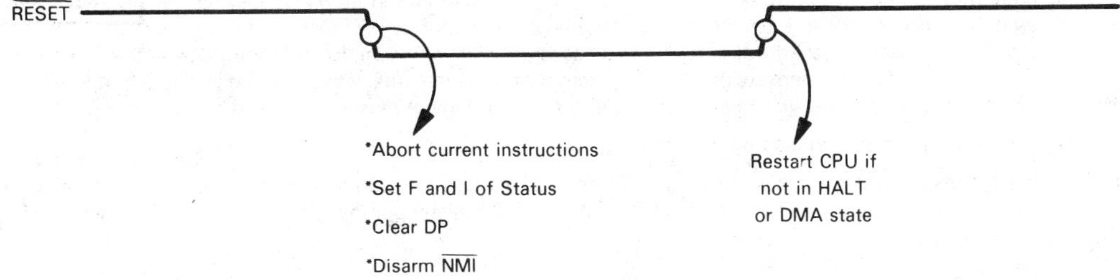

**EXTAL and XTAL are inputs for a parallel resonant crystal;** alternatively, EXTAL may be driven by an external TTL-level compatible clock by grounding the XTAL pin.

**The Enable pin E distributes the clocking signal to the rest of the system.** It is a standard 6800 Bus system timing signal and is usually connected to the E inputs of MC6800 family devices.

**Q is a new clocking output signal that has no counterpart in the MC6800, MC6801, or MC6802 versions.** Its positive transition indicates when stable address exist on the system busses.

**Memory Ready (MRDY)** is an input control signal that is used to extend the data access time when slow memories are used. It is also used to extend the access time in multiprocessor applications when shared memories are used.

**The Address Bus lines (A0 to A15) and Data Bus lines (D0 to D7) are standard 6800 peripheral-compatible busses.** Their relationship with bus control signals is detailed later.

**R/$\overline{\text{W}}$ is the same as the MC6800 signal.** It is valid with the positive transition of Q.

**MC6809 BUS STATE CONTROLS**

**Control signals on the MC6809 Control Bus may be divided into bus state controls, bus data identification, and interrupt processing.** There are some lines here that do not exist on the MC6800.

**These are the bus state control lines:**

**DMA/Bus Request ($\overline{\text{DMA/BREQ}}$):** This is an input line used for DMA or memory refresh operations. When asserted low, it suspends CPU operation (by stretching the internal CPU clock), takes the processor off the bus and tristates the system busses. (There is no equivalent to this line on the MC6800 — in fact, it takes two lines, TSC and DBE, just to float the system busses.)

**No DBE (Data Bus Enable) input is provided on the MC6809.** The equivalent of DBE is generated internally by the processor.

**$\overline{\text{HALT}}$:** When this input is asserted low, the CPU ceases operation at the end of the current instruction and the system busses (Address, Data and R/$\overline{\text{W}}$) are tristated. The CPU may remain in the halted state indefinitely without loss of data.

**Bus Available (BA):** This output line (when driven high by internal logic) indicates that the system busses (Address, Data and R/$\overline{\text{W}}$) are in their high impedance state and available to external devices for Direct Memory Access (DMA) transactions or any other form of bus sharing activities permitted. BA high does not imply that the bus will be available for more than one cycle, however. When driven low (by internal logic) an additional bus cycle at high impedance occurs before resuming operation.

**Bus State (BS): This is an encoded output** which, in conjunction with output BA, indicates the current state of the CPU. Combinations are listed in Table 9-20.

Table 9-20. MC6809 Bus Status Signals

| BA | BS | Function |
|---|---|---|
| 0 | 0 | Normal Operation (Running) |
| 0 | 1 | Interrupt Acknowledge |
| 1 | 0 | SYNC Acknowledge |
| 1 | 1 | BUS GRANT or HALT Acknowledge |
| Status indications are valid on the leading edge of Q. | | |

**MC6809 VMA CONDITION**

**No VMA (Valid Memory Address) output is provided on the MC6809 — instead, when the processor does not need to use the system busses for a data transfer, it simultaneously sets all address lines high ($\text{FFFF}_{16}$) and R/$\overline{\text{W}}$ = 1.** This is a "dummy" read of address FFFF. During this dummy read, both BA and BS = 0. The only other required read of address FFFF occurs during a fetch of the low-order Reset vector address. During this access of FFFF, however, BA = 0 and BS = 1 (see Table 9-20). Thus, the status of lines BA and BS permits the user to differentiate between these two situations. (Note that MRDY will not be used to extend one of these dummy cycles since there is no logical reason to extend these cycles.)

**These are the three interrupt processing signals:**

**Non-Maskable Interrupt ($\overline{\text{NMI}}$):** This interrupt cannot be masked. It is an edge-sensitive (as opposed to level-sensitive) input that responds to a high-to-low transition. On $\overline{\text{NMI}}$, the full register complement is stacked. $\overline{\text{NMI}}$ has the highest priority.

**$\overline{\text{IRQ}}$ is a hardware Interrupt Request input.** An interrupt generated at $\overline{\text{IRQ}}$ stacks the full complement of CPU registers. $\overline{\text{IRQ}}$ has lowest priority.

**$\overline{\text{FIRQ}}$ is a Fast Hardware Interrupt Request input.** It provides fast response by stacking only the return address and the Status register. It has higher priority than $\overline{\text{IRQ}}$ but less than $\overline{\text{NMI}}$.

## MC6809 TIMING AND INSTRUCTION EXECUTION

**MC6809 CLOCK OPTIONS**

**An internal divide-by-four circuit on the MC6809 permits the use of inexpensive, parallel resonant crystals. Alternatively, EXTAL may be driven by an external TTL-level compatible clock.** Since the internal divide-by-four circuit is still utilized, the bus frequency is 1/4 input frequency.

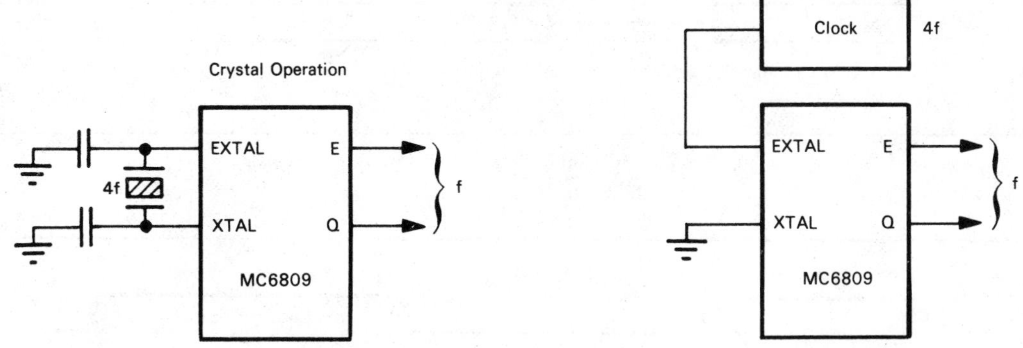


**The phase relationship between the MC6809 timing outputs E and Q is shown below. Q is a quadrature clocking signal that leads E.**

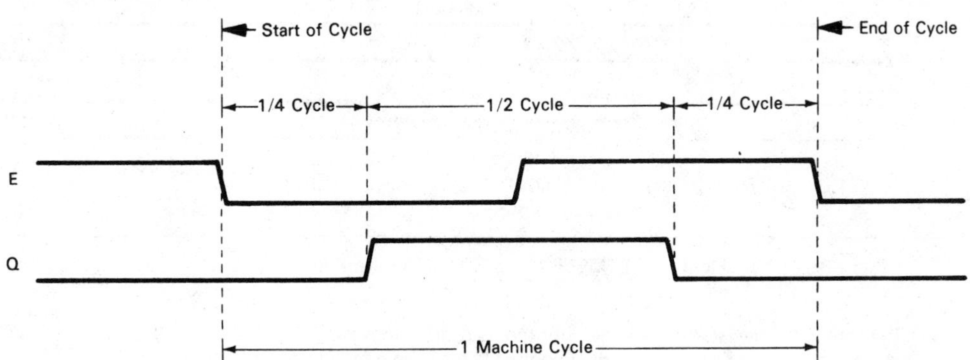

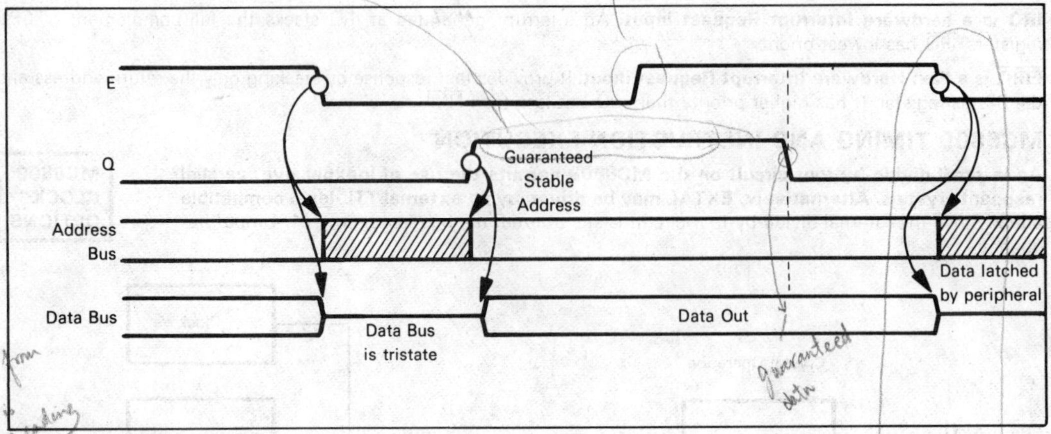

Figure 9-70. MC6809 E and Q Timing for Write Cycles

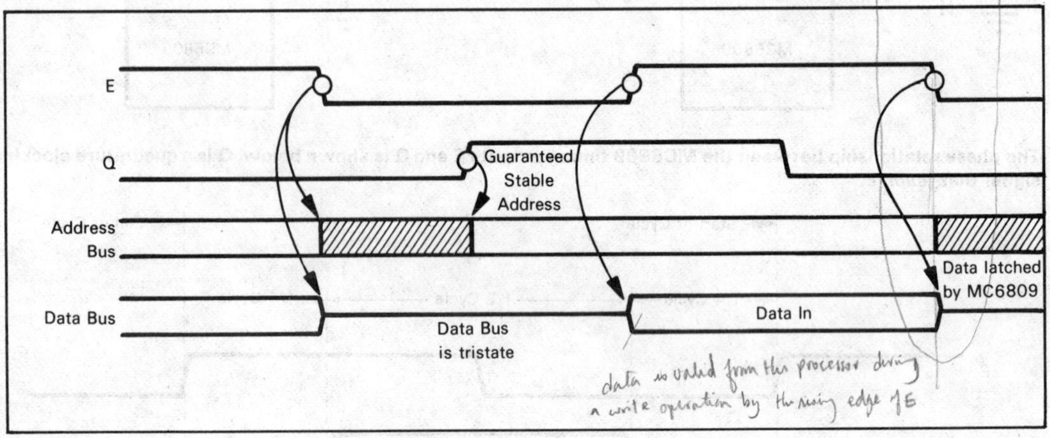

Figure 9-71. MC6809 E and Q Timing for Read Cycles

**MC6809 WRITE TIMING**

Addresses from the CPU may start to change after the hold time from the falling edge of E, but they are guaranteed to be stable on the leading edge of Q, as shown in Figure 9-70. The timing shown in this figure is for an MC6809 write cycle.

During the write cycle, the processor starts to propagate data onto the Data Bus at the positive transition of Q; this data is guaranteed to be valid on the trailing edge of Q.

**MC6809 READ TIMING**

Figure 9-71 illustrates the timing for an MC6809 read cycle.

Peripherals generally propagate data into the system via the Data Bus during E high. Data needs to be stable a short time before and after E goes low. This is the hold time.

Note that the Data Bus is floated during the interval when both E and Q are low (on a write cycle) or for 1/2 cycle when E is low (on a read cycle.) This interval allows "turn-around" time on the bidirectional Data Bus.

**MC6809 ACCESSING SLOW DEVICES**

**Several control signals are provided to increase timing parameters so that the MC6809 can be easily interfaced to slow devices.**

If E (high) is too short for the external device logic to respond to during the write cycle, the slow device may be accommodated if we stretch the bus clocks. MRDY permits this stretching. By asserting MRDY low, the clocks are stretched as indicated in the following illustration:

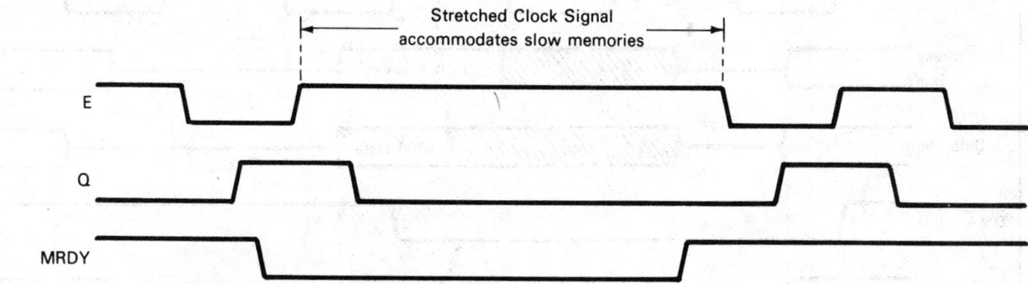


A low input on MRDY when E goes high causes E to remain high; stretching terminates when MRDY is returned high. Stretching will always be an integral number of high-frequency clock cycles (that is, 1/4 bus cycles) and must not exceed 10 microseconds in order to maintain the integrity of the CPU internal registers.

Note that MRDY alters the system E signal. Devices which require a constant clock frequency must therefore use a different clock source if this clock stretching technique is implemented.

## MC6809 DIRECT MEMORY ACCESS

**The MC6809 bus state control monitoring signals permit all three of the most widely used DMA techniques (Halt mode, cycle stealing, and bus multiplexing) to be implemented. With the on-chip clock version of the MC6809, cycle-stealing DMA is controlled by the chip itself.**

**MC6809 HALT MODE DMA**

**Consider first Halt mode DMA.** This is the simplest mode, as one simply shuts down the CPU while transactions take place on the bus. The MC6809 Halt state is equivalent to the Halt on the 6800, or the Hold state of the 8080A. The CPU will float its Address Bus, Data Bus, and R/$\overline{W}$ line and suspend instruction execution in response to a low level applied to the $\overline{HALT}$ input. The CPU will maintain this condition indefinitely (without loss of data) until the $\overline{HALT}$ input is driven high again. While in this state, BA and BS are asserted high by internal CPU logic. When $\overline{HALT}$ is driven low, the CPU will continue to run until the end of the current instruction before it enters the Hold state. The worst case latency is 20 machine cycles. This occurs with the Software Interrupt instructions SWI2 and SWI3.

**MC6809 BUS GRANT**

CPU output lines Bus Available (BA) and Bus State (BS) both go high in the Halt mode. These lines may be asynchronously decoded to yield a BUS GRANT signal.

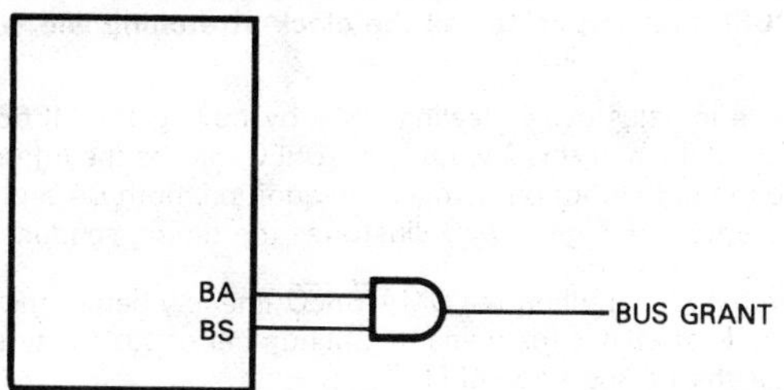

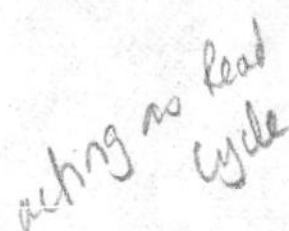

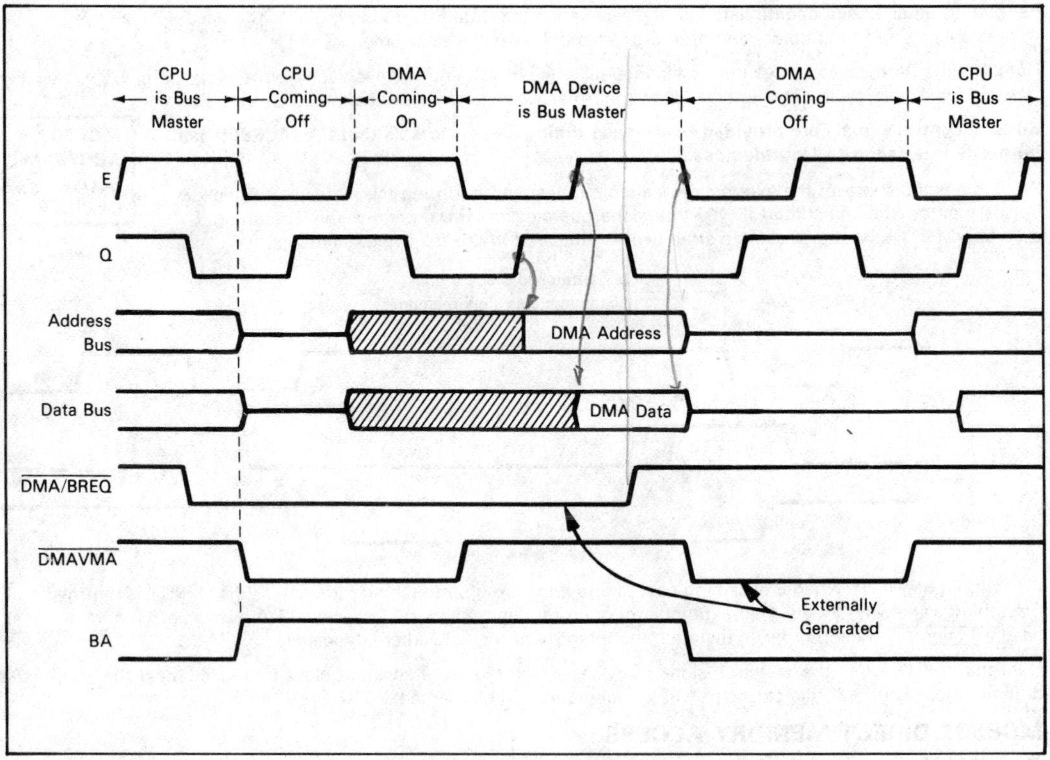

CPU is Bus Master | CPU Coming Off | DMA Coming On | DMA Device is Bus Master | DMA Coming Off | CPU is Bus Master

E

Q

Address Bus

DMA Address

Data Bus

DMA Data

$\overline{\text{DMA/BREQ}}$

$\overline{\text{DMAVMA}}$

BA

Externally Generated

Figure 9-72. MC6809 Timing and Signals for Cycle-Stealing Single-Cycle DMA

In most cases, it will be sufficient to use BA alone as a BUS GRANT signal.

With the above as background, we can summarize the Halt mode DMA activity as follows:

- The external device asserts the CPU $\overline{\text{HALT}}$ line low.
- At the end of the current instruction, the CPU suspends operation, floats the system busses (Address, Data and R/$\overline{\text{W}}$), and outputs BA high to signify to the DMA device that it may take over the busses and commence a DMA transaction.
- The bus clocks E and Q continue to furnish synchronization signals to the DMA interface.
- At the end of the transaction, the external device asserts $\overline{\text{HALT}}$ high. This terminates the DMA activity by making BA =0 and restores the CPU to normal operation one cycle later.

**MC6809 CYCLE-STEALING DMA**

**Now consider cycle-stealing DMA. This mode is easily implemented because the internal circuitry of the MC6809 incorporates all the clock stretching and bus floating logic required.**

The external DMA device initiates cycle-stealing DMA by pulling the MC6809 Bus Request line $\overline{\text{DMA/BREQ}}$ low. Recognition of this low on $\overline{\text{DMA/BREQ}}$ causes the internal CPU clocks to be stretched, while the bus clocks (E and Q) continue to function normally. In addition, both BA and BS go high, and the system busses (Address, Data and R/$\overline{\text{W}}$) are floated. Figure 9-72 illustrates the timing sequence for cycle-stealing DMA.

A DMA transaction is initiated by pulling the $\overline{\text{DMA/BREQ}}$ line low before the trailing edge of Q. This suspends operation of the internal clocks (it stretches them an integral number of basic machine cycles), and starts to float the system busses (a hold time after the trailing edge of E).

**EXTERNAL VMA**

**To prevent false reads or writes to memory and peripherals as the address and R/$\overline{\text{W}}$ lines are floated, the system must generate an external VMA signal (denoted $\overline{\text{DMAVMA}}$).** This

DMAVMA signal is used to disable the memory and peripherals until the DMA device has control of the system busses. A circuit that could be used to generate this DMAVMA signal is as follows:

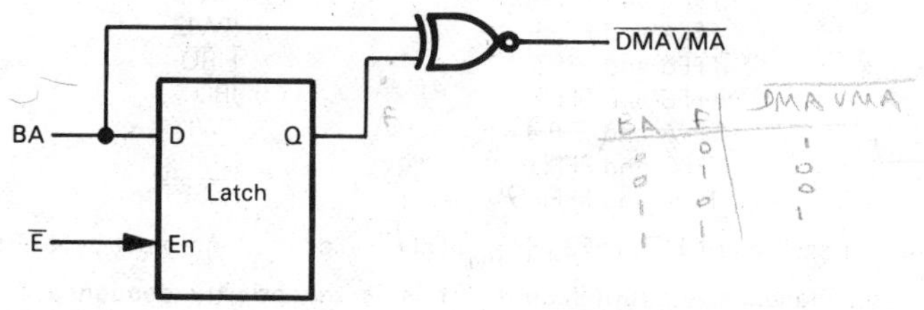


The CPU acknowledges DMA/BREQ by asserting BA and BS high. This is the BUS GRANT signal. It signifies to the DMA device that the CPU has been removed from the busses, and that a DMA transaction may take place. The bus clock signals E and Q continue to furnish bus timing to the DMA interface.

At the end of the transfer, the external device returns DMA/BREQ high, restoring the CPU to normal operation. This must occur before the trailing edge of Q, and the DMA device must get off the bus a hold time after the trailing edge of E (in the same cycle). The CPU busses will begin to emerge from their floating condition after the dead cycle. Again, the system must provide a low VMA signal (DMAVMA) to prevent false accesses while the Address Bus and R/W line are going through this floating state.

**One significant difference between the DMA logic of the MC6809 and that of the MC6800 is the "self-refresh" capability of the MC6809. With the MC6800, there was a maximum duration specified for DMA operations: the DMAREQ signal had to be returned high periodically to allow internal circuitry of the MC6800 to be refreshed. With the MC6809, however, the microprocessor itself will periodically recover the system busses to perform a single MPU cycle and thus refresh itself.**

**MC6809 DYNAMIC MEMORY REFRESH OPERATIONS**

Dynamic memory refresh can also be implemented on a cycle-stealing basis by making the refresh controller a high priority DMA device, and accessing the required number of consecutive locations within the time required to maintain data integrity. Another way of refreshing dynamic memory would be to simply perform a high-speed scan through 64 or 128 consecutive memory locations. This is easily done through a single-instruction subroutine consisting of 63 (or 127) pre-bytes and an RTS (or RTI).

## MC6809 INTERRUPT PROCESSING AND RESET

Interrupt capabilities implemented on the MC6809 are:

- Hardware Interrupts NMI, FIRQ, and IRQ
- Software Interrupts SWI, SWI2 and SWI3
- RESTART

**NMI and IRQ are equivalent to the corresponding interrupts on the MC6800.**

**FIRQ is a Fast Interrupt Request that has no counterpart on the MC6800. It is a maskable, hardware interrupt of higher priority than IRQ. Its implementation provides the MC6809 with an easy to use two-level vectored interrupt scheme.** An interrupt on IRQ automatically vectors to its own software handler routine, while an interrupt on FIRQ automatically vectors to its unique software handler routine. The higher priority device is connected to FIRQ to achieve priority response.

Within each of these levels, software polling may be used if more than one interrupt device is connected on each interrupt input. However, as noted in the MC6800 description, software polling greatly increases interrupt latency and can quickly become untenable.

An alternate scheme that permits direct vectoring by the interrupting device itself to anywhere in memory may be implemented. This is described later.

**MC6809 INTERRUPT VECTOR ADDRESSES**

**The MC6809 sets aside the sixteen highest addressable memory locations for interrupt processing purposes. Seven 16-bit addresses are stored in these locations (one pair of locations is reserved for future definition). These seven addresses identify the starting addresses of the service routines for the seven possible sources of interrupt.**

**This is how the memory locations are used to store the interrupt vectors:**

| | |
|---|---|
| FFF0 and FFF1 | Reserved |
| FFF2 and FFF3 | SWI3 |
| FFF4 and FFF5 | SWI2 |
| FFF6 and FFF7 | $\overline{\text{FIRQ}}$ |
| FFF8 and FFF9 | $\overline{\text{IRQ}}$ |
| FFFA and FFFB | SWI |
| FFFC and FFFD | $\overline{\text{NMI}}$ |
| FFFE and FFFF | $\overline{\text{RESET}}$ |

The lower address of each pair (FFF0, FFF2, FFF4, ...FFFE) holds the high-order byte of the starting address.

**MC6809 INTERRUPT PRIORITIES**

In the event of simultaneous interrupt requests, **this is the priority sequence** during the acknowledge process:

Highest
1) $\overline{\text{RESET}}$
2) Non-Maskable Interrupt ($\overline{\text{NMI}}$)
3) Software Interrupt (SWI)
4) Fast Interrupt Request $\overline{\text{FIRQ}}$
5) Standard Hardware Interrupt ($\overline{\text{IRQ}}$)

Lowest

**We will begin our discussion of MC6809 interrupt processing by describing the various interrupts.**

**MC6809 FAST INTERRUPT REQUEST**

**Consider first $\overline{\text{FIRQ}}$. $\overline{\text{FIRQ}}$ permits high-speed response to hardware interrupts by stacking only a subset of the register complement** — only the return address and the Stack register contents are pushed onto the Stack. At the end of the interrupt, these two items only are restored from the Stack. Status register flag bits F and I are set to mask out the present $\overline{\text{FIRQ}}$ and further $\overline{\text{IRQ}}$ and $\overline{\text{FIRQ}}$ interrupts. (If you wish to admit multiple-level interrupts, you can now clear the F and I flags.)

**MC6809 STANDARD HARDWARE INTERRUPTS**

**We will refer to $\overline{\text{IRQ}}$ as the standard hardware interrupt. It provides slower response than FIRQ, because it stacks the entire machine state. Thus, $\overline{\text{IRQ}}$ functions in the same way as the MC6800 $\overline{\text{IRQ}}$.** $\overline{\text{FIRQ}}$ can interrupt $\overline{\text{IRQ}}$, but $\overline{\text{IRQ}}$ cannot interrupt $\overline{\text{FIRQ}}$, since $\overline{\text{FIRQ}}$ disables $\overline{\text{IRQ}}$ by setting the I bit of the Status register.

**MC6809 SOFTWARE INTERRUPTS SWI, SWI2 AND SWI3**

**The MC6809 includes three software interrupts. SWI has higher priority than $\overline{\text{IRQ}}$ and $\overline{\text{FIRQ}}$, and disables these interrupts by setting the Status flags F and I. SWI2 and SWI3 do not disable any interrupts. All three save the entire machine status by pushing the contents of all the active registers onto the Stack.**

SWI is implemented on the MC6800, but the MC6800 has no counterpart to SWI2 and SWI3. Note that these instructions cause the MC6809 to go through the complete logic of an interrupt request, even though the interrupting source is within the CPU.

**MC6809 NON-MASKABLE INTERRUPT**

**The non-maskable interrupt $\overline{\text{NMI}}$, as with the MC6800, cannot be disabled. Like $\overline{\text{IRQ}}$, it stacks the entire machine status.**

Because $\overline{\text{NMI}}$ is not masked, repeated $\overline{\text{NMI}}$ interrupts occurring before the previous ones have been terminated by an RTI (Return from Interrupt) instruction can cause the Stack to overflow. This will cause a fatal error.

**MC6809 RESET**

A detailed discussion of **$\overline{\text{RESET}}$ versus Interrupt response** is included with the MC6800 description and will not be repeated here. However, the following points should be noted:

- If the $\overline{\text{HALT}}$ or $\overline{\text{DMA/BREQ}}$ inputs are asserted low when $\overline{\text{RESET}}$ makes its low-to-high transition, it will be latched, and the CPU will wait until the resumption of a running state before completing the reset.
- A single-bus-cycle low on $\overline{\text{RESET}}$ will start the reset sequence.
- Asserting $\overline{\text{RESET}}$ will not bring the CPU out of tristate during a HALT or DMA condition.
- Because a Schmitt trigger is used on the $\overline{\text{RESET}}$ input, a simple RC network can be used to reset the CPU. This is much less stringent than the 100 nanosecond rise time limit of the MC6800.
- NMI is disabled by RESET until after you have loaded the Stack Pointer(s).

Normally, the reset action takes five bus cycles. However, since DMA may occur during reset, the actual reset may take considerably longer.

**Through the use of some external logic, it is possible for the interrupting device to force a vectored jump to anywhere in memory.** This scheme makes use of the Interrupt Acknowledge (IACK) signal.

Table 9-20 shows the IACK is indicated by BA = 0 and BS = 1. These status indications are valid on the leading edge of Q.

**MC6809 INTERRUPT VECTORING BY EXTERNAL DEVICES**

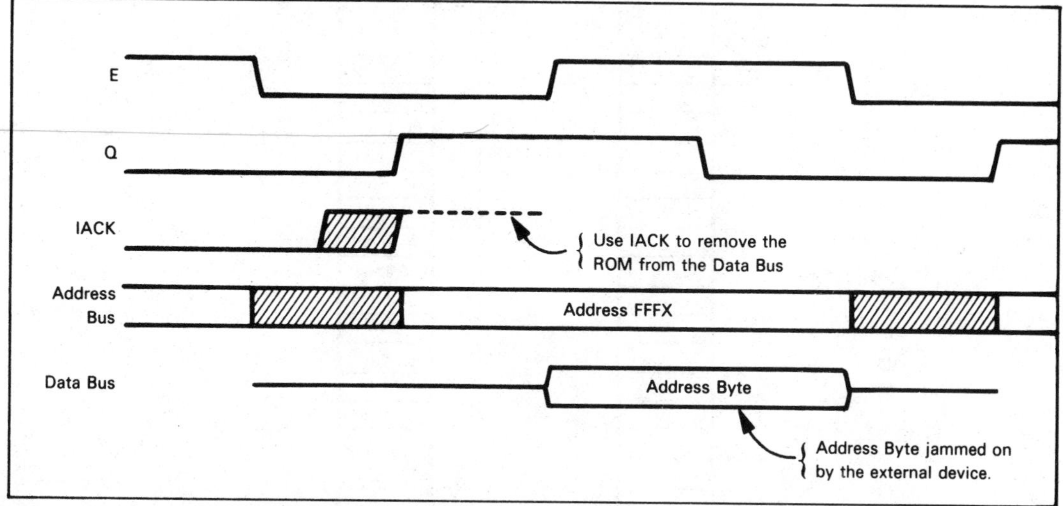


Figure 9-73. MC6809 Signals for Externally Vectored Interrupts

IACK indicates that a byte of vector address is being retrieved from one of the memory locations FFF0 to FFFF as a result of an interrupt ($\overline{RESET}$, $\overline{NMI}$, $\overline{FIRQ}$, $\overline{IRQ}$, SWI, SWI2 or SWI3). IACK is valid during both the high-order and low-order vector address byte fetches.

Note that the address locations corresponding to the seven vectors are all of the form FFFX, where X is between 0 and F; thus, only the last four bits of the address differ. By externally decoding these four low-order bits plus the IACK signals BA and BS, you can determine what type of interrupt has been accepted, disable the ROM containing addresses FFF0 to FFFF, and jam onto the Data Bus the address of an appropriate interrupt service routine. This is done in turn for both the high-order and low-order address bytes by external device logic. Figure 9-73 illustrates the sequence for externally vectoring an interrupt.

Note that the address byte jammed onto the Data Bus is loaded into the Program Counter by the CPU as its normal response to an interrupt request, but now the 16-bit address loaded is the address supplied by the external device, not the address normally retrieved from the applicable address pairs FFF0/FFF1 to FFFE/FFFF.

At the end of this transaction, the program commences execution at the address supplied by the interrupting device. Thus, a vectored jump to the device service routine has been effected.

**This technique can drastically reduce interrupt response time as compared to a polled approach.**

**Stack Pointer SP is used during interrupts. For all interrupts except $\overline{FIRQ}$, the full complement of registers is stacked.** The sequence in which the registers are saved on the Stack can be illustrated as follows:

**MC6809 STACKING DURING INTERRUPTS**

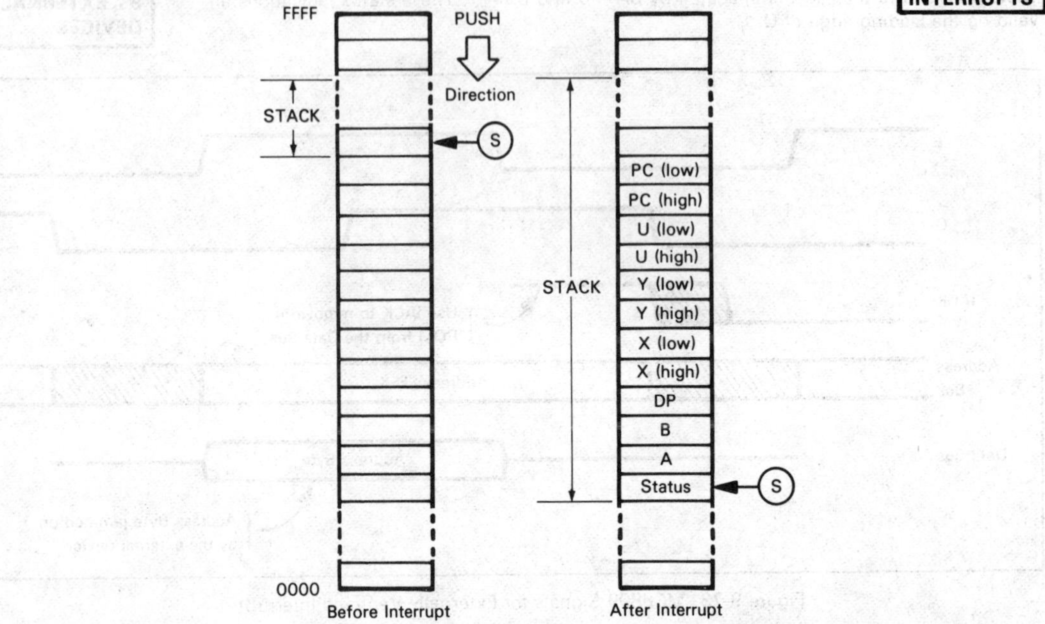


**The MC6809 Stack Pointer(s) points to the last item placed in the Stack, instead of to the next empty location as with the MC6800, MC6801, and MC6802.** The new stacking order interchanges the order of Accumulators A and B to make A the high-order byte instead of B, as is the case on the MC6800, MC6801, and MC6802.

**MC6809 HARDWARE-SOFTWARE SYNCHRONIZATION**

**The MC6809 provides two methods of achieving external process synchronization. The first method we will consider is similar to the one implemented on the MC6800. It uses the CWAI instruction,** which is similar to the MC6800 sequence CLI WAI. However, CWAI does not float the system busses as WAI does on the MC6800. (No WAI instruction exists on the MC6809.)

When the CWAI instruction is executed, the processor logically ANDs the immediate-byte of the instruction into the status register, stacks the entire machine status, then sits idle until an interrupt occurs. When an interrupt occurs, it can be processed immediately, as no time need be spent in stacking machine status.

The CWAI instruction is an immediate mode instruction, with the immediate data being a mask byte. During execution, this byte is automatically ANDed with the Status register byte to clear interrupt bits F and I if required.

When an interrupt occurs, it will (if it hasn't been masked) cause a transfer to the appropriate interrupt service routine. Note that when an $\overline{FIRQ}$ occurs, it will enter its service routine with the entire machine status stacked (instead of just the Program Counter and Status register); however, the corresponding RTI instruction will correctly unstack it, since the state of the stacked E bit will properly indicate how much status was stacked.

**MC6809 SYNC INSTRUCTION**

**The second method of synchronization uses the new MC6809 SYNC instruction. When executed, SYNC causes the processor to cease further execution and wait for an interrupt to occur. Any of the interrupts $\overline{NMI}$, $\overline{FIRQ}$ or $\overline{IRQ}$ may release the processor from the SYNC state. If the interrupt is enabled, the processor will service it; if it is disabled, the processor simply continues on to the next instruction in sequence, without stacking the machine status.** The logic of the SYNC Instruction is illustrated in Figure 9-74.

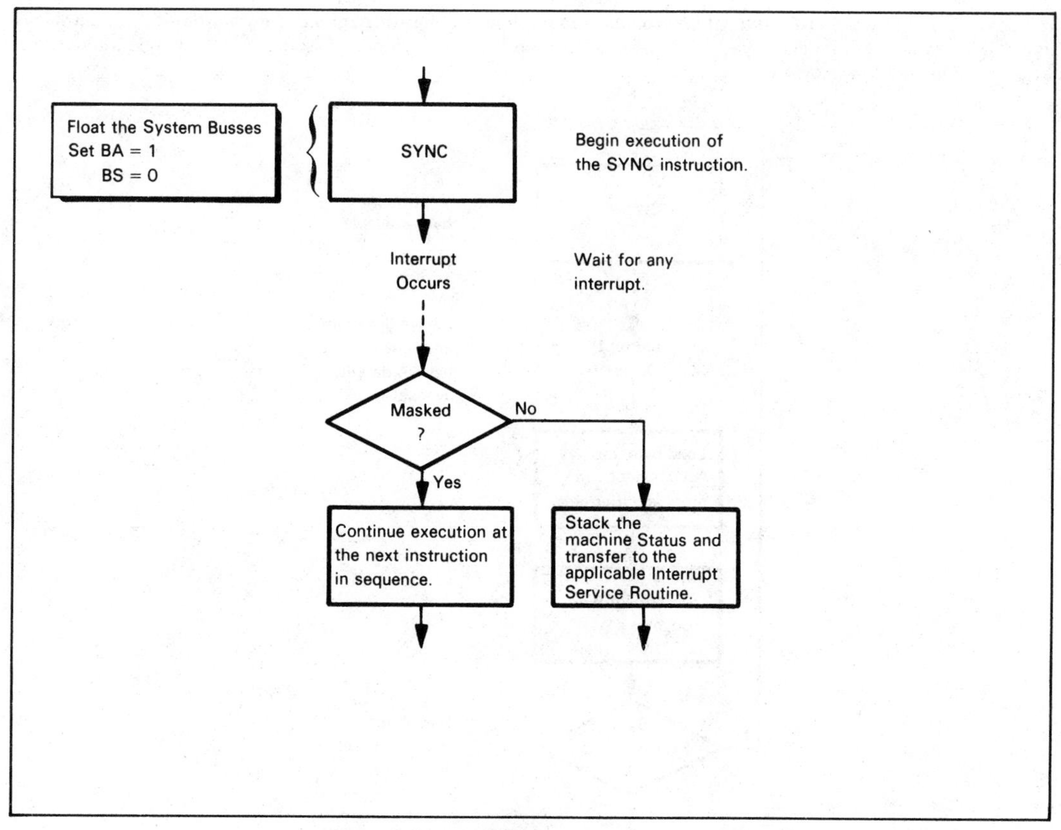


Figure 9-74. MC6809 SYNC Instruction Logic

**One obvious use of the SYNC instruction would be to implement high-throughput program/device synchronization.** The following diagram illustrates this concept. (To keep it simple, we have assumed that only one interrupting device is connected to the system.)

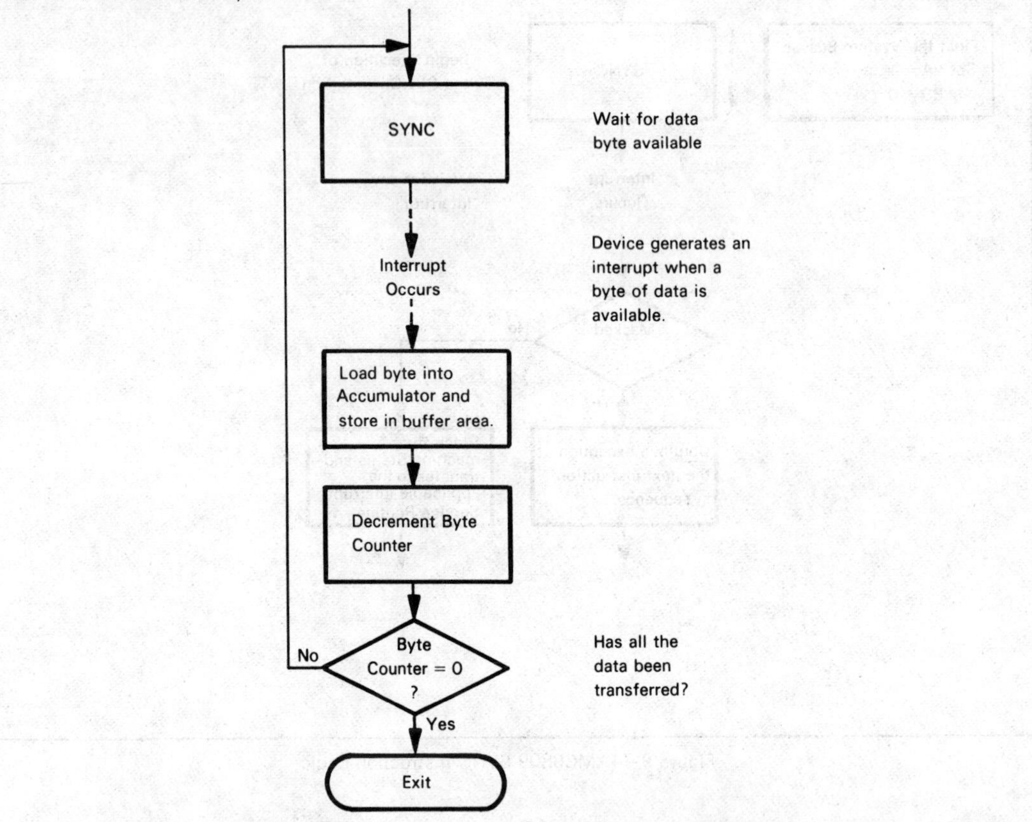


External logic can determine when the CPU is in the SYNC state by decoding the MC6809 BA and BS signals. A SYNC acknowledge status is indicated by BA = 1 and BS = 0, as shown in Table 9-20. Note that since BA = 1, the system busses are floated.

**MC6809 USE OF SYNC FOR DMA**

**SYNC can also be used to mechanize block transfer of data under DMA control. When SYNC is executed, the busses are floated and BA = 1, BS = 0 announces to the DMA device that it may take over the system busses.** At the end of each block transfer, the DMA device advises the CPU by asserting an interrupt request, and the program resumes execution.

Note that the MC6800 does not have a SYNC instruction. Block transfer DMA for the 6800 can be implemented via the WAI instruction as described in the MC6800 section.

## THE MC6809 INSTRUCTION SET

**Table 9-21 lists the MC6809 instruction mnemonics, while Table 9-22 summarizes the instructions which differ from those that appear in the MC6800 instruction set.** Note that all MC6800 addressing modes have been implemented, plus the enhanced modes that we described at the beginning of this section.

When comparing the MC6809 instruction set to the MC6800 set, you will notice that Direct Page addressing for the MC6809 applies to all memory reference instructions, not just the primary memory reference instructions as is the case for the MC6800. In addition, the Direct page can be dynamically relocated.

**During our discussion of the MC6800, we noted the paucity of index registers and the lack of data mobility between them. These deficiencies have been corrected and the MC6809 set includes two types of instructions for register-to-register transfers — the Exchange and the Transfer instructions.** The only restriction on the use of these instructions is that the source and destination registers must be the same size (i.e., both 8 bis or both 16 bits).

**An examination of the MC6809 set reveals that some of the familiar MC6800 instructions are missing. However, provision has been made to perform the missing operations in alternate ways.** For example, the instruction to clear the Carry bit C is implemented on the MC6800 as CLC; to perform this on the MC6809, one must use ANDCC #$FE. The result of these changes is that, even though the MC6809 is fully software compatible (at the source code level) and much more powerful, it uses fewer mnemonics than the MC6800 (59 versus 72).

**MC6809 MISSING MNEMONICS**

**The MC6809 contains many instructions that the MC6800 does not.** Some of these we have already noted, such as Synchronize with Interrupt (SYNC), Clear and Wait for Interrupt (CWAI), Exchange Registers (EXG), Transfer Register (TFR), and the Software Interrupts SWI2 and SWI3. Some of the remaining differences are simply extensions of the existing instructions to make them apply to the new registers — e.g., ANDCC, LDY, etc. — while others are totally new — e.g., Sign Extend (SEX) and Load Effective Address (LEA).

**MC6809 ADDED MNEMONICS**

**Some mnemonics that are used with both the MC6800 and the MC6809 have slightly altered meanings.** This is illustrated below for the "Load Accumulator" instruction.

| MC6800/MC6801/MC6802 | MC6809 |
|---|---|
| Generic Form: LDA | Generic Form: LD |
| LDAA = Load Accumulator A | LDA = Load Accumulator A |
| LDAB = Load Accumulator B | LDB = Load Accumulator B |
| | LDD = Load Accumulator D |
| | LDS = Load Hardware Stack Pointer |
| | LDU = Load User Stack Pointer |
| | LDX = Load Index Register X |
| | LDY = Load Index Register Y |

The "Store Accumulator" instruction has similarly been altered.

**The Push and Pull instructions have been enhanced such that any, all, any subset, or none of the CPU registers can be pushed or pulled from the stacks.** PSHS and PULS access the Hardware Stack, while PSHU and PULU access the User Stack. These instructions require a Post Byte, as shown in the following illustration:

**MC6809 PUSH AND PULL INSTRUCTIONS**

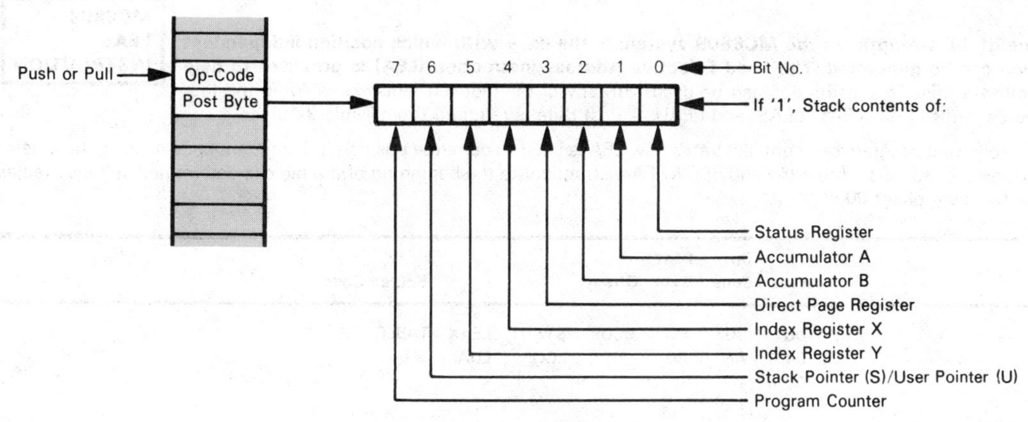

To illustrate, the assembler instruction PSHS D is encoded as follows:

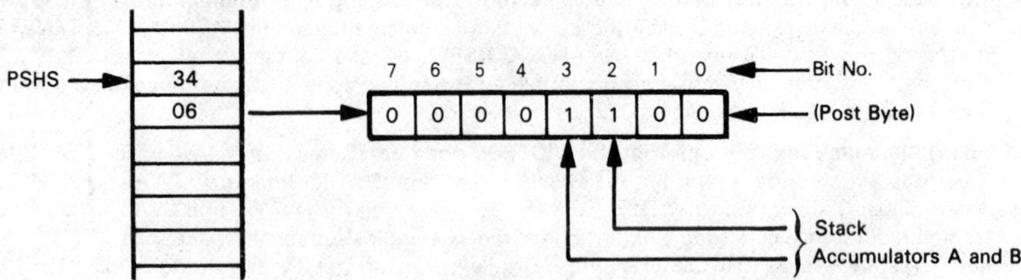


Note the interpretation of bit 6. When executing PSHS, if bit 6 = 1, the contents of U are saved. When executing PSHU, if bit 6 = 1, the contents of SP are saved. Note that PSHS cannot save the contents of SP and PSHU cannot save the contents of U.

**MC6809 EXCHANGE REGISTER AND TRANSFER REGISTER POST BYTE**

**The Exchange Registers and Transfer Register instructions also require a Post Byte to identify the source and destination registers, as shown in the following diagram:**

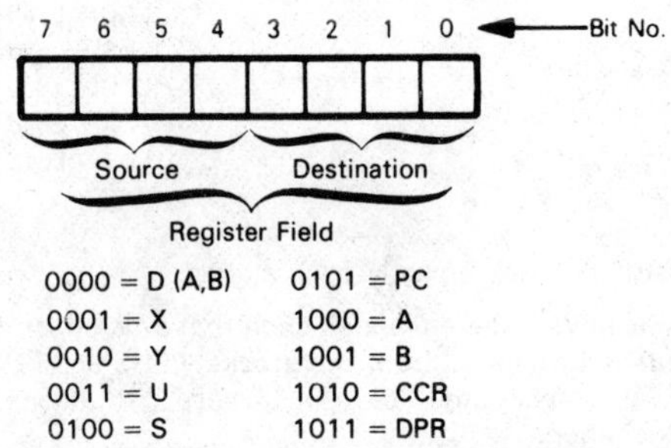


**MC6809 LEA INSTRUCTION**

**One of the strengths of the MC6809 system is the ease with which position independent code can be generated. The Load Effective Address instruction (LEA) is provided to help facilitate this.** This instruction can be used with any of the indexed registers, yielding the four source forms LEAX, LEAY, LEAS, and LEAU. A Post Byte is required (from Table 9-19).

The following program segment illustrates how LEA is used to generate position independent code. During the assembly process, the offset (from the end of the LEA instruction) to the beginning of the table is determined and inserted as the two-byte offset 0009.

| Address | Op Code | Post Byte | Offset | | Source Code | |
|---|---|---|---|---|---|---|
| 0100 | 30 | 8D | 0009 | START | LEAX | TABLE,PCR |
| 0104 | A6 | 80 | | LOOP | LDA | ,X+ |
| 0106 | . | . | | | . | |
| . | . | . | | | . | |
| . | . | . | | | . | |
| . | . | . | | | . | |
| . | . | . | | | . | |
| . | | | | | . | |
| . | | | | | . | |
| . | | | | | . | |
| 010D | | | | TABLE | FCC | /TABLE OF CHARACTERS/ |

Assume that the program is stored at the locations shown. During execution, the offset 0009 is added to the updated Program Counter value 0104 to yield the start of table address 010D. This value is loaded into Index Register X, rather than put out on the Address Bus. When the indexed instruction LDA,X+ is executed, this newly computed address (stored in the Index register) is used to access data from the table.

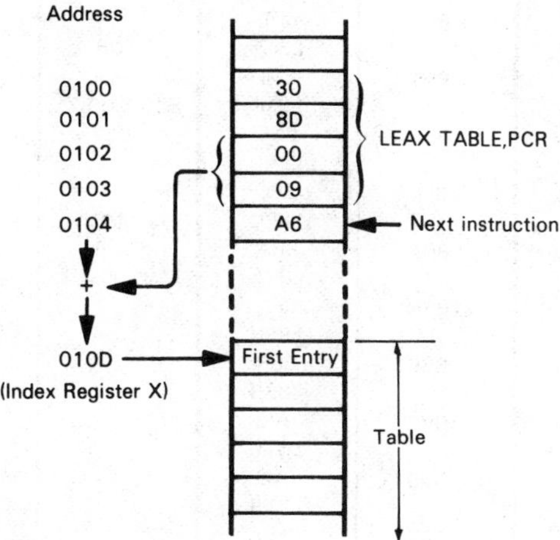


PCR = Program Counter Relative

Notice what happens if the above block of code is moved to another location in memory as shown below.

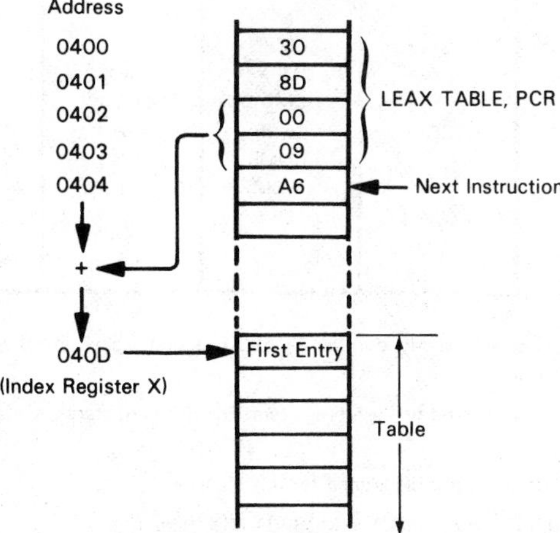


During execution, the new table address 040D is formed in Index Register X when LEAX is executed and used by the instruction LDA,X+ to correctly abstract entries from the table. Truly, this is position independent code.

**The instructions shown shaded in Table 9-21 are the new (or modified) instructions. They are summarized in detail in Table 9-22. The remaining instructions have already been summarized in the MC6800 section (Table 9-1).** It should be noted that many of the unchanged instructions take fewer machine cycles to execute on the MC6809 than on the MC6800.

When comparing the MC6800 family processors, it should be noted that the MC6800 and MC6802 have the same instruction set, and the MC6801 has a superset of the MC6800, but a subset of the MC6809.

Table 9-21. MC6809 Mnemonics (New and Modified Instructions are Shaded)

| Instruction | Source Forms | Instruction | Source Forms | Instruction | Source Forms | Instruction | Source Forms |
|---|---|---|---|---|---|---|---|
| ABX | | BLS | BLS | DEC | DECA | OR | ORA |
| ADC | ADCA | | LBLS | | DECB | | ORB |
| | ADCB | BLT | BLT | | DEC | | ORCC |
| ADD | ADDA | | LBLT | EOR | EORA | PSH | PSHS[11] |
| | ADDB | BMI | BMI | | EORB | | PSHU |
| | ADDD | | LBMI | EXG R1, R2[2] | | PUL | PULS[12] |
| AND | ANDA | BNE | BNE | INC | INCA | | PULU |
| | ANDB | | LBNE | | INCB | ROL | ROLA |
| | ANDCC | BPL | BPL | | INC | | ROLB |
| ASL[3] | ASLA | | LBPL | JMP | | | ROL |
| | ASLB | BRA | BRA | JSR | | ROR[6] | RORA |
| | ASL | | LBRA | LD | LDA[10] | | RORB |
| ASR[3, 6] | ASRA | BRN | BRN | | LDB[10] | | ROR |
| | ASRB | | LBRN | | LDD | RTI[8] | |
| | ASR | BSR | BSR | | LDS | RTS | |
| BCC | BCC | | LBSR | | LDU | SBC[3] | SBCA |
| | LBCC | BVC | BVC | | LDX | | SBCB |
| BCS | BCS | | LBVC | | LDY | SEX | |
| | LBCS | BVS | BVS | LEA | LEAS | ST | STA[10] |
| BEQ | BEQ | | LBVS | | LEAU | | STB[10] |
| | LBEQ | CLR | CLRA | | LEAX | | STD |
| BGE | BGE | | CLRB | | LEAY | | STS |
| | LBGE | | CLR | LSL[3] | LSLA | | STU |
| BGT | BGT | CMP[3] | CMPA | | LSLB | | STX |
| | LBGT | | CMPB | | LSL | | STY |
| BHI | BHI | | CMPD | LSR[6] | LSRA | SUB[3] | SUBA |
| | LBHI | | CMPS | | LSRB | | SUBB |
| BHS | BHS | | CMPU | | LSR | | SUBD |
| | LBHS | | CMPX[7] | MUL[4] | | SWI[9] | SWI |
| BIT | BITA | | CMPY | NEG[3] | NEGA | | SWI2 |
| | BITB | COM | COMA | | NEGB | | SWI3 |
| BLE | BLE | | COMB | | NEG | SYNC | |
| | LBLE | | COM | NOP | | TFR R1, R2[2] | |
| BLO | BLO | CWAI | | | | TST[5] | TSTA |
| | LBLO | DAA | | | | | TSTB |
| | | | | | | | TST |

**Notes**

1. The unshaded instructions are described in the MC6800 section. They have the same object codes for both the MC6800 and the MC6809 processors.
2. R1 and R2 may be any pair of 8-bit or 16-bit registers. The 8-bit registers are A, B, DP and CC. The 16-bit registers are X, Y, U, S, D, and PC.
3. The Auxiliary or Half-Carry bit H is undefined for these cases.
4. This MUL sets the Z bit if appropriate. The MC6801 MUL does not.
5. This instruction does not affect the C bit. On the MC6800/6801/6802 it clears C.
6. These do not affect the overflow bit (V). On the MC6800/6801/6802 they may.
7. This instruction correctly sets all flags. On the MC6800/6802 it does not.
8. On the MC6809, the E status bit is checked during RTI to determine how much to unstack — the complete register complement or just the Stack register and Return Address.
9. SWI sets bits F and I: SWI2 and SWI3 have no effect on F and I.
10. These instructions are implemented on the MC6800 with slightly different mnemonics, as discussed above.
11. This instruction is implemented on the MC6800 as PSH.
12. This instruction is implemented on the MC6800 as PUL.

In Table 9-22, the following symbols are used in addition to those used in Table 9-1.

| | |
|---|---|
| ACD,D | Accumulator D |
| b0-b7 | Bits of Post Byte or other registers |
| U | User Stack Pointer |
| Y | Y Index Register |
| DP | Direct Page Register |
| B4 | Instruction Byte 4 |
| DISP16 | A 16-bit, twos complement displacement |
| REG | A 16-bit register (S, U, X, or Y, as the context demands) |
| [PC'] | Contents of the Program Counter after it has "stepped over" the offset bytes in a multi-byte instruction — thus, PC' is the address of the next instruction in sequence. |
| R1, R2 | Register pairs, both 8-bit or both 16-bit |
| LIST | List of registers to be stored on or retrieved from the Stack |
| EA | Effective Address |
| OFFSET,R | This symbology is used to denote all forms of indexed addressing and all forms of indirect addressing. For this addressing scheme, the total byte count is the sum of the base count indicated in Table 9-22 and the appropriate value from the following chart. |

| Type | Form | Non-indirect | | Bytes | Indirect | | Bytes |
|---|---|---|---|---|---|---|---|
| | | **Assembler Form** | **Post-Byte Op-code** | | **Assembler Form** | **Post-Byte Op-code** | |
| Constant Offset from R | No Offset | , R | 1RR00100 | 0 | [, R] | 1RR10100 | 0 |
| | 5-Bit Offset | n, R | 0RRnnnnn | 0 | | defaults to 8-bit | |
| | 8-Bit Offset | n, R | 1RR01000 | 1 | [n,R] | 1RR11000 | 1 |
| | 16-Bit Offset | n, R | 1RR01001 | 2 | [n,R] | 1RR11001 | 2 |
| Accumulator Offset from R | A — Register Offset | A, R | 1RR00110 | 0 | [A,R] | 1RR10110 | 0 |
| | B — Register Offset | B, R | 1RR00101 | 0 | [B, R] | 1RR10101 | 0 |
| | D — Register Offset | D, R | 1RR01011 | 0 | [D, R] | 1RR11011 | 0 |
| Auto Increment/ Decrement R | Increment by 1 | , R + | 1RR00000 | 0 | | not allowed | |
| | Increment by 2 | , R + + | 1RR00001 | 0 | [, R + +] | 1RR10001 | 0 |
| | Decrement by 1 | , -R | 1RR00010 | 0 | | not allowed | |
| | Decrement by 2 | , - -R | 1RR00011 | 0 | [,--R] | 1RR10011 | 0 |
| Constant Offset from PC | 8-Bit Offset | n, PCR | 1XX01100 | 1 | [n, PCR] | 1XX11100 | 1 |
| | 16-Bit Offset | n, PCR | 1XX01101 | 2 | [n, PCR] | 1XX11101 | 2 |
| Extended Indirect | 16-Bit Address | — | — | - | [n] | 10011111 | 2 |

R = X, Y, U, or S
X = Don't Care

Note: This chart conforms to Motorola nomenclature; their use of square brackets [ ] indicates to the assembler that the addressing mode is indirect — thus, their use of [ ] differs from the use in Table 9-22.

Table 9-22. A Summary of the New and Enhanced Instructions for the MC6809

| TYPE | MNEMONIC | OPERAND(S) | BYTES | STATUS E | F | C | Z | S | V | H | I | OPERATION PERFORMED |
|---|---|---|---|---|---|---|---|---|---|---|---|---|
| PRIMARY MEMORY REFERENCE | LDD | ADR8<br>ADR16<br>OFFSET,R | 2<br>3<br>2+ | | | | X | X | 0 | | | [ACA] ← [MEM], [ACB] ← [MEM + 1]<br>Load double Accumulator using base page direct, extended direct, indirect or indexed addressing. |
| | STD | ADR8<br>ADR16<br>OFFSET,R | 2<br>3<br>2+ | | | | X | X | 0 | | | [MEM] ← [ACA], [MEM + 1] ← [ACB]<br>Store double Accumulator using direct, extended, indirect or indexed addressing. |
| | LDU | ADR8<br>ADR16<br>OFFSET,R | 2<br>3<br>2+ | | | | X | X | 0 | | | [REG(HI)] ← [MEM], [REG(LO)] ← [MEM + 1]<br>Load specified register (U or Y) using direct, extended, indirect or indexed addressing. |
| | LDY | ADR8<br>ADR16<br>OFFSET,R | 3<br>4<br>3+ | | | | X | X | 0 | | | Sign status reflects REG bit 15. |
| | STU | ADR8<br>ADR16<br>OFFSET,R | 2<br>3<br>2+ | | | | X | X | 0 | | | [MEM] ← [REG(HI)], [MEM + 1] ← [REG(LO)]<br>Store contents of specified register (U or Y) using direct, extended, indirect or indexed addressing. Sign status reflects REG bit 15. |
| | STY | ADR8<br>ADR16<br>OFFSET,R | 3<br>4<br>3+ | | | | X | X | 0 | | | |
| SECONDARY MEMORY REFERENCE (MEMORY OPERATE) | ADDD | ADR8<br>ADR16<br>OFFSET, R | 2<br>3<br>2+ | | | X | X | X | X | X | | [ACD] ← [ACD] + [MEM]: [MEM + 1]<br>Add 16-bit value from locations MEM and MEM + 1 to D Accumulator using direct, extended, indirect or indexed addressing. |
| | CMPD | ADR8<br>ADR16<br>OFFSET,R | 3<br>4<br>3+ | | | X | X | X | X | | | [ACD] – [MEM]: [MEM + 1]<br>Compares 16-bit number from locations M and M + 1 with contents of D Accumulator and sets status bits as appropriate. Only Status register is affected. |
| | CMPS<br>CMPU<br>CMPY<br>CMPX | ADR8<br>ADR16<br>OFFSET,R<br>ADR8<br>ADR16<br>OFFSET,R | 3<br>4<br>3+<br>2<br>3<br>2+ | | | X<br><br><br>X | X<br><br><br>X | X<br><br><br>X | X<br><br><br>X | | | [REG] – [MEM]: [MEM + 1]<br>Compares 16-bit number from locations M and M + 1 with contents of register (S, U, Y or X) specified in the mnemonic and sets status bits as appropriate. Only Status register is affected. |
| | LSL | ADR8<br>ADR16<br>OFFSET,R | 2<br>3<br>2+ | | | X | X | X | X | | | C ← 7 ← 0 ← 0 [M] $0 = b_7 \veebar b_6$<br>Logical Shift Left. |
| | SUBD | ADR8<br>ADR16<br>OFFSET,R | 2<br>3<br>2+ | | | X | X | X | X | | | [ACD] ← [ACD] - [MEM]: [MEM + 1]<br>Subtract 16-bit number contained in locations MEM and MEM + 1 from number contained in D Accumulator using direct, extended, indirect or indexed addressing. |

Table 9-22. A Summary of the New and Enhanced Instructions for the MC6809 (Continued)

| TYPE | MNEMONIC | OPERAND(S) | BYTES | STATUS E | F | C | Z | S | V | H | I | OPERATION PERFORMED |
|---|---|---|---|---|---|---|---|---|---|---|---|---|
| IMMEDIATE | LDD | DATA16 | 3 | | | | X | X | 0 | | | [ACA] ← [B2], [ACB] ← [B3]<br>Load Accumulator immediate. (Sign status reflects bit 15) |
| | LDU | DATA16 | 3 | | | | X | X | 0 | | | [U(HI)] ← [B2], [U(LO)] ← [B3]<br>Load User Pointer immediate. |
| | LDY | DATA16 | 4 | | | | X | X | 0 | | | [Y(HI)] ← [B3], [Y(LO)] ← [BA] |
| IMMEDIATE OPERATE | ADDD | DATA16 | 3 | | | X | X | X | X | X | | [ACD] ← [ACD] + [B2]: [B3]<br>Add 16-bit number following Op-code to contents of D Accumulator. |
| | SUBD | DATA16 | 3 | | | X | X | X | X | | | [ACD] ← [ACD] - [B2]: [B3]<br>Subtract 16-bit number following Op-Code from contents of D Accumulator. |
| | CMPD | DATA16 | 4 | | | X | X | X | X | | | [ACD] – [B3]: [B4]<br>Compare immediate contents of D Accumulator and 16-bit number following (two byte) Op-code. Only status bits are affected. |
| | CMPS<br>CMPU<br>CMPY | DATA16 | 4 | | | X | X | X | X | | | [REG] – [B3]: [B4]<br>Compare immediate contents of designated Register (S, U, Y or X) specified in instruction with 16-bit number following (two byte) Op-code. Only Status bits are affected. |
| | CMPX | DATA16 | 3 | | | X | X | X | X | | | |
| JUMP | LBRA | DISP16 | 3 | | | | | | | | | [PC] ← [PC'] + DISP16<br>Unconditional long branch relative to present Program Counter contents. |
| | LBSR | DISP16 | 3 | | | | | | | | | [[SP] - 1] ← [PC(LO)], [[SP] - 2] ← [PC(HI)], [SP] ← [SP] - 2<br>[PC] ← [PC'] + DISP16<br>Unconditional long branch to subroutine located relative to present Program Counter contents. |
| BRANCH ON CONDITION | | | | | | | | | | | | [PC] ← [PC'] + DISP if condition true |
| | BHS | DISP | 2 | | | | | | | | | C = 0 |
| | BLO | DISP | 2 | | | | | | | | | C = 1 |
| | | | | | | | | | | | | [PC] ← [PC'] + DISP16 if condition true |

Table 9-22. A Summary of the New and Enhanced Instructions for the MC6809 (Continued)

| TYPE | MNEMONIC | OPERAND(S) | BYTES | STATUS | | | | | | | | OPERATION PERFORMED |
|---|---|---|---|---|---|---|---|---|---|---|---|---|
| | | | | E | F | C | Z | S | V | H | I | |
| BRANCH ON CONDITION (Continued) | LBCC | DISP16 | 4 | | | | | | | | | Conditions are the same as shown in the Branch On Condition Table for the MC6800. |
| | LBCS | DISP16 | 4 | | | | | | | | | |
| | LBEQ | DISP16 | 4 | | | | | | | | | |
| | LBGE | DISP16 | 4 | | | | | | | | | |
| | LBGT | DISP16 | 4 | | | | | | | | | |
| | LBHI | DISP16 | 4 | | | | | | | | | |
| | LBHS | DISP16 | 4 | | | | | | | | | |
| | LBLE | DISP16 | 4 | | | | | | | | | |
| | LBLO | DISP16 | 4 | | | | | | | | | |
| | LBLS | DISP16 | 4 | | | | | | | | | |
| | LBLT | DISP16 | 4 | | | | | | | | | |
| | LBMI | DISP16 | 4 | | | | | | | | | |
| | LBNE | DISP16 | 4 | | | | | | | | | |
| | LBPL | DISP16 | 4 | | | | | | | | | |
| | LBVC | DISP16 | 4 | | | | | | | | | |
| | LBVS | DISP16 | 4 | | | | | | | | | |
| REGISTER TO REGISTER MOVE | EXG | R1, R2 | 2 | | | | | | | | | [R1] ←→ [R2]<br>Exchange contents of specified registers. Status register not affected unless R1 or R2 is Status register. |
| | TFR | R1, R2 | 2 | | | | | | | | | [R2] ← [R1]<br>Transfer contents of R1 to R2. Status register is not affected unless R2 is Status register. |
| REGISTER-REGISTER OPERATE | ABX | | 1 | | | | | | | | | [X] ← [X] + [B]<br>Add unsigned contents of B Accumulator to Index register. |
| | MUL | | 1 | | | | X | | | | | [D] ← [A] x [B]<br>Multiply unsigned numbers in Accumulators A and B and place result in D. Carry bit is set if Accumulator B bit 7 is set. |
| | SEX | | 1 | | | | X | X | 0 | | | [A] ← $FF_{16}$ if Accumulator B bit 7 = 1<br>[A] ← $00_{16}$ if Accumulator B bit 7 = 0<br>Transform an 8-bit twos complement number in B to a 16-bit twos complement number in D. |

Table 9-22. A Summary of the New and Enhanced Instructions for the MC6809 (Continued)

| TYPE | MNEMONIC | OPERAND(S) | BYTES | STATUS | | | | | | | | OPERATION PERFORMED |
|---|---|---|---|---|---|---|---|---|---|---|---|---|
| | | | | E | F | C | Z | S | V | H | I | |
| | LEAS | OFFSET,R | 2+ | | | | | | | | | [S] ← EA |
| | LEAU | OFFSET,R | 2+ | | | | | | | | | [U] ← EA    EA is the Effective Address |
| | LEAX | OFFSET,R | 2+ | | | | X | | | | | [X] ← EA |
| | LEAY | OFFSET,R | 2+ | | | | X | | | | | [Y] ← EA<br>Form the Effective Address EA according to the addressing variation used. Load this address into designated register (for later use) rather than outputting it on Address Bus at this time. |
| | LSL | ACX | 1 | | | X | X | X | X | | | C ← 7 ← 0 ← 0   $0 = b_7 \veebar b_6$<br>(ACX) |
| STACK | PSHS | LIST | 2 | | | | | | | | | Test Post Byte and stack as follows.<br>Condition:<br>b7 = 1; [SP] ← [SP] -1, [[SP]] ← [PC(LO)]<br>[SP] ← [SP] - 1, [[SP]] ← [PC(HI)]<br>b6 = 1; [SP] ← [SP] - 1, [[SP]] ← [U(LO)]<br>[SP] ← [SP] - 1, [[SP]] ←[U(HI)]<br>b5 = 1; [SP] ← [SP] - 1, [[SP]] ← [Y(LO)]<br>[SP] ← [SP] - 1, [[SP]] ← [Y(HI)]<br>b4 = 1; [SP] ← [SP] - 1, [[SP]] ← [X(LO)]<br>[SP] ← [SP] - 1, [[SP]] ← [X(HI)]<br>b3 = 1; [SP] ← [SP] - 1, [[SP]] ← [DP]<br>b2 = 1; [SP] ← [SP] - 1, [[SP]] ← [B]<br>b1 = 1; [SP] ← [SP] - 1, [[SP]] ← [A]<br>b0 = 1; [SP] ← [SP] - 1, [[SP]] ← [SR]<br>Push any, all, none or any subset of registers onto Hardware Stack (except the Hardware Stack Pointer itself). |

Table 9-22. A Summary of the New and Enhanced Instructions for the MC6809 (Continued)

| TYPE | MNEMONIC | OPERAND(S) | BYTES | STATUS | | | | | | | | OPERATION PERFORMED |
|---|---|---|---|---|---|---|---|---|---|---|---|---|
| | | | | E | F | C | Z | S | V | H | I | |
| STACK (Continued) | PSHU | LIST | 2 | | | | | | | | | Test Post Byte and stack as follows.<br>Condition:<br>b7 = 1; [U] ← [U] - 1, [[U]] ← [PC(LO)]<br>[U] ← [U] - 1, [[U]] ← [PC(HI)]<br>b6 = 1; [U] ← [U] - 1, [[U]] ← [SP(LO)]<br>[U] ← [U] - 1, [[U]] ← [SP(HI)]<br>b5 = 1; [U] ← [U] - 1, [[U]] ← [Y(LO)]<br>[U] ← [U] - 1, [[U]] ← [Y(HI)]<br>b4 = 1; [U] ← [U] - 1, [[U]] ← [X(LO)]<br>[U] ← [U] - 1, [[U]] ← [X(HI)]<br>b3 = 1; [U] ← [U] - 1, [[U]] ← [DP]<br>b2 = 1; [U] ← [U] - 1, [[U]] ← [B]<br>b1 = 1; [U] ← [U] - 1, [[U]] ← [A]<br>b0 = 1; [U] ← [U] - 1, [[U]] ← [SR]<br>Push any, all, none or any subset of registers onto User Stack (except the User Stack Pointer itself). |
| | PULS | LIST | 2 | | | | | | | | | Test Post Byte and unstack as follows.<br>Condition:<br>b0 = 1; [SR] ← [[SP]], [SP] ← [SP] + 1<br>b1 = 1; [A] ← [[SP]], [SP] ← [SP] + 1<br>b2 = 1; [B] ← [[SP]], [SP] ← [SP] + 1<br>b3 = 1; [DP] ← [[SP]], [SP] ← [SP] + 1<br>b4 = 1; [X(HI)] ← [[SP]], [SP] ← [SP] + 1<br>[X(LO)] ← [[SP]], [SP] ← [SP] + 1<br>b5 = 1; [Y(HI)] ← [[SP]], [SP] ← [SP] + 1<br>[Y(LO)] ← [[SP]], [SP] ← [SP] + 1<br>b6 = 1; [U(HI)] ← [[SP]], [SP] ← [SP] + 1<br>[U(LO)] ← [[SP]], [SP] ← [SP] + 1<br>b7 = 1; [PC(HI)] ← [[SP]], [SP] ← [SP] + 1<br>[PC(LO)] ← [[SP]], [SP] ← [SP] + 1<br>Pull any, all, none or any subset of registers from Hardware Stack (except the Hardware Stack Pointer itself). The Status register bits are determined by byte pulled from Stack. |

Table 9-22. A Summary of the New and Enhanced Instructions for the MC6809 (Continued)

| TYPE | MNEMONIC | OPERAND(S) | BYTES | STATUS E | F | C | Z | S | V | H | I | OPERATION PERFORMED |
|---|---|---|---|---|---|---|---|---|---|---|---|---|
| STACK (Continued) | PULU | LIST | 2 | | | | | | | | | Test Post Byte and unstack as follows.<br>Condition:<br>b0 = 1; [SR] ← [[U]], [U] ← [U] + 1<br>b1 = 1; [A] ← [[U]], [U] ← [U] + 1<br>b2 = 1; [B] ← [[U]], [U] ← [U] + 1<br>b3 = 1; [DP] ← [[U]], [U] ← [U] + 1<br>b4 = 1; [X(HI)] ← [[U]], [U] ← [U] + 1<br>[X(LO)] ← [[U]], [U] ← [U] + 1<br>b5 = 1; [Y(HI)] ← [[U]], [U] ← [U] + 1<br>[Y(LO)] ← [[U]], [U] ← [U] + 1<br>b6 = 1; [SP(HI)] ← [[U]], [U] ← [U] + 1<br>[SP(LO)] ← [[U]], [U] ← [U] + 1<br>b7 = 1; [PC(HI)] ← [[U]], [U] ← [U] + 1<br>[PC(LO)] ← [[U]], [U] ← [U] + 1<br>Pull any, all, none or any subset of registers from User Stack (except the User Stack Pointer itself). Status register bits are determined by byte pulled from Stack. |
| INTERRUPT | RTI | | 1 | | | | | | | | | Pull registers from Hardware Stack in accordance with value of E of Status Register.<br>If E = 0, pull the subset.<br>[SR] ← [[SP]], [SP] ← [SP] + 1<br>[PC(HI)] ← [[SP]], [SP] ← [SP] + 1<br>[PC(LO)] ← [[SP]], [SP] ← [SP] + 1<br>If E = 1, pull the full complement.<br>[SR] ← [[SP]], [SP] ← [SP] + 1<br>[A] ← [[SP]], [SP] ← [SP] + 1<br>[B] ← [[SP]], [SP] ← [SP] + 1<br>[DP] ← [[SP]], [SP] ← [SP] + 1<br>[X(HI)] ← [[SP]], [SP] ← [SP] + 1<br>[X(LO)] ← [[SP]], [SP] ← [SP] + 1<br>[Y(HI)] ← [[SP]], [SP] ← [SP] + 1<br>[Y(LO)] ← [[SP]], [SP] ← [SP] + 1<br>[U(HI)] ← [[SP]], [SP] ← [SP] + 1<br>[U(LO)] ← [[SP]], [SP] ← [SP] + 1<br>[PC(HI)] ← [[SP]], [SP] ← [SP] + 1<br>[PC(LO)] ← [[SP]], [SP] ← [SP] + 1<br>Status bits are as received from Stack. |

Table 9-22. A Summary of the New and Enhanced Instructions for the MC6809 (Continued)

| TYPE | MNEMONIC | OPERAND(S) | BYTES | STATUS | | | | | | | | OPERATION PERFORMED |
|---|---|---|---|---|---|---|---|---|---|---|---|---|
| | | | | E | F | C | Z | S | V | H | I | |
| INTERRUPT (Continued) | CWAI | | 2 | | | | | | | | | [SR] ← [SR] Λ [B2] This may clear SR bits.<br>E ← 1<br>[SP] ← [SP] - 1, [[SP]] ← [PC]<br>[SP] ← [SP] - 1, [[SP]] ← [PC]<br>[SP] ← [SP] - 1, [[SP]] ← [U]<br>[SP] ← [SP] - 1, [[SP]] ← [U]<br>[SP] ← [SP] - 1, [[SP]] ← [Y]<br>[SP] ← [SP] - 1, [[SP]] ← [Y]<br>[SP] ← [SP] - 1, [[SP]] ← [X]<br>[SP] ← [SP] - 1, [[SP]] ← [X]<br>[SP] ← [SP] - 1, [[SP]] ← [DP]<br>[SP] ← [SP] - 1, [[SP]] ← [B]<br>[SP] ← [SP] - 1, [[SP]] ← [A]<br>[SP] ← [SP] - 1, [[SP]] ← [SR]<br>Pushes registers onto Stack and waits for an interrupt. When non-masked interrupt occurs, vectors to corresponding interrupt service routine. $\overline{FIRQ}$ enters its service routine with all registers saved, but since E = 1, they will unstack correctly on RTI. (System busses are not floated by CWAI.) |

Table 9-22. A Summary of the New and Enhanced Instructions for the MC6809 (Continued)

| TYPE | MNEMONIC | OPERAND(S) | BYTES | STATUS | | | | | | | | OPERATION PERFORMED |
|---|---|---|---|---|---|---|---|---|---|---|---|---|
| | | | | E | F | C | Z | S | V | H | I | |
| INTERRUPT (Continued) | SWI | | 1 | | | | | | | | | E ← 1<br>[SP] ← [SP] - 1, [[SP]] ← [PC(LO)]<br>[SP] ← [SP] - 1, [[SP]] ← [PC(HI)]<br>[SP] ← [SP] - 1, [[SP]] ← [U(LO)]<br>[SP] ← [SP] - 1, [[SP]] ← [U(HI)]<br>[SP] ← [SP] - 1, [[SP]] ← [Y(LO)]<br>[SP] ← [SP] - 1, [[SP]] ← [Y(HI)]<br>[SP] ← [SP] - 1, [[SP]] ← [X(LO)]<br>[SP] ← [SP] - 1, [[SP]] ← [X(HI)]<br>[SP] ← [SP] - 1, [[SP]] ← [DP]<br>[SP] ← [SP] - 1, [[SP]] ← [B]<br>[SP] ← [SP] - 1, [[SP]] ← [A]<br>[SP] ← [SP] - 1, [[SP]] ← [SR]<br>1 ← 1, F ← 1, [PC] ← [FFFA]: [FFFB]<br>Transfer control to interrupt subroutine. |
| | SWI2 | | 2 | | | | | | | | | E ← 1<br>Push registers onto Hardware Stack (same as above).<br>[PC] ← [FFF4]: [FFF5]<br>Transfer control to interrupt subroutine. |
| | SWI3 | | 2 | | | | | | | | | E ← 1<br>Push registers onto Hardware Stack (same as above).<br>[PC] ← [FFF2]: [FFF3]<br>Transfer control to interrupt subroutine. |
| | SYNC | | 1 | | | | | | | | | Stop processing instructions: float system busses: wait for an interrupt. When an interrupt occurs, resume processing as follows:<br>i) If interrupt is enabled, transfer to the service routine.<br>ii) If interrupt is disabled, continue execution at next instruction in sequence. |
| STATUS | ANDCC | DATA | 2 | | | 1 | | | | | | [SR] ← [SR] Λ DATA<br>AND immediate. Used to clear SR bits. |
| | ORCC | DATA | 2 | | | | | | | | | [SR] ← [SR] V DATA<br>OR immediate. Used to set SR bits. |
| | BRN | DISP | 2 | | | | | | | | | Branch Never. This is a No Operation |
| | LBN | DISP16 | 4 | | | | | | | | | Long Branch Never. This is a No Operation. |

# DATA SHEETS

This section contains specific electrical and timing data for the following devices:

- MC6800 CPU
- MC6802 CPU/RAM
- MC6870A Clock
- MC6871A Clock
- MC6871B Clock
- MC6875 Clock
- MC6820 PIA
- MC6850 ACIA
- MC6852 SSDA
- MC6840 PTM
- MC6844 DMAC
- MC6846 ROM-I/O-Timer
- MC6801 One-Chip Microcomputer
- MC6809 CPU

**TABLE 1 – MAXIMUM RATINGS**

| Rating | Symbol | Value | Unit |
|---|---|---|---|
| Supply Voltage | $V_{CC}$ | -0.3 to +7.0 | Vdc |
| Input Voltage | $V_{in}$ | -0.3 to +7.0 | Vdc |
| Operating Temperature Range—$T_L$ to $T_H$<br>MC6800, MC68A00, MC68B00<br>MC6800C, MC68A00C<br>MC6800BQCS, MC6800CQCS | $T_A$ | <br>0 to +70<br>-40 to +85<br>-55 to +125 | °C |
| Storage Temperature Range | $T_{stg}$ | -55 to +150 | °C |
| Thermal Resistance<br>Plastic Package<br>Ceramic Package | $\theta_{JA}$ | <br>70<br>50 | °C/W |

This device contains circuitry to protect the inputs against damage due to high static voltages or electric fields; however, it is advised that normal precautions be taken to avoid application of any voltage higher than maximum rated voltages to this high impedance circuit.

**TABLE 2 – ELECTRICAL CHARACTERISTICS** ($V_{CC}$ = 5.0 V, ± 5%, $V_{SS}$ = 0, $T_A$ = $T_L$ to $T_H$ unless otherwise noted)

| Characteristic | | Symbol | Min | Typ | Max | Unit |
|---|---|---|---|---|---|---|
| Input High Voltage | Logic<br>φ1,φ2 | $V_{IH}$<br>$V_{IHC}$ | $V_{SS}$ + 2.0<br>$V_{CC}$ – 0.6 | –<br>– | $V_{CC}$<br>$V_{CC}$ + 0.3 | Vdc |
| Input Low Voltage | Logic<br>φ1,φ2 | $V_{IL}$<br>$V_{ILC}$ | $V_{SS}$ – 0.3<br>$V_{SS}$ – 0.3 | –<br>– | $V_{SS}$ + 0.8<br>$V_{SS}$ + 0.4 | Vdc |
| Input Leakage Current<br>($V_{in}$ = 0 to 5.25 V, $V_{CC}$ = max)<br>($V_{in}$ = 0 to 5.25 V, $V_{CC}$ = 0.0 V) | <br>Logic*<br>φ1,φ2 | $I_{in}$ | <br>–<br>– | <br>1.0<br>– | <br>2.5<br>100 | μAdc |
| Three-State (Off State) Input Current<br>($V_{in}$ = 0.4 to 2.4 V, $V_{CC}$ = max) | D0-D7<br>A0-A15,R/$\overline{W}$ | $I_{TSI}$ | –<br>– | 2.0<br>– | 10<br>100 | μAdc |
| Output High Voltage<br>($I_{Load}$ = -205 μAdc, $V_{CC}$ = min)<br>($I_{Load}$ = -145 μAdc, $V_{CC}$ = min)<br>($I_{Load}$ = -100 μAdc, $V_{CC}$ = min) | <br>D0-D7<br>A0-A15,R/$\overline{W}$,VMA<br>BA | $V_{OH}$ | <br>$V_{SS}$ + 2.4<br>$V_{SS}$ + 2.4<br>$V_{SS}$ + 2.4 | <br>–<br>–<br>– | <br>–<br>–<br>– | Vdc |
| Output Low Voltage ($I_{Load}$ = 1.6 mAdc, $V_{CC}$ = min) | | $V_{OL}$ | – | – | $V_{SS}$ + 0.4 | Vdc |
| Power Dissipation | | $P_D$ | – | 0.5 | 1.0 | W |
| Capacitance<br>($V_{in}$ = 0, $T_A$ = 25°C, f = 1.0 MHz) | <br>φ1<br>φ2<br>D0-D7<br>Logic Inputs | $C_{in}$ | <br>–<br>–<br>–<br>– | <br>25<br>45<br>10<br>6.5 | <br>35<br>70<br>12.5<br>10 | pF |
| | A0-A15,R/$\overline{W}$,VMA | $C_{out}$ | – | – | 12 | pF |

**TABLE 3 – CLOCK TIMING** ($V_{CC}$ = 5.0 V, ±5%, $V_{SS}$ = 0, $T_A$ = $T_L$ to $T_H$ unless otherwise noted)

| Characteristics | | Symbol | Min | Typ | Max | Unit |
|---|---|---|---|---|---|---|
| Frequency of Operation | MC6800<br>MC68A00<br>MC68B00 | f | 0.1<br>0.1<br>0.1 | –<br>–<br>– | 1.0<br>1.5<br>2.0 | MHz |
| Cycle Time (Figure 1) | MC6800<br>MC68A00<br>MC68B00 | $t_{cyc}$ | 1.000<br>0.666<br>0.500 | –<br>–<br>– | 10<br>10<br>10 | μs |
| Clock Pulse Width<br>(Measured at $V_{CC}$ – 0.6 V) | φ1,φ2 – MC6800<br>φ1,φ2 – MC68A00<br>φ1,φ2 – MC68B00 | $PW_{\phi H}$ | 400<br>230<br>180 | –<br>–<br>– | 9500<br>9500<br>9500 | ns |
| Total φ1 and φ2 Up Time | MC6800<br>MC68A00<br>MC68B00 | $t_{ut}$ | 900<br>600<br>440 | –<br>–<br>– | –<br>–<br>– | ns |
| Rise and Fall Times<br>(Measured between $V_{SS}$ + 0.4 and $V_{CC}$ – 0.6) | | $t_{\phi r}$, $t_{\phi f}$ | – | – | 100 | ns |
| Delay Time or Clock Separation (Figure 1)<br>(Measured at $V_{OV}$ = $V_{SS}$ + 0.6 V @ $t_r$ = $t_f$ ≤ 100 ns)<br>(Measured at $V_{OV}$ = $V_{SS}$ + 1.0 V @ $t_r$ = $t_f$ ≤ 35 ns) | | $t_d$ | <br>0<br>0 | <br>–<br>– | <br>9100<br>9100 | ns |

Data sheets on pages 9-D2 through 9-D46 reprinted by permission of Motorola Semiconductor Products, Inc.

**TABLE 4 – READ/WRITE TIMING** (Reference Figures 2 through 6)

| Characteristic | Symbol | MC6800 | | | MC68A00 | | | MC68B00 | | | Unit |
|---|---|---|---|---|---|---|---|---|---|---|---|
| | | Min | Typ | Max | Min | Typ | Max | Min | Typ | Max | |
| Address Delay | $t_{AD}$ | | | | | | | | | | ns |
| C = 90 pF | | – | – | 270 | – | – | 180 | – | – | 150 | |
| C = 30 pF | | – | – | 250 | – | – | 165 | – | – | 135 | |
| Peripheral Read Access Time $t_{ac} = t_{ut} - (t_{AD} + t_{DSR})$ | $t_{acc}$ | – | – | 530 | – | – | 360 | – | – | 250 | ns |
| Data Setup Time (Read) | $t_{DSR}$ | 100 | – | – | 60 | – | – | 40 | – | – | ns |
| Input Data Hold Time | $t_H$ | 10 | – | – | 10 | – | – | 10 | – | – | ns |
| Output Data Hold Time | $t_H$ | 10 | 25 | – | 10 | 25 | – | 10 | 25 | – | ns |
| Address Hold Time (Address, R/$\overline{W}$, VMA) | $t_{AH}$ | 30 | 50 | – | 30 | 50 | – | 30 | 50 | – | ns |
| Enable High Time for DBE Input | $t_{EH}$ | 450 | – | – | 280 | – | – | 220 | – | – | ns |
| Data Delay Time ($\overline{Write}$) | $t_{DDW}$ | – | – | 225 | – | – | 200 | – | – | 160 | ns |
| Processor Controls | | | | | | | | | | | |
| Processor Control Setup Time | $t_{PCS}$ | 200 | – | – | 140 | – | – | 110 | – | – | ns |
| Processor Control Rise and Fall Time | $t_{PCr}$, $t_{PCf}$ | – | – | 100 | – | – | 100 | – | – | 100 | ns |
| Bus Available Delay | $t_{BA}$ | – | – | 250 | – | – | 165 | – | – | 135 | ns |
| Three-State Delay | $t_{TSD}$ | – | – | 270 | – | – | 270 | – | – | 220 | ns |
| Data Bus Enable Down Time During $\phi$1 Up Time | $t_{\overline{DBE}}$ | 150 | – | – | 120 | – | – | 75 | – | – | ns |
| Data Bus Enable Rise and Fall Times | $t_{DBEr}$, $t_{DBEf}$ | – | – | 25 | – | – | 25 | – | – | 25 | ns |

**FIGURE 1 – CLOCK TIMING WAVEFORM**

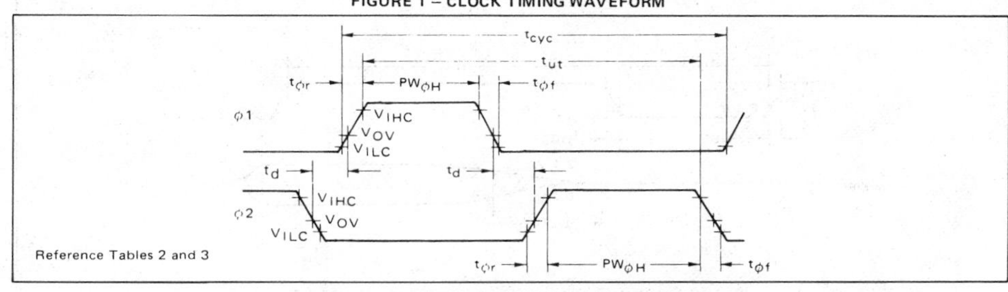


**FIGURE 2 – READ DATA FROM MEMORY OR PERIPHERALS**

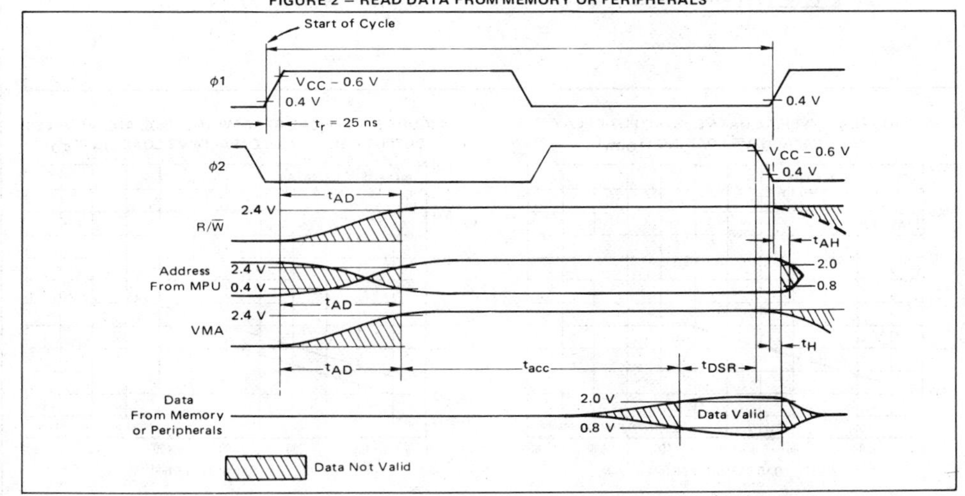

**MOTOROLA** *Semiconductor Products Inc.*

FIGURE 3 – WRITE IN MEMORY OR PERIPHERALS

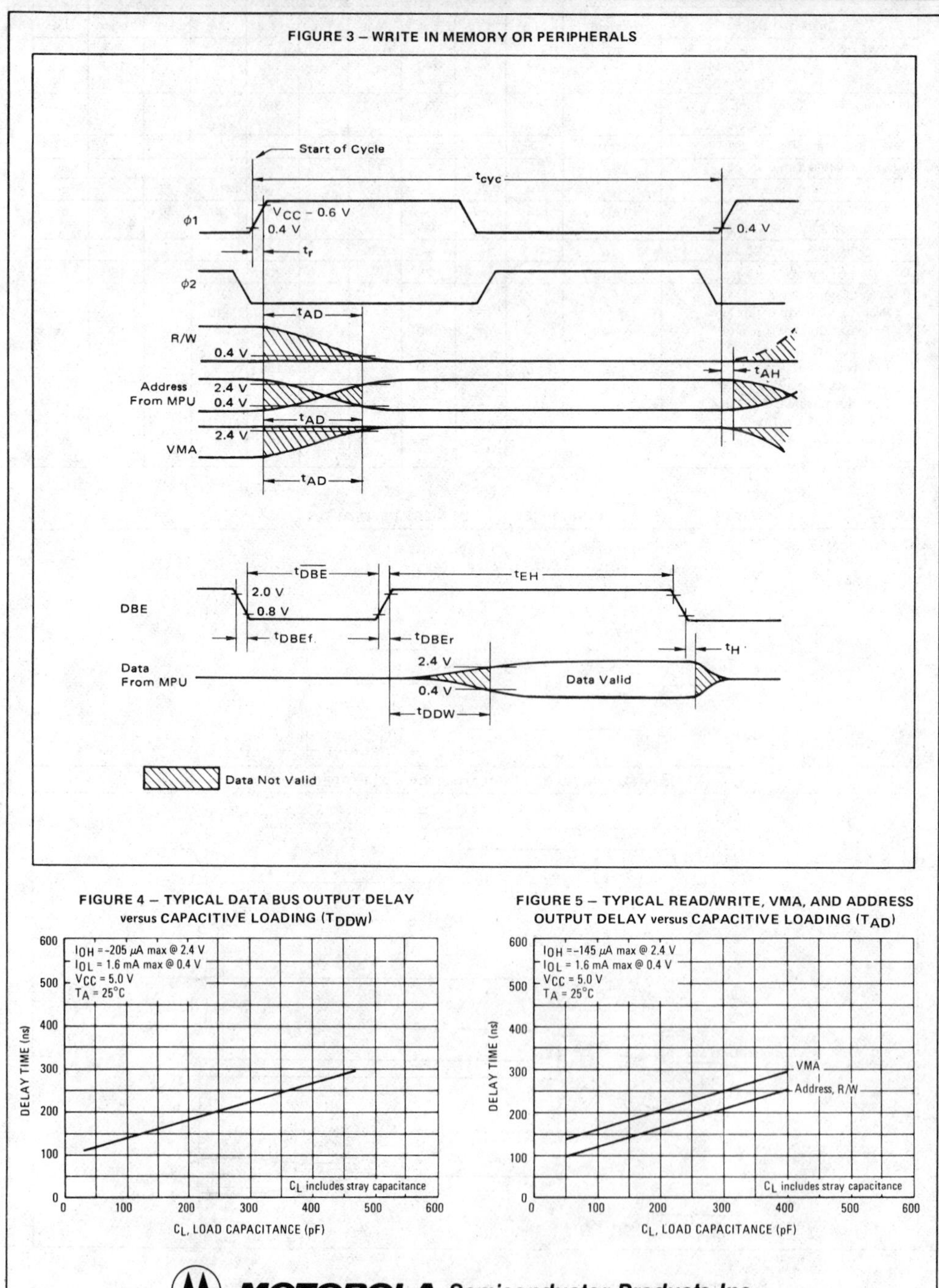

**FIGURE 6 – BUS TIMING TEST LOADS**

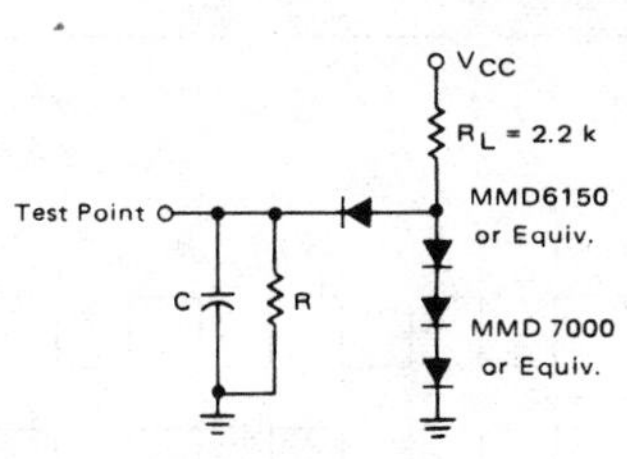


C = 130 pF for D0–D7, E
= 90 pF for A0–A15, R/W, and VMA
(Except $t_{AD2}$)
= 30 pF for A0–A15, R/W, and VMA
($t_{AD2}$ only)
= 30 pF for BA

R = 11.7 kΩ for D0–D7
= 16.5 kΩ for A0–A15, R/W, and VMA
= 24 kΩ for BA

TEST CONDITIONS

The dynamic test load for the Data Bus is 130 pF and one standard TTL load as shown. The Address, R/W, and VMA outputs are tested under two conditions to allow optimum operation in both buffered and unbuffered systems. The resistor (R) is chosen to insure specified load currents during $V_{OH}$ measurement.

Notice that the Data Bus lines, the Address lines, the Interrupt Request line, and the DBE line are all specified and tested to guarantee 0.4 V of dynamic noise immunity at both "1" and "0" logic levels.

FIGURE 12 – THREE STATE CONTROL TIMING

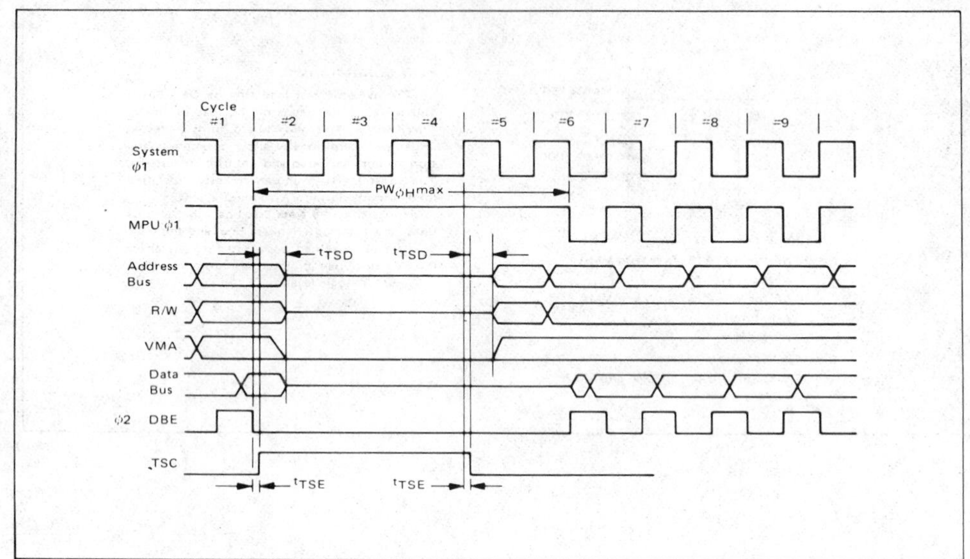


FIGURE 13 – $\overline{\text{HALT}}$ AND SINGLE INSTRUCTION EXECUTION FOR SYSTEM DEBUG

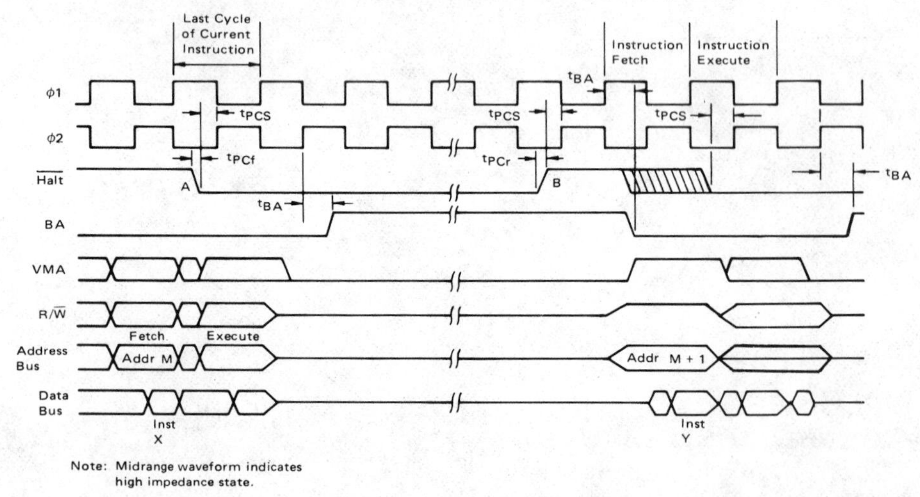


Note: Midrange waveform indicates high impedance state.

## MAXIMUM RATINGS

| Rating | Symbol | Value | Unit |
|---|---|---|---|
| Supply Voltage | $V_{CC}$ | -0.3 to +7.0 | Vdc |
| Input Voltage | $V_{in}$ | -0.3 to +7.0 | Vdc |
| Operating Temperature Range | $T_A$ | 0 to +70 | °C |
| Storage Temperature Range | $T_{stg}$ | -55 to +150 | °C |
| Thermal Resistance | $\theta_{JA}$ | 70 | °C/W |

This device contains circuitry to protect the inputs against damage due to high static voltages or electric fields; however, it is advised that normal precautions be taken to avoid application of any voltage higher than maximum rated voltages to this high impedance circuit.

## ELECTRICAL CHARACTERISTICS ($V_{CC}$ = 5.0 V ± 5%, $V_{SS}$ = 0, $T_A$ = 0 to 70°C unles otherwise noted.)

| Characteristic | | Symbol | Min | Typ | Max | Unit |
|---|---|---|---|---|---|---|
| Input High Voltage | Logic, EXtal<br>$\overline{\text{Reset}}$ | $V_{IH}$ | $V_{SS}$ + 2.0<br>$V_{SS}$ + 4.0 | –<br>– | $V_{CC}$<br>$V_{CC}$ | Vdc |
| Input Low Voltage | Logic, EXtal<br>$\overline{\text{Reset}}$ | $V_{IL}$ | $V_{SS}$ – 0.3<br>$V_{SS}$ – 0.3 | – | $V_{SS}$ + 0.8<br>$V_{SS}$ + 2.3 | Vdc |
| Input Leakage Current<br>($V_{in}$ = 0 to 5.25 V, $V_{CC}$ = max) | Logic* | $I_{in}$ | – | 1.0 | 2.5 | μAdc |
| Output High Voltage<br>($I_{Load}$ = -205 μAdc, $V_{CC}$ = min)<br>($I_{Load}$ = -145 μAdc, $V_{CC}$ = min)<br>($I_{Load}$ = -100 μAdc, $V_{CC}$ = min) | <br>D0-D7<br>A0-A15, R/$\overline{\text{W}}$, VMA, E<br>BA | $V_{OH}$ | <br>$V_{SS}$ + 2.4<br>$V_{SS}$ + 2.4<br>$V_{SS}$ + 2.4 | <br>–<br>–<br>– | <br>–<br>–<br>– | Vdc |
| Output Low Voltage<br>($I_{Load}$ = 1.6 mAdc, $V_{CC}$ = min) | | $V_{OL}$ | – | – | $V_{SS}$ + 0.4 | Vdc |
| Power Dissipation | | $P_D$** | – | 0.600 | 1.2 | W |
| Capacitance ≠<br>($V_{in}$ = 0, $T_A$ = 25°C, f = 1.0 MHz) | <br>D0-D7<br>Logic Inputs, EXtal | $C_{in}$ | <br>–<br>– | <br>10<br>6.5 | <br>12.5<br>10 | pF |
| | A0-A15, R/$\overline{\text{W}}$, VMA | $C_{out}$ | – | – | 12 | pF |
| Frequency of Operation (Input Clock ÷4)<br>(Crystal Frequency) | | f<br>$f_{XTal}$ | 0.1<br>1.0 | –<br>– | 1.0<br>4.0 | MHz |
| Clock Timing<br>Cycle Time | | $t_{cyc}$ | 1.0 | – | 10 | μs |
| Clock Pulse Width<br>(Measured at 2.4 V) | | $PW_{\phi Hs}$<br>$PW_{\phi L}$ | 450 | – | 9500 | ns |
| Fall Time<br>(Measured between $V_{SS}$ + 0.4 V and $V_{SS}$ + 2.4 V) | | $t_\phi$ | – | – | 25 | ns |

*Except $\overline{\text{IRQ}}$ and $\overline{\text{NMI}}$, which require 3 kΩ pullup load resistors for wire-OR capability at optimum operation. Does not include EXtal and Xtal, which are crystal inputs.

**In power-down mode, maximum power dissipation is less than 40 mW.

≠Capacitances are periodically sampled rather than 100% tested.

## READ/WRITE TIMING (Figures 2 through 6; Load Circuit of Figure 4.)

| Characteristic | Symbol | Min | Typ | Max | Unit |
|---|---|---|---|---|---|
| Address Delay | $t_{AD}$ | – | – | 270 | ns |
| Peripheral Read Access Time<br>$t_{acc} = t_{ut} - (t_{AD} + t_{DSR})$ $(t_{ut} = t_{cyc} - t_\phi)$ | $t_{acc}$ | – | – | 530 | ns |
| Data Setup Time (Read) | $t_{DSR}$ | 100 | – | – | ns |
| Input Data Hold Time | $t_H$ | 10 | – | – | ns |
| Output Data Hold Time | $t_H$ | 30 | – | – | ns |
| Address Hold Time (Address, R/$\overline{\text{W}}$, VMA) | $t_{AH}$ | 20 | – | – | ns |
| Data Delay Time (Write) | $t_{DDW}$ | – | 165 | 225 | ns |
| Processor Controls<br>Processor Control Setup Time<br>Processor Control Rise and Fall Time<br>(Measured between 0.8 V and 2.0 V) | <br>$t_{PCS}$<br>$t_{PCr}$, $t_{PCf}$ | <br>200<br>– | <br>–<br>– | <br>–<br>100 | <br>ns<br>ns |

FIGURE 2 – READ DATA FROM MEMORY OR PERIPHERALS

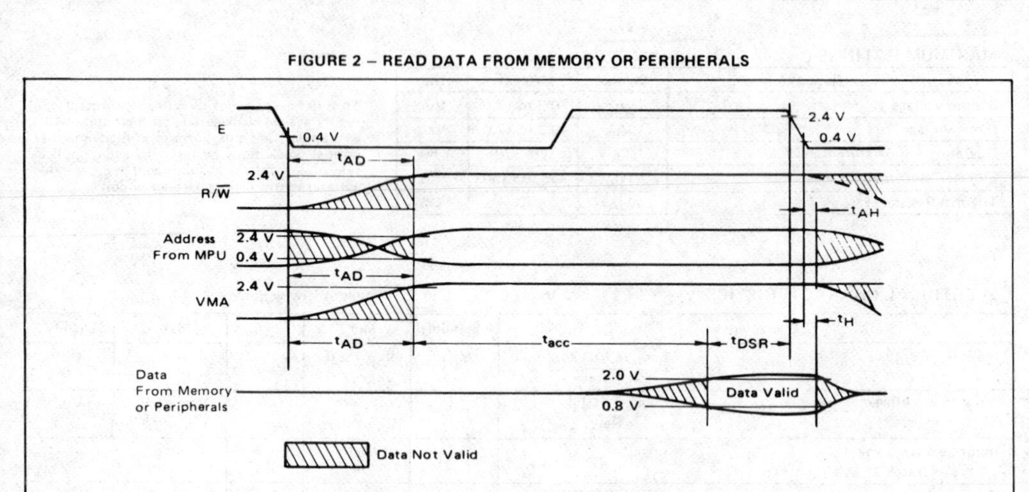


FIGURE 3 – WRITE DATA IN MEMORY OR PERIPHERALS

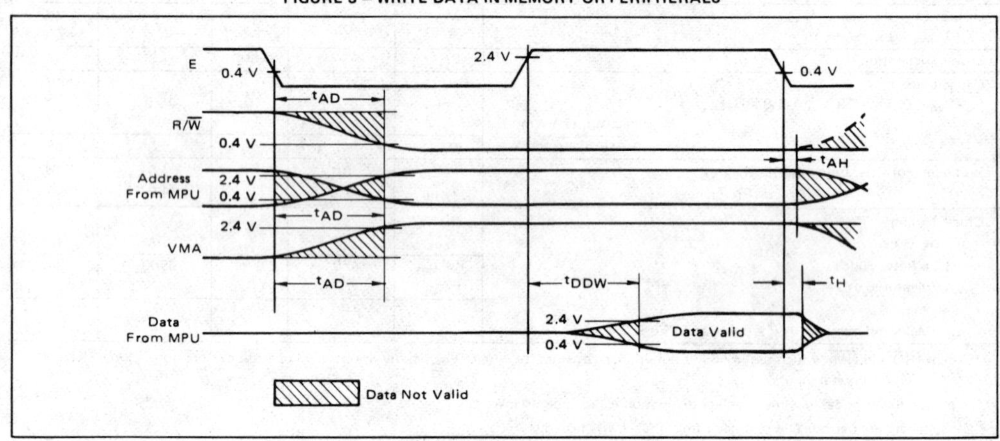


FIGURE 4 – BUS TIMING TEST LOAD

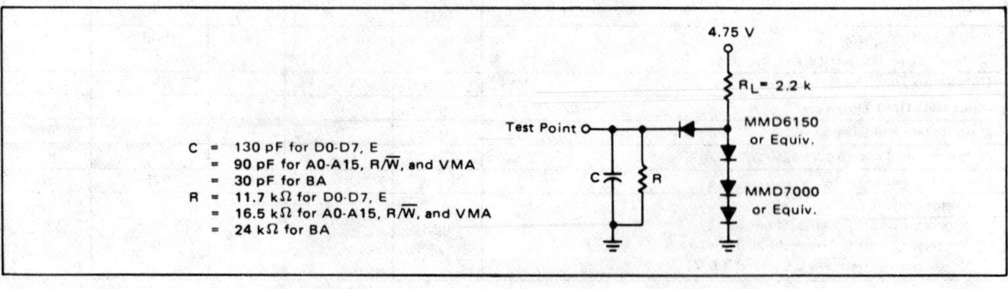

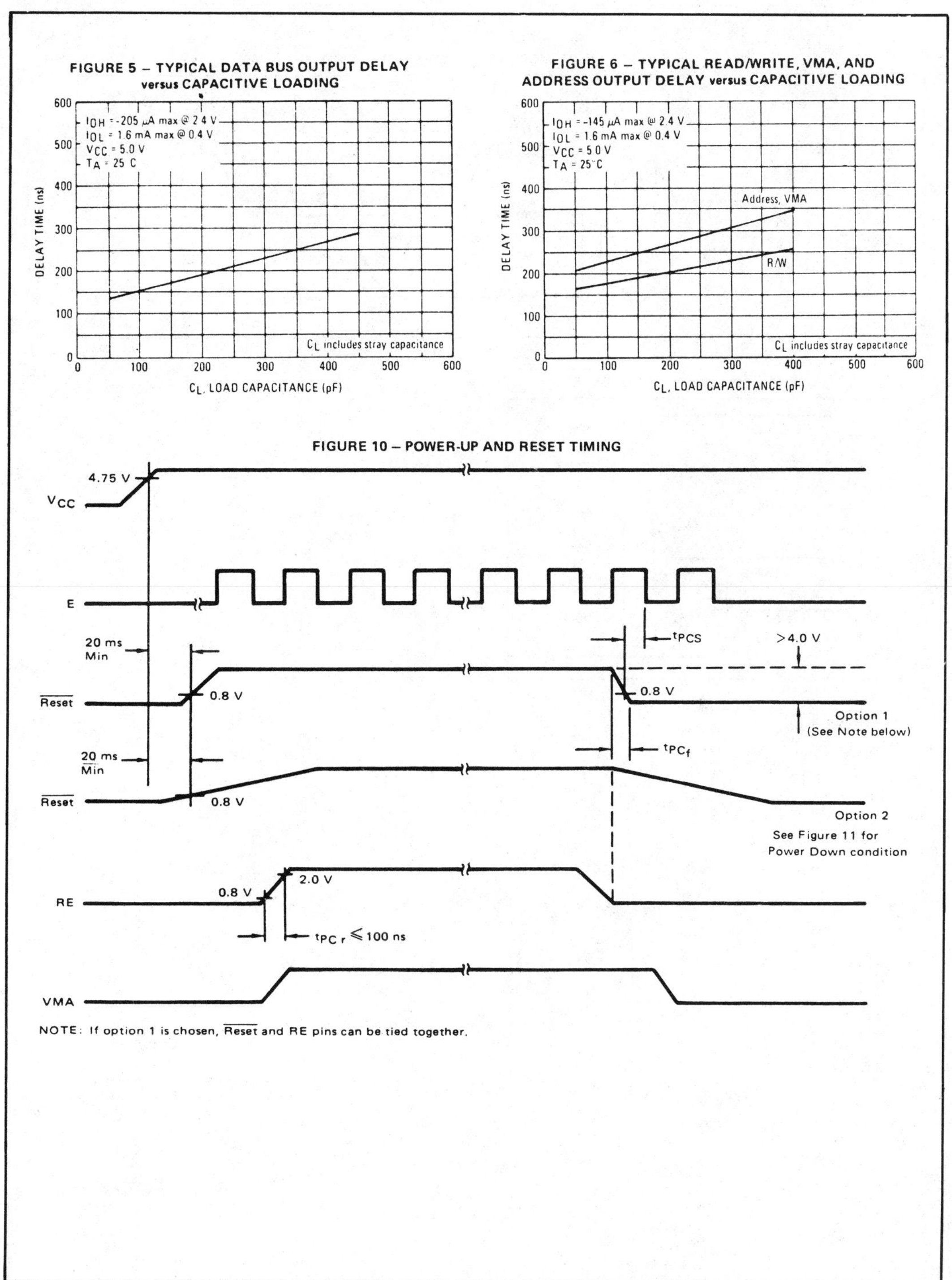
FIGURE 5 – TYPICAL DATA BUS OUTPUT DELAY versus CAPACITIVE LOADING
$I_{OH}$ = -205 μA max @ 2.4 V
$I_{OL}$ = 1.6 mA max @ 0.4 V
$V_{CC}$ = 5.0 V
$T_A$ = 25 C
DELAY TIME (ns)
$C_L$ includes stray capacitance
$C_L$, LOAD CAPACITANCE (pF)
FIGURE 6 – TYPICAL READ/WRITE, VMA, AND ADDRESS OUTPUT DELAY versus CAPACITIVE LOADING
$I_{OH}$ = -145 μA max @ 2.4 V
$I_{OL}$ = 1.6 mA max @ 0.4 V
$V_{CC}$ = 5.0 V
$T_A$ = 25°C
Address, VMA
R/W
DELAY TIME (ns)
$C_L$ includes stray capacitance
$C_L$, LOAD CAPACITANCE (pF)
FIGURE 10 – POWER-UP AND RESET TIMING
4.75 V
$V_{CC}$
E
20 ms Min
Reset
0.8 V
$t_{PCS}$
>4.0 V
Option 1 (See Note below)
$t_{PCf}$
Option 2
See Figure 11 for Power Down condition
RE
2.0 V
$t_{PCr}$ ≤ 100 ns
VMA
NOTE: If option 1 is chosen, Reset and RE pins can be tied together.

FIGURE 13 – MEMORY READY CONTROL FUNCTION

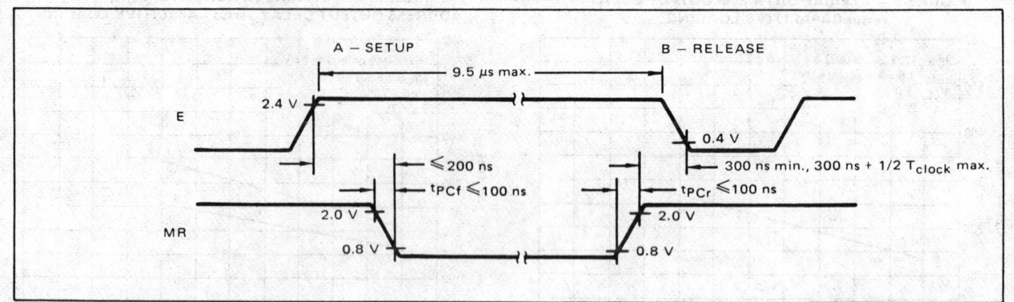

FIGURE 11 – POWER-DOWN SEQUENCE

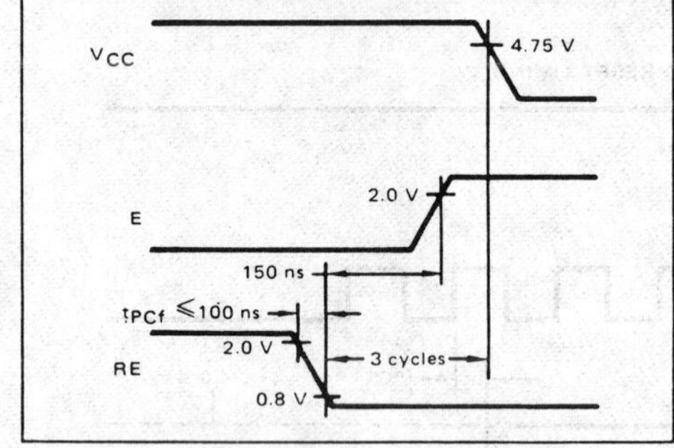

# MC6870A

**limited function microprocessor clock**
**250 kHz to 2.5 MHz**

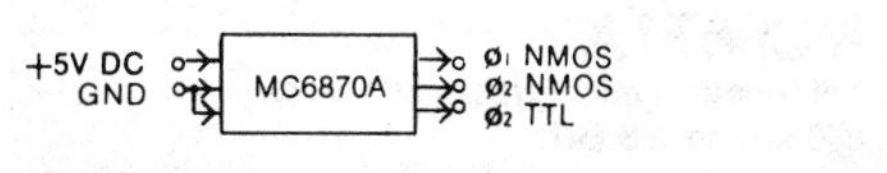


**DIMENSIONS**

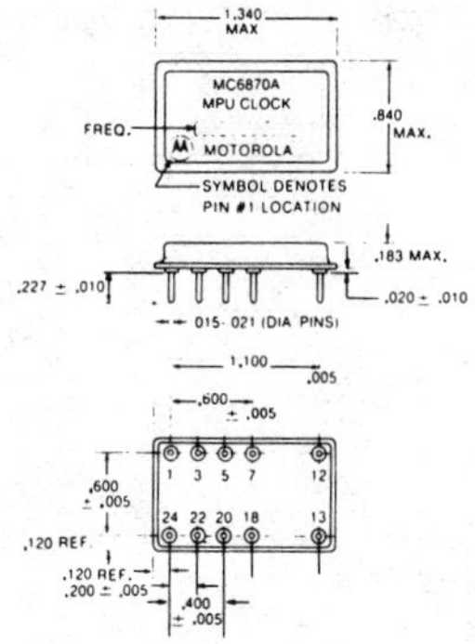

| PIN | CONNECTION |
|---|---|
| 1 | GND |
| 3 | NC |
| 5 | Ø2 TTL |
| 7 | $V_{cc}$ (+5VDC) |
| 12 | Ø2 NMOS |
| 13 | Ø1 NMOS |
| 18 | GND |
| 20 | NC |
| 22 | NC |
| 24 | NC |

Note: All dimensions are in inches

**WAVEFORM TIMING**
(ALL TIME IN NANOSECONDS)

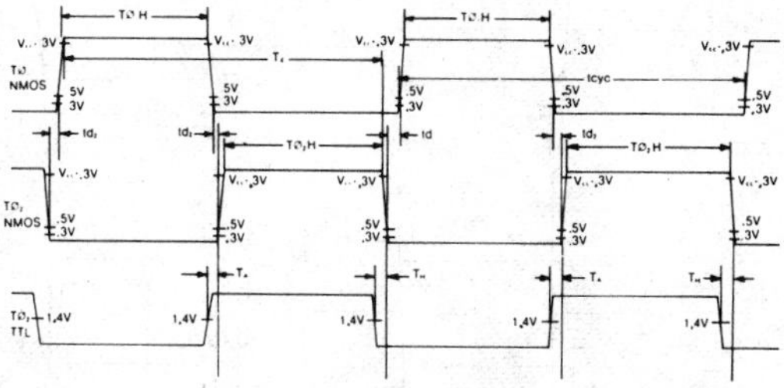

**TEST CIRCUIT**

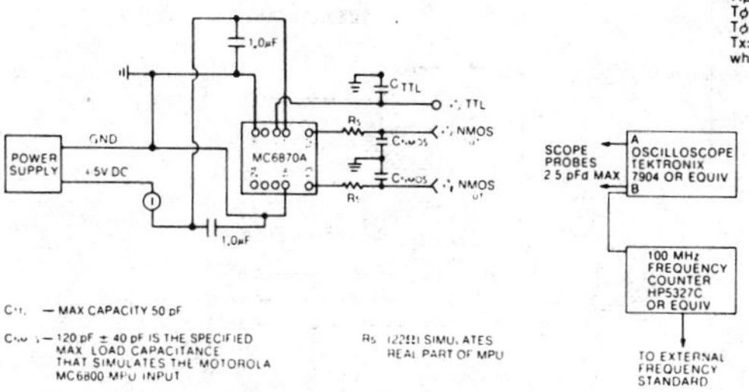

$C_{TTL}$ — MAX CAPACITY 50 pF

$C_{NMOS}$ — 120 pF ± 40 pF IS THE SPECIFIED MAX. LOAD CAPACITANCE THAT SIMULATES THE MOTOROLA MC6800 MPU INPUT

$R_S$ (22Ω) SIMULATES REAL PART OF MPU

## specifications

| Rating | Symbol | Value | Unit |
|---|---|---|---|
| Supply Voltage | $V_{cc}$ | 5.00±5% | Vdc |
| Operating Temperature Range | $T_A$ | 0 to +70 | °C |
| Storage Temperature | $T_{stg}$ | −55 to +125 | °C |
| Power Supply Drain (max.) | $I_{pd}$ | 100 | mA |

ELECTRICAL CHARACTERISTICS ($V_{cc}$ = 5.0 ± 5%, $V_{ss}$ = 0, $T_A$ = 0° to 70°C, unless otherwise noted)

| Characteristic | Symbol | Min | Typ | Max | Unit |
|---|---|---|---|---|---|
| **Frequency** | | | | | |
| Operating Frequency | $f_c$ | .250 | | 2.5 | MHz |
| Frequency stability (inclusive of calibration tolerance at +25°C, operating temperature, input voltage change, load change, aging, shock and vibration) | | | ±.01 | | % |
| **NMOS Outputs at 1.0 MHz Operation**** | | | | | |
| Pulse Width (meas. at $V_{cc}$= −.3V dc level) | TØ1H<br>TØ2H | 430<br>450 | | | ns<br>ns |
| Logic Levels | $V_{OLC}$<br>$V_{OHC}$ | $V_{ss}$-.1<br>$V_{cc}$-.3 | —<br>— | $V_{ss}$+.3<br>$V_{cc}$+.1 | Vdc<br>Vdc |
| Rise and Fall Times | $t_r$<br>$t_f$ | 5<br>5 | 12<br>12 | 50<br>50 | ns<br>ns |
| *Overshoot/Undershoot<br>Logic "1"<br>Logic "0" | $V_{OS}$ | $V_{cc}$-.5<br>$V_{ss}$-.5 | | $V_{cc}$+.5<br>$V_{ss}$+.5 | Vdc<br>Vdc |
| Pulse duration of any overshoot or undershoot | $T_{OS}$ | | | 40 | ns |
| Period @ 0.3V dc Level | $t_{cyc}$ | | 1.00 | | us |
| Edge Timing @ $V_{cc}$=0.3V dc | Tx | 940 | | | ns |
| NMOS Relationship @ +0.5V dc Level | $t_{d1}$<br>$t_{d2}$ | 0<br>0 | | 8.0 | us |
| **TTL Outputs** | | | | | |
| In ref. to Ø2 NMOS @ 0.3V dc | | | | | |
| Ø2 TTL @ +1.4V dc | $T_A$<br>$T_H$ | 15<br>10 | 30<br>25 | 45<br>40 | ns<br>ns |
| **Logic Levels** | $V_{OH}$<br>$V_{OL}$ | 2.4 | 3.2<br>.3 | .4 | Vdc<br>Vdc |
| Rise and Fall Times<br>.4V and 2.4V<br>2.4V and .4V | $t_r$<br>$t_f$ | | | 15<br>15 | ns<br>ns |
| Logic "0" Sink (/Gate) | $I_{OL}$ | | | −1.6 | mA |
| Logic "1" Source (/Gate) | $I_{OH}$ | | | +40 | uA |
| Current Output Shorted | $I_{SC}$ | −18 | | −57 | mA |
| **Load** | | | | | |
| NMOS—Load Capacity Ø1, Ø2 | $C_{NMOS}$ | 80 | 120 | 160 | pf |
| TTL—No. of Loads | | | | 5 | ttl |
| TTL—Load Capacity | $C_{TTL}$ | | | 50 | pf |

*Into specified test load

**Apply the following parameters for frequencies other than 1.0 MHz:
TØ1H=0.5 (P-140) ns
TØ2H=0.5 (P-100) ns
Tx=(P-60) ns
where P=desired period of operation in nanoseconds

**MOTOROLA INC.** COMPONENT PRODUCTS DEPT.

# MC6871A

**full function microprocessor clock**
**850 kHz to 2.5 MHz**

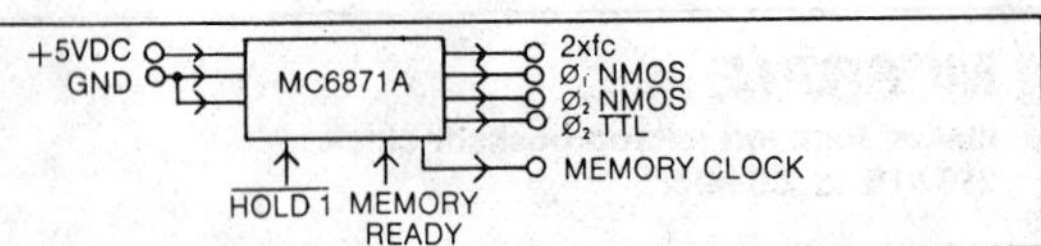


## specifications

| Rating | Symbol | Value | Unit |
|---|---|---|---|
| Supply Voltage | $V_{cc}$ | 5.00±5% | Vdc |
| Operating Temperature Range | $T_A$ | 0 to +70 | °C |
| Storage Temperature | $T_{stg}$ | −55 to +125 | °C |
| Power Supply Drain (max.) | $I_{pd}$ | 100 | mA |

ELECTRICAL CHARACTERISTICS ($V_{cc}$ = 5.0 ± 5%, $V_{ss}$ = 0, $T_A$ = 0° to 70°C, unless otherwise noted)

| Characteristic | Symbol | Min | Typ | Max | Unit |
|---|---|---|---|---|---|
| **Frequency** | | | | | |
| Operating Frequency | $f_c$ | .850 | | 2.5 | MHz |
| Frequency stability (inclusive of calibration tolerance at +25°C, operating temperature, input voltage change, load change, aging, shock and vibration) | | | ±.01 | | % |
| **NMOS Outputs at 1.0 MHz Operation***** | | | | | |
| Pulse Width (meas. at $V_{cc}$= −.3V dc level) | TØ1H<br>TØ2H | 430<br>450 | | | ns<br>ns |
| Logic Levels | $V_{OLC}$<br>$V_{OHC}$ | $V_{ss}$-.1<br>$V_{cc}$-.3 | —<br>— | $V_{ss}$+.3<br>$V_{cc}$+.1 | Vdc<br>Vdc |
| Rise and Fall Times | $t_r$<br>$t_f$ | 5<br>5 | 12<br>12 | 50<br>50 | ns<br>ns |
| *Overshoot/Undershoot<br>Logic "1"<br>Logic "0" | $V_{OS}$ | $V_{cc}$-.5<br>$V_{ss}$-.5 | | $V_{cc}$+.5<br>$V_{ss}$+.5 | Vdc<br>Vdc |
| Pulse duration of any overshoot or undershoot | $T_{OS}$ | | | 40 | ns |
| Period @ 0.3V dc Level | $t_{cyc}$ | | 1.00 | | us |
| Edge Timing @ $V_{cc}$=0.3V dc | Tx | 940 | | | ns |
| NMOS Relationship @ +0.5V dc Level | $t_{d1}$<br>$t_{d2}$ | 0<br>0 | | 8.0 | us |
| **TTL Outputs** | | | | | |
| In ref. to Ø2 NMOS @ 0.3V dc | | | | | |
| Ø2 TTL @ 1.4V dc | $T_A$<br>$T_H$ | 15<br>10 | 30<br>25 | 45<br>40 | ns<br>ns |
| Memory Clock @ 1.4V dc | $T_C$<br>$T_J$ | 30<br>20 | 50<br>40 | 70<br>60 | ns<br>ns |
| 2xfc @ 1.4V dc | $T_B$ | 40 | 80 | 120 | ns |
| **Logic Levels** | $V_{OH}$<br>$V_{OL}$ | 2.4 | 3.2<br>.3 | .4 | Vdc<br>Vdc |
| Rise and Fall Times<br>.4V and 2.4V<br>2.4V and .4V | $t_r$<br>$t_f$ | | | 15<br>15 | ns<br>ns |
| Logic "0" Sink (/Gate) | $I_{OL}$ | | | −1.6 | mA |
| Logic "1" Source (/Gate) | $I_{OH}$ | | | +40 | uA |
| Current Output Shorted | $I_{SC}$ | −18 | | −57 | mA |
| **Load** | | | | | |
| NMOS—Load Capacity Ø1, Ø2 | $C_{NMOS}$ | 80 | 120 | 160 | pf |
| TTL—No. of Loads | | | | 5 | ttl |
| TTL—Load Capacity | $C_{TTL}$ | | | 50 | pf |
| **Logic Inputs** ("0" Level Applies HOLD or MEMORY READY)** | | | | | |
| Holds Ø1 NMOS 'High', Ø2 NMOS 'Low', Ø2 TTL 'Low' | $\overline{\text{HOLD 1}}$ | −.2 | | +.4 | Vdc |
| Holds Ø1 NMOS 'Low', Ø2 NMOS 'High', Ø2 TTL 'High', and MEMORY CLOCK 'High' | MEMORY READY | −.2 | | +.4 | Vdc |

*Into specified test load

**Must be externally held at "1" level (2.4V min., 5.0V max.) if not used

***Apply the following parameters for frequencies other than 1 MHz:
TØ1H=0.5 (P-140) ns
TØ2H=0.5 (P-100) ns
Tx=(P-60) ns
where P=desired period of operation in nanoseconds

| PIN | CONNECTION |
|---|---|
| 1 | GND |
| 3 | MEMORY CLOCK |
| 5 | Ø2 TTL |
| 7 | $V_{cc}$ (+5VDC) |
| 12 | Ø2 NMOS |
| 13 | Ø1 NMOS |
| 18 | GND |
| 20 | $\overline{\text{HOLD 1}}$ |
| 22 | MEMORY READY |
| 24 | 2xfc |

**DIMENSIONS**

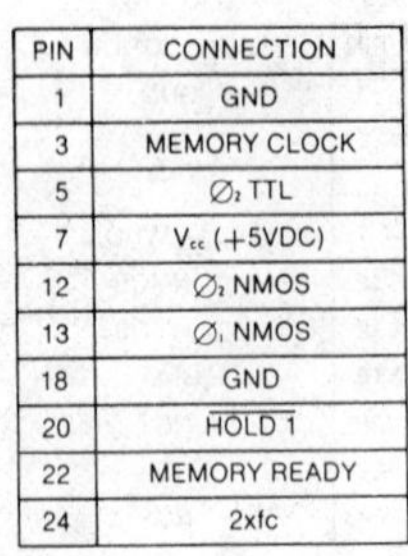
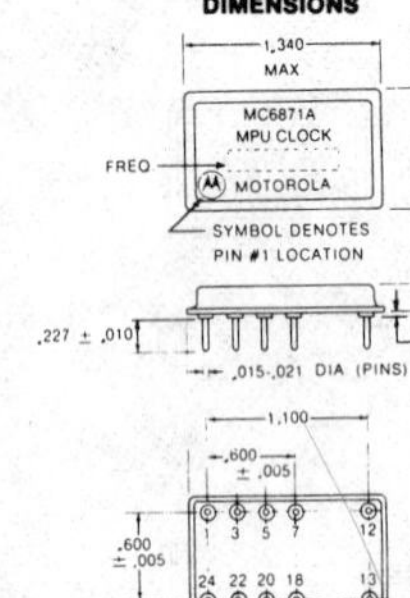


Note: All dimensions are in inches

**WAVEFORM TIMING**

(ALL TIME IN NANOSECONDS)

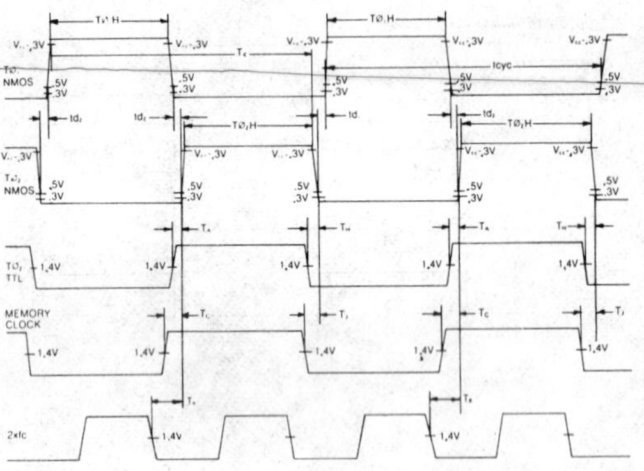


**TEST CIRCUIT**

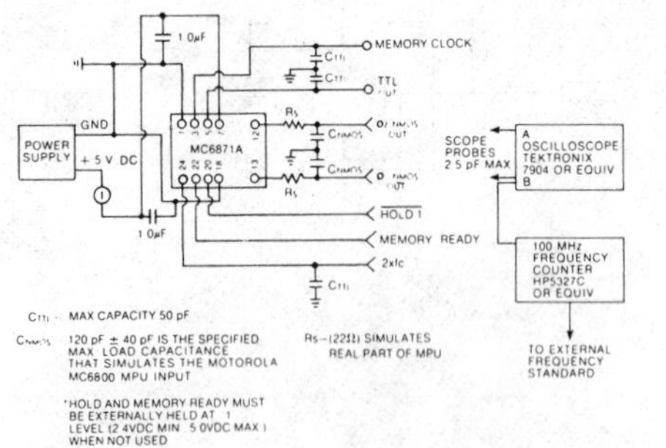


$C_{TTL}$ — MAX CAPACITY 50 pF

$C_{NMOS}$ — 120 pF ± 40 pF IS THE SPECIFIED MAX. LOAD CAPACITANCE THAT SIMULATES THE MOTOROLA MC6800 MPU INPUT

Rs — (22Ω) SIMULATES REAL PART OF MPU

*HOLD AND MEMORY READY MUST BE EXTERNALLY HELD AT "1" LEVEL (2.4VDC MIN., 5.0VDC MAX.) WHEN NOT USED

 **MOTOROLA INC.** COMPONENT PRODUCTS DEPT.

# MC6871B

**alternate function microprocessor clock**
**250 kHz to 2.5 MHz**

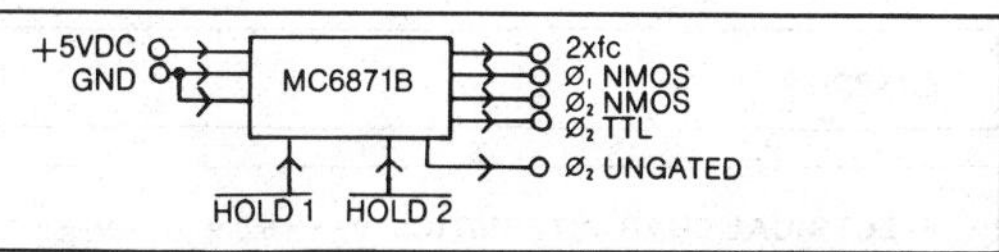


## specifications

| Rating | Symbol | Value | Unit |
|---|---|---|---|
| Supply Voltage | $V_{cc}$ | 5.00±5% | Vdc |
| Operating Temperature Range | $T_A$ | 0 to +70 | °C |
| Storage Temperature | $T_{stg}$ | −55 to +125 | °C |
| Power Supply Drain (max.) | $I_{pd}$ | 100 | mA |

ELECTRICAL CHARACTERISTICS ($V_{cc}$ = 5.0 ± 5%, $V_{ss}$ = 0, $T_A$ = 0° to 70°C, unless otherwise noted)

| Characteristic | Symbol | Min | Typ | Max | Unit |
|---|---|---|---|---|---|
| **Frequency** | | | | | |
| Operating Frequency | $f_c$ | .250 | | 2.5 | MHz |
| Frequency stability (inclusive of calibration tolerance at +25°C, operating temperature, input voltage change, load change, aging, shock and vibration) | | | ±.01 | | % |
| **NMOS Outputs at 1.0 MHz Operation***** | | | | | |
| Pulse Width (meas. at $V_{cc}$ = −.3V dc level) | $TØ_1H$ | 430 | | | ns |
| | $TØ_2H$ | 450 | | | ns |
| Logic Levels | $V_{OLC}$ | $V_{ss}$-.1 | — | $V_{ss}$+.3 | Vdc |
| | $V_{OHC}$ | $V_{cc}$-.3 | — | $V_{cc}$+.1 | Vdc |
| Rise and Fall Times | $t_r$ | 5 | 12 | 50 | ns |
| | $t_f$ | 5 | 12 | 50 | ns |
| *Overshoot/Undershoot Logic "1" | | $V_{cc}$-.5 | | $V_{cc}$+.5 | Vdc |
| Logic "0" | $V_{OS}$ | $V_{ss}$-.5 | | $V_{ss}$+.5 | Vdc |
| Pulse duration of any overshoot or undershoot | $T_{OS}$ | | | 40 | ns |
| Period @ 0.3V dc Level | $t_{cyc}$ | | 1.00 | | us |
| Edge Timing @ $V_{cc}$=0.3V dc | Tx | 940 | | | ns |
| NMOS Relationship @ +0.5V dc | $t_{d1}$ | 0 | | | |
| | $t_{d2}$ | 0 | | 8.0 | us |
| **TTL Outputs** | | | | | |
| In ref. to Ø2 NMOS @ 0.3V dc | | | | | |
| Ø2 TTL @ 1.4V dc | $T_A$ | 15 | 30 | 45 | ns |
| | $T_H$ | 10 | 25 | 40 | ns |
| Ø2 Ungated @ 1.4V dc | $T_C$ | 30 | 50 | 70 | ns |
| | $T_J$ | 20 | 40 | 60 | ns |
| 2xfc @ 1.4V dc | $T_B$ | 40 | 80 | 120 | ns |
| **Logic Levels** | $V_{OH}$ | 2.4 | 3.2 | | Vdc |
| | $V_{OL}$ | | .3 | .4 | Vdc |
| Rise and Fall Times .4V and 2.4V | $t_r$ | | | 15 | ns |
| 2.4V and .4V | $t_f$ | | | 15 | ns |
| Logic "0" Sink (/Gate) | $I_{OL}$ | | | −1.6 | mA |
| Logic "1" Source (/Gate) | $I_{OH}$ | | | +40 | uA |
| Current Output Shorted | $I_{SC}$ | −18 | | −57 | mA |
| **Load** | | | | | |
| NMOS—Load Capacity Ø1, Ø2 | $C_{NMOS}$ | 80 | 120 | 160 | pf |
| TTL—No. of Loads | | | | 5 | ttl |
| TTL—Load Capacity | $C_{TTL}$ | | | 50 | pf |
| **Logic Inputs** ("0" Level applies HOLD)** | | | | | |
| Holds Ø1 NMOS 'High', Ø2 NMOS 'Low', Ø2 TTL 'Low' | $\overline{\text{HOLD 1}}$ | −.2 | | +.4 | Vdc |
| Holds Ø1 NMOS 'Low', Ø2 NMOS 'High', Ø2 TTL 'High' | $\overline{\text{HOLD 2}}$ | −.2 | | +.4 | Vdc |

*Into specified test load

**Must be externally held at "1" level (2.4V min., 5.0V max.) if not used

***Apply the following parameters for frequencies other than 1 MHz
TØ1H=0.5 (P-140) ns
TØ2H=0.5 (P-100) ns
Tx=(P-60) ns
where P=desired period of operation in nanoseconds

**DIMENSIONS**

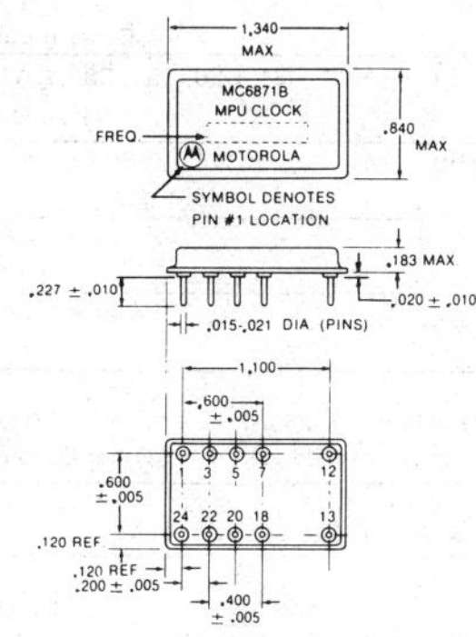


| PIN | CONNECTION |
|---|---|
| 1 | GND |
| 3 | Ø2 TTL UNGATED |
| 5 | Ø2 TTL |
| 7 | $V_{cc}$ (+5VDC) |
| 12 | Ø2 NMOS |
| 13 | Ø1 NMOS |
| 18 | GND |
| 20 | $\overline{\text{HOLD 1}}$ |
| 22 | $\overline{\text{HOLD 2}}$ |
| 24 | 2xfc |

Note: 4xfc available on request

Note: All dimensions are in inches

**WAVEFORM TIMING.**

ALL TIME IN NANOSECONDS

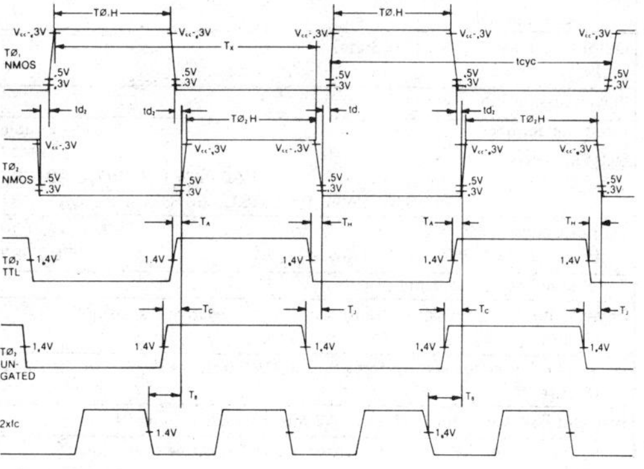


**TEST DIAGRAM**

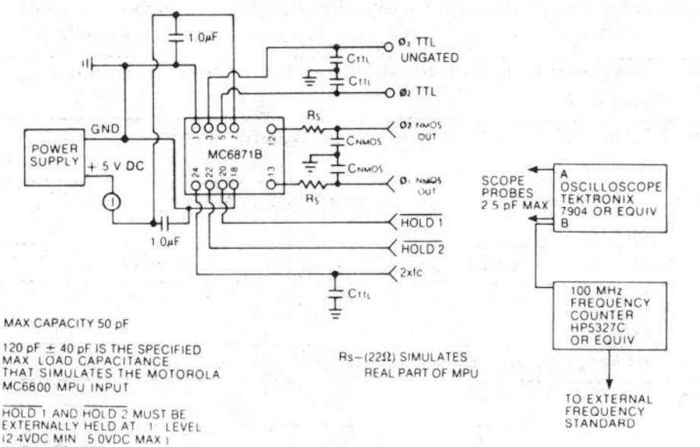

**MOTOROLA INC.** COMPONENT PRODUCTS DEPT.
2553 N. Edgington Franklin Park, Ill. 60131 312/451-1000

**ELECTRICAL CHARACTERISTICS** ($V_{CC}$ = 5.0 V ±5%, $V_{SS}$ = 0, $T_A$ = 0 to 70°C unless otherwise noted.)

| Characteristic | Symbol | Min | Typ | Max | Unit |
|---|---|---|---|---|---|
| Input High Voltage — Enable<br>Other Inputs | $V_{IH}$ | $V_{SS}$ + 2.4<br>$V_{SS}$ + 2.0 | –<br>– | $V_{CC}$<br>$V_{CC}$ | Vdc |
| Input Low Voltage — Enable<br>Other Inputs | $V_{IL}$ | $V_{SS}$ -0.3<br>$V_{SS}$ -0.3 | –<br>– | $V_{SS}$ + 0.4<br>$V_{SS}$ + 0.8 | Vdc |
| Input Leakage Current — R/W, $\overline{Reset}$, RS0, RS1, CS0, CS1, $\overline{CS2}$, CA1, CB1, Enable<br>($V_{in}$ = 0 to 5.25 Vdc) | $I_{in}$ | – | 1.0 | 2.5 | μAdc |
| Three-State (Off State) Input Current — D0-D7, PB0-PB7, CB2<br>($V_{in}$ = 0.4 to 2.4 Vdc) | $I_{TSI}$ | – | 2.0 | 10 | μAdc |
| Input High Current — PA0-PA7, CA2<br>($V_{IH}$ = 2.4 Vdc) | $I_{IH}$ | -100 | -250 | – | μAdc |
| Input Low Current — PA0-PA7, CA2<br>($V_{IL}$ = 0.4 Vdc) | $I_{IL}$ | – | -1.0 | -1.6 | mAdc |
| Output High Voltage<br>($I_{Load}$ = -205 μAdc, Enable Pulse Width < 25 μs) — D0-D7<br>($I_{Load}$ = -100 μAdc, Enable Pulse Width <25 μs) — Other Outputs | $V_{OH}$ | <br>$V_{SS}$ + 2.4<br>$V_{SS}$ + 2.4 | <br>–<br>– | <br>–<br>– | Vdc |
| Output Low Voltage<br>($I_{Load}$ = 1.6 mAdc, Enable Pulse Width < 25 μs) | $V_{OL}$ | – | – | $V_{SS}$ + 0.4 | Vdc |
| Output High Current (Sourcing)<br>($V_{OH}$ = 2.4 Vdc) — D0-D7<br>Other Outputs<br>($V_O$ = 1.5 Vdc, the current for driving other than TTL, e.g., Darlington Base) — PB0-PB7, CB2 | $I_{OH}$ | <br>-205<br>-100<br>-1.0 | <br>–<br>–<br>-2.5 | <br>–<br>–<br>-10 | <br>μAdc<br>μAdc<br>mAdc |
| Output Low Current (Sinking)<br>($V_{OL}$ = 0.4 Vdc) | $I_{OL}$ | 1.6 | – | – | mAdc |
| Output Leakage Current (Off State) — $\overline{IRQA}$, $\overline{IRQB}$<br>($V_{OH}$ = 2.4 Vdc) | $I_{LOH}$ | – | 1.0 | 10 | μAdc |
| Power Dissipation | $P_D$ | – | – | 650 | mW |
| Input Capacitance — Enable<br>($V_{in}$ = 0, $T_A$ = 25°C, f = 1.0 MHz) — D0-D7<br>PA0-PA7, PB0-PB7, CA2, CB2<br>R/W, $\overline{Reset}$, RS0, RS1, CS0, CS1, $\overline{CS2}$, CA1, CB1 | $C_{in}$ | –<br>–<br>–<br>– | –<br>–<br>–<br>– | 20<br>12.5<br>10<br>7.5 | pF |
| Output Capacitance — $\overline{IRQA}$, $\overline{IRQB}$<br>($V_{in}$ = 0, $T_A$ = 25°C, f = 1.0 MHz) — PB0-PB7 | $C_{out}$ | –<br>– | –<br>– | 5.0<br>10 | pF |
| Peripheral Data Setup Time (Figure 1) | $t_{PDSU}$ | 200 | – | – | ns |
| Delay Time, Enable negative transition to CA2 negative transition (Figure 2, 3) | $t_{CA2}$ | – | – | 1.0 | μs |
| Delay Time, Enable negative transition to CA2 positive transition (Figure 2) | $t_{RS1}$ | – | – | 1.0 | μs |
| Rise and Fall Times for CA1 and CA2 input signals (Figure 3) | $t_r, t_f$ | – | – | 1.0 | μs |
| Delay Time from CA1 active transition to CA2 positive transition (Figure 3) | $t_{RS2}$ | – | – | 2.0 | μs |
| Delay Time, Enable negative transition to Peripheral Data valid (Figures 4, 5) | $t_{PDW}$ | – | – | 1.0 | μs |
| Delay Time, Enable negative transition to Peripheral CMOS Data Valid ($V_{CC}$ – 30% $V_{CC}$, Figure 4; Figure 12 Load C) — PA0-PA7, CA2 | $t_{CMOS}$ | – | – | 2.0 | μs |
| Delay Time, Enable positive transition to CB2 negative transition (Figure 6, 7) | $t_{CB2}$ | – | – | 1.0 | μs |
| Delay Time, Peripheral Data valid to CB2 negative transition (Figure 5) | $t_{DC}$ | 20 | – | – | ns |
| Delay Time, Enable positive transition to CB2 positive transition (Figure 6) | $t_{RS1}$ | – | – | 1.0 | μs |
| Rise and Fall Time for CB1 and CB2 input signals (Figure 7) | $t_r, t_f$ | – | – | 1.0 | μs |
| Delay Time, CB1 active transition to CB2 positive transition (Figure 7) | $t_{RS2}$ | – | – | 2.0 | μs |
| Interrupt Release Time, $\overline{IRQA}$ and $\overline{IRQB}$ (Figure 8) | $t_{IR}$ | – | – | 1.6 | μs |
| Reset Low Time* (Figure 9) | $t_{RL}$ | 2.0 | – | – | μs |

*The Reset line must be high a minimum of 1.0 μs before addressing the PIA.

## MAXIMUM RATINGS

| Rating | Symbol | Value | Unit |
|---|---|---|---|
| Supply Voltage | $V_{CC}$ | –0.3 to +7.0 | Vdc |
| Input Voltage | $V_{in}$ | –0.3 to +7.0 | Vdc |
| Operating Temperature Range | $T_A$ | 0 to +70 | °C |
| Storage Temperature Range | $T_{stg}$ | –55 to +150 | °C |
| Thermal Resistance | $\theta_{JA}$ | 82.5 | °C/W |

This device contains circuitry to protect the inputs against damage due to high static voltages or electric fields; however, it is advised that normal precautions be taken to avoid application of any voltage higher than maximum rated voltages to this high impedance circuit.

## BUS TIMING CHARACTERISTICS

**READ** (Figures 10 and 12)

| Characteristic | Symbol | Min | Typ | Max | Unit |
|---|---|---|---|---|---|
| Enable Cycle Time | $t_{cycE}$ | 1.0 | – | – | μs |
| Enable Pulse Width, High | $PW_{EH}$ | 0.45 | – | 25 | μs |
| Enable Pulse Width, Low | $PW_{EL}$ | 0.43 | – | – | μs |
| Setup Time, Address and R/W valid to Enable positive transition | $t_{AS}$ | 160 | – | – | ns |
| Data Delay Time | $t_{DDR}$ | – | – | 320 | ns |
| Data Hold Time | $t_H$ | 10 | – | – | ns |
| Address Hold Time | $t_{AH}$ | 10 | – | – | ns |
| Rise and Fall Time for Enable input | $t_{Er}, t_{Ef}$ | – | – | 25 | ns |

**WRITE** (Figures 11 and 12)

| Characteristic | Symbol | Min | Typ | Max | Unit |
|---|---|---|---|---|---|
| Enable Cycle Time | $t_{cycE}$ | 1.0 | – | – | μs |
| Enable Pulse Width, High | $PW_{EH}$ | 0.45 | – | 25 | μs |
| Enable Pulse Width, Low | $PW_{EL}$ | 0.43 | – | – | μs |
| Setup Time, Address and R/W valid to Enable positive transition | $t_{AS}$ | 160 | – | – | ns |
| Data Setup Time | $t_{DSW}$ | 195 | – | – | ns |
| Data Hold Time | $t_H$ | 10 | – | – | ns |
| Address Hold Time | $t_{AH}$ | 10 | – | – | ns |
| Rise and Fall Time for Enable input | $t_{Er}, t_{Ef}$ | – | – | 25 | ns |

**FIGURE 1 – PERIPHERAL DATA SETUP TIME**
**(Read Mode)**

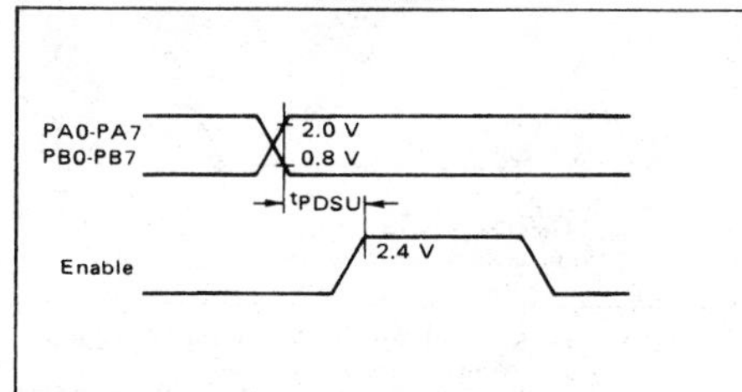


**FIGURE 2 – CA2 DELAY TIME**
**(Read Mode; CRA-5 = CRA-3 = 1, CRA-4 = 0)**

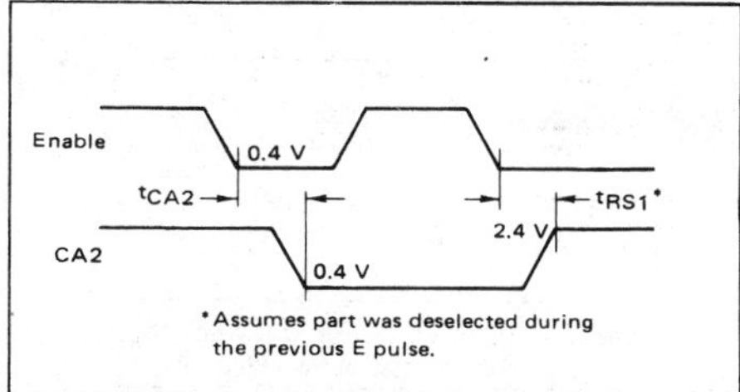


**FIGURE 3 – CA2 DELAY TIME**
**(Read Mode; CRA-5 = 1, CRA-3 = CRA-4 = 0)**

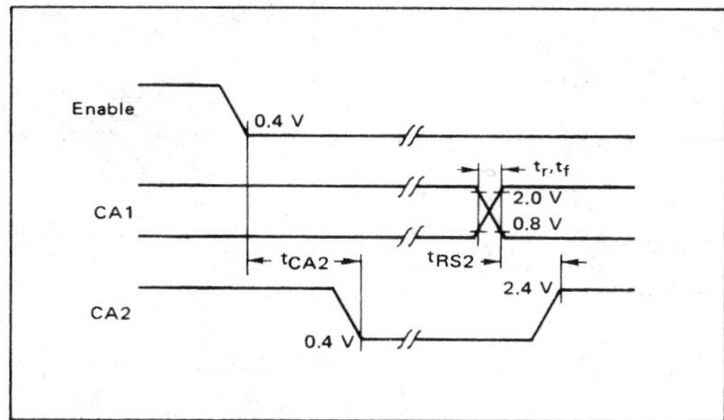

**FIGURE 4 – PERIPHERAL CMOS DATA DELAY TIMES**
**(Write Mode; CRA-5 = CRA-3 = 1, CRA-4 = 0)**

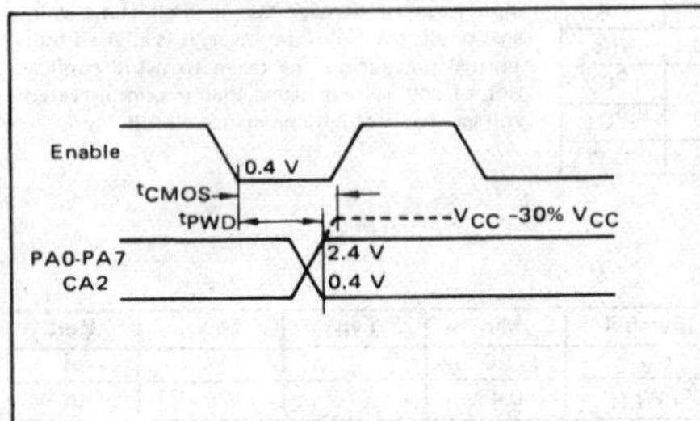


**FIGURE 5 – PERIPHERAL DATA AND CB2 DELAY TIMES**
**(Write Mode; CRB-5 = CRB-3 = 1, CRB-4 = 0)**

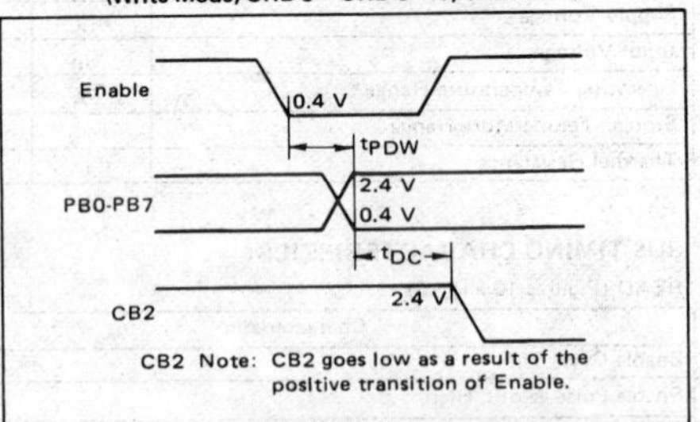


CB2 Note: CB2 goes low as a result of the positive transition of Enable.

**FIGURE 6 – CB2 DELAY TIME**
**(Write Mode; CRB-5 = CRB-3 = 1, CRB-4 = 0)**

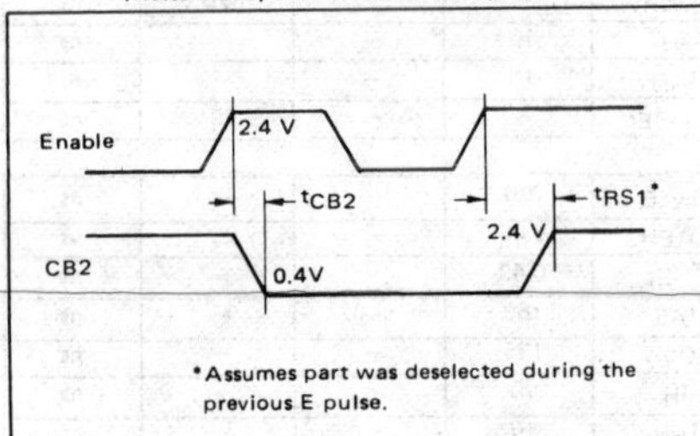


*Assumes part was deselected during the previous E pulse.

**FIGURE 7 – CB2 DELAY TIME**
**(Write Mode; CRB-5 = 1, CRB-3 = CRB-4 = 0)**

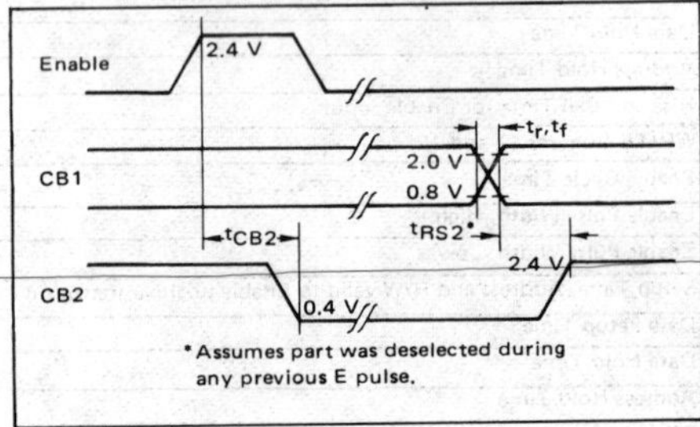


*Assumes part was deselected during any previous E pulse.

**FIGURE 8 – $\overline{IRQ}$ RELEASE TIME**

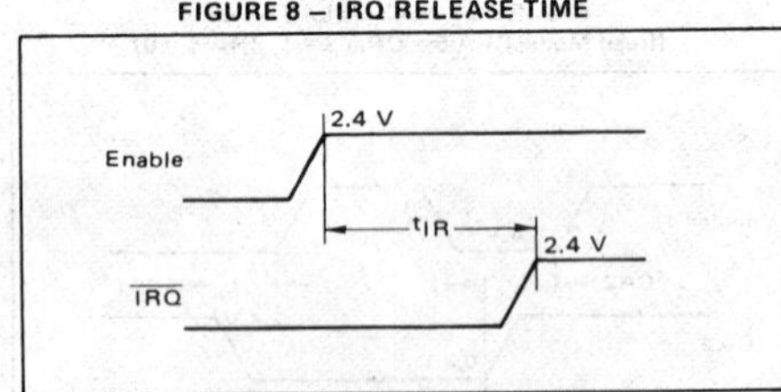


**FIGURE 9 – $\overline{RESET}$ LOW TIME**

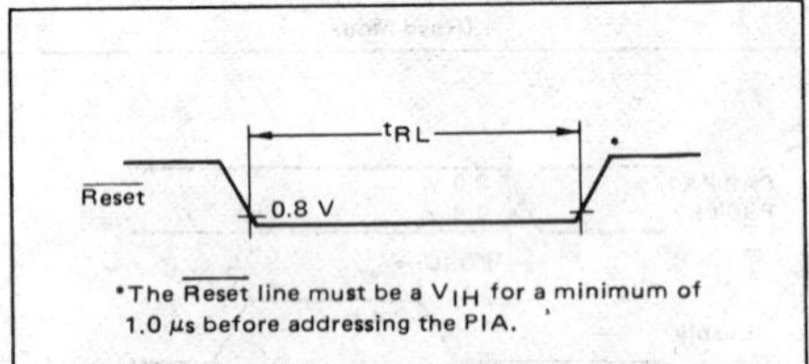


*The Reset line must be a $V_{IH}$ for a minimum of 1.0 μs before addressing the PIA.

**FIGURE 10 – BUS READ TIMING CHARACTERISTICS**
**(Read Information from PIA)**

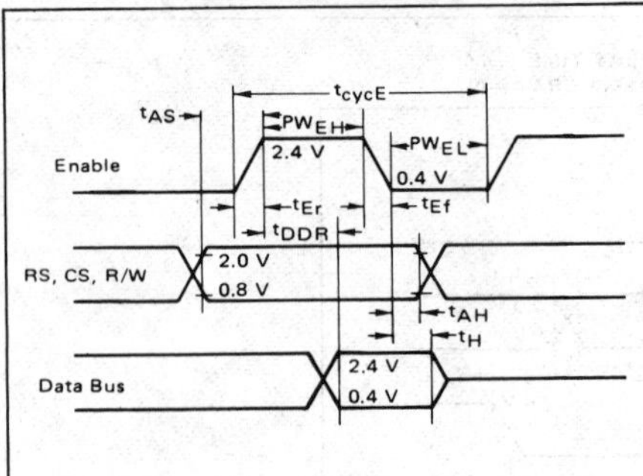


**FIGURE 11 – BUS WRITE TIMING CHARACTERISTICS**
**(Write Information into PIA)**

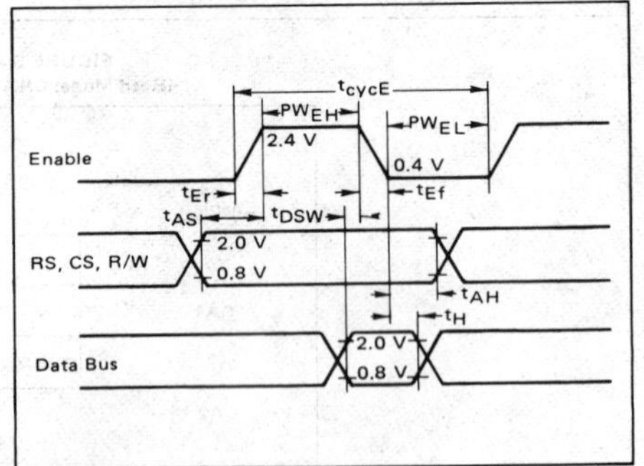

**MAXIMUM RATINGS**

| Rating | Symbol | Value | Unit |
|---|---|---|---|
| Supply Voltage | $V_{CC}$ | -0.3 to +7.0 | Vdc |
| Input Voltage | $V_{in}$ | -0.3 to +7.0 | Vdc |
| Operating Temperature Range | $T_A$ | 0 to +70 | °C |
| Storage Temperature Range | $T_{stg}$ | -55 to +150 | °C |
| Thermal Resistance | $\theta_{JA}$ | 82.5 | °C/W |

This device contains circuitry to protect the inputs against damage due to high static voltages or electric fields; however, it is advised that normal precautions be taken to avoid application of any voltage higher than maximum rated voltages to this high-impedance circuit.

**ELECTRICAL CHARACTERISTICS** ($V_{CC}$ = 5.0 V ±5%, $V_{SS}$ = 0, $T_A$ = 0 to 70°C unless otherwise noted.)

| Characteristic | | Symbol | Min | Typ | Max | Unit |
|---|---|---|---|---|---|---|
| Input High Voltage | | $V_{IH}$ | $V_{SS}$ + 2.0 | – | $V_{CC}$ | Vdc |
| Input Low Voltage | | $V_{IL}$ | $V_{SS}$ -0.3 | – | $V_{SS}$ + 0.8 | Vdc |
| Input Leakage Current ($V_{in}$ = 0 to 5.25 Vdc) | R/W,CS0,CS1,$\overline{CS2}$,Enable | $I_{in}$ | – | 1.0 | 2.5 | μAdc |
| Three-State (Off State) Input Current ($V_{in}$ = 0.4 to 2.4 Vdc) | D0-D7 | $I_{TSI}$ | – | 2.0 | 10 | μAdc |
| Output High Voltage | D0-D7 | $V_{OH}$ | | | | Vdc |
| ($I_{Load}$ = -205 μAdc, Enable Pulse Width <25 μs) | | | $V_{SS}$ + 2.4 | – | – | |
| ($I_{Load}$ = -100 μAdc, Enable Pulse Width <25 μs) | Tx Data, $\overline{RTS}$ | | $V_{SS}$ + 2.4 | – | – | |
| Output Low Voltage ($I_{Load}$ = 1.6 mAdc, Enable Pulse Width <25 μs) | | $V_{OL}$ | – | – | $V_{SS}$ + 0.4 | Vdc |
| Output Leakage Current (Off State) ($V_{OH}$ = 2.4 Vdc) | $\overline{IRQ}$ | $I_{LOH}$ | – | 1.0 | 10 | μAdc |
| Power Dissipation | | $P_D$ | – | 300 | 525 | mW |
| Input Capacitance | | $C_{in}$ | | | | pF |
| ($V_{in}$ = 0, $T_A$ = 25°C, f = 1.0 MHz) | D0-D7 | | – | 10 | 12.5 | |
| | E, Tx Clk, Rx Clk, R/W, RS, Rx Data, CS0, CS1, $\overline{CS2}$, $\overline{CTS}$, $\overline{DCD}$ | | – | 7.0 | 7.5 | |
| Output Capacitance | $\overline{RTS}$, Tx Data | $C_{out}$ | – | – | 10 | pF |
| ($V_{in}$ = 0, $T_A$ = 25°C, f = 1.0 MHz) | $\overline{IRQ}$ | | – | – | 5.0 | |
| Minimum Clock Pulse Width, Low (Figure 1) | ÷16, ÷64 Modes | $PW_{CL}$ | 600 | – | – | ns |
| Minimum Clock Pulse Width, High (Figure 2) | ÷16, ÷64 Modes | $PW_{CH}$ | 600 | – | – | ns |
| Clock Frequency | ÷1 Mode | $f_C$ | – | – | 500 | kHz |
| | ÷16, ÷64 Modes | | – | – | 800 | |
| Clock-to-Data Delay for Transmitter (Figure 3) | | $t_{TDD}$ | – | – | 1.0 | μs |
| Receive Data Setup Time (Figure 4) | ÷1 Mode | $t_{RDSU}$ | 500 | – | – | ns |
| Receive Data Hold Time (Figure 5) | ÷1 Mode | $t_{RDH}$ | 500 | – | – | ns |
| $\overline{\text{Interrupt Request}}$ Release Time (Figure 6) | | $t_{IR}$ | – | – | 1.2 | μs |
| $\overline{\text{Request-to-Send}}$ Delay Time (Figure 6) | | $t_{RTS}$ | – | – | 1.0 | μs |
| Input Transition Times (Except Enable) | | $t_r, t_f$ | – | – | 1.0* | μs |

*1.0 μs or 10% of the pulse width, whichever is smaller.

**BUS TIMING CHARACTERISTICS**

**READ** (Figures 7 and 9)

| Characteristic | Symbol | Min | Typ | Max | Unit |
|---|---|---|---|---|---|
| Enable Cycle Time | $t_{cycE}$ | 1.0 | – | – | μs |
| Enable Pulse Width, High | $PW_{EH}$ | 0.45 | – | 25 | μs |
| Enable Pulse Width, Low | $PW_{EL}$ | 0.43 | – | – | μs |
| Setup Time, Address and R/W valid to Enable positive transition | $t_{AS}$ | 160 | – | – | ns |
| Data Delay Time | $t_{DDR}$ | – | – | 320 | ns |
| Data Hold Time | $t_H$ | 10 | – | – | ns |
| Address Hold Time | $t_{AH}$ | 10 | – | – | ns |
| Rise and Fall Time for Enable input | $t_{Er}, t_{Ef}$ | – | – | 25 | ns |

**WRITE** (Figure 8 and 9)

| Characteristic | Symbol | Min | Typ | Max | Unit |
|---|---|---|---|---|---|
| Enable Cycle Time | $t_{cycE}$ | 1.0 | – | – | μs |
| Enable Pulse Width, High | $PW_{EH}$ | 0.45 | – | 25 | μs |
| Enable Pulse Width, Low | $PW_{EL}$ | 0.43 | – | – | μs |
| Setup Time, Address and R/W valid to Enable positive transition | $t_{AS}$ | 160 | – | – | ns |
| Data Setup Time | $t_{DSW}$ | 195 | – | – | ns |
| Data Hold Time | $t_H$ | 10 | – | – | ns |
| Address Hold Time | $t_{AH}$ | 10 | – | – | ns |
| Rise and Fall Time for Enable input | $t_{Er}, t_{Ef}$ | – | – | 25 | ns |

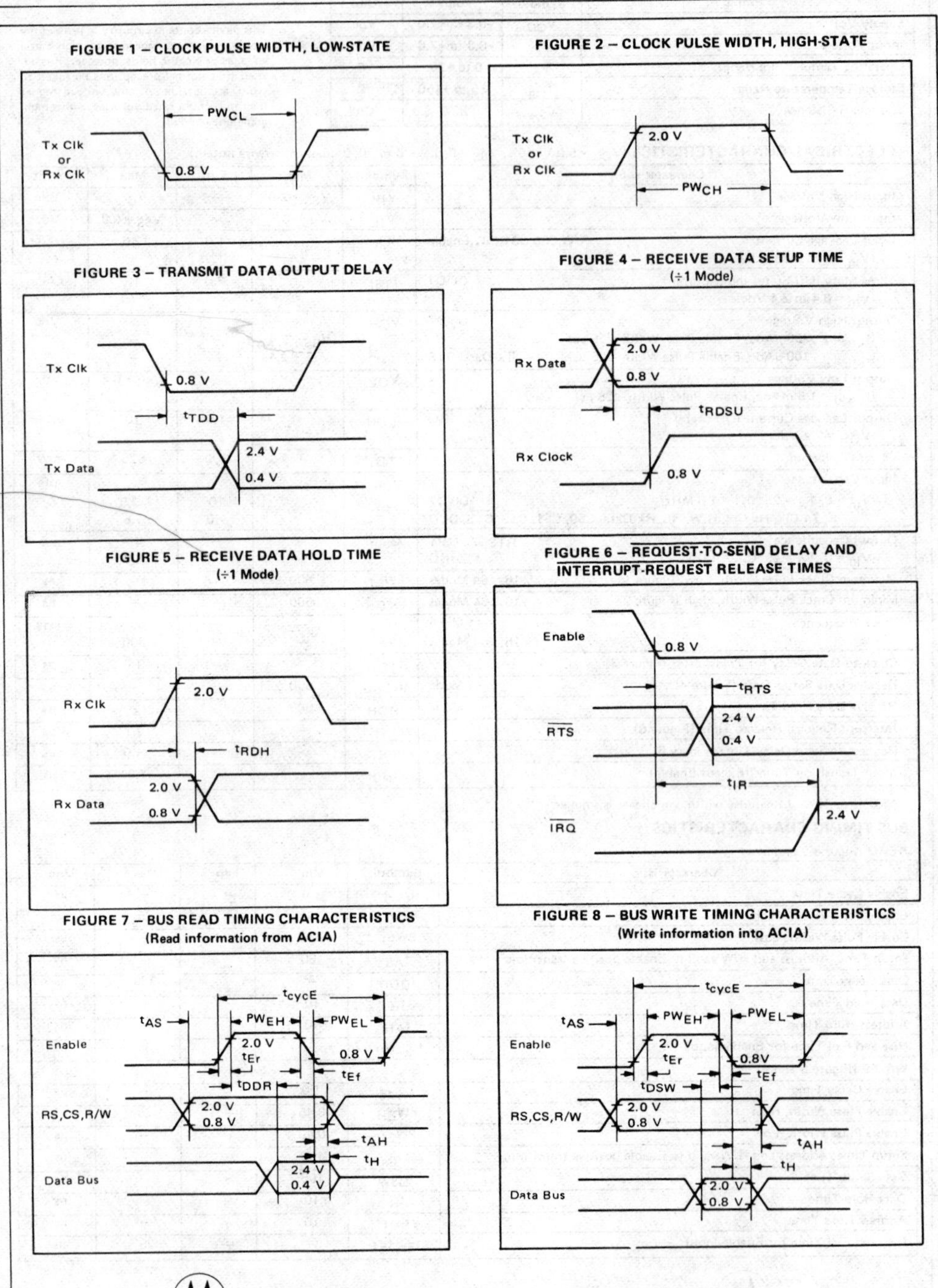

FIGURE 1 – CLOCK PULSE WIDTH, LOW-STATE
PWCL
Tx Clk or Rx Clk
0.8 V
FIGURE 2 – CLOCK PULSE WIDTH, HIGH-STATE
2.0 V
Tx Clk or Rx Clk
PWCH
FIGURE 3 – TRANSMIT DATA OUTPUT DELAY
Tx Clk
0.8 V
tTDD
2.4 V
Tx Data
0.4 V
FIGURE 4 – RECEIVE DATA SETUP TIME (÷1 Mode)
2.0 V
Rx Data
0.8 V
tRDSU
Rx Clock
0.8 V
FIGURE 5 – RECEIVE DATA HOLD TIME (÷1 Mode)
Rx Clk
2.0 V
tRDH
2.0 V
Rx Data
0.8 V
FIGURE 6 – REQUEST-TO-SEND DELAY AND INTERRUPT-REQUEST RELEASE TIMES
Enable
0.8 V
tRTS
2.4 V
RTS
0.4 V
tIR
2.4 V
IRQ
FIGURE 7 – BUS READ TIMING CHARACTERISTICS (Read information from ACIA)
tcycE
tAS
PWEH
PWEL
Enable
2.0 V
tEr
0.8 V
tEf
tDDR
RS,CS,R/W
2.0 V
0.8 V
tAH
tH
Data Bus
2.4 V
0.4 V
FIGURE 8 – BUS WRITE TIMING CHARACTERISTICS (Write information into ACIA)
tcycE
tAS
PWEH
PWEL
Enable
2.0 V
tEr
0.8V
tEf
tDSW
RS,CS,R/W
2.0 V
0.8 V
tAH
tH
Data Bus
2.0 V
0.8 V

## MAXIMUM RATINGS

| Rating | Symbol | Value | Unit |
|---|---|---|---|
| Supply Voltage | $V_{CC}$ | −0.3 to +7.0 | Vdc |
| Input Voltage | $V_{in}$ | −0.3 to +7.0 | Vdc |
| Operating Temperature Range − $T_L$ to $T_H$<br>MC6852, MC68A52, MC68B52<br>MC6852C, MC68A52C<br>MC6800BJCS, MC6852CJCS | $T_A$ | $T_L$ $T_H$<br>0 to +70<br>−40 to +85<br>−55 to +125 | °C |
| Storage Temperature Range | $T_{stg}$ | −55 to +150 | °C |
| Thermal Resistance<br>Plastic Package<br>Ceramic Package<br>Cerdip Package | $\theta_{JA}$ | <br>120<br>60<br>65 | °C/W |

This device contains circuitry to protect the inputs against damage due to high static voltages or electric fields; however, is is advised that normal precautions be taken to avoid application of any voltage higher than maximum rated voltages to this high-impedance circuit.

## ELECTRICAL CHARACTERISTICS ($V_{CC}$ = 5.0 V ±5%, $V_{SS}$ = 0, $T_A$ = $T_L$ to $T_H$ unless otherwise noted.)

| Characteristic | Symbol | Min | Typ | Max | Unit |
|---|---|---|---|---|---|
| Input High Voltage | $V_{IH}$ | $V_{SS}$ + 2.0 | – | – | Vdc |
| Input Low Voltage | $V_{IL}$ | – | – | $V_{SS}$ + 0.8 | Vdc |
| Input Leakage Current ($V_{in}$ = 0 to 5.25 Vdc) Tx Clk, Rx Clk, Rx Data, Enable, Reset, RS, R/W, CS, DCD, CTS | $I_{in}$ | – | 1.0 | 2.5 | μAdc |
| Three-State (Off State) Input Current ($V_{in}$ = 0.4 to 2.4 Vdc, $V_{CC}$ = 5.25 Vdc) D0–D7 | $I_{TSI}$ | – | 2.0 | 10 | μAdc |
| Output High Voltage<br>($I_{Load}$ = −205 μAdc, Enable Pulse Width < 25 μs) D0–D7<br>($I_{Load}$ = −100 μAdc, Enable Pulse Width < 25 μs) Tx Data, DTR, TUF | $V_{OH}$ | <br>$V_{SS}$ + 2.4<br>$V_{SS}$ + 2.4 | <br>–<br>– | <br>–<br>– | Vdc |
| Output Low Voltage ($I_{Load}$ = 1.6 mAdc, Enable Pulse Width < 25 μs) | $V_{OL}$ | – | – | $V_{SS}$ + 0.4 | Vdc |
| Output Leakage Current (Off State) ($V_{OH}$ = 2.4 Vdc) IRQ | $I_{LOH}$ | – | 1.0 | 10 | μAdc |
| Power Dissipation | $P_D$ | – | 300 | 525 | mW |
| Input Capacitance ($V_{in}$ = 0, $T_A$ = 25°C, f = 1.0 MHz)<br>D0–D7<br>All Other Inputs | $C_{in}$ | <br>–<br>– | <br>–<br>– | <br>12.5<br>7.5 | pF |
| Output Capacitance ($V_{in}$ = 0, $T_A$ = 25°C, f = 1.0 MHz)<br>Tx Data, SM/DTR, TUF<br>IRQ | $C_{out}$ | – | – | <br>10<br>5.0 | pF |

## ELECTRICAL CHARACTERISTICS ($V_{CC}$ = 5.0 V ± 5%, $V_{SS}$ = 0, $T_A$ = $T_L$ to $T_H$ unless otherwise noted.)

| Characteristic | Symbol | MC6852 | | MC68A52 | | MC68B52 | | Unit |
|---|---|---|---|---|---|---|---|---|
| | | Min | Max | Min | Max | Min | Max | |
| Minimum Clock Pulse Width, Low (Figure 1) | $PW_{CL}$ | 700 | – | 400 | – | 280 | – | ns |
| Minimum Clock Pulse Width, High (Figure 2) | $PW_{CH}$ | 700 | – | 400 | – | 280 | – | ns |
| Clock Frequency | $f_C$ | – | 600 | – | 1000 | – | 1500 | kHz |
| Receive Data Setup Time (Figure 3, 7) | $t_{RDSU}$ | 350 | – | 200 | – | 160 | – | ns |
| Receive Data Hold Time (Figure 3) | $t_{RDH}$ | 350 | – | 200 | – | 160 | – | ns |
| Sync Match Delay Time (Figure 3) | $t_{SM}$ | – | 1.0 | – | 0.666 | – | 0.500 | μs |
| Clock-to-Data Delay for Transmitter (Figure 4) | $t_{TDD}$ | – | 1.0 | – | 0.666 | – | 0.500 | μs |
| Transmitter Underflow (Figure 4, 6) | $t_{TUF}$ | – | 1.0 | – | 0.666 | – | 0.500 | μs |
| DTR Delay Time (Figure 5) | $t_{DTR}$ | – | 1.0 | – | 0.666 | – | 0.500 | μs |
| Interrupt Request Release Time (Figure 5) | $t_{IR}$ | – | 1.6 | – | 1.1 | – | 0.850 | μs |
| Reset Minimum Pulse Width | $t_{Res}$ | 1.0 | – | 0.666 | – | 0.500 | – | μs |
| CTS Setup Time (Figure 6) | $t_{CTS}$ | 200 | – | 150 | – | 120 | – | ns |
| DCD Setup Time (Figure 7) | $t_{DCD}$ | 500 | – | 350 | – | 250 | – | ns |
| Input Rise and Fall Times (except Enable) (0.8 V to 2.0 V) | $t_r$, $t_f$ | – | 1.0* | – | 1.0* | – | 1.0* | μs |

*1.0 μs or 10% of the pulse width, whichever is smaller

**FIGURE 1 – CLOCK PULSE WIDTH, LOW-STATE**

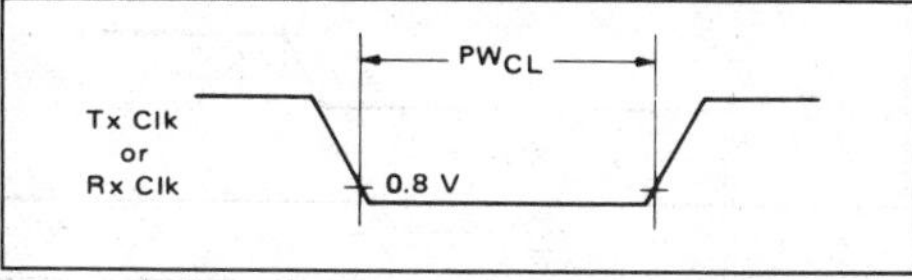


**FIGURE 2 – CLOCK PULSE WIDTH, HIGH-STATE**

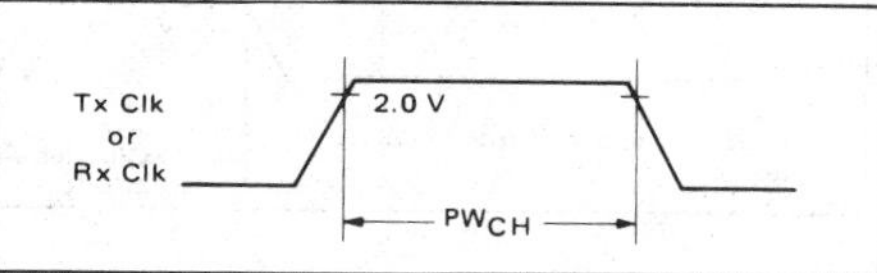

## BUS TIMING CHARACTERISTICS

| Characteristic | Symbol | MC6852 Min | MC6852 Max | MC68A52 Min | MC68A52 Max | MC68B52 Min | MC68B52 Max | Unit |
|---|---|---|---|---|---|---|---|---|
| Enable Cycle Time | $t_{cycE}$ | 1.0 | – | 0.666 | – | 0.5 | – | μs |
| Enable Pulse Width, High | $PW_{EH}$ | 0.45 | 25 | 0.28 | 25 | 0.22 | 25 | μs |
| Enable Pulse Width, Low | $PW_{EL}$ | 0.43 | – | 0.28 | – | 0.21 | – | μs |
| Setup Time, Address and R/$\overline{W}$ valid to Enable positive transition | $t_{AS}$ | 160 | – | 140 | – | 70 | – | ns |
| Data Delay Time | $t_{DDR}$ | – | 320 | – | 220 | – | 180 | ns |
| Data Hold Time | $t_H$ | 10 | – | 10 | – | 10 | – | ns |
| Address, $\overline{CS}$, R/$\overline{W}$ Hold Time | $t_{AH}$ | 10 | 100 | 10 | 100 | 10 | 100 | ns |
| Rise and Fall Time for Enable input | $t_{Er}, t_{Ef}$ | – | 25 | – | 25 | – | 25 | ns |
| **WRITE (Figures 9 and 10)** | | | | | | | | |
| Enable Cycle Time | $t_{cycE}$ | 1.0 | – | 0.666 | – | 0.5 | – | μs |
| Enable Pulse Width, High | $PW_{EH}$ | 0.45 | 25 | 0.28 | 25 | 0.22 | 25 | μs |
| Enable Pulse Width, Low | $PW_{EL}$ | 0.43 | – | 0.28 | – | 0.21 | – | μs |
| Setup Time, Address and R/$\overline{W}$ valid to Enable positive transition | $t_{AS}$ | 160 | – | 140 | – | 70 | – | ns |
| Data Setup Time | $t_{DSW}$ | 195 | – | 80 | – | 60 | – | ns |
| Data Hold Time | $t_H$ | 10 | – | 10 | – | 10 | – | ns |
| Address, $\overline{CS}$, R/$\overline{W}$ Hold Time | $t_{AH}$ | 10 | 100 | 10 | 100 | 10 | 100 | ns |
| Rise and Fall Time for Enable input | $t_{Er}, t_{Ef}$ | – | 25 | – | 25 | – | 25 | ns |

**FIGURE 3 – RECEIVE DATA SETUP AND HOLD TIMES AND SYNC MATCH DELAY TIME**

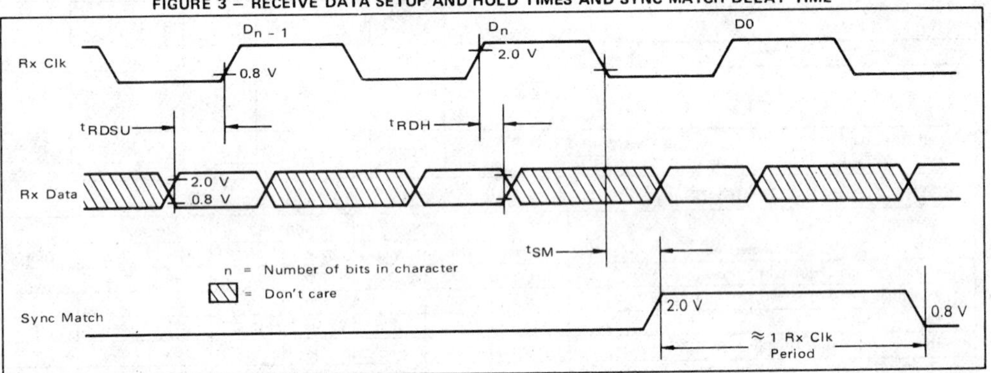


**FIGURE 4 – TRANSMIT DATA OUTPUT DELAY AND TRANSMITTER UNDERFLOW DELAY TIME**

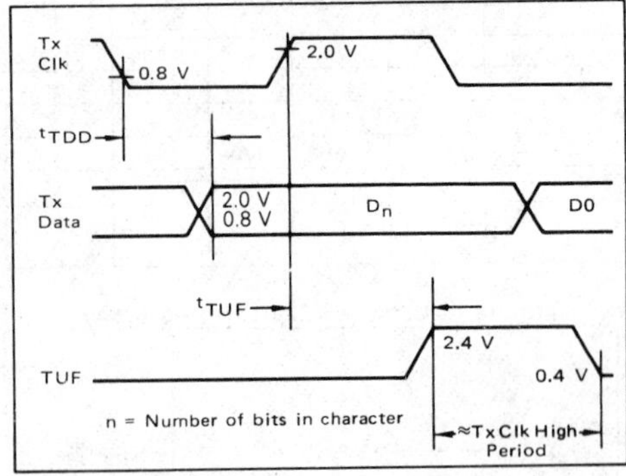


**FIGURE 5 – $\overline{\text{DATA TERMINAL READY}}$ AND $\overline{\text{INTERRUPT REQUEST}}$ RELEASE TIMES**

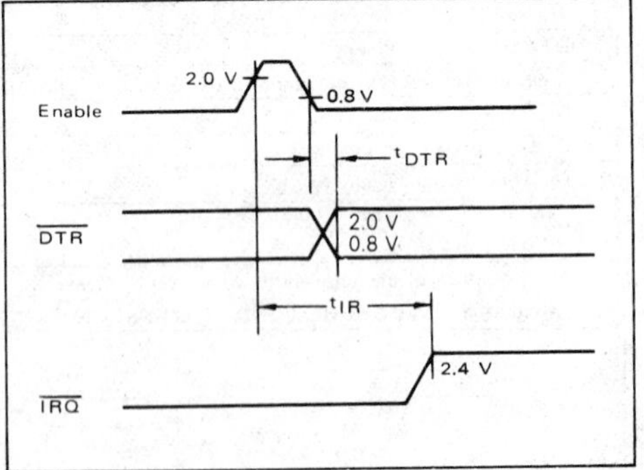

FIGURE 6 – $\overline{\text{CLEAR-TO-SEND}}$ SETUP TIME

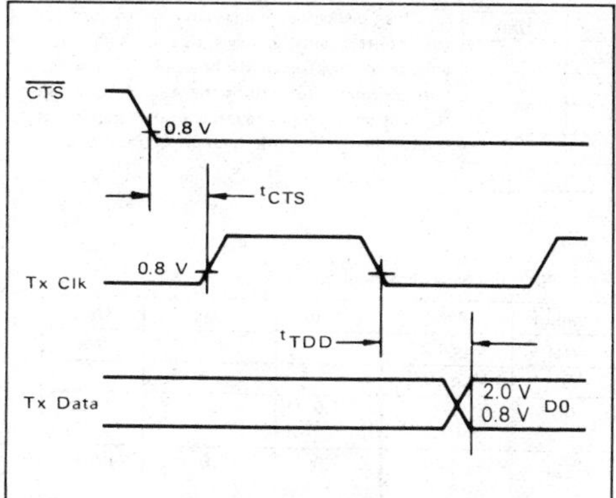


FIGURE 7 – $\overline{\text{DATA CARRIER DETECT}}$ SETUP TIME

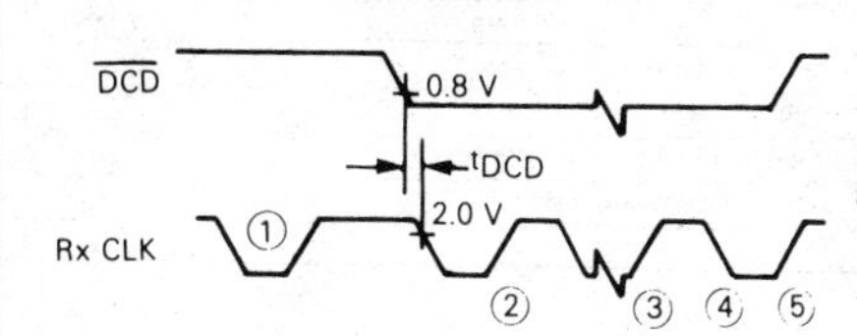


Notes:

1. Must occur before $\overline{\text{DCD}}$ goes low.
2. First data bit placed in Rx shift register.
3. Last data bit of byte placed in Rx shift register.
4. Rx data byte transferred from shift register to Rx FIFO.
5. Clock edge required for generation of $\overline{\text{IRQ}}$ by RDA status.

Note: refer to Figure 3 for the Rx data setup and hold times.

FIGURE 8 – BUS READ TIMING CHARACTERISTICS
(Read information from SSDA)

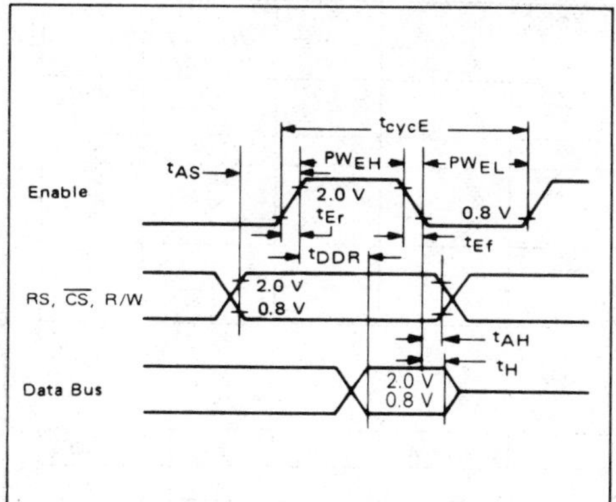


FIGURE 9 – BUS WRITE TIMING CHARACTERISTICS
(Write information into SSDA)

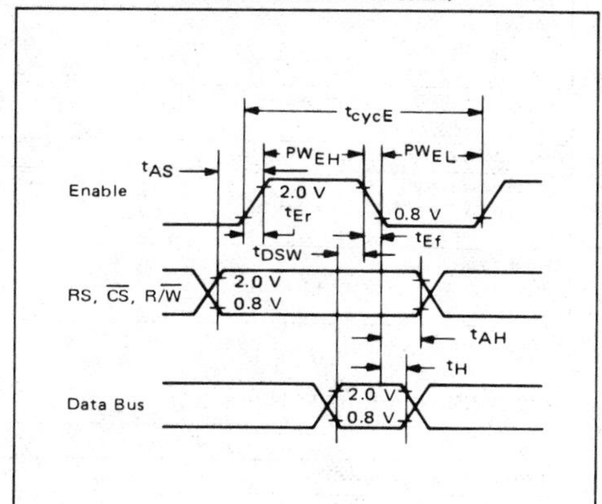


FIGURE 10 – BUS TIMING TEST LOADS

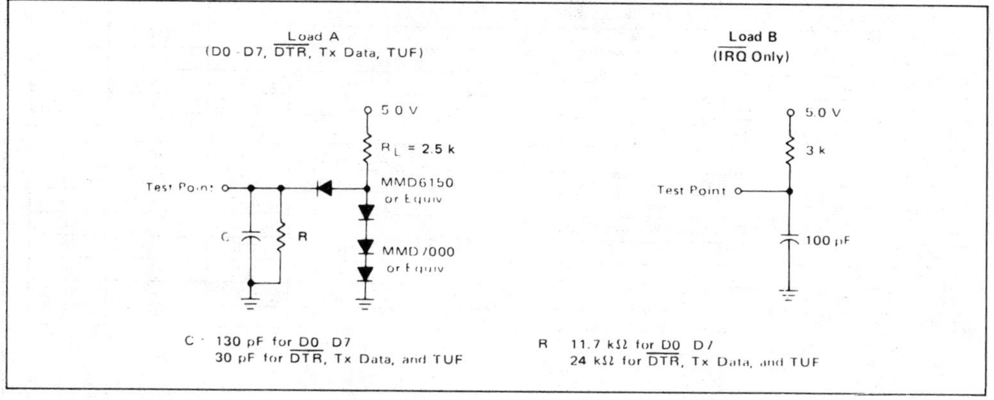

## MAXIMUM RATINGS

| Rating | Symbol | Value | Unit |
|---|---|---|---|
| Supply Voltage | $V_{CC}$ | -0.3 to +7.0 | Vdc |
| Input Voltage | $V_{in}$ | -0.3 to +7.0 | Vdc |
| Operating Temperature Range | $T_A$ | 0 to +70 | °C |
| Storage Temperature Range | $T_{stg}$ | -55 to +150 | °C |
| Thermal Resistance | $\theta_{JA}$ | 82.5 | °C/W |

This device contains circitry to protect the inputs against damage due to high static voltages or electric fields; however, it is advised that normal precautions be taken to avoid application of any voltage higher than maximum rated voltages to this high-impedance circuit.

## ELECTRICAL CHARACTERISTICS ($V_{CC}$ = 5.0 V ±5%, $V_{SS}$ = 0, $T_A$ = 0 to 70°C unless otherwise noted)

| Characteristic | | Symbol | Min | Typ | Max | Unit |
|---|---|---|---|---|---|---|
| Input High Voltage | | $V_{IH}$ | $V_{SS}$ +2.0 | – | $V_{CC}$ | Vdc |
| Input Low Voltage | | $V_{IL}$ | $V_{SS}$ -0.3 | – | $V_{SS}$ +0.8 | |
| Input Leakage Current ($V_{in}$ = 0 to 5.25 V) | | $I_{in}$ | – | 1.0 | 2.5 | μAdc |
| Three-State (Off State) Input Current ($V_{in}$ = 0.4 to 2.4 V) | D0–D7 | $I_{TSI}$ | – | 2.0 | 10 | μAdc |
| Output High Voltage | | $V_{OH}$ | | | | Vdc |
| ($I_{load}$ = -205 μA) | D0–D7 | | $V_{SS}$ +2.4 | – | – | |
| ($I_{load}$ = -200 μA) | Other Outputs | | $V_{SS}$ +2.4 | – | – | |
| Output Low Voltage | | $V_{OL}$ | | | | Vdc |
| ($I_{load}$ = 1.6 mA) | D0–D7 | | – | – | $V_{SS}$ +0.4 | |
| ($I_{load}$ = 3.2 mA) | O1–O3, $\overline{IRQ}$ | | – | – | $V_{SS}$ +0.4 | |
| Output Leakage Current (Off State) ($V_{OH}$ = 2.4 Vdc) | $\overline{IRQ}$ | $I_{LOH}$ | – | 1.0 | 10 | μAdc |
| Power Dissipation | | $P_D$ | – | – | 550 | mW |
| Input Capacitance | | $C_{in}$ | | | | pF |
| ($V_{in}$ = 0, $T_A$ = 25°C, f = 1.0 MHz) | D0–D7 | | – | – | 12.5 | |
| | All others | | – | – | 7.5 | |
| Output Capacitance | | $C_{out}$ | | | | pF |
| ($V_{in}$ = 0, $T_A$ = 25°C, f = 1.0 MHz) | $\overline{IRQ}$ | | – | – | 5.0 | |
| | O1, O2, O3 | | – | – | 10 | |

## BUS TIMING CHARACTERISTICS

| Characteristic | Symbol | Min | Max | Unit |
|---|---|---|---|---|
| **READ (See Figures 2 and 8)** | | | | |
| Enable Cycle Time | $t_{cycE}$ | 1.0 | 10 | μs |
| Enable Pulse Width, High | $PW_{EH}$ | 0.45 | 4.5 | μs |
| Enable Pulse Width, Low | $PW_{EL}$ | 0.43 | – | μs |
| Setup Time, Address and R/$\overline{W}$ valid to enable positive transition | $t_{AS}$ | 160 | – | ns |
| Data Delay Time | $t_{DDR}$ | – | 320 | ns |
| Data Hold Time | $t_H$ | 10 | – | ns |
| Address Hold Time | $t_{AH}$ | 10 | – | ns |
| Rise and Fall Time for Enable input | $t_{Er}, t_{Ef}$ | – | 25 | ns |
| **WRITE (See Figures 3 and 8)** | | | | |
| Enable Cycle Time | $t_{cycE}$ | 1.0 | 10 | μs |
| Enable Pulse Width, High | $PW_{EH}$ | 0.45 | 4.5 | μs |
| Enable Pulse Width, Low | $PW_{EL}$ | 0.43 | – | μs |
| Setup Time, Address and R/$\overline{W}$ valid to enable positive transition | $t_{AS}$ | 160 | – | ns |
| Data Setup Time | $t_{DSW}$ | 195 | – | ns |
| Data Hold Time | $t_H$ | 10 | – | ns |
| Address Hold Time | $t_{AH}$ | 10 | – | ns |
| Rise and Fall Time for Enable input | $t_{Er}, t_{Ef}$ | – | 25 | ns |

## AC OPERATING CHARACTERISTICS

| Characteristic | | Symbol | Min | Max | Unit |
|---|---|---|---|---|---|
| Input Rise and Fall Times | $\overline{C}$, $\overline{G}$ and $\overline{Reset}$ | $t_r, t_f$ | – | 1.0* | μs |
| Input Pulse Width Low (Figure 4) | $\overline{C}$, $\overline{G}$ and $\overline{Reset}$ | $PW_L$ | $t_{cycE} + t_{su} + t_{hd}$ | – | ns |
| Input Pulse Width High (Figure 5) | $\overline{C}$, $\overline{G}$ | $PW_H$ | $t_{cycE} + t_{su} + t_{hd}$ | – | ns |
| Input Setup Time (Figure 6)<br>(Synchronous Mode) | $\overline{C}$, $\overline{G}$ and $\overline{Reset}$<br>$\overline{C3}$ (÷8 Prescaler Mode only) | $t_{su}$ | 200<br>– | –<br>– | ns |
| Input Hold Time (Figure 6)<br>(Synchronous Mode) | $\overline{C}$, $\overline{G}$ and $\overline{Reset}$<br>$\overline{C3}$ (÷8 Prescaler Mode only) | $t_{hd}$ | 50<br>– | –<br>– | ns |
| Output Delay, O1–O3 (Figure 7)<br>($V_{OH}$ = 2.4 V, Load A)<br>($V_{OH}$ = 2.4 V, Load C)<br>($V_{OH}$ = 0.7 $V_{DD}$, Load C) | <br>TTL<br>MOS<br>CMOS | <br>$t_{co}$<br>$t_{cm}$<br>$t_{cmos}$ | <br>–<br>–<br>– | <br>700<br>450<br>2.0 | <br>ns<br>ns<br>μs |
| Interrupt Release Time | | $t_{IR}$ | – | 1.6 | μs |

*$t_r$ and $t_f$ ≤ 1 x Pulse Width or 1.0 μs, whichever is smaller.

**FIGURE 2 – BUS READ TIMING CHARACTERISTICS**
**(Read Information from PTM)**

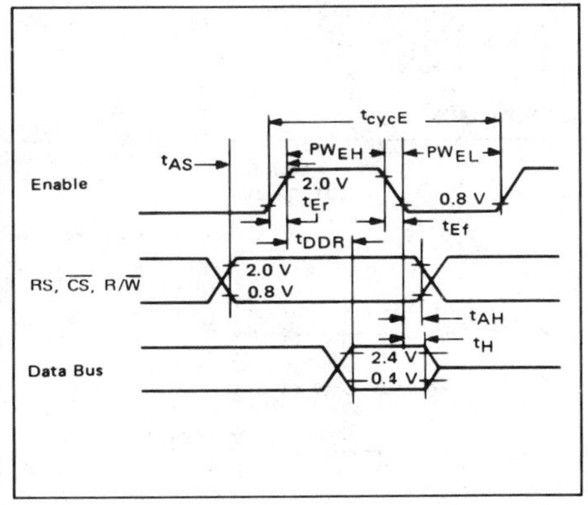


**FIGURE 3 – BUS WRITE TIMING CHARACTERISTICS**
**(Write Information into PTM)**

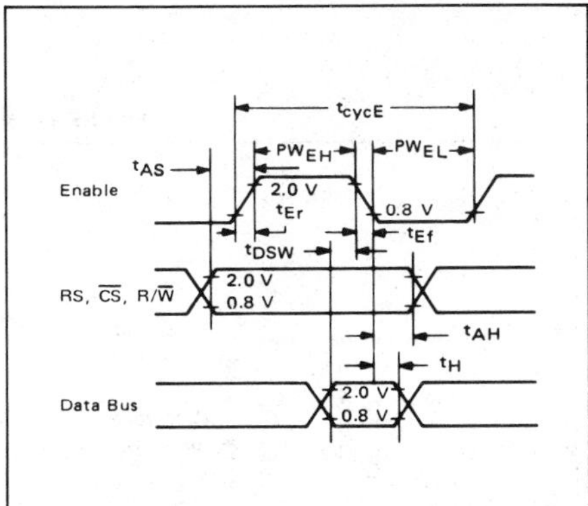


**FIGURE 4 – INPUT PULSE WIDTH LOW**

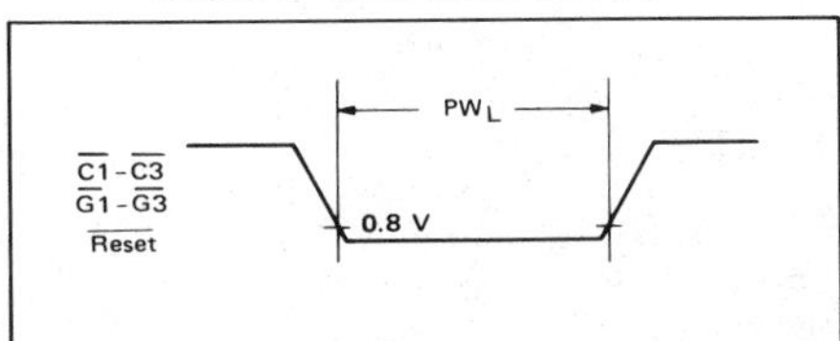


**FIGURE 5 – INPUT PULSE WIDTH HIGH**

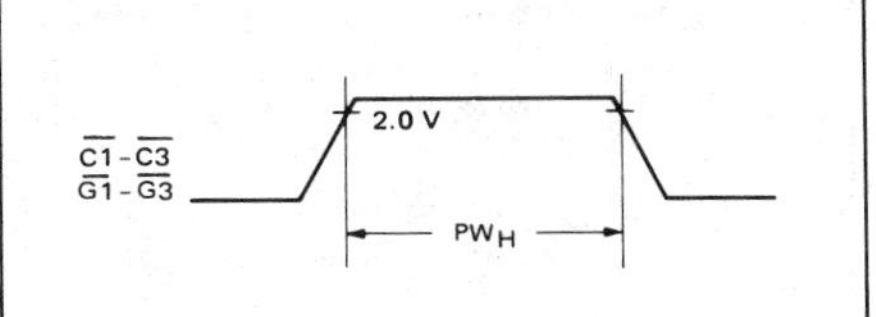

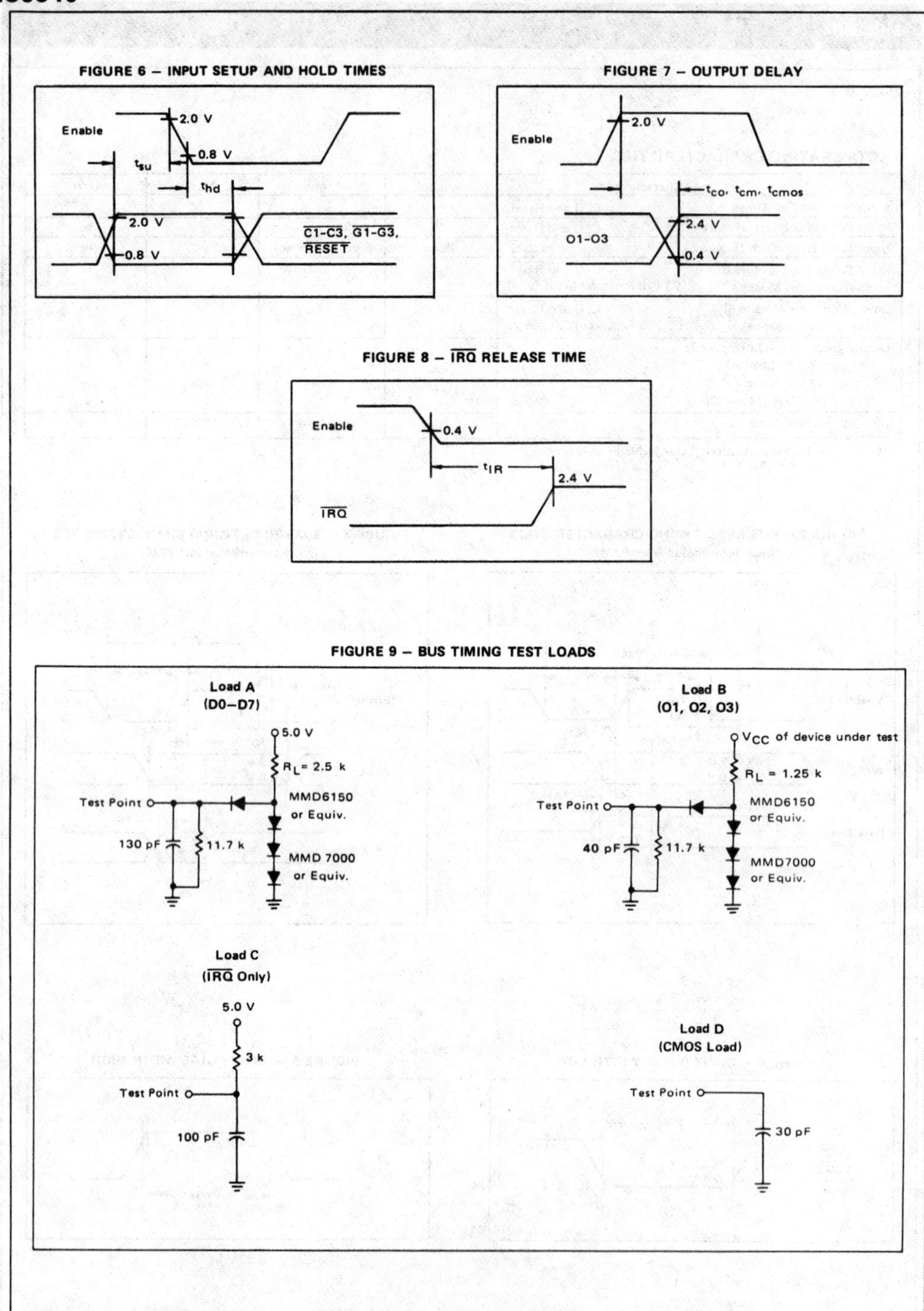

FIGURE 6 – INPUT SETUP AND HOLD TIMES
Enable
2.0 V
0.8 V
tsu
thd
2.0 V
0.8 V
C1-C3, G1-G3, RESET
FIGURE 7 – OUTPUT DELAY
Enable
2.0 V
tco, tcm, tcmos
2.4 V
O1-O3
0.4 V
FIGURE 8 – IRQ RELEASE TIME
Enable
0.4 V
tIR
2.4 V
IRQ
FIGURE 9 – BUS TIMING TEST LOADS
Load A
(D0–D7)
5.0 V
RL = 2.5 k
Test Point
MMD6150
or Equiv.
130 pF
11.7 k
MMD 7000
or Equiv.
Load B
(O1, O2, O3)
VCC of device under test
RL = 1.25 k
Test Point
MMD6150
or Equiv.
40 pF
11.7 k
MMD7000
or Equiv.
Load C
(IRQ Only)
5.0 V
3 k
Test Point
100 pF
Load D
(CMOS Load)
Test Point
30 pF

## MAXIMUM RATINGS

| Rating | Symbol | Value | Unit |
|---|---|---|---|
| Supply Voltage | $V_{CC}$* | -0.3 to +7.0 | Vdc |
| Input Voltage | $V_{in}$* | -0.3 to +7.0 | Vdc |
| Operating Temperature Range | $T_A$ | 0 to +70 | °C |
| Storage Temperature Range | $T_{stg}$ | -55 to +150 | °C |
| Thermal Resistance | $R_{\theta JA}$ | 82.5 | °C/W |

* In respect to $V_{ss}$.

Permanent device damage may occur if ABSOLUTE MAXIMUM RATINGS are exceeded. Functional operation should be restricted to RECOMMENDED OPERATING CONDITIONS. Exposure to higher than recommended voltages for extended periods of time could affect device reliability.

## RECOMMENDED OPERATING CONDITIONS

| Rating | Symbol | Value | Unit |
|---|---|---|---|
| Power Supply Voltage | $V_{CC}$ | +4.75 to +5.25 | Vdc |
| Input Voltage | $V_{IL}$<br>$V_{IH}$ | -0.3 to +0.8<br>2.0 to $V_{CC}$ | Vdc |
| Operating Ambient Temperature Range | $T_A$ | 0 to +70 | °C |

## ELECTRICAL CHARACTERISTICS ($V_{CC}$ = 5.0 V ±5%, $V_{SS}$ = 0, $T_A$ = -20 to +75°C unless otherwise noted)

| Characteristic | | Symbol | Min | Typ | Max | Unit |
|---|---|---|---|---|---|---|
| Input High Voltage | | $V_{IH}$ | $V_{SS}$+2.0 | – | $V_{CC}$ | Vdc |
| Input Low Voltage | | $V_{IL}$ | $V_{SS}$-0.3 | – | $V_{SS}$+0.8 | Vdc |
| Input Leakage Current ($V_{in}$ = 0 to 5.25 V) | TxRQ0-3,φ2 DMA, $\overline{RES}$, DGRNT | $I_{in}$ | – | – | 2.5 | μAdc |
| Three-State Leakage Current ($V_{in}$ = 0.4 to 2.4 V) | A0-A15, R/$\overline{W}$<br>D0-D7 | $I_{TSI}$ | -10 | – | 10 | μAdc |
| Output High Voltage<br>($I_{Load}$ = -205 μAdc)<br>($I_{Load}$ = -145 μAdc)<br>($I_{Load}$ = -100 μAdc) | <br>D0-D7<br>A0-15, R/$\overline{W}$<br>All Others | $V_{OH}$ | <br>$V_{SS}$+2.4<br>$V_{SS}$+2.4<br>$V_{SS}$+2.4 | <br>–<br>–<br>– | <br>–<br>–<br>– | Vdc |
| Output Low Voltage ($I_{Load}$ = 1.6 mAdc) | | $V_{OL}$ | – | – | $V_{SS}$+0.4 | Vdc |
| Source Current ($V_{in}$ = 0 Vdc, Figure 10) | $\overline{CS}$/Tx AKB | $I_{CSS}$ | – | 10 | – | |
| Power Dissipation | | $P_D$ | – | 500 | – | mW |
| Capacitance ($V_{in}$ = 0, $T_A$ = 25°C, f = 1.0 MHz) | φ2 DMA<br>D0-D7, $\overline{CS}$, A0-A4, R/$\overline{W}$<br>All Others | $C_{in}$ | –<br>–<br>– | –<br>–<br>– | 20<br>12.5<br>10 | pF |
| | | $C_{out}$ | – | – | 12 | pF |

 **MOTOROLA** *Semiconductor Products Inc.*

**BUS TIMING CHARACTERISTICS** (Load Condition Figure 11)

| Characteristic | | Symbol | Min | Max | Unit |
|---|---|---|---|---|---|
| **READ TIMING (Figure 4)** | | | | | |
| Address Setup Time | A0-A4, R/$\overline{W}$, $\overline{CS}$ | $t_{AS}$ | 160 | – | ns |
| Address Input Hold Time | A0-A4, R/$\overline{W}$, $\overline{CS}$ | $t_{AHI}$ | 10 | – | ns |
| Data Delay Time | D0-D7 | $t_{DDR}$ | – | 320 | ns |
| Data Access Time | D0-D7 | $t_{ACC}$ | – | 480 | ns |
| Data Output Hold Time | D0-D7 | $t_{DHR}$ | 10 | – | ns |
| **WRITE TIMING (Figure 4)** | | | | | |
| Address Setup Time | A0-A4, R/$\overline{W}$, $\overline{CS}$ | $t_{AS}$ | 160 | – | ns |
| Address Input Hold Time | A0-A4, R/$\overline{W}$, $\overline{CS}$ | $t_{AHI}$ | 10 | – | ns |
| Data Setup Time | D0-D7 | $t_{DSW}$ | 195 | – | ns |
| Data Input Hold Time | D0-D7 | $t_{DHW}$ | 10 | – | ns |

**CLOCK TIMING**

| Characteristic | | Symbol | Min | Max | Unit |
|---|---|---|---|---|---|
| **φ2 DMA (See Figure 4)** | | | | | |
| Cycle Time | | $t_{cyc}$ | 1000 | – | ns |
| Pulse Width–High | | $PW_H$ | 450 | – | ns |
| Low | | $PW_L$ | 430 | – | |
| Rise and Fall Time | | $t_{\phi r}, t_{\phi f}$ | – | 25 | ns |
| **DMA TIMING (Load Condition Figure 11)** | | | | | |
| Tx RQ Setup Time (Figure 5) | | | | | ns |
| φ2 DMA Rising Edge | | $t_{TQS1}$ | 120 | – | |
| φ2 DMA Falling Edge | | $t_{TQS2}$ | 210 | – | |
| Tx RQ Hold Time (Figure 5) | | | | | ns |
| φ2 DMA Rising Edge | | $t_{TQH1}$ | 20 | – | |
| φ2 DMA Falling Edge | | $t_{TQS2}$ | 20 | – | |
| DGRNT Setup Time (Figure 6) | | $t_{DGS}$ | 155 | – | ns |
| DGRNT Hold Time (Figure 6) | | $t_{DGH}$ | 10 | – | ns |
| Address Output Delay Time (Figure 15) | A0-A15, R/$\overline{W}$, $\overline{Tx\ STB}$ | $t_{AD}$ | – | 270 | ns |
| Address Output Hold Time (Figure 15) | A0-15, R/$\overline{W}$ | $t_{AHO}$ | 30 | – | ns |
| | $\overline{Tx\ STB}$ | | 35 | – | |
| Address Three-State Delay Time (Figure 8) | A0-A15, R/$\overline{W}$ | $t_{ATSD}$ | – | 700 | ns |
| Address Three-State Recovery Time (Figure 8) | | $t_{ATSR}$ | – | 400 | ns |
| Delay Time (Figure 7) | $\overline{DRQH}$, $\overline{DRQT}$ | $t_{DQD}$ | – | 375 | ns |
| Tx AK Delay Time | | | | | ns |
| φ2 DMA Rising Edge (Figure 7) | | $t_{TKD1}$ | – | 400 | |
| DGRNT Rising Edge (Figure 10) | | $t_{TKD2}$ | – | 190 | |
| $\overline{IRQ}/\overline{DEND}$ Delay Time | | | | | ns |
| φ2 DMA Falling Edge (Figure 8) | | $t_{DED1}$ | – | 300 | |
| DGRNT Rising Edge (Figure 10) | | $t_{DED2}$ | – | 190 | |

FIGURE 4 – READ/$\overline{\text{WRITE}}$ OPERATION SEQUENCE

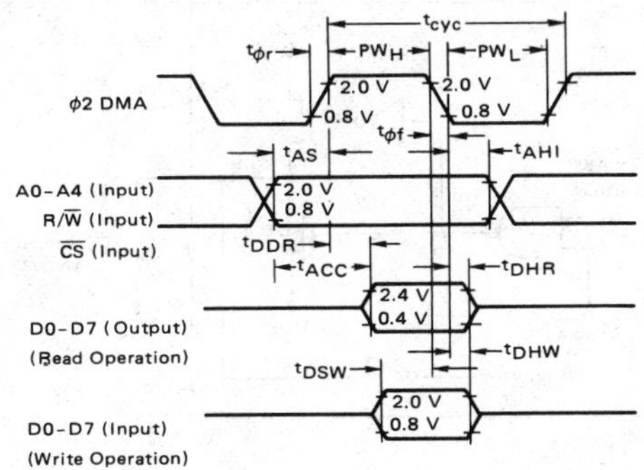


FIGURE 5 – Tx RQ INPUT TIMING

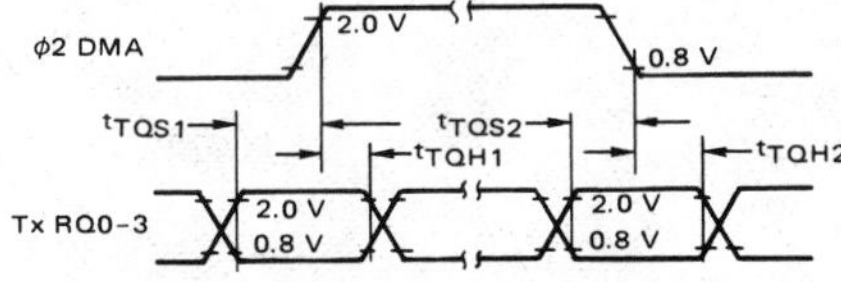


FIGURE 6 – DGRNT INPUT TIMING

Setup Timing

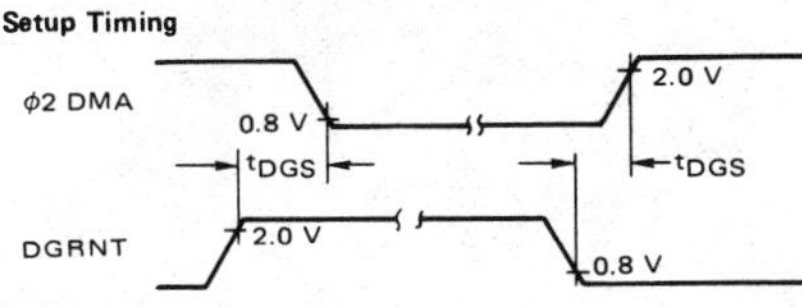


Hold Timing

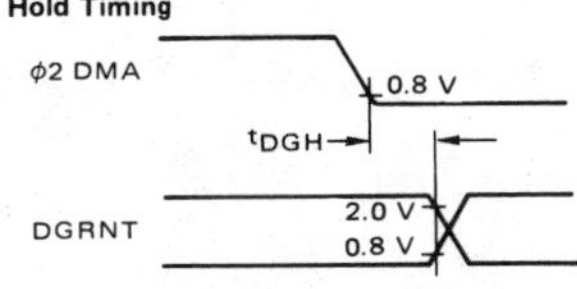


FIGURE 7 – $\overline{\text{DRQH}}$, $\overline{\text{DRQT}}$, Tx AK OUTPUT TIMING

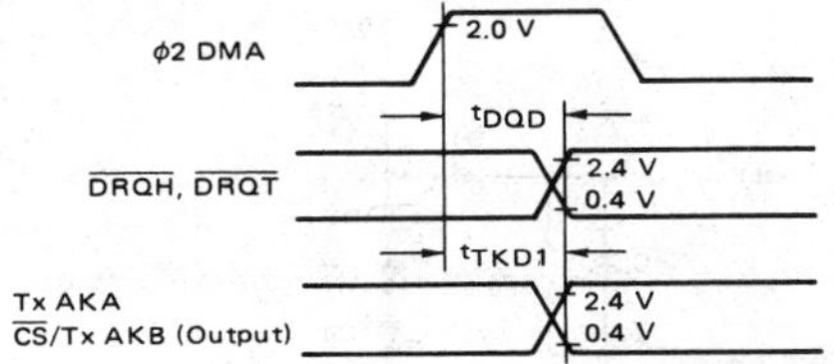


FIGURE 8 – ADDRESS, $\overline{\text{IRQ}}$/$\overline{\text{DEND}}$ OUTPUT TIMING

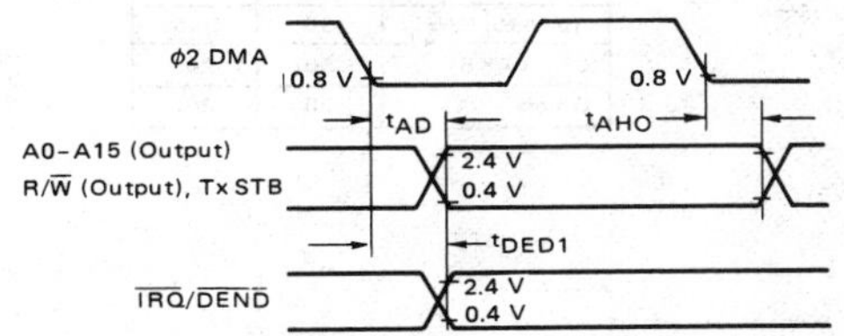


FIGURE 9 – ADDRESS THREE-STATE TIMING

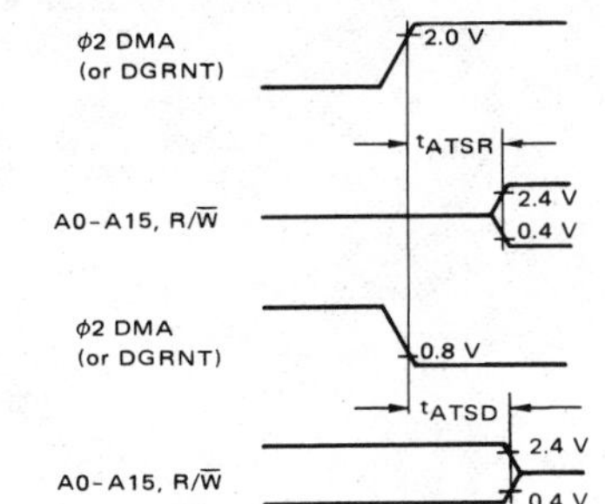


FIGURE 10 – Tx AKB, $\overline{\text{IRQ}}$/$\overline{\text{DEND}}$
OUTPUT TIMING FROM DGRNT INPUT

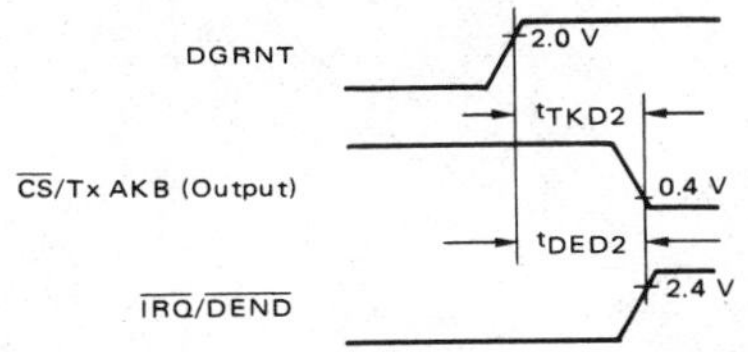

**FIGURE 11 – TEST LOADS**

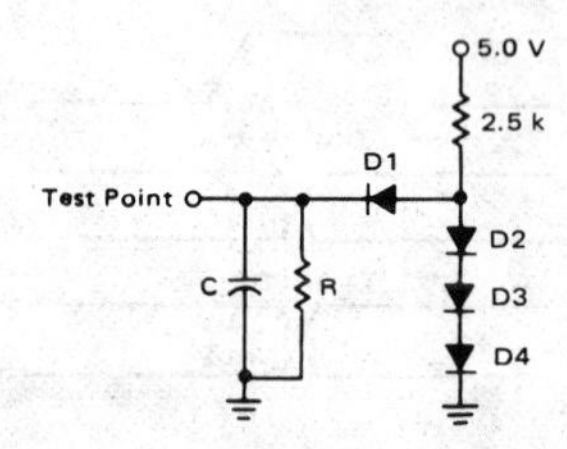


| Test Pin | C = pF | R = kΩ |
|---|---|---|
| D0–D7 | 130 | 11.7 |
| A0–A15, R/$\overline{W}$ | 90 | 16.5 |
| $\overline{CS}$/Tx AKB | 50 | 24 |
| Others | 30 | 24 |

**FIGURE 12 – $\overline{CS}$/Tx AKB SOURCE CURRENT TEST CIRCUIT**

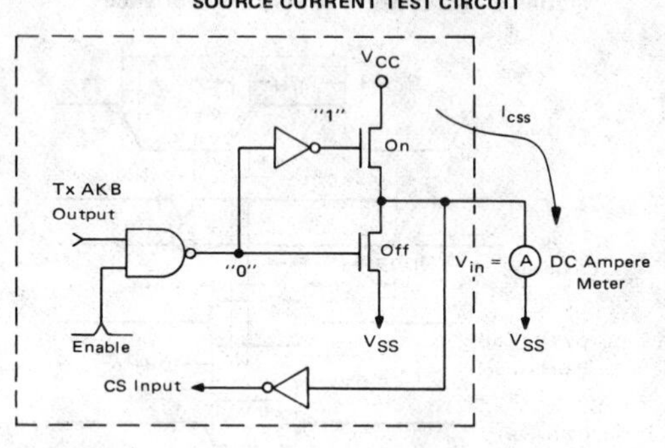

## MAXIMUM RATINGS

| Rating | Symbol | Value | Unit |
|---|---|---|---|
| Supply Voltage | $V_{CC}$ | -0.3 to +7.0 | Vdc |
| Input Voltage | $V_{in}$ | -0.3 to +7.0 | Vdc |
| Operating Temperature Range | $T_A$ | 0 to +70 | °C |
| Storage Temperature Range | $T_{stg}$ | -55 to +150 | °C |
| Thermal Resistance | $\theta_{JA}$ | 70 | °C/W |

This device contains circuitry to protect the inputs against damage due to high static voltages or electric fields; however, is is advised that normal precautions be taken to avoid application of any voltage higher than maximum rated voltages to this high-impedance circuit.

## ELECTRICAL CHARACTERISTICS ($V_{CC}$ = 5.0 V ± 5%, $V_{SS}$ = 0, $T_A$ = 0 to 70°C unless otherwise noted.)

| Characteristic | | Symbol | Min | Typ | Max | Unit |
|---|---|---|---|---|---|---|
| Input High Voltage | All Inputs | $V_{IH}$ | $V_{SS}$ + 2.0 | – | $V_{CC}$ | Vdc |
| Input Low Voltage | All Inputs | $V_{IL}$ | $V_{SS}$ – 0.3 | – | $V_{SS}$ + 0.8 | Vdc |
| Clock Overshoot/Undershoot – Input High Level | | $V_{OS}$ | $V_{CC}$ – 0.5 | – | $V_{CC}$ + 0.5 | Vdc |
| – Input Low Level | | | $V_{SS}$ – 0.5 | – | $V_{SS}$ + 0.5 | |
| Input Leakage Current ($V_{in}$ = 0 to 5.25 Vdc) | R/$\overline{W}$, $\overline{Reset}$, CS0, CS1, CP1, $\overline{CTG}$, $\overline{CTC}$, E, A0-A10 | $I_{in}$ | – | 1.0 | 2.5 | μAdc |
| Three-State (Off State) Input Current ($V_{in}$ 0.4 to 2.4 Vdc) | D0-D7, PP0-PP7, CP2 | $I_{TSI}$ | – | 2.0 | 10 | μAdc |
| Output High Voltage | | $V_{OH}$ | | | | Vdc |
| ($I_{Load}$ = -205 μAdc,) | D0-D7 | | $V_{SS}$ + 2.4 | – | – | |
| ($I_{Load}$ = -200 μAdc) | Other Outputs | | $V_{SS}$ + 2.4 | – | – | |
| Output Low Voltage | | $V_{OL}$ | | | | Vdc |
| ($I_{Load}$ = 1.6 mAdc) | D0-D7 | | – | – | $V_{SS}$ + 0.4 | |
| ($I_{Load}$ = 3.2 mAdc) | Other Outputs | | – | – | $V_{SS}$ + 0.4 | |
| Output High Current (Sourcing) | | $I_{OH}$ | | | | μAdc |
| ($V_{OH}$ = 2.4 Vdc) | D0-D7 | | -205 | – | – | |
| | Other Outputs | | -200 | – | – | |
| ($V_O$ = 1.5 Vdc, the current for driving other than TTL, e.g., Darlington Base) | CP2, PP0-PP7 | | -1.0 | – | -10 | mAdc |
| Output Low Current (Sinking) | | $I_{OL}$ | | | | mAdc |
| ($V_{OL}$ = 0.4 Vdc) | D0-D7 | | 1.6 | – | – | |
| | Other Outputs | | 3.2 | – | – | |
| Output Leakage Current (Off State) ($V_{OH}$ = 2.4 Vdc) | $\overline{IRQ}$ | $I_{LOH}$ | – | – | 10 | μAdc |
| Power Dissipation | | $P_D$ | – | – | 1000 | mW |
| Capacitance | | $C_{in}$ | – | – | 20 | pF |
| ($V_{in}$ = 0, $T_A$ = 25°C, f = 1.0 MHz) | D0-D7 | | – | – | 12.5 | |
| | PP0-PP7, CP2 | | – | – | 10 | |
| | A0-A10, R/$\overline{W}$, $\overline{Reset}$, CS0, CS1, CP1, $\overline{CTC}$, $\overline{CTG}$ | | – | – | 7.5 | |
| | $\overline{IRQ}$ | $C_{out}$ | | – | 5.0 | pF |
| | PP0-PP7, CP2, CTO | | | – | 10 | |
| Frequency of Operation | | f | 0.1 | – | 1.0 | MHz |
| Clock Timing | | | | | | |
| Cycle Time | | $t_{cycE}$ | 1.0 | – | – | μs |
| Reset Low Time | | $t_{RL}$ | 2 | – | – | μs |
| Interrupt Release | | $t_{IR}$ | – | – | 1.6 | μs |

**MOTOROLA** Semiconductor Products Inc.

**READ/WRITE TIMING** (Figures 3 and 4).

| Characteristic | Symbol | Min | Typ | Max | Unit |
|---|---|---|---|---|---|
| Enable Pulse Width, Low | $PW_{EL}$ | 430 | – | – | ns |
| Enable Pulse Width, High | $PW_{EH}$ | 430 | – | – | ns |
| Set Up Time (Address CS0, CS1, R/$\overline{W}$) | $t_{AS}$ | 160 | – | – | ns |
| Data Delay Time | $t_{DDR}$ | – | – | 320 | ns |
| Data Hold Time | $t_H$ | 10 | – | – | ns |
| Address Hold Time | $t_{AH}$ | 10 | – | – | ns |
| Rise and Fall Time | $t_{Ef}, t_{Er}$ | – | – | 25 | ns |
| Data Set Up Time | $t_{DSW}$ | 195 | – | – | ns |

**BUS TIMING**

Peripheral I/O Lines

| Characteristic | Symbol | Min | Typ | Max | Unit |
|---|---|---|---|---|---|
| Peripheral Data Setup | $t_{PDSU}$ | 200 | – | – | ns |
| Rise and Fall Times CP1, CP2 | $t_{Pr}, t_{Pc}$ | – | – | 1.0 | μs |
| Delay Time E to CP2 Fall | $t_{CP2}$ | – | – | 1.0 | μs |
| Delay Tme I/O Data CP2 Fall | $t_{DC}$ | 20 | – | – | ns |
| Delay Time E to CP2 Rise | $t_{RS1}$ | – | – | 1.0 | μs |
| Delay Time CP1 to CP2 Rise | $t_{RS2}$ | – | – | 2.0 | μs |
| Peripheral Data Delay | $t_{PDW}$ | – | – | 1.0 | μs |
| Peripheral Data Setup Time for Latch | $t_{PSU}$ | 100 | – | – | ns |
| Peripheral Data Hold Time for Latch | $t_{PDH}$ | 15 | – | – | ns |

**Timer-Counter Lines**

| Characteristic | | Symbol | Min | Typ | Max | Unit |
|---|---|---|---|---|---|---|
| Input Rise and Fall Time | CTC and CTG | $t_{CR}, t_{CF}$ | – | – | 100 | ns |
| Input Pulse Width High (Asynchronous Mode) | | $t_{PWH}$ | $t_{cyc}$ + 250 | – | – | ns |
| Input Pulse Width Low (Asychronous Mode) | | $t_{PWL}$ | $t_{cyc}$ + 250 | – | – | ns |
| Input Setup Time (Synchronous Mode) | | $t_{su}$ | 200 | – | – | ns |
| Input Hold Time (Synchronous Mode) | | $t_{hd}$ | 50 | – | – | ns |
| Output Delay | | $t_{CTO}$ | – | – | 1.0 | μs |

**FIGURE 3 – BUS READ TIMING**
**Read Information from MC6846)**

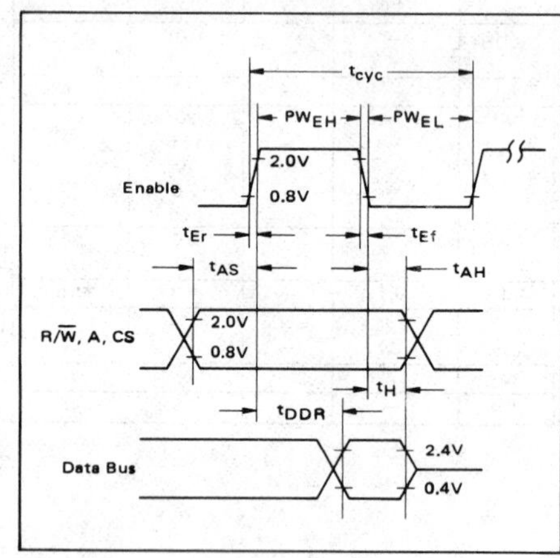


**FIGURE 4 – BUS WRITE TIMING**
**(Write Information from MPU)**

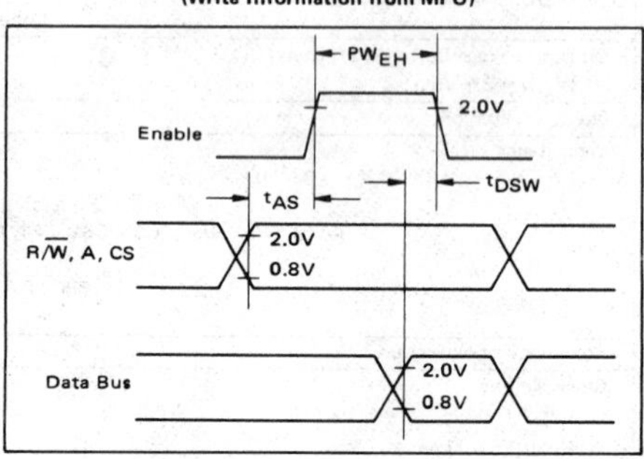


**FIGURE 5 – PERIPHERAL PORT LATCH SETUP AND HOLD TIME**

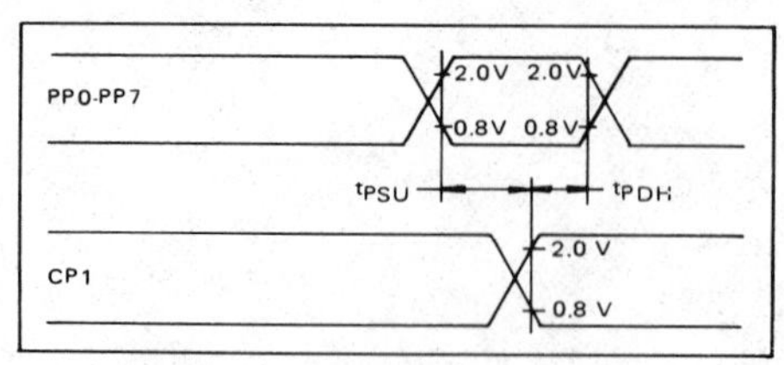

## MAXIMUM RATINGS

| Rating | Symbol | Value | Unit |
|---|---|---|---|
| Supply Voltage | $V_{CC}$ | −0.3 to +7.0 | Vdc |
| Input Voltage | $V_{in}$ | −0.3 to +7.0 | Vdc |
| Operating Temperature Range | $T_A$ | 0 to 70 | °C |
| Storage Temperature Range | $T_{stg}$ | −55 to +150 | °C |

This device contains circuitry to protect the inputs against damage due to high static voltages or electric fields; however, it is advised that normal precautions be taken to avoid application of any voltage higher than maximum rated voltages to this high-impedance circuit. For proper operation it is recommended that $V_{in}$ and $V_{out}$ be constrained to the range $V_{SS} \leq (V_{in}$ or $V_{out}) \leq V_{CC}$

## THERMAL CHARACTERISTICS

| Characteristic | Symbol | Value | Rating |
|---|---|---|---|
| Thermal Resistance<br>Plastic Package<br>Ceramic Package | $\theta_{JA}$ | <br>100<br>50 | °C/W |

## ELECTRICAL CHARACTERISTICS ($V_{CC}$ = 5.0 V ±5%, $V_{CC}$ = 0, $T_A$ = 70°C unless otherwise noted)

| Characteristic | | Symbol | Min | Typ | Max | Unit |
|---|---|---|---|---|---|---|
| Input High Voltage | $\overline{RESET}$<br>Other Inputs* | $V_{IH}$ | $V_{SS}$+4.0<br>$V_{SS}$+2.0 | –<br>– | $V_{CC}$<br>$V_{CC}$ | Vdc |
| Input Low Voltage | All Inputs* | $V_{IL}$ | $V_{SS}$−0.3 | – | $V_{SS}$+0.8 | Vdc |
| Input Load Current<br>($V_{in}$ = 0 to 2.4 Vdc) | Port 4<br>SC1 | $I_{in}$ | –<br>– | –<br>– | 0.5<br>0.8 | mAdc |
| Input Leakage Current<br>($V_{in}$ = 0 to 5.25 Vdc) | $\overline{NMI}$, $\overline{IRQ1}$, $\overline{RESET}$ | $I_{in}$ | – | 1.5 | 2.5 | μA |
| Three-State (Off State) Input Current<br>($V_{in}$ = 0.5 to 2.4 Vdc) | P10-P17, P30-P37<br>P20-P24 | $I_{TSI}$ | –<br>– | 2.0<br>10.0 | 10<br>100 | μA |
| Output High Voltage<br>($I_{load}$ = −205 μAdc, $V_{CC}$ = min)<br>($I_{load}$ = −145 μAdc, $V_{CC}$ = min)<br>($I_{load}$ = −100 μAdc, $V_{CC}$ = min) | <br>P30-P37<br>P40-P47, E, SC1, SC2<br>Other Outputs | $V_{OH}$ | <br>$V_{SS}$+2.4<br>$V_{SS}$+2.4<br>$V_{SS}$+2.4 | <br>–<br>–<br>– | <br>–<br>–<br>– | Vdc |
| Output Low Voltage<br>($I_{load}$ = 2.0 mAdc, $V_{CC}$ = min) | All Outputs | $V_{OL}$ | – | – | $V_{SS}$+0.5 | Vdc |
| Darlington Drive Current<br>($V_O$ = 1.5 Vdc) | P10-P17 | $I_{OH}$ | 1.0 | 2.5 | 10.0 | mAdc |
| Power Dissipation | | $P_D$ | – | – | 1200 | mW |
| Input Capacitance<br>($V_{in}$ = 0, $T_A$ = 25°C, $f_o$ = 1.0 MHz) | P30-P37, P40-P47, SC1<br>Other Inputs | $C_{in}$ | –<br>– | –<br>– | 12.5<br>10.0 | pF |
| $V_{CC}$ Standby | Powerdown<br>Powerup | $V_{SBB}$<br>$V_{SB}$ | 4.0<br>4.75 | –<br>– | 5.25<br>5.25 | Vdc |
| Standby Current | Powerdown | $I_{SBB}$ | – | – | 6.0 | mAdc |
| Frequency of Operation<br>MC6801 External Clock<br>MC6801 Crystal<br>MC6801-1 External Clock<br>MC6801-1 Crystal | <br>EXTAL2<br>XTAL1, EXTAL2<br>EXTAL2<br>XTAL1, EXTAL2 | <br>$4f_o$<br>$f_{XTAL}$<br>$4f_o$<br>$f_{XTAL}$ | <br>2.0<br>3.579<br>2.0<br>3.579 | <br>–<br>–<br>–<br>– | <br>4.0<br>4.0<br>5.0<br>5.0 | MHz |

*Except Mode Programming Levels; See Figure 17.

**PERIPHERAL PORT TIMING** (Refer to Figures 3-6)

| Characteristics | Symbol | Min | Typ | Max | Unit |
|---|---|---|---|---|---|
| Peripheral Data Setup Time | $t_{PDSU}$ | 200 | – | – | ns |
| Peripheral Data Hold Time | $t_{PDH}$ | 200 | – | – | ns |
| Delay Time, Enable Positive Transition to $\overline{OS3}$ Negative Transition | $t_{OSD1}$ | – | – | 350 | ns |
| Delay Time, Enable Positive Transition to $\overline{OS3}$ Positive Transition | $t_{OSD2}$ | – | – | 350 | ns |
| Delay Time, Enable Negative Transition to Peripheral Data Valid<br>Port 1<br>Port 2, 3, 4 | $t_{PWD}$ | –<br>– | –<br>– | 500<br>350 | ns |
| Delay Time, Enable Negative Transition to Peripheral CMOS Data Valid | $t_{CMOS}$ | – | – | 2.0 | μs |
| Input Strobe Pulse Width | $t_{PWIS}$ | 200 | – | – | ns |
| Input Data Hold Time | $t_{IH}$ | 50 | – | – | ns |
| Input Data Setup Time | $t_{IS}$ | 20 | – | – | ns |

**FIGURE 3 — DATA SETUP AND HOLD TIMES (MPU READ)**

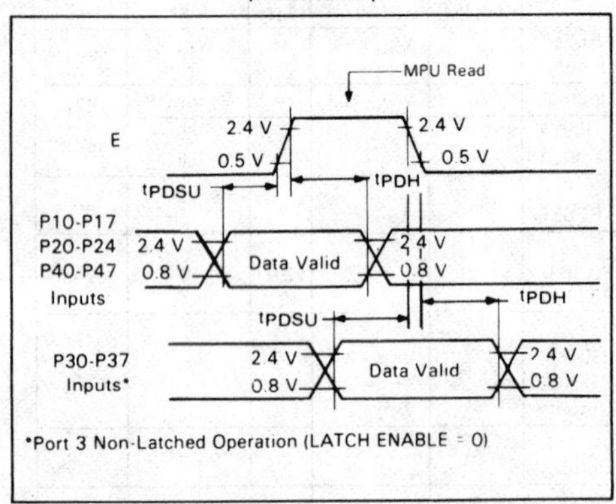


**FIGURE 4 — DATA SETUP AND HOLD TIMES (MPU WRITE)**

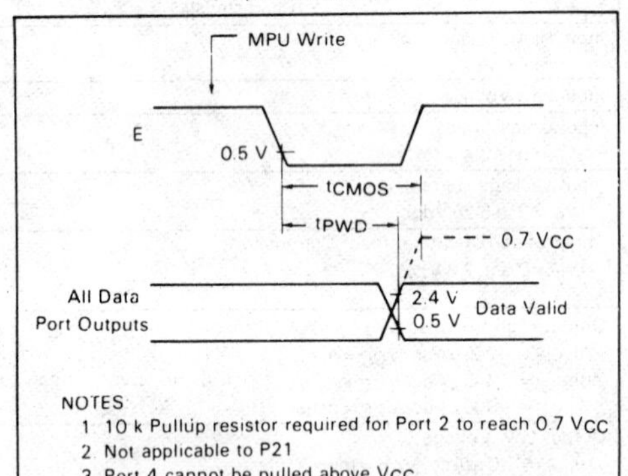


**FIGURE 5 — PORT 3 OUTPUT STROBE TIMING (SINGLE CHIP MODE)**

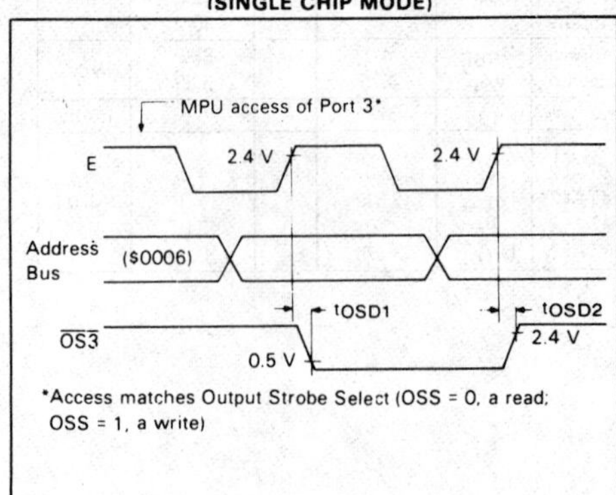


**FIGURE 6 — PORT 3 LATCH TIMING (SINGLE CHIP MODE)**

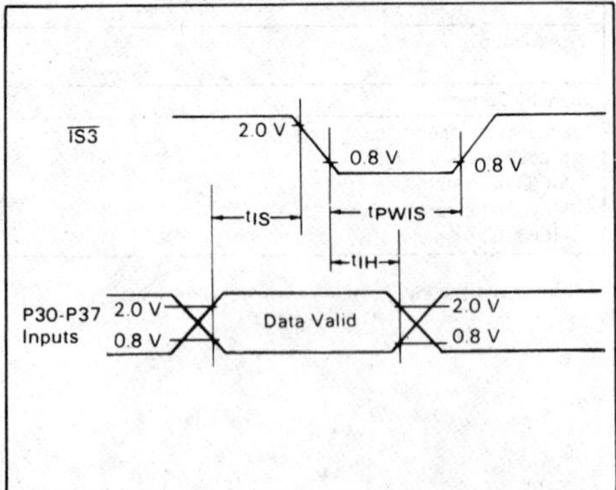

**BUS TIMING** (Refer to Figures 9 and 10 and 22b)

| Characteristic | Symbol | MC6801 ($f_o$ = 1.0 MHz) Min | Typ | Max | MC6801-1 ($f_o$ = 1.25 MHz) Min | Typ | Max | Unit |
|---|---|---|---|---|---|---|---|---|
| Cycle Time | $t_{cyc}$ | 1 | — | 2 | 0.8 | — | 2 | μs |
| Address Strobe Pulse Width High | $PW_{ASH}$ | 200 | ¼$t_{cyc}$ | — | 150 | ¼$t_{cyc}$ | — | ns |
| Address Strobe Rise Time | $t_{ASR}$ | 5 | — | 30 | 5 | — | 30 | ns |
| Address Strobe Fall Time | $t_{ASF}$ | 5 | — | 30 | 5 | — | 30 | ns |
| Address Strobe Delay Time | $t_{ASD}$ | 60 | ⅛$t_{cyc}$ | — | 30 | ⅛$t_{cyc}$ | — | ns |
| Enable Rise Time | $t_{ER}$ | 5 | — | 30 | 5 | — | 30 | ns |
| Enable Fall Time | $t_{EF}$ | 5 | — | 30 | 5 | — | 30 | ns |
| Enable Pulse Width High Time | $PW_{EH}$ | 450 | ½$t_{cyc}$ | — | 340 | ½$t_{cyc}$ | — | ns |
| Enable Pulse Width Low Time | $PW_{EL}$ | 450 | ½$t_{cyc}$ | — | 350 | ½$t_{cyc}$ | — | ns |
| Address Strobe to Enable Delay Time | $t_{ASED}$ | 60 | — | — | 30 | — | — | ns |
| Address Delay Time | $t_{AD}$ | — | — | 260 | — | — | 220 | ns |
| Data Delay Write Time | $t_{DDW}$ | — | — | 225 | — | — | 225 | ns |
| Data Set-up Time | $t_{DSR}$ | 80 | — | — | 70 | — | — | ns |
| Data Hold Time<br>Read<br>Write | <br>$t_{HR}$<br>$t_{HW}$ | <br>10<br>20 | <br>—<br>— | <br>—<br>— | <br>10<br>20 | <br>—<br>— | <br>—<br>— | ns |
| Address Setup Time for Latch | $t_{ASL}$ | 20 | — | — | 20 | — | — | ns |
| Address Hold Time for Latch | $t_{AHL}$ | 20 | — | — | 20 | — | — | ns |
| Address Hold Time | $t_{AH}$ | 20 | — | — | 20 | — | — | ns |
| Address, R/$\overline{W}$ Set-up Time Before E | $t_{AS}$ | 200 | — | — | 140 | — | — | ns |
| A0-A7 Set-up Time Before E | $t_{ASM}$ | 190 | — | — | 130 | — | — | ns |
| Peripheral Read Access Time:<br>Non-Multiplexed Bus<br>Multiplexed Bus | <br>$t_{ACCN}$<br>$t_{ACCM}$ | <br>—<br>— | <br>—<br>— | <br>570<br>560 | <br>—<br>— | <br>—<br>— | <br>410<br>400 | ns |
| Oscillator Stabilization Time | $t_{RC}$ | 100 | — | — | 100 | — | — | ms |
| Processor Control Setup Time | $t_{PCS}$ | 200 | — | — | 200 | — | — | ns |

FIGURE 7 — CMOS LOAD

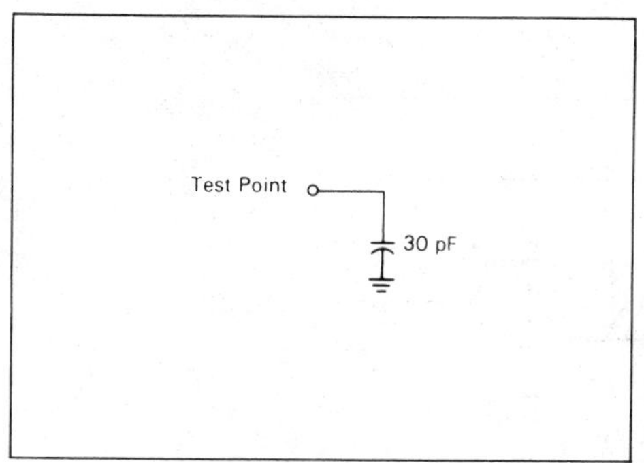


FIGURE 8 — TIMING TEST LOAD PORTS 1, 2, 3, 4

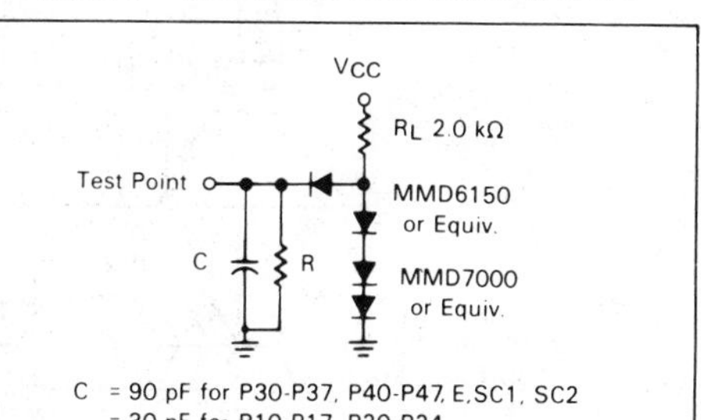

**FIGURE 9 — EXPANDED NON-MULTIPLEXED BUS TIMING**

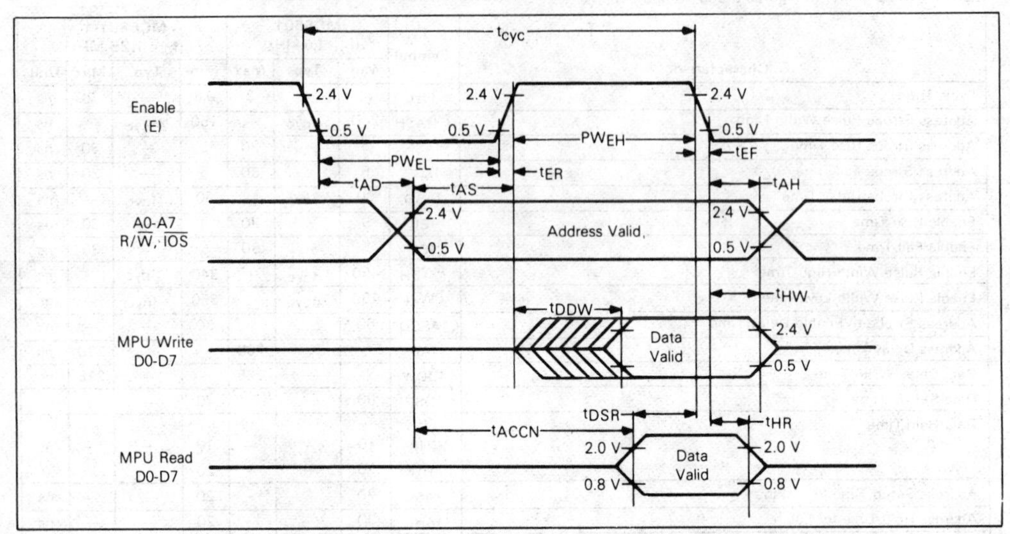


**FIGURE 10 — EXPANDED MULTIPLEXED BUS TIMING**

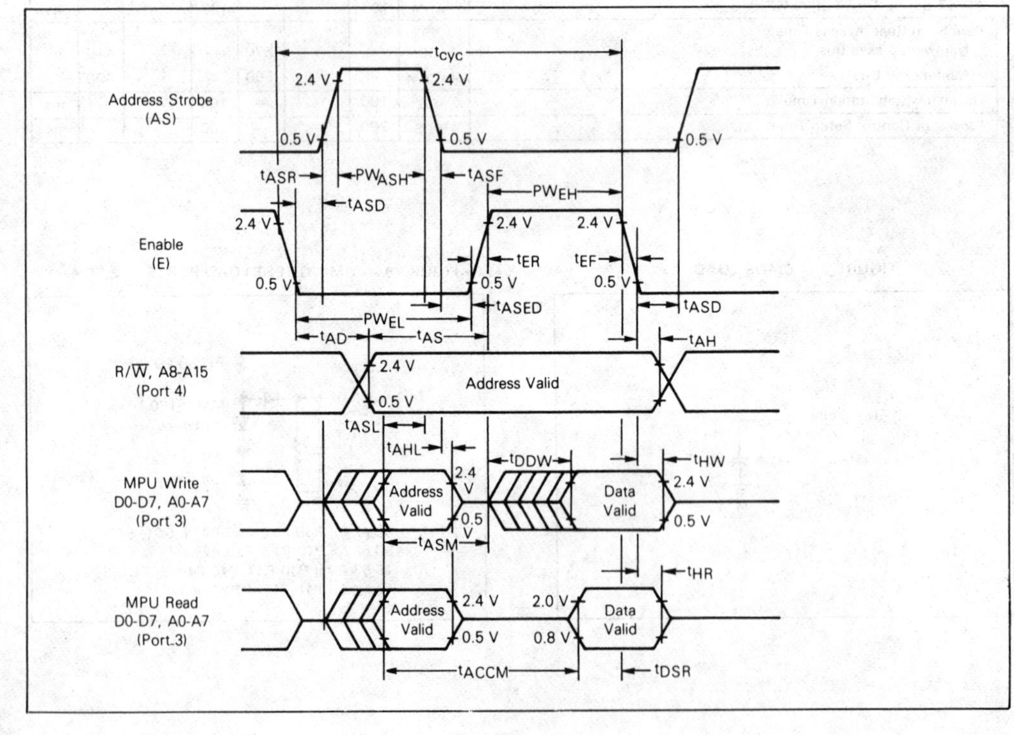

FIGURE 17 — MODE PROGRAMMING TIMING

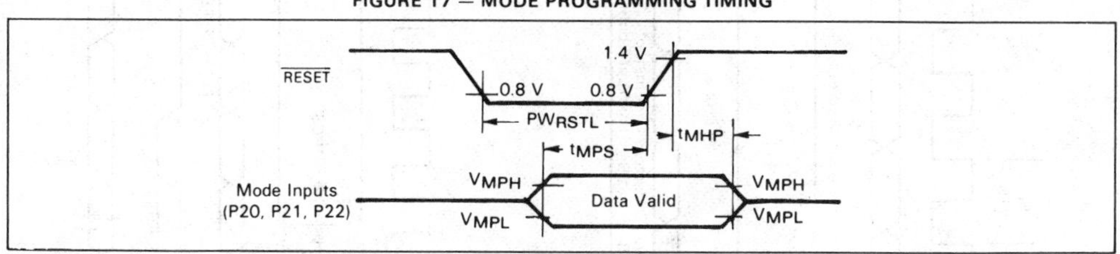


**MODE PROGRAMMING** (Refer to Figure 17)

| Characteristic | Symbol | Min | Typ | Max | Unit |
|---|---|---|---|---|---|
| Mode Programming Input Voltage Low | $V_{MPL}$ | — | — | 2.2 | Vdc |
| Mode Programming Input Voltage High | $V_{MPH}$ | 4.0 | — | — | Vdc |
| $\overline{\text{RESET}}$ Low Pulse Width | $PW_{RSTL}$ | 3.0 | — | — | E-Cycles |
| Mode Programming Set-Up Time | $t_{MPS}$ | 2.0 | — | — | E-Cycles |
| Mode Programming Hold Time | $t_{MHP}$ | 150 | — | — | ns |

FIGURE 18 — TYPICAL MODE PROGRAMMING CIRCUIT

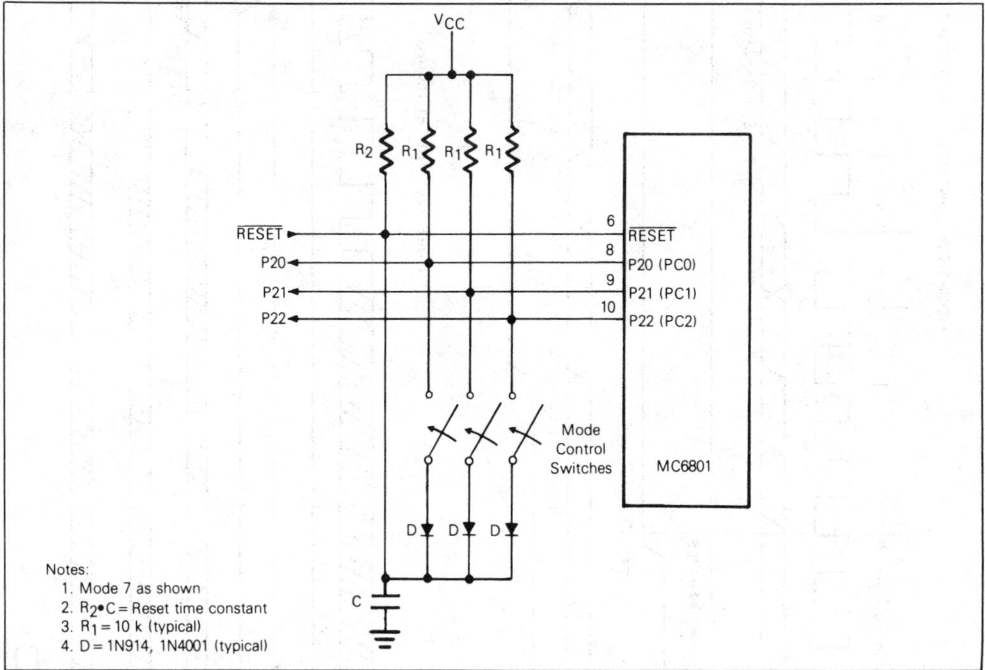


**MEMORY MAPS**

The MCU can provide up to 64K byte address space depending on the operating mode. A memory map for each operating mode is shown in Figure 19. In Modes 1R and 6R, the ROM has been relocated by a mask option. The first 32 locations of each map are reserved for the MCU's internal register area, as shown in Table 4, with exceptions as indicated.

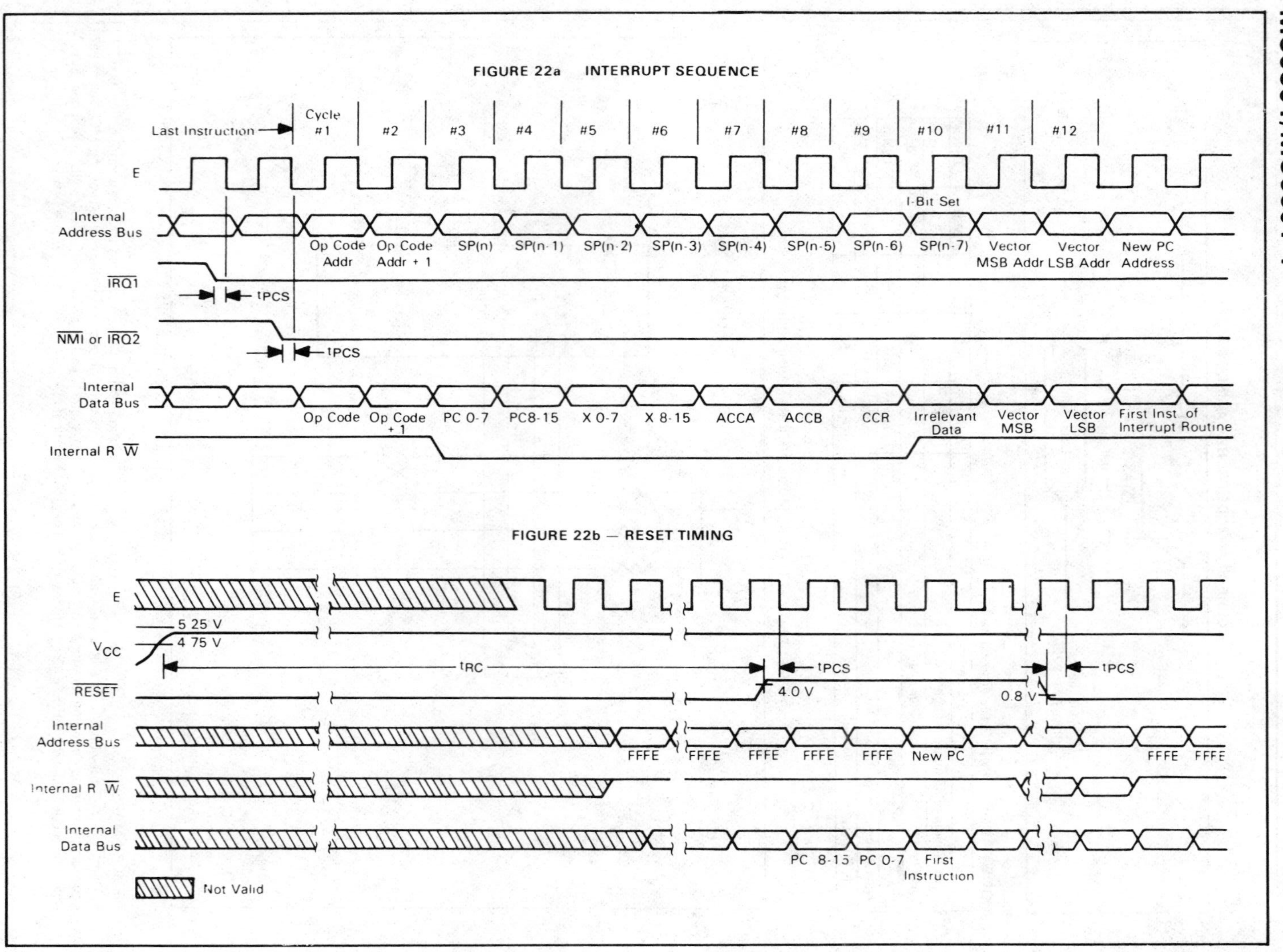
FIGURE 22a INTERRUPT SEQUENCE
Last Instruction
Cycle #1
#2
#3
#4
#5
#6
#7
#8
#9
#10
#11
#12
E
Internal Address Bus
Op Code Addr
Op Code Addr + 1
SP(n)
SP(n-1)
SP(n-2)
SP(n-3)
SP(n-4)
SP(n-5)
SP(n-6)
SP(n-7)
Vector MSB Addr
Vector LSB Addr
New PC Address
I-Bit Set
IRQ1
tPCS
NMI or IRQ2
tPCS
Internal Data Bus
Op Code
Op Code +1
PC 0-7
PC8-15
X 0-7
X 8-15
ACCA
ACCB
CCR
Irrelevant Data
Vector MSB
Vector LSB
First Inst. of Interrupt Routine
Internal R W
FIGURE 22b — RESET TIMING
E
VCC
5 25 V
4 75 V
tRC
tPCS
tPCS
4.0 V
0.8 V
RESET
Internal Address Bus
FFFE
FFFE
FFFE
FFFE
FFFF
New PC
FFFE
FFFE
Internal R W
Internal Data Bus
PC 8-15
PC 0-7
First Instruction
Not Valid

**FIGURE 23 — MC6801 OSCILLATOR CHARACTERISTICS**

**(a) Nominal Recommended Crystal Parameters**

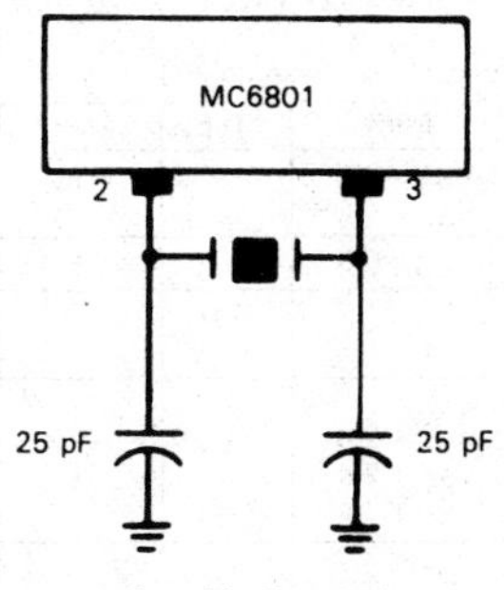


$C_L$ = 24 pF (typical)

**MC6801 Nominal Crystal Parameters**

| | 3.58 MHz | 4.00 MH | 5.0 MHz |
|---|---|---|---|
| RS | 60 Ω | 50 Ω | 30-50 Ω |
| $C_0$ | 3.5 pF | 6.5 pF | 4.6 pF |
| $C_1$ | 0.015 pF | 0.025 pF | 0.01-0.02 pF |
| Q | >40 k | >30 k | >20 k |

*Note: These are representative AT-cut crystal parameters only. Crystals of other types of cuts may also be used.

**NOTE**
TTL-compatible oscillators may be obtained from:

Motorola Component Products
Attn: Data Clock Sales
2553 N. Edginton St.
Franklin Park, IL 60131
Tel: 312-451-1000
Telex: 025-4400

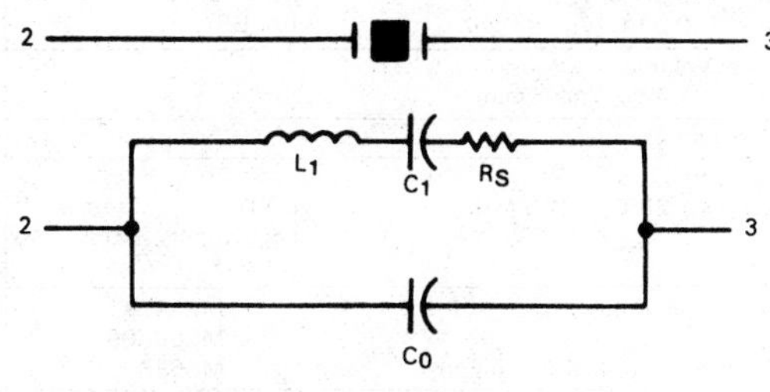


Equivalent Circuit

**(b) Oscillator Stabilization Time ($t_{RC}$)**

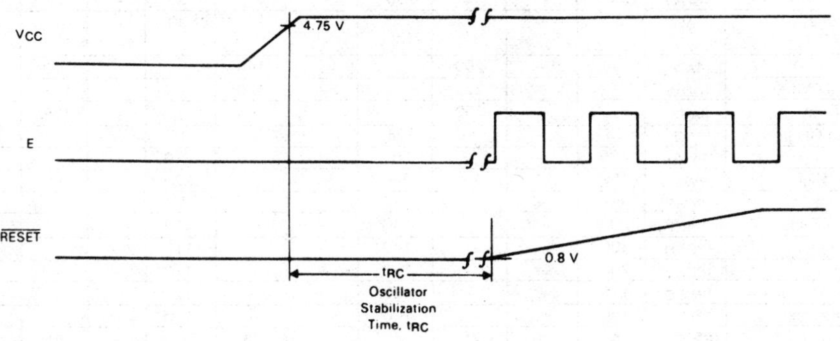

## MAXIMUM RATINGS

| Rating | Symbol | Value | Unit |
|---|---|---|---|
| Supply Voltage | $V_{CC}$ | -0.3 to +7.0 | Vdc |
| Input Voltage | $V_{in}$ | -0.3 to +7.0 | Vdc |
| Operating Temperature Range | $T_A$ | 0 to +70 | °C |
| Storage Temperature Range | $T_{stg}$ | -55 to +150 | °C |
| Thermal Resistance | $\theta_{JA}$ | 70 | °C/W |

This device contains circuitry to protect the inputs against damage due to high static voltages or electric fields; however, it is advised that normal precautions be taken to avoid application of any voltage higher than maximum rated voltages to this high impedance circuit.

## ELECTRICAL CHARACTERISTICS ($V_{CC}$ = 5.0 V ±5%, $V_{SS}$ = 0, $T_A$ = 0 to 70°C unless otherwise noted.)

| Characteristic | | Symbol | Min | Typ | Max | Unit |
|---|---|---|---|---|---|---|
| Input High Voltage | Logic, EXtal<br>$\overline{RESET}$ | $V_{IH}$ | $V_{SS}$ + 2.0<br>$V_{SS}$ + 4.0 | —<br>— | $V_{DD}$<br>$V_{DD}$ | Vdc |
| Input Low Voltage | Logic, EXtal, $\overline{RESET}$ | $V_{IL}$ | $V_{SS}$ - 0.3 | — | $V_{SS}$ + 0.8 | Vdc |
| Input Leakage Current<br>($V_{in}$ = 0 to 5.25 V, $V_{CC}$ = max) | Logic | $I_{in}$ | — | 1.0 | 2.5 | μAdc |
| Output High Voltage<br>($I_{Load}$ = -205 μAdc, $V_{CC}$ = min)<br>($I_{Load}$ = -145 μAdc, $V_{CC}$ = min)<br>($I_{Load}$ = -100 μAdc, $V_{CC}$ = min) | <br>D0-D7<br>A0-A15, R/$\overline{W}$, Q, E<br>BA, BS | $V_{OH}$ | <br>$V_{SS}$ + 2.4<br>$V_{SS}$ + 2.4<br>$V_{SS}$ + 2.4 | <br>—<br>—<br>— | <br>—<br>—<br>— | Vdc |
| Output Low Voltage<br>($I_{Load}$ = 2.0 mAdc, $V_{CC}$ = min) | | $V_{OL}$ | — | — | $V_{SS}$ +0.5 | Vdc |
| Power Dissipation | | $P_D$ | — | — | 1.0 | W |
| Capacitance #<br>($V_{in}$ = 0, $T_A$ = 25°C, f = 1.0 MHz) | <br>D0-D7<br>Logic Inputs, EXtal<br>A0-A15, R/W | $C_{in}$<br><br><br>$C_{out}$ | <br>—<br>—<br>— | <br>10<br>7<br>— | <br>15<br>10<br>12 | pF |
| Frequency of Operation<br><br>(Crystal or External Input) | MC6809<br>MC68A09<br>MC68B09 | f<br>$f_{XTAL}$<br>$f_{XTAL}$ | —<br>—<br>— | —<br>—<br>— | 4<br>6<br>8 | MHz |
| Three-State (Off State) Input Current<br>($V_{in}$ = 0.4 to 2.4 V, $V_{CC}$ = max) | D0-D7<br>A0-A15, R/W | $I_{TSI}$ | —<br>— | 2.0<br>— | 10<br>100 | μAdc |

## READ/WRITE TIMING (Reference Figures 1 and 2)

| Characteristic | Symbol | MC6809 | | | MC68A09 | | | MC68B09 | | | Unit |
|---|---|---|---|---|---|---|---|---|---|---|---|
| | | Min | Typ | Max | Min | Typ | Max | Min | Typ | Max | |
| Cycle Time | $t_{CYC}$ | 1000 | — | — | 667 | — | — | 500 | — | — | ns |
| Total Up Time | $t_{UT}$ | 975 | — | — | 640 | — | — | 480 | — | — | ns |
| Peripheral Read Access Time $t_{ac}$ = ($t_{AD}$ = $t_{DSR}$) | $t_{ACC}$ | 695 | — | — | 440 | — | — | 320 | — | — | ns |
| Data Setup Time (Read) | $t_{DSR}$ | 80 | — | — | 60 | — | — | 40 | — | — | ns |
| Input Data Hold Time | $t_{DHR}$ | 10 | — | — | 10 | — | — | 10 | — | — | ns |
| Output Data Hold Time | $t_{DHW}$ | 30 | — | — | 30 | — | — | 30 | — | — | ns |
| Address Hold Time (Address, R/$\overline{W}$) | $t_{AH}$ | 30 | — | — | 30 | — | — | 30 | — | — | ns |
| Address Delay | $t_{AD}$ | — | — | 200 | — | — | 140 | — | — | 110 | ns |
| Data Delay Time (Write) | $t_{DDW}$ | — | — | 225 | — | — | 180 | — | — | 145 | ns |
| $E_{low}$ to $Q_{high}$ Time | $t_{AVS}$ | — | — | 250 | — | — | 165 | — | — | 125 | ns |
| Address Valid to $Q_{high}$ | $t_{AQ}$ | 25 | — | — | 25 | — | — | 15 | — | — | ns |
| Processor Clock Low | $t_{PWEL}$ | 450 | — | — | 295 | — | — | 210 | — | — | ns |
| Processor Clock High | $t_{PWEH}$ | 450 | — | — | 280 | — | — | 220 | — | — | ns |
| MRDY Set Up Time | $t_{PCSR}$ | 60 | — | — | 60 | — | — | 60 | — | — | ns |
| Interrupts Set Up Time | $t_{PCS}$ | 200 | — | — | 140 | — | — | 110 | — | — | ns |
| $\overline{HALT}$ Set Up Time | $t_{PCSH}$ | 200 | — | — | 140 | — | — | 110 | — | — | ns |
| $\overline{RESET}$ Set Up Time | $t_{PCSR}$ | 200 | — | — | 140 | — | — | 110 | — | — | ns |
| $\overline{DMA/BREQ}$ Set Up Time | $t_{PCSD}$ | 125 | — | — | 125 | — | — | 125 | — | — | ns |
| Crystal Osc Start Time | $t_{rc}$ | 100 | — | — | 100 | — | — | 100 | — | — | ms |
| E Rise and Fall Time | $t_{ER}$, $t_{EF}$ | 5 | — | 25 | 5 | — | 25 | 5 | — | 20 | ns |
| Processor Control Rise/Fall | $t_{PCR}$, $t_{PLF}$ | — | — | 100 | — | — | 100 | — | — | 100 | ns |
| Q Rise and Fall Time | $t_{QR}$, $t_{QF}$ | 5 | — | 25 | 5 | — | 25 | 5 | — | 20 | ns |
| Q Clock High | $t_{PWQH}$ | 450 | — | — | 280 | — | — | 220 | — | — | ns |

Data sheets on pages 9-D31 through 9-D39 reprinted by permission of Motorola Semiconductor Products, Inc.

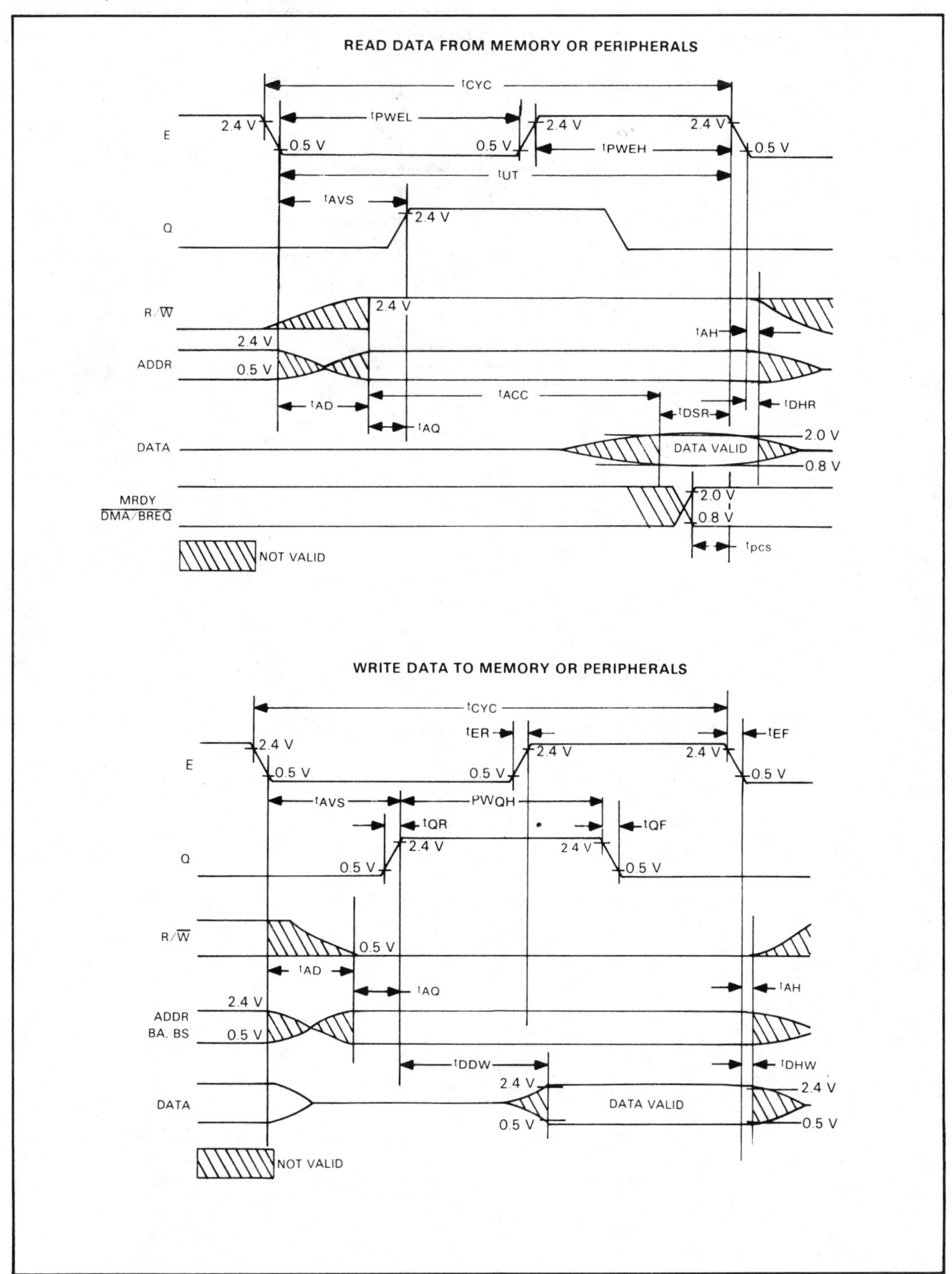
READ DATA FROM MEMORY OR PERIPHERALS
tCYC
tPWEL
tPWEH
tUT
tAVS
E
Q
R/W
ADDR
DATA
MRDY
DMA/BREQ
2.4 V
0.5 V
tAH
tACC
tAD
tAQ
tDSR
tDHR
DATA VALID
2.0 V
0.8 V
tpcs
NOT VALID
WRITE DATA TO MEMORY OR PERIPHERALS
tCYC
tER
tEF
tAVS
PWQH
tQR
tQF
tAD
tAQ
tAH
ADDR
BA, BS
tDDW
tDHW
DATA
DATA VALID
NOT VALID

**BUS TIMING TEST LOAD**

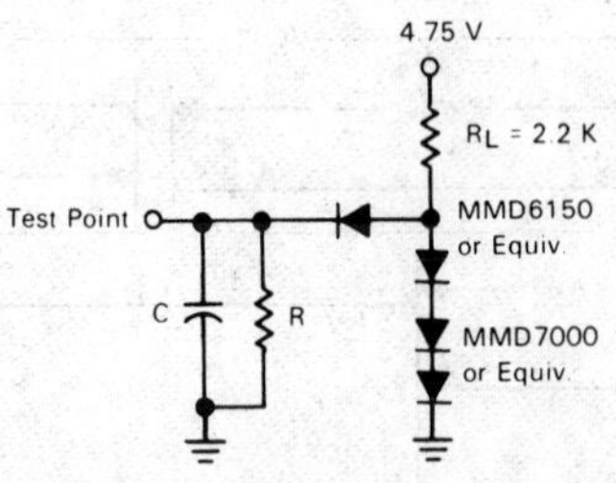


C = 30 pF for BA, BS
130 pF for D0-D7, E, Q
90 pF for A0-A15, R/W

R = 11.7 kΩ for D0-D7
16.5 kΩ for A0-A15, E, Q
24 kΩ for BA, BS

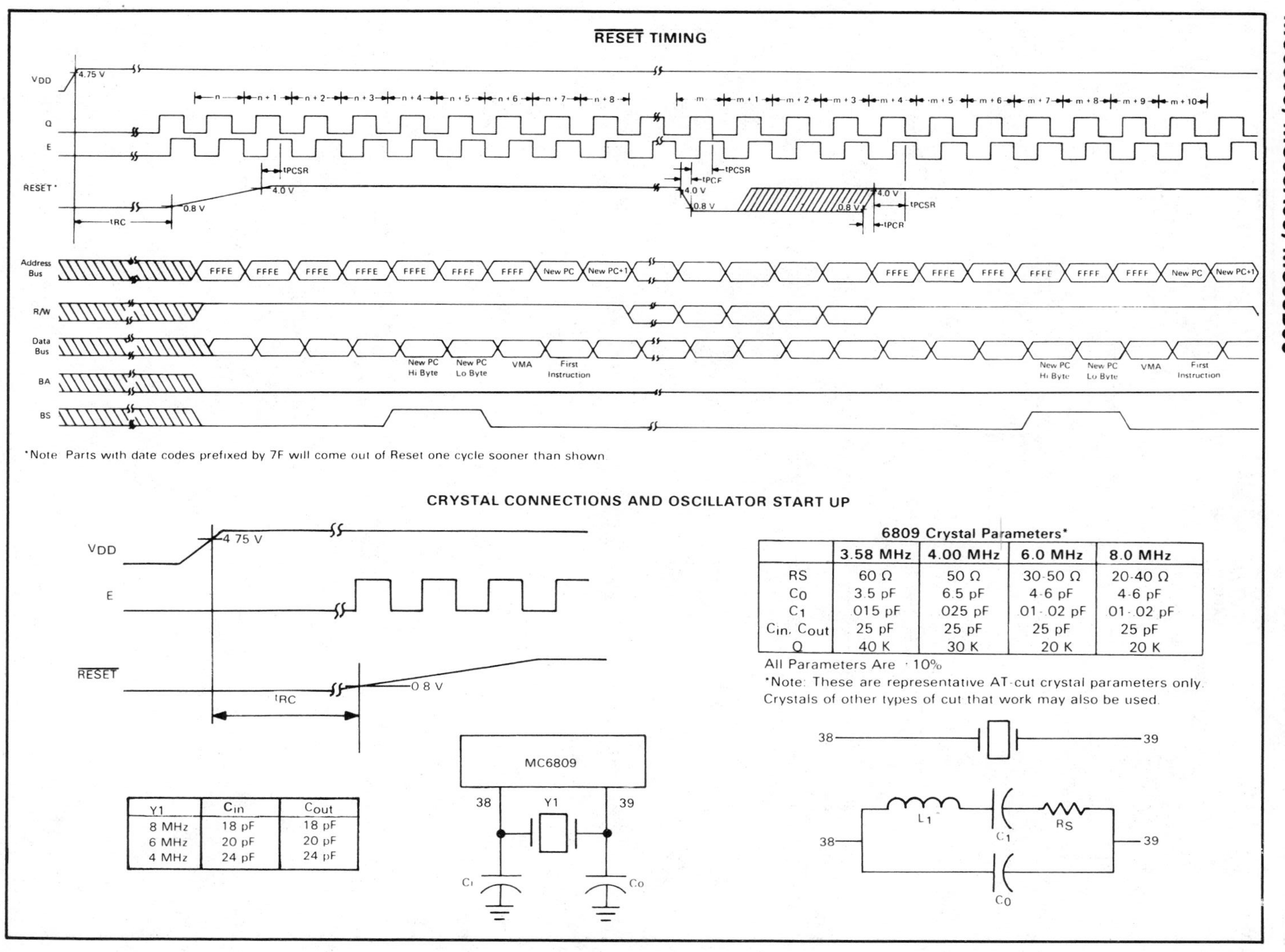


*Note: Parts with date codes prefixed by 7F will come out of Reset one cycle sooner than shown

| Y1 | $C_{in}$ | $C_{out}$ |
|---|---|---|
| 8 MHz | 18 pF | 18 pF |
| 6 MHz | 20 pF | 20 pF |
| 4 MHz | 24 pF | 24 pF |

**6809 Crystal Parameters***

| | 3.58 MHz | 4.00 MHz | 6.0 MHz | 8.0 MHz |
|---|---|---|---|---|
| RS | 60 Ω | 50 Ω | 30-50 Ω | 20-40 Ω |
| $C_0$ | 3.5 pF | 6.5 pF | 4-6 pF | 4-6 pF |
| $C_1$ | .015 pF | .025 pF | .01-.02 pF | .01-.02 pF |
| $C_{in}$, $C_{out}$ | 25 pF | 25 pF | 25 pF | 25 pF |
| Q | 40 K | 30 K | 20 K | 20 K |

All Parameters Are ±10%

*Note: These are representative AT-cut crystal parameters only. Crystals of other types of cut that work may also be used.

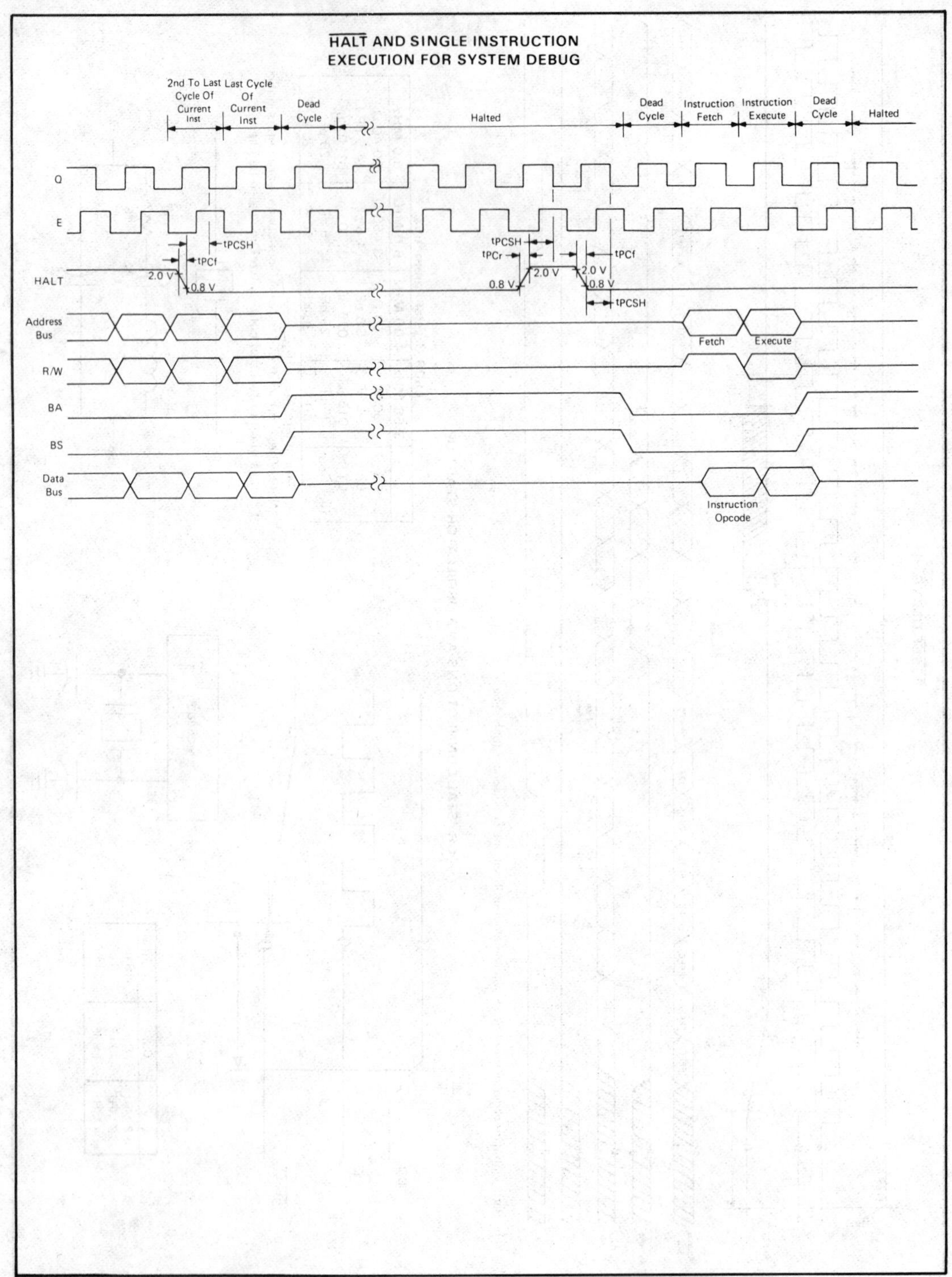
HALT AND SINGLE INSTRUCTION
EXECUTION FOR SYSTEM DEBUG
2nd To Last Cycle Of Current Inst
Last Cycle Of Current Inst
Dead Cycle
Halted
Dead Cycle
Instruction Fetch
Instruction Execute
Dead Cycle
Halted
Q
E
tPCSH
tPCf
tPCr
2.0 V
0.8 V
HALT
Address Bus
Fetch
Execute
R/W
BA
BS
Data Bus
Instruction Opcode

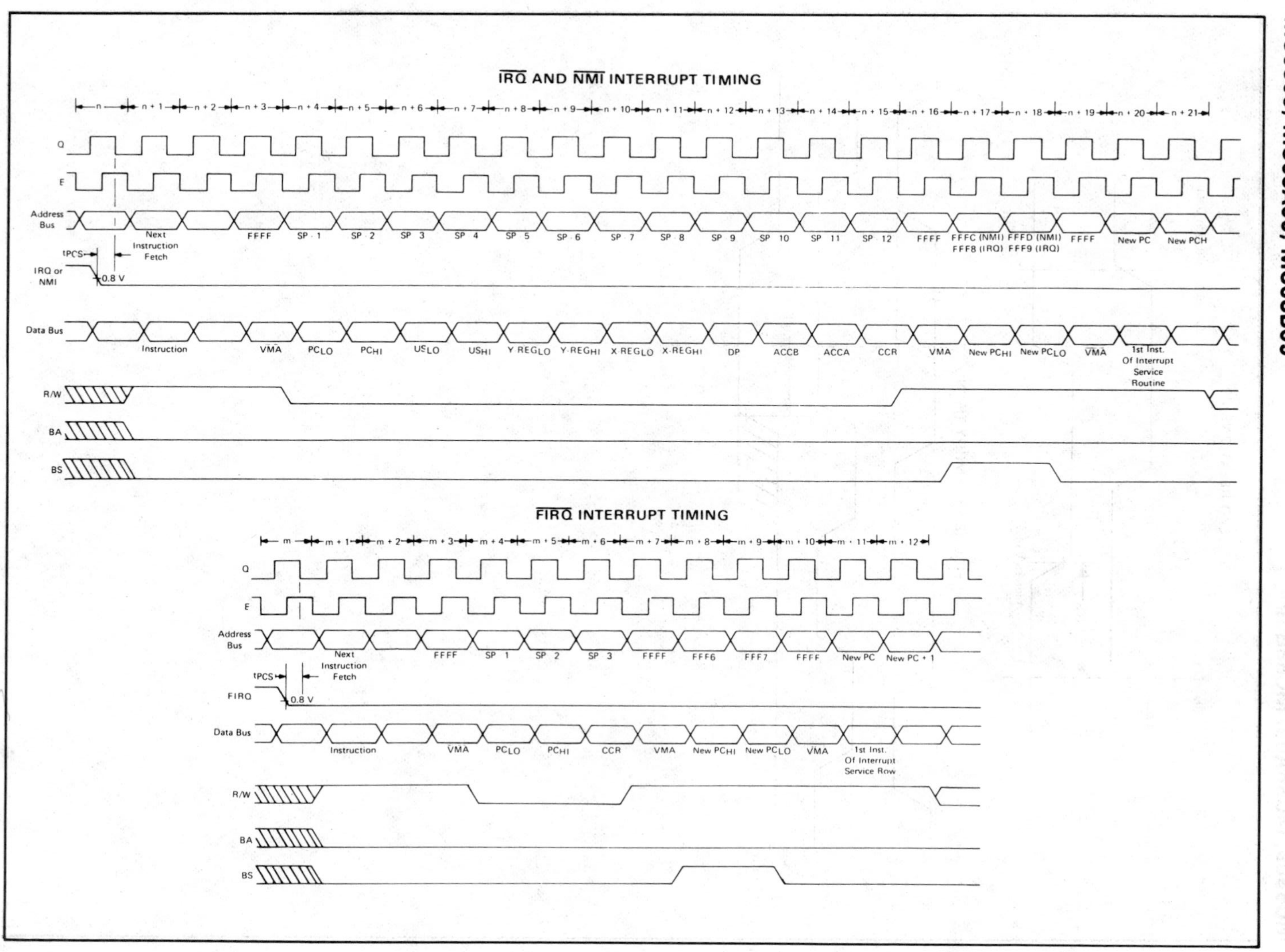

IRQ AND NMI INTERRUPT TIMING
n
n + 1
n + 2
n + 3
n + 4
n + 5
n + 6
n + 7
n + 8
n + 9
n + 10
n + 11
n + 12
n + 13
n + 14
n + 15
n + 16
n + 17
n + 18
n + 19
n + 20
n + 21
Q
E
Address Bus
Next Instruction Fetch
FFFF
SP 1
SP 2
SP 3
SP 4
SP 5
SP 6
SP 7
SP 8
SP 9
SP 10
SP 11
SP 12
FFFF
FFFC (NMI) FFF8 (IRQ)
FFFD (NMI) FFF9 (IRQ)
FFFF
New PC
New PCH
tPCS
IRQ or NMI
0.8 V
Data Bus
Instruction
VMA
PCLO
PCHI
USLO
USHI
Y REGLO
Y REGHI
X REGLO
X REGHI
DP
ACCB
ACCA
CCR
VMA
New PCHI
New PCLO
VMA
1st Inst. Of Interrupt Service Routine
R/W
BA
BS
FIRQ INTERRUPT TIMING
m
m + 1
m + 2
m + 3
m + 4
m + 5
m + 6
m + 7
m + 8
m + 9
m + 10
m + 11
m + 12
Q
E
Address Bus
Next Instruction Fetch
FFFF
SP 1
SP 2
SP 3
FFFF
FFF6
FFF7
FFFF
New PC
New PC + 1
tPCS
FIRQ
0.8 V
Data Bus
Instruction
VMA
PCLO
PCHI
CCR
VMA
New PCHI
New PCLO
VMA
1st Inst. Of Interrupt Service Row
R/W
BA
BS

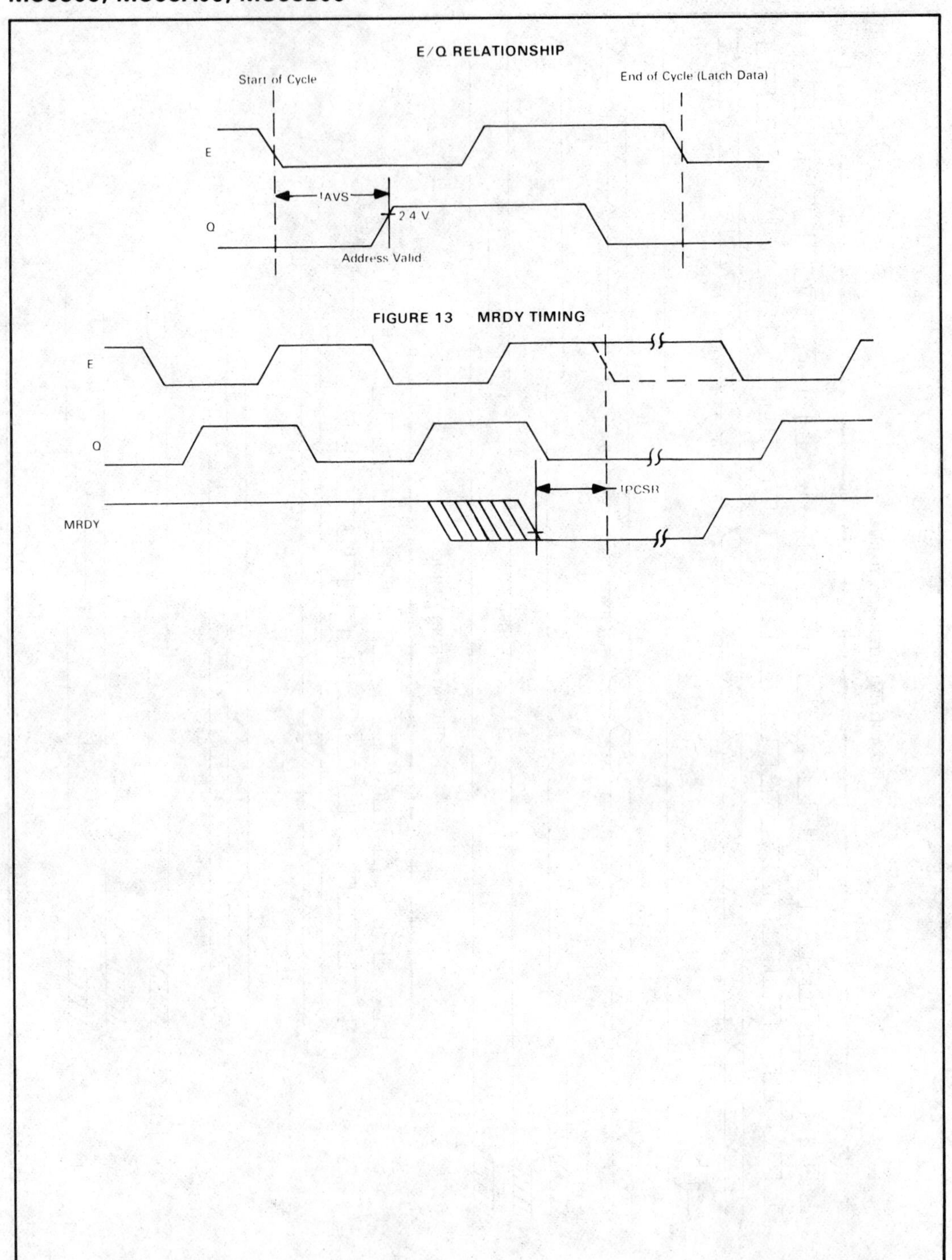


FIGURE 13 MRDY TIMING

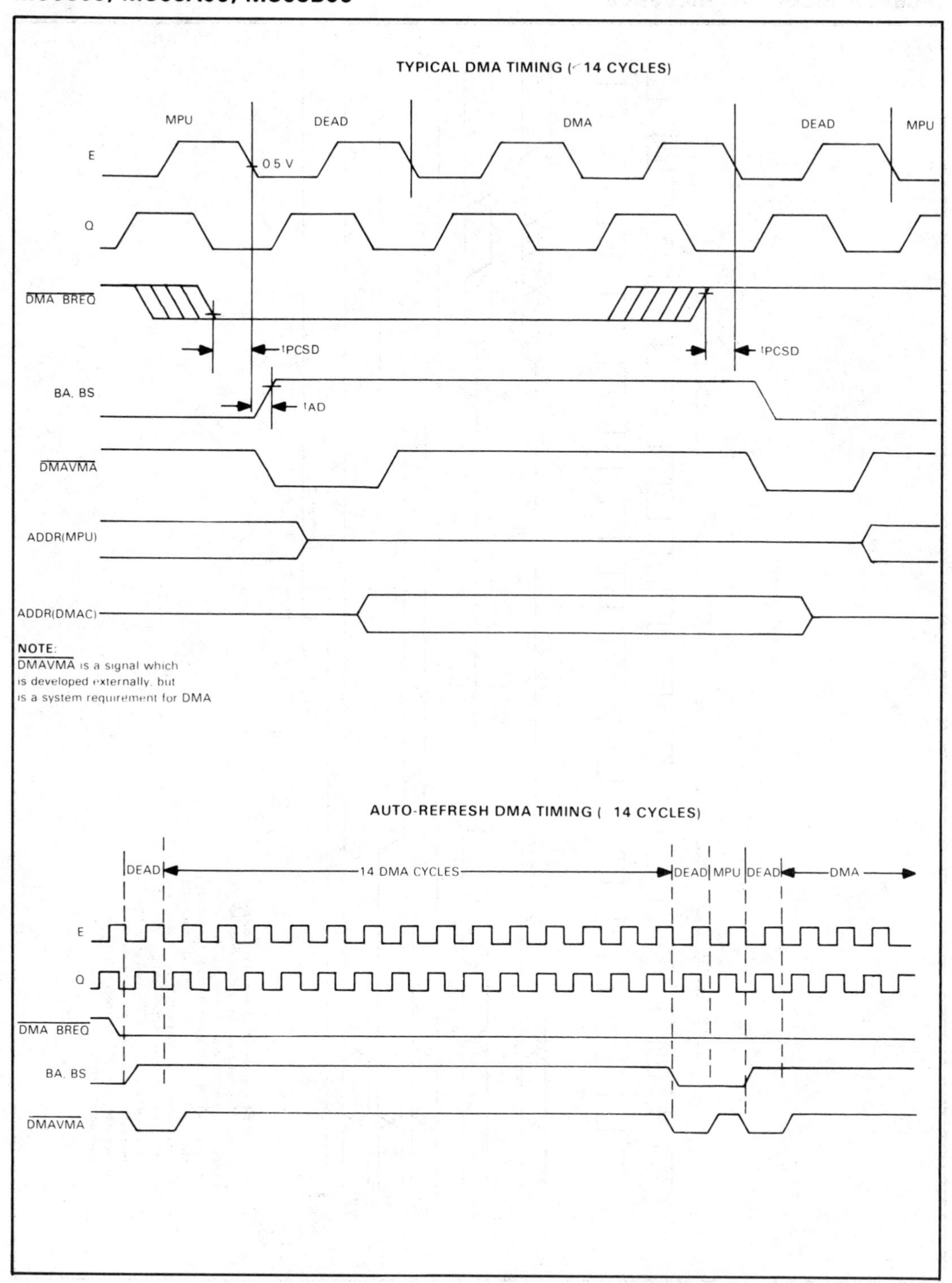
TYPICAL DMA TIMING (< 14 CYCLES)
MPU
DEAD
DMA
DEAD
MPU
E
0.5 V
Q
DMA BREQ
tPCSD
tPCSD
BA, BS
tAD
DMAVMA
ADDR(MPU)
ADDR(DMAC)
NOTE:
DMAVMA is a signal which
is developed externally, but
is a system requirement for DMA
AUTO-REFRESH DMA TIMING (> 14 CYCLES)
DEAD
14 DMA CYCLES
DEAD
MPU
DEAD
DMA
E
Q
DMA BREQ
BA, BS
DMAVMA

## SYNC TIMING

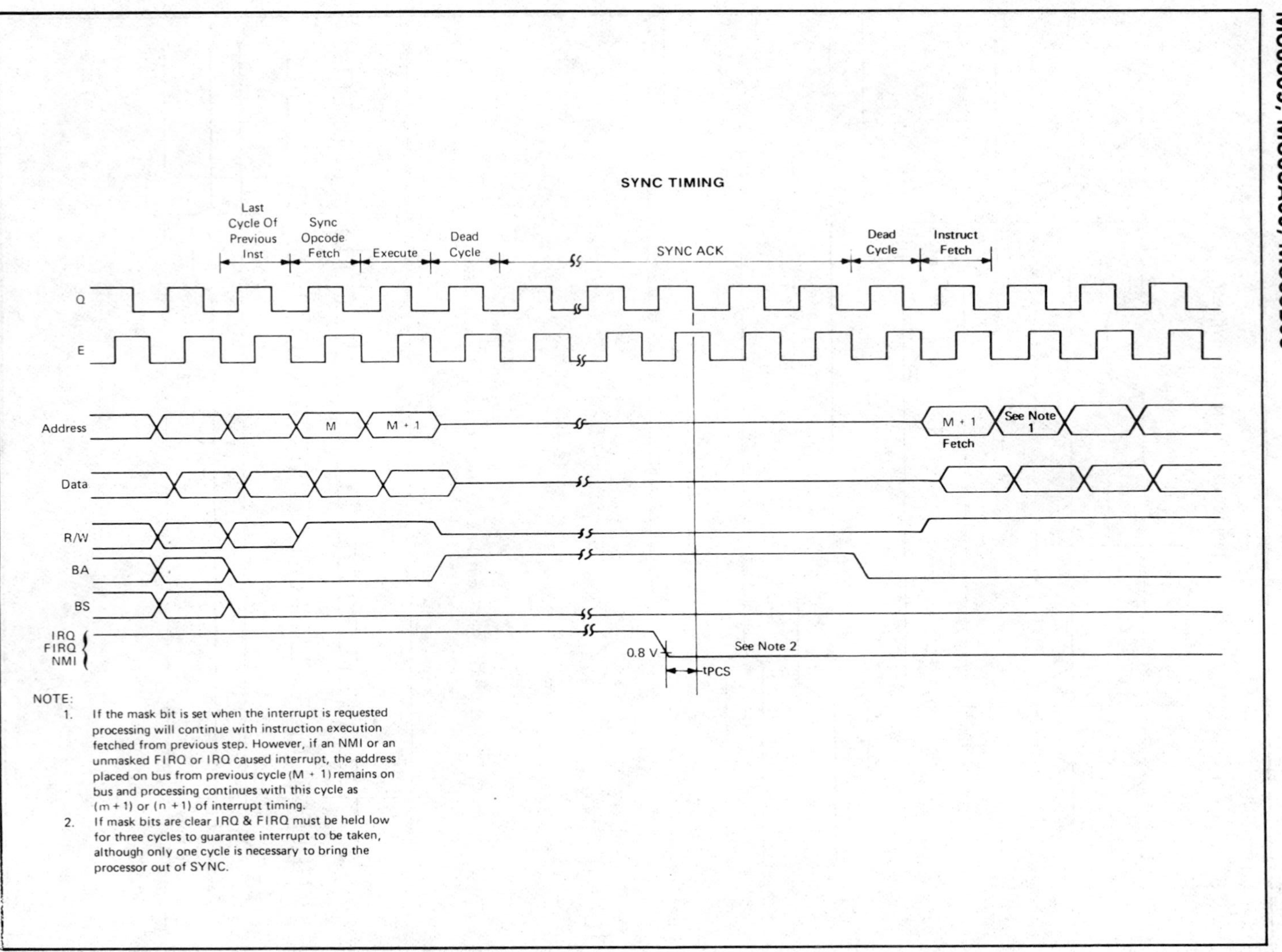


NOTE:

1. If the mask bit is set when the interrupt is requested processing will continue with instruction execution fetched from previous step. However, if an NMI or an unmasked FIRQ or IRQ caused interrupt, the address placed on bus from previous cycle (M + 1) remains on bus and processing continues with this cycle as (m + 1) or (n + 1) of interrupt timing.
2. If mask bits are clear IRQ & FIRQ must be held low for three cycles to guarantee interrupt to be taken, although only one cycle is necessary to bring the processor out of SYNC.

# Chapter 10
# THE MOS TECHNOLOGY MCS6500

**In many ways MCS6500 series microprocessors can be compared to the Zilog Z80, which we described in Chapter 7. Just as the Z80 is an enhancement of the 8080A, which is described in Chapter 4, so MOS Technology's products are enhancements of the MC6800, which we described in Chapter 9.**

**But there are some interesting conceptual differences between the way MOS Technology went about enhancing the MC6800, as compared to the product enhancement philosophy adopted by Zilog.**

**The Z80 is indeed an enhancement of the 8080A, but only to the extent that the 8080A instruction set is a subset of the Z80 instruction set; there are architectural similarities between the Z80 and the 8080A, but System Bus philosophies are markedly different. It would be hard to look upon the Z80 as simply another member of the 8080A family of microcomputer devices.**

**The MCS6500 product line, by way of contrast, can be looked upon as a CPU whose philosophical concepts agree closely with the MC6800 product line —without being in any way compatible, either in terms of instruction set or System Bus philosophy.** While on the surface it may appear as though MCS6500 CPUs represent some form of an MC6800 superset, this is not the case. System Busses are sufficiently different that you could not consider replacing an MC6800 CPU with an MCS6500 equivalent, leaving other logic unaltered. Instruction sets are similar, but deceptively so. In reality, the instruction sets are sufficiently different that converting an MC6800 source program to its MCS6500 equivalent is no simple task. It would be completely impossible to take an MC6800 program ROM and use it to drive an MCS6500 CPU. Recall that you can take an 8080A program ROM and use it to drive a Z80 CPU.

**Since this chapter is devoted to the MOS Technology product line, let us begin by summarizing the components of this product line, and the principal CPU enhancements that have been made.**

The MOS Technology devices described in this chapter consist of ten CPUs, plus four support circuits and a one-chip microcomputer. A fifth support circuit is described in Chapter 9.

The ten CPUs share the same instruction set and addressing modes, but have minor differences in packaging and system interface. Table 10-1 summarizes the ten CPUs.

The four support circuits that are described in this chapter are the MCS6522 Peripheral Interface Adapter, the MCS6530 and MCS6532 Combination Logic Device, and the MCS6551 Asynchronous Communication Interface Adapter. The MCS6520 PIA is identical to the MC6820 PIA; for a description of this device see Chapter 9.

**MCS6500 support devices are described in this chapter rather than in Volume 3 because, like the MC6800, the MCS6500 relies on a synchronizing clock signal. While it would be possible to use MCS6500 support devices with other microprocessors, the extra logic needed in order to create MCS6500 compatible bus interfaces would not be sufficiently rewarded by the specific capabilities of the support parts themselves.** MCS6500 support devices can be used with MC6800 microprocessors and, conversely, MC6800 support devices can be used with the MCS6500 CPU.

**In order to enhance the MC6800 CPU, MOS Technology made a number of useful yet obvious instruction set changes; they also made a number of subjective architectural changes which might have significant impact in particular applications, but which in general result in products that adhere quite closely to MC6800 philosophy.**

**The most important enhancement that MOS Technology has made is to develop a whole family of CPU devices.**

**The second most important feature of the MCS6500 line of CPU devices is the fact that the MCS650X series CPUs contain on-chip clock logic;** therefore, when using these CPUs, you do not need an MC6870 series clock device. However, you will need an external crystal oscillator or RC network — which is typical of any microprocessor with on-chip clock logic.

**Another important feature of all MCS6500 series CPUs is that you cannot float the Address and Data Busses separately during Φ1 high and Φ1 low clock pulses, and there is no HALT condition. Also, you cannot stretch clock pulses.** Slow memories are accommodated in the more traditional manner, by allowing you to insert extra machine cycles, equivalent to 8080A Wait states.

Table 10-1. A Comparison of MCS6500 Series and the MC6800 CPU Devices

| CPU | CPU Pins and Signals | | | | | | | | | | | | | | Comments |
|---|---|---|---|---|---|---|---|---|---|---|---|---|---|---|---|
| | Address Bus | Data Bus | Φ0 | Φ1 | Φ2 | RDY | $\overline{IRQ}$ | $\overline{NMI}$ | SYNC | $\overline{RES}$/$\overline{RESET}$* | SO | R/$\overline{W}$ | DBE | Pins | |
| 6502 | A0-A15 | D0-D7 | I | O | O | I | I | I | O | I | I | O | | 40 | This is the on-chip-clock version of the 6512. |
| 6503 | A0-A11 | D0-D7 | I | | O | | I | I | | I | | O | | 28 | This is the on-chip-clock version of the 6513. |
| 6504 | A0-A12 | D0-D7 | I | | O | | I | | | I | | O | | 28 | This is the on-chip-clock version of the 6514. |
| 6505 | A0-A11 | D0-D7 | I | | O | I | I | | | I | | O | | 28 | This is the on-chip-clock version of the 6515. |
| 6506 | A0-A11 | D0-D7 | I | O | O | | I | | | I | | O | | 28 | On-chip-clock version, 4K memory, $\overline{IRQ}$, Φ1 (out) and Φ2 (out). |
| 6507 | A0-A12 | D0-D7 | I | | O | I | | | | I | | O | | 28 | 8K memory without $\overline{IRQ}$ and with RDY. |
| 6512 | A0-A15 | D0-D7 | | I | I/O | I | I | I | O | I | I | O | I | 40 | This CPU is most like the MC6800. The HALT, VMA, TSC and BA signals are not present. SYNC, SO, Φ2 (out) and RDY are added. |
| 6513 | A0-A11 | D0-D7 | | I | I | | I | I | | I | | O | | 28 | 4K memory with $\overline{IRQ}$ and $\overline{NMI}$. |
| 6514 | A0-A11 | D0-D7 | | I | I | | I | | | I | | O | | 28 | 8K memory with $\overline{IRQ}$. |
| 6515 | A0-A11 | D0-D7 | | I | I | I | I | | | I | | O | | 28 | 4K memory with $\overline{IRQ}$ and RDY. |
| MC6800 | A0-A15 | D0-D7 | | I | I | | I | I | | I | | O | I | 40 | The MC6800 TSC, VMA, BA and HALT signals are not implemented on any MCS6500 CPU. |

*The second name is the name used by MC6800 literature for the same signal.

Within CPU Pins and Signals columns, I identifies an input signal present,
O identifies an output signal present,
I/O identifies a signal that appears twice, at two pins, one as an input, the other as an output.

65xx parts use a 1 MHz clock.
65xx A parts use a 2 MHz clock.
65xx B parts use a 3 MHz clock.

If you are making extensive use of clock stretching, or DMA data transfers during Halt states, in an MC6800 microcomputer system, switching to an MCS6500 CPU will require considerable system redesign.

**In order to refresh dynamic memory in an MCS6500 system, you must "steal" machine cycles by inserting Wait states, as you would for slow memories.**

**MOS Technology, the principal manufacturer of the MCS6500 product line, is located at:**

MOS TECHNOLOGY, INC.
950 Rittenhouse Road
Norristown, PA 19401

Second sources are:

SYNERTEK, INC.
1901 Old Middlefield Way
Mountain View, CA 94043

ROCKWELL INTERNATIONAL
Microelectronic Devices
P.O. Box 3669, RC55
Anaheim, CA 92803

Since Honeywell acquired Synertek, MOS Technology has become the smallest of the three 6500 series sources. Many new parts are being designed by Rockwell and Synertek, therefore it may be more accurate to treat all three 6500 sources as equal.

**The MCS6500 devices use a single +5 V power supply. Using a 1 microsecond clock, instruction execution times range from 2 to 12 microseconds.**

**All MCS6500 devices have TTL-level compatible signals.**

**N-channel, silicon gate, depletion load MOS technology is used for MCS6500 devices.**

Three series of 6500 microprocessors are available, differing only in clock speed. For details see Table 10-1.

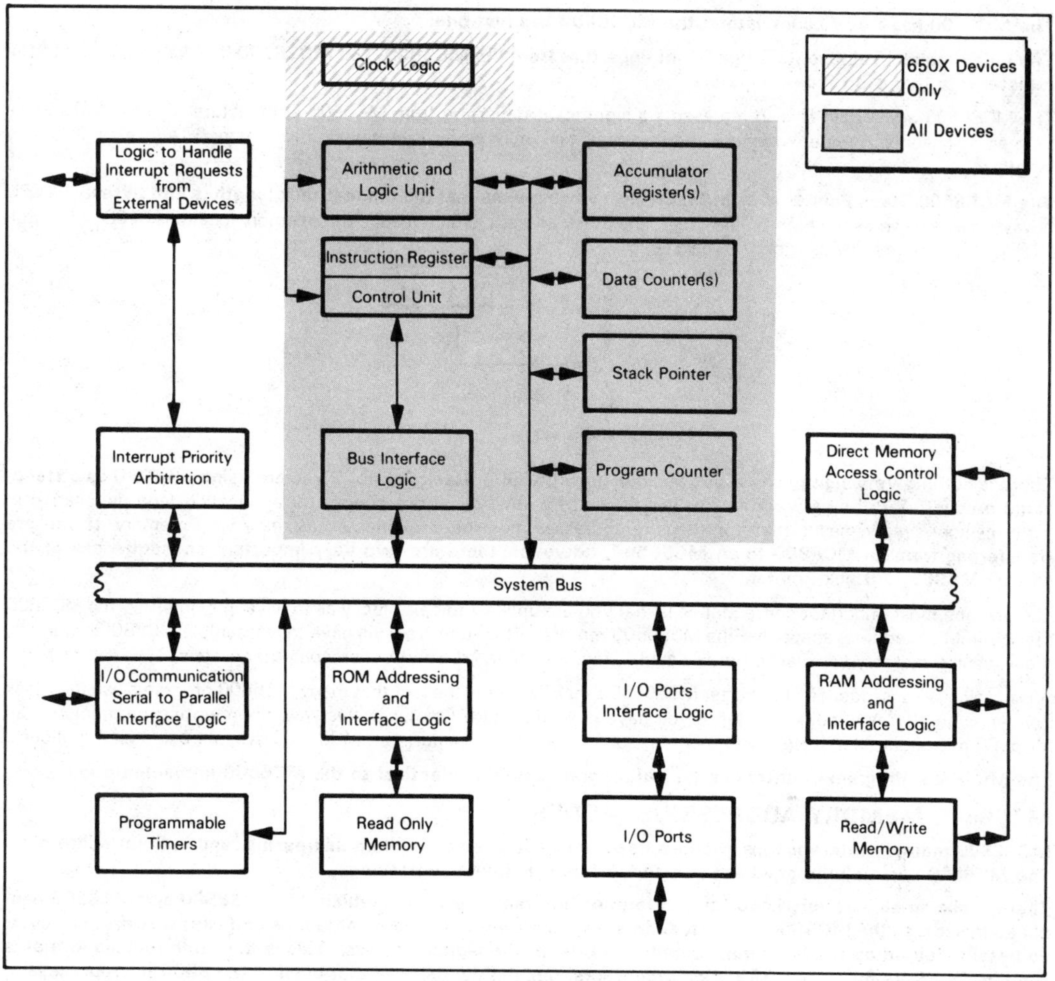

Figure 10-1. Logic of MCS6500 Series CPU Devices

# THE MCS6500 SERIES CPUs

**Functions implemented on each of the MCS6500 CPUs are illustrated in Figure 10-1. As this figure would imply, capabilities offered by the various MCS6500 CPUs differ in scope rather than function.**

## MCS6500 SERIES CPU PROGRAMMABLE REGISTERS

**The MCS6500 series CPUs all have the same programmable registers; they may be illustrated as follows:**

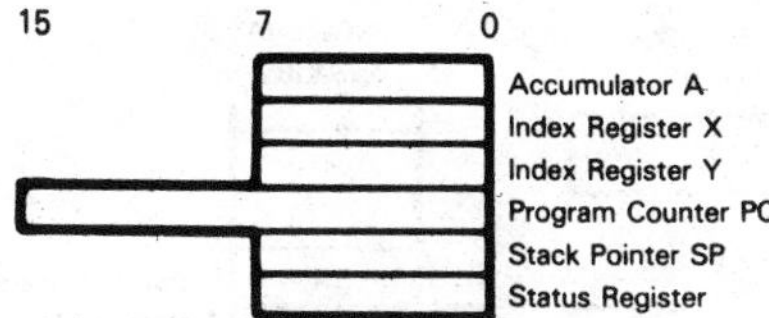

**The MC6800 has two Accumulators; the MCS6500 has just one.**

**The Index register represents a significant departure from the MC6800. The MCS6500 breaks one 16-bit Index register into two 8-bit Index registers.**

The MCS6500 Stack Pointer also represents a significant departure from MC6800 architecture. The MC6800 Stack Pointer is sixteen bits wide, which means that the Stack may be located anywhere in memory, and may be of any length.

**The MCS6500 Stack Pointer is eight bits wide, which means that maximum Stack length is 256 bytes.** The CPU always inserts $01_{16}$ as the high-order byte of any Stack address, which means that memory locations $0100_{16}$ through $01FF_{16}$ are permanently assigned to the Stack:

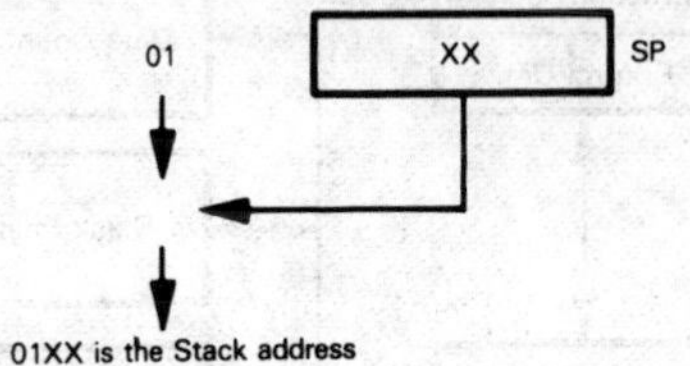


**There is nothing very significant about the shorter MCS6500 Stack Pointer if you are using this CPU as a stand-alone product.** A 256-byte Stack is usually sufficient for any typical microcomputer application; and its location in early memory simply means that low memory addresses must be implemented as read/write memory. **If you are transferring from an MC6800 to an MCS6500, however, there are two very important consequences of the shorter MCS6500 Stack Pointer.**

The first and most important consequence is that you are unlikely to be so lucky as to have implemented the MC6800 Stack within the address space that the MCS6500 requires. Therefore, you will have to reassemble MC6800 programs, repartitioning memory in order to run the same programs in an MCS6500 microcomputer system.

A less obvious consequence of a shorter MCS6500 Stack Pointer is the fact that many MC6800 programs use the Stack Pointer as an alternate Index register. If you have used the Stack Pointer in this way when writing programs for an MC6800 microcomputer system, the program conversion, when going to an MCS6500 system, could be significant.

**The MCS6500 Program Counter is a typical program counter, identical to the MC6800 implementation.**

## MCS6500 MEMORY ADDRESSING MODES

**MCS6500 memory reference instructions use direct addressing, indexed addressing, and indirect addressing. The MC6800 has no indirect addressing and different indexed addressing.**

**There is one small, but very important, difference between the way in which the MCS6500 and MC6800 handle addresses. In the MCS6500, 16-bit addresses are stored with the eight least significant bits first (at lower address) followed by the eight most significant bits (at the higher address). This is the same technique that is used in the 8080, 8085, and Z80 microprocessors, but the opposite of that used in the 6800 microprocessor.**

**The MC6800 and MCS6500 have identical direct addressing.** Three-byte instructions use the second and third bytes of the object code to provide a direct, 16-bit address; therefore, 65,536 bytes of memory can be addressed directly. The commonly used memory reference instructions also have a two-byte object code variation, where the second byte directly addresses one of the first 256 bytes of memory.

**MCS6500 direct indexed addressing differs markedly from MC6800 indexed addressing.**

**The MCS6500 offers base page, indexed addressing.** In this case, the instruction has two bytes of object code. The contents of either the X or Y Index registers are added to the second object code byte in order to compute a memory address. This may be illustrated as follows:

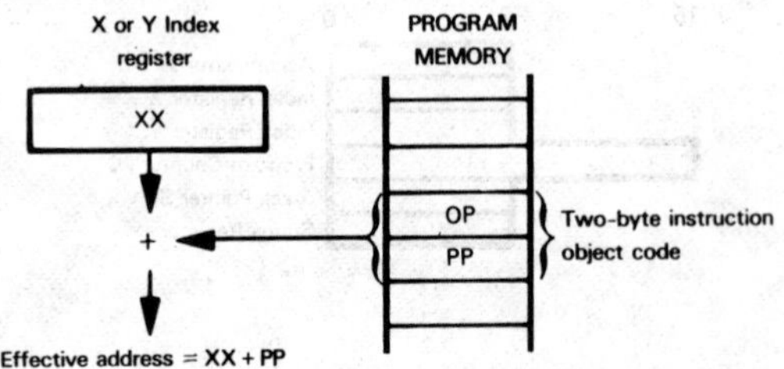

Base page, indexed addressing, as illustrated above, is wraparound — which means that there is no carry. If the sum of the Index register and second object code byte contents is more than $FF_{16}$, the carry bit will be discarded. This may be illustrated as follows:

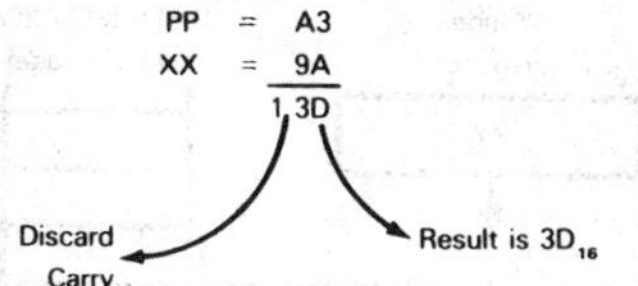


**Absolute indexed addressing is also provided.** In this case, the contents of either the X or the Y Index register are added to a 16-bit direct address provided by the second and third bytes of an instruction's object code. This may be illustrated as follows:

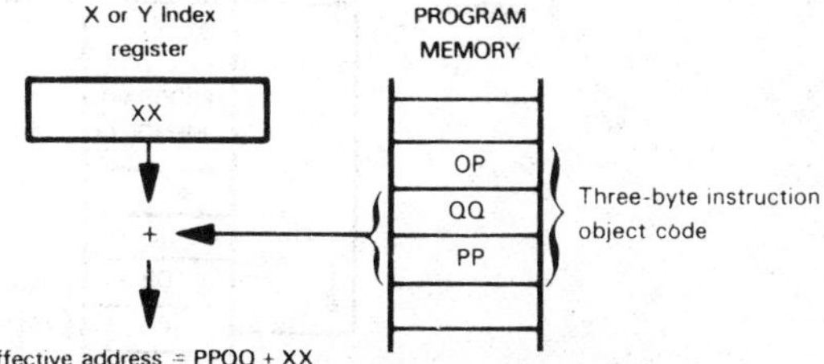


**Indirect addressing represents a feature of the MCS6500 which the MC6800 does not have. Instructions that use simple indirect addressing have three bytes of object code.** The second and third object code bytes provide a 16-bit address; therefore, the indirect address can be located anywhere in memory. This is straightforward indirect addressing, as described in Volume 1, Chapter 6.

**MCS6500 indirect, indexed addressing comes in two forms: there is pre-indexed indirect addressing and there is post-indexed indirect addressing.**

In each case the instruction object code is two bytes long and the second object code byte provides an 8-bit address.

**Instructions with pre-indexed indirect addressing add the contents of the X Index register and the second object code byte** to access a memory location in the first 256 bytes of memory, where the indirect address will be found:

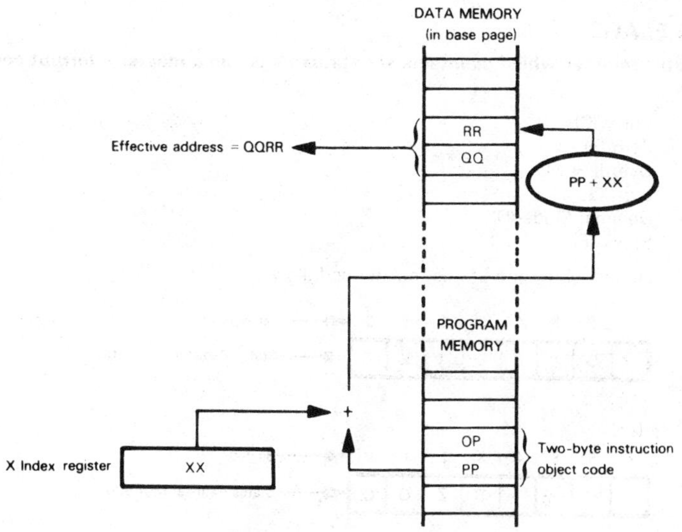


When using pre-indexed indirect addressing, once again wraparound addition is used, which means that when the X Index register contents are added to the second object code byte, any carry will be discarded. Note that only the X Index register can be used with pre-indexed indirect addressing.

**The Y Index register is used for post-indexed indirect addressing;** now the second object code byte identifies a location in the first 256 bytes of memory where an indirect address will be found. The contents of the Y Index register are added to this indirect address. This may be illustrated as follows:

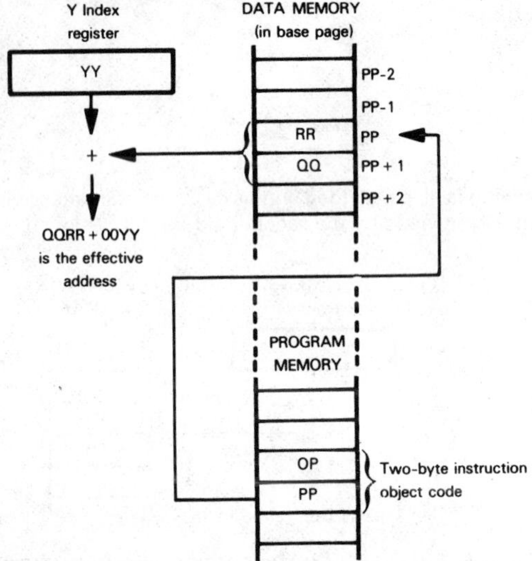


Note that only the Y Index register can be used with post-indexed indirect addressing.

**MCS6500 Branch and Branch-on-Condition instructions use program relative, direct addressing as described for the MC6800.** These instructions have two bytes of object code. The second object code byte is treated as an 8-bit, signed binary number, which is added to the Program Counter after the Program Counter contents have been incremented to address the next sequential instruction. This allows displacements in the range +127 through -128 bytes from the next instruction.

The MCS6500 literature uses the term implied addressing, as Motorola's MC6800 literature does, to describe instructions that identify one of the programmable registers. **The MCS6500 does not have implied addressing as the term is used in this book.**

## MCS6500 STATUS FLAGS

**The MCS6500 has a Status register which maintains six status flags and a master interrupt control bit. These are the six status flags:**

Carry (C)
Zero (Z)
Overflow (O)
Sign (S)
Decimal Mode (D)
Break (B)

Statuses are assigned bit positions within the Status register as follows:

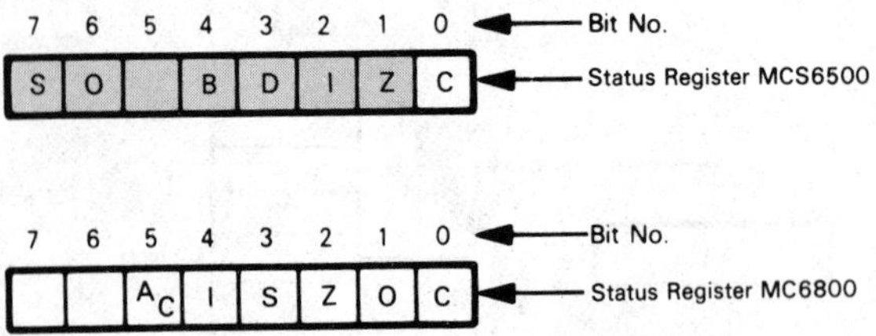


In the illustration above, MCS6500 statuses and status bit assignments that differ from MC6800 equivalents have been shaded.

The Carry, Zero and Sign statuses are standard and are identical in function to those of the MC6800.

Carry represents any carry out of bit 7 during arithmetic or logical operations.

Zero is set to 1 when any arithmetic or logical operation results in a 0 value. Zero is set to 0 otherwise.

The Sign status will acquire the value of the high-order (Sign) bit of any arithmetic operation result. Thus, a Sign status value of 1 identifies a negative result and a Sign status of 0 identifies a positive result. The Sign status will be set or reset on the assumption that you are using signed binary arithmetic. If you are not using signed binary arithmetic, you can ignore the Sign status, or you can use it to identify the value of the high-order result bit.

The Decimal Mode and Break statuses have no MC6800 equivalent.

**The Decimal Mode status, when set, causes the Add-with-Carry and Subtract-with-Carry instructions to perform BCD operations.** Thus, when the Decimal Mode status is set and an Add-with-Carry or Subtract-with-Carry instruction is executed, CPU logic assumes that both source 8-bit values are valid BCD numbers — and the result generated will also be a valid BCD number. Because MCS6500 CPUs perform decimal addition and subtraction, there is no need for an Intermediate Carry status. This status is used for decimal adjust operations only, as described in Volume 1.

**The Break status pertains to software interrupts.** MCS6500 supports software interrupts, just as the MC6800 does. When a software interrupt is executed, however, MCS6500 CPU logic will set the Break status flag.

**I is a standard master interrupt enable/disable flag.** When I equals 1, interrupts are disabled; when I equals 0, interrupts are enabled.

**The Overflow status is a typical overflow, except that it can also be used as a control input.** Recall that an Overflow status represents a carry when performing signed binary arithmetic. The Overflow status has been discussed in detail in Volume 1; it equals the exclusive-OR of carries out of bits 6 and 7 when performing arithmetic operations. Some MCS6500 CPUs allow external logic to set or reset the Overflow status, in which case it can be used subsequently as a general logic indicator; you must be very careful when using the Overflow status in this way, since the same status flag will be modified by arithmetic instructions. It is up to you, as a programmer, to make sure that an instruction which modifies the Overflow status is not executed in between the time external logic sets or resets this status, and subsequent program logic tests it.

## MCS6500 CPU PINS AND SIGNALS

**Figures 10-2 through 10-10 illustrate pins and signals for the nine CPUs of the MCS6500 family. Shaded pins in Figures 10-2 and 10-7 identify signals which are identical to the MC6800, both in pin location and signal type. Most of the 28-pin MCS6500 series CPUs have signals which are identical to those of the MC6800; however, between a 40-pin DIP and a 28-pin DIP, it is impossible to talk about pin compatibility.**

MCS6500 signals may be divided between those that have MC6800 equivalents and those that do not. We are going to describe all of the MCS6500 series signals, as a group. **In order to determine which signals are available on the different MCS6500 CPUs, see Table 10-1.**

**Let us begin with the signals which are direct reproductions of MC6800 signals.**

**DATA BUS ENABLE (DBE).** Only the MCS6512 CPU supports this signal. This signal is input low in order to float the Data Bus. DBE is frequently tied to the Φ2 clock input, in which case Φ2 and DBE are identical signals.

**READ/WRITE (R/$\overline{\text{W}}$).** When high, this signal indicates that the CPU wishes to read data off the Data Bus; when low, this signal indicates that the CPU is outputting data on the Data Bus. The normal standby state for this signal is "read" (high).

**INTERRUPT REQUEST ($\overline{\text{IRQ}}$).** This signal is used by external logic to request an interrupt. If interrupts have been enabled, then the CPU will acknowledge an interrupt at the end of the currently executing instruction. There is a small difference between MCS6500 and MC6800 interrupt acknowledge logic. **The MC6800 cannot acknowledge an interrupt while it is in the Halt state. The MCS6500 has no Halt state,** therefore this situation cannot arise.

**NONMASKABLE INTERRUPT ($\overline{\text{NMI}}$).** This signal differs from $\overline{\text{IRQ}}$ in that it cannot be inhibited. Typically this input is used for catastrophic interrupts such as power failure. Not all of the MCS6500 series CPUs provide this signal.

**$\overline{\text{RESET}}$.** This is a typical RESET signal. Reset logic within an MCS6500 microcomputer system is identical to Reset logic within an MC6800 microcomputer system.

**Next consider MC6800 signals which are the same on some MCS6500 CPUs, but not on others.**

**The clock signals $\Phi1$ and $\Phi2$ are identical to MC6800 clock signals for the MCS651X series CPUs.** These CPUs require external clock signals whose waveforms are identical to the MC6800. **The MCS650X series CPUs have clock logic on the CPU chip; these CPUs output $\Phi2$;** the MCS6502 and the MCS6506 output $\Phi1$ as well.

**The Data Bus of the MCS6500 series CPUs is identical to that of the MC6800.** The Data Bus is a tristate, 8-bit bidirectional bus via which data is transferred between memory and all MCS6500 microcomputer system devices. **However, only the MCS6512 has a DBE input for external control of the bus.** On MCS6500 CPUs other than the MCS6512, an internal Data Bus Enable is connected to $\Phi2$; in these devices the Data Bus is always floated during the first part of a machine cycle

**We will now look at the CPU signals which are unique to the MCS6500 microcomputer system.**

**The Address Bus** in MCS6500 microcomputer systems is not a tristate bus and cannot be floated. Also, the 28-pin MCS6500 series CPUs have either 12 or 13 Address Bus lines, allowing a total memory space of either 4K or 8K bytes. The Address Bus is used in the normal way by the CPU to output memory addresses.

**READY (RDY) is an input control signal** which, in MCS6500 microcomputer systems, performs the task of MC6800 TSC, DBE and $\overline{\text{HALT}}$ signals. The RDY input causes the equivalent of a Wait machine cycle to be inserted within the normal machine cycle sequence. In order to generate a Wait machine cycle, RDY must make a high-to-low transition during a $\Phi1$ high clock pulse in any machine cycle other than a write. We will illustrate the use of the RDY signal, and discuss a number of its non-obvious ramifications, following this summary description of MCS6500 signals.

**The Set Overflow flag (SO) signal can be used to set to 1 the Overflow bit** of the Status register. When the SO input makes a high-to-low transition, the Overflow status is set to 1. The SO input can make a high-to-low transition at any time; this is an asynchronous input.

You cannot use the SO input signal to reset the Overflow bit of the Status register to 0.

**The SYNC signal is used to identify instruction fetch machine cycles.** There are a number of important uses for this signal, which we will discuss along with general instruction timing.

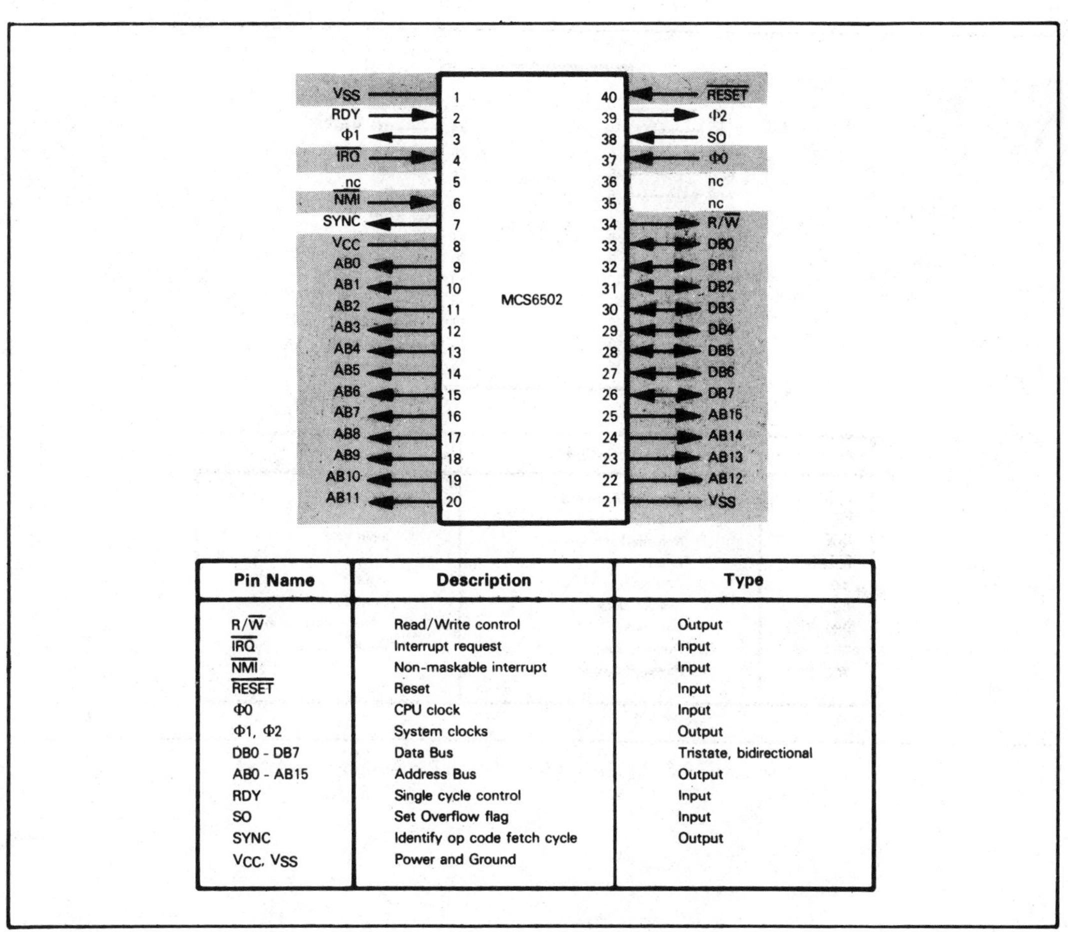


| Pin Name | Description | Type |
|---|---|---|
| R/$\overline{W}$ | Read/Write control | Output |
| $\overline{IRQ}$ | Interrupt request | Input |
| $\overline{NMI}$ | Non-maskable interrupt | Input |
| $\overline{RESET}$ | Reset | Input |
| Φ0 | CPU clock | Input |
| Φ1, Φ2 | System clocks | Output |
| DB0 - DB7 | Data Bus | Tristate, bidirectional |
| AB0 - AB15 | Address Bus | Output |
| RDY | Single cycle control | Input |
| SO | Set Overflow flag | Input |
| SYNC | Identify op code fetch cycle | Output |
| $V_{CC}$, $V_{SS}$ | Power and Ground | |

Figure 10-2. MCS6502 Signals and Pin Assignments

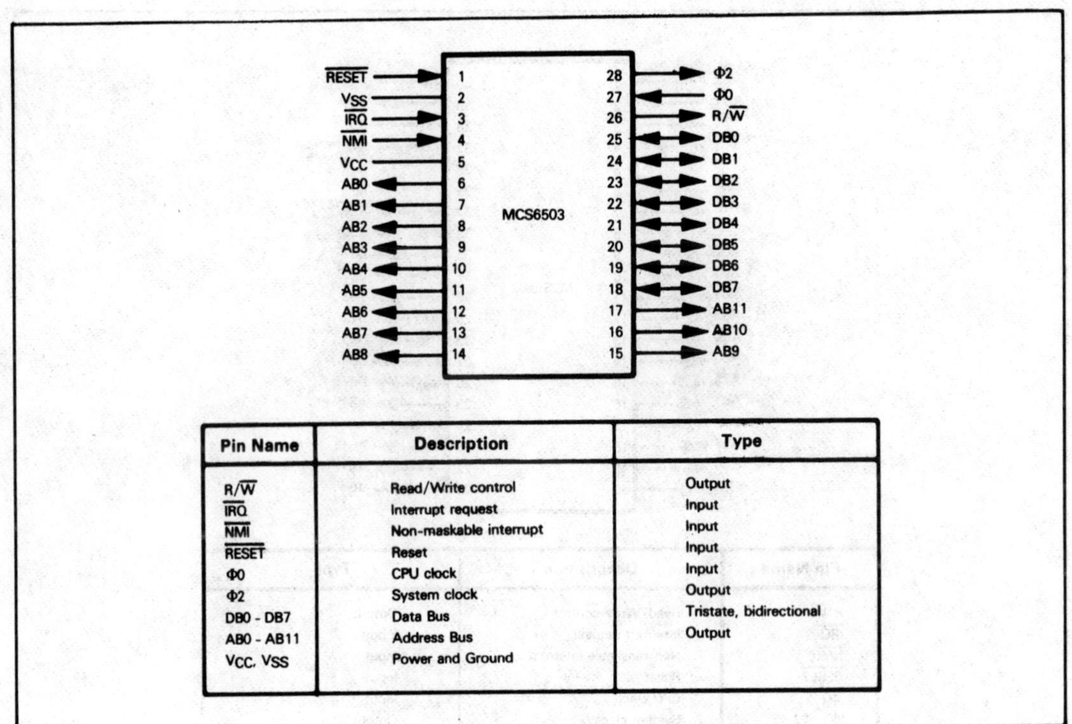


| Pin Name | Description | Type |
|---|---|---|
| R/$\overline{W}$ | Read/Write control | Output |
| $\overline{IRQ}$ | Interrupt request | Input |
| $\overline{NMI}$ | Non-maskable interrupt | Input |
| $\overline{RESET}$ | Reset | Input |
| Φ0 | CPU clock | Input |
| Φ2 | System clock | Output |
| DB0 - DB7 | Data Bus | Tristate, bidirectional |
| AB0 - AB11 | Address Bus | Output |
| $V_{CC}$, $V_{SS}$ | Power and Ground | |

Figure 10-3. MCS6503 Signals and Pin Assignments

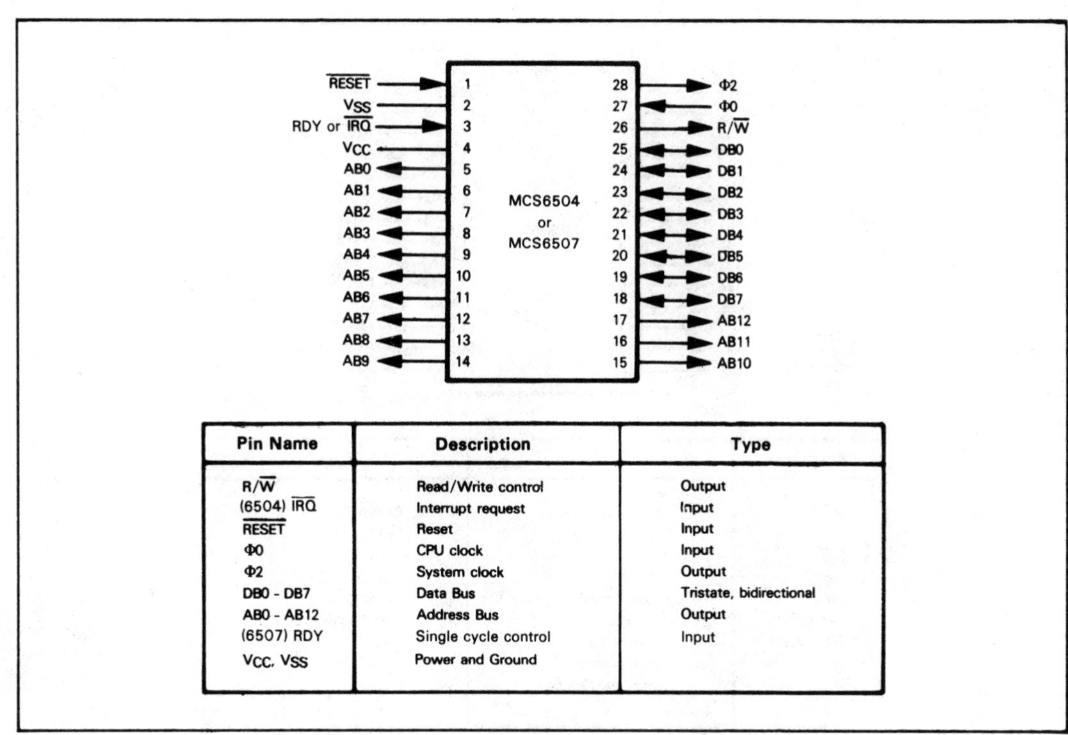


| Pin Name | Description | Type |
|---|---|---|
| R/$\overline{W}$ | Read/Write control | Output |
| (6504) $\overline{IRQ}$ | Interrupt request | Input |
| $\overline{RESET}$ | Reset | Input |
| Φ0 | CPU clock | Input |
| Φ2 | System clock | Output |
| DB0 - DB7 | Data Bus | Tristate, bidirectional |
| AB0 - AB12 | Address Bus | Output |
| (6507) RDY | Single cycle control | Input |
| $V_{CC}$, $V_{SS}$ | Power and Ground | |

Figure 10-4. MCS6504 Signals and Pin Assignments

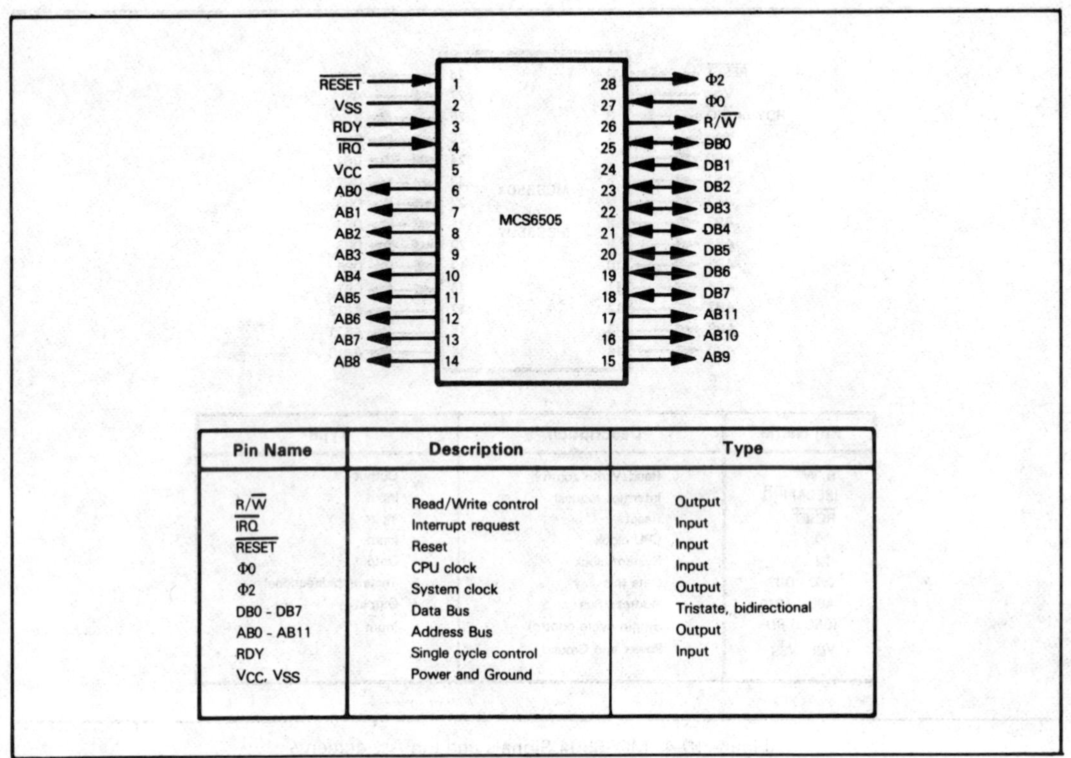


| Pin Name | Description | Type |
|---|---|---|
| R/$\overline{W}$ | Read/Write control | Output |
| $\overline{IRQ}$ | Interrupt request | Input |
| $\overline{RESET}$ | Reset | Input |
| Φ0 | CPU clock | Input |
| Φ2 | System clock | Output |
| DB0 - DB7 | Data Bus | Tristate, bidirectional |
| AB0 - AB11 | Address Bus | Output |
| RDY | Single cycle control | Input |
| $V_{CC}$, $V_{SS}$ | Power and Ground | |

Figure 10-5. MCS6505 Signals and Pin Assignments

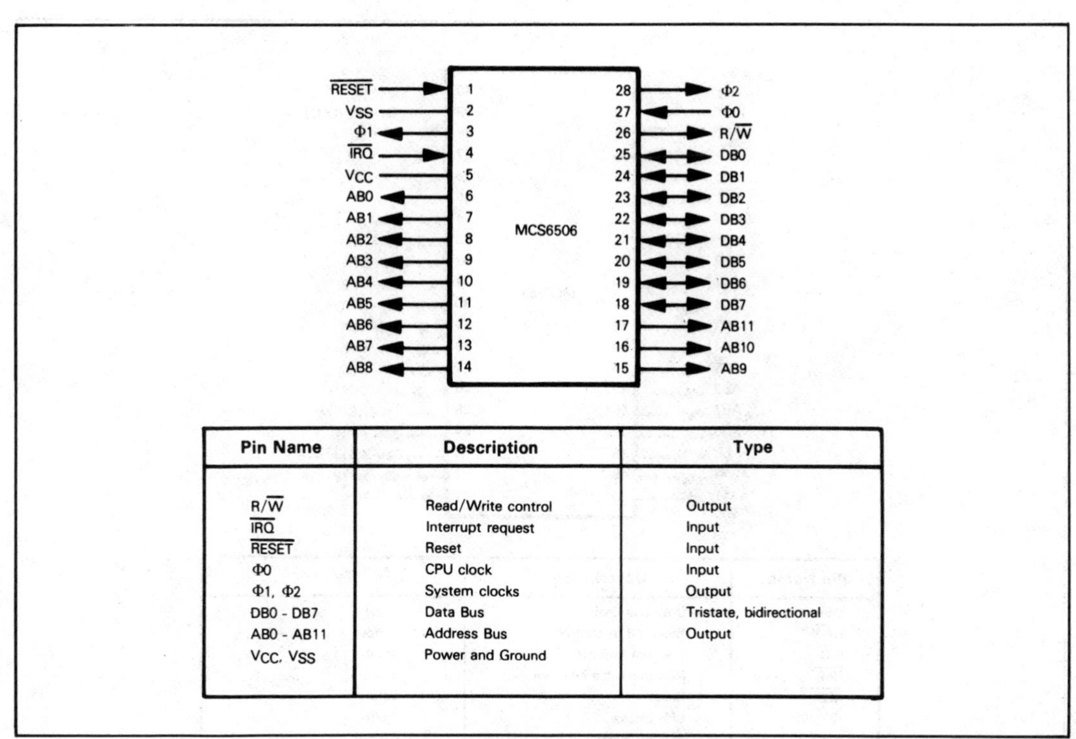


| Pin Name | Description | Type |
|---|---|---|
| R/$\overline{\text{W}}$ | Read/Write control | Output |
| $\overline{\text{IRQ}}$ | Interrupt request | Input |
| $\overline{\text{RESET}}$ | Reset | Input |
| Φ0 | CPU clock | Input |
| Φ1, Φ2 | System clocks | Output |
| DB0 - DB7 | Data Bus | Tristate, bidirectional |
| AB0 - AB11 | Address Bus | Output |
| $V_{CC}$, $V_{SS}$ | Power and Ground | |

Figure 10-6. MCS6506 Signals and Pin Assignments

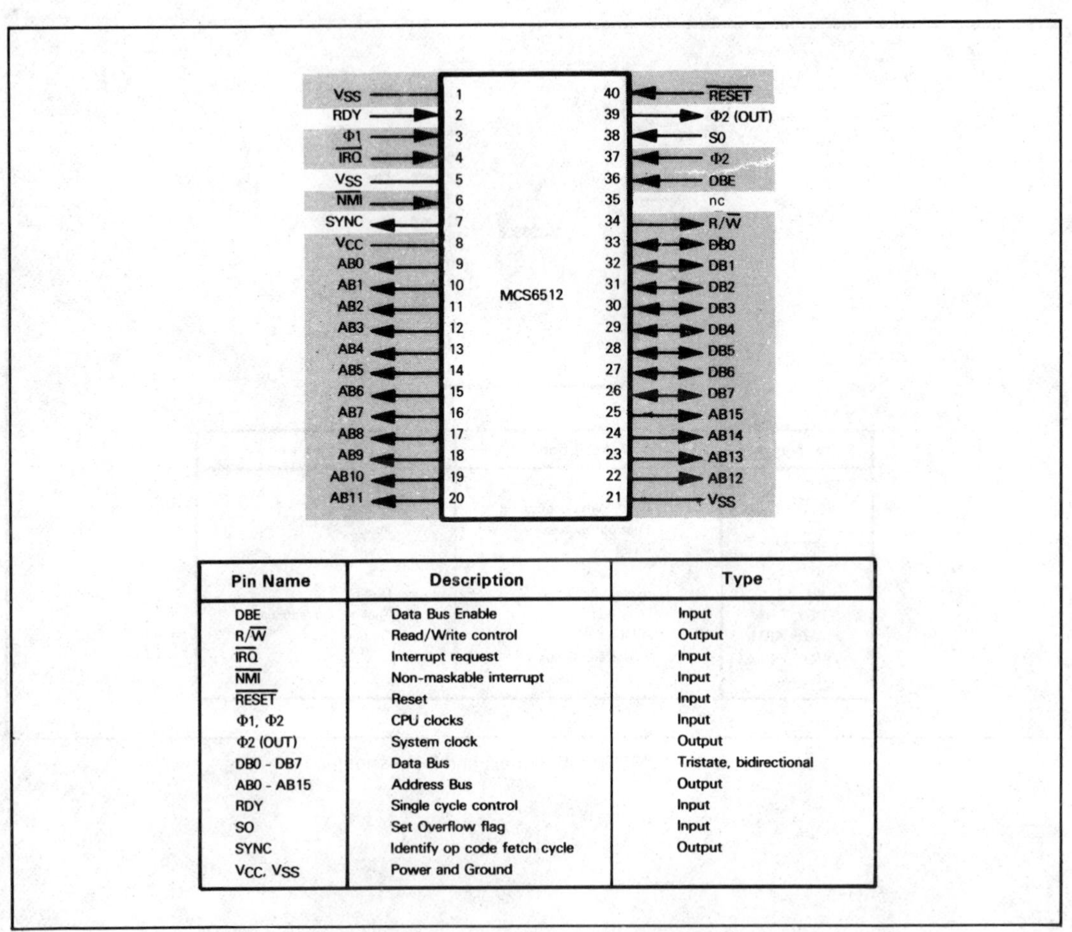


| Pin Name | Description | Type |
|---|---|---|
| DBE | Data Bus Enable | Input |
| R/W | Read/Write control | Output |
| IRQ | Interrupt request | Input |
| NMI | Non-maskable interrupt | Input |
| RESET | Reset | Input |
| Φ1, Φ2 | CPU clocks | Input |
| Φ2 (OUT) | System clock | Output |
| DB0 - DB7 | Data Bus | Tristate, bidirectional |
| AB0 - AB15 | Address Bus | Output |
| RDY | Single cycle control | Input |
| SO | Set Overflow flag | Input |
| SYNC | Identify op code fetch cycle | Output |
| VCC, VSS | Power and Ground | |

Figure 10-7. MCS6512 Signals and Pin Assignments

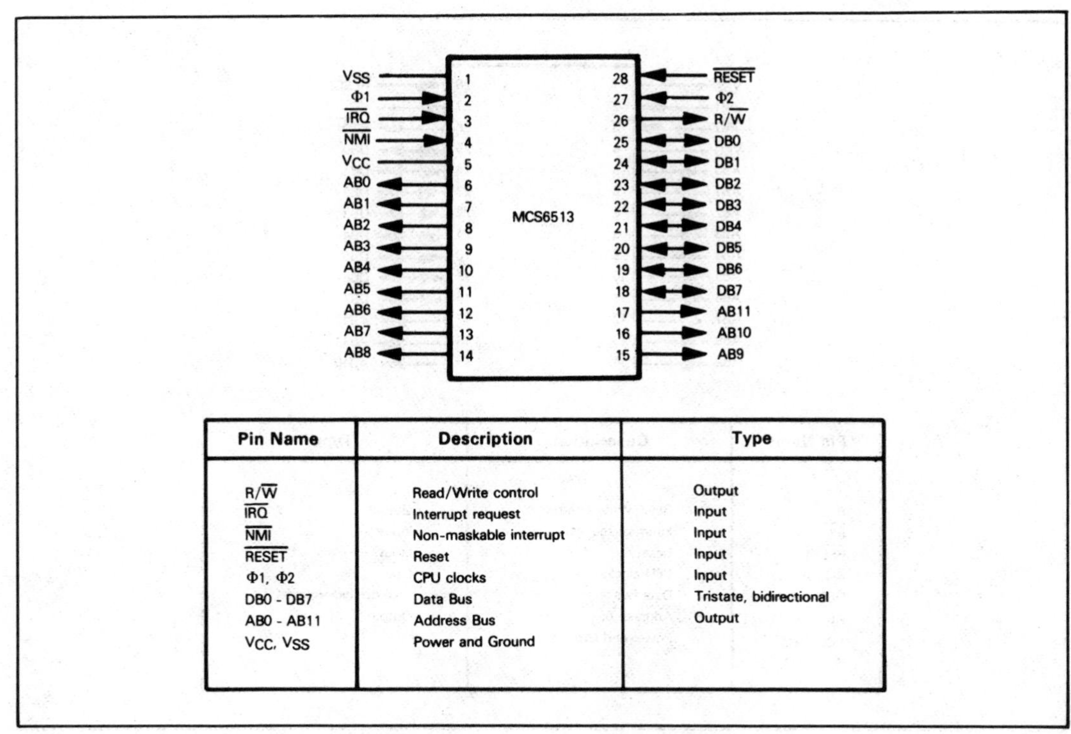


| Pin Name | Description | Type |
| --- | --- | --- |
| $R/\overline{W}$ | Read/Write control | Output |
| $\overline{IRQ}$ | Interrupt request | Input |
| $\overline{NMI}$ | Non-maskable interrupt | Input |
| $\overline{RESET}$ | Reset | Input |
| $\Phi 1$, $\Phi 2$ | CPU clocks | Input |
| DB0 - DB7 | Data Bus | Tristate, bidirectional |
| AB0 - AB11 | Address Bus | Output |
| $V_{CC}$, $V_{SS}$ | Power and Ground | |

Figure 10-8. MCS6513 Signals and Pin Assignments

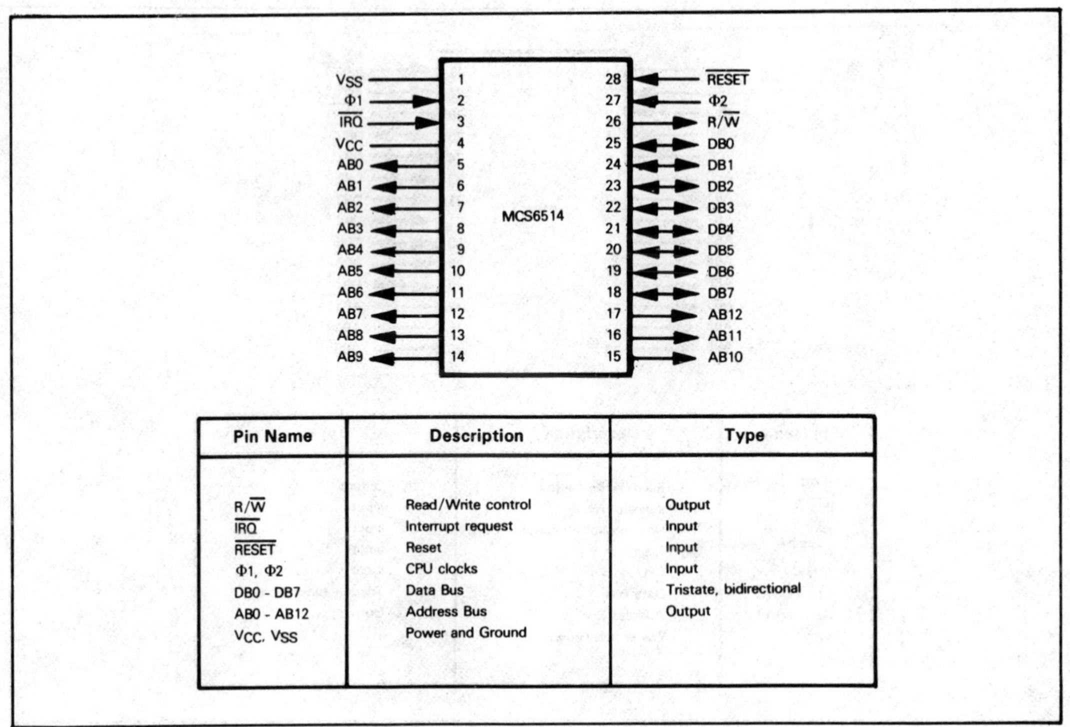


| Pin Name | Description | Type |
|---|---|---|
| R/W | Read/Write control | Output |
| IRQ | Interrupt request | Input |
| RESET | Reset | Input |
| Φ1, Φ2 | CPU clocks | Input |
| DB0 - DB7 | Data Bus | Tristate, bidirectional |
| AB0 - AB12 | Address Bus | Output |
| $V_{CC}$, $V_{SS}$ | Power and Ground | |

Figure 10-9. MCS6514 Signals and Pin Assignments

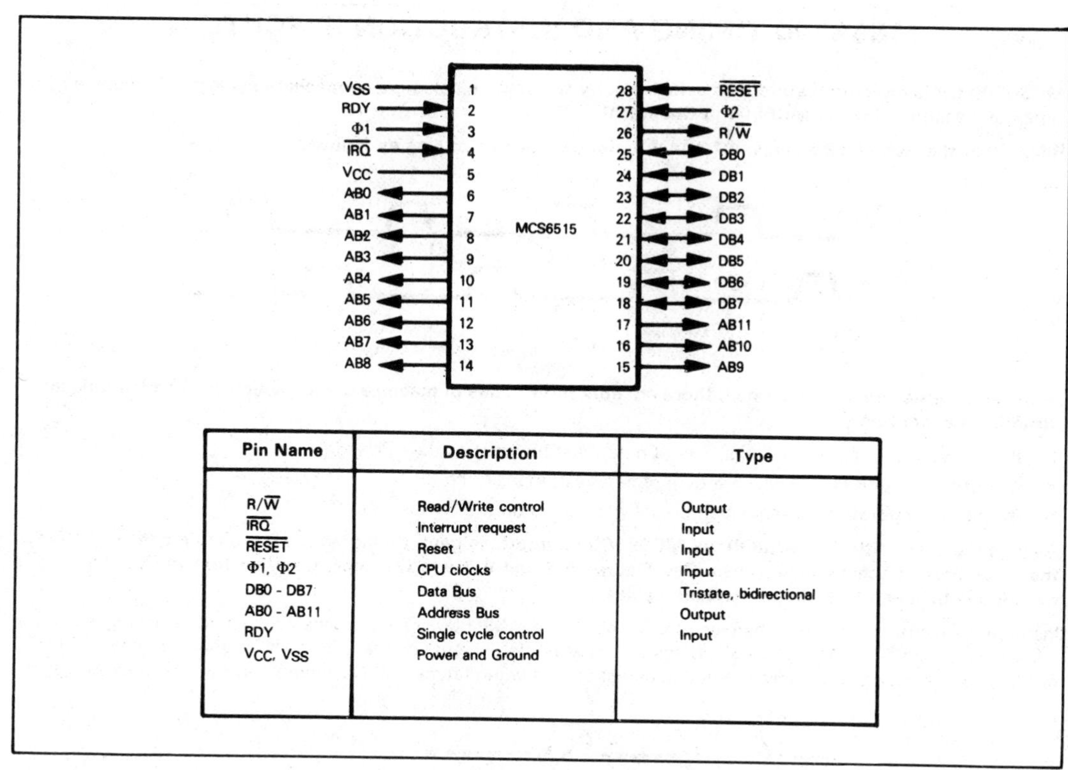


| Pin Name | Description | Type |
|---|---|---|
| R/$\overline{W}$ | Read/Write control | Output |
| $\overline{IRQ}$ | Interrupt request | Input |
| $\overline{RESET}$ | Reset | Input |
| Φ1, Φ2 | CPU clocks | Input |
| DB0 - DB7 | Data Bus | Tristate, bidirectional |
| AB0 - AB11 | Address Bus | Output |
| RDY | Single cycle control | Input |
| $V_{CC}$, $V_{SS}$ | Power and Ground | |

Figure 10-10. MCS6515 Signals and Pin Assignments

# MCS6500 TIMING AND INSTRUCTION EXECUTION

**MCS6500 CPUs execute instructions using exactly the same clock signals, machine cycles and machine cycle types as described for the MC6800 in Chapter 9.**

**Recall that the two clock signals, Φ1 and Φ2, define machine cycles as follows:**

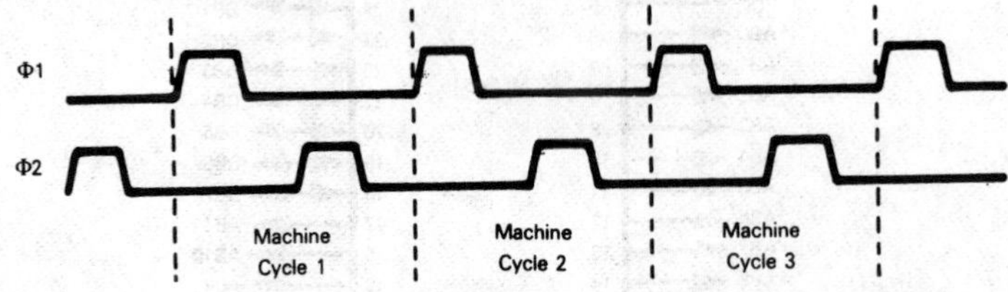


**So far as external logic is concerned, there are only three types of machine cycles which can occur during an instruction's execution:**

1) **A read operation** during which a byte of data must be input to the CPU.
2) **A write operation** during which a byte of data is output by the CPU.
3) **An internal operation** during which no activity occurs on the System Bus.

**As was the case with the MC6800, all MCS6500 instructions have timing which is a simple concatenation of the three basic machine cycle types. See Figures 9-3 and 9-4 and the accompanying text in Chapter 9 for a description of these three basic machine cycles.**

Instruction execution differences between the MC6800 and MCS6500 arise only when we depart from simple instruction execution logic. The MCS6500 SYNC signal is also a difference to be noted; the SYNC signal identifies MCS6500 machine cycles during which any instruction object code is being fetched. SYNC timing may be illustrated as follows:

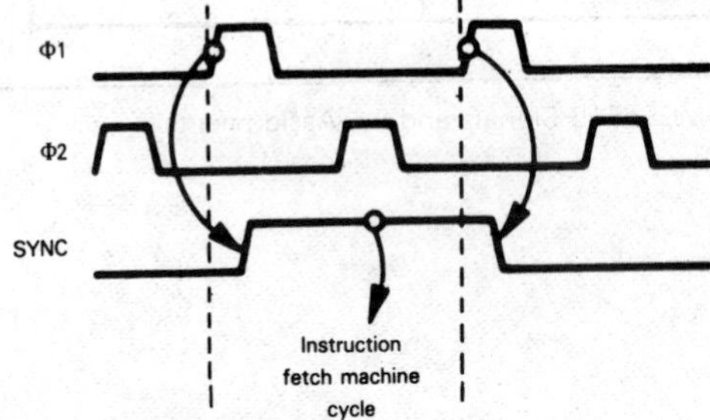


MCS6500 CPUs do not allow the Φ1 and Φ2 clocks to be stretched, nor do they allow the Address Bus to be floated; some MCS6500 CPU versions do not allow the Data Bus to be floated. Also, there is no Halt state. **The single RDY signal is used to interface slow memories, to refresh dynamic memories or to perform Direct Memory Access operations.**

**What the RDY input signal does is allow you to insert one or more Wait machine cycles in between two normal instruction execution machine cycles:**

**MCS6500 WAIT STATE**

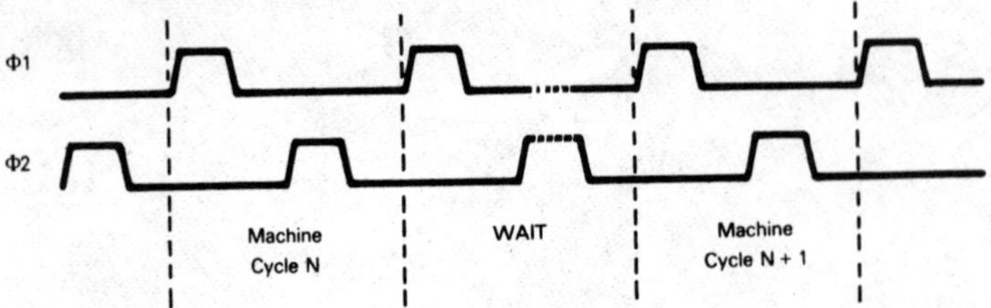

The RDY input allows Wait machine cycles to be inserted within any instruction's normal sequence of machine cycles. For Wait machine cycles to occur, the RDY input must make a high-to-low transition during a Φ1 high clock pulse. This transition may occur during any nonwrite machine cycle. Timing may be illustrated as follows:

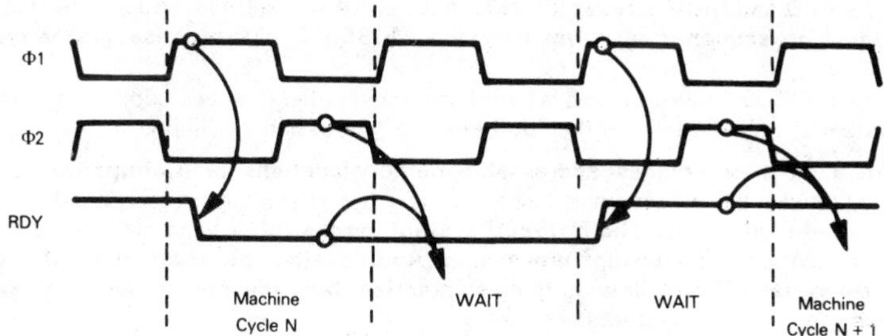


Wait machine cycles will be inserted until RDY is sensed high during a Φ2 high pulse.

If a RDY high-to-low transition occurs during a write machine cycle, then the Wait states will still be inserted, but the insertion will occur following the next nonwrite machine cycle.

**A non-obvious feature of the MCS6500 RDY signal is the fact that there is no acknowledge response from the CPU to external logic.** This can be a problem. To guarantee that the machine cycle following the RDY high-to-low transition will be a Wait, you must make sure that RDY never makes a high-to-low transition during a write cycle. Fortunately, you can use the R/$\overline{W}$ output to detect write cycles and thus generate a safe RDY input. Here is simple sample logic:

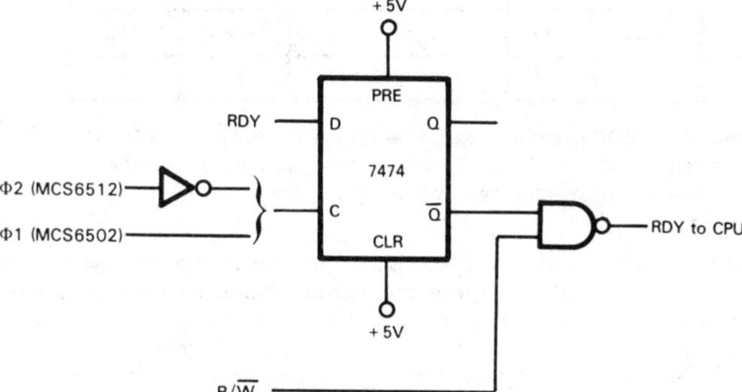


Since the same Φ2 clock pulse that triggers the 7474 flip-flop also triggers any change in R/$\overline{W}$ signal level, R/$\overline{W}$ is NANDed with $\overline{Q}$ after taking the 7474 settling delay — which also gives R/$\overline{W}$ time to acquire its new level.

If you are interfacing slow memories, performing Direct Memory Access or refreshing dynamic memories, in each case the extra time provided for the secondary operation is the Wait state generated via the RDY input, as we have just described.

**MCS6500 SLOW MEMORY INTERFACE**

**When interfacing slow memories,** the logic of the Wait state is self-evident. The slow memory simply has additional machine cycles in which to respond to the memory access, and memory select logic holds RDY low for any required time delay.

**When using a Wait state to perform Direct Memory Access or dynamic memory refresh operations,** there is a further complication. During the Wait state, the Data and Address Busses are not floated. Alternate Data and Address Busses must therefore be provided, connected via a tristate buffer to any memory device which is being accessed.

## MCS6500 INTERRUPT PROCESSING AND SYSTEM RESET

**The MCS6500 microcomputer system handles interrupts and reset operations quite similarly to the way that the MC6800 does, but there are a number of significant differences. Like the MC6800, the MCS6500 provides two interrupt inputs (IRQ and NMI), a reset (RESET) input and a software interrupt-type instruction. However, the interrupt processing sequence performed by the MCS6500 differs in several ways from that of the MC6800.**

Like the MC6800, the MCS6500 interrupt logic is based on polling rather than vectoring. For a discussion of this aspect of the interrupt system you should refer to the 6800 interrupt discussion in Chapter 9.

**The MCS6500 sets aside the six highest addressable memory locations for interrupt processing purposes.** Three 16-bit addresses are stored in these six memory locations, identifying the interrupt service routines' starting address for the four possible sources of interrupts. **The MC6800 system, on the other hand, sets aside the eight highest addressable memory locations for interrupt processing. Additionally, the assignments for these locations are different for the two systems. The following table summarizes how the memory locations are used for interrupt processing purposes for the two systems.**

| Interrupt Source | Address Used (Hex) | | | |
|---|---|---|---|---|
| | 6500 | | 6800 | |
| | MS Byte | LS Byte | MS Byte | LS Byte |
| IRQ | FFFF | FFFE | FFF8 | FFF9 |
| BRK Instruction | FFFF | FFFE | — | — |
| NMI | FFFB | FFFA | FFFC | FFFD |
| SWI Instruction | — | — | FFFA | FFFB |
| RESET | FFFD | FFFC | FFFE | FFFF |

**You can see that all of the MCS6500 memory assignments are different from those of the MC6800 system.** Additionally, as we have previously noted, the MCS6500 stores 16-bit addresses with the eight least significant bits at the lower address followed by the eight most significant bits at the higher address. This is the opposite of the system used in the 6800 microprocessor.

**Also note that the interrupt request (IRQ) and BRK instructions share the two memory locations (FFFF, FFFE) used to store the interrupt vector. The 6800 system, on the other hand, provided separate locations for the software interrupt (SWI) instruction.** Because IRQ and the BRK instruction use the same locations to store their interrupt vectors, the interrupt processing sequence which your program must perform will be a bit more complicated than a similar routine in the 6800: your program must determine whether the interrupt that it is serving is due to the IRQ input or execution of a BRK instruction.

**MCS6500 INTERRUPT PRIORITIES**

**There is an inherent priority in the MCS6500 interrupt structure which is essentially the same as that of the 6800 system.** In the event of simultaneous interrupt requests, this is the priority sequence during the acknowledge process:

| | | |
|---|---|---|
| Highest | (1) | Reset |
| | (2) | Nonmaskable interrupt (NMI) |
| | (3) | Break instruction |
| Lowest | (4) | Normal external interrupt (IRQ) |

**The operation and use of these interrupts is basically the same as we described for the MC6800 in Chapter 9, and you should refer to that description for a detailed discussion of the interrupts. The one significant difference is that the MCS6500 saves only the Program Counter and the Status register as it responds to an interrupt request.** This is the same approach used in 8080 systems but differs from the MC6800 which saves the contents of all the CPU registers during the interrupt acknowledge sequence. With the MCS6500, if you want to save the contents of the CPU registers, you must execute individual instructions to perform the operations which the MC6800 performs automatically.

**MCS6500 BREAK INSTRUCTION**

**The Break instruction provided by the MCS6500 is comparable to the software interrupt (SWI) instruction of the MC6800 but there are differences.** First, just as was the case with the hardware interrupt, **the Break instruction saves only the Program Counter and the Status register contents,** while the MC6800 SWI saves all of the CPU registers. Next, you will recall that **the Break instruction shares the vector storage locations with the IRQ interrupt while the SWI had its own separate vector storage locations.** When the Break instruction is executed, the Break status bit in the Status (P) register is set to 1 and then the Program Counter and Status register are pushed onto the Stack. Your interrupt routine must provide the instructions to differentiate between a Break instruction and a regular interrupt response. Since the contents of the Status register will have already been stored on the Stack, you must pull the contents of the Status register from the Stack to check the value of the B (break) status flag.

**One final difference between the Break instruction and the SWI of the MC6800 is that they have different op-codes.** This is hardly surprising, but it is significant because the op-code for the BRK instruction is 00. This choice of op-codes means that the BRK instruction can be used to patch programs in fusible-link PROMs, since blowing all the fuses makes the contents of a PROM word 00. Thus, an erroneous instruction in your PROM program can be corrected by changing the first object code byte to 00 and inserting a patch via the interrupt vector routine.

**There are two other minor differences that you should note between the interrupt systems of the MCS6500 and MC6800:**

1) Neither the MCS6500 nor the MC6800 will respond to an interrupt if the interrupt enable status bit has been set to 1. Additionally, the MC6800 will not respond to an interrupt while in the Halt state. The MCS6500 has no Halt state, but Wait states induced by the RDY line may be looked upon as equivalent. If an interrupt request occurs while Wait states are being created by an MCS6500 CPU in response to the RDY control input, then the interrupt response process will begin with the first non-Wait machine cycle.

2) The MCS6500 Stack is 256 bytes long and is implemented in memory locations $0100_{16}$ through $01FF_{16}$. The MC6800 Stack can have any length within the allowed memory space, and can be located anywhere in memory.

**The MCS6500 series microcomputers have no interrupt acknowledge signal.** You must create this signal by decoding off the Address Bus the interrupt acknowledge address $FFFF_{16}$, which is the second address to be output during the interrupt acknowledge sequence. Creating an interrupt acknowledge signal in this fashion is described later in this chapter.

## MCS6500 CPU CLOCK LOGIC

**Clock logic required by the MCS651X series of CPUs is identical to that which has already been described for the MC6800 in Chapter 9. Indeed, you can use any of the MC6870 series clock devices in order to create timing inputs.**

**The MCS650X series CPUs have on-chip logic; all they need is an external crystal or RC network. A number of possible circuits, described in MOS Technology literature, are reproduced in Figure 10-11.**

There are 1 MHz, 2 MHz, and 3 MHz versions of 6500 series microcomputers. See Table 10-1.

## MCS6500 CPU INTERFACE LOGIC

Look again at Table 10-1 and you will see that the 28-pin CPUs are remarkable in that they output so few control signals; in fact, the MCS6513, MCS6514, and MCS6515 output just one control signal: R/$\overline{W}$. The remaining 28-pin CPUs additionally output clock signals only. There is no interrupt acknowledge, no synchronization output, nor any control signal which external logic can use to determine what is going on within the CPU. **Of all the microprocessors described in this book, none provides so few control output signals.** So long as you are building relatively straightforward microcomputer systems, this does not present a problem. The Address and Data Busses are never floated by 28-pin CPUs; therefore, external logic, upon detecting a select address on the Address Bus, will simply respond by reading or writing — depending upon the level of the R/$\overline{W}$ signal. The fact that R/$\overline{W}$ is high in its idle state, indicating a read, simply means that selected external logic will place the contents of its addressed memory location on the Data Bus. If the R/$\overline{W}$ signal is really in its standby state, then the CPU will ignore the Data Bus contents and no harm is done. Thus, for simple microcomputer systems, the MCS6500 series CPUs are remarkably simple devices to work with. If a microcomputer system becomes complex, however, problems may arise. **DMA logic must account for the fact that there is no detectable standby state for memory or I/O devices to detect; any device selected by the address on the Address Bus is continuously responding to a read or write command.**

**When designing microcomputer systems around an MCS6500 CPU, if you are going to share the System Bus in any way, you must be very cautious about ensuring that you have accounted for the passive role of support logic surrounding the CPU.**

Despite the paucity of control signals on the MCS6500 bus, you can, in fact, do anything that you could do on any other bus. Using the MCS6500, it is simply going to take a little more logic. Some suggestions are given later in this chapter, when we explain how you can use non-6500 support devices (in particular 8080A support devices) with a 6500 CPU.

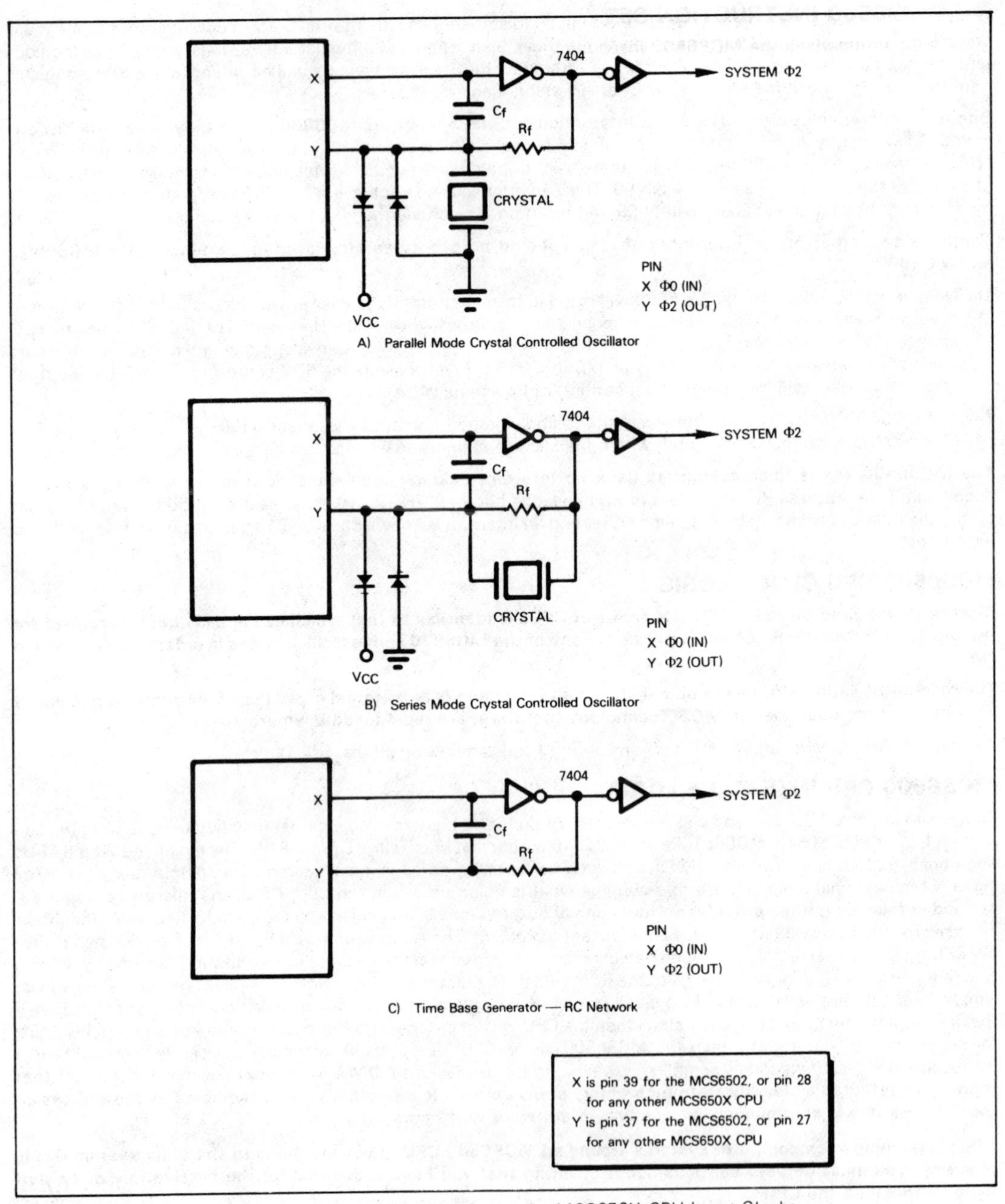


Figure 10-11. Time Base Generation for MCS650X CPU Input Clocks

## THE MCS6500 INSTRUCTION SET

**Table 10-2 summarizes the MCS6500 instruction set.** This instruction set follows the philosophy of the MC6800 very closely.

## THE BENCHMARK PROGRAM

The benchmark program is coded for the MCS6500 as follows:

```
        LDY   IOCNT       LOAD BUFFER LENGTH INTO Y INDEX
LOOP    LDA   (IOBUF),Y   LOAD NEXT SOURCE BYTE
        STA   (TABLE),Y   STORE IN NEXT DESTINATION BYTE
        DEY               DECREMENT Y
        BNE   LOOP        RETURN FOR MORE BYTES
        LDA   IOCNT       AT END ADD NUMBER OF BYTES
        CLC               TO CURRENT TABLE BASE ADDRESS
        ADC   TABLE+1
        STA   TABLE+1
```

This is the memory map assumed:

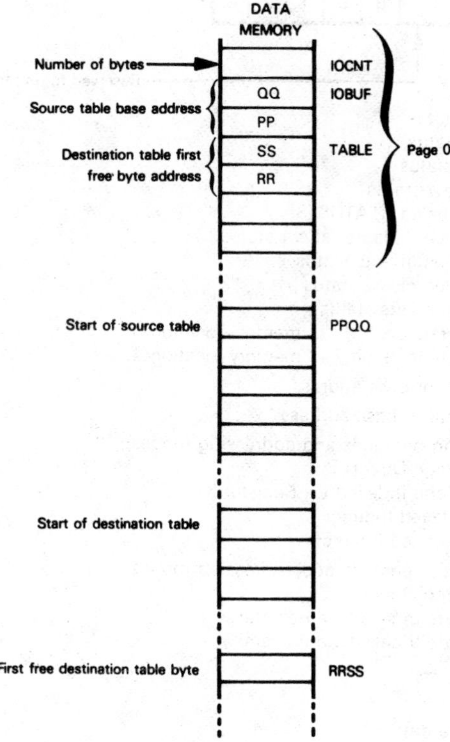


The programming example illustrated above makes use of indirect addressing. Somewhere in the first 256 bytes of memory we store the number of bytes to be transferred, the beginning address for the source table, and the address for the first free destination table byte. By loading the byte count into the Y Index register, we can use this register both as an index for moving data from source to destination, and as a counter.

After moving the block of data, we must add the number of moved data bytes to the destination table first free byte address; this reflects the fact that the destination table has been incrementally filled.

**When comparing the MCS6500 with the MC6800, we see that we have indeed reduced the number of instructions** from 11 to 9; the number of instructions within the iterative loop has been reduced from 5 to 4. We cannot make a more substantial reduction in the number of instructions because the MC6800 program uses the Stack Pointer as an Index register — which is not an option with the MCS6500. We might argue that the MCS6500 has an advantage by not immobilizing the Stack while the instruction sequence is executed; however, the MCS6500 has the disadvantage of requiring both the source and destination tables to have a maximum length of 256 bytes; the MC6800 program makes no such demand.

Symbols are used in Table 10-2 as follows:

Registers:
- A — Accumulator
- X — Index Register X
- Y — Index Register Y
- PC — Program Counter
- SP — Stack Pointer
- SR — Status register, with bits assigned as follows:

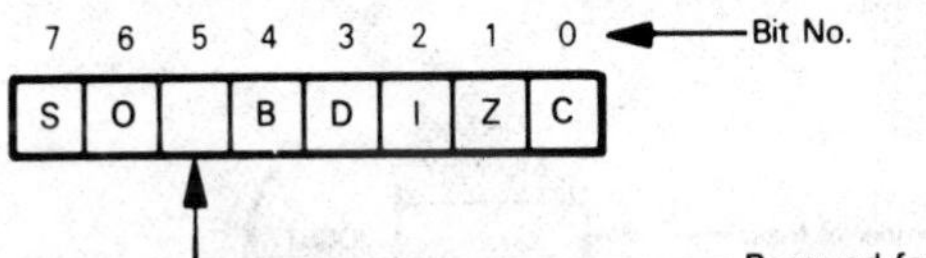


Statuses:
- S — Sign status
- Z — Zero status
- C — Carry status
- O — Overflow status

Symbols in the column labeled STATUSES:
- (blank) — operation does not affect status
- X — operation affects status
- 0 — operation clears status
- 1 — operation sets status
- 6 — status reflects bit 6 of memory location
- 7 — status reflects bit 7 of memory location

ADR — 8 bits of immediate or base address

ADR16 — 16 bits of immediate or base address

a8 — Any of the following operands and addressing modes:
- ADR — Base Page Direct
- ADR,X — Base Page Indexed via Register X
- (ADR,X) — Pre-Indexed Indirect
- (ADR),Y — Post-Indexed Indirect

a16 — Any of the following operands and addressing modes:
- ADR16 — Extended Direct
- ADR16,X — Absolute Indexed via Register X
- ADR16,Y — Absolute Indexed via Register Y

B — Break status

D — Decimal Mode status

DATA — 8 bits of immediate data

DISP — An 8-bit, signed address displacement

I — Interrupt disable status

LABEL — 16-bit immediate address, destination of Jump-on-Subroutine call

M ( ) — The memory location addressed via the mode specified in parenthesis

PC(HI) — The most significant 8 bits of the Program Counter

PC(LO) — The least significant 8 bits of the Program Counter

| | |
|---|---|
| [ ] | Contents of location enclosed within brackets. If a register designation is enclosed within the brackets, then the designated register's contents are specified. If a memory address is enclosed within the brackets, then the contents of the addressed memory location are specified. |
| [[ ]] | Implied memory addressing; the contents of the memory location designated by the contents of a register or address calculation. |
| Λ | Logical AND |
| V | Logical OR |
| ∀ | Logical Exclusive-OR |
| ← → | Data is transferred in the direction of the arrow |
| ←→ | Data is exchanged between the two locations designated on either side of the arrow |

Table 10-2. A Summary of the MCS6500 Microcomputer Instruction Set

| TYPE | MNEMONIC | OPERAND(S) | BYTES | STATUSES S | Z | C | O | | | OPERATION PERFORMED |
|---|---|---|---|---|---|---|---|---|---|---|
| I/O AND PRIMARY MEMORY REFERENCE | LDA | ADR<br>ADR,X<br>(ADR,X)<br>(ADR),Y } a8<br>ADR16<br>ADR16,X<br>ADR16,Y } a16 | 2<br>2<br>2<br>2<br>3<br>3<br>3 | X | X | | | | | [A]←[ADR] or<br>[A]←[[X] + ADR] or<br>[A]←[[[X] + ADR]] or<br>[A]←[[ADR + 1,ADR] + [Y]] or<br>[A]←[ADR16] or<br>[A]←[ADR16 + [X]] or<br>[A]←[ADR16 + [Y]]<br>Load Accumulator from memory using any of the following addressing modes:<br>Base page direct<br>Base page indexed (X register)<br>Pre-indexed indirect<br>Post-indexed indirect<br>Extended direct<br>Absolute indexed (Register X or Register Y) |
| | STA | a8<br>a16 | 2<br>3 | | | | | | | M(a8) ←[A] or M(a16) ←[A]<br>Store Accumulator to memory using any of the addressing modes permitted with LDA. |
| | LDX | ADR or ADR,Y<br>ADR16 or ADR16,Y | 2<br>3 | X | X | | | | | [X]←[ADR] or [X]←[ADR16] or<br>[X]←[[Y] + ADR] or [X]←[ADR16 + [Y]<br>Load Index Register X from memory using direct, extended, base page indexed or absolute indexed addressing, indexing through Register Y. |
| | STX | ADR or ADR,Y<br>ADR16 | 2<br>3 | | | | | | | [ADR]←[X] or [ADR16]←[X] or<br>[[Y] + ADR]←[X]<br>Store Index Register X to memory using direct, extended or base page indexed addressing, indexing through Register Y. |
| | LDY | ADR or ADR,X<br>ADR16 or ADR16,X | 2<br>3 | X | X | | | | | [Y]←[ADR] or [Y]←[ADR16] or<br>[Y]←[[X] + ADR] or [Y]←[ADR16 + [X]]<br>Load Index Register Y from memory using direct, extended, base page indexed or absolute indexed addressing, indexing through Register Y. |
| | STY | ADR or ADR,X<br>ADR16 | 2 | | | | | | | [ADR]←[Y] or [ADR16]←[Y] or<br>[[X] + ADR]←[Y]<br>Store Index Register Y to memory using direct, extended, or base page indexed addressing, indexing through Register X. |
| MEMORY OPERATE | ADC | a8<br>a16 | 2<br>3 | X | X | X | X | | | [A]←[A] + M(a8) + C or<br>[A]←[A] + M(a16) + C<br>Add contents of memory location, with carry, to those of Accumulator, using any of the addressing modes permitted with LDA. Zero flag is not valid in Decimal Mode. |
| | AND | a8<br>a16 | 2<br>3 | X | X | | | | | [A]←[A] $\wedge$ M(a8) or [A]←[A] $\wedge$ M(a16)<br>AND contents of Accumulator with those of memory location addressed via any of the modes permitted with LDA. |
| | BIT | ADR8<br>ADR16 | 2<br>3 | 7 | X | | 6 | | | [A] $\wedge$ [ADR8] or [A] $\wedge$ [ADR16]<br>AND contents of Accumulator with those of memory location. Only the status bits are affected. Direct or extended addressing modes may be used. |

Table 10-2. A Summary of the MCS6500 Microcomputer Instruction Set (Continued)

| TYPE | MNEMONIC | OPERAND(S) | BYTES | STATUSES | | | | | | OPERATION PERFORMED |
|---|---|---|---|---|---|---|---|---|---|---|
| | | | | S | Z | C | O | | | |
| SECONDARY MEMORY REFERENCE (MEMORY OPERATE) (CONTINUED) | CMP | a8<br>a16 | 2<br>3 | X | X | X | | | | [A] - M(a8) or [A] - M(a16)<br>Compare contents of Accumulator with those of memory location, affecting status bit only. Any of the addressing modes permitted with LDA may be used. |
| | EOR | a8<br>a16 | 2<br>3 | X | X | | | | | [A]←[A] $\veebar$ M(a8) or [A]←[A] $\veebar$ M(a16)<br>Exclusive-OR contents of Accumulator with those of memory location, using any of the addressing modes permitted with LDA. |
| | ORA | a8<br>a16 | 2<br>3 | X | X | | | | | [A]←[A] V M(a8) or [A]←[A] V M(a16)<br>OR contents of Accumulator with those of memory location, using any of the addressing modes permitted with LDA. |
| | SBC | a8<br>a16 | 2<br>3 | X | X | X | X | | | [A]←[A] - M(a8) - $\overline{C}$ or [A]←[A] - M(a16) - $\overline{C}$<br>Subtract contents of memory location, with borrow, from contents of Accumulator. Any addressing mode permitted with LDA may be used. Note that Carry reflects the complement of the borrow. |
| | INC | ADR8 or ADR,X<br>ADR16 or ADR16,X | 2<br>3 | X | X | | | | | [ADR]←[ADR] + 1 or [ADR16]←[ADR16] + 1 or<br>[[X] + ADR]←[[X] + ADR] + 1 or<br>[ADR16 + [X]]←[ADR16 + [X]] + 1<br>Increment contents of memory location using direct, extended, base page indexed or absolute indexed addressing, indexing through Register X. |
| | DEC | ADR or ADR,X<br>ADR16 or ADR16,X | 2<br>3 | X | X | | | | | [ADR]←[ADR] - 1 or [ADR16]←[ADR16] - 1 or<br>[[X] + ADR]←[[X] + ADR] - 1 or<br>[ADR16 + [X]]←[ADR16 + [X]] - 1<br>Decrement contents of memory location using direct, extended, base page indexed or absolute indexed addressing, indexing through Register X. |
| | CPX | ADR<br>ADR16 | 2<br>3 | X | X | X | | | | [X] - [ADR] or [X] - [ADR16]<br>Compare contents of X register with those of memory location, using direct or extended addressing. Only the status flags are affected. |
| | CPY | ADR<br>ADR16 | 2<br>3 | X | X | X | | | | [Y] - [ADR] or [Y] - [ADR16]<br>Compare contents of Y register with those of memory location using direct or extended addressing. Only the status flags are affected. |
| | ROL | ADR or ADR,X<br>ADR16 or ADR16,X | 2<br>3 | X | X | X | | | | C ← 7 ← 0 ← (C)<br>[ADR] or [ADR16] or<br>[[X] + ADR] or<br>[ADR16 + [X]]<br>Rotate contents of memory location left through Carry, using direct, extended, base page indexed or absolute indexed addressing, indexing through Register X. |
| | ASL | ADR or ADR,X<br>ADR16 or ADR16,X | 2<br>3 | X | X | X | | | | C ← 7 ← 0 ← 0<br>[ADR] or [ADR16] or<br>[[X] + ADR] or [ADR16 + [X]]<br>Arithmetic shift left contents of memory location using direct, extended, base page indexed or absolute indexed addressing, indexing through Register X. |
| | LSR | ADR or ADR,X<br>ADR16 or ADR16,X | 2<br>3 | 0 | X | X | | | | 0 → 7 → 0 → C<br>[ADR] or [ADR16] or<br>[[X] + ADR] or [ADR16 + [X]]<br>Logical shift right contents of memory location, using direct, extended, base page indexed or absolute indexed addressing, indexing through Register X. |

Table 10-2. A Summary of the MCS6500 Microcomputer Instruction Set (Continued)

| TYPE | MNEMONIC | OPERAND(S) | BYTES | STATUSES | | | | | | OPERATION PERFORMED |
|---|---|---|---|---|---|---|---|---|---|---|
| | | | | S | Z | C | O | | | |
| IMMEDIATE | LDA | DATA | 2 | X | X | | | | | [A]←DATA<br>Load Accumulator with immediate data. |
| | LDX | DATA | 2 | X | X | | | | | [X]←DATA<br>Load Index Register X with immediate data. |
| | LDY | DATA | 2 | X | X | | | | | [Y]←DATA<br>Load Index Register Y with immediate data. |
| IMMEDIATE OPERATE | ADC | DATA | 2 | X | X | X | X | | | [A]←[A] + DATA + C<br>Add immediate, with Carry, to Accumulator. The Zero flag is not valid in Decimal Mode. |
| | AND | DATA | 2 | X | X | | | | | [A]←[A] $\wedge$ DATA<br>AND immediate with Accumulator. |
| | CMP | DATA | 2 | X | X | X | | | | [A] - DATA<br>Compare immediate with Accumulator. Only the status flags are affected. |
| | EOR | DATA | 2 | X | X | | | | | [A]←[A] $\forall$ DATA<br>Exclusive-OR immediate with Accumulator. |
| | ORA | DATA | 2 | X | X | | | | | [A]←[A] $\vee$ DATA<br>OR immediate with Accumulator. |
| | SBC | DATA | 2 | X | X | X | X | | | [A]←[A] - DATA - $\overline{C}$<br>Subtract immediate, with borrow, from Accumulator. Note that Carry reflects the complement of the borrow. |
| | CPX | DATA | 2 | X | X | X | | | | [X] - DATA<br>Compare immediate with Index Register X. Only the status flags are affected. |
| | CPY | DATA | 2 | X | X | X | | | | [Y] - DATA<br>Compare immediate with Index Register Y. Only the status flags are affected. |
| JUMP | JMP | LABEL<br>(LABEL) | 3 | | | | | | | [PC]← LABEL or [PC]←[LABEL]<br>Jump to new location, using extended or indirect addressing. |
| | JSR | LABEL | 3 | | | | | | | [[SP]]←[PC(HI)],<br>[[SP]-1]←[PC(LO)],<br>[SP]←[SP]-2,<br>[PC]← LABEL<br>Jump to subroutine beginning at address given in bytes 2 and 3 of the instruction. |
| BRANCH ON CONDITION | BCC | DISP | 2 | | | | | | | If C = 0, then [PC]←[PC] + 1 + DISP<br>Branch relative if Carry flag is cleared. |
| | BCS | DISP | 2 | | | | | | | If C = 1, then [PC]←[PC] + 1 + DISP<br>Branch relative if Carry flag is set. |
| | BEQ | DISP | 2 | | | | | | | If Z = 1, then [PC]←[PC] + 1 + DISP<br>Branch relative if result is equal to zero. |
| | BMI | DISP | 2 | | | | | | | If S = 1, then [PC]←[PC] + 1 + DISP<br>Branch relative if result is negative. |
| | BNE | DISP | 2 | | | | | | | If Z = 0, then [PC]←[PC] + 1 + DISP<br>Branch relative if result is not zero. |
| | BPL | DISP | 2 | | | | | | | If S = 0, then [PC]←[PC] + 1 + DISP<br>Branch relative if result is positive. |
| | BVC | DISP | 2 | | | | | | | If O = 0, then [PC]←[PC] + 1 + DISP<br>Branch relative if Overflow flag is cleared. |

Table 10-2. A Summary of the MCS6500 Microcomputer Instruction Set (Continued)

| TYPE | MNEMONIC | OPERAND(S) | BYTES | STATUSES S | STATUSES Z | STATUSES C | STATUSES O | | | OPERATION PERFORMED |
|---|---|---|---|---|---|---|---|---|---|---|
| BRANCH ON CONDITION (CONTINUED) | BVS | DISP | 2 | | | | | | | If O = 1, then [PC]←[PC] + 1 + DISP<br>Branch relative if Overflow flag is set. |
| REGISTER-REGISTER MOVE | TAX | | 1 | X | X | | | | | [A]→[X]<br>Move Accumulator contents to Index Register X. |
| | TXA | | 1 | X | X | | | | | [X]→[A]<br>Move contents of Index Register X to Accumulator. |
| | TAY | | 1 | X | X | | | | | [A]→[Y]<br>Move Accumulator contents to Index Register Y. |
| | TYA | | 1 | X | X | | | | | [Y]→[A]<br>Move contents of Index Register Y to Accumulator. |
| | TSX | | 1 | X | X | | | | | [SP]→[X]<br>Move contents of Stack Pointer to Index Register X. |
| | TXS | | 1 | | | | | | | [X]→[SP]<br>Move contents of Index Register X to Stack Pointer. |
| REGISTER OPERATE | DEX | | 1 | X | X | | | | | [X]←[X]-1<br>Decrement contents of Index Register X. |
| | DEY | | 1 | X | X | | | | | [Y]←[Y]-1<br>Decrement contents of Index Register Y. |
| | INX | | 1 | X | X | | | | | [X]←[X] + 1<br>Increment contents of Index Register X. |
| | INY | | 1 | X | X | | | | | [Y]←[Y] + 1<br>Increment contents of Index Register Y. |
| | ROL | A | 1 | X | X | X | | | | C ← 7 ← 0 ← (C) [A]<br>Rotate contents of Accumulator left through Carry. |
| | ASL | A | 1 | X | X | X | | | | C ← 7 ← 0 ← 0 [A]<br>Arithmetic shift left contents of Accumulator. |
| | LSR | A | 1 | 0 | X | X | | | | 0 → 7 → 0 → C [A]<br>Logical shift right contents of Accumulator. |
| STACK | PHA | | 1 | | | | | | | [[SP]]←[A], [SP]←[SP]-1<br>Push Accumulator contents onto Stack. |
| | PLA | | 1 | X | X | | | | | [A]←[[SP] + 1], [SP]←[SP] + 1<br>Load Accumulator from top of Stack (PULL). |
| | PHP | | 1 | | | | | | | [[SP]]←[SR], [SP]←[SP]-1<br>Push Status register contents onto Stack. |

Table 10-2. A Summary of the MCS6500 Microcomputer Instruction Set (Continued)

| TYPE | MNEMONIC | OPERAND(S) | BYTES | STATUSES | | | | | | OPERATION PERFORMED |
|---|---|---|---|---|---|---|---|---|---|---|
| | | | | S | Z | C | O | | | |
| STACK (CONTINUED) | PLP | | 1 | X | X | X | X | | | [SR]←[[SP] + 1], [SP]←[SP] + 1<br>Load Status register from top of Stack (PULL). |
| | RTS | | 1 | | | | | | | [PC(LO)]←[[SP] + 1]<br>[PC(HI)]←[[SP] + 2],<br>[SP]←[SP] + 2,<br>[PC]←[PC] + 1<br>Return from subroutine. |
| INTERRUPT | CLI | | 1 | | | | | | | I←0<br>Enable interrupts by clearing interrupt disable bit of Status register. |
| | SEI | | 1 | | | | | | | I←1<br>Disable interrupts. |
| | RTI | | 1 | X | X | X | X | | | [SR]←[[SP] + 1],<br>[PC(LO)]←[[SP] + 2],<br>[PC(HI)]←[[SP] + 3],<br>[SP]←[SP] + 3,<br>[PC]←[PC] + 1<br>Return from interrupt; restore Status register and Program Counter from top of Stack. |
| | BRK | | 1 | | | | | | | [[SP]]←[PC(HI)],<br>[[SP]-1]←[PC(LO)],<br>[[SP]-2]←[SR],<br>[SP]←[SP]-3,<br>[PC(LO)]←[FFFE], [PC(HI)]←[FFFF],<br>I←1, B←1<br>Programmed interrupt. BRK cannot be disabled. |
| STATUS | CLC | | 1 | | | 0 | | | | C←0<br>Clear Carry flag. |
| | SEC | | 1 | | | 1 | | | | C←1<br>Set Carry flag. |
| | CLD | | 1 | | | | | | | D←0<br>Clear Decimal Mode. |
| | SED | | 1 | | | | | | | D←1<br>Set Decimal Mode. |
| | CLV | | 1 | | | 0 | | | | O←0<br>Clear Overflow flag. |
| | NOP | | 1 | | | | | | | No Operation. |

The following symbols are used in the object codes in Table 10-3.

Address mode selection:

aaa

- 000 pre-indexed indirect — (ADR,X)
- 001 direct — ADR
- 010 immediate — DATA
- 011 extended direct — ADR16
- 100 post-indexed indirect — (ADR),Y
- 101 base page indexed — ADR,X
- 110 absolute indexed — ADR16,Y
- 111 absolute indexed — ADR16,X

bb

- 00 direct — ADR
- 01 extended direct — ADR16
- 10 base page indexed — ADR,X
- 11 absolute indexed — ADR16,X

bbb

- 001 direct — ADR
- 010 accumulator — A
- 011 extended direct — ADR16
- 101 base page indexed — ADR,X
- 111 absolute indexed — ADR16,X

cc

- 00 immediate — DATA
- 01 direct — ADR
- 11 extended direct — ADR16

ddd

- 000 immediate — DATA
- 001 direct — ADR
- 011 extended direct — ADR16
- 101 base page indexed — ADR,Y in LDX; ADR,X in LDY
- 111 absolute indexed — ADR16,Y in LDX; ADR16,X in LDY

pp the second byte of a two- or three-byte instruction.

qq the third byte of a three-byte instruction.

x one bit choosing the address mode.

Two numbers in the Machine Cycles column (for example, 2 - 6) indicate that execution time depends on the addressing mode.

Table 10-3. Summary of MCS6500 Object Codes, with MC6800 Mnemonics

| MNEMONIC | OPERAND(S) | OBJECT CODE | BYTES | MACHINE CYCLES | MC6800 INSTRUCTION |
|---|---|---|---|---|---|
| ADC | | 011aaa01 | | | ADCA |
| | DATA or a8 | pp | 2 | 2-6 | ADR8 or DATA |
| | a16 | qq | 3 | 4 | ADR16 |
| AND | | 001aaa01 | | | ANDA |
| | DATA or a8 | pp | 2 | 2-6 | ADR8 or DATA |
| | a16 | qq | 3 | 4 | ADR16 |
| ASL | A | 000bbb10 | 1 | 2 | ASL A |
| | ADR or ADR,X | pp | 2 | 5-6 | ADR8 |
| | ADR16 or ADR16,X | qq | 3 | 6-7 | ADR16 |
| BCC | DISP | 90 pp | 2 | 2 | BCC DISP |
| BCS | DISP | B0 pp | 2 | 2 | BCS DISP |
| BEQ | DISP | F0 pp | 2 | 2 | BEQ DISP |
| BIT | | 0010x100 | | | BITA |
| | ADR (x=0) | pp | 2 | 3 | ADR8 or DATA |
| | ADR16 (x=1) | qq | 3 | 4 | ADR16 |
| BMI | DISP | 30 pp | 2 | 2 | BMI DISP |
| BMI | DISP | 30 pp | 2 | 2 | BMI DISP |
| BNE | DISP | D0 pp | 2 | 2 | BNE DISP |
| BPL | DISP | 10 pp | 2 | 2 | BPL DISP |
| BRK | | 00 | 1 | 7 | (SWI) |
| BVC | DISP | 50 pp | 2 | 2 | BVC DISP |
| BVS | DISP | 70 pp | 2 | 2 | BVS DISP |
| CLC | | 18 | 1 | 2 | CLC |
| CLD | | D8 | 1 | 2 | |
| CLI | | 58 | 1 | 2 | CLI |
| CLV | | B8 | 1 | 2 | CLV |
| CMP | | 110aaa01 | | | CMPA |
| | DATA or a8 | pp | 2 | 2-6 | ADR8 or DATA |
| | a16 | qq | 3 | 4 | ADR16 |
| CPX | | 1110cc00 | | | CPX |
| | DATA or ADR | pp | 2 | 2-3 | ADR8 |
| | ADR16 | qq | 3 | 4 | DATA 16 or ADR16 |
| CPY | | 1100cc00 | | | |
| | DATA or ADR | pp | 2 | 2-3 | |
| | ADR16 | qq | 3 | 4 | |
| DEC | | 110bb110 | | | DEC |
| | ADR or ADR,X | pp | 2 | 5-6 | ADR8 |
| | ADR16 or ADR16,X | qq | 3 | 6-7 | ADR16 |
| DEX | | CA | 1 | 2 | DEX |
| DEY | | 88 | 1 | • 2 | |
| EOR | | 010aaa01 | | | EORA |
| | DATA or a8 | pp | 2 | 2-6 | ADR8 or DATA |
| | a16 | qq | 3 | 4 | ADR16 |
| INC | | 111bb110 | | | INC |
| | ADR or ADR,X | pp | 2 | 5-6 | ADR8 |
| | ADR16 or ADR16,X | qq | 3 | 6-7 | ADR16 |
| INX | | E8 | 1 | 2 | INX |
| INY | | C8 | 1 | 2 | |

| MNEMONIC | OPERAND(S) | OBJECT CODE | BYTES | MACHINE CYCLES | MC6800 INSTRUCTION |
|---|---|---|---|---|---|
| JMP | LABEL (x 0) | 01x01100 | 3 | 3-5 | JMP ADR16 |
| | or (LABEL)(x 1) | ppqq | | | |
| JSR | LABEL | 20 ppqq | 3 | 6 | JSR ADR16 |
| LDA | | 101aaa01 | | | LDAA |
| | DATA or a8 | pp | 2 | 2-6 | ADR8 or DATA |
| | a16 | qq | 3 | 4 | ADR16 |
| LDX | DATA or | 101ddd10 | | | LDX |
| | ADR or ADR,Y | pp | 2 | 2-4 | ADR8 |
| | ADR16 or ADR16,Y | qq | 3 | 4 | ADR16 or DATA16 |
| LDY | DATA or | 101ddd00 | | | |
| | ADR or ADR,X | pp | 2 | 2-4 | |
| | ADR16 or ADR16,Y | qq | 3 | 4 | |
| LSR | A | 010bbb10 | 1 | 2 | LSR A |
| | ADR or ADR,X | pp | 2 | 5-6 | ADR8 |
| | ADR16 or ADR16,X | qq | 3 | 6-7 | ADR16 |
| NOP | | EA | 1 | 2 | NOP |
| ORA | | 000aaa01 | | | ORA |
| | DATA or a8 | pp | 2 | 2-6 | ADR8 or DATA |
| | a16 | qq | 3 | 4 | ADR16 |
| PHA | | 48 | 1 | 3 | PSHA |
| PHP | | 08 | 1 | 3 | |
| PLA | | 68 | 1 | 4 | PULA |
| PLP | | 28 | 1 | 4 | |
| ROL | A | 001bbb10 | 1 | 2 | ROL A |
| | ADR or ADR,X | pp | 2 | 5-6 | ADR8 |
| | ADR16 or ADR16,X | qq | 3 | 6-7 | ADR16 |
| RTI | | 40 | 1 | 6 | RTI |
| RTS | | 60 | 1 | 6 | RTS |
| SBC | | 111aaa01 | | | SBCA |
| | DATA or a8 | pp | 2 | 2-6 | ADR8 or DATA |
| | a16 | qq | 3 | 4 | ADR16 |
| SEC | | 38 | 1 | 2 | SEC |
| SED | | F8 | 1 | 2 | |
| SEI | | 78 | 1 | 2 | SEI |
| STA | (aaa 010) | 100aaa01 | | | STAA |
| | a8 | | 2 | 3-6 | ADR8 |
| | a16 | | 3 | 4-5 | ADR16 |
| STX | ADR(bb=00) | 100bb110 | | | STX |
| | or ADR,Y(bb=10) | | 2 | 3-4 | ADR8 |
| | ADR16 (bb=01) | | 3 | 4 | ADR16 |
| STY | ADR (bb=00) | 100bb100 | | | |
| | or ADR,X (bb=10) | pp | 2 | 3-4 | |
| | ADR16 (bb=01) | qq | 3 | 4 | |
| TAX | | AA | 1 | 2 | |
| TAY | | A8 | 1 | 2 | |
| TSX | | BA | 1 | 2 | TSX |
| TXA | | 8A | 1 | 2 | |
| TXS | | 9A | 1 | 2 | TXS |
| TYA | | 98 | 1 | 2 | |

# SUPPORT DEVICES THAT MAY BE USED WITH THE MCS6500 SERIES MICROPROCESSORS

**The MCS6500 and MC6800 microprocessors are similar enough for MC6800 support devices to be used with an MCS6500 series central processing unit.**

**The similarities between the MC6800 and MCS6500 extend also to the way in which you use other support devices with these two microprocessors. Therefore, you should read the MC6800 section in Chapter 9 that describes using the MC6800 CPU with other support devices before you read this text. Comments regarding 8080A and Z80 support devices being used with the MC6800 apply for the most part to the MCS6500.**

**But the MCS6500 does have some limitations.** The most prominent limitation is the fact that no MCS6500 microprocessor floats its System Bus. Only the MCS6512 has any bus floating capability at all; you can float its Data Bus. Within an MCS6500 microcomputer system, **if you wish to float the System Bus or perform direct memory access operations, you must have an external tristate buffer.** This tristate buffer receives as inputs the System Bus from the MCS6500; it creates as outputs the System Bus which will be used by support devices. This may be illustrated as follows:

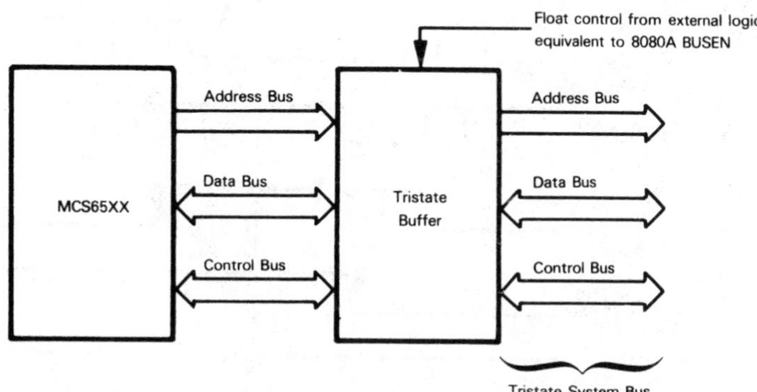


**If you are going to use an MCS6500 CPU with support devices from other microprocessor families,** you will in all probability use the MCS6502 or the MCS6512. It would make little sense to begin with the limitations of a 28-pin 6500 CPU and then expand it to interface with non-6500 support devices. We will therefore consider only MCS6502 and MCS6512 busses expanded to generate 8080A compatible interfaces. **Logic may be illustrated as follows:**

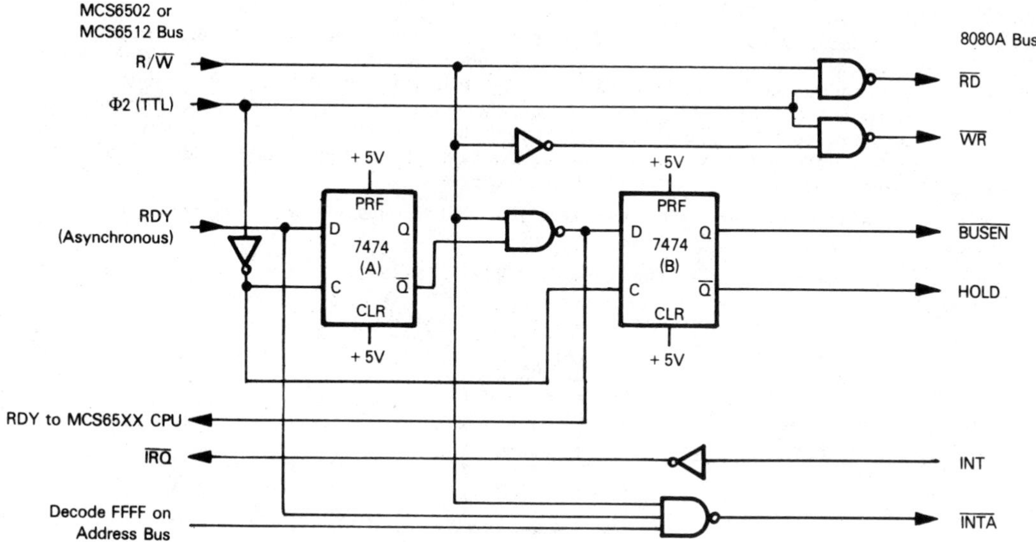

The logic illustrated above is quite similar to that which we described for the MC6800 in Chapter 9. The Read (RD) and Write ($\overline{WR}$) control signals are generated by separating out R/$\overline{W}$ via two NAND gates that are conditioned by Φ2 (TTL). This is the same logic that we illustrated for the MC6800.

HOLD and Bus Enable ($\overline{BUSEN}$) signals require more complex generation out of an MCS6500 bus — but still the logic is quite simple. Since the MCS6500 has no Hold condition, we must use the Wait State created in response to a RDY input. The 7474 D-type flip-flop marked (A) synchronizes an asynchronous RDY input to ensure that it makes a high-to-low transition while Φ1 is high, as is required by MCS6500 logic. To ensure that the synchronous Ready output does not occur during a Write cycle, the (A) flip-flop output is NANDed with R/$\overline{W}$ to create a valid MCS6500 RDY input. We use the next high-to-low transition of Φ2 (TTL) to identify the beginning of the Wait State. Timing may be illustrated as follows:

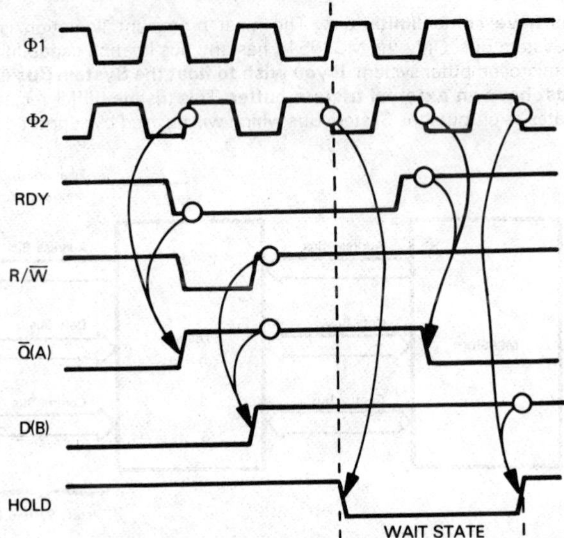


As illustrated by the timing above, the HOLD and $\overline{BUSEN}$ signals will accurately identify time intervals when the MCS6500 CPU is in a Wait State. But remember, busses are not floated by the MCS6500 CPU while it is in the Wait State. You must therefore use either the HOLD or $\overline{BUSEN}$ signal as a float control strobe on a tristate buffer (as illustrated earlier).

If we look at the interrupt request and acknowledge signals of the 8080A bus, the interrupt request represents no problem; we simply invert INT to create $\overline{IRQ}$. Generating an interrupt acknowledge is not so straightforward. We must decode the second address byte of the interrupt acknowledge sequence ($FFFF_{16}$) off the Address Bus, without the comfort of a valid memory address (VMA) signal. The logic shown uses the combination of R/$\overline{W}$ high, indicating a necessary read condition, together with the initial asynchronous RDY high, indicating no Wait request, to validate the $FFFF_{16}$ address on the Address Bus. You must also keep in mind that the BRK instruction and the $\overline{IRQ}$ input use the same memory locations (FFFE, FFFF) to store their interrupt vectors.

Thus, a 7474 D-type flip-flop together with four NAND gates and two inverters will create an 8080A-compatible System Bus for an MCS6502 or MCS6512 CPU.

You can generate an 8080A-compatible system clock from Φ2 (TTL) as follows:

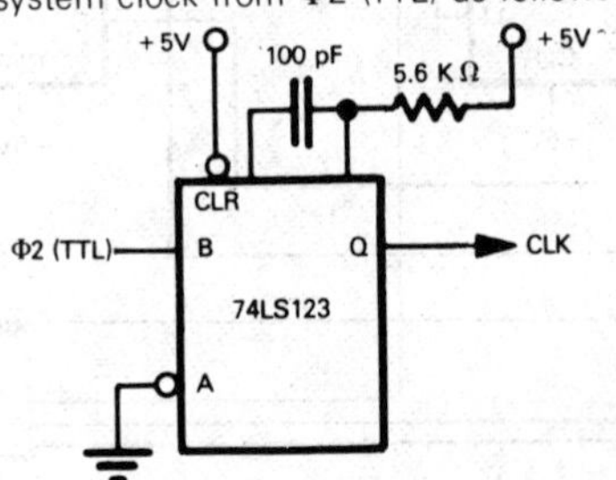


The clock logic illustrated above is identical to that which we described for the MC6800.

# THE MCS6522 PERIPHERAL INTERFACE ADAPTER

**The MCS6522 PIA is an enhanced version of the MC6820 (described in Chapter 9), which is also manufactured by MOS Technology as the MCS6520 Peripheral Interface Adapter. As such, the MCS6522 PIA can be used interchangeably in MC6800 or MCS6500 microcomputer systems.**

**The MCS6522 PIA is a general purpose I/O device which, like the MC6820 PIA, provides 16 I/O pins, configured as two 8-bit I/O ports. As compared to the MC6820 PIA, the MCS6522 provides more handshaking logic associated with parallel data transfers occurring via I/O Port A. Counter/timer and elementary serial I/O logic have been added to MCS6522 Port B.**

**Figure 10-12 illustrates that part of our general purpose microcomputer system logic which has been implemented on the MCS6522 PIA.**

**The MCS6522 PIA is packaged as a 40-pin DIP. It uses a single +5V power supply. All inputs and outputs are TTL-level compatible. I/O Port A and B pins are also CMOS logic compatible. I/O Port B pins may be used as a power source to directly drive the base of a transistor switch.**

**The device is implemented using N-channel, silicon gate MOS technology.**

## THE MCS6522 PIA PINS AND SIGNALS

**The MCS6522 PIA pins and signals are illustrated in Figure 10-13. Signals which are identical to the MC6820, both in function and pin assignment, are shaded.**

**We will summarize all signal functions, those which are unique to the MCS6522 as well as those which are common to the MC6820, before describing the various MCS6522 PIA operations which can be performed.**

**Consider first the various Data Busses.**

**D0 - D7 represents the bidirectional Data Bus** via which all communications between the CPU and the MCS6522 occur. **This Data Bus is identical to that of the MC6820.** When the MCS6522 is not selected, the Data Bus buffer is placed in a high impedance state — which is absolutely necessary, since MCS6500 CPUs (with the exception of the MCS6512) cannot float the System Data Bus.

**PA0 - PA7 and PB0 - PB7 represent Data Busses connecting I/O Ports A and B with external logic. In terms of simple data transfers, these two I/O ports are identical on the MCS6522 and MC6820 devices.** In each case the 16 I/O port pins may be looked upon as 16 individual signal lines, or as two 8-bit I/O busses. Each I/O port pin can be individually assigned to input or output, but an individual pin cannot support bidirectional data transfers.

**There are differences between I/O Ports A and B. Some of these differences are found in MC6800 I/O ports; others represent enhancements of the MCS6522. Let us first look at I/O port differences which are common to the MC6820 as well as the MCS6522:**

1) An I/O Port B pin which has been assigned to output will enter a tristate condition during an input operation; this is not the case for an I/O Port A pin. This means that loads placed on I/O Port B pins will not modify data waiting to be read by the CPU.

2) I/O Port A pins will register logical 1 when +2V or more are input; logical 0 results from an input of +0.4V or less. I/O Port B pins will register logical 1 when power levels below +2V are input.

3) As outputs, I/O Port B pins may be used as a source of up to a milliampere, at +1.5V, to directly drive the base of a transistor switch. This is not feasible using I/O Port A pins.

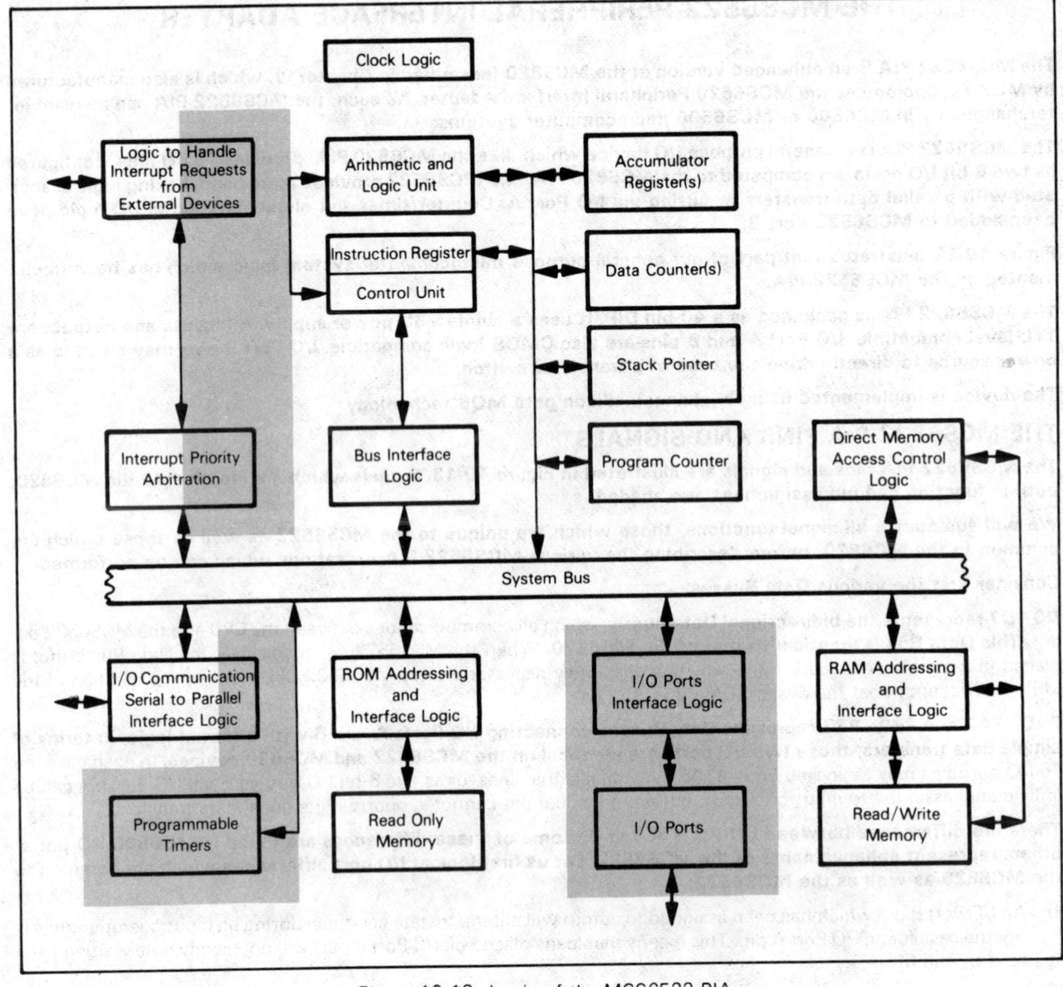


Figure 10-12. Logic of the MCS6522 PIA

**The different I/O Port A and B characteristics are a function of port pin design.**

I/O Port A pins contain "passive" pullups which are resistive and allow the output voltage to go to +5V for logic 1:

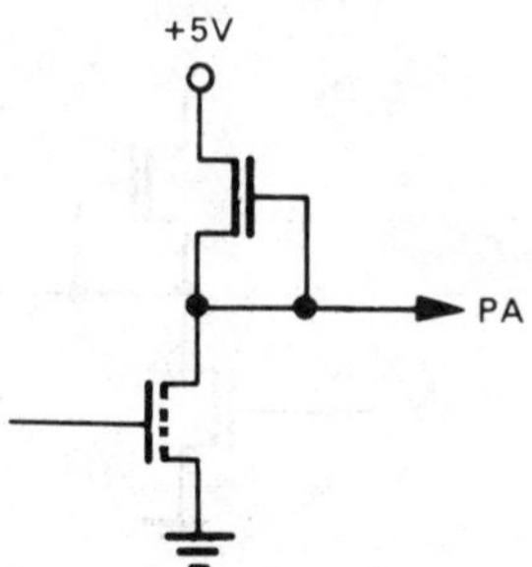


The Port A pins can drive two standard TTL loads.

I/O Port B pins are push-pull devices: the pullup is switched "off" in the 0 state and "on" for a logic 1:

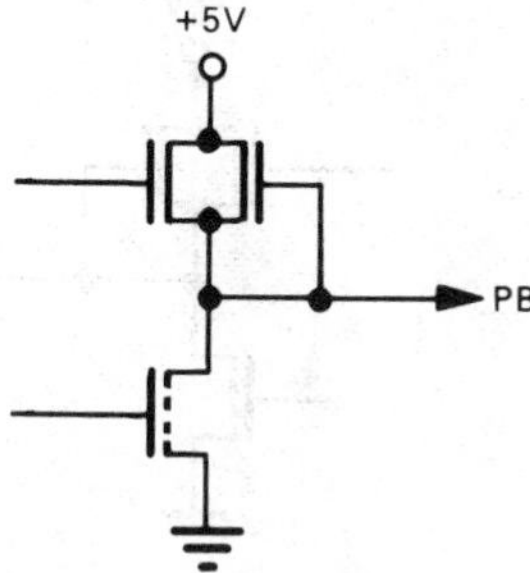


The pullup can source up to 3 ma at 1.5 V; that is why an I/O Port B pin can drive a diode, LED or similar device.

**Let us now look at differences between MCS6522 I/O Port A and B pins which are the result of MCS6522 logic enhancements:**

1) There are two programmable counters connected to I/O Port B logic. The MC6820 has no counter logic.
2) There is an 8-bit Shift register associated with I/O Port B logic. The Shift register provides an elementary serial I/O capability which may be adequate for certain types of control logic, but falls short of what is needed to support serial data communications. The MC6820 has no serial I/O capability whatsoever.
3) I/O Port A provides CA2 as an output control signal when the CPU reads or writes data. I/O Port B provides CB2 as an output control signal when the CPU writes data only.

**The MCS6522 PIA has six device select pins.**

**CS1 and $\overline{\text{CS2}}$ are two typical select signals, exactly equivalent to MC6820 signals bearing the same names.** Note that the MCS6522 has no CS0 select. For the MCS6522 device to be selected, CS1 must receive a high input while $\overline{\text{CS2}}$ simultaneously receives a low input.

**RS0, RS1, RS2 and RS3 address one of 16 locations within the MCS6522.** Thus an MCS6522 device will appear to a programmer as 16 memory locations. Note that **the MC6820** has only two address lines, RS0 and RS1, and **appears to a programmer as four memory locations.**

**MCS6522 ADDRESSING**

Addressing logic associated with the MCS6522 is, in fact, quite simple. Combining the two chip select signals, CS1 and $\overline{\text{CS2}}$, with the four address select signals, R0, R1, R2 and R3, simply means that total device logic will be derived from six of the 16 Address Bus lines — and **to the programmer, the MCS6522 PIA will appear as 16 contiguous memory locations.** Table 10-4 identifies the 16 addressable locations of the MCS6522. For the moment it is not important that you understand the nature of these addressable locations; rather, let us concentrate on the select lines RS0 - RS3. Throughout this description of the MCS6522, we are going to identify addressable locations by a label and a "select code". The "select code" consists of the signal levels given in the left-hand column of Table 10-4. To a programmer, a "select code" will simply become some index which must be added to a base address. Suppose, for example, that your interfacing logic will cause an MCS6522 to consider

**The different I/O Port A and B characteristics are a function of port pin design.**

I/O Port A pins contain "passive" pullups which are resistive and allow the output voltage to go to +5V for logic 1:

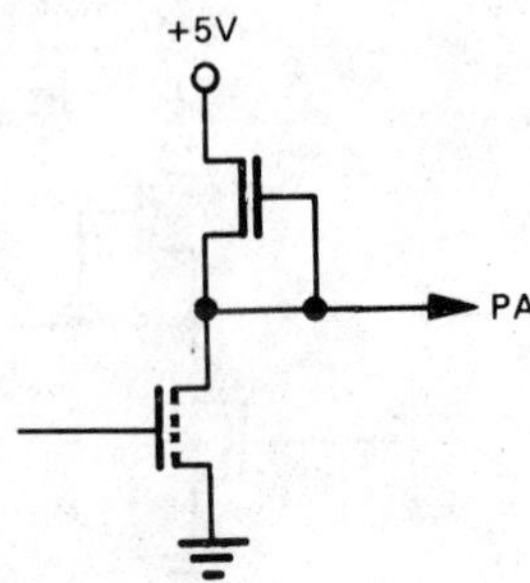


The Port A pins can drive two standard TTL loads.

I/O Port B pins are push-pull devices; the pullup is switched "off" in the 0 state and "on" for a logic 1:

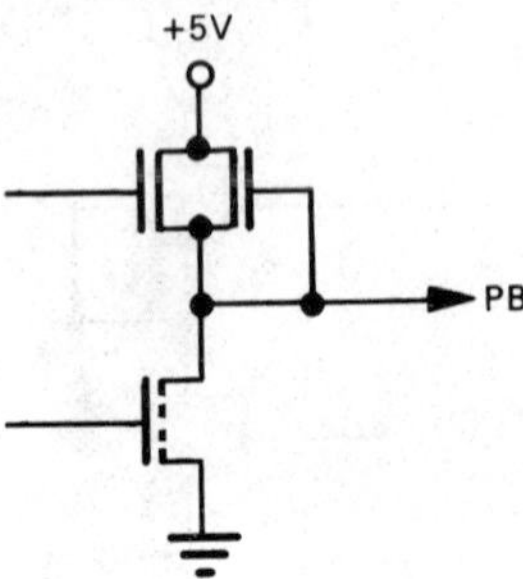


The pullup can source up to 3 ma at 1.5 V; that is why an I/O Port B pin can drive a diode, LED or similar device.

**Let us now look at differences between MCS6522 I/O Port A and B pins which are the result of MCS6522 logic enhancements:**

1) There are two programmable counters connected to I/O Port B logic. The MC6820 has no counter logic.
2) There is an 8-bit Shift register associated with I/O Port B logic. The Shift register provides an elementary serial I/O capability which may be adequate for certain types of control logic, but falls short of what is needed to support serial data communications. The MC6820 has no serial I/O capability whatsoever.
3) I/O Port A provides CA2 as an output control signal when the CPU reads or writes data. I/O Port B provides CB2 as an output control signal when the CPU writes data only.

**The MCS6522 PIA has six device select pins.**

**CS1 and $\overline{\text{CS2}}$ are two typical select signals, exactly equivalent to MC6820 signals bearing the same names.** Note that the MCS6522 has no CS0 select. For the MCS6522 device to be selected, CS1 must receive a high input while $\overline{\text{CS2}}$ simultaneously receives a low input.

**RS0, RS1, RS2 and RS3 address one of 16 locations within the MCS6522.** Thus an MCS6522 device will appear to a programmer as 16 memory locations. Note that **the MC6820** has only two address lines, RS0 and RS1, and **appears to a programmer as four memory locations.**

**MCS6522 ADDRESSING**

Addressing logic associated with the MCS6522 is, in fact, quite simple. Combining the two chip select signals, CS1 and $\overline{\text{CS2}}$, with the four address select signals, R0, R1, R2 and R3, simply means that total device logic will be derived from six of the 16 Address Bus lines — and **to the programmer, the MCS6522 PIA will appear as 16 contiguous memory locations.** Table 10-4 identifies the 16 addressable locations of the MCS6522. For the moment it is not important that you understand the nature of these addressable locations; rather, let us concentrate on the select lines RS0 - RS3. Throughout this description of the MCS6522, we are going to identify addressable locations by a label and a "select code". The "select code" consists of the signal levels given in the left-hand column of Table 10-4. To a programmer, a "select code" will simply become some index which must be added to a base address. Suppose, for example, that your interfacing logic will cause an MCS6522 to consider

Table 10-4. Addressing MCS6522 Internal Registers

| Label | Select Lines | | | | Addressed Location |
|---|---|---|---|---|---|
| | RS3 | RS2 | RS1 | RS0 | |
| DEV | 0 | 0 | 0 | 0 | Input/Output register for I/O Port B |
| DEV+1 | 0 | 0 | 0 | 1 | Input/Output register for I/O Port A, with handshaking |
| DEV+2 | 0 | 0 | 1 | 0 | I/O Port B Data Direction register |
| DEV+3 | 0 | 0 | 1 | 1 | I/O Port A Data Direction register |
| DEV+4 | 0 | 1 | 0 | 0 | Read Timer 1 Counter low-order byte<br>Write to Timer 1 Latch low-order byte |
| DEV+5 | 0 | 1 | 0 | 1 | Read Timer 1 Counter high-order byte<br>Write to Timer 1 Latch high-order byte and initiate count |
| DEV+6 | 0 | 1 | 1 | 0 | Access Timer 1 Latch low-order byte |
| DEV+7 | 0 | 1 | 1 | 1 | Access Timer 1 Latch high-order byte |
| DEV+8 | 1 | 0 | 0 | 0 | Read low-order byte of Timer 2 and reset Counter interrupt<br>Write to low-order byte of Timer 2 but do not reset interrupt |
| DEV+9 | 1 | 0 | 0 | 1 | Access high-order byte of Timer 2; reset Counter interrupt on write |
| DEV+A | 1 | 0 | 1 | 0 | Serial I/O Shift register |
| DEV+B | 1 | 0 | 1 | 1 | Auxiliary Control register |
| DEV+C | 1 | 1 | 0 | 0 | Peripheral Control register |
| DEV+D | 1 | 1 | 0 | 1 | Interrupt Flag register |
| DEV+E | 1 | 1 | 1 | 0 | Interrupt Enable register |
| DEV+F | 1 | 1 | 1 | 1 | Input/Output register for I/O Port A, without handshaking |

itself selected when any address is output in the range $C000_{16}$ through $C00F_{16}$. Select code $0000_2$ now corresponds to memory address $C000_{16}$; select code $0111_2$ now corresponds to memory address $C007_{16}$. That is the relationship between select code and memory address.

**There are four timing and control signals which interface an MCS6522 with external logic. These four signals are CA1, CA2, CB1 and CB2. Superficially, these four signals are identical to their MC6820 equivalents. But there are some secondary differences.**

CA1 and CA2 are control signals associated with I/O Port A. CA1 is an input signal whereas CA2 is bidirectional. CB1 and CB2 are equivalent signals associated with I/O Port B, however, CB1 is bidirectional, although it is used as an input by Shift register logic only.

**There are two control signals associated with the MCS6522 CPU interface.**

$\Phi 2$ is the phase two clock which is output by any of the MCS6500 CPUs. **The MCS6522 uses $\Phi 2$ as a standard synchronization signal, equivalent to the E signal used by the MC6820.** The trailing edge of each $\Phi 2$ pulse synchronizes all logic and timing within the MCS6522. $\Phi 2$ is used optionally by Shift register logic to clock serial input or output data.

**$R/\overline{W}$ is the standard read/write control signal output by all MCS6500 CPUs. This signal is identical to that on the MC6820.** Recall that when $R/\overline{W}$ is high, a read operation is specified and data transfer from the MCS6522 PIA to the CPU will occur. When $R/\overline{W}$ is low, a write operation is specified and data transfer from the CPU to the PIA will occur.

**The MCS6522 has a single interrupt request signal $\overline{IRQ}$. In contrast, the MC6820 has two interrupt requests $\overline{IRQA}$ and $\overline{IRQB}$.** If you are simply going to wire-OR interrupt requests and connect them to the CPU $\overline{IRQ}$ pin, then having two requests, $\overline{IRQA}$ and $\overline{IRQB}$, makes no sense; combining them is preferable. On the other hand, if you are going to include any type of interrupt priority arbitration logic, such as the MC6828, then by combining $\overline{IRQA}$ and $\overline{IRQB}$ into a single interrupt request, you can no longer vector separately to interrupt requests arising at either I/O Port A or I/O Port B logic. You must vector a single interrupt request, arising from either of these ports; then you must execute instructions to test status bits and determine the exact interrupt source.

**RESET is a standard Reset input.** When input low, the contents of all MCS6522 registers will be set to 0. Reset logic of the MCS6522 and MC6820 is identical.

## MCS6522 PARALLEL DATA TRANSFER OPERATIONS

**The two 8-bit I/O ports (A and B) are controlled by four internal MCS6522 registers:**

1) **Data Direction Register A (DEV+3) determines whether the pins on I/O Port A are input or output.**
2) **Data Direction Register B (DEV+2) determines whether the pins on I/O Port B are input or output.**
3) **The Peripheral Control register (DEV+C) determines which polarity of transition (rising edge or falling edge) will be recognized on the input status lines (CA1 and CB1) and also how the other status lines (CA2 and CB2) will operate.**
4) **The Auxiliary Control register (DEV+B) specifies whether the I/O port inputs are latched and is also used to control the timers and shift register operations.**

**When I/O ports A and B are being used for parallel data transfers, then their operation is nearly identical. There are however some significant differences between the two ports. Therefore, we will first describe the operation of I/O Port A and then point out the differences that exist on I/O Port B.**

**MCS6522 I/O PORT A DATA TRANSFER**

When you examine I/O Port A operations, **the first addressable location to look at is 0011 (DEV+3) — the I/O Port A Data Direction register.** You must load a mask into this register in order to assign individual I/O port pins to input or output. A 0 in any bit of the Data Direction register will cause the corresponding I/O Port A pin to input data only. A 1 in any bit position will cause the corresponding I/O Port A pin to output data only.

You access I/O Port A, either to read or write data, via select code $0001_2$ (DEV+1) or $1111_2$ (DEV+F).

But before we discuss why I/O Port A has two select codes, **we must describe the way in which read and write operations occur in conjunction with pins having been assigned to input or output.** Read and write logic is best illustrated as follows:

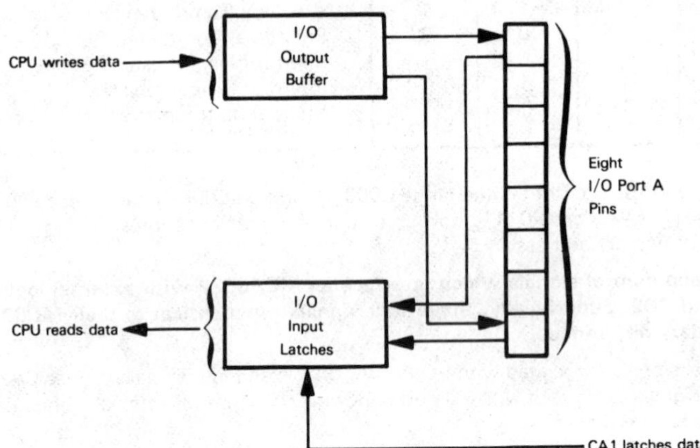


Data being output is written to the I/O Output buffer; signal levels are created immediately at those I/O pins which have been declared as output pins. I/O pins which have been declared as input pins are, in effect, disconnected from the I/O Output buffer — and are in no way affected by I/O Output buffer contents.

I/O input latches will reflect the signal level of every I/O Port A pin, whether it has been assigned to input or output. You have the option of enabling or disabling the input latching function for I/O Port A using bit 0 of the Auxiliary Control register. The bit assignments for the Auxiliary Control register are illustrated in Figure 10-14 and this register is addressed as select code 1011 or location DEV+B. Writing a one into bit 0 of the Auxiliary Control register enables the input latching function for Port A and a 0 disables the latching function. If input latching is disabled then the data that is on the Port A I/O pins is always the data that will be presented to the CPU. With these input latches disabled, this I/O port operates the same as the 6820 PIA which has no input latches. When the latching function is enabled, then the data will be latched by an active transition on CA1. Note that 'active transition' is defined by bit 0 of the Peripheral Control register.

For the most part, this scheme is inconsequential to you as an MCS6522 user, since whatever you write to output pins will be output, and you will read whatever external logic inputs to input pins. The only caution is that you cannot read back what you write to output pins. Latch timing and transient signal levels at output pins can modify data as it travels from I/O Output buffers to I/O Input latches.

Irrespective of whether I/O Port A pins have been assigned to input or output, control signals CA1 and CA2 can be used to provide handshaking. External logic uses CA1 to communicate with the microcomputer system; CA2 may be a control input or a control output signal.

After you have specified data direction and latching options, you must select your CA1 and CA2 control options by writing appropriate codes into bits 0 - 3 of the Peripheral Control register, which is illustrated in Figure 10-15.

When you access I/O Port A via select code $0001_2$ (DEV+1), then as soon as data is written into the I/O Port A buffer, the CA2 signal may output low, or it may pulse low; you determine how CA2 will respond by the code you load into the Peripheral Control register. Bits 3, 2 and 1 of the Peripheral Control register determine the way in which control signal CA2 will function. If these three bits are 100, then when you address I/O Port A via select code $0001_2$, CA2 will go low as soon as the I/O port is accessed:

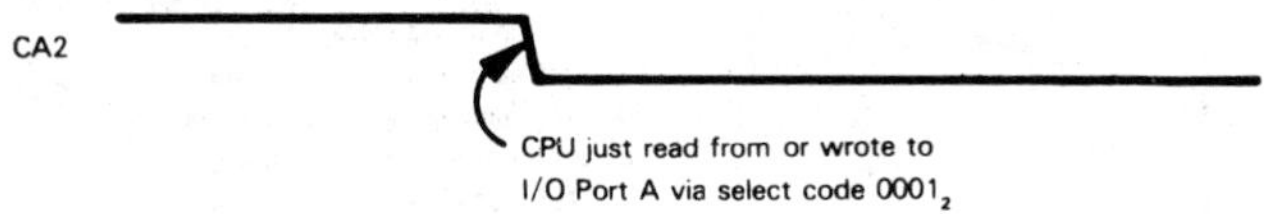

CA2
CPU just read from or wrote to
I/O Port A via select code 0001₂

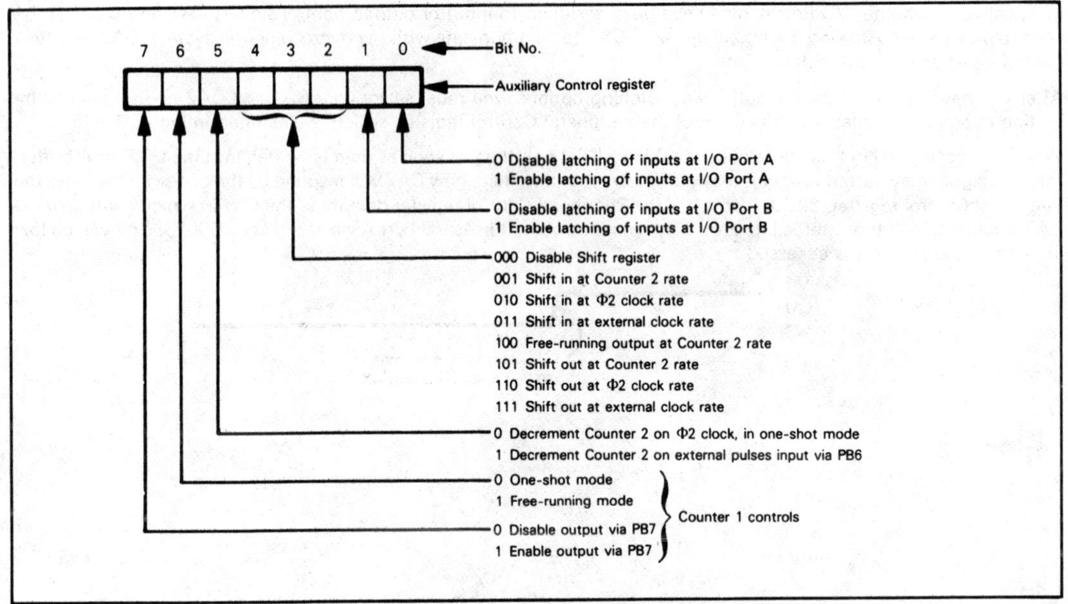


Figure 10-14. Auxiliary Control Register Bit Assignments

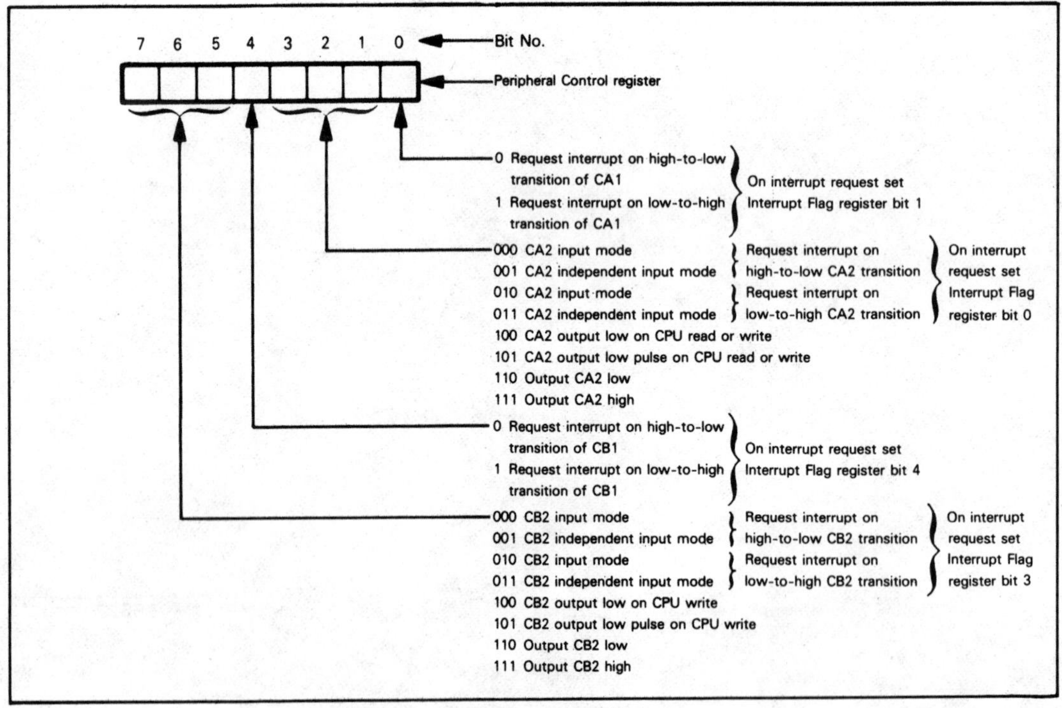


Figure 10-15. Peripheral Control Register Bit Assignments

If bits 3, 2 and 1 of the Peripheral Control register contain 101, then CA2 will pulse low for one clock period when you access the I/O Port via the select code $0001_2$:

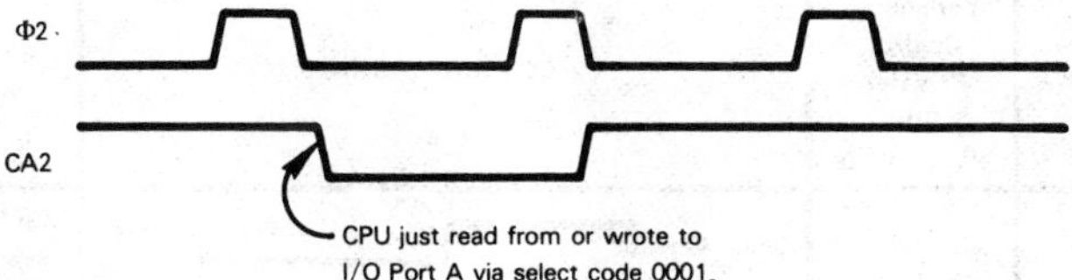
Φ2
CA2
CPU just read from or wrote to
I/O Port A via select code 0001₂

If bits 3, 2 and 1 of the Peripheral Control register contain any other values, CA2 will not be affected by the CPU accessing I/O Port A via select code $0001_2$ (DEV+1).

**If CA2 makes an active transition when you access I/O Port A, then any interrupts pending for CA1 or CA2 will be cleared.**

If you access I/O Port A via the select code $1111_2$ (DEV+F), then CA2 is unaffected, regardless of what Peripheral Control register bits 3, 2, and 1 contain.

Notice that bits 3, 2 and 1 of the Peripheral Control register primarily determine whether control signal CA2 will be an input or an output control. We have seen two of the output control options. The remaining two output options force CA2 to be either output high or low.

Let us look at the CA2 input options, which are also specified via Peripheral Control register bits 3, 2 and 1. If any input option has been specified, then it makes no difference whether you access I/O Port A via the select code $0001_2$ (DEV+1) or $1111_2$ (DEV+F); since CA2 has been specified as input control, it cannot be output low or pulsed low when you access I/O Port A.

The CA2 input options available to you are as follows:

1) You can specify that a CA2 input high-to-low, or low-to-high transition will generate an interrupt request.
2) You can specify that any interrupt pending from a CA2 active transition will, or will not be cleared when I/O Port A is accessed via the select code $0001_2$ (DEV+1). Accessing I/O Port A via the select code $1111_2$ (DEV+F) will never affect any pending interrupt statuses. **In Figure 10-15, CA2 "input mode" means prior CA2 active transition interrupt requests are cleared when you access I/O Port A via select code $0001_2$ (DEV+1); no such interrupt reset occurs in "independent input" mode.**

Peripheral Control register bit 0 determines whether input control signal CA1 will generate an interrupt request on a high-to-low, or a low-to-high transition. One or the other transition will always cause an interrupt — and the only way of ignoring CA1 interrupts is to individually disable them. We will describe how this is done later when we discuss interrupt logic in general.

If you access I/O Port A via the select code $0001_2$ (DEV+1), and you cause CA2 to output low by storing 100 in bits 3, 2 and 1 of the Peripheral Control register, then CA2 will return high again when CA1 makes its active transition. This may be illustrated as follows:

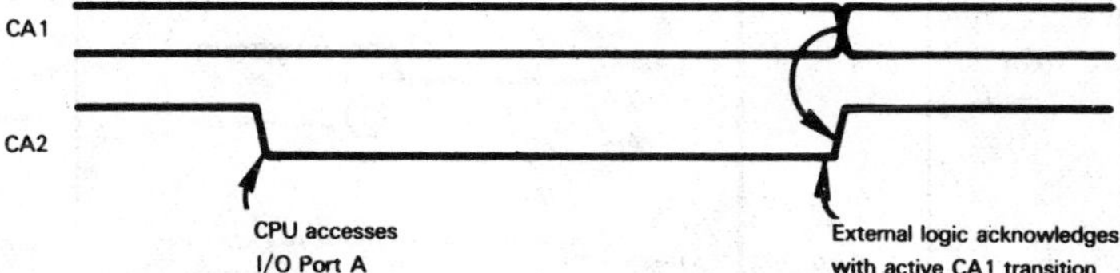
CA1
CA2
CPU accesses
I/O Port A
External logic acknowledges
with active CA1 transition

**While handshaking options available with I/O Port A may seem complex, in reality they are quite simple. For easy reference, options are summarized in Table 10-5.**

**Next, consider I/O Port B.**

**MCS6522 I/O PORT B DATA TRANSFER**

**If you look upon I/O Port B simply as a data transfer conduit, then it is very similar to I/O Port A, simply lacking a few I/O Port A features.**

Like I/O Port A, I/O Port B has a Data Direction register (select code $0010_2$ or label DEV+2), which you use to identify input and output pins. You must load a mask into this register in order to assign individual I/O port pins to input or output. A 0 in any bit of the Data Direction register will cause the corresponding I/O Port B pin to input data only. A 1 in any bit position will cause the corresponding I/O Port B pin to output data only.

Table 10-5. Summary of I/O Port A Handshaking Control Signals

| I/O Port A Select Code (Binary) | Peripheral Control Register Bits 3 2 1 0 | CONTROL SIGNALS | Interrupt Reset |
|---|---|---|---|
| 0001 or 1111 | 0 0 0 0 | CA1 ←<br>CA2 ← | On 0001 select code access or programmed reset |
| 0001 or 1111 | 0 0 0 1 | CA1 ←<br>CA2 ← | On 0001 select code access or programmed reset |
| 0001 or 1111 | 0 0 1 0 | CA1 ←<br>CA2 ← | Programmed reset only |
| 0001 or 1111 | 0 0 1 1 | CA1 ←<br>CA2 ← | Programmed reset only |
| 0001 or 1111 | 0 1 0 0 | CA1 ←<br>CA2 ← | On 0001 select code access or programmed reset |
| 0001 or 1111 | 0 1 0 1 | CA1 ←<br>CA2 ← | On 0001 select code access or programmed reset |
| 0001 or 1111 | 0 1 1 0 | CA1 ←<br>CA2 ← | Programmed reset only |
| 0001 or 1111 | 0 1 1 1 | CA1 ←<br>CA2 ← | Programmed reset only |
| 0001 | 1 0 0 0 | CA1 ←<br>CA2 → | At (A) or programmed reset |
| 1111 | 1 0 0 0 | CA1 ←<br>CA2 → | Programmed reset only |

Table 10-5. Summary of I/O Port A Handshaking Control Signals (Continued)

| I/O Port A Select Code (Binary) | Peripheral Control Register Bits 3 2 1 0 | CONTROL SIGNALS | Interrupt Reset |
|---|---|---|---|
| 0001 | 1 0 0 1 | CA1 ← (I); CA2 → (A) | At (A) or programmed reset |
| 1111 | 1 0 0 1 | CA1 ← (I); CA2 → | Programmed reset only |
| 0001 | 1 0 1 0 | CA1 ← (I); CA2 → (A) | At (A) or programmed reset |
| 1111 | 1 0 1 0 | CA1 ← (I); CA2 → unaffected | Programmed reset only |
| 0001 | 1 0 1 1 | CA1 ← (I); CA2 → (A) | At (A) or programmed reset |
| 1111 | 1 0 1 1 | CA1 ← (I); CA2 → unaffected | Programmed reset only |
| 0001 or 1111 | 1 1 0 0 | CA1 ← (I); CA2 → (Held low) | On 0001 select code access or programmed reset |
| 0001 or 1111 | 1 1 0 1 | CA1 ← (I); CA2 → (Held low) | On 0001 select code access or programmed reset |
| 0001 or 1111 | 1 1 1 0 | CA1 ← (I); CA2 → (Held high) | On 0001 select code access or programmed reset |
| 0001 or 1111 | 1 1 1 1 | CA1 ← (I); CA2 → (Held high | On 0001 select code access or programmed reset |

(I) Interrupt request (A) CPU access

You must enable or disable the input latching function for I/O Port B by loading a 1 or 0 into bit 1 of the Auxiliary Control register, just as you had to do for I/O Port A.

Subsequently, you access I/O Port B via the single select code $0000_2$.

You have to load an appropriate code into bits 4 - 7 of the Peripheral Control register to define the way in which control signals CB1 and CB2 will operate, just as you had to load a code into bits 3 - 0 of the Peripheral Control register to define control signal CA1 and CA2 operations. The only difference between control signals CB1 and CB2, as compared to control signals CA1 and CA2, pertains to codes 100 and 101 in bits 7, 6, 5 or 3, 2, 1 of the Peripheral Control register. Code 100 causes CA2 or CB2 to output low when appropriate conditions exist, while code 101 causes the signal to pulse. For I/O Port A, "appropriate conditions" consist of the CPU reading or writing, while selecting I/O Port A via the select code $0001_2$ (DEV+1). For I/O Port B, "appropriate conditions" consist of the CPU writing, but not reading, accessing I/O Port B via the select code $0000_2$ (DEV) — the only select code available for I/O Port B.

I/O Port B also has a simpler interface with the CPU Data Bus. Rather than having separate output buffer and input latches, there is a single output buffer, which is accessed by the CPU when reading from, or writing to I/O Port B. Coupled with the different pin configuration, which we have already described for I/O Port B, you can guarantee that bit levels written to I/O Port B output pins will subsequently be read back accurately.

The more limited capabilities of I/O Port B reflect the fact that pins 7 and 6 of this I/O port may be used by Interval Timer logic. Thus, the MCS6522 will frequently be configured with I/O Port A providing parallel I/O, while I/O Port B provides various types of control dialogue.

## MCS6522 INTERVAL TIMER LOGIC

**The most important point to note regarding the additional functions associated with I/O Port B is that they have logical priority over simple data transfers;** what this means is that the Interval Timers and Shift register may, under some circumstances, use I/O Port B pins, control signals and interrupt logic. When Interval Timer or Shift register requirements are in conflict with simple data transfer, then Interval Timer or Shift register requirements will prevail.

Let us look at a specific example; **pins of I/O Port B are used by Interval Timer logic as follows:**

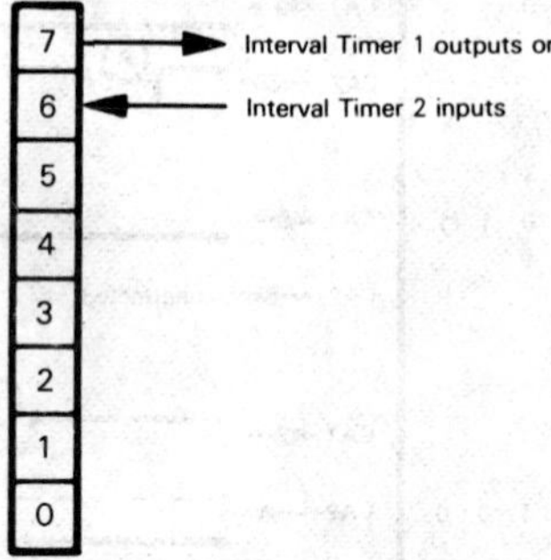


Suppose you have identified I/O Port B pin 7, via the Data Direction register, as an input pin; Interval Timer 1 uses this pin to output pulses or square waves and will override the Data Direction register.

**It is a good idea not to use I/O Port B for parallel data transfer while you are using Interval Timer or Shift register logic. Also, exercise caution when using both Interval Timers, or when using the Serial Shift register in conjunction with Interval Timers.**

**Let us first examine Interval Timer 1. This is the more versatile of the two MCS6522 Interval Timers; it is most easily understood if visualized as follows:**

**MCS6522 INTERVAL TIMER 1**

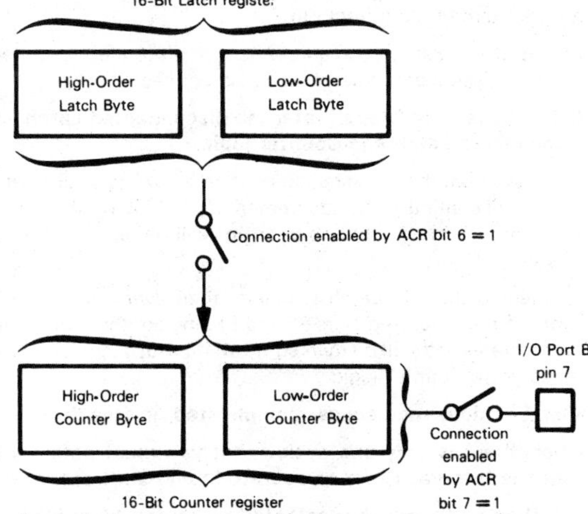


**You select from among its many functions by appropriately loading bits 7 and 6 of the Auxiliary Control register (ACR).**

Interval Timer 1 addressing via select codes may be illustrated as follows:

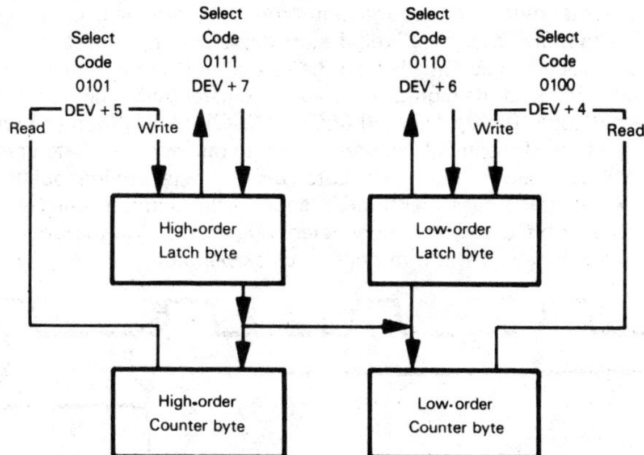


Select codes $0110_2$ (DEV+6) and $0111_2$ (DEV+7) are quite straightforward. The former accesses the low-order Latch byte to read or write; the latter accesses the high-order Latch byte to read or write.

Select codes $0100_2$ (DEV+4) and $0101_2$ (DEV+5) are not so straightforward. If you access the MCS6522 PIA with select code $0100_2$ (DEV+4), you will write into the low-order Latch byte, but you will read the contents of the low-order Counter byte.

If you access the MCS6522 PIA with select code $0101_2$ (DEV+5), you will read the contents of the high-order Counter byte; but upon writing, you will access the high-order Latch byte and the high-order Counter byte, while simultaneously transferring the low-order Latch byte contents to the low-order Counter byte. This allows a clean method of loading 16 bits of data into the Counter byte following the execution of a single instruction.

Writing to select code $0101_2$ (DEV+5) will also initiate a new Timer interval.

The two Counter registers constitute a 16-bit entity which is decremented on the trailing edges of the $\Phi 2$ clock pulse. The initial value loaded into the Counter registers identifies the interval of the Counter. An active time-out of the Counter is marked by an interrupt request.

If the Counter is connected to pin 7 of I/O Port B, then an active time-out will also cause the signal output at pin 7 of I/O Port B to invert or pulse low, depending on the mode in which the Interval Timer is operating.

A 1 in bit 7 of the Auxiliary Control register will connect Counter logic to pin 7 of I/O Port B. A 0 in bit 7 of the Auxiliary Control register disconnects Counter logic from pin 7.

Via bit 6 of the Auxiliary Control register, you can connect or disconnect Counter and Latch logic. A 0 in bit 6 of the Auxiliary Control register is a disconnect, whereas a 1 is a connect.

**Referring to Figure 10-14, "One-Shot Mode" refers to disconnected Latch and Counter logic, while "Free Running Mode" refers to connected Latch and Counter logic.**

If Counter logic is disconnected from the Latch registers, then following Counter initiation there will be one active time-out, after which the Counter will continuously redecrement from $0000_{16}$, through $FFFF_{16}$, and back to $0000_{16}$. Subsequent counts are inactive — which means that no interrupt will be requested, and if connected to pin 7 of I/O Port B, no signal changes will be output.

If Counter logic is connected to the two Latch registers, then every time the Counter times out, it is immediately reloaded with the contents of the Latch registers — and begins another active time out. Under these circumstances, every Counter time out is active — and will be marked by an interrupt request, plus a signal level change at pin 7 of I/O Port B, if this pin is connected to Counter logic.

**While the Interval Timer 1 options may appear complicated, in fact they are very simple.**

**To you, as a programmer, there is only one option that you must define when using Interval Timer 1 of the MCS6522: do you want the Interval Timer to operate in one-shot or free running mode?**

**MCS6522 INTERVAL TIMER 1 ONE-SHOT MODE**

**Let us first consider one-shot mode, which is selected by having a 0 in bit 6 of the Auxiliary Control register.**

Recall that in one-shot mode the Counter is disconnected from the Latch registers. For practical reasons, however, this disconnection is not complete; you have to initiate a time out by loading an initial value into the high-order and low-order Counter bytes; but the Counter is continuously running. Were you to load the low-order byte, and then the high-order byte into the Counter register, problems could arise, because the low-order byte would start decrementing before you had completed loading the high-order byte. To resolve this problem, you initially load the low-order Counter register byte value into the low-order Latch register byte; then you directly load the high-order Counter register byte. You do this by writing into the memory addresses associated with select codes $0100_2$ (DEV+4) and $0101_2$ (DEV+5). When you write into select code $0100_2$ (DEV+4), you load the low-order byte of the initial Counter value into the low-order Latch register byte. When you write into select code $0101_2$ (DEV+5), you load the high-order Latch register byte, but immediately the 16 Latch register bits are loaded into the Counter, which starts decrementing. As soon as the Counter times out, an interrupt is requested; and if, via Auxiliary Control register bit 7, you have connected I/O port pin 7 to the Counter, then a low pulse will be output via pin 7. The low pulse will have a width of one Φ2 clock period:

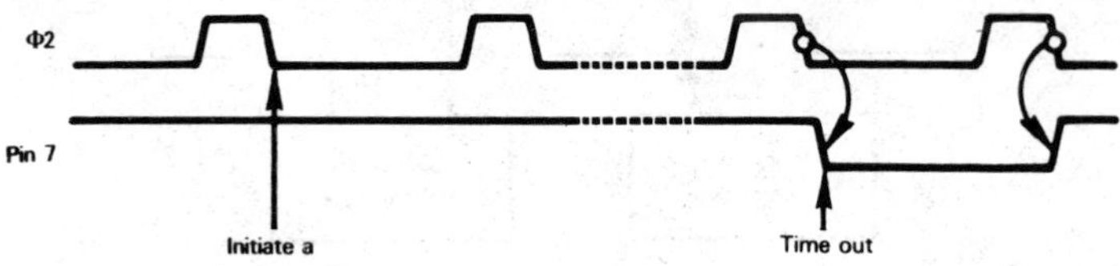


Note that when using an MCS6522, the onus is upon you to make sure that all programmable signal levels are at their correct level. In the illustration above, Φ2 is not a programmable signal, so you can ignore it. The pin 7 level is programmable; it is up to you to make sure that a high level is being output at pin 7, or else a low pulse will not occur.

What we are saying is that Interval Timer 1 logic will not insure that pin 7 is normally outputting a high level. You must first define pin 7 as an output by writing a 0 into bit 7 of the I/O Port B Data Direction register. Then you must output a 1 to bit 7 of I/O Port B. Having thus established a continuous high level being output at pin 7, you can be sure of a low pulse marking an active time out.

Following a time out in the one-shot mode, the Counter decrements continuously via $FFFF_{16}$ to $0000_{16}$. On subsequent time outs no interrupt request occurs and no low pulse is output via pin 7 of I/O Port B.

**If you have specified the free running mode by loading 1 into bit 6 of the Auxiliary Control register,** then as soon as the Counter times out, Latch register contents are immediately transferred to the Counter register, which again decrements to an active time out. Thus a sequence of interrupt requests, with optional signal output via pin 7 of I/O Port B, will occur — but there are some differences.

**MCS6522 INTERVAL TIMER 1 FREE RUNNING MODE**

When using Interval Timer 1 in free running mode, you initialize exactly as you do for the one-shot mode, you load the low-order and high-order Counter bytes via select codes $0100_2$ (DEV+4) and $0101_2$ (DEV+5). As soon as you write into select code $0101_2$, the Latch contents are transferred to the Counter, which starts decrementing. While the Counter is decrementing you can reset the next Counter initial value by writing into the Latch register using select codes $0110_2$ (DEV+6) and $0111_2$ (DEV+7). Now as soon as the Counter times out, the new value you have loaded into the Latch register becomes the next initial Counter value.

If you have connected I/O Port B pin 7 to the Counter by storing 1 in Auxiliary Control register bit 7, then each time the Counter times out, the signal output via pin 1 of I/O Port B is inverted, generating a square wave; this may be illustrated as follows:

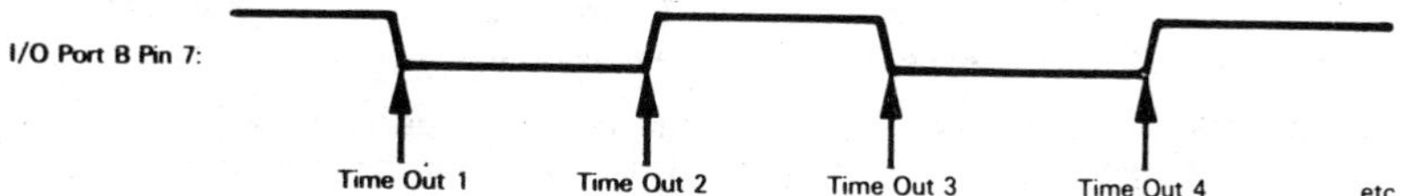


Remember, you can, at any time, read the contents of Interval Timer 1 Counter or Latch registers. This gives you a complete ability to test and modify Timer intervals In any way, under program control, while Interval Timer 1 is operating.

**Now consider Interval Timer 2.**

**MCS6522 Interval Timer 2 has logic which is markedly different from Interval Timer 1, which we have just described. Interval Timer 2 offers two modes of operation:**

**MCS6522 INTERVAL TIMER 2**

**1) One-shot mode with no signal output.**

**2) Pulse counting mode.**

You select one of the two Interval Timer 2 options by appropriately setting bit 5 of the Auxiliary Control register, as illustrated in Figure 10-14.

One-shot mode, with no signal output, is identical in operation to one-shot mode with no signal output, as described for Interval Timer 1.

Pulse counting mode is an alternative one-shot mode; the Interval Timer 2 Counter decrements on high-to-low transitions of signal input via pin 6 of I/O Port B. Thus, in the pulse count mode, Interval Timer 2 will count out after the number of high-to-low transitions specified by the initial Counter value. For example, if you initially load $2000_{16}$ into the Interval Timer 2 Counter, then after 8192 high-to-low transitions of the signal input via pin 6, an active time out will occur.

Following an active time out, an interrupt is requested. Subsequently, Interval Timer 2 continues to decrement continuously from $0000_{16}$ through $FFFF_{16}$ and back to $0000_{16}$; on subsequent time outs however, no interrupt request is generated. Subsequent time outs are passive.

Since the logic capabilities of Interval Timer 2 differ from Interval Timer 1, as we might expect, the register organization and addressing logic associated with Interval Timer 2 also differs. It may be illustrated as follows:

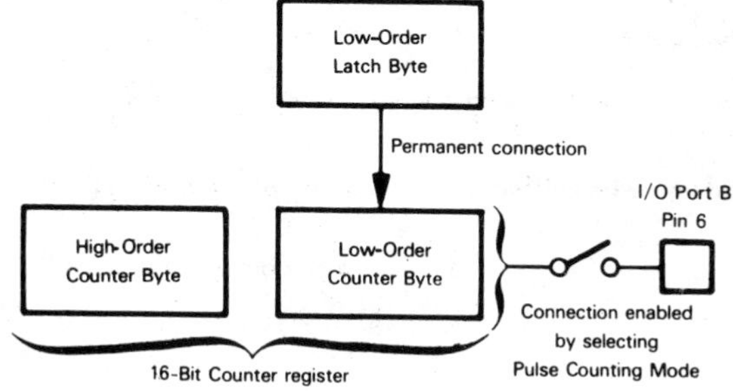

Interval Timer 2 is accessed via two select codes, $1000_2$ (DEV+8) and $1001_2$ (DEV+9); addressing may be illustrated as follows:

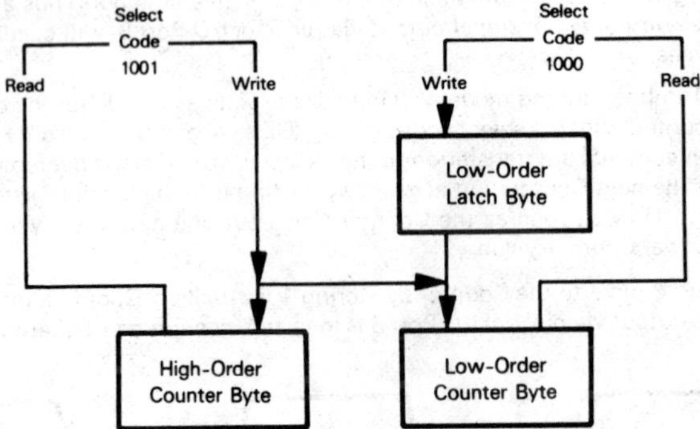


Since Interval Timer 2 has no free running option, there is no need for a high-order Latch register byte; the sole purpose of such a location is to store a high-order Counter byte, waiting to be loaded into the Counter register when it times out. You do need a low-order Latch register byte, because when loading the Counter register, you still have to make two accesses. You cannot load the low-order Counter byte, and then load the high-order Counter byte; the Counter is continuously decrementing and would start decrementing the low-order Counter byte while you were loading the high-order Counter byte.

The initiation procedure for Interval Timer 2, whether you are in one-shot mode or pulse counting mode, is to write the low-order Counter byte to select code $1000_2$ (DEV+8), then the high-order Counter byte to select code $1001_2$ (DEV+9). As soon as you write the high-order Counter byte to select code $1001_2$ (DEV+9), Interval Timer 2 logic transfers the contents of the low-order Latch byte to the low-order Counter byte — and initiates decrementing.

If you are in one-shot mode, the Counter register is decremented on each high-to-low transition of the Φ2 clock pulse.

If you are in pulse counting mode, the Counter decrements on each high-to-low transition of a signal input via pin 6 of I/O Port B.

That is the only difference between the two modes.

## MCS6522 SHIFTER LOGIC

**MCS6522 Shifter logic may be illustrated as follows:**

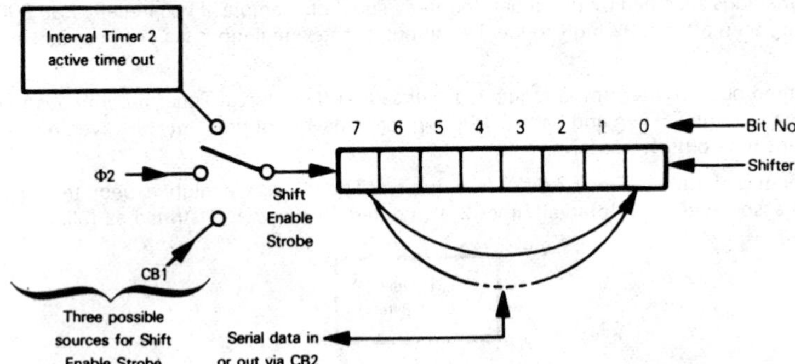


**As illustrated above, serial data may be shifted into bit 0 or out of the Shift register bit 7. Serial data is transferred via control signal CB2.**

When you shift into bit 0 the data transfer is accompanied by a one-bit left shift of the Shifter contents. When you shift out of bit 7, the data transfer is accompanied by a one-bit left rotate of the Shifter contents.

**Every serial bit data transfer is enabled by a strobe signal.** The strobe may be derived from:

1) A signal input by external logic via CB1.
2) The Φ2 clock signal.
3) Interval Timer 2 active time-outs.

If the enable strobe is derived from external logic via CB1 or from Φ2, then the high-to-low transition of either signal triggers the enable strobe.

If the shift enable strobe is derived from Interval Timer 2, then only the low-order eight Counter bits for Interval Timer 2 are decremented.

**There are seven modes in which the Shifter can be operated;** three are input modes and four are output modes. You select an appropriate mode by the code loaded into bits 4, 3, and 2 of the Auxiliary Control register. Let us examine the response of Shifter logic to the eight possible Auxiliary Control register bit combinations.

**Mode 000; disable Shift register.** When Auxiliary Control register bits 4, 3, and 2 are 000, the Shift register is disabled. Control signals CB1 and CB2 respond as defined by bits 7, 6, and 5 of the Peripheral Control register. While the Shift register is disabled, the CPU can still write into it and read from it; you, as a programmer, can therefore use it as a storage location for a single data byte.

**Mode 001; input under Interval Timer 2 strobe.** Auxiliary Control register bits 4, 3, and 2 set to 001 specify serial data shifted in, as timed by Interval Timer 2. However, only the low-order byte of Interval Timer 2 is active, which means that 256 is the maximum initial Interval Timer 2 count which can be used. A low pulse with a width of one Φ2 clock is output via CB1 on each Interval Timer 2 time-out, as a signal that external logic must provide the next serial data bit to be input. Interrupts are generated, as usual, following each time-out; an additional interrupt is generated after eight bits in the Shift register have been serially output.

When Interval Timer 2 is being used to strobe the Shift register in Mode 001, then it operates in a unique mode which is not available at any other time.

Whenever Interval Timer 2 times out, the contents of the low-order Latch byte are immediately transferred to the low-order Counter byte — and decrementing resumes. Thus, Interval Timer 2 is operating in a free running mode, with only the low-order Counter byte active. As this would imply, you must initiate Interval Timer 2 by loading the appropriate initial count into the low-order Timer 2 Latch byte — before enabling the Shift register in Mode 001. Following a time-out you can, of course, reload the Interval Timer 2 low-order Latch byte to modify the next time interval. Timing may be illustrated as follows:

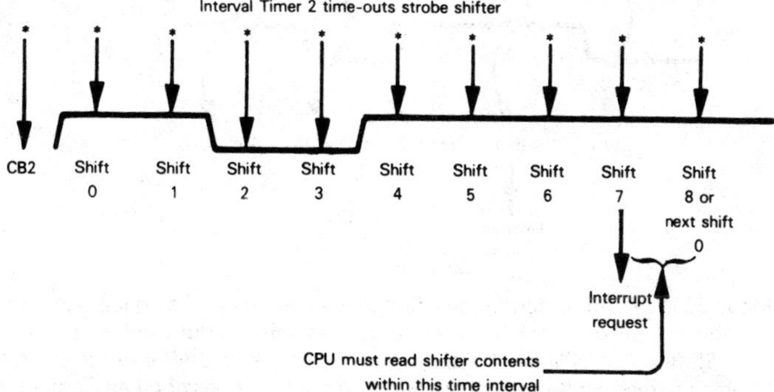


Note that it is your responsibility as a programmer to ensure that all logic needed by the Shifter has been appropriately set for operations illustrated above. This means that you must program Interval Timer 2 to redecrement following each time-out by writing a 0 into select mode $1001_2$ (DEV+9), the high-order Timer 2 Counter byte.

Since control signals CB1 and CB2 are being used by the Shift register in this mode of operation, Shift register requirements will override any CB1 and CB2 control signal specifications that have been made via bits 7, 6, 5, and 4 of the Peripheral Control register.

**Mode 010; input under Φ2 clock strobe.** This mode is specified by 010 in bits 4, 3, and 2 of the Auxiliary Control register.

In Mode 010, and in all other Shift register modes that are clocked by Φ2, shifting stops on the eighth shift — which is marked by an interrupt request. Timing may be illustrated as follows:

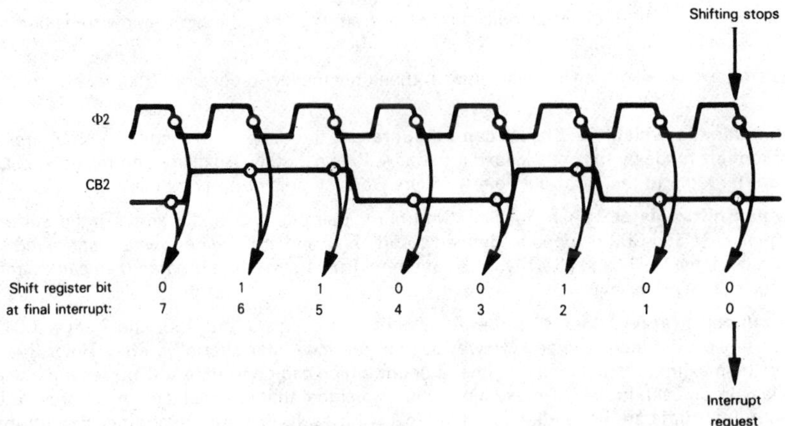


**Mode 011; input under external pulse strobe.** This mode is specified by 011 in bits 4, 3, and 2 of the Auxiliary Control register. This mode is equivalent to the standard serial input found in most serial I/O devices, where external logic provides the clocking signal which is used to time in serial data. In this case, external logic provides a clocking signal via CB1; a high-to-low transition of CB1 is interpreted by the Shift register as a strobe to input the next serial data bit from CB2.

Timing may be illustrated as follows:

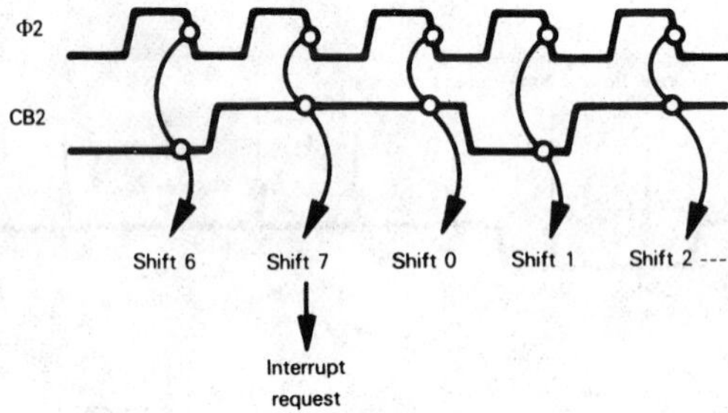


As was the case with Mode 001, shifting is continuous. So far as external logic is concerned it is shifting in an endless stream of serial data bits. Shifter logic generates an interrupt request every eighth shift so that the CPU will know when to read the contents of the Shifter. The CPU has the time interval between a Shifter interrupt and the next high-to-low transition of CB1 within which to read Shifter register contents. If the CPU does not read Shifter register contents in this time interval then an error will occur but no error status will be reported.

Shift register use of control signals CB1 and CB2 overrides specifications made for these signals via bits 7, 6, 5 and 4 of the Peripheral Control register; however, the policy of overriding adopted by the designers of the MCS6522 is somewhat subtle. Since control signal CB2 is used as a serial data input signal, any specifications made for this signal via the Peripheral Control register are totally ignored. Specifications made for control signal CB1, however, remain. If you have enabled the input latches of I/O Port B via bit 1 of the Auxiliary Control register, then the active transition for control signal CB1 which is specified by bit 4 of the Peripheral Control register will apply. Thus you will generate an interrupt whenever CB1 makes an active transition in the process of clocking in serial data. The two possibilities may be illustrated as follows:

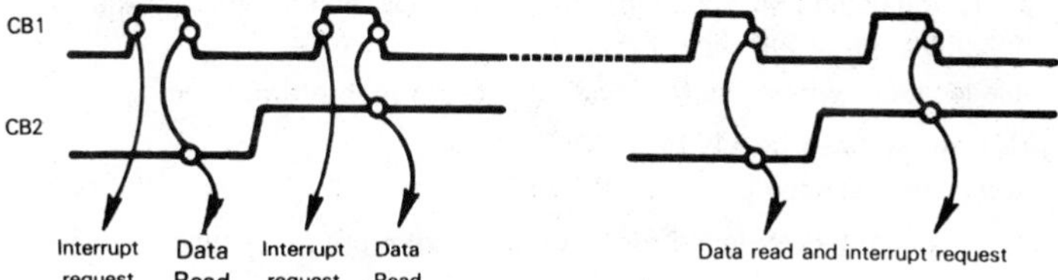


You can disable interrupts occurring as a result of active CB1 transitions via the Interrupt Enable register, which we have yet to describe.

**Let us now look at the output modes of the Shift register.** In all output modes, the Shift register transfers the contents of bit 7 to control signal CB2. Simultaneously, bit 7 contents are shifted back into bit 0. This may be illustrated as follows:

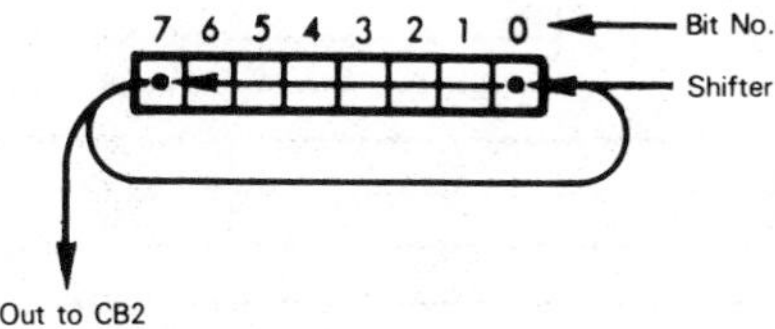


Depending upon the serial output option you choose, CB1 may or may not be used as a companion control signal.

**Mode 100; free-running output under Interval Timer 2 strobe.** This mode is selected via 100 in bits 4, 3, and 2 of the Auxiliary Control register. Data is shifted out of Shift register bit 7, clocked by Interval Timer 2, as described for input mode 001. Data shifted out appears on CB2. Shifting is continuous, which means that the bit pattern in the Shift register will output endlessly.

**Mode 101; output under Interval Timer 2 strobe.** This mode is specified by 101 in bits 4, 3, and 2 of the Auxiliary Control register. It differs from Mode 100, which we have just described, in that once eight bits have been shifted out of the Shifter, an interrupt is requested and shifting halts.

You can output continuously under Mode 101 by making appropriate use of Shift register interrupts and Interval Timer 2. The Shift register interrupt occurs on the eighth shift out of the Shifter; but within the time it takes for Interval Timer 2 to again time-out, you can reload the Shifter. If you reload the Shifter during this time interval, then on the next time-out of Interval Timer 2, shifting will begin again, and thus become an uninterrupted bit stream on signal CB2.

**Mode 110; shift out under $\Phi 2$ pulse.** This mode is selected via 110 in bits 4, 3, and 2 of the Auxiliary Control register. In this mode eight bits are shifted out of the Shift register, clocked by $\Phi 2$. Then shifting ceases.

These are the steps you must adopt when using the Shifter in Mode 110:

1) Disable the Shifter by loading 000 into bits 4, 3, and 2 of the Auxiliary Control register.
2) Load a byte of data into the Shifter. Remember the data you load will be shifted high-order bit first.
3) Enable the Shifter by loading 110 into bits 4, 3, and 2 of the Auxiliary Control register.
4) Again disable the Shifter by loading 000 into bits 4, 3, and 2 of the Auxiliary Control register.

In Mode 110, data will be shifted out on every high-to-low transition of the $\Phi 2$ clock pulse. Thus the entire shift operation will be completed in eight clock pulses.

**Mode 111; shift out under external pulse strobe.** This mode is identical to Mode 101, except that instead of output being timed by Interval Timer 2, external logic provides the output timing pulse via control signal CB1. As was the case for input mode 011, the high-to-low transition of the external timing signal input via CB1 causes serial data to be shifted out of the Shift register. Once again, unless you have disabled CB1 interrupts via the Interrupt Enable register, the condition of bit 4 in the Peripheral Control register will cause the interrupts to be requested each time control signal CB1 makes a high-to-low or a low-to-high transition.

## MCS6522 INTERRUPT LOGIC

Interrupt logic is one of the first things you must initialize when starting to use an MCS6522. It is the last subject we describe, because in order to understand MCS6522 interrupts, you must first be aware of the numerous ways in which interrupt requests may originate within this device.

There are two addressable locations within the MCS6522 dedicated to interrupt logic:

1) The Interrupt Flag register, selected by $1101_2$ (DEV+D).
2) The Interrupt Enable register, selected by $1110_2$ (DEV+E).

These two registers have individual bits assigned to the different interrupt requesting sources as follows:

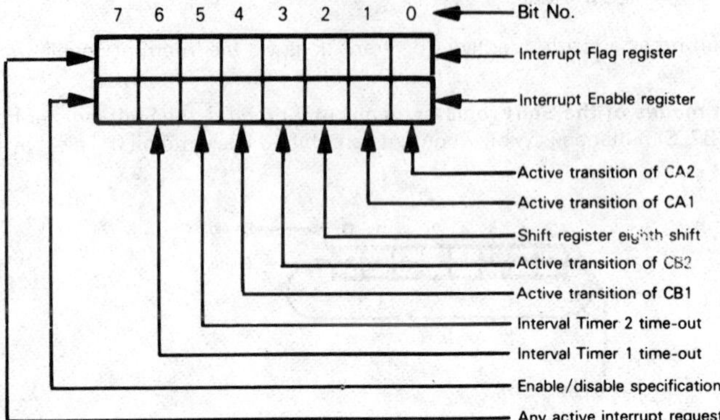


**The Interrupt Flag register identifies those interrupts which are active.** A 1 in any bit position indicates an active interrupt, whereas a 0 indicates an inactive interrupt.

**You can selectively enable or disable individual interrupts via the Interrupt Enable register.** You enable individual interrupts by writing to the Interrupt Enable register with a 1 in bit 7. Thus you could enable "time-out for Timer 1" and "active transitions of signal CB1" by outputting $D0_{16}$ to the Interrupt Enable register:

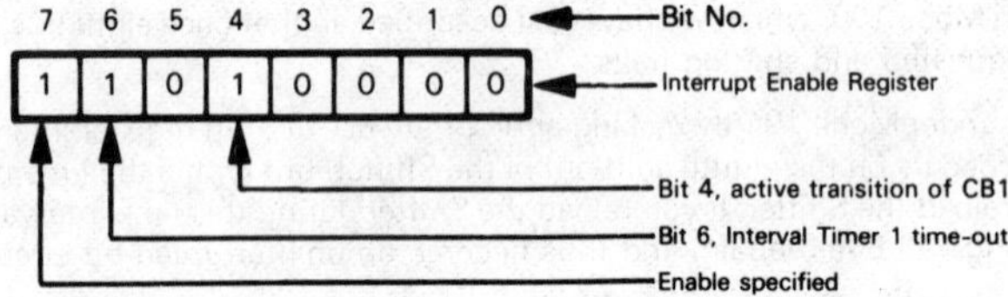


You selectively disable interrupts by writing to the Interrupt Enable register with bit 7 set to 0. Thus you would disable time-outs from Timer 1 and active transitions of signal CB1 by outputting $50_{16}$ to the Interrupt Enable register.

If an active interrupt exists in the Interrupt Flag register for an interrupt which has been enabled via the Interrupt Enable register, then bit 7 of the Interrupt Flag register will be set — and an interrupt request will be passed on to the CPU by setting IRQ low. The interrupt service routine executed in response to an interrupt request from the MCS6522 must read the contents of the Interrupt Flag register in order to determine the source of the interrupt, and thus the manner in which the interrupt must be serviced.

You can clear any bit in the Interrupt Flag register, except bit 7, by writing a 1 to that bit. Writing 0 to a bit has no effect. Thus, if interrupt requests were being made from time-out of Timer 1 and an active transition on CA1:

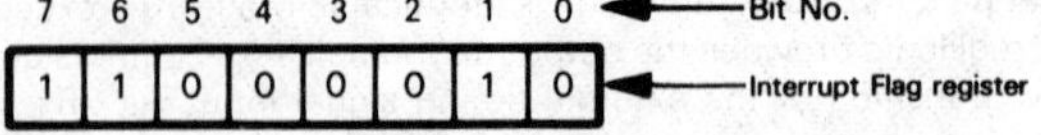


Writing either $82_{16}$ or $02_{16}$ to select code $1101_2$ (DEV+D) would clear the interrupt due to an active transition on CA1 (bit 1); however, bits 7 and 6 would remain set.

There are a number of ways in which interrupt requests are automatically cleared, and the corresponding Interrupt Flag register bits get reset. These are summarized in Table 10-6.

Table 10-6. A Summary of MCS6522 Interrupt Setting and Resetting

| | Set | Cleared By |
|---|---|---|
| 6 | Time-out of Timer 1 | Reading Timer 1 Low-Order Counter or writing T1 High-Order Latch |
| 5 | Time-out of Timer 2 | Reading Timer 2 Low-Order Counter or writing T2 High-Order Counter |
| 4 | Active transition of the signal on CB1 | Reading from or writing to I/O Port B |
| 3 | Active transition of the signal on CB2 (input mode) | Reading from or writing to I/O Port B in input mode only |
| 2 | Completion of eight shifts | Reading or writing the Shift register |
| 1 | Active transition of the signal on CA1 | Reading from or writing to I/O Port A using address $0001_2$ |
| 0 | Active transition of the signal on CA2 (input mode) | Reading from or writing to I/O Port A Output register (ORA) using address $0001_2$ in input mode only |

# THE MCS6530 MULTIFUNCTION SUPPORT LOGIC DEVICE

**This is a device which appears to have been designed by MOS Technology as an answer to one-chip microcomputers. For new designs you should use the R6531, introduced by Rockwell, in preference to the R6530.**

In order to compete in low-end, high volume, price sensitive markets, MOS Technology came up with the MCS6530, which provides 1K bytes of ROM, 64 bytes of RAM, two I/O ports, a Programmable Interval Timer and interrupt logic. The realities of the MCS6530 are such that if you use the Interval Timer and interrupt logic, one of the I/O ports is only partially functional. Nevertheless, an MCS6530 multifunction support device, together with an MCS6500 series CPU, can compete effectively with the two-chip microcomputers described in this book.

If we look at the MCS6530 simply as a member of the MCS6500 microcomputer family of devices, it is best visualized as a memory device which, in addition, provides a significant subset of the MCS6522 logic capabilities.

Figure 10-16 illustrates that part of our general purpose microcomputer logic which has been implemented on the MCS6530 multifunction logic device. Figure 10-16 also applies to the R6531 and the MCS6532, which we will describe next.

**The MCS6530 is packaged as a 40-pin DIP. It uses a single +5 V power supply. All inputs and outputs are TTL-level compatible. I/O Port A and B pins are also CMOS compatible. PA0 and PB0 may be used as a power source to directly drive the base of a transistor switch.**

**The MCS6530 is implemented using N-channel silicon gate MOS technology.**

**Figure 10-17 illustrates the logic provided by an MCS6530 multifunction logic device.**

## THE MCS6530 MULTIFUNCTION DEVICE PINS AND SIGNALS

**The MCS6530 multifunction device pins and signals are illustrated in Figure 10-18.**

**These signals are identical to signals with the same names which we have already described for the MCS6522:**

| | |
|---|---|
| D0 - D7 | the bidirectional Data Bus |
| $\Phi 2$ | the system clock input |
| R/$\overline{\text{W}}$ | the Read/Write control output by the CPU |
| $\overline{\text{RESET}}$ | which is a standard reset input |

**I/O port pins PA0 - PA7 and PB0 - PB7 are functionally similar to equivalent I/O port pins of the MCS6522, but there are some differences.**

**Pin 17 may be specified,** when you order the MCS6530, **as $\overline{\text{IRQ}}$ only, PB7 only, or as the programmable dual function pin $\overline{\text{IRQ}}$/PB7.**

Electrical characteristics of all 16 MCS6530 I/O port pins are equivalent to MCS6522 I/O Port B pins, rather than I/O Port A pins.

**MCS6530 pins 18 and 19 may implement I/O Port B pins PB6 and PB5, or they may serve as chip select pins.** Note carefully that these are not programmable dual function pins. Each pin will either have one function or the other; and when ordering the part, you must indicate which function the pin is to serve. Pins 18 and 19 are logically independent, and the function assigned to one in no way restricts the choices available to you when assigning functions to the other pins.

**If pins 18 and/or 19 have been assigned to chip select logic, then they contribute to device addressing in a unique way.**

**MCS6530 ADDRESSING LOGIC**

**The MCS6530 has ten address lines, A0 - A9;** this is sufficient to address 1024 bytes of ROM. In addition, the MCS6530 has 64 bytes of RAM plus assorted I/O and Interval Timer logic which needs to be addressed. RS0, CS1 and CS2 are used to discriminate between ROM addresses, RAM addresses and additional logic addresses. But there is no predefined way in which the different addressable locations of the MCS6530 will be accessed — which is only to be expected since CS1 and CS2 are not permanent features of every MCS6530 device. **When RS0 is high, ROM will always be selected. When RS0 is low, RAM or additional logic may be accessed** — and the way in which the access works is entirely up to you.

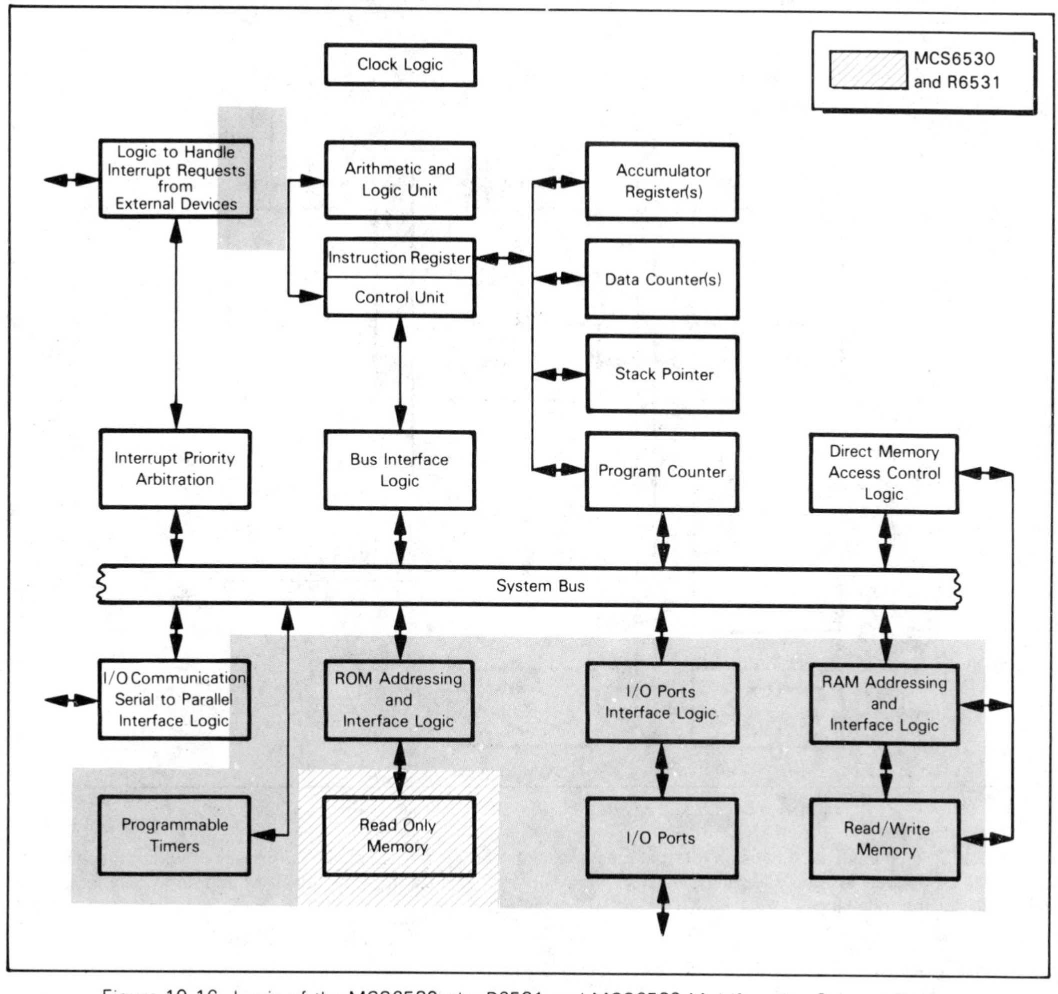


Figure 10-16. Logic of the MCS6530, the R6531 and MCS6532 Multifunction Support Devices

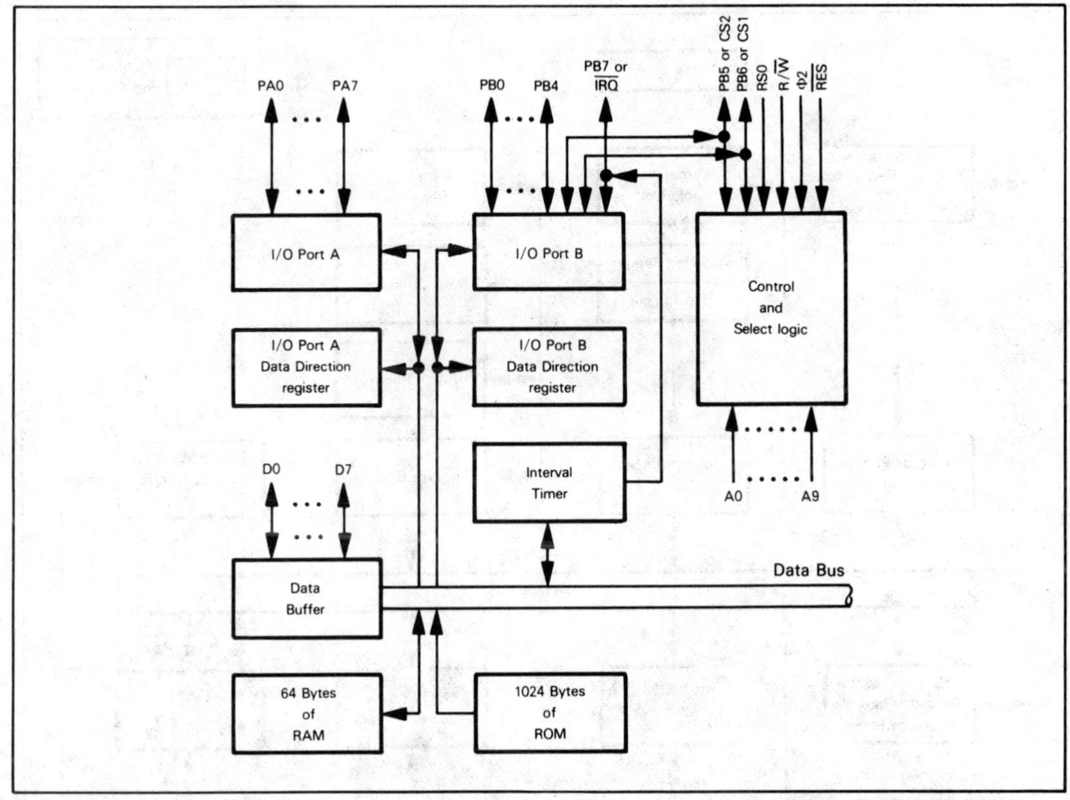


Figure 10-17. Logic Provided by the MCS6530 Multifunction Device

RAM and additional logic each have an internal master select; and what you specify is the way in which these master selects will be derived. As you will see upon examining Table 10-7, master selects for RAM and additional logic each will consist of the following:

1) RS0 set to 0.
2) Address lines A4 - A9 with specific values which you define.
3) CS1 and CS2, if implemented, with specific values which you define.

As seen by a programmer, the address space of an MCS6530 can be divided in many flexible ways.

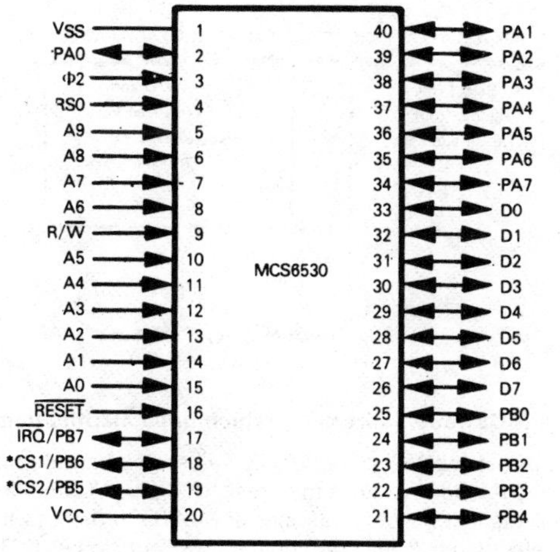

| | | MCS6530 | | |
|---|---|---|---|---|
| VSS | 1 | | 40 | PA1 |
| PA0 | 2 | | 39 | PA2 |
| Φ2 | 3 | | 38 | PA3 |
| RS0 | 4 | | 37 | PA4 |
| A9 | 5 | | 36 | PA5 |
| A8 | 6 | | 35 | PA6 |
| A7 | 7 | | 34 | PA7 |
| A6 | 8 | | 33 | D0 |
| R/$\overline{\text{W}}$ | 9 | | 32 | D1 |
| A5 | 10 | | 31 | D2 |
| A4 | 11 | | 30 | D3 |
| A3 | 12 | | 29 | D4 |
| A2 | 13 | | 28 | D5 |
| A1 | 14 | | 27 | D6 |
| A0 | 15 | | 26 | D7 |
| $\overline{\text{RESET}}$ | 16 | | 25 | PB0 |
| $\overline{\text{IRQ}}$/PB7 | 17 | | 24 | PB1 |
| •CS1/PB6 | 18 | | 23 | PB2 |
| •CS2/PB5 | 19 | | 22 | PB3 |
| VCC | 20 | | 21 | PB4 |

| Pin Name | Description | Type |
|---|---|---|
| D0 - D7 | Data Bus to CPU | Tristate, bidirectional |
| Φ2 | System Clock | Input |
| R/$\overline{\text{W}}$ | Read/Write control | Input |
| $\overline{\text{RESET}}$ | Reset | Input |
| PA0 - PA7 | Port A Peripheral Data Bus | Tristate, Input or Output |
| PB0 - PB7 | Port B Peripheral Data Bus | Tristate, Input or Output |
| $\overline{\text{IRQ}}$ | Interrupt from Interval Timer; special function of input pin PB7 | Input |
| CS1, CS2 | Chip Select | Input |
| A0 - A9 | Address lines | Input |
| RS0 | ROM Select | Input |
| $V_{CC}$, $V_{SS}$ | Power and Ground | |

•Mutually exclusive functions. One or the other must be specified when the chip is ordered.

Figure 10-18. MCS6530 Multifunction Device Signals and Pin Assignments

Usually RS0 will be connected to a high-order address line; let us assume it is A10, so that we can develop real examples. Now ROM will be accessed by addresses in the range $0400_{16}$ through $07FF_{16}$.

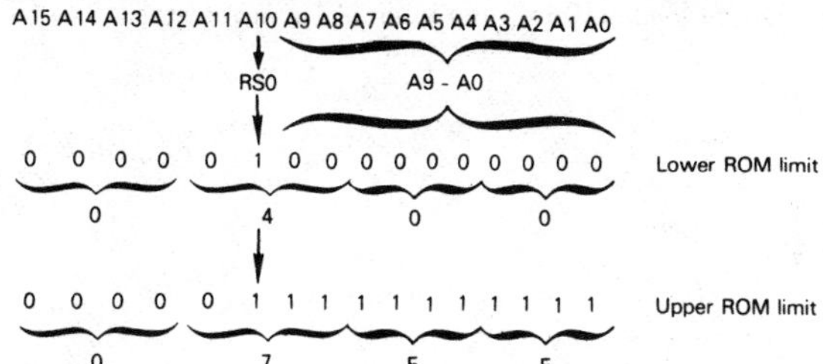


RAM may respond to any 64 contiguous addresses in the range $0000_{16}$ through $03FF_{16}$.

Similarly, I/O and timer logic will be selected by 16 contiguous memory addresses in the same address space.

In summary, we may illustrate addressing and select options as follows:

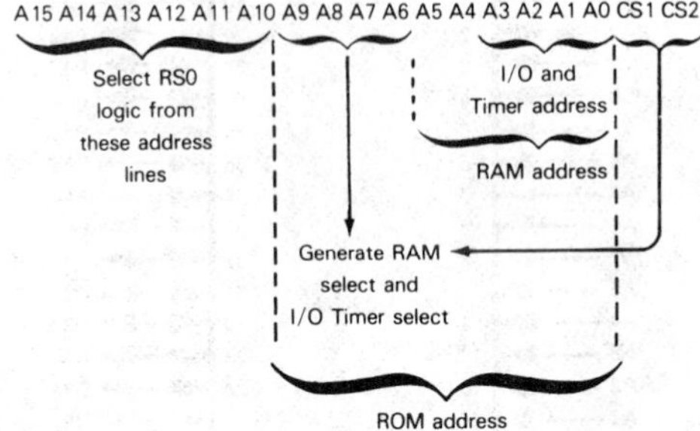


**There are a number of aspects to MCS6530 addressing which need clarification.**

First of all, you may well ask why pins 18 and 19 can optionally be assigned as additional chip select inputs. After all, with RSO low, you have more than enough address lines to access RAM plus I/O and timer logic. The purpose of having CS1 and CS2, as additional chip selects, is to allow a number of MCS6530 devices to interface with a single CPU — without requiring complex device select logic. If the additional chip select signals CS1 and CS2 are not available, you can still have more than one MCS6530 connected to a CPU, but additional support logic must selectively suppress Φ2 for all but one MCS6530 device. Remember, RSO, R/$\overline{W}$ and the Address Bus are all signals with two active and no passive states. These signals are always selecting some MCS6530 location.

Since the whole purpose of the MCS6530 is to support very low cost, simple microcomputer configurations, the ability to minimize device select logic becomes very important.

Observe that address logic is used not only to access individual addressable locations within the MCS6530, but also to perform certain programming functions. We will describe these programming functions in greater detail later. It is interesting to note that both the MC6800 and MCS6500 microcomputer devices use address logic to provide control functions in support devices. In contrast, 8080A devices will be very spartan when it comes to device addressing, frequently having two I/O or memory addresses to access numerous different locations — with complex sequencing schemes determining how locations will be accessed.

## MCS6530 PARALLEL DATA TRANSFER OPERATIONS

Parallel data transfer operations, when using the MCS6530 are exactly as described for the MCS6522 I/O Port B.

Each I/O port of the MCS6530 has a Data Direction register. Into this register you load a mask which has a 1 in every bit position corresponding to an output I/O port pin and a 0 corresponding to an input I/O port pin. Subsequently the CPU reads and writes data by accessing the assigned I/O port address.

## MCS6530 INTERVAL TIMER AND INTERRUPT LOGIC

MCS6530 Interval Timer logic differs significantly from MCS6522 logic. The MCS6530 Interval Timer is a single 8-bit register which can be loaded with any initial value. The initial value decrements on high-to-low transitions of the Φ2 clock pulse, or multiples of the Φ2 clock pulse; and on decrementing to 0, an interrupt request is generated. Thus the largest time interval is generated by loading 0 into the Interval Timer register.

Table 10-7. Addressing the MCS6530 Multifunction Support Logic Device

| Primary Select | | | Accessed Locations | | | | |
|---|---|---|---|---|---|---|---|
| RSO | RAM Select* | I/O Timer Select* | | | | | |
| 1 | X | X | A0 - A9 directly address one of 1024 ROM bytes | | | | |
| 0 | 1 | 0 | A0 - A5 directly address one of 64 RAM bytes | | | | |
| | | | Secondary Select | | | | Interpretation |
| | | | A3 | A2 | A1 | A0 | |
| 0 | 0 | 1 | X | 0 | 0 | 0 | Access I/O Port A |
| 0 | 0 | 1 | X | 0 | 0 | 1 | Access I/O Port A Data Direction register |
| 0 | 0 | 1 | X | 0 | 1 | 0 | Access I/O Port B |
| 0 | 0 | 1 | X | 0 | 1 | 1 | Access I/O Port B Data Direction register |
| 0 | 0 | 1W | 0 | 1 | X | X | Disable $\overline{IRQ}$ |
| 0 | 0 | 1W | 1 | 1 | X | X | Enable $\overline{IRQ}$ |
| 0 | 0 | 1W | X | 1 | 0 | 0 | Write to timer, then decrement every Φ2 pulse |
| 0 | 0 | 1W | X | 1 | 0 | 1 | Write to timer, then decrement every 8 Φ2 pulses |
| 0 | 0 | 1W | X | 1 | 1 | 0 | Write to timer, then decrement every 64 Φ2 pulses |
| 0 | 0 | 1W | X | 1 | 1 | 1 | Write to timer, then decrement every 1024 Φ2 pulses |
| 0 | 0 | 1R | X | 1 | X | 0 | Read timer |
| 0 | 0 | 1R | X | 1 | X | 1 | Read interrupt flag |

* RAM select and I/O select are "true" if 1, or "false" if 0; true and false are functions of your specification. You specify the combination of address lines that create a "true" line condition.

X represents "don't care". Bits may be 0 or 1.
1R represents Select during a read.
1W represents Select during a write.

As defined in Table 10-7, the Interval Timer has four addresses which you can use when loading an initial timer value. Each address specifies a different decrement interval. The four decrement intervals are 1, 8, 64 or 1024 Φ2 clock pulses.

Suppose the MCS6500 microcomputer system is being driven by a 500 nanosecond clock. The four decrement options mean that the Interval Timer may be decremented once every 1/2, 4, 32 or 512 microseconds. The timeout will occur anywhere from 1 to 256 decrements following the write into the Interval Timer.

Following a timeout, an interrupt will be requested. When an interrupt request occurs, the interrupt flag will be set. This flag may be read by the CPU using the address shown in Table 10-7.

The interrupt request will appear as a low level on pin 17 if the following conditions are met:

1) Address line A3 is 1 when reading from or writing to the timer.
2) PB7 has been programmed as an input by loading a 0 into bit 7 of the I/O Port B Data Direction register. (This is not necessary if the pin is factory masked to be $\overline{IRQ}$ only.)

The interrupt to pin 17 is disabled when address line A3 is 0 on a timer read or write.

The interrupt request is cleared (that is, $\overline{IRQ}$ returns high) the next time the timer is written or read.

Once the Interval Timer has timed out, it will decrement once more, from 0 back to 0. Then it will stop. Post-interrupt decrementing occurs on every Φ2 clock cycle, regardless of whether pre-interrupt decrements occurred every 1, 8, 64 or 1024 Φ2 clock cycles.

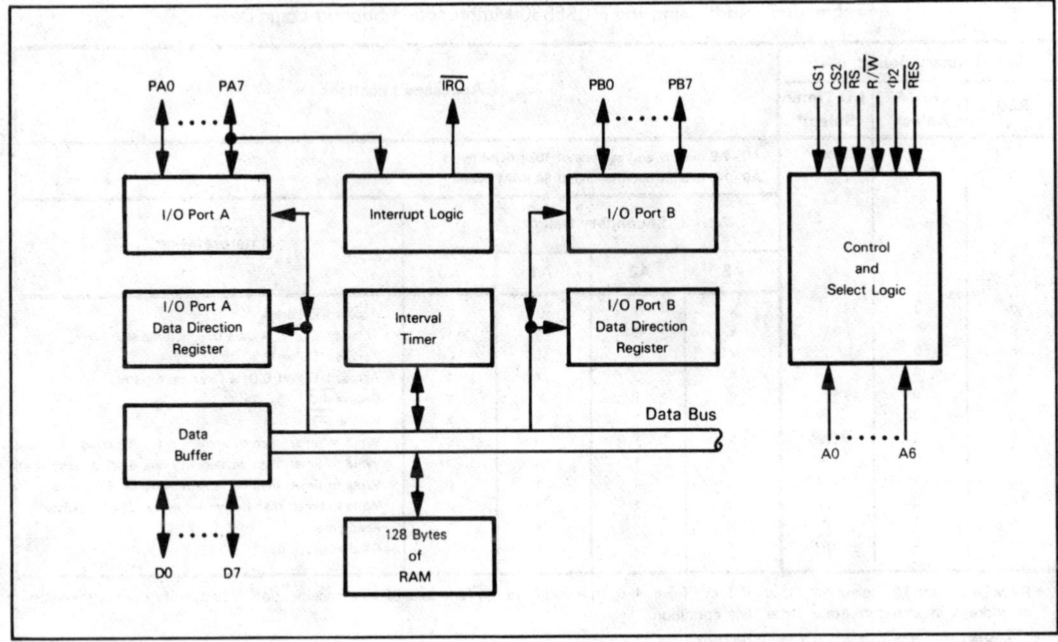


Figure 10-19. Logic Provided by the MCS6532 Multifunction Device

# THE MCS6532 MULTIFUNCTION SUPPORT LOGIC DEVICE

**This device is a variation of the MCS6530 which we have just described. As for the R6530, we recommend using the R6531, introduced by Rockwell, in preference to the R6532.**

The MCS6532 provides no ROM memory, but twice the RAM — 128 bytes.

External logic can request an interrupt via the MCS6532 using a control signal which may be likened to the MCS6522 CA1 or CB1 control input.

The mask defined addressing options of the MCS6530 have been removed from the MCS6532; otherwise the balance of logic on the two devices is identical.

**Figure 10-16 also illustrates that part of our general purpose microcomputer system logic which has been implemented on the MCS6532 multifunction device. Figure 10-19 illustrates the logic functions provided by the MCS6532.**

**The MCS6532 multifunction device is packaged as a 40-pin DIP. It uses a single +5V power supply. All inputs and outputs are TTL compatible. I/O Port A and B pins are also CMOS logic compatible. Pins of I/O Port B may be used as a power source to directly drive the base of a transistor switch.**

**The device is implemented using N-channel silicon gate MOS technology.**

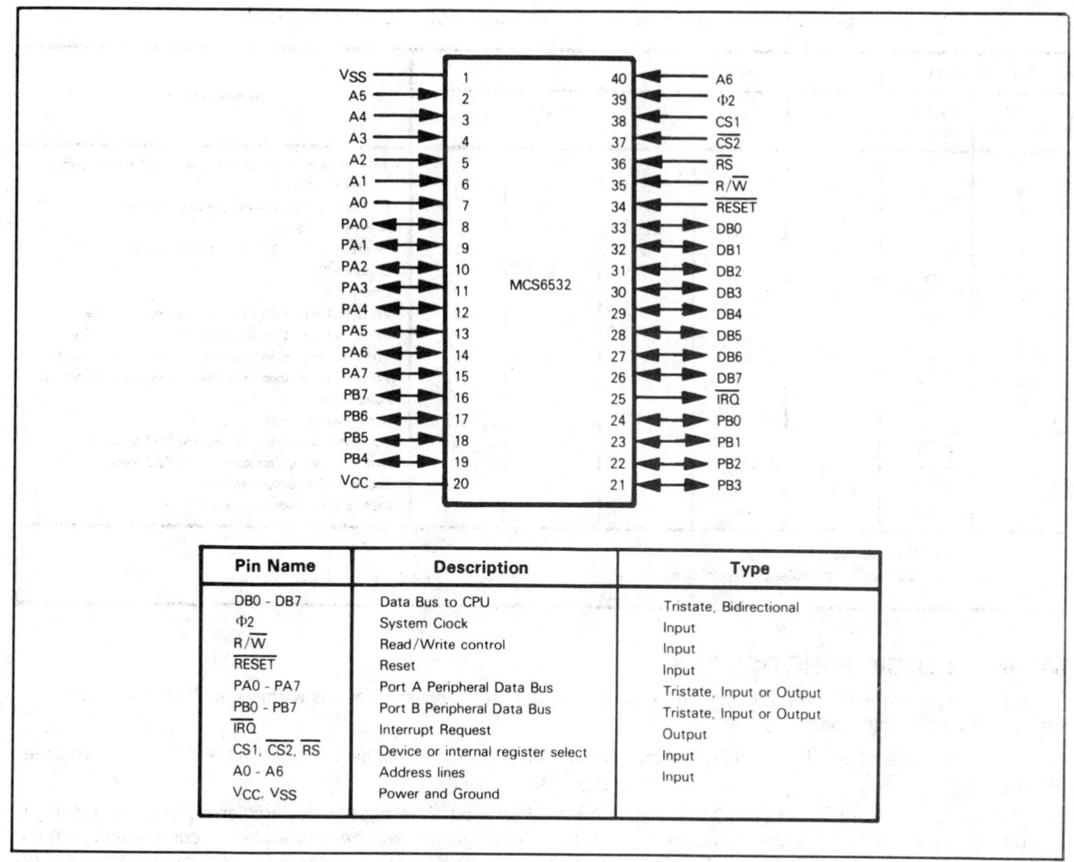


| Pin Name | Description | Type |
|---|---|---|
| DB0 - DB7 | Data Bus to CPU | Tristate, Bidirectional |
| Φ2 | System Clock | Input |
| R/$\overline{W}$ | Read/Write control | Input |
| $\overline{RESET}$ | Reset | Input |
| PA0 - PA7 | Port A Peripheral Data Bus | Tristate, Input or Output |
| PB0 - PB7 | Port B Peripheral Data Bus | Tristate, Input or Output |
| $\overline{IRQ}$ | Interrupt Request | Output |
| CS1, $\overline{CS2}$, $\overline{RS}$ | Device or internal register select | Input |
| A0 - A6 | Address lines | Input |
| $V_{CC}$, $V_{SS}$ | Power and Ground | |

Figure 10-20. MCS6532 Multifunction Device Signals and Pin Assignments

## MCS6532 MULTIFUNCTION DEVICE PINS AND SIGNALS

The MCS6532 multifunction device pins and signals are illustrated in Figure 10-20. These are the only differences between MCS6532 and MCS6530 signals:

1) $\overline{IRQ}$, CS1 and $\overline{CS2}$ are assigned, unique pins by the MCS6532; the MCS6530 requires you to choose individually between these three signals and the three high order bits of I/O Port B.
2) For the MCS6532 to be selected, $\overline{RS}$ and $\overline{CS2}$ must be low while CS1 is high. Recall that with the MCS6530, RS0 is a signal which discriminates between ROM and other addressable locations; you define the way in which CS1 and CS2, if present, will function when you order an MCS6530 part.

**MCS6532 ADDRESSING**

Addressing the MCS6532 is a good deal simpler than addressing the MCS6530, since the MCS6532 has no ROM present, and it has separate Chip Select signals. You still must define RAM select and I/O timer select as a function of $\overline{RS}$, CS1 and $\overline{CS2}$ and address lines A0 - A6. By connecting RS, CS1 and $\overline{CS2}$ to higher address lines, you can assign RAM or I/O timer logic various address spaces. This ability to define RAM and I/O Timer select as a mask option is a convenience, where with the MCS6530 it was frequently a necessity. With the MCS6532 you can accept whatever standard "off-the-shelf" option is being provided, and still have enough flexibility using RS, CS1 and CS2 to include a number of MCS6532 devices in a microcomputer configuration.

Table 10-8. Addressing the MCS6532 Multifunction Support Logic Device

| Primary Select | | Secondary Select | | | | | Interpretation |
|---|---|---|---|---|---|---|---|
| RAM Select | I/O Timer Select | A4 | A3 | A2 | A1 | A0 | |
| 1 | 0 | X | X | X | X | X | A0 - A6 directly addresses one of 128 RAM bytes. |
| 0 | 1 | X | X | 0 | 0 | 0 | Access I/O Port A |
| 0 | 1 | X | X | 0 | 0 | 1 | Access I/O Port A Data Direction register |
| 0 | 1 | X | X | 0 | 1 | 0 | Access I/O Port B |
| 0 | 1 | X | X | 0 | 1 | 1 | Access I/O Port B Data Direction register |
| 0 | 1W | 1 | 0 | 1 | X | X | Disable $\overline{IRQ}$ |
| 0 | 1W | 1 | 1 | 1 | X | X | Enable $\overline{IRQ}$ |
| 0 | 1W | 1 | X | 1 | 0 | 0 | Write to timer, then decrement every Φ2 pulse |
| 0 | 1W | 1 | X | 1 | 0 | 1 | Write to timer, then decrement every 8 Φ2 pulses |
| 0 | 1W | 1 | X | 1 | 1 | 0 | Write to timer, then decrement every 64 Φ2 pulses |
| 0 | 1W | 1 | X | 1 | 1 | 1 | Write to timer, then decrement every 1024 Φ2 pulses |
| 0 | 1R | X | X | 1 | X | 0 | Read timer |
| 0 | 1R | X | X | 1 | X | 1 | Read interrupt flags |
| 0 | 1W | 0 | X | 1 | X | 0 | Request interrupt on high-to-low PA7 transition |
| 0 | 1W | 0 | X | 1 | X | 1 | Request interrupt on low-to-high PA7 transition |
| 0 | 1W | 0 | X | 1 | 0 | X | Enable PA7 interrupt request |
| 0 | 1W | 0 | X | 1 | 1 | X | Disable PA7 interrupt request |

X represents "don't care". Bits may be 0 or 1.
1R represents Read access. 1W represents Write access.

## MCS6532 LOGIC FUNCTIONS

Table 10-8 summarizes the way in which addressing is used both to access locations within the MCS6532 and to provide various logic functions.

The only logic of the MCS6532 which differs from the MCS6530 and needs to be described is the external interrupt request capability.

External logic requests interrupts via I/O Port A pin PA7. I/O Port A pin PA7 must be declared an input pin by loading 0 into bit 7 of the I/O Port A Data Direction register. Data Direction registers have been described in conjunction with the MCS6522. A low-to-high or high-to-low transition on a signal input to PA7 will generate the interrupt request. An interrupt request will be accompanied by bit 6 of the Interrupt Flag register being set. Table 10-8 defines the way in which you select interrupt options.

MCS6532 interrupt acknowledge logic requires the CPU to read the Interrupt Flags register. This read operation resets MCS6532 interrupt logic.

# THE R6531 MULTIFUNCTION SUPPORT DEVICE

**The R6531 is an enhancement of the MCS6530 multifunction support device, described earlier in this chapter. The 6531 was designed by Rockwell; we therefore precede the device number with the letter R.**

**The R6531 is clearly superior to the MCS6530 or the MCS6532;** therefore the R6531 is the part of choice in new designs. However, the R6531 is neither pin nor program compatible with the MCS6530 or the MCS6532; replacing these parts with an R6531 in existing designs is therefore unlikely to be cost effective.

**Figure 10-16 also illustrates that part of our general purpose microcomputer logic which has been implemented on the R6531 multifunction device.**

**The R6531 is packaged as either a 40-pin DIP, or a 52-pin quad in-line package. It uses a single +5 V power supply; optionally, an additional +5 V read/write memory standby power supply may be selected. All inputs and outputs are TTL-level compatible.**

The R6531 is implemented using N- channel silicon gate MOS technology.

**Figure 10-21 illustrates the logic provided by the R6531 multifunction device.** Most of this logic is a variation of either MCS6522 or MCS6530 logic; however, there are numerous small differences. Since the R6531 is likely to be the part of choice in many 6500-based microcomputer systems, we will describe this part in detail, contrasting it with the MCS6522 and the MCS6530, but not relying upon these prior part descriptions for any logic discussion.

## THE R6531 MULTIFUNCTION DEVICE PINS AND SIGNALS

**The R6531 multifunction device pins and signals are illustrated in Figure 10-22 for the four possible pin and package options.**

The R6531 can be selected as a 40-pin DIP or as a 52-pin quad in-line package. Each package offers the option of a special read/write memory standby power supply. In addition, there are a number of pin and address options which you must specify when ordering an R6531. **Package, pin and mask options are summarized in Table 10-9.**

**D0-D7 represents the bidirectional Data Bus** via which all communications between the CPU and the R6531 occur. When the R6531 is not selected, the Data Bus buffer is placed in a high impedance state.

**PA0-PA7 and PB0-PB6 are two I/O ports, each pin of which is software programmable to act as either an input or an output.** Note that Port A is eight bits wide while Port B is seven bits wide. Port B is only six bits wide when using the 40-pin R6531 DIP with the standby power supply ($V_{RR}$) option.

In output operation, all Port A and B pins are push-pull drivers, identical to the MCS6522 I/O Port B pins.

**All I/O Port B pins have optional alternative functions.**

**The 52-pin quad in-line package variations of the R6531 have two additional I/O ports: I/O Ports C and D.** C is an output-only port, while D is an input-only port. Port C pins are, like those of Ports A and B, push-pull drivers.

**The R6531 has three optional device select signals: CS1, CS2 and CS3.** CS1 and CS2 can be selected as a mask option with any R6531 package. CS3 is available only on the 52-pin quad in-line package. All three of these device select signals share pins with I/O port lines, as shown in Figure 10-22. You select this function for these lines as a mask option. If you choose the device select option for any of these pins, then you cannot use the associated I/O port pin for any other purpose. We will explain how these select lines are used later, when we describe R6531 device addressing.

**There are two control signals associated with the R6531 CPU interface.**

**Φ2 is the phase 2 clock which is output by all MCS6500 series microprocessors.** The R6531 uses Φ2 as a standard synchronization signal. The trailing edge of each Φ2 pulse synchronizes all logic and timing within the R6531. Φ2 is used optionally by the shift register to clock serial data input or output; it is also used optionally by the counter/timer.

**R/$\overline{\text{W}}$ is the standard read/write control signal** output by all MCS6500 series microprocessors. Recall that when R/$\overline{\text{W}}$ is high, a read operation is specified and data is transferred from the R6531 to the CPU. When R/$\overline{\text{W}}$ is low, a write operation is specified and data is transferred from the CPU to the R6531.

**$\overline{\text{RES}}$ is a standard system reset input.** When $\overline{\text{RES}}$ is held low for four or more Φ2 cycles, it resets all the R6531 interval registers to zero, with the exception of the interval timer and the serial I/O logic. Thus, after reset, the R6531 is in the following state:

- I/O Port A and B lines are all inputs
- I/O Port C lines all output a high level (1)
- All interrupts are disabled, as are the interval timer and the serial I/O logic.

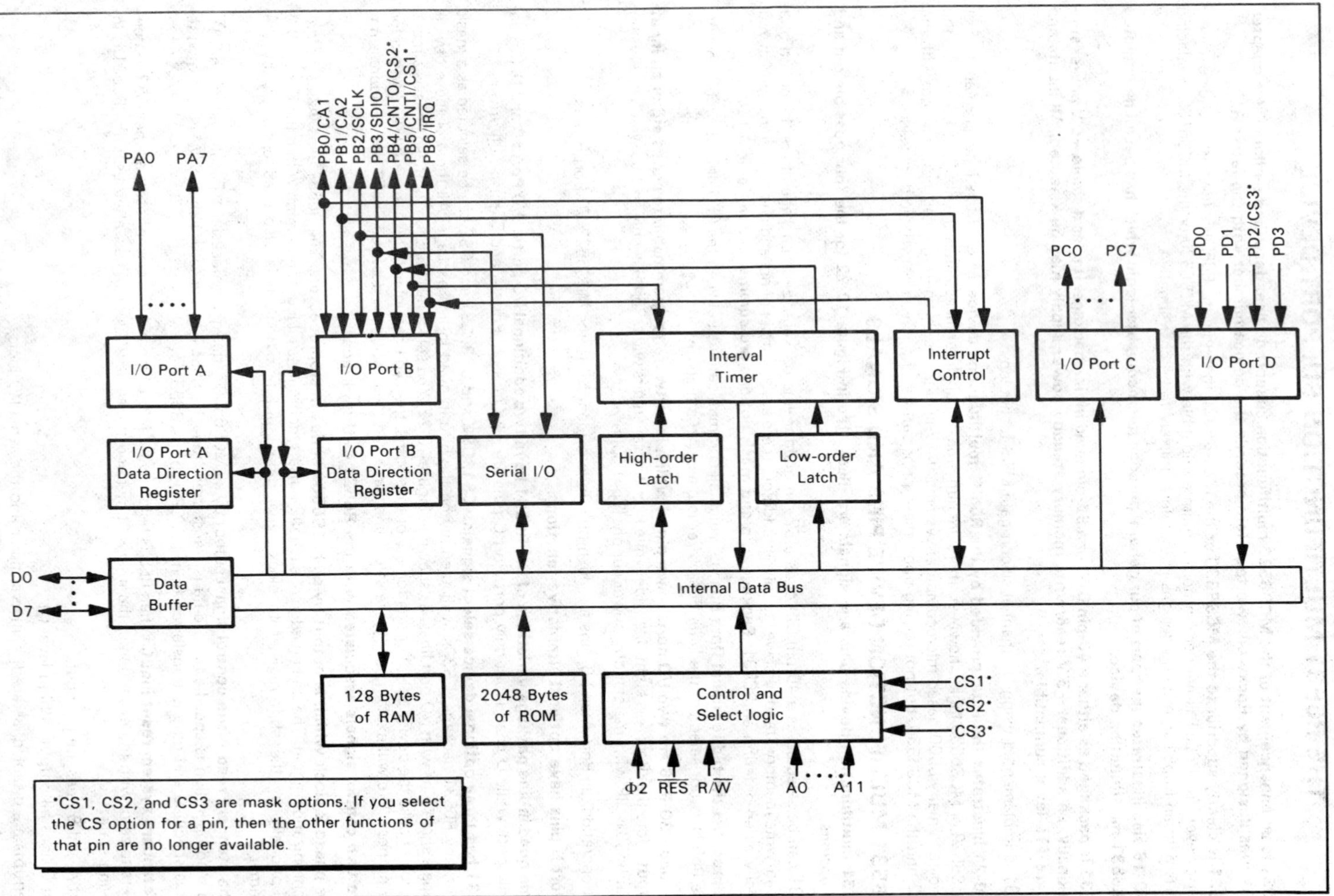


Figure 10-21. Logic Provided by the R6531 Multifunction Device

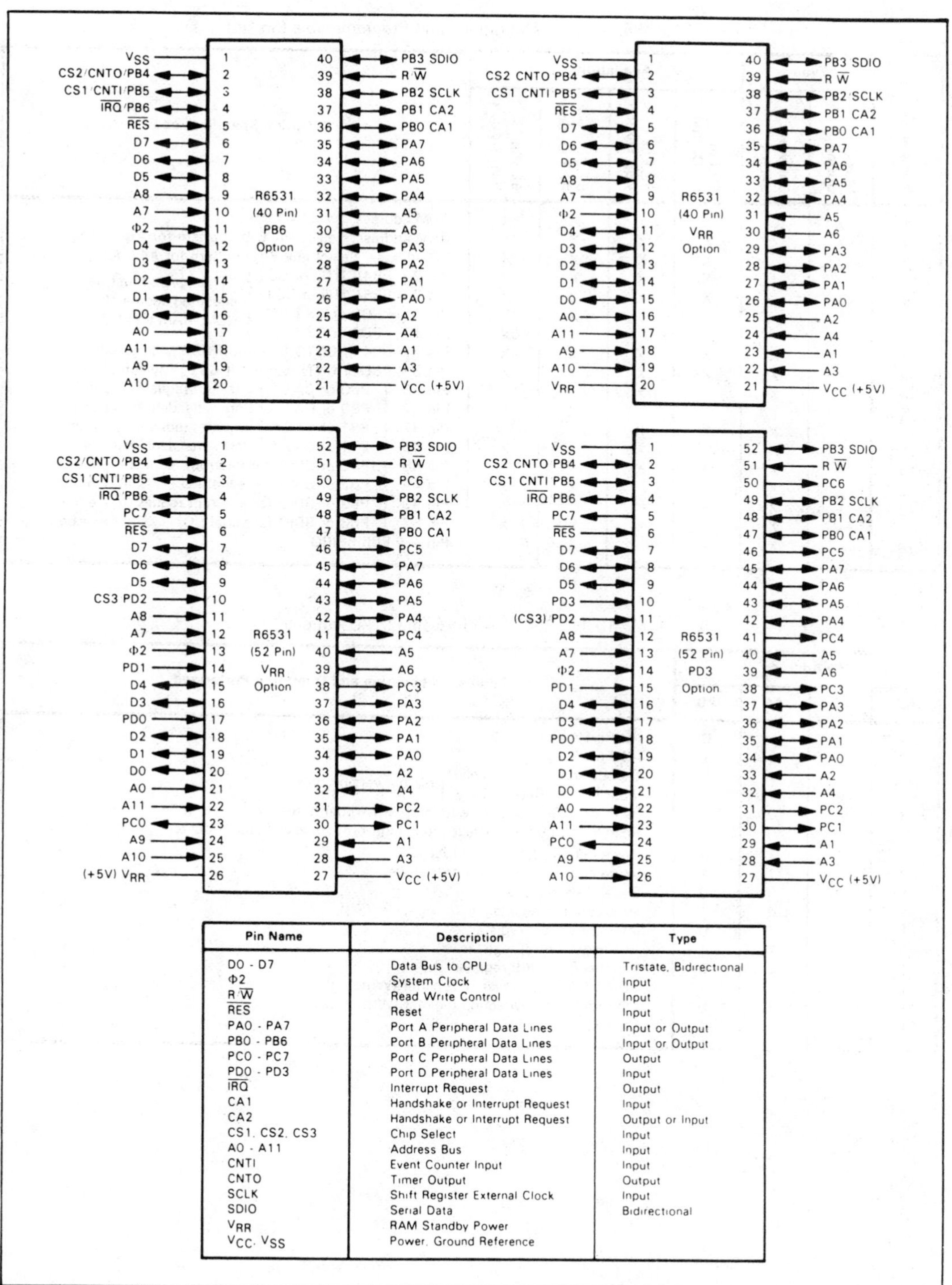


| Pin Name | Description | Type |
|---|---|---|
| D0 - D7 | Data Bus to CPU | Tristate, Bidirectional |
| Φ2 | System Clock | Input |
| R/$\overline{W}$ | Read Write Control | Input |
| $\overline{RES}$ | Reset | Input |
| PA0 - PA7 | Port A Peripheral Data Lines | Input or Output |
| PB0 - PB6 | Port B Peripheral Data Lines | Input or Output |
| PC0 - PC7 | Port C Peripheral Data Lines | Output |
| PD0 - PD3 | Port D Peripheral Data Lines | Input |
| $\overline{IRQ}$ | Interrupt Request | Output |
| CA1 | Handshake or Interrupt Request | Input |
| CA2 | Handshake or Interrupt Request | Output or Input |
| CS1, CS2, CS3 | Chip Select | Input |
| A0 - A11 | Address Bus | Input |
| CNTI | Event Counter Input | Input |
| CNTO | Timer Output | Output |
| SCLK | Shift Register External Clock | Input |
| SDIO | Serial Data | Bidirectional |
| $V_{RR}$ | RAM Standby Power | |
| $V_{CC}$, $V_{SS}$ | Power, Ground Reference | |

Figure 10-22. R6531 Multifunction Device Signals and Pin Assignments

Table 10-9. R6531 Mask Definitions and Programmable Pin Options

| Number | Type | | Availability | | | | Option Specification |
|---|---|---|---|---|---|---|---|
| | Mask Option | Software Select | 40 Pin B6 Option | 40 Pin $V_{RR}$ Option | 52 Pin PD3 Option | 52 Pin $V_{RR}$ Option | |
| 1 | X | | X | X | X | X | ROM address. Select A11 = 0 or 1. |
| 2 | X | | X | X | X | X | RAM address. Select any 6-bit pattern for A6 - A11. |
| 3 | X | | X | X | X | X | I/O address. Select any 8-bit pattern for A4 - A11. |
| 4 | X | | X | X | X | X | Pin 2 = PB4/CNTO or CS2 } "True levels must be |
| 5 | X | | X | X | X | X | Pin 3 = PB5/CNTI or CS1 } specified separately for |
| 6 | X | | | | X | | Pin 11 = PD2 or CS3 } ROM, RAM and I/O. |
| 7 | X | | | | | X | Pin 10 = PD2 or CS3 } |
| 8 | | X | X | X | X | X | Pin 2 = PB4 or CNTO (but not if CS2 is selected) |
| 9 | | X | X | X | X | X | Pin 3 = PB5 or CNTI (but not if CS1 is selected) |
| 10 | | X | X | X | | | Pin 36 } PB0 or CA1 for interrupt request } either |
| 11 | | X | | | X | X | Pin 47 } PB0 or CA1 for Port A handshaking } or both |
| 12 | | X | X | X | | | Pin 37 } PB1 or CA2 for interrupt request } either |
| 13 | | X | | | X | X | Pin 48 } PB1 or CA2 for Port A handshaking } or both |
| 14 | | X | X | X | | | Pin 38 } PB2 or SCLK for interrupt request } either |
| 15 | | X | | | X | X | Pin 49 } PB2 or SCLK for serial I/O } or both |
| 16 | | X | X | X | | | Pin 40 } PB3 or SDIO for interrupt request } either |
| 17 | | X | | | X | X | Pin 52 } PB3 or SDIO for serial I/O } or both |
| 18 | | X | X | | X | X | Pin 4 = PB6 or $\overline{IRQ}$ |

Table 10-10. R6531 Addressable I/O Locations

| I/O Address | | | | Addressed Location and Operation Performed |
|---|---|---|---|---|
| A3 | A2 | A1 | A0 | |
| 0 | 0 | 0 | 0 | I/O Port A |
| 0 | 0 | 0 | 1 | I/O Port B |
| 0 | 0 | 1 | 0 | Output Port C (Write only) } 52-pin version only |
| 0 | 0 | 1 | 1 | Input Port D (Read only) } |
| 0 | 1 | 0 | 0 | Read from Counter, write to latch, low-order byte |
| 0 | 1 | 0 | 1 | Read from Counter, write to latch, high-order byte and start Counter |
| 0 | 1 | 1 | 0 | Write only, to latch low-order byte |
| 0 | 1 | 1 | 1 | Write only, to latch high-order byte |
| 1 | 0 | 0 | 0 | Serial Data register |
| 1 | 0 | 0 | 1 | Interrupt Flag register |
| 1 | 0 | 1 | 0 | Interrupt Enable register |
| 1 | 0 | 1 | 1 | Auxiliary Control register |
| 1 | 1 | 0 | 0 | Peripheral Control register |
| 1 | 1 | 0 | 1 | I/O Port A Data Direction register (Write only) |
| 1 | 1 | 1 | 0 | I/O Port B Data Direction register (Write only) |
| 1 | 1 | 1 | 1 | Unused |

**There are five signals associated with R6531 interrupt logic; all five signals share pins with I/O ports.**

**I/O Port B pin 6 can be set aside to output $\overline{IRQ}$, a general interrupt request.** If I/O Port B pin 6 is so designated, then any interrupt request condition will cause a low $\overline{IRQ}$ output. If $\overline{IRQ}$ is not enabled, interrupt requests will set appropriate status flags, which must be tested by a status polling program.

**Signals input at I/O Port B pins 0, 1, 2 and 3 can generate interrupt requests.** CA1 and CA2, input to I/O Port B pins 0 and 1, are selected as a pair; if selected, they generate interrupt requests on high-to-low transitions. At I/O Port B pins 2 and 3, SCLK and SDIO (in addition to optionally serving as serial data input logic) can independently be selected, as a pair, to generate interrupt requests on low-to-high transitions.

If you use R6531 serial I/O logic, then serial data is input or output via SDIO. The serial data transfer can, optionally, be clocked by SCLK.

**Under program control, you can assign I/O Port B pins 4 and 5 to counter/timer logic.** CNTO is used to generate square wave outputs, while CNTI is the input for external event counter logic.

## R6531 ADDRESSING LOGIC

**The R6531 has variable addressing for ROM, RAM, and I/O, each of which you must select as three separate device mask options. This logic is similar to the MCS6530 device addressing; it may be summarized as follows:**

**R6531 ADDRESS SPACES**

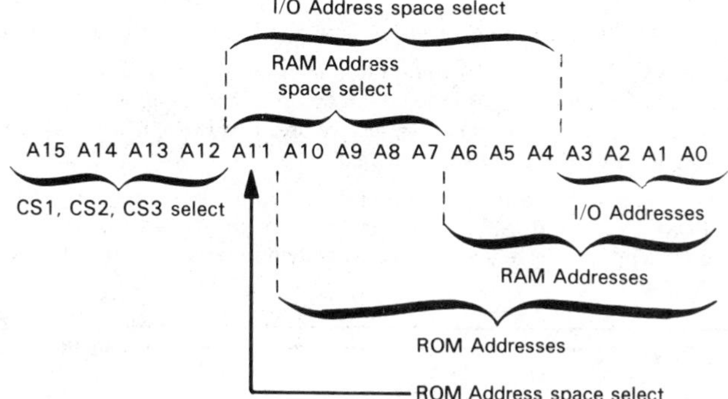


Address lines A12 through A15 should be used to select CS3, CS2, and/or CS1, depending on which (if any) of these three select signals are active. From a programmer's point of view, the logic which creates "true" select signals out of the four address lines A12 through A15 defines the four high-order bits of the address spaces separately assigned to ROM, RAM, and I/O. Note carefully that ROM, RAM, and I/O may have the same select levels. For example, if CS3, CS2, and CS1 are all active, then ROM, RAM, and I/O might share the same 4096 address space as follows:

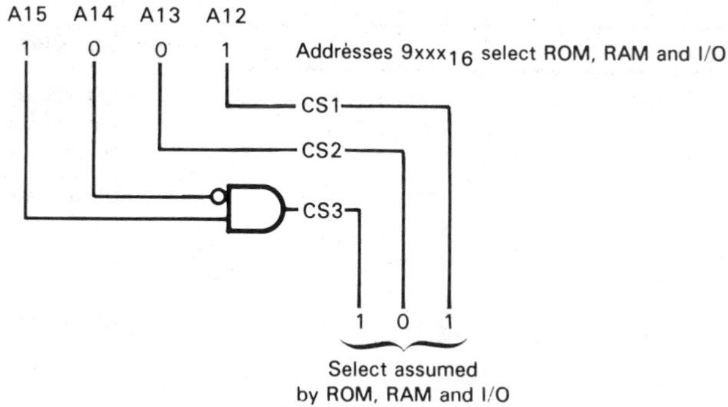

On the other hand, ROM, RAM, and I/O may be selected by different levels at CS3, CS2, and CS1. This may be illustrated as follows:

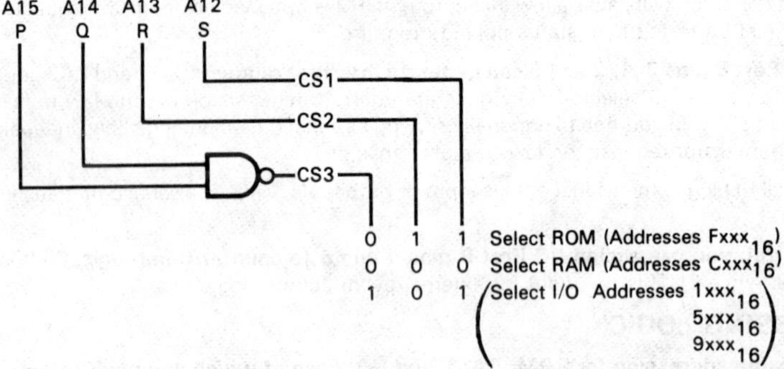


External logic will generate CS3, CS2, and/or CS1 from the four high-order address lines A12 through A15, but mask options (which you specify) determine which CS3, CS2, and CS1 combinations will be considered as "true" selects by ROM, RAM, and I/O.

Any of the three select signals CS3, CS2, and CS1, if not active, become "don't care" signals.

You do not have to use all four address lines A12 through A15 in order to generate select signals, but any address lines, if ignored, will (of course) duplicate address spaces to which the R6531 will respond. If, for example, A15 and A14 are unused, then the two high-order address bits can have any values, and ROM, RAM, and I/O will consider themselves selected, providing select logic has been otherwise satisfied.

Address lines A0 through A11 connect directly to address inputs of the R6531. However, you must specify address line levels which will select ROM, RAM, and I/O. Each of these three may have separate and distinct address space specifications. For each address bit, you have the option of specifying that the bit must be low, high, or don't care. Here are some possibilities:

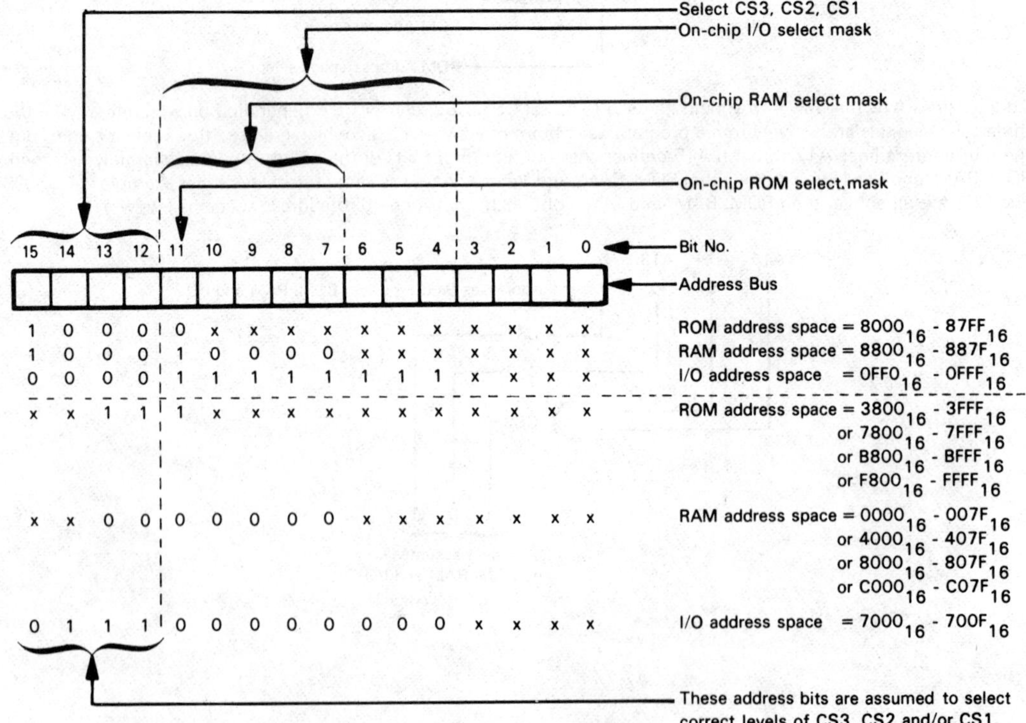

Rockwell's R6531 prototyping circuit specifies ROM, RAM, and I/O address spaces as follows:

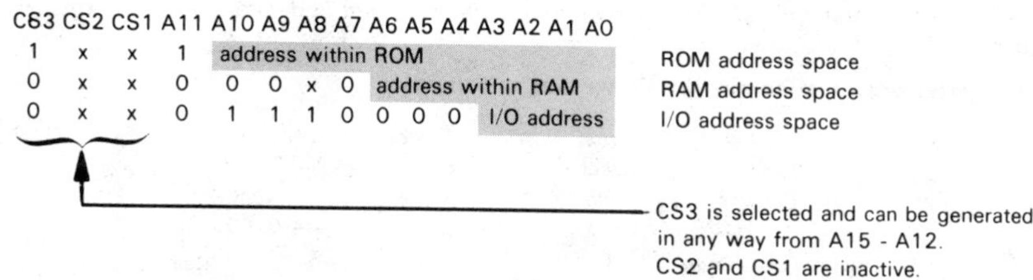


Address bit A8 is a RAM "don't care" bit so that RAM can be selected as the first or third 128 bytes of memory. This allows RAM to serve either as page 0 read/write data, or as the page 1 Stack.

**R6531 DEVICE SELECT LOGIC**

**The 40-pin version of the R6531 gives you the option of assigning I/O Port B lines 4 and 5 to device select inputs CS2 and CS1. The 52-pin version of the R6531 gives you the additional option of using I/O Port D line 2 as a third device select input, CS3.** Note that if you select CS1 and/or CS2, then you cannot use these pins for either the program selectable counter options CNTI and CNTO, or for any other I/O functions. Similarly, if you select CS3, you cannot use line 2 of I/O Port D to input data.

**R6531 I/O ADDRESSES**

The 16 I/O port addresses are used to access addressable locations, specify I/O Port A and B pin directions, and initialize counter/timer operations. **Table 10-10 summarizes R6531 I/O addressing options.**

## R6531 PARALLEL DATA TRANSFER OPERATIONS

**All versions of the R6531 have an 8-bit I/O Port A and a 6- or 7-bit I/O Port B, each line of which can be an input or an output. The 52-pin versions of the R6531 have, in addition, an 8-bit output-only Port C and a 4-bit input-only Port D.**

All output lines (Port C and those lines of Ports A and B programmed as outputs) have push-pull type drivers capable of driving a single TTL load. For more information, see the data sheet at the end of this chapter.

**R6531 DATA DIRECTION REGISTER**

**You define the direction for each pin of I/O Ports A and B via their respective Data Direction registers.** A 1 written into a Data Direction register bit causes the associated I/O port pin to act as an output; a 0 written into a Data Direction register bit forces the associated pin to act as an input.

**When I/O port bits are assigned to any special function, then the special function pin direction must be specified via the Data Direction register.** If, for example, you write a 1 to bit 5 of Data Direction Register B, then I/O Port B pin 5 becomes an output pin. However, if you try to use this pin to input CNTI, the signal which counter/timer logic uses to count external events, then the device will malfunction.

**All seven I/O Port B pins can be assigned to special functions.** Any pin that is assigned to a special function should not be used to transfer parallel data; however, unassigned pins can be used to transfer parallel data. If, for example, I/O Port B pins 6, 4, 1 and 0 are assigned to $\overline{IRQ}$, CS2, CA2 and CA1, respectively, then these four pins cannot be used to transfer parallel data; however, PB5, PB3, and PB2 can still be used to transfer parallel data.

**I/O Port A is the primary I/O port for R6531 devices.** No pins of I/O Port A provide special functions; however, signals CA1 and CA2 at I/O Port B pins 0 and 1 can be used to provide primitive handshaking logic for I/O Port A.

I/O Port A handshaking logic uses pins 0 and 1 of I/O Port B. Pin 0 receives a control input and pin 1 generates a control output. Pin 1 is normally high, but switches low when you read or write to I/O Port A. Pin 1 remains low until a high-to-low transition occurs at the pin 0 input.

**Ports C and D, available on the 52-pin version of the R6531 device, do not have Data Direction registers,** since they are output-only and input-only, respectively. Remember, I/O Port D pin 2 can optionally function as a chip select, in which case it cannot be used to input data.

## R6531 INTERVAL TIMER LOGIC

The simplest method of understanding R6531 interval timer logic is to first understand register organization, and then operating modes.

**Interval timer register organization may be illustrated as follows:**

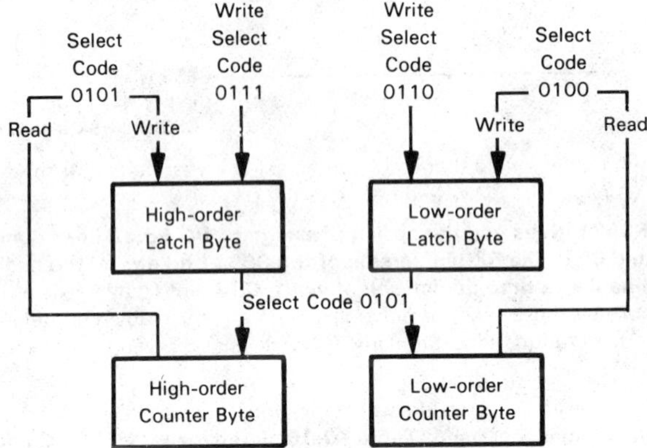


You write an initial timer constant into the latches. This initial constant is downloaded into the counter when you write to the high-order latch byte using select code 5 (0101). This select code also starts the counter. Subsequently, if the interval timer is free running, the initial value in the latch bytes will automatically be downloaded into the counter bytes following every time-out.

**R6531 COUNTER READ ON THE FLY**

**You can read the counter on the fly, but you must do so in two halves; this protects against a decrement modifying the high-order counter byte in between the two counter read operations.** Suppose, for example, the counter contains $C300_{16}$. If you read the high-order byte, then the counter decrements to $C2FF_{16}$; then when you read the counter low-order byte, this is what happens:

| Counter Contents | Operation | Value Read |
|---|---|---|
| C300 | Read Counter high-order byte | C3xx |
| C2FF | | |
| C2FF | Read Counter low-order byte | C3FF |

Thus you have erroneously read $C3FF_{16}$ instead of $C2FF_{16}$. There are many ways of protecting against this error. Here is one possibility:

Read Counter high-order byte
Read Counter low-order byte
Re-read Counter high-order byte

If the first and second high-order counter byte readings are the same, you have no problem.

If the first and second high-order byte readings differ, you must determine which value is correct. If the low-order counter byte is 00 or higher, then the decrement which changed the high-order byte must have occurred after you read the low-order byte; therefore, use the first high-order byte reading. If the low-order byte is $FF_{16}$ or less, then the decrement which modified the high-order byte occurred before you read the low-order byte; therefore, use the second high-order byte.

**There are a number of counter options available to you.** You select counter options using appropriate Auxiliary Control/register settings (which we will define later).

**R6531 EVENT COUNTER MODE**

**Event counter mode** decrements the counter whenever he CNTI signal makes a high-to-low transition.

**R6531 INTERVAL TIMER MODE**

**Interval timer mode** decrements the counter whenever the Φ2 system clock makes a high-to-low transition. In other words, interval timer mode counts Φ2 system clock pulses.

**R6531 PULSE WIDTH MEASUREMENT MODE**

**External trigger mode** counts Φ2 clock pulses as described for interval timer mode; however, the counter does not start to decrement until CNTI makes a high-to-low transition. This may be illustrated as follows:

CNTI

Φ2

Counter Contents | ppqq | ppqq | ppqq-1 | ppqq-2

**R6531 FREE-RUNNING MODE**

**R6531 ONE-SHOT MODE**

**Event counter, interval timer and external trigger modes can all be free running or one-shot.** In free-running mode, whenever the counter decrements to zero, it will automatically reload from the latches and restart. Furthermore, every time the counter decrements to zero it will set a bit in the Interrupt Flag register. Free-running mode may be illustrated as follows:

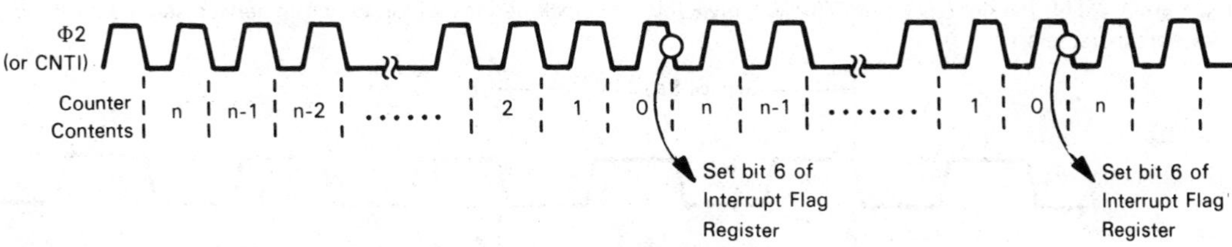


In one-shot mode, the counter continues to decrement after it reaches zero, but it sets the interrupt flag only once, when it first decrements to zero. One-shot mode may be illustrated as follows:

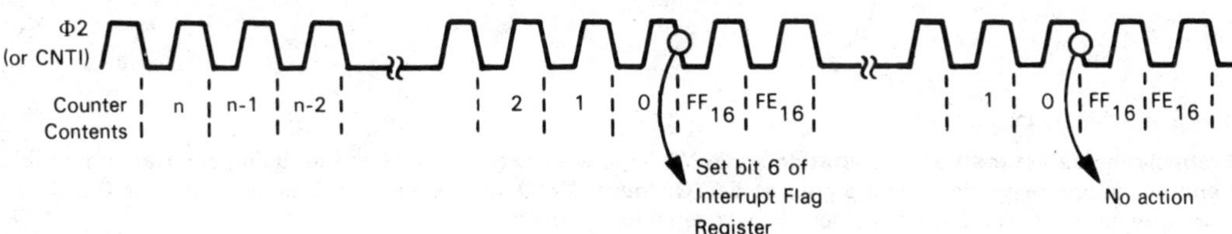


In both modes you can stop the decrementing by disabling the counter, or you can restart the decrementing by loading a new value from the latches. When a flag is set in the Interrupt Flag register, an interrupt request occurs if interrupts have been appropriately enabled. Interrupt logic is described later.

**R6531 SQUARE WAVE OUTPUT**

There is one additional option that you have in any of the counter/timer modes or combination of modes. **You may specify that the CNTO output at I/O Port B pin 4 generates a square wave output.**

Initially, CNTO is output high. When you start the counter/timer, CNTO switches low. Following a time-out CNTO switches high again. In free-running mode, however, CNTO simply switches level following each time-out.

## R6531 SERIAL INPUT/OUTPUT

**R6531 serial I/O logic consists of an 8-bit serial data register connected to I/O Port B pins 2 and 3.** Serial data must be input or output via I/O Port B pin 3, which must be programmed to act as the SDIO signal. You determine the serial data direction using an appropriate Auxiliary Control register bit setting. Serial data transfer may be clocked by either the Φ2 system clock or an external clock. The external clock must be input at I/O Port B pin 2. Of course, this pin must be programmed to function as the SCLK option. If serial data is clocked by Φ2, then the serial data rate is half of the Φ2 clock rate. If the external clock is used, then any clock rate up to half of Φ2 may be used.

**If serial I/O is clocked by Φ2, then the derived serial data rate (half of Φ2) is output via SCLK.**

**In the external clock mode only, an interrupt request may be generated after every eighth shift in or out.** Providing interrupts have been enabled appropriately, this interrupt request may be used to service the serial data transfer.

**You must exercise extreme caution when using R6531 serial I/O logic since this logic is very primitive and easier to misuse than use.**

The R6531 Serial Data register is not buffered. If you are transmitting or receiving serial data continuously, you have one bit time at each character boundary within which to service the serial data transfer, or else face serial data underflow/overflow. This may be illustrated as follows:

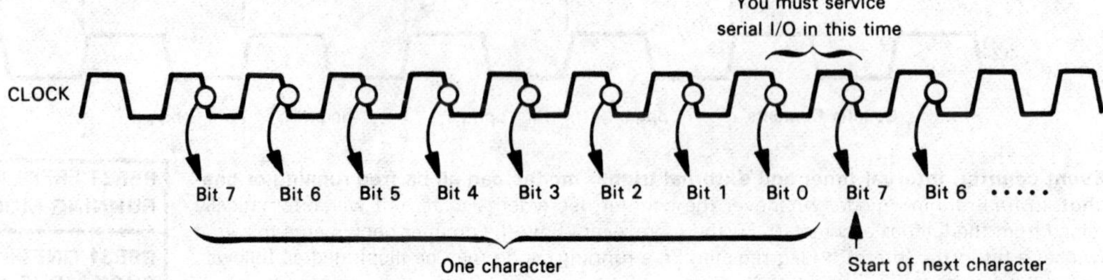


You cannot operate serial data transfer logic continuously and at maximum speed, since serial data will then be transferred at half the Φ2 clock rate. This will give you two clock periods within which to service serial data transfer between characters:

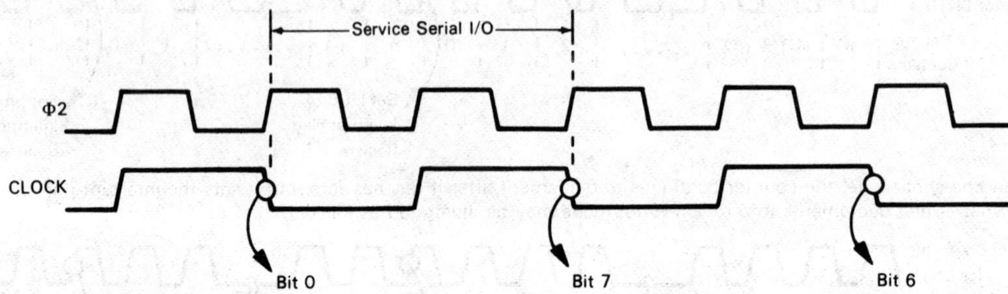


and that is simply insufficient.

**Probably the safest method of operating serial I/O logic is in external clock mode, using counter/timer logic to generate a square wave timing signal at CNTO. Input CNTO as the serial I/O clock signal at SCLK.** Using counter/timer logic, you have some control over serial logic timing.

When transmitting serial data, operate the counter/timer in free running timer mode. The initial value you load into the counter/timer latches now determines the pulse rate output at CNTO; this becomes the serial data transfer clock rate input at SCLK. Providing the pulse rate is slow enough, you can use the serial data transfer interrupt request, which will be generated every eighth clock pulse, to write another data byte into the serial data register.

When receiving serial data, you do not need to use counter/timer logic; instead, the transmitter can generate its own companion clock signal which becomes the SCLK input.

In an asynchronous configuration which is transmitting data at a fixed baud rate, you can use counter/timer logic to generate SCLK for serial data input. See the SY6551 description in this chapter, or Section C of Volume 3, where tables are given for baud rate generation as a function of system clock frequencies for a number of different devices.

## R6531 CONTROL REGISTERS

**The R6531 has an Auxiliary Control register and a Peripheral Control register. You use these two registers to control parallel data transfer, counter/timer, and serial I/O operations. Auxiliary Control register bit assignments may be illustrated as follows:**

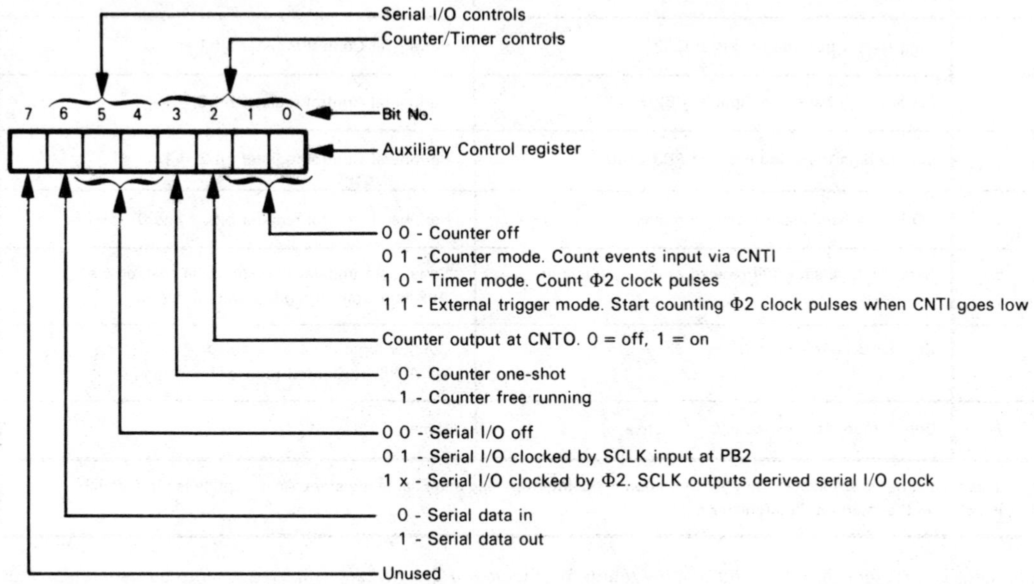


**Auxiliary Control register bits 0, 1, 2 and 3 control the counter/timer.** Bits 0 and 1 are used to enable the counter/timer, selecting event counter, interval timer, or external trigger modes. Bit 2 selects the CNTO output at I/O Port B bit 4. Bit 3 selects one-shot or free running operation.

**Auxiliary Control register bits 4, 5 and 6 control serial I/O logic.** Bits 4 and 5 enable serial I/O logic, selecting either external or internal clocking. Bit 6 determines the serial data transfer direction.

**The Peripheral Control register controls parallel data transfer modes at I/O Port A, together with the signals that will be used by interrupt logic. Peripheral control register bit settings may be illustrated as follows:**

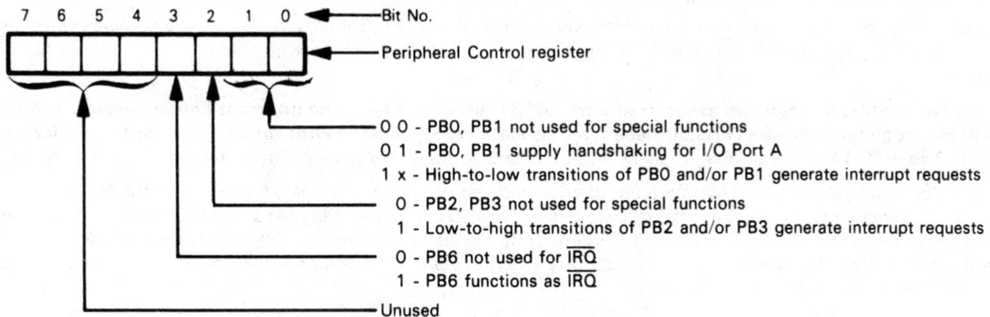


Peripheral Control register bits 0 and 1 apply to parallel data transfer at I/O Port A.

Normal operation means that signals will be input or output as specified by the Data Direction register, with no accompanying handshake or interrupt logic.

We described I/O Port A handshaking logic earlier.

The negative edge detect option allows an interrupt request to occur whenever a high-to-low transition is input via CA1 or CA2 at I/O Port B pin 0 or 1. The actual interrupt request will reach the CPU only if associated interrupt logic has been enabled and $\overline{IRQ}$ is active.

Table 10-11. R6531 Interrupt Conditions

| Bit* | Condition | Enable |
|---|---|---|
| 0 | High-to-low transition input at CA1 | Peripheral Control register bit 1 = 1 |
| 1 | High-to-low transition input at CA2 | Peripheral Control register bit 1 = 1 |
| 2 | Low-to-high transition input at PB2/SCLK | Peripheral Control register bit 2 = 1 |
| 3 | Low-to-high transition input at PB3/SDIO | Peripheral Control register bit 2 = 1 |
| 4 | I/O Port A handshaking service request | Peripheral Control register bits 1 and 0 = 01 |
| 5 | Serial Data register full/receive or empty/transmit | Serial data transfer logic must be enabled via Auxiliary Control register bits 5 and 4 |
| 6 | Counter decrements to 0 | Counter logic must be enabled via Auxiliary Control register bits 1 and 0 |
| 7 | One or more of Conditions 0 - 6 active | None |

*This bit number is associated with the Condition in the Interrupt Flag and Enable registers. An exception is bit 7, which is active in the Interrupt Flag register only.

Peripheral Control register bits 2 and 3 apply to interrupt logic. Bit 2 allows interrupt requests to be generated when signals input at I/O Port B bit 3 or 2 make low-to-high transitions. Peripheral Control register bit 3 is used to enable $\overline{IRQ}$ at I/O Port B bit 6.

**I/O Port B pins may be used to input or output data if they have not been assigned special functions; but if they have been assigned special functions, they may not be used to transfer data.**

## R6531 INTERRUPT LOGIC

**Interrupts can be generated by the R6531 based on external signal transitions or internal I/O Port A counter/timer and serial data transfer operations. In all, there are seven conditions capable of generating an interrupt request; these conditions, together with their associated register bits, are summarized in Table 10-11.**

The Peripheral Control register, which we have already described, enables $\overline{IRQ}$, plus the level detection interrupt logic at I/O Port B pins 0, 1, 2 and 3. $\overline{IRQ}$ is an open drain signal; therefore, it can be wire ORed for a number of R6531 devices.

**There are two additional registers associated with R6531 interrupt logic: the Interrupt Enable register and the Interrupt Flag register. Individual bits of these two registers are associated with specific interrupt conditions as defined in Table 10-11.** Interrupt Flag register bit 7, you should note, is a general "interrupt request pending" bit.

Whenever a condition capable of generating an interrupt request occurs, its associated bit is set in the Interrupt Flag register. At the same time, bit 7 of the Interrupt Flag register is set. An Interrupt Flag register bit setting becomes an interrupt request only if the interrupt is enabled. The interrupt is enabled by writing a 1 to the corresponding Interrupt Enable register bit. Here, for example, are some arbitrary Interrupt Flag and Interrupt Enable register bit settings, showing the resulting active interrupt requests:

```
   Interrupt Flag register: 10110010  11011001  10001010
 Interrupt Enable register: 00000000  01111111  01010110

   (X) Interrupt requests:             X XX  X         X
```

If there are one or more active interrupt requests, then $\overline{IRQ}$ will be output low — providing you have enabled $\overline{IRQ}$ via Peripheral Control register bit 3. If $\overline{IRQ}$ is not enabled, then Interrupt Enable register bit settings become meaningless. If $\overline{IRQ}$ is enabled, it will remain low for as long as there are any active interrupt requests within the R6531.

Interrupt Flag register bit settings remain set until they are specifically reset. You reset bits by writing to the Interrupt Flag register with 1 in those bit positions that need to be cleared. For example, if you write $2E_{16}$ to the Interrupt Flag register, you will reset bits 5, 3,2 and 1. In addition, Interrupt Flag register bit 6 is reset when you read the contents of the low-order counter byte using I/O address 4, or when you write to the high-order latch byte using I/O address 5 or 7. Interrupt Flag register bits 5 and 4 may be reset in a similar way, by writing to the Serial Data register or Port A, respectively.

If $\overline{IRQ}$ is not enabled, then you can use the Interrupt Flag register in order to poll an R6531 device, and thus detect conditions in need of service. You will, in any event, read the contents of the Interrupt Flag register when acknowledging an interrupt request in order to determine the source or sources of the interrupt request(s).

# THE SY6551 ASYNCHRONOUS COMMUNICATIONS INTERFACE ADAPTER (ACIA)

**The SY6551 ACIA is a fairly standard asynchronous serial I/O device, designed by Synertek to support 6800 and 6500 series microcomputer systems. The SY6551 may be looked upon as an enhancement of the MC6850 ACIA, which we described in Chapter 9.** On-chip baud rate generation represents the principal SY6551 enhancement; the SY6551 also has more Modem signals and programmable options.

As with the MC6850, **we describe the SY6551 in Volume 2 rather than Volume 3 because of the Φ2 clock and special control signals shared by 6800 and 6500 series microcomputers.** Interfacing the SY6551 ACIA to other microprocessors would not be difficult; however, the SY6551 offers no special capabilities to compensate for even small additional interfacing requirements. In particular, the INS8250, described in Volume 3, offers a number of capabilities and programmable options not provided by the SY6551.

The SY6551 ACIA is packaged as a 28-pin DIP. It is fabricated using N-channel silicon gate MOS technology. All signals are TTL-level compatible. A single +5 V power supply is required.

**This discussion of the SY6551 assumes that you understand asynchronous serial I/O protocol. If you do not, see Volume 1, Chapter 5. The SY6551 uses Non-Return to Zero (NRZ) serial I/O coding.**

## THE SY6551 PINS AND SIGNALS

**The SY6551 ACIA pins and signals are illustrated in Figure 10-23. Signals may be divided into the following four categories:**

1) CPU interface/control
2) Serial input
3) Serial output
4) Modem control

**We will first consider signals on the CPU interface.**

**D0-D7 constitutes an 8-bit bidirectional Data Bus** connecting the SY6551 to the CPU.

When data is output to the SY6551 by the CPU, either a byte of parallel data or a control code will be transmitted.

A byte of parallel data will be serialized and transmitted serially, in NRZ format, according to the asynchronous protocol variations which have been specified under program control.

Either data or status may be input from the SY6551 ACIA to the CPU via the Data Bus. Data consists of an 8-bit parallel data unit extracted from the NRZ serial input data stream. Status consists of the contents of the ACIA Status register.

**SY6551 DEVICE ADDRESSING**

**The SY6551 ACIA is accessed by the CPU as four memory locations. SY6551 select logic consists of two chip select signals, CS0 and $\overline{\text{CS1}}$.** For the SY6551 to be selected, CS0 must be high and $\overline{\text{CS1}}$ must be low. Once selected, **the address inputs RS0 and RS1 determine which of the four addressable locations within the SY6551 ACIA will be accessed.** Addresses are interpreted as shown in Table 10-12.

We will say more about SY6551 addressable locations later, when describing device operations.

While the SY6551 ACIA is selected, **internal logic is synchronized on the trailing edge of the Φ2 signal.** Φ2 is the standard output of all MC6800 and 6500 series microprocessors; it is equivalent to the E signal of MC6800 microprocessors.

**R/$\overline{\text{W}}$ is the control input which determines whether a read or write operation is in progress.** When R/$\overline{\text{W}}$ is high, the CPU is reading data out of the SY6551. When R/$\overline{\text{W}}$ is low, the CPU is writing data to the SY6551.

**Let us examine serial input and output signals.**

**Serial data is transmitted via TxD; it is received via RxD.**

**XTAL1, XTAL2, and RxC are used by serial data transfer timing logic.**

You may connect a crystal across XTAL1 and XTAL2 and use the crystal frequency to generate the baud rate internally, under program control

Alternatively, you can input a clock signal at XTAL1 while leaving XTAL2 floating. The clock signal input at XTAL1 is also used to generate the baud rate internally, under program control.

In either case you can, under program control, cause receive logic to be timed by a signal input via RxC. If you do not program RxC to serve as the receive logic clock signal, then RxC outputs a clock signal with a frequency that is 16 times the programmed baud rate.

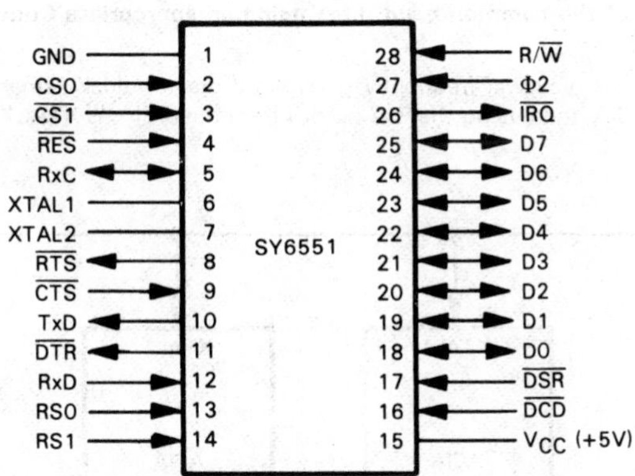


| Pin Name | Description | Type |
|---|---|---|
| D0 - D7 | Data Bus | Tristate, Bidirectional |
| CS0, $\overline{CS1}$ | Chip Select | Input |
| Φ2 | Internal Synchronization | Input |
| RS0, RS1 | Register Select | Input |
| R/$\overline{W}$ | Read/Write Control | Input |
| XTAL1, XTAL2 | Internal Baud Rate Generator Crystal Connections | |
| TxD | Transmit Data | Output |
| RxC | External Transmit/Receive Clock | Input or Output |
| RxD | Receive Data | Input |
| $\overline{CTS}$ | Clear-to-Send | Input |
| $\overline{RTS}$ | Request-to-Send | Output |
| $\overline{DCD}$ | Data Carrier Detect | Input |
| $\overline{DSR}$ | Data Set Ready | Input |
| $\overline{DTR}$ | Data Terminal Ready | Output |
| $\overline{IRQ}$ | Interrupt Request | Output |
| $\overline{RES}$ | Device Reset | Input |
| $V_{CC}$, GND | Power, Ground | |

Figure 10-23. SY6551 ACIA Signals and Pin Assignments

Table 10-12. SY6551 Addressable Locations

| RS1 | RS0 | Addressed Location |
|---|---|---|
| 0 | 0 | Read from Receive buffer<br>Write to Transmit buffer |
| 0 | 1 | Read from Status register<br>Write to device reset |
| 1 | 0 | Read from, or write to Command register |
| 1 | 1 | Read from, or write to Control register |

**When generating a baud rate internally, you should connect a 1.8432 MHz crystal across XTAL1 and XTAL2. You may then specify any of the common baud rates using an appropriate Control register setting, which we will describe later.**

In multiple-ACIA configurations, you will frequently generate a master clock signal by connecting a crystal across XTAL1 and XTAL2 for one ACIA, then using the RxC output from this ACIA as XTAL1 inputs to other ACIAs. This may be illustrated as follows:

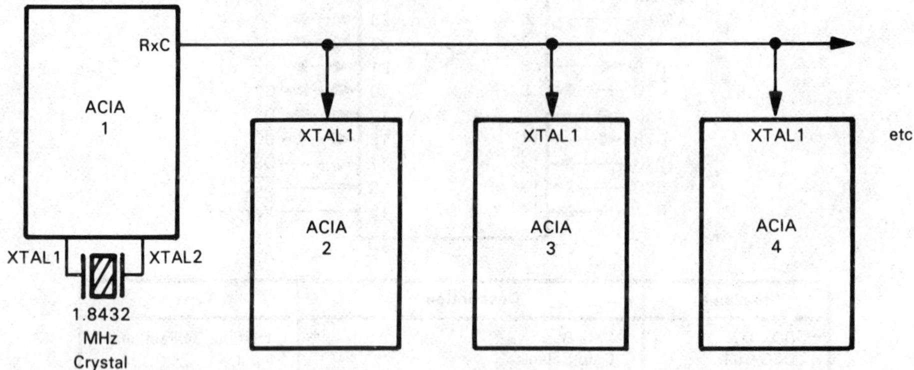


As illustrated above, just one SY6551 has a crystal connected across XTAL1 and XTAL2. This device generates a baud rate internally and outputs, at RxC, a clock signal with a frequency of 16 times the baud rate. This 16x clock signal is input to all other SY6551 devices in the configuration, thus ensuring that all devices operate at exactly the same serial data frequency.

**If you input a clock signal to RxC, this clock signal, divided by 16, times the received serial data stream.**

**The SY6551 has all five standard Modem control signals: $\overline{\text{RTS}}$ (Request to Send), $\overline{\text{CTS}}$ (Clear to Send), $\overline{\text{DTR}}$ (Data Terminal Ready), $\overline{\text{DSR}}$ (Data Set Ready), and $\overline{\text{DCD}}$ (Data Carrier Detect). See Volume 1, Chapter 5 for a general discussion of these Modem control signals.**

**Only the $\overline{\text{CTS}}$ input directly affects ST6551 logic.**

The $\overline{\text{CTS}}$ signal must be low for the transmitter to be enabled. When $\overline{\text{CTS}}$ goes high, the transmitter is immediately disabled. The $\overline{\text{RTS}}$ and $\overline{\text{DTR}}$ outputs simply respond to appropriate Command register bit settings. The $\overline{\text{DSR}}$ and $\overline{\text{DCD}}$ inputs, similarly, modify Status register bits, and can generate interrupts, if interrupts have been appropriately enabled. It is up to your program logic to make sure that $\overline{\text{RTS}}$, $\overline{\text{DTR}}$, $\overline{\text{DSR}}$, and $\overline{\text{DCD}}$ are interpreted in the accepted way.

**The SY6551 has a master reset input, $\overline{\text{RES}}$.** This signal, when input low, resets all internal registers. **You can also reset the SY6551 by writing to addressable location 1.** These two resets are described in detail later on.

## SY6551 DATA TRANSFER AND CONTROL OPERATIONS

**SY6551 transmit and receive logic are each single buffered;** that is to say, there is a single buffer storage location between the serial transmit/receive logic and the Data Bus. **The SY6551 has, in addition, a Status register, a Command register, and a Control register.** Data flows may be illustrated as follows:

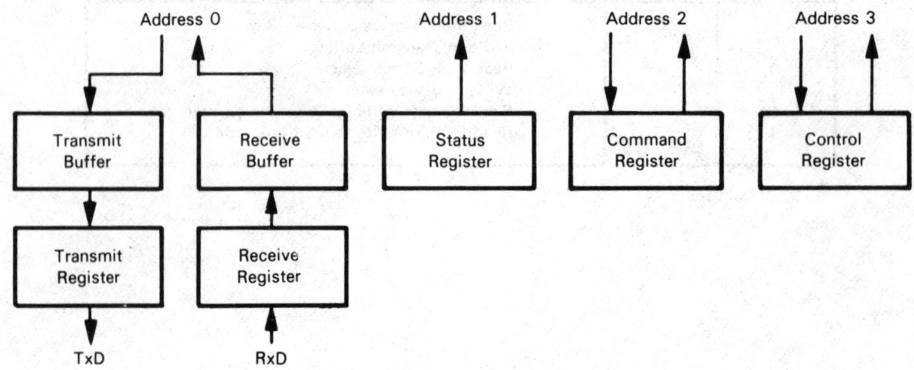

The Transmit and Receive buffers are write-only and read-only locations, respectively; they are accessed as memory location 0 within the SY6551 ACIA.

The Status register is a read-only location accessed as address 1 within the SY6551 ACIA. When you write to address 1, you perform a software reset in the device.

The Command and Control registers are read/write locations, accessed via addresses 2 and 3, respectively.

In the normal course of events, the SY6551 will transmit and receive data as a contiguous stream of characters. **Transmit logic always transmits the low-order bit of a character first; receive logic assumes that it first receives the low-order bit of a character.**

**SY6551 TRANSMIT**

**You have the option of transmitting data with or without interrupts.** You will normally transmit data with interrupts, in which case the transmitter generates an interrupt request whenever it starts transmitting the start bit of a new character. The CPU responds to this request by executing an interrupt service routine which writes the next character to the Transmit buffer. This may be illustrated as follows:

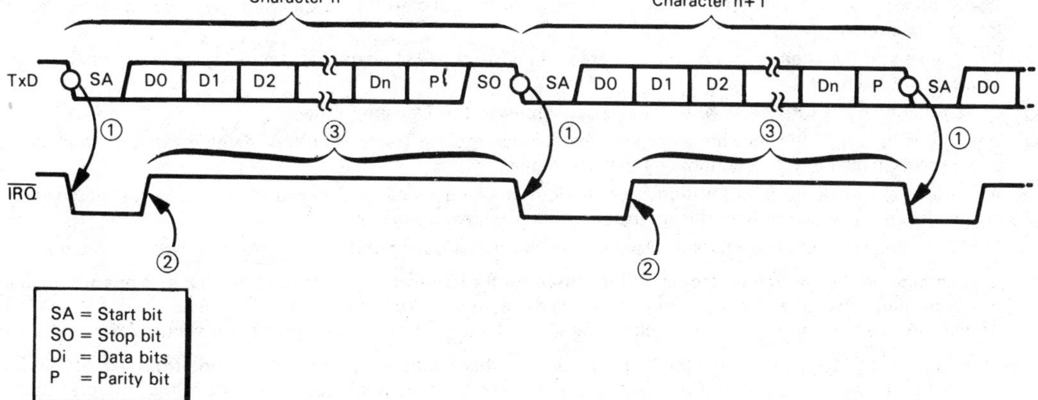


① SY6551 generates an interrupt request at the beginning of start bit transmission.

② $\overline{\text{IRQ}}$ is reset, and the interrupt condition cleared, when the CPU reads Status register contents.

③ During this time the CPU must write the next character to the Transmit buffer, otherwise a continuous mark is transmitted.

If you are transmitting data with interrupts disabled, then a monitoring program would have to continuously poll the Status register to determine when the next character should be written to the Transmit buffer.

**If the CPU does not write a new character to the transmitter within the allowed time, then the SY6551 will underflow and transmit a continuous, high marking signal; however, it continues to generate interrupt requests every character time.** This is not an error condition; it may be illustrated as follows:

**SY6551 UNDERRUN**

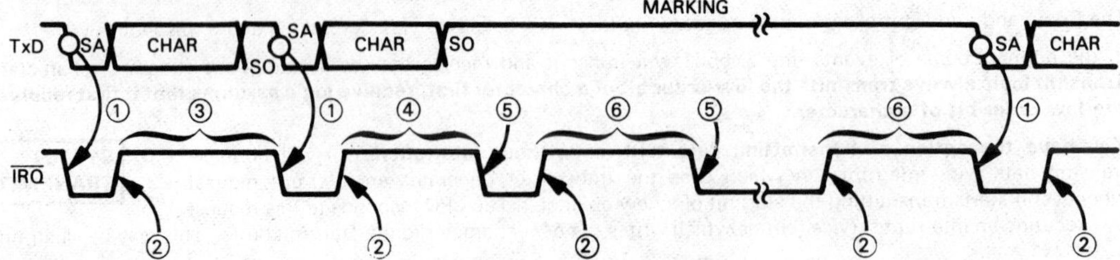


① The SY6551 generates an interrupt request at the beginning of start bit transmission, as it would do for normal transmit operations.

② $\overline{IRQ}$ is reset and the interrupt condition is cleared whenever the CPU reads Status register contents, whatever the cause of the interrupt.

③ During this time the CPU must write the next character to the Transmit buffer.

④ During this time the CPU does not write the next character to the Transmit buffer; therefore, an underrun occurs and transmit logic outputs a continuous marking signal.

⑤ Although transmit logic is outputting a continuous marking signal, an interrupt request is generated every character time. You can disable this interrupt via the Command register.

⑥ The CPU must write another character to the Transmit buffer during this time in order to end the underrun.

**If $\overline{CTS}$ goes high while the transmitter is active, then the transmitter will immediately suspend operations and output a continuous marking signal.** Interrupt requests will continue to be generated every character time. When $\overline{CTS}$ goes high again, the transmitter starts transmitting a new character, which will be the character in the Transmit buffer.

No status bit reports $\overline{CTS}$ having gone high. You must deduce this condition by noting that an interrupt request has occurred with no other possible cause. We will discuss later the way in which you should read and interpret Status register contents.

**You can operate the receiver with interrupts enabled or disabled. If interrupts are enabled, receive logic generates an interrupt request while receiving the last stop bit of a character. The CPU now has one character time within which to read the received character.** Timing may be illustrated as follows:

**SY6551 RECEIVE**

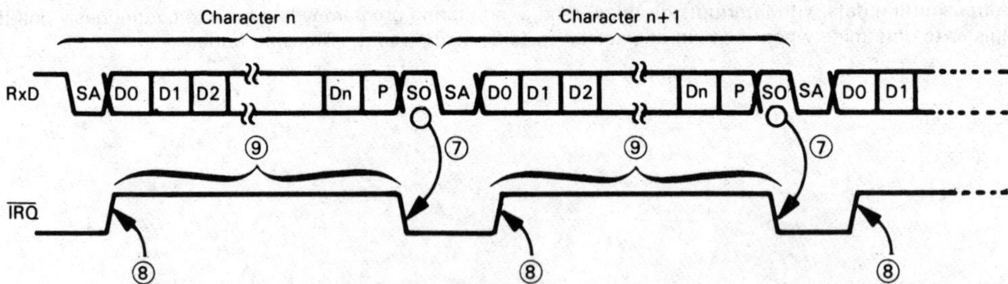


⑦ An interrupt request is generated on the 9th clock pulse of the received character's stop bit. Recall that each bit time within the SY6551 is 16 clock pulses wide.

⑧ As usual, when the CPU reads the contents of the Status register, interrupt conditions are cleared.

⑨ During this time the CPU must read the contents of the Receive buffer.

**If the CPU does not read the received character in time, then subsequently received characters are lost.** Timing may be illustrated as follows:

**SY6551 OVERRUN**

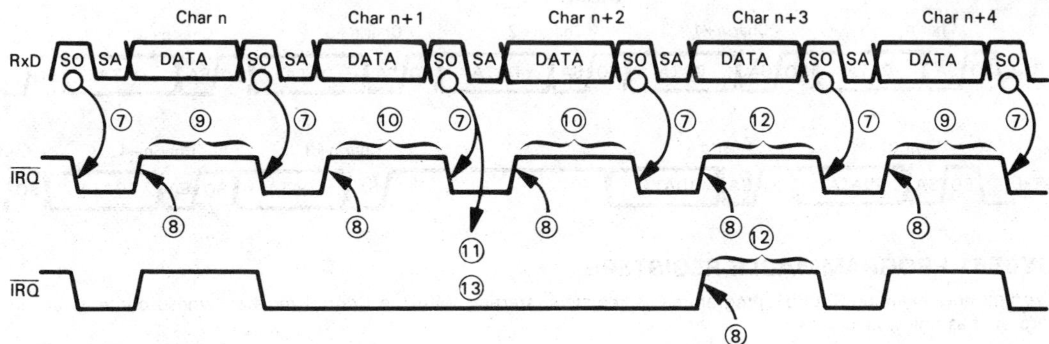


⑦, ⑧ and ⑨ identify correct receive operations, as described above.

⑩ identifies a character time within which the CPU does not read the contents of the Receive buffer; therefore, at ⑪ the overrun status is set.

In the upper $\overline{\text{IRQ}}$ illustration, interrupt requests continue to occur and are cleared by the CPU reading Status register contents. But the CPU does not read Receive buffer contents until ⑫. Thus, characters n+2 and n+3 are lost. At ⑫ the CPU reads character n+1, which will have been in the Receive buffer while characters n+2 and n+3 were discarded.

If the CPU does not acknowledge the interrupt request, then, as illustrated at ⑬, the interrupt request will remain active until ⑧.

**A Modem will transmit $\overline{\text{DCD}}$ low while sending data to receive logic.** If the Modem goes off line for any reason, $\overline{\text{DCD}}$ will be input high and a short time later the received serial data stream will become a continuous, high marking signal. **An interrupt request is generated at the SY6551 when $\overline{\text{DCD}}$ or $\overline{\text{DSR}}$ makes an active transition: low-to-high or high-to-low.** Further transitions of $\overline{\text{DCD}}$ and $\overline{\text{DSR}}$ will be ignored until the CPU services the pending interrupt request. Then the next transition of $\overline{\text{DCD}}$ or $\overline{\text{DSR}}$ will again generate an interrupt request.

**SY6551 MODEM DISCONNECT**

**By writing an appropriate Command register code, you can transmit a continuous break; however, interrupts are disabled,** in contrast to an underrun break, during which time interrupts remain enabled.

**SY6551 PROGRAMMED BREAK**

Receive logic, upon receiving a continuous break, will treat the low signal as data, generating an interrupt request every character time, but reporting a framing error, in the absence of a stop bit, for every character.

**The SY6551 can also operate in echo mode. In the simplest case, the SY6551 retransmits whatever it receives with a one-half bit time delay. However, if $\overline{\text{CTS}}$ goes high while the SY6551 is operating in echo mode, then the receiver continues to operate, but the transmitter ceases to retransmit.** Unfortunately, there is no way in which the CPU can detect this condition. Normally, the CPU assumes that $\overline{\text{CTS}}$ high caused the interrupt request if no interrupting condition can be found in the Status register. But when operating in the echo mode, receive logic is still functioning, and the Receive buffer full condition is reported in the Status register. Thus, the default $\overline{\text{CTS}}$ high condition cannot be detected.

**SY6551 ECHO MODE**

The SY6551 responds to an overrun in echo mode by retransmitting a continuous, high marking signal while received characters are being lost. This may be illustrated as follows:

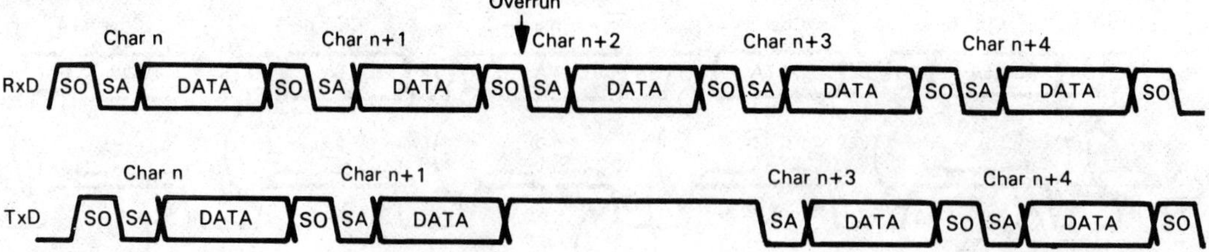


## SY6551 PROGRAMMABLE REGISTERS

We will now examine SY6551 programmable registers, starting with the Control register, whose contents are interpreted as follows:

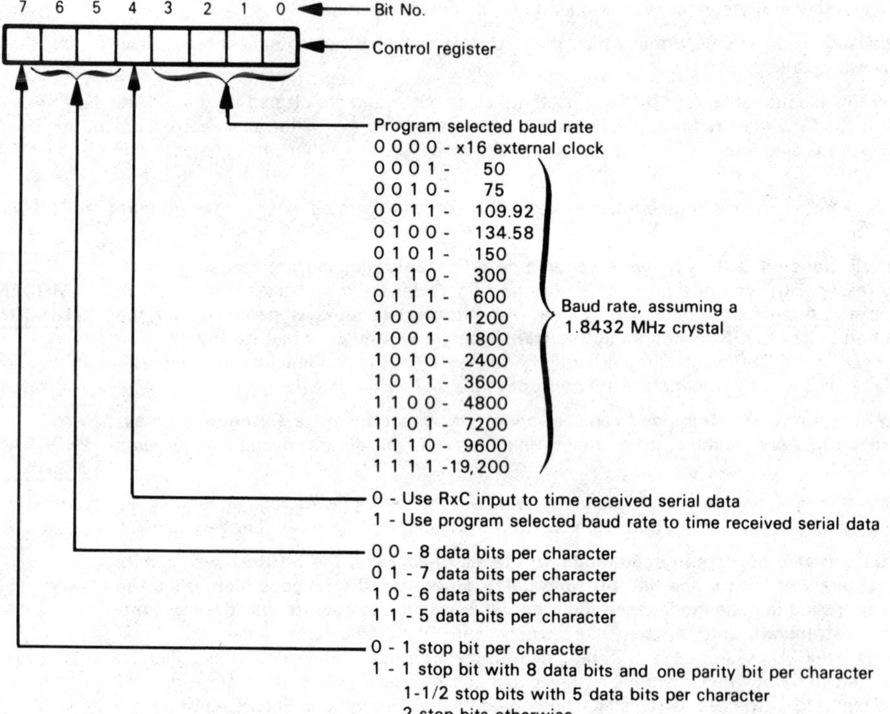


Assuming that you have connected a 1.8432 MHz crystal across XTAL1 and XTAL2, **Control register bits 0, 1, 2, and 3 generate baud rates as shown above.** If the crystal frequency is not 1.8432 MHz, then the baud rate will vary by the ratio of the actual crystal frequency to 1.8432 MHz.

**Control register bit 4 determines whether the received serial data rate is controlled by the internal baud rate generator or an external clock.** If this bit is 0, then an external clock, input via RxC, controls the received serial data rate. If Control register bit 4 is 1, then the internal baud rate generator controls the received serial data rate, and RxC outputs a clock signal whose frequency is 16 times the computed baud rate.

**Control register bits 5, 6, and 7 allow you to specify the common asynchronous character bit combinations.**

The SY6551 restricts the use of 2 or 1-1/2 stop bits. But this will rarely be a restriction, since 1-1/2 stop bits are generally used only with five data bits, to generate BAUDOT codes. Also, the use of two stop bits with eight data bits is rare. Therefore, unless yours is a non-standard application, SY6551 stop bit restrictions will cause you no problems.

**The SY6551 Command register bits are interpreted as follows:**

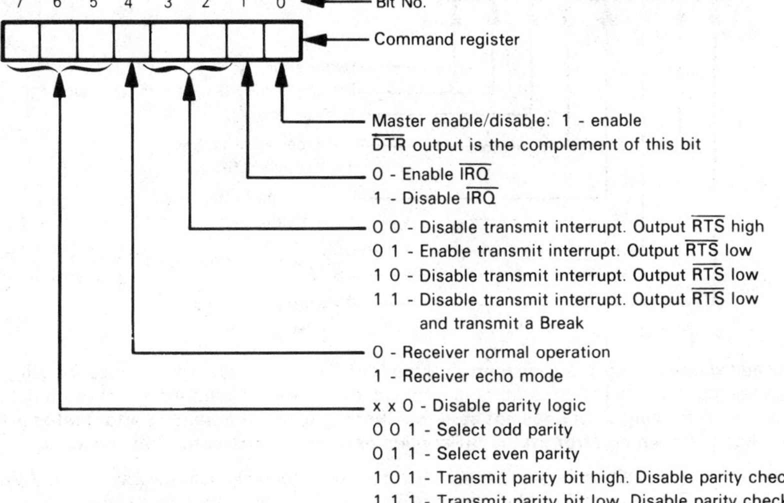


**Command register bit 0 is the master enable/disable for the SY6551.** If this bit is 0, then transmit and receive logic are both disabled. If this bit is 1, then transmit and receive logic are both enabled. **Command register bit 0 also sets or resets** the **$\overline{DTR}$** Modem output. The $\overline{DTR}$ output is the complement of Command register bit 0.

**Command register bit 1 enables or disables interrupt requests output via $\overline{IRQ}$.** Note that this bit does not enable or disable interrupt request logic within the SY6551; it merely allows or prevents the interrupt condition from generating a low $\overline{IRQ}$ output. The effect of Command register bit 1 depends on Command register bit 0. If Command register bit 0 holds a 0, then the transmitter and receiver are disabled; in that case the contents of Command register bit 1 are inconsequential, since no interrupt requests will occur.

**Command register bits 3 and 2 control transmitter logic.** The transmitter interrupts may be disabled or enabled; the device may be requesting to transmit, or it may be transmitting a break.

Code 00 in bits 3 and 2 disables the transmitter. You can use this code to disable the transmitter while the receiver is enabled.

You use code 01 during normal operations; this code causes $\overline{RTS}$ to be output low while data is transmitted with active interrupts.

Code 10 causes data to be transmitted with interrupt logic disabled. $\overline{RTS}$ is output low.

Code 11 causes $\overline{RTS}$ to be output low while a continuous break (low) signal is output, with interrupts disabled.

Command register bit 4, if 0, specifies normal receiver operation. If this bit is 1, then the SY6551 operates in echo mode, in which case the data stream received is retransmitted after a delay of one-half bit time.

**Command register bits 5, 6, and 7 control parity options.** You can enable or disable parity logic. If enabled, you can select odd parity or even parity. You can also force the parity bit to be 1 or 0, in which case parity checking logic is disabled, since parity is no longer being used for its usual purpose.

**You will interrogate the Status register in order to monitor normal operations and detect errors. Status register bits are interpreted as follows:**

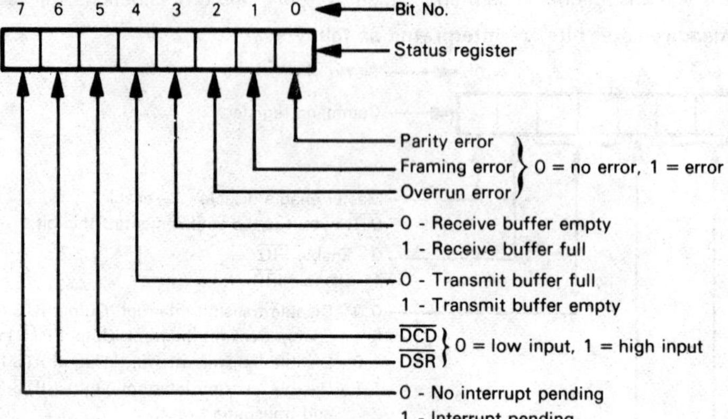


**Parity, framing, and overrun errors are absolutely standard.** The parity error will be reported if parity has been enabled and the wrong parity is detected. A framing error will be reported if start and stop bits do not correctly frame the received character. **A framing error does not stop receiver logic, and the framing error status is reset after one character time. Thus the framing error status bit applies only to the character just received.**

**The SY6551 overrun error condition is not standard.** An overrun error occurs, in the usual way, if the CPU does not read the contents of the Receive buffer within the allowed time. Normally, an overrun results in the next received character overwriting the contents of the Receiver buffer. But following an overrun, the SY6551 discards the next received character. Thus, following an overrun error, the CPU will normally read the most recently received character; however, in the case of the SY6551, following an overrun error you will read the last valid character transmitted before the overrun occurred. This event sequence was illustrated earlier.

**Status register bits 3 and 4 report the condition of the Receive and Transmit buffers, respectively.**

Receive logic will set Status register bit 3 to 1 whenever a new character has been assembled by receiver logic. You have one character time in which to read Receive buffer contents. When you read the contents of the Receive buffer, Status register bit 3 is reset to 0. If you do not read the Receive buffer contents within the allowed one-character time, then an overrun error will occur, as described above.

Status register bit 4 is set to 1 whenever the Transmit buffer contents are moved to the Transmit register. At this time you should write the next character to the Transmit buffer. Writing to the Transmit buffer resets Status register bit 4 to 0. If you do not write to the Transmit buffer while the current character is being transmitted, then Transmit logic will output a mark signal while waiting for the next character to transmit. This is not an error condition.

Status register bits 5 and 6 report the levels of the $\overline{DCD}$ and $\overline{DSR}$ Modem inputs.

Status register bit 7 reports the presence or absence of any condition capable of requesting an interrupt.

**A program controlling the SY6551 will usually be interrupt driven. Following an interrupt request, a service routine must read the Status register in order to determine the interrupt request condition. Figure 10-24 illustrates the sequence in which you should examine Status register bits.**

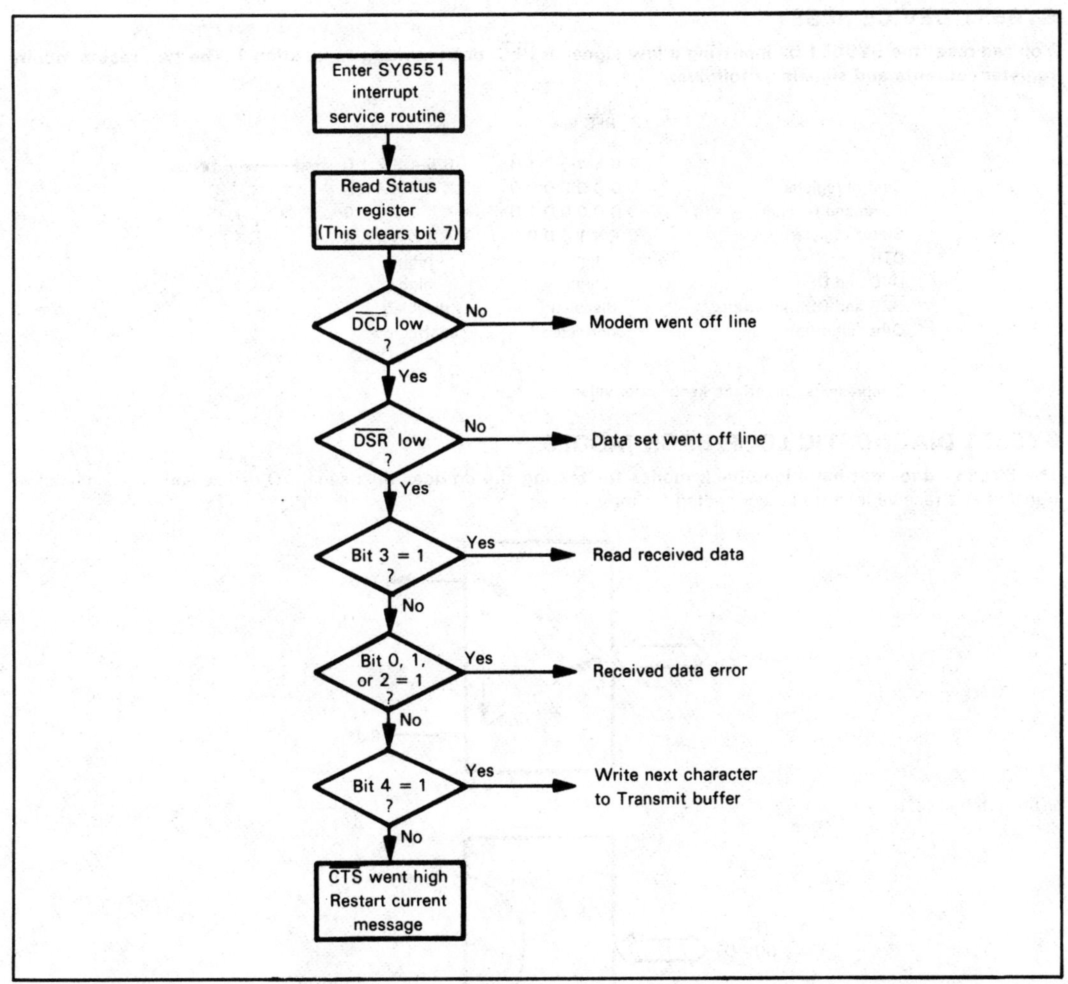


Figure 10-24. SY6551 Interrupt Service Routine, Status Register Testing Logic Portion

## SY6551 DEVICE RESET

**You can reset the SY6551 by inputting a low signal at $\overline{RES}$, or by writing to location 1. The two resets modify register contents and signals as follows:**

| | $\overline{RES}$ low | Write to 1 | |
|---|---|---|---|
| | 7 6 5 4 3 2 1 0 | 7 6 5 4 3 2 1 0 | ← Bit No. |
| Control register | 0 0 0 0 0 0 0 0 | X X X X X X X X | |
| Command register | 0 0 0 0 0 0 1 0 | X X X 0 0 0 1 0 | |
| Status register | 0 X X 1 0 0 0 0 | X X X X X 0 X X | |
| $\overline{DTR}$ | high | high | |
| $\overline{DCD}$ and $\overline{DSR}$ | high | high | |
| $\overline{DCD}$ and $\overline{DSR}$ interrupts | disabled | disabled | |
| Other interrupts | unaffected | unaffected | |

X represents "no effect, keeps prior value".

## SY6551 DIAGNOSTIC LOOP-BACK MODES

**The SY6551 does not have loop-back modes for testing the device.** Most serial I/O devices automatically allow transmit and receive logic to be connected for internal test:

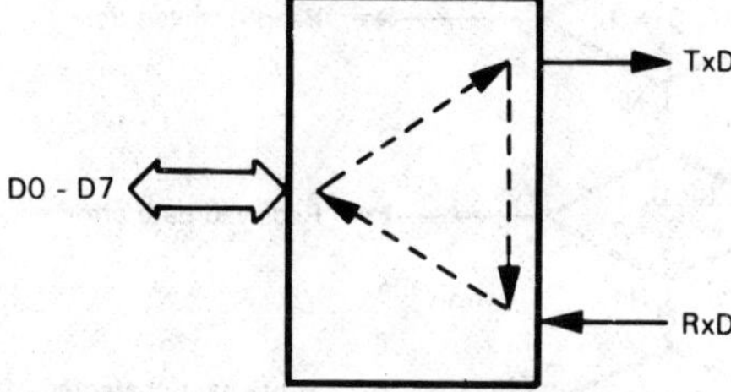


or for external test:

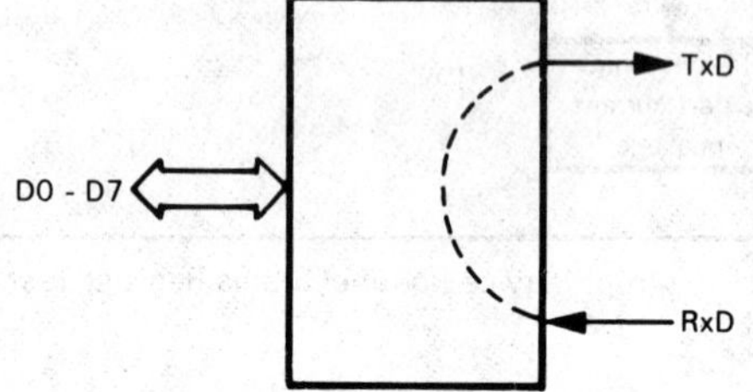

**Synertek recommends the following circuit in order to provide local and remote loop-back capabilities:**

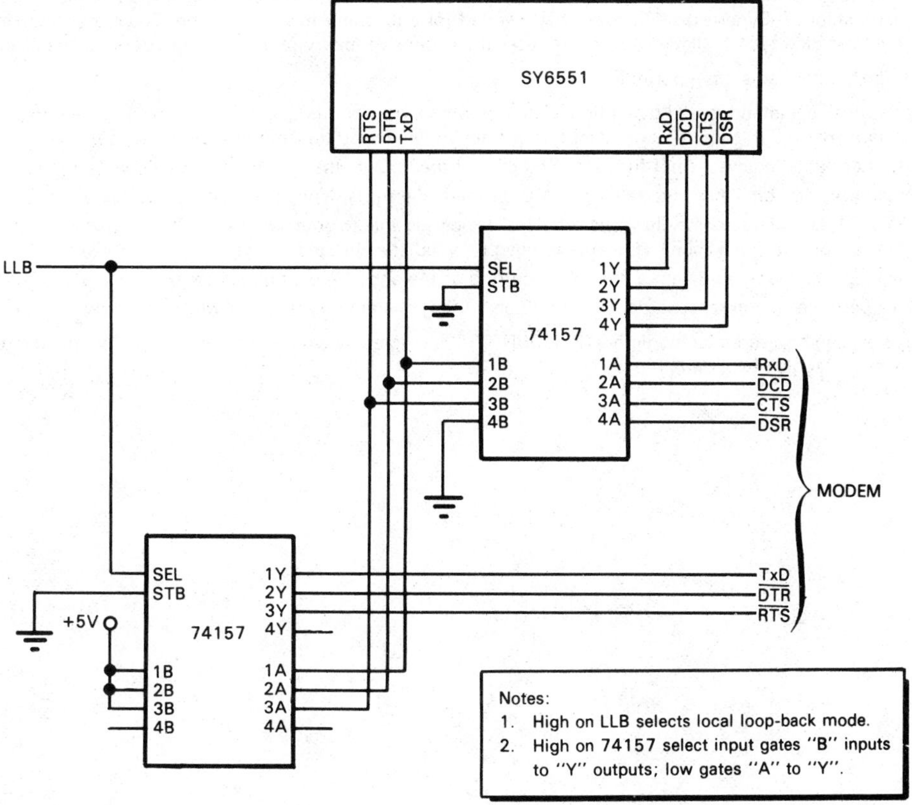


When LLB is high, the following occurs:

1) The TxD, $\overline{DTR}$ and $\overline{RTS}$ outputs from the SY6551 are disconnected from the Modem.
2) The RxD, $\overline{DCD}$, $\overline{CTS}$, and $\overline{DSR}$ inputs from the Modem are disconnected from the SY6551.
3) TxD is connected to RxD.
4) $\overline{DTR}$ is connected to $\overline{DCD}$.
5) $\overline{RTS}$ is connected to $\overline{CTS}$.

For normal operation LLB will be low.

Remote loop-back is programmed as follows:

Control Register bit 4 = 1. Transmit clock = Receive clock.

Command Register bits 4,3,2,1 = 1 1 0 0

Select Echo mode with interrupts disabled.

## EARLY SY6551 DESIGN PROBLEMS

Synertek has had the wisdom to publish certain functional problems that have been discovered in the first batch of SY6551 parts shipped. Synertek ought to be commended for publishing this information. Too often, manufacturers keep such information secret, allowing user after user the expensive luxury of discovering errors for themselves.

The following six problems are reported:

1) Either a Break command issued by writing 11 to Command register bits 3 and 2, or an external reset occurring at the instant that the transmitter is transmitting a start bit will cause transmitter logic to hang up.
2) Transmitter parity logic does not function. You cannot predict whether the parity bit will be 1 or 0.
3) Command register bit 1 has inverted logic. A 0 disables interrupts, while a 1 enables interrupts.
4) The SY6551, like all other asynchronous serial I/O devices, is able to detect a false start bit. However, after detecting a false start bit, the SY6551 is unable to detect a valid start bit and hangs up.
5) Receive logic is unable to detect a stop bit occurring at the end of a continuous break character.
6) Receive parity logic will report a parity error when a $00_{16}$ character is received with odd parity.

All these errors can be cleared by toggling $\overline{DTR}$ or $\overline{DCD}$. $\overline{DTR}$ is toggled by writing 0 and then 1 to command register bit 0. $\overline{DCD}$ must be toggled by external logic.

# DATA SHEETS

This section contains specific electrical and timing data for the following devices:

- MCS6500 Series CPUs
- MCS6530 Multifunction Device
- R6531 Multifunction Support Device
- SY6551 Asynchronous Communications Interface Adapter

## COMMON CHARACTERISTICS

**MAXIMUM RATINGS**

| RATING | SYMBOL | VALUE | UNIT |
|---|---|---|---|
| SUPPLY VOLTAGE | Vcc | -0.3 to +7.0 | Vdc |
| INPUT VOLTAGE | Vin | -0.3 to +7.0 | Vdc |
| OPERATING TEMPERATURE | $T_A$ | 0 to +70 | °C |
| STORAGE TEMPERATURE | $T_{STG}$ | -55 to +150 | °C |

This device contains input protection against damage due to high static voltages or electric fields; however, precautions should be taken to avoid application of voltages higher than the maximum rating.

**ELECTRICAL CHARACTERISTICS** (Vcc = 5.0V ± 5%, Vss = 0, $T_A$ = 25° C)

$\emptyset_1$, $\emptyset_2$ applies to MCS6512, 13, 14, 15, $\emptyset_{o\ (in)}$ applies to MCS6502, 03, 04, 05 and 06

| CHARACTERISTIC | SYMBOL | MIN. | TYP. | MAX. | UNIT |
|---|---|---|---|---|---|
| Input High Voltage | $V_{IH}$ | | | | Vdc |
| Logic, $\emptyset_{o(in)}$ | | Vss + 2.4 | - | Vcc | |
| $\emptyset_1$, $\emptyset_2$ | | Vcc - 0.2 | - | Vcc + 0.25 | |
| Input Low Voltage | $V_{IL}$ | | | | Vdc |
| Logic, $\emptyset_{o(in)}$ | | Vss - 0.3 | - | Vss + 0.4 | |
| $\emptyset_1$, $\emptyset_2$ | | Vss - 0.3 | - | Vss + 0.2 | |
| Input High Threshold Voltage<br>$\overline{RES}$, $\overline{NMI}$, RDY, $\overline{IRQ}$, Data, S.O. | $V_{IHT}$ | Vss + 2.0 | - | - | Vdc |
| Input Low Threshold Voltage<br>$\overline{RES}$, $\overline{NMI}$, RDY, $\overline{IRQ}$, Data, S.O. | $V_{ILT}$ | - | - | Vss + 0.8 | Vdc |
| Input Leakage Current<br>($V_{in}$ = 0 to 5.25V, Vcc = 0) | $I_{in}$ | | | | |
| Logic (Excl. RDY, S.O.) | | - | - | 2.5 | µA |
| $\emptyset_1$, $\emptyset_2$ | | - | - | 100 | µA |
| $\emptyset_{o(in)}$ | | - | - | 10.0 | µA |
| Three-State (Off State) Input Current<br>($V_{in}$ = 0.4 to 2.4V, Vcc = 5.25V)<br>Data Lines | $I_{TSI}$ | - | - | 10 | µA |
| Output High Voltage<br>($I_{LOAD}$ = -100µAdc, Vcc = 4.75V)<br>SYNC, Data, A0-A15, R/W | $V_{OH}$ | Vss + 2.4 | - | - | Vdc |
| Output Low Voltage<br>($I_{LOAD}$ = 1.6mAdc, Vcc = 4.75V)<br>SYNC, Data, A0-A15, R/W | $V_{OL}$ | - | - | Vss + 0.4 | Vdc |
| Power Dissipation | $P_D$ | - | .25 | .70 | W |
| Capacitance<br>($V_{in}$ = 0, $T_A$ = 25°C, f = 1MHz) | C | | | | pF |
| Logic | $C_{in}$ | - | - | 10 | |
| Data | | - | - | 15 | |
| A0-A15, R/W, SYNC | $C_{out}$ | - | - | 12 | |
| $\emptyset_{o(in)}$ | $C_{\emptyset o(in)}$ | - | - | 15 | |
| $\emptyset_1$ | $C_{\emptyset 1}$ | - | 30 | 50 | |
| $\emptyset_2$ | $C_{\emptyset 2}$ | - | 50 | 80 | |

Note: $\overline{IRQ}$ and $\overline{NMI}$ require 3K pull-up resistors.

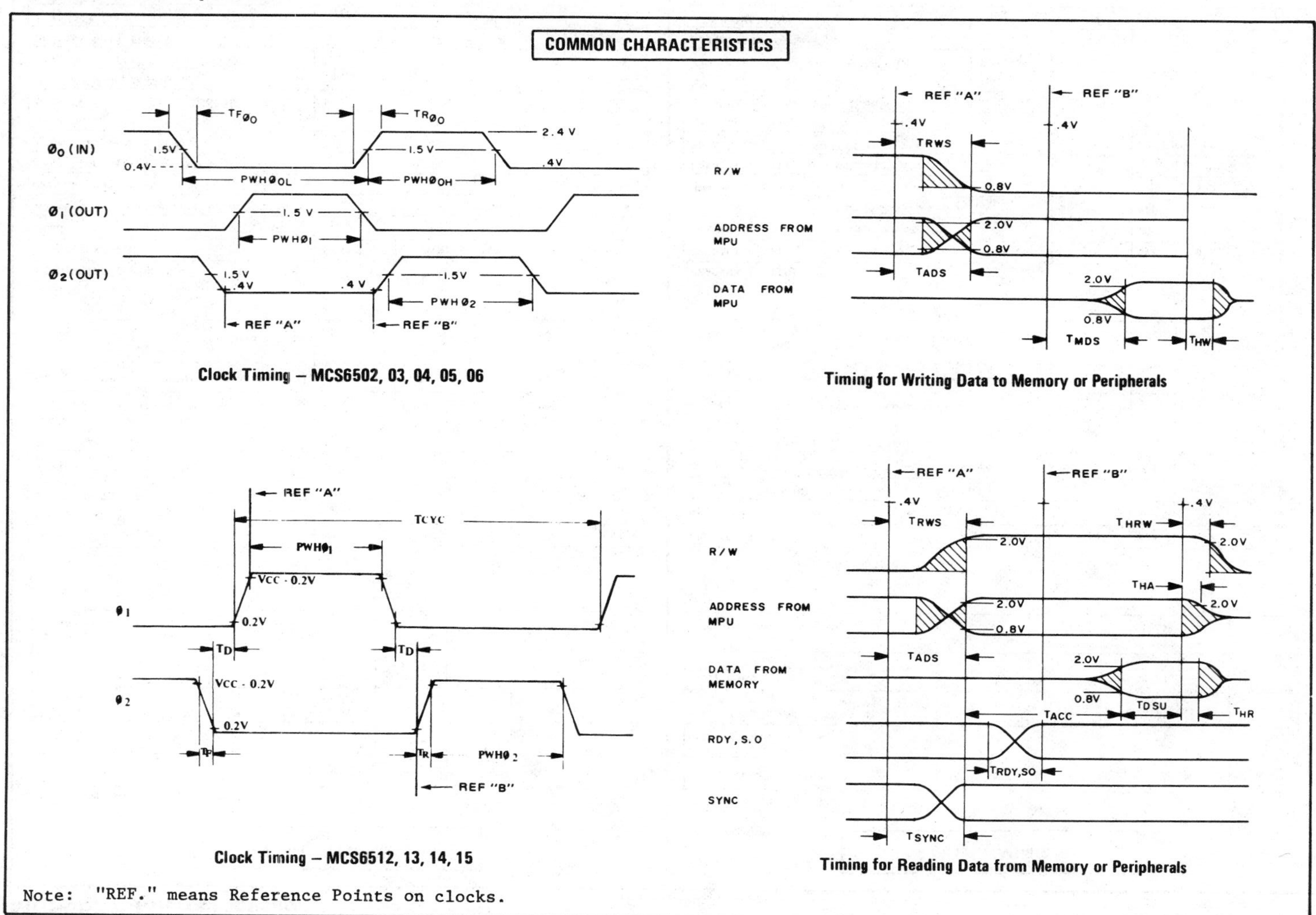


Clock Timing – MCS6502, 03, 04, 05, 06

Timing for Writing Data to Memory or Peripherals

Clock Timing – MCS6512, 13, 14, 15

Timing for Reading Data from Memory or Peripherals

Note: "REF." means Reference Points on clocks.

## 1 MH$_z$ TIMING

**Clock Timing – MCS6512, 13, 14, 15**

| CHARACTERISTIC | SYMBOL | MIN. | TYP. | MAX. | UNIT |
|---|---|---|---|---|---|
| Cycle Time | $T_{CYC}$ | 1000 | --- | --- | nsec |
| Clock Pulse Width Ø1 (Measured at Vcc - 0.2v) Ø2 | PWH Ø1<br>PWH Ø2 | 430<br>470 | --- | --- | nsec |
| Fall Time (Measured from 0.2v to Vcc - 0.2v) | $T_F$ | --- | --- | 25 | nsec |
| Delay Time between Clocks (Measured at 0.2v) | $T_D$ | 0 | --- | --- | nsec |

CLOCK TIMING -MCS6502, 03, 04, 05, 06

| CHARACTERISTIC | SYMBOL | MIN. | TYP. | MAX. | UNITS |
|---|---|---|---|---|---|
| Cycle Time | $T_{CYC}$ | 1000 | -- | -- | ns |
| $\phi_{o(IN)}$ Pulse Width (measured at 1.5V) | $PWH\phi_o$ | 460 | -- | 520 | ns |
| $\phi_{o(IN)}$ Rise, Fall Time | $TR\phi_o, TF\phi_o$ | -- | -- | 10 | ns |
| Delay Time Between Clocks (measured at 1.5V) | $T_D$ | 5 | -- | -- | ns |
| $\phi_{1(OUT)}$ Pulse Width (measured at 1.5V) | $PWH\phi_1$ | $PWH\phi_{oL}-20$ | -- | $PWH\phi_{oL}$ | ns |
| $\phi_{2(OUT)}$ Pulse Width (measured at 1.5V) | $PWH\phi_2$ | $PWH\phi_{oH}-40$ | -- | $PWH\phi_{oH}-10$ | ns |
| $\phi_{1(OUT)}$, $\phi_{2(OUT)}$ Rise, Fall Time (Load = 30pf + 1 TTL) (measured .8V to 2.0 V) | $T_R$, $T_F$ | -- | -- | 25 | ns |

READ/WRITE TIMING

| CHARACTERISTIC | SYMBOL | MIN. | TYP. | MAX. | UNITS |
|---|---|---|---|---|---|
| Read/Write Setup Time from **MCS6500** | $T_{RWS}$ | -- | 100 | 300 | ns |
| Address Setup Time from **MCS6500** | $T_{ADS}$ | -- | 100 | 300 | ns |
| Memory Read Access Time | $T_{ACC}$ | -- | -- | 575 | ns |
| Data Stability Time Period | $T_{DSU}$ | 100 | -- | -- | ns |
| Data Hold Time - Read | $T_{HR}$ | 10 | -- | -- | ns |
| Data Hold Time - Write | $T_{HW}$ | 30 | 60 | -- | ns |
| Data Setup Time from **MCS6500** | $T_{MDS}$ | -- | 150 | 200 | ns |
| RDY, S.O. Setup Time | $T_{RDY}$ | 100 | -- | -- | ns |
| SYNC Setup Time from **MCS6500** | $T_{SYNC}$ | -- | -- | 350 | ns |
| Address Hold Time | $T_{HA}$ | 30 | 60 | -- | ns |
| R/W Hold Time | $T_{HRW}$ | 30 | 60 | -- | ns |

## 2 MH$_z$ TIMING

**Clock Timing – MCS6512, 13, 14, 15, 16**

| CHARACTERISTIC | SYMBOL | MIN. | TYP. | MAX. | UNIT |
|---|---|---|---|---|---|
| Cycle Time | $T_{CYC}$ | 500 | --- | --- | nsec |
| Clock Pulse Width Ø1 (Measured at Vcc - 0.2v) Ø2 | PWH Ø1<br>PWH Ø2 | 215<br>235 | --- | --- | nsec |
| Fall Time (Measured from 0.2v to Vcc - 0.2v) | $T_F$ | --- | --- | 12 | nsec |
| Delay Time between Clocks (Measured at 0.2v) | $T_D$ | 0 | --- | --- | nsec |

CLOCK TIMING - MCS6502, 03, 04, 05, 06

| CHARACTERISTIC | SYMBOL | MIN. | TYP. | MAX. | UNITS |
|---|---|---|---|---|---|
| Cycle Time | $T_{CYC}$ | 500 | -- | -- | ns |
| $\phi_{o(IN)}$ Pulse Width (measured at 1.5V) | $PWH\phi_o$ | 240 | -- | 260 | ns |
| $\phi_{o(IN)}$ Rise, Fall Time | $TR\phi_o, TF\phi_o$ | -- | -- | 10 | ns |
| Delay Time Between Clocks (measured at 1.5V) | $T_D$ | 5 | -- | -- | ns |
| $\phi_{1(OUT)}$ Pulse Width (measured at 1.5V) | $PWH\phi_1$ | $PWH\phi_{oL}-20$ | -- | $PWH\phi_{oL}$ | ns |
| $\phi_{2(OUT)}$ Pulse Width (measured at 1.5V) | $PWH\phi_2$ | $PWH\phi_{oH}-40$ | -- | $PWH\phi_{oH}-10$ | ns |
| $\phi_{1(OUT)}$, $\phi_{2(OUT)}$ Rise, Fall Time (Load = 30pf + 1 TTL) (measured .8V to 2.0 V) | $T_R$, $T_F$ | -- | -- | 25 | ns |

READ/WRITE TIMING

| CHARACTERISTIC | SYMBOL | MIN. | TYP. | MAX. | UNITS |
|---|---|---|---|---|---|
| Read/Write Setup Time from **MCS6500A** | $T_{RWS}$ | -- | 100 | 150 | ns |
| Address Setup Time from **MCS6500A** | $T_{ADS}$ | -- | 100 | 150 | ns |
| Memory Read Access Time | $T_{ACC}$ | -- | -- | 300 | ns |
| Data Stability Time Period | $T_{DSU}$ | 50 | -- | -- | ns |
| Data Hold Time - Read | $T_{HR}$ | 10 | -- | -- | ns |
| Data Hold Time - Write | $T_{HW}$ | 30 | 60 | -- | ns |
| Data Setup Time from **MCS6500A** | $T_{MDS}$ | -- | 75 | 100 | ns |
| RDY, S.O. Setup Time | $T_{RDY}$ | 50 | -- | -- | ns |
| SYNC Setup Time from **MCS6500A** | $T_{SYNC}$ | -- | -- | 175 | ns |
| Address Hold Time | $T_{HA}$ | 30 | 60 | -- | ns |
| R/W Hold Time | $T_{HRW}$ | 30 | 60 | -- | ns |

## MAXIMUM RATINGS

| RATING | SYMBOL | VOLTAGE | UNIT |
|---|---|---|---|
| Supply Voltage | VCC | -.3 to +7.0 | V |
| Input/Output Voltage | $V_{IN}$ | -.3 to +7.0 | V |
| Operating Temperature Range | $T_{OP}$ | 0 to 70 | $^{o}C$ |
| Storage Temperature Range | $T_{STG}$ | -55 to +150 | $^{o}C$ |

All inputs contain protection circuitry to prevent damage due to high static charges. Care should be exercised to prevent unnecessary application of voltage outside the specification range.

## ELECTRICAL CHARACTERISTICS (VCC = 5.0v ± 5%, VSS = 0v, $T_A$ = 25° C)

| CHARACTERISTIC | SYMBOL | MIN. | TYP. | MAX. | UNIT |
|---|---|---|---|---|---|
| Input High Voltage | $V_{IH}$ | $V_{SS}+2.4$ | | VCC | V |
| Input Low Voltage | $V_{IL}$ | $V_{SS}-.3$ | | $V_{SS}+.4$ | V |
| Input Leakage Current; $V_{IN} = V_{SS} + 5v$<br>AØ-A9, RS, R/W, $\overline{RES}$, Ø2, PB6*, PB5* | $I_{IN}$ | | 1.0 | 2.5 | µA |
| Input Leakage Current for High Impedance State (Three State); $V_{IN}$ = .4v to 2.4v; DØ-D7 | $I_{TSI}$ | | ±1.0 | ±10.0 | µA |
| Input High Current; $V_{IN}$ = 2.4v<br>PAØ-PA7, PBØ-PB7 | $I_{IH}$ | -100. | -300. | | µA |
| Input Low Current; $V_{IN}$ = .4v<br>PAØ-PA7, PBØ-PB7 | $I_{IL}$ | | -1.0 | -1.6 | MA |
| Output High Voltage<br>VCC = MIN, $I_{LOAD} \leq -100\mu A$ (PAØ-PA7,PBØ-PB7,DØ-D7)<br>$I_{LOAD} \leq -3$ MA (PAØ,PBØ) | $V_{OH}$ | <br>VSS+2.4<br>VSS+1.5 | | | V |
| Output Low Voltage<br>VCC = MIN, $I_{LOAD} \leq 1.6MA$ | $V_{OL}$ | | | VSS+.4 | V |
| Output High Current (Sourcing);<br>VOH ≥ 2.4v (PAØ-PA7,PBØ-PB7,DØ-D7)<br>≥ 1.5v Available for other than TTL (Darlingtons) (PAØ,PBØ) | $I_{OH}$ | <br>-100<br>-3.0 | <br>-1000<br>-5.0 | | <br>µA<br>MA |
| Output Low Current (Sinking); VOL ≤ .4v (PAØ-PA7) (PBØ-PB7) | $I_{OL}$ | 1.6 | | | MA |
| Clock Input Capacitance | $C_{Clk}$ | | | 30 | pf |
| Input Capacitance | $C_{IN}$ | | | 10 | pf |
| Output Capacitance | $C_{OUT}$ | | | 10 | pf |
| Power Dissipation | $P_D$ | | 500 | 1000 | MW |

*When programmed as address pins
All values are D.C. readings

## WRITE TIMING CHARACTERISTICS

| CHARACTERISTIC | SYMBOL | MIN. | TYP. | MAX. | UNIT |
|---|---|---|---|---|---|
| Clock Period | $T_{CYC}$ | 1 | | 10 | μS |
| Rise & Fall Times | TR, TF | | | 25 | NS |
| Clock Pulse Width | TC | 470 | | | NS |
| R/W valid before positive transition of clock | TWCW | 180 | | | NS |
| Address valid before positive transition of clock | TACW | 180 | | | NS |
| Data Bus valid before negative transition of clock | TDCW | 300 | | | NS |
| Data Bus Hold Time | THW | 10 | | | NS |
| Peripheral data valid after negative transition of clock | TCPW | | | 1 | μS |
| Peripheral data valid after negative transition of clock driving CMOS (Level=VCC-30%) | TCMOS | | | 2 | μS |

## READ TIMING CHARACTERISTICS

| CHARACTERISTIC | SYMBOL | MIN. | TYP. | MAX. | UNIT |
|---|---|---|---|---|---|
| R/W valid before positive transition of clock | TWCR | 180 | | | NS |
| Address valid before positive transition of clock | TACR | 180 | | | NS |
| Peripheral data valid before positive transition of clock | TPCR | 300 | | | NS |
| Data Bus valid after positive transition of clock | TCDR | | | 395 | NS |
| Data Bus Hold Time | THR | 10 | | | NS |
| $\overline{\text{IRQ}}$ (Interval Timer Interrupt) valid before positive transition of clock | TIC | 200 | | | NS |

Loading = 30 pf + 1 TTL load for PAØ-PA7, PBØ-PB7

=130 pf + 1 TTL load for DØ-D7

## MCS652X and MCS653X

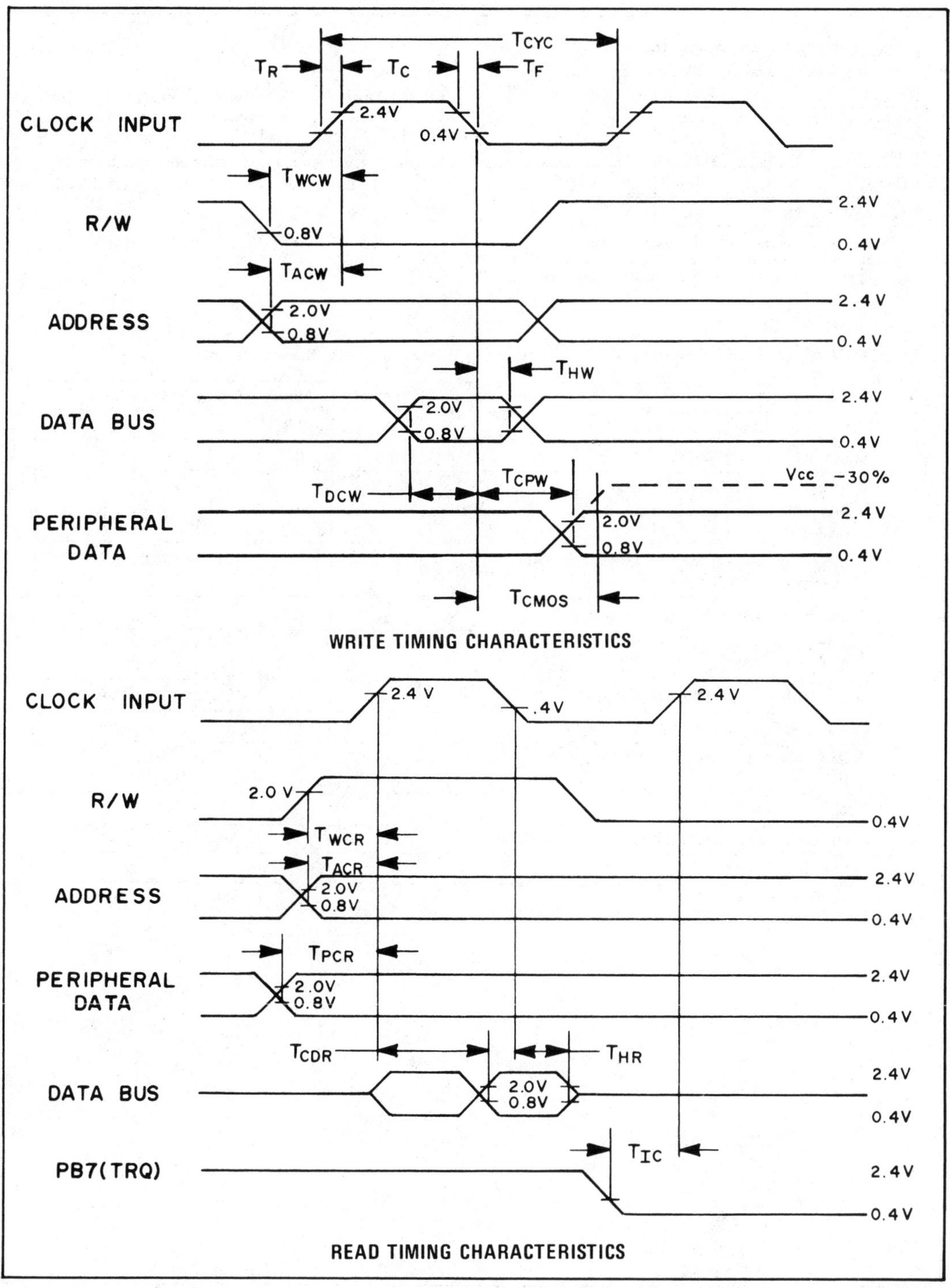

## ABSOLUTE MAXIMUM RATINGS

| Rating | Symbol | Allowable Range |
|---|---|---|
| Supply Voltage | $V_{CC}$ | -0.3V to +7.0V |
| Input/Output Voltage | $V_{IN}$ | -0.3V to +7.0V |
| Operating Temperature | $T_{OP}$ | 0°C to 70°C |
| Storage Temperature | $T_{STG}$ | -55°C to 150°C |

All inputs contain protection circuitry to prevent damage to high static charges. Care should be exercised to prevent unnecessary application of voltages in excess of the allowable limits.

Stresses above those listed under "Absolute Maximum Ratings" may cause permanent damage to the device. This is a stress rating only and functional operation of the device at these or any other conditions above those indicated in the operational sections of this specification is not implied.

## ELECTRICAL CHARACTERISTICS ($V_{CC}$ = 5.0V ± 5%, $T_A$ = 25°C, unless otherwise noted)

| Characteristic | Symbol | Min | Typ | Max | Unit |
|---|---|---|---|---|---|
| Input High Voltage | $V_{IH}$ | 2.0 | – | $V_{CC}$ | V |
| Input Low Voltage | $V_{IL}$ | -0.3 | – | 0.8 | V |
| Input Leakage Current: $V_{IN}$=0 to 5V. ($\phi$2, R/$\overline{W}$, $\overline{RES}$, $CS_0$, $\overline{CS_1}$, $RS_0$, $RS_1$, $\overline{CTS}$, RxD, $\overline{DCD}$, $\overline{DSR}$) | $I_{IN}$ | – | ±1.0 | ±2.5 | μA |
| Input Leakage Current for High Impedance State (Three State) | $I_{TSI}$ | – | ±2.0 | ±10.0 | μA |
| Output High Voltage: $I_{LOAD}$=-100μA | $V_{OH}$ | 2.4 | – | – | V |
| Output Low Voltage: $I_{LOAD}$=1.6mA ($DB_0$-$DB_7$, TxD, RxC, $\overline{RTS}$, $\overline{DTR}$, $\overline{IRQ}$) | $V_{OL}$ | – | – | 0.4 | V |
| Output High Current (Sourcing): $V_{OH}$=2.4V | $I_{OH}$ | -100 | -1000 | – | μA |
| Output Low Current (Sinking): $V_{OL}$=0.4V | $I_{OL}$ | 1.6 | – | – | μA |
| Output Leakage Current (off state): $V_{OUT}$=5V ($\overline{IRQ}$) | $I_{OFF}$ | – | 1.0 | 10.0 | μA |
| Clock Capacitance ($\phi$2) | $C_{CLK}$ | – | – | 20 | pF |
| Input Capacitance (except XTAL1 and XTAL2) | $C_{IN}$ | – | – | 10 | pF |
| Output Capacitance | $C_{OUT}$ | – | – | 10 | pF |
| Power Dissipation | $P_D$ | – | 350 | 500 | mw |

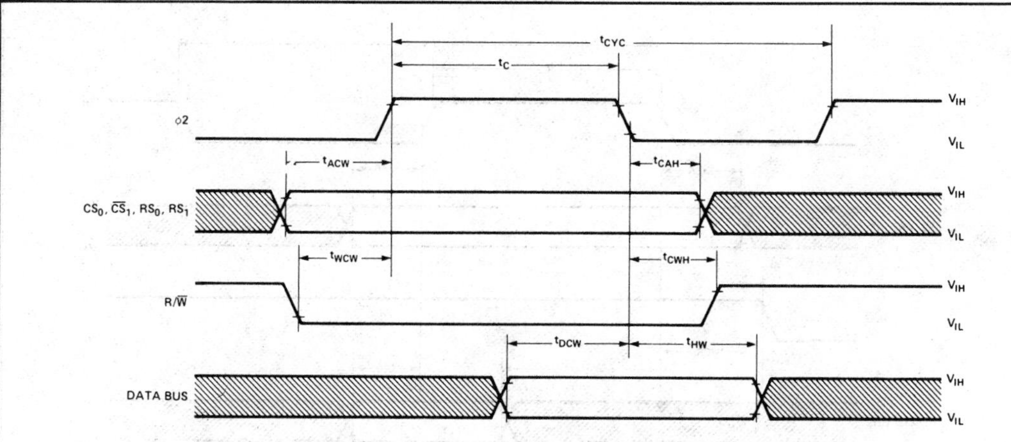


**Write Timing Characteristics**

**WRITE CYCLE** ($V_{CC}$ = 5.0V ± 5%, $T_A$ = 0 to 70°C, unless otherwise noted)

| Characteristic | Symbol | SY6551 | | SY6551A | | Unit |
|---|---|---|---|---|---|---|
| | | Min | Max | Min | Max | |
| Cycle Time | $t_{CYC}$ | 1.0 | 40 | 0.5 | 40 | μs |
| φ2 Pulse Width | $t_C$ | 470 | – | 235 | – | ns |
| Address Set-Up Time | $t_{ACW}$ | 180 | – | 90 | – | ns |
| Address Hold Time | $t_{CAH}$ | 0 | – | 0 | – | ns |
| R/$\overline{W}$ Set-Up Time | $t_{WCW}$ | 180 | – | 90 | – | ns |
| R/$\overline{W}$ Hold Time | $t_{CWH}$ | 0 | – | 0 | – | ns |
| Data Bus Set-Up Time | $t_{DCW}$ | 300 | – | 150 | – | ns |
| Data Bus Hold Time | $t_{HW}$ | 10 | – | 10 | – | ns |

($t_r$ and $t_f$ = 10 to 30 ns)

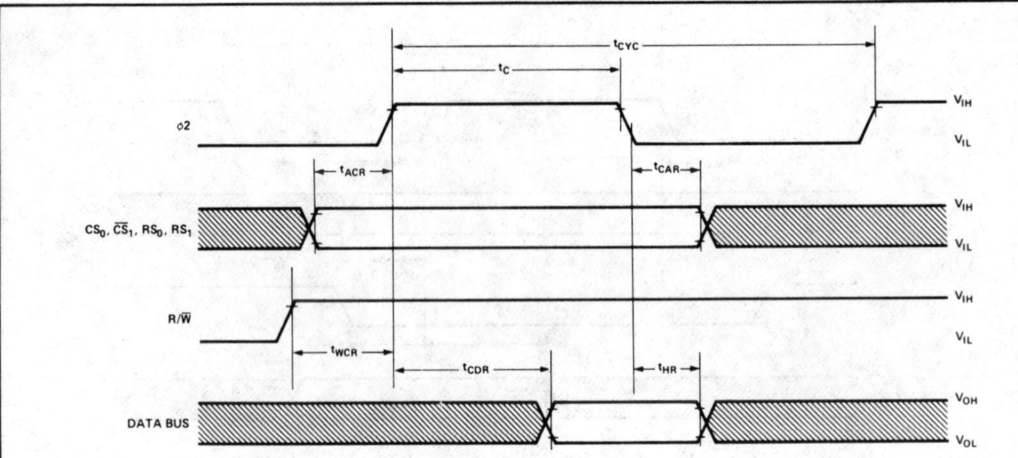


**Read Timing Characteristics**

**READ CYCLE** ($V_{CC}$ = 5.0V ± 5%, $T_A$ = 0 to 70°C, unless otherwise noted)

| Characteristic | Symbol | SY6551 Min | SY6551 Max | SY6551A Min | SY6551A Max | Unit |
|---|---|---|---|---|---|---|
| Cycle Time | $t_{CYC}$ | 1.0 | 40 | 0.5 | 40 | μs |
| Pulse Width (φ2) | $t_C$ | 470 | – | 235 | – | ns |
| Address Set-Up Time | $t_{ACR}$ | 180 | – | 90 | – | ns |
| Address Hold Time | $t_{CAR}$ | 0 | – | 0 | – | ns |
| R/$\overline{W}$ Set-Up Time | $t_{WCR}$ | 180 | – | 90 | – | ns |
| Read Access Time | $t_{CDR}$ | – | 395 | – | 200 | ns |
| Read Hold Time | $t_{HR}$ | 10 | – | 10 | – | ns |

($t_r$ and $t_f$ = 10 to 30 ns)

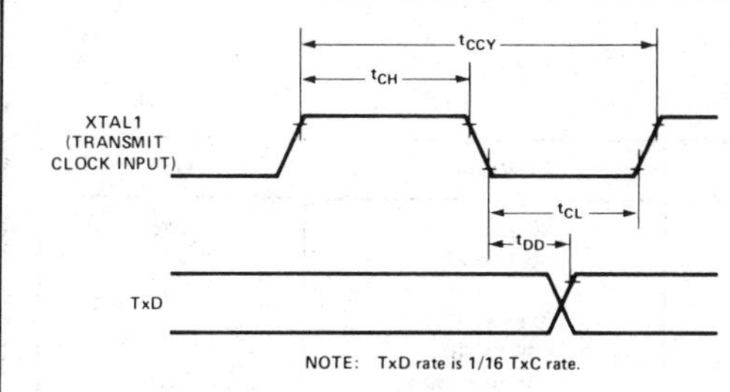


Figure 4a. Transmit Timing with External Clock

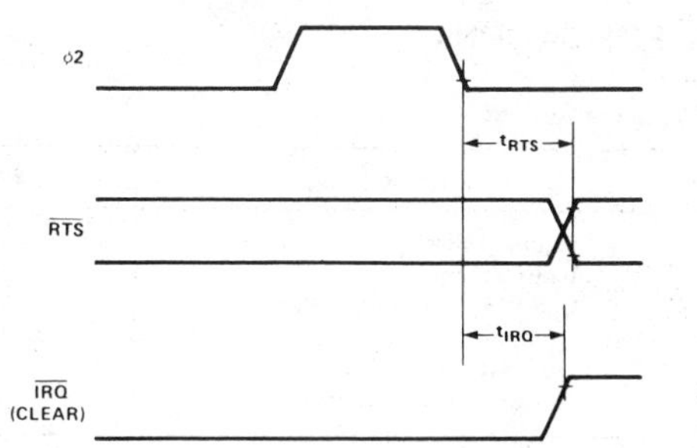


Figure 4b. Interrupt and RTS Timing

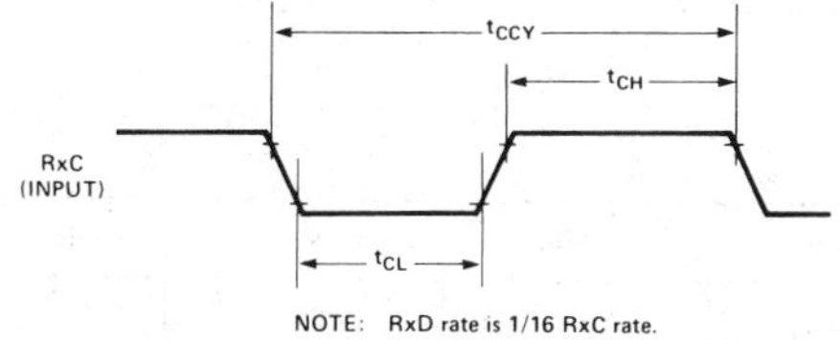


Figure 4c. Receive External Clock Timing

## TRANSMIT/RECEIVE CHARACTERISTICS

| Characteristic | Symbol | SY6551 | | SY6551A | | Unit |
|---|---|---|---|---|---|---|
| | | Min | Max | Min | Max | |
| Transmit/Receive Clock Rate | $t_{CCY}$ | 0.5* | – | 0.5* | – | μs |
| Transmit/Receive Clock High Time | $t_{CH}$ | 235 | – | 235 | – | ns |
| Transmit/Receive Clock Low Time | $t_{CL}$ | 235 | – | 235 | – | ns |
| XTAL1 to TxD Propagation Delay | $t_{DD}$ | – | 500 | – | 500 | ns |
| $\overline{RTS}$ Propagation Delay | $t_{RTS}$ | – | 500 | – | 500 | ns |
| $\overline{IRQ}$ Propagation Delay (Clear) | $t_{IRQ}$ | – | 500 | – | 500 | ns |

($t_r$, $t_f$ = 10 to 30 nsec)

*The baud rate with external clocking is: Baud Rate = $\frac{1}{16 \times T_{CCY}}$

## SPECIFICATIONS

### Maximum Ratings

| Rating | Symbol | Value | Unit |
|---|---|---|---|
| Supply Voltage | $V_{CC}$ | -0.3 to +7.0 | Vdc |
| Input Voltage | $V_{in}$ | -0.3 to +7.0 | Vdc |
| Operating Temperature Range | T | | °C |
| Commercial | | 0 to +70 | |
| Industrial | | -40 to +85 | |
| Storage Temperature Range | $T_{stg}$ | -55 to +150 | °C |

This device contains circuitry to protect the inputs against damage due to high static voltages, however, it is advised that normal precautions be taken to avoid application of any voltage higher than maximum rated voltages to this circuit.

### Electrical Characteristics

(VCC = 5V ± 10% for R6531, VCC = 5V ± 5% for R6531A)

| Characteristic | Symbol | Min | Max | Unit |
|---|---|---|---|---|
| Input High Voltage | $V_{IH}$ | 2.0 | VCC | V |
| Input Low Voltage | $V_{IL}$ | -0.3 | +0.8 | V |
| Input Leakage Current; $V_{IN} = V_{SS} + 5V$, $V_{CC} = +5V$ A0-A11, CS, R/$\overline{W}$, $\overline{RES}$, φ2, PD0-PD3 | $I_{IN}$ | | 2.5 | μA |
| Leakage Current for High Impedance State, $V_{CC} = +5V$ (Three State); $V_{IN}$ = 0.4V to 2.4V; D0-D7, PA0-PA7, PB0-PB6 | $I_{TSI}$ | | ±10.0 | μA |
| Output High Voltage VCC = MIN, $I_{LOAD} \leq -200$ μA (PA0-PA7, PB-PB6, D0-D7) | $V_{OH}$ | VSS + 2.4 | | V |
| Output Low Voltage VCC = MIN, $I_{LOAD} \leq 2.1$ mA | $V_{OL}$ | | VSS + 0.4 | V |
| Output High Current (Sourcing); VOH ≥ 2.4V (PA0-PA7, PB0-PB6, PC0-PC7, PD0-PD3, D0-D7) | $I_{OH}$ | -200 | | μA |
| Output Low Current (Sinking); $V_{OL} \leq 0.4V$ (PA0-PA7) (PB0-PB6) (PC0-PC7) | $I_{OL}$ | 2.1 | | mA |
| Clock Input Capacitance, $V_{CC}$ = 5V | $C_{Clk}$ | | 20 | pF |
| Input Capacitance, $V_{CC}$ = 5V | $C_{IN}$ | | 10 | pF |
| Output Capacitance, $V_{CC}$ = 5V, chip deselected | $C_{OUT}$ | | 10 | pF |
| Power Dissipation | $P_D$ | | 1.0 | W |

*When programmed as address pins

All values are D.C. readings

## Write Timing Characteristics

| Characteristic | Symbol | 1 MHz Min | 1 MHz Max | 2 MHz Min | 2 MHz Max | Unit |
|---|---|---|---|---|---|---|
| Clock Period | $T_{CYC}$ | 1 | 10 | 0.5 | 10 | μs |
| Rise & Fall Times | $T_R, T_F$ | | 25 | | 15 | ns |
| Clock Pulse Width | $T_C$ | 470 | | 235 | | ns |
| R/$\overline{W}$ valid before positive transition of clock | $T_{WCW}$ | 180 | | 120 | | ns |
| Address valid before positive transition of clock | $T_{ACW}$ | 180 | | 120 | | ns |
| Data Bus valid before negative transition of clock | $T_{DCW}$ | 270 | | 135 | | ns |
| Data Bus Hold Time | $T_{HW}$ | 10 | | 10 | | ns |
| Peripheral data valid after negative transition of clock | $T_{CPW}$ | | 900 | | 450 | ns |

## Read Timing Characteristics

| Characteristic | Symbol | 1 MHz Min | 1 MHz Max | 2 MHz Min | 2 MHz Max | Unit |
|---|---|---|---|---|---|---|
| R/$\overline{W}$ valid before positive transition of clock | $T_{WCR}$ | 180 | | 120 | | ns |
| Address valid before positive transition of clock | $T_{ACR}$ | 180 | | 120 | | ns |
| Peripheral data valid before positive transition of clock | $T_{PCR}$ | 270 | | 135 | | ns |
| Data Bus valid after positive transition of clock | $T_{CDR}$ | | 350 | | 180 | ns |
| Data Bus Hold Time | $T_{HR}$ | 10 | | 10 | | ns |
| IRQ valid after negative transition of clock | $T_{IC}$ | | 900 | | 450 | ns |

Loading = 100 pF + 1 TTL load for PA0-PA7, PB0-PB6, PC0-PC7
= 100 pF + 1 TTL load for D0-D7 (R6531A)
= 130 pF + 1 TTL load for D0-D7 (R6531)

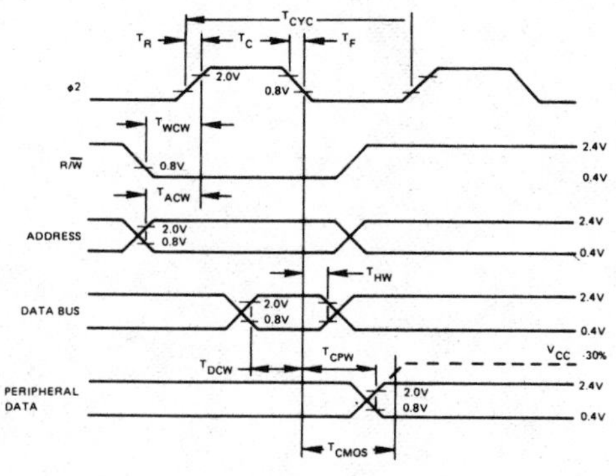

**Write Timing Characteristics**

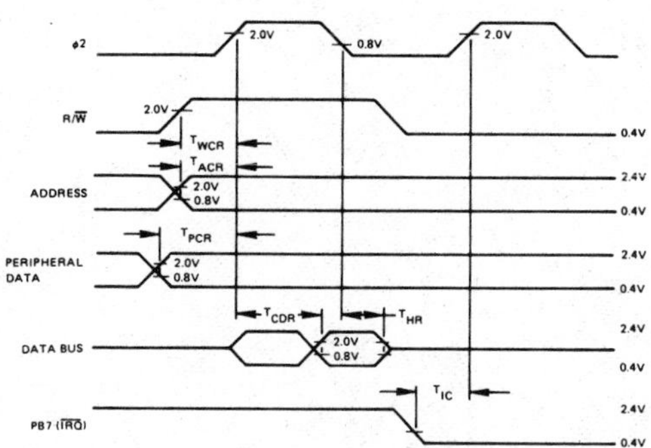


**Read Timing Characteristics**

# Chapter 11
# THE SIGNETICS 2650A

**The 2650A is functionally identical to the 2650 microprocessor which has been described in previous editions of this book. The 2650A is a redesigned chip that is smaller and cheaper to produce than the old 2650.**

**The 2650A-1 is a new higher-speed version of the 2650A.**

**Within the frame of reference of the microcomputers being described in this book, the Signetics 2650A is a very minicomputer-like device.**

**The Signetics 2650A has a wealth of memory addressing modes; a large number of CPU-generated control signals are aimed at allowing TTL logic to surround the microcomputer device itself, rather than requiring a family of support devices, as do most products described in this book.** However, you will have very little trouble using support devices of the 8080A with the Signetics 2650A CPU. MC6800 support devices can be used with the Signetics 2650A — but with more difficulty.

**There are two support devices designed by Signetics specifically for the 2650A. They are:**

1) **The 2656 System Memory Interface (SMI).** This is a multifunction support device that provides read-only memory, read/write memory and parallel I/O logic on a single chip.
2) **The 2651 Programmable Communications Interface (PCI).** This is a universal synchronous/asynchronous data communications controller.

**The 2656 and 2651 are both described in Volume 3.** This is because the two devices can be used as easily with a 2650A, or with any other microprocessor.

**Interesting features of the 2650A, which are described on the following pages, are the imaginative use of status flags, a rich variety of very informative control signals, and the use of the second object code byte, in multibyte instructions, to encode memory addressing options.**

**Figure 11-1 illustrates the logical functions implemented on the 2650A CPU chip. Memory and other external logic will connect directly to the 2650A address, data and control lines, without need for interface devices (other than buffer amplifiers needed to meet signal loads).**

The 2650A uses a single +5V power supply.

Using a clock with a 0.8 microsecond period, 2650A instruction execution times vary between 4.8 and 9.6 microseconds. Using a clock with a 0.5 microsecond period, instruction execution times vary between 3.0 and 6.0 microseconds.

All 2650A signals are TTL compatible.

The principal manufacturer for the 2650A is:

SIGNETICS CORPORATION
811 East Arques Avenue
Sunnyvale, CA 94086

Signetics has a second sourcing agreement with National Semiconductor, whereby National Semiconductor is supposed to second source the 2650A. At the present time it does not look as though National Semiconductor will exercise this second source option.

## THE 2650A CPU LOGIC

**The 2650A CPU has a typical microcomputer organization. The Arithmetic and Logic Unit, the Control Unit and programmable registers are all implemented on the 2650A CPU.**

**The additions and omissions shown in Figure 11-1, as compared to typical CPU logic, need some preliminary explanation.**

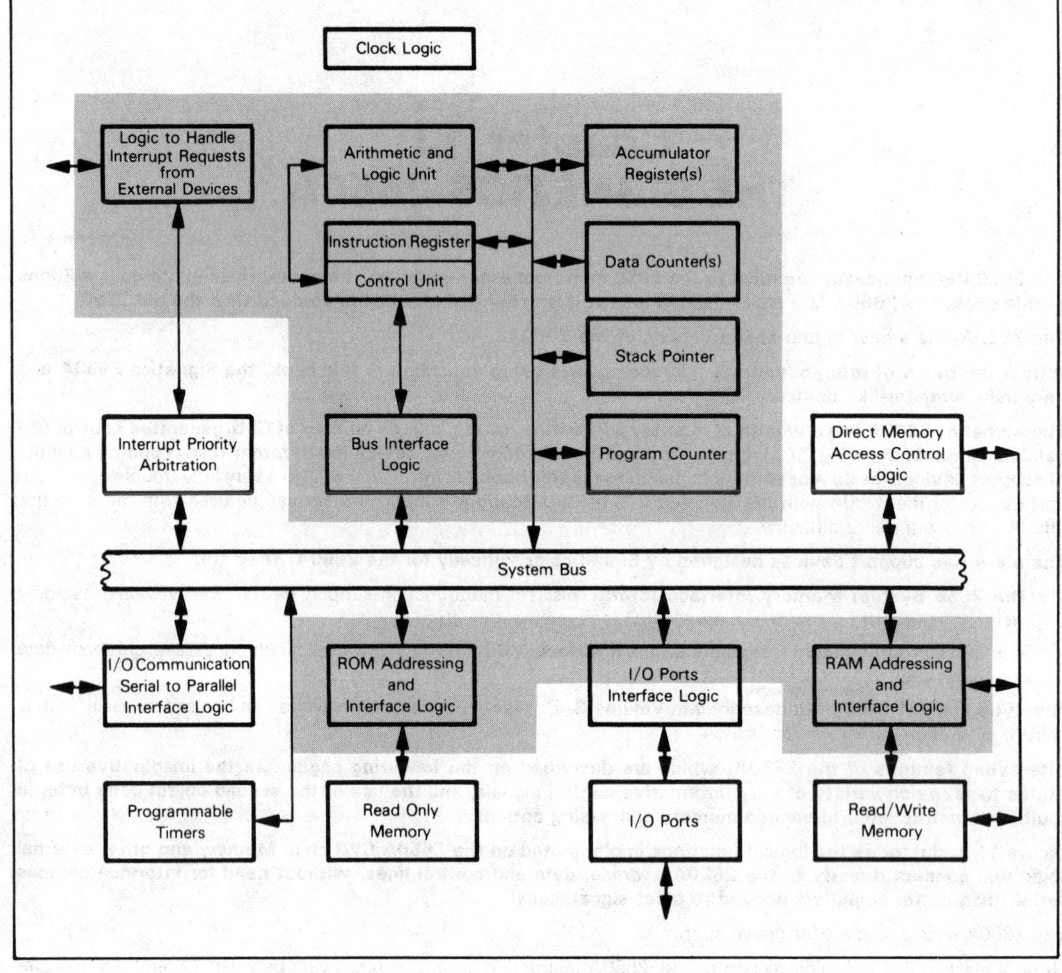


Figure 11-1. Logic of the 2650A Microcomputer CPU

Although the 2650A has just one interrupt request line and one interrupt acknowledge line, CPU logic allows every interrupting device to force a vectored branch to its own unique interrupt service routine; for this reason, logic to handle interrupt requests is shown as an integral part of CPU chip logic.

Standard ROM and RAM devices can be connected directly to 2650A bus lines; therefore, the 2650A is shown as providing complete memory interface logic. Note, however, that TTL load levels will almost certainly require that signal buffer amplifiers interface memory devices to the 2650A CPU.

I/O port interface logic is shown as only partially implemented on the 2650A CPU chip. A 2650A-based microcomputer system with one or two I/O ports will require no special I/O port logic; control signals allow the Data Bus to be used either as a conduit to external devices or to memory. But if a 2650A-based microcomputer system has more than two separately addressable I/O ports, external I/O port select logic must be added.

Figure 11-1 excludes clock logic from the CPU chip. The 2650A CPU does indeed require external logic to create its clock signal; however, a single TTL level clock signal with relatively lax tolerances is required. Therefore, external generation of the clock signal will be both inexpensive and free of problems.

## 2650A PROGRAMMABLE REGISTERS

**In addition to a 15-bit Program Counter, the 2650A has seven 8-bit programmable registers which may be illustrated as follows:**

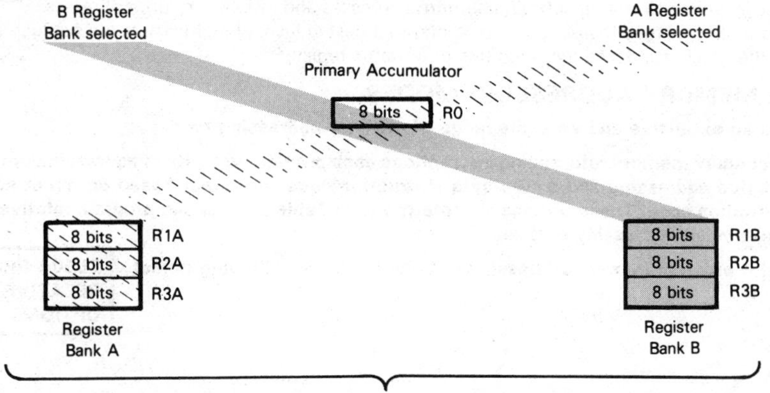


**2650A ACCUMULATOR**

**2650A INDEX REGISTERS**

**R0 is a primary Accumulator. This register is always accessible.**

**The remaining six 8-bit registers form two 3-register banks.** A status bit (which will be described later) is used to identify one of the two register banks as accessible at any given time. Thus, depending on the status bit setting, Registers R0, R1A, R2A and R3A may be accessible, or else Registers R0, R1B, R2B and R3B may be accessible.

**The six secondary registers serve as both secondary Accumulators and Index registers.**
The 2650A has no Data Counters, as do most microcomputers; rather, it uses the minicomputer philosophy of adding an index, out of an Index register, to a memory address which is computed from information provided by every Memory Reference instruction.

**2650A PROGRAM COUNTER**

**2650A MEMORY PAGES**

**The Program Counter is 15 bits wide;** therefore up to 32,768 bytes of memory may be addressed in the normal course of events.

**The two high-order bits of the Program Counter represent page select bits.** 2650A memory is divided into four pages with 8192 bytes of memory per page; this scheme is illustrated as follows:

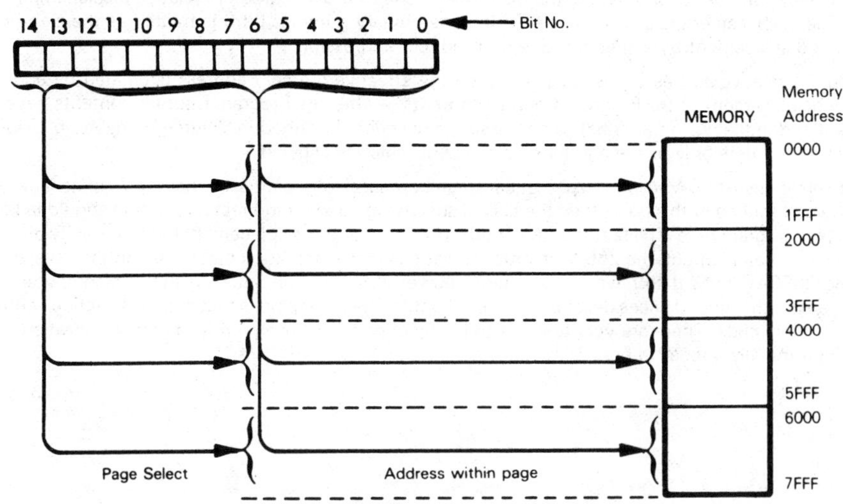

**Pages are selected by Branch instructions,** but we will defer to the discussion of addressing modes a description of how this is done.

**2650A STACK**

**The 2650A has a primitive Stack,** implemented on the CPU chip; this Stack is eight addresses deep, and its use is limited to storing subroutine return addresses and interrupt return addresses. Subroutines and interrupts may therefore be combined to a nested level of eight. There are no Push and Pop type instructions, and the Stack is indexed via three bits of a Status register.

## THE 2650A MEMORY ADDRESSING MODES

**The 2650A has an extensive and versatile range of memory addressing modes.**

**Primary and secondary memory referencing instructions each provide two sets of addressing options, one based on program relative addressing and a two-byte instruction code, the other based on direct addressing and a three-byte instruction code. These options are referred to in Table 11-1 as the program relative addressing options and the extended addressing options.**

**2650A PROGRAM RELATIVE ADDRESSING OPTIONS**

**Instructions with program relative addressing options have the following object code:**

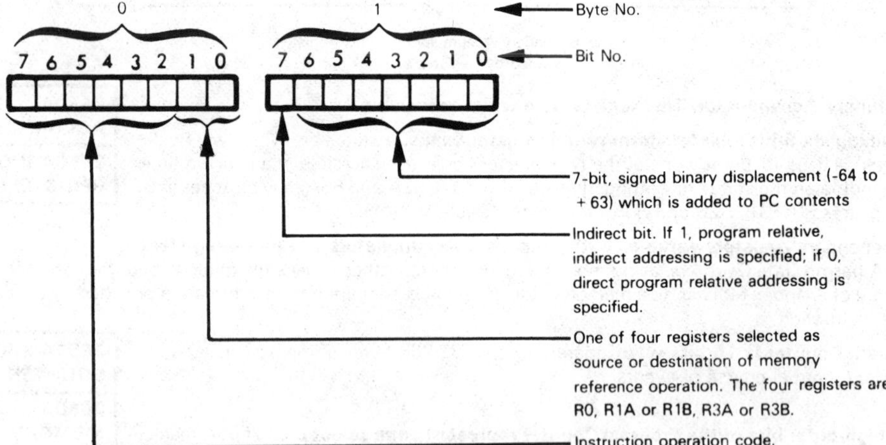


In the above illustration, the second byte of the instruction code provides a program relative displacement in the range +63 to -64. The displacement is provided as a 7-bit signed binary number; bit 6 is treated as the sign bit. The high-order bit of the displacement byte specifies direct or indirect addressing.

If direct, program relative addressing is specified, then the effective memory address is created by adding the 7-bit signed binary displacement to the Program Counter contents — after the Program Counter contents have been incremented. Direct and indirect program relative addressing have been described in Volume 1, Chapter 6; 2650A program relative addressing differs only in the shorter displacement which is allowed.

If we are to relate the 2650A to our hypothetical microcomputer of Volume 1, Chapter 7, or to any of the other microcomputers described in this book, then the task of specifying direct or indirect addressing should fall to a bit within the first object program byte. The fact that the 2650A uses a bit of the displacement byte to specify direct or indirect addressing means that, in effect, the 2650A instruction set has more than 256 object code options available to it. This feature of the 2650A allows it to have a much more powerful instruction set — in the minicomputer sense of the word — than any of the other devices described in this chapter. The price paid is that most instructions generate two or three bytes of object code. There are very few one-byte object codes. Consequently, memory utilization is not as efficient as it might initially appear to be.

In all probability, indirect, program relative addressing will be more commonly used than direct, program relative addressing. This is because microcomputer programs usually reside in read-only memory. If direct, program relative addressing is used, then data bytes must be located within 64 bytes of the memory reference instruction. That excludes having instructions in ROM and data in RAM; therefore, only unalterable constants can be addressed using program relative direct addressing.

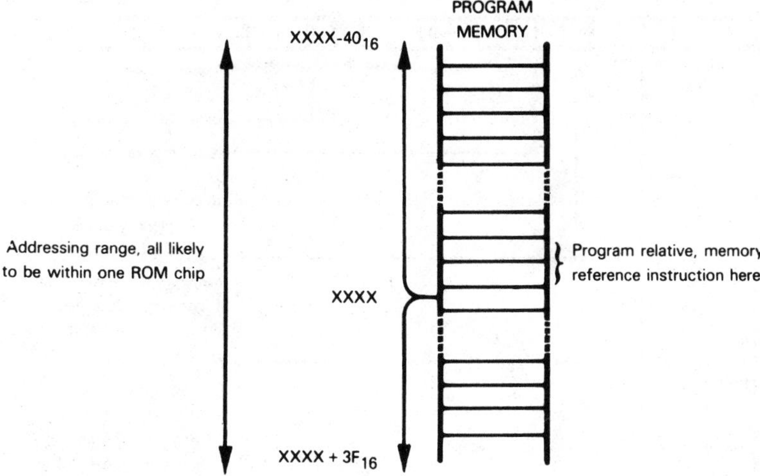


Indirect, program relative addressing, on the other hand, only requires memory addresses to be positioned within 64 bytes of the memory reference instruction; this is illustrated as follows, using arbitrary memory addresses to make the illustration easier to understand:

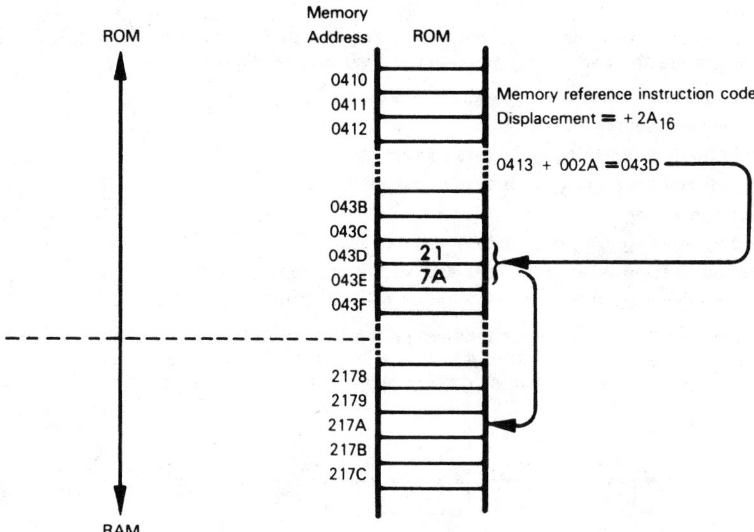

**Extended addressing options of the 2650A microcomputer may be illustrated as follows:**

**2650A EXTENDED ADDRESSING OPTIONS**

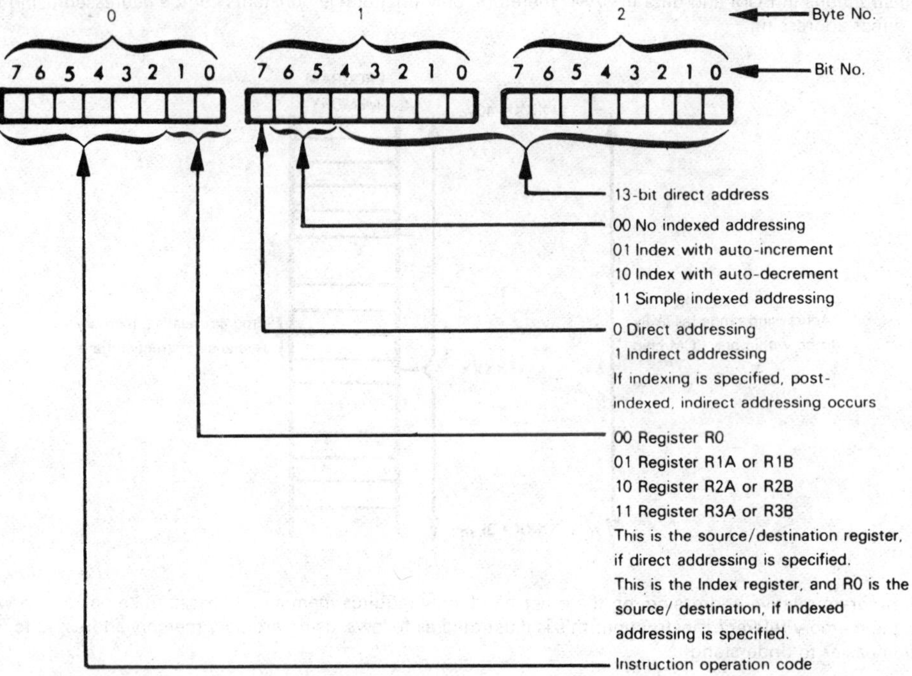


**All of the addressing options illustrated above have been described in Volume 1, Chapter 6. To summarize, however, these are the addressing combinations which are allowed:**

**1) Direct addressing (absolute or program relative)**
**2) Direct indexed addressing**
**3) Direct indexed addressing with auto-increment**
**4) Direct indexed addressing with auto-decrement**
**5) Indirect addressing**
**6) Indirect addressing with post-index**
**7) Indirect addressing with post-index and auto-increment**
**8) Indirect addressing with post-index and auto-decrement**

**There is a small difference between indexed addressing as described in Volume 1, Chapter 6, and indexed addressing as implemented by the 2650A.** The 2650A memory reference instructions provide a 13-bit absolute address, which represents the full addressing range of any memory bank; an 8-bit index value is added to this displacement, as follows:

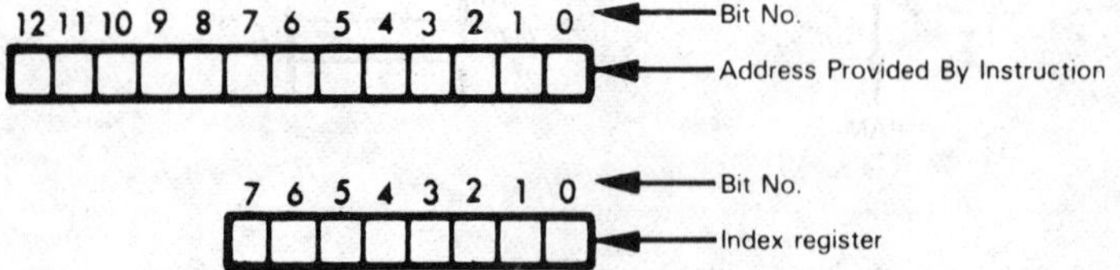


Effective address = 13-bit absolute address + 8-bit index.

If you are not clear on the difference between pre-indexed, indirect addressing and post-indexed, indirect addressing, refer again to Volume 1, Chapter 6, before proceeding with this discussion of the 2650A microcomputer.

The fact that the 2650A has a 13-bit absolute address and an 8-bit index means that post-indexed, indirect addressing is very viable. The 13-bit absolute address identifies the memory location, anywhere within an 8192-byte program page, where an indirect address will be found. The indirect address becomes the base of a 256-byte table, which may be indexed via any one of the six Index registers. The Index register contents are treated as an unsigned binary number.

Now look again at indexed addressing the way it is in most microcomputers, and the way it is described in Volume 1, Chapter 6. A 16-bit Index register indexes tables that are up to 65,536 bytes in length, and that is clearly ridiculous in microcomputers. The usual programming procedure, when using microcomputers that have a 16-bit Index register, is to use only the low-order byte of the Index register for indexing. The base address is created out of the high-order byte of the Index register, plus the displacement:

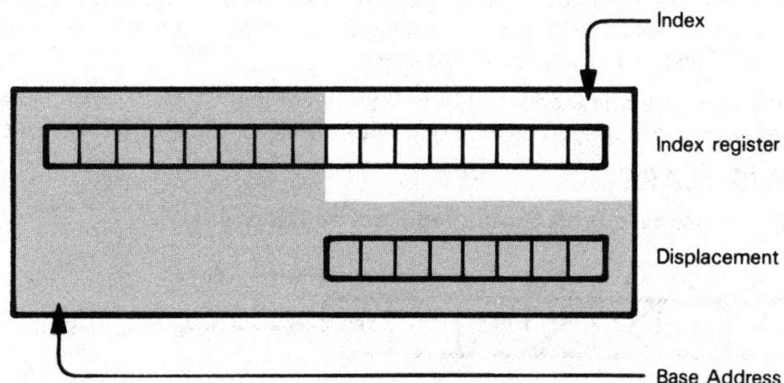


If the base address is created half out of an Index register and half out of a displacement, then clearly post-indexed, indirect addressing is impossible.

Any minicomputer programmer will attest to the fact that post-indexed, indirect addressing is far more useful than pre-indexed, indirect addressing.

**2650A BRANCH INSTRUCTION ADDRESSING**

**The 2650A has a wide variety of Branch and Branch-on-Condition instructions, which have the following object code and format:**

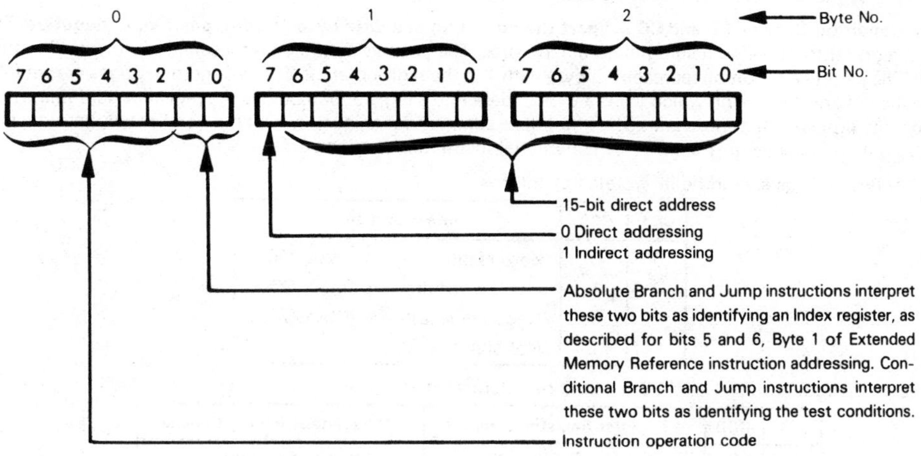

**Most 2650A Jump and Branch instructions are conditional; that means that only direct or indirect addressing may be used.**

**Notice that the branch direct address is 15 bits wide. Therefore, a Branch instruction may reference any byte within the maximum 32K-byte memory allowed by the 2650A.**

**2650A MEMORY PAGE SELECTION**

**Branch instructions are, in fact, the means provided by the 2650A microcomputer to select a page of memory.** The two high-order bits of a Branch instruction's direct address select an 8K-byte memory bank, which remains selected until another Branch instruction modifies the selection.

The 2650A has two unconditional Branch instructions. These instructions also have a 15-bit direct address; therefore, they also select a memory page. In addition to allowing direct or indirect addressing, these two instructions allow indexed addressing to be specified, as described for the extended addressing options.

Since Branch instructions specify a 15-bit direct address, in the vast majority of cases simple direct addressing will be used. Indexed addressing will be valuable only in special logic sequences, such as branch tables. Branch instructions with indirect addressing will rarely have any justifiable value.

Conditional Branch instructions use bits 0 and 1 of byte 0 to determine if a test condition has been met. The way in which these two bits are used is discussed below, along with the description of 2650A Status registers.

## THE 2650A STATUS FLAGS

**The 2650A microcomputer has two 8-bit Status registers as follows:**

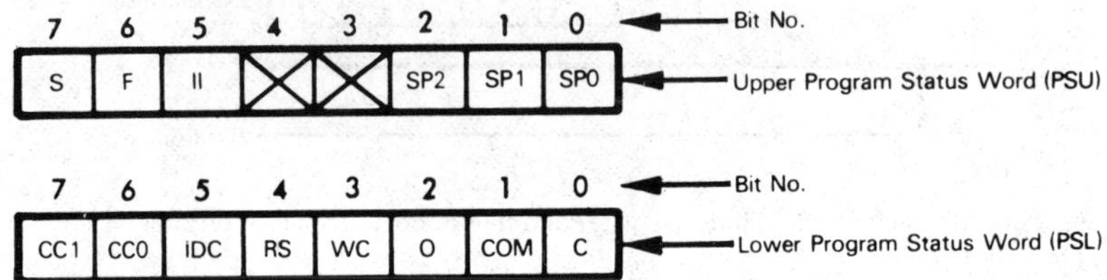


**S and F represent a Sense Input bit and a Flag Output bit,** both of which are connected directly to two CPU device pins. These two bits allow one input and one output signal to directly interface external devices to the CPU, under program control.

**The Interrupt Inhibit bit is the master interrupt disable flag for the 2650A microcomputer system.**

**SP0, SP1 and SP2 constitute a 3-bit Stack Pointer.** Recall that the 2650A has a Stack eight addresses deep; the current top-of-Stack is addressed by this 3-bit Stack Pointer.

**The two Condition Codes CC0 and CC1 report the condition of a data byte as zero, positive or negative.** The zero condition represents a byte containing eight binary zeros. The positive condition represents a byte with 0 in the high-order bit. The negative condition represents a byte with 1 in the high-order bit. These Condition Codes are set following the execution of any instruction which loads a byte of data into a register or modifies the register's contents. These two Condition bits represent a minor variation of the more common technique, in which a conditional instruction tests a register's contents directly, at the time the conditional instruction is executed.

The CC0 and CC1 flags should be interpreted as follows:

| CC1 | CC0 | Interpretation | |
|---|---|---|---|
| 0 | 0 | Zero result: | 00000000 |
| 0 | 1 | Positive result: | 0XXXXXXX |
| 1 | 0 | Negative result: | 1XXXXXXX |
| 1 | 1 | Not significant | |

For Compare instructions, CC1 and CC0 should be interpreted as follows:

| CC1 | CC0 | Register-Register Compare | Register-Memory Compare |
|---|---|---|---|
| 0 | 0 | Register 0 = Register X | Register X = Memory |
| 0 | 1 | Register 0 > Register X | Register X > Memory |
| 1 | 0 | Register 0 < Register X | Register X < Memory |

**IDC is a standard intermediate Carry bit,** reflecting the carry out of bit 3.

**O, the Overflow bit, and C, the Carry/Borrow bit, are standard Overflow and Carry statuses as described in Volume 1, Chapter 2.**

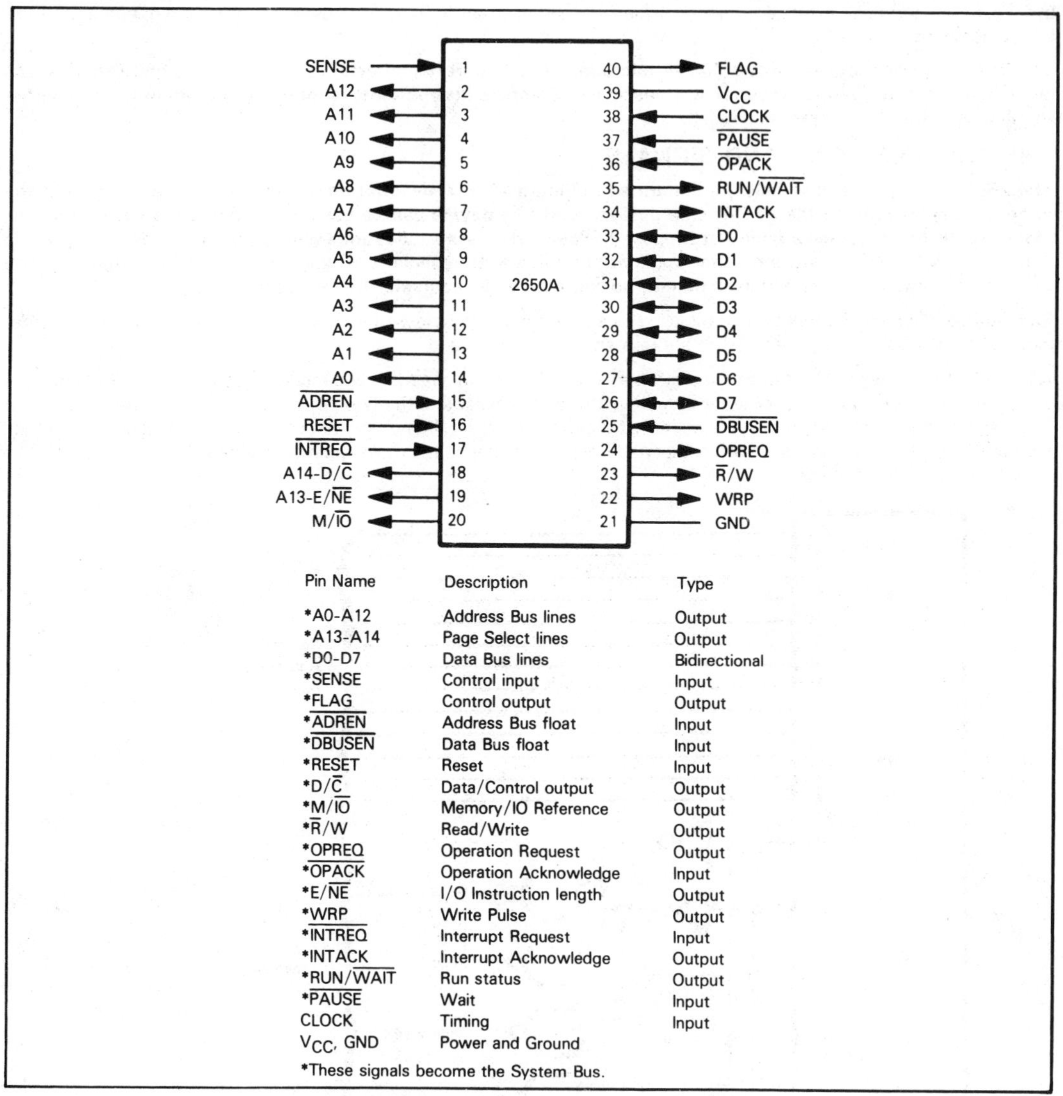


| Pin Name | Description | Type |
|---|---|---|
| *A0-A12 | Address Bus lines | Output |
| *A13-A14 | Page Select lines | Output |
| *D0-D7 | Data Bus lines | Bidirectional |
| *SENSE | Control input | Input |
| *FLAG | Control output | Output |
| *ADREN | Address Bus float | Input |
| *DBUSEN | Data Bus float | Input |
| *RESET | Reset | Input |
| *D/C | Data/Control output | Output |
| *M/IO | Memory/IO Reference | Output |
| *R/W | Read/Write | Output |
| *OPREQ | Operation Request | Output |
| *OPACK | Operation Acknowledge | Input |
| *E/NE | I/O Instruction length | Output |
| *WRP | Write Pulse | Output |
| *INTREQ | Interrupt Request | Input |
| *INTACK | Interrupt Acknowledge | Output |
| *RUN/WAIT | Run status | Output |
| *PAUSE | Wait | Input |
| CLOCK | Timing | Input |
| $V_{CC}$, GND | Power and Ground | |

*These signals become the System Bus.

Figure 11-2. 2650A CPU Signals and Pin Assignments

**RS, the Register Bank Select bit, specifies the current bank of Accumulator/Index registers:** either R1A, R2A and R3A or R1B, R2B and R3B.

Recall that addition, subtraction, shift and rotate instructions optionally may or may not include the Carry status; in other words, a microcomputer may have an Add-with-Carry or an Add-without-Carry instruction; it may have a Rotate-simple or a Rotate-through-Carry instruction. **The WC bit specifies whether the Carry will or will not be included** in 2650A instructions of this type. **If the C status is included in a rotate, the IDC status will also be included,** operating as a branch carry out of bit 3. This is a unique 2650A feature.

**The Compare status determines whether Compare instructions will treat data as signed or unsigned binary numbers.** Consider an instruction which compares the contents of Register R0 with the contents of a memory byte. Clearly the result of the comparison will differ significantly, depending on whether the high-order bit of each byte is being interpreted as a sign bit, or whether positive numbers only are being compared. If the COM status flag is set to 1, the two bytes are assumed to be positive numbers. If the COM status is set to 0, the two bytes are assumed to contain signed binary numbers.

**The WC and COM statuses of the 2650A microcomputer are very powerful features; their significance is that they double the available number of Arithmetic and Compare instructions, respectively, without increasing the number of instruction object codes.**

## THE 2650A CPU PINS AND SIGNALS

**The 2650A CPU pins and signals are illustrated in Figure 11-2. A description of these signals will highlight the underlying philosophy of the 2650A chip design: that this device can be used with standard off-the-shelf TTL logic, rather than requiring a family of support devices. There are applications where the Signetics philosophy is viable and will work; there are other applications where the specialized devices provided by Signetics and other microcomputer manufacturers cannot be reproduced at equivalently low cost.**

**The Address Bus is 13 lines wide;** it is used to address a single byte within 8192 bytes of memory. The low-order eight address lines may also be used to address an external device.

**A13 and A14 are page select lines.** As described in the discussion of addressing modes, only Branch instructions provide 15-bit memory addresses. When a Branch instruction is executed, the two high-order bits of the address, output on pins 18 and 19, are used by external memory to select or deselect 8K memory pages. Subsequent memory reference instructions that provide only a 13-bit memory address will reference the most recently selected 8K memory bank. This may be illustrated as follows:

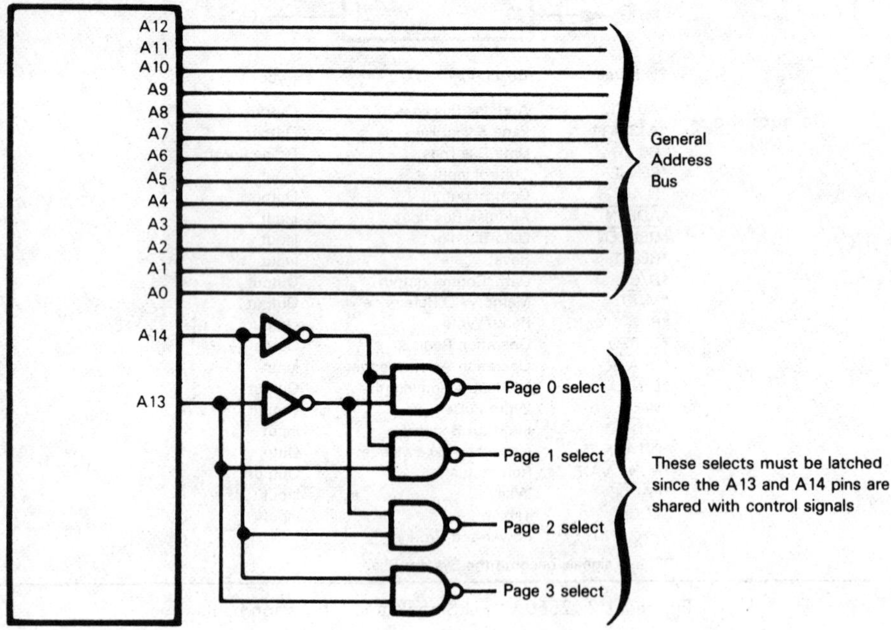


**Control lines of the 2650A microcomputer may be grouped into categories as follows:**

1) **CPU execution control**
2) **Data and Address Bus access control**
3) **Data and Address Bus contents identification**
4) **Interrupt processing**
5) **Direct, external device interface**

**2650A CPU EXECUTION CONTROL SIGNALS**

**CPU execution control signals, being of primary importance, will be discussed first.**

**CLOCK is the master timing signal required by the 2650A CPU.** Depending upon the way in which external logic is implemented, CLOCK may or may not be needed by other devices that surround the 2650A; in most cases CLOCK will not be needed by other devices, since system control will normally be handled by 2650A control inputs and outputs.

**RESET is the master reset input which every microcomputer has.** As is standard for most microcomputers, when the CPU is reset, the Program Counter is cleared, with the result that the instruction stored in memory location 0 is executed. The CPU will typically be reset when first powered up.

**$\overline{\text{PAUSE}}$ causes the CPU to enter a Wait state.** $\overline{\text{PAUSE}}$ is an input signal which may be used by external direct memory access logic to stop the CPU while memory is being accessed. The Halt instruction also causes the CPU to enter the Wait state. A Wait state will be terminated by a Reset or by external logic removing its $\overline{\text{PAUSE}}$ input.

**2650A BUS ACCESS CONTROL SIGNALS**

**There are two bus access control signals on the 2650A: $\overline{\text{DBUSEN}}$ and $\overline{\text{ADREN}}$. These two signals float the Data and Address Busses, respectively.** On the Address Bus, only the 13 Address Bus lines A0 - A12 are floated; the two page select lines A13 and A14 are not floated.

**2650A BUS CONTENTS IDENTIFICATION SIGNALS**

**The most interesting feature of 2650A control signals is the scheme employed for identifying events on the Data and Address Busses.**

**The inception of any operation which will involve external devices is identified by OPREQ going high.**

Normally, the first step in any operation that involves external logic is for an address to be output on the Address Bus. **If memory is being accessed, then M/$\overline{\text{IO}}$ is output high. $\overline{\text{R}}$/W is output high to identify a write operation or low to identify a read operation.** As soon as memory has responded to the memory read or write operation, it inputs $\overline{\text{OPACK}}$ low. If $\overline{\text{OPACK}}$ low does not arrive in time for the CPU to continue processing the current instruction at the next clock cycle, then the CPU temporarily enters the Wait state and outputs RUN/$\overline{\text{WAIT}}$ low to indicate this condition. Now as soon as $\overline{\text{OPACK}}$ is input low, the Wait state will end and the CPU will continue execution.

**The CPU will also output a write strobe, WRP, when writing to memory. This strobe is output when data is steady on the Data Bus.**

**When an I/O device is being accessed by one of the I/O instructions, M/$\overline{\text{IO}}$ is output low.** You will see in Table 11-1 that the 2650A instruction set includes two sets of I/O instructions; one set does not identify an I/O port, and has a one-byte object code; the other set identifies an I/O port via a second byte of object code. Let us assume that the short I/O instructions will always reference I/O Port 0, while the long I/O instructions will specify one of 256 I/O ports. The E/$\overline{\text{NE}}$ signal, if low, identifies a short I/O instruction, therefore an instruction which accesses I/O Port 0; if high, this signal indicates that the current contents of the low-order eight address lines contain an I/O port address, and should be so decoded. In fact, the I/O port which is selected by a short I/O instruction can be defined by you. You can look upon E/$\overline{\text{NE}}$ as a signal which, when low, is a unique select line. When high, E/$\overline{\text{NE}}$ identifies the low-order eight Address Bus lines as providing the I/O port address. Thus, you can generate I/O port select logic as follows:

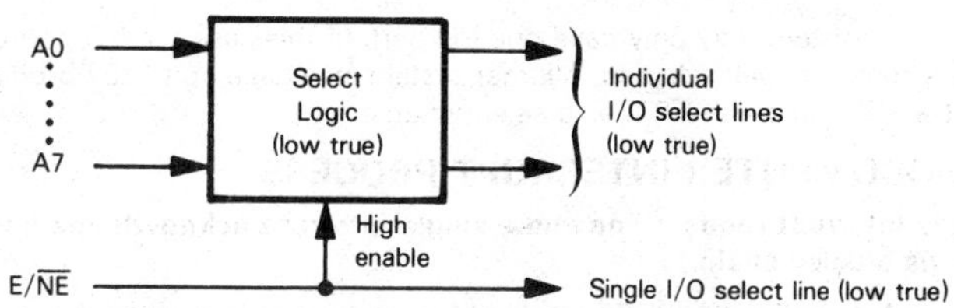


**Once an I/O port has been selected, and external logic knows from the M/$\overline{\text{IO}}$ and E/$\overline{\text{NE}}$ controls which I/O port is selected,** I/O logic needs to know whether an input or output I/O operation is to occur, and whether data or control/status information is to be transmitted. (Volume 1, Chapter 5 discusses at length the difference between data, controls and status.) The $\overline{\text{R}}$/W control indicates whether data is being transmitted from the CPU to external devices, or whether external devices are supposed to transmit data to the CPU; then D/$\overline{\text{C}}$ identifies the output as either data or control information. Conversely, when $\overline{\text{R}}$/W identifies the CPU as requiring input from an I/O device, D/$\overline{\text{C}}$ indicates whether the input should be data or status.

**When external device logic responds to the I/O request, it concludes by inputting $\overline{OPACK}$ low.** Figure 11-3 illustrates how control signals may be used to interpret events on the Address and Data Busses.

**2650A INTERRUPT CONTROL SIGNALS**

**2650A interrupt handling is very straightforward. An interrupt is requested by setting $\overline{INTREQ}$ low. The interrupt is acknowledged by the CPU outputting INTACK high.**

**2650A EXTERNAL DEVICE CONTROL SIGNALS**

**The SENSE and FLAG signals allow the 2650A to directly control external devices.** The condition of a SENSE input is immediately translated into a 0 or 1 within the Sense bit of the 2650A Status register. A 0 or 1 in the Flag bit of the 2650A Status register is immediately reflected by a low or high signal output at the Flag pin.

## INTERFACING MEMORY TO THE 2650A MICROCOMPUTER

**Given the wealth of control signals provided by the 2650A microcomputer, most types of memory can be interfaced with very little difficulty.** The only peculiarity of the 2650A which external logic must be able to cope with is the fact that memory is paged into 8192-byte pages. Any memory device whose addressing range is smaller than a page must have select logic which takes into account not only high-order address lines on the 13-line Address Bus but, in addition, the two page select lines. The two page select lines change status occasionally when a new page is being selected; therefore, page select must be stored in an external buffer.

The 2650A CPU also expects to receive an $\overline{OPACK}$ acknowledgement from memory. If memory can respond to an access within the allowed time, then you can simply tie $\overline{OPACK}$ to ground for all memory accesses. I/O accesses must still be able to respond with a high or low $\overline{OPACK}$, depending upon prevailing conditions. Here is appropriate logic:

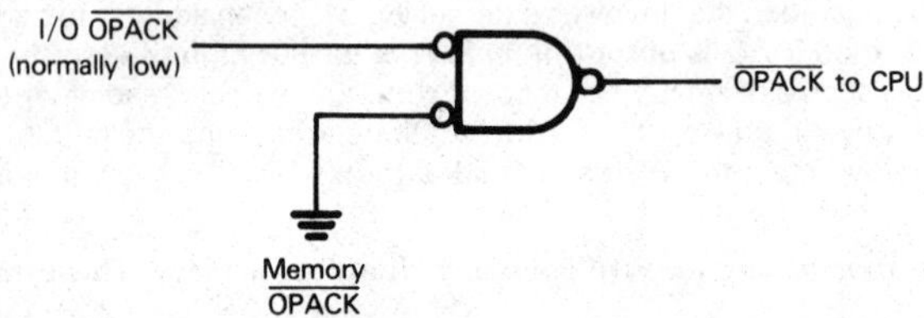


I/O $\overline{OPACK}$ is normally low. I/O logic drives $\overline{OPACK}$ high at the beginning of an I/O access if the I/O device requires extra time to respond to OPREQ.

The $\overline{OPACK}$ input during memory access operations is equivalent to the 8080A READY input. You should refer to the extensive discussion of the 8080A READY input given in Chapter 4 in order to find ways of using $\overline{OPACK}$ logic in a 2650A microcomputer system.

## INTERFACING I/O DEVICES TO THE 2650A MICROCOMPUTER

**The simplest way of interfacing external devices to the 2650A microcomputer is to use the microcomputer's I/O instructions, plus the control signals which identify I/O operations.**

A very small microcomputer system may only have one I/O port. In this case the I/O port can connect directly to the Data Bus and can always consider itself selected. A larger system may have up to 257 8-bit ports, with select lines that simply connect to the Data Bus and use E/$\overline{NE}$ as a select enable signal.

## THE 2650A MICROCOMPUTER INTERRUPT PROCESS

**The 2650A has a single interrupt request line and a single interrupt acknowledge line. Interrupt priorities will therefore be handled via a daisy chain.**

**When the CPU acknowledges an interrupt, first it disables all further interrupts. Next, it pushes the contents of the Program Counter onto the address Stack and zeros the Program Counter.**

**The CPU will now insert the first byte of a ZBSR instruction code into the Instruction register; this instruction code is a Branch-to-Subroutine using program relative addressing. The interrupting device must submit a byte of data on the Data Bus, which will be interpreted as the second byte of the ZBSR instruction.**

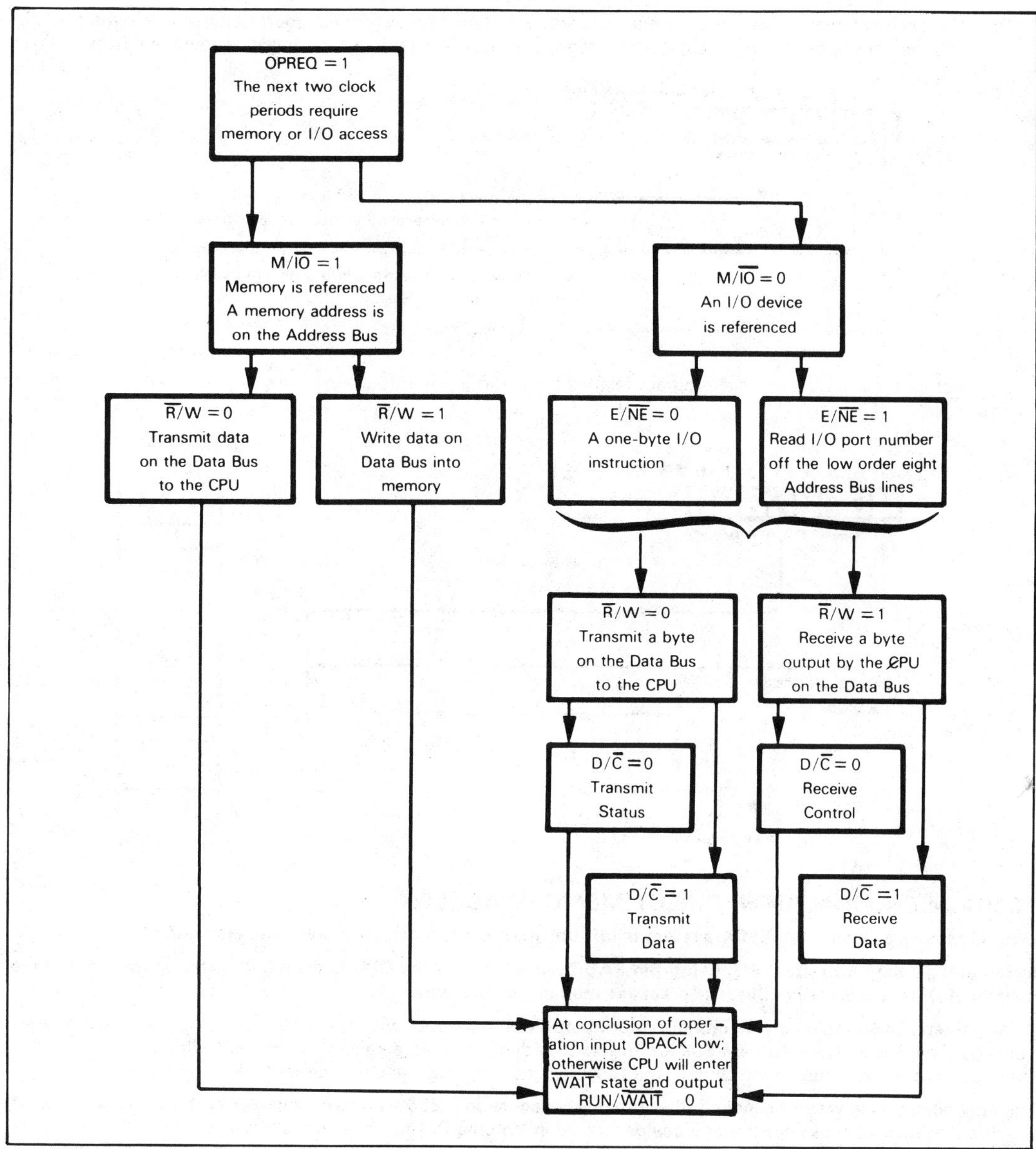


Figure 11-3. How Control Signals Identify Address and Data Bus Use for the 2650A Microcomputer

Look again at the discussion of 2650A addressing modes and you will see that with the Program Counter set to 0, the byte of data input by the interrupting device becomes a displacement vector.

Assume that each external device has the beginning address of its interrupt service routine stored somewhere within the first 64 bytes of the zero memory page. The interrupting device must input the following byte of data:

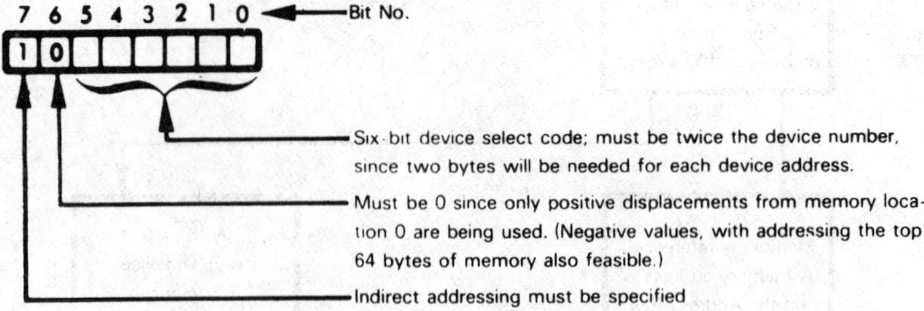


This byte of data causes an indirect program relative jump to the interrupting device's interrupt service routine, as follows:

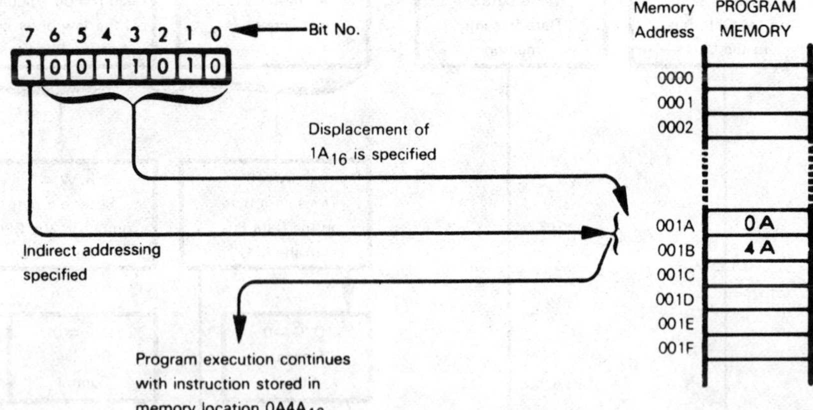


## 2650A MICROCOMPUTER DIRECT MEMORY ACCESS

**Direct memory access in a 2650A system is left up to external logic. Two schemes are possible.**

**External logic may stop the CPU, using the $\overline{\text{PAUSE}}$ input; while the CPU is disabled, external logic may take control of Data and Address Busses to access memory in any way.**

**Alternatively, DMA logic may be implemented to operate in parallel with the CPU.** The 2650A has periods when both the Data Bus and the Address Bus are floated. Handling DMA in parallel with normal instruction execution is made possible if you combine the OPREQ and $\overline{\text{OPACK}}$ handshake signals with normal timing sequences.

**The only economical way of handling direct memory access in a 2650A microcomputer system is to use one of the direct memory access control devices described in Volume 3.** Timing requirements are given with the discussions of these devices. The flexibility of the 2650A System Bus is such that you will have very little difficulty generating an interface with any of these direct memory access control parts.

## THE 2650A MICROCOMPUTER INSTRUCTION SET

**The 2650A microcomputer instruction set is the most minicomputer-like of the microcomputers discussed in this book. It is particularly rich in addressing modes and memory reference instructions. The instruction set is listed in Table 11-1.**

Memory reference instructions are shown as offering program relative addressing options or extended addressing options. See the discussion of 2650A addressing options for a definition of these terms.

Note that in the statuses column, CC identifies the CC0 and CC1 statuses. These two statuses are used to test for a zero, positive or negative branch condition; these two statuses are described along with the 2650A Status registers.

The TMI Immediate Operate instruction compares a register's contents with a mask provided by the instruction operand. This instruction allows any bit combination to be tested for, in any CPU register.

The Decimal Adjust (DAR) instruction of the 2650A differs from the instructions with the same name as implemented on a number of other microcomputers. The Decimal Adjust instruction can be used to perform binary decimal arithmetic. Referring to the discussion of binary decimal arithmetic given in Volume 1, the 2650A DAR instruction performs Step 3 of the binary-coded-decimal addition operation described in Chapter 3.

## THE 2650A BENCHMARK PROGRAM

**This is how the 2650A may implement our benchmark program:**

```
        LODA,R1   TLENGTH        LOAD DISPLACEMENT TO FIRST FREE TABLE BYTE
        LODA,R2   IOBFL          LOAD I/O BUFFER FILLED LENGTH
LOOP    LODA,R0   *IOBUF,R2      LOAD NEXT I/O BUFFER BYTE
        STRA,R0   *TABLE,R1,+    STORE IN TABLE, AUTO-INCREMENT R1
        BDRR,R2   LOOP           DECREMENT R2, RETURN TO LOOP ON NON-ZERO
        STRA,R1   TLENGTH        AT END, RESTORE NEW TABLE LENGTH
```

The benchmark program, as illustrated for the 2650A, assumes that both the data table and the I/O buffer have maximum lengths of 256 bytes.

The displacement to the first free byte of the data table is stored in a memory location identified by the label TLENGTH.

The number of filled I/O buffer bytes is stored in a memory location identified by the label IOBFL. It is assumed that the I/O buffer can be read backwards; in other words, the last I/O buffer byte becomes the first byte stored in the permanent data table.

The instruction with label LOOP begins by loading the last byte in the I/O buffer, using indirect, indexed addressing without auto-increment or auto-decrement. Subsequently, Index Register R2 is decremented; if it does not decrement to 0, execution returns to the instruction labeled LOOP.

The instruction which stores data in TABLE uses indirect, post-indexed addressing, with the contents of Index Register R1 auto-incremented. Thus, at the conclusion of data movement, Index Register R1 contains the displacement to the next free byte of TABLE.

Comparing the 2650A benchmark program with other benchmark programs shown in this book might suggest that the 2650A has the shortest, and therefore the fastest and most efficient benchmark program. This is not necessarily the case. Certainly the 2650A instruction set provides a source program which is likely to be shorter than any other microcomputer's source program, but that is because instructions are very minicomputer-like. The number of bytes required to implement the 2650A object program, and the time taken to execute the program, may bear no relationship to the length of the source program. For example, the program loop, although it contains only three instructions (LODA, STRA and BDRR), will require eight bytes of object program.

Once again, we caution against drawing fast conclusions from benchmark programs.

The following symbols are used in Table 11-1:

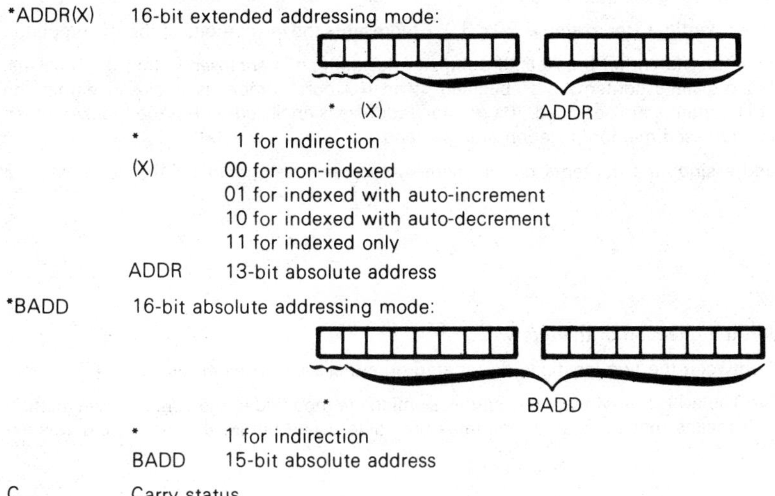

*ADDR(X) 16-bit extended addressing mode:



- * 1 for indirection
- (X) 00 for non-indexed
  - 01 for indexed with auto-increment
  - 10 for indexed with auto-decrement
  - 11 for indexed only
- ADDR 13-bit absolute address

*BADD 16-bit absolute addressing mode:



- * 1 for indirection
- BADD 15-bit absolute address

C Carry status

CC — The two Condition Code bits CC1 and CC0

CC1 ☐☐ CC0

CIDC — The Carry and Inter-Digit Carry

C ☐☐ IDC

dataNE — The non-extended data port

DATA2 — 2-bit data unit

DATA8 — 8-bit data unit

*DISP — 8-bit relative addressing mode:

☐☐☐☐☐☐☐☐

* DISP

* 1 for indirection

DISP 7-bit signed displacement

EAA — Effective address generated by *BADD

EAD — Effective address generated by *ADDR(X)

EAR — PC relative address generated by *DISP

IDC — Inter-Digit Carry status

O — Overflow status

P — An 8-bit port number

PC — Program Counter

PSU — Upper byte of Program Status Word

PSL — Lower byte of Program Status Word

r — One of the seven CPU registers

RAS(SP) — The Return Address Stack location indicated by the Stack Pointer

R0 — Accumulator

SP — Stack Pointer

status NE — The Non-Extended status port

ZEA — A zero page relative address generated by DISP

x<y,z> — Bits y through z of the quantity x; for example, R0<3,0> represents the lower 4 bits of the Accumulator.

[ ] — Contents of location enclosed within brackets. If a register designation is enclosed within the brackets, then the designated register's contents are specified. If an I/O port number is enclosed within the brackets, then the I/O contents are specified. If a memory address is enclosed within the brackets, then the contents of the addressed memory location are specified.

[[ ]] — Implied memory addressing; the contents of the memory location designated by the contents of a register.

$\wedge$ — Logical AND

$\vee$ — Logical OR

$\forall$ — Logical Exclusive-OR

$\leftarrow$ — Data is transferred in the direction of the arrow

$\longleftrightarrow$ — Data is exchanged between the two locations designated on either side of the arrow.

Under the heading of STATUSES in Table 11-1, an X indicates statuses which are modified in the course of the instruction's execution. If there is no X, it means that the status maintains the value it had before the instruction was executed.

Table 11-1. Summary of Signetics 2650A Instruction Set

| TYPE | MNEMONIC | OPERAND(S) | BYTES | STATUSES | | | | | | OPERATION PERFORMED |
|---|---|---|---|---|---|---|---|---|---|---|
| | | | | C | O | IDC | CC | | | |
| I/O | REDD | ,r | 1 | | | | X | | | [r]←[dataNE] Read data at non-extended port into specified register. |
| | REDC | ,r | 1 | | | | X | | | [r]←[statusNE] Read non-extended status into specified register. |
| | REDE | ,r P | 2 | | | | X | | | [r]←[P] Read into specified register from Port P. |
| | WRTD | ,r | 1 | | | | | | | [dataNE]←[r] Write specified register contents to non-extended data port. |
| | WRTC | ,r | 1 | | | | | | | [statusNE]←[r] Write specified register contents to non-extended status port. |
| | WRTE | ,r P | 2 | | | | | | | [P]←[r] Write specified register contents to Port P. |
| PRIMARY MEMORY REFERENCE | LODR | ,r *DISP | 2 | | | | X | | | [r]←[EAR] Load specified register from relative location. |
| | LODA | ,r *ADDR(X) | 3 | | | | X | | | [r]←[EAD] Load specified register from extended location. |
| | STRR | ,r *DISP | 2 | | | | | | | [EAR]←[r] Store specified register contents in relative location. |
| | STRA | ,r *ADDR(X) | 3 | | | | | | | [EAD]←[r] Store specified register contents in extended location. |
| SECONDARY MEMORY REFERENCE (MEMORY OPERATE) | ADDR | ,r *DISP | 2 | X | X | X | X | | | [r]←[r] + [EAR] Add contents of relative location to specified register. |
| | ADDA | ,r *ADDR(X) | 3 | X | X | X | X | | | [r]←[r] + [EAD] Add contents of extended location to specified register. |
| | SUBR | ,r *DISP | 2 | X | X | X | X | | | [r]←[r] - [EAR] Subtract contents of relative location from specified register. |
| | SUBA | ,r *ADDR(X) | 3 | X | X | X | X | | | [r]←[r] - [EAD] Subtract contents of extended location from specified register. |
| | ANDR | ,r *DISP | 2 | | | | X | | | [r]←[r] Λ [EAR] AND contents of relative location with those of specified register. |
| | ANDA | ,r *ADDR(X) | 3 | | | | X | | | [r]←[r] Λ [EAD] AND contents of extended location with those of specified register. |
| | IORR | ,r *DISP | 2 | | | | X | | | [r]←[r] V [EAR] OR contents of relative location with those of specified register. |
| | IORA | ,r *ADDR(X) | 3 | | | | X | | | [r]←[r] V [EAD] OR contents of extended location with those of specified register. |
| | EORR | ,r *DISP | 2 | | | | X | | | [r]←[r] ⊻ [EAR] Exclusive-OR contents of relative location with those of specified register. |
| | EORA | ,r *ADDR(X) | 3 | | | | X | | | [r]←[r] ⊻ [EAD] Exclusive-OR contents of extended location with those of specified register. |

Table 11-1. Summary of Signetics 2650A Instruction Set (Continued)

| TYPE | MNEMONIC | OPERAND(S) | BYTES | STATUSES | | | | | | OPERATION PERFORMED |
|---|---|---|---|---|---|---|---|---|---|---|
| | | | | C | O | IDC | CC | | | |
| SECONDARY MEMORY REFERENCE (MEMORY OPERATE) (CONTINUED) | COMR | ,r *DISP | 2 | | | | X | | | If [r] > [EAR]; then CC = 01<br>If [r] = [EAR]; then CC = 00<br>If [r] < [EAR]; then CC = 10<br>Compare contents of relative location with those of specified register; set the CC accordingly. |
| | COMA | ,r, *ADDR(X) | 3 | | | | X | | | If [r] > [EAD]; then CC = 01<br>If [r] = [EAD]; then CC = 00<br>If [r] < [EAD]; then CC = 10<br>Compare contents of extended location with those of specified register; set the CC accordingly. |
| IMMEDIATE | LODI | ,r DATA8 | 2 | | | | X | | | [r]←DATA8<br>Load immediate into specified register. |
| IMMEDIATE OPERATE | ADDI | ,r DATA8 | 2 | X | X | X | X | | | [r]←[r] + DATA8<br>Add immediate to specified register contents. |
| | SUBI | ,r DATA8 | 2 | X | X | X | X | | | [r]←[r] - DATA8<br>Subtract immediate from specified registers contents. |
| | ANDI | ,r DATA8 | 2 | | | | X | | | [r]←[r] Λ DATA8<br>AND immediate with specified register contents. |
| | IORI | ,r DATA8 | 2 | | | | X | | | [r]←[r] V DATA8<br>OR immediate with specified register contents. |
| | EORI | ,r DATA8 | 2 | | | | X | | | [r]←[r]] ⊻ DATA8<br>Exclusive-OR immediate with specified register contents. |
| | COMI | ,r DATA8 | 2 | | | | X | | | If [r] > DATA8; [CC]←01<br>If [r] = DATA8; [CC]←00<br>If [r] < DATA8; [CC]←10<br>Compare immediate with specified register; set the CC accordingly. |
| | TMI | ,r DATA8 | 2 | | | | X | | | If all selected bits are set, CC = 00; otherwise CC = 10<br>Test bits in specified register corresponding to 1s in immediate data. If all tested bits are 1s set CC accordingly. |
| JUMP | ZBRR | *DISP | 2 | | | | | | | [PC]←ZEA<br>Branch to zero page address. |
| | BXA | *BADD | 3 | | | | | | | [PC]←EAA<br>Branch to extended address. |
| | ZBSR | *DISP | 2 | | | | | | | [SP]←[SP] + 1<br>[RAS(SP)]←[PC] + 2<br>[PC]←ZEA<br>Call zero page subroutine. |
| | BSXA | *BADD | 3 | | | | | | | [SP]←[SP] + 1<br>[RAS(SP)]←[PC] + 3<br>[PC]←EAA<br>Call extended subroutine. |

Table 11-1. Summary of Signetics 2650A Instruction Set (Continued)

| TYPE | MNEMONIC | OPERAND(S) | BYTES | STATUSES | | | | | | OPERATION PERFORMED |
|---|---|---|---|---|---|---|---|---|---|---|
| | | | | C | O | IDC | CC | | | |
| BRANCH ON CONDITION | BCTR | ,DATA2 *DISP | 2 | | | | | | | If DATA2 = CC, then [PC]←EAR<br>Branch relative if DATA2 equals CC. |
| | BCTA | ,DATA2 *DISP | 3 | | | | | | | If DATA2 = CC, then [PC]←EAA<br>Branch absolute if DATA2 equals CC. |
| | BCFR | ,DATA2 *DISP | 2 | | | | | | | If DATA2 ≠ CC, then [PC]←EAR<br>Branch relative if DATA2 is not equal to CC. |
| | BCFA | ,DATA2 *BADD | 3 | | | | | | | If DATA2 ≠ CC, then [PC]←EAA<br>Branch absolute if DATA2 is not equal to CC. |
| | BIRR | ,r *DISP | 2 | | | | | | | [r]←[r] + 1<br>If [r] ≠ 0, [PC]←EAR<br>Increment specified register. If nonzero result, branch relative. |
| | BIRA | ,r *BADD | 3 | | | | | | | [r]←[r] + 1<br>If [r] ≠ 0, then [PC]←EAA<br>Increment specified register. If nonzero result, branch absolute. |
| | BDRR | ,r *DISP | 2 | | | | | | | [r]←[r] - 1<br>If [r] ≠ 0, then [PC]←EAR<br>Decrement specified register. If nonzero result, branch relative. |
| | BDRA | ,r *BADD | 3 | | | | | | | [r]←[r] - 1<br>If [r] ≠ 0; then [PC]←EAA<br>Decrement specified register. If nonzero result, branch absolute. |
| | BRNR | ,r *DISP | 2 | | | | | | | If [r] ≠ 0; then [PC]←EAR<br>If specified register is nonzero, branch relative. |
| | BRNA | ,r *BADD | 3 | | | | | | | If [r] ≠ 0; then [PC]←EAA<br>If specified register is nonzero, branch absolute. |
| CONDITIONAL SUBROUTINE BRANCH | BSTR | ,DATA2 *DISP | 2 | | | | | | | If DATA2 = CC; then [SP]←[SP] + 1<br>[RAS(SP)]←[PC] + 2<br>[PC]←EAR<br>If DATA2 equals CC, then call subroutine at relative address. |
| | BSTA | ,DATA2 *BADD | 3 | | | | | | | If DATA2 = CC; then [SP]←[SP] + 1<br>[RAS(SP)]←[PC] + 3<br>[PC]←EAA<br>If DATA2 equals CC, then call subroutine at absolute address. |
| | BSFR | ,DATA2 *DISP | 2 | | | | | | | If DATA2 ≠ CC; then [SP]←[SP] + 1<br>[RAS(SP)]←[PC] + 2<br>[PC]←EAR<br>If DATA2 not equal to CC, then call subroutine at relative address. |
| | BSFA | ,DATA2 *BADD | 3 | | | | | | | If DATA2 ≠ CC; then [SP]←[SP] + 1<br>[RAS(SP)]←[PC] + 3<br>[PC]←EAA<br>If DATA2 not equal to CC, call subroutine at absolute address. |

Table 11-1. Summary of Signetics 2650A Instruction Set (Continued)

| TYPE | MNEMONIC | OPERAND(S) | BYTES | STATUSES | | | | | | OPERATION PERFORMED |
|---|---|---|---|---|---|---|---|---|---|---|
| | | | | C | O | IDC | CC | | | |
| CONDITIONAL SUBROUTINE BRANCH (CONTINUED) | BSNR | ,r *DISP | 2 | | | | | | | If [r] ≠ 0; then [SP]←[SP] + 1<br>[RAS(SP)]←[PC] + 2<br>[PC]←EAR<br>If specified register is nonzero, call subroutine at relative address. |
| | BSNA | ,r *BADD | 3 | | | | | | | If [r] ≠ 0; then [SP]←[SP] + 1<br>[RAS(SP)]←[PC] + 3<br>[PC]←EAA<br>If specified register is nonzero, call subroutine at absolute address. |
| | RETC | ,DATA2 | 1 | | | | | | | If DATA2 = CC, then [PC]←[RAS(SP)]<br>[SP]←[SP] - 1<br>If DATA2 equals CC, then return from subroutine. |
| REGISTER-REGISTER MOVE | LODZ | r | 1 | | | | X | | | [R0]←[r]<br>Load Accumulator (Register 0) with specified register contents. |
| | STRZ | r | 1 | | | | X | | | [r]←[R0]<br>Store contents of Accumulator (Register 0) into specified register. |
| REGISTER-REGISTER OPERATE | ADDZ | ,r | 1 | X | X | X | X | | | [R0]←[R0] + [r]<br>Add specified register to Register 0. |
| | SUBZ | ,r | 1 | X | X | X | X | | | [R0]←[R0] - [r]<br>Subtract specified register from Register 0. |
| | ANDZ | ,r | 1 | | | | X | | | [R0]←[R0] Λ [r]<br>AND specified register with Register 0. |
| | IORZ | ,r | 1 | | | | X | | | [R0]←[R0] V [r]<br>OR specified register with Register 0. |
| | EORZ | ,r | 1 | | | | X | | | [R0]←[R0] ⊻ [r]<br>Exclusive-OR specified register with Register 0. |
| | COMZ | ,r | 1 | | | | X | | | If [R0] > [r]; then CC = 01<br>If [R0] = [r]; then CC = 00<br>If [R0] < [r]; then CC = 10<br>Compare specified register with Register 0; set the CC accordingly. |
| REGISTER OPERATE | RRL | ,r | 1 | X | X | X | X | | | C IDC 7 0 WC = 0<br>Or<br>C IDC 7 0 WC = 1<br>If WC is 0, rotate the specified register left. If WC is 1, rotate through Carry and Intermediate Carry. |

Table 11-1. Summary of Signetics 2650A Instruction Set (Continued)

| TYPE | MNEMONIC | OPERAND(S) | BYTES | STATUSES | | | | | | OPERATION PERFORMED |
|---|---|---|---|---|---|---|---|---|---|---|
| | | | | C | O | IDC | CC | | | |
| REGISTER OPERATE (CONTINUED) | RRR | ,r | 1 | X | X | X | X | | | WC = 0<br>Or<br>WC = 1<br>If WC is 0, rotate the specified register right. If WC is 1, rotate through Carry and Intermediate Carry. |
| | DAR | ,r | 1 | | | | | | | Decimal adjust the specified register. |
| INTERRUPT | RETE | ,DATA2 | 1 | | | | | | | If DATA2 = CC; then [PC]←[RAS(SP)]<br>[SP]←[SP] - 1<br>Enable interrupts<br>If DATA2 equals CC, then return from subroutine and enable interrupts. |
| STATUS | LPSU | | 1 | | | | | | | [PSU]←[R0]<br>Load Register 0 into PSU. |
| | LPSL | | 1 | | | | | | | [PSL]←[R0]<br>Load Register 0 into PSL. |
| | SPSU | | 1 | | | | | | | [R0]←[PSU]<br>Load PSU into Register 0. |
| | SPSL | | 1 | | | | | | | [R0]←[PSL]<br>Load PSL into Register 0. |
| | PPSU | DATA8 | 2 | | | | | | | If [DATA8<i>]=1; then [PSU<i>]←1<br>Set bits in PSU which correspond to 1s in immediate data. |
| | PPSL | DATA8 | 2 | | | | | | | If [DATA8<i>]=1; then [PSL<i>]←1<br>Set bits in PSL which correspond to 1s in immediate data. |
| | CPSU | DATA8 | 2 | | | | | | | If [DATA8<i>]=1 then [PSU<i>]←0<br>Clear bits of PSU which correspond to 1s in immediate data. |
| | CPSL | DATA8 | 2 | | | | | | | If [DATA8<i>]=1 then [PSL<i>]←0<br>Clear bits of PSL which correspond to 1s in immediate data. |
| | TPSU | DATA8 | 2 | | | | X | | | If DATA8 = [PSU], then CC = 00; else CC = 10<br>Compare immediate with PSU; set CC accordingly. |
| | TPSL | DATA8 | 2 | | | | X | | | If DATA8 = [PSL], then CC = 00; else CC = 10<br>Compare immediate with PSL; set CC accordingly. |
| | NOP | | 1 | | | | | | | No Operation. |
| | HALT | | 1 | | | | | | | Processor enters Wait state. |

Table 11-2. Signetics 2650A Instruction Object Codes

| INSTRUCTION | | OBJECT CODE | BYTES | MACHINE CYCLES |
|---|---|---|---|---|
| ADDA,r | *ADDR(X) | 100011aa<br>bccqqqqq<br>QQ | 3 | 4 |
| ADDI,r | DATA8 | 100001aa<br>PP | 2 | 2 |
| ADDR,r | *DISP | 100010aa<br>beeeeeee | 2 | 3 |
| ADDZ,r | | 100000aa | 1 | 2 |
| ANDA,r | *ADDR(X) | 010011aa<br>bccqqqqq<br>QQ | 3 | 4 |
| ANDI,r | DATA8 | 010001aa<br>PP | 2 | 2 |
| ANDR,r | *DISP | 010010aa<br>beeeeeee | 2 | 3 |
| ANDZ,r | | 010000aa | 1 | 2 |
| BCFA,DATA2 | *BADD | 100111ff<br>bqqqqqqq<br>QQ | 3 | 3 |
| BCFR,DATA2 | *DISP | 100110ff<br>beeeeeee | 2 | 3 |
| BCTA,DATA2 | *BADD | 000111ff<br>bqqqqqqq<br>QQ | 3 | 3 |
| BCTR,DATA2 | *DISP | 000110ff<br>beeeeeee | 2 | 3 |
| BDRA,r | *BADD | 111111aa<br>bqqqqqqq<br>QQ | 3 | 3 |
| BDRR,r | *DISP | 111110aa<br>beeeeeee | 2 | 3 |
| BIRA,r | *BADD | 110111aa<br>bqqqqqqq<br>QQ | 3 | 3 |
| BIRR,r | *DISP | 110110aa<br>beeeeeee | 2 | 3 |
| BRNA,r | *BADD | 010111aa<br>bqqqqqqq<br>QQ | 3 | 3 |
| BRNR,r | *DISP | 010110aa<br>beeeeeee | 2 | 3 |
| BSFA,DATA2 | *BADD | 101111ff<br>bqqqqqqq<br>QQ | 3 | 3 |
| BSFR,DATA2 | *DISP | 101110ff<br>beeeeeee | 2 | 3 |
| BSNA,r | *BADD | 011111aa<br>bqqqqqqq<br>QQ | 3 | 3 |
| BSNR,r | *DISP | 011110aa<br>beeeeeee | 2 | 3 |
| BSTA,DATA2 | *BADD | 001111ff<br>bqqqqqqq<br>QQ | 3 | 3 |
| BSTR,DATA2 | *DISP | 001110ff<br>beeeeeee | 2 | 3 |
| BSXA | *BADD | BF<br>bqqqqqqq<br>QQ | 3 | 3 |
| BXA | *BADD | 9F<br>bqqqqqqq<br>QQ | 3 | 3 |
| COMA,r | *ADDR(X) | 111011aa<br>bccqqqqq<br>QQ | 3 | 4 |
| COMI,r | DATA8 | 111001aa<br>PP | 2 | 2 |
| COMR,r | *DISP | 111010aa<br>beeeeeee | 2 | 3 |
| COMZ,r | | 111000aa | 1 | 2 |
| CPSL | DATA8 | 75<br>PP | 2 | 3 |
| CPSU | DATA8 | 74<br>PP | 2 | 3 |
| DAR,r | | 100101aa | 1 | 3 |
| EORA,r | *ADDR(X) | 001011aa<br>bccqqqqq<br>QQ | 3 | 4 |
| EORI,r | DATA8 | 001001aa<br>PP | 2 | 2 |
| EORR,r | *DISP | 001010aa<br>beeeeeee | 2 | 3 |
| EORZ,r | | 001000aa | 1 | 2 |
| HALT | | 40 | 1 | 2 |
| IORA,r | *ADDR(X) | 011011aa<br>bccqqqqq<br>QQ | 3 | 4 |
| IORI,r | DATA8 | 011001aa<br>PP | 2 | 2 |
| IORR,r | *DISP | 011010aa<br>beeeeeee | 2 | 3 |
| IORZ,r | | 011000aa | 1 | 2 |
| LODA,r | *ADDR(X) | 000011aa<br>bccqqqqq<br>QQ | 3 | 4 |
| LODI,r | DATA8 | 000001aa<br>PP | 2 | 2 |
| LODR,r | *DISP | 000010aa<br>beeeeeee | 2 | 3 |
| LODZ,r | | 000000aa | 1 | 2 |
| LPSL | | 93 | 1 | 2 |
| LPSU | | 92 | 1 | 2 |
| NOP | | C0 | 1 | 2 |
| PPSL | DATA8 | 77<br>PP | 1 | 3 |
| PPSU | DATA8 | 76<br>PP | 2 | 3 |
| REDC,r | | 001100aa | 1 | 2 |
| REDD,r | | 011100aa | 1 | 2 |
| REDE,r | P | 010101aa<br>PP | 2 | 3 |
| RETC,DATA2 | | 000101ff | 1 | 3 |
| RETE,DATA2 | | 001101ff | 1 | 3 |
| RRL,r | | 110100aa | 1 | 2 |
| RRR,r | | 010100aa | 1 | 2 |
| SPSL | | 13 | 1 | 2 |
| SPSU | | 12 | 1 | 2 |
| STRA,r | *ADDR(X) | 110011aa<br>bccqqqqq<br>QQ | 3 | 4 |
| STRR,r | *DISP | 110010aa<br>beeeeeee | 2 | 3 |
| STRZ,r | | 110000aa | 1 | 2 |

Table 11-2. Signetics 2650A Instruction Object Codes (Continued)

| INSTRUCTION | OBJECT CODE | BYTES | MACHINE CYCLES |
|---|---|---|---|
| SUBA,r *ADDR(X) | 101011aa | 3 | 4 |
| | bccqqqqq | | |
| | QQ | | |
| SUBI,r DATA8 | 101001aa | 2 | 2 |
| | PP | | |
| SUBR,r *DISP | 101010aa | 2 | 3 |
| | beeeeeee | | |
| SUBZ,r | 101000aa | 1 | 2 |
| TMI,r DATA8 | 111101aa | 2 | 3 |
| | PP | | |
| TPSL DATA8 | B5 | 2 | 3 |
| | PP | | |
| TPSU DATA8 | B4 | 2 | 3 |
| | PP | | |
| WRTC,r | 101100aa | 1 | 2 |
| WRTD,r | 111100aa | 1 | 2 |
| WRTE,r P | 110101aa | 2 | 3 |
| | PP | | |
| ZBRR *DISP | 9B | 2 | 3 |
| | beeeeeee | | |
| ZBSR *DISP | BB | 2 | 3 |
| | beeeeeee | | |

The following symbols are used in Table 11-2:

| | |
|---|---|
| aa | Two bits which, in conjunction with the Register Bank Select bit in the PSL, choose the register |
| b | One bit selecting the indirection option |
| cc | Two bits choosing the indexing mode:<br>00 No indexing<br>01 Indexing with auto-increment<br>10 Indexing with auto-decrement<br>11 Indexing only |
| eeeeeee | 7-bit signed address displacement |
| ff | 2-bit test value |
| PP | eight bits of immediate data |
| q | One bit of absolute or extended address |
| Q | One byte (eight bits) of absolute or extended address |

## SUPPORT DEVICES THAT MAY BE USED WITH THE 2650A MICROPROCESSOR

**Interfacing the 2650A with 8080A support devices is very straightforward. Figure 11-4 shows how 8080A control signals may be generated from 2650A control signals. Figure 11-5 provides the same information for the MC6800.**

**But there are some ambiguities not immediately apparent when you look at Figure 11-4.** To begin with, the 2650A uses a request/acknowledge handshaking control protocol which is alien to an 8080A-based system. Thus $\overline{\text{OPACK}}$, which is shown creating RDYIN in Figure 11-4, may well be grounded in a configuration that is not going to insert Wait states into 2650A instruction execution cycles. OPREQ will be used as a contributor to the chip select logic of 8080A support devices. M/$\overline{\text{IO}}$, which is shown discriminating between memory and I/O control signals in Figure 11-4, may alternatively be used as a contributor to chip select logic. **Figures 11-6 through 11-9 illustrate 8251 and 8255 devices connected to a 2650A CPU, being selected within memory or I/O spaces.** Note that where devices are selected within the 2650A I/O space, C/$\overline{\text{D}}$ could be generated from the 2650A C/$\overline{\text{D}}$ control output rather than using address line ADR0.

**Figure 11-10 shows how 2650A priority interrupts may be generated using an 8214 Priority Interrupt Control Unit.**

**Interfacing MC6800 support devices to a 2650A CPU is again complicated by the synchronizing signal required by MC6800 support devices. But the 2650A is flexible enough to make this interface possible.**

We must use OPREQ in order to generate the synchronizing enable signal for MC6800 support devices. Unfortunately, there is a significant variation in the leading edge of OPREQ. Therefore, **logic to create an ENABLE synchronizing signal must have the following three parts:**

1) Create a continuous clock signal to substitute for the MC6800 ENABLE synchronizing signal.
2) Make sure that during a write cycle MC6800 device select logic is true across one pulse of the ENABLE signal. Chip select logic must be true from shortly before the beginning ofthe ENABLE signal positive transition until shortly after the end of the negative transition.

3) During a read cycle, again make sure that chip select logic for the MC6800 support device is valid for one ENABLE cycle only; but this time stretch the ENABLE true pulse so that the 2650A CPU can latch the data on the negative transition of OPREQ before ENABLE goes low.

**Timing for the above three conditions is illustrated in Figure 11-11.** But note that since the minimum cycle time for MC6800 support devices is 1 microsecond, the 2650A CPU must also operate at this frequency — rather than using a 0.8 microsecond clock, which is the fastest allowed.

**Figure 11-12 illustrates a 2650A-6850 ACIA interface. Figure 11-13 illustrates a 2650A-6820 PIA interface.** Important aspects of 2650A interface timing are defined in Figure 11-14.

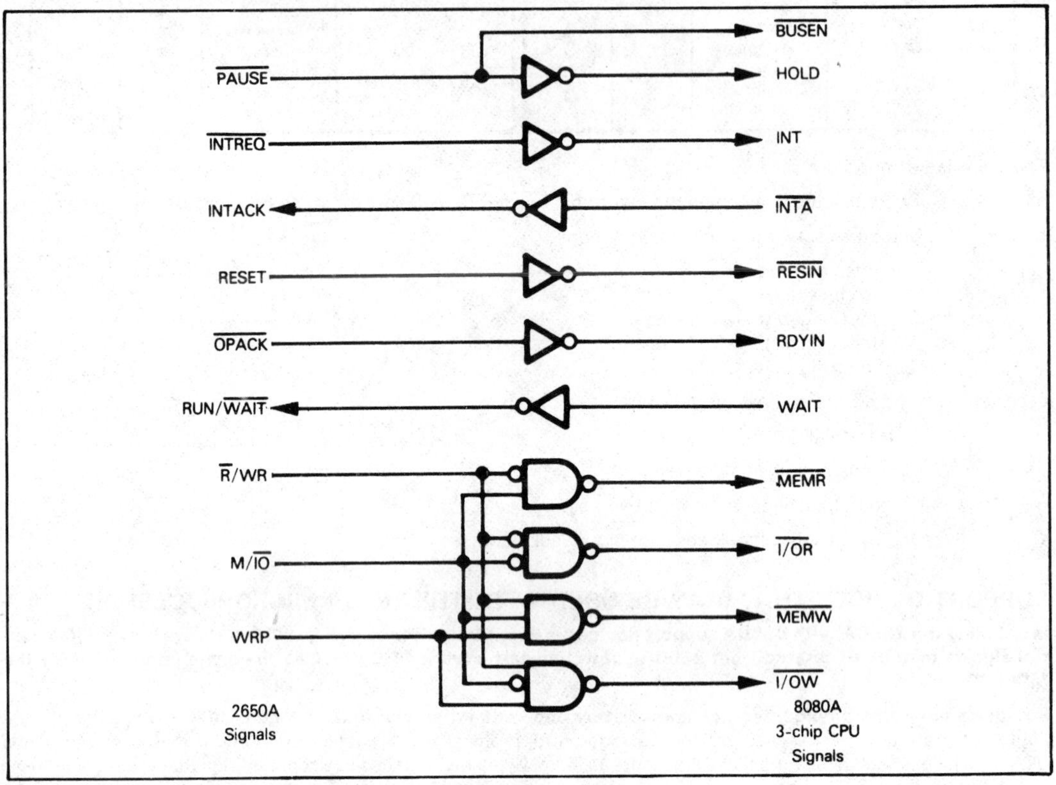

BUSEN
PAUSE
HOLD
INTREQ
INT
INTACK
INTA
RESET
RESIN
OPACK
RDYIN
RUN/WAIT
WAIT
R/WR
MEMR
M/IO
I/OR
MEMW
WRP
I/OW
2650A Signals
8080A 3-chip CPU Signals

Figure 11-4. 2650A-8080A Signal Equivalents

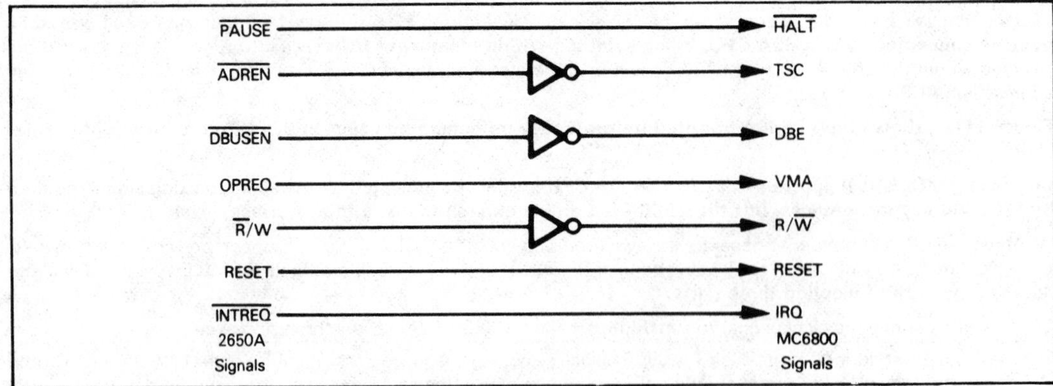


Figure 11-5. 2650A-MC6800 Signal Equivalents

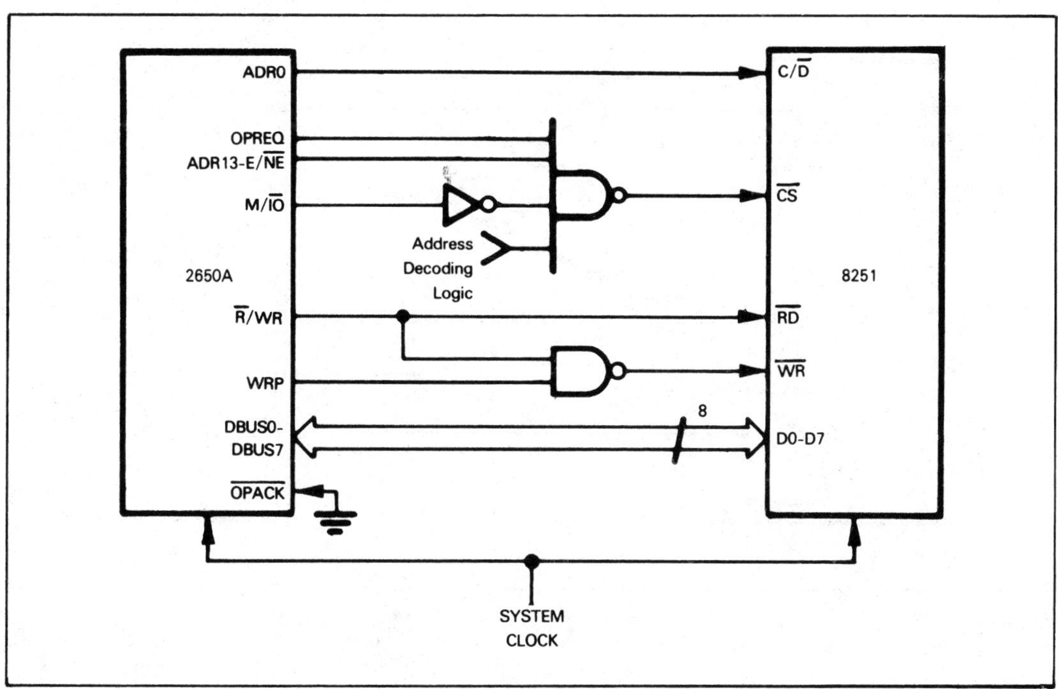


Figure 11-6. An 8251 USART Accessed by a 2650A as an I/O Device

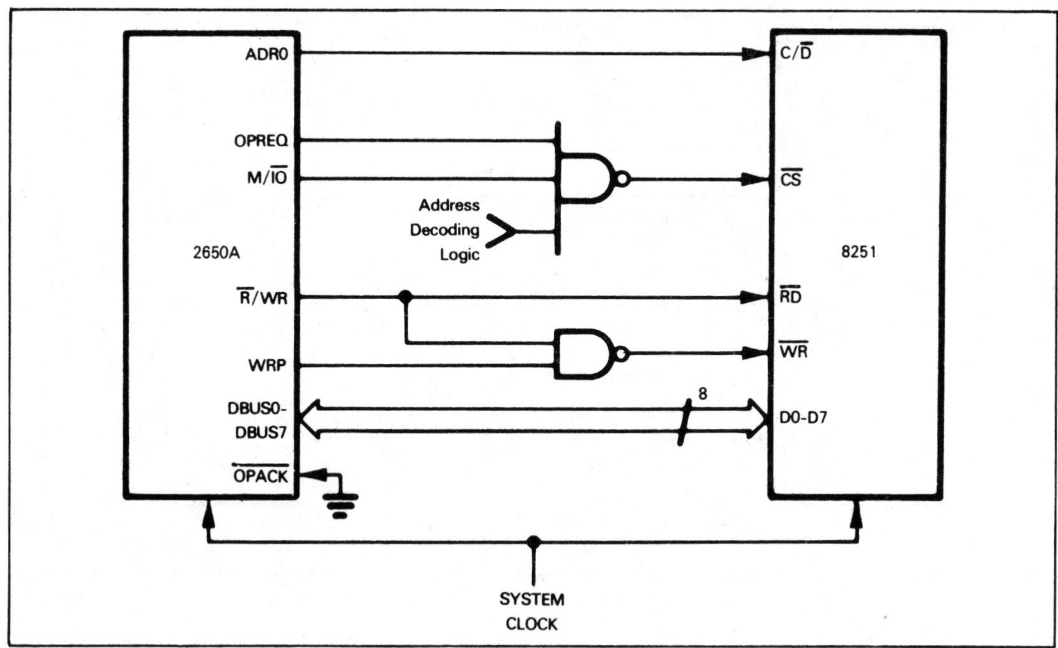


Figure 11-7. An 8251 USART Accessed by a 2650A as a Memory Device

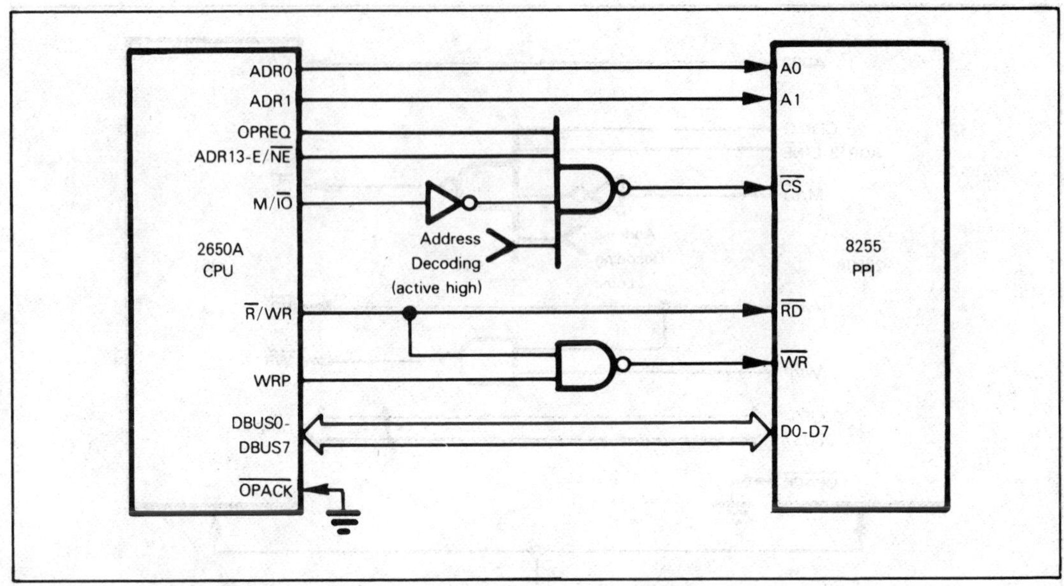


Figure 11-8. An 8255 PPI Accessed by a 2650A as an I/O Device

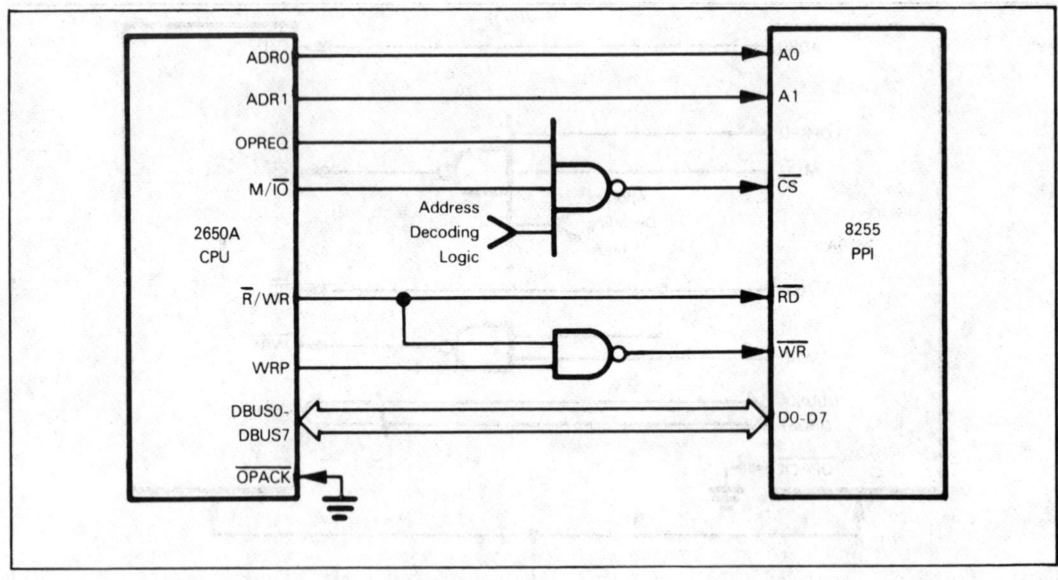


Figure 11-9. An 8255 PPI Accessed by a 2650A as a Memory Device

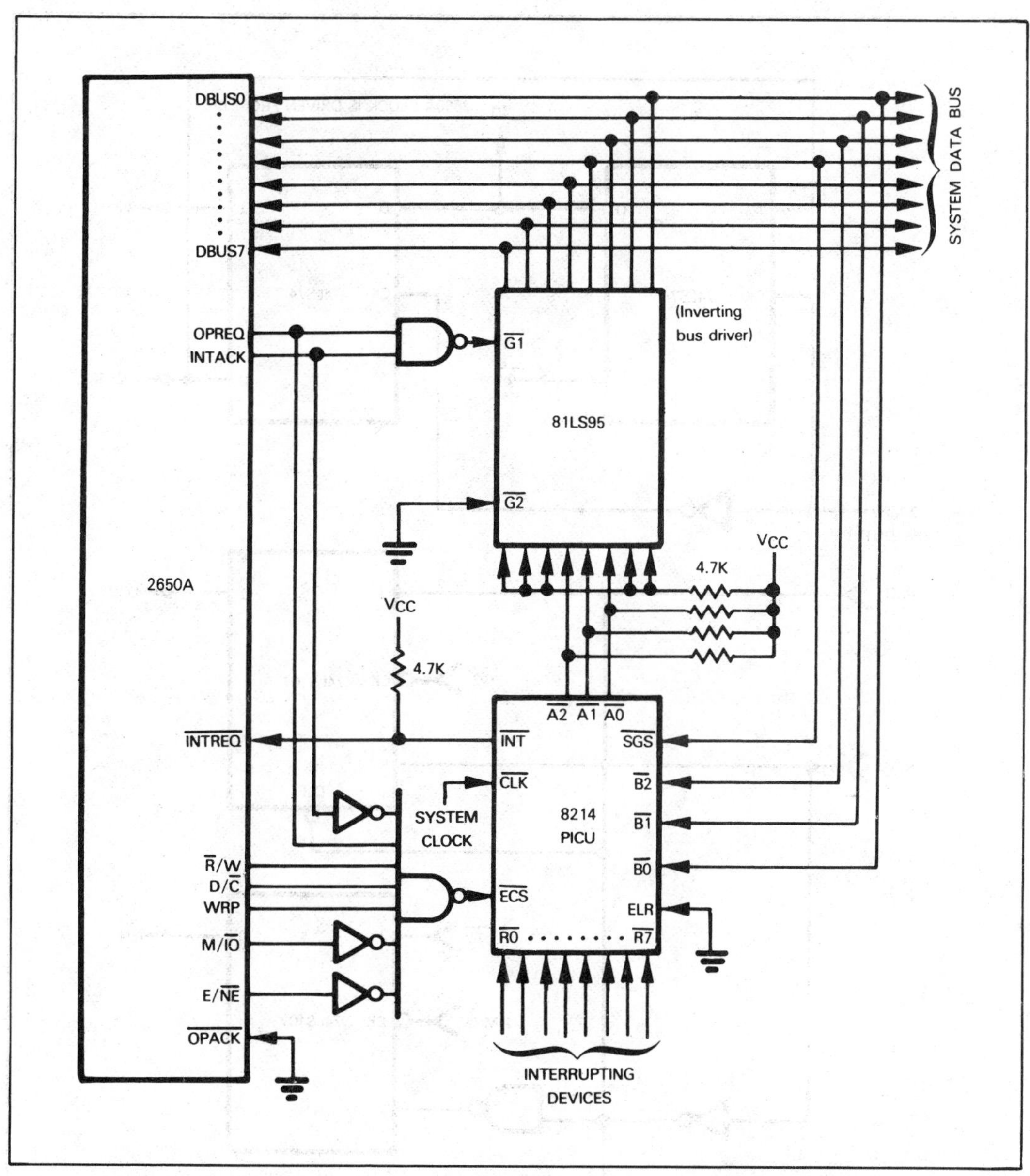


Figure 11-10. Vectored Interrupt Using the 8214 PICU with a 2650A CPU

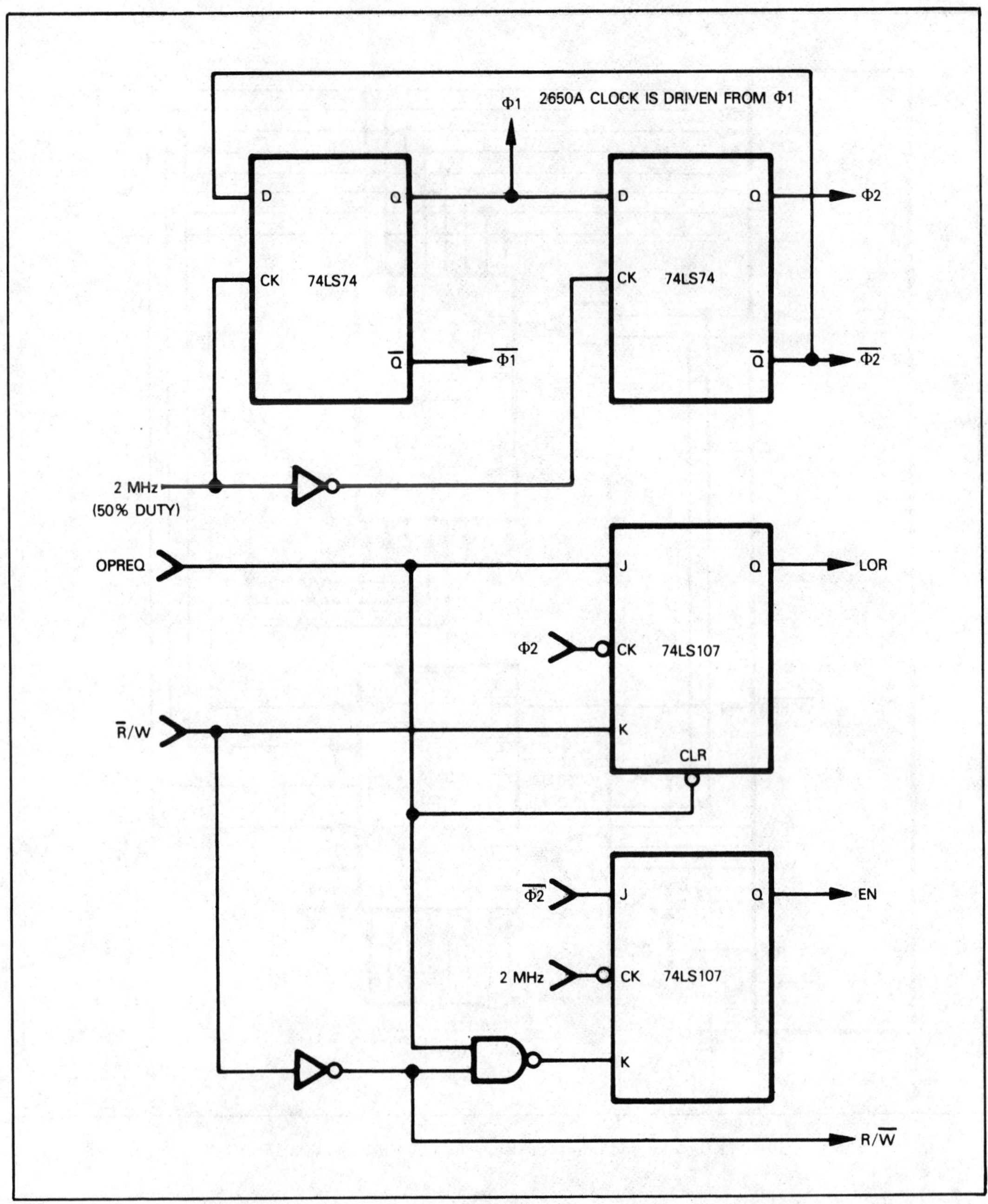


Figure 11-11. Synchronization Circuits in a 2650A-MC68XX Interface

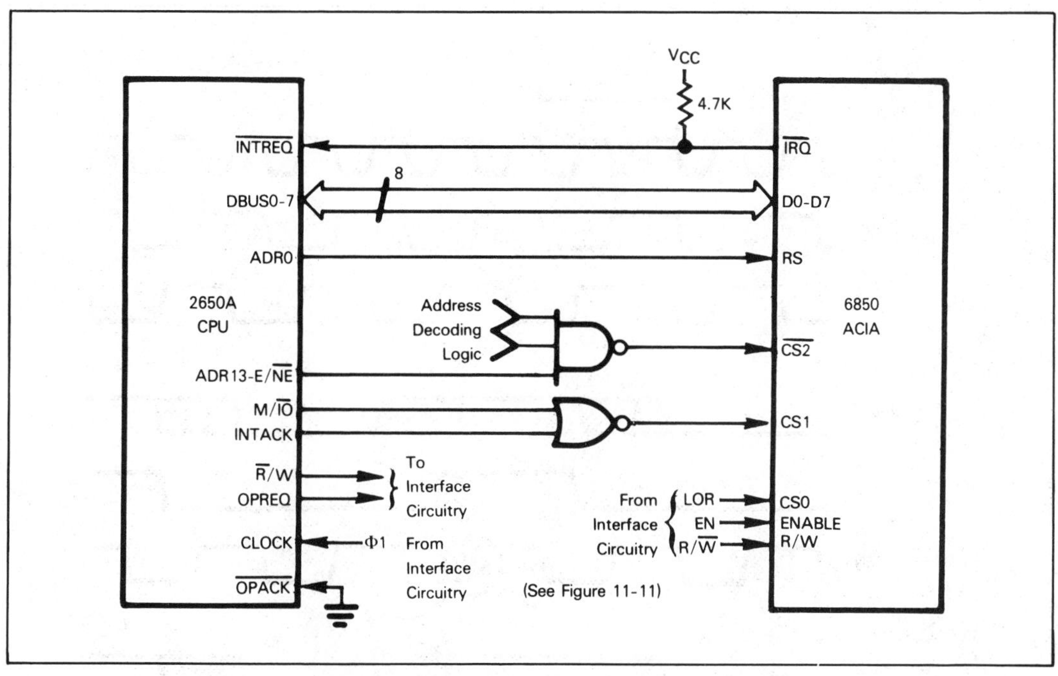


Figure 11-12. An MC6850 ACIA Connected to a 2650A

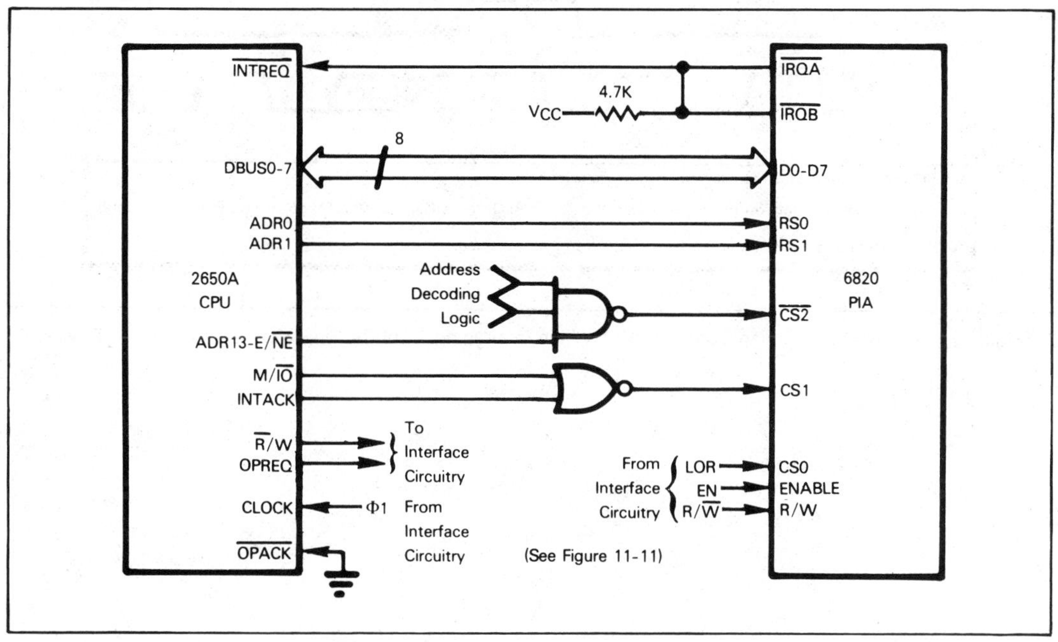


Figure 11-13. An MC6820 PIA Connected to a 2650A

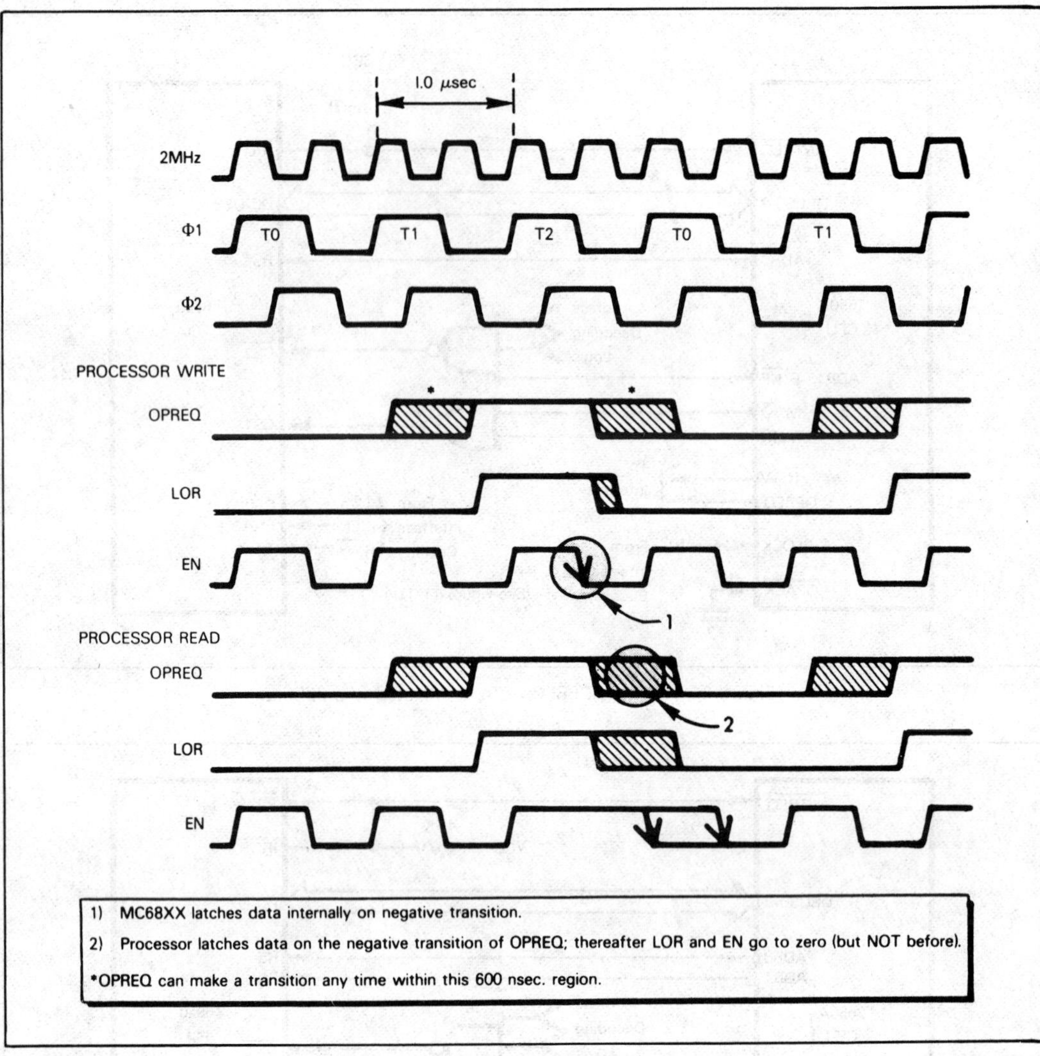
1.0 μsec
2MHz
Φ1
T0
T1
T2
T0
T1
Φ2
PROCESSOR WRITE
OPREQ
LOR
EN
1
PROCESSOR READ
OPREQ
2
LOR
EN
1) MC68XX latches data internally on negative transition.
2) Processor latches data on the negative transition of OPREQ; thereafter LOR and EN go to zero (but NOT before).
*OPREQ can make a transition any time within this 600 nsec. region.

Figure 11-14. Important Timing Considerations When Interfacing a 2650A CPU with MC68XX Series Devices

# DATA SHEETS

This section contains specific electrical and timing data for the 2650A microprocessor.

## ABSOLUTE MAXIMUM RATINGS[1]

| | PARAMETER | RATING |
|---|---|---|
| $T_A$ | Operating ambient temperature[2] | 0°C to 70°C |
| $T_{STG}$ | Storage temperature | −65°C to +150°C |
| $P_D$ | Package power dissipation[2] | 1.6W |
| | All input, output, and supply voltages with respect to GND[3] | −0.5V to +6V |

## DC ELECTRICAL CHARACTERISTICS $T_A$ = 0°C to 70°C, $V_{CC}$ = 5V ±5%.

| | PARAMETER | TEST CONDITIONS | LIMITS Min | Typ | Max | UNIT |
|---|---|---|---|---|---|---|
| | Current | | | | | μA |
| $I_{IL}$ | Input load | $V_{IN}$ = 0 to 5.25V | −10 | | 10 | |
| $I_{LOH}$ | Output high leakage | $\overline{ADREN}$, $\overline{DBUSEN}$ = 2.2V $V_{OUT}$ = 4V | −10 | | 10 | |
| $I_{LOL}$ | Output low leakage | $\overline{ADREN}$, $\overline{DBUSEN}$ = 2.2V $V_{OUT}$ = 0.45V | −10 | | 10 | |
| | Voltage levels | | | | | V |
| $V_{IH}$ | Input high | | 2.2 | | $V_{CC}$ | |
| $V_{IL}$ | Input low | | −0.5 | | 0.8 | |
| $V_{OH}$ | Output high | $I_{OH}$ = −100μA | 2.4 | | | |
| $V_{OL}$ | Output low | $I_{OL}$ = 1.6ma | 0 | | 0.45 | |
| $I_{CC}$ | Power supply current | $V_{CC}$ = 5.25V $T_A$ = 0°C | | | 150 | mA |
| | Capacitance | | | | | pF |
| $C_{IN}$ | Input | $f_c$ = 1MHz | | | 20 | |
| $C_{OUT}$ | Output | Unmeasured pins tied to ground | | | 20 | |

NOTES

1. Stresses above those listed under "Absolute Maximum Ratings" may cause permanent damage to the device. This is a stress rating only and functional operation of the device at these or at any other condition above those indicated in the operation sections of this specification is not implied.
2. For operating at elevated temperatures the device must be derated based on +150°C maximum junction temperature and thermal resistance of 50°C/W junction to ambient (IWA ceramic package).
3. This product includes circuitry specifically designed for the protection of its internal devices from the damaging effects of excessive static charge. However, it is suggested that conventional precautions be taken to avoid applying any voltages larger than the rated maxima.

## AC CHARACTERISTICS $T_A = 0°C$ to $+70°C$, $V_{CC} = 5V \pm 5\%$[1, 2, 3, 4]

| PARAMETER | | LIMITS | | UNIT |
|---|---|---|---|---|
| | | Min | Max | |
| $t_{AS}$ | Address stable | 50 | | ns |
| $t_{TVD}$ | 3-State enable delay time | | 250 | ns |
| $t_{VTD}$ | 3-State disable delay time | | 150 | ns |
| $t_{DS}$ | Data stable | 50 | | ns |
| $t_{DIH}$ | Data in hold | 0 | | ns |
| $t_{DIA}$ | Data in access time (2650A-1)<br>(2650A) | $t_{CP} + t_{CH} - 200$<br>$t_{CP} + t_{CH} - 300$ | | ns |
| $t_{CH}$ | Clock high phase (2650A-1)<br>(2650A) | 250<br>400 | | ns |
| $t_{CL}$ | Clock low phase (2650A-1)<br>(2650A) | 250<br>400 | | ns |
| $t_{CP}$ | Clock period (2650A-1)<br>(2650A) | 500<br>800 | | ns |
| $t_{PC}$ | Processor cycle time[5] (2650A-1)<br>(2650A) | 1500<br>2400 | | ns |
| $t_{OR}$ | OPREQ pulse width[6] | $t_{CP} + t_{CH} - 50$ | $t_{CP} + t_{CH} + 75$ | ns |
| $t_{COR}$ | Clock to OPREQ time (2650A-1)<br>(2650A) | 50<br>50 | 200<br>300 | ns |
| $t_{OAD}$ | $\overline{\text{OPACK}}$ delay time (2650A-1)<br>(2650A) | | $t_{CP} - 250$<br>$t_{CP} - 350$ | ns |
| $t_{OAH}$ | $\overline{\text{OPACK}}$ hold time | $t_{CP}$ | | ns |
| $t_{CSS}$ | Control signal stable | 50 | | ns |
| $t_{WPD}$ | Write pulse delay | $t_{CH} - 50$ | $t_{CH} + 100$ | ns |
| $t_{WPW}$ | Write pulse width[6] | $t_{CL} - 50$ | $t_{CL} + 125$ | ns |
| $t_{IRH}$ | INTREQ hold time | 0 | | ns |
| $t_{PSE}$ | Pause delay | | $t_{CP}$ | ns |
| $t_{RST}$ | Reset width | $3t_{CP}$ | | ns |

NOTES
1. Input levels swing between 0.4 and 2.4 volts.
2. Input signal transition times are 20ns.
3. All voltage measurements are referenced to ground. All time measurements are at the 50% level for inputs and at 0.8V and 2.0V for outputs.
4. Output load is 100pF.
5. Processor cycle time consists of three clock periods.
6. These values assume that $\overline{\text{OPACK}}$ is returned in time to not cause the processor to idle. Otherwise, the specified maximum will increase by an integral number of clock cycles.

READ TIMING

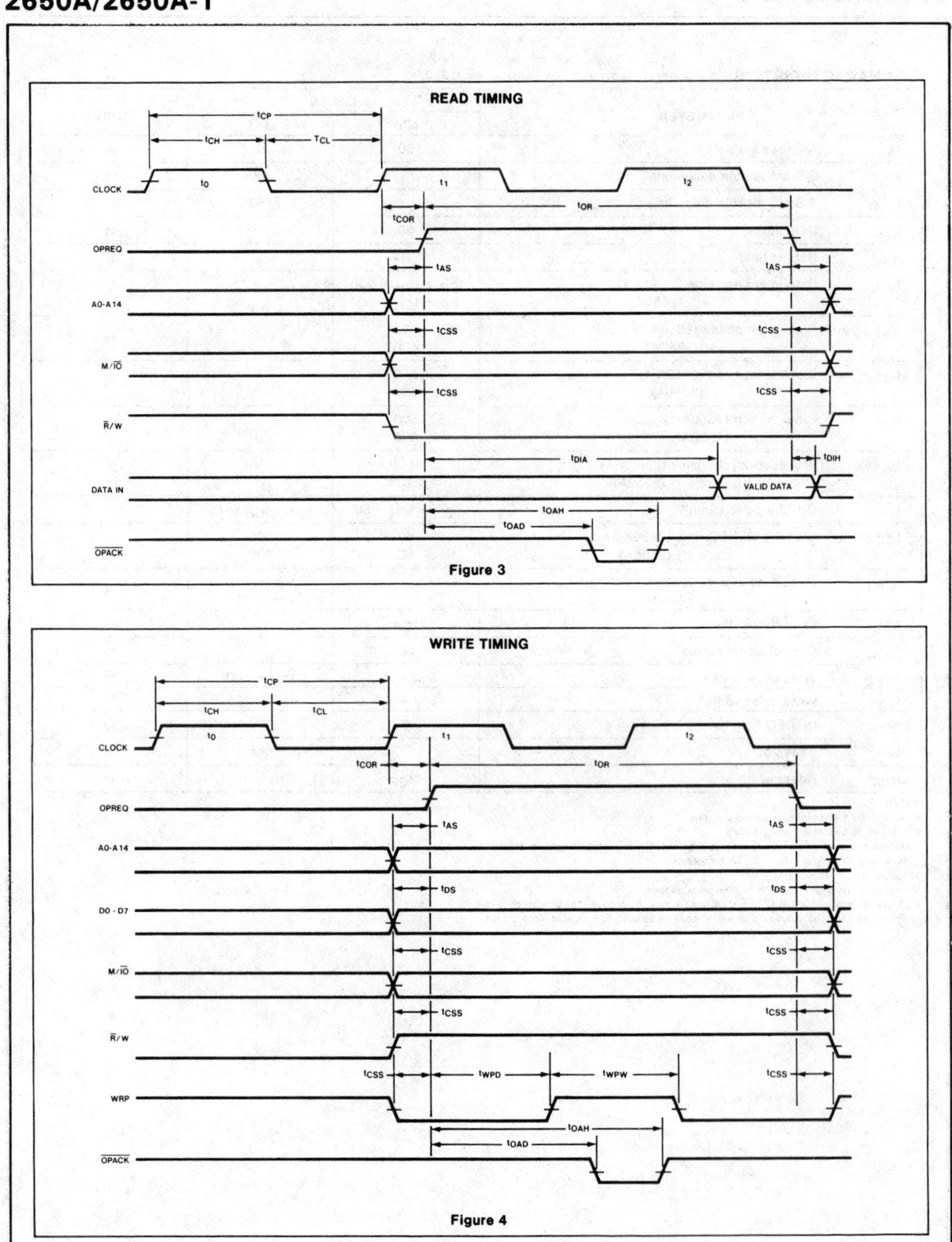


Figure 3

WRITE TIMING



Figure 4

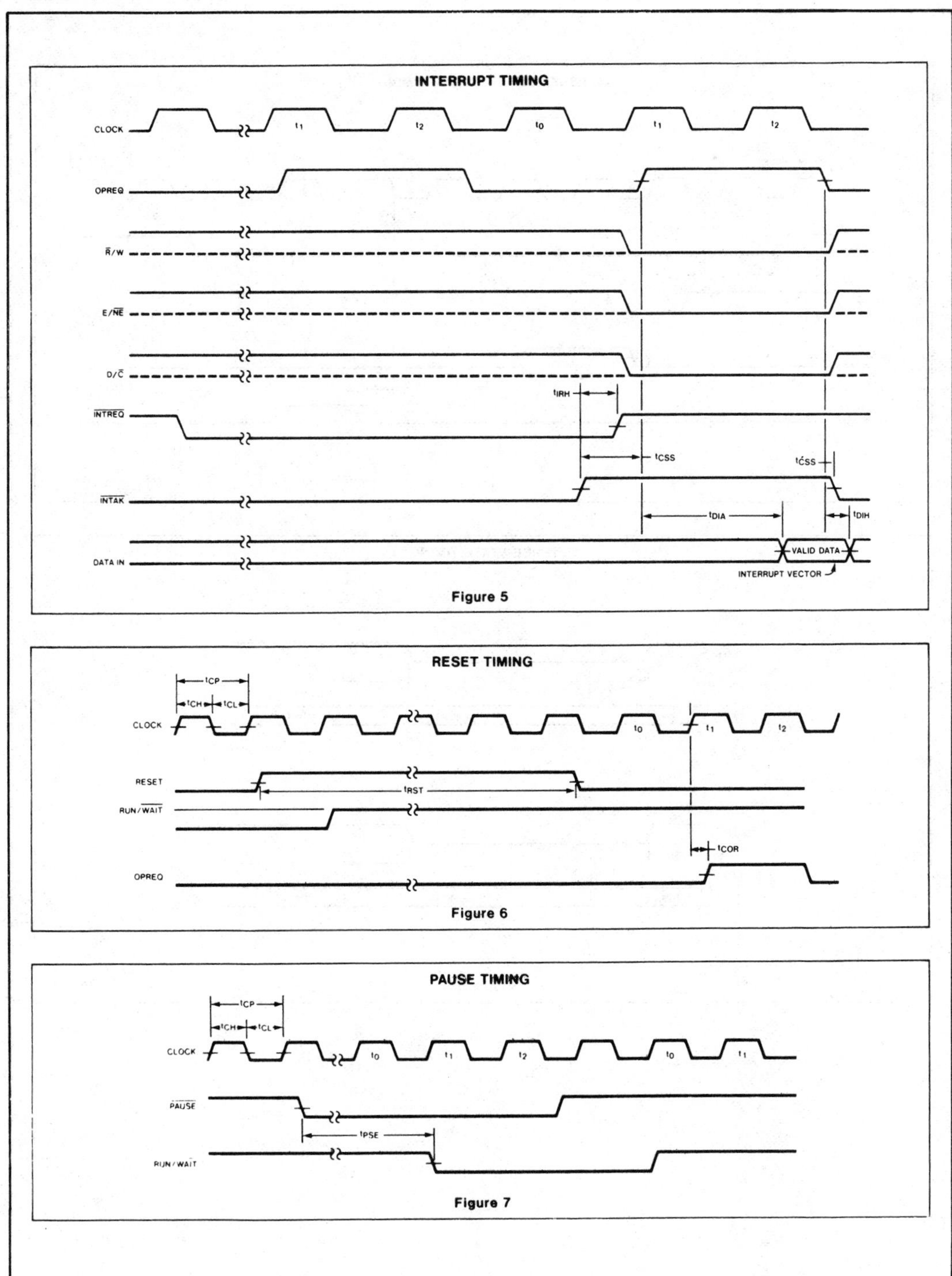


Figure 5

Figure 6

Figure 7

RESET DURING PAUSE TIMING

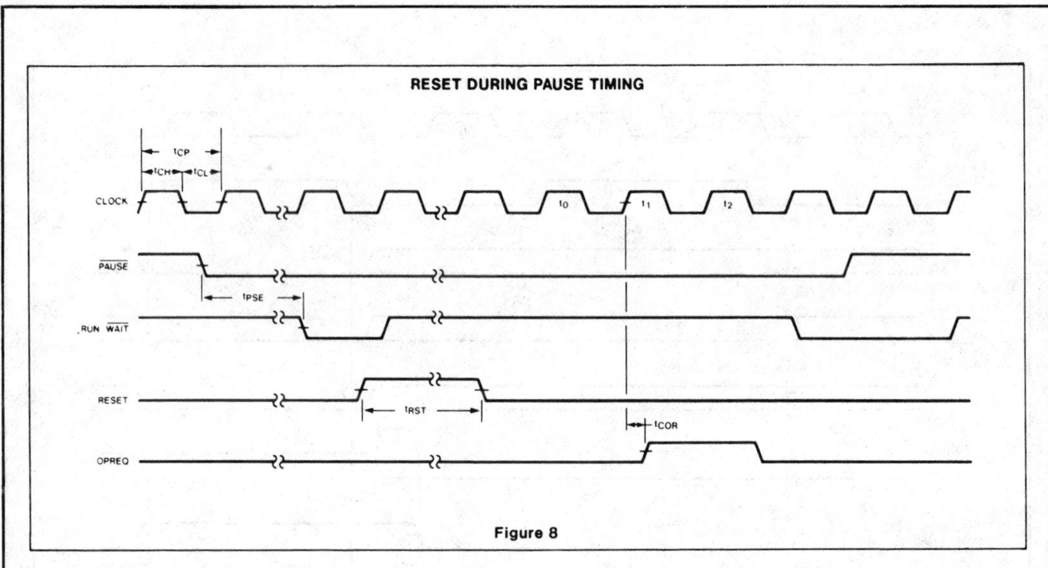


Figure 8

THREE-STATE TIMING

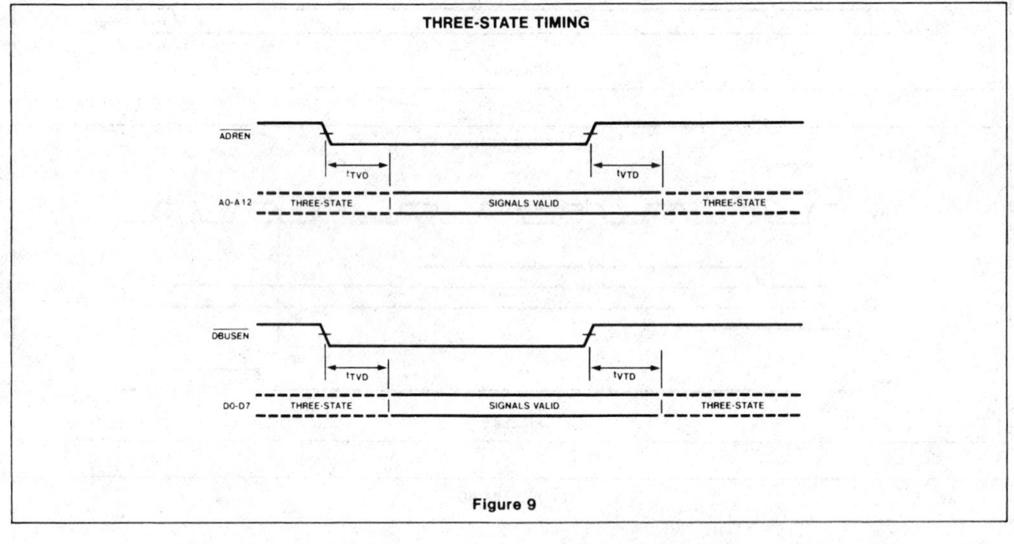


Figure 9

# Chapter 12
# THE RCA COSMAC

**We are going to describe the single-chip CPU referred to as the CDP1802. This is a one-chip implementation of the previous two-chip CPU, consisting of the CDP1801 and CDP18101.**

COSMAC is a "low end" microprocessor; it is well suited to simple, high-volume applications with limited programming needs. As compared to many other microprocessors described in this book, COSMAC is a poor choice for low-volume, program intensive applications; this is because COSMAC is relatively difficult to program optimally.

But where does the transition from a simple application to a complex application occur? For COSMAC, it is sudden — an application either is or is not suited to COSMAC, with very little grey area.

**The principal advantage of COSMAC is that it requires very little power, since it is fabricated using CMOS technology. If your application is going to be battery powered for any length of time, CMOS logic is strongly favored.** In addition, if speed is not essential in your application, then power consumption can be further reduced by using a lower clock frequency. The advent of one-chip microcomputers has clouded the previously clear-cut power supply advantage associated with CMOS technology. **There are occasions when a multi-chip COSMAC (or IM6100) microcomputer system, even though it is all CMOS, will use approximately the same amount of power as a single-chip NMOS microcomputer;** the single-chip microcomputer will be capable of doing the same job. **Before immediately assuming that your application demands CMOS technology for power supply purposes, it is worth checking the power supply requirements of an equivalent NMOS one-chip microcomputer.**

**Both the power and the inflexibility of COSMAC are based on a subtly clever use of CPU logic, coupled with a somewhat primitive interface between CPU and external memory. Providing you can accommodate all "program housekeeping" using CPU registers for your read/write memory, COSMAC is a superb microprocessor. "Program housekeeping" includes maintaining the program and data memory address required by subroutines, interrupts, and data accesses in general.** A large class of microprocessor applications fit these restrictions and are well suited to COSMAC.

Devices described in this chapter include the CDP1802 Central Processing Unit and the CDP1852 8-bit input/output port. There is also a CMOS Universal Asynchronous Receiver/Transmitter (UART) — the CDP1854 device. This part is described in Volume 3.

COSMAC is fabricated using CMOS technology. It operates with a single power supply and is very insensitive to noise. The power supply can vary between +3V and +12V.

CMOS technology also results in COSMAC having a very low power consumption and a broad operating temperature range. It is one of the few products described in this book that operates within the full military specification temperature range of -55°C to +125°C.

**You should be cautious with your power supply when using COSMAC.** CMOS is indeed immune to noise in the power supply; the power supply can swing wildly between +3V and +12V without affecting the 1 and 0 levels at individual gates. However, timing swings accompany power supply swings. This would not be a problem if all signals changed frequency together; however, as we will discuss later in this chapter, signals do not change in unison. Thus, **it is quite possible that a COSMAC system which works perfectly well with a +5V power supply is inoperable with a +8V power supply, because signal transitions have shifted sufficiently for +5V logic to no longer apply.**

Using a +10V power supply, a 155 nanosecond clock results in instruction execution times of 2.5 or 3.75 microseconds. In reality, a 200 nanosecond (or slower) clock should be used. Even though faster clocks are allowed, **users have experienced design problems when attempting to run COSMAC microcomputer systems with clocks that are faster than 200 nanoseconds.**

The principal manufacturer for the COSMAC is:

RCA SOLID STATE DIVISION
P.O. Box 3200
Somerville, N.J. 08876

The second sources are:

HUGHES AIRCRAFT INC.
Industrial Electronics Group
500 Superior Avenue
Newport Beach, CA 92663

SOLID STATE SCIENTIFIC INC.
Montgomeryville Industrial Park
Montgomeryville, PA 18936

# THE COSMAC CPU

**Functions implemented on the CDP1802 CPU are illustrated in Figure 12-1.**

Logic to handle an external interrupt request is provided by the COSMAC CPU, along with an elementary ability to handle interrupt priority arbitration.

An unusual feature of COSMAC, as compared to other CPUs described in this book, is the fact that COSMAC provides an elementary DMA capability using CPU logic.

## COSMAC PROGRAMMABLE REGISTERS

These are the programmable registers of the COSMAC CPU:

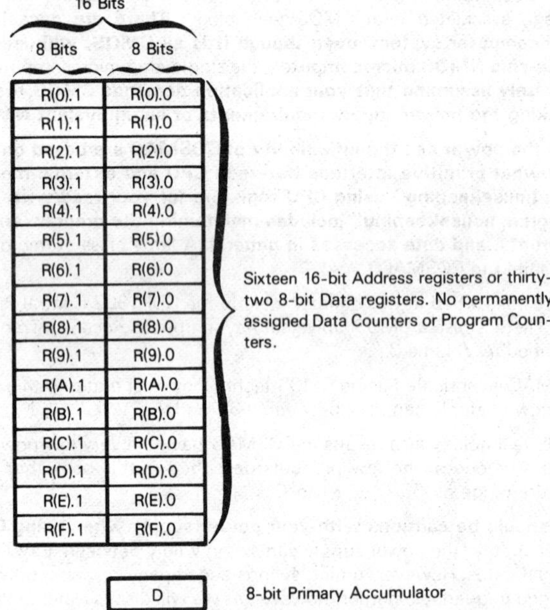


**The D register functions as a primary Accumulator.**

**The sixteen 16-bit registers may serve as Program Counters, Data Counters, or scratchpad memory.**

As scratchpad memory, each 16-bit register consists of two 8-bit registers whose contents can be transferred to or from the primary Accumulator (D register).

The nomenclature RN is used to define a 16-bit general purpose register. N may be any number in the range 0 - 15. When general purpose registers are being treated as 8-bit data storage units, R(N).1 is used to identify the high-order byte of General Purpose Register RN and R(N).0 is used to identify the low-order byte of General Purpose Register RN. For example, R6 identifies the seventh 16-bit general purpose register. This general purpose register contains a high-order byte, identified as R(6).1 and a low-order byte, identified as R(6).0.

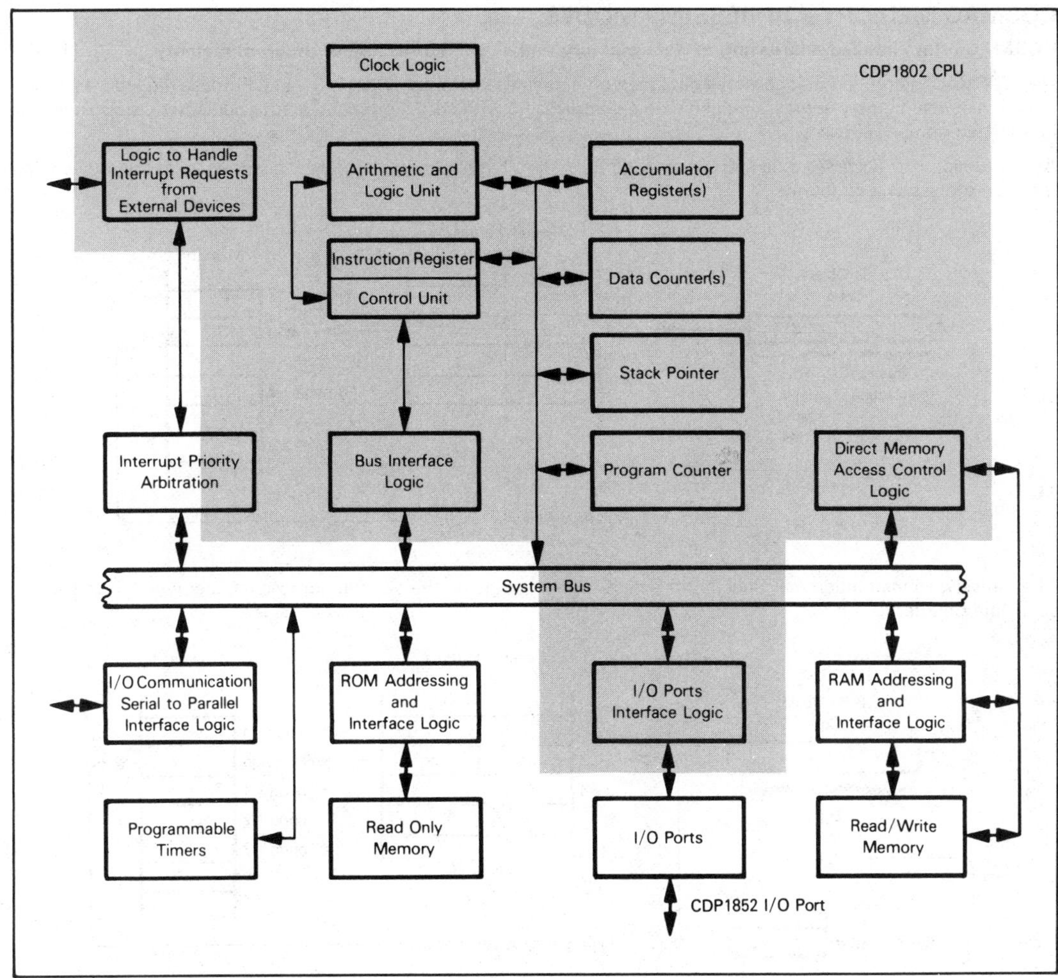


Figure 12-1. Logic of the CDP1802 COSMAC CPU and the CDP1852 I/O Port

**The 4-bit P register identifies the 16-bit register which at any point in time is functioning as the Program Counter.**

**The 4-bit X register identifies the 16-bit register which at any point in time is functioning as the Data Counter.**

**The T register is a simple, 8-bit buffer within which X and P register contents are stored following an interrupt.**

**COSMAC literature identifies a third 4-bit register, called the N register.** On first reading, the N register may look like the X register, but in reality, the N register represents the low-order four bits of the Instruction register. The N register is not a programmable register as we define it.

**The first three 16-bit registers have dedicated functions.**

**Register R0 is the Memory Address register used by the DMA logic of COSMAC.**

**Following an interrupt acknowledge, Register R1 is assumed to contain the beginning address for the interrupt service routine; General Purpose Register R2 serves as a primitive Stack Pointer.** A single instruction allows you to push the contents of the T register into the memory location addressed by General Purpose Register R2. Another single instruction loads P and X with the contents of the memory location addressed by General Purpose Register R2.

## COSMAC MEMORY ADDRESSING MODES

**COSMAC offers implied addressing of data memory and direct addressing of program memory.**

Any COSMAC instruction that accesses data memory indicates one of the sixteen General Purpose registers as providing the required memory address. Implied memory addressing with auto-increment or auto-decrement is also available in a limited number of cases.

An instruction that accesses data memory may directly identify the general purpose register wherein the implied data memory address will be found:

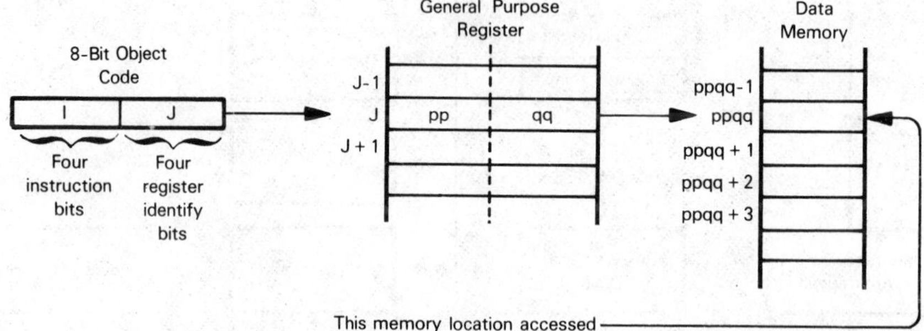


Alternatively, an instruction may specify that the X register points to the general purpose register which is to be used as a Data Counter:

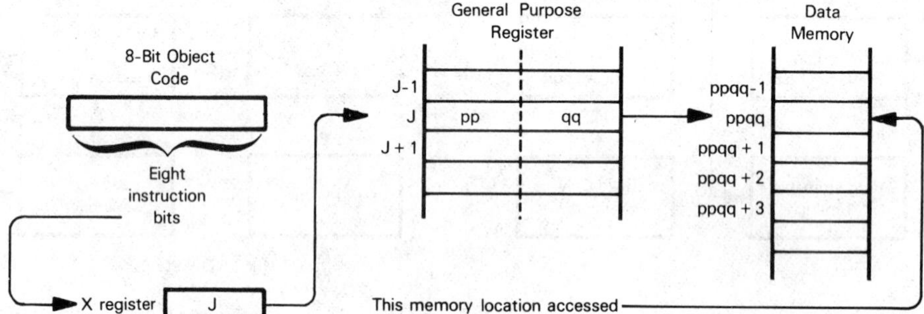


Branch instructions use direct memory addressing. COSMAC has two-byte and three-byte Branch instructions. A two-byte Branch instruction uses paged, direct addressing; the second byte of object code replaces the low-order byte of the 16-bit general purpose register currently serving as Program Counter:

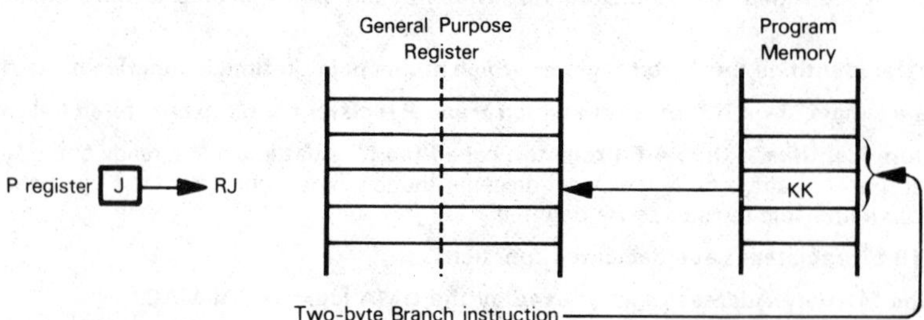


In the illustration above, the P register contains a hexadecimal digit represented by J. General Purpose Register RJ is therefore currently serving as the Program Counter. A two-byte Branch instruction contains an 8-bit value, represented by KK, in the second object program byte. When a branch is executed, KK is loaded into R(J).0, the low-order byte of General Purpose Register RJ. This represents straightforward, absolute paged direct addressing as described in Volume 1.

The second and third object code bytes of a three-byte Branch instruction provide a 16-bit address which replaces the entire contents of the general purpose register currently serving as Program Counter. This is equivalent to simple non-paged direct addressing as described in Volume 1. When a 16-bit address is stored in memory, the high-order address byte precedes the low-order address byte as follows:

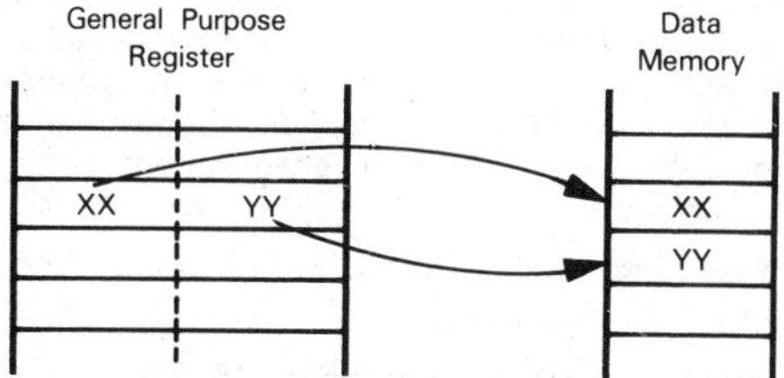


**Program and data memory in a COSMAC microcomputer system may be common or separate.** Because COSMAC has a wealth of control signals, it is almost as easy to implement program and data memory with duplicated memory addresses and address spaces as it is to implement program and data memory with separate addresses and address spaces. Thus COSMAC can have separate program and data memories, as described for the SMS300, or it can have a shared address space, as is the case for all other microcomputers described in this book.

## COSMAC STATUS FLAGS

**COSMAC has no Status register, but it does have seven flags which, in a rather unusual way, provide status information.**

**Two of the seven status flags are orthodox:**

**There is the Data Flag (DF), which is equivalent to the Carry status as we describe it.**

**There is an Interrupt Enable flag** which must be set to 1 if interrupts are enabled; this flag is reset to 0 in order to disable interrupts.

**Five of the seven status flags are direct logic control statuses.**

**There are four I/O flags ($\overline{EF1}$ - $\overline{EF4}$) which are connected through inverters to CPU input pins. External logic can input high or low signals at these four pins.** Subsequently, COSMAC Branch-on-Condition instructions can test any one of these four pins, then branch or not branch, depending on the status of the pin.

The fifth condition status is referred to as **the Q status.** This status **can be set or reset directly by appropriate COSMAC instructions.** Subsequent Branch-on-Condition instructions will test the Q status in order to determine whether or not the branch will occur. In addition, the Q status is output to a pin which external logic can use in any way.

We may summarize the I/O and Q statuses as follows:

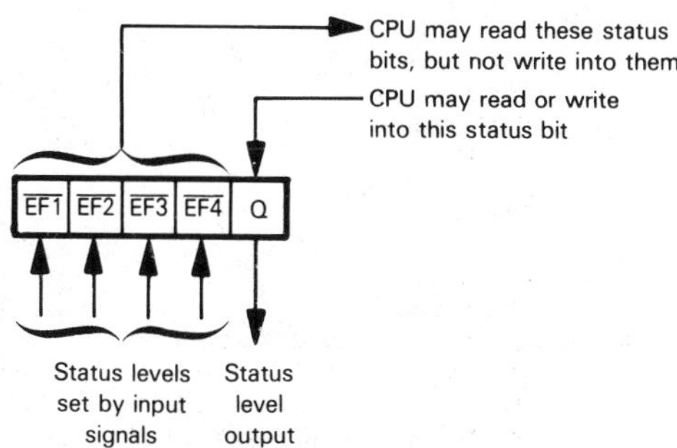


In addition, there are three I/O control signals output by COSMAC (N0, N1, and N2). These three signals can be used as control/status outputs to external logic. These three signals are described below, together with other COSMAC signals.

## COSMAC CPU PINS AND SIGNALS

**COSMAC CPU pins and signals are illustrated in Figure 12-2. A description of these signals is useful as a guide to the way in which the COSMAC microprocessor works. Signal names in Figure 12-2 conform with those used by COSMAC literature.**

**BUS0 - BUS7 is a standard bidirectional parallel Data Bus, usually called D0 - D7 for other microprocessors described in this book. All parallel data communications between the COSMAC CPU and external logic, memory, or I/O occur via this Data Bus.**

**MA0 - MA7 represent an 8-bit Address Bus. Most other microprocessors described in this book use the symbols A0 - A7 for equivalent Address Bus lines.** The fact that COSMAC has only eight address lines is very important. On the one hand, it frees up eight CPU DIP pins, which are used to provide extra control signals. The disadvantage of having just eight Address Bus lines is that all addresses must be multiplexed; the high-order address byte is output, followed by the low-order address byte. RCA provides memory devices that include address decode logic. An additional advantage of multiplexed address lines is that ROMs of varying sizes but identical pinouts can be constructed to recognize their own address space, thus giving users extra flexibility in constructing custom products.

**The remaining signals may be divided into timing, status, and control signals.**

**The timing signals are CLOCK, $\overline{\text{XTAL}}$, TPA, and TPB.**

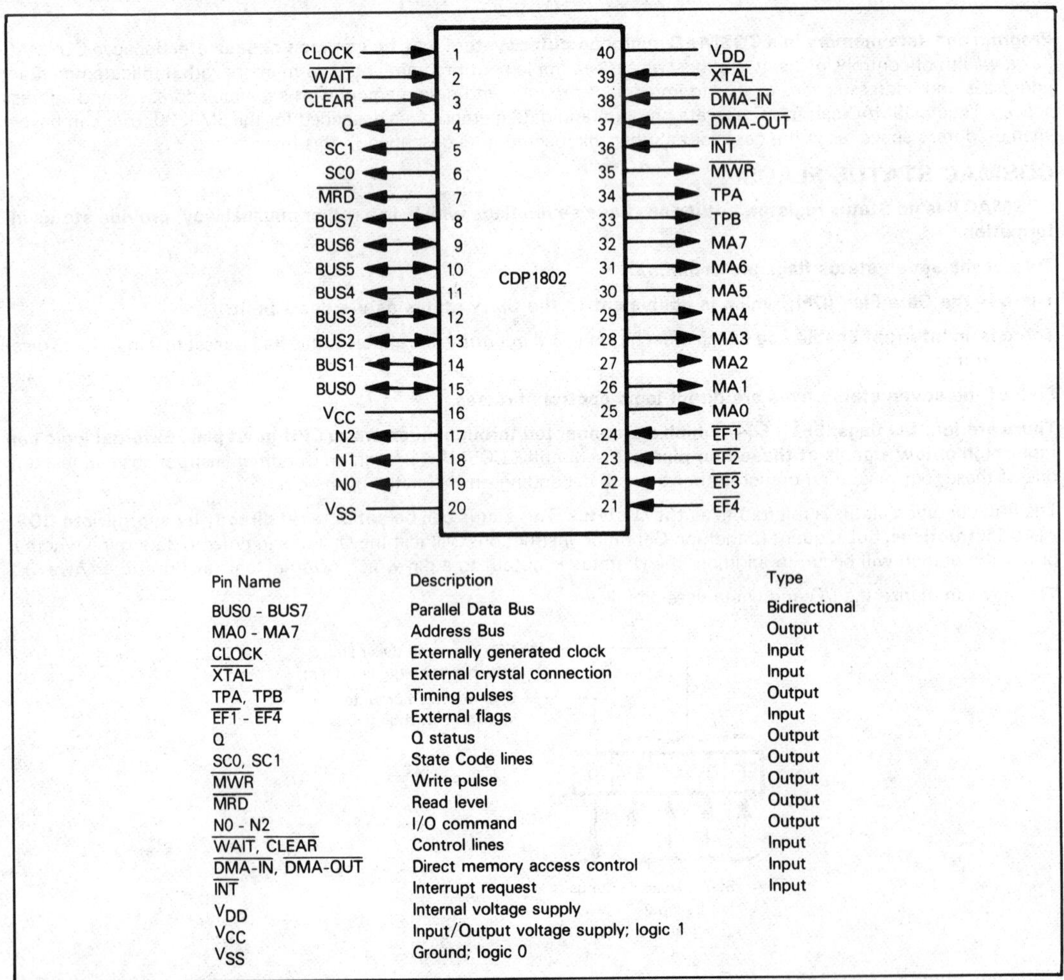


| Pin Name | Description | Type |
|---|---|---|
| BUS0 - BUS7 | Parallel Data Bus | Bidirectional |
| MA0 - MA7 | Address Bus | Output |
| CLOCK | Externally generated clock | Input |
| $\overline{\text{XTAL}}$ | External crystal connection | Input |
| TPA, TPB | Timing pulses | Output |
| $\overline{\text{EF1}}$ - $\overline{\text{EF4}}$ | External flags | Input |
| Q | Q status | Output |
| SC0, SC1 | State Code lines | Output |
| $\overline{\text{MWR}}$ | Write pulse | Output |
| $\overline{\text{MRD}}$ | Read level | Output |
| N0 - N2 | I/O command | Output |
| $\overline{\text{WAIT}}$, $\overline{\text{CLEAR}}$ | Control lines | Input |
| $\overline{\text{DMA-IN}}$, $\overline{\text{DMA-OUT}}$ | Direct memory access control | Input |
| $\overline{\text{INT}}$ | Interrupt request | Input |
| $V_{DD}$ | Internal voltage supply | |
| $V_{CC}$ | Input/Output voltage supply; logic 1 | |
| $V_{SS}$ | Ground; logic 0 | |

Figure 12-2. CDP1802 COSMAC CPU Signals and Pin Assignments

**CLOCK is the principal timing signal** input by external clock logic. Any frequency up to 6.4 MHz, when using a +10V power supply, is advertised, but **frequencies above 5 MHz are not recommended.**

If you are using the on-chip clock logic, then you must connect an external crystal, with a parallel resistor, to the $\overline{\text{XTAL}}$ and CLOCK pins.

**TPA and TPB are timing pulses output by the CPU to control external logic.**

**CLOCK, TPA, and TPB timing is illustrated in Figure 12-3.**

**The status signals are $\overline{\text{EF1}}$ - $\overline{\text{EF4}}$, Q, and SC0 - SC1.**

We have already encountered signals **$\overline{\text{EF1}}$ - $\overline{\text{EF4}}$.** These **are four signals which external logic can input high or low;** they are tested by conditional Branch instructions.

**Q is output continuously, reflecting the level of the Q status flag,** which you can set or reset by executing appropriate COSMAC instructions. External logic can use the Q output signal in any way.

**The two state signals SC0 and SC1 are output by the CPU to identify the type of machine cycle which is in progress. SC0 and SC1 are output as follows:**

| SC1 | SC0 | Machine Cycle Operation |
|---|---|---|
| 0 | 0 | Instruction Fetch |
| 0 | 1 | Instruction Execute |
| 1 | 0 | DMA Access |
| 1 | 1 | Interrupt Acknowledge |

Typically, external logic will use the SC0 and SC1 signals as an integral part of device select logic in order to ensure that no device considers itself selected inappropriately.

**Remaining signals may be classified generally as controls.**

**A low $\overline{\text{MWR}}$ pulse identifies a memory write operation, an I/O data input operation, or the two operations occurring simultaneously.**

**$\overline{\text{MRD}}$ low identifies a memory read operation, an I/O data output operation, or the two operations occurring simultaneously.**

You should always keep in mind the possibility of using the high $\overline{\text{MWR}}$ and $\overline{\text{MRD}}$ signal levels in a COSMAC microcomputer system. This is because the delays between signal transitions can vary markedly with clock frequency. Sometimes you will find it easier to use the NOT $\overline{\text{MWR}}$ or the NOT $\overline{\text{MRD}}$ condition to generate a strobe, rather than relying on the low pulse.

**When an Input or Output instruction is executed, as against a Memory Reference instruction, a nonzero value is output via the three I/O command pins N0, N1, and N2.** If all three pins are low, no I/O operation is in progress. How you use the three I/O command pins is up to you. They can, if you wish, identify an I/O port, in which case you can immediately address up to seven I/O ports. Alternatively, you can use these pins to distinguish between command, status or data.

**External logic can control the CPU via the $\overline{\text{WAIT}}$ and $\overline{\text{CLEAR}}$ inputs. These two inputs combine to force the CPU into the following states:**

| $\overline{\text{CLEAR}}$ | $\overline{\text{WAIT}}$ | CPU State |
|---|---|---|
| 0 | 0 | Load |
| 0 | 1 | Reset |
| 1 | 0 | Pause |
| 1 | 1 | Run |

**In the Load state,** the CPU is idled and external logic can load memory directly, using the direct memory access logic provided by the CPU itself. That is to say, no instructions are executed and output signals are inactive; however, if $\overline{\text{DMA-IN}}$ is input low, then a DMA-IN machine cycle will be executed, as described later in this chapter.

**The Reset state is a typical reset.** During a reset, the Instruction register, the X and P registers, R0, and the Q status are all reset to zero. The Reset state must last for at least nine clock pulses. You should end the Reset state by entering the Run state. Thus, you may look upon $\overline{\text{WAIT}}$ as a signal which is maintained high during a normal sequence of Run and Reset states; $\overline{\text{CLEAR}}$ then becomes equivalent to the single $\overline{\text{RESET}}$ signal provided by other microprocessors.

When you enter the Run state following a Reset, the P register will contain 0; therefore, General Purpose Register R0 acts as a Program Counter. General Purpose Register R0 contains 0000; therefore, the first instruction fetched following a Reset will have its object code stored in memory location 0000. When the COSMAC CPU is reset, interrupts are enabled. **You must** therefore **disable interrupts with the first instruction of your bootstrap program.** If you do not do this, any stray interrupts will be acknowledged with unpredictable results.

**The Pause mode stops all internal CPU operations other than the CLOCK signal.** Note that COSMAC is a static device. CPU operations can halt for any length of time with no loss of data.

**The Run mode is the condition in which the CPU will normally operate.**

$\overline{\text{DMA-IN}}$ and $\overline{\text{DMA-OUT}}$ are control signals input by external logic in order to perform direct memory access operations. $\overline{\text{DMA-IN}}$ requests a data transfer from external logic to memory; $\overline{\text{DMA-OUT}}$ requests a data transfer from memory to external logic. In each case, memory is addressed by General Purpose Register R0. External logic is implicitly identified — it is the source of the $\overline{\text{DMA-IN}}$ and $\overline{\text{DMA-OUT}}$ signals. Following a DMA transfer, General Purpose Register R0 contents are incremented.

**$\overline{\text{INT}}$ is a standard interrupt request input.**

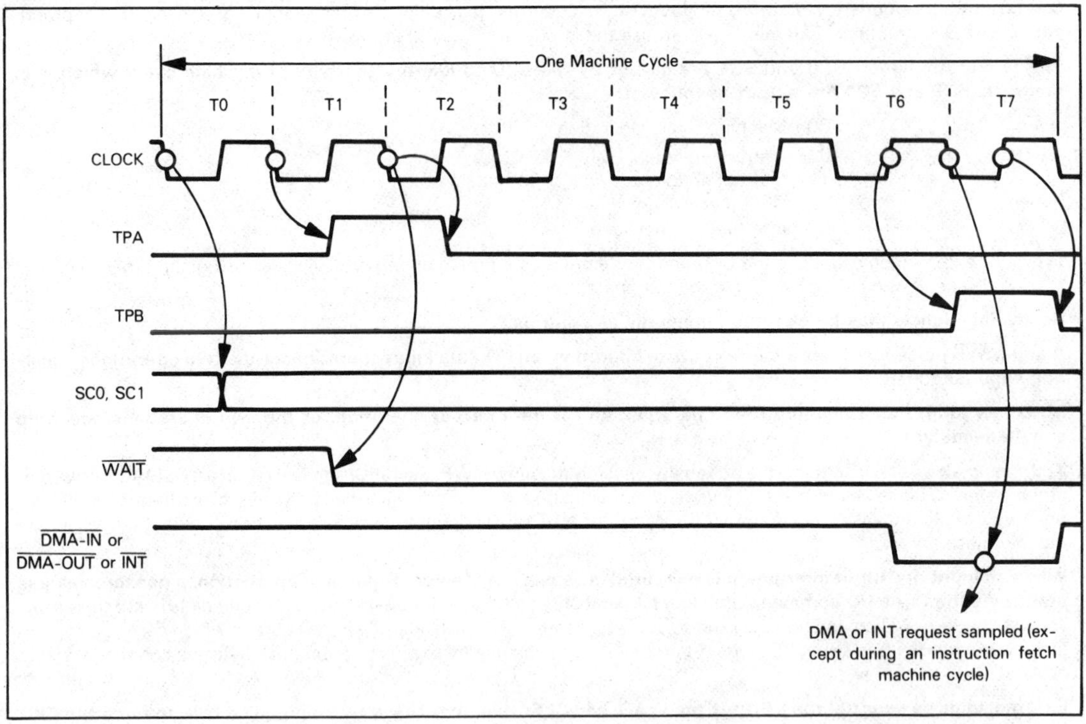

Figure 12-3. COSMAC Machine Cycle Timing

# COSMAC TIMING AND INSTRUCTION EXECUTION

**COSMAC signal timing varies with the frequency of the clock signal. Variations are non-linear. In the data sheets at the end of this chapter, delays are given for various clock frequencies. We recommend that you use one of the clock frequencies shown in the data sheets; you cannot accurately predict delays for other clock frequencies by interpolation or extrapolation. If you are using a clock frequency that is not shown in the data sheets, you should create your own data sheets by viewing waveforms on an oscilloscope and measuring delays experimentally.**

**COSMAC TIMING VARIATIONS**

**In the timing diagrams which follow, we have made some attempt to highlight the wide variations in timing that can separate a trigger signal transition and a subsequent dependent signal transition.** In an NMOS device we might show a control pulse dependent on a clock signal as follows:

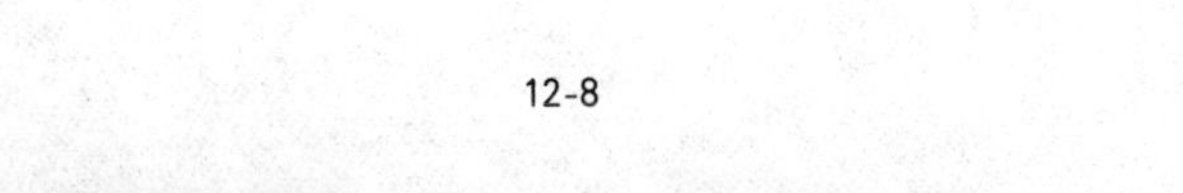

The same clock pulse might be more accurately illustrated for COSMAC as follows:

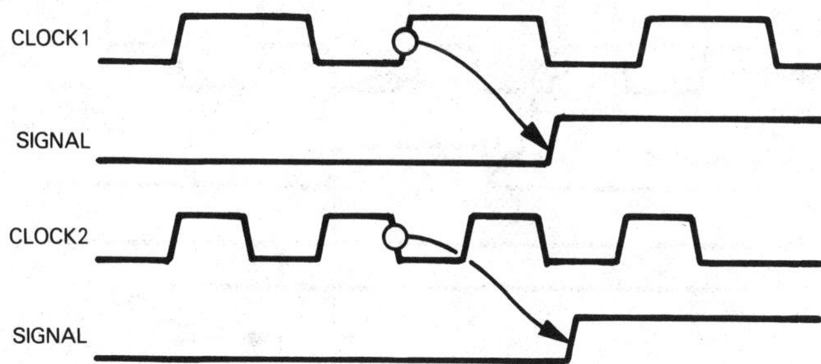


**COSMAC INSTRUCTION MACHINE CYCLE**

**All COSMAC instructions are executed as a sequence of machine cycles. Each machine cycle has eight clock periods, as illustrated in Figure 12-3.** Two timing signals, TPA and TPB, are output as an integral part of every machine cycle's timing.

Most COSMAC instructions execute in two machine cycles: an instruction fetch machine cycle and an instruction execute machine cycle. A few three-byte instructions execute in three machine cycles.

**For any memory reference instruction, a 16-bit memory address is output, one byte at a time, on the 8-bit Address Bus, as illustrated in Figure 12-4.** The high-order address byte appears first and should be read on the trailing edge of TPA. The low-order address byte is read with the accompanying data strobe.

**COSMAC NEGATIVE SET-UP TIME**

**When using certain clock frequencies, the high-order address byte does not appear on the Address Bus until some time after the trailing edge of TPA. This is identified in the data sheets by a negative set-up time,** which may be illustrated as follows:

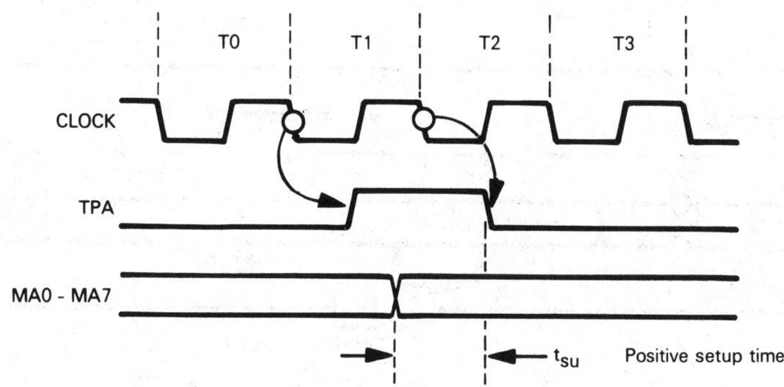

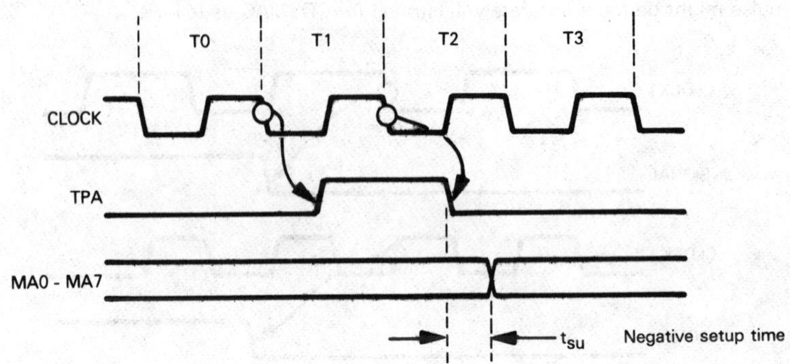

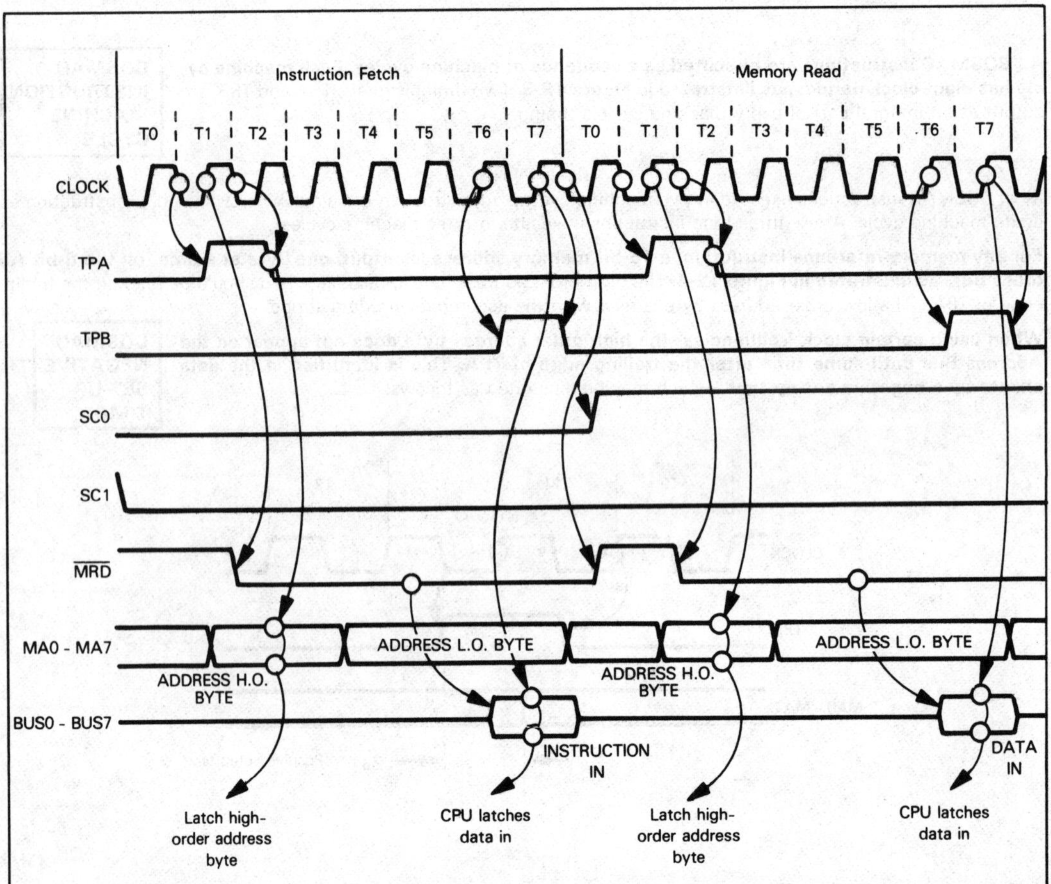

Figure 12-4. COSMAC Memory Read Instruction Timing

**If your clock frequency results in negative set-up times, then you must be sure to include extra logic that accounts for this fact. Note carefully that negative set-up times occur in a number of different places within any machine cycle.**

## COSMAC MEMORY READ TIMING

**Figure 12-4 illustrates timing for a two-machine cycle memory read instruction's execution.** An instruction fetch operation occurs in the first machine cycle and a memory read operation occurs in the second machine cycle. The only difference between these two machine cycles is the level of the SC0 control output and the source of the memory address which appears on the Address Bus.

The trailing edge of TPA is normally used as the high-order address byte strobe. When there is a negative set-up time, the trailing edge of TPA occurs before the high-order address byte is stable on the Address Bus. You will now have to use some clock signal transition occurring after TPA as your high-order address byte strobe.

$\overline{MRD}$ low occurs early on in a memory read or instruction fetch machine cycle. Therefore, as soon as the low-order address byte has been read by a memory device, it can immediately respond to a read request. The combination of $\overline{MRD}$ low and some appropriate clock signal transition must be used to generate a low-order address byte strobe. This strobe logic will be highly dependent on your clock frequency. The CPU reads data off the Data Bus on the rising edge of the T7 clock pulse. At this time, data on the Data Bus must be stable.

## COSMAC MEMORY WRITE INSTRUCTION TIMING

**A two-machine-cycle memory write instruction's timing is illustrated in Figure 12-5.** Memory strobes the high-order address byte exactly as it would for a memory read. A low $\overline{MWR}$ pulse acts as the low-order address byte strobe and a data output strobe. The CPU has valid data on the Data Bus before the high-order address byte output is complete; since the low-order address byte is stable on the Address Bus for a considerable time, there are no timing problems associated with the low-order address byte or data output.

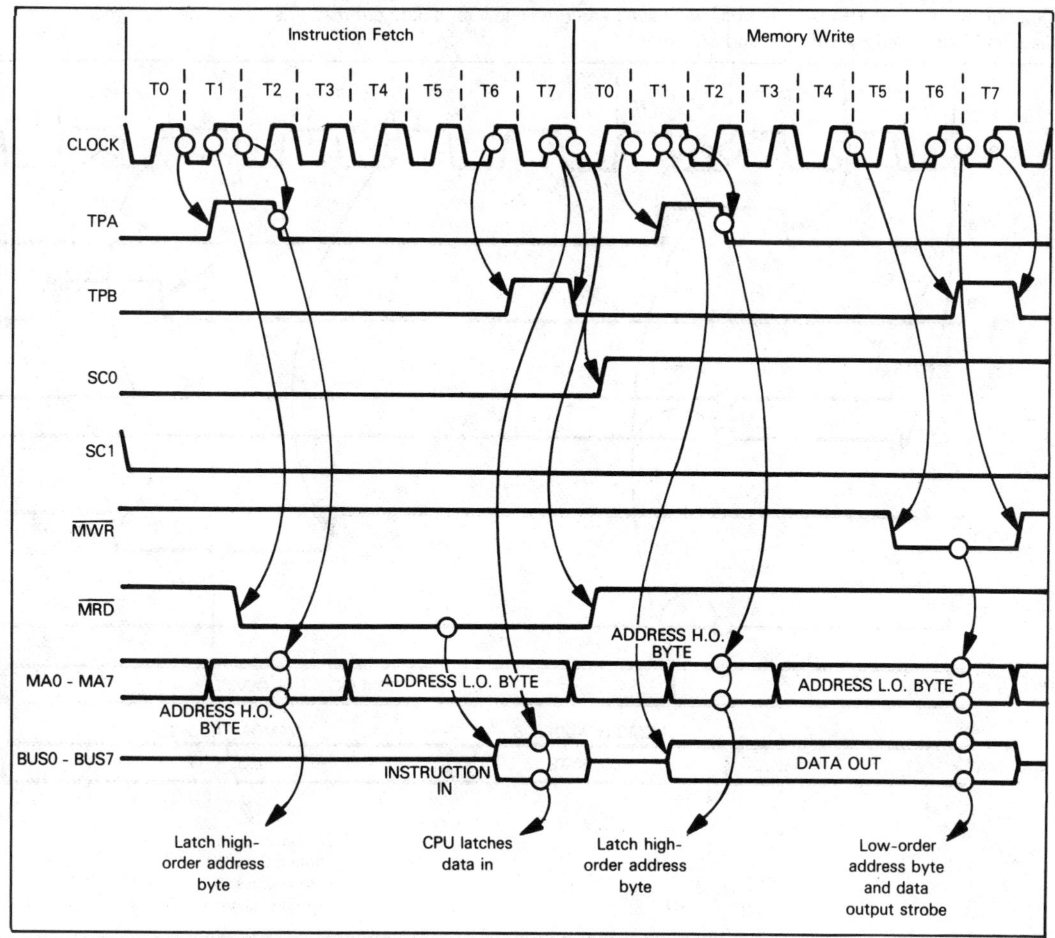


Figure 12-5. COSMAC Memory Write Instruction Timing

## COSMAC DATA INPUT, DATA OUTPUT, AND DIRECT MEMORY ACCESS

**COSMAC DMA and I/O logic are combined. We will therefore describe them together, beginning with direct memory access.**

**External logic initiates a DMA-IN or DMA-OUT operation by inputting the appropriate DMA control signal low.** As illustrated in Figure 12-3, the CPU samples the $\overline{\text{DMA-IN}}$ and $\overline{\text{DMA-OUT}}$ lines at the end of T6 in non-instruction fetch machine cycles. Upon detecting one or the other of these two signals low, the CPU performs a direct memory access operation during the next machine cycle. **Figure 12-6 illustrates timing for a DMA-IN machine cycle; Figure 12-7 illustrates timing for a DMA-OUT machine cycle.** As illustrated in these two figures, a DMA machine cycle consists of a simultaneous memory and I/O access.

**Consider first the DMA-IN machine cycle illustrated in Figure 12-6.** As "DMA-IN" would imply, data is to flow from an external device to memory. The external device is implicitly identified; it is the device which drove the $\overline{\text{DMA-IN}}$ control signal low in the previous machine cycle. The memory location to be accessed is addressed by Register R0. A DMA-IN machine cycle therefore consists of a data input machine cycle superimposed on a memory write machine cycle. In many microprocessors, superimposing these two operations within a single machine cycle would be impossible, since the Address Bus is used to identify memory locations and I/O devices; also, memory and I/O accesses occur during the same part of a machine cycle. In the case of COSMAC, the two operations can occur within a single machine cycle. The memory location to be accessed is identified in the usual way by outputting a memory address on the 8-bit Address Bus. Memory interface logic selects a memory location and writes into it as it would for any memory write machine cycle. Timing is illustrated in Figure 12-5. The external device which requested the $\overline{\text{DMA-IN}}$ can use the combination of a high TPA pulse together with SC0 low, SC1 high, and $\overline{\text{MRD}}$ high as a control signal forcing data onto the Data Bus. By the time TPA is high, $\overline{\text{MRD}}$ will have been driven low for a data out machine cycle. The DMA machine cycle is itself identified by SC0 low and SC1 high.

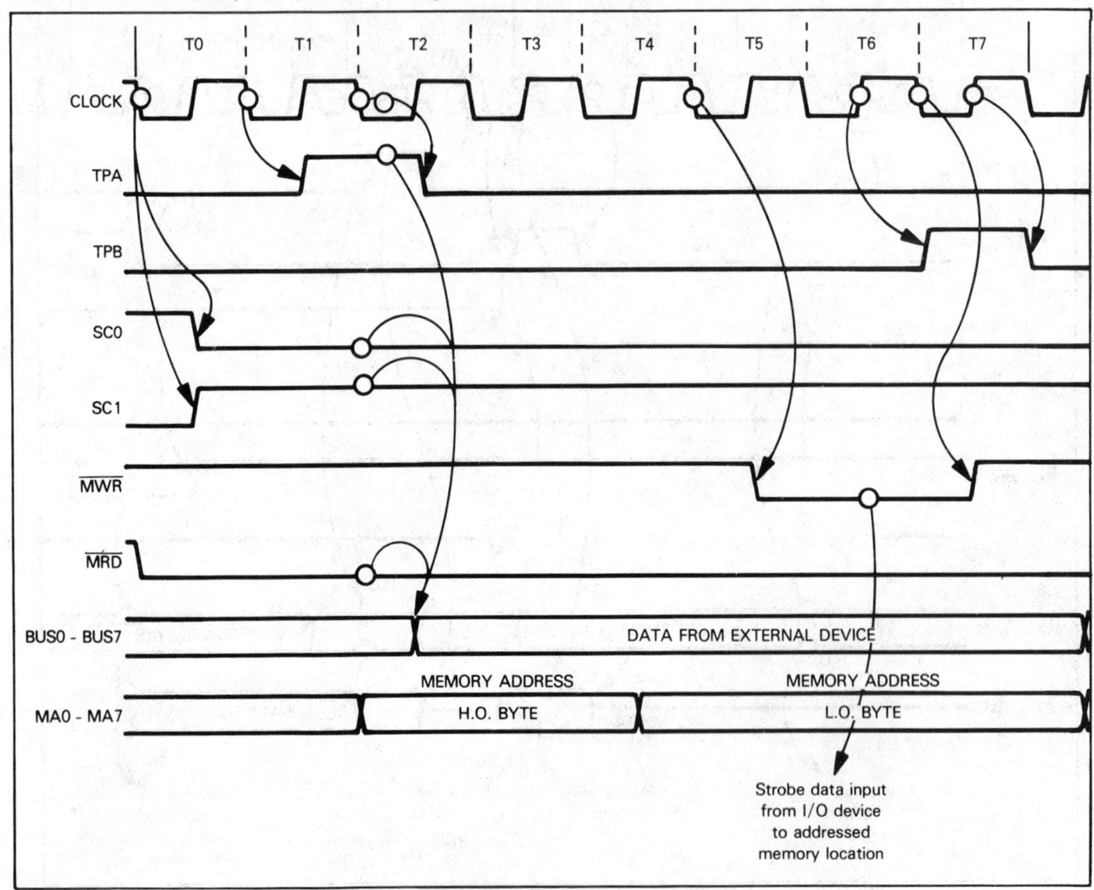


Figure 12-6. COSMAC DMA-IN Machine Cycle

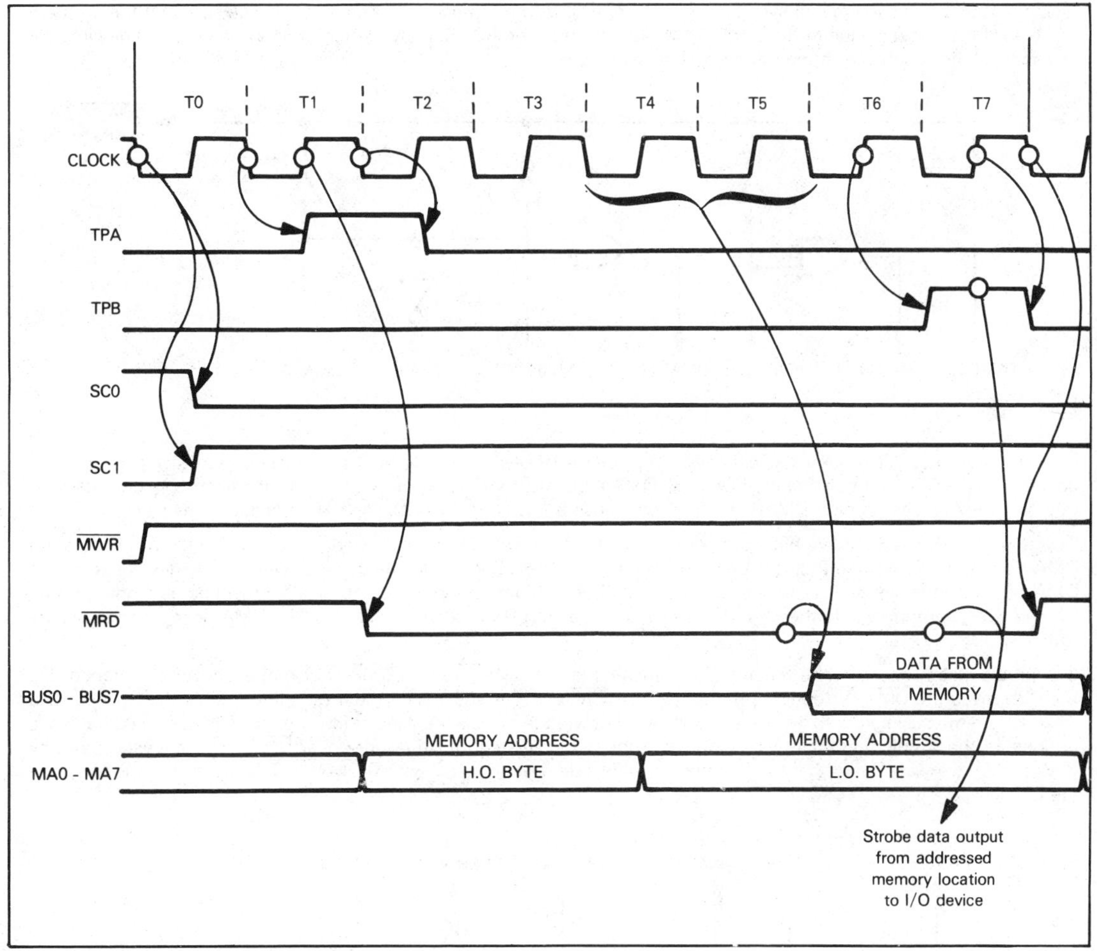


Figure 12-7. COSMAC DMA-OUT Machine Cycle

**For the DMA-OUT machine cycle, illustrated in Figure 12-7, the memory access portion of the machine cycle does not differ from a memory read, as illustrated in Figure 12-4.** The signal causing the addressed memory location to place data on the Data Bus will be generated, as shown in Figure 12-7, from the combination of $\overline{\text{MRD}}$ low and some appropriate clock transition; the appropriate clock transition will depend on the clock frequency you are using. The I/O device requesting the $\overline{\text{DMA-OUT}}$ machine cycle can use the high TPB pulse as a strobe to read data off the Data Bus.

External logic may know whether a DMA-IN or a DMA-OUT operation is being performed, since the I/O device generated the initial DMA request. In this case, external logic does need a CPU control signal identifying the direction of the DMA transfer. In Figure 12-6 we could show input data appearing on the Data Bus soon after the beginning of the DMA-IN machine cycle, as identified by SC0 low and SC1 high. It is only necessary for the data to be stable on the Data Bus while the $\overline{\text{MWR}}$ pulse is low, since this is the memory write strobe which will cause the input data to be written into memory.

**During any DMA machine cycle, the address output on the Address Bus comes from Register R0, which is then incremented so as to point to the next memory location;** this is in anticipation of a data block being transferred via direct memory access.

**If more than one device is capable of generating a DMA request, the CPU does nothing to help you resolve priority conflicts.** In every DMA machine cycle, the CPU assumes that only one external device is requesting direct memory access, and that this device can uniquely identify itself. If more than one device is capable of requesting direct memory access, then you must have your own external DMA arbitration logic. You must also be sure that the program has placed the correct value in the single DMA Address register (R0). Some variation of daisy-chaining is the simplest and most obvious scheme; it may be illustrated as follows:

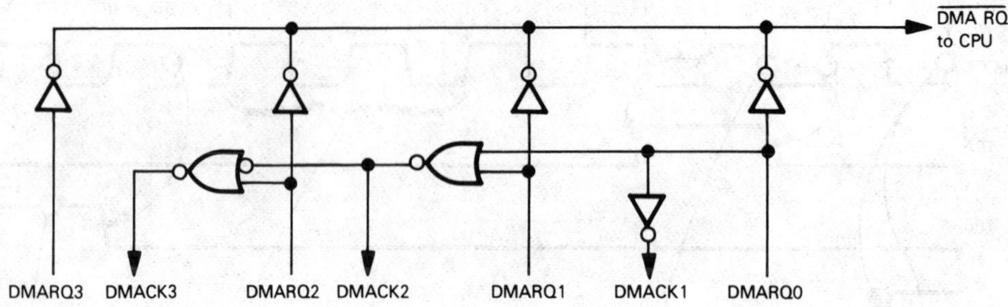


In the primitive logic illustrated above, DMARQ may be the $\overline{\text{DMA-IN}}$ or the $\overline{\text{DMA-OUT}}$ request line. In each case, the signal input to the CPU is simply the wire-OR of all DMA requests from external devices. Thus, if one or more devices is requesting DMA access, a high DMARQn input will cause a low $\overline{\text{DMA-IN}}$ or $\overline{\text{DMA-OUT}}$ to occur at the CPU.

Device 0 is considered to have highest priority. This device has no DMA acknowledge input. If Device 0 is requesting DMA access, it will assume that it is being serviced by the next DMA machine cycle. Lower priority devices require a DMA acknowledge signal. This signal can be the NOR of all higher priority DMA requests. Providing all higher priority DMA requests are low, no higher priority device is requesting DMA service; therefore the DMA acknowledge will be true.

One problem can arise with the scheme illustrated above. If a $\overline{\text{DMA-IN}}$ and a $\overline{\text{DMA-OUT}}$ request occur simultaneously, the CPU gives the $\overline{\text{DMA-IN}}$ request priority over the $\overline{\text{DMA-OUT}}$ request. You must therefore couple the $\overline{\text{DMA-IN}}$ and $\overline{\text{DMA-OUT}}$ requests in order to generate the DMA acknowledge signals returned to lower priority devices. You have two options. In the simpler case, $\overline{\text{DMA-IN}}$ requests from all devices can have priority over $\overline{\text{DMA-OUT}}$ requests from any device; that is to say, Device 3 $\overline{\text{DMA-IN}}$ requests will have priority over Device 0 $\overline{\text{DMA-OUT}}$ requests. Here is appropriate logic:

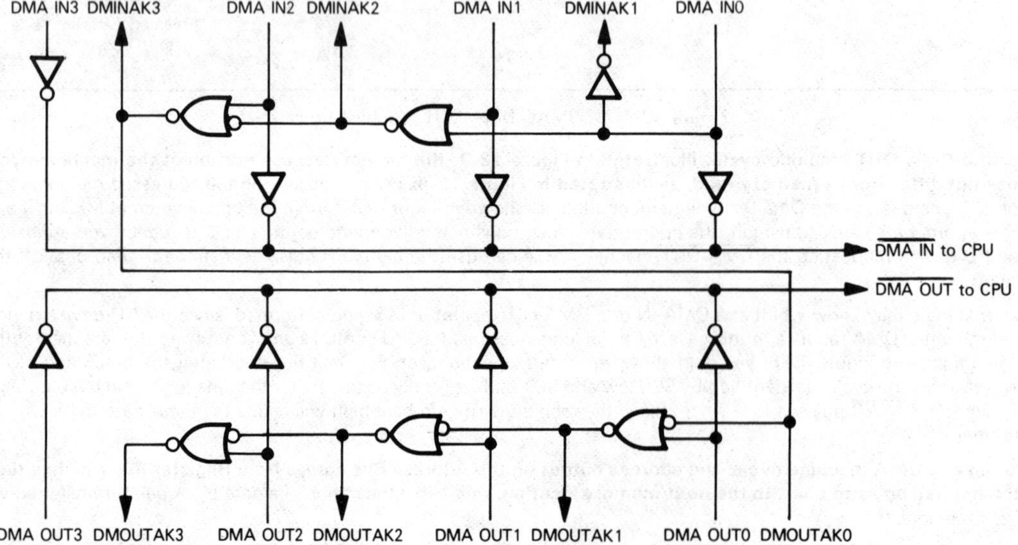

A more reasonable scheme would be to give Device 0 $\overline{\text{DMA-IN}}$ and $\overline{\text{DMA-OUT}}$ requests priority over Device 1 $\overline{\text{DMA-IN}}$ and $\overline{\text{DMA-OUT}}$ requests, and so on. This can be accomplished as follows:

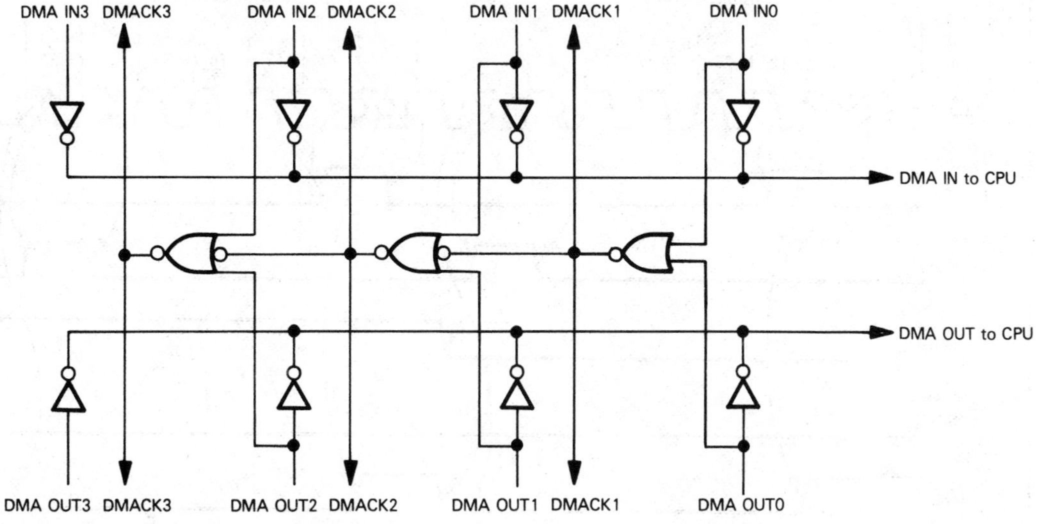

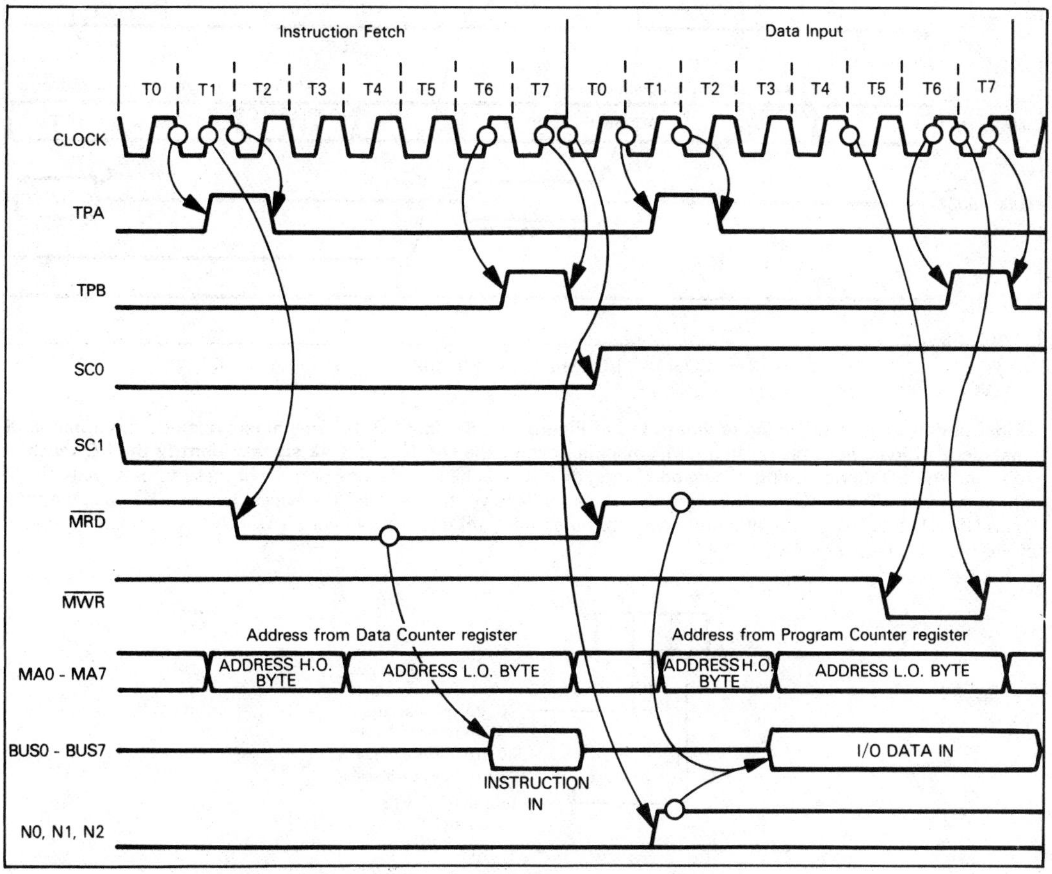

Instruction Fetch
Data Input
T0 T1 T2 T3 T4 T5 T6 T7 T0 T1 T2 T3 T4 T5 T6 T7
CLOCK
TPA
TPB
SC0
SC1
$\overline{\text{MRD}}$
$\overline{\text{MWR}}$
Address from Data Counter register
Address from Program Counter register
MA0 - MA7
ADDRESS H.O. BYTE
ADDRESS L.O. BYTE
BUS0 - BUS7
INSTRUCTION IN
I/O DATA IN
N0, N1, N2

Figure 12-8. COSMAC I/O Data Input Instruction Execution Timing

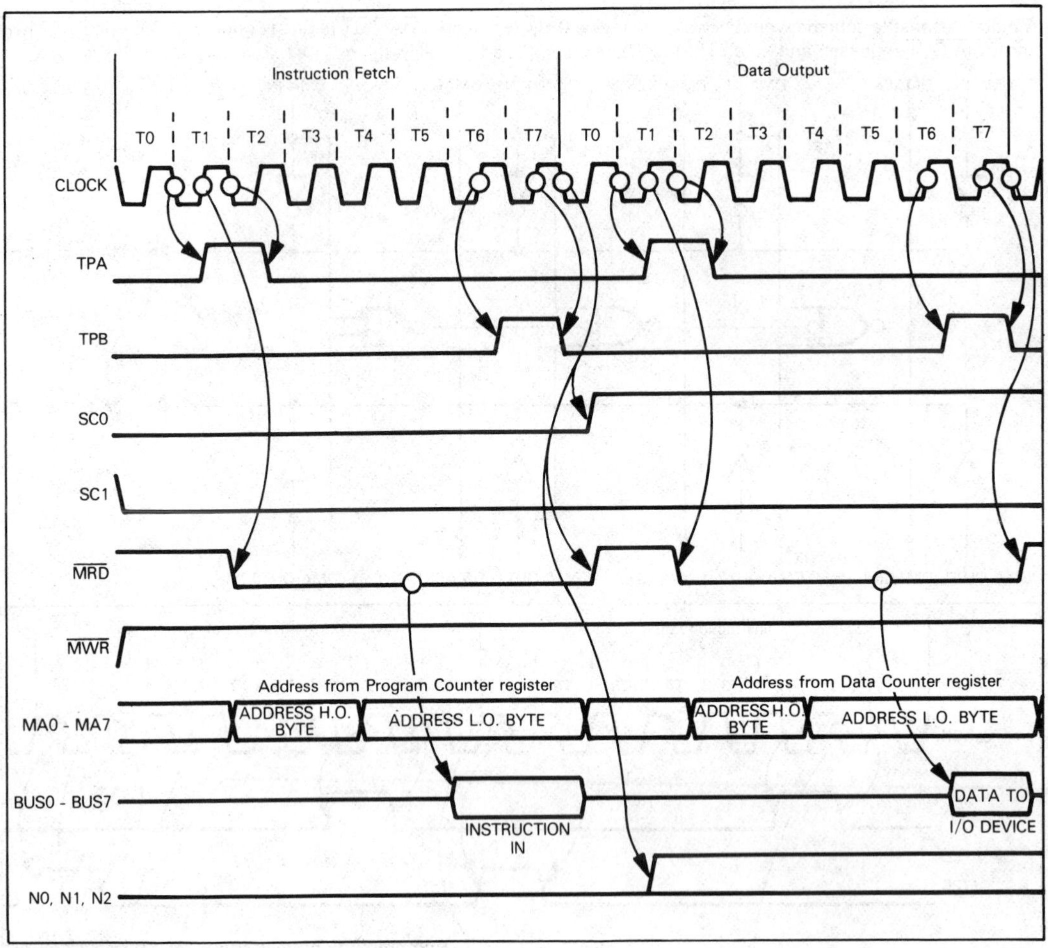

Figure 12-9. COSMAC I/O Data Output Instruction Execution Timing

**I/O instruction execution timing is illustrated in Figures 12-8 and 12-9. I/O machine cycles do have one additional piece of logic not present in a DMA machine cycle: the N0, N1, and N2 signals identify the I/O machine cycle, and the I/O device being accessed.** During any I/O machine cycle, one or more of these three signals will be high; thus, seven I/O devices may be identified. If you have fewer than seven I/O devices, then you can use the three signals N0, N1, and N2 to differentiate between data and control information. For a COSMAC system with three I/O devices, here is one possibility:

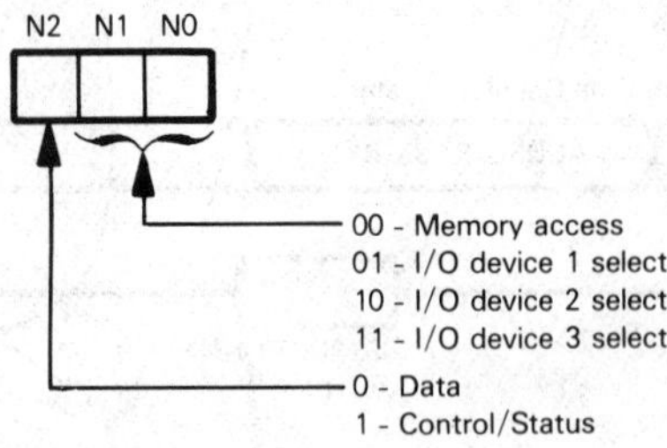

**The fact that I/O operations are in reality half of a DMA operation results in an anomaly.** The $\overline{\text{MRD}}$ and $\overline{\text{MWR}}$ control signals are logically inverted during an I/O operation if you think of them as I/O control signals. $\overline{\text{MRD}}$ low, which signals a memory read operation, identifies an I/O output operation. $\overline{\text{MWR}}$ low, which signals a memory write operation, identifies an I/O input operation.

**When an output instruction is executed, the Data Counter is incremented. The Data Counter is not affected when an input instruction is executed.** The programming ramifications of COSMAC I/O instructions are discussed in more detail later in this chapter.

## A SUMMARY OF COSMAC INTERRUPT PROCESSING

External logic can, at any time, request an interrupt by inputting a low signal at $\overline{\text{INT}}$. $\overline{\text{INT}}$ signal timing is given in Figure 12-3. Providing interrupts are enabled, following execution of the current instruction **the CPU will respond to the interrupt request with these three steps:**

1) The contents of the X and P registers are moved to the T register.
2) 1 is loaded into the P register and 2 is loaded into the X register.
3) Interrupts are disabled.

Steps 1 and 2 may be illustrated as follows:

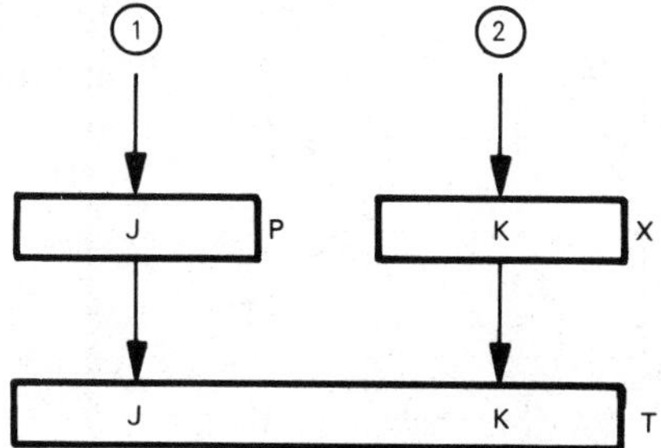


The interrupt service routine now begins executing with the instruction addressed by General Purpose Register R1. Any data accessed by the interrupt service routine must be addressed by General Purpose Register R2.

In the event that an interrupt service routine may itself be interrupted, you can store the T register contents in memory, at the location addressed by General Purpose Register R2 (which is now pointed to by X).

**The four input signals, $\overline{\text{EF1}}$ - $\overline{\text{EF4}}$, are the only means directly available for external logic to identify itself when more than one external device can request an interrupt.** Use of these external flag signals means that the interrupt service routine must begin with a number of Branch-on-Condition instructions that test the input flags to determine which is high.

More complex interrupt priority arbitration schemes must rely upon external logic to create an identifying code for the CPU to read out of an I/O port.

## THE COSMAC INSTRUCTION SET

**Table 12-1 summarizes the COSMAC instruction set.**

**You should allow for some anomalies in the COSMAC instruction set before starting to write programs.**

**There are four instructions which access the Data Counter.** They are:

1) LDX - transfer the contents of the memory location addressed by the Data Counter to the CPU Accumulator (D register).
2) LDXA - same as LDX, but post-increment the Data Counter.
3) IRX - increment the Data Counter.
4) STXD - store the CPU Accumulator (D register) contents in the memory location addressed by the Data Counter, then post-decrement the Data Counter.

**These four instructions are sometimes difficult to use.** Usually, a pair of instructions that increment and decrement a memory address will pre-increment and post-decrement, or post-increment and pre-decrement. In either case you can use the Data Counter as a Stack Pointer. Post-increment and post-decrement logic simply makes programming more difficult. The problem is further compounded by the fact that there is an LDX instruction, but no STX instruction;

also, there is an Increment Data Counter (IRX) instruction, but no Decrement Data Counter instruction. The fact that there is no Decrement Data Counter instruction is annoying, since every output instruction increments the Data Counter — something you don't always wish to do.

**COSMAC has no Jump-to-Subroutine instructions. You must maintain a separate Program Counter within the CPU registers in order to address subroutines. In very simple programs, this is a perfectly workable scheme;** what it means is that all subroutines are single level (that is to say, a subroutine will be called by a main program and never by another subroutine).

Consider the following register/memory scheme in a small COSMAC microcomputer system:

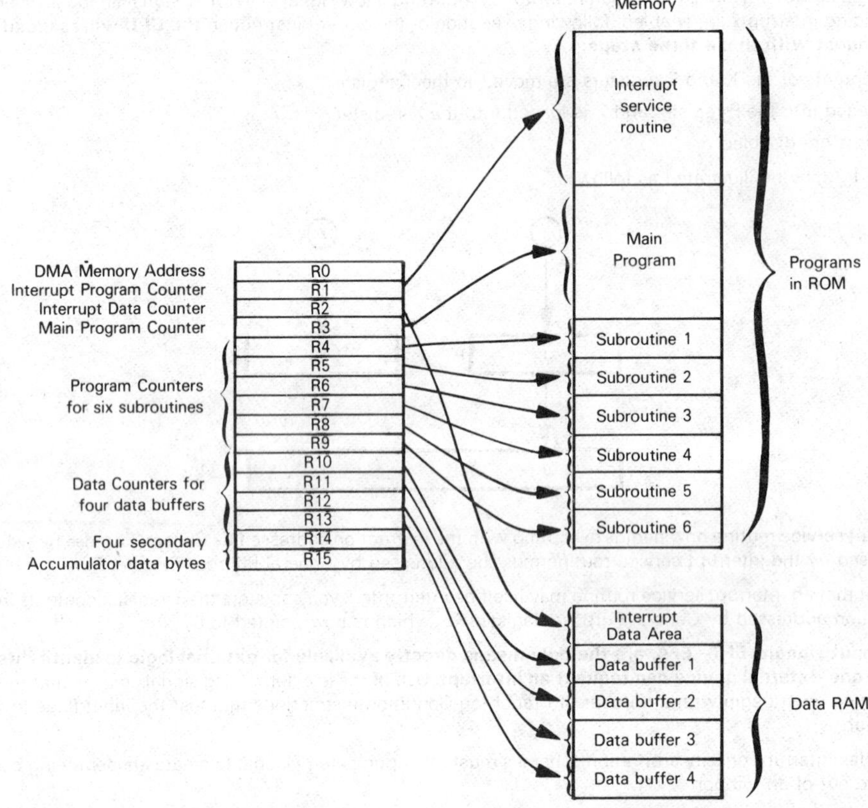


The scheme illustrated above shows data memory being divided into four stacks, each of which has its own Data Counter. The program consists of a main program and six subroutines. The main program has a Program Counter, and each subroutine has its own Program Counter. In order to call a subroutine, you simply switch from the main Program Counter to a subroutine Program Counter. In order to return from a subroutine, you simply switch from the subroutine Program Counter to the main Program Counter. This may be illustrated as follows:

```
..MAIN PROGRAM. IT USES DATA BUFFER 1.
            -
            -
            -
            -
            SETP    5           ..CALL SUBROUTINE 2
            -                   ..SUBROUTINE 2 RETURNS HERE
            -
            -
            -
..SUBROUTINE 2 BEGINS AT INSTRUCTION START
```

```
RET     SETP    3       ..RETURN TO MAIN PROGRAM
START   SETX    11      ..SUBROUTINE 2 USES DATA BUFFER 2
        -
        -
        -
        -
        SETX    10      ..RESTORE MAIN PROGRAM DATA COUNTER
        BR      RET     ..BRANCH TO RETURN INSTRUCTION
```

Subroutine 2 program logic illustrated above is self-evident, except for the return procedure.

Initially, Register 5 holds the address of the subroutine 2 instruction labeled START (that is, the SETX 11 instruction). Therefore, when the SETP 5 instruction is executed in the main program, execution branches to instruction START within subroutine 2. This instruction selects Register 11 as the Data Counter for subroutine 2. After the body of subroutine 2 has been executed, the return procedure begins with the SETX 10 instruction, which restores the Data Counter pointer required by the main program. This is assumed to be Register 10. The next instruction branches to RET, which is the instruction preceding the start of subroutine 2. This instruction loads the value 3 into the P register, thus selecting Register R3 as the next Program Counter — this causes execution to return to the main program. But notice that Register R5, which was the Program Counter for subroutine 2, is left addressing START, since R5 will have been incremented while executing instruction RET. Thus, the next time the main program calls subroutine 2, Register R5 will be pointing to START, which is the correct entry point for subroutine 2. The instruction execution path may now be illustrated as follows:

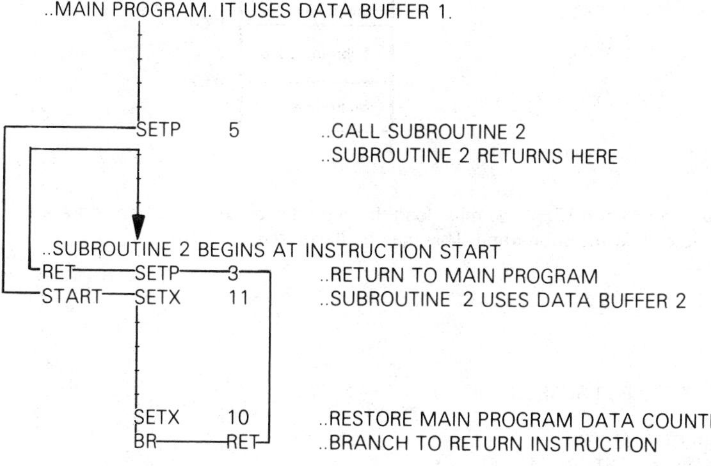
..MAIN PROGRAM. IT USES DATA BUFFER 1.
SETP 5 ..CALL SUBROUTINE 2
..SUBROUTINE 2 RETURNS HERE
..SUBROUTINE 2 BEGINS AT INSTRUCTION START
RET SETP 3 ..RETURN TO MAIN PROGRAM
START SETX 11 ..SUBROUTINE 2 USES DATA BUFFER 2
SETX 10 ..RESTORE MAIN PROGRAM DATA COUNTER
BR RET ..BRANCH TO RETURN INSTRUCTION

Note that when the SETP 5 instruction is executed, Register 3 is left pointing at the next memory location. If desired, a list of parameters can be stored following the SETP 5 instruction and then picked up by the subroutine via LDA 3 instructions. For example,

```
        SETP    5
        06              ..NUMBER OF BYTES
        'S'             ..ASCII MESSAGE
        'I'
        'G'
        'N'
        'O'
        'N'
RET     SETP    3
START   LDA     3
        PLO     6
        SETX    3
LOOP    OUT     PORT$NUMBER
        DEC     6
        GLO     6
        BNZ     LOOP
        BR      RET
```

**By keeping a number of short subroutines on a single 256-byte page of memory, you can increase the number of addressable subroutines.** Consider the following scheme:

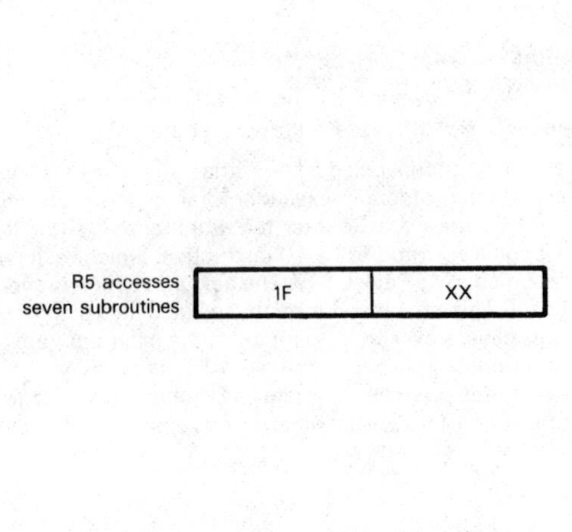


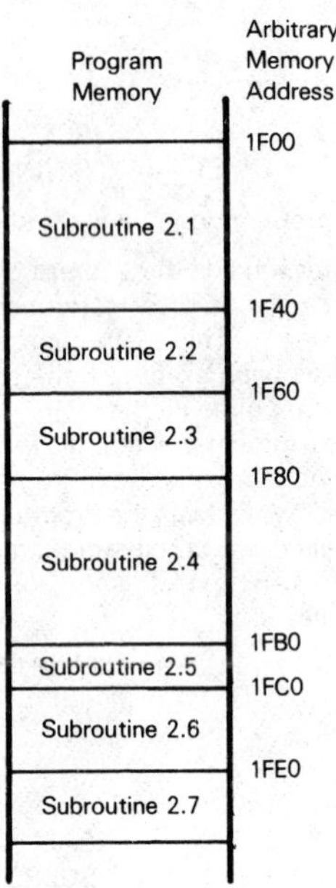


In order to call one of the seven subroutines held on Page $1F_{16}$, you must load the correct subroutine starting address into the low-order byte of Register R5 prior to calling the subroutine. This may be illustrated as follows:

```
..MAIN PROGRAM. IT USES DATA BUFFER 1.
        -
        -
        -
        -
        LDI     61H         ..INITIALIZE R(5).0 FOR SUBROUTINE 2.3
        PLO     5
        SETP    5           ..CALL SUBROUTINE 2.3
        -                   ..SUBROUTINE 2.3 RETURNS HERE
        -
        -
        -
..SUBROUTINE 2.3 IS ORIGINED AT 1F61H
        ORG     1F60H
RET     SETP    3           ..RETURN TO MAIN PROGRAM
START   SETX    11          ..SUBROUTINE 2.3 USES DATA BUFFER 2
        -
        -
        -
        -
        SETX    10          ..RESTORE MAIN PROGRAM DATA COUNTER
        BR      RET         ..BRANCH TO RETURN INSTRUCTION
```

You can use a similar scheme to increase the number of addressable data buffers. For example, you could have a large number of short data buffers on a single 256-byte page of data memory. This may be illustrated as follows:

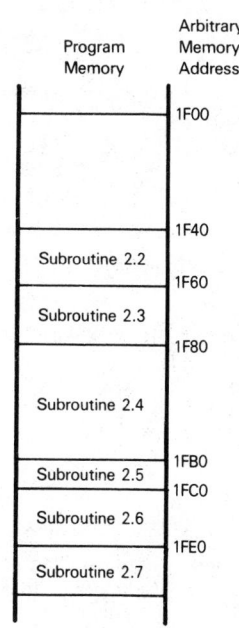

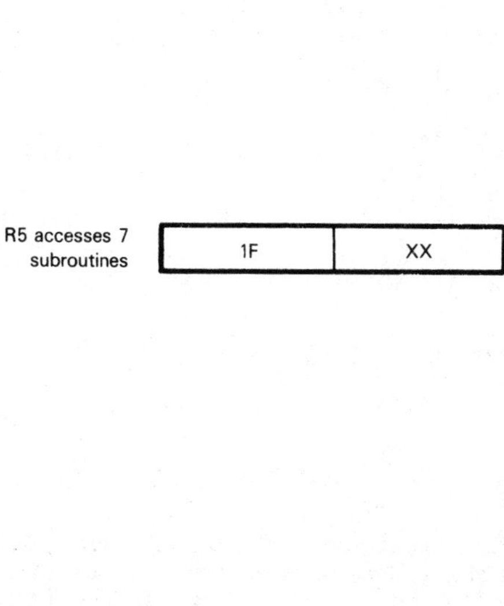


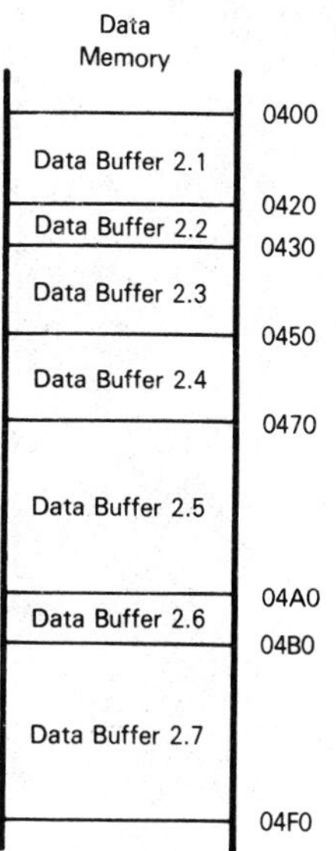

We must now modify our instruction sequence as follows:

```
..MAIN PROGRAM. IT USES DATA BUFFER 1
          -
          -
          -
          -
          LDI     61H         ..INITIALIZE R(5).0 FOR SUBROUTINE 2.3
          PLO     5
          SETP    5           ..CALL SUBROUTINE 2.3
          -                   ..SUBROUTINE 2.3 RETURNS HERE
          -
          -
          -
..SUBROUTINE 2.3 IS ORIGINED AT 1F61H. IT USES DATA BUFFER 2.3
          ORG     1F60H
RET       SETP    3           ..RETURN TO MAIN PROGRAM
START     LDI     30H         ..INITIALIZE R(11).0 FOR DATA COUNTER
          PLO     11
          SETX    11
          -
          -
          -
          -
          SETX    10          ..RESTORE MAIN PROGRAM DATA COUNTER
          BR      RET         ..BRANCH TO RETURN INSTRUCTION
```

**COSMAC NESTED SUBROUTINE**

**There is no simple way of handling nested subroutines using the COSMAC instruction set.** The problem is that if a subroutine can be called by another subroutine, then you have no obvious return logic. Suppose, for example, that subroutine X can be called by subroutine A, B, or C, or by the main program. If subroutines A, B, and C each have their own Program Counter, then how is subroutine X going to know which Program Counter to select when returning? In order to resolve this problem, you will need a special subroutine to call subroutines, with another special subroutine to return from subroutines. Consider the following register assignments:

| | |
|---|---|
| R0 | DMA memory address |
| R1 | Interrupt Program Counter |
| R2 | Interrupt Data Counter |
| R3 | Main Program Counter |
| R4 | Call subroutine Program Counter |
| R5 | Return subroutine Program Counter |
| R6 | Stack Pointer |
| R7 | |
| R8 | |
| R9 | |
| R10 | |
| R11 | |
| R12 | |
| R13 | |
| R14 | |
| R15 | |

Every time a subroutine is called, Register R4 must be selected as the new Program Counter. Register R4 switches to a special subroutine whose only purpose is to save the contents of Register R3 in an external stack, which is addressed by R6. If additional registers are dedicated to serving as Data Counters, then the contents of these registers may also have to be saved on the external stack. After register contents have been appropriately saved, the CALL subroutine must select the required subroutine. There are many ways in which you can identify the required subroutine; one technique would be to use an additional register as a pointer to a data table within which all subroutine addresses are stored. For example, R7 might point to such a data table. Now the calling program must load into R7 the address of the location in the data table where the required subroutine address is stored. Now the CALL subroutine will use R7 as a pointer to two bytes of data, which must be loaded into R3 before the CALL subroutine terminates execution by selecting R3 as the next Program Counter.

When a subroutine completes execution, it returns by selecting Register R5 as the Program Counter in order to call a RETURN subroutine. The RETURN subroutine must reload R3, and any dedicated Data Counter registers' contents from the external stack, which is addressed by R6. Having done this, the RETURN subroutine selects R3 as the next Program Counter, thus affecting a return from subroutine.

It takes 128 microseconds to execute a well-written CALL subroutine. It takes 112 microseconds to execute a well-written RETURN subroutine. These times assume a 2 MHz clock.

**RCA's COSMAC Programming Manual describes some additional techniques for handling nested subroutines.**

**COSMAC INTERRUPT SERVICE ROUTINE PROGRAMS**

**Programming interrupt service routines is quite simple — providing you do not use subroutines within the interrupt service routine.** Remember, as soon as an interrupt is acknowledged, R1 becomes the Program Counter and R2 becomes the Data Counter; the previous Program Counter and Data Counter pointers are stored in the memory location which was addressed by the Data Counter when the interrupt occurred. Now, providing there are no subroutines in the interrupt service routine, you can simply execute a program which is addressed by R1, while using R2 to access data memory. **If you do execute subroutines, you must consider all of the problems associated with using subroutines in a main program, but you must add a new complication: R1 is now the main Program Counter.** You must either have special subroutines that are called only by the interrupt service routine, or you must write some type of instruction sequence which switches to using the main Program Counter register within the interrupt service routine before you start calling subroutines.

**COSMAC INPUT/OUTPUT PROGRAMS**

**COSMAC I/O instructions are quite unusual. The most unusual (and useful) aspect of COSMAC I/O instructions is the fact that they transfer data between memory and an I/O device.** Most microprocessors transfer data between the CPU and I/O devices. When you are inputting or outputting one byte of data at a time, it makes more sense for the data transfer to occur between the CPU and the I/O device, since the single byte of data is likely to be generated in the CPU for an output operation, or is likely to be operated on by the CPU after being input. When blocks of data are being input or output, it makes more sense for the data transfer to occur between memory and an I/O device, since the block of data must be held in a memory buffer.

COSMAC input instructions transfer the data to the CPU Accumulator and the memory location addressed by the Data Counter, thus giving you the benefit of both possibilities. If your program is in read-only memory, you can avoid input data being written into memory by selecting the same register to act as Program Counter and Data Counter. Now the input data will be stored in the Accumulator (D register), but the attempt to write the input byte into memory will be thwarted, since the selected memory location will be a read-only memory location.

COSMAC output instructions increment the Data Counter after performing the output operation. This makes it easy to output a block of data from data memory.

If you select the same register to act as Program Counter and Data Counter during an output operation, then the Program Counter will be incremented twice: once for the normal instruction fetch increment, and a second time for the data output. This allows you to perform immediate output operations.

## THE BENCHMARK PROGRAM

**Now consider our benchmark program; for COSMAC it looks like this:**

```
        LDI     TABHI    ..LOAD TABLE BASE ADDRESS HIGH ORDER BYTE
        PHI     R15      ..INTO R15 AND R13
        PHI     R13      ..R15 POINTS TO NEXT FREE TABLE BYTE
        LDI     00
        PLO     R13      ..R13 POINTS TO FIRST BYTE IN TABLE
        PLO     R14
        LDN     R13      ..ASSUME THAT DISPLACEMENT TO FIRST
        PLO     R15      ..FREE BYTE IS STORED IN FIRST TABLE BYTE
        LDI     IOBFHI   ..LOAD IOBUF START ADDRESS INTO R14
        PHI     R14
        LDN     R14      ..LOAD DISPLACEMENT TO END OF FILLED IOBUF
        PLO     R14
LOOP:   LDN     R14      ..LOAD NEXT BYTE FROM IOBUF
        STR     R15      ..STORE IN NEXT FREE TABLE BYTE
```

```
        INC     R15      ..INCREMENT R15
        DEC     R14      ..DECREMENT R14
        GLO     R14      ..TEST LOW ORDER BYTE OF R14
        BNZ     LOOP     ..IF NOT ZERO RETURN TO LOOP
        GLO     R15      ..AT END RESET FIRST BYTE OF
        STR     R13      ..TABLE TO NEW FIRST FREE BYTE ADDRESS
```

This is the memory map assumed by the benchmark program above:

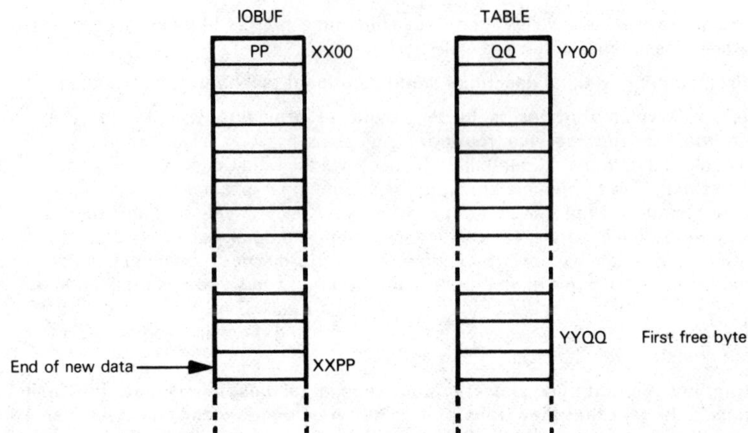


Tables IOBUF and TABLE are both origined on page boundaries; that is to say, the low-order eight bits of the origin address are zeros. Data in table IOBUF is stored backwards. The first byte of data to be moved from IOBUF to TABLE is stored at the highest memory address of IOBUF. This highest memory address, illustrated above by XXPP, is derived by adding the contents of the first IOBUF table byte to the origin address. Thus, the first byte of IOBUF stores that length of table IOBUF which is currently filled. COSMAC program logic can now decrement the initial IOBUF address from XXPP and, upon testing the low-order byte equal to zero, logic knows that all data has been transferred.

The destination table stores the displacement to the first free table byte in the first byte of TABLE. Thus the address of the first free byte equals the origin plus the contents of the first TABLE byte.

Since the displacement to the first free byte of TABLE is stored in a single data byte, clearly TABLE cannot be more than 256 bytes long. Thus, IOBUF must contain less than 256 bytes at any time.

If you look at the COSMAC program, it appears rather long. The instruction loop itself contains only six instructions, which compares well with many other benchmark programs. What is deceptive about the benchmark program is the fact that we have taken a large number of instructions in order to load initial addresses into general purpose registers. Remember, COSMAC has sixteen such general purpose registers, and the whole programming philosophy of this microcomputer is that you load addresses into general purpose registers once, at the beginning of the program, and never again. In fact, the benchmark program points up both the strength and the weakness of the COSMAC instruction set. Its strength is that large numbers of addresses can be permanently stored within CPU registers, thence memory access becomes a trivial task. Its weakness is that it takes a lot of instructions to get memory addresses into general purpose registers in the first place — and that becomes a liability if you have to re-use the same general purpose register in a number of different ways within one program.

The following symbols are used in Table 12-1:

| | |
|---|---|
| ADR8 | 8-bit address |
| ADR16 | 16-bit address |
| D | D register |
| DATA8 | 8-bit data unit |
| DEV | 3-bit code: 1 through 7 |
| DF | Data Flag or Carry |
| EFn | Pin status: EF1, EF2, EF3, or EF4 |
| IE | Interrupt Enable bit |

n One of the numbers 1, 2, 3, 4

N 4-bit register select unit

N210 Three output pins, N2, N1, N0

P 4-bit Program Counter Pointer register

Q Q status output flip-flop

R(z) Specifies a register:
if z is N the instruction operand specifies the register
P the contents of the P register specify the register
X the contents of the X register specify the register

T T register

X 4-bit Data Counter Pointer register

x<y,z> Bits y through z of a register or memory location. For example, T<7,4> represents the high-order four bits of the T register.

[] Contents of location enclosed within brackets. If a register designation is enclosed within the brackets, then the designated register's contents are specified. If an I/O port number is enclosed within the brackets, then the I/O port contents are specified. If a memory address is enclosed within the brackets, then the contents of the addressed memory location are specified.

[[]] Implied memory addressing; the contents of the memory location designated by the contents of a register.

Λ Logical AND

V Logical OR

⊻ Logical Exclusive-OR

← Data is transferred in the direction of the arrow.

Under the heading of STATUSES in Table 12-1, an X indicates statuses which are modified in the course of the instruction's execution. If there is no X, it means that the status maintains the value it had before the instruction was executed.

Table 12-1. COSMAC Instruction Set Summary

| TYPE | MNEMONIC | OPERAND(S) | BYTES | STATUSES | | | | | | OPERATION PERFORMED |
|---|---|---|---|---|---|---|---|---|---|---|
| | | | | OF | IE | | | | | |
| I/O | INP | DEV | 1 | | | | | | | [[R(X)]]←[D]←BUS<br>N210←[N<2,0>]<br>Input data from Bus to Register D and memory. Output device number (DEV) at pins N2, N1, N0. |
| | OUT | DEV | 1 | | | | | | | BUS ← [[R(X)]], [R(X)] ← [R(X)] + 1<br>N210←[N<2,0>]<br>[R(X)]←[R(X)] + 1<br>Output memory to Bus; output device number (DEV) at pins N2, N1, N0; increment Data Counter. |
| PRIMARY MEMORY REFERENCE | LDN | N | 1 | | | | | | | [D]←[[R(N)]]<br>Load D register via specified register. N may not be 0. |
| | LDA | N | 1 | | | | | | | [D]←[[R(N)]]<br>[R(N)]←[R(N)] + 1<br>Load D register via specified register. Increment specified register. |
| | STR | N | 1 | | | | | | | [[R(N)]]←[D]<br>Store D register via specified register. |
| | LDX | | 1 | | | | | | | [D]←[[R(X)]]<br>Load D register using implied addressing. |
| | LDXA | | 1 | | | | | | | [D]←[[R(X)]]<br>[R(X)]←[R(X)] + 1<br>Load D register using implied addressing. Increment Data Counter. |
| | STXD | | 1 | | | | | | | [[R(X)]]←[D]<br>[R(X)]←[R(X)]-1<br>Store D register using implied addressing. Decrement Data Counter. |
| SECONDARY MEMORY REFERENCE MEMORY OPERATE | OR | | 1 | | | | | | | [D]←[[R(X)]] V [D]<br>OR with D register using implied addressing. |
| | XOR | | 1 | | | | | | | [D]←[[R(X)]]⊻[D]<br>Exclusive-OR with D register using implied addressing. |
| | AND | | 1 | | | | | | | [D]←[[R(X)]] Λ [D]<br>AND with D register using implied addressing. |
| | ADD | | 1 | X | | | | | | [D]←[[R(X)]] + [D]<br>Add to D register using implied addressing. |
| | ADC | | 1 | X | | | | | | [D]←[[R(X)]] + [D] + [DF]<br>Add with Carry to D register using implied addressing. |
| | SD | | 1 | X | | | | | | [D]←[[R(X)]]-[D]<br>Subtract D from memory using implied addressing. |
| | SDB | | 1 | X | | | | | | [D]←[[R(X)]]-[D]-[DF]<br>Subtract with borrow from memory using implied addressing. |
| | SM | | 1 | X | | | | | | [D]←[D]-[[R(X)]]<br>Subtract memory from D using implied addressing. |
| | SMB | | 1 | X | | | | | | [D]←[D]-[[R(X)]]-[DF]<br>Subtract memory with borrow from D using implied addressing. |

Table 12-1. COSMAC Instruction Set Summary (Continued)

| TYPE | MNEMONIC | OPERAND(S) | BYTES | STATUSES | | | | | | OPERATION PERFORMED |
|---|---|---|---|---|---|---|---|---|---|---|
| | | | | OF | IE | | | | | |
| IMMEDIATE | LDI | DATA8 | 2 | | | | | | | [D]← DATA8<br>Load immediate to D register. |
| IMMEDIATE OPERATE | ORI | DATA8 | 2 | | | | | | | [D]← DATA8 V [D]<br>OR immediate with D register. |
| | XRI | DATA8 | 2 | | | | | | | [D]← DATA8 ⊻ [D]<br>Exclusive-OR immediate with D register. |
| | ANI | DATA8 | 2 | | | | | | | [D]← DATA8 Λ [D]<br>AND immediate with D register. |
| | ADI | DATA8 | 2 | X | | | | | | [D]← DATA8 + [D]<br>Add immediate to D register. |
| | ADCI | DATA8 | 2 | X | | | | | | [D]← DATA8 + [D] + [DF]<br>Add immediate with Carry to D register. |
| | SDI | DATA8 | 2 | X | | | | | | [D]← DATA8- [D]<br>Subtract D register from immediate data. |
| | SDBI | DATA8 | 2 | X | | | | | | [D]← DATA8- [D]- [DF]<br>Subtract D register with borrow from immediate data. |
| | SMI | DATA8 | 2 | X | | | | | | [D]←[D]-DATA8<br>Subtract immediate from D register. |
| | SMBI | DATA8 | 2 | X | | | | | | [D]←[D]-DATA8- [DF]<br>Subtract immediate with borrow from D register. |
| BRANCH AND SKIP | BR | ADR8 | 2 | | | | | | | [R(P)<7,0>]← ADR8<br>Branch within same page to given address. |
| | LBR | ADR16 | 3 | | | | | | | [R(P)]← ADR16<br>Branch to given address |
| | SKP | | 1 | | | | | | | [R(P)]←[R(P)] + 1<br>Skip next byte. |
| | LSKP | | 1 | | | | | | | [R(P)]←[R(P)] + 2<br>Skip next two bytes. |
| | NBR | ADR8 | 2 | | | | | | | Same as SKIP |
| | NLBR | ADR16 | 3 | | | | | | | Same as LSKP |
| BRANCH AND SKIP ON CONDITION | BZ | ADR8 | 2 | | | | | | | If [D]=0; then [R(P)<7,0>]← ADR8<br>Branch within same page on D register zero. |
| | BNZ | ADR8 | 2 | | | | | | | If [D]≠0; then [R(P)<7,0>]← ADR8<br>Branch within same page on D register nonzero. |
| | BDF | ADR8 | 2 | | | | | | | If [DF]=1; then [R(P)<7,0>]← ADR8<br>Branch within same page on Carry set. |

Table 12-1. COSMAC Instruction Set Summary (Continued)

| TYPE | MNEMONIC | OPERAND(S) | BYTES | STATUSES | | | | | | OPERATION PERFORMED |
|---|---|---|---|---|---|---|---|---|---|---|
| | | | | OF | IE | | | | | |
| BRANCH AND SKIP ON CONDITION (CONTINUED) | BNF | ADR8 | 2 | | | | | | | If [DF]=0; then [R(P)<7,0>]← ADR8<br>Branch within same page on Carry reset. |
| | BQ | ADR8 | 2 | | | | | | | If Q=1; then [R(P)<7,0>]← ADR8<br>Branch within same page on output flip-flop set. |
| | BNQ | ADR8 | 2 | | | | | | | If Q=0; then [R(P)<7,0>]← ADR8<br>Branch within same page on output flip-flop reset. |
| | Bn | ADR8 | 2 | | | | | | | If EFn=1; then [R(P)<7,0>]← ADR8<br>Branch within same page on specified external flag set. |
| | BNn | ADR8 | 2 | | | | | | | If EFn=0; then [R(P)<7,0>]← ADR8<br>Branch within same page on specified external flag reset. |
| | LBZ | ADR16 | 3 | | | | | | | If [D]=0; then [R(P)]← ADR16<br>Branch absolute on D register zero. |
| | LBNZ | ADR16 | 3 | | | | | | | If [D]≠0; then [R(P)]← ADR16<br>Branch absolute on D register nonzero. |
| | LBDF | ADR16 | 3 | | | | | | | If [DF]=1; then [R(P)]← ADR16<br>Branch absolute on Carry set. |
| | LBNF | ADR16 | 3 | | | | | | | If [DF]=0; then [R(P)]← ADR16<br>Branch absolute on Carry reset. |
| | LBQ | ADR16 | 3 | | | | | | | If [Q]=1; then [R(P)]← ADR16<br>Branch absolute on output flip-flop set. |
| | LBNQ | ADR16 | 3 | | | | | | | If [Q]=0; then [R(P)]← ADR16<br>Branch absolute on output flip-flop reset. |
| | LSZ | | 1 | | | | | | | If [D]=0; then [R(P)]←[R(P)] + 2<br>Skip two bytes if D register zero. |
| | LSNZ | | 1 | | | | | | | If [D]≠0; then [R(P)]←[R(P)] + 2<br>Skip two bytes if D register nonzero. |
| | LSDF | | 1 | | | | | | | If [DF]=1; then [R(P)]←[R(P)] + 2<br>Skip two bytes if Carry set. |
| | LSNF | | 1 | | | | | | | If [DF]=0; then [R(P)]←[R(P)] + 2<br>Skip two bytes if Carry reset. |
| | LSQ | | 1 | | | | | | | If [Q]=1; then [R(P)]←[R(P)] + 2<br>Skip two bytes if output flip-flop set. |
| | LSNQ | | 1 | | | | | | | If [Q]=0; then [R(P)]←[R(P)] + 2<br>Skip two bytes if output flip-flop reset. |
| | LSIE | | 1 | | | | | | | If [IE]=1; then [R(P)]←[R(P)] + 2<br>Skip two bytes if interrupts are enabled. |

Table 12-1. COSMAC Instruction Set Summary (Continued)

| TYPE | MNEMONIC | OPERAND(S) | BYTES | STATUSES OF | IE | | | | | OPERATION PERFORMED |
|---|---|---|---|---|---|---|---|---|---|---|
| REGISTER-REGISTER MOVE | GLO | N | 1 | | | | | | | [D]←[R(N)<7,0>]<br>Load D with low byte of specified register. |
| | GHI | N | 1 | | | | | | | [D]←[R(N)<15,8>]<br>Load D with high byte of specified register. |
| | PLO | N | 1 | | | | | | | [R(N)<7,0>]←[D]<br>Store D to low byte of specified register. |
| | PHI | N | 1 | | | | | | | [R(N)<15,8>]←[D]<br>Store D to high byte of specified register. |
| REGISTER OPERATE | INC | N | 1 | | | | | | | [R(N)]←[R(N)] + 1<br>Increment specified register. |
| | DEC | N | 1 | | | | | | | [R(N)]←[R(N)]-1<br>Decrement specified register. |
| | IRX | | | | | | | | | [R(X)]←[R(X)] + 1<br>Increment Data Counter. |
| | SHR | | 1 | X | | | | | | 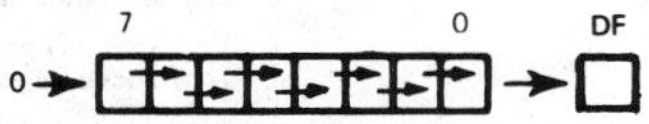 Shift D register right one bit. Shift bit 0 into Carry; reset bit 7. |
| | SHRC | | 1 | X | | | | | | 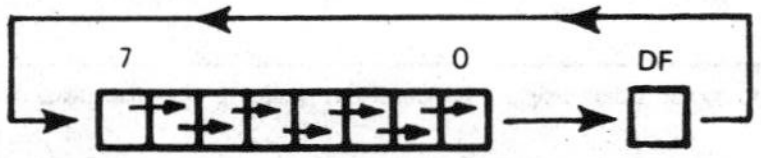 Shift D register right one bit through Carry. |
| | SHL | | 1 | X | | | | | |  Shift D register left one bit. Shift bit 7 into Carry; reset bit 0. |
| | SHLC | | 1 | X | | | | | | 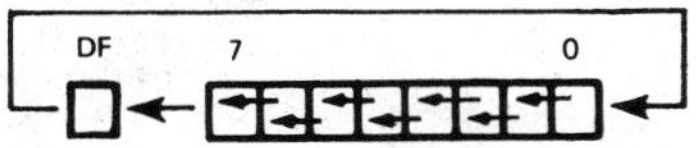 Shift D register left one bit through Carry. |

Table 12-1. COSMAC Instruction Set Summary (Continued)

| TYPE | MNEMONIC | OPERAND(S) | BYTES | STATUSES | | | | | | OPERATION PERFORMED |
|---|---|---|---|---|---|---|---|---|---|---|
| | | | | OF | IE | | | | | |
| STACK | SAV | | 1 | | | | | | | [[R(X)]]←[T]<br>Save T register in memory. |
| | MARK | | 1 | | | | | | | [T<7,4>]←[X]<br>[T<3,0>]←[P]<br>[[R(2)]]←[T]<br>[R(2)]←[R(2)]-1<br>[X]←[P]<br>Save X and P in T; then push onto Stack via Register 2. Decrement Register 2. Move P to X. |
| | RET | | 1 | | | | | | | [X]←[[R(X)]<7,4>]<br>[P]←[[R(X)]<3,0>]<br>[R(X)]←[R(X)] + 1<br>[IE]←1<br>Pop memory into X and P using implied addressing. Increment Data Counter. Enable interrupts. |
| | DIS | | 1 | | | | | | | [X]←[[R(X)]<7,4>]<br>[P]←[[R(X)]<3,0>]<br>[R(X)]←[R(X(] + 1<br>[IE]←0<br>Pop memory into X and P using implied addressing. Increment Data Counter. Disable interrupts. |
| STATUS | SEP | N | 1 | | | | | | | [P]←N<br>Set P register to N. |
| | SEX | N | 1 | | | | | | | [X]←N<br>Set X register to N. |
| | SEQ | | 1 | | | | | | | [Q]←1<br>Set output flip-flop. |
| | REQ | | 1 | | | | | | | [Q]←0<br>Reset output flip-flop. |
| | IDL | | 1 | | | | | | | Idle CPU. Wait for Interrupt/DMA-IN/DMA-OUT. |
| | NOP | | 1 | | | | | | | No Operation |

The following symbols are used in Table 12-2:

aaaa 4 bits selecting one of the 16 registers
bbb 3-bit data unit output to N2, N1, N0 lines
PP 8-bit address
QQ Second 8 bits of a 16-bit address
XX 8-bit immediate data unit

Table 12-2. COSMAC Instruction Set Object Codes

| INSTRUCTION | OBJECT CODE | BYTES | MACHINE CYCLES |
|---|---|---|---|
| ADC | 74 | 1 | 2 |
| ADCI DATA8 | 7C | 2 | 2 |
| | XX | | |
| ADD | F4 | 1 | 2 |
| ADI DATA8 | FC | 2 | 2 |
| | XX | | |
| AND | F2 | 1 | 2 |
| ANI DATA8 | FA | 2 | 2 |
| | XX | | |
| BDF ADR8 | 33 | 2 | 2 |
| | PP | | |
| BNF ADR8 | 3B | 2 | 2 |
| | PP | | |
| BNQ ADR8 | 39 | 2 | 2 |
| | PP | | |
| BNZ ADR8 | 3A | 2 | 2 |
| | PP | | |
| BNI ADR8 | 3C | 2 | 2 |
| | PP | | |
| BNZ ADR8 | 3D | 2 | 2 |
| | PP | | |
| BN3 ADR8 | 3E | 2 | 2 |
| | PP | | |
| BN4 ADR8 | 3F | 2 | 2 |
| | PP | | |
| BQ ADR8 | 31 | 2 | 2 |
| | PP | | |
| BR ADR8 | 30 | 2 | 2 |
| | PP | | |
| BZ ADR8 | 32 | 2 | 2 |
| | PP | | |
| B1 ADR8 | 34 | 2 | 2 |
| | PP | | |
| B2 ADR8 | 35 | 2 | 2 |
| | PP | | |
| B3 ADR8 | 36 | 2 | 2 |
| | PP | | |
| B4 ADR8 | 37 | 2 | 2 |
| | PP | | |
| DEC N | 0010aaaa | 1 | 2 |
| DIS | 71 | 1 | 2 |
| GHI N | 1001aaaa | 1 | 2 |
| GLO N | 1000aaaa | 1 | 2 |
| IDL | 00 | 1 | 2 |
| INC N | 0001aaaa | 1 | 2 |
| INP P | 01101bbb | 1 | 2 |
| IRX | 60 | 1 | 2 |
| LBDF ADR16 | C3 | 3 | 3 |
| | PP | | |
| | QQ | | |

| INSTRUCTION | OBJECT CODE | BYTES | MACHINE CYCLES |
|---|---|---|---|
| LBNF ADR16 | C3 | 3 | 3 |
| | PP | | |
| | QQ | | |
| LBNQ ADR16 | C9 | 3 | 3 |
| | PP | | |
| | QQ | | |
| LBNZ ADR16 | CA | 3 | 3 |
| | PP | | |
| | QQ | | |
| LBQ ADR16 | C1 | 3 | 3 |
| | PP | | |
| | QQ | | |
| LBR ADR16 | C0 | 3 | 3 |
| | PP | | |
| | QQ | | |
| LBZ ADR16 | C2 | 3 | 3 |
| | PP | | |
| | QQ | | |
| LDA N | 0100aaaa | 1 | 2 |
| LDI DATA8 | F8 | 2 | 2 |
| | XX | | |
| LDN N | 0000aaaa | 1 | 2 |
| LDX | F0 | 1 | 2 |
| LDXA | 72 | 1 | 2 |
| LSDF | CF | 1 | 3 |
| LSIE | CC | 1 | 3 |
| LSNF | C7 | 1 | 3 |
| LSNQ | C5 | 1 | 3 |
| LSNZ | C6 | 1 | 3 |
| LSQ | CD | 1 | 3 |
| LSKP | C8 | 1 | 3 |
| LSZ | CF | 1 | 3 |
| MARK | 79 | | 2 |
| NBR | 38 | 2 | 2 |
| NLBR | C8 | 3 | 3 |
| NOP | C4 | 1 | 3 |
| OR | F1 | 1 | 2 |
| ORI DATA8 | F9 | 2 | 2 |
| | XX | | |
| OUT P | 01100bbb | 1 | 2 |
| PHI N | 1011aaaa | 1 | 2 |
| PLO N | 1010aaaa | 1 | 2 |
| REQ | 7B | 1 | 2 |
| RET | 70 | 1 | 2 |
| SAV | 78 | 1 | 2 |
| SEQ | 7A | 1 | 2 |
| SEP N | 1101aaaa | 1 | 2 |
| SEX N | 1110aaaa | 1 | 2 |

Table 12-2. COSMAC Instruction Set Object Codes (Continued)

| INSTRUCTION | OBJECT CODE | BYTES | MACHINE CYCLES | INSTRUCTION | OBJECT CODE | BYTES | MACHINE CYCLES |
|---|---|---|---|---|---|---|---|
| SD | F5 | 1 | 2 | SM | F7 | 1 | 2 |
| SDB | 75 | 1 | 2 | SMB | 77 | 1 | 2 |
| SDBI DATA8 | 7D | 2 | 2 | SMBI DATA8 | 7F | 2 | 2 |
| | XX | | | | XX | | |
| SDI DATA8 | FD | 2 | 2 | SMI | FF | 2 | 2 |
| | XX | | | | XX | | |
| SHL | FE | 1 | 2 | STR N | 0101aaaa | 1 | 2 |
| SHLC | 7E | 1 | 2 | STXD | 73 | 1 | 2 |
| SHR | F6 | 1 | 2 | XOR | F3 | 1 | 2 |
| SHRC | 76 | 1 | 2 | XRI DATA8 | FB | 2 | 2 |
| SKP | 38 | 1 | 2 | | XX | | |

## USING COSMAC WITH OTHER MICROPROCESSOR SUPPORT DEVICES

**Using the COSMAC microprocessor with other microprocessor support devices will rarely make economic sense. We are therefore not going to describe how other microprocessor system busses can be generated from the COSMAC System Bus.**

The principal advantage of COSMAC is its CMOS technology. The architecture, instruction set, and signal timing of COSMAC are not in themselves attractive enough to warrant selecting this CPU, as compared to many other popular 8-bit microprocessors described in this book. Thus, the principal reason for describing bus-to-bus conversion logic does not exist in this case. If you are going to use 8080A or 6800 support devices in your microcomputer application, you will almost certainly want to use the 8080A or 6800 CPU in preference to COSMAC.

The one other CMOS microprocessor described in this book, the IM6100, has support devices which are very dependent on the peculiarities of the IM6100; therefore, they are not useful in a COSMAC microcomputer system.

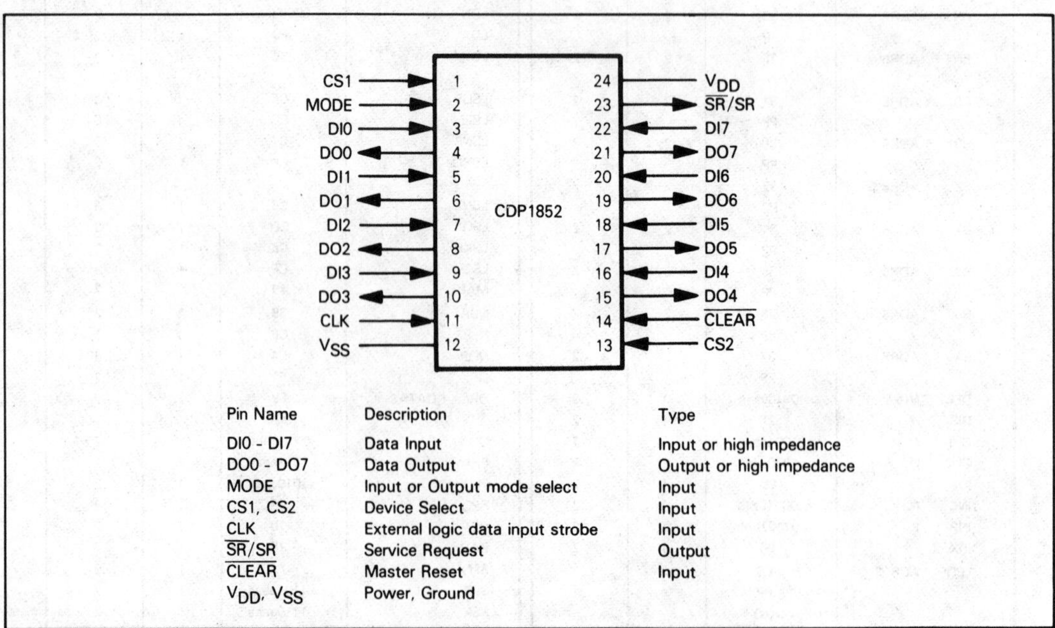


| Pin Name | Description | Type |
|---|---|---|
| DI0 - DI7 | Data Input | Input or high impedance |
| DO0 - DO7 | Data Output | Output or high impedance |
| MODE | Input or Output mode select | Input |
| CS1, CS2 | Device Select | Input |
| CLK | External logic data input strobe | Input |
| $\overline{SR}$/SR | Service Request | Output |
| $\overline{CLEAR}$ | Master Reset | Input |
| $V_{DD}$, $V_{SS}$ | Power, Ground | |

Figure 12-10. CDP1852 I/O Port Pins and Signals

# THE CDP1852 PARALLEL I/O PORT

**The CDP1852 parallel I/O port provides a COSMAC microcomputer system with bidirectional parallel I/O logic. Although we classify the device as bidirectional, it must be operated in input mode or output mode at any given time.**

**Figure 12-1 illustrates that part of our general microcomputer functional logic which is implemented by the CDP1852 device.**

**The CDP1852 is fabricated using CMOS technology; it is packaged as a 24-pin DIP.**

**There are two versions of the CDP1852 I/O port, differentiated by their power supplies. The CDP1852D will operate with power supplies ranging between +3 and +12 volts. The CDP1852CD requires a power supply ranging between +4 and +6 volts.**

## CDP1852 PINS AND SIGNALS

**CDP1852 I/O port pins and signals are illustrated in Figure 12-10.**

**There are two Data Busses. Data is input to the CDP1852 device via DI0-DI7; data output occurs at DO0-DO7.** If the CDP1852 device is operating in input mode, then DO0-DO7 will be connected to the CPU Data Bus (BUS0-BUS7). If the CDP1852 device is operating in output mode, then DI0-DI7 will be connected to the CPU Data Bus (BUS0-BUS7).

**The mode of the CDP1852 device is determined by the MODE input.** If MODE is low, then the CDP1852 device is operating in input mode. In this mode, data will be transferred from external logic to the CDP1852 device via the DI0-DI7 signals; this data will be read by the CPU via the DO0-DO7 signals. When MODE is high, the CDP1852 device is operating in output mode. In output mode data will flow from the CPU to the CDP1852 device via the DI0-DI7 signals, while external logic will read this data via the DO0-DO7 signals.

**External logic strobes data into the CDP1852 device via a high-to-low transition of the CLK signal in input mode. CLK high is a prerequisite for data input when the CDP1852 device is operated in output mode.**

**CS1 and CS2 are select signals used by the CPU to access a CDP1852 device.** CS1 is high true in input mode and low true in output mode. CS2 is always high true.

**$\overline{\text{SR}}$/SR is a handshaking control signal;** in input mode $\overline{\text{SR}}$ is used by the CPU, while in output mode SR is used by external logic.

**$\overline{\text{CLEAR}}$ is a master reset input.** When input low, it resets all data bits within the CDP1852 to 0 and it outputs SR low.

## CDP1852 OPERATIONS OVERVIEW

**The CDP1852 I/O port can operate in input mode or output mode.** Input mode is specified by a low MODE input and output is specified by a high MODE input.

In input mode, external logic transmits data to the CDP1852 I/O port via DI0-DI7. External logic uses CLK to strobe data into the I/O port. Data is output via DO0-DO7, which holds valid data whenever CS1 and CS2 are both high. **In the general case, input mode timing may be illustrated as follows:**

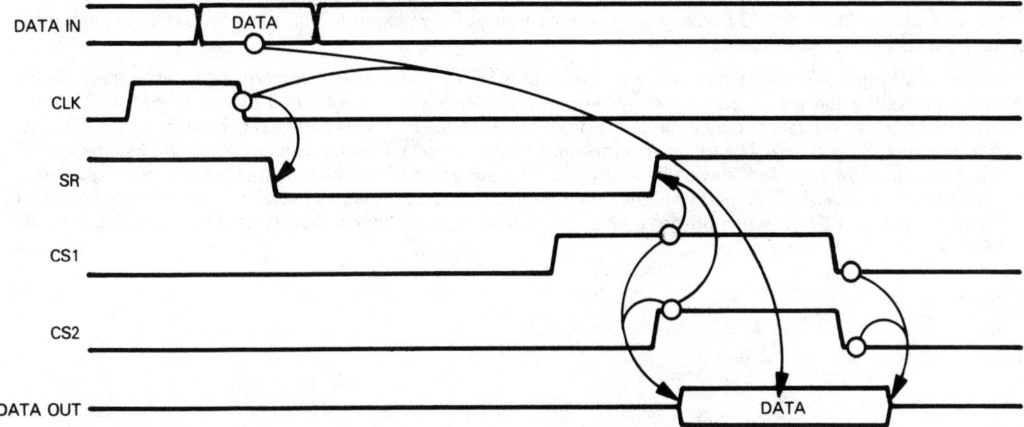

SR is an acknowledge signal sent back to external logic. SR goes low as soon as external logic provides a high-to-low CLK transition. SR returns high as soon as the CDP1852 I/O port ceases to be selected via CS1 and CS2. Thus, external logic can look upon SR low as a "device busy" signal, and the low-to-high SR transition as an input acknowledge.

**When the CDP1852 I/O port is operated in output mode,** the CPU Data Bus is connected to DI0-DI7. The combination of CS1 low, CS2 high, and CLK high latches data input into the CDP1852 I/O port. The output lines DO0-DO7 are always enabled; therefore, as soon as new data is latched into the I/O port, this data appears at the output pins. **Timing may be illustrated as follows:**

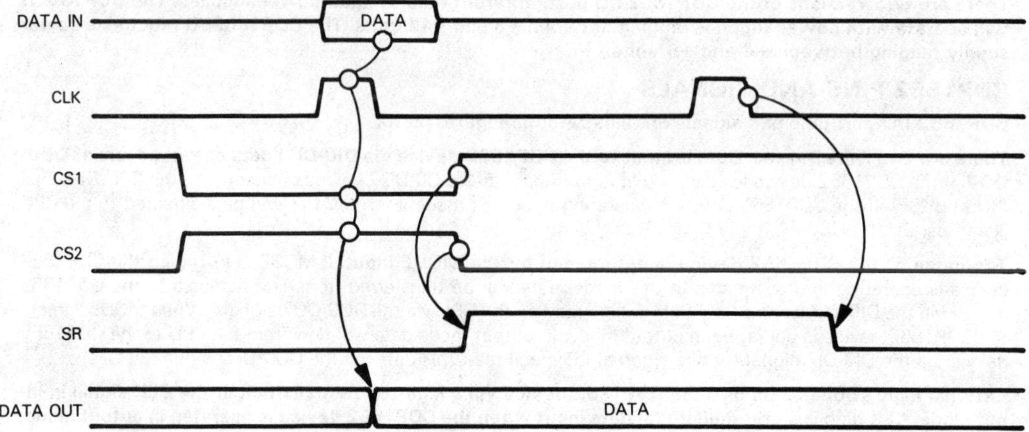


SR is pulsed high in output mode. SR goes high as soon as new data is strobed into the CDP1852 I/O port, and remains high until the next high-to-low CLK transition. External logic can use the SR high pulse as a data input strobe.

## CDP1852 INPUT OPERATIONS

**The CDP1852 can be operated as an input port using programmed input or DMA input. We will first examine programmed input.**

**Figure 12-11 illustrates the CDP1852 I/O port operating in input mode with programmed input. Before examining this figure, you should be familiar with Figure 12-8 and its associated text.**

The logic in Figure 12-11 assumes that external logic uses the eight data input lines DI0-DI7 and two control lines CLK and $\overline{SR}$.

When external logic has new data available, it will place the data on DI0-DI7 and pulse CLK high. This latches the data into the CDP1852 I/O port and simultaneously sets $\overline{SR}$ low. External logic will not attempt to input more data until $\overline{SR}$ is no longer low.

Since the $\overline{SR}$ signal is connected to one of the flag inputs $\overline{EF1\text{-}EF4}$ of the CPU, program logic can monitor the $\overline{SR}$ signal by testing the proper status flag. When an input instruction is executed by the COSMAC CPU, the CDP1852 I/O port will respond by gating data onto the CPU Data Bus. This gating is controlled by the two chip select inputs CS1 and CS2. The CPU reads this data on the low $\overline{MWR}$ strobe. External logic can use the low $\overline{SR}$ pulse as its acknowledge and "device busy" signal; $\overline{SR}$ is pulsed low from the time that the external logic data is strobed into the CDP1852 I/O port until the time that this I/O port ceases to be selected after being selected for an input operation. Thus, when $\overline{SR}$ goes high again, external logic knows that its data has been input to the CPU.

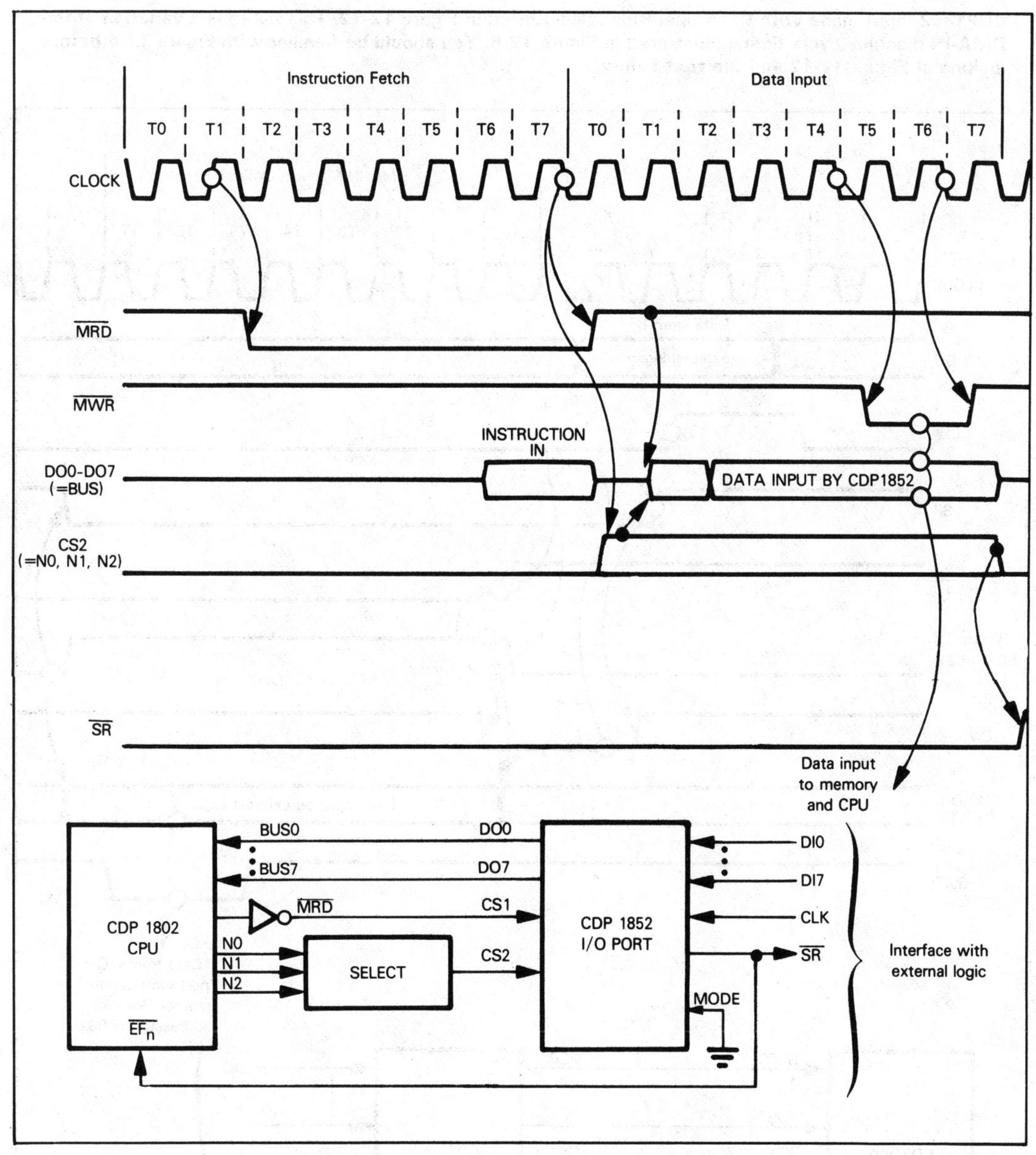


Figure 12-11. CDP1852 I/O Port in Input Mode with Programmed Input

**CDP1852 input mode with DMA operation is illustrated in Figure 12-12. This figure is a variation of the DMA-IN machine cycle timing illustrated in Figure 12-6. You should be familiar with Figure 12-6 before looking at Figure 12-12 and the text below.**

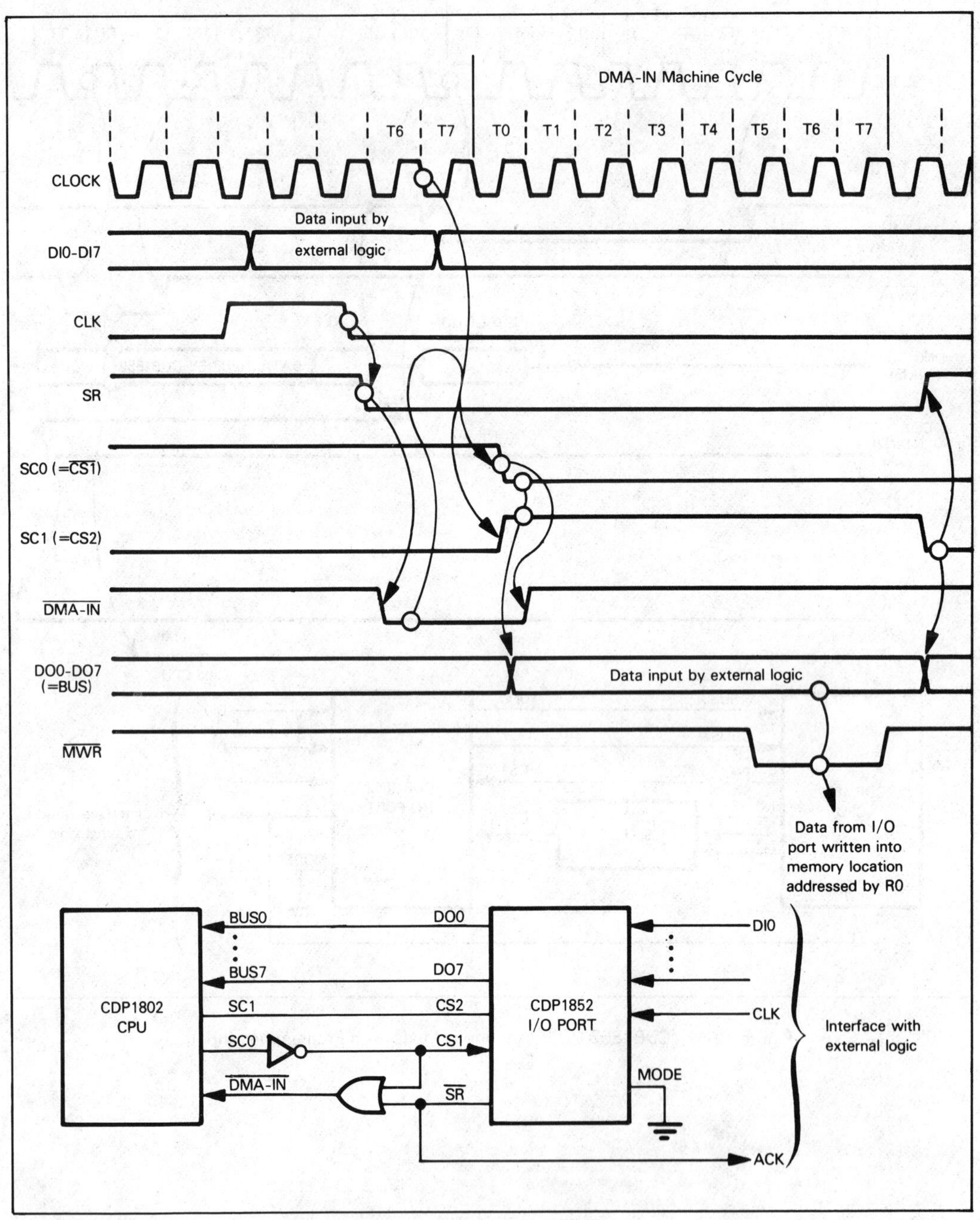


Figure 12-12. CDP1852 I/O Port in Input Mode with DMA Input

External logic initiates a data input operation by placing data at the DI0-DI7 pins of the CDP1852 device and applying the CLK strobe. On the trailing edge of the CLK strobe, data is latched into the CDP1852 I/O port and $\overline{\text{SR}}$ is output low.

The $\overline{\text{DMA-IN}}$ signal is input low when $\overline{\text{SR}}$ goes low. But we only want one DMA-IN machine cycle to occur at a time. If you examine Figure 12-3, you will see that the $\overline{\text{DMA-IN}}$ signal is sampled at the end of the T6 clock pulse in all non-instruction fetch machine cycles. In addition, we now want to suppress $\overline{\text{DMA-IN}}$ during a DMA machine cycle. We therefore create $\overline{\text{DMA-IN}}$ as the NAND of SR and SC0. SC0 will be low only for instruction fetch and DMA machine cycles. Since DMA is not sampled during instruction fetch, the net effect of our logic is to disable $\overline{\text{DMA-IN}}$ during a DMA machine cycle. Thus, in Figure 12-12, $\overline{\text{DMA-IN}}$ will be sampled low at the end of T6, which means that the next machine cycle becomes a DMA-IN machine cycle. During this machine cycle $\overline{\text{SR}}$ remains low; however, $\overline{\text{DMA-IN}}$ goes high shortly after SC0 goes low.

We use SC0 and SC1 to create the CDP1852 select inputs. SC1 is tied directly to CS2, while CS0 is inverted and then becomes SC1. Therefore, shortly after the beginning of the DMA-IN machine cycle, the data that was input via DI0-DI7 appears at DO0-DO7, which are connected to the COSMAC Data Bus (BUS0-BUS7). Data remains stable on the bus for almost the entire DMA-IN machine cycle. The $\overline{\text{MWR}}$ low pulse, when it appears, strobes the data from the Data Bus into the memory location addressed by Register R0.

External logic can use $\overline{\text{SR}}$ as its handshaking signal. When $\overline{\text{SR}}$ goes low, external logic knows that the CPU has been informed of data present at the CDP1852 I/O port. When $\overline{\text{SR}}$ goes high again, external logic knows that the DMA-IN machine cycle is complete; therefore, external logic is free to input the next byte of data.

## CDP1852 OUTPUT OPERATIONS

**Now consider a CDP1852 device operating in output mode.**

**There are two ways in which it would make sense to operate the CDP1852 device in output mode: the CPU could initiate the operation by executing an output instruction, or external logic could initiate the operation by applying a low signal at $\overline{\text{DMA-OUT}}$. Figure 12-13 provides timing and signal connections for the CPU initiating the output operation with an output instruction. Figure 12-14 provides timing and signal connections for external logic initiating the output operation by applying a low signal at $\overline{\text{DMA-OUT}}$.**

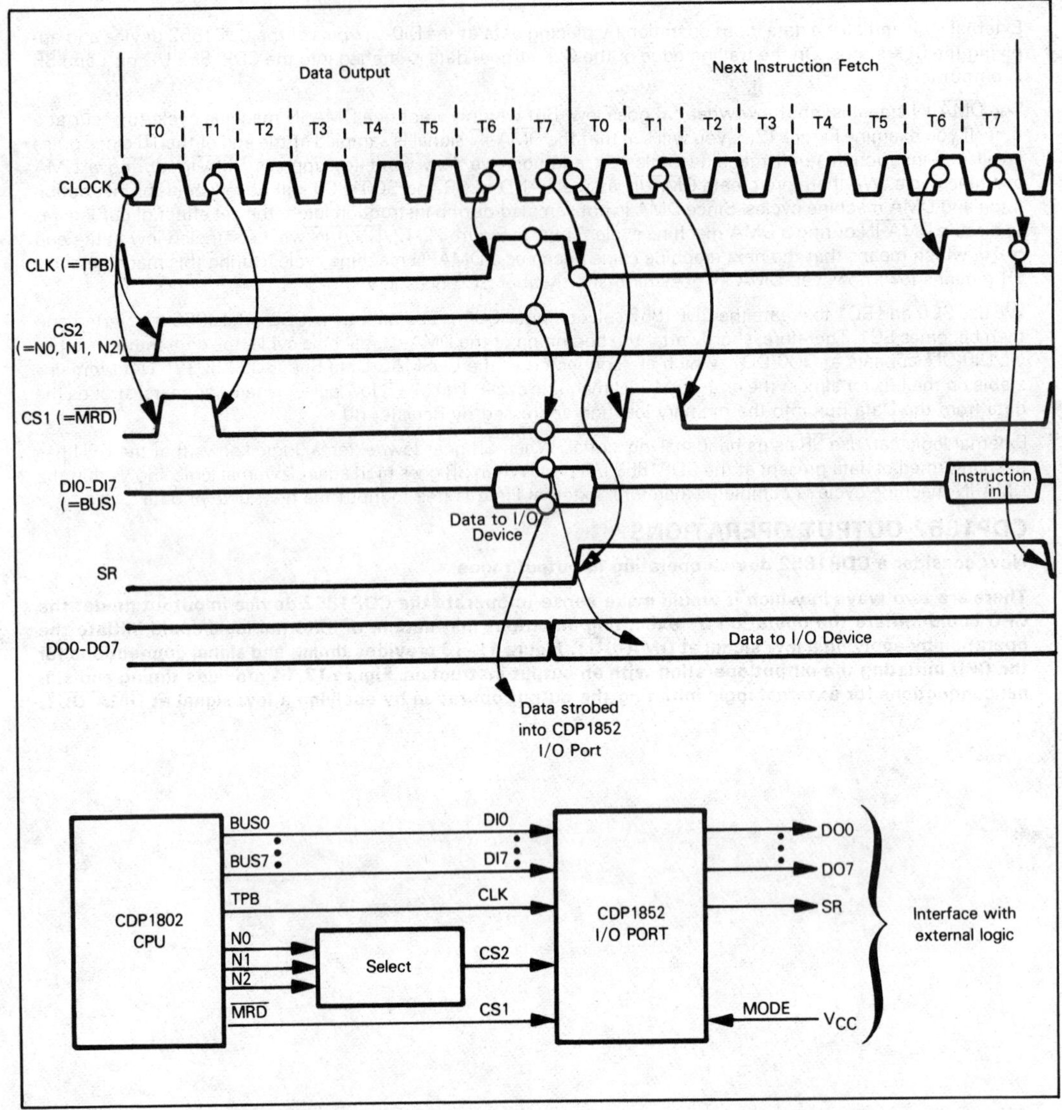


Figure 12-13. CDP1852 I/O Port in Output Mode with Programmed Output

**First consider the CDP1852 I/O port operating in output mode with programmed output, as illustrated in Figure 12-13. Before looking at this figure in detail, you should be familiar with Figure 12-9 and its associated text.**

When a CDP1852 I/O port is being operated in output mode, the output lines DO0-DO7 are always active, outputting the contents

When a CDP1852 I/O port is being operated in output mode, the output lines DO0-DO7 are always active, outputting the contents of the I/O port. Data input via DI0-DI7 is latched into the I/O port by the combination of CLK high, CS2 high, and CS1 low. In Figure 12-13 we connect CLK to TPB; this becomes the actual data strobe. This data strobe is conditioned by CS2 being high and CS1 being low. CS1 is tied to the memory read control signal MRD, which must be low during an output operation. CS2 is connected to the I/O select lines N0, N1, and N2, thus creating the required device select when more than one CDP1852 I/O port is present. As soon as the data input is strobed into the CDP1852 I/O port, it is output via DO0-DO7, and the service request signal SR goes high. SR is held high until the falling edge of TPB during the next machine cycle, which will be an instruction fetch. The fact that the next machine cycle is an instruction fetch is not relevant to external logic, which simply knows that it is going to receive a signal pulsed high for one machine cycle to identify the presence of new output data.

There are certain frequencies of operation where TPB is not pulsed high while the CPU is outputting stable data on the Data Bus. Under these circumstances, you will have to use some alternative logic to generate CLK.

**Figure 12-14 illustrates CDP1852 output mode operation using the CPU direct memory access logic. Before looking at this figure, you should be familiar with Figure 12-7 and associated discussion.**

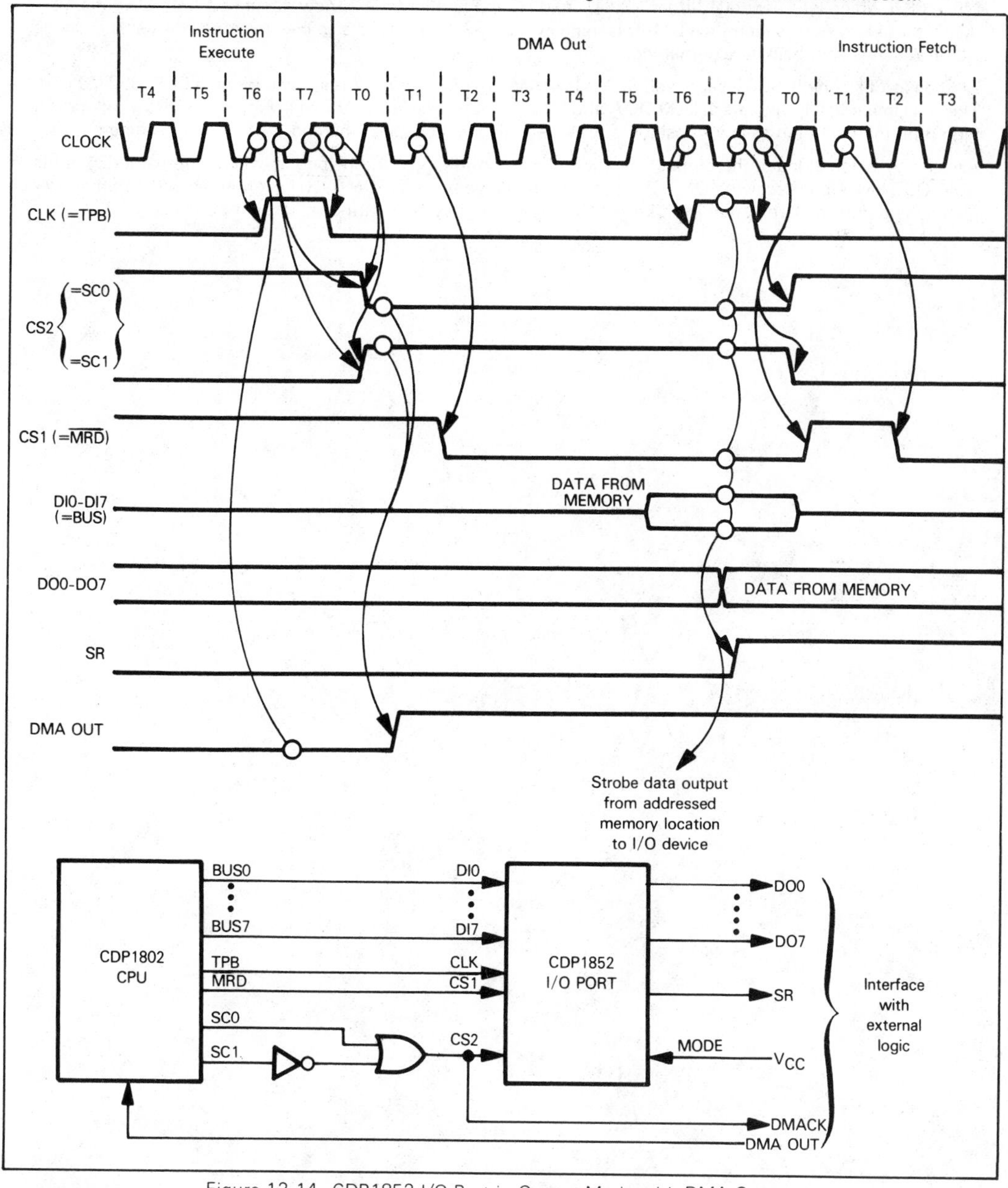


Figure 12-14. CDP1852 I/O Port in Output Mode with DMA Output

External logic initiates the data output in Figure 12-14 by inputting a low signal via $\overline{\text{DMA-OUT}}$. This signal must be low at the end of T6 in a non-instruction fetch machine cycle. The DMA-OUT machine cycle is identified by SC0 high and SC1 low; this combination is sent back to external logic as a DMA acknowledge. External logic must use this DMA acknowledge in order to set $\overline{\text{DMA-OUT}}$ high again. If $\overline{\text{DMA-OUT}}$ remains low for the DMA-OUT machine cycle, then a number of DMA-OUT machine cycles will be executed.

During the DMA-OUT machine cycle, valid data is output from the memory location addressed by R0. The presence of valid data on the Data Bus is identified by the TPB high pulse with $\overline{\text{MRD}}$ low. The CPU Data Bus is connected to the CDP1852 DI0-DI7 input lines. This data input is clocked into the CDP1852 device by CLK high, CS2 high, and CS1 low. In order to achieve these conditions, we once again connect CLK to TPB and CS1 to $\overline{\text{MRD}}$. CS2, which was generated from N0, N1, and N2 in Figure 12-13, is now generated from SC0 and SC1. When these two signals identify a DMA machine cycle, CS2 is true. CS2 also becomes the DMA acknowledge signal which is sent back to external logic.

As soon as CLK is high, SC0 is high, and SC1 is low, data input via DI0-DI7 is strobed into the CDP1852 I/O port. This data immediately appears at DO0-DO7, and SR is output high. As illustrated in Figure 12-13, SR will remain high until the next high-to-low transition of CLK — which will occur at the end of the next machine cycle.

As seen by external logic, the output operation illustrated in Figure 12-14 begins when external logic inputs $\overline{\text{DMA-OUT}}$ low. Upon receiving DMACK high, external logic must set $\overline{\text{DMA-OUT}}$ high again. When SR subsequently is output high, external logic knows that new data has been output and must be read.

# DATA SHEETS

The section contains specific electrical and timing data for the following devices:

- CDP1802 CPU
- CDP1852 I/O Port

**MAXIMUM RATINGS,** *Absolute-Maximum Values:*

DC SUPPLY-VOLTAGE RANGE, ($V_{DD}$)
(Voltage referenced to $V_{SS}$ Terminal)
CDP1802 . . . . . . . . . . . . . . . . . . . . . . . . . . . . –0.5 to +11 V
CDP1802C . . . . . . . . . . . . . . . . . . . . . . . . . . . . –0.5 to +7 V
INPUT VOLTAGE RANGE, ALL INPUTS . . . . . . . . . . . . . . . . . –0.5 to $V_{DD}$ +0.5 V
DC INPUT CURRENT, ANY ONE INPUT . . . . . . . . . . . . . . . . . ±10 mA
POWER DISSIPATION PER PACKAGE ($P_D$):
For $T_A$ = –40 to +60°C (PACKAGE TYPE E) . . . . . . . . . . . . . . 500 mW
For $T_A$ = +60 to +85°C (PACKAGE TYPE E) . . . . Derate Linearly at 12 mW/°C to 200 mW
For $T_A$ = –55 to +100°C (PACKAGE TYPE D) . . . . . . . . . . . . . 500 mW
For $T_A$ = +100 to +125°C (PACKAGE TYPE D) Derate Linearly at 12 mW/°C to 200 mW
DEVICE DISSIPATION PER OUTPUT TRANSISTOR
For $T_A$ = FULL PACKAGE-TEMPERATURE RANGE (All Package Types) . . . . . . 100 mW
OPERATING-TEMPERATURE RANGE ($T_A$):
PACKAGE TYPE D . . . . . . . . . . . . . . . . . . . . . . . . . –55 to +125°C
PACKAGE TYPE E . . . . . . . . . . . . . . . . . . . . . . . . . –40 to +85°C
STORAGE TEMPERATURE RANGE ($T_{stg}$) . . . . . . . . . . . . . . –65 to +150°C
LEAD TEMPERATURE (DURING SOLDERING):
At distance 1/16± 1/32 inch (1.59 ± 0.79 mm) from case for 10 s max. . . . . . . . . . +265°C

**STATIC ELECTRICAL CHARACTERISTICS at $T_A$ = –40 to +85°C, except as noted.**

| CHARACTERISTIC | CONDITIONS | | | LIMITS | | | | | | UNITS |
|---|---|---|---|---|---|---|---|---|---|---|
| | | | | CDP1802D CDP1802E | | | CDP1802CD CDP1802CE | | | |
| | $V_O$ (V) | $V_{IN}$ (V) | $V_{CC}$, $V_{DD}$ (V) | Min. | Typ.* | Max. | Min. | Typ.* | Max. | |
| Quiescent Device Current, $I_L$ | – | – | 5 | – | 0.01 | 50 | – | 0.02 | 200 | µA |
| | – | – | 10 | – | 1 | 200 | – | – | – | |
| Output Low Drive (Sink) Current, $I_{OL}$ (Except $\overline{XTAL}$) | 0.4 | 0,5 | 5 | 1.1 | 2.2 | – | 1.1 | 2.2 | – | mA |
| | 0.5 | 0,10 | 10 | 2.2 | 4.4 | – | – | – | – | |
| $\overline{XTAL}$ Output $I_{OL}$ | 0.4 | 5 | 5 | 75 | 150 | – | 75 | 150 | – | µA |
| Output High Drive (Source) Current $I_{OH}$ (Except $\overline{XTAL}$) | 4.6 | 0,5 | 5 | -0.27 | -0.55 | – | -0.27 | -0.55 | – | mA |
| | 9.5 | 0,10 | 10 | -0.55 | -1.1 | – | – | – | – | |
| $\overline{XTAL}$ Output $I_{OH}$ | 4.6 | 0 | 5 | -38 | -75 | – | -38 | -75 | – | µA |
| Output Voltage Low-Level $V_{OL}$ | – | 0,5 | 5 | – | 0 | 0.05 | – | 0 | 0.05 | V |
| | – | 0,10 | 10 | – | 0 | 0.05 | – | – | – | |
| Output Voltage High Level, $V_{OH}$ | – | 0,5 | 5 | 4.95 | 5 | – | 4.95 | 5 | – | |
| | – | 0,10 | 10 | 9.95 | 10 | – | – | – | – | |
| Input Low Voltage $V_{IL}$ | 0.5,4.5 | – | 5 | – | – | 1.5 | – | – | 1.5 | V |
| | 0.5,4.5 | – | 5,10 | – | – | 1 | – | – | 1 | |
| | 1,9 | – | 10 | – | – | 3 | – | – | – | |
| Input High Voltage $V_{IH}$ | 0.5,4.5 | – | 5 | 3.5 | – | – | 3.5 | – | – | |
| | 0.5,4.5 | – | 5,10 | 4 | – | – | 4 | – | – | |
| | 1,9 | – | 10 | 7 | – | – | – | – | – | |
| Input Leakage Current $I_{IN}$ | Any Input | 0,5 | 5 | – | $\pm10^{-4}$ | ±1 | – | $\pm10^{-4}$ | ±1 | µA |
| | | 0,10 | 10 | – | $\pm10^{-4}$ | ±1 | – | – | – | |

*Typical values are for $T_A$ = 25°C.

**STATIC ELECTRICAL CHARACTERISTICS at $T_A$ = –40 to +85°C, except as noted.**

| CHARACTERISTIC | CONDITIONS | | | LIMITS | | | | | | UNITS |
|---|---|---|---|---|---|---|---|---|---|---|
| | $V_O$ (V) | $V_{IN}$ (V) | $V_{CC}$, $V_{DD}$ (V) | CDP1802D CDP1802E | | | CDP1802CD CDP1802CE | | | |
| | | | | Min. | Typ.* | Max. | Min. | Typ.* | Max. | |
| 3-State Output Leakage Current $I_{OUT}$ | 0,5 | 0,5 | 5 | – | $\pm10^{-4}$ | ±1 | – | $\pm10^{-4}$ | ±1 | μA |
| | 0,10 | 0,10 | 10 | – | $\pm10^{-4}$ | ±1 | – | – | – | |
| Minimum Data Retention Voltage, $V_{DR}$ | $V_{DD} = V_{DR}$ | | | – | 2 | 2.4 | – | 2 | 2.4 | V |
| Data Retention Current, $I_{DR}$ | $V_{DD}$ = 2.4 V | | | – | 0.01 | 1 | – | 0.5 | 5 | μA |

*Typical values are for $T_A$ = 25°C.

**RECOMMENDED OPERATING CONDITIONS at $T_A$ = –40 to + 85°C Unless Otherwise Specified**

*For maximum reliability, nominal operating conditions should be selected so that operation is always within the following ranges:*

| CHARACTERISTIC | CONDITIONS | | LIMITS | | UNITS |
|---|---|---|---|---|---|
| | $V_{CC}$[1] (V) | $V_{DD}$ (V) | CDP1802D CDP1802E | CDP1802CD CDP1802CE | |
| Supply-Voltage Range | – | – | 4 to 10.5 | 4 to 6.5 | V |
| Input Voltage Range | – | – | $V_{SS}$ to $V_{CC}$ | $V_{SS}$ to $V_{CC}$ | V |
| Maximum Clock Input Rise or Fall Time, $t_r$ or $t_f$ | 4–10.5 | 4–10.5 | 1 | 1 | μs |
| Instruction Time[2] (See Fig. 8) | 5 | 5 | 6.4 | 6.4 | μs |
| | 5 | 10 | 5.1 | – | |
| | 10 | 10 | 3.2 | – | |
| Maximum DMA Transfer Rate | 5 | 5 | 312 | 312 | KBytes/sec |
| | 5 | 10 | 390 | – | |
| | 10 | 10 | 625 | – | |
| Maximum Clock Input Frequency, $f_{CLOCK}$[3] | 5 | 5 | DC – 2.5 | DC – 2.5 | MHz |
| | 5 | 10 | DC – 3.1 | – | |
| | 10 | 10 | DC – 5 | – | |

NOTES:
1: $V_{CC} \leqslant V_{DD}$; for CDP1802C, $V_{DD} = V_{CC}$ = 5 volts.
2. Equals 2 machine cycles – one Fetch and one Execute operation for all instructions except Long Branch and Long Skip, which require 3 machine cycles – one Fetch and two Execute operations.
3. Load Capacitance ($C_L$) = 50 pF.

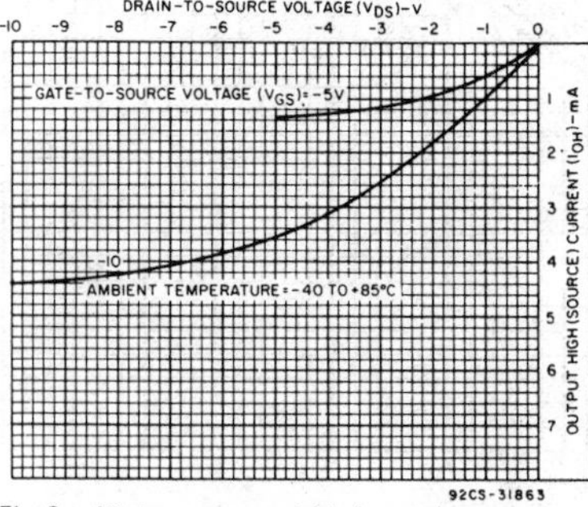


*Fig. 2 – Minimum output high (source) current characteristics.*

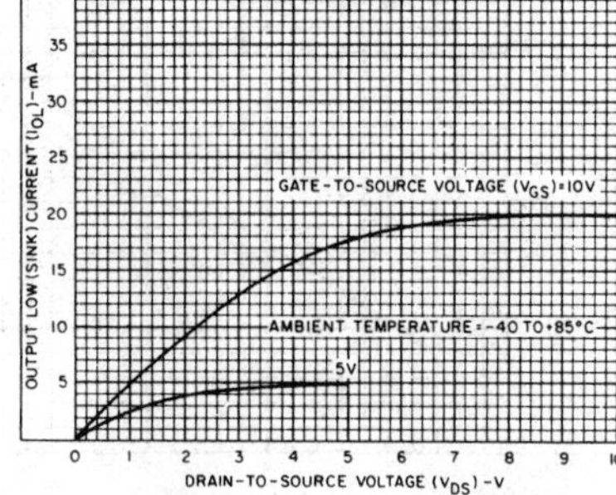


*Fig. 3 – Minimum output low (sink) current characteristics.*

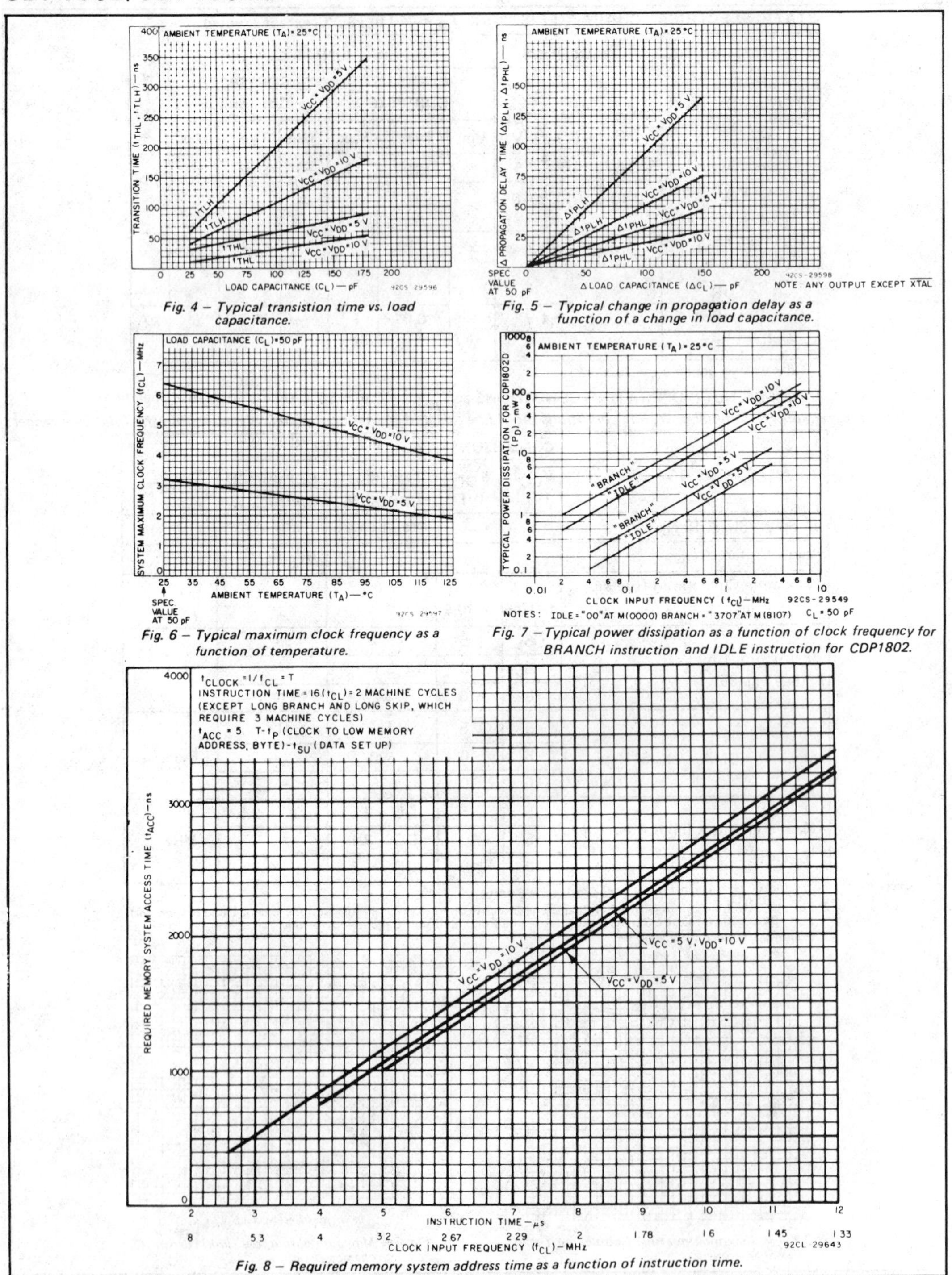


*Fig. 4 – Typical transistion time vs. load capacitance.*

*Fig. 5 – Typical change in propagation delay as a function of a change in load capacitance.*

*Fig. 6 – Typical maximum clock frequency as a function of temperature.*

*Fig. 7 – Typical power dissipation as a function of clock frequency for BRANCH instruction and IDLE instruction for CDP1802.*

*Fig. 8 – Required memory system address time as a function of instruction time.*

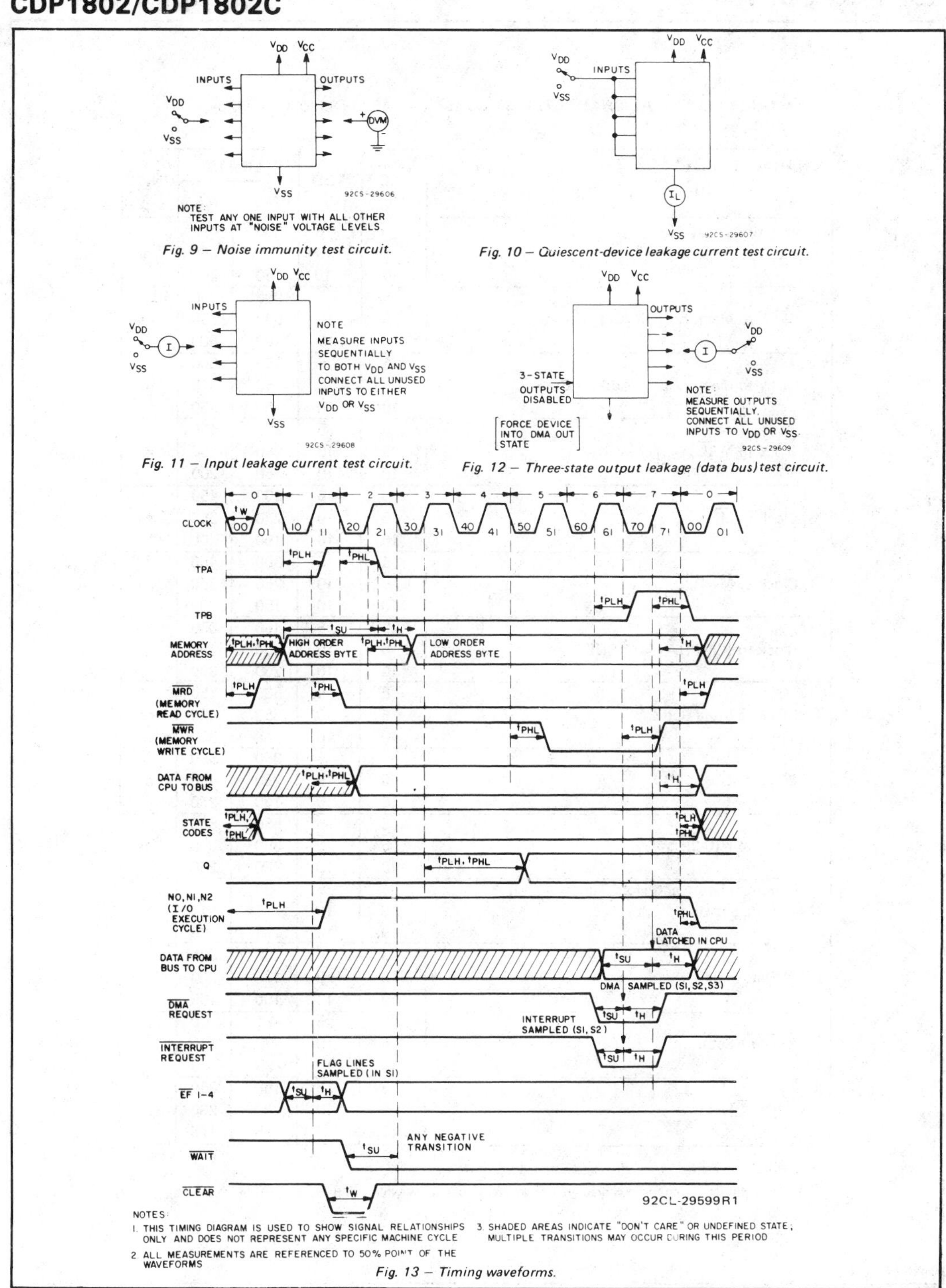


*Fig. 9 – Noise immunity test circuit.*

*Fig. 10 – Quiescent-device leakage current test circuit.*

*Fig. 11 – Input leakage current test circuit.*

*Fig. 12 – Three-state output leakage (data bus) test circuit.*

NOTES:

1. THIS TIMING DIAGRAM IS USED TO SHOW SIGNAL RELATIONSHIPS ONLY AND DOES NOT REPRESENT ANY SPECIFIC MACHINE CYCLE
2. ALL MEASUREMENTS ARE REFERENCED TO 50% POINT OF THE WAVEFORMS
3. SHADED AREAS INDICATE "DON'T CARE" OR UNDEFINED STATE; MULTIPLE TRANSITIONS MAY OCCUR DURING THIS PERIOD

*Fig. 13 – Timing waveforms.*

**DYNAMIC ELECTRICAL CHARACTERISTICS at $T_A$ = –40 to +85°C, $C_L$ = 50 pF, $V_{DD}$ ±5%, except as noted.**

| CHARACTERISTIC | $V_{CC}$ (V) | $V_{DD}$ (V) | LIMITS Typ.• | LIMITS Max. | UNITS |
|---|---|---|---|---|---|
| Propagation Delay Time, $t_{PLH}$, $t_{PHL}$: Clock to TPA, TPB | 5 | 5 | 300 | 450 | ns |
| | 5 | 10 | 250 | 350 | |
| | 10 | 10 | 150 | 200 | |
| Clock-to-Memory High-Address Byte | 5 | 5 | 900 | 1350 | ns |
| | 5 | 10 | 500 | 750 | |
| | 10 | 10 | 400 | 600 | |
| Clock-to-Memory Low-Address Byte | 5 | 5 | 350 | 500 | ns |
| | 5 | 10 | 250 | 375 | |
| | 10 | 10 | 150 | 250 | |
| Clock to $\overline{MRD}$, $t_{PLH}$ | 5 | 5 | 300 | 450 | ns |
| | 5 | 10 | 250 | 350 | |
| | 10 | 10 | 150 | 200 | |
| Clock to $\overline{MRD}$, $t_{PHL}$ | 5 | 5 | 300 | 450 | ns |
| | 5 | 10 | 250 | 350 | |
| | 10 | 10 | 150 | 200 | |
| Clock to $\overline{MWR}$, $t_{PLH}$, $t_{PHL}$ | 5 | 5 | 300 | 450 | ns |
| | 5 | 10 | 250 | 350 | |
| | 10 | 10 | 150 | 200 | |
| Clock to (CPU DATA to BUS) | 5 | 5 | 450 | 650 | ns |
| | 5 | 10 | 350 | 450 | |
| | 10 | 10 | 200 | 300 | |
| Clock to State Code | 5 | 5 | 500 | 750 | ns |
| | 5 | 10 | 350 | 450 | |
| | 10 | 10 | 250 | 300 | |
| Clock to Q | 5 | 5 | 350 | 550 | ns |
| | 5 | 10 | 250 | 400 | |
| | 10 | 10 | 150 | 250 | |
| Clock to N(0-2), $t_{PLH}$ | 5 | 5 | 550 | 800 | ns |
| | 5 | 10 | 350 | 500 | |
| | 10 | 10 | 250 | 350 | |
| Minimum Setup and Hold Times, $t_{SU}$, $t_H$▼ Data Set Up | 5 | 5 | -30 | 0 | ns |
| | 5 | 10 | -25 | 10 | |
| | 10 | 10 | -10 | 20 | |
| Data Hold | 5 | 5 | 200 | 300 | |
| | 5 | 10 | 125 | 200 | |
| | 10 | 10 | 100 | 150 | |
| $\overline{DMA}$ Setup | 5 | 5 | -75 | 0 | ns |
| | 5 | 10 | -50 | 0 | |
| | 10 | 10 | -25 | 0 | |
| $\overline{DMA}$ Hold | 5 | 5 | 150 | 250 | |
| | 5 | 10 | 100 | 200 | |
| | 10 | 10 | 75 | 125 | |

•Typical values are for $T_A$ = 25°C and nominal $V_{DD}$.

▼Maximum limits of minimum characteristics are the values above which all devices function.

DYNAMIC ELECTRICAL CHARACTERISTICS (cont'd)

| CHARACTERISTIC | $V_{CC}$ (V) | $V_{DD}$ (V) | LIMITS Typ. | Max. | UNITS |
|---|---|---|---|---|---|
| Minimum Setup and Hold Times, $t_{SU}$, $t_H$▼ Interrupt Setup | 5 | 5 | -75 | 0 | ns |
| | 5 | 10 | -50 | 0 | |
| | 10 | 10 | -25 | 0 | |
| Interrupt Hold | 5 | 5 | 150 | 250 | |
| | 5 | 10 | 100 | 200 | |
| | 10 | 10 | 75 | 125 | |
| $\overline{WAIT}$ Setup | 5 | 5 | -15 | 0 | ns |
| | 5 | 10 | -25 | 25 | |
| | 10 | 10 | 0 | 50 | |
| $\overline{EF1-4}$ Setup | 5 | 5 | -30 | 0 | ns |
| | 5 | 10 | -20 | 0 | |
| | 10 | 10 | -10 | 0 | |
| $\overline{EF1-4}$ Hold | 5 | 5 | 150 | 250 | |
| | 5 | 10 | 100 | 200 | |
| | 10 | 10 | 75 | 125 | |
| Minimum Pulse Width, $t_{WL}$▼ $\overline{CLEAR}$ Pulse Width | 5 | 5 | 300 | 600 | ns |
| | 5 | 10 | 200 | 400 | |
| | 10 | 10 | 150 | 300 | |
| $\overline{CLOCK}$ Pulse Width, $t_{WL}$ | 5 | 5 | 150 | 200 | ns |
| | 5 | 10 | 120 | 160 | |
| | 10 | 10 | 75 | 100 | |
| Typical Total Power Dissipation f = 2 MHz | 5 | 5 | 4 | – | mW |
| Idle "00" at M(0000), $C_L$ = 50 pF f= 4 MHz | 10 | 10 | 30 | – | |
| Effective Input Capacitance, $C_{IN}$ Any Input | | | 5 | – | pF |
| Effective 3-State Terminal Capacitance DATA BUS | | | 7.5 | – | pF |

•Typical values are for $T_A$ = 25°C and nominal $V_{DD}$.
▼Maximum limits of minimum characteristics are the values above which all devices function.

TIMING SPECIFICATIONS as a function of T ($T=1/f_{CLOCK}$) at $T_A$ = −40 to +85°C.

| CHARACTERISTIC | $V_{CC}$ (V) | $V_{DD}$ (V) | LIMITS Min. | Typ.• | UNITS |
|---|---|---|---|---|---|
| High-Order Memory-Address Byte Setup to $\overline{TPA}$ Time, $t_{SU}$ | 5 | 5 | 2T-800 | 2T-600 | ns |
| | 5 | 10 | 2T-635 | 2T-475 | |
| | 10 | 10 | 2T-400 | 2T-300 | |
| High-Order Memory-Address Byte Hold after TPA Time, $t_H$ | 5 | 5 | T/2+0 | T/2+30 | |
| | 5 | 10 | T/2+0 | T/2+20 | |
| | 10 | 10 | T/2+0 | T/2+10 | |
| Low-Order Memory-Address Byte Hold after WR Time, $t_H$ | 5 | 5 | T+0 | T+30 | |
| | 5 | 10 | T+0 | T+20 | |
| | 10 | 10 | T+0 | T+10 | |
| CPU Data to Bus Hold after WR Time, $t_H$ | 5 | 5 | T+25 | T+120 | |
| | 5 | 10 | T+10 | T+75 | |
| | 10 | 10 | T+0 | T+50 | |

•Typical values are for $T_A$ = 25°C.

**MAXIMUM RATINGS,** *Absolute-Maximum Values:*

DC SUPPLY-VOLTAGE RANGE, ($V_{DD}$)
(Voltage referenced to $V_{SS}$ Terminal)
CDP1852 . . . . . . . . . . −0.5 to +11 V
CDP1852C . . . . . . . . . . −0.5 to +7 V
INPUT VOLTAGE RANGE, ALL INPUTS . . . . . . . . . . −0.5 to $V_{DD}$ +0.5 V
DC INPUT CURRENT, ANY ONE INPUT . . . . . . . . . . ±10 mA
POWER DISSIPATION PER PACKAGE ($P_D$):
For $T_A$ = −40 to +60°C (PACKAGE TYPE E) . . . . . . . . . . 500 mW
For $T_A$ = +60 to +85°C (PACKAGE TYPE E) . . . . . Derate Linearly at 12 mW/°C to 200 mW
For $T_A$ = −55 to +100°C (PACKAGE TYPE D) . . . . . . . . . . 500 mW
For $T_A$ = +100 to +125°C (PACKAGE TYPE D) . . . . . Derate Linearly at 12 mW/°C to 200 mW
DEVICE DISSIPATION PER OUTPUT TRANSISTOR
FOR $T_A$ = FULL PACKAGE-TEMPERATURE RANGE (All Package Types) . . . . . . 100 mW
OPERATING-TEMPERATURE RANGE ($T_A$):
PACKAGE TYPES D, H . . . . . . . . . . −55 to +125°C
PACKAGE TYPE E . . . . . . . . . . −40 to +85°C
STORAGE TEMPERATURE RANGE ($T_{stg}$) . . . . . . . . . . −65 to +150°C
LEAD TEMPERATURE (DURING SOLDERING):
At distance 1/16 ± 1/32 inch (1.59 ± 0.79 mm) from case for 10 s max. . . . . . . . +265°C

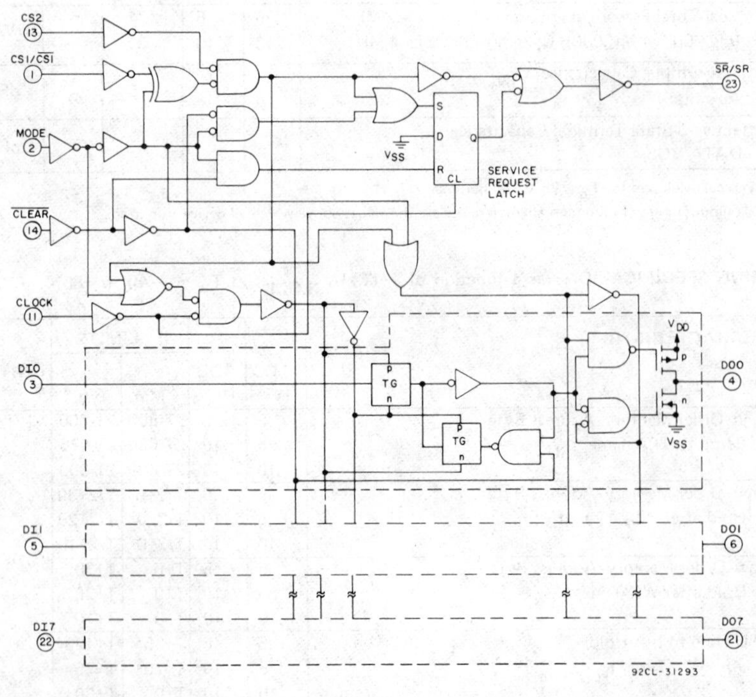


*Fig. 2 – CDP1852 logic diagram.*

**RECOMMENDED OPERATING CONDITIONS at $T_A$ = Full Package Temperature Range**

*For maximum reliability, operating conditions should be selected so that operation is always within the following ranges:*

| CHARACTERISTIC | LIMITS | | | | UNITS |
|---|---|---|---|---|---|
| | CDP1852 | | CDP1852C | | |
| | Min. | Max. | Min. | Max. | |
| DC Operating-Voltage Range | 4 | 10.5 | 4 | 6.5 | V |
| Input Voltage Range | $V_{SS}$ | $V_{DD}$ | $V_{SS}$ | $V_{DD}$ | V |

**STATIC ELECTRICAL CHARACTERISTICS at $T_A$ = –40 to +85°C**

| CHARACTERISTIC | CONDITIONS | | | LIMITS | | | | | | UNITS |
|---|---|---|---|---|---|---|---|---|---|---|
| | $V_O$ (V) | $V_{IN}$ (V) | $V_{DD}$ (V) | CDP1852 | | | CDP1852C | | | |
| | | | | Min. | Typ.* | Max. | Min. | Typ.* | Max. | |
| Quiescent Device Current, $I_{DD}$ | – | 0,5 | 5 | – | – | 10 | – | – | 50 | μA |
| | – | 0,10 | 10 | – | – | 50 | – | – | – | |
| Output Low Drive (Sink) Current, $I_{OL}$ | 0.4 | 0,5 | 5 | 1.6 | 3.2 | – | 1.6 | 3.2 | – | mA |
| | 0.5 | 0,10 | 10 | 3 | 6 | – | – | – | – | |
| Output High Drive (Source) Current, $I_{OH}$ | 4.6 | 0,5 | 5 | –1.15 | –2.3 | – | –1.15 | –2.3 | – | mA |
| | 9.5 | 0,10 | 10 | –3 | –6 | – | – | – | – | |
| Output Voltage Low-Level $V_{OL}$▲ | – | 0,5 | 5 | – | 0 | 0.1 | – | 0 | 0.1 | V |
| | – | 0,10 | 10 | – | 0 | 0.1 | – | – | – | |
| Output Voltage HighLevel, $V_{OH}$ | – | 0,5 | 5 | 4.9 | 5 | – | 4.9 | 5 | – | |
| | – | 0,10 | 10 | 9.9 | 10 | – | – | – | – | |
| Input Low Voltage, $V_{IL}$ | 0.5,4.5 | – | 5 | – | – | 1.5 | – | – | 1.5 | V |
| | 0.5,9.5 | – | 10 | – | – | 3 | – | – | – | |
| Input High Voltage, $V_{IH}$ | 0.5,4.5 | – | 5 | 3.5 | – | – | 3.5 | – | – | |
| | 0.5,9.5 | – | 10 | 7 | – | – | – | – | – | |
| Input Current, $I_{IN}$ | – | 0,5 | 5 | – | – | ±1 | – | – | ±1 | μA |
| | – | 0,10 | 10 | – | – | ±2 | – | – | – | |
| 3-State Output Leakage Current $I_{OUT}$ | 0,5 | 0,5 | 5 | – | – | ±1 | – | – | ±1 | μA |
| | 0,10 | 0,10 | 10 | – | – | ±2 | – | – | – | |
| Operating Current, $I_{DD1}$# | – | 0,5 | 5 | – | 130 | 200 | – | 150 | 200 | μA |
| | – | 0,10 | 10 | – | 400 | 600 | – | – | – | |
| Input Capacitance $C_{IN}$ | – | – | – | – | 5 | 7.5 | – | 5 | 7.5 | pF |
| Output Capacitance, $C_{OUT}$ | – | – | – | – | 5 | 7.5 | – | – | – | |

* Typical values are for $T_A$ = 25°C.

▲ $I_{OL}$ = $I_{OH}$ = 1 μA

\# Operating current is measured at 2 MHz in an CDP1802 system with open outputs and a program of 6N55, 6NAA, 6N55, 6NAA, ---- .

**DYNAMIC ELECTRICAL CHARACTERISTICS at $T_A$ = −40 to +85°C, $V_{DD}$ = ±5%, $t_r,t_f$ = 20 ns, $V_{IH}$ = 0.7 $V_{DD}$, $V_{IL}$ = 0.3 $V_{DD}$, $C_L$ = 100 pF, and 1 TTL Load**
**LIMITS AT $V_{DD}$ = 10 V APPLY TO THE CDP1852 ONLY**

| CHARACTERISTIC | $V_{DD}$ (V) | LIMITS Min. | LIMITS Typ.* | LIMITS Max. | UNITS |
|---|---|---|---|---|---|
| **MODE 0 – Input Port** | | | | | |
| Minimum Select Pulse Width, $t_{SW}$ | 5 | – | 180 | 360 | ns |
| | 10 | – | 90 | 180 | |
| Minimum Write Pulse Width, $t_{WW}$ | 5 | – | 90 | 180 | |
| | 10 | – | 45 | 90 | |
| Minimum Clear Pulse Width, $t_{CLR}$ | 5 | – | 80 | 160 | |
| | 10 | – | 40 | 80 | |
| Minimum Data Setup Time, $t_{SD}$ | 5 | – | −10 | 0 | |
| | 10 | – | −5 | 0 | |
| Minimum Data Hold Time, $t_{DH}$ | 5 | – | 75 | 150 | |
| | 10 | – | 35 | 75 | |
| Data Out Hold Time, $t_{DOH}$▲ | 5 | 30 | 185 | 370 | |
| | 10 | 15 | 100 | 200 | |
| SR Output Transition Time | 5 | – | 30 | 60 | |
| | 10 | – | 15 | 30 | |
| Data Output Transition Time | 5 | – | 30 | 60 | |
| | 10 | – | 15 | 30 | |
| Propagation Delay Times, $t_{PLH}$, $t_{PHL}$: Select to Data Out▲ | 5 | 30 | 185 | 370 | |
| | 10 | 15 | 100 | 200 | |
| Clear to SR | 5 | – | 170 | 340 | |
| | 10 | – | 85 | 170 | |
| Clock to SR | 5 | – | 110 | 220 | |
| | 10 | – | 55 | 110 | |
| Select to SR | 5 | – | 120 | 240 | |
| | 10 | – | 60 | 120 | |
| **MODE 1 – Output Port** | | | | | |
| Minimum Clock Pulse Width, $t_{CL}$ | 5 | – | 130 | 260 | ns |
| | 10 | – | 65 | 130 | |
| Minimum Write Pulse Width, $t_{WW}$ | 5 | – | 130 | 260 | |
| | 10 | – | 65 | 130 | |
| Minimum Clear Pulse Width, $t_{CLR}$ | 5 | – | 60 | 120 | |
| | 10 | – | 30 | 60 | |
| Minimum Data Setup Time, $t_{DS}$ | 5 | – | −10 | 0 | |
| | 10 | – | −5 | 0 | |
| Minimum Data Hold Time, $t_{DH}$ | 5 | – | 75 | 150 | |
| | 10 | – | 35 | 75 | |
| Minimum Clock-after-Select Hold Time | 5 | – | −10 | 0 | |
| | 10 | – | −5 | 0 | |
| SR Output Transition Time | 5 | – | 30 | 60 | |
| | 10 | – | 15 | 30 | |
| Data Output Transition Time | 5 | – | 30 | 60 | |
| | 10 | – | 15 | 30 | |

▲ Minimum value is measured from CS2; maximum value is measured from CS1.

* Typical values are for $T_A$ = 25°C and nominal $V_{DD}$.

**DYNAMIC ELECTRICAL CHARACTERISTICS (Cont'd)**

| CHARACTERISTIC | $V_{DD}$ (V) | LIMITS Min. | Typ.* | Max. | UNITS |
|---|---|---|---|---|---|
| Propagation Delay Times, $t_{PLH}$, $t_{PHL}$: Clear to Data Out | 5 | – | 140 | 280 | ns |
| | 10 | – | 70 | 140 | |
| Write to Data Out | 5 | – | 220 | 440 | |
| | 10 | – | 110 | 220 | |
| Data In to Data Out | 5 | – | 100 | 200 | |
| | 10 | – | 50 | 100 | |
| Clear to SR | 5 | – | 120 | 240 | |
| | 10 | – | 60 | 120 | |
| Clock to SR | 5 | – | 120 | 240 | |
| | 10 | – | 60 | 120 | |
| Select to SR | 5 | – | 120 | 240 | |
| | 10 | – | 60 | 120 | |

* Typical values are for $T_A = 25°C$ and nominal $V_{DD}$.

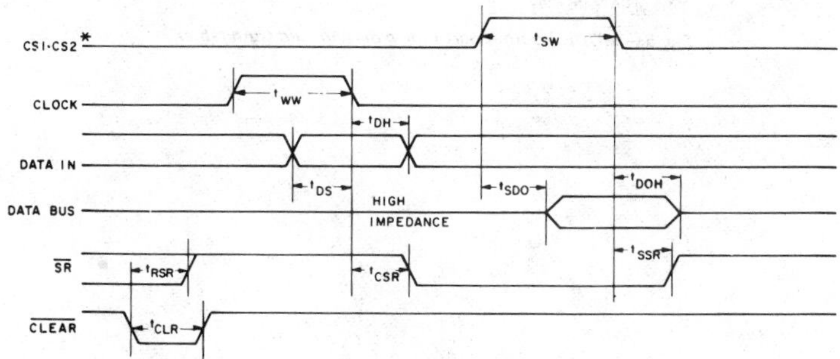


* CSI·CS2 IS THE OVERLAP OF CSI=1 AND CS2=1

| INPUTS | | | OUTPUTS | |
|---|---|---|---|---|
| CLOCK | CS1·CS2† | $\overline{CLEAR}$ | DATA OUT | $\overline{SR}$ OUT |
| X | 0 | 0 | HIGH Z | 1 |
| X | 0 | 1 | HIGH Z | SR LATCH● |
| 0 | 1 | 0 | 0 | 0 |
| 0 | 1 | 1 | DATA LATCH | 0 |
| 1 | 1 | X | DATA IN | 0 |

| INPUTS | | | OUTPUTS |
|---|---|---|---|
| CLOCK | CSI·CS2† | $\overline{CLEAR}$ | $\overline{SR}$ LATCH● |
| X | X | 0 | 1 |
| X | 1 | X | 1 |
| ↓ | 0 | 1 | 0 |
| ↑ | 0 | 1 | NO CHANGE |

† CSI·CS2 = 1 ⇒ CS1 = 1 and CS2 = 1.

● SR Latch is internal to the device (See Fig. 2).

92CM-31292

*Fig. 3 – MODE 0 input port timing diagram and truth tables.*

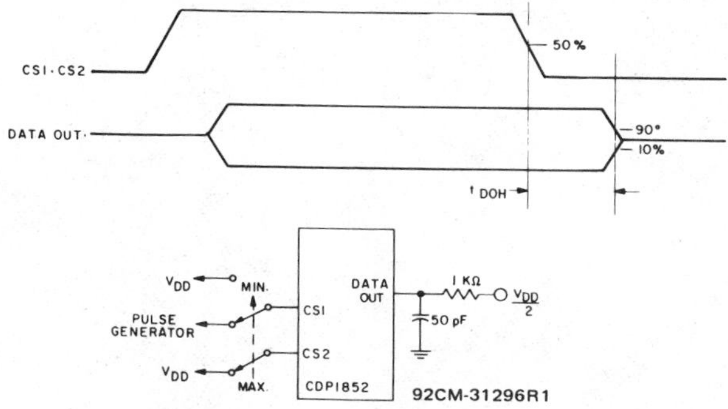


*Fig. 4 – Data out hold time waveforms and test circuit.*

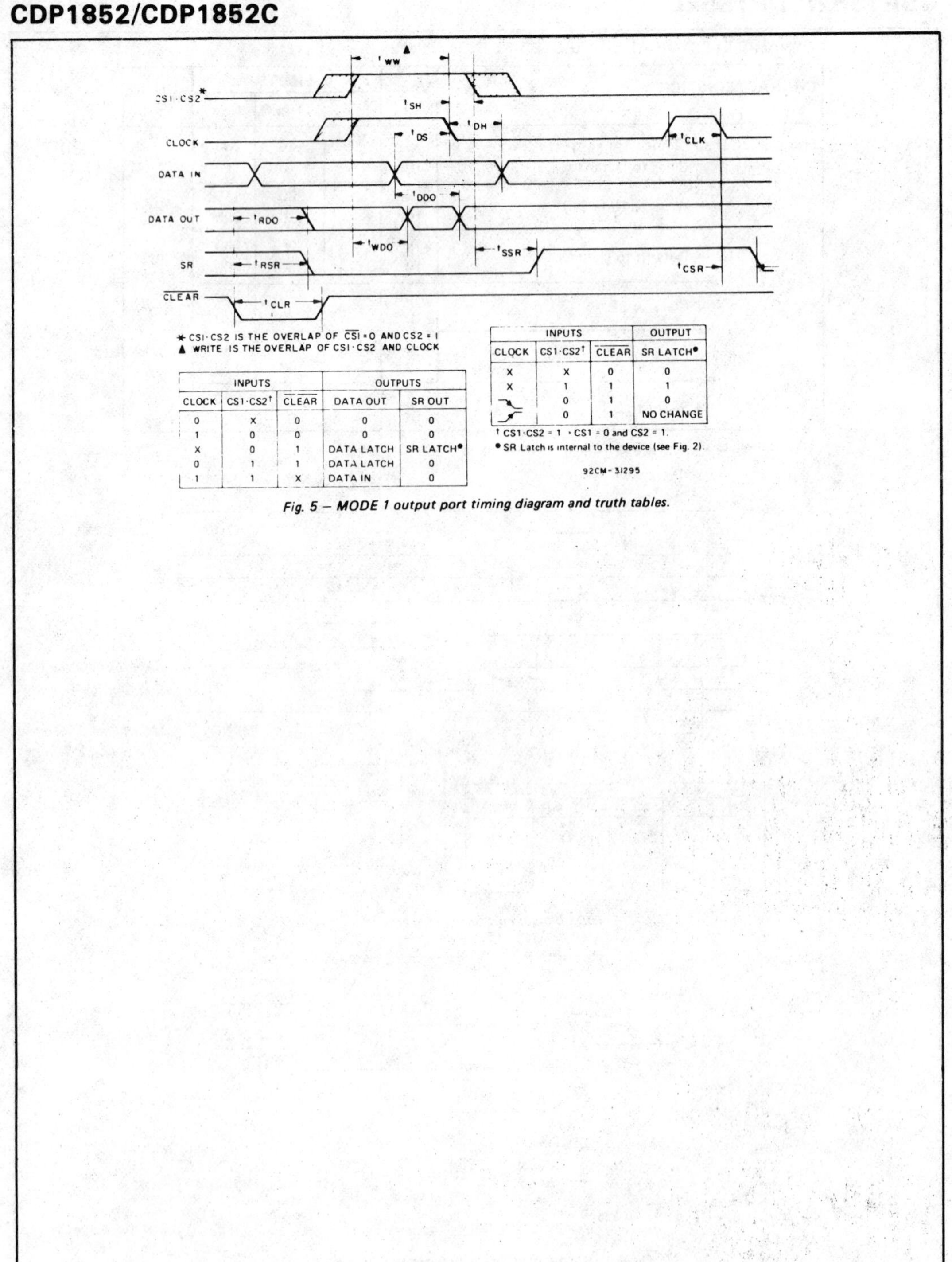


* CS1·CS2 IS THE OVERLAP OF $\overline{\text{CS1}}$ = 0 AND CS2 = 1
▲ WRITE IS THE OVERLAP OF CS1·CS2 AND CLOCK

| INPUTS | | | OUTPUTS | |
|---|---|---|---|---|
| CLOCK | CS1·CS2† | $\overline{\text{CLEAR}}$ | DATA OUT | SR OUT |
| 0 | X | 0 | 0 | 0 |
| 1 | 0 | 0 | 0 | 0 |
| X | 0 | 1 | DATA LATCH | SR LATCH● |
| 0 | 1 | 1 | DATA LATCH | 0 |
| 1 | 1 | X | DATA IN | 0 |

| INPUTS | | | OUTPUT |
|---|---|---|---|
| CLOCK | CS1·CS2† | $\overline{\text{CLEAR}}$ | SR LATCH● |
| X | X | 0 | 0 |
| X | 1 | 1 | 1 |
| ↓ | 0 | 1 | 0 |
| ↑ | 0 | 1 | NO CHANGE |

† CS1·CS2 = 1 → $\overline{\text{CS1}}$ = 0 and CS2 = 1.
● SR Latch is internal to the device (see Fig. 2).

92CM-31295

*Fig. 5 – MODE 1 output port timing diagram and truth tables.*

# Chapter 13
# IM6100 MICROCOMPUTER DEVICES

**The IM6100 is an almost exact reproduction of the PDP-8E minicomputer.** The IM6100 has the same instruction set as the PDP-8E; however, there are differences in direct memory access logic. Also, the IM6100 cannot use the PDP-8E extended arithmetic element or user flag options.

Rather than concentrating on differences between the IM6100 and the PDP-8E, we will in this chapter relate the IM6100 to other microprocessors described in this book. This reflects the fact that minicomputer concepts are simply not viable in the microcomputer world. The PDP-8E was developed at a time when Central Processing Units were very expensive and it was reasonable to demand that controllers surrounding the Central Processing Unit contain a lot of internal intelligence. This intelligence, in turn, demanded complex System Bus signals that identified the state of the CPU as it progressed through an instruction's execution. Microcomputers are inexpensive, and their low cost is defeated if they have to be surrounded by expensive device controllers. Therefore, it will be more valuable in this chapter to show how the IM6100 can be used in a microcomputer system with a simple bus and standard microcomputer support devices, rather than comparing it with the PDP-8E minicomputer.

**The PDP-8 is a 12-bit minicomputer, therefore the IM6100 is a 12-bit microcomputer.**

The very existence of the IM6100 is testimony to one of the less well understood aspects of minicomputers versus microcomputers: people tend to place too much emphasis on "creeping featurism". The majority of applications that are going to use a microcomputer could be implemented with almost any microcomputer described in this book. The economics of exact chip counts and product development expense is worth exploring, but in most cases detailed comparative evaluations of instruction sets and addressing modes are a waste of time and money; enhancement of one product as compared to another will rarely have any significant economic impact. This is true of microcomputers today, and it was also true of minicomputers yesterday. The PDP-8 was the first popular minicomputer. Compared to nearly any other minicomputer on the market today, the PDP-8 is a very primitive device. Yet there are more PDP-8s in the world than any other minicomputer. Despite the large number of new, more powerful minicomputers that are available, the PDP-8 continues, from year to year, to rank among the leaders in minicomputer sales volume.

It is this popularity of the PDP-8, for all its shortcomings as a minicomputer, that has given birth to the IM6100. Many design features of the IM6100 are dubious, when looked upon from the microcomputer user's point of view. It is safe to say that no microcomputer designer would have seen fit to develop a product even remotely like the IM6100, but for the predecessor PDP-8. The IM6100 exists to participate in the continuing sales volume of PDP-8, and to take advantage of the huge library of PDP-8 software which is available — much of it at no cost.

You must look at the IM6100 (and the microNOVA) from a totally different perspective, as compared to any other microcomputer described in this book; do not look for justification of IM6100 design features in terms of a microcomputer application's needs; rather, accept the IM6100 for what it is — a very low-cost reproduction of something which already exists; a product whose existence is justified by a large established product market and a prior base of existing software.

**In addition to the IM6100 CPU, we are going to describe the IM6101 Parallel Interface Element and the IM6102 MEDIC multifunction support device. The IM6402 UART is also available; it is described in Volume 3.**

All IM6100 microcomputer devices use a single power supply which may range between +4V and +11V.

Using a 250 nanosecond clock input, instruction execution times range from 5 to 11 microseconds.

All IM6100 microcomputer devices use CMOS technology, which means that they are highly immune to noise in the power supply and they consume very little power. Recall that COSMAC is the only other microprocessor described in this book that offers CMOS technology.

The principal manufacturer of the IM6100 is:

INTERSIL, INC.
10900 North Tantau Avenue
Cupertino, CA 95014

The second source is:

HARRIS SEMICONDUCTOR DIVISION
P.O. Box 883
Melbourne, FLA 32901

## THE IM6100 CPU

**Functions implemented on the IM6100 CPU are illustrated in Figure 13-1. IM6101 Parallel Interface Element logic is also shown.**

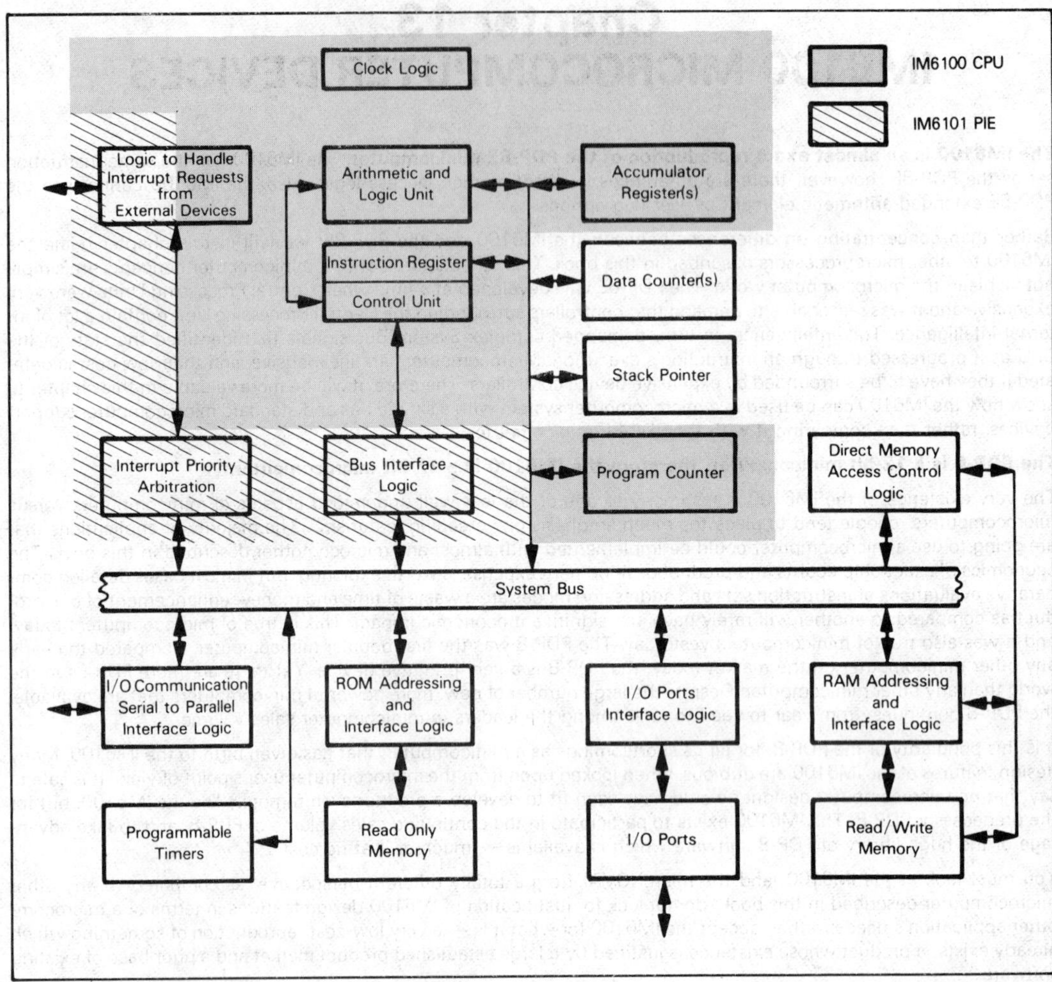


Figure 13-1. Logic of the IM6100 CPU and the IM6101 Parallel Interface Element

Bus interface logic is shown as implemented by the IM6101. This is because the bus control signals input to and output by the CPU do not conform with the standard PDP-8 bus, or with typical microcomputer busses. You are going to need additional logic either to create a PDP-8 bus equivalent, or to reduce IM6100 control signals to manageable microcomputer bus proportions. The IM6101 creates a microcomputer type of System Bus.

Direct memory access control logic is shown as absent. The CPU has logic which will respond to a DMA request by floating the System Bus; however, the actual DMA transfer, including creation of memory addresses, is the responsibility of external logic.

Observe that clock logic is provided on the CPU chip.

## IM6100 PROGRAMMABLE REGISTERS

**The IM6100 has just three programmable registers as we define them: an Accumulator, a Program Counter and the MQ register. All three registers are twelve bits wide.**

**The Accumulator is a typical primary Accumulator.** With a single exception, it is the only source or destination within the CPU for data being operated on.

**The MQ register is a simple buffer for the Accumulator.** The only operation you can perform on the MQ register contents is to OR them with the Accumulator contents; the result is returned to the Accumulator. You may also exchange the contents of the Accumulator and the MQ register.

**The Program Counter, being 12 bits wide, limits the IM6100 to an address space of 4096 memory words.** The IM6102 allows this address space to be expanded to 32,768 memory words.

**Intersil literature describes additional registers, but these are not programmable registers as we define them.**

The IM6100 has no Data Counter. There is a Memory Address register within the CPU, but you have no direct access to this register. It is a simple depository for addresses which are automatically computed by CPU logic during the execution of memory reference instructions.

## IM6100 MEMORY SPACE

Memory addressing modes that we are about to describe apply to a single 4096-word memory bank. If you have more than one such memory bank, then each one must be considered as a separate and distinct entity. This is important, because the nature of the IM6100 demands that if program memory is in ROM, then both ROM and RAM must be present in external memory. Thus, if you have more than one bank, each memory bank must include ROM and RAM.

## IM6100 MEMORY ADDRESSING MODES

**IM6100 memory reference instructions use absolute, paged, direct addressing and indirect addressing.**

All IM6100 instruction object codes occupy a single 12-bit word. There are no two-word or three-word object codes. All memory reference instructions have the following object code format:

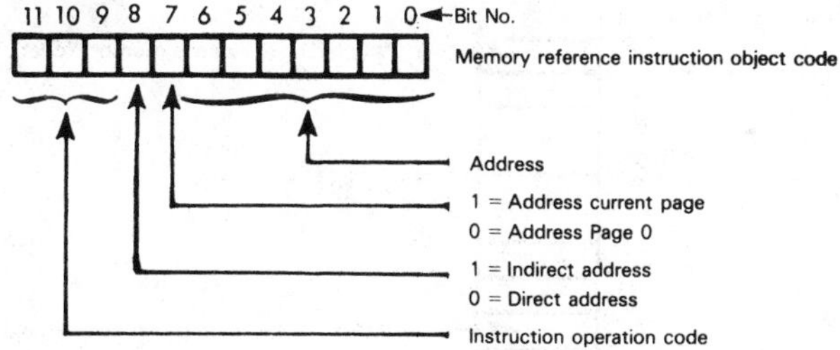


**A memory reference instruction that uses direct addressing has seven address bits; thus memory is divided into 128-word pages. The memory page bit gives you the option of directly addressing a memory word on Page 0, or within the instruction's page:**

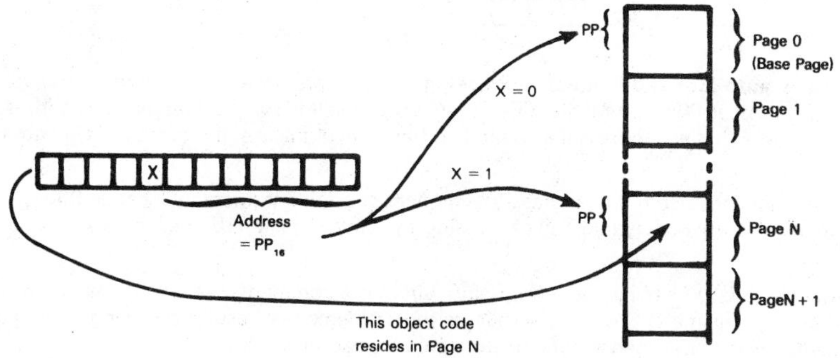

This is standard, absolute paged direct addressing, as described in Volume 1, Chapter 6.

A memory reference instruction with indirect addressing simply takes the 12-bit word accessed by the direct memory address and interprets this 12-bit word's contents as the effective memory address. This is standard indirect addressing. In the case of the IM6100, **a memory reference instruction can access an indirect memory address either on the base page or on the instruction's current page.**

**You can use indirect addressing to create the equivalent of a two-word, nonpaged direct addressing Jump instruction.**

To do this, store the 12-bit absolute direct address directly following the Jump Indirect instruction. This may be illustrated as follows:

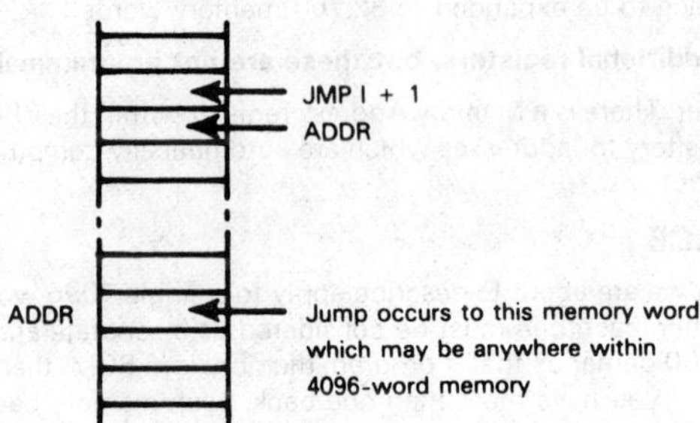


You cannot use this technique with any memory reference instruction other than a Jump. That is because any other instruction would leave the Program Counter pointing to the indirect address as the next object code to be executed.

For memory reference instructions other than a Jump, reserve a few memory words at the end of the current page to store indirect addresses. This may be illustrated as follows:

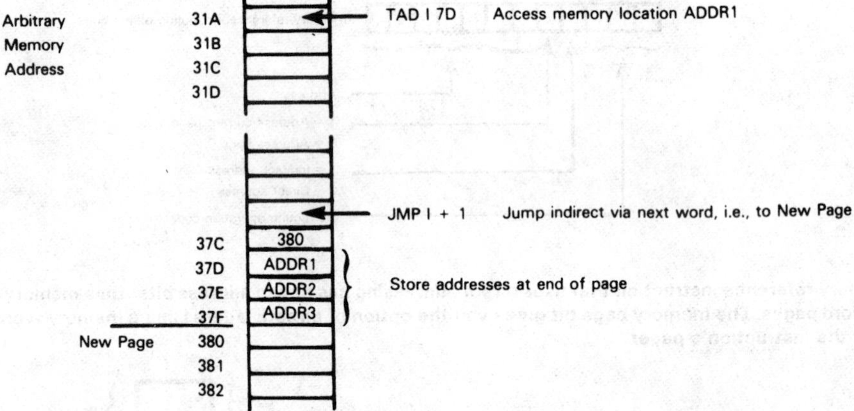


**The IM6100 also has auto-indexed indirect addressing.** If you store an indirect address in any one of the eight memory words with addresses $008_{16}$ through $00F_{16}$ then, when the IM6100 CPU fetches this address, it will also increment and return it. Note that the address that is fetched from one of these eight locations is incremented before it is used as an address.

For example, you can store the beginning address (minus one) of a table in memory location $008_{16}$. You can subsequently read sequential table words by indirectly accessing the table. The IM6100 benchmark program illustrates this use of auto-indexing.

It is just as well that the IM6100 has indirect addressing with auto-increment, because it has no Data Counter or implied memory addressing. Volume 1, Chapter 6 discusses the problems that result from using direct addressing to access sequential memory locations when programs are stored in read-only memory.

**Note that the IM6100 makes no distinction between program and data memory.** Thus Jump instructions use exactly the same memory addressing options as memory read or write instructions. The concept of separate program and data memory is a microcomputer phenomenon, because it was only with the advent of the microcomputer that programs started to be stored in read-only memory. Minicomputers use read/write memory for programs and data — and frequently a minicomputer will make no clear separation between the memory spaces that will be assigned to programs as against data.

**The way in which the IM6100 handles subroutine calls represents an excellent illustration of the fact that minicomputer concepts can run into trouble in the world of microcomputers.**

**IM6100 SUBROUTINES IN READ-ONLY MEMORY**

**When a JMS instruction is executed, the return address is stored in the first word of the subroutine's object code.**

The scheme certainly made sense to the PDP-8 designers; they visualized memory as a general read/write depository for programs and data. This scheme is nonviable when programs are stored in read-only memory, since you cannot write a return address in read-only memory. In order to use subroutines with an IM6100, you must origin all subroutines in read/write memory, then jump to a program sequence stored in read-only memory. This may be illustrated as follows:

```
/BASE PAGE STARTS HERE
          -
          -
          -
SUBA      0                /FIRST WORD OF SUBROUTINE SUBA
          JMP I    •+1     /JUMP INDIRECT TO SUBROUTINE IN ROM
          PPQ              /PPQ REPRESENTS THE STARTING ADDRESS IN ROM
          -
          -
          -
          *PPQ             /SUBROUTINE ORIGIN IN ROM
          -
          -
          -
          JMP I    SUBA    /LAST INSTRUCTION OF SUBROUTINE IN ROM
/MAIN PROGRAM WHICH CALLS SUBROUTINE SUBA
          -
          -
          -
          JMS      SUBA    /SUBROUTINE CALL
          DCA      DATA    /EVENTUAL SUBROUTINE RETURN
```

Let us examine the path of instruction execution illustrated above.

Begin by looking at the JMS SUBA instruction in the main program which calls subroutine SUBA. SUBA is a label representing a location in the base page of memory. When the JMS SUBA instruction is executed, the address of the next instruction, arbitrarily illustrated above as a DCA instruction, will be stored in the memory word with label SUBA. The first instruction executed following the Jump-to-Subroutine is the instruction stored in the memory location following SUBA; this is the JMP I •+1 instruction. This instruction jumps indirect via the address stored in the next memory location; we represent this memory location's contents with PPQ. PPQ is the address of the first instruction to be executed within the subroutine. This instruction, and all subsequent subroutine instructions are stored in read-only memory. The last instruction executed by the subroutine in read-only memory is the JMP I SUBA instruction. This instruction performs an indirect jump via the address stored at SUBA. This is the address of the DCA DATA instruction. This execution sequence may be illustrated as follows:

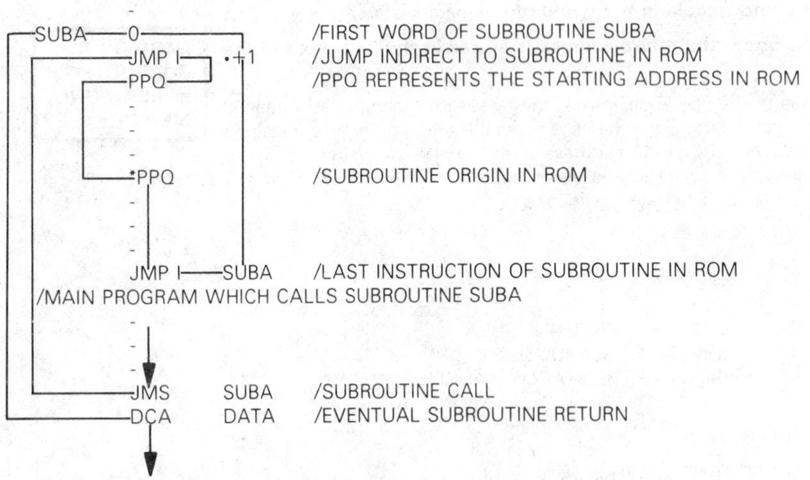
/BASE PAGE STARTS HERE
SUBA 0 /FIRST WORD OF SUBROUTINE SUBA
JMP I .+1 /JUMP INDIRECT TO SUBROUTINE IN ROM
PPQ /PPQ REPRESENTS THE STARTING ADDRESS IN ROM
*PPQ /SUBROUTINE ORIGIN IN ROM
JMP I SUBA /LAST INSTRUCTION OF SUBROUTINE IN ROM
/MAIN PROGRAM WHICH CALLS SUBROUTINE SUBA
JMS SUBA /SUBROUTINE CALL
DCA DATA /EVENTUAL SUBROUTINE RETURN

**Handling subroutine calls through RAM has some non-obvious repercussions.**

First of all, at least the first page of the first 4096-word memory bank (Page 0) must be read/write memory; this is due to the way the IM6100 handles interrupts, which we will discuss later. In all probability, there will be more than one page of read/write memory.

Next, if you are going to initiate subroutines in Page 0 RAM, then when you power up the system, you must load this RAM from ROM. This is because RAM will lose its contents when powered down. Thus, every restart or reset procedure must include the execution of an instruction sequence which moves a block of data from ROM to Page 0 RAM.

Possibly the most serious problem associated with calling subroutines through Page 0 RAM is the fact that, apart from interrupt handling, existing PDP-8 software does not do that. Thus, if you are going to implement programs in read-only memory, the existing PDP-8 software base is not available to you — and that is one of the principal reasons for the IM6100's existence. Converting existing PDP-8 programs, so that subroutines are called through Page 0 RAM, is not a simple task. If you look again at the discussion of direct, paged addressing given in Volume 1, Chapter 6, you will see that there are very significant problems associated with memory mapping. Programs cannot lie across page boundaries; therefore, the addition of a few instructions to any one program can have serious consequences. In some cases it may be possible to generate special assemblers and compilers that convert existing source programs into object programs which partition memory into ROM for programs and RAM for data, allowing subroutines to be called via the base page — but that assumes the base page has free space available for this purpose.

**There is a hardware solution to the IM6100 Jump-to-Subroutine problem.** This solution uses an external read/write memory Stack to store subroutine return addresses in the manner of a conventional stack. Necessary logic and minor programming ramifications are described later in this chapter.

## IM6100 STATUS FLAGS

**The IM6100 has a single Carry status; it is called the Link or L status in PDP-8 and IM6100 literature.**

## IM6100 CPU PINS AND SIGNALS

**IM6100 CPU pins and signals are illustrated in Figure 13-2.** Once again, the minicomputer ancestry of the IM6100 is evident from the complex control signals input and output by the CPU. Minicomputer designers favor a rich variety of control signals on a System Bus because that makes the job of designing peripheral device controllers easier. Microcomputers rely on low-cost support devices, and complex System Busses simply increase the complexity and cost of surrounding the CPU with support logic. After reading this summary of IM6100 pins and signals, compare it to the 8080A described in Chapter 4; then compare it with the MCS6500 described in Chapter 10. The MCS6500 represents the ultimate in simplicity.

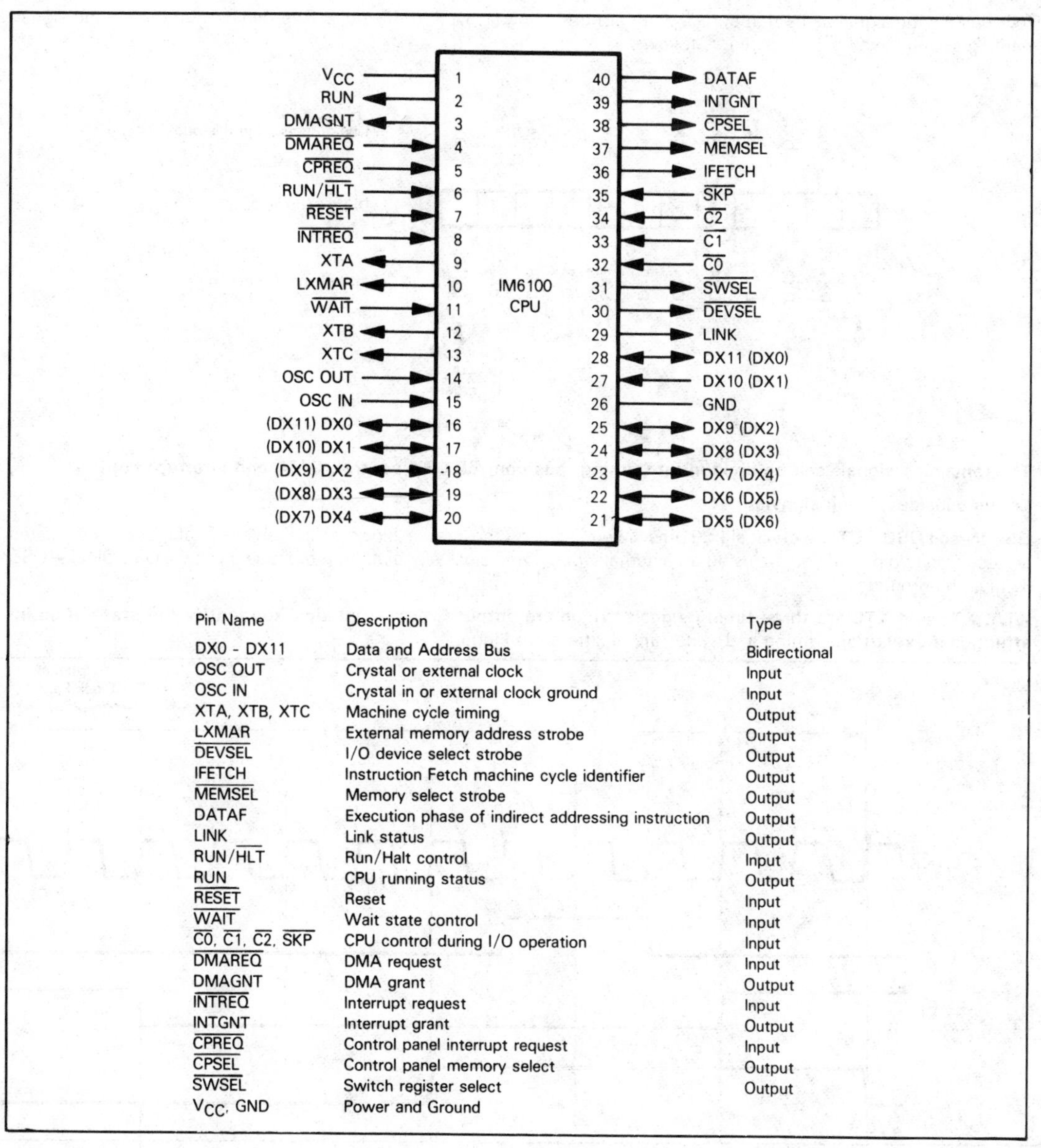


| Pin Name | Description | Type |
|---|---|---|
| DX0 - DX11 | Data and Address Bus | Bidirectional |
| OSC OUT | Crystal or external clock | Input |
| OSC IN | Crystal in or external clock ground | Input |
| XTA, XTB, XTC | Machine cycle timing | Output |
| LXMAR | External memory address strobe | Output |
| $\overline{DEVSEL}$ | I/O device select strobe | Output |
| IFETCH | Instruction Fetch machine cycle identifier | Output |
| $\overline{MEMSEL}$ | Memory select strobe | Output |
| DATAF | Execution phase of indirect addressing instruction | Output |
| LINK | Link status | Output |
| RUN/$\overline{HLT}$ | Run/Halt control | Input |
| RUN | CPU running status | Output |
| $\overline{RESET}$ | Reset | Input |
| $\overline{WAIT}$ | Wait state control | Input |
| $\overline{C0}$, $\overline{C1}$, $\overline{C2}$, $\overline{SKP}$ | CPU control during I/O operation | Input |
| $\overline{DMAREQ}$ | DMA request | Input |
| DMAGNT | DMA grant | Output |
| $\overline{INTREQ}$ | Interrupt request | Input |
| INTGNT | Interrupt grant | Output |
| $\overline{CPREQ}$ | Control panel interrupt request | Input |
| $\overline{CPSEL}$ | Control panel memory select | Output |
| $\overline{SWSEL}$ | Switch register select | Output |
| $V_{CC}$, GND | Power and Ground | |

Figure 13-2. IM6100 CPU Signals and Pin Assignments

**The IM6100 has a single 12-bit multiplexed Data and Address Bus, represented by pins DX0 - DX11.** Memory and I/O interface logic must use appropriate control signals in order to demultiplex data and addresses off this single bus.

**IM6100 BIT NUMBERING**

Intersil literature numbers the bits of registers and memory words from left to right; that is to say, with the 0 bit representing the high-order bit. In this book we consistently number bits of registers and words from right to left; that is to say, with the low-order bit represented by the 0 bit. Data/Address Bus lines are confusing when you compare the discussion in this chapter with Intersil literature. In Figure 13-2, DX0 - DX11 signals are identified first with labels that conform to Intersil literature; the bracketed labels that follow show the signal name that agrees with bit numbering as used in this book. The two bit-numbering and signal-naming systems may be compared as follows:

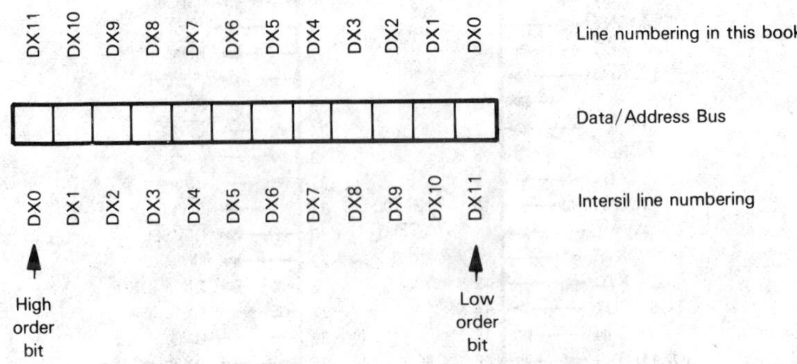


**The remaining signals can be divided into timing, bus control, CPU control, DMA and interrupt control.**

**Let us consider timing signals first.**

**OSC IN and OSC OUT are clock signal pins.** If you are using the internal clock logic, then a crystal must be connected across these two pins. If you are using an externally generated clock signal, then it must be input via OSC OUT — OSC IN must be grounded.

**XTA, XTB and XTC are three timing signals which are output for external logic to identify the state of an instruction's execution.** Timing and states are illustrated in Figure 13-3.

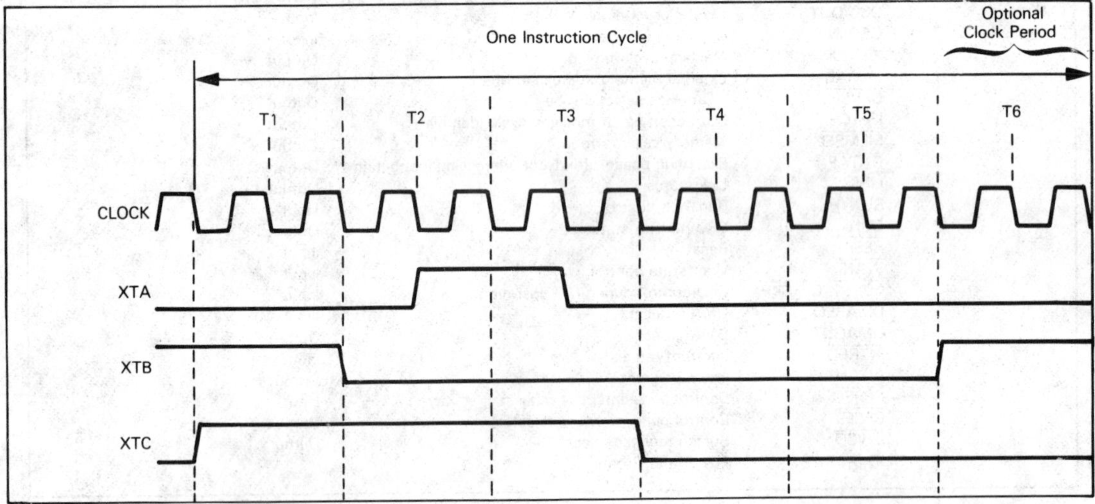


Figure 13-3. IM6100 Machine Cycles and Clock Periods

**Let us now look at the signals output by the CPU to define events on the System Bus.**

**LXMAR** is output as a high pulse which external logic can use to strobe an address off the Data/Address Bus.

**$\overline{\text{DEVSEL}}$** is output as a low pulse when information on the Address/Data Bus must be interpreted by I/O devices as device identification or I/O operation control.

**IFETCH** is output high for the duration of an instruction fetch machine cycle. IFETCH may be used as a synchronization signal identifying the beginning of a new instruction cycle.

**$\overline{\text{MEMSEL}}$** is output as a low pulse during a memory reference operation. Memory interface logic determines whether a memory read or a memory write is in progress via the condition of the XTA, XTB and XTC signals. (Only XTB is really necessary for this purpose.)

**DATAF** is a signal output high during the execute phase of an instruction that uses indirect addressing.

**LINK** is a signal output at all times to represent the level of the Link status. We include this signal among control outputs because you can use it as a direct external logic control signal. By executing instructions to set or reset the Link status you can modify the level of this control signal on a real time basis.

**Let us now consider the control signals input by external logic to control CPU operations.**

**RUN/$\overline{\text{HLT}}$** is a control input which allows external logic to halt the CPU. This signal is similar to the Halt input which some 8-bit microcomputers have, but its purpose in the IM6100 is to give control panel logic some means of executing program instructions one at a time. This helps in debugging.

**RUN** is output high when the CPU is running; it is output low when the CPU has been halted.

**$\overline{\text{RESET}}$** is a typical reset input. When input low, it clears all CPU registers except the Program Counter, which is loaded with $FFF_{16}$.

**$\overline{\text{WAIT}}$** is used by slow external logic which needs to acquire more time to respond to a memory or I/O access. As long as $\overline{\text{WAIT}}$ is input low, the CPU will maintain register and signal levels, but not advance the state of an instruction's execution.

**$\overline{\text{C0}}$, $\overline{\text{C1}}$, $\overline{\text{C2}}$ and $\overline{\text{SKP}}$ are very unusual input control signals.** During an I/O operation (that is, while an IOT instruction is being executed), **external logic can use these four control signals in order to determine CPU operations.**

Control signals $\overline{\text{C0}}$, $\overline{\text{C1}}$ and $\overline{\text{C2}}$ are interpreted by the CPU as follows:

| $\overline{\text{C2}}$ | $\overline{\text{C1}}$ | $\overline{\text{C0}}$ | |
|---|---|---|---|
| L | L | X | Transfer data from DX0 - DX11 to Program Counter (execute an absolute jump) |
| L | H | X | Add data on DX0 - DX11 to Program Counter (execute a program relative jump) |
| H | L | L | Load data from DX0 - DX11 to Accumulator |
| H | L | H | OR data from DX0 - DX11 with Accumulator |
| H | H | L | Transfer Accumulator contents to DX0 - DX11, then clear Accumulator |
| H | H | H | Transfer Accumulator contents to DX0 - DX11 but do not clear Accumulator |

X represents "don't care"; $\overline{\text{C0}}$ may be low or high.

**If external logic inputs $\overline{\text{SKP}}$ low during an IOT instruction, then the CPU will skip the instruction which immediately follows the IOT.** SKP logic is separate and distinct from $\overline{\text{C0}}$, $\overline{\text{C1}}$ and $\overline{\text{C2}}$ logic.

Two signals support DMA operation. **External logic requests DMA access by inputting a low signal via $\overline{\text{DMAREQ}}$.** As soon as the current instruction has completed execution, **the CPU responds by outputting DMAGNT high.** At this point the Data/Address Bus is floated. External logic must provide all DMA transfer signals; the only thing the CPU does in response to a DMA request is float the Data/Address Bus for a single instruction cycle. The bus is floated for as long as $\overline{\text{DMAREQ}}$ is held low. $\overline{\text{DMAREQ}}$ and DMAGNT are rarely used. The IM6102 provides simultaneous DMA logic, which is preferred.

Interrupt logic reflects the IM6100's minicomputer heritage. **Normal interrupts are requested via $\overline{\text{INTREQ}}$ being input low. Upon acknowledging an interrupt, the CPU will output INTGNT high.** Microcomputers are no different; but an IM6100 control panel interrupt request has its own dedicated $\overline{\text{CPREQ}}$ signal. Microcomputers do not assume the possible presence of a control panel.

Two additional control signals are provided to support the presence of a control panel. The IM6100 control panel will have its own memory in order to support logic required by switches and indicators of the control panel. **Following a control panel interrupt, $\overline{\text{CPSEL}}$ is output low instead of $\overline{\text{MEMSEL}}$, so that programs can be executed out of control panel memory, rather than out of main memory.**

There is also an instruction which reads the contents of control panel switches and ORs them with the contents of the Accumulator. **$\overline{\text{SWSEL}}$ is output low in order to inform control panel logic that switch levels must be returned as data on the Data/Address Bus.**

## IM6100 TIMING AND INSTRUCTION EXECUTION

**An IM6100 instruction's execution is timed by a sequence of machine cycles,** each of which is subdivided into clock periods. A machine cycle may have five or six clock periods. Machine cycles and clock periods are identified by the CLOCK, XTA, XTB, and XTC signals, **as illustrated in Figure 13-3.** Note that each clock period consists of two external clock cycles.

**IM6100 machine cycles, like those of almost any other microcomputer, consist of memory or I/O read cycles,**

**memory or I/O write cycles and CPU operation cycles. Specific events occur only during specific clock periods of a machine cycle.**

**IM6100 CLOCK PERIOD ASSIGNMENTS**

A memory or I/O device address is output during T1.

Data is input during T2. The I/O control input lines C0, C1, C2 and SKP must be input during T2, with timing conforming to data input.

Internal CPU operations occur during T3, T4 and T5.
Data is output during T6.

**In order to best understand the nature of different IM6100 machine cycles, we will begin by looking at the basic data input, data output and no operation machine cycles. Then we will look at specific interpretations of these machine cycles for various types of instruction execution.**

## IM6100 NO OPERATION MACHINE CYCLE

An IM6100 "no operation" machine cycle may have five or six clock periods. Only the XTA, XTB and XTC signals change levels during a no operation machine cycle, therefore **Figure 13-3** (excluding the sixth clock period) **illustrates a no operation machine cycle.**

## IM6100 DATA INPUT MACHINE CYCLE

**Data input machine cycle timing is illustrated in Figure 13-4.** Observe that there are four different sources for data being input to the CPU. The four different sources are identified by individual select lines.

## IM6100 DATA OUTPUT MACHINE CYCLE

**Data output machine cycle timing is illustrated in Figure 13-5.** Data output occurs during the T6 clock period of the machine cycle, and is identified by a low Select pulse; otherwise, timing is the same as illustrated in Figure 13-4.

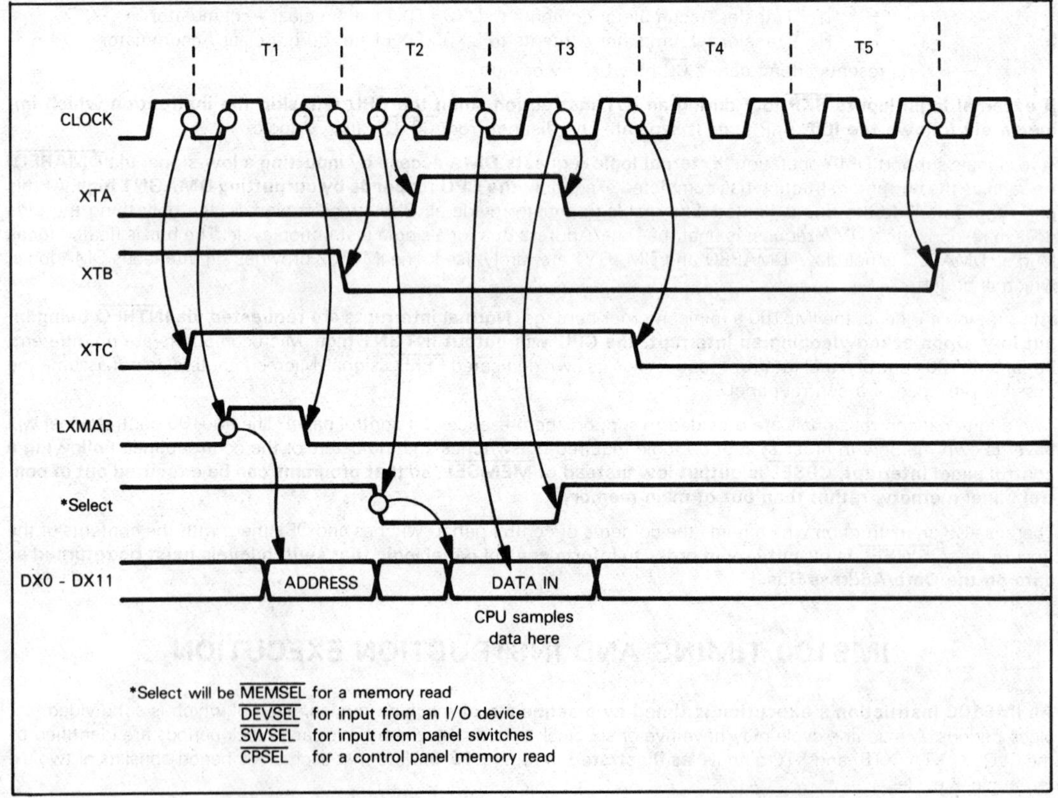


Figure 13-4. IM6100 Data Input Machine Cycle Timing

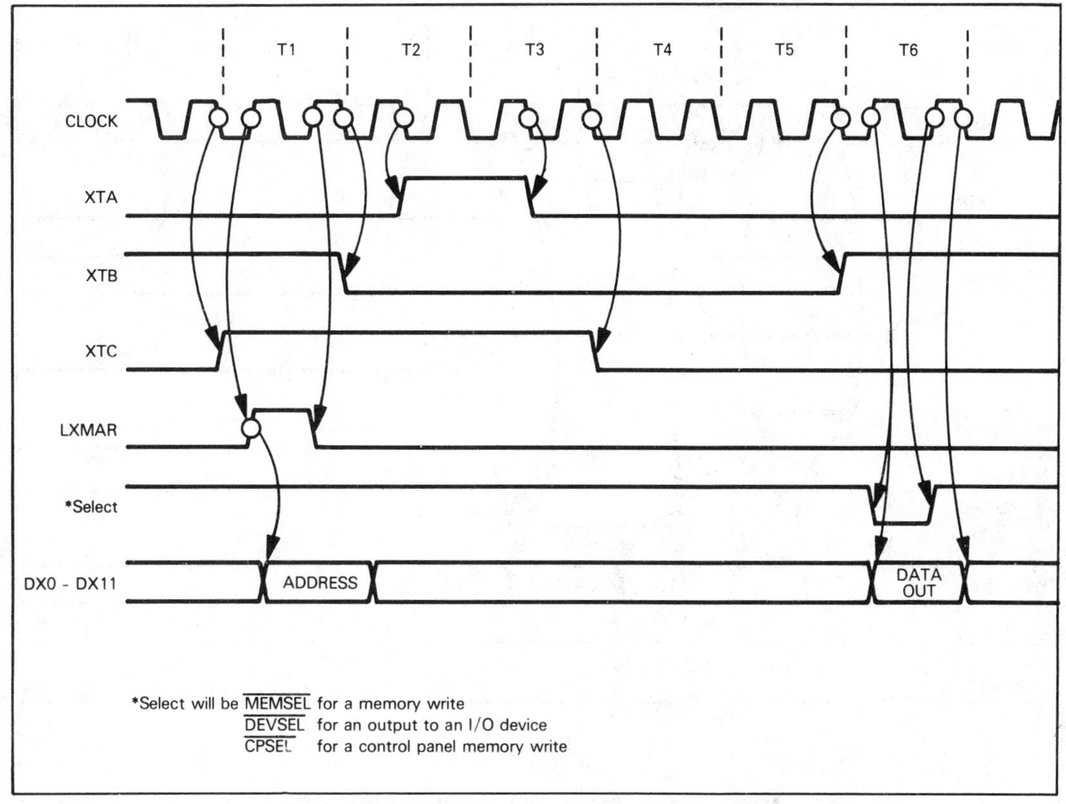

Figure 13-5. IM6100 Data Output Machine Cycle Timing

## IM6100 ADDRESS DEMULTIPLEXING

The minicomputer flavor of the IM6100 can cause some initial confusion when you try to interface devices to its System Bus. **Normally, if we encounter a multiplexed Data and Address Bus, we immediately demultiplex the bus to create separate Data and Address Busses.** Indeed, this is easy enough to do when working **with the IM6100,** but **it is not necessary.** Providing the address stable time on the Data/Address Bus is satisfactory, memory and I/O devices can simultaneously use the LXMAR high pulse as an address or device select strobe. Since there are separate subsequent control strobes for memory, I/O devices and control panel logic, the fact that an ambiguous address appeared earlier is irrelevant. Without the subsequent control strobe, a memory device that was spuriously selected by an I/O instruction, for example, will not perform a read or write operation. Moreover, the IM6101 Parallel Interface Element creates unique select strobes for individual I/O devices, as we will see later in this chapter. **The only occasion when you will almost certainly want to demultiplex the IM6100 Data/Address Bus is if you are creating a System Bus which is compatible with some other microcomputer — for example, the 8080A.**

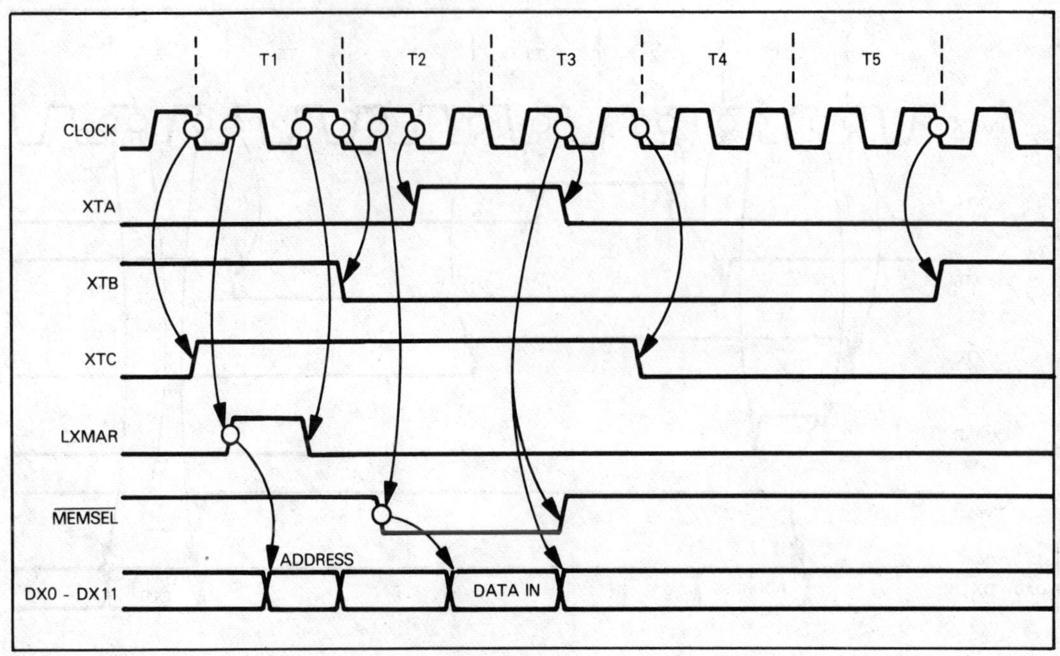


Figure 13-6. IM6100 Memory Read Machine Cycle Timing

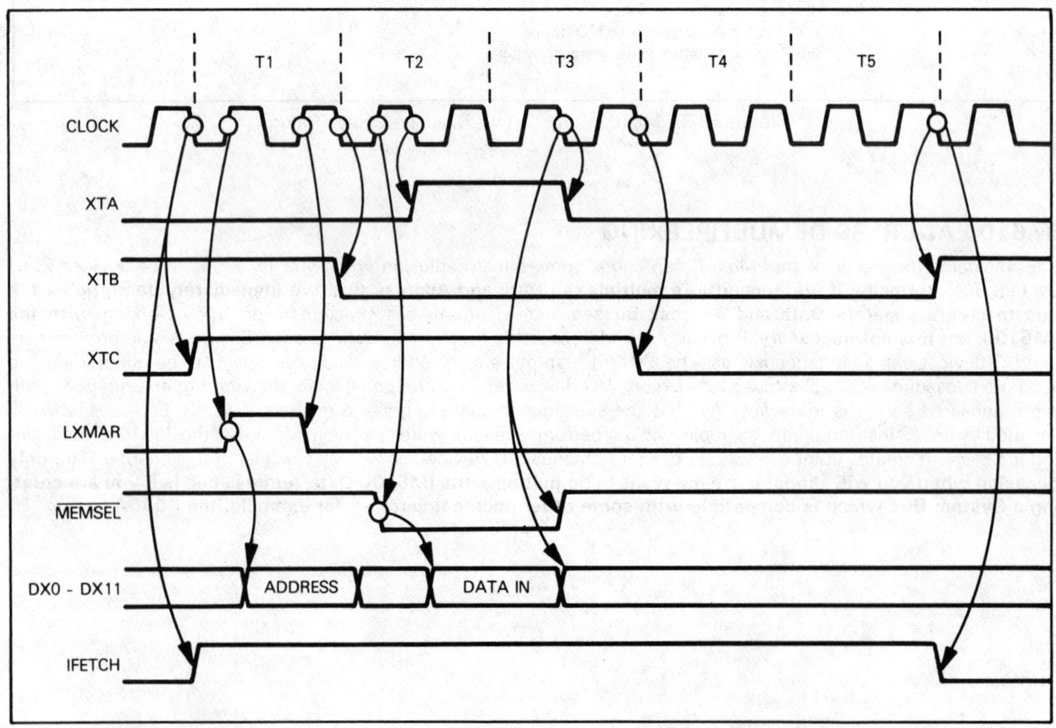


Figure 13-7. IM6100 Instruction Fetch Machine Cycle

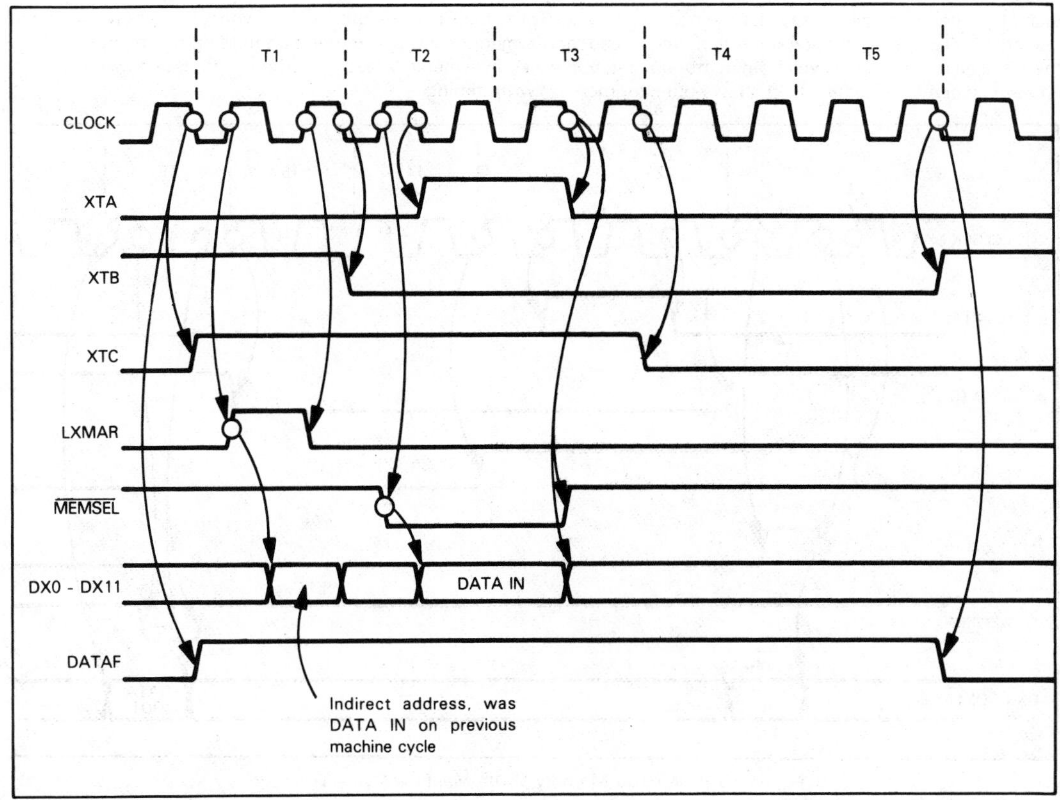


Figure 13-8. Machine Cycle Timing for Memory Read from Indirectly Addressed Location

## IM6100 MEMORY READ MACHINE CYCLE TIMING

**Figure 13-6 represents the memory read variation of Figure 13-4.** $\overline{\text{MEMSEL}}$ is pulsed low for a select, but otherwise the two figures are identical.

**IM6100 INSTRUCTION FETCH MACHINE CYCLE**

Logically there is no difference between an instruction fetch machine cycle and a memory read machine cycle; however, **the IM6100 outputs IFETCH high for the duration of the instruction fetch, memory read machine cycle. Timing is illustrated in Figure 13-7.**

**IM6100 INDIRECTLY ADDRESSED MEMORY READ CYCLE**

There is one additional memory read machine cycle which is specifically identified via its own signal. Memory reference instructions AND, TAD, and ISZ, if they specify indirect addressing, output DATAF high for the duration of the machine cycle that carries the indirect address as an address, rather than data. **Figure 13-8 illustrates timing for a machine cycle during which the CPU reads from an indirectly addressed memory location.** DATAF is not output high when JMP or JMS instructions specifying indirect addressing are executed.

The IM6100 has two instructions that read data from memory to the Accumulator: the AND and TAD instructions. Without indirect addressing, each of these instructions will be executed in two machine cycles; the first machine cycle will be an instruction fetch, as illustrated in Figure 13-7, while the second machine cycle will be a memory read, as illustrated in Figure 13-6. If either of these instructions specifies indirect addressing, then the instruction will be executed in three machine cycles. The first machine cycle will be a simple instruction fetch, as illustrated in Figure 13-7. The second machine cycle will be a simple memory read, as illustrated in Figure 13-6; however, during this machine cycle the effective memory address will be read as data. The third machine cycle will be an indirect addressing memory read, as illustrated in Figure 13-8. The data input during the second machine cycle will be output as an address during the third machine cycle.

The ISZ instruction reads from memory, increments the data just read, and writes it back. The sequence of machine cycles used to execute ISZ is almost the same as sequences for AND and TAD; the only difference is that, for ISZ, a memory write cycle follows the last memory read cycle. Thus, the CPU executes an ISZ without indirection in three machine cycles: an instruction fetch, a memory read, and a memory write. If indirect addressing has been specified, there will be four machine cycles: an instruction fetch followed by a memory read, an indirect addressing memory read, and a memory write. Figure 13-9 shows ordinary memory write timing.

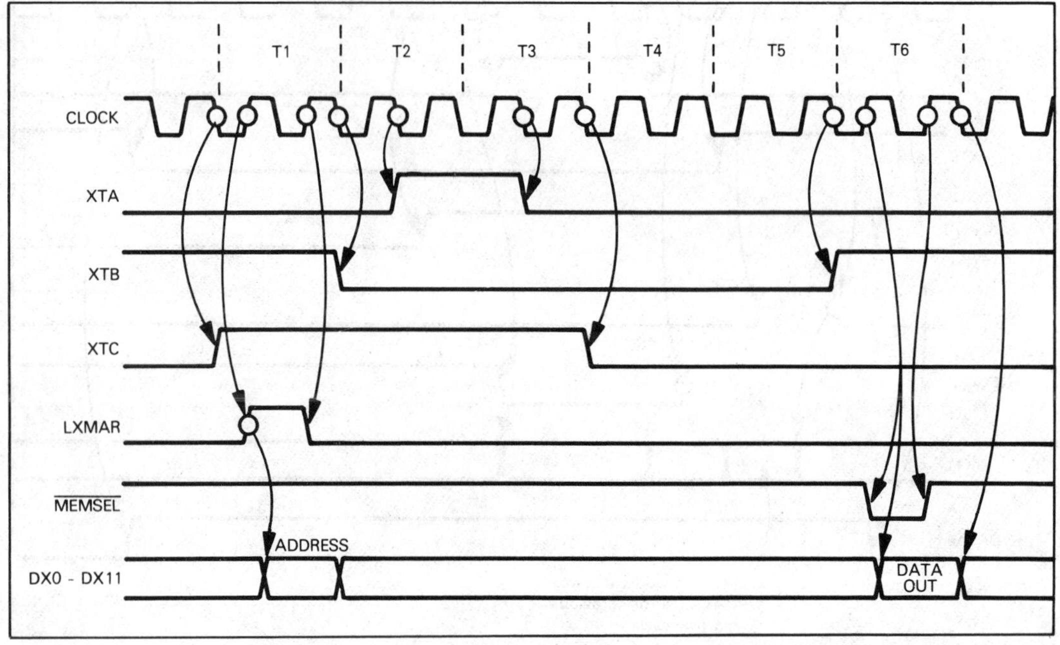


Figure 13-9. IM6100 Memory Write Machine Cycle Timing

## IM6100 MEMORY WRITE MACHINE CYCLE

**A simple IM6100 memory write machine cycle is illustrated in Figure 13-9.** This figure is identical to Figure 13-5, except that $\overline{\text{MEMSEL}}$ is shown generating a low strobe in T6.

The IM6100 has two instructions that write to memory: the DCA and the ISZ instructions. Also, any memory reference instruction that specifies indirect addressing with auto-increment must write into memory. This is because when auto-increment addressing is specified, the indirect address which is fetched from one of the memory locations $08_{16}$ through $0F_{16}$ is incremented, then written back to the same memory location.

**IM6100 INDIRECTLY ADDRESSED MEMORY WRITE CYCLE**

**A simple memory write machine cycle with indirect addressing will have timing** identical to Figure 13-9, except that DATAF will pulse high for the duration of the machine cycle, **as illustrated in Figure 13-10.** The memory address output during this indirect addressing, memory write machine cycle will have been input as data during the previous machine cycle, which will be a simple memory read machine cycle with timing as illustrated in Figure 13-6.

**IM6100 INDIRECT ADDRESSING WITH AUTO-INCREMENT TIMING**

**Any memory reference instruction that specifies indirect addressing with auto-increment will insert a write during T6 of the second machine cycle.** During this machine cycle, the indirect address will be fetched from one of the memory locations with addresses $08_{16}$ through $0F_{16}$. During the T6 clock period this address, having been incremented, is written back to the same memory location. During a third machine cycle, the memory read or write required by the instruction will occur. **Figure 13-11 illustrates timing for an indirect addressing with auto-increment machine cycle.** Observe that a memory read and a memory write occur in this single machine cycle, albeit to and from the same memory location.

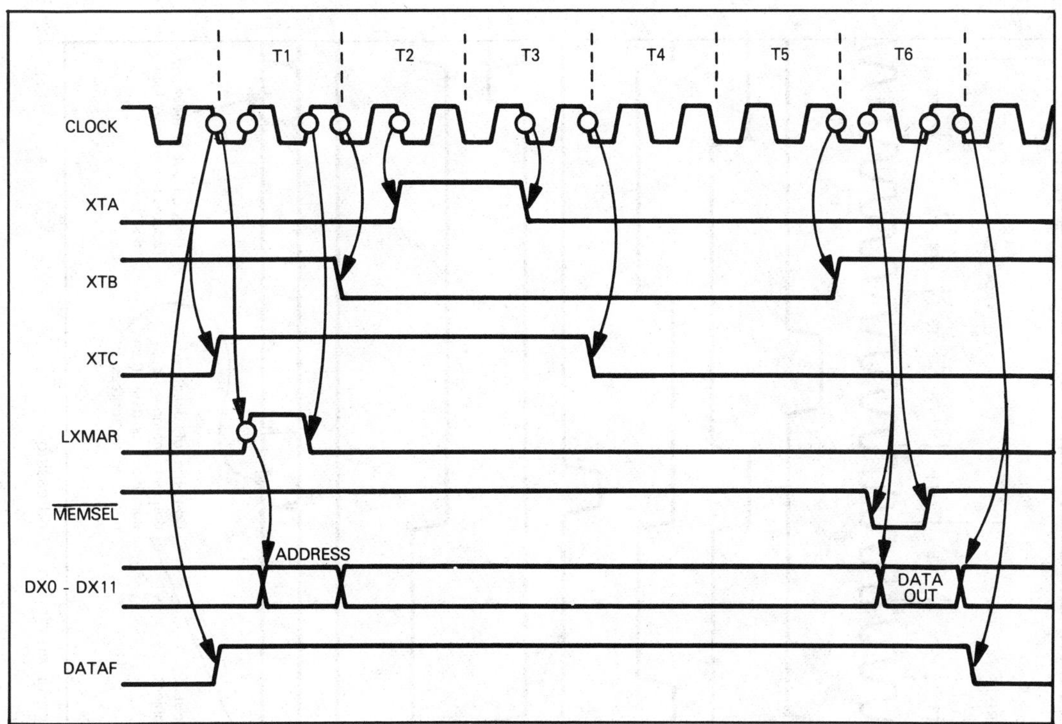


Figure 13-10. Machine Cycle Timing for Memory Write to Indirectly Addressed Location

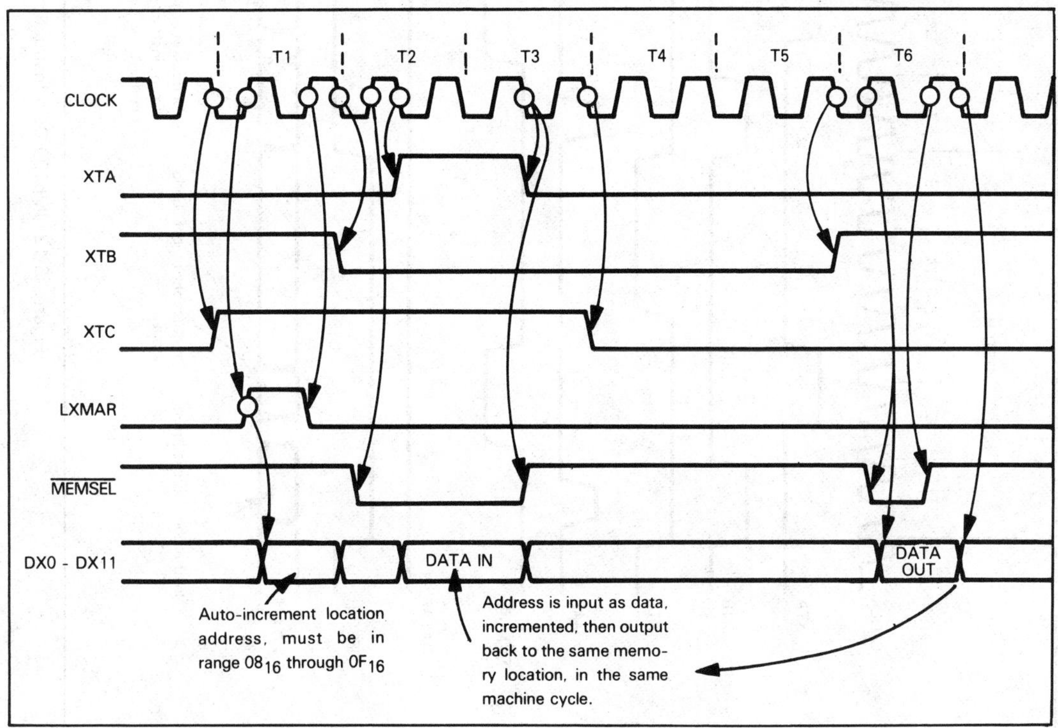


Figure 13-11. Auto-Increment Machine Cycle for an IM6100 Memory Reference Instruction that Specifies Indirect Addressing with Auto-Increment

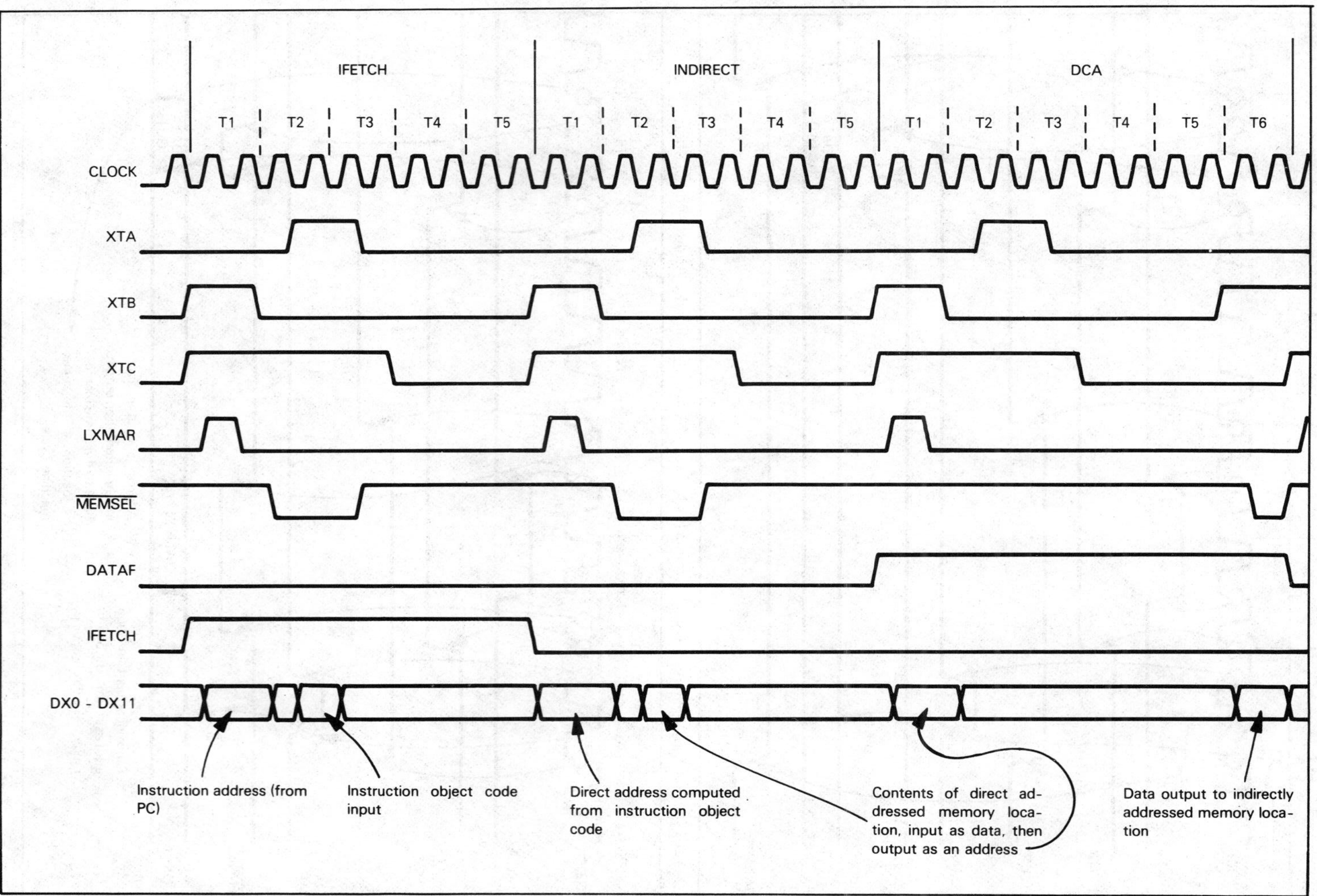


Figure 13-12. IM6100 DCA Instruction Timing with Indirect Addressing

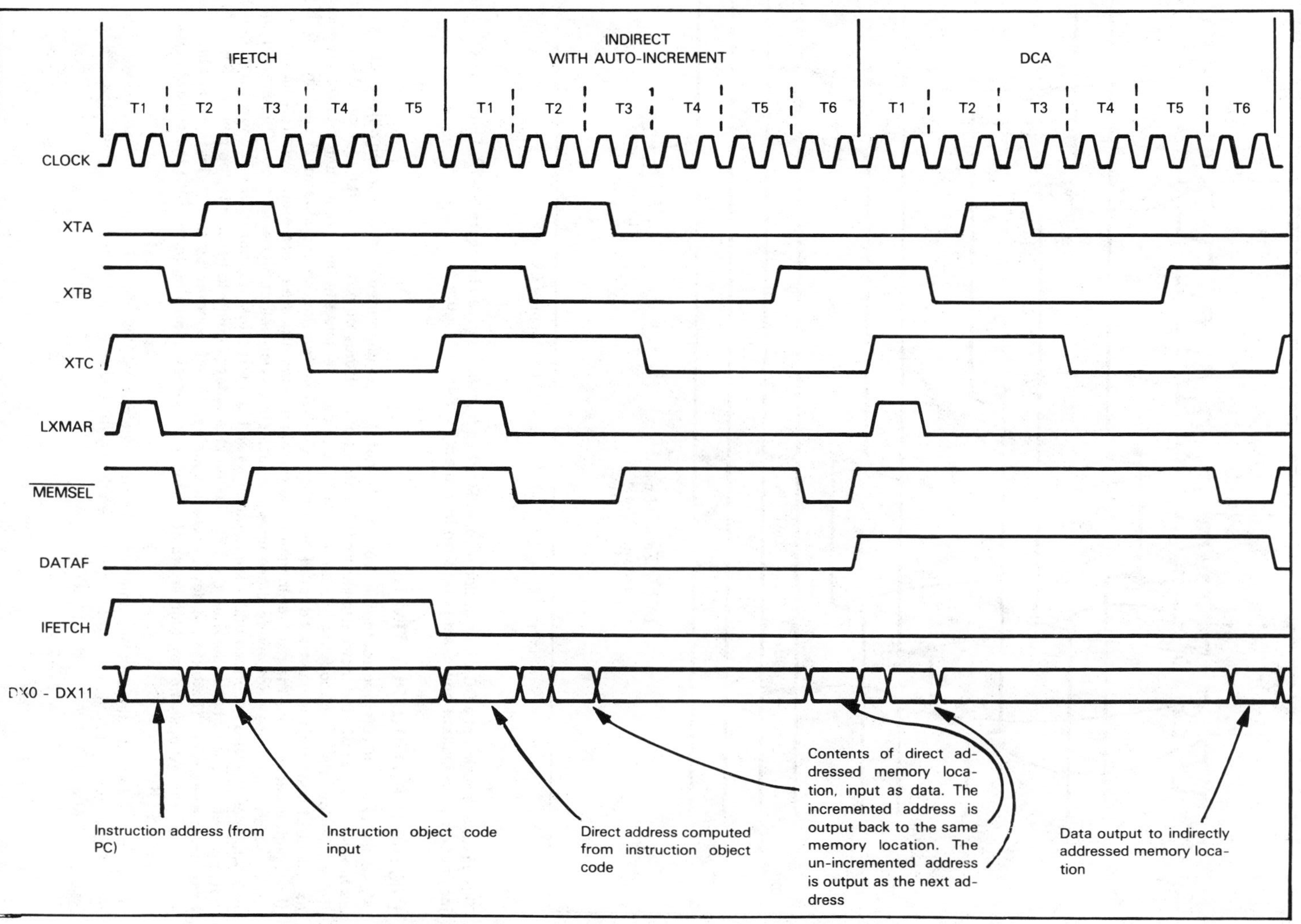


Figure 13-13. IM6100 DCA Instruction Timing with Indirect Addressing and Auto-Increment

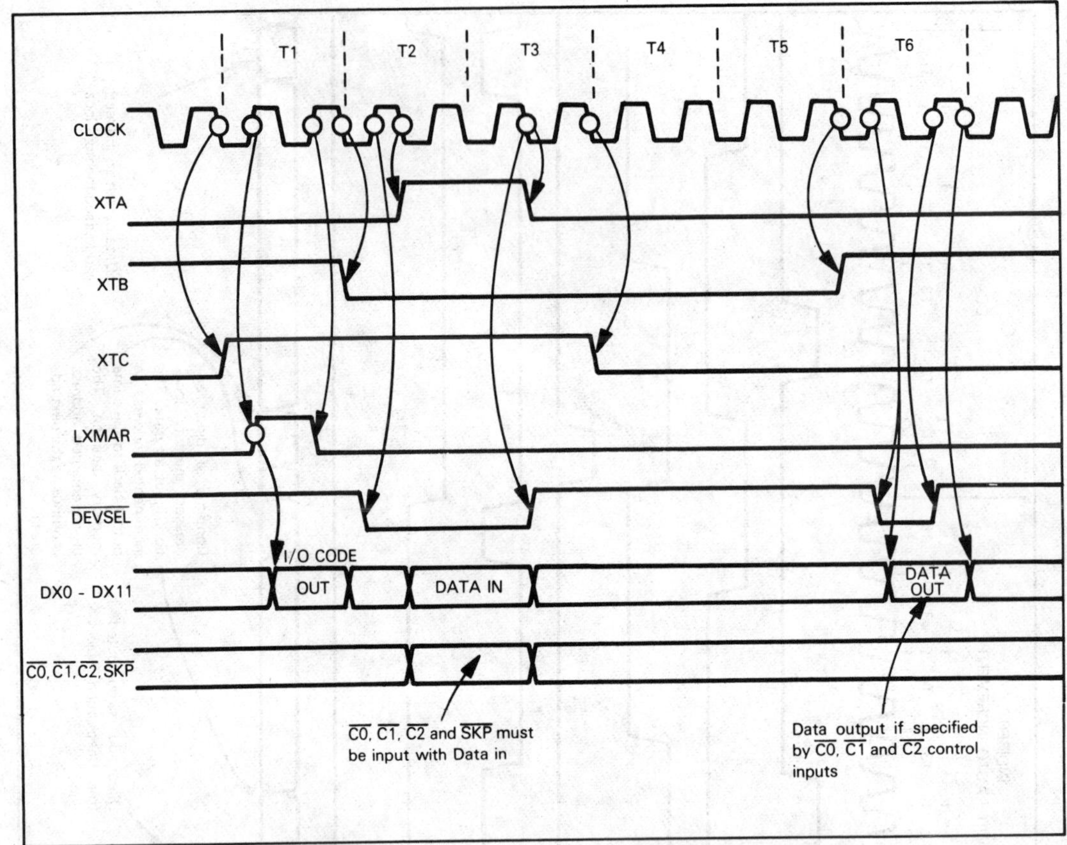


Figure 13-14. IM6100 I/O Data Input Machine Cycle

**Timing for execution of a DCA instruction with indirect addressing is given in Figure 13-12. Timing for this same instruction with indirect addressing and auto-increment is given in Figure 13-13.**

## IM6100 INPUT/OUTPUT TIMING

**A peculiarity of IM6100 input/output instructions is that they are undefined. The instruction object code's three high-order bits identify the instruction as an I/O instruction, but they do not identify the type of I/O instruction. By convention, six object code bits constitute an I/O device code, and the three remaining bits are interpreted as a control code (this is illustrated later). In reality, the I/O instruction object code must contain 110 in the three high-order bits, but the manner in which the remaining nine bits are interpreted is entirely up to external logic, which may or may not divide these nine bits into six device select bits and three I/O operation control bits. As far as the CPU is concerned, when it executes an I/O instruction, it outputs $\overline{\text{DEVSEL}}$ low instead of outputting $\overline{\text{MEMSEL}}$ low, but otherwise the CPU has no idea what is going to happen in the course of the I/O instruction's execution. The external device which considers itself selected by the I/O instruction object code determines the I/O operations which are to occur by appropriately inputting to the CPU the control signals $\overline{\text{C0}}$, $\overline{\text{C1}}$, $\overline{\text{C2}}$ and $\overline{\text{SKP}}$.**

If you are familiar with standard microprocessors such as the 8080A, this IM6100 I/O logic will appear very strange. The I/O device must tell the CPU what is to happen during the course of the I/O instruction's execution. All the CPU knows is that an I/O operation is in progress.

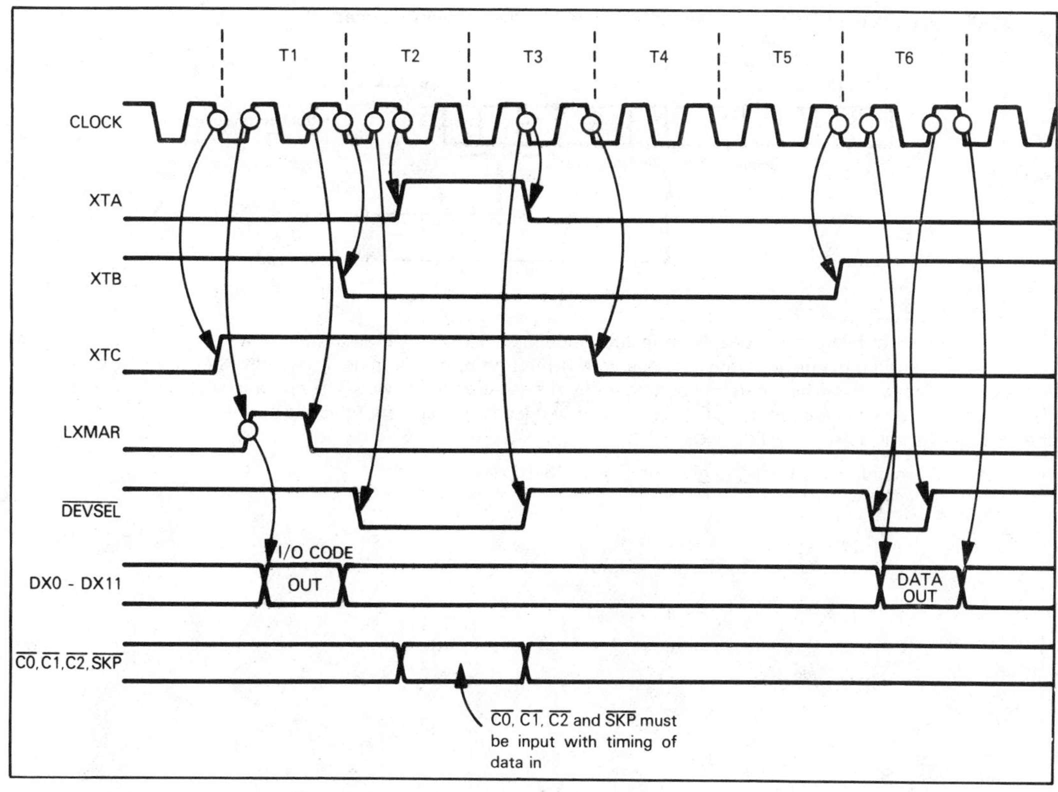


Figure 13-15. IM6100 I/O Data Output Machine Cycle

**Every IM6100 I/O instruction executes in three machine cycles.**

**The first machine cycle is a standard instruction fetch, as illustrated in Figure 13-7.**

**The second machine cycle is a variation of the data input or data output machine cycle, as illustrated in Figures 13-14 and 13-15.**

**The third I/O instruction machine cycle is a "no operation"** machine cycle. **The no operation machine cycle has six clock periods.** The clock, XTA, XTB, XTC, and LXMAR signals are active, but the Select lines and the Data/Address Bus are not.

The most important difference between the I/O input and output machine cycles illustrated in Figures 13-14 and 13-15, as against the standard input and output machine cycles illustrated in Figures 13-5 and 13-6, is the fact that the control inputs $\overline{C0}$, $\overline{C1}$, $\overline{C2}$ and $\overline{SKP}$ must be accounted for. Timing for these four signals, as inputs, must conform to data input timing. Thus, every I/O machine cycle must include a $\overline{DEVSEL}$ low pulse at read time so that the selected I/O device knows when to input the four control signals. The CPU uses these control inputs to determine whether a data input or a data output is to occur. **I/O logic will normally hold $\overline{C1}$ and $\overline{C2}$ high in between I/O operations so the default IOC instruction is a data output.** This is necessary since there is very little time separating the LXMAR high pulse and data output. $\overline{C0}$ may normally be held low or high, depending on whether the Accumulator is to be cleared or not following data output.

The I/O instruction object code, rather than an address, is output on the Data/Address Bus during T1 of any I/O instruction's second machine cycle.

By PDP-8E convention, the I/O instruction object code has the following format:

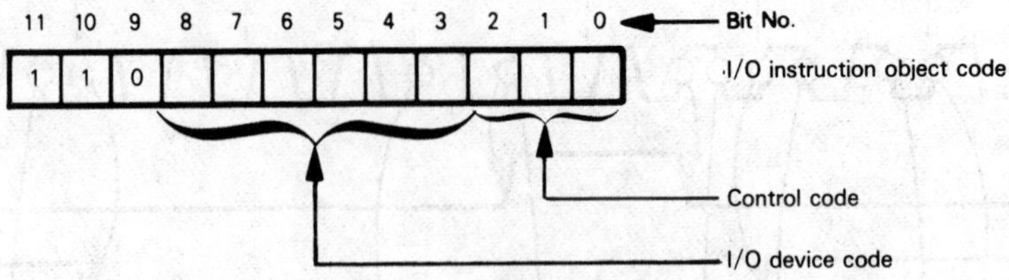


The interpretation of bits 0 through 8 is, in reality, undefined. The illustration above shows standard PDP-8E format using this convention; I/O devices must decode lines 3 through 8 to determine if they have been selected; lines 0, 1 and 2 identify operations which must be performed by the selected I/O device. The operations which the selected I/O device must perform include returning $\overline{C0}$, $\overline{C1}$, $\overline{C2}$ and $\overline{SKP}$ levels, which determine the nature of the I/O instruction for the CPU and for the selected I/O device.

A complete I/O instruction's timing is given in Figure 13-16.

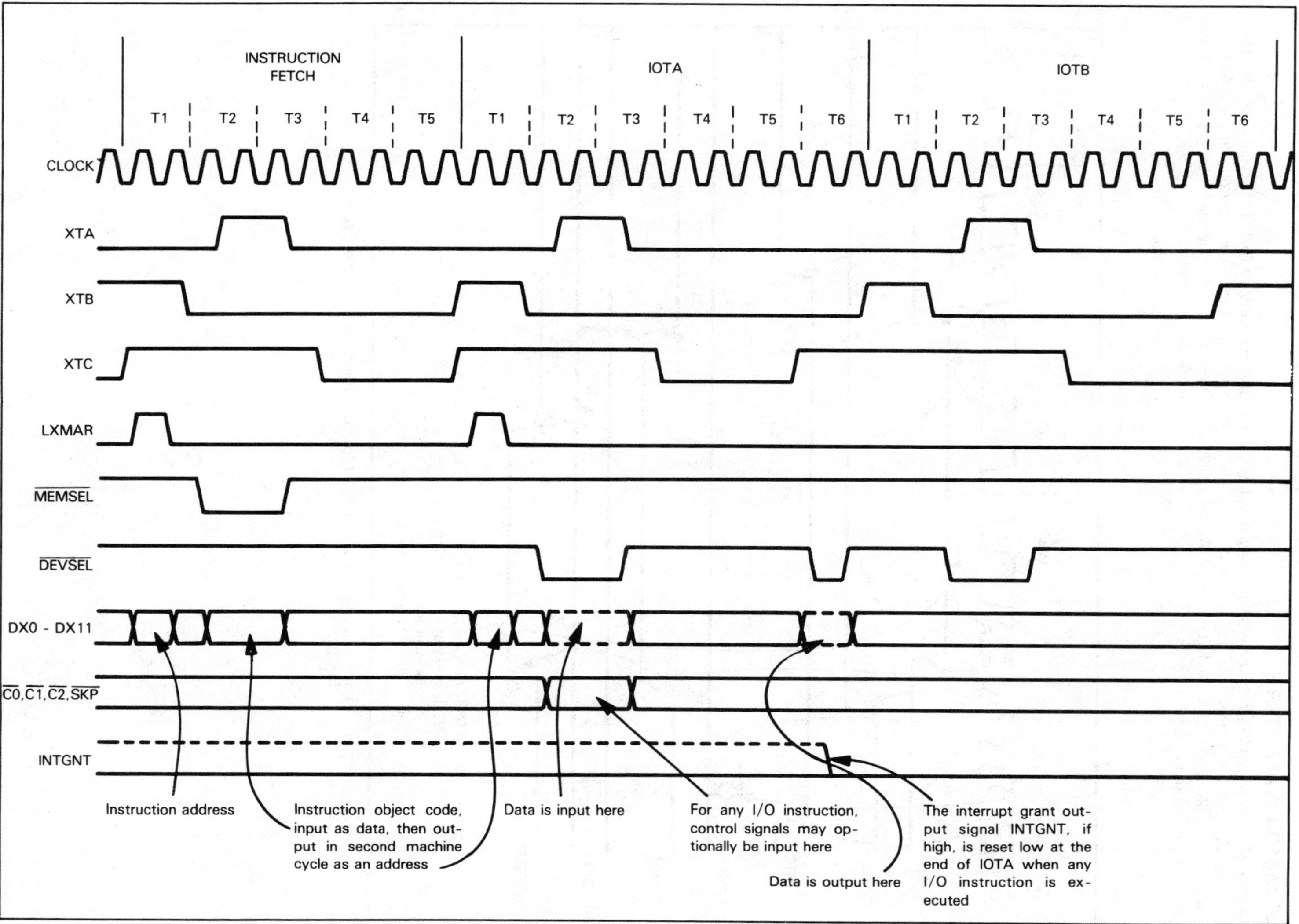


Figure 13-16. IM6100 I/O Instruction Timing

## THE IM6100 WAIT STATE

**External logic may insert Wait states within a data input or data output machine cycle.** In each case, external logic requests the Wait state via a low $\overline{\text{WAIT}}$ input. The Wait state will generate additional T2 clock periods during a data input operation. Timing is illustrated in Figure 13-17. Additional T6 clock periods will be generated during a data output operation, as illustrated in Figure 13-18.

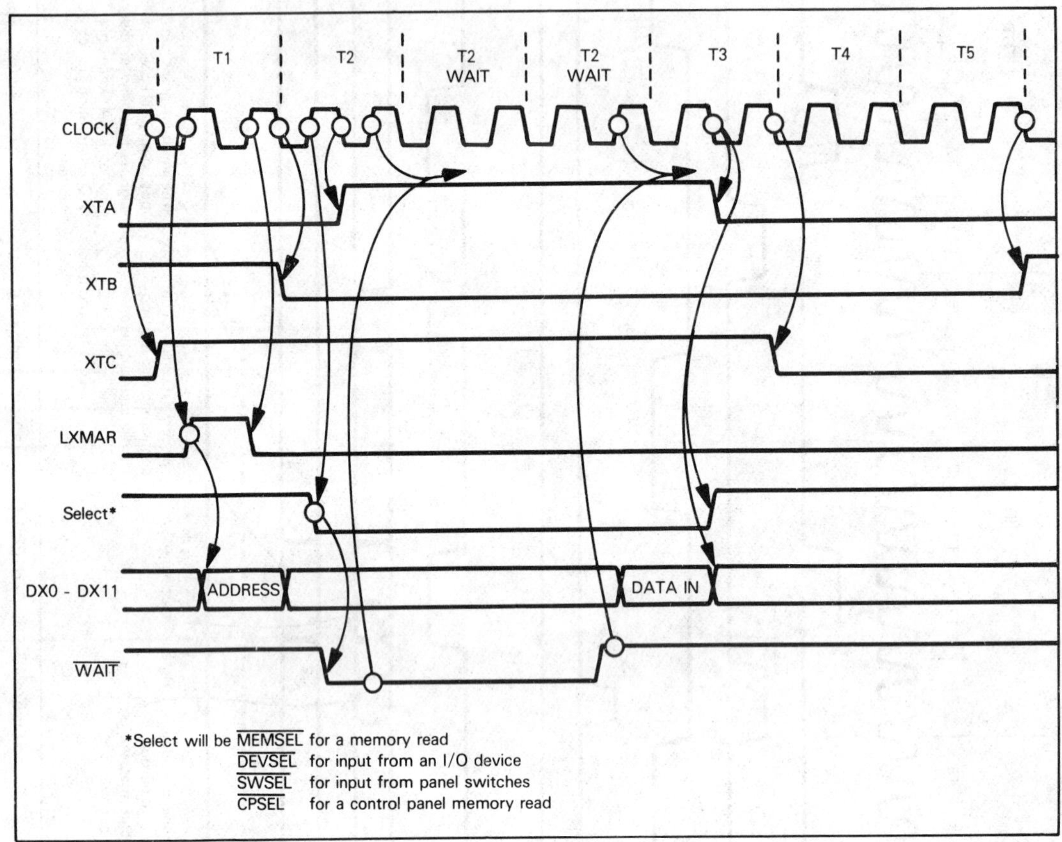


Figure 13-17. Wait States within an IM6100 Data Input Machine Cycle

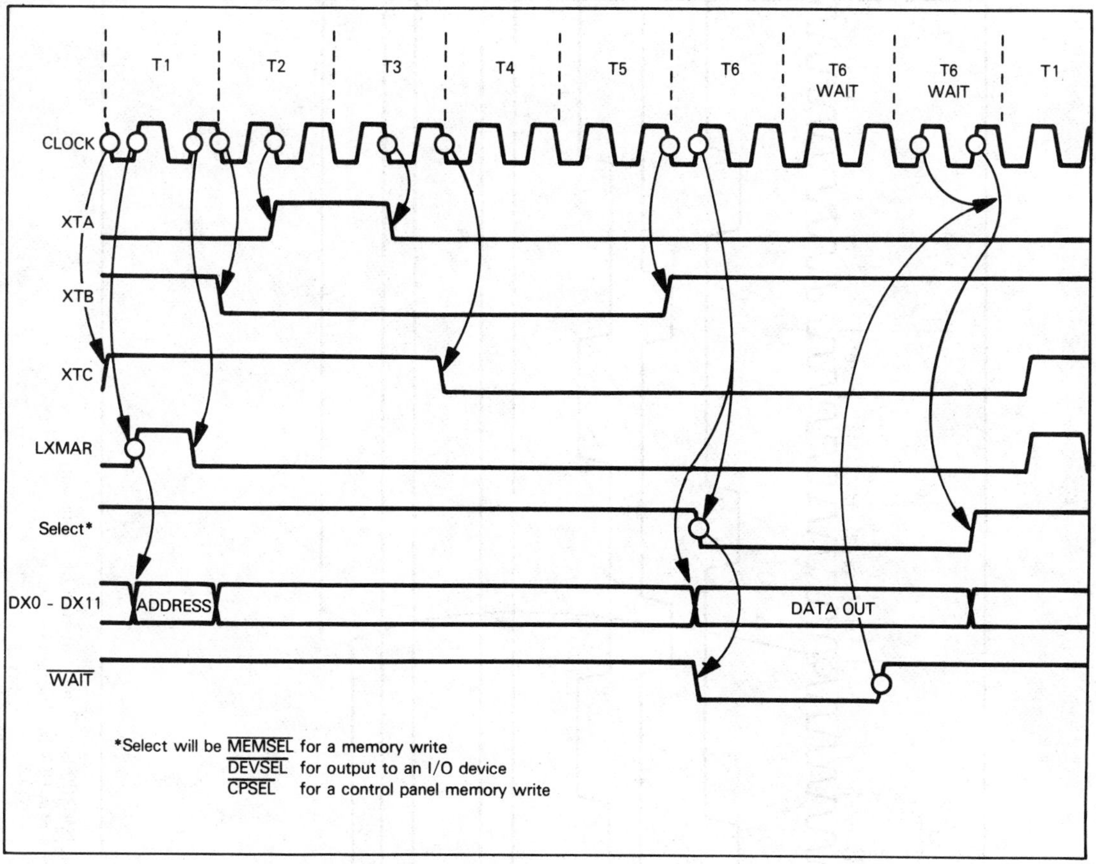

*Select will be $\overline{MEMSEL}$ for a memory write
$\overline{DEVSEL}$ for output to an I/O device
$\overline{CPSEL}$ for a control panel memory write

Figure 13-18. Wait States within an IM6100 Data Output Machine Cycle

In Chapter 4, we described ways in which READY input signals can be generated in order to create Wait states of one, or of a few clock periods. Although the Chapter 4 discussion is for the 8080A microprocessor, the logic applies equally well for the IM6100.

## IM6100 HOLD AND HALT CONDITIONS

**The IM6100 has a single Halt state which is equivalent to the Hold and Halt conditions of other microprocessors. The Halt state can be initiated by executing a Halt instruction, or by inputting a low signal via RUN/$\overline{HLT}$.**

**The IM6100 has two control signals associated with its Halt state. RUN/$\overline{HLT}$ is an input which can be used to initiate and terminate Halt states.** What is unusual about the RUN/$\overline{HLT}$ control input is that **the low-to-high transition of this signal is active.** This may be illustrated as follows:

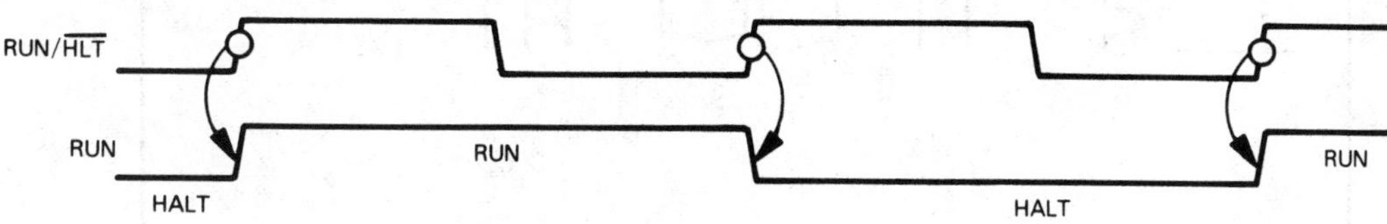

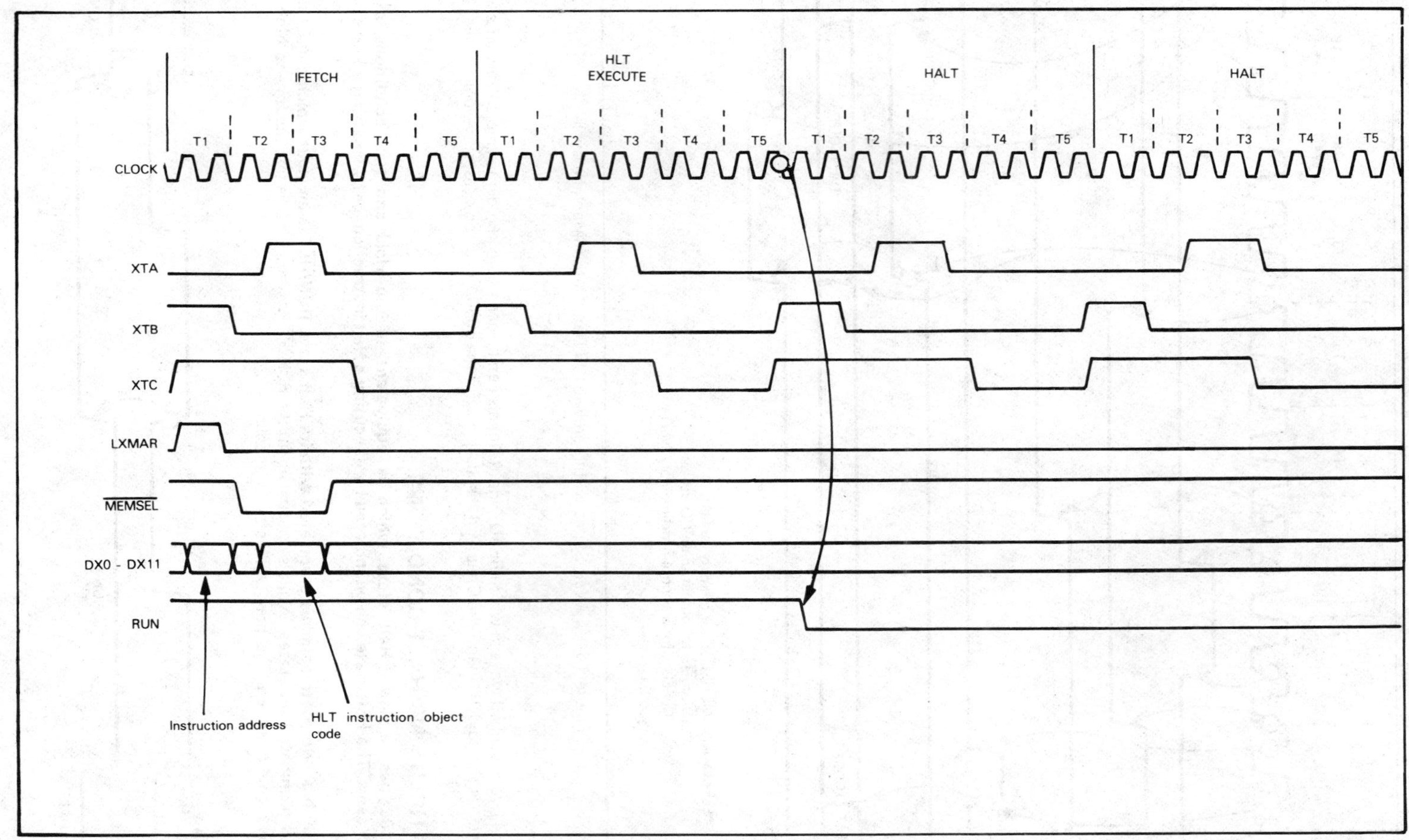


Figure 13-19. An IM6100 Halt State Initiated by Execution of a HLT Instruction

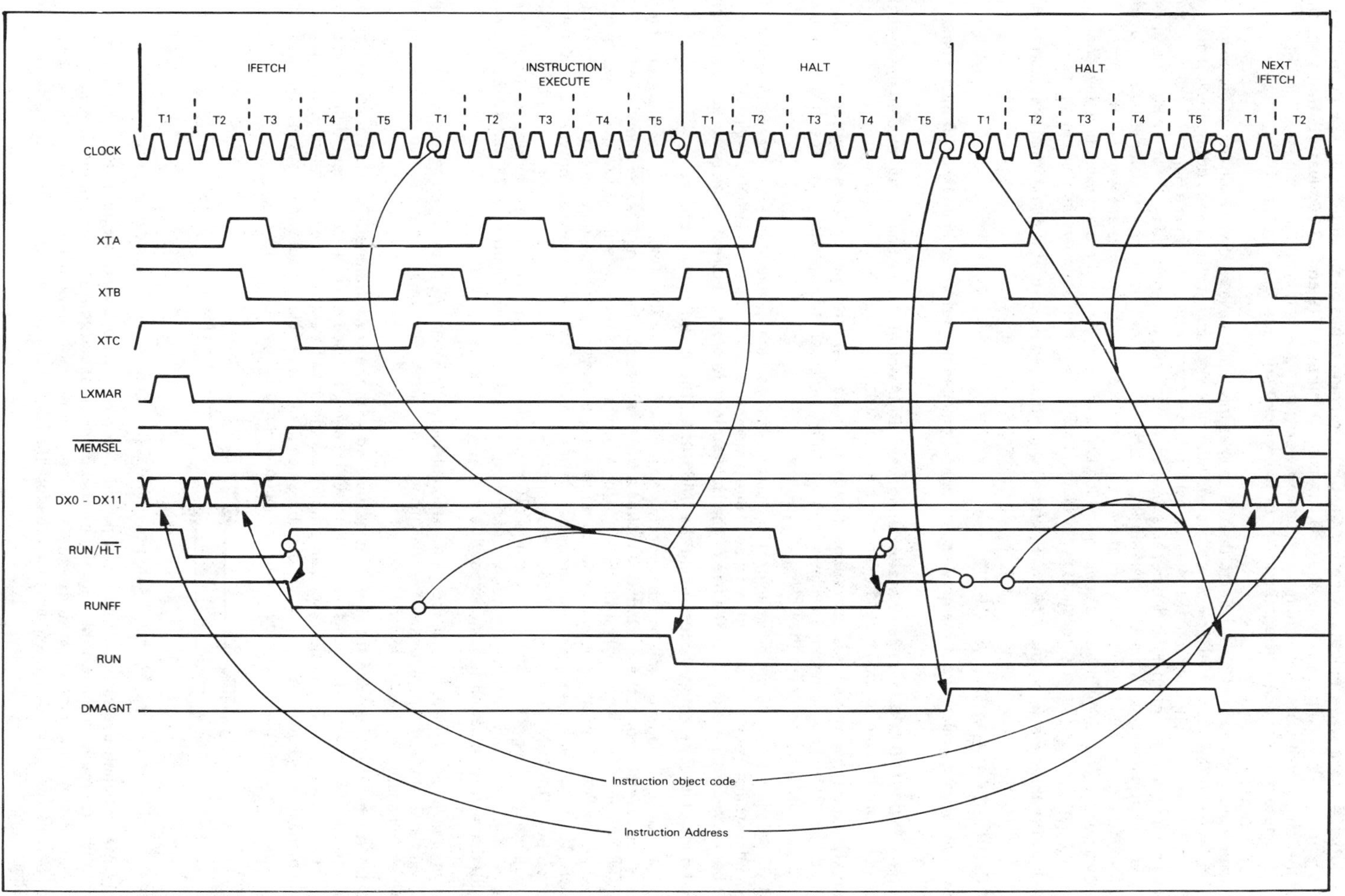


Figure 13-20. An IM6100 Halt State Initiated and Terminated by the RUN/HLT Input

**The RUN output signal always indicates whether the CPU is running or has been halted.** RUN is output high while the CPU is running; RUN is output low when the CPU has halted. **Figures 13-19 and 13-20 illustrate Halt state timing.** Note that once a Halt state has been initiated, either by executing the Halt instruction or by inputting RUN/$\overline{\text{HLT}}$ low, the **Halt state will last some integral number of five-clock-period machine cycles.**

If a Halt state is initiated by the RUN/$\overline{\text{HLT}}$ input, then as soon as this input makes a low-to-high transition, an internal Run flip-flop is reset to 0. This internal flip-flop is sampled in the middle of the first clock period during the last machine cycle of the currently executing instruction. If the internal flip-flop is reset at this time, then a Halt state will begin with the next machine cycle. This internal flip-flop remains reset until the next low-to-high transition of the RUN/$\overline{\text{HLT}}$ input. During every Halt machine cycle the internal Halt flip-flop is sampled in the middle of the first Halt machine cycle clock period. As soon as the internal flip-flop is detected high again, the Halt state terminates at the end of the current Halt machine cycle with a "transition" Halt cycle, during which DMAGNT is held high. Program execution then continues with an instruction fetch on the next machine cycle. Figure 13-20 shows Halt state termination timing.

**Observe that the three clock signals XTA, XTB, and XTC continue to be output in the normal way during Halt machine cycles.**

## IM6100 DIRECT MEMORY ACCESS

**There are two ways in which direct memory access operations can be performed in an IM6100 microcomputer system.**

**You can put the IM6100 CPU into a Hold state,** during which DMA operations are being performed. In this case the CPU will slow down in order to accommodate direct memory access.

**Alternatively, direct memory access operations may occur in parallel with instruction execution** by exploiting clock periods T3, T4 and T5 of machine cycles within which no write operation occurs. This type of parallel direct memory access does not slow down the CPU.

The IM6102 MEDIC device, described later in this chapter, enables parallel direct memory access in an IM6100 microcomputer system. For a discussion of this type of direct memory access, refer to the IM6102 device description. **In the text below we will consider only the use of the Hold state to implement direct memory access operations.**

**Note that parallel direct memory access using the IM6102 MEDIC is definitely preferred.**

IM6100 Hold state DMA logic is similar to that which we have described for the 8080A in Chapter 4. **External logic that wishes to take control of the System Bus makes a DMA request by inputting $\overline{\text{DMAREQ}}$ low.** The CPU samples $\overline{\text{DMAREQ}}$ in the middle of the first clock period of a machine cycle. Upon sensing $\overline{\text{DMAREQ}}$ low, the CPU acknowledges the DMA request at the end of the currently executing instruction, providing no higher priority control input exists. Table 13-1 and associated text summarize control priorities. **When the CPU acknowledges a DMA request, it outputs DMAGNT high** and suspends program execution. The Data/Address Bus is floated and all select lines are output high; the clock signals XTA, XTB and XTC continue to function, clocking five-clock-period machine cycles. External logic must now use the System Bus to perform all DMA transfers. **Figures 13-21 and 13-22 illustrate DMA initiation and termination timing, respectively.**

$\overline{\text{DMAREQ}}$ is sampled in the middle of the first clock period of every DMA machine cycle. Upon sensing $\overline{\text{DMAREQ}}$ high, the CPU will terminate DMA operations at the conclusion of the current DMA machine cycle, and will then proceed with the next scheduled instruction fetch.

**External DMA logic is responsible for all events associated with the DMA transfer.** This includes having special device select lines. The device select lines output by the CPU cannot be used, since these are held high during a DMA transfer. This is not a significant problem; you can simply AND the DMA Select with the CPU Select in order to generate a valid memory or I/O device Select. This is possible since the inactive select input will always be held high while the active select input is pulsed low. You will have a negative-logic OR:

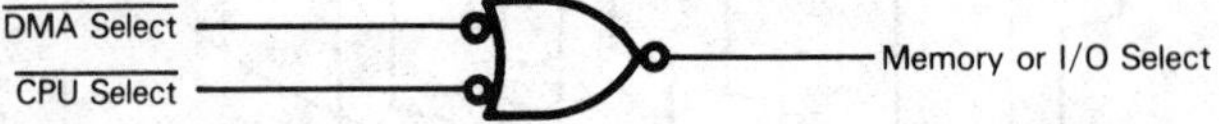


the select line will be active (that is, low) if either the DMA Select line or the CPU Select line is active.

**Since all DMA machine cycles have five clock periods, memory write timing during a DMA transfer cannot agree exactly with memory write timing during normal program execution.** This is not a problem, since there is sufficient time within a machine cycle to execute a memory write. Logic beyond the IM6100 does not know the difference between one clock period and another, therefore the DMA memory write can occur at any time within the DMA machine cycle.

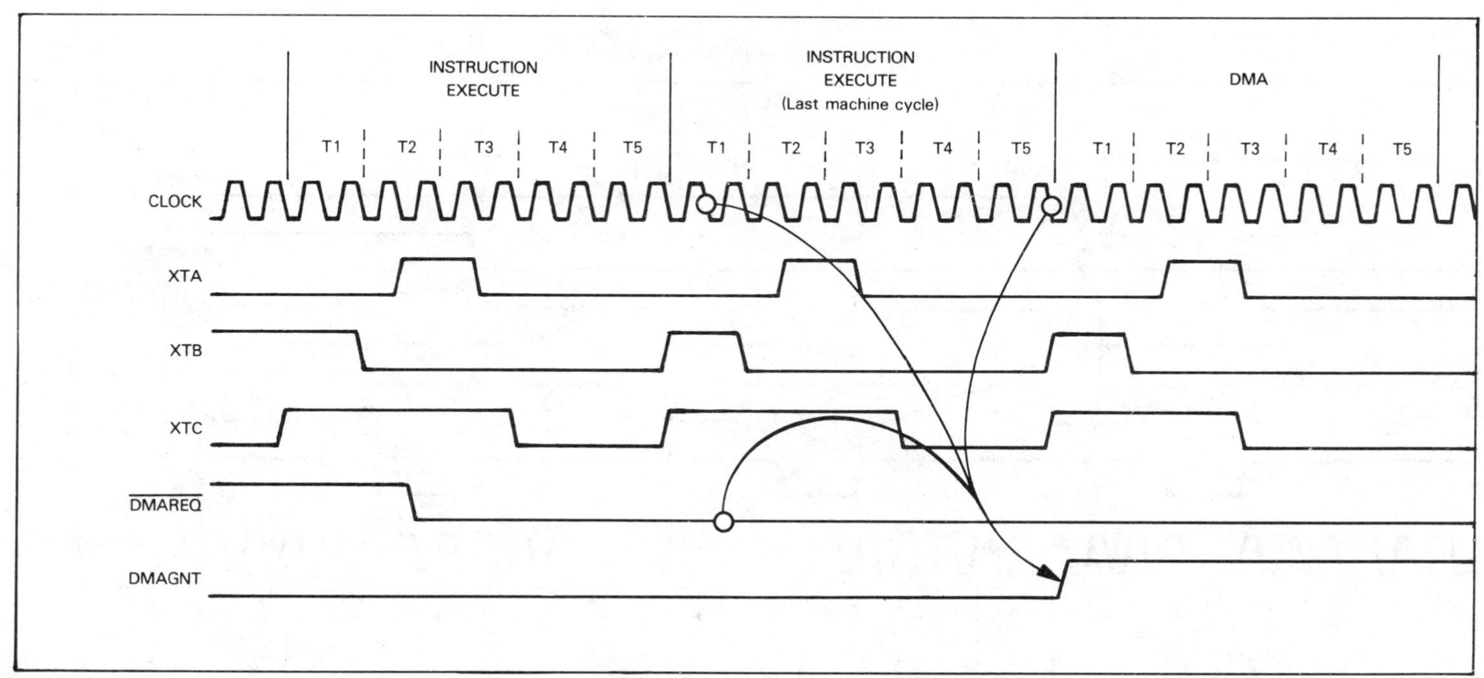


Figure 13-21. IM6100 DMA Initiation Timing

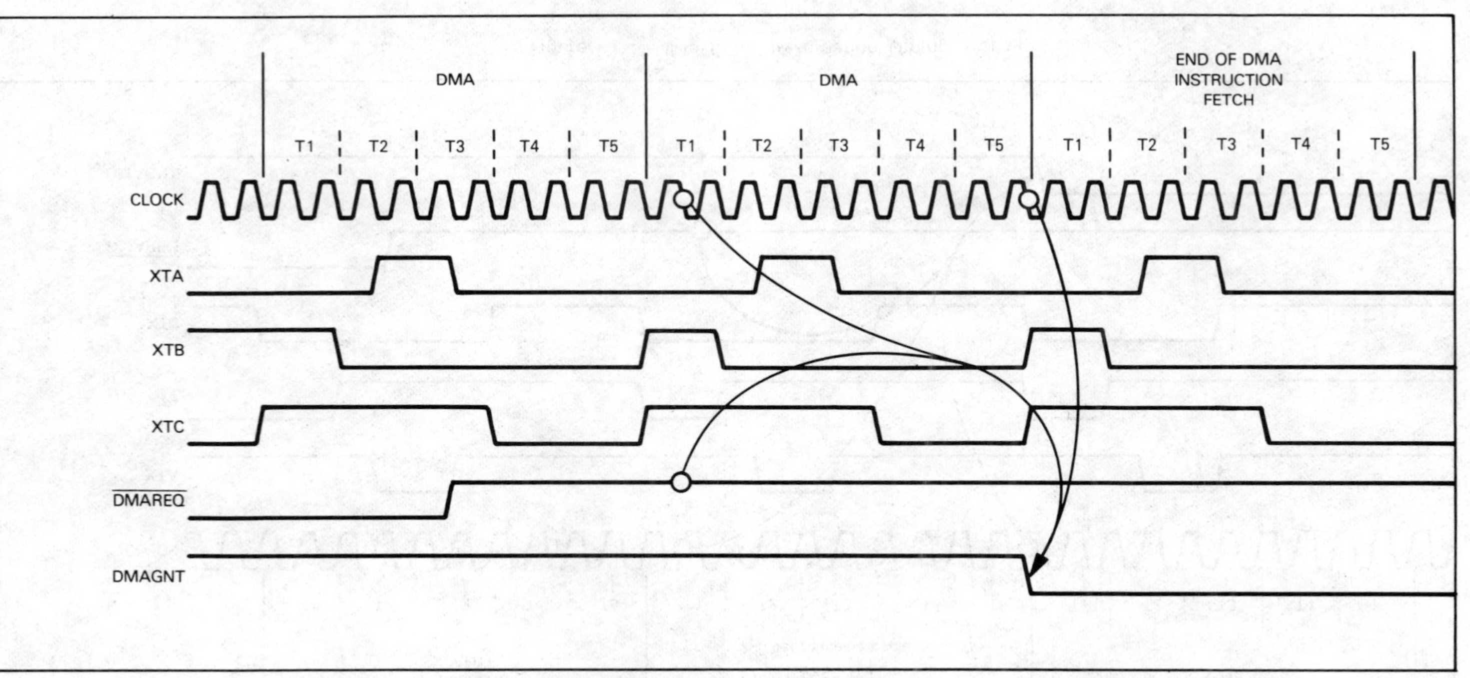


Figure 13-22. IM6100 DMA Termination Timing

**The Halt state has priority over the DMA state.** Thus, a DMA request will not be acknowledged while the CPU is in a Halt state; however, while the CPU has acknowledged a DMA request and is executing DMA machine cycles, it will respond to a Halt request generated by a low-to-high transition of the RUN/$\overline{\text{HLT}}$ input. In the Halt state the Data/Address Bus is not floated, therefore **you must make sure that RUN/$\overline{\text{HLT}}$ does not pulse low while the CPU is acknowledging a DMA request.** This is simple enough to do. Here is appropriate logic:

**Table 13-1 summarizes operation priorities within IM6100 CPU logic.**

**You will have no trouble using the DMA control devices described in Volume 3 in order to implement direct memory access in an IM6100 microcomputer system;** however, the IM6102 is preferred in IM6100 microcomputer systems. The DMA control devices described in Volume 3 are all NMOS devices, therefore you will need CMOS-to-NMOS bidirectional drivers. These drivers may buffer the CPU from the rest of the system, or, if most of the system is implemented using CMOS technology, these buffers will isolate the DMA logic from the rest of the system.

## THE IM6100 RESET

**You must input the $\overline{\text{RESET}}$ signal low in order to reset the IM6100 CPU.** The CPU samples this signal in the middle of the first clock period during the last machine cycle of an instruction's execution. Upon detecting $\overline{\text{RESET}}$ low, the CPU enters a Reset condition beginning with the next machine cycle. The Reset condition is maintained for an exact number of five-clock-period machine cycles while the $\overline{\text{RESET}}$ input is low. When the CPU detects $\overline{\text{RESET}}$ high in the middle of the first clock period of a Reset machine cycle, the processor will begin program execution at the end of that Reset machine cycle, thus terminating the Reset state.

**Timing for the initiation and termination of a Reset condition is identical to timing for DMA initiation and termination, as illustrated in Figures 13-21 and 13-22. In these two figures, by substituting $\overline{\text{RESET}}$ for $\overline{\text{DMAREQ}}$, and by eliminating the DMAGNT signal, you create Reset initiation and termination timing.**

**During a Reset condition the following events occur:**

1) The Program Counter is set to $FFF_{16}$.
2) The Accumulator and Link flag are cleared.
3) The Data/Address Bus is floated.
4) All Select lines are output high.
5) The three clock signals, XTA, XTB, and XTC, continue to output, timing five-clock-period machine cycles.

The only difference between a Reset condition and a DMA condition is the fact that during the Reset condition the Accumulator and flags are cleared and the Program Counter is set to $FFF_{16}$. You will normally initiate a bootstrap loader program at memory location $FFF_{16}$ in order to restart the microcomputer system following a reset.

## IM6100 INTERRUPT LOGIC

**The IM6100 has two separate and distinct interrupt requests, one for the control panel and another for external devices in general. We will now discuss external devices' interrupt request logic, leaving control panel interrupt request logic to the control panel discussion which follows.**

**Any external device wishing to request an interrupt does so by inputting a low signal via $\overline{\text{INTREQ}}$.** The CPU samples this signal in the middle of the first clock period, during the last machine cycle of the current instruction's execution. Upon detecting $\overline{\text{INTREQ}}$ low, the CPU will acknowledge the interrupt at the conclusion of the current instruction's execution, providing no high priority control input exists. Priorities are summarized in Table 13-1. **Upon acknowledging a valid interrupt request, the IM6100 CPU goes through these steps:**

1) The interrupt grant signal INTGNT is output high.
2) Interrupt acknowledge logic is disabled.
3) Program Counter contents are stored in memory location 000.
4) An instruction fetch machine cycle is executed, with the next instruction's object code fetched from memory location 001.

**Timing is illustrated in Figure 13-22a.**

**IM6100 interrupt logic is, by microprocessor standards, quite primitive.** A single interrupt service routine, origined at memory location 001, must be executed in response to every external interrupt request.

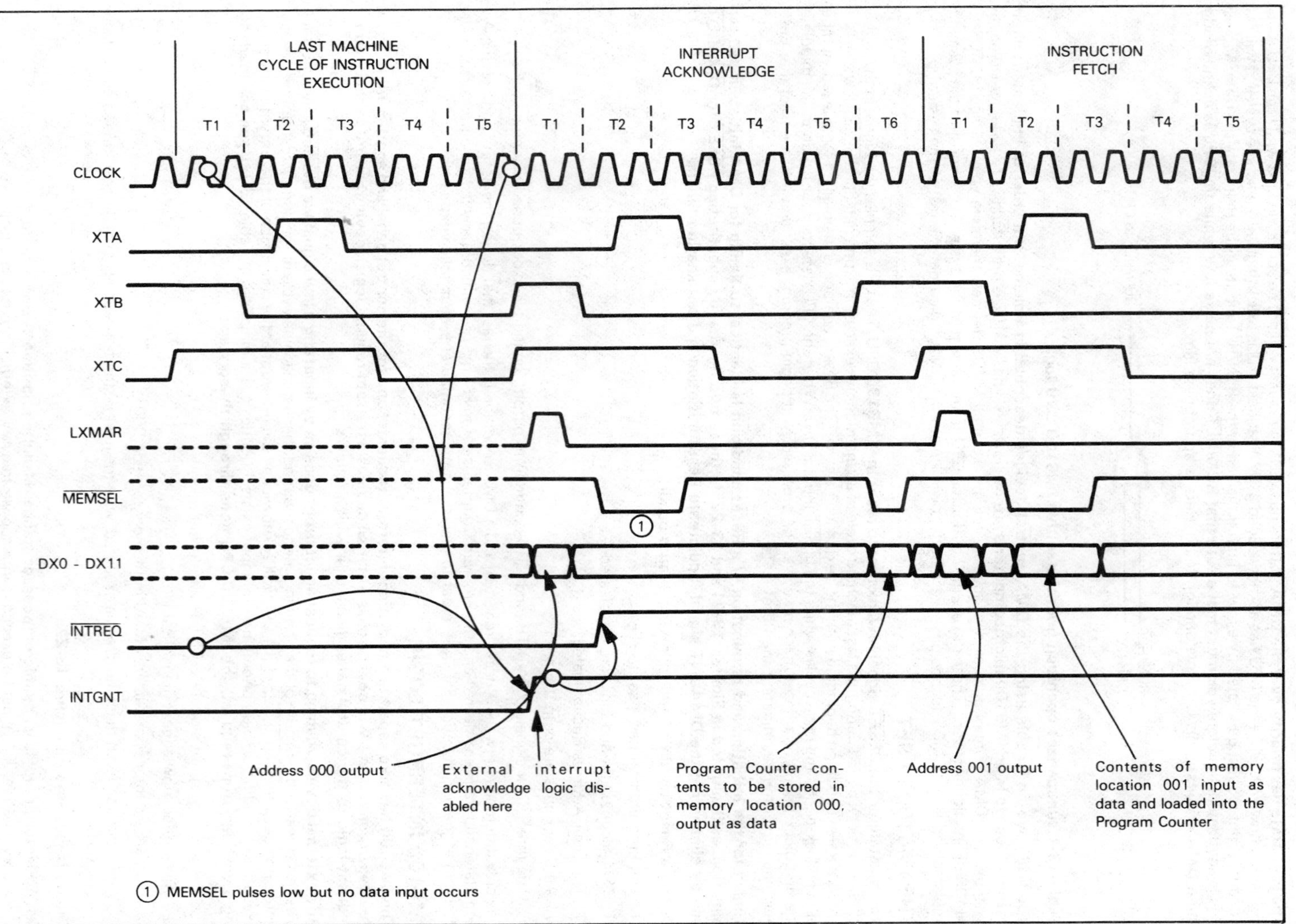


Figure 13-22a. IM6100 Interrupt Acknowledge Timing

**IM6100 INTERRUPT PROCESSING INSTRUCTIONS**

**There is a group of eight I/O instructions which are treated as interrupt processing instructions.** These are:

SKON - Skip if interrupt On
ION - Enable interrupts
IOF - Disable interrupts
SRQ - Skip if there is an active interrupt request
GTF - Get flags
RTF - Return flags
SGT - Undefined I/O operation
CAF - Clear all flags

**Figure 13-16 illustrates instruction execution timing for these eight instructions.**

**When any I/O instruction,** including the eight instructions above, **is executed, the INTGNT signal is reset low.** INTGNT reset timing is illustrated in Figure 13-16.

In the simplest case, here is an appropriate interrupt service routine that can be used to determine device priorities:

```
        *001            /INTERRUPT SERVICE ROUTINE ORIGINED AT 001
        JMP I   .+1     /JUMP INDIRECT VIA ADDRESS IN NEXT WORD
        INTS            /LABEL OF INTERRUPT SERVICE ROUTINE
        -
        -
        -
INTS    IOT DEV1,INT    /DEV1 ACTIVE?
        SKP             /IF NOT, SKIP OVER
        JMP I DEV1A     /IF SO, SERVICE DEV1
        IOT DEV2,INT
        SKP
        JMP I DEV2A
        IOT DEV3,INT
        SKP
        JMP I DEV3A
        -
        -
        -
        etc
DEV1A   ADDR1
DEV2A   ADDR2
DEV3A   ADDR3
```

The instruction sequence above begins (at memory location 1) with a Jump Indirect instruction that holds the start of the interrupt service routine in memory location 2. This interrupt service routine origin is identified by the label INTS. INTS may be anywhere in program memory.

The instruction sequence beginning at INTS is a sequence of I/O, Jump Indirect, and Skip instructions. The I/O instructions identify, sequentially, the devices that can request an interrupt. Each identified device is provided with a control code given the label INT. This control code must be interpreted by the addressed device as a command to return a low pulse via $\overline{SKP}$ during I/O data input time, if the device is requesting an interrupt. Thus, if there is an interrupt request, the next instruction, which is a Skip instruction, will be stepped over and the Jump Indirect to the appropriate device interrupt service routine will be performed. The IOT instruction may thus be illustrated as follows:

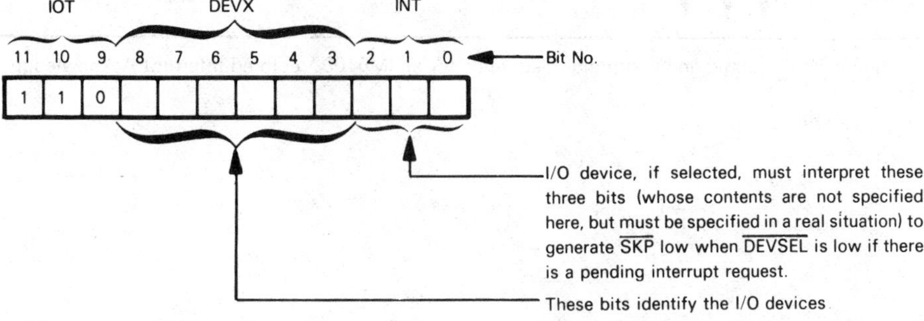

Thus, the first device in the program chain which has an active interrupt request will return $\overline{SKP}$ high, which means that the next Jump Indirect instruction will be executed.

All of the Jump Indirect instructions identify a location which must be on the same page of memory. Within this location the actual address of the interrupt service routine for the selected device is stored.

The problem with the polling scheme described above is that it demands a certain amount of intelligence from the peripheral controller. We could eliminate this intelligence by reading the contents of a device Status register, then jumping or not jumping, based upon a particular bit setting within the status register.

But remember, as the interrupt service routine increases in length, interrupt response time also goes up.

**IM6100 VECTORED INTERRUPT ACKNOWLEDGE**

**You can implement a vectored interrupt acknowledge using daisy chain logic, as illustrated for the 8048 microcomputer in Chapter 6.** Consider Figure 6-14. Eight separate interrupt acknowledge signals are generated together with a three-bit code identifying the acknowledged device — which is the highest priority device requesting an interrupt. This three-bit code could be held in a 12-bit buffer, which the CPU reads as an I/O port. If logic associated with this I/O port, upon being accessed, inputs control signals C2 low and C1 high, then the three-bit code (shifted left appropriately to meet the needs of Branch logic) will be added to the Program Counter. This implements a program relative jump, and then a vectored branch. **Figure 13-23 illustrates an appropriate instruction sequence.**

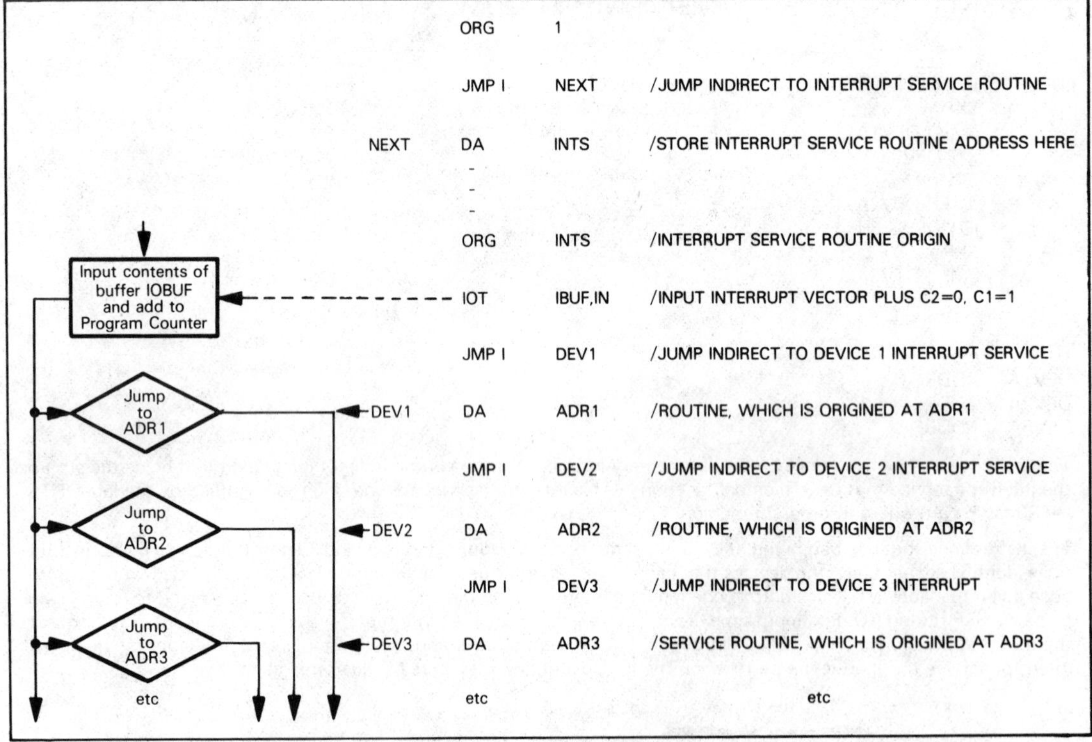


Figure 13-23. Logic and Instruction Sequence for an IM6100 Vectored Interrupt Acknowledge

Let us examine Figure 13-23.

When the interrupt is acknowledged, the Indirect Jump instruction stored in memory location 1 is fetched. This instruction causes program execution to jump to the memory location whose address is stored in the next memory word, which is assigned the label NEXT, but is location 2. The address stored in location 2 is referred to by the label INTS.

The main interrupt service routine is stored in memory, origined at INTS. The first instruction to be executed is an IOT instruction, which inputs data from a location identified by the label IBUF. IBUF is assumed to be the label of the 12-bit buffer which has the 3-bit device vector stored in bits 1, 2 and 3. During the IOTA machine cycle, this buffer's contents will be transmitted to the CPU. Simultaneously, C2 is input low while C1 is input high; therefore, the buffer contents will be added to the Program Counter. Adding the buffer contents to the Program Counter will cause one of eight instructions to be executed next. These eight instructions are all Indirect Jump instructions, which are immediately followed by the address to be jumped to indirectly. Thus, one of eight routines origined at ADR1 through ADR8 will be executed.

Although INTGNT is reset low with the first I/O instruction executed within an interrupt service routine, note that once you acknowledge an interrupt, all further interrupts are disabled until you execute an ION instruction. The ION instruction re-enables interrupts, but not until the conclusion of the instruction fetch for the next instruction to be executed. You will therefore normally leave interrupts disabled for the duration of an interrupt service routine, re-enabling the interrupts by executing an ION instruction directly before you exit the interrupt service routine via a Jump Indirect instruction. Thus the following two instructions will normally conclude an interrupt service routine:

```
-
-
-
ION                 /RE-ENABLE INTERRUPTS
JMP I    0          /RETURN FROM INTERRUPT SERVICE ROUTINE
```

Since interrupts will not be re-enabled until after the Jump Indirect instruction object code has been fetched, you will succeed in returning from the interrupt before another interrupt request gets acknowledged, if pending.

**You can, if you wish, re-enable interrupts within an interrupt service routine in order to accommodate nested interrupts.** If you do this, then prior to re-enabling interrupts within the interrupt service routine, you must save the return address, which is stored in memory location 0, in a software stack. But remember, nested interrupts rarely make sense in a microcomputer system. The low cost of microprocessor Central Processing Units invariably makes it more economical to generate multi-CPU configurations in preference to time sharing a single CPU with nested interrupts.

**The preferred method of handling multiple interrupts in an IM6100 microcomputer system is to use the IM6102 MEDIC, together with IM6101 PIE devices.** These devices automatically implement daisy-chain interrupt priorities with vectored interrupt logic. That is to say, you obtain the same result illustrated in Figure 13-23, but without any of the complexities associated with special logic of the type illustrated in Figure 6-14.

## IM6100 CONTROL PANEL LOGIC

**Since the IM6100 reproduces the logic of a microcomputer, the possible presence of a minicomputer control panel is assumed.** Control panel logic for a minicomputer can be quite complex; given the limitations of the IM6100 CPU, this could present problems. These problems are resolved, however, by allowing the control panel to have its own memory. Control panel memory is used to store programs that implement control panel logic. **Control panel memory is separate and distinct from main memory. Control panel memory addresses can (and usually do) overlap with main memory addresses. External logic can discriminate between a main memory location and a control panel memory location with the same address because control panel memory locations are selected by the $\overline{\text{CPSEL}}$ strobe, whereas main memory locations are selected by the $\overline{\text{MEMSEL}}$ strobe. Timing for control panel memory and main memory accesses are identical, with the exception of the different select strobes.**

**IM6100 CONTROL PANEL SWITCH REGISTER**

**There is a single instruction, the OSR instruction, which accesses a control panel switch register.** The switch register is assumed to be a 12-bit register holding data that is input via control panel switches. The OSR instruction reads the switch register contents and ORs this data on a bit-by-bit basis with the contents of the CPU Accumulator. When the **OSR instruction** is executed, timing is a variation of a memory read instruction with direct addressing. **Timing is illustrated in Figure 13-24.**

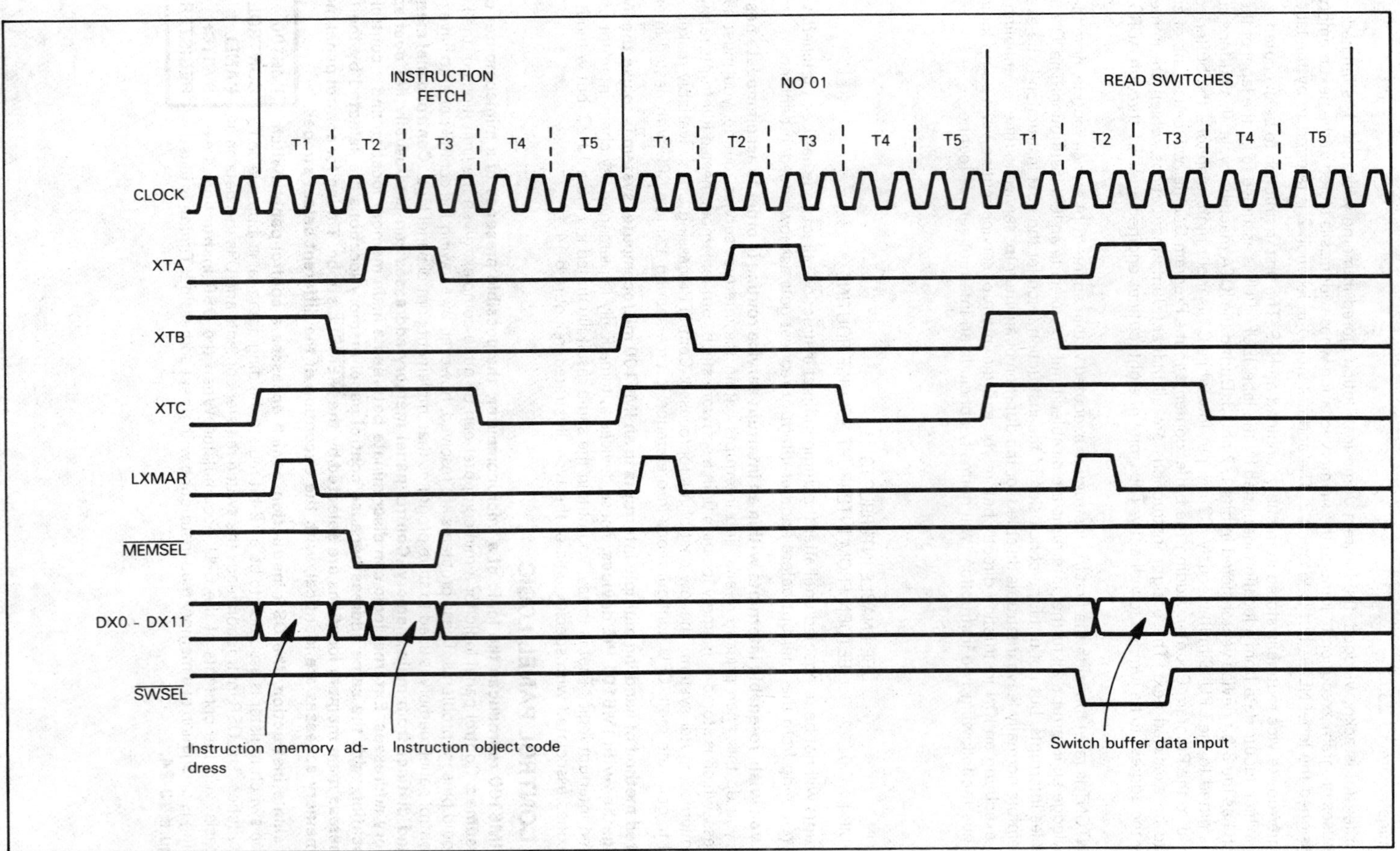


Figure 13-24. IM6100 OSR Instruction Timing

There is nothing very complex about accessing the Switch register; it is a single location, accessible via a single instruction. The same is not true for control panel memory, which can be accessed by any memory reference instruction, although its address space is parallel with main memory (i.e., control panel memory and main memory use the same memory addresses). **You must therefore execute a special control panel interrupt request in order to initiate execution of any program that is stored in control panel memory.**

Following a control panel interrupt request, all direct memory accesses are identified by a low $\overline{CPSEL}$ pulse instead of a low $\overline{MEMSEL}$ pulse. This means that all instruction fetch machine cycles will fetch an instruction object code out of control panel memory, not out of main memory. Thus as soon as a control panel interrupt request has been acknowledged, a program stored in control panel memory will be executed. Furthermore, all direct memory reference instructions contained within this program will also access data locations within control panel memory, not within main memory.

**You request a control panel interrupt by inputting a low signal via $\overline{CPREQ}$. Timing for the request acknowledge sequence is identical to the general interrupt timing given in Figure 13-22a, providing you substitute $\overline{CPREQ}$ for $\overline{INTREQ}$.**

A control panel interrupt request is a higher priority interrupt request than the general external interrupt request. (See Table 13-1 for a summary of priorities). If the two interrupt requests occur simultaneously, the control panel interrupt request will be acknowledged, while the external interrupt request will not be acknowledged. In fact, only a Reset has higher priority than a control panel interrupt request, therefore **no INTGNT output occurs following a control panel interrupt request.**

**A control panel interrupt request** has higher priority than Halt or DMA, therefore the control panel interrupt request **will be acknowledged while the CPU is halted.** The Halt condition will be terminated and the CPU will enter a run condition as soon as the control panel interrupt request is acknowledged. At the end of the control panel interrupt service routine the CPU will return to the Halt state.

The control panel interrupt's priority over external interrupts extends for the duration of the external interrupt service routine. **A control panel interrupt request will be acknowledged even if it occurs while an external interrupt service routine is being executed.** That is to say, if you disable external interrupts, this has no effect on control panel interrupt logic; a control panel interrupt request will, nonetheless, be acknowledged.

**When a control panel interrupt request is acknowledged, the following events occur:**

1) Program Counter contents are stored in control panel memory location 0. This is not the same as main memory location 0; therefore, if a control panel interrupt request is acknowledged while an external interrupt service routine is being executed, no harm is done. A control panel interrupt can be nested within an external interrupt.
2) All interrupts are disabled. External interrupts and further control panel interrupts will be ignored.
3) The Program Counter is set to $FFF_{16}$. Thus the control panel interrupt service routine must be origined at control panel memory location $FFF_{16}$.
4) The CPU will output $\overline{CPSEL}$ instead of $\overline{MEMSEL}$ for all memory accesses (except as explained below).

**When an AND, TAD, ISZ or DCA instruction is executed within a control panel interrupt service routine, if indirect addressing is specified, then control panel memory is accessed for the direct addressing machine cycle; however, main memory is accessed for the indirect addressing machine cycle — that is, for the machine cycle during which DATAF is high. We can reproduce Figure 13-12 for execution of an indirect addressing DCA instruction within a control panel interrupt service routine, as shown in Figure 13-25.** Thus, you cannot indirectly address control panel memory. If you are going to indirectly access data within a control panel interrupt service routine, the address of the data can be held in control panel memory, but the data itself must be held in main memory.

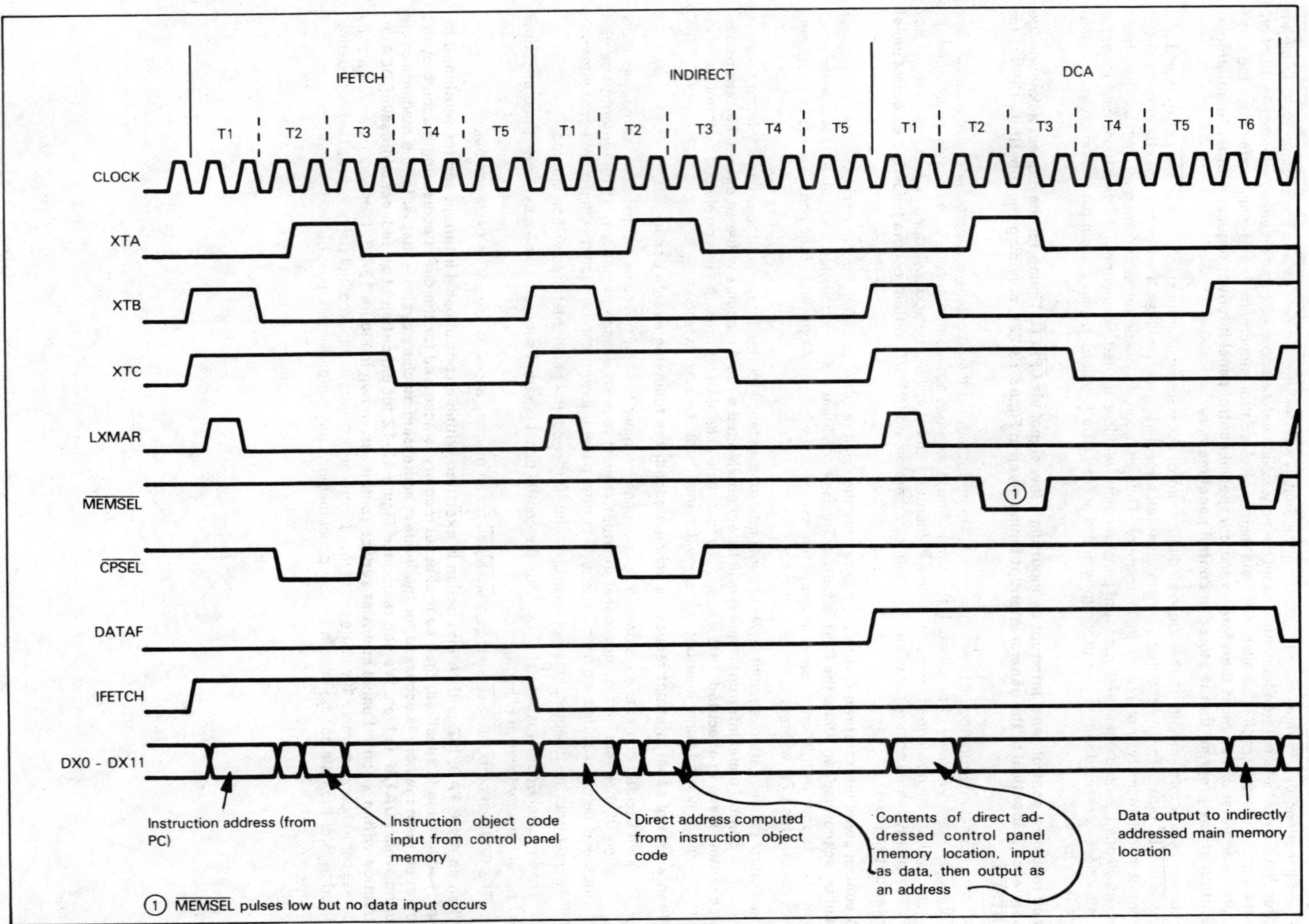


Figure 13-25. IM6100 DCA Instruction in Control Panel Memory — Timing with Indirect Addressing

**You must leave all interrupts disabled while executing the control panel interrupt service routine.** This is a prerequisite for the CPU to output $\overline{CPSEL}$ pulses instead of $\overline{MEMSEL}$ pulses. If you enable interrupts within a control panel interrupt service routine, you will immediately disable $\overline{CPSEL}$ and re-enable $\overline{MEMSEL}$, and therefore program logic will exit the control panel service routine. When you execute any I/O instruction, you re-enable control panel interrupts and external interrupts. Thus, executing any I/O instruction will also cause you to exit the control panel interrupt service routine. Therefore, **you cannot use I/O instructions within a control panel interrupt service routine.**

**In order to return from a control panel memory interrupt service routine, therefore, you simply re-enable interrupts and execute an indirect jump via memory location 0.** The following two instructions will terminate the control panel interrupt service routine:

```
ION              /ENABLE INTERRUPTS
JMP I   0        /RETURN FROM INTERRUPT
```

When the ION instruction is executed, all interrupts are re-enabled; however, this does not happen until the following instruction object code has been fetched. This instruction is a Jump Indirect. When the direct address (000) is output, $\overline{CPSEL}$ is pulsed low; therefore the contents of control panel memory location 0 are fetched. But when the indirect address which was fetched from control panel memory location 000 is output, $\overline{MEMSEL}$ is pulsed low; therefore we branch back to main memory for the next instruction fetch. ION disables $\overline{CPSEL}$, so all future memory accesses select main memory.

The RTF instruction is another I/O instruction which is frequently used (instead of ION) in the control panel interrupt service routine exit sequence.

**Note that a Reset enables all interrupts; therefore, if a reset occurs in the middle of a control panel interrupt service routine, then when program execution restarts, it will restart out of main memory, as described earlier in this chapter for the reset operation.**

Table 13-1. IM6100 External Signal Sampling Priorities

| Priority | Operation | Associated Signals |
|---|---|---|
| First (highest) | Reset | $\overline{RESET}$ |
| Second | Control panel interrupt request | $\overline{CPREQ}$, $\overline{CPSEL}$ |
| Third | Halt | RUN/$\overline{HLT}$, RUN |
| Fourth | DMA | $\overline{DMAREQ}$, DMAGNT |
| Fifth (lowest) | External interrupt request | $\overline{INTREQ}$, INTGNT |

## EXTERNAL CONTROL SIGNAL PRIORITIES

**Table 13-1 summarizes the sequence in which external control signals are sampled by the IM6100 CPU.** As a consequence of these priorities, a $\overline{RESET}$ input will always be accepted and the IM6100 CPU will always be reset, irrespective of what operations the CPU happens to be performing.

A control panel interrupt request will be acknowledged unless the CPU is in the process of being reset. Thus, if the CPU is in a Halt state, the Halt state will be terminated and the CPU will enter a Run state while the control panel interrupt service routine is executed. If a Hold state DMA operation is in progress, then the DMA operation will be suspended for the duration of the control panel interrupt service routine.

The third highest priority condition is the Halt state. This means that a Halt condition will be terminated to execute a control panel interrupt service routine; however, a Halt condition has priority over DMA.

An external device interrupt request is acknowledged as the lowest priority external control input. Thus an external device's interrupt service routine will be slowed down by DMA logic, it will be stopped by a Halt and it will be interrupted by a control panel interrupt service routine.

## IM6100 INSTRUCTION SET

The IM6100 instruction set is unusual because of limitations imposed by the fact that every single instruction generates a single 12-bit object code.

The IM6100 is very deficient in memory reference instructions; it has absolutely no immediate instructions, but it has an incredible wealth of register operate instructions and I/O instructions. **Instructions are summarized in Table 13-2.**

Look first at the memory reference instructions. There is no simple memory read instruction or memory write instruction. The TAD instruction performs a binary add of memory with the Accumulator, leaving the result in the Accumulator. In order to read the contents of a memory word, you must clear the Accumulator, and then add memory to the Accumulator.

DCA is a deposit and clear instruction which is close to a memory write. When this instruction is executed the contents of the Accumulator are written to memory and the Accumulator is then cleared.

The only Boolean logic instructions provided AND the contents of memory with the Accumulator. You can also OR the MQ register and Accumulator contents. If you require XOR, you must create it using the operations available.

There is a single Jump instruction which uses absolute, paged direct or indirect addressing. There are no conditional Jump instructions; however, there are a wealth of conditional Skip instructions. In order to perform conditional branches, you must use skip logic.

The total absence of immediate instructions results from the fact that no instructions have two words of object code. Where you would have used an immediate instruction, you must instead use the TAD instruction to add a constant to the zeroed Accumulator. It is important to note that given the architecture of the IM6100 CPU, immediate instructions are not very valuable — and the lack of them is not consequential. Since you only have one Accumulator and no Data Counters, you do not need immediate instructions in order to load initial addresses or data.

IM6100 I/O instructions are also unusual. At one extreme, you could say that the IM6100 only has one I/O instruction, which outputs a 9-bit code on the Data/Address Bus, which external logic can interpret in any way. In practice, the PDP-8 minicomputer interprets this 9-bit code as follows:

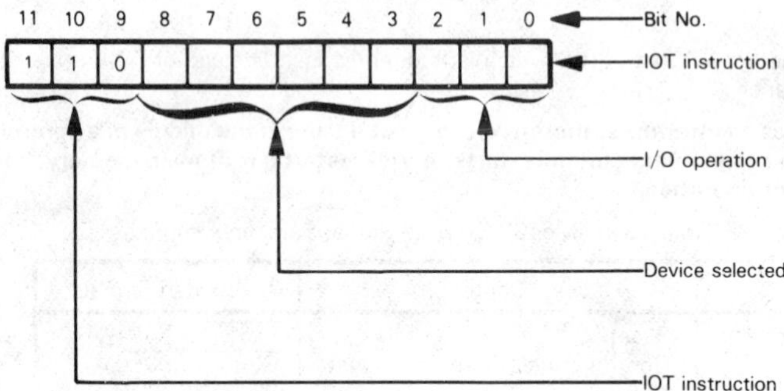


If you are designing a product from scratch, there is no reason why you must use the 9-bit code output by an IOT instruction as illustrated above. If you are using existing PDP-8 software, you are forced to conform to the above IOT instruction interpretation.

The most unusual feature of IM6100 I/O instructions is the fact that external devices can talk back and control the CPU via the $\overline{C0}$, $\overline{C1}$, $\overline{C2}$ and $\overline{SKP}$ control inputs which we have already described.

## THE IM6100 BENCHMARK PROGRAM

**The IM6100 benchmark program may be illustrated as follows:**

```
        CLA              /CLEAR THE ACCUMULATOR
        TAD     IOBUF    /LOAD IO BUF BASE ADDRESS INTO
        DCA     8        /AUTO-INCREMENT LOCATION
        TAD     TABLE    /LOAD TABLE FIRST FREE BYTE ADDRESS
        DCA     9        /INTO AUTO-INCREMENT LOCATION
        TAD     CNT      /LOAD BYTE COUNT
        CIA              /COMPLEMENT AC AND INCREMENT
        DCA     INDEX    /SAVE IN RAM
LOOP    TAD I   8        /LOAD NEXT WORD FROM IOBUF
        DCA I   9        /STORE IN NEXT FREE TABLE WORD
        ISZ     INDEX    /INCREMENT BYTE COUNT COMPLEMENT
        JMP     LOOP     /RETURN FOR MORE
        TAD     9        /AT END RESTORE NEW TABLE FIRST
        DCA     TABLE    /FREE BYTE ADDRESS
```

The benchmark program illustrated above uses auto-increment memory locations 8 and 9 to indirectly address IOBUF and TABLE. These two tables can be of any length within the constraints of the available 4096-word address space. Three other words in the base page are reserved to store the IOBUF base address, the address of the first free byte in TABLE and the byte count. An additional memory word in the base page is used to store the complement of the byte count. This location is represented by the label INDEX. Note that IOBUF and TABLE must initially be set to the beginning address of each, minus one, since the address values will be incremented before they are used.

The following symbols are used in Table 13-2.

| | |
|---|---|
| A | Accumulator |
| *ADDR | Addressing operands. * indicates indirect mode specified. ADDR may be zero page or current page address as described in the text. |
| CMND | Three-bit I/O command. |
| DEV | Six-bit Device address |
| EA | Effective Address generated by *ADDR operands. |
| IE | Interrupt Enable flip-flop |
| L | Link status |
| MQ | MQ register |
| PC | Program Counter |
| SR | Switch register — a 12-bit register external to the CPU. |
| x<y> | The yth bit of the quantity x. For example, A<0> specifies the low bit of the Accumulator. |
| [ ] | Contents of location enclosed within brackets. If a register designation is enclosed within the brackets, then the designated register's contents are specified. If a memory address is enclosed within the brackets, then the contents of the addressed memory location are specified. |
| ∧ | Logical AND |
| V | Logical OR |
| ← | Data is transferred in the direction of the arrow. |

Under the heading of STATUS in Table 13-2, an X indicates that the Link is modified in the course of the instruction's execution. If there is no X, it means that the Link maintains the value it had before the instruction was executed.

Table 13-2. IM6100 Instruction Set Summary

| TYPE | MNEMONIC | OPERAND(S) | 12-BIT WORDS | STATUS C | | | | | | OPERATION PERFORMED |
|---|---|---|---|---|---|---|---|---|---|---|
| I/O | IOT | DEV,CMND | 1 | | | | | | | [DEV]←[CMND]<br>Issue the command to the device. |
| PRIMARY MEMORY REFERENCE | DCA | *ADDR | | | | | | | | [EA]←[A]<br>[A]←0<br>Deposit the Accumulator in memory; then clear Accumulator. |
| MEMORY OPERATE | AND | *ADDR | 1 | | | | | | | [A]←[A] Λ [EA]<br>AND Accumulator with memory. |
| | TAD | *ADDR | 1 | X | | | | | | [A]←[A] + [EA]<br>Add memory to Accumulator. |
| | ISZ | *ADDR | 1 | | | | | | | [EA]←[EA] + 1<br>If [EA] = 0; skip<br>Increment memory and skip if zero. |
| JUMP | JMP | *ADDR | | | | | | | | [PC]←EA<br>Branch unconditional. |
| | JMS | *ADDR | | | | | | | | [EA]←[PC] + 1<br>[PC]←EA + 1<br>Jump to subroutine unconditional. |
| REGISTER OPERATE | IAC | 1 | | X | | | | | | [A]←[A] + 1<br>Increment Accumulator. |
| | RAL | 1 | | X | | | | | | L 11 0<br>Rotate Accumulator left one bit through Link. |
| | RTL | | 1 | X | | | | | | L 11 0<br>Rotate Accumulator left two bits through Link. |
| | RAR | | 1 | X | | | | | | L 11 0<br>Rotate accumulator right one bit through Link. |

Table 13-2. IM6100 Instruction Set Summary (Continued)

| TYPE | MNEMONIC | OPERAND(S) | 12-BIT WORDS | STATUS C | | | | | | OPERATION PERFORMED |
|---|---|---|---|---|---|---|---|---|---|---|
| REGISTER OPERATE (CONTINUED) | RTR | | 1 | X | | | | | | Rotate Accumulator right two bits through Link. |
| | BSW | | 1 | | | | | | | Swap the two halves of the Accumulator. |
| | CMA | | 1 | | | | | | | $[A] \leftarrow \overline{[A]}$ Complement Accumulator contents. |
| | CIA | | 1 | | | | | | | $[A] \leftarrow \overline{[A]} + 1$ Negate (twos complement) Accumulator contents. (same as CMA IAC) |
| | CLA | | 1 | | | | | | | $[A] \leftarrow 0$ Clear Accumulator. |
| | CLA IAC | | 1 | | | | | | | $[A] \leftarrow 1$ Clear, then increment Accumulator. |
| | STA | | 1 | | | | | | | $[A] \leftarrow FFF_{16}$ Set Accumulator bits to all ones. (same as CLA CMA) |
| BRANCH ON CONDITION | SNL | | 1 | | | | | | | If $[L]=1$; $[PC] \leftarrow [PC]+2$ Skip on Link set. |
| | SZL | | 1 | | | | | | | If $[L]=0$; $[PC] \leftarrow [PC]+2$ Skip on Link reset. |
| | SZA | | 1 | | | | | | | If $[A]=0$; $[PC] \leftarrow [PC]+2$ Skip on Accumulator zero. |
| | SNA | | 1 | | | | | | | If $[A] \neq 0$; $[PC] \leftarrow [PC]+2$ Skip on Accumulator nonzero. |
| | SZA SNL | | 1 | | | | | | | If $[A]=0$ or $[L]=1$; $[PC] \leftarrow [PC]+2$ Skip if either Accumulator zero or Link set. |
| | SNA SZL | | 1 | | | | | | | If $[A] \neq 0$ and $[L]=0$; $[PC] \leftarrow [PC]+2$ Skip if Accumulator nonzero and Link reset. |
| | SMA | | 1 | | | | | | | If $A<11>=1$; $[PC] \leftarrow [PC]+2$ Skip if Accumulator negative. |
| | SPA | | 1 | | | | | | | If $A<11>=0$; $[PC] \leftarrow [PC]+2$ Skip if Accumulator positive or zero. |

Table 13-2. IM6100 Instruction Set Summary (Continued)

| TYPE | MNEMONIC | OPERAND(S) | 12-BIT WORDS | STATUS | | | | | | OPERATION PERFORMED |
|---|---|---|---|---|---|---|---|---|---|---|
| | | | | C | | | | | | |
| BRANCH ON CONDITION (CONTINUED) | SMA SNL | | 1 | | | | | | | If A<11>=1 or [L]=1; then [PC]←[PC]+2<br>Skip if Accumulator negative or Link set. |
| | SPA SZL | | 1 | | | | | | | If A<11>=0 and [L]=0; then [PC]←[PC]+2<br>Skip if Accumulator positive and Link reset. |
| | SMA SZA | | 1 | | | | | | | If [A] ≤ 0; then [PC]←[PC]+2<br>Skip if Accumulator zero or negative. |
| | SPA SNA | | 1 | | | | | | | If [A] > 0; then [PC]←[PC]+2<br>Skip if Accumulator positive. |
| | SMA SZA SNL | | 1 | | | | | | | If [A] ≤ 0 or [L]=1<br>Skip if Accumulator less than or equal to zero or if Link set. |
| | SPA SNA SZL | | 1 | | | | | | | If [A] > 0 and L=0<br>Skip if Accumulator positive and Link reset. |
| BRANCH ON CONDITION AND OPERATE | SZA CLA | | 1 | | | | | | | If [A]=0; [PC]←[PC]+2.<br>[A]←0<br>Skip on Accumulator zero. Clear Accumulator. |
| | SNA CLA | | 1 | | | | | | | If [A]≠0; [PC]←[PC]+2.<br>[A]←0<br>Skip on Accumulator nonzero. Clear Accumulator. |
| | SMA CLA | | 1 | | | | | | | If [A] < 0; [PC]←[PC]+2.<br>[A]←0<br>Skip on Accumulator negative. Clear Accumulator. |
| | SPA CLA | | 1 | | | | | | | If [A] ≥ 0; [PC]←[PC]+2.<br>[A]←0<br>Skip on Accumulator greater than or equal zero. Clear Accumulator. |
| REGISTER-REGISTER MOVE | LAS | | 1 | | | | | | | [A]←[SR]<br>Load Accumulator from Switch register (same as CLA OSR). |
| | MQL | | 1 | | | | | | | [MQ]←[A]<br>[A]←0<br>Load MQ register from Accumulator. Clear Accumulator. |
| | SWP | | 1 | | | | | | | [A]←→[MQ]<br>Exchange Accumulator and MQ (same as MQA MQL). |
| | CAM | | 1 | | | | | | | [A]←0<br>[MQ]←0<br>Clear Accumulator and MQ (same as CLA MQL). |
| | ACL | | 1 | | | | | | | [A]←[MQ]<br>Load MQ into Accumulator (same as CLA MQA). |
| | CLA SWP | | 1 | | | | | | | [A]←0<br>[A]←→[MQ]<br>Clear Accumulator; then swap Accumulator and MQ. |

Table 13-2. IM6100 Instruction Set Summary (Continued)

| TYPE | MNEMONIC | OPERAND(S) | 12-BIT WORDS | STATUS | | | | | | OPERATION PERFORMED |
|---|---|---|---|---|---|---|---|---|---|---|
| | | | | C | | | | | | |
| REGISTER-REGISTER OPERATE | OSR | | 1 | | | | | | | [A]←[A] V [SR]<br>OR Accumulator with Switch register. |
| | MQA | | 1 | | | | | | | [A]←[A] V [MQ]<br>OR Accumulator with MQ. |
| STATUS AND REGISTER OPERATE | CLL RAL | | 1 | X | | | | | | [L]←0 <br>Clear Link, then rotate Accumulator left one bit through Link. |
| | CLL RTL | | 1 | X | | | | | | [L]←0 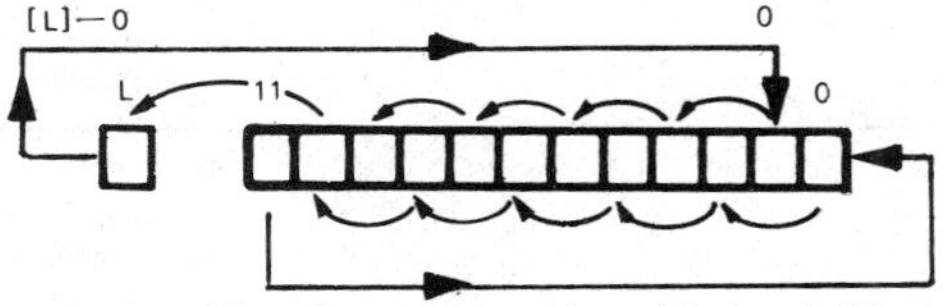<br>Clear Link, then rotate Accumulator left two bits through Link. |
| | CLL RAR | | 1 | X | | | | | | [L]←0 <br>Clear Link, then rotate Accumulator right one bit through Link. |
| | CLL RTR | | 1 | X | | | | | | [L]←0 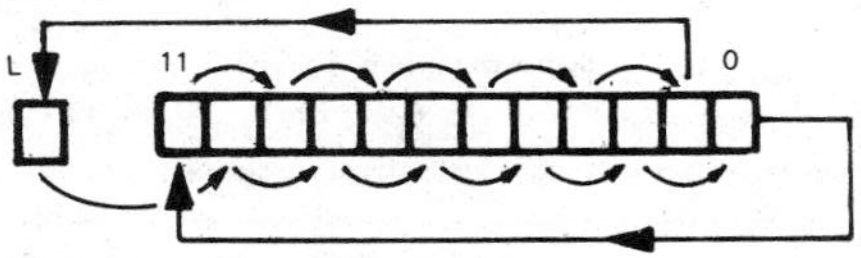<br>Clear Link, then rotate Accumulator right two bits through Link. |
| | CLA CLL | | 1 | | | | | | | [A]←0<br>[L]←0<br>Clear Accumulator and Link. |
| | GTL | | 1 | | | | | | | [A]←0<br>[A <0>]←[L]<br>Clear Accumulator, then rotate Link into low bit (same as CLA RAL). |

Table 13-2. IM6100 Instruction Set Summary (Continued)

| TYPE | MNEMONIC | OPERAND(S) | 12-BIT WORDS | STATUS | | | | | | OPERATION PERFORMED |
|---|---|---|---|---|---|---|---|---|---|---|
| | | | | C | | | | | | |
| BRANCH | SKP | | 1 | | | | | | | [PC]←[PC] + 2<br>Skip next instruction. |
| INTERRUPT | | | | | | | | | | Execution of any of the following instructions will reset INTGNT. |
| | SKON | | 1 | | | | | | | If [IE]=1; [PC]←[PC] + 2<br>If interrupts enabled, skip next instruction. |
| | ION | | 1 | | | | | | | [IE]←1<br>Enable interrupts. |
| | IOF | | 1 | | | | | | | [IE]←0<br>Disable interrupts. |
| | SRQ | | 1 | | | | | | | Skip next instruction if Interrupt Request bus is low. |
| | GTF | | 1 | | | | | | | A<11> ← [L]<br>A<9> ← $\overline{\text{INTREQ}}$<br>A<7> ← [IE]<br>Get flags. |
| | RTF | | 1 | X | | | | | | [L]← A<11>; [IE]←1<br>Return Link and enable interrupts after the execution of the next sequential instruction. |
| | SGT | | 1 | | | | | | | I/O device logic determines operation |
| | CAF | | 1 | X | | | | | | [L]←0<br>[A]←0<br>[IE]←0<br>Clear all flags. |
| STATUS | CML | | 1 | X | | | | | | [L]←$\overline{[L]}$<br>Complement Link. |
| | CLL | | 1 | X | | | | | | [L]←0<br>Reset Link. |
| | STL | | 1 | X | | | | | | [L]←1<br>Set Link. |
| | HLT | | 1 | | | | | | | Halt |
| | NOP | | 1 | | | | | | | No Operation |

The following symbols are used in Table 13-3:

| | |
|---|---|
| a | One bit which determines if indirect addressing is used. |
| b | One bit which determines if current or zero page is used. |
| ccccccc | Seven-bit page address. |
| dddddd | Six-bit device code. |
| eee | Three-bit I/O command. |

Most instructions are described in this manner:

mnemonic xxxx
yyy

where xxxx is the octal object code associated with the mnemonic and yyy is the hexadecimal object code associated with the mnemonic. IM6100 literature uses octal notation.

Some instructions have this form in the input clock cycles column:

a/b/c

a is the number of cycles required using direct addressing.
b is the number of cycles required using indirect addressing.
c is the number of cycles required using auto-indexed addressing.

Table 13-3. IM6100 Instruction Set Object Codes

| INSTRUCTION | OBJECT CODE | 12-BIT WORDS | INPUT CLOCK CYCLES |
|---|---|---|---|
| ACL | 7701<br>FC1 | 1 | 20 |
| AND *ADDR | 000abccccccc | 1 | 20/30/32 |
| BSW | 7002<br>E02 | 1 | 30 |
| CAF | 6007<br>C07 | 1 | 34 |
| CAM | 7621<br>F91 | 1 | 20 |
| CIA | 7041<br>E21 | 1 | 20 |
| CLA | 7200<br>E80 | 1 | 20 |
| CLA CLL | 7300<br>EC0 | 1 | 20 |
| CLA IAC | 7201<br>E81 | 1 | 20 |
| CLA SWP | 7721<br>FD1 | 1 | 20 |
| CLL | 7100<br>E40 | 1 | 20 |
| CLL RAL | 7104<br>E44 | 1 | 30 |
| CLL RAR | 7110<br>E48 | 1 | 30 |
| CLL RTL | 7106<br>E46 | 1 | 30 |
| CLL RTR | 7112<br>E4A | 1 | 30 |
| CMA | 7040<br>E20 | 1 | 20 |
| CML | 7020<br>E10 | 1 | 20 |
| DCA *ADDR | 011abccccccc | 1 | 22/32/34 |
| GTF | 6004<br>C04 | 1 | 34 |
| GTL | 7204<br>E84 | 1 | 20 |
| HLT | 7402<br>F02 | 1 | 20 |
| IAC | 7001<br>E01 | 1 | 20 |
| IOF | 6002<br>C02 | 1 | 34 |
| ION | 6001<br>C01 | 1 | 34 |
| IOT DEV,CMND | 110dddddddeee | 1 | 20 |
| ISZ *ADDR | 010abccccccc | 1 | 20 |
| JMP *ADDR | 101abccccccc | 1 | 20/30/32 |
| JMS *ADDR | 100abccccccc | 1 | 22/32/34 |
| LAS | 7604<br>F84 | 1 | 30 |
| MQA | 7501<br>F41 | 1 | 20 |
| MQL | 7421<br>F11 | 1 | 20 |
| NOP | 7000<br>E00 | 1 | 20 |
| OSR | 7404<br>F04 | 1 | 30 |
| RAL | 7004<br>E04 | 1 | 30 |
| RAR | 7010<br>E08 | 1 | 30 |
| RTF | 6005<br>C05 | 1 | 34 |
| RTL | 7006<br>E06 | 1 | 30 |
| RTR | 7012<br>E0A | 1 | 30 |
| SGT | 6006<br>C06 | 1 | 34 |
| SKON | 6000<br>C00 | 1 | 34 |
| SKP | 7410<br>F08 | 1 | 20 |
| SMA | 7500<br>F40 | 1 | 20 |
| SMA CLA | 7700<br>FC0 | 1 | 20 |
| SMA SNL | 7520<br>F50 | 1 | 20 |
| SMA SZA | 7540<br>F60 | 1 | 20 |
| SMA SZA SNL | 7560<br>F70 | 1 | 20 |
| SNA | 7450<br>F28 | 1 | 20 |
| SNA CLA | 7650<br>FA8 | 1 | 20 |
| SNA SZL | 7470<br>F38 | 1 | 20 |
| SNL | 7420<br>F10 | 1 | 20 |
| SPA | 7510<br>F48 | 1 | 20 |
| SPA CLA | 7710<br>FC8 | 1 | 20 |
| SPA SNA | 7550<br>F68 | 1 | 20 |
| SPA SNA SZL | 7570<br>F78 | 1 | 20 |
| SPA SZL | 7530<br>F58 | 1 | 20 |
| SRQ | 6003<br>C03 | 1 | 34 |
| STA | 7240<br>EA0 | 1 | 20 |
| STL | 7120<br>E50 | 1 | 20 |
| SWP | 7521<br>F51 | 1 | 20 |
| SZA | 7440<br>F20 | 1 | 20 |
| SZA CLA | 7640<br>FA0 | 1 | 20 |
| SZA SNL | 7460<br>F30 | 1 | 20 |
| SZL | 7430<br>F18 | 1 | 20 |
| TAD *ADDR | 001abccccccc | 1 | 20/30/32 |

# SOME SPECIAL IM6100 HARDWARE CONSIDERATIONS

**The apparently complex System Bus of the IM6100 has some non-obvious advantages. The wealth of bus signals makes it very easy to generate System Busses compatible with other microprocessors and to circumvent certain limitations of the IM6100 instruction set.**

## IMPLEMENTING A HARDWARE STACK

**Consider first the problem of the Jump-to-Subroutine instruction,** which we described earlier in this chapter. Recall that the IM6100 Jump-to-Subroutine instruction cannot work when programs are stored in read-only memory, because the subroutine return address is stored in the first word of the subroutine — which will be a read-only memory location. **We can circumvent this problem by creating a special read/write memory stack which is addressed by an up-down counter. Appropriate logic is illustrated in Figure 13-28.**

Before examining the logic in this figure, let us look at what we are trying to accomplish.

Remember, a Jump-to-Subroutine instruction contains a write machine cycle during which the Program Counter contents are stored in the first memory location of the subroutine. **Timing for execution of the Jump-to-Subroutine instruction with indirect addressing, along with the logic that accompanies the instruction's execution, is illustrated in Figure 13-26.** Timing for direct addressing or auto-increment addressing variations of the Jump-to-Subroutine instruction can be readily deduced from Figures 13-12 and 13-13.

**We are going to identify the Jump-to-Subroutine object code; then, for the rest of the Jump-to-Subroutine instruction's execution, we will deflect memory write accesses to an external read/write memory stack. Timing and an appropriate event sequence are illustrated in Figure 13-27. Figure 13-28 illustrates the logic used to implement timing in Figure 13-27. Figure 13-28 also shows the logic used to return from subroutines; we will describe this later.**

In Figures 13-27 and 13-28 we use a 7474 D-type flip-flop to generate a low true select signal ($\overline{\text{QSEL}}$). This select signal is used to differentiate between stack and normal memory accesses; the trailing low-to-high transition of this select signal is also used to increment the up-down counter, which generates the stack address. Thus, any "write to stack" operation will be a "write and then increment address" operation. The write select signal $\overline{\text{QSEL}}$ is generated low true by decoding 100 on Data/Address Bus lines 11, 10 and 9, while the Data/Address Bus is carrying an instruction object code. We can identify this condition by the combination of IFETCH high and XTC high. This combination generates the DIN input to the 7474 flip-flop, which is clocked by DCLK, the AND of $\overline{\text{MEMSEL}}$ and IFETCH. Since the low-to-high clock transition is active, it is very important that data be stable on the Data/Address Bus until well after $\overline{\text{MEMSEL}}$ has made its low-to-high transition. This may be illustrated as follows:

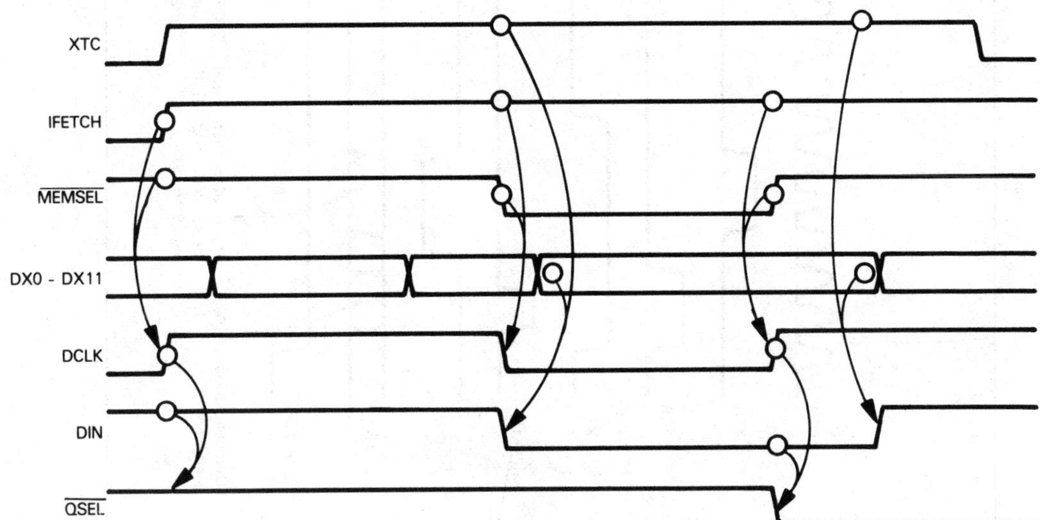

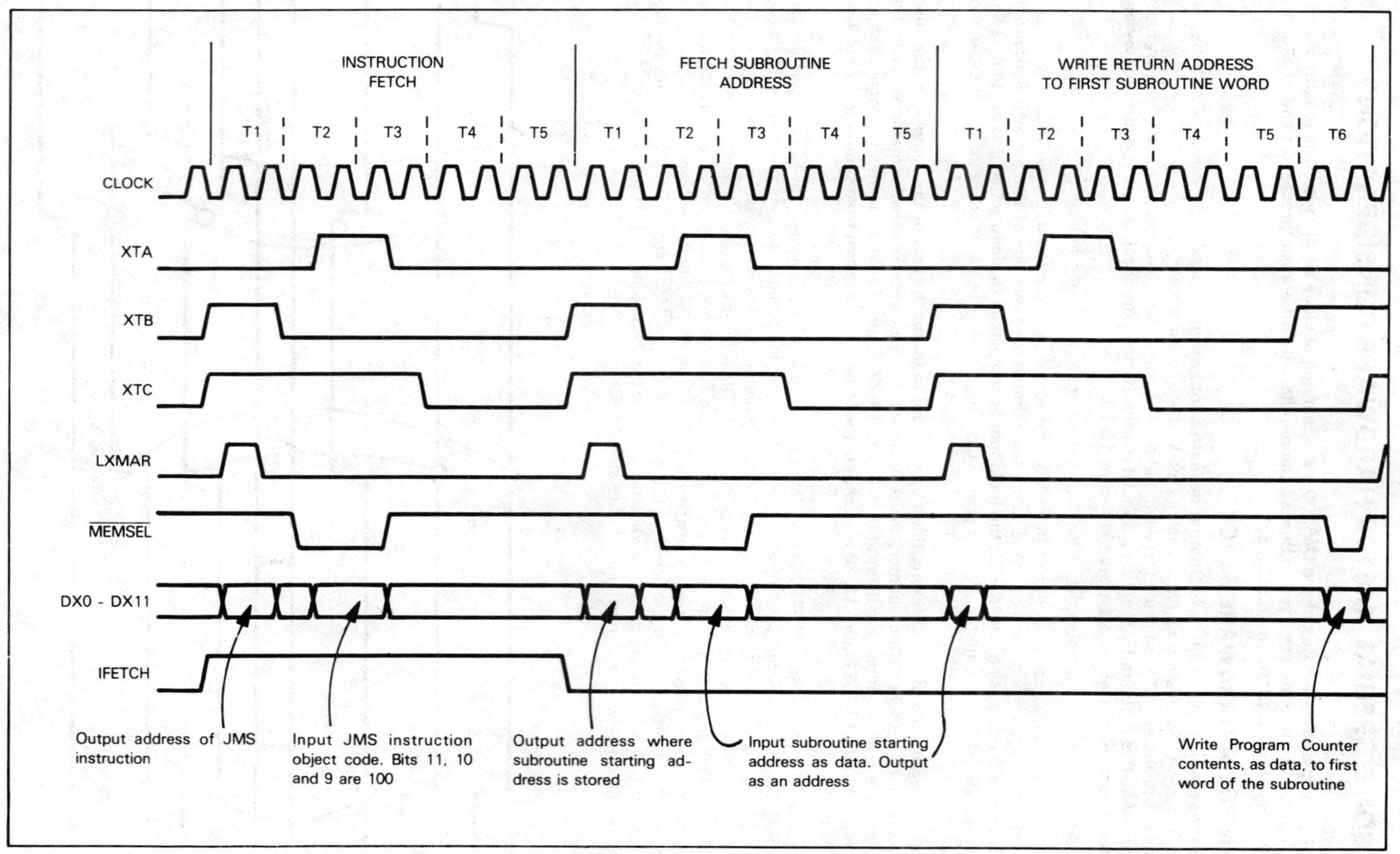


Figure 13-26. IM6100 Jump-to-Subroutine Instruction Timing with Indirect Addressing

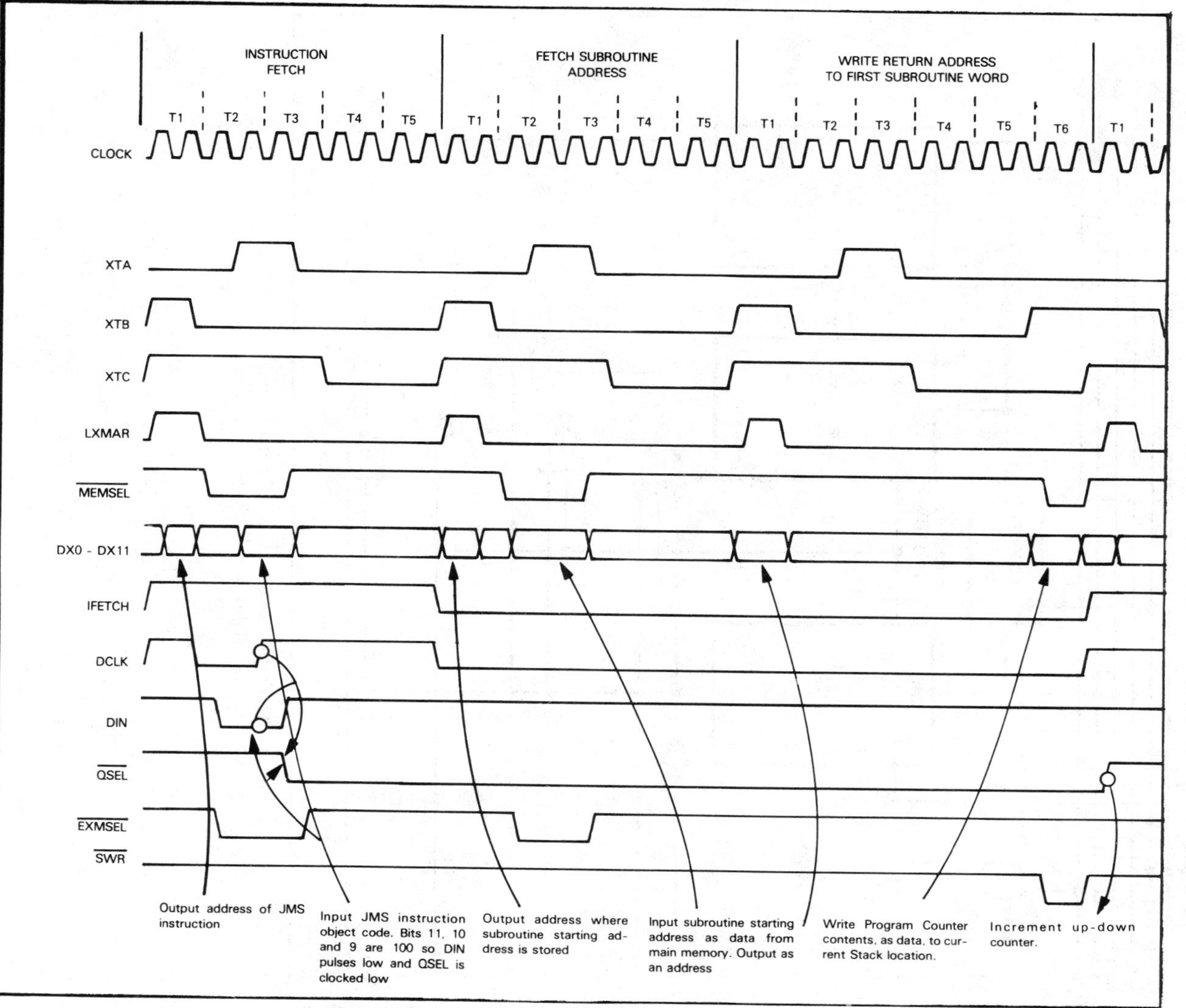


Figure 13-27. IM6100 Jump-to-Subroutine Instruction Timing with Stack Access Logic

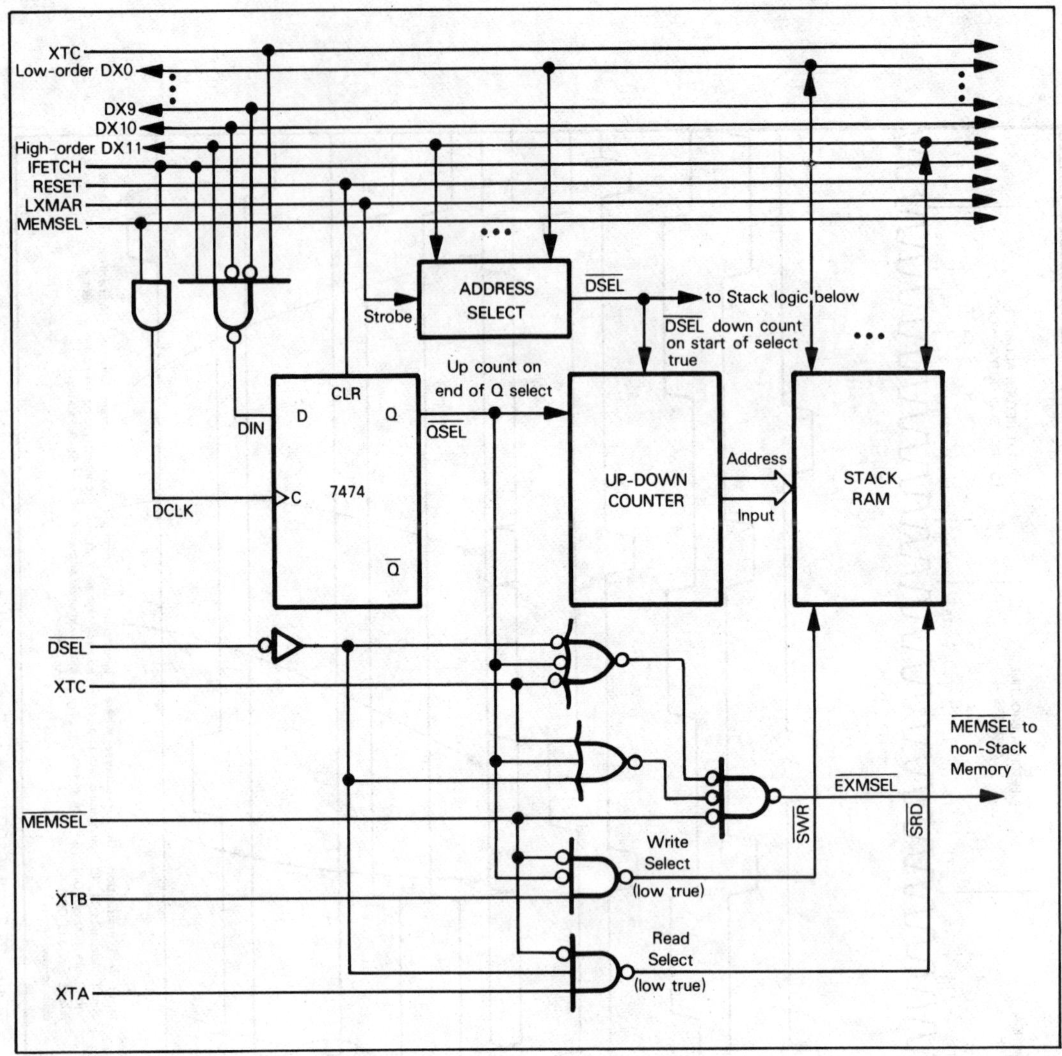


Figure 13-28. Using an External Stack Memory to Avoid IM6100 JMS ROM Problems

Once $\overline{QSEL}$ has gone low, it will remain low until the next instruction fetch. DCLK will make its next low-to-high transition at the beginning of T1 for the next instruction fetch machine cycle, at which time DIN will be high again. $\overline{QSEL}$ will then go high, which is what we require. That is to say, $\overline{QSEL}$ remains low only for the non-instruction fetch machine cycles of the Jump-to-Subroutine instruction.

While $\overline{QSEL}$ is low, we want to divert all memory write select pulses from $\overline{MEMSEL}$ to the stack. We do this by generating $\overline{EXMSEL}$ for standard memory selects. $\overline{EXMSEL}$ is generated as the OR of $\overline{MEMSEL}$ with two conditioning inputs. The truth table for $\overline{EXMSEL}$ may be illustrated as follows:

| $\overline{DESL}$ | XTC | $\overline{QSEL}$ | $\overline{EXMSEL}$ | Condition |
|---|---|---|---|---|
| L | L | L | $\overline{MEMSEL}$ | Will never arise |
| L | L | H | $\overline{MEMSEL}$ | Return from subroutine; non-read part of machine cycle |
| L | H | L | $\overline{MEMSEL}$ | Will never arise |
| L | H | H | H | Return from subroutine; read part of machine cycle |
| H | L | L | H | JMS, write part of machine cycle |
| H | L | H | $\overline{MEMSEL}$ | Normal machine cycle |
| H | H | L | $\overline{MEMSEL}$ | JMS, read part of machine cycle |
| H | H | H | $\overline{MEMSEL}$ | Normal machine cycle |

**A memory read that implements indirect addressing for a JMS instruction will access normal memory; however, you cannot use a Jump-to-Subroutine instruction with auto-increment memory addressing, since the incremented address will be written back to the stack instead of being written to the auto-increment location in Page 0.**

**A return from subroutine is executed via a Jump Indirect instruction.** The Jump Indirect instruction in a normal PDP-8E program will reference the first subroutine word as the location in which the indirect address is stored. For our adaptation, we must select one memory address that is referenced by all Jump Indirect instructions that return from subroutines. This may be illustrated as follows:

```
          IM6100 Subroutine                      PDP-8E Subroutine
      /PDP-8E stores subroutine return address at START
      /IM6100 does not use this logic
      START      JMP       .+1              START      *
                  -                                    -
                  -                                    -
                  -                                    -
                  -                                    -
                  -                                    -
      /Return from subroutine
                 JMP I     FFF                         JMP I     START
```

We have shown the address $FFF_{16}$ being used as the single address which will always be referenced by Jump Indirect instructions which are returning from an IM6100 subroutine. Our logic in Figure 13-28 will decode the address selected (in this case $FFF_{16}$) using the LXMAR high pulse as a strobe. Whenever the required address is detected while LXMAR is high, $\overline{DSEL}$ will be output low. The leading high-to-low transition of $\overline{DSEL}$ must be used as a down count trigger for the up-down counter. Thus, all "read from stack" operations will be "decrement and then read" operations. The $\overline{DSEL}$ signal will remain low until another address is detected — that is to say, until the next occurrence of a high LXMAR pulse with another address on the Data/Address Bus. While $\overline{DSEL}$ is low, all memory read operations will be deflected to the stack and away from normal memory. See the truth table given earlier, and the logic of Figure 13-28 for verification of this logic.

**The net effect of Figure 13-28 logic is that all subroutine return addresses will be stored in an external stack. IM6100 and PDP-8E Jump-to-Subroutine instructions will be identical. There will, however, be differences in the Return-from-Subroutine instructions within an IM6100 program as compared to a PDP-8E program. A PDP-8E program which is to run on an IM6100 must have all Return-from-Subroutine Jump Indirect instructions modified to access the single memory location which has been assigned to identify the external stack.**

## SUPPORT DEVICES THAT MAY BE USED WITH THE IM6100

**Since the 8080A System Bus is the most useful, in that it supports the most readily available support devices, we will begin by looking at how 8080A-compatible signals may be generated from the standard IM6100 System Bus. Figure 13-29 provides necessary bus conversion logic. The bus conversion is quite simple.**

The most complex portion of Figure 13-29 is the logic which demultiplexes the Address and Data Busses. A 12-bit address buffer must be present, using LXMAR as a latching strobe. This buffer will create the Address Bus, while DX0 - DX11 otherwise implements the Data Bus. Remaining control signals are generated using simple gates. Note that no attempt is made to generate signals that reproduce 8080A clock signals or exact machine cycle timing. Since the 8080A System Bus is asynchronous, this presents no problem. So long as control signals have the required pulse widths and logic levels, they will work with 8080A support devices. Thus an 8080A System Bus as illustrated in Figure 13-29 can be used in a microcomputer system where the IM6100 is the CPU and 8080A support devices provide additional logic; however, Figure 13-29 does not generate a System Bus which could be used in a microcomputer system where an IM6100 and an 8080A were communicating with each other. For those 8080A support devices that do need a clock signal, one can be derived from XTA, XTB and/or XTC.

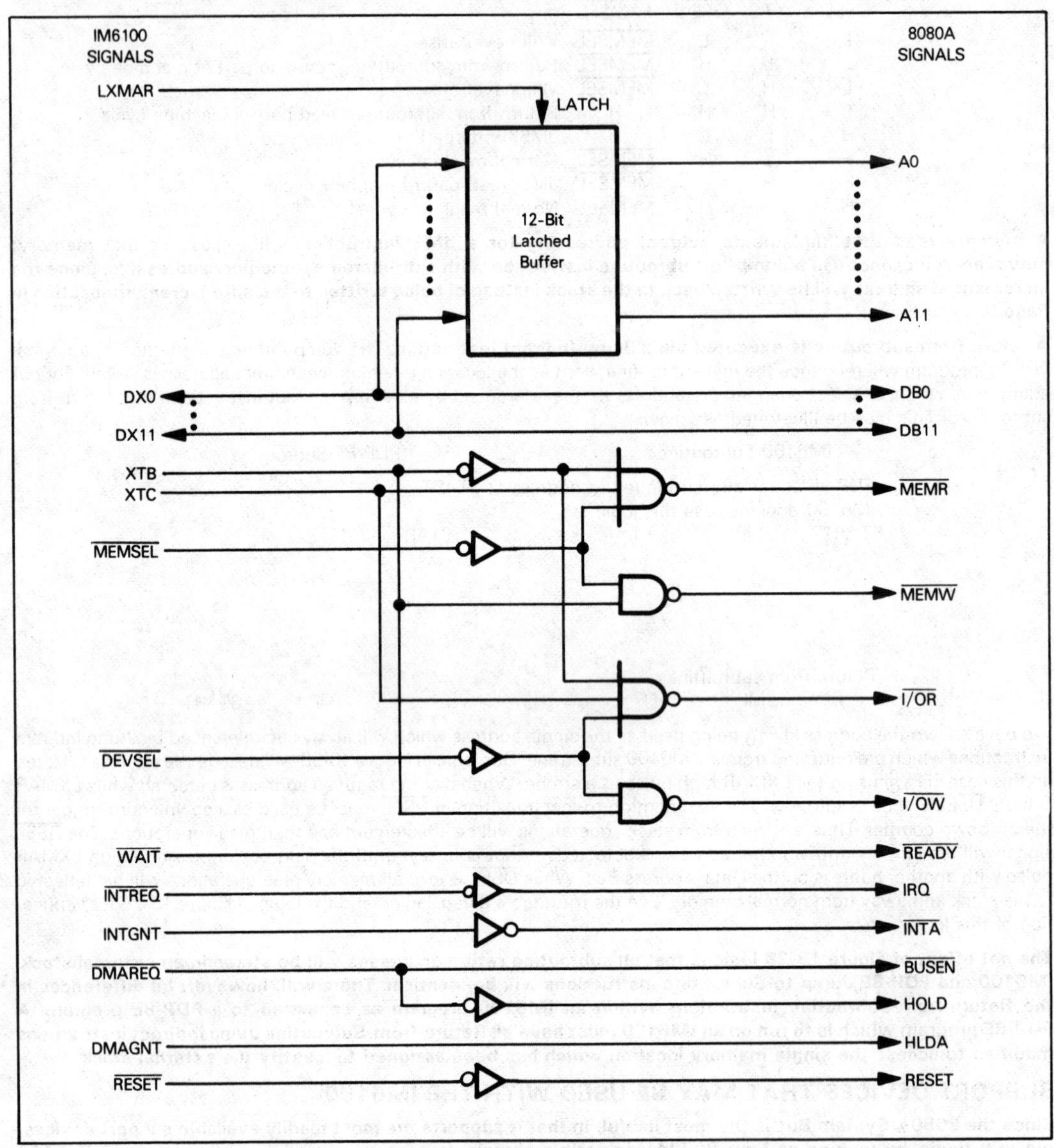


Figure 13-29. IM6100 System Bus Converted to an 8080A-Compatible System Bus

**Generating 8085-compatible signals from the IM6100 bus is not so straightforward.** This is because the 8085 generates state signals S0 and S1, and an IO/Memory discriminator (IO/M) whose levels must be specified for the entire duration of read and write machine cycles that access memory or I/O devices. The IM6100 generates RUN and IFETCH signals that extend for the duration of a machine cycle, but memory or I/O access control signals are not generated in this fashion. **If you look at timing for the 8085 support devices — the 8155, the 8355 and the 8755 — it would appear that the IM6100 System Bus can generate adequate control inputs for these support devices. However, we have no experimental verification of this fact.**

**We do not recommend using MC6800 or MCS6500 support devices with the IM6100 because of the peculiar synchronous nature of the MC6800 and MCS6500 microcomputer systems.** It would be very hard to make IM6100 machine cycle timing conform to MC6800 or MCS6500 machine cycle timing. Moreover, MC6800 and MCS6500 support devices are not attractive enough to make this logic exercise worthwhile.

## THE IM6101 PARALLEL INTERFACE ELEMENT (PIE)

**The IM6100 CPU, being a copy of the PDP-8 minicomputer, has a number of features which are not well suited to the average microcomputer application; but that is no fault of the IM6100 chip designer — his product was specified for him. The IM6101, on the other hand, is a well thought out part that goes a long way towards rectifying the problems that you are likely to encounter if you try to design logic around the IM6100 CPU.**

**The IM6101 is best visualized as a control signal interface on the IM6100 System Bus, connecting an IM6100 CPU and its support devices.** This concept may be illustrated as follows:

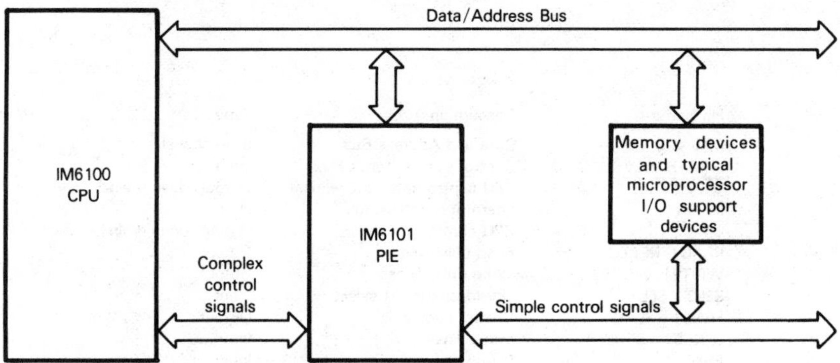


Conceptually, what is important about the illustration above is the fact that the IM6101 does not lie on the address or data path of the microcomputer system. Like a typical DMA controller, the IM6101 generates and receives control signals, while memory and I/O devices communicate directly with the System, Data and Address Busses.

**Functionally, Figure 13-1 illustrates that part of our general microcomputer system logic which is implemented on the IM6101 Parallel Interface Element (PIE).**

The IM6101, like all members of the IM6100 family, is fabricated using CMOS technology; it requires a single power supply that may range between +4V and +10V and is packaged as a 40-pin DIP.

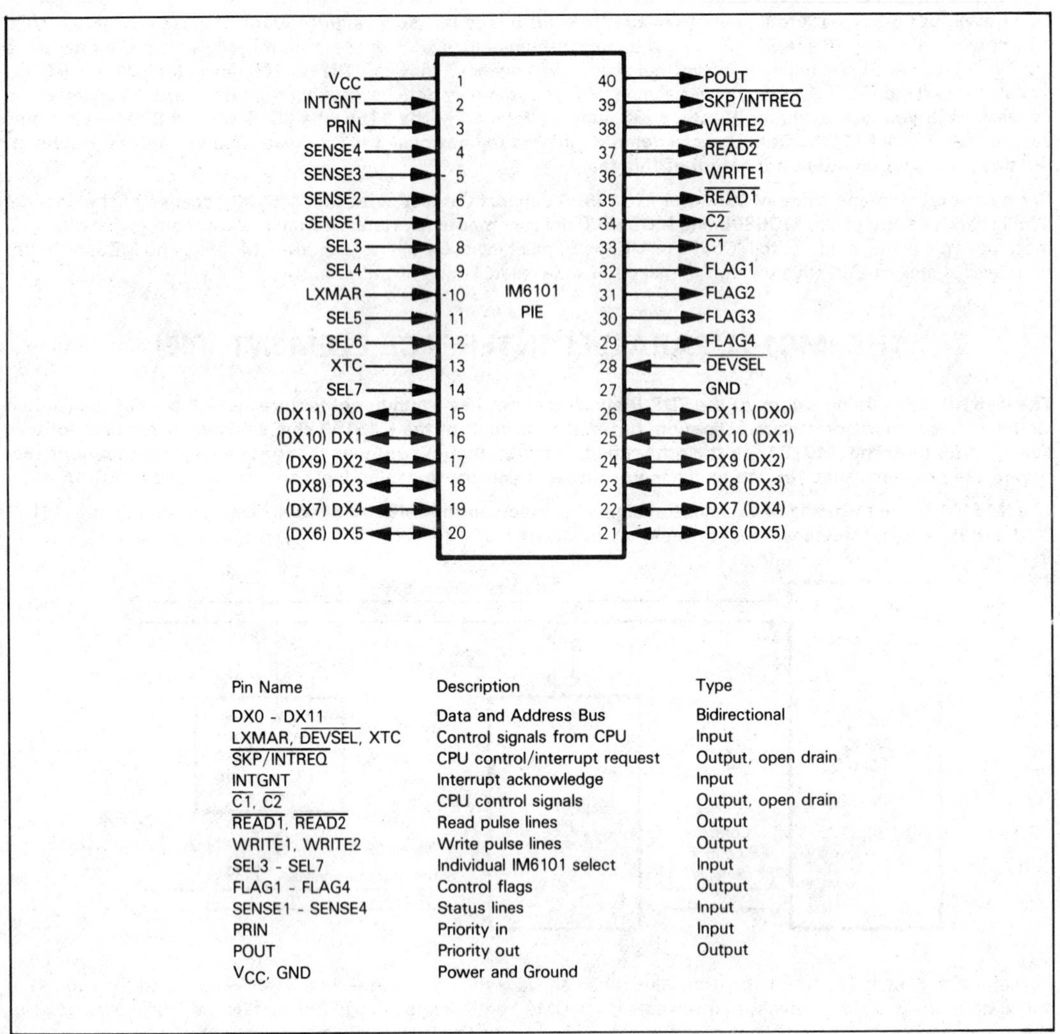


| Pin Name | Description | Type |
|---|---|---|
| DX0 - DX11 | Data and Address Bus | Bidirectional |
| LXMAR, $\overline{\text{DEVSEL}}$, XTC | Control signals from CPU | Input |
| $\overline{\text{SKP/INTREQ}}$ | CPU control/interrupt request | Output, open drain |
| INTGNT | Interrupt acknowledge | Input |
| $\overline{\text{C1}}$, $\overline{\text{C2}}$ | CPU control signals | Output, open drain |
| $\overline{\text{READ1}}$, $\overline{\text{READ2}}$ | Read pulse lines | Output |
| WRITE1, WRITE2 | Write pulse lines | Output |
| SEL3 - SEL7 | Individual IM6101 select | Input |
| FLAG1 - FLAG4 | Control flags | Output |
| SENSE1 - SENSE4 | Status lines | Input |
| PRIN | Priority in | Input |
| POUT | Priority out | Output |
| $V_{CC}$, GND | Power and Ground | |

Figure 13-30. IM6101 Parallel Interface Element Signals and Pin Assignments

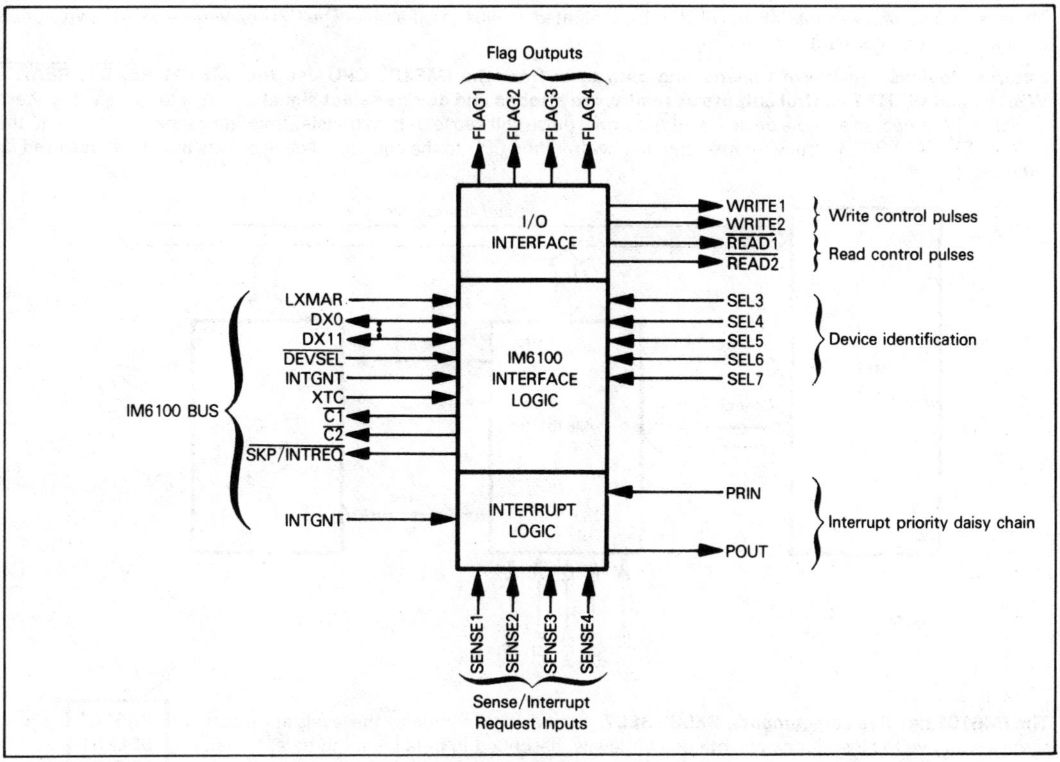

Flag Outputs

FLAG1 FLAG2 FLAG3 FLAG4

I/O INTERFACE

$\overline{\text{WRITE1}}$
$\overline{\text{WRITE2}}$
$\overline{\text{READ1}}$
$\overline{\text{READ2}}$

Write control pulses
Read control pulses

IM6100 BUS

LXMAR
DX0
DX11
$\overline{\text{DEVSEL}}$
INTGNT
XTC
$\overline{\text{C1}}$
$\overline{\text{C2}}$
$\overline{\text{SKP/INTREQ}}$
INTGNT

IM6100 INTERFACE LOGIC

SEL3
SEL4
SEL5
SEL6
SEL7

Device identification

INTERRUPT LOGIC

PRIN
POUT

Interrupt priority daisy chain

SENSE1 SENSE2 SENSE3 SENSE4

Sense/Interrupt Request Inputs

Figure 13-31. Logic of the IM6101 PIE

## IM6101 PARALLEL INTERFACE ELEMENT PINS AND SIGNALS

**Figure 13-30 illustrates the pins and signals of the IM6101 Parallel Interface Element. Figure 13-31 illustrates the important logic components of the IM6101.**

**We will begin by summarizing IM6101 signals.**

The IM6101 communicates directly with the IM6100 CPU via the Data/Address Bus (DX0 - DX11) together with the three control signals LXMAR, $\overline{\text{DEVSEL}}$ and XTC. As per our discussion of the IM6100 Data/Address Bus, remember that we number bus lines, register bits and word bits in an opposite sense to Intersil literature. Thus, in Figure 13-30, Data/Address Bus line signals are shown as they appear in Intersil literature, with our equivalents, in brackets, adjacent to them.

Interrupt requests are transmitted to the CPU via $\overline{\text{INTREQ}}$ (which shares a pin with $\overline{\text{SKP}}$). The IM6101 receives in response the CPU interrupt acknowledge signal INTGNT.

The CPU communicates with the IM6101 PIE via IOT instructions. The IM6101 therefore returns $\overline{\text{C1}}$, $\overline{\text{C2}}$ and $\overline{\text{SKP}}$ as I/O controls. Recall that IM6100 I/O logic demands that the selected I/O device return I/O control signals which specify the I/O operations to occur. The IM6101 does not return $\overline{\text{C0}}$; this signal must be generated externally. $\overline{\text{SKP}}$ shares a pin with $\overline{\text{INTREQ}}$.

The fact that $\overline{\text{INTREQ}}$ and $\overline{\text{SKP}}$ outputs share a pin presents no problem since the two signals are active at different times in any machine cycle. You could, if you wish, separate the two signals via the following logic:

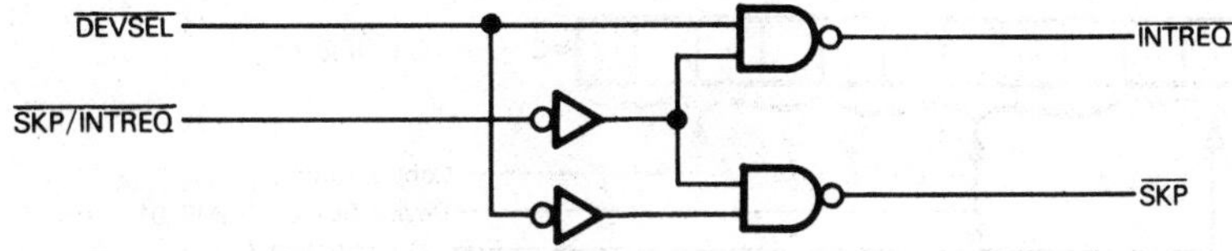

There is, in fact, no need for $\overline{SKP/INTREQ}$ to be separated as illustrated above. The CPU distinguishes the two signals on the single line via instruction timing.

**External devices capable of transmitting data to or from the IM6100 CPU use the IM6101 $\overline{READ1}$, $\overline{READ2}$, WRITE1 and WRITE2 control outputs as read/write strobes and device select signals.** That is to say, each of these signals will connect to a single device. A $\overline{READ}$ signal pulse will cause data to transfer from the connected device to the IM6100 CPU. A WRITE pulse will cause data to flow from the CPU to the connected device. **This may be illustrated as follows:**

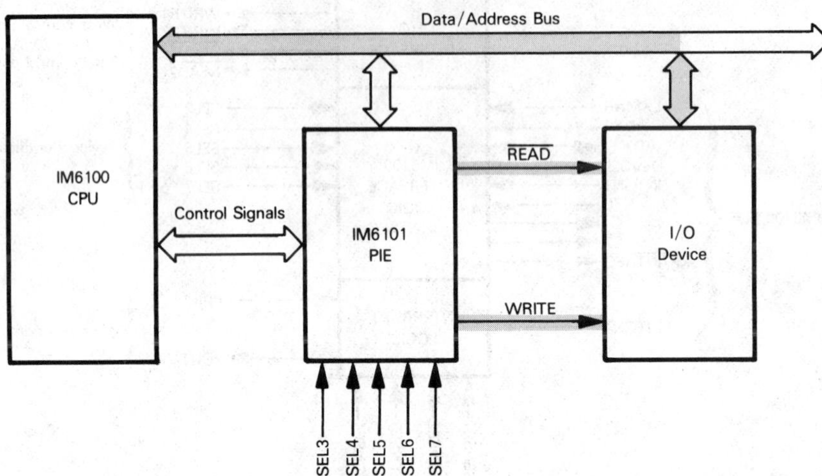


**IM6101 SELECT LOGIC**

**The IM6101 has five select inputs, SEL3 - SEL7.** Internal logic compares the levels at these five signals with five I/O instruction object code bit levels (described in detail later) in order to determine whether the IM6101 is or is not selected when an I/O instruction is being executed. In other words, the five signals SEL3 - SEL7 allow you to specify a unique device code for the IM6101 by tying signals selectively to power or ground. A device code of 0 is not allowed, since special internal CPU I/O instructions use this device code. The five select lines SEL3 - SEL7 therefore allow 31 unique device codes to be specified for IM6101 devices.

**The IM6101 PIE provides eight any-purpose control signals.** FLAG1 - FLAG4 constitute four flag outputs which may be set or reset under program control. SENSE1 - SENSE4 represent four status inputs which may optionally be used as interrupt request lines.

When more than one IM6101 PIE is present in a microcomputer system, the PRIN and POUT signals allow daisy-chained priority interrupt logic to be generated. For a discussion of daisy-chain logic, see Volume 1.

**Figure 13-36 illustrates a large IM6100 microcomputer system that includes more than one IM6101 PIE.**

## IM6101 FUNCTIONAL LOGIC

**IM6101 PROGRAMMING**

**You access an IM6101 Parallel Interface Element using I/O instructions;** this is how the IM6101 will interpret an I/O instruction code as it appears on the Data/Address Bus:

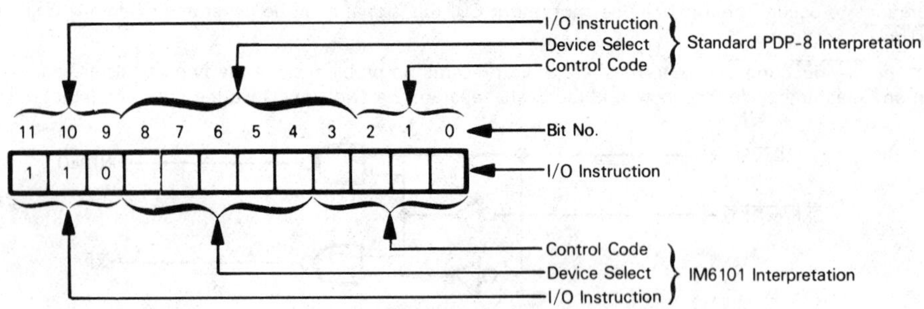

**Note that the IM6101 and the PDP-8 differ in their interpretation of the I/O instruction code.**

**IM6101 logic identifies an I/O instruction object code by examining Data/Address Bus bits 9, 10 and 11 during an IOTA machine cycle. Timing is illustrated in Figure 13-16.**

Now, if you look at Figure 13-16 and then examine the signals input to the IM6101, there appears to be a possibility for confusion. The only control inputs received by the IM6101 are LXMAR, $\overline{\text{DEVSEL}}$ and XTC. What is to stop the IM6101 from being confused by an address output during the instruction fetch machine cycle? LXMAR will be high at this time. An address can certainly look like an I/O instruction object code; in fact, any address in the range $C10_{16}$ through $DFF_{16}$ will look like an I/O instruction object code. Since the IM6101 does not receive the IFETCH signal as an input, it cannot identify an instruction fetch machine cycle. There is no problem, however, because the PIE detects the subsequent $\overline{\text{DEVSEL}}$ low pulse — or lack of low pulse. Indeed, an address in the range mentioned above, output during an instruction fetch machine cycle, may match an IM6101 selection code; however, without the subsequent low $\overline{\text{DEVSEL}}$ pulse, the IM6101 will not respond to this selection. Since $\overline{\text{DEVSEL}}$ is pulsed low during IOTA, but not during an instruction fetch machine cycle, possible problems of ambiguity are resolved.

In order to determine whether or not it is selected, IM6101 logic compares I/O instruction object code bits 8 through 4 with select inputs SEL3 through SEL7, as described earlier.

Here is how the bits are compared:

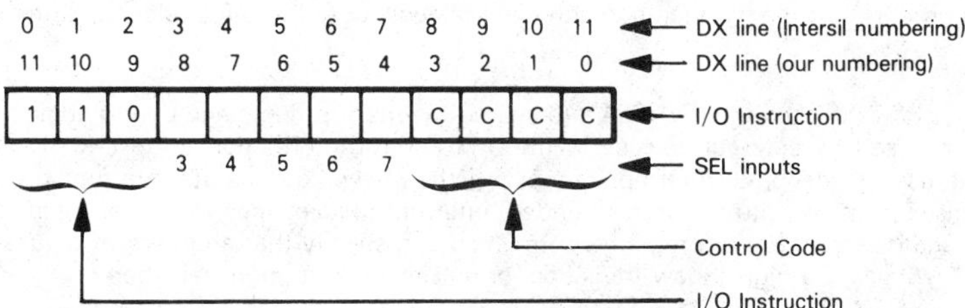


**The low-order four bits of the I/O instruction object code are used by IM6101 logic to generate 16 specific I/O instructions, which are defined in Table 13-4.** This table shows the standard instruction mnemonics recognized by the Intersil assembler, together with the low-order four object code bits' settings.

Table 13-4. IM6101 Interpretation of I/O Instruction Control Bits 3-0

| Instruction Mnemonic | Control Bit | | | | Interpretation |
|---|---|---|---|---|---|
| | 3 | 2 | 1 | 0 | |
| READ1 | 0 | 0 | 0 | 0 | Generate a low pulse output on $\overline{\text{READ1}}$. |
| READ2 | 1 | 0 | 0 | 0 | Generate a low pulse output on $\overline{\text{READ2}}$. |
| WRITE1 | 0 | 0 | 0 | 1 | Generate an active pulse output on WRITE1. |
| WRITE2 | 1 | 0 | 0 | 1 | Generate an active pulse output on WRITE2. |
| SKIP1 | 0 | 0 | 1 | 0 | Test the SENSE1 status. If it is active, output a low pulse via $\overline{\text{SKP/INTREQ}}$, to be interpreted by the IM6100 CPU as an $\overline{\text{SKP}}$ pulse. |
| SKIP2 | 0 | 0 | 1 | 1 | Test the SENSE2 status. If it is active, output a low pulse via $\overline{\text{SKP/INTREQ}}$, to be interpreted by the IM6100 CPU as an $\overline{\text{SKP}}$ pulse. |
| SKIP3 | 1 | 0 | 1 | 0 | Test the SENSE3 status. If it is active, output a low pulse via $\overline{\text{SKP/INTREQ}}$, to be interpreted by the IM6100 CPU as an $\overline{\text{SKP}}$ pulse. |
| SKIP4 | 1 | 0 | 1 | 1 | Test the SENSE4 status. If it is active, output a low pulse via $\overline{\text{SKP/INTREQ}}$, to be interpreted by the IM6100 CPU as an $\overline{\text{SKP}}$ pulse. |
| RCRA | 0 | 1 | 0 | 0 | Place the contents of Control Register A on the Data Bus as data. The IM6100 CPU will OR Control Register A contents with the Accumulator contents. |
| WCRA | 0 | 1 | 0 | 1 | Write the contents of the Accumulator to Control Register A. |
| WCRB | 1 | 1 | 0 | 1 | Write the contents of the Accumulator to Control Register B. |
| WVR | 1 | 1 | 0 | 0 | Write the contents of the Accumulator to the Interrupt Vector register. |
| SFLAG1 | 0 | 1 | 1 | 0 | Set Output Signal FLAG1 high and set Control Register A bit 8 to one. |
| SFLAG3 | 1 | 1 | 1 | 0 | Set Output Signal FLAG3 high and set Control Register A bit 10 to one. |
| CFLAG1 | 0 | 1 | 1 | 1 | Reset Output Signal FLAG1 low and reset Control Register A bit 8 to zero. |
| CFLAG3 | 1 | 1 | 1 | 1 | Reset Output Signal FLAG3 low and reset bit 10 of Control Register A to zero. |

**Let us look at the operations which may be performed when the instructions identified in Table 13-4 are executed.**

IM6101 I/O INSTRUCTIONS

**The two read instructions, READ1 and READ2, cause data to be transferred from an external device to the CPU. Timing is illustrated in Figure 13-32.** The IM6101 outputs a low $\overline{\text{READ1}}$ or $\overline{\text{READ2}}$ pulse, which acts as both a select signal and a strobe signal for the external device which is to transmit data to the IM6100 CPU. The IM6101 transmits $\overline{\text{C1}}$ low and $\overline{\text{C2}}$ high to the CPU in order to identify the I/O instruction as a Read. The actual data transfer occurs directly between the selected device and the IM6100 CPU via the Data/Address Bus.

IM6101 READ INSTRUCTION

The two **write instructions, WRITE1 and WRITE2,** cause the IM6101 to send back $\overline{\text{C1}}$ and $\overline{\text{C2}}$ high at data input time in order to signal a write operation to the IM6100 CPU. Subsequently the IM6101 outputs a WRITE pulse via WRITE1 or WRITE2. Under program control you may select a high write pulse or a low write pulse. An external device will use the write pulse both as a select and as a signal identifying stable data on the Data/Address Bus, which is to be read by the selected device. **Timing is illustrated in Figure 13-33.**

IM6101 WRITE OPERATION

Remaining IM6101 I/O instructions affect control signals and interrupt logic.

The IM6101 has eight control signals: four Flag outputs and four Sense inputs. The Flag outputs, FLAG1 through FLAG4, are simple control outputs. Under program control, the levels of these four outputs can be set or reset, but the manner in which external logic uses these four signals is undefined.

IM6101 FLAG OUTPUTS

The four Sense inputs, SENSE1 through SENSE4, are shared by interrupt logic and control logic. These signals can be used by external devices to transmit control information to an IM6101, and/or they can be used to generate interrupt requests. When used to generate interrupt requests, the four Sense inputs constitute four independent interrupt request lines which can be individually enabled and disabled. Under program control, you can specify that an interrupt request will occur when a sense line is high, low, makes a high-to-low transition, or makes a low-to-high transition.

IM6101 SENSE INPUTS

**The various programmable options of the IM6101 are specified by writing control codes to two control registers.**

IM6101 CONTROL REGISTERS

**Control Register A can be written into (by WCRA) or its contents can be read (by RCRA). Control Register A contents are interpreted as follows:**

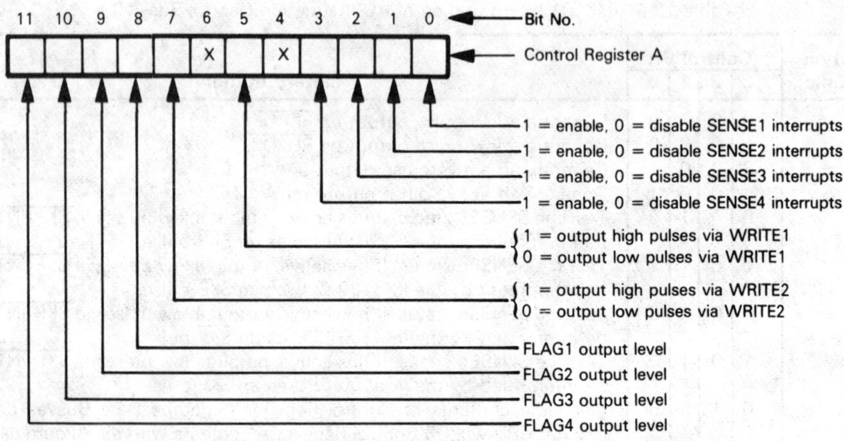

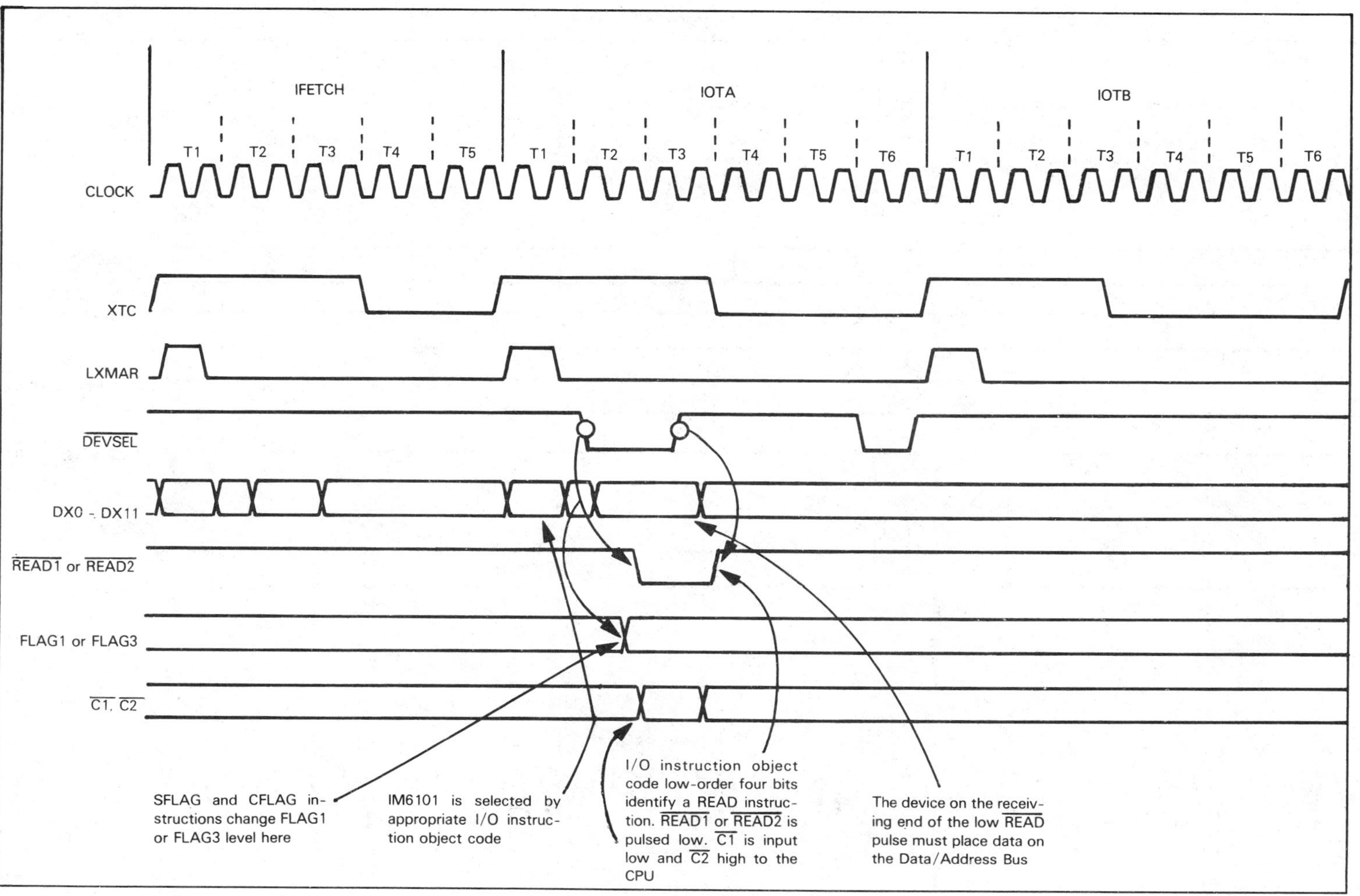
IFETCH
IOTA
IOTB
T1 T2 T3 T4 T5
T1 T2 T3 T4 T5 T6
T1 T2 T3 T4 T5 T6
CLOCK
XTC
LXMAR
DEVSEL
DX0 - DX11
READ1 or READ2
FLAG1 or FLAG3
C1, C2
SFLAG and CFLAG instructions change FLAG1 or FLAG3 level here
IM6101 is selected by appropriate I/O instruction object code
I/O instruction object code low-order four bits identify a READ instruction. READ1 or READ2 is pulsed low. C1 is input low and C2 high to the CPU
The device on the receiving end of the low READ pulse must place data on the Data/Address Bus

Figure 13-32. An IM6101 I/O Read Instruction's Timing

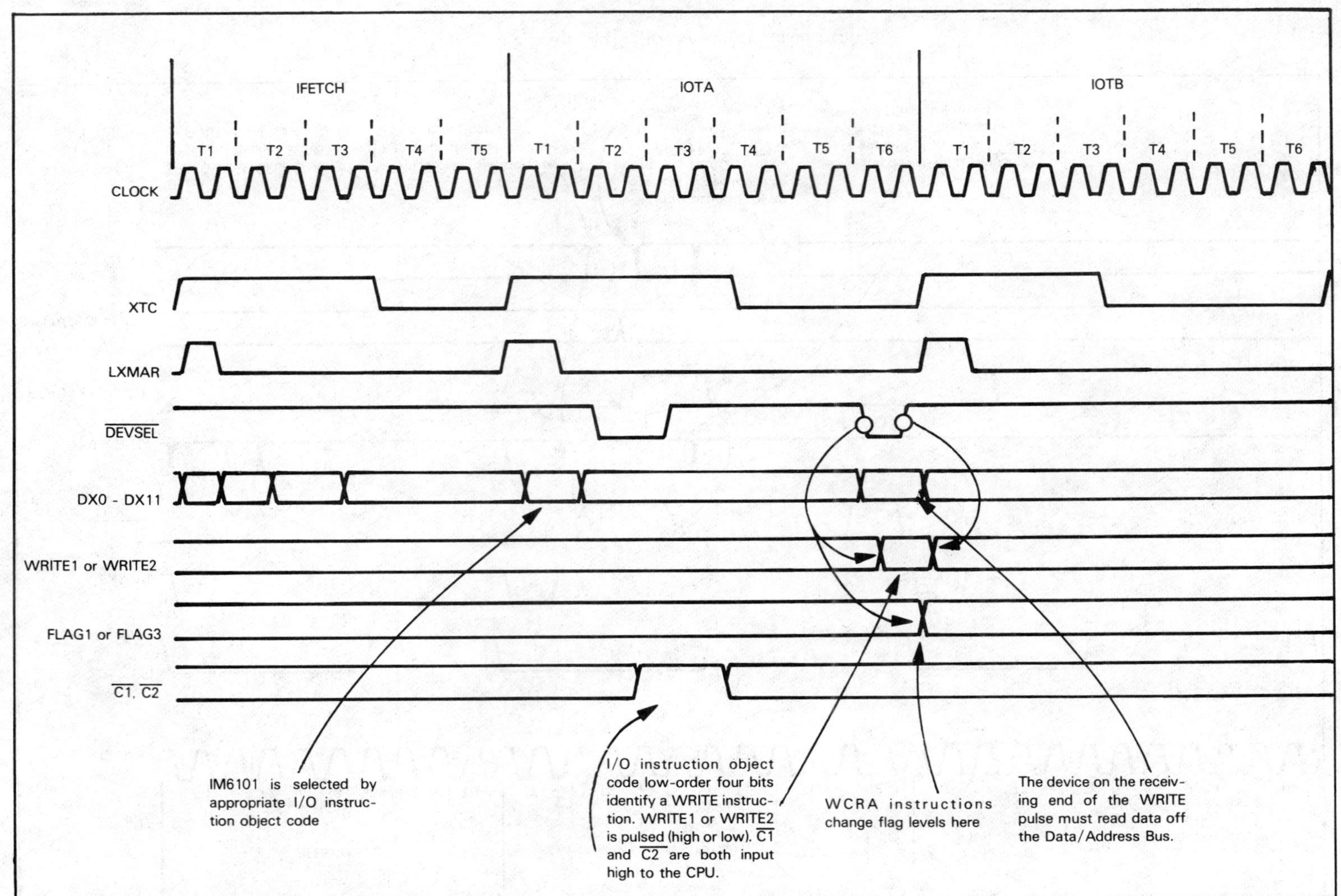
IFETCH
IOTA
IOTB
T1
T2
T3
T4
T5
T1
T2
T3
T4
T5
T6
T1
T2
T3
T4
T5
T6
CLOCK
XTC
LXMAR
DEVSEL
DX0 - DX11
WRITE1 or WRITE2
FLAG1 or FLAG3
C1, C2
IM6101 is selected by appropriate I/O instruction object code
I/O instruction object code low-order four bits identify a WRITE instruction. WRITE1 or WRITE2 is pulsed (high or low). C1 and C2 are both input high to the CPU.
WCRA instructions change flag levels here
The device on the receiving end of the WRITE pulse must read data off the Data/Address Bus.

Figure 13-33. An IM6101 I/O Write Instruction's Timing

The levels of the four Flag outputs, FLAG1 - FLAG4, are determined by the contents of the four high-order Control Register A bits. In addition, specific control instructions shown in Table 13-4 allow FLAG1 and FLAG3 to be set or reset (by SFLAG1, SFLAG2, CFLAG1, CFLAG2). You can therefore modify FLAG1 and FLAG3 in two ways — by executing specific I/O instructions, or by loading appropriate information into the flag bits of Control Register A.

Bits 5 and 7 of Control Register A determine whether the Write output signals WRITE1 and WRITE2 will pulse high or low when a write IOT instruction is executed. Note that you cannot program read pulse levels; a read IOT instruction pulses one of the read lines low.

**You use bits 0 through 3 of Control Register A to determine whether the status inputs SENSE1 - SENSE4 are to function as interrupt requests or as statuses which will trigger IM6100 CPU skip control logic.** You can define the function of each signal in any way and thus create any combination of interrupt requests and skip controls.

**Control Register B determines what will constitute an "active" state for each of the four individual sense inputs.** Each sense input has two control bits in Control Register B, one of which determines whether signal level or transition will constitute the active state; the other control bit determines polarity. Here is Control Register B format:

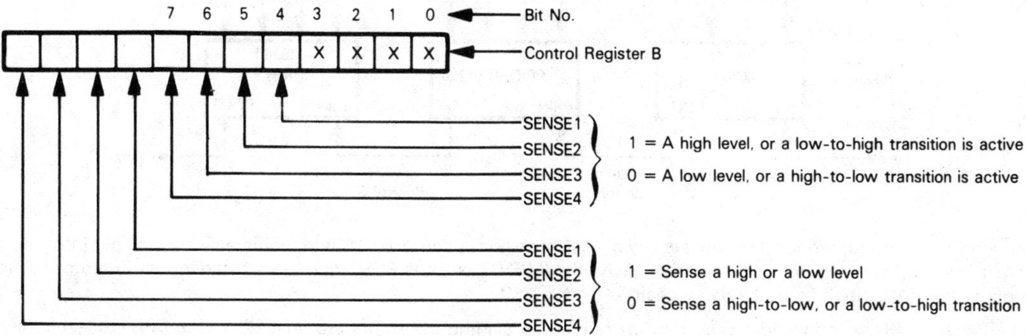


By appropriately setting the two bits of Control Register B which are assigned to any sense input, you can cause a high level, a low level, a high-to-low transition or a low-to-high transition to be the active sense signal state.

Note carefully that Control Register B determines only what will constitute an active sense condition. Control Register B does not hold sense input information.

**You write to Control Registers A and B by executing the WCRA and WCRB instructions, respectively. Timing is as illustrated in Figure 13-15 for a standard device output operation.**

**You can read the contents of Control Register A by executing the RCRA instruction, but you cannot read the contents of Control Register B.** When the RCRA instruction is executed, timing conforms to Figure 13-14.

Recall that instructions which transfer data between the IM6100 CPU and the IM6101 PIE treat the IM6101 PIE as a standard I/O device — selected by a 5-bit device code. READ1, READ2, WRITE1 and WRITE2 instructions, in contrast, select an IM6101 via a 5-bit device code, but subsequently cause a data transfer to occur between the IM6100 and the I/O device which is connected to the selected IM6101 $\overline{\text{READ}}$ or WRITE control signal.

**IM6101 FLAG INSTRUCTIONS**

**There are four instructions which directly control the level of FLAG1 and FLAG3 flag outputs. These four instructions are SFLAG1, SFLAG3, CFLAG1 and CFLAG3.** When any one of these four instructions is executed, the flag output changes state during T2 of IOTA, as illustrated in Figure 13-32. In addition to changing the level of the flag output, these instructions modify the associated Control Register A bit.

**When you write to Control Register A (via a WCRA instruction) you can modify all four flag output levels,** since the four flag outputs reflect associated bit levels in Control Register A. However, any changes in flag levels will occur during T6 of IOTA, as illustrated in Figure 13-33.

**IM6101 SKIP INSTRUCTIONS**

You cannot sample the level of the Sense inputs, since there is no register which stores Sense input levels in the form of binary data. **You must execute a SKIP instruction in order to test a Sense input's level.** A SKIP instruction tests for an "active" Sense signal condition. This "active" condition is defined within Control Register B. As explained for Control Register B, the "active" Sense signal condition may be a high level, a low level, a high-to-low transition, or a low-to-high transition.

**A particular Sense line can be used with skip logic or with interrupt logic.** If interrupt logic has been enabled for the Sense line, then as soon as the active condition occurs at the Sense line, an interrupt will be requested. If interrupt logic has not been enabled for the Sense line, then the active condition of the Sense input will be recorded in an internal flip-flop. Subsequently, **when a SKIP instruction identifying the Sense line is executed, a skip pulse will be returned to the IM6100 CPU if the "active" Sense input has occurred. The Sense flip-flop is then cleared.**

## IM6101 INTERRUPT HANDLING LOGIC

**The IM6101 has typical daisy-chain priority interrupt logic, implemented via the PRIN and POUT signals.**

PRIN must be a high input if an IM6101 is to generate an interrupt request based on one of the four sense lines. Therefore, the IM6101 electrically closest to the CPU must have its PRIN input connected to a high logic level so that its interrupt request logic will always be enabled. So long as no interrupt request is active at this highest priority IM6101, a high signal will be output via POUT; it becomes the PRIN input for the next IM6101 in the daisy chain.

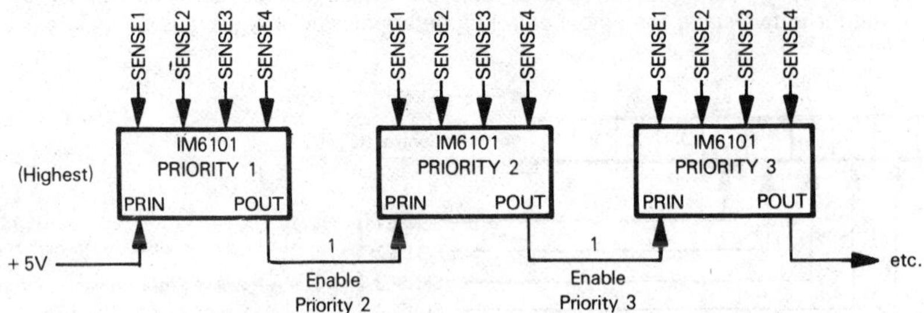


As soon as an interrupt request occurs via one of the sense lines at an IM6101, it immediately sends an out interrupt request low level via $\overline{\text{SKP/INTREQ}}$; simultaneously, the IM6101 outputs POUT low, thus disabling all interrupt request logic at lower priority PIEs in the daisy chain.

The IM6100 CPU acknowledges the interrupt request, providing interrupts are enabled at the CPU, by executing a "Jump-to-Subroutine at memory address 000" instruction. Thus, the interrupt return address is stored in memory location 000, and the instruction object code stored in memory location 001 becomes the first instruction executed following the interrupt acknowledge. Upon acknowledging an interrupt, the IM6100 outputs INTGNT high. The first IOT instruction executed, of any type or to any device, resets INTGNT low. We have described IM6100 interrupt logic earlier in this chapter.

**The IM6101 has an Interrupt Vector register which you write into via the WVR instruction.** The Vector register contents are interpreted as follows:

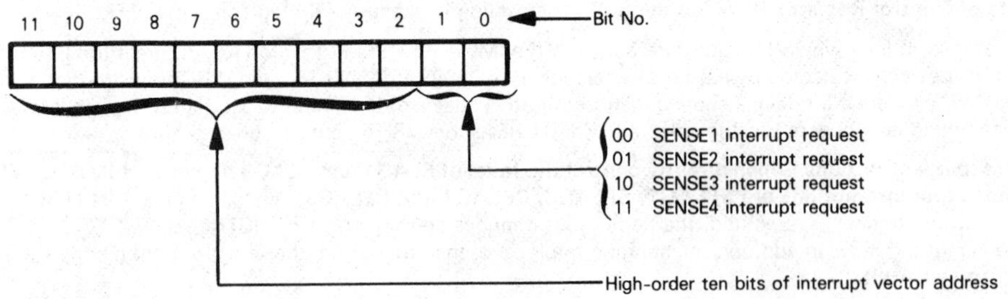


**When an "active" condition occurs at one of the Sense inputs, and interrupt logic for this Sense input has been enabled, then the IM6101 will generate an interrupt request by outputting $\overline{\text{SKP/INTREQ}}$ low.** As soon as the CPU acknowledges the interrupt by outputting INTGNT high, the IM6101 device which has highest priority in the daisy chain (and is requesting an interrupt) will trap the INTGNT signal. When the next I/O instruction is executed, this IM6101 device will place on the Data Bus the contents of the Interrupt Vector register, while simultaneously outputting $\overline{\text{C1}}$ and $\overline{\text{C2}}$ low. This causes an absolute Jump to be executed, with the contents of the interrupt vector becoming the address of the instruction that program logic jumps to. The location addressed by the interrupt vector should contain a

Jump Indirect instruction, since a single word in the interrupt service routine is allocated to each Sense line of an individual IM6101. This may be illustrated as follows:

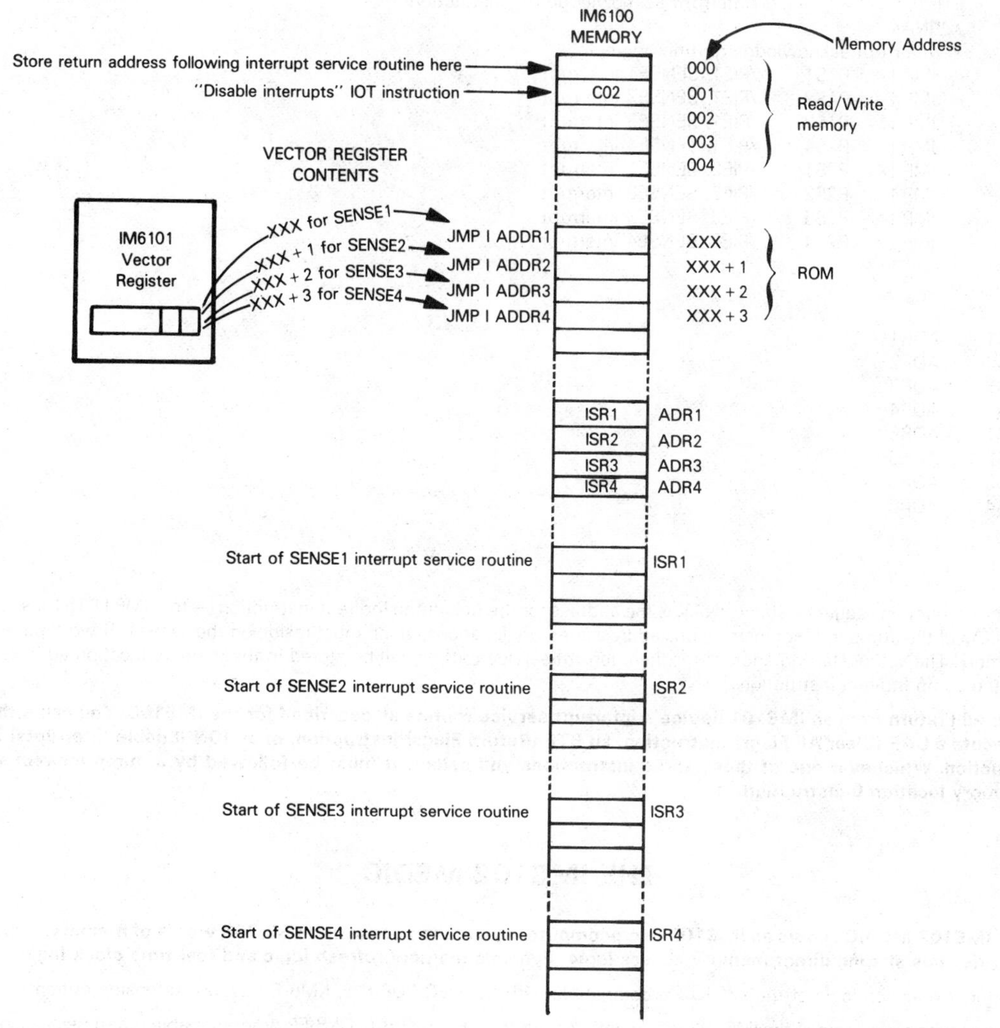


**IM6101 SENSE INTERRUPT PRIORITY**

As we have just stated, the INTGNT signal output by the IM6100 CPU remains high from the time the interrupt is acknowledged until an I/O instruction is subsequently executed by the CPU. **While the INTGNT signal is high, the acknowledged IM6101 device freezes its internal interrupt logic;** that is to say, no further active transitions at Sense inputs will be recognized. Therefore, the Sense input which will be acknowledged is the highest priority Sense input at the instant that INTGNT goes high. **Sense inputs have the following priority at any single IM6101 device:**

Highest Priority: SENSE1
SENSE2
SENSE3
Lowest Priority: SENSE4

Normally, an IOF instruction will be the first I/O instruction executed by the CPU within an interrupt service routine. This instruction disables interrupts at the CPU, where they are already disabled; therefore, it constitutes a no operation

I/O instruction which simply serves to reset the INTGNT signal low. Thus, the interrupt acknowledge routine which will service one or more IM6101 devices may be illustrated as follows:

```
        *1
        IOF                 /Interrupt acknowledge I/O instruction
        *INAK
        /Interrupt acknowledge routine origin
        JMP I    P1S1       /PIE1, SENSE1 interrupt
        JMP I    P1S2       /PIE1, SENSE2 interrupt
        JMP I    P1S3       /PIE1, SENSE3 interrupt
        JMP I    P1S4       /PIE1, SENSE4 interrupt
        JMP I    P2S1       /PIE2, SENSE1 interrupt
        JMP I    P2S2       /PIE2, SENSE2 interrupt
        JMP I    P2S3       /PIE2, SENSE3 interrupt
        JMP I    P2S4       /PIE2, SENSE4 interrupt
        .
        .
        .
P1S1    ADR1
P1S2    ADR2
P1S3    ADR3
P1S4    ADR4
P2S1    ADR5
P2S2    ADR6
P2S3    ADR7
P2S4    ADR8
        .
        .
        .
```

In the instruction sequence above, INAK is the address for the first Jump Indirect instruction — the JMP I P1S1 instruction. All of the Jump Indirect instructions address memory locations which must reside on the same 128-word page of memory. The actual starting address for the interrupt service routine will be stored in the memory location addressed by the Jump Indirect instruction.

**You will return from an IM6101 device's interrupt service routine as described for the IM6100. You can either execute a CAF (Clear All Flags) instruction, an RTF (Return Flags) instruction, or an ION (Enable Interrupts) instruction. Whichever one of these three instructions you select, it must be followed by a Jump Indirect via memory location 0 instruction.**

## THE IM6102 MEDIC

**The IM6102 MEDIC allows an IM6100 microcomputer system to access up to 32,768 words of memory. It also provides bus sharing direct memory access logic, dynamic memory refresh logic and real-time clock logic.**

Memory expansion logic of the IM6102 is compatible with the DEC PDP-8/E, KM8-E memory extension option.

The real-time clock logic of the IM6102 is compatible with the DEC PDP-8/E, DK8-EP programmable real-time clock option.

IM6102 direct memory access logic is not a reproduction of any PDP-8E option.

**Figure 13-34 illustrates that part of our general microcomputer functional logic which is implemented on the IM6102 MEDIC.**

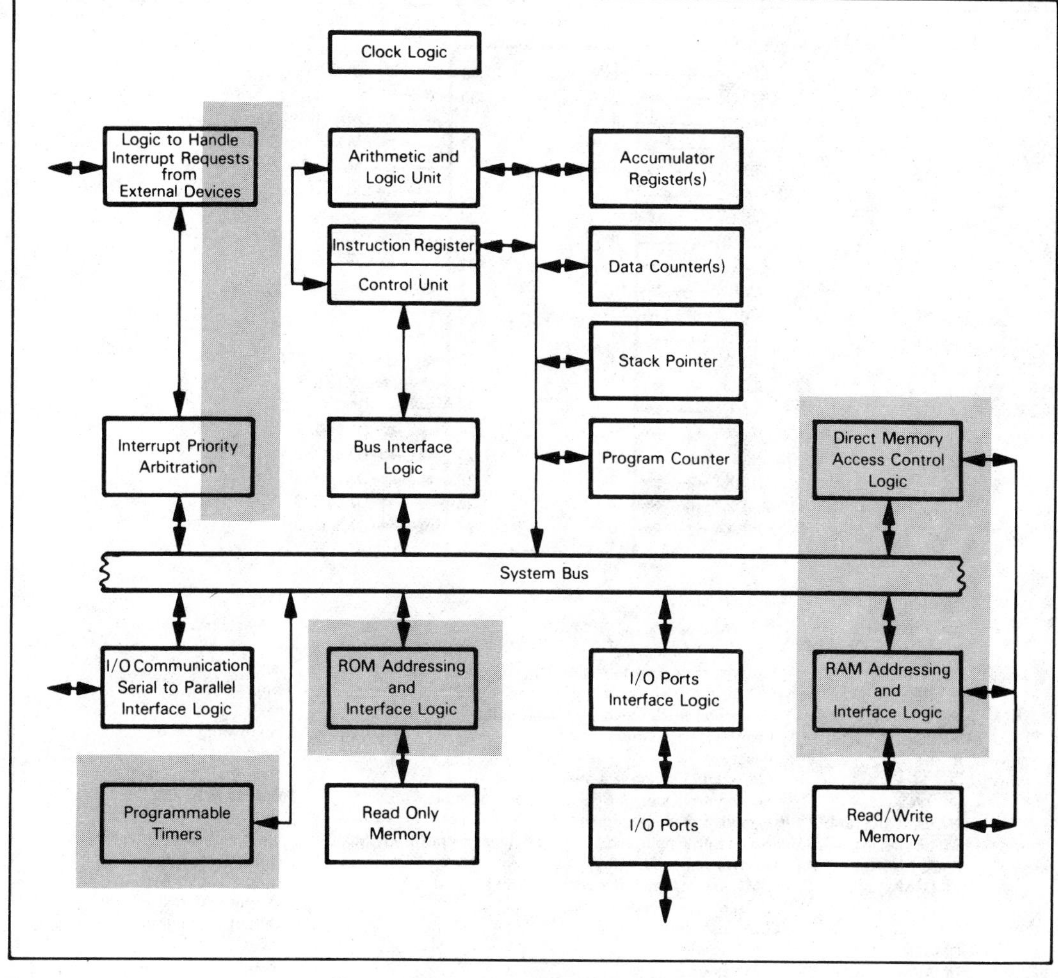


Figure 13-34. Logic of the IM6102 MEDIC

**The IM6102, like all members of the IM6100 family, is fabricated using CMOS technology; it requires a single power supply that may range between +4V and +10V. The IM6102 is packaged as a 40-pin DIP.**

## IM6102 MEDIC PINS AND SIGNALS

**Figure 13-35 illustrates the pins and signals of the IM6102 MEDIC.** We will summarize these pins and signals before proceeding to examine their functions in detail.

**Table 13-5 identifies selected pins of the IM6102 that should be tied to power or ground when specific functions of the device are not used.**

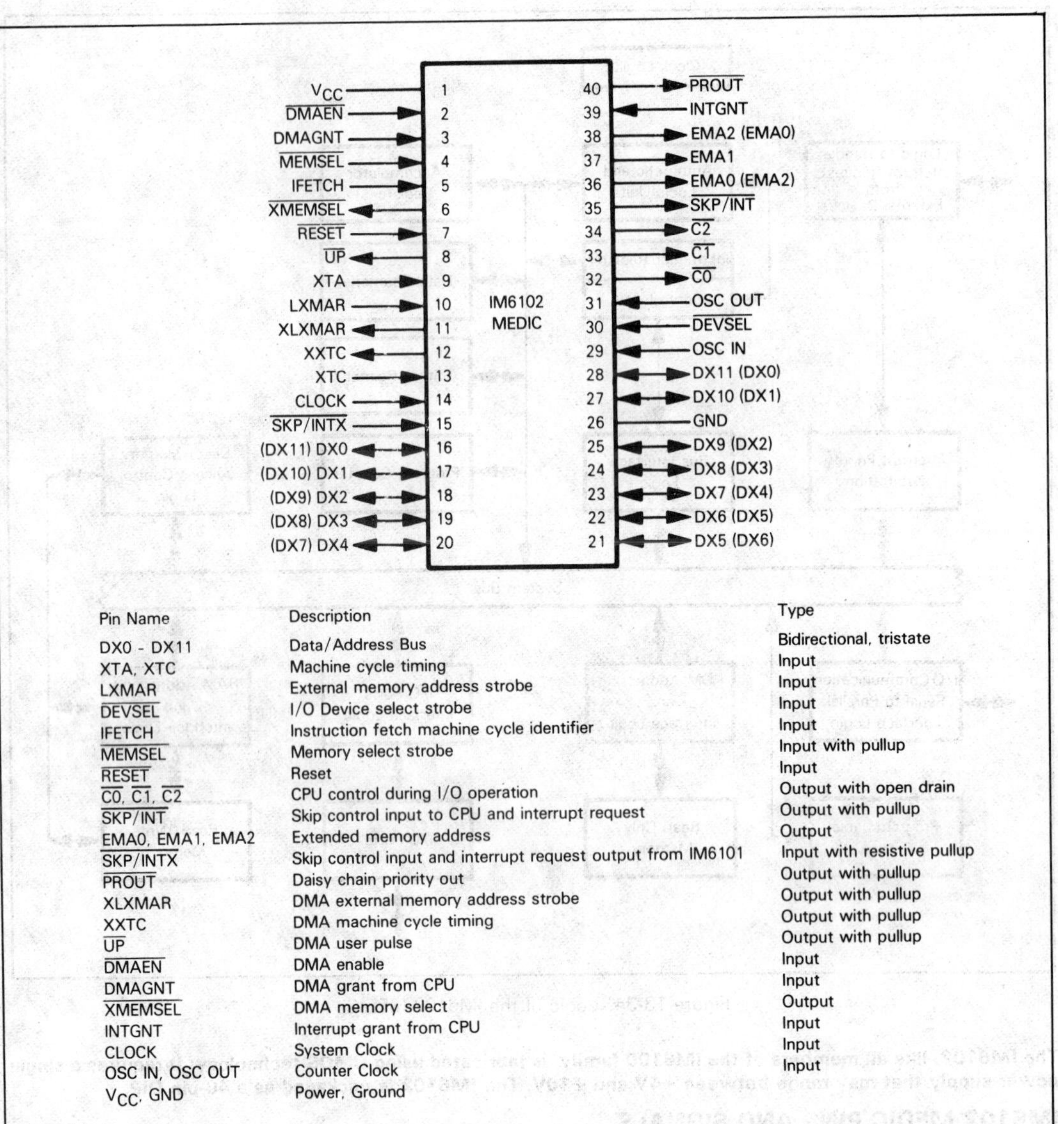


| Pin Name | Description | Type |
|---|---|---|
| DX0 - DX11 | Data/Address Bus | Bidirectional, tristate |
| XTA, XTC | Machine cycle timing | Input |
| LXMAR | External memory address strobe | Input |
| DEVSEL | I/O Device select strobe | Input |
| IFETCH | Instruction fetch machine cycle identifier | Input |
| MEMSEL | Memory select strobe | Input with pullup |
| RESET | Reset | Input |
| C0, C1, C2 | CPU control during I/O operation | Output with open drain |
| SKP/INT | Skip control input to CPU and interrupt request | Output with pullup |
| EMA0, EMA1, EMA2 | Extended memory address | Output |
| SKP/INTX | Skip control input and interrupt request output from IM6101 | Input with resistive pullup |
| PROUT | Daisy chain priority out | Output with pullup |
| XLXMAR | DMA external memory address strobe | Output with pullup |
| XXTC | DMA machine cycle timing | Output with pullup |
| UP | DMA user pulse | Output with pullup |
| DMAEN | DMA enable | Input |
| DMAGNT | DMA grant from CPU | Input |
| XMEMSEL | DMA memory select | Output |
| INTGNT | Interrupt grant from CPU | Input |
| CLOCK | System Clock | Input |
| OSC IN, OSC OUT | Counter Clock | Input |
| $V_{CC}$, GND | Power, Ground | |

Figure 13-35. IM6102 MEDIC Signals and Pin Assignments

Table 13-5. IM6102 MEDIC Pins that should be Tied to Power or Ground when Certain Functions are Unused

| PIN NUMBER | PIN NAME | REAL-TIME CLOCK ONLY | DMA ONLY | EXTENDED MEMORY CONTROL ONLY | EXTENDED MEMORY CONTROL AND DYNAMIC MEMORY REFRESH |
|---|---|---|---|---|---|
| 2 | $\overline{\text{DMAEN}}$ | GND | USED | GND | GND |
| 3 | DMAGNT | USED | USED | USED | USED |
| 6 | $\overline{\text{XMEMSEL}}$ | N/C | USED | N/C | USED |
| 8 | $\overline{\text{UP}}$ | N/C | USED | N/C | N/C |
| 11 | XLXMAR | N/C | USED | N/C | USED |
| 12 | XXTC | N/C | USED | N/C | USED |
| 15 | $\overline{\text{SKP/INTX}}$ | $V_{CC}$ | $V_{CC}$ | USED | USED |
| 29 | OSC IN | USED | GND | GND | GND |
| 31 | OSC OUT | USED | N/C | N/C | N/C |
| 34 | $\overline{\text{C2}}$ | USED | USED | N/C | N/C |
| 36 | EMA0 | N/C | N/C | USED | USED |
| 37 | EMA1 | N/C | N/C | USED | USED |
| 38 | EMA2 | N/C | N/C | USED | USED |
| 40 | $\overline{\text{PROUT}}$ | USED | USED | N/C | N/C |

**Only one IM6102 MEDIC can be present in an IM6100 system.**

**Let us first look at the IM6102 signals which connect directly with the IM6100 CPU.**

**DX0 - DX11 is the system Data/Address Bus.** As in the IM6100 and IM6101 descriptions, our Data/Address Bus signal names are shown in brackets next to names used in Intersil literature. Addresses and data will flow directly between the IM6102 and the IM6100, via the Data/Address Bus, when the CPU is accessing the IM6102 via the I/O instructions described in Table 13-6.

Of the IM6100 control and timing signals, **XTA, XTC, LXMAR, $\overline{\text{DEVSEL}}$, IFETCH and $\overline{\text{MEMSEL}}$ are input to the IM6102.** Note specifically that XTB and DATAF are not transmitted to the IM6102; functions performed by these signals are implied by logic within the IM6102.

**IM6102 RESET**

**$\overline{\text{RESET}}$ is a standard reset input.** $\overline{\text{RESET}}$ input timing must conform to IM6100 reset timing. **When the IM6102 is reset, all of its internal registers and flags are cleared.**

**The IM6102 generates the four I/O control signals required by the CPU: $\overline{\text{C0}}$, $\overline{\text{C1}}$, $\overline{\text{C2}}$ and $\overline{\text{SKP}}$.** However, $\overline{\text{SKP}}$ and the interrupt request signal $\overline{\text{INT}}$ share a single pin, as is the case with the IM6101 devices.

**If IM6102 and IM6101 devices are present together in an IM6100 microcomputer system, then the IM6102 must be the device with highest interrupt priority. IM6101 devices having lower priority will use the PROUT output of the IM6102 to initiate interrupt priority daisy chain logic. Interrupt requests from IM6101 devices must be input to the IM6102 via $\overline{\text{SKP/INTX}}$. The IM6102 will pass the interrupt request on to the IM6100 via $\overline{\text{SKP/INT}}$ at the proper time. This is illustrated in Figure 13-36.**

In order to address additional "fields" of memory, EMA0, EMA1, and EMA2 act as three high-order address lines, extending the normal 12-bit memory address available on DX0 - DX11 to a 15-bit address as follows:

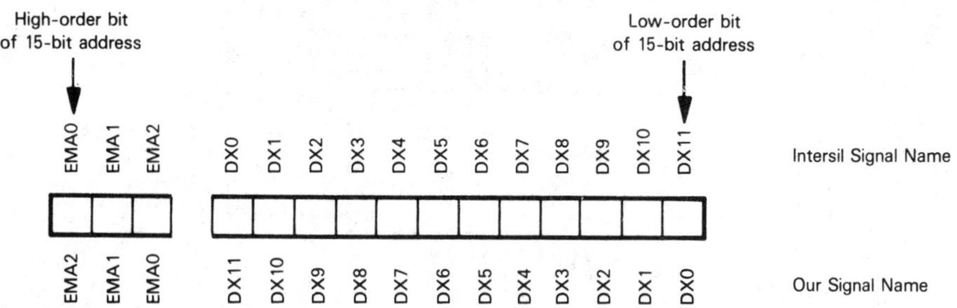

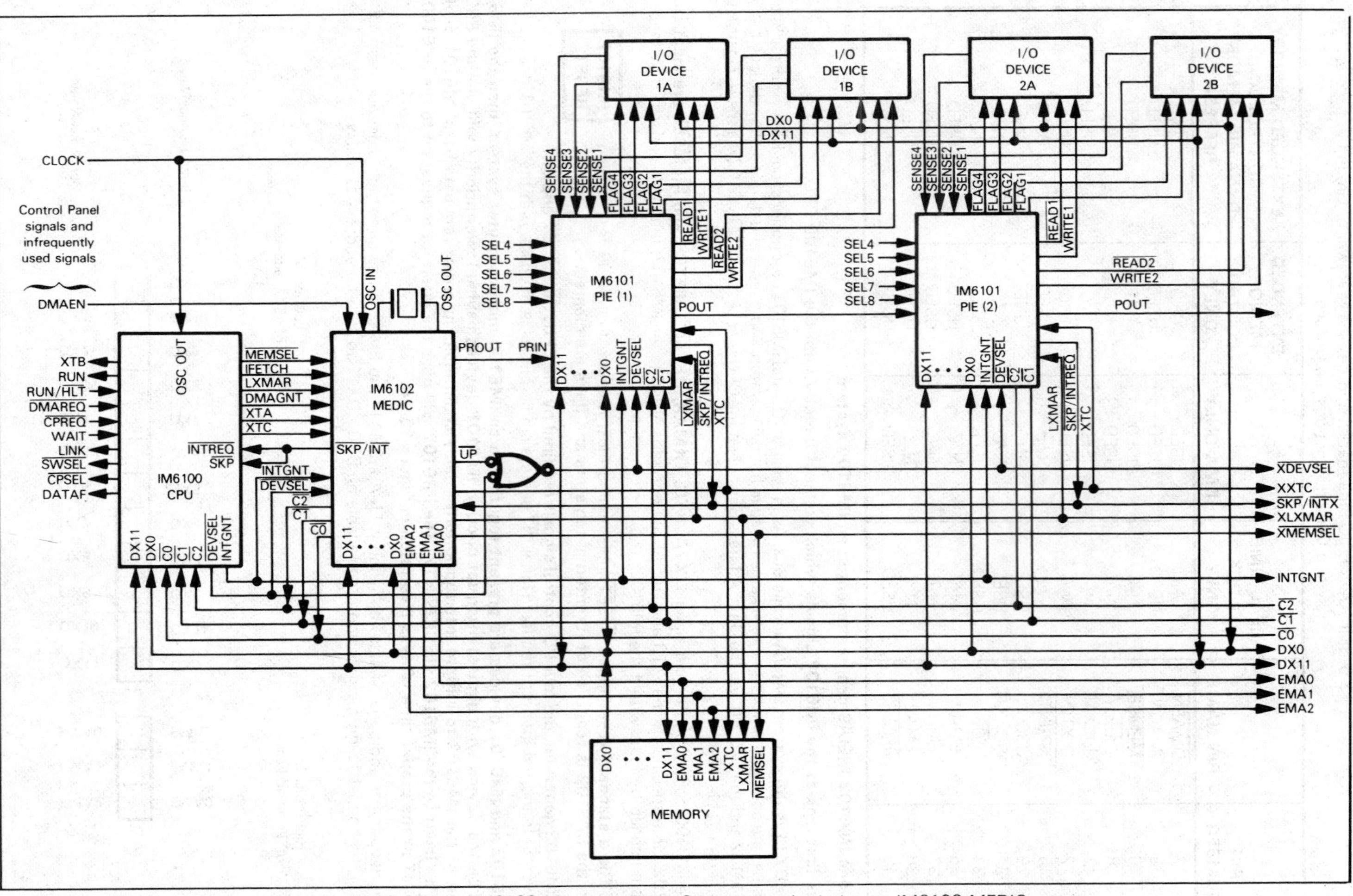


Figure 13-36. An IM6100 Microcomputer System that Includes an IM6102 MEDIC and IM6101 PIE Device

**Any interrupt request** from the IM6102 **is acknowledged by the CPU via INTGNT,** the standard interrupt acknowledge signal output by the CPU.

For direct memory access and dynamic memory refresh functions, **the IM6102 generates XLXMAR, XXTC, and $\overline{\text{XMEMSEL}}$,** signals derived from LXMAR, XTC and $\overline{\text{MEMSEL}}$, respectively. In addition, **UP is generated as an I/O device pulse.**

**$\overline{\text{DMAEN}}$ is a master DMA enable** which must be input low to the IM6102 to enable any DMA operation. **DMAGNT is the standard DMA grant output by the CPU;** DMAGNT is received by the IM6102, which suspends DMA operations if DMAGNT is high — in which case some other DMA operation, not initiated by the IM6102, is in progress.

**Counter/timer logic of the IM6102 is driven by an external crystal which must be connected across OSC IN and OSC OUT.**

**The IM6102 MEDIC requires two sets of clock logic. A crystal must be connected across OSC IN and OSC OUT: this crystal is used by the IM6102 real-time logic only. The master IM6100 microcomputer system clock signal must also be input to the IM6102.** Since no such clock signal is output by the IM6100 CPU, you must generate this clock signal externally. This means you cannot use the IM6100 internal clock logic if you are also using an IM6102 MEDIC. External logic must generate the clock signal, which is input to the OSC OUT pin of the IM6100 CPU, and to the CLOCK input of the IM6102 MEDIC.

**The crystal connecting the OSC IN and OSC OUT pins of the IM6102 should have the following characteristics:**

$$R_S \leq 150 \text{ ohms}$$
$$C_M = 3 \text{ to } 30 \text{ fF } (10^{-15}\text{F})$$
$$C_O = 10 \text{ to } 50 \text{ pF (12 pF preferred)}$$
$$\text{Static capacitance} \simeq 5 \text{ pF}$$

## THE IM6100 - IM6102 INTERFACE

**Figure 13-36 illustrates an IM6100 microcomputer system that includes an IM6102 MEDIC and a number of IM6101 devices** (two are shown). The IM6102 has been designed on the assumption that there will be no more than one of these devices in a single IM6100 microcomputer system. The IM6102 will be the highest priority device in an interrupt daisy chain.

**The CPU communicates with the IM6102 device via a specific set of I/O instructions, which are summarized in Table 13-6.** A few of the I/O instructions shown in Table 13-6 are general instructions that affect all devices connected to an IM6100 CPU, but most of the instructions in Table 13-6 are specific to the single IM6102 device that can be present in the system. If you look at Table 13-6, you may notice the possibility for confusion in instruction object codes. First of all, none of the instruction object codes identify an I/O device — yet in our earlier discussion of IM6100 I/O instruction object codes we saw that five or six object code bits were set aside to provide device identification. This problem is resolved in two ways:

1) A few of the instructions shown in Table 13-6 are general I/O instructions which must be acted upon by all I/O devices in the IM6100 microcomputer system. Since all I/O devices will respond to these instructions, the lack of an I/O device code presents no problem.
2) There is only one IM6102 device allowed per IM6100 microcomputer system. Therefore, the I/O device numbers which happen to be usurped by IM6102 I/O instruction object codes given in Table 13-6 must not be used for IM6101 devices, or any other I/O devices in the IM6100 microcomputer system. That is to say, **the following I/O device codes cannot be used if an IM6102 is present:**

| Instruction Mnemonics | Binary Device Code Used by IM6102 |
|---|---|
| CLZE, CLSK, CLDE, CLAB, CLEN, CLSA, CLBA, CLCA | xxx00101xxxx |
| CDF, CIF, RDF, RIF, RIB, RMF, LIF, LCAR, RCAR, LWCR, LEAR, REAR, LFSR, RFSR, SKOF, WRVR | xxx01000xxxx<br>xxx01001xxxx<br>xxx01010xxxx<br>xxx01011xxxx |

**Five of the 31 allowed IM6101 device codes are used by the IM6102 IOT instructions, therefore a maximum of 26 IM6101 devices may be present in an IM6100 microcomputer system that includes an IM6102.**

## IM6102 EXTENDED MEMORY CONTROL

**The IM6102 implements extended memory addressing via the simple expedient of creating three additional high-order address lines,** over and above the 12 address lines output on the Data/Address Bus. **These three high-order address lines are EMA0, EMA1 and EMA2.** Together with the address output on the Data/Address Bus, these three address lines create 15-bit memory addresses, as illustrated earlier in our discussion of IM6102 signals. Note again that since we number signals and bits in the opposite sense to Intersil literature, **our signal names compare with Intersil signal names as follows:**

| | Highest order bit | | Lowest order bit |
|---|---|---|---|
| Intersil signal name: | EMA0 | EMA1 | EMA2 |
| Our signal name: | EMA2 | EMA1 | EMA0 |

**IM6102 DATA FIELD REGISTER**

**IM6102 INSTRUCTION FIELD REGISTER**

**There are two 3-bit registers within the IM6102 which hold the value to be output via EMA2, EMA1 and EMA0. These are the Instruction Field register and the Data Field register.** The EMA2, EMA1 and EMA0 outputs will always come from one of these two registers.

**The Instruction Field register contents are output as three high-order address lines most of the time. The Data Field register contents are output as the three high-order address lines only during the third machine cycle of an AND, TAD, ISZ or DCA instruction — when the instruction is using indirect addressing to reference memory.** This machine cycle is identified by the DATAF signal. See Figure 13-13 for DATAF signal timing.

The DATAF signal is not input to the IM6102; logic internal to the device recognizes the third, direct addressing machine cycle of an AND, TAD, ISZ or DCA instruction that specifies indirect addressing. **Figure 13-40 is a reproduction of Figure 13-13, including EMA outputs of the IM6102.**

**IM6100 MEMORY FIELDS**

**Neither the Instruction Field register nor the Data Field register contents increment along with the Program Counter.** Suppose, for example, the Instruction Field register contains the value 3. If the Program Counter contents increment from $FFF_{16}$ to $000_{16}$, the effective address will change from $3FFF_{16}$ to $3000_{16}$. The effective address will not increment from $3FFF_{16}$ to $4000_{16}$. This means that the **IM6102 memory extension logic divides memory into separate and distinct 4096-word "fields".** Since there are three extended memory address lines, there can be a total of eight 4096-word "fields", for a maximum of 32,768 words of memory.

There are some important programming implications in the fact that the Instruction Field and Data Field register contents do not increment. We will examine these programming implications later.

**IM6100-IM6102 RESET BOOTSTRAP**

**When the IM6102 is reset, the Data Field and Instruction Field registers both contain 0.** But the Program Counter is initialized with the value $FFF_{16}$ when the IM6100 is reset. Therefore, initial program execution begins with a bootstrap program origined at location $FFF_{16}$, the highest address within the first 4096-word memory field.

**IM6100-IM6102 INTERRUPT ACKNOWLEDGE**

**Following an interrupt acknowledge, the Instruction Field and Data Field registers' contents are saved** in the Save Field register, **then zeros are loaded into the Instruction Field and Data Field registers.** Thus, interrupt service routines will be origined at memory location 1 of the first 4096-word memory field and the interrupt service routine return address will be stored in location 0 of this same memory field, just as though there were no additional memory fields present. Thus, additional memory fields have no effect on restart logic or interrupt acknowledge logic.

**IM6100 BASE PAGE IN EXTENDED MEMORY**

**Base page logic is reproduced in every 4096-word memory field** of an IM6100 microcomputer system. That is to say, a memory reference instruction that specifies base page addressing will access one of the first 128 words within the current memory field. Moreover, auto-increment memory addressing logic will apply to addresses stored in memory words $008_{16}$ through $00F_{16}$ of every 4096-word memory field.

**IM6102 EXTENDED MEMORY ADDRESSING REGISTERS**

**Let us examine the way in which you will use the Instruction Field, Data Field and associated registers of the IM6102 extended memory address control logic. These registers, and instructions which access them, are illustrated in Figure 13-37.**

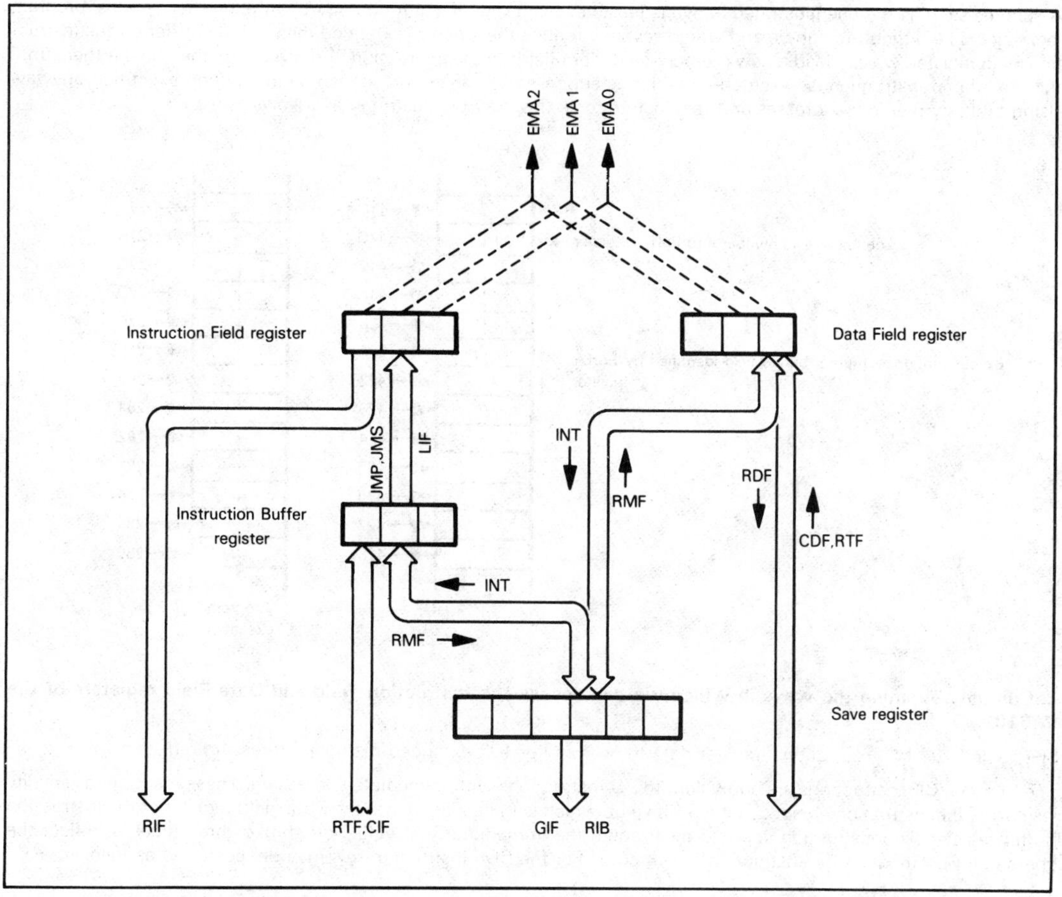

Figure 13-37. IM6102 Extended Memory Addressing Registers and Data Paths

**IM6102 INSTRUCTION BUFFER REGISTER**

**Note that the Instruction Field register has a Buffer register.** This is necessary, since the instruction that loads a new value into the Instruction Field register would otherwise cause an immediate branch into the next sequential memory location of a new memory field. Using arbitrary memory addresses, this may be illustrated as follows:

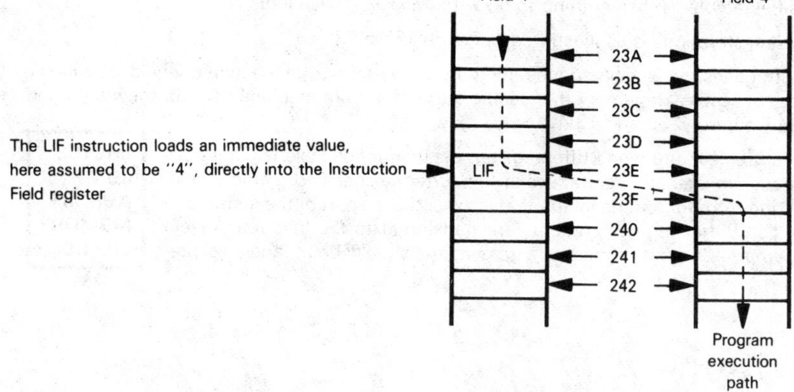

A scheme such as the one illustrated above is feasible, using the LIF instruction, but, without other options, program logic would be difficult to handle and would severely reduce the value of extended memory. By buffering the Instruction Field register, we can load a new memory field identifier into the Instruction Buffer register, then hold it there until the next Jump instruction is executed — which is supposed to cause non-sequential instruction execution anyway. Using arbitrary memory addresses and real instructions, this may be illustrated as follows:

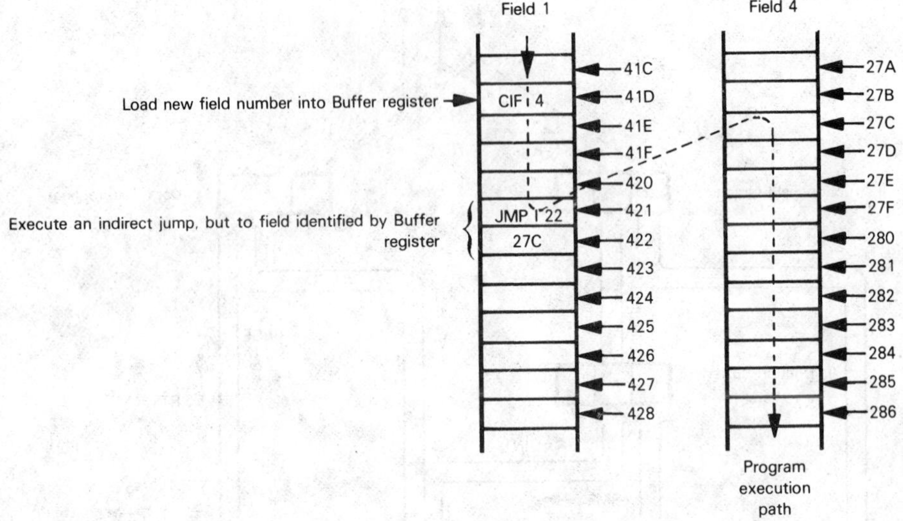


**Let us now examine the ways in which we can access the Instruction Field and Data Field registers of the IM6102.**

Special IM6102 I/O instructions transfer data to or from IM6102 extended memory addressing registers.

The CDF and CIF instructions are equivalent to I/O instructions with immediate addressing. These instructions specify (as part of the instruction object code) a 3-bit value which is to be loaded into the Data Field register or the Instruction Buffer register. The instruction operand must equal the immediate 3-bit value left shifted three times to reflect the operand bit positions in the instruction object code. For the CDF instruction this may be illustrated as follows:

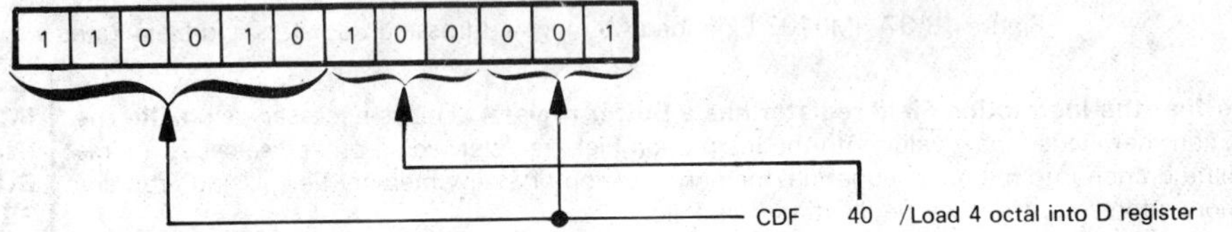


This is a quirk of the Intersil assembler; it has nothing to do with IM6102 device logic.

Timing for execution of these instructions is as illustrated in Figure 13-15.

AND, TAD, ISZ and DCA instructions that specify indirect memory addressing go to the memory field identified by the Data Field register for the direct access of memory that occurs during the third machine cycle of the instruction's execution; this is illustrated in Figures 13-39 and 13-40.

**IM6102 JUMP ACROSS MEMORY FIELDS**

When you load a new value into the Instruction Buffer register, the Instruction Field register does not change, and therefore program execution continues in the currently specified memory field. But when the next Jump or Jump-to-Subroutine instruction is executed, as part of the instruction execution logic, the Instruction Buffer register contents are transferred to the Instruction Field register, so the Jump or Jump-to-Subroutine occurs across memory field boundaries, as previously illustrated.

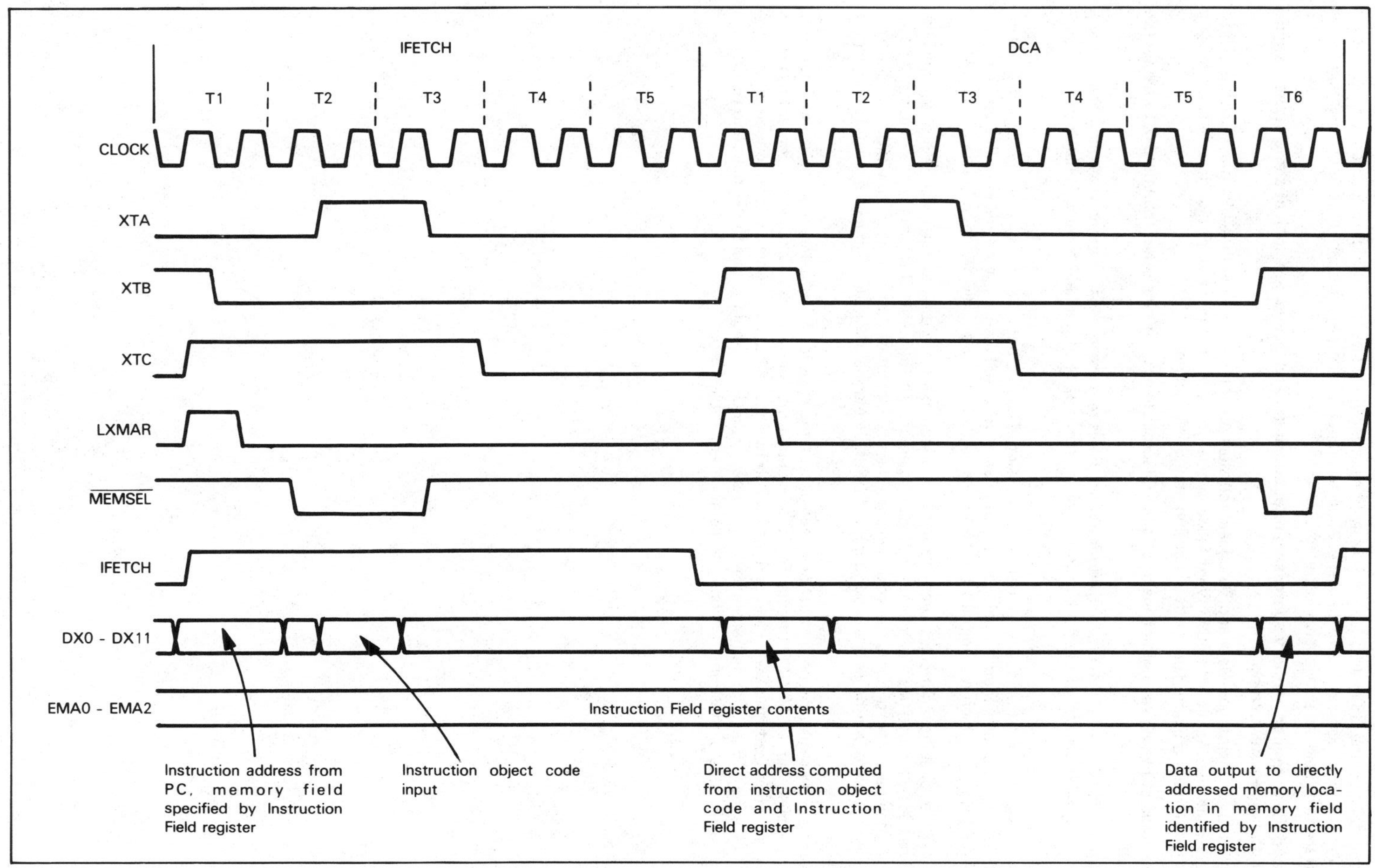


Figure 13-38. IM6100 DCA Instruction Timing with Direct Addressing Using Extended Memory Addressing

You do have the option, via the LIS instruction, of directly transferring the Instruction Buffer register contents to the Instruction Field register. This will cause program execution to branch to the next sequential memory location in the newly specified memory field, as previously illustrated.

**Having examined the extended memory addressing registers in general, let us now look at some of the specific ways in which these registers work.**

First of all, recall that the Instruction Field and Data Field registers do not increment with the Program Counter. Thus, program memory is divided rigidly into 4096-word fields, where you can only move from one field to another via a Jump or Jump-to-Subroutine instruction, or by executing an LIS instruction.

**Let us examine some of the ways in which instructions will execute out of fields other than field 0. Consider the DCA instruction.**

Using direct memory addressing, the instruction and the word that is referenced must lie in the same memory field; the referenced word may be in page 0 of the field, or in the instruction's page of the field. Timing is illustrated in Figure 13-38.

Now consider a DCA instruction that specifies indirect addressing. The instruction and the word that contains the indirect address must lie in the same memory field, but the ultimately accessed memory word will lie in the field specified by the Data Field register — which may or may not be the same field. Timing is illustrated in Figure 13-39.

A DCA instruction that specifies indirect addressing with auto-increment will directly reference one of the memory words with address $08_{16}$ through $0F_{16}$ in the current field of memory. The contents of this memory location will be incremented and written back; the incremented value will become the address of the memory word ultimately accessed. However, this memory word will be in the field identified by the Data Field register. Timing is illustrated in Figure 13-40.

You also have register-to-register type instructions that access the Instruction Buffer register and the Data Field register. This is because the IM6100 CPU treats IM6102 extended memory addressing registers' contents as status flags. The GTF instruction loads the Data Field and Instruction Buffer registers' contents into the low-order CPU Accumulator bits, while the RTF instruction transfers the low-order six CPU Accumulator bits to the Instruction Buffer and Data Field registers. Results of these instructions are illustrated in Table 13-6.

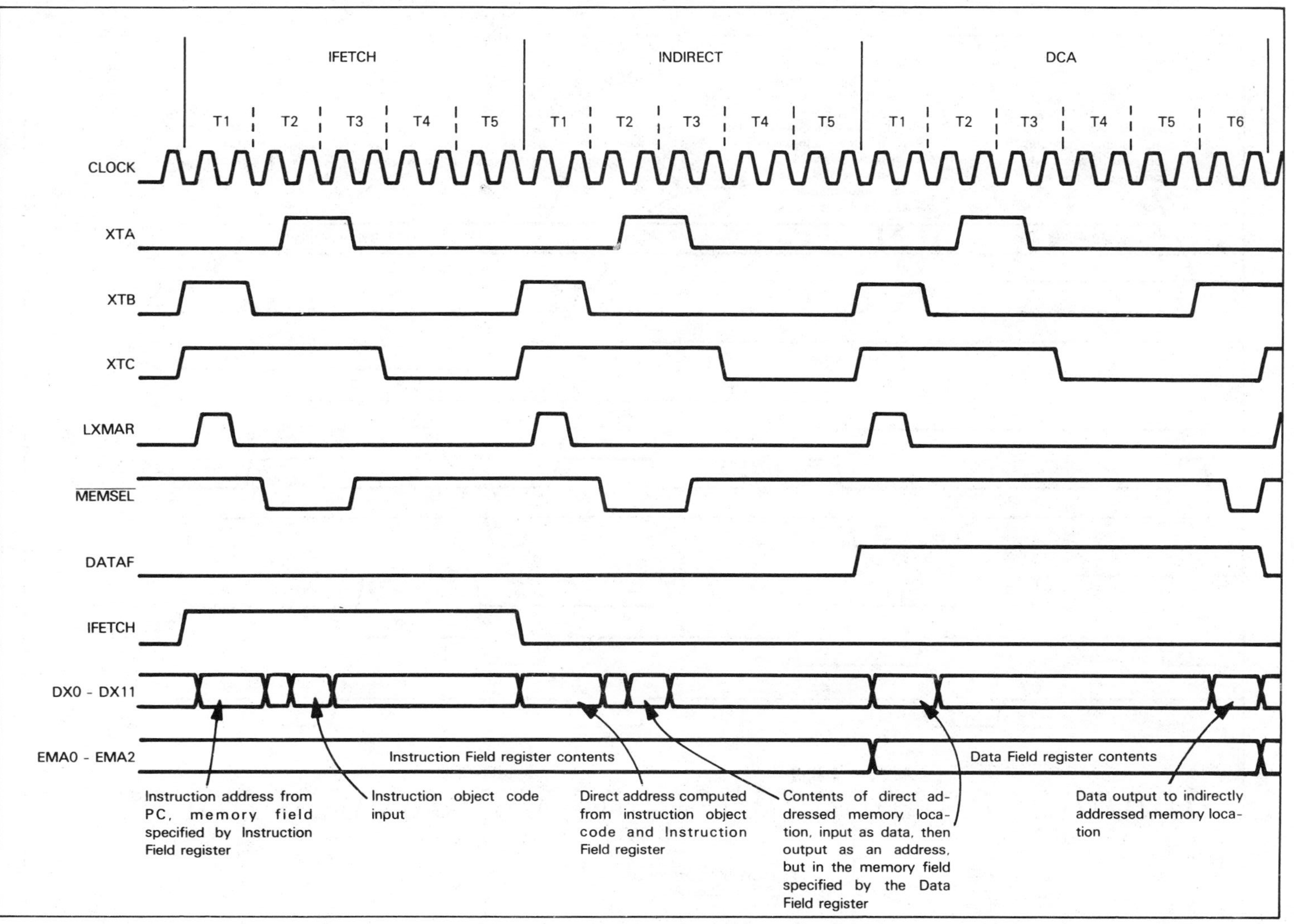


Figure 13-39. IM6100 DCA Instruction Timing with Indirect Addressing Using Extended Memory Addressing

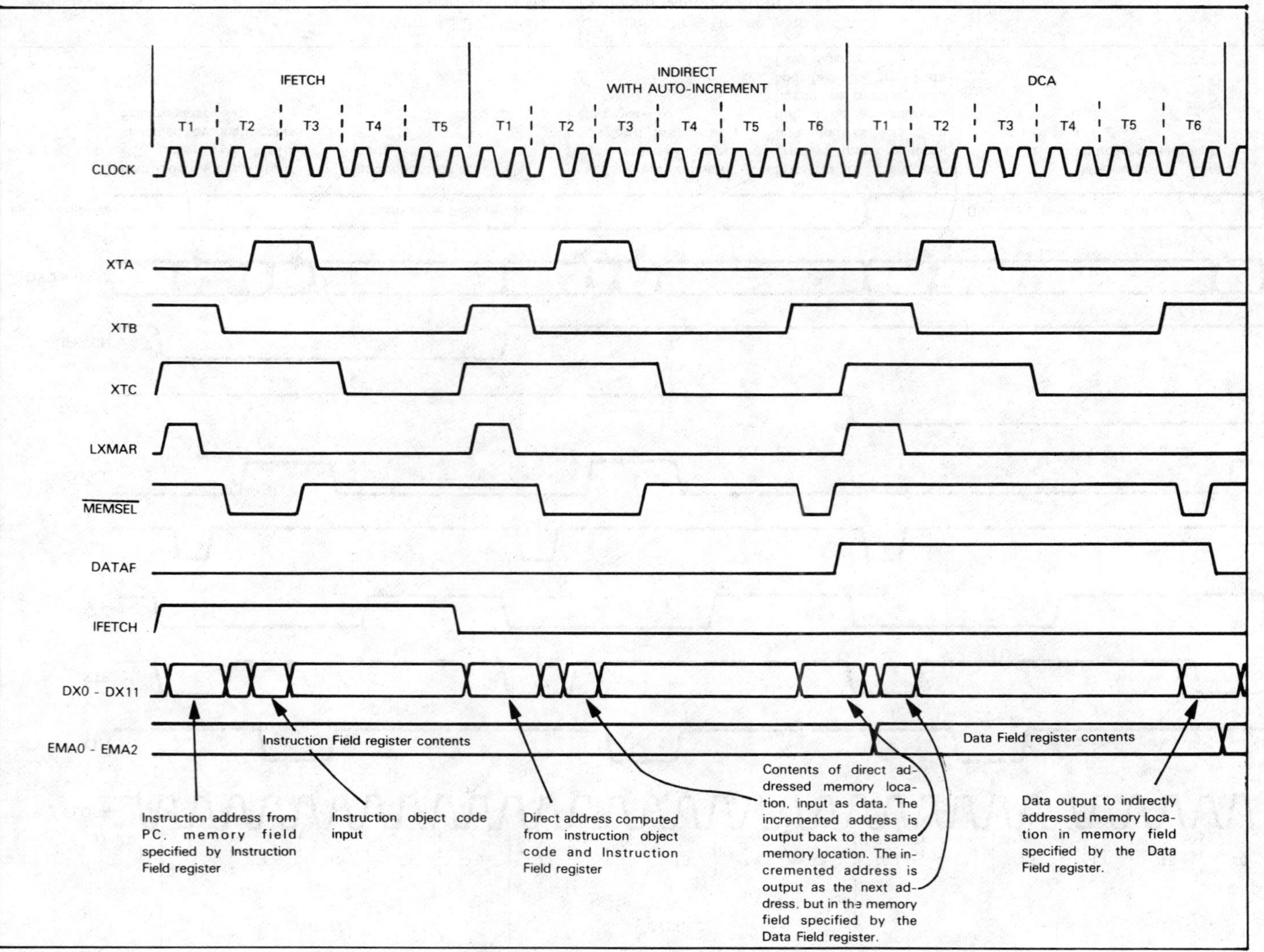


Figure 13-40. IM6100 DCA Instruction Timing with Indirect Addressing and Auto-Increment Using Extended Memory Addressing

## IM6102 EXTENDED MEMORY PROGRAMMING CONSIDERATIONS

**IM6100 EXTENDED MEMORY JUMP**

**Here is the necessary instruction sequence for program logic to branch from any memory field into memory field 3:**

```
        -
        -
        -
        CIF     30        /PREPARE TO JUMP TO MEMORY FIELD 3
        -
        -
        -
        CDF     20        /SET DATA FIELD TO 2
        JMP I   .+1       /JUMP TO LOCATION ADDR IN FIELD 3
        ADDR
        -
        -
        -
```

Observe that the CIF and CDF instruction operands require the field number to be specified in bit positions 3, 4 and 5:

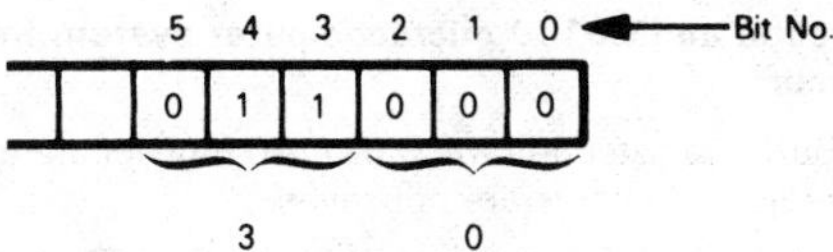


The Intersil assembler assumes octal data in the operand field unless otherwise defined.

**IM6100 EXTENDED MEMORY SUBROUTINE ACCESSES**

**Calling subroutines and returning from subroutines across field boundaries is not nearly as simple as the Jump illustrated above.** The problem is that a subroutine has no way of knowing out of which field it was called. Thus, when it is time to return from the subroutine, the normal return sequence will not work. Your program logic must therefore include special instructions that transmit to the subroutine the field number out of which the subroutine was called. The technique most commonly used is to load the program field number into the Data Field register before calling the subroutine. If we arbitrarily assume that a subroutine in memory field 1 is to be called by a program in memory field 4, accessing data in memory field 5, then the subroutine calling sequence can be illustrated as follows:

```
/Below is the subroutine calling sequence
        CDF     40        /LOAD PROGRAM FIELD INTO DATA FIELD REGISTER
        CIF     10        /LOAD SUBROUTINE FIELD INTO INSTRUCTION BUFFER REGISTER
        JMS I   SADR      /JUMP TO SUBROUTINE IN MEMORY FIELD 1
        CDF     50        /AFTER RETURNING FROM SUBROUTINE, RESTORE DATA FIELD REGISTER
        -
        -
        -
SADR    SUBR              /12-BIT SUBROUTINE ADDRESS
/SUBROUTINE IN MEMORY FIELD 1 BEGINS BELOW
SUBR    0                 /RETURN ADDRESS IS STORED HERE
        CLA               /CLEAR ACCUMULATOR AND INPUT DATA FIELD REGISTER CONTENTS
        RDF
        TAD     RET       /ADD 110010000010 TO CREATE INSTRUCTION FIELD REGISTER RESTORATION
                          /INSTRUCTION
        DCA     EXIT      /AND INSERT AT EXIT
        -       \
        -        }        Body of subroutine occurs here
        -       /
EXIT    0                 /THIS BECOMES A CIF N INSTRUCTION
        JMP I   SUBR      /RETURN TO CALLING PROGRAM
RET     CIF     00        /DATA USED TO CREATE INSTRUCTION AT EXIT
```

Before executing a Jump-to-Subroutine instruction, the CDF instruction loads the current program memory field number into the Data Field register. Next, the CIF instruction loads the subroutine's memory field into the Instruction Buffer register. Now when the Jump-to-Subroutine instruction is executed, a subroutine in field 1 will be accessed, since the Instruction Buffer register contents are transferred to the Instruction Field register.

Instructions at the beginning of the subroutine must load the Data Field register contents into the Accumulator, then add the appropriate binary digit pattern to create a CIF instruction which will restore the correct Instruction Field register contents prior to returning from the subroutine. A memory word at location EXIT is reserved for this instruction. This memory word occurs directly in front of the Jump Indirect instruction, which actually causes the return to occur.

**There are two problems with the subroutine logic illustrated above.** They are:

1) A subroutine's object code must reside in read/write memory, since the return address and the memory word labeled EXIT are both going to be written into.

2) Subroutines must be rewritten as soon as you add extended memory. But note that a subroutine which has been written to work with extended memory will also work in the absence of extended memory, providing you do not pass parameters to the subroutine via the Accumulator.

If you want to store subroutines in read-only memory and have these subroutines called out of extended memory, then you must use an external read/write memory stack as described earlier in this chapter. You could locate the word labeled EXIT on page 0, but this is a very expensive solution to the problem, since page 0 has just 128 memory locations — and these get used up very quickly.

## IM6102 EXTENDED MEMORY INTERRUPT CONSIDERATIONS

**When an interrupt is acknowledged in an IM6100 microcomputer system that is using extended memory addressing, the following events occur:**

1) The contents of the Instruction Buffer register and the Data Field register are transferred to the Save Field register. Note that the Instruction Field register contents are not saved.

2) Zero values are loaded into the Instruction Field register and the Data Field register.

3) The Program Counter contents are saved in memory word 0 of memory field 0.

4) The instruction located in memory word 1 of memory field 0 is fetched and executed.

Thus, **the interrupt acknowledge scheme is the same whether or not the IM6100 microcomputer system uses extended memory addressing.**

The standard IM6100 interrupt acknowledge procedure would appear to pose a problem.

From our earlier discussion of programming logic that jumps from one memory field to another, recall that you will normally load the Instruction Buffer register with the number of the destination memory field. This number is held in the Instruction Buffer register until a Jump or Jump-to-Subroutine instruction is executed, at which time the Instruction Buffer register contents are moved to the Instruction Field register. Thus, the Instruction Buffer register and the Instruction Field register contents will differ from the time you load a new value into the Instruction Buffer register until you subsequently execute a Jump or Jump-to-Subroutine instruction. During this time, if an interrupt were to be acknowledged, the Instruction Buffer register contents would be saved and the Instruction Field register contents would be lost. Subsequently, upon returning from the interrupt, you would return to the memory field identified by the Instruction Buffer register — which would be the wrong memory field. The memory field within which the program was executing when the interrupt was acknowledged was the memory field identified by the Instruction Field register. In order to overcome this problem, **IM6102 logic disables external device interrupts (but not control panel interrupts) when any instruction that loads data into the Instruction Buffer register is executed. The IM6102 keeps external device interrupts disabled until a Jump or Jump-to-Subroutine is subsequently executed. Interrupts are also re-enabled when an LIF instruction is executed.**

**IM6102 INTERRUPT VECTOR REGISTER**

**The IM6102 has vectored interrupt acknowledge logic, as is the case for the IM6101 devices.** The IM6102 has an 11-bit Interrupt Vector register. The WRVR instruction transfers the contents of the CPU Accumulator to the Interrupt Vector register, but the low-order Interrupt Vector register bit is automatically set or reset by the IM6102 counter/timer logic, as described later.

From the discussion of IM6100 interrupt acknowledge logic given early in this chapter, recall that the INTGNT signal is output high by the CPU from the time an interrupt is acknowledged until the end of the second machine cycle for the first I/O instruction executed following the interrupt acknowledge. **IM6102 interrupt acknowledge logic uses the INTGNT high signal occurring during an I/O instruction's execution as a signal to output the Interrupt Vector register contents with $\overline{C1}$ and $\overline{C2}$ I/O control inputs both low. Timing conforms to standard I/O data input timing.**

**The interrupt service routine initiation instruction sequence described earlier in this chapter for the IM6101 applies also for the IM6102.** However, the IM6102 generates only two vector addresses, whereas the IM6101 generates four vector addresses.

**The logic used to return from interrupt service routines is also identical in IM6100 microcomputer systems that do and do not employ extended memory addressing.** In both cases you return from an interrupt service routine by jumping indirect via the address stored in memory location 0 of memory field 0. **But in a microcomputer system that employs extended memory addressing, your interrupt service routine's return logic must restore the Instruction Buffer and Data Field registers' contents from the Save Field register prior to returning from the interrupt.** This is done via the RMF instruction, as follows:

```
RMF              /LOAD INSTRUCTION BUFFER AND DATA FIELD REGISTERS FROM THE SAVE FIELD
ION              /RE-ENABLE INTERRUPTS
JMP I    0       /JUMP INDIRECT VIA SAVED ADDRESS IN LOCATION 0 OF FIELD 0
```

When the RMF instruction is executed, the Save Field register contents are transferred to the Instruction Buffer and Data Field registers, and interrupts are disabled. When the subsequent Jump Indirect instruction is executed, the Instruction Buffer register contents are transferred to the Instruction Field register. Interrupts are enabled by the ION instruction. Thus, program execution returns to the point of interrupt — which may be within an instruction sequence stored in any memory field.

## IM6102 DYNAMIC MEMORY REFRESH AND DIRECT MEMORY ACCESS LOGIC

If you look again at the various machine cycle timing diagrams, you will see that with the exception of data output machine cycles, the second half of the machine cycle is used for operations internal to the CPU. This time is therefore available to perform a second memory access. **The IM6102 uses the second half of non-data output machine cycles in order to perform a second memory access, either to refresh dynamic memory or to perform a direct memory access operation. Figures 13-41 and 13-42 illustrate timing for a DMA read and a DMA write, respectively. A memory refresh machine cycle differs from a DMA machine cycle only in pulse timing,** as defined in the data sheets at the end of this chapter. Also, there is no low UP pulse during a memory refresh machine cycle.

**IM6102 DMA CONTROL SIGNALS**

**External devices that are accessed during a DMA operation use the Data/Address Bus (including the three extended memory address signals) and three control signals: XXTC, $\overline{\text{XMEMSEL}}$, and $\overline{\text{UP}}$. XXTC becomes, in effect, a single read/write control.** If this signal is high, then it identifies data being transferred from memory to an external device — a DMA read machine cycle. If XXTC is low, then a DMA write machine cycle is specified — data being transferred from an external device to memory. In either case, the low $\overline{\text{XMEMSEL}}$ pulse is interpreted as a memory enable strobe, while the low $\overline{\text{UP}}$ pulse is interpreted as an I/O device strobe. **A DMA operation will occur in an allowed machine cycle only if $\overline{\text{DMAEN}}$ is low on the rising edge of XTA.** $\overline{\text{DMAEN}}$ is a master external DMA enable/disable control.

**IM6102 DMA REGISTERS**

**IM6102 DMA logic uses these four registers:**

A 12-bit Word Count register.

A 12-bit Current Address register.

A 3-bit Extended Current Address register.

A 7-bit Status register.

**The Current Address register identifies the memory location which is to be accessed during the next DMA or dynamic memory refresh operation.** The contents of this register are incremented after each DMA or dynamic memory refresh operation.

The Extended Current Address register is a 3-bit register which creates the three high-order address lines of a 15-bit address. **The Extended Current Address register is equivalent to the Instruction Field register of extended memory address control logic.** Thus, during DMA or dynamic memory refresh operations, the 15-bit address seen by external memory is created as follows:

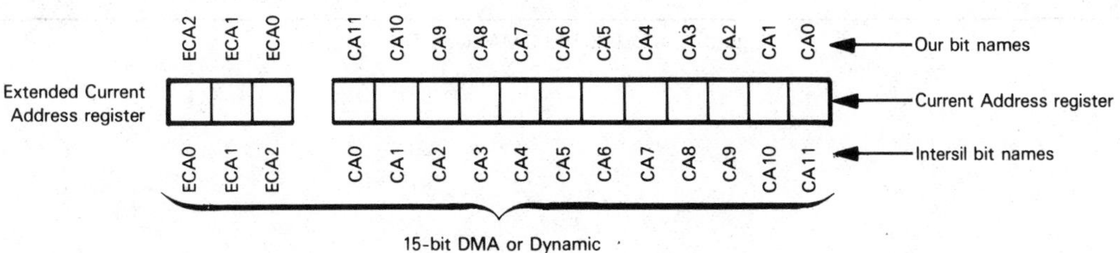

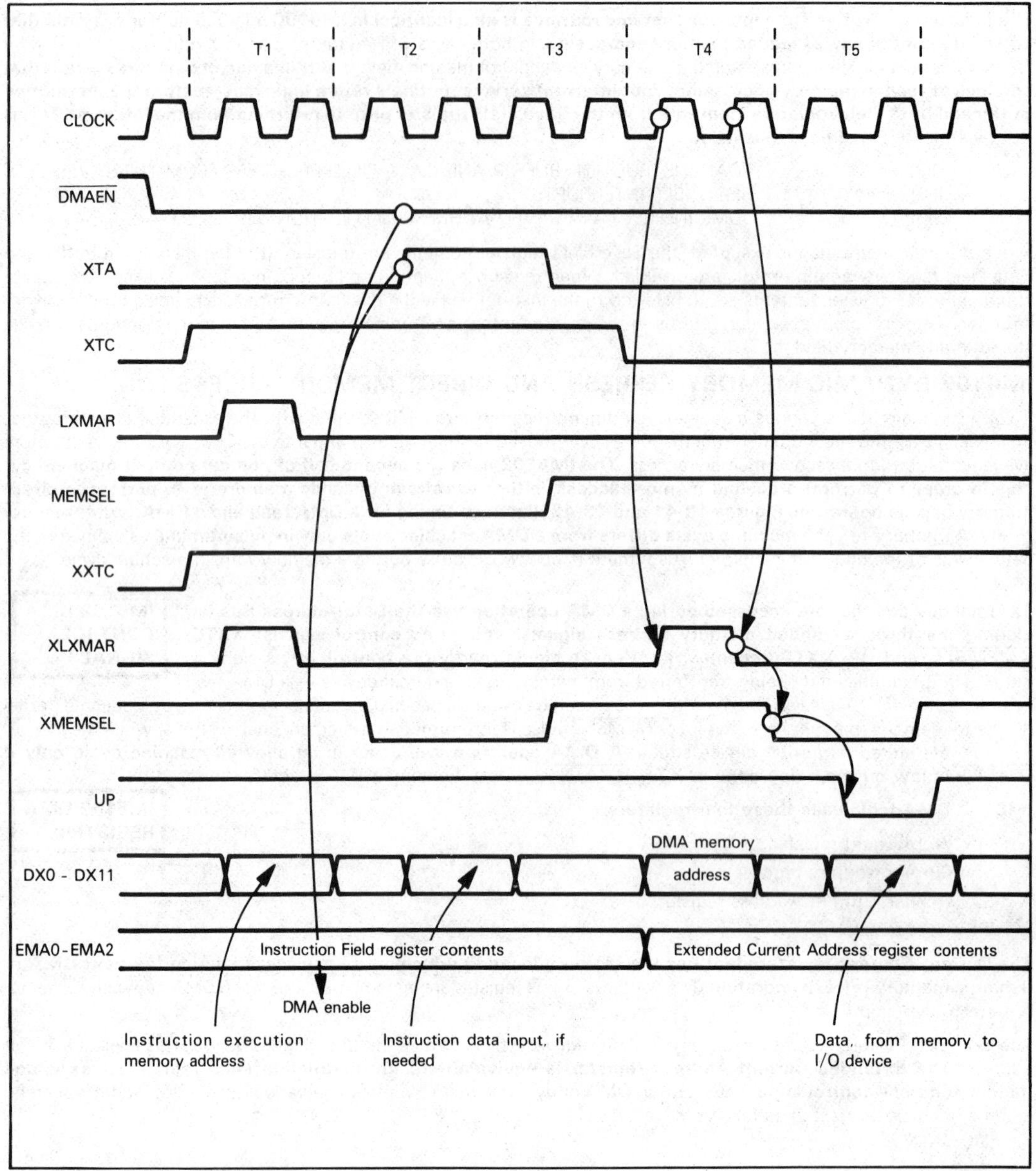


Figure 13-41. IM6102 DMA Read Timing

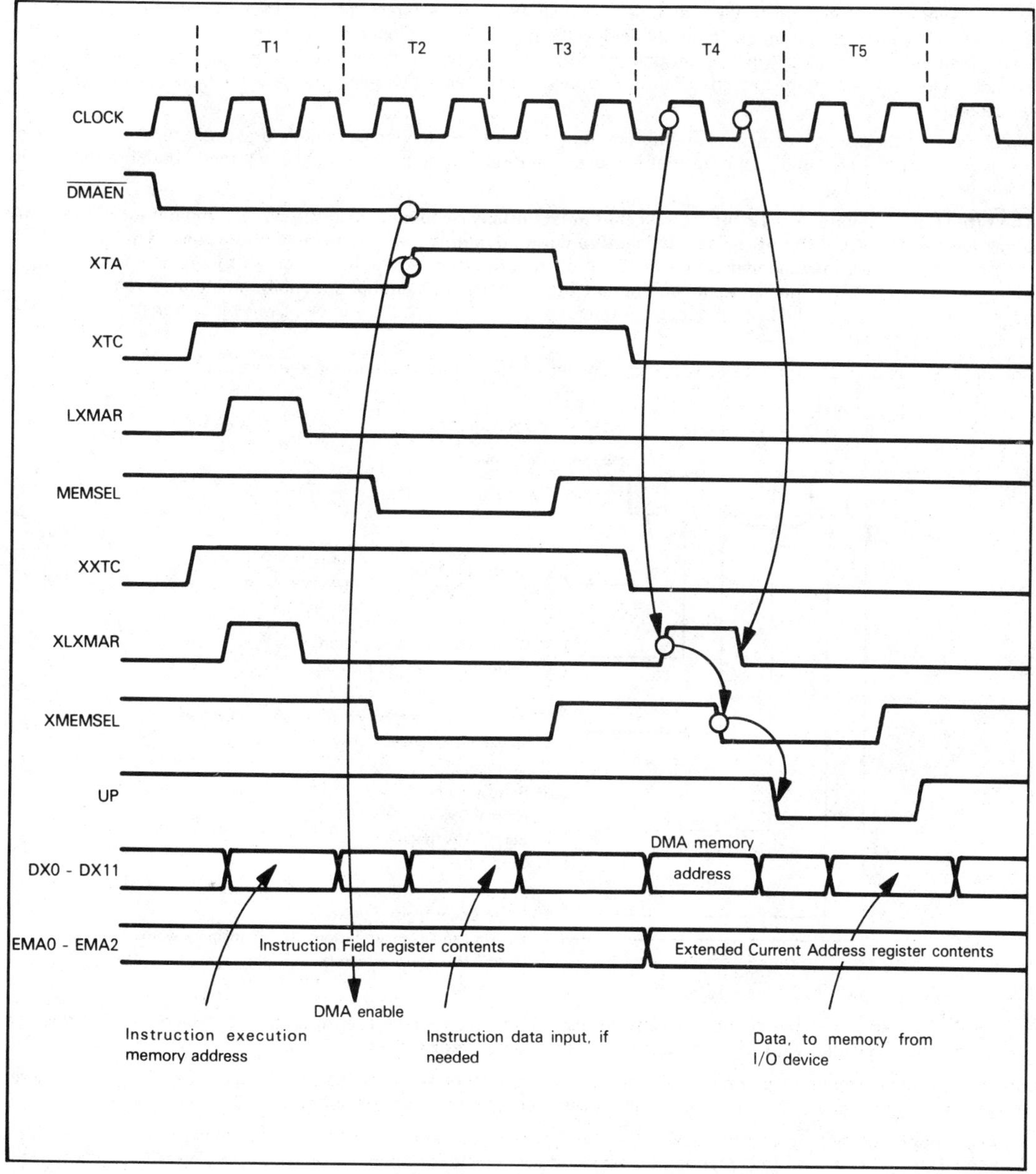


Figure 13-42. IM6102 DMA Write Timing

But there is a significant difference between the Extended Current Address register and the Instruction Field register of extended memory address control logic. **Under program control you can specify that the Extended Current Address register will increment** along with the Current Address register. That is to say, when the Current Address register increments from $FFF_{16}$ to $000_{16}$, the Extended Current Address register can be forced to increment. Extended memory address control logic, in contrast, does not allow the Instruction Field register to increment when the Program Counter increments from $FFF_{16}$ to $000_{16}$.

Dynamic memory refresh logic requires that the Extended Current Address register be allowed to increment along with the Current Address register. Dynamic memory refresh requires that you load 0 into the Extended Current Address and

Current Address registers, which then increment as a single 15-bit Address register. Thus, dynamic memory refresh logic automatically moves from one memory field to the next. If the Extended Current Address register did not increment, then in order to refresh more than one memory field, you would have to execute instructions between each memory field to increment the Extended Current Address register and thus select the new dynamic memory field to be refreshed.

Direct memory access logic does not benefit from the fact that the Extended Current Address register contents can increment automatically. A block of data that is moved via direct memory access logic will rarely be more than 4096 words in length.

**The Word Count register is a 12-bit register that must initially be loaded with the twos complement of the DMA block length. The Word Count register is inactive during dynamic memory refresh operations.** The Word Count register's contents are incremented after every DMA operation. When this register's contents increment from $FFF_{16}$ to $000_{16}$, an end of DMA is signaled via an appropriate Status register bit setting; optionally, an interrupt request may be generated. Depending on the DMA mode, DMA operations may cease at the end of a DMA block transfer, or the DMA operation may restart.

The DMA Status and Control register is a 7-bit register whose contents are interpreted as follows:

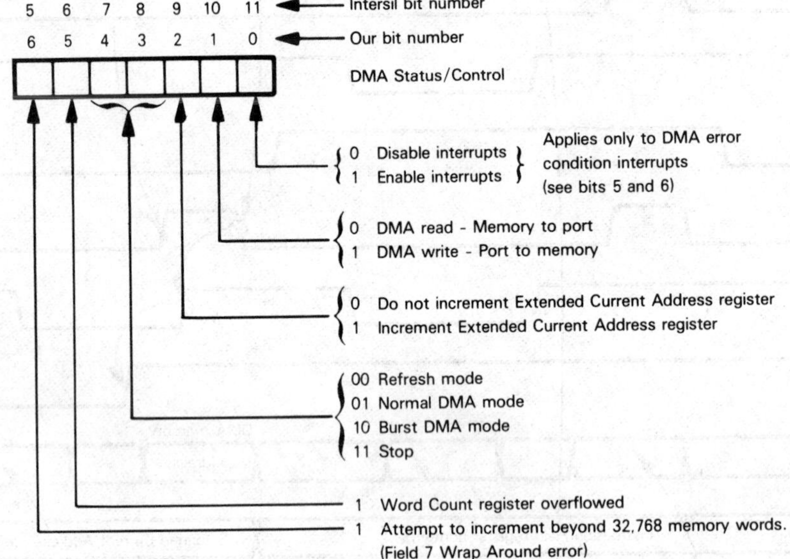


Status/Control register bit 0 is an interrupt enable/disable bit which allows interrupt requests to be generated when error conditions associated with bits 5 or 6 of the Status/Control register occur.

Status/Control register bit 1 determines whether the DMA operation will be a Read or a Write. A DMA Read constitutes a transfer from memory to an I/O device, while a Write constitutes a transfer from the I/O device to memory.

Status/Control register bit 2 determines whether the Extended Current Address register increments as part of a 15-bit address. If this bit is 0, then the Extended Current Address register does not increment. If this bit is 1, then when the Current Address register increments from $FFF_{16}$ to $000_{16}$ the Extended Current Address register increments by 1. When the Extended Current Address register contains 111, however, it cannot increment to 000. If the Extended Current Address register is supposed to increment when it contains 111, then instead a "field 7 wrap around error" occurs and Status/Control register bit 6 is set to 1. At this time an interrupt request will also occur if Status/Control register bit 0 has been set to 1. Once a field 7 wrap around error occurs, Status/Control register bit 6 can be reset to 0 by execution of a CAF or an RFSR instruction. A reset operation resets all Status/Control register bits to 0.

Whenever the Word Count register increments from $FFF_{16}$ to $000_{16}$, Status/Control register bit 5 is set to 1. If Status/Control register bit 0 has also been set to 1, then an interrupt request will accompany the Word Count register incrementing from $FFF_{16}$ to $000_{16}$. If you want to identify the end of a DMA data transfer with an interrupt request, you do so by enabling interrupts via bit 0 of the DMA Status/Control register. When the Word Count register increments from $FFF_{16}$ to $000_{16}$, you have, in effect, reached the end of a DMA block — which will be identified with an interrupt request, providing the DMA Status/Control register bit 0 is 1.

**IM6102 DMA MODES**

**Status/Control register bits 3 and 4 allow IM6102 DMA logic to be disabled, or one of three modes to be selected.**

**In Refresh mode, a sequence of DMA Read machine cycles is executed;** however, the $\overline{UP}$ signal is not output and $\overline{DMAEN}$ as an input is ignored. Thus external logic cannot suppress dynamic memory refresh by inputting $\overline{DMAEN}$ low. But in refresh mode the rest of the Status/Control register is active, which means that you must set bit 2 to 1 if the Extended Current Address register is to increment, in which case a field 7 wrap around error will occur if the Extended Current Address register attempts to increment from 111 to 000.

**IM6102 DMA PROGRAMMING**

**In normal DMA mode, a DMA operation will be performed during every allowed machine cycle, providing $\overline{DMAEN}$ is low at the beginning of the machine cycle.** However, an LWCR instruction must be executed to start a normal DMA mode operation. As illustrated in Figures 13-41 and 13-42, $\overline{DMAEN}$ is sampled on the rising edge of XTA. If $\overline{DMAEN}$ is high at this time, then no DMA operation will occur. Logic internal to the IM6102 decodes the instruction object code which the IM6102 receives along with the IM6100 in order to identify machine cycles when no memory write operation is scheduled and a DMA operation can therefore be performed. When the Word Count register increments from $FFF_{16}$ to $000_{16}$, a normal DMA operation stops, Status/Control register bit 5 is set (as already described) and if interrupts have been enabled, an interrupt request is generated. IM6102 DMA logic remains in normal mode at this time; however, it must be restarted under program control by executing another LWCR instruction. Thus, the following instruction sequence will initiate normal DMA mode:

```
CLA             /CLEAR ACCUMULATOR
TAD     DMAD    /FETCH STARTING DMA ADDRESS
LCAR            /LOAD INTO CURRENT ADDRESS REGISTER. CLEAR ACCUMULATOR
TAD     SR      /FETCH STATUS/CONTROL REGISTER SETTINGS
LFSR            /LOAD INTO STATUS/CONTROL REGISTER. CLEAR ACCUMULATOR
TAD     WC      /FETCH TWOS COMPLEMENT OF WORD COUNT
LWCR            /LOAD INTO WORD COUNT REGISTER AND START DMA OPERATION.
```

**Burst DMA mode is identical to normal DMA mode, except that when the Word Count register increments from $FFF_{16}$ to $000_{16}$ the mode immediately reverts to dynamic memory refresh.** Burst mode is used when DMA operations are being performed with dynamic memory, in which case you must be careful to keep DMA transfer blocks short enough not to interfere with dynamic memory decay times. Remember, while a DMA operation is being performed, no dynamic memory refreshes are occurring.

**In Stop mode, no DMA or dynamic memory refresh operations occur;** however, any of the DMA registers may be accessed.

## IM6102 PROGRAMMABLE REAL-TIME CLOCK LOGIC

**The IM6102 has relatively simple real-time clock logic, which computes time intervals using pulses generated by an external crystal. The crystal is connected across the OSC IN and OSC OUT pins of the IM6102 device.** Crystal characteristics were defined earlier, together with the description of IM6102 pins.

**A 12-bit Clock Counter register is at the heart of IM6102 real-time clock logic.** The contents of this register are incremented at time intervals which you select under program control. By selecting the appropriate increment time interval and initial Clock Counter register value, you can compute almost any time interval up to 40,950 milliseconds.

**The Clock Counter register has an associated Clock Buffer register.** You actually transfer data between the Clock Buffer register and the CPU Accumulator. The Clock Buffer register contents are transferred to the Clock Counter register to start computing a time interval. While the Clock Counter register is incrementing, you can, under program control, load a new value into the Clock Buffer register; the next time interval computed will then differ from the time interval currently being computed.

**IM6102 real-time clock registers and the instructions which access them may be illustrated as follows:**

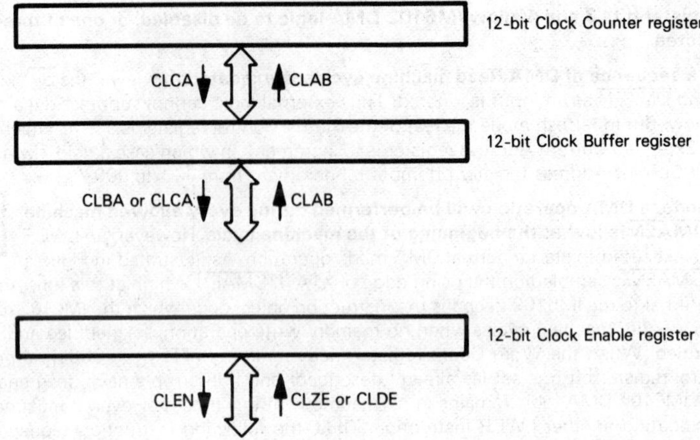


**The programmable options of the IM6102 real-time clock logic are selected by loading appropriate bits into the Clock Enable register. This register's bits are assigned as follows:**

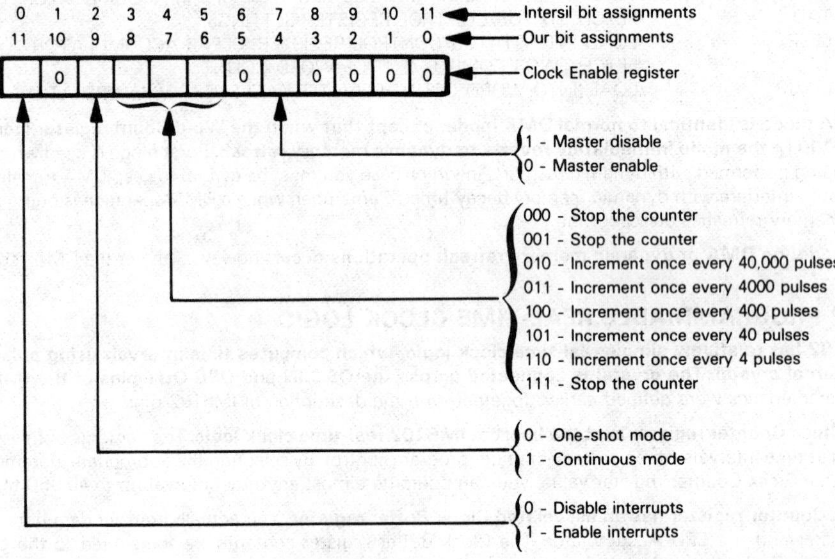


Clock Enable register bit 4 is a master enable/disable control. When set to 1, this bit stops IM6102 real-time clock logic. When the IM6102 is reset, this bit is cleared; after a reset, therefore, real-time clock logic can run. The CAF instruction resets bit 4 to 0.

Clock Enable register bits 6, 7 and 8 select the interval between increment pulses. With a 4 MHz oscillator, the time interval between Clock Counter register increments may vary between 1 microsecond and 10 milliseconds, as follows:

| Bits 8 7 6 | Time interval between increments |
|---|---|
| 0 1 0 | 10 msec |
| 0 1 1 | 1 msec |
| 1 0 0 | 100 $\mu$sec |
| 1 0 1 | 10 $\mu$sec |
| 1 1 0 | 1 $\mu$sec |

**Following a reset, or execution of a CAF instruction,** all Clock Enable register bits are reset to 0; therefore **real-time clock logic is effectively disabled.** This is because the Clock Counter register increment logic is stopped, even though clock logic in general has been enabled by bit 4.

**Clock Enable register bit 9 is used to select One-shot mode or Continuous mode. If** this bit is 0, then **One-shot mode is selected; as soon as the Clock Counter register increments from $FFF_{16}$ to $000_{16}$, a clock overflow flag is set and the clock stops.** If bit 9 is 1, then when the Clock Counter register increments from $FFF_{16}$ to $000_{16}$, the clock overflow flag is set, but the Clock Buffer register contents transfer to the Clock Counter register, which starts incrementing again.

**Clock Enable register bit 11 enables or disables timer interrupts.** Timer interrupts can occur when the Clock Counter register overflows. **From our earlier discussion of the IM6102 Interrupt Vector register, recall that the low-order bit of this register is set in response to an interrupt request coming from real-time clock logic.** Thus, if Clock Enable register bit 11 is set to 1, then an interrupt request will occur whenever the Clock Counter register increments from $FFF_{16}$ to $000_{16}$. In response to an interrupt acknowledge, the address vector transmitted to the CPU will uniquely identify IM6102 real-time clock logic.

Programming the IM6102 real-time clock logic is very straightforward; it may be illustrated by the following instruction sequence:

```
CLA             /CLEAR THE ACCUMULATOR
TAD     INIT    /LOAD STARTING VALUE INTO THE CLOCK
CLAB            /COUNTER BUFFER
TAD     ENAB    /LOAD CONTROL CODE INTO THE CLOCK
CLDE            /ENABLE REGISTER AND START THE CLOCK
```

## IM6102 MEDIC INSTRUCTIONS

**There are a number of special I/O instructions recognized by an IM6102 MEDIC. These instructions, together with their object codes and operands, are listed in Table 13-6. Note carefully that the operands (where they occur) consist of two octal digits. The high-order octal digit can have any value in the range 0 through 7. The low-order octal digit must be 0.**

**The following abbreviations are used in Table 13-6:**

| | |
|---|---|
| AC | CPU Accumulator |
| AC <x-y> | CPU Accumulator bits x through y inclusive. For example, AC <4-0> represents bits 4, 3, 2, 1, and 0 of the CPU Accumulator |
| CAR | Current Address register |
| CBR | Clock Buffer register |
| CC | Clock Counter register |
| COF | Clock Overflow status |
| DF | Data Field register |
| ECAR | Extended Current Address register |
| EN | Clock Enable register |
| H | High level voltage — positive logic "1" |
| IB | Instruction Field buffer |
| IE | CPU Interrupt Enable status |
| IF | Instruction Field register |

| | |
|---|---|
| IIFF | Interrupt Inhibit Flip-Flop (IM6102 internal interrupt enable/disable status) |
| L | Low level voltage — positive logic "0" |
| LINK | CPU Link status bit |
| n | An octal operand digit in the range 0 through 7 |
| SF | Save Field register |
| SF <2,1,0> | Save Field register bits 2, 1, 0 |
| SF <5,4,3> | Save Field register bits 5, 4, 3 |
| SR | DMA Status register |
| SR6 | DMA Status register bit 6 — the Field 7 wrap around carry error bit |
| SR5 | DMA Status register bit 5 — the Word Count Overflow error bit |
| VR | Interrupt Vector register |
| WCR | DMA Word Count register |
| xxx | Three bits of object code corresponding to "n", described above |
| [ ] | Contents of location enclosed within brackets |
| $\wedge$ | Logical AND |
| $\vee$ | Logical OR |
| $\leftarrow$ | Data is transferred in the direction of the arrow |

Table 13-6. IM6102 MEDIC I/O Instructions

| TYPE | MNEMONIC | OPERAND | OBJECT CODE | CONTROLS TO · CPU $\overline{C0}$ | $\overline{C1}$ | $\overline{C2}$ | $\overline{SKP}$ | | | OPERATION PERFORMED |
|---|---|---|---|---|---|---|---|---|---|---|
| GENERAL | CAF | | 6007<br>C07 | H | H | H | H | | | [SR5]←0, [SR6]←0, [COF]←0, [EN]←0, [CBR]←0<br>Clear all flags: clear Word Count Overflow error bit, Field 7 wrap around carry error bit, and Clock Overflow flag; clear Clock Enable register and Clock Buffer. |
| EXTENDED MEMORY ADDRESS CONTROL | CDF | n0 | 62n1<br>110010xxx001 | H | H | H | H | | | [DF]←n<br>Load Data Field register immediate |
| | CIF | n0 | 62n2<br>110010xxx010 | H | H | H | H | | | [IB]←n<br>Load Instruction Field buffer immediate |
| | CDF,CIF | n0 | 62n3<br>110010xxx011 | H | H | H | H | | | [DF]←n, [IB]←n<br>Load Data Field register and Instruction Field buffer immediate |
| | GTF | | 6004<br>C04 | L | L | H | H | | | Read flags into CPU Accumulator as follows:<br>Bit No.: 11 10 9 8 7 6 5 4 3 2 1 0<br>CPU Accumulator: [ ] [ ] [ ] [X] [ ] [ ] [X] [X] [X] [X] [X] [X]<br>Bit 11: LINK; bit 9: $\overline{INTREQ}$; bit 8: IIFF; bit 7: IE; bits 5–0: Save Field register<br>These are from IM6102 MEDIC<br>These are from IM6100 CPU |
| | LIF | | 6254<br>CAC | H | H | H | H | | | [IF]←[IB]<br>Load Instruction Field register, re-enable interrupts |
| | RDF | | 6214<br>C8C | H | L | H | H | | | [AC<5-3>]←[AC<5-3>] V [DF]<br>OR Data Field register into bits 6, 5, 4, and 3 of the CPU Accumulator |
| | RIB | | 6234<br>C9C | H | L | H | H | | | [AC<5-0>]←[AC<5-0>] V [SF]<br>Save Field register into the low-order 6 bits of the CPU Accumulator |
| | RIF | | 6224<br>C94 | H | L | H | H | | | [AC<5-3>]←[AC<5-3>] V [IF]<br>OR Instruction Field register into bits 5, 4, and 3 of the CPU Accumulator. |
| | RMF | | 6244<br>CA4 | H | H | H | H | | | [IB]←[SF<5,4,3>], [DF]←[SF<2,1,0>]<br>Restore memory field. The Instruction Buffer will load the Instruction Field after the next JMP, JMS, or LIF instruction. |
| | RTF | | 6005<br>C05 | H | H | H | H | | | Return flags from CPU as follows:<br>Bit No.: 11 10 9 8 7 6 5 4 3 2 1 0<br>CPU Accumulator: [X] [ ] [ ] [ ] [ ] [ ] [X] [X] [X] [X] [X] [X]<br>Bit 11 → LINK; bits 5–3 → [IB]; bits 2–0 → [DF]<br>After the next JMS, JMP, or LIF instruction, interrupts wil be enabled and the Instruction Buffer will load the Instruction Field. |

Table 13-6. IM6102 MEDIC I/O Instructions (Continued)

| TYPE | MNEMONIC | OPERAND | OBJECT CODE | CONTROLS TO CPU $\overline{C0}$ | $\overline{C1}$ | $\overline{C2}$ | $\overline{SKP}$ | | | OPERATION PERFORMED |
|---|---|---|---|---|---|---|---|---|---|---|
| DIRECT MEMORY ACCESS CONTROL | LCAR | | 6205<br>C85 | L | H | H | H | | | [CAR]←[AC]; [AC]←0<br>Transfer CPU Accumulator contents to Current Address register, then clear Accumulator. |
| | LEAR | n0 | 62n6<br>110010xxx110 | H | H | H | H | | | [ECAR]←n<br>Load the Extended Current Address register immediate. |
| | LFSR | | 6245<br>CA5 | L | H | H | H | | | [SR]←[AC<4-0>]; [AC]←0<br>Transfer low-order five bits of CPU Accumulator contents to DMA Status register, then clear Accumulator. |
| | LWCR | | 6225<br>C95 | L | H | H | H | | | [WCR]←[AC]; [AC]←0<br>Start DMA and clear Word Count Overflow status. Transfer CPU Accumulator to DMA Word Count register then clear Accumulator. |
| | RCAR | | 6215<br>C8D | L | L | H | H | | | [AC]←[CAR]<br>Transfer Current Address register contents to the CPU. |
| | REAR | | 6235<br>C9D | H | L | H | H | | | [AC<5-3>]←[AC<5-3>] V [ECAR]<br>OR Extended Current Address register contents with CPU Accumulator bits 5, 4, and 3. |
| | RFSR | | 6255<br>CAD | H | L | H | H | | | [AC<6-0>]←[AC<6-0>] V [SR]; [SR6]←0<br>OR DMA Status register contents with CPU Accumulator bits 6-0; then clear bit 6 of the DMA Status register. |
| | SKOF | | 6265<br>CB5 | H | H | H | L/H | | | If DMA Word Count register has overflowed, return low $\overline{SKP}$ pulse. |
| REAL-TIME CLOCK CONTROL | CLAB | | 6133<br>C5B | H | H | H | H | | | [CBR]←[AC]; [CC]←[CBR]<br>Transfer the CPU Accumulator contents to the Clock Buffer register, then transfer the Clock Buffer register contents to the Clock Counter register. |
| | CLBA | | 6136<br>C5E | L | L | H | H | | | [AC]←[CBR]<br>Transfer the Clock Buffer register contents to the CPU Accumulator |
| | CLCA | | 6137<br>C5F | L | L | H | H | | | [CBR]←[CC]; [AC]←[CBR]<br>Transfer the Clock Counter register contents to the Clock Buffer register, then transfer the Clock Buffer register contents to the CPU Accumulator. |
| | CLDE | | 6132<br>C5A | H | H | H | H | | | [EN]←[EN] V [AC]<br>Set to 1 all Clock Enable register bits which correspond to 1 bits in the CPU Accumulator |
| | CLEN | | 6134<br>C5C | L | L | H | H | | | [AC]←[EN]<br>Transfer Clock Enable register contents to the CPU Accumulator |
| | CLSA | | 6135<br>C5D | L | L | H | H | | | [AC]←0; [AC<11>]←[COF]; [COF]←0<br>Clear CPU Accumulator, transfer Clock Overflow Flag to high bit of Accumulator, and then reset Clock Overflow Flag |
| | CLSK | | 6131<br>C59 | H | H | H | L/H | | | If Clock Overflow Flag is set return a low $\overline{SKP}$ pulse. |
| | CLZE | | 6130<br>C58 | H | H | H | H | | | [EN]←[EN] Λ $\overline{[AC]}$<br>Reset to 0 all Clock Enable register bits which correspond to 1 bits in the CPU Accumulator. |
| INTERRUPT CONTROL | WRVR | | 6275<br>CBD | L | H | H | H | | | [VR]←[AC<11-1>]; [AC]←0<br>Transfer upper 10 bits of CPU Accumulator to the Interrupt Vector register, then clear Accumulator. |

# DATA SHEETS

This section contains specific electrical and timing data for the following devices:

- IM6100 CPU
- IM6101 PIE
- IM6102 MEDIC

# IM6100

## ABSOLUTE MAXIMUM RATINGS

| | | | |
|---|---|---|---|
| Supply Voltage | IM6100/C +4.0V to +7.0V<br>IM6100A +4.0V to 11.0V | Operating Temperature Range<br>Commercial | <br>0°C to +75°C |
| Input or Output Voltage Applied | GND −0.3V to $V_{CC}$ +0.3V | Industrial | −40°C to +85°C |
| Storage Temperature Range | −65°C to +125°C | Military | −55°C to +125°C |

**DC CHARACTERISTICS** $V_{cc}$ = 5.0V ± 10% (IM6100), 10.0V ± 10% (IM6100A), $T_A$ = Commercial, Industrial or Military

| PARAMETER | SYMBOL | CONDITIONS | MIN | TYP | MAX | UNITS |
|---|---|---|---|---|---|---|
| Logical "1" Input Voltage | $V_{IH}$ | | 70% $V_{cc}$ | | | V |
| Logical "0" Input Voltage | $V_{IL}$ | | | | 20%$V_{CC}$ | V |
| Input Leakage | $I_{IL}$ | OV ≤ $V_{IN}$ ≤ $V_{CC}$ | −1.0 | | 1.0 | μA |
| Logical "1" Output Voltage | $V_{OH2}$ | $I_{OUT}$=0 | $V_{cc}$−0.01 | | | V |
| Logical "1" Output Voltage | $V_{OH1}$ | $I_{OH}$=−0.2mA | 2.4 | | | V |
| Logical "0" Output Voltage | $V_{OL2}$ | $I_{OUT}$=0 | | | GND +0.01 | V |
| Logical "0" Output Voltage | $V_{OL1}$ | $I_{OL}$=1.6 mA | | | 0.45 | V |
| Output Leakage | $I_O$ | OV ≤ $V_o$ ≤ $V_{cc}$ | −1.0 | | 1.0 | μA |
| Supply Current | $I_{CC}$ | $V_{CC}$ = 5.0 volts<br>$V_{CC}$ = 10.0 volts<br>$C_L$= 50 pF; TA = 25°C<br>$F_{CLOCK}$ = Operating Frequency | | | 2.5<br>10.0 | mA<br>mA |
| Input Capacitance | $C_{IN}$ | | | 5.0 | | pF |
| Output Capacitance | $C_O$ | | | 8.0 | | pF |

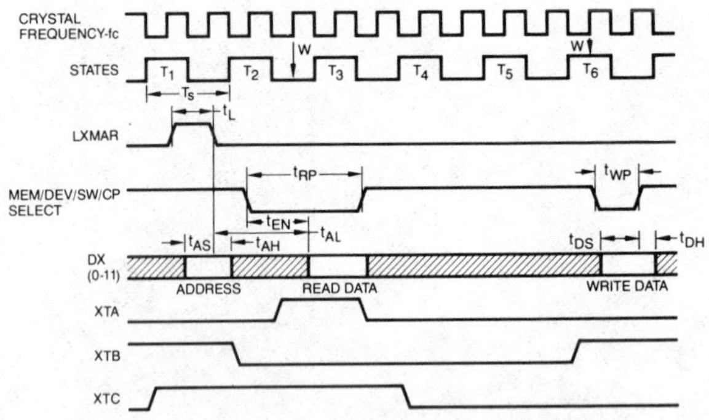


**IM6100 TIMING AND STATE SIGNALS**

**AC CHARACTERISTICS ($T_A$ = 25° C), Derate 0.390/°C**

| PARAMETER | SYMBOL | IM6100 $V_{CC}$ = 5.0 $f_c$ = 4MHz | IM6100A $V_{CC}$ = 10.0 $f_c$ = 8 MHz | IM6100C $V_{CC}$ = 5.0 $f_c$ = 3.3MHz | UNITS |
|---|---|---|---|---|---|
| Major State Time | $T_s$ | 500 | 250 | 600 | ns |
| LXMAR Pulse Width | $t_L$ | 240 | 120 | 280 | ns |
| Address Setup Time | $t_{AS}$ | 50 | 30 | 60 | ns |
| Address Hold Time | $t_{AH}$ | 250 | 125 | 280 | ns |
| Access Time From LXMAR | $t_{AL}$ | 500 | 250 | 600 | ns |
| Output Enable Time | $t_{EN}$ | 240 | 120 | 280 | ns |
| Read Pulse Width | $t_{RP}$ | 700 | 350 | 800 | ns |
| Write Pulse Width | $t_{WP}$ | 240 | 120 | 280 | ns |
| Data Setup Time | $t_{DS}$ | 240 | 120 | 280 | ns |
| Data Hold Time | $t_{DH}$ | 100 | 50 | 160 | ns |

**Data sheets on pages 13-D2 through 13-D6 reprinted by permission of Intersil, Incorporated.**

## ABSOLUTE MAXIMUM RATINGS

Supply Voltage
- IM6101 +8.0V
- IM6101A +12.0V

Applied Input or Output Voltage GND – 0.3V to $V_{CC}$ +0.3V

Storage Temperature Range –65°C to 150°C

Operating Temperature Range
- Industrial –40°C to 85°C
- Military –55°C to 125°C

Operating Voltage Range
- IM6101 4V to 7V
- IM6101A 4V to 11V

## DC CHARACTERISTICS $V_{CC}$ = Operating Voltage Range $T_A$ = Temperature Range

| PARAMETER | SYMBOL | CONDITIONS | MIN | TYP | MAX | UNITS |
|---|---|---|---|---|---|---|
| Logical "1" Input Voltage | $V_{IH}$ | | 70% $V_{CC}$ | | | V |
| Logical "0" Input Voltage | $V_{IL}$ | | | | 20% $V_{CC}$ | V |
| Input Leakage | $I_{IL}$ | $0V \leqslant V_{IN} \leqslant V_{CC}$ | –1.0 | | 1.0 | μA |
| Logical "1" Output Voltage | $V_{OH2}$ | $I_{OUT} = 0$ | $V_{CC}$ - 0.01 | | | V |
| Logical "1" Output Voltage | $V_{OH1}$ | $I_{OH} = -0.2$ mA | 2.4 | | | V |
| Logical "0" Output Voltage | $V_{OL2}$ | $I_{OUT} = 0$ | | | GND + 0.01 | V |
| Logical "0" Output Voltage | $V_{OL1}$ | $I_{OL} = 2.0$ mA | | | 0.45 | V |
| Output Leakage | $I_O$ | $0V \leqslant V_O \leqslant V_{CC}$ | –1.0 | | 1.0 | μA |
| Supply Current | $I_{CC1}$ | $V_{IN} = V_{CC}$ | | 1.0 | | μA |
| | $I_{CC2}$ | $V_{CC} = 5V$ $f_{IM6100} = 4$ MHz | | 1.0 | | mA |
| Input Capacitance | $C_I$ | | | 5 | 7 | pf |
| Output Capacitance | $C_O$ | | | 8 | 10 | pf |
| Input/Output Capacitance | $C_{ID}$ | | | 8 | 10 | pf |

## AC CHARACTERISTICS $T_A$ = 25°C $C_L$ = 50pf

| PARAMETER | SYMBOL | CONDITIONS | MIN | TYP | MAX | UNITS |
|---|---|---|---|---|---|---|
| Delay from DEVSEL to READ | $t_{DR}$ | IM6101 $V_{CC}$ = 5V<br>IM6101A $V_{CC}$ = 10V | | 150<br>75 | | ns<br>ns |
| Delay from DEVSEL to WRITE | $t_{DW}$ | IM6101 $V_{CC}$ = 5V<br>IM6101A $V_{CC}$ = 10V | | 150<br>75 | | ns<br>ns |
| Delay from DEVSEL to FLAG | $t_{DF}$ | IM6101 $V_{CC}$ = 5V<br>IM6101A $V_{CC}$ = 10V | | 200<br>100 | | ns<br>ns |
| Delay from DEVSEL to C1, C2 | $t_{DC}$ | IM6101 $V_{CC}$ = 5V<br>IM6101A $V_{CC}$ = 10V | | 200<br>100 | | ns<br>ns |
| Delay from DEVSEL to SKP/INT | $t_{DI}$ | IM6101 $V_{CC}$ = 5V<br>IM6101A $V_{CC}$ = 10V | | 200<br>100 | | ns<br>ns |
| Delay from DEVSEL to DX | $t_{DA}$ | IM6101 $V_{CC}$ = 5V<br>IM6101A $V_{CC}$ = 10V | | 200<br>100 | | ns<br>ns |
| LXMAR pulse width | $t_{LXMAR}$ | IM6101 $V_{CC}$ = 5V<br>IM6101A $V_{CC}$ = 10V | | 200<br>100 | | ns<br>ns |
| Address setup time | $t_{ADDS}$ | IM6101 $V_{CC}$ = 5V<br>IM6101A $V_{CC}$ = 10V | | 50<br>25 | | ns<br>ns |
| Address hold time | $t_{ADDH}$ | IM6101 $V_{CC}$ = 5V<br>IM6101A $V_{CC}$ = 10V | | 100<br>50 | | ns<br>ns |
| Data setup time | $t_{DS}$ | IM6101 $V_{CC}$ = 5V<br>IM6101A $V_{CC}$ = 10V | | 200<br>100 | | ns<br>ns |
| Data hold time | $t_{DH}$ | IM6101 $V_{CC}$ = 5V<br>IM6101A $V_{CC}$ = 10V | | 50<br>25 | | ns<br>ns |

## TIMING DIAGRAM

Timing for a typical IOT transfer is shown below. During IFETCH the processor obtains from memory an IOT instruction of the form 6XXX. During the IOTA the processor places that instruction back on the DX lines ③ and pulses LXMAR transferring address and control information for the IOT transfer to all peripheral devices. A low going pulse on DEVSEL while XTC is high ④ is used by the addressed PIE along with decoded control information to generate C1, C2, SKP and controls for data transfers to the processor. Control outputs READ1 and READ2 are used to gate peripheral data to the DX lines during this time. A low going pulse on DEVSEL while XTC is low ⑤ is used to generate WRITE1 and WRITE2 controls. These signals are used to clock processor accumulator instruction data into peripheral devices.

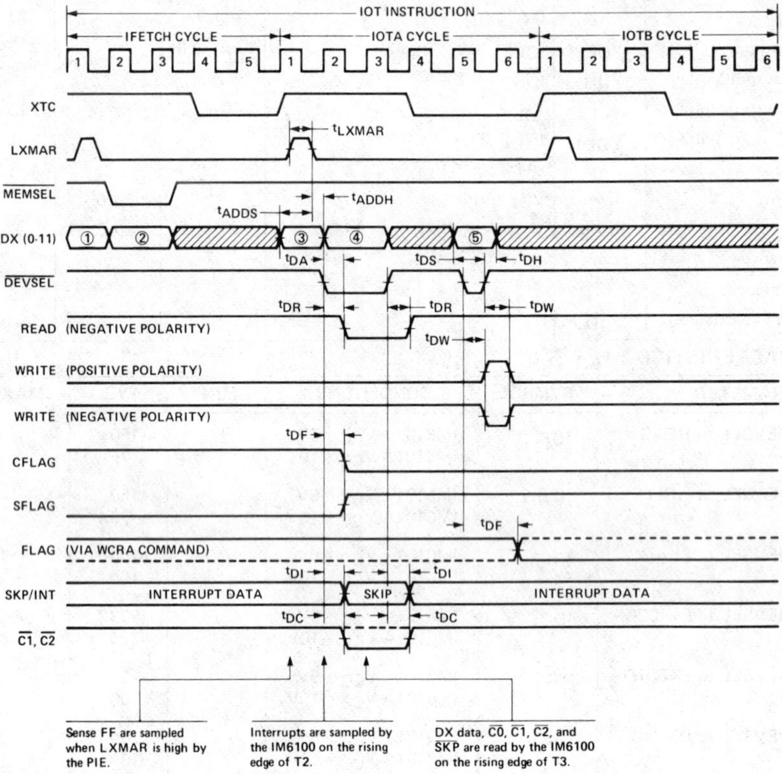


All PIE timing is generated from IM6100 signals LXMAR, DEVSEL, and XTC. No additional timing signals, clocks, or one shots are required. Propagation delays, pulse width, data setup and hold times are specified for direct interfacing with the IM6100.

## ABSOLUTE MAXIMUM RATINGS

IM6102I
IM6102M

| | |
|---|---|
| Supply Voltage | 8V |
| Input or Output Voltage applied | GND -0.3V to $V_{CC}$ + 0.3V |
| Storage Temperature Range | -65°C to +150°C |
| Operating Temperature Range | IM6102I -40°C to +85°C |
| | IM6102M -55°C to +125°C |
| Operating Voltage Range | 4–7V |

## DC CHARACTERISTICS $V_{CC}$ = 5.0V ± 10% $T_A$ = Industrial or Military

| PARAMETER | SYMBOL | CONDITIONS | MIN | TYP | MAX | UNITS |
|---|---|---|---|---|---|---|
| Logical "1" Input Voltage | $V_{IH}$ | | $V_{CC}$ -2.0 | | | V |
| Logical "0" Input Voltage | $V_{IL}$ | | | | 0.8 | V |
| Input Leakage | $I_{IL}$ | OV ≤ $V_{IN}$ ≤ $V_{CC}$ except pins 15, 29, 31 | -1.0 | | 1.0 | μA |
| Logical "1" Output Voltage | $V_{OH}$ | $I_{OH}$ = -0.2 mA except pins 32, 33, 34 | 2.4 | | | V |
| Logical "0" Output Voltage | $V_{OL}$ | $I_{OL}$ = 2.0mA | | | 0.45 | V |
| Output Leakage | $I_O$ | OV ≤ $V_O$ ≤ $V_{CC}$ | -1.0 | | 1.0 | μA |
| Supply Current | $I_{CC}$ | $V_{CC}$ = 5.0V | | | 2.5 | mA |
| | | $C_L$ = 50 pF; TA = 25°C<br>$F_{CLOCK}$ = Operating Frequency | | | | |
| Input Capacitance | $C_{IN}$ | | | 7.0 | 8.0 | pF |
| Output Capacitance | $C_O$ | | | 8.0 | 10.0 | pF |

## AC CHARACTERISTICS

$V_{CC}$ = 5.0V ± 10% $T_A$ = Industrial or Military $C_L$ = 50pF fc = 4MHZ : $T_S$ = 2/fc = 500ns All times in ns

| PARAMETER | SYMBOL | MIN | TYP | MAX |
|---|---|---|---|---|
| LXMAR pulse width IN | $t_{LIN}$ | 250 | | |
| XTA pulse width IN | $t_{XAI}$ | 500 | 150 | |
| Address setup time IN: DX-LXMAR (↓) | $t_{AIS}$ | | 100 | |
| Address hold time IN: LXMAR (↓)-DX | $t_{AIH}$ | | 100 | |
| Data output enable time: DEVSEL (↓)-DX | $t_{DEN}$ | | 200 | |
| Controls output enable time: DEVSEL (↓)-lines C0, C1, C2, S/I | $t_{CEN}$ | | 100 | |
| Write pulse width IN | $t_{DVW}$ | | 75 | |
| Data input setup time: DX-DEVSEL (↑) | $t_{DIS}$ | | 0 | |
| Data input hold time: DEVSEL (↑)-DX | $t_{DIH}$ | | 50 | |
| RESET input pulse width | $t_{RST}$ | | 100 | |
| SKP/INTX to SKP/INT propagation delay | $t_{SID}$ | | 100 | |
| DMA control signals delay: XTC-XTC*; MEMSEL- MEMSEL*, LXMAR-LXMAR* | $t_{DMLX}$ | | 100 | |
| Enable/Disable time from DMAGNT to EMA lines | $t_{DEM}$ | | 100 | |
| MEMSEL* pulse width - DMA READ | $t_{MDR}$ | | 500 | |
| MEMSEL* pulse width - DMA WRITE | $t_{MDW}$ | | 625 | |
| MEMSEL* pulse width - DMA READ/REFSH | $t_{MDRR}$ | | 500 | |
| MEMSEL* pulse width - DMA WRITE/REFSH | $t_{MDWR}$ | | 375 | |

| PARAMETER | SYMBOL | MIN | TYP | MAX |
|---|---|---|---|---|
| LXMAR* pulse width | $t_{LD}$ | | 250 | |
| DMA READ access time: LXMAR* (↓)-UP (↑) | $t_{DRAT}$ | | 500 | |
| DX & EMA address setup time wrt LXMAR* (↓) | $t_{DXAS}$ | | 375 | |
| | $t_{EMAS}$ | | 375 | |
| DX & EMA address hold time wrt LXMAR* (↓) | $t_{DXAH}$ | | 125 | |
| | $t_{EMAH}$ | | 125 | |
| DMA READ enable time: MEMSEL* (↓)-UP (↑) | $t_{DREN}$ | | 375 | |
| UP pulse width DMA READ | $t_{RUP}$ | | 250 | |
| DMA WRITE access time: LXMAR* (↓)-MEMSEL* (↑) | $t_{DWAT}$ | | 500 | |
| DMA WRITE enable time: UP (↓)-MEMSEL* (↑) | $t_{DWEN}$ | | 375 | |
| MEMSEL* setup time DMA WRITE MEMSEL*(↓)-LXMAR* (↓) | $t_{MWS}$ | | 125 | |
| DMAEN setup time w.r.t. XTA (↑) | $t_{DMS}$ | | 50 | |
| DMAEN hold time w.r.t. XTA (↑) | $t_{DMH}$ | | 50 | |
| UP pulse width DMA WRITE | $t_{WUP}$ | | 500 | |

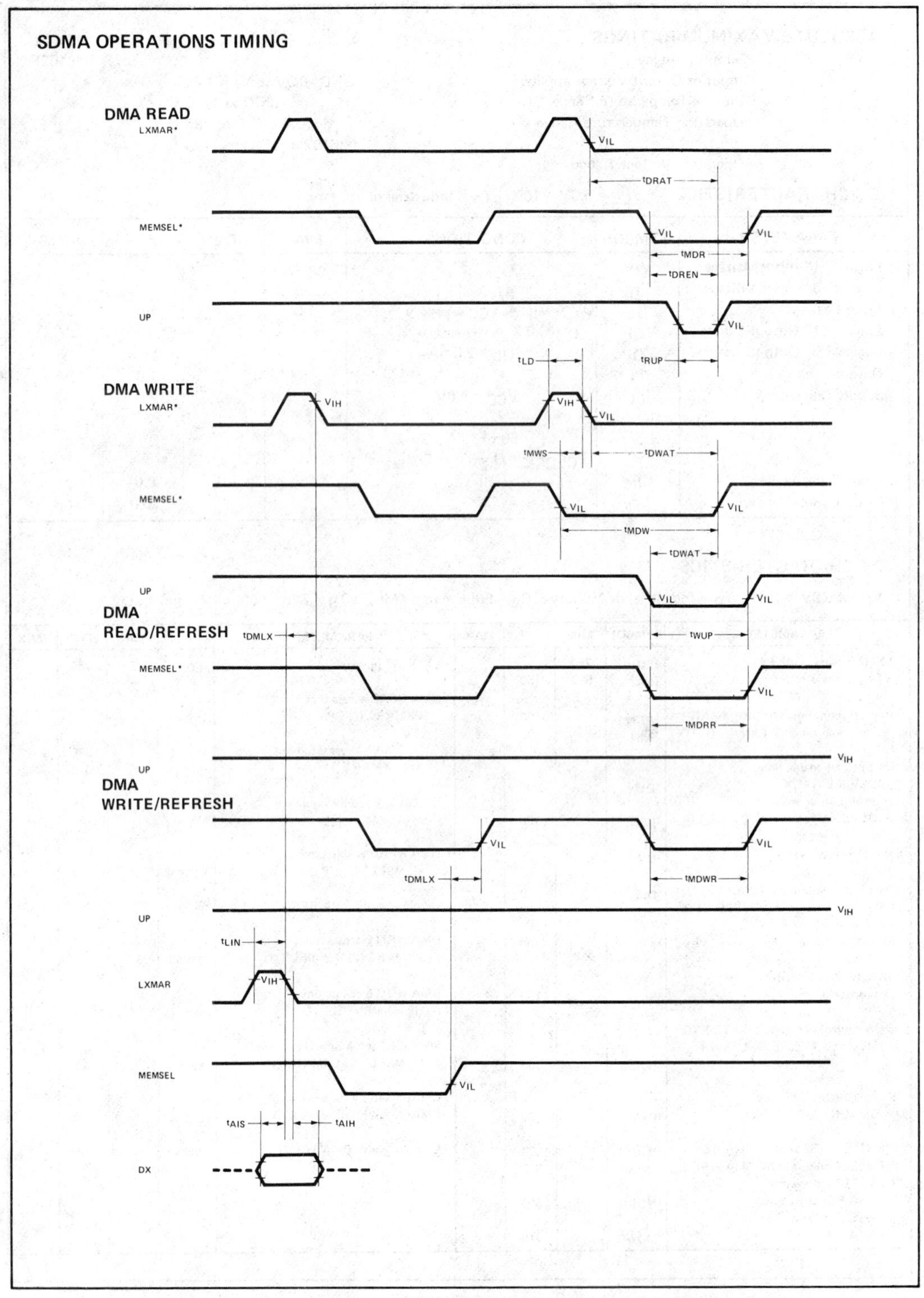
SDMA OPERATIONS TIMING
DMA READ
LXMAR*
MEMSEL*
UP
VIL
tDRAT
tMDR
tDREN
tLD
tRUP
DMA WRITE
LXMAR*
VIH
tMWS
tDWAT
MEMSEL*
tMDW
UP
tWUP
DMA
READ/REFRESH
tDMLX
MEMSEL*
tMDRR
UP
DMA
WRITE/REFRESH
tDMLX
tMDWR
UP
tLIN
LXMAR
MEMSEL
tAIS
tAIH
DX

# Chapter 14
# THE 8X300 (OR SMS300)

**We have described this product in previous editions under the designation SMS300. However, its manufacturer now calls it 8X300, and that is the standard part number.**

**The 8X300 is described by its manufacturer as a "microcontroller" rather than a "microprocessor". This distinction draws attention to the unique capabilities of the 8X300 which make it the most remarkable device described in this book.**

**The 8X300 is designed to serve as a signal processor or logic controller, operating at very high speed. The 8X300 can handle applications of this type at more than ten times the speed of most other devices described in this book. On the other hand, the 8X300 has a very limited ability to access read/write memory, or to perform arithmetic operations — particularly when handling multibyte arithmetic.**

If yours is a high-speed, signal processing application, then give the 8X300 serious consideration; otherwise, the 8X300 is probably not for you.

We describe the 8X300 in Chapter 14 because it lies between the 8-bit microcomputers, which we have just described, and the 16-bit devices described beginning with Chapter 15. The 8X300 accesses program memory as 16-bit words, while accessing data in 8-bit units.

**Although Scientific Micro Systems was originally considered the prime source for the 8X300 (then known as the SMS300), the only manufacturer of 8X300 parts to date has been Signetics.** Signetics has always manufactured parts for itself and for Scientific Micro Systems, even through Signetics was looked upon as the second source. The second source designation came from the fact that the part was initially designed by Scientific Micro Systems, which contracted with Signetics for production. Scientific Micro Systems no longer sells the 8X300 or related components.

All 8X300 devices are manufactured using bipolar technology. For this reason, devices have very fast logic; but conversely, they consume a great deal of power.

At present, the sole source for 8X300 components is:

SIGNETICS
P.O. Box 9052
811 E. Arques Avenue
Sunnyvale, CA 94086

## THE 8X300 MICROCONTROLLER

**Figure 14-1 illustrates that part of our general microcomputer logic which is implemented by the 8X300 Microcontroller. Figure 14-2 provides a functional overview of this device.**

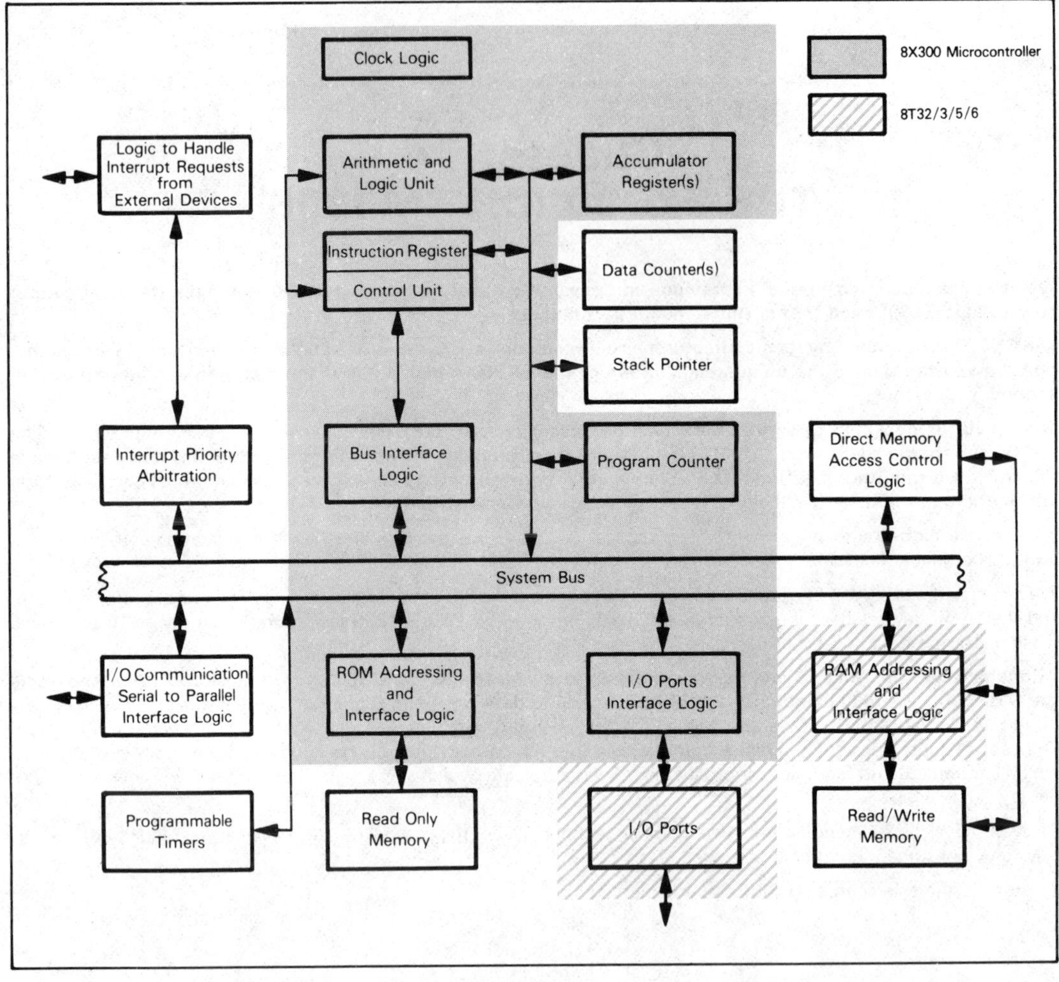


**Figure 14-1. Logic of the 8X300 Microcontroller and 8T32/3/5/6**

The 8X300 is manufactured using bipolar LSI technology; it is packaged as a 50-pin DIP. A single +5V power supply is required.

Using a 150 nanosecond clock, instructions execute in 250 nanoseconds. However, comparing 8X300 instruction execution times with other microcomputer instruction times can be misleading. A single 8X300 instruction, when simply manipulating data, can be the equivalent of five "typical" microcomputer instructions; on the other hand, it may take four or more 8X300 instructions to perform a memory access which could be accomplished using one "typical" microcomputer instruction.

It is important to note that the very fast 8X300 clock demands external logic with appropriately fast response times. You are therefore highly restricted in the size of memory, and the type of I/O device which you can include in an 8X300 microcomputer system.

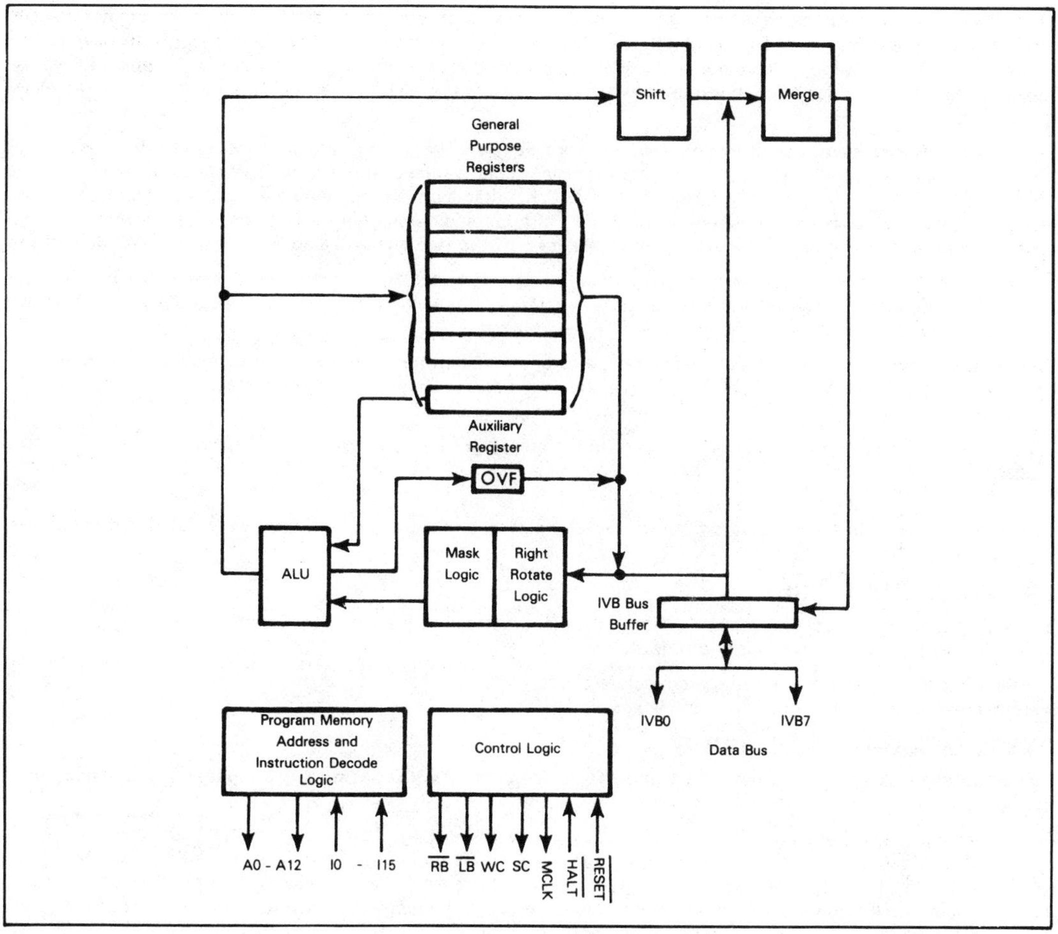

Figure 14-2. A Logic Overview of the 8X300 Microcontroller

## 8X300 ADDRESSABLE REGISTERS

**Addressable registers of the 8X300 may be illustrated as follows:**

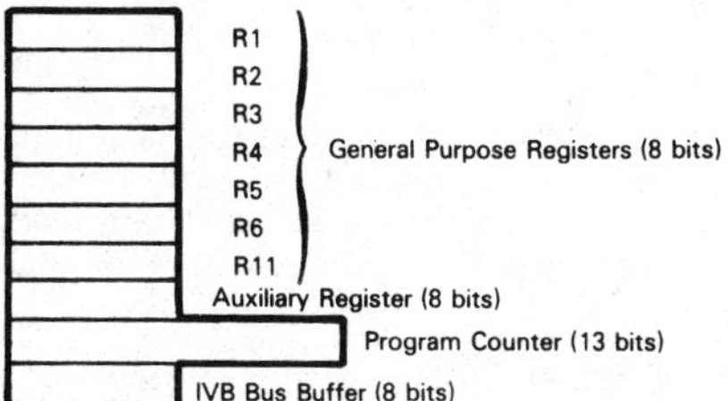

**The seven General Purpose registers and the Auxiliary register constitute eight primary Accumulators.** The result of any ALU operation may be stored in the Auxiliary register, or in any one of the seven General Purpose registers. ALU operations that require a single data input may receive this input from any General Purpose register, or from the Auxiliary register. ALU operations that require two data inputs will receive the second data input from the Auxiliary register only.

**The 8X300 IVB Bus is equivalent to a microprocessor Data Bus.** The IVB Bus buffer operates as a source or destination for data in the same way as a general purpose register; it can be the destination of an ALU operation, or it can be the source for one ALU input. Strictly speaking, the IVB Bus buffer is not a programmable register, in that there are no instructions that will simply load data into the IVB Bus buffer or read data out of the IVB Bus buffer. However, **any instruction that outputs data on the IVB Bus or reads data off the IVB Bus will also write into the IVB Bus buffer.**

The strange general purpose register numbering reflects instruction object code interpretations which we will describe later in this chapter. 8X300 assembly language uses register designations to identify a number of operations that have nothing to do with programmable registers; do not be confused.

**The Program Counter is thirteen bits wide; thus, a total of 8192 program memory words may be addressed.** The Program Counter is one feature of 8X300 logic which is not unusual; at all times, this register addresses the next program memory location from which an instruction code will be fetched.

Manufacturer's literature describes an Instruction Address register, but this is not a programmable register; it is simply a location within which effective program memory addresses are computed before being output to the program memory.

**Observe that the 8X300 has no Data Counter, Stack Pointer, or other logic via which external data memory can be addressed.**

## 8X300 STATUS FLAGS

**The 8X300 has a single status flag,** referred to in the manufacturer's literature as the Overflow (OVF) flag. This flag is, in fact, **a Carry status, as we would define it.**

In keeping with the generally unusual architecture of the 8X300, the Overflow status flag is addressed as though it were the low order bit of General Purpose Register 8 (10 octal).

## 8X300 MEMORY ADDRESSING

**The 8X300 can access program memory and I/O devices; the 8X300 has no logic capable of addressing data memory.**

**8X300 PROGRAM MEMORY ADDRESSING**

Program memory is addressed in 16-bit words; up to 8192 words of program memory can be addressed. You can address program memory in order to fetch instruction object codes, but that is all. You cannot store data tables in program memory, because there is absolutely no way of transferring the contents of a program memory word to any data register. Also, there is absolutely no way in which you can write into program memory.

**8X300 DATA AND I/O ADDRESSING**

**All data and external logic is addressed as 8-bit data units, via 512 I/O port addresses.** If you want to have read/write memory present in an 8X300 system, you must set aside a block of contiguous I/O port addresses in order to select individual bytes of read/write memory; alternatively, you must access 8-bit buffers, via I/O port addresses, in order to create the memory address and Data Busses which are needed by external read/write memory. For example, you could address 65,536 bytes of external read/write memory by allocating two 8-bit I/O ports to hold 16 bits of data which will create a memory Address Bus; a third 8-bit I/O port must be set aside as a buffer, holding data being written out to external memory or being read from external memory.

**8T32/3/5/6 IV BYTES**

The 8T32/3/5/6 Interface Vector Bytes (IV Bytes), which are described later in this chapter, have been designed to operate as I/O ports, read/write memory and the 8X300 Microcontroller external logic interface. Because of the unique architecture of the 8X300, and particularly because of its very high speed, you will probably find that the IV Bytes currently have no substitutes in any 8X300 microcomputer system.

**8T32/3/5/6 IV BYTE ADDRESSING**

Looking at the 8X300 from the frame of reference of any other microcomputer described in this book, an IV Byte is a simple, 8-bit parallel I/O port. But unlike the I/O ports of other microprocessors, 8X300 instructions that access an I/O port do not identify the I/O port that is to be accessed. You must first execute an instruction which selects an I/O port; then any instruction which specifies an I/O port access will access the most recently selected I/O port. You can have two I/O ports simultaneously selected, since the 8X300 divides a total of 512 addressable I/O ports into a left bank and a right bank — within each bank a single IV Byte can be selected.

As we have already stated, if you want to have read/write memory present in an 8X300 microcomputer system, you must create the address and Data Bus required by the external read/write memory using IV bytes. This is no different than using I/O ports of any other microcomputer system described in this book in order to create Address and Data Busses. The reason the 8X300 can get away with such an apparently clumsy method of accessing read/write memory is because of the very high speed of instruction execution — and because of the fact that the 8X300 is simply not designed for data manipulations that use a lot of read/write memory. For the type of signal processing and logic control applications that are well suited to an 8X300, 512 bytes of external read/write memory will be more than sufficient.

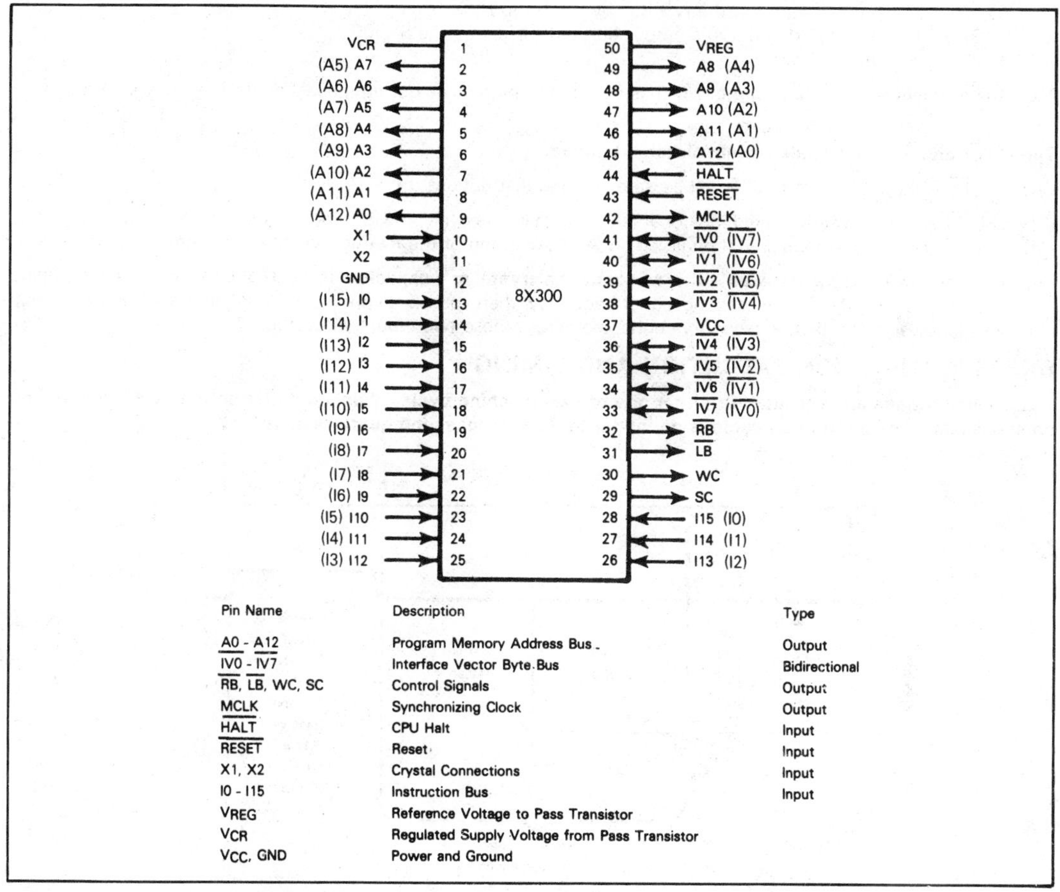


| Pin Name | Description | Type |
|---|---|---|
| A0 - A12 | Program Memory Address Bus | Output |
| IV0 - IV7 | Interface Vector Byte Bus | Bidirectional |
| RB, LB, WC, SC | Control Signals | Output |
| MCLK | Synchronizing Clock | Output |
| HALT | CPU Halt | Input |
| RESET | Reset | Input |
| X1, X2 | Crystal Connections | Input |
| I0 - I15 | Instruction Bus | Input |
| VREG | Reference Voltage to Pass Transistor | |
| VCR | Regulated Supply Voltage from Pass Transistor | |
| VCC, GND | Power and Ground | |

Figure 14-3. 8X300 Microcontroller Signals and Pin Assignments

## 8X300 PINS AND SIGNALS

**8X300 pins and signals are illustrated in Figure 14-3.**

Signetics literature numbers bits and busses beginning with 0 for the high-order bit or line. We number bits and busses in the opposite direction, with 0 representing the low-order bit or line. In Figure 14-3, therefore, signals are identified first with the nomenclature used by Signetics documentation, then in parentheses with the signal name using our numbering system. Furthermore, all bit numbers throughout this chapter refer to our numbering system.

**All addresses are output to program memory via the Address Bus lines A0 - A12. Note carefully that addresses cannot be output via A0 - A12 to data memory.** The only time an address will be output via the Address Bus is during an instruction fetch operation. **The fetched instruction object code will be returned via the sixteen instruction pins, I0 - I15.**

**IV0 - IV7 is a combined Address and Data Bus via which external logic is accessed by the 8X300.** You will find it easiest to understand this bus if you visualize it as a multiplex I/O port address and I/O Data Bus.

**The two control signals, $\overline{\text{RB}}$ and $\overline{\text{LB}}$, may be looked upon as an extension to the IVB Bus** when an I/O port address is being output via this bus. Whenever an address is being output on the IVB Bus, either $\overline{\text{RB}}$ or $\overline{\text{LB}}$ will be low, while the other signal is high. You can use these two signals in order to decode the address on the IVB Bus as selecting one or two of the 256 I/O port banks. We will describe how to output I/O port addresses, as against data, later in this chapter.

**The WC and SC control outputs further define the contents of the IVB Bus as follows:**

| SC | WC | |
|---|---|---|
| 0 | 0 | Data is input to the 8X300 via the IVB Bus |
| 0 | 1 | Data is output on the IVB Bus by the 8X300 |
| 1 | 0 | An I/O port address is output on the IVB Bus by the 8X300 |
| 1 | 1 | Never output |

**MCLK is a synchronizing clock signal** which is output as a high pulse during the last quarter of every instruction cycle.

**The $\overline{\text{HALT}}$ and $\overline{\text{RESET}}$ signals are absolutely standard.**

When $\overline{\text{HALT}}$ is input low, the 8X300 will cease executing instructions until $\overline{\text{HALT}}$ is input high again.

When $\overline{\text{RESET}}$ is input low and is held low for at least one machine cycle, the Program Counter contents are set to zero; subsequently, program execution will begin again with execution of the instruction stored in memory location zero.

**The two inputs X1 and X2 are used either to connect a crystal or a capacitor.** If the 8X300 Microcontroller is being used at maximum speed (125 nanosecond signal frequency) then you must connect a crystal across X1 and X2. If you are using a slower clock, then a capacitor connected across these two inputs will suffice.

## 8X300 INSTRUCTION EXECUTION AND TIMING

**8X300 instructions are executed in either one or two machine cycles. Minimum instruction cycle time is 250 nanoseconds. Each instruction cycle is divided into 62.5 nanosecond quarters as follows:**

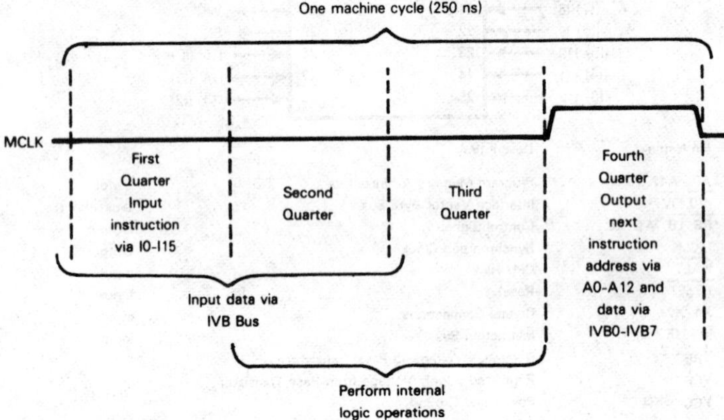


During the fourth quarter of a machine cycle, the address for the next machine cycle's instruction object code is output via the Address Bus, A0 - A12.

During the first quarter of the next machine cycle, the addressed instruction object code is input via the Instruction Bus, I0 - I15.

During the second and third quarters of a machine cycle, data is input off the IVB Bus by the 8X300, if necessary; then any internal operations on data are performed.

During the fourth quarter, in addition to the next address being output to program memory, data is output to the IVB Bus, if necessary.

Within the rather simple-looking instruction timing illustrated above, some very complex event sequences can occur as a result of the 8X300 Microcontroller's unique internal logic organization. Timing and propagation delays are quite complex and must be examined with care using vendor data sheets as your guide.

The 8X300 Microcontroller's internal logic is unique because **a good deal of it is distributed along various data paths. This is illustrated in Figure 14-2.**

Consider the implications of the shift, merge, rotate and mask logic positions.

**8X300 ROTATE AND MASK LOGIC**

Data entering the Arithmetic and Logic Unit, either from the IVB Bus Buffer, or from a general purpose register, must pass through both the rotate and mask logic. The rotate logic optionally allows the entering eight data bits to be right-rotated by any number of bit positions:

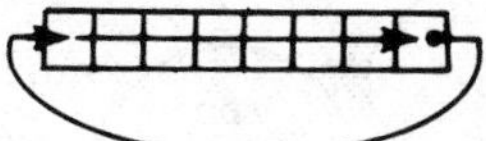

The mask logic optionally allows you to take the output from the rotate logic and mask off any number of bits, beginning with the high-order bit:

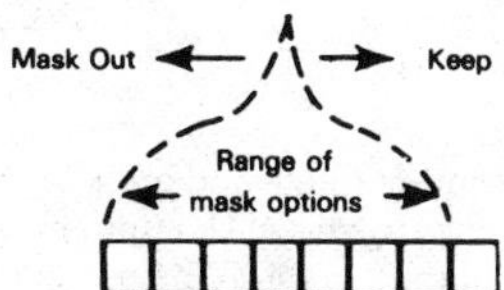


Masked out bit positions are replaced by 0.

Thus, the data entering the ALU from either a general purpose register or the IVB Bus register may be rotated and/or masked before being operated on.

Combining the rotate and mask logic that we have just described, the input to the ALU may be illustrated as follows:

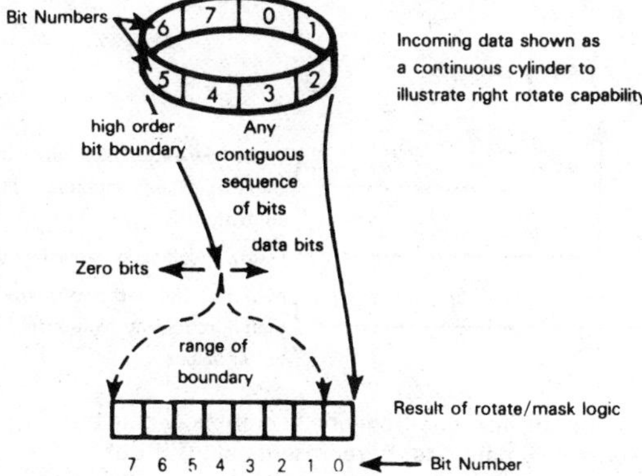


Suppose an input is right-rotated three bit positions, then the two high-order bits are masked off; this would be the result:

| | 7 | 6 | 5 | 4 | 3 | 2 | 1 | 0 | Bit No. |
|---|---|---|---|---|---|---|---|---|---|
| Initial value: | A7 | A6 | A5 | A4 | A3 | A2 | A1 | A0 | |
| After right rotate: | A2 | A1 | A0 | A7 | A6 | A5 | A4 | A3 | |
| After mask: | 0 | 0 | A0 | A7 | A6 | A5 | A4 | A3 | |

The result of the rotate/mask logic illustrated above becomes an Arithmetic and Logic Unit (ALU) input; it may be the only ALU input, or it may be one of two ALU inputs. If it is the only ALU input, it will simply be passed through the ALU.

If it is one of two ALU inputs, then the second input is the unmodified contents of an 8-bit Auxiliary register. You may Add, AND or XOR the two operands:

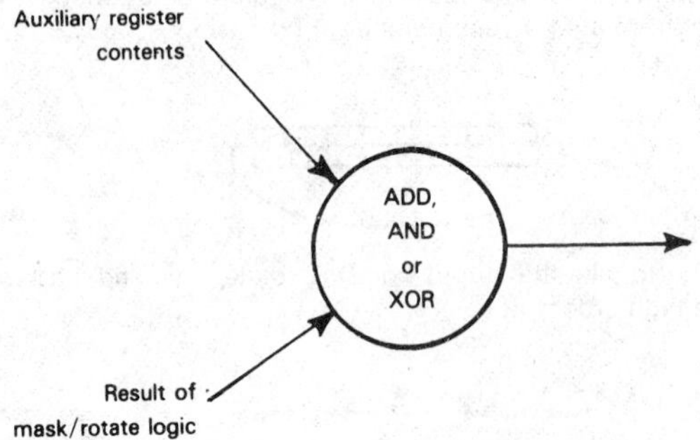


Thus, the ALU output may be the unmodified result of rotate and mask logic, or it may be the output from an arithmetic or logical operation, as illustrated above. In either case, the ALU output may be stored in the Auxiliary register, or in one of the general purpose registers; or it may be output to the IVB Bus.

**8X300 SHIFT AND MERGE LOGIC**

Data being transferred to the IVB Bus passes through shift and merge logic. This shift and merge logic combines in a very unusual way. ALU output, if shifted, may be shifted left from one to seven bits. However, zeros are not shifted in to the low-order bits; rather, any prior contents of the IVB Buffer are moved into the vacated bit positions.

In addition, you can specify the number of high-order bits which will retain their IVB Buffer values. This may be illustrated as follows:

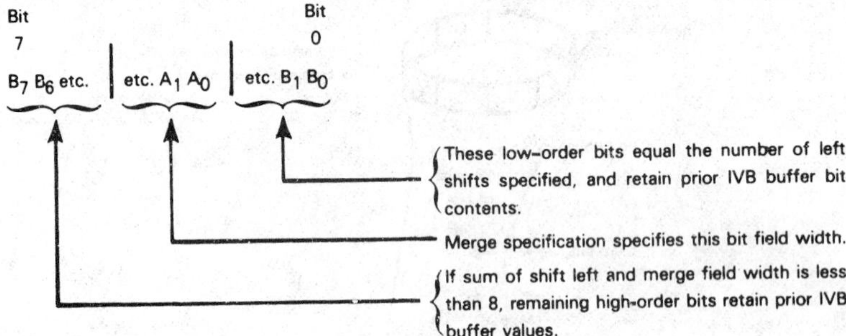


Thus you create a new IVB Bus output by inserting from one to eight new data bits anywhere in the old data bit field. In the illustration above, $A_i$ represents new data bits; $B_i$ represents old IVB Buffer bits.

Suppose you specify a 2-bit left shift and a 3-bit merge; this would be the result:

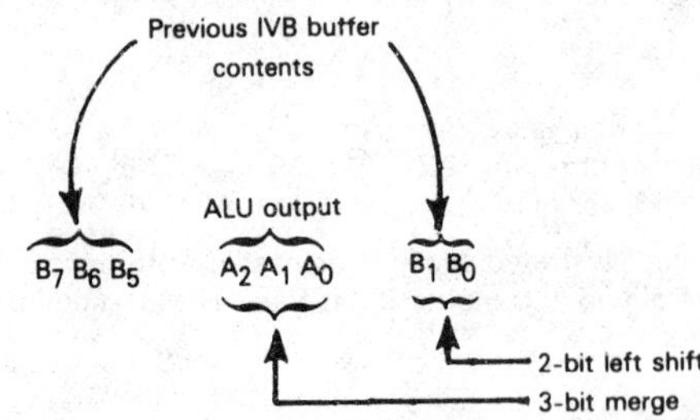

Figures 14-4 through 14-7 illustrate the four possible data paths that may be specified by 8X300 instructions. In all four figures, data entering the ALU from the Auxiliary register is optional, but, if present, requires an Add, AND or XOR operation to be performed.

## THE 8X300 INSTRUCTION SET

**We cannot neatly categorize instructions as we have done for any other product described in this book; one 8X300 instruction may perform a data move, plus five additional operations. Therefore, in order to summarize the 8X300 instruction set in Table 14-2, we list individual instructions that perform many operations under each of the instruction classes that may apply.**

Table 14-2 will help you understand what the true comparison is between the 8X300 instruction set and other microcomputer instruction sets. However, **Table 14-2 will do nothing to help you understand 8X300 assembly language.** This is because of the strange assembly language mnemonics adopted by Scientific Micro Systems for the 8X300 Assembler. But without some understanding of 8X300 instruction codes, any further discussion of assembly language mnemonics will have little meaning; therefore let us take a look at these object codes, and simultaneously look at the assembly language syntax that goes with them.

**The one general statement that can be made for all 8X300 instructions is that every instruction has a single, 16-bit object code; the 3 high-order object code bits define the instruction class, while the next 13 bits provide additional operand or qualifying data. This may be illustrated as follows:**

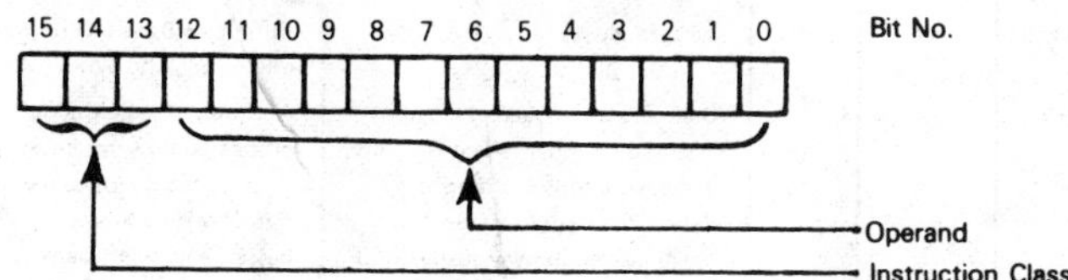


Now we are going to make the discussion which follows conform to the rest of this book by numbering instruction words and data byte bits from right to left; and we are going to use hexadecimal object code notation. Signetics' literature, by way of contrast, numbers data words from left to right, and uses a form of bastardized octal notation to describe instruction object codes.

**The first four classes of 8X300 instructions have identical object code formats which may be illustrated as follows:**

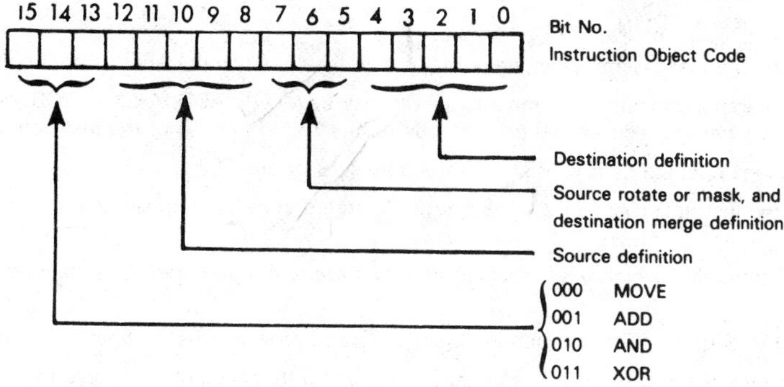


The "Source definition" and "Destination definition" are defined as register numbers; since each definition is five bits wide, a register number in the range $00_{16}$ through $1F_{16}$ ($00_8$ through $37_8$) may be specified. But you get to specify a lot more than a source or destination register. Table 14-1 summarizes the possibilities.

Table 14-1. 8X300 Source and Destination Object Code Interpretations

| CODE | | | INTERPRETATION | |
|---|---|---|---|---|
| BINARY | OCTAL | HEX | SOURCE DEFINITION | DESTINATION DEFINITION |
| 00000 | 00 | 00 | Auxiliary register | |
| 00001 | 01 | 01 | General Purpose Register R1 | |
| 00010 | 02 | 02 | General Purpose Register R2 | |
| 00011 | 03 | 03 | General Purpose Register R3 | |
| 00100 | 04 | 04 | General Purpose Register R4 | |
| 00101 | 05 | 05 | General Purpose Register R5 | |
| 00110 | 06 | 06 | General Purpose Register R6 | |
| 00111 | 07 | 07 | All zero input | Output an 8-bit I/O port address to a left bank IV Byte |
| 01000 | 10 | 08 | OVF status (low-order bit only) | Not allowed |
| 01001 | 11 | 09 | General Purpose Register R11 | |
| 01010 through 01110 | 12 through 16 | 0A through 0E | No operation | |
| 01111 | 17 | 0F | All zero input | Output an 8-bit I/O port address to a right bank IV Byte. |
| 10XXX | 2X | 10 to 17 | Contents of left bank IV Byte selected by most recent 07 output is loaded into IVB buffer; this data is then right rotated X bit positions, on its way to the ALU. IVB buffer holds unrotated input. | ALU output is shifted left 7-X bit positions. After passing through merge logic, merge logic output will be stored in IVB buffer, and in left bank IV Byte most recently selected by an 07 output. |
| 11XXX | 3X | 18 to 1F | Identical to 10XXX, except that right bank IV Byte most recently selected by a 0F (or 17) output is accessed. | |

**8X300 assembly language syntax closely follows the object code format; this may be illustrated as follows:**

```
LABEL    OP        S, N, D
```

LABEL represents any normal assembly language instruction label; as usual, LABEL is optional.

OP represents the operation or instruction mnemonic. OP may be MOVE, ADD, AND, or XOR, depending on which of the four instructions is being executed. OP corresponds to bits 15, 14 and 13 of the instruction code.

The assembly language operand field consists of three terms: S, N and D.

With reference to the instruction object code we have illustrated above, S represents bits 8 through 12, the source definition.

N represents bits 5 through 7 which may provide rotation, mask or merge parameters, depending on the nature of S and D.

D represents bits 0 through 4 of the instruction object code and provides the destination definition.

The problem with the S, N and D terms of the operand field is that they are not really operands as one would normally define them in an assembly language instruction set. These three fields also help identify part of the instruction operation, or mnemonic. If you approach 8X300 assembly language realizing that its operand field is really an extension of the mnemonic field, you will have less trouble understanding individual instructions.

The various ways in which a Move, Add, AND,or XOR instruction may be executed are illustrated in Figures 14-4 through 14-7. Let us look at these possibilities in more detail.

**When a register is specified as both the source and destination of data, Figure 14-4 defines the operation.** Referring to this figure, note that the source data is rotated, but it is not masked. The second ALU input will only occur if you are executing an Add, AND, or XOR instruction; and in each case the second ALU input will be the unmodified contents of the Auxiliary register.

The classes of instruction illustrated in Figure 14-4 can be listed under the following categories:

1) A Register-Register Move. This involves specifying a Move instruction with different registers as the data source and destination, but no right rotate.
2) Register Operate. By specifying the same register as the source and destination for a MOVE, you can create a Register Operate instruction if you also specify some degree of right rotation. You can create additional Register Operate instructions by specifying the Auxiliary register as both source and destination for an Add, AND or XOR instruction.
3) Register-Register Operate. By specifying an Add, AND or XOR operation that does not use the Auxiliary register as both source and destination, you create Register-Register Operate instructions.

Consider some possibilities.

In order to complement any register's contents, load $FF_{16}$ into the Auxiliary register (using an XMIT instruction), then XOR the General Purpose register contents with the Auxiliary register contents, returning the results to the General Purpose register. These two instructions can be executed in 500 nanoseconds.

You can AND or XOR Auxiliary register bits with other data bits from the same Auxiliary register by specifying the Auxiliary register as the source and destination for an AND or XOR instruction with right rotate. The ability to perform logical operations on bits within a single 8-bit unit is very useful if you are treating the contents of a register as status, representing individual signal levels rather than treating the bits contiguously, as data items.

Apparently absent instructions, such as Register Increment, Register Decrement, OR and Compare, can be generated by using the Auxiliary register to hold appropriate intermediate data.

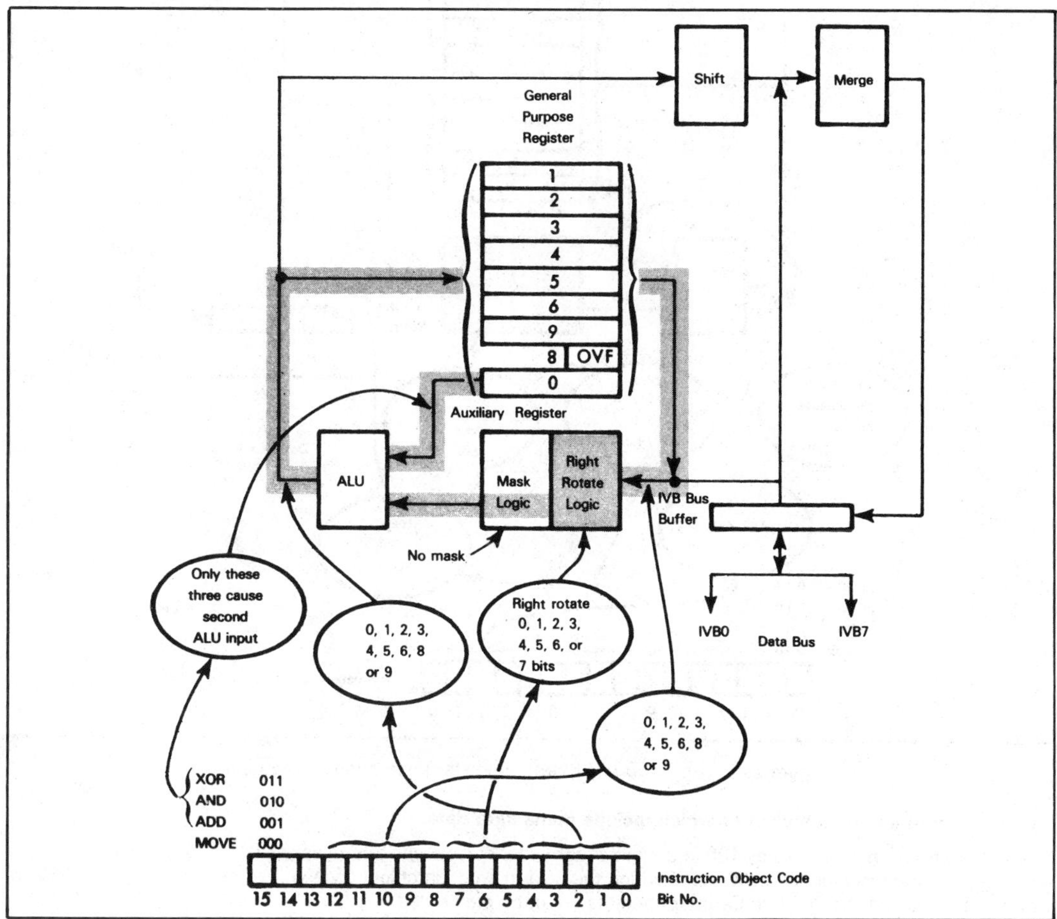


Figure 14-4. An 8X300 Register-to-Register Instruction's Execution

**Figure 14-5 illustrates Move, Add, AND and XOR instructions where the IVB Bus is the data source and a general purpose register is the data destination.** Referring to Figure 14-5, observe that the mask and right rotate logic are both involved. Bits 5, 6 and 7 of the instruction object code, which in Figure 14-4 specify the amount of right rotation, in Figure 14-5 specify the degree of masking which will occur. Bits 8, 9 and 10 in Figure 14-5 specify the amount of right rotation which will occur.

8X300 assembly language mnemonics do not discriminate between this new use of bits 5, 6 and 7. You will still write assembly language instructions with the format:

```
LABEL    OP       S, N, D
```

S now defines the right rotate while N defines the masking operation.

Now consider instructions which specify an IV byte as the data destination. **Figure 14-6 illustrates instructions where a General Purpose register is the instruction source; Figure 14-7 illustrates IV byte-to-IV byte operations.**

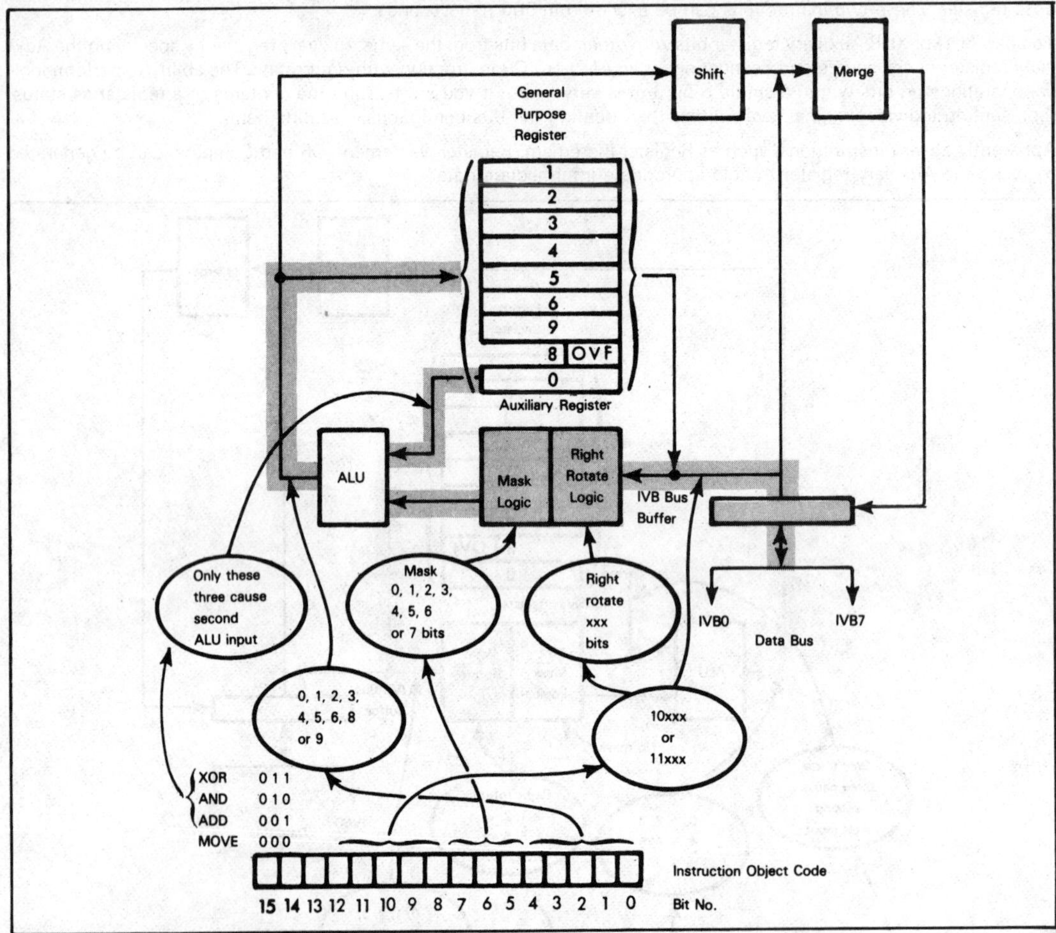


Figure 14-5. An 8X300 IV Byte-to-Register Instruction's Execution

**There are three instruction classes which include immediate data.**

**The XEC instruction,** identified by 100 in the three high-order object code bits, uses the 13 operand bits to compute a temporary program memory address out of which the next instruction object code will be fetched. When an XEC instruction is executed the Program Counter contents are not incremented.

**The NZT instruction,** specified by 101 in the three high-order object code bits, provides the 8X300 with its conditional logic.

**The XMIT instruction,** represented by 110 in the three high-order object code bits, provides the 8X300 with its immediate instructions.

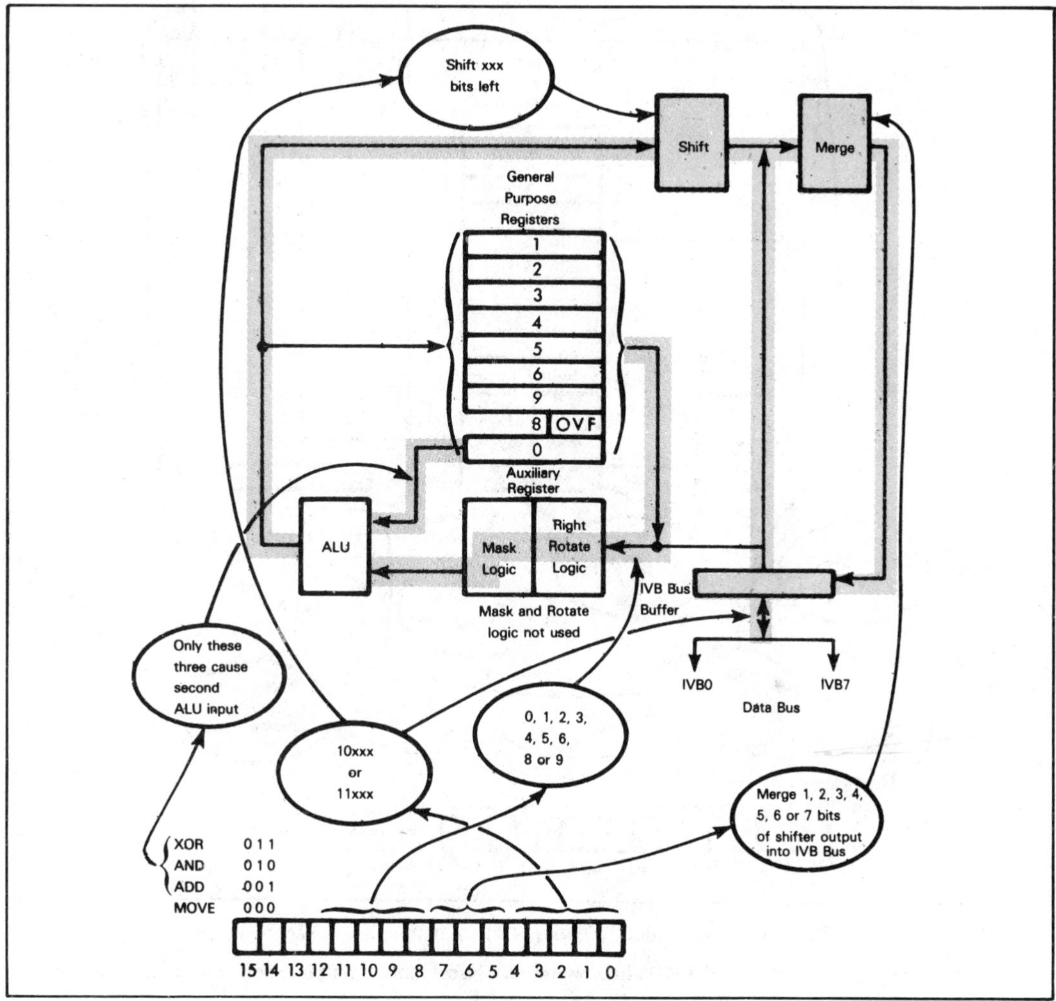


Figure 14-6. An 8X300 Register-to-IV Byte Instruction's Execution

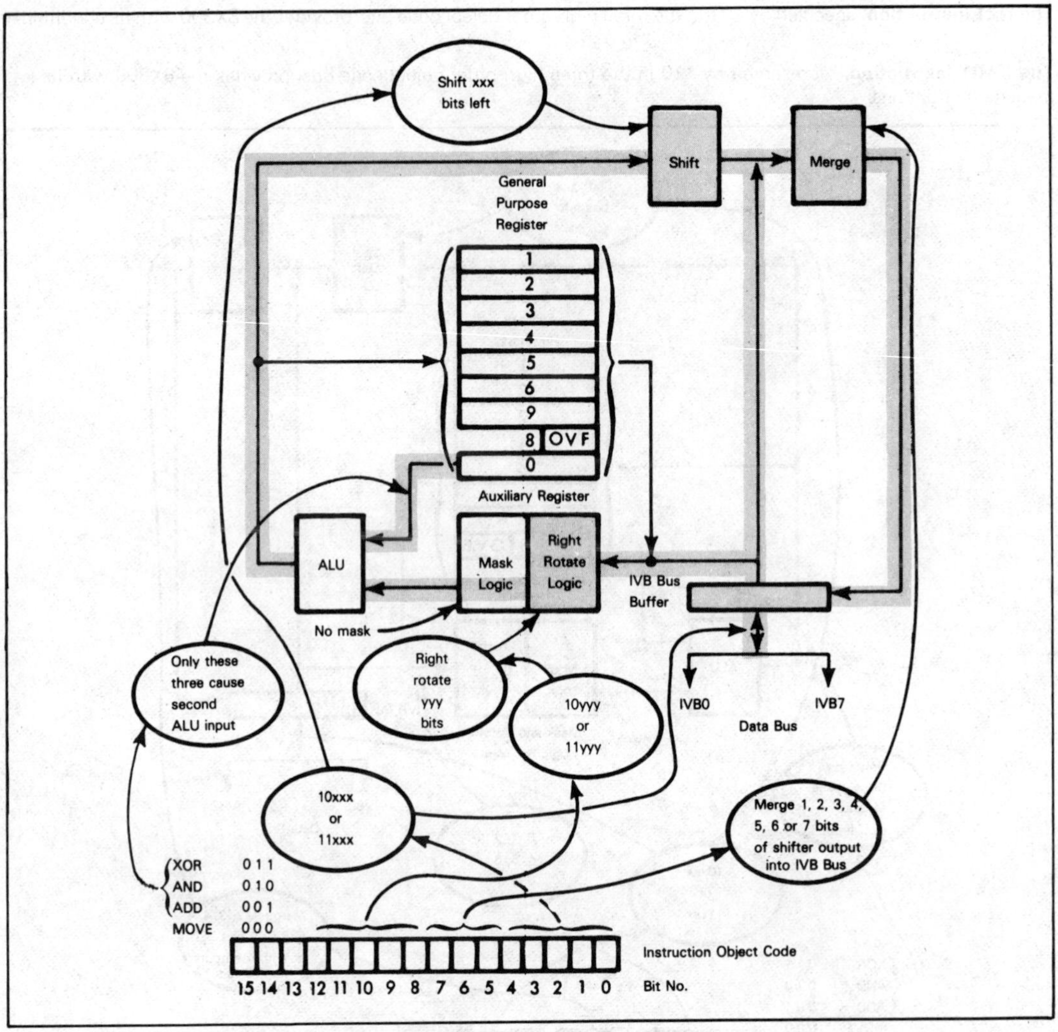

Figure 14-7. An 8X300 IV Byte-to-IV Byte Instruction's Execution

**All three instructions, XEC, NZT and XMIT, use one of the two following instruction object code formats:**

Format A:

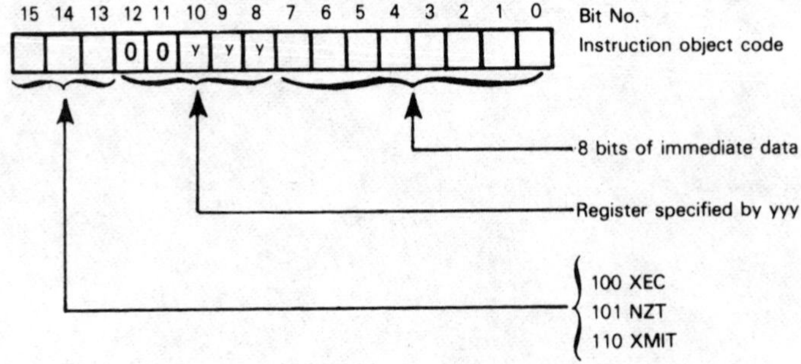

Format B:

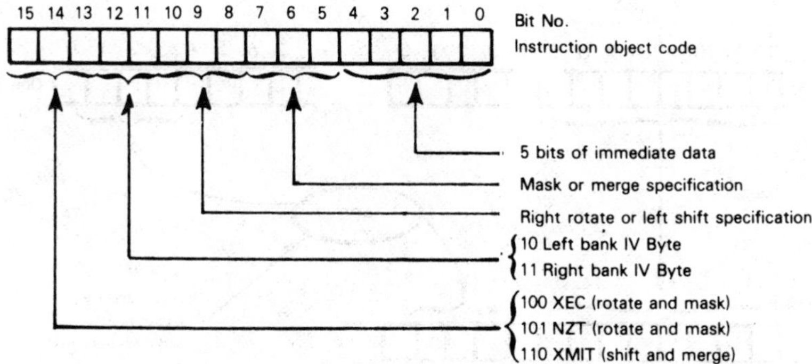


For all three instructions, XEC, NZT and XMIT, the Format A object code uses bits 8 through 12 to specify a General Purpose register, or the Auxiliary register.

The Format B instruction object code uses bits 5 through 12 to specify the currently selected left bank or right bank IV byte, where byte contents will be subject to a mask and a rotate, as illustrated in Figure 14-5.

**Let us take another look at how the XEC, NZT and XMIT instructions use the data generated by their operand bits.**

**The XEC instruction** allows you to stay at one object code, continuously re-executing this single object code, while it points to another object code which actually gets executed. The address of the object code which actually gets executed is computed in one of two ways:

1) For the Format A object code, the current five high-order Program Counter bits are concatenated with the 8-bit sum of the specified register contents, plus the immediate data:

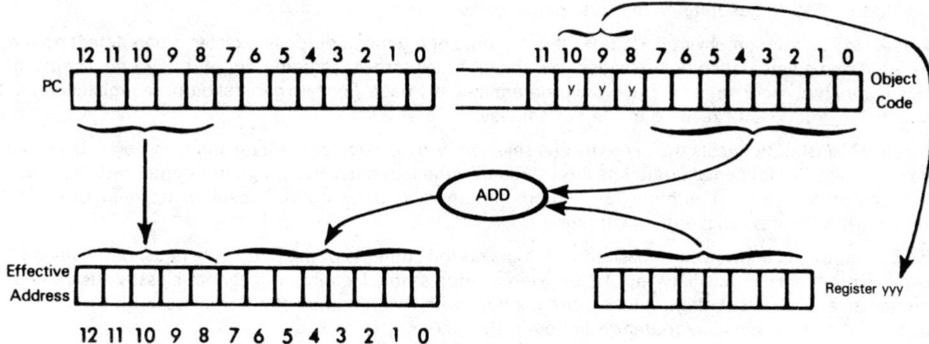

2) With the second object code format, the 8 high-order current Program Counter bits are concatenated with the 5-bit sum of the immediate data, plus the rotated and masked IV byte data:

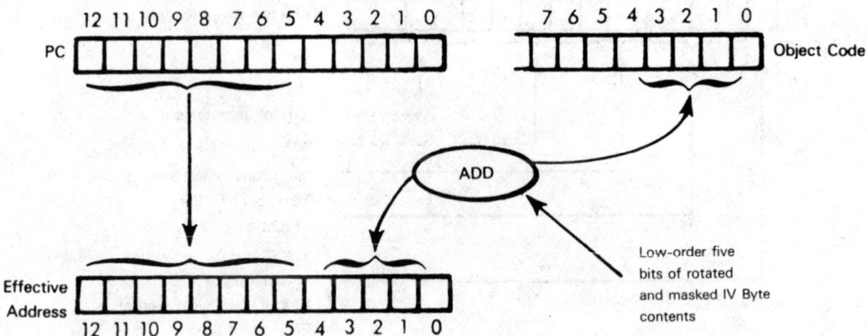


You may use XEC instructions in one of two ways:

1) You may create a branch table of Jump instructions: based on the contents of any General Purpose register or IV byte, you may jump to one of 256 locations using Format A instruction object code, or one of 32 locations using Format B instruction object code.

2) External logic may directly control the sequence in which instructions are executed. The XEC instruction is equivalent to a single instruction which requires 500 nanoseconds to execute: 250 nanoseconds to process the XEC instruction's object code and another 250 nanoseconds to execute the object code fetched in response to the XEC instruction. If you are using the Format B instruction, external logic can use the second 250 nanosecond time interval to load new data into the selected IV byte. Thus, external logic can indefinitely control instruction execution sequence within an 8X300 microcomputer system.

**The NZT instruction** uses the 13 operand bits to identify a data byte that will be tested for a zero or a nonzero value. Additional operand bits are used to identify a branch address. If the identified data has a nonzero value, then the branch address is used to generate an absolute paged jump.

The Format A NZT instruction object code tests the contents of a general purpose register; upon detecting a nonzero value, the eight immediate data bits are loaded into the eight low-order Program Counter bits — thus causing an absolute paged branch to occur within a 256-word program memory page. For zero general purpose register contents, the next sequential instruction is executed in the normal way.

The Format B NZT instruction tests the contents of a selected IV byte, subject to rotate and mask logic. Upon detecting a nonzero result, the five immediate data bits are loaded into the low-order five Program Counter bits thus causing an absolute, paged branch to occur within a 32-word program memory page. If a zero result is detected, program execution continues with the next sequential instruction.

Thus the NZT instruction allows you to base branch logic on the contents of the Overflow status, or on any bit field, in any general purpose register, auxiliary register or external addressable location. We cannot classify such a wide-ranging instruction as a single instruction; it would not conform with the definition of a single assembly language instruction as used by any other microcomputer described in this book.

**In the case of the XMIT instruction,** the immediate data gets loaded into the general purpose register specified by a Format A instruction, or the external IV byte specified by a Format B instruction. In the case of a Format B instruction, the immediate data is shifted and merged, as illustrated in Figure 14-7, before being output to the identified IV byte. Recall that the identified IV byte will be the byte most recently selected by a Move instruction that specifies Register 7 or F as the destination.

**The Jump instruction** is the only one which remains to be described; it is also the simplest to describe. When this instruction is executed, the 13 operand bits are loaded directly into the Program Counter; thus you perform a simple unconditional jump to any location in program memory.

**Observe that the 8X300 has no subroutine or interrupt handling logic.**

Subroutine logic can be created using the XEC instruction and an appropriate jump table, but this is rather clumsy. In most cases it will be simpler to do without subroutines.

The lack of interrupt logic is probably inconsequential. Given the fact that the 8X300 can execute instructions in 300 nanoseconds, polling on status will invariably be a satisfactory way of allowing external logic to control events within the 8X300 microcomputer system.

A very effective way of allowing external logic to control the 8X300 microcomputer system is to have the system continuously re-execute an ineffective instruction as the result of an XEC. For example, the XEC could point to an instruction which simply moves the contents of a General Purpose register back into itself. Using Format B for the XEC instruction, external logic could modify the contents of the selected external IV byte in order to force program execution to branch in one of 31 different directions.

## THE 8X300 BENCHMARK PROGRAM

The benchmark program we have been using throughout this book is particularly ill suited to the 8X300; in fact, it could well illustrate a benchmark program that a competitor would select in order to make the 8X300 look bad. This is because the 8X300 is not good at memory addressing. The 8X300 would never be used in an application that principally reads blocks of data into read/write memory, then moves blocks of data around read/write memory.

The 8X300 has no ability to address read/write memory; as we have already described earlier in this chapter, should you require the presence of read/write memory in an 8X300 system, you are going to have to create a memory Address Bus and Data Bus for the external read/write memory; IV bytes must be used to create these busses.

We will therefore change the benchmark program so that a sequence of data bytes entering via the left bank IV byte must immediately be output via a right bank IV byte. The first byte read will be interpreted as identifying the number of data bytes to follow. Now the benchmark will appear as follows:

```
        XMIT    AUX,377       LOAD 377 OCTAL INTO THE AUXILIARY REGISTER TO DECREMENT COUNTER
        XMIT    20,0,SRCE     SELECT SOURCE IV BYTE IN LEFT BANK
        XMIT    30,0,DST      SELECT DESTINATION IV BYTE IN RIGHT BANK
        MOVE    R1,0,SRCE     LOAD COUNTER INTO R1
LOOP    MOVE    SRCE,0,DST    MOVE NEXT DATA BYTE
        ADD     R1,0,R1       DECREMENT COUNTER
        NZT     R1,LOOP
```

The following symbols are used in Table 14-2:

| | |
|---|---|
| A | Auxiliary register |
| ADDR | 13-bit address value |
| DATA5 | 5-bit data unit |
| DATA8 | 8-bit data unit |
| DISP5 | 5-bit address value |
| DISP8 | 8-bit address value |
| IV1, IV2 | IV Byte |
| (L) | Optional Field length for IV Byte |
| PC | Program Counter |
| (R) | Optional rotate value for register |
| RX, RY | Any General Purpose registers |
| x<y,z> | Bits y through z of the specified value. For example, PC<7,0> is the low byte of the Program Counter. |
| [[ ]] | Contents of location enclosed within brackets. If a register designation is enclosed within the brackets, then the designated register's contents are specified. If a memory address is enclosed within the brackets, then the contents of the addressed memory location are specified. |
| $\wedge$ | Logical AND |
| $\forall$ | Logical Exclusive-OR |
| ← | Data is transferred in the direction of the arrow. |

Under the heading of STATUS in Table 14-2, an X indicates OVF is modified in the course of the instructions execution. If there is no X, it means that the status maintains the value it had before the instruction was executed.

Table 14-2. 8X300 Instruction Set

| TYPE | MNEMONIC | OPERAND(S) | BYTES | STATUS OV | OPERATION PERFORMED |
|---|---|---|---|---|---|
| I/O | MOVE | IV1,(L),IV2 | 2 | | [IV2]←[IV1] Move data from IV Byte to IV Byte. |
| | MOVE | IV1,(L),RX | 2 | | [RX]←[IV1] Move data from IV Byte to register. |
| | MOVE | RX,(L),IV1 | 2 | | [IV1]←[RX] Move data from register to IV Byte. |
| | ADD | IV1,(L),IV2 | 2 | X | [IV2]←[IV1] + [A] Add IV Byte to Auxiliary register, store result in IV Byte. |
| | ADD | IV1,(L),RX | 2 | X | [RX]←[IV1] + [A] Add IV Byte to Auxiliary register, store result in register. |
| | ADD | RX,(L),IV1 | 2 | X | [IV1]←[RX] + [A] Add register to Auxiliary register, store result in IV Byte. |
| | AND | IV1,(L),IV2 | 2 | | [IV2]←[IV1] $\wedge$ [A] AND IV Byte with Auxiliary register, store result in IV Byte. |
| | AND | IV1,(L),RX | 2 | | [RX]←[IV1] $\wedge$ [A] AND IV Byte with Auxiliary register, store result in register. |
| | AND | RX,(L),IV1 | 2 | | [IV1]←[RX] $\wedge$ [A] AND register with Auxiliary register, store result in IV Byte. |
| | XOR | IV1,(L),IV2 | 2 | | [IV2]←[IV1] $\veebar$ [A] Exclusive-OR IV Byte with Auxiliary register, store result in IV Byte. |
| | XOR | IV1,(L),RX | 2 | | [RX]←[IV1] $\veebar$ [A] Exclusive-OR IV Byte with Auxiliary register, store result in register. |
| | XOR | RX,(L),IV1 | 2 | | [IV1]←[RX] $\veebar$ [A] Exclusive-OR register with Auxiliary register, store result in IV Byte. |
| | XMIT | DATA5,(L),IV1 | 2 | | [IV1]← DATA5 Transmit immediate to IV Byte. |
| REGISTER-REGISTER MOVE | MOVE | RX,(R),RY | 2 | | [RY]←[RX] Move contents of one General Purpose register to another. |

Table 14-2. 8X300 Instruction Set (Continued)

| TYPE | MNEMONIC | OPERAND(S) | BYTES | STATUS OV | OPERATION PERFORMED |
|---|---|---|---|---|---|
| REGISTER OPERATE | MOVE | RX,(R),RX | 2 | | Rotate contents of a general purpose register and store result in the same register. |
| REGISTER-REGISTER OPERATE | ADD | RX,(R),RY | 2 | X | [RY]←[RX] + [A]<br>Add Register X to Auxiliary register, store result in Register Y. |
| | AND | RX,(R),RY | 2 | X | [RY]←[RX] Λ [A]<br>AND Register X with Auxiliary register, store result in Register Y. |
| | XOR | RX,(R),RY | 2 | X | [RY]←[RX] ⊻ [A]<br>Exclusive-OR Register X with Auxiliary register, store result in Register Y. |
| IMMEDIATE | XMIT | DATA8,RX | 2 | | [RX]← DATA8<br>Load immediate to General Purpose register. |
| BRANCH ON CONDITION | NZT | RX,DISP8 | 2 | | If [RX] ≠ 0; [PC <7,0>]← DISP8<br>Branch if register contents nonzero. |
| | NZT | IV1,(L),DISP5 | 2 | | If [IV1] ≠ 0; [PC <4,0>]← DISP5<br>Branch if IV Byte is nonzero. |
| JUMP | JMP | ADDR | 2 | | [PC]← ADDR<br>Unconditional jump. |
| | XEC | RX,DISP8 | 2 | | Execute instruction at the following address:<br>[ADDR <12,8>]←[PC <12,8>]<br>[ADDR <7,0>]←[RX] + DISP8.<br>Do not increment PC. |
| | XEC | IV1,(L),DISP5 | 2 | | Execute instruction at the following address:<br>[ADDR <12,5>]←[PC <12,5>]<br>[ADDR <4,0>]←[IV1] + DISP5<br>Do not increment PC |

The following symbols are used in Table 14-3.

a one bit of immediate address.
ddddd 5 bits choosing destination register or IV Byte.
i one bit of immediate data
lll three bits specifying length of IV Byte field.
rrr three bits specifying the number of rotates performed.
sssss 5 bits choosing source register or IV Byte.

The sssss and ddddd fields are restricted in the following ways:

If sssss or ddddd represents a register, it must be in the range $00_8$ — $17_8$.
If sssss or ddddd represetns an IV Byte, it must be in the range of $20_8$ — $37_8$.

Table 14-3. 8X300 Instruction Set Object Codes

| INSTRUCTION | | OBJECT CODE | BYTES | MACHINE CYCLES |
|---|---|---|---|---|
| ADD | IV1,(L),IV2 | 001ssssslllddddd | 2 | 1 |
| | IV1,(L),RX | | | |
| | RX,(L),IV1 | | | |
| ADD | RX,(R),RY | 001sssssrrrddddd | 2 | 1 |
| AND | IV1,(L),IV2 | 010ssssslllddddd | 2 | 1 |
| | IV1,(L),RX | | | |
| | RX,(L),IV1 | | | |
| AND | RX,(R),RY | 010sssssrrrddddd | 2 | 1 |
| JMP | ADDR | 111aaaaaaaaaaaaa | 2 | 1 |
| MOVE | IV1,(L),IV2 | 000ssssslllddddd | 2 | 1 |
| | IV1,(L),RX | | | |
| | RX,(L),IV1 | | | |
| MOVE | RX,(R),RX | 000sssssrrrsssss | 2 | 1 |
| MOVE | RX,(R(,RY | 000sssssrrrddddd | 2 | 1 |
| NZT | IV1,(L),DISP5 | 101ssssslllaaaaa | 2 | 1 |
| NZT | RX,DISP8 | 101sssssaaaaaaaa | 2 | 1 |
| XEC | IV1,(L),DISP | 100ssssslllaaaaa | 2 | 1 |
| XEC | RX,DISP | 100sssssaaaaaaaa | 2 | 1 |
| XMIT | DATA5,IV1 | 110ddddd llliiiii | 2 | 1 |
| XMIT | DATA8 | 110dddddiiiiiiii | 2 | 1 |
| XOR | IV1,(L),IV2 | 011ssssslllddddd | 2 | 1 |
| | IV1,(L),RX | | | |
| | RX,(L),IV1 | | | |
| XOR | RX,(R),RY | 011sssssrrrddddd | 2 | 1 |

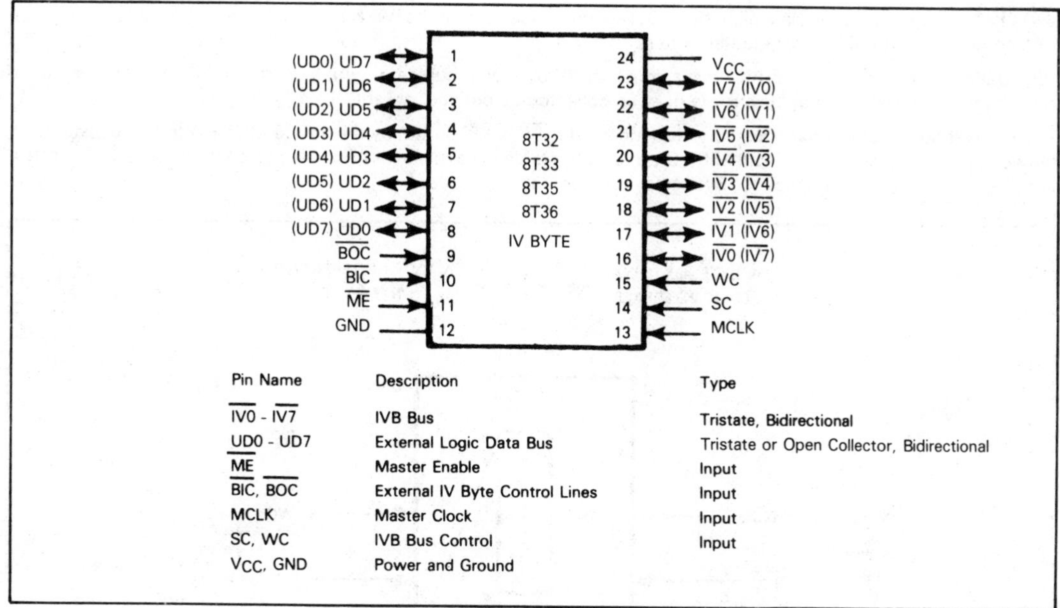


| Pin Name | Description | Type |
|---|---|---|
| IV0 - IV7 | IVB Bus | Tristate, Bidirectional |
| UD0 - UD7 | External Logic Data Bus | Tristate or Open Collector, Bidirectional |
| ME | Master Enable | Input |
| BIC, BOC | External IV Byte Control Lines | Input |
| MCLK | Master Clock | Input |
| SC, WC | IVB Bus Control | Input |
| $V_{CC}$, GND | Power and Ground | |

Figure 14-8. 8T32/3/5/6 Interface Vector Byte Signals and Pin Assignments

## THE 8T32, 8T33, 8T35, AND 8T36 INTERFACE VECTOR BYTE (IV BYTE)

**This device serves as an I/O port and IVB Bus interface for all external logic communicating with the 8X300 Microcontroller.**

**The various Interface Vector Bytes are summarized in Table 14-4. This table identifies part differences.**

**Table 14-4. Interface Vector Byte Options**

| Part Name | Data Input via UD0 - UD7 | UD Pins Logic | IV Byte Address Logic |
|---|---|---|---|
| 8T31 | Synchronous, when MCLK is high | Tristate | None |
| 8T32 | Synchronous, when MCLK is high | Tristate | Present |
| 8T33 | Synchronous, when MCLK is high | Open Collector | Present |
| 8T35 | Asynchronous, independent of MCLK | Open Collector | Present |
| 8T36 | Asynchronous, independent of MCLK | Tristate | Present |

**The IV Byte is implemented using bipolar LSI technology and is packaged as a 24-pin DIP. It requires a single +5V power supply.**

### 8T32/3/5/6 IV BYTE PINS AND SIGNALS

**Figure 14-8 illustrates the pins and signals of the IV Byte. Figure 14-9 illustrates how an IV Byte will normally be used.**

**As described for Figure 14-3, we show signal numbers in Figure 14-8 first as given in Signetics literature, then in brackets as we would number these signals.**

**$\overline{IV0}$ - $\overline{IV7}$** represent the pins via which the IV Byte communicates with the IVB Bus. These pins represent the IV Byte interface with the 8X300 microcomputer system.

**Pins UD0 - UD7** represent the 8-bit bus via which the IV Byte communicates with logic beyond the 8X300 microcomputer system. These pins may be tristate or open collector, as defined in Table 14-4.

**$\overline{ME}$ is a master enable signal.** This signal is connected to $\overline{LB}$ or $\overline{RB}$, output by the 8X300 Microcontroller to distinguish between two banks of I/O ports with 256 I/O ports addressable in each bank. $\overline{ME}$ is just one contributor to device select logic; we will describe the whole IV Byte select process later.

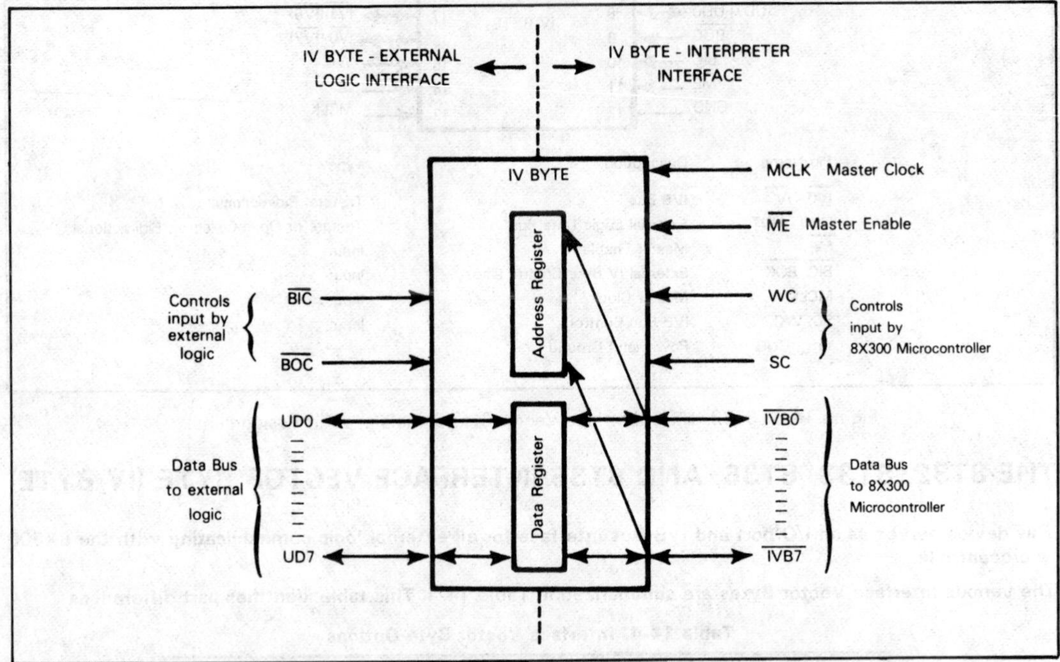


Figure 14-9. 8T32/3/5/6 IV Byte Control Signals and Interfaces

**$\overline{BIC}$ and $\overline{BOC}$ are signals which control data flow between the IV Byte and external logic, via the UD Bus.** $\overline{BIC}$ and $\overline{BOC}$ must be input to the IV Byte by external logic. MCLK, output by the 8X300 Microcontroller, synchronizes actual data transfers. $\overline{BIC}$, $\overline{BOC}$, and MCLK combine to control events on the UD Bus as follows:

| $\overline{BIC}$ | $\overline{BOC}$ | MCLK | |
|---|---|---|---|
| 1 | 0 | X | IV Byte output data to external logic |
| 0 | X | 1 | External logic input data to IV Byte (synchronous parts) |
| 0 | X | X | External logic input data to IV Byte (asynchronous parts) |
| 0 | X | 0 | Disable UD Bus for 8T31, 8T32, 8T33. Input data to IV Byte for 8T35, 8T36 |
| 1 | 1 | X | No operation |

X signifies "don't care"; the signal may be low or high.

**SC and WC control the IVB Bus which connects all IVB bytes with the 8X300 Microcontroller.** Control signals SC and WC are automatically output by the 8X300 Interpreter. $\overline{BIC}$ contributes to IVB Bus logic in order to resolve access conflicts; external logic accessing the IV Byte via the UD Bus will have priority over an 8X300 Microcontroller access occurring via the IVB Bus. MCLK synchronizes data transfers occurring via the IVB Bus for synchronous and asynchronous parts. IVB Bus control logic also requires $\overline{ME}$ to be low; observe that UD Bus logic ignores $\overline{ME}$. Combining SC, WC, $\overline{BIC}$, MCLK and $\overline{ME}$, this is how IVB Bus interface logic responds to control signals:

| SC | WC | $\overline{BIC}$ | MCLK | $\overline{ME}$ | |
|---|---|---|---|---|---|
| X | X | X | X | 1 | IV Byte not selected; no operation. |
| 0 | 0 | X | X | 0 | IV Byte must place data contents on IVB Bus. |
| 0 | 1 | 1 | 1 | 0 | IV Byte reads IVB Bus as data. |
| 1 | 0 | X | 1 | 0 | IV Byte reads IVB Bus as a select address. (not 8T31). |
| 1 | 1 | 0 | 1 | 0 | |
| 1 | 1 | 1 | 1 | 0 | IV Byte reads IVB Bus as a select address, and as data. 8T31 reads IVB Bus as data only. |

**Data is inverted when it flows across an IV Byte.** If data is input by external logic via UD0 - UD7, then the complement of this data will be read by the 8X300 on $\overline{IVB0}$ - $\overline{IVB7}$. Conversely, if the 8X300 outputs data via $\overline{IVB0}$ - $\overline{IVB7}$, then external logic will read the complement of this data via UD0 - UD7.

If the 8X300 Microcontroller reads back data which it wrote out, then it reads back the exact data it wrote out, and not the complement of the data it wrote out. Conversely, if external logic reads back the data it wrote out, then it too will read back the exact data it wrote out, and not the complement of the data it wrote out.

## 8T32/3/5/6 IV BYTE OPERATION

**There is no device address logic on the external logic interface of any IV Byte. The IV Byte inputs and outputs data via the UD0 - UD7 lines depending on the condition of the $\overline{BIC}$ and $\overline{BOC}$ signals.** Synchronous IV Bytes, as identified in Table 14-4, will input data via UD0 - UD7 only while MCLK is high. Asynchronous IV Bytes ignore MCLK when recieving data input from external logic. All data output via UD0 - UD7 is asynchronous.

**On the Microcontroller interface of an IV Byte, all devices (with the exception of the 8T31) have address logic and select logic.** The 8T31 will always respond on the Microcontroller interface if the SC, WC, $\overline{ME}$, $\overline{BIC}$, and MCLK signals are at the correct levels.

**All IV Bytes (with the exception of the 8T31) have an internal Address regiser.** The contents of this internal Address register are usually created when the IV Byte is manufactured. You can buy an IV Byte whose internal address has not been set, in which case you may set the address following a procedure described later.

The Microcontroller must output select addresses to select IV Bytes. Any IV Byte that detects a select address coinciding with its internal address will consider itself selected. It will remain selected until a new select address that does not coincide with its internal address is detected. Once an IV Byte has been selected, it will respond to data input or output operations specified by control signals on the Interpreter interface. An IV Byte which is not selected will not respond to input or output operations specified by control signals on the Interpreter interface. Select logic has no effect on the external logic interface of the IV Byte.

Address and select logic does not exist in the 8T31 IV Byte, which will therefore always respond to control signal levels on the Interpreter interface.

**8T32/3/5/6 IV BYTE ACCESS LOGIC**

**Let us now look at dialogue occurring between an IV Byte and the 8X300 Interpreter via the IVB Bus.** Note carefully that the following discussion applies only to the IV Byte-8X300 interface. The IV Byte-external logic interface is controlled entirely by external logic manipulating the $\overline{BIC}$ and $\overline{BOC}$ control signals.

At any time, just one IV Byte should consider itself selected on the left bank of IV Bytes, and just one IV Byte should consider itself selected on the right bank of IV Bytes. In order to select an IV Byte, you execute a Move instruction which outputs data to Register 7 fhe left bank, or F for the right bank. There is no Register 7 or F; in response to either of these Move instruction destination definitions, the 8X300 outputs data on the IVB Bus, just as it would for any normal data output operation, but control signals SC and WC are set to 1 and 0, respectively. A destination Register of 7 causes $\overline{LB}$ to be output low, while the destination address F causes $\overline{RB}$ to be output low. Thus, the net effect of executing a Move instruction specifying Register 7 or F as the destination is that the data moved is the address of the IV Byte which is going to consider itself selected; all other IV Bytes will at this time deselect themselves. If no IV Byte has a select address equal to the address output, then all IV Bytes will be deselected.

Once an IV Byte selects itself, it will remain selected until a subsequent Move to Register 7 or F causes a new Byte to select itself.

Remember, the 8T31 has no select logic; it always considers itself selected.

All 8X300 instructions that specify the IVB Bus as the source or destination of data will automatically access the single selected IV Byte — on the left or right bank of IV Bytes, whichever is being accessed by the Move instruction. Table 14-1 describes the way in which you specify whether the IV Byte selected on the left bank or right bank will be accessed.

Observe that external logic will always have priority over the 8X300, should both simultaneously attempt to output data to an IV Byte. $\overline{BIC}$ will be input low by external logic whenever it is attempting to write to the IV Byte; but $\overline{BIC}$ low inhibits any attempt by the 8X300 Microcontroller to write data into the IV Byte.

When inputting data from external logic using a synchronous IV Byte, you will have no timing problems. Data will be input only while MCLK is high, at which time the 8X300 is guaranteed not to be accessing the IV Byte.

When using asynchronous IV Bytes, data will be input by external logic to the IV Byte at any time. Unless you provide your own logic to guard against it, there is nothing to prevent external logic from inputting data to an asynchronous IV Byte while the 8X300 is partway through accessing the same IV Byte, in which case the 8X300 operation will be inaccurate.

## 8T32/3/5/6 IV BYTE ADDRESSES

**IV Bytes can be bought from Signetics with predefined addresses 01 through $0A_{16}$. IV Bytes with addresses $0B_{16}$ through $32_{16}$ are held in smaller quantities. You can, if you wish, buy an IV Byte whose address has not been set.** This IV Byte will, in fact, have an address of $FF_{16}$. You must create the address you want by resetting individual address bits to 0. This is an operation you can do just once. Once an address bit has been reset to 0, it cannot be set to 1 again. **The following procedure is described by Signetics for resetting individual address bits to 0:**

Table 14-5. Specifications for Signals Illustrated in Figures 14-10 and 14-11

| PARAMETER | | TEST CONDITIONS | LIMITS Min | Typ | Max | UNITS |
|---|---|---|---|---|---|---|
| $V_{CCP}$ | Programming supply voltage | | | | | |
| | Address | | 7.5 | | 8.0 | V |
| | Protect | | | 0 | | V |
| $I_{CCP}$ | Programming supply current | $V_{CCP} = 8.0V$ | | | 250 | mA |
| | Max time $V_{CCP} > 5.25V$ | | | | 1.0 | s |
| | Programming voltage | | | | | |
| | Address | | 17.5 | | 18.0 | V |
| | Protect | | 13.5 | | 14.0 | V |
| | Programming current | | | | | |
| | Address | | | | 75 | mA |
| | Protect | | | | 150 | mA |
| | Programming pulse rise time | | | | | |
| | Address | | 1 | | 1 | μs |
| | Protect | | 100 | | | μs |
| | Programming pulse width | | 5 | | 1 | ms |

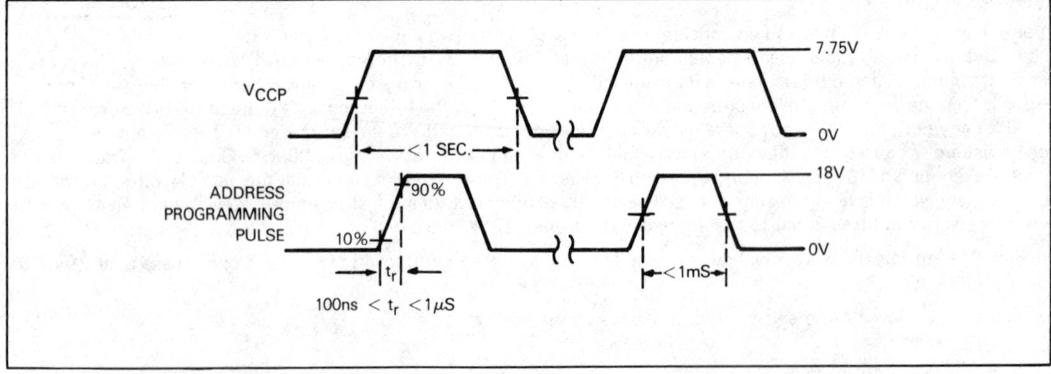


Figure 14-10. 8T32/3/5/6 IV Byte Address Programming Pulse

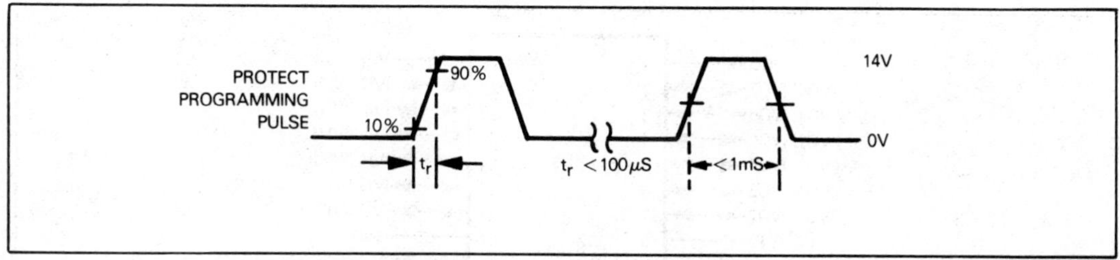


Figure 14-11. 8T32/3/5/6 IV Byte Protect Programming Pulse

1) Set all control signals to their inactive state; $\overline{BIC}$, $\overline{BOC}$, and $\overline{ME}$ must be tied to power while SC, WC, and MCLK are held at ground. Leave all IVB Bus pins open.
2) Increase $V_{CC}$ to 7.75V ± 0.25V.
3) After $V_{CC}$ has stablized, apply a single programming pulse at the UB Bus line corresponding to the bit which must be reset to 0. Figure 14-10 provides timing for the Address Programming pulse. The current should be limited to 75mA.
4) If the entire programming operation occurs in less than one second, return $V_{CC}$ to 7.75V. If the programming operation takes more than one second, $V_{CC}$ must now be reduced to 0V.
5) Repeat Steps 3 and 4 for each additional UD line whose corresponding address bit must be reset to zero.
6) Verify that the proper address exists by inserting this address via the IVB Bus, with $\overline{ME}$ and WC low, while SC and MCLK are high. Next, input data via the IVB Bus and read it via the UD Bus. If the correct address exists within the IV Byte, the inverted data will appear at the UD Bus.
7) If the address is correct, proceed to Step 8. If the address is incorrect, you may be able to save the IV Byte by hunting for the actual address using trial and error. If the actual address has one or more bits high which should be low, then you can repeat Steps 2 and 3 in an attempt to pull these bits low. If an incorrect bit has been pulled low, then you must either modify the address that you were seeking to create, or you must throw away the IV Byte.
8) Set $V_{CC}$ and all control inputs to 0 volts. Leave IVB and UD Bus line pins open.
9) Apply a protect programming pulse as illustrated in Figure 14-11 to every UD Bus pin. This includes UD Bus pins which were accessed during Steps 2 and 3, as well as UD Bus pins which were not accessed during Steps 2 and 3. The current should be limited to 150mA.
10) Apply +7V to each UD Bus pin and measure the amperage. It must be less than 1mA. If it is more than 1mA, then the particular line has been damaged and the IV Byte should be discarded.

Table 14-5 provides specifications for the pulses illustrated in Figures 14-10 and 14-11.

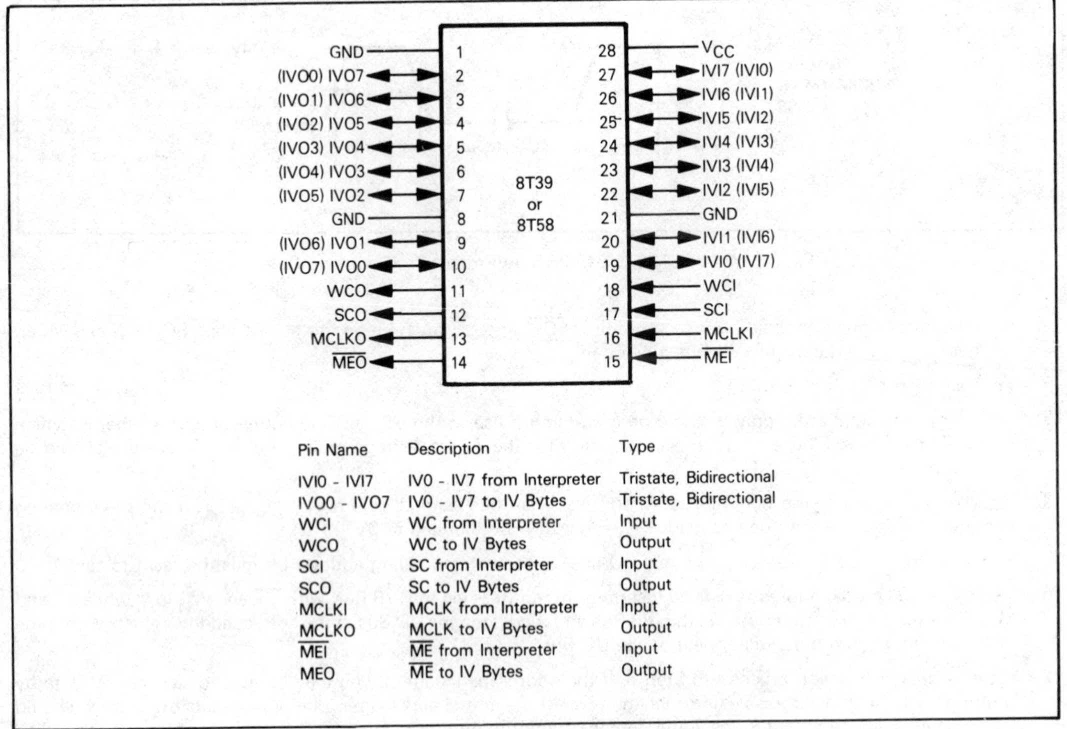


| Pin Name | Description | Type |
|---|---|---|
| IVI0 - IVI7 | IV0 - IV7 from Interpreter | Tristate, Bidirectional |
| IVO0 - IVO7 | IV0 - IV7 to IV Bytes | Tristate, Bidirectional |
| WCI | WC from Interpreter | Input |
| WCO | WC to IV Bytes | Output |
| SCI | SC from Interpreter | Input |
| SCO | SC to IV Bytes | Output |
| MCLKI | MCLK from Interpreter | Input |
| MCLKO | MCLK to IV Bytes | Output |
| $\overline{MEI}$ | $\overline{ME}$ from Interpreter | Input |
| MEO | $\overline{ME}$ to IV Bytes | Output |

Figure 14-12. 8T39 and 8T58 Bus Expander Signals and Pin Assignments

# THE 8T39 AND 8T58 BUS EXPANDERS

**These two devices buffer the IVB Bus and control signals output by the 8X300 Microcontroller. Up to 16 IV Bytes may be connected to one Bus Expander, which will present a load equivalent to one IV Byte on the 8X300 Bus. The 8T39 Bus Expander contains internal address and select logic, while the 8T58 Bus Expander does not.**

**The two Bus Expander parts are implemented using bipolar LSI technology and are packaged in 28-pin DIPs. These parts require a +5V power supply.**

**Figure 14-12 identifies the pins and signals of the two Bus Expander parts. These signals are not described, since they are identical to the signals with the same names as already described for the Microcontroller and IV Bytes.** Notice that the signals are input on one side of the Bus Expander and output on the other side of the Bus Expander. The input signals will connect to the 8X300 Microcontroller, while the output signals will generate a bus to which up to 16 IV Bytes may be connected.

**A 15 nanosecond propagation delay will occur across each Bus Expander for signals input and then output. You must make sure that you add this delay time when computing the total access time for external logic responding to an 8X300 Microcontroller access.**

The 8T39 Bus Expander has internal addressing and select logic. The 8T58 Bus Expander has no internal addressing or select logic. For the 8T39 only, the four high-order address lines are examined when the 8X300 outputs an IV Byte address. The actual response of the 8T39 to addresses is identical to that which we have described for IV Bytes. The 16 IV Bytes connected to an 8T39 Bus Expander must have addresses corresponding to the fixed four high-order address bits specified by the Bus Expander.

There are four address options available to you when buying an 8T39 Bus Expander. These four address options, and the allowed IV Byte addresses that may be connected to each option, are identified in Table 14-6.

Table 14-6. 8T39 Bus Expander Addresses and IV Byte Addresses That May Be Connected

| Part Number | 8T39 Internal Address | IV Byte addresses that may be connected |
|---|---|---|
| 8T39-00 | 0000XXXX | $00\text{-}0F_{16}$ |
| 8T39-01 | 0001XXXX | $10_{16}\text{-}1F_{16}$, $20_{16}\text{-}2F_{16}$, $40_{16}\text{-}4F_{16}$, $80_{16}\text{-}8F_{16}$ |
| 8T39-03 | 0011XXXX | $30_{16}\text{-}3F_{16}$, $50_{16}\text{-}5F_{16}$, $60_{16}\text{-}6F_{16}$, $90_{16}\text{-}9F_{16}$, $A0_{16}\text{-}AF_{16}$, $C0_{16}\text{-}CF_{16}$ |
| 8T39-07 | 0111XXXX | $70_{16}\text{-}7F_{16}$, $B0_{16}\text{-}BF_{16}$, $D0_{16}\text{-}DF_{16}$, $E0_{16}\text{-}EF_{16}$ |
| 8T39-17 | 1111XXXX | $F0_{16}\text{-}FF_{16}$ |

# DATA SHEETS

The following section contains specific electrical and timing data for the following devices:

- 8X300 Interpreter
- 8T32 IV Byte
- 8T39 Bus Expander

## DC ELECTRICAL CHARACTERISTICS

| PARAMETER | | TEST CONDITIONS | LIMITS | | | UNIT |
|---|---|---|---|---|---|---|
| | | | Min | Typ | Max | |
| $V_{IH}$ | High level input voltage | | | | | |
| | X1,X2 | | .6 | | | V |
| | All others | | 2 | | | V |
| $V_{IL}$ | Low level input voltage | | | | | |
| | X1,X2 | | | | .4 | V |
| | All others | | | | .8 | V |
| $V_{CL}$ | Input clamp voltage (Note 1) | $V_{CC}$ = 4.75V<br>$I_I$ = -10mA | | | -1.5 | V |
| $I_{IH}$ | High level input current | | | | | |
| | X1,X2 | $V_{CC}$ = 5.25V<br>$V_{IH}$ = .6V | | 2700 | | μA |
| | All others | $V_{CC}$ = 5.25V<br>$V_{IH}$ = 4.5V | | <1 | 50 | μA |
| $I_{IL}$ | Low level input current | | | | | |
| | X1,X2 | $V_{CC}$ = 5.25V<br>$V_{IL}$ = .4V | | -2500 | | μA |
| | $\overline{\text{IVBO-7}}$ | $V_{CC}$ = 5.25V<br>$V_{IL}$ = .4V | | -140 | -200 | μA |
| | IO-I15 | $V_{CC}$ = 5.25V<br>$V_{IL}$ = .4V | | -880 | -1600 | μA |
| | $\overline{\text{HALT}}$, $\overline{\text{RESET}}$ | $V_{CC}$ = 5.25V<br>$V_{IL}$ = .4V | | -230 | -400 | μA |
| $V_{OL}$ | Low level output voltage | | | | | |
| | A0-A12 | $V_{CC}$ = 4.75V<br>$I_{OL}$ = 4.25mA | | .35 | .55 | V |
| | All others | $V_{CC}$ = 4.75V<br>$I_{OL}$ = 16mA | | .35 | .55 | V |
| $V_{OH}$ | High level output voltage | $V_{CC}$ = 4.75V<br>$I_{OH}$ = 3mA | 2.4 | | | V |
| $I_{OS}$ | Short circuit output current (Note 2) | $V_{CC}$ = 5.25V | -30 | | -140 | mA |
| $V_{CC}$ | Supply voltage | | 4.75 | 5 | 5.25 | V |
| $I_{CC}$ | Supply current | $V_{CC}$ = 5.25V | | 300 | 450 | mA |
| $I_{REG}$ | Regulator control | $V_{CC}$ = 5.0V | -14 | | -21 | mA |
| $I_{CR}$ | Regulator current (Note 3) | $V_{CR}$ = 0 | | | 290 | mA |
| $V_{CR}$ | Regulator voltage (Note 3) | $V_{REG}$ = 0V | 2.2 | | 3.2 | V |

NOTES

1 Crystal inputs X1 and X2 do not have clamp diodes.

2 Only one output may be grounded at a time.

3 (Limits apply for $V_{CC}$ = 5V ± 5% and 0°C ≤ $T_A$ ≤ 70°C unless specified otherwise.)

signetics

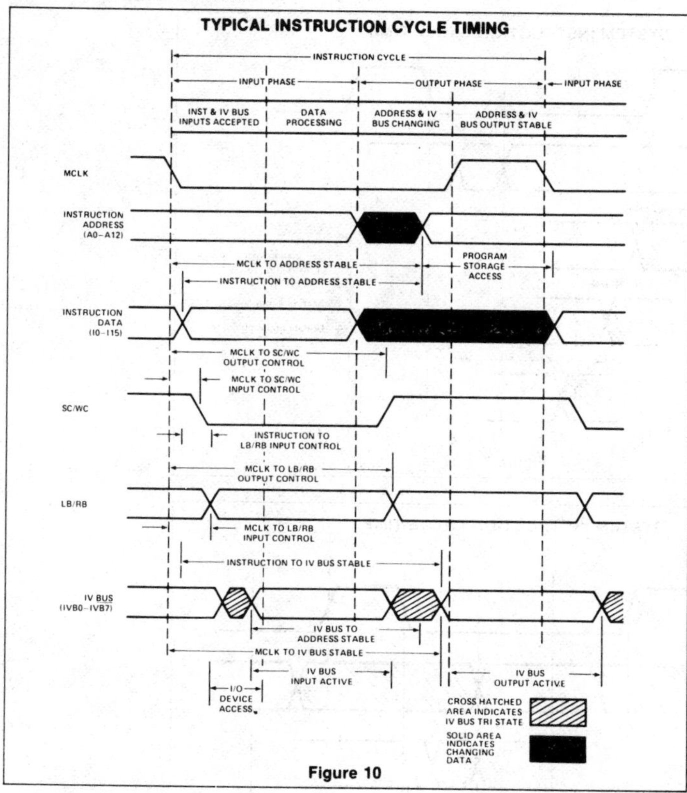


Figure 10

## ABSOLUTE MAXIMUM RATINGS

Supply Voltage $V_{CC}$ ........ 7V
Logic Input Voltage ........ 5.5V
Crystal Input Voltage ........ 2V

## AC ELECTRICAL CHARACTERISTICS $V_{CC} = 5V \pm 5\%$ and $0°C \leq T_A < 70°C$

| DELAY DESCRIPTION | PROPAGATION DELAY TIME | CYCLE TIME LIMIT |
|---|---|---|
| X1 falling edge to MCLK (driven from external pulse generator) | 75ns | |
| MCLK to SC/WC falling edge (input phase) | 25ns | |
| MCLK to SC/WC rising edge (output phase) | | ½ cycle + 25ns |
| MCLK to LB/RB (input phase) | 35ns | |
| Instruction to LB/RB output (input phase) | 35ns | |
| MCLK to LB/RB (output phase) | | ¼ cycle + 35ns |
| MCLK to IV data (output phase) | 185ns | ½ cycle + 60ns |
| IV data (input phase) to IV data (output phase) | 115ns | |
| Instruction to Address | 185ns | ½ cycle + 40ns |
| MCLK to Address | 185ns | ½ cycle + 40ns |
| IV data (input phase) to Address | 115ns | |
| MCLK to IV data (input phase) | | ½ cycle - 55ns |
| MCLK to Halt falling edge to prevent current cycle | | ¼ cycle - 40ns |
| Reset rising edge to first MCLK | | 0 to 1 cycle |

NOTE
1. Reference to MCLK is to the falling edge when loaded with 300pF.
2. Loading on Address lines is 150pF.

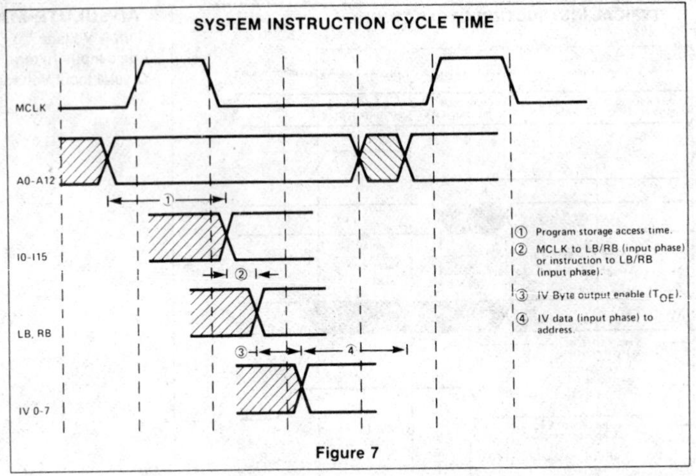


Figure 7

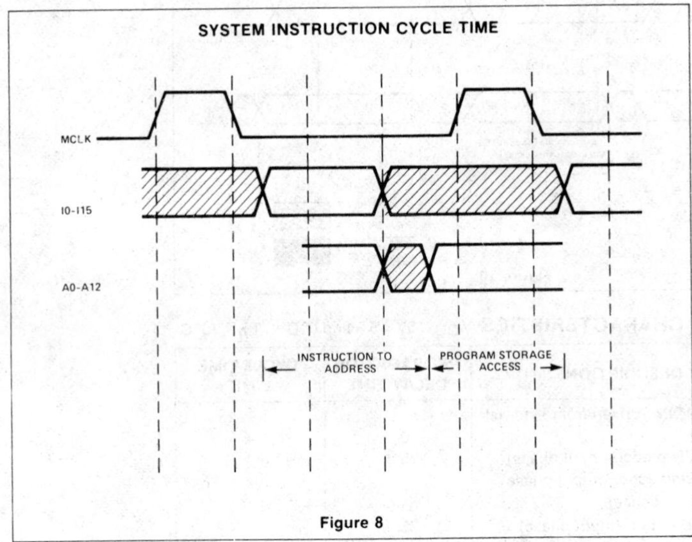


Figure 8

## DC ELECTRICAL CHARACTERISTICS $V_{CC}$ = 5V ± 5%, 0°C ≤ $T_A$ ≤ 70°C unless otherwise specified

| | PARAMETER | TEST CONDITIONS | LIMITS Min | Typ | Max | UNIT |
|---|---|---|---|---|---|---|
| | Input voltage | | | | | V |
| $V_{IH}$ | High | | 2.0 | | | |
| $V_{IL}$ | Low | | | | .8 | |
| $V_{IC}$ | Clamp | $I_I$ = −5mA<br>$V_{CC}$ = 4.75V | | | −1 | |
| | Output voltage | | | | | V |
| $V_{OH}$ | High | | 2.4 | | | |
| $V_{OL}$ | Low | | | | .55 | |
| | Input current[3] | $V_{CC}$ = 5.25V | | | | μA |
| $I_{IH}$ | High | $V_{IH}$ = 5.25V | | <10 | 100 | |
| $I_{IL}$ | Low | $V_{IL}$ = .5V | | -350 | -550 | |
| | Output current[4] | | | | | mA |
| $I_{OS}$ | Short circuit | $V_{CC}$ = 4.75V | | | | |
| | UD bus | | 10 | | | |
| | IV bus | | 20 | | | |
| $I_{CC}$ | $V_{CC}$ supply current | $V_{CC}$ = 5.25V | | 100 | 150 | mA |

## PROGRAMMING SPECIFICATIONS[5]

| | PARAMETER | TEST CONDITIONS | LIMITS Min | Typ | Max | UNITS |
|---|---|---|---|---|---|---|
| $V_{CCP}$ | Programming supply voltage | | | | | |
| | Address | | 7.5 | | 8.0 | V |
| | Protect | | | 0 | | V |
| $I_{CCP}$ | Programming supply current | $V_{CCP}$ = 8.0V | | | 250 | mA |
| | Max time $V_{CCP}$ > 5.25V | | | | 1.0 | s |
| | Programming voltage | | | | | |
| | Address | | 17.5 | | 18.0 | V |
| | Protect | | 13.5 | | 14.0 | V |
| | Programming current | | | | | |
| | Address | | | | 75 | mA |
| | Protect | | | | 150 | mA |
| | Programming pulse rise time | | | | | |
| | Address | | .1 | | 1 | μs |
| | Protect | | 100 | | | μs |
| | Programming pulse width | | .5 | | 1 | ms |

NOTES

3. The input current includes the tri-state/open collector leakage current of the output driver on the data lines.
4. Only one output may be shorted at a time.
5. If all programming can be done in less than 1 second, VCC may remain at 7.75V for the entire programming cycle.

## AC ELECTRICAL CHARACTERISTICS

| PARAMETER | INPUT | TEST CONDITION | LIMITS | | | UNIT |
|---|---|---|---|---|---|---|
| | | | Min | Typ | Max | |
| $t_{PD}$ User data delay (Note 1) | UDX<br>MCLK*<br>BIC† | $C_L$ = 50pF | | 25<br>45<br>40 | 38<br>61<br>55 | ns |
| $t_{OE}$ User output enable | BOC | $C_L$ = 50pF | 18 | 26 | 47 | ns |
| $t_{OD}$ User output disable | BIC<br>BOC | $C_L$ = 50pF | 18<br>16 | 28<br>23 | 35<br>33 | ns |
| $t_{PD}$ IV data delay (Note 1) | IVBX<br>MCLK | $C_L$ = 50pF | | 38<br>48 | 53<br>61 | ns |
| $t_{OE}$ IV output enable | ME<br>SC<br>WC | $C_L$ = 50pF | 14 | 19 | 25 | ns |
| $t_{OD}$ IV output disable | ME<br>SC<br>WC | $C_L$ = 50pF | 13 | 17 | 32 | ns |
| $t_W$ Minimum pulse width | MCLK<br>BIC† | | 40<br>35 | | | ns |
| $t_{SETUP}$ Minimum setup time | UD□<br>BIC*<br>IVX<br>ME<br>SC<br>WC | (Note 2) | 15<br>25<br>55<br>30<br>30<br>30 | | | ns |
| $t_{HOLD}$ Minimum hold time | UDX□<br>BIC*<br>IVX<br>ME<br>SC<br>SC | (Note 2) | 25<br>10<br>10<br>5<br>5<br>5 | | | ns |

* Applies for 8T32 and 8T33 only.
† Applies for 8T35 and 8T36 only.
□ Times are referenced to MCLK for 8T32 and 8T33, and are referenced to BIC for 8T35 and 8T36.

NOTES:

1. Data delays referenced to the clock are valid only if the input data is stable at the arrival of the clock and the hold time requirement is met.
2. Set up and hold times given are for "normal" operation. BIC setup and hold times are for a user write operation. SC setup and hold times are for an IV Byte select operation. WC setup and hold times are for an IV Bus write operation. ME setup and hold times are for both IV write and select operations.

## ABSOLUTE MAXIMUM RATINGS

| PARAMETER | | RATING | UNIT |
|---|---|---|---|
| $V_{CC}$ | Power supply voltage | -0.5 to +7 | Vdc |
| $V_{IN}$ | Input voltage | -0.5 to +5.5 | Vdc |
| $V_O$ | Off-state output voltage | -0.5 to +5.5 | Vdc |
| $T_A$ | Operating temperature range | -55 to +125 | °C |
| $T_{stg}$ | Storage temperature range | -65 to +150 | °C |

ADDRESS PROGRAMMING PULSE

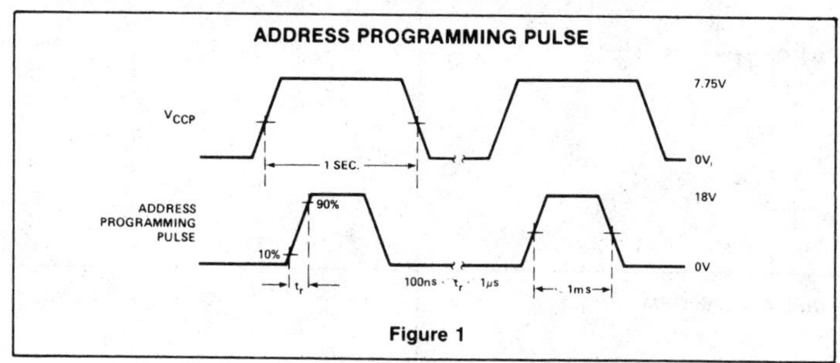


Figure 1

PROTECT PROGRAMMING PULSE

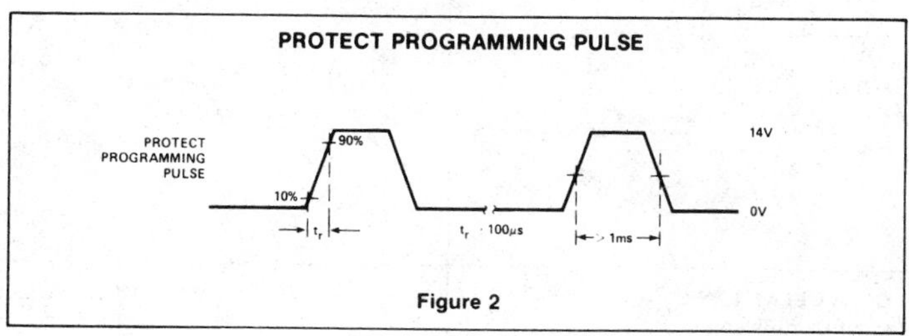


Figure 2

## PARAMETER MEASUREMENT INFORMATION

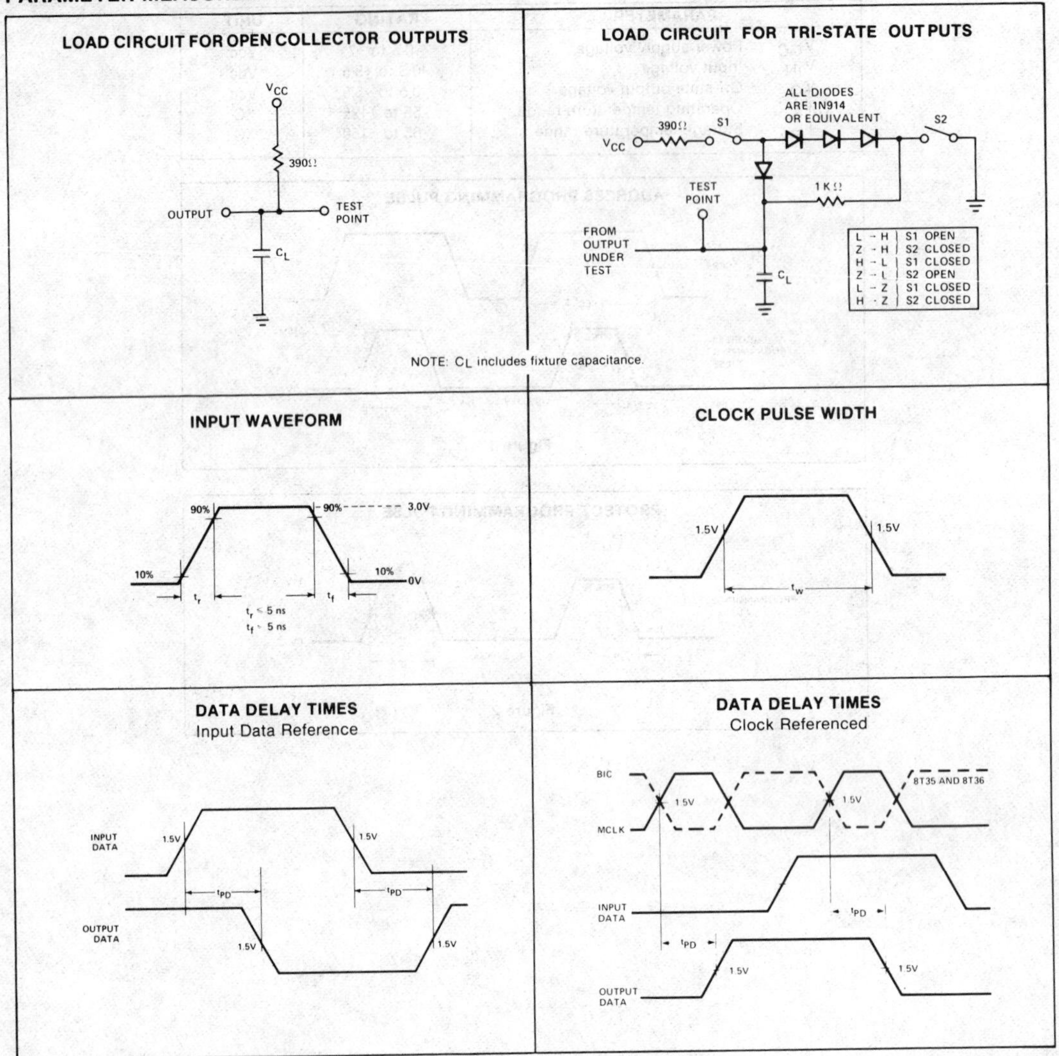

## PARAMETER MEASUREMENT INFORMATION (Cont'd)

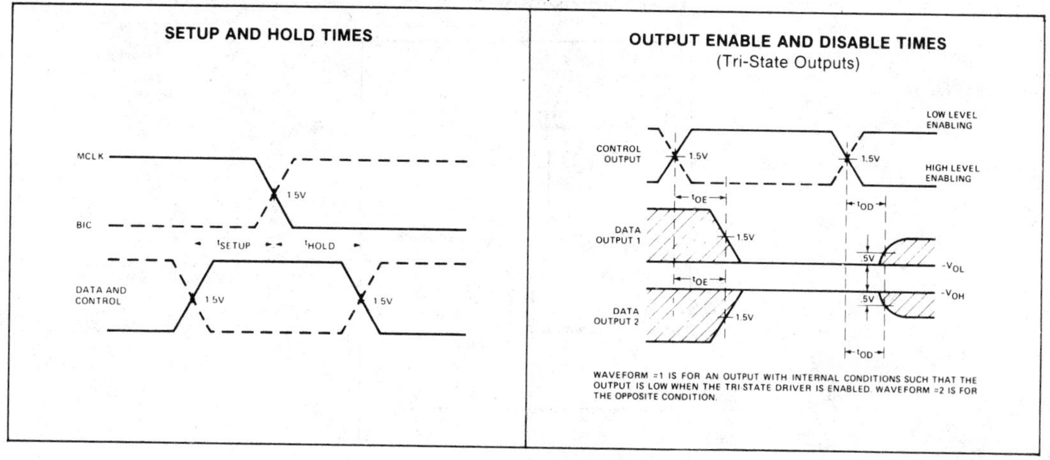

## 8T39 BUS EXPANDER

### TEST LOAD CIRCUIT

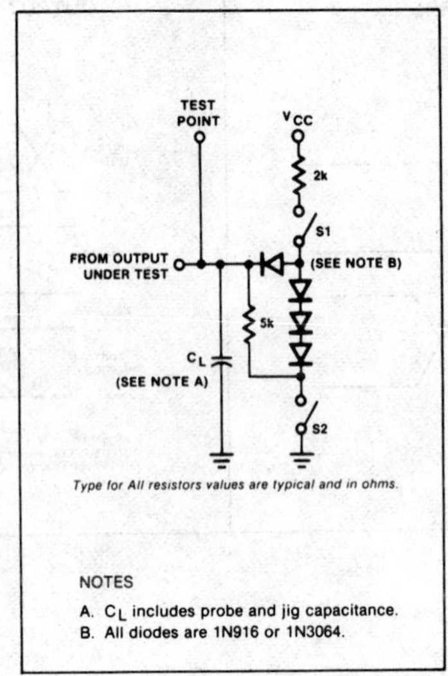


NOTES
A. $C_L$ includes probe and jig capacitance.
B. All diodes are 1N916 or 1N3064.

### DC ELECTRICAL CHARACTERISTICS $V_{CC} = 5V \pm 5\%, 0°C \leqslant T_A \leqslant 70°C$

| PARAMETER | | TEST CONDITIONS | LIMITS | | | UNIT |
|---|---|---|---|---|---|---|
| | | | Min | Typ | Max | |
| | Input voltage | | | | | V |
| $V_{IL}$ | Low | | | | .8 | |
| $V_{IH}$ | High | | 2.0 | | | |
| $V_{IC}$ | Clamp | | | | -1 | |
| | Output voltage | $V_{CC} = 4.75V$ | | | | V |
| $V_{OL}$ | Low | $I_{OL} = 16mA$ | | | .55 | |
| $V_{OH}$ | High | $I_{OH} = -3.2mA$ | 2.4 | | | |
| | Input current | $V_{CC} = 5.25V$ | | | | uA |
| $I_{IL}$ | Low | $V_{IL} = .5V$ | | | -250 | |
| $I_{IH}$ | High | $V_{IH} = 5.25V$ | | < 10 | 100 | |
| $I_{OS}$ | Short circuit output current | $V_{CC} = 4.75V$ | -40 | | | mA |
| $I_{CC}$ | Supply current | $V_{CC} = 5.25V$ | | | 200 | mA |

### AC ELECTRICAL CHARACTERISTICS $V_{CC} = 5V \pm 5\%, 0°C \leqslant T_A \leqslant 70°C, C_L = 300pF$

| PARAMETER | | TO | FROM | TEST CONDITIONS | LIMITS | | | UNIT |
|---|---|---|---|---|---|---|---|---|
| | | | | | Min | Typ | Max | |
| | Path delay | | | | | | | ns |
| tpd | Data | DOX<br>DIX | DIX<br>DOX | | | | 15 | |
| tpd | Control | $\overline{ME}$ (out)<br>MCLK (out)<br>SC (out<br>WC (out) | $\overline{ME}$ (in)<br>MCLK (in)<br>SC (in)<br>WC (in) | | | | 15 | |

## 8T39BUS EXPANDER

### VOLTAGE WAVEFORMS

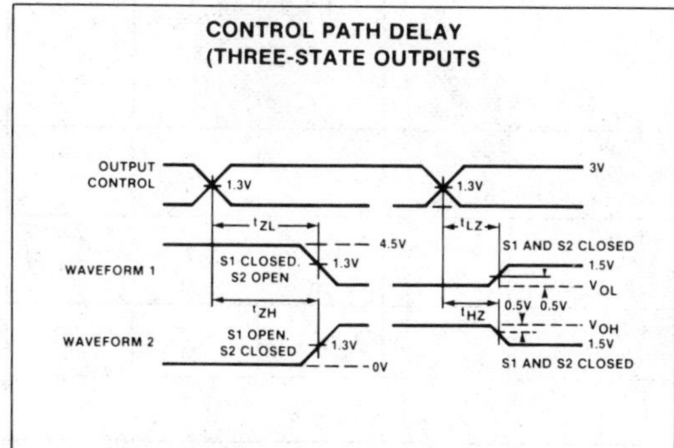


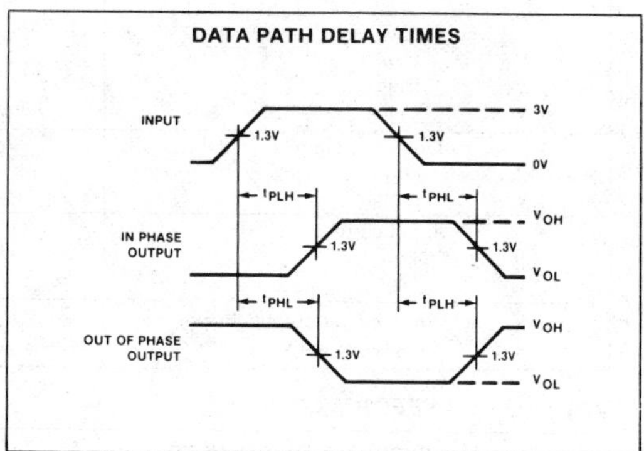


## 8T58 TRANSPARENT BUS EXPANDER

### ABSOLUTE MAXIMUM RATINGS

| | PARAMETER | RATING | UNIT |
|---|---|---|---|
| $V_{CC}$ | Power supply voltage | +7 | Vdc |
| $V_{IN}$ | Input voltage | +5.5 | Vdc |
| $V_O$ | Off-state output voltage | +5.5 | Vdc |
| $T_A$ | Operating temperature range | 0 to +70 | °C |
| $T_{STG}$ | Storage temperature range | -65 to +150 | °C |

NOTE Includes tri-state leakage.

### AC ELECTRICAL CHARACTERISTICS $V_{CC} = 5V \pm 5\%$, $0°C \le T_A \le 70°C$, $C_L = 300pF$

| PARAMETER | | TO | FROM | TEST CONDITIONS | LIMITS | | | UNIT |
|---|---|---|---|---|---|---|---|---|
| | | | | | Min | Typ | Max | |
| $t_{pd}$ | Path delay Data | DOX<br>DIX | DIX<br>DOX | | | | 15 | ns |
| $t_{pd}$ | Control | $\overline{ME}$(OUT)<br>MCLK(OUT)<br>SC(OUT)<br>WC(OUT) | $\overline{ME}$(IN)<br>MCLK(IN)<br>SC(IN)<br>WC(IN) | | | | 15 | ns |
| $t_{oe}$ | Data Output Enable | DIX<br>DOX | $\overline{ME}$(IN)<br>SC(IN)<br>WC(IN) | | 28 | | 56 | ns |
| $t_{od}$ | Data Output Disable | DIX<br>DOX | $\overline{ME}$(IN)<br>SC(IN)<br>WC(IN) | | 15 | | | |

# 8T58 TRANSPARENT BUS EXPANDER

| PARAMETER | | TEST CONDITIONS | LIMITS Min | Typ | Max | UNIT |
|---|---|---|---|---|---|---|
| | Input voltage | | | | | V |
| $V_{IL}$ | Low | | | | .8 | |
| $V_{IH}$ | High | | 2.0 | | | |
| $V_{IC}$ | Clamp | -5mA at $V_{CC}$ min | | | -1 | |
| | Output voltage | $V_{CC}$ = 4.75V | | | | V |
| $V_{OL}$ | Low | $I_{OL}$ = 50mA | | | .55 | |
| $V_{OH}$ | High | $I_{OH}$ = -3.2mA | 2.4 | | | |
| | Input current | $V_{CC}$ = 5.25V | | | | μA |
| $I_{IL}$ | Low[1] | $V_{IL}$ = .5V | | | -250 | |
| $I_{IH}$ | High[1] | $V_{IH}$ = 5.25V | | <10 | 100 | |
| $I_{OS}$ | Short circuit output current | $V_{CC}$ = 4.75V | -40 | | | mA |
| $I_{CC}$ | Supply current | $V_{CC}$ = 5.25V | | | 200 | mA |

## VOLTAGE WAVEFORMS

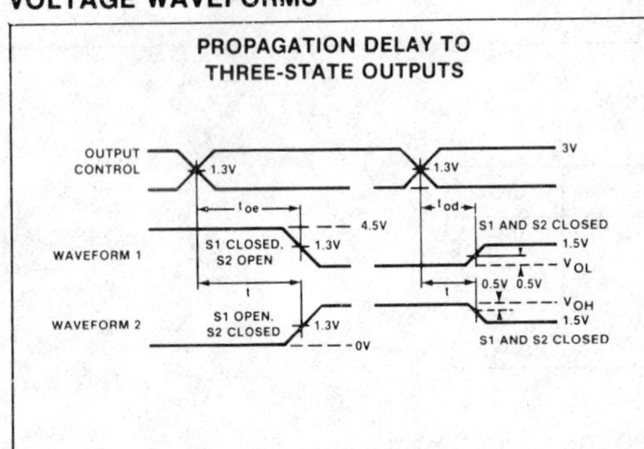


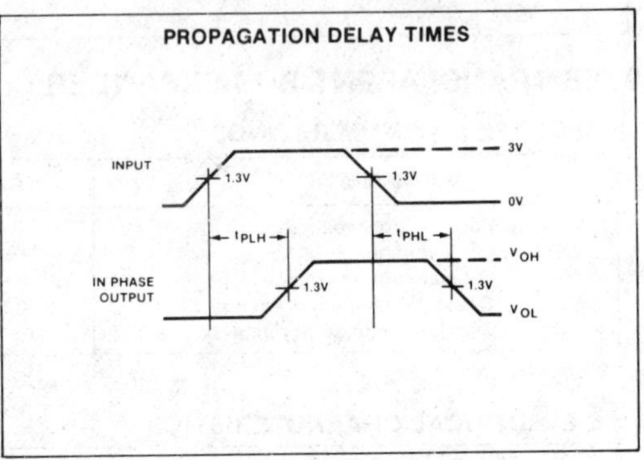


## TEST LOAD CIRCUIT

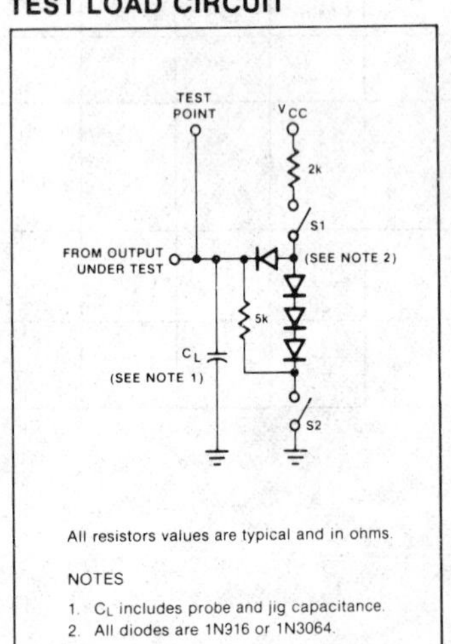


All resistors values are typical and in ohms.

NOTES

1. $C_L$ includes probe and jig capacitance.
2. All diodes are 1N916 or 1N3064.

## TYPICAL APPLICATION

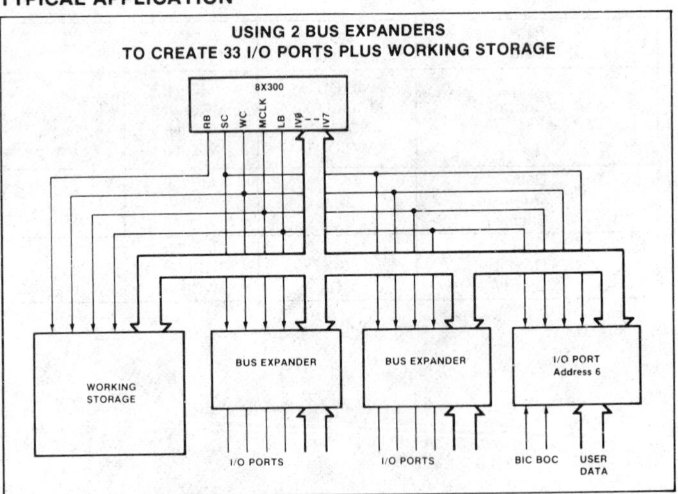

# Chapter 15
# THE GENERAL INSTRUMENT 1650 SERIES MICROCOMPUTERS

The 1650 series of one-chip microcomputers have been manufactured by General Instrument to compete in the high-volume, price sensitive, digital logic replacement market. If we compare the 1650 series of one-chip microcomputers to other one-chip microcomputers, they are most similar to the 3870; in reality, they are copies of no other product. They are unique devices in their own right.

Describing the 1650 family of microcomputers at this point in the book is, perhaps, not strictly accurate, since they are not 16-bit microcomputers, nor do they have any relationship to the CP1600 described in the previous chapter.

The 1650 series have separate on-chip program and data memories. Program memory is 12 bits wide, while data memory is 8 bits wide. Table 15-1 summarizes the 1650 options. None of these microcomputers are expandable. If your application outgrows the 1670, then you must look elsewhere for a replacement.

The prime source for the 1650 series of microcomputers is:

GENERAL INSTRUMENT CORP.
Microelectronics Division
600 West John Street
Hicksville, New York 11802

In Europe a second source for the 1650 is:

INTERMETALL
19 Hans-Bun Strasse
7800 Freiburg
West Germany

The 1650 series microcomputers use a single +5V power supply. With an oscillator frequency of 1 MHz, instructions execute in four or eight microseconds.

1650 series devices are packaged as 18-pin, 28-pin, or 40-pin DIPs. They are manufactured using NMOS ion implantation technology and have TTL-compatible signals.

**Figure 15-1 illustrates that part of our general microcomputer system logic which is implemented on the 1650 series one-chip microcomputers.** Once again, we must warn against making direct comparisons using these figures; logic shown as present says nothing about the extent to which the logic has been implemented. Read/write memory is shown only half present because between 11 and 39 bytes of on-chip read/write memory are provided by the various 1650 options. 64 words is the smallest amount of read/write memory provided by any other one-chip microcomputer.

## A 1650 FUNCTIONAL OVERVIEW

**Logic of the 1650 series microcomputers is illustrated functionally in Figure 15-2.**

The Arithmetic and Logic Unit and the Control Unit are inaccessible to you as a user, therefore we will ignore this portion of the microcomputer.

Table 15-1. 1650 Series One-Chip Microcomputer Options

| Part Number | Program Memory 12-Bit Words | Data Memory Bytes | I/O Lines | Input Only Lines | Output Only Lines | Stack Levels | Interrupts | Power Supply | Package Pins |
|---|---|---|---|---|---|---|---|---|---|
| 1650 | 512 | 23 | 8 x 4 | - | - | 2 | No | + 5V | 40 |
| 1655 | 512 | 23 | 8 x 1 | 4 x 1 | 8 x 1 | 2 | No | + 5V | 28 |
| 1670 | 1024 | 39 | 8 x 4 | - | - | 4 | Yes | + 5V | 40 |
| 1645 | 256 | 16 | 4 x 1 | 4 x 1 | 4 x 1 | 3 | Yes | + 5V | 18 |

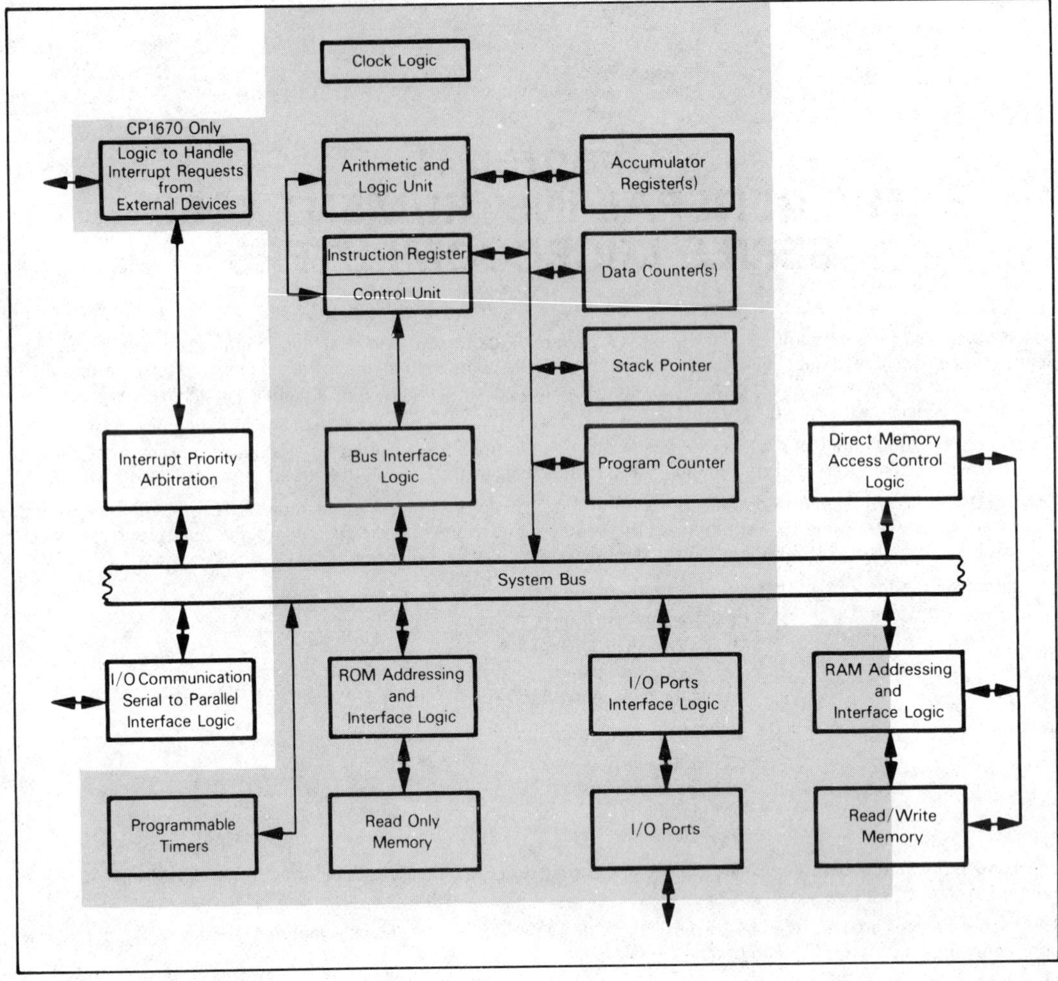


Figure 15-1. Logic of the 1650 Series Microcomputers

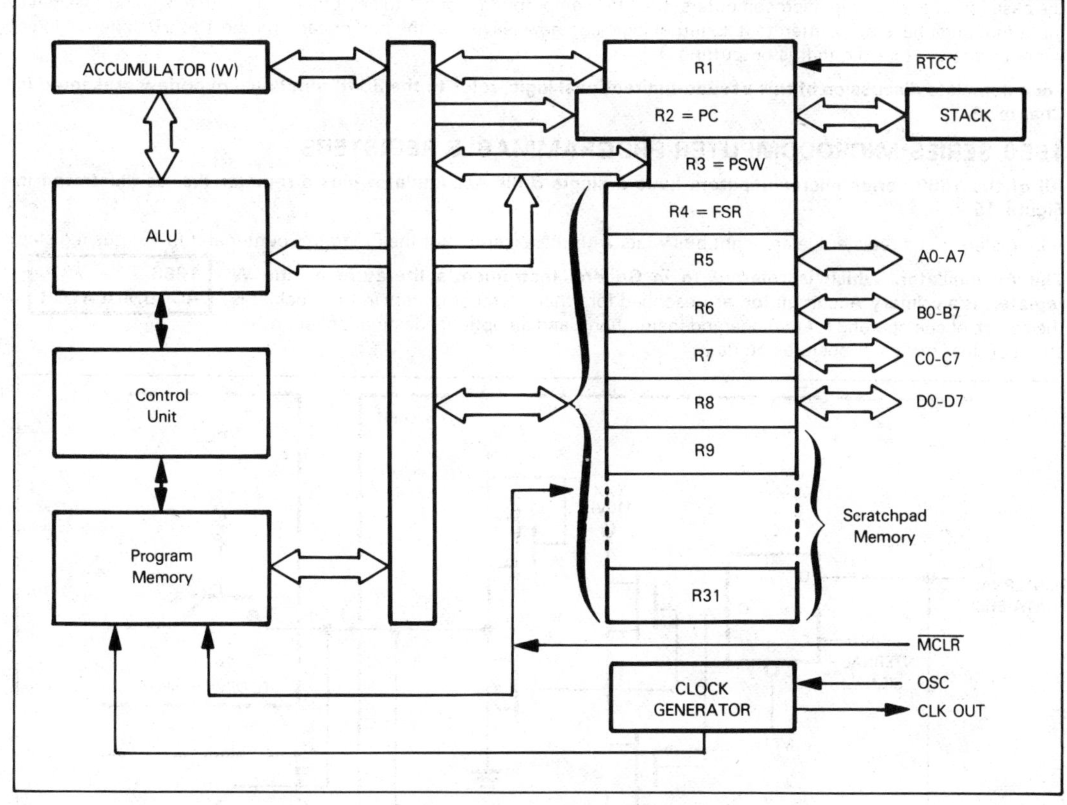


Figure 15-2. 1650 Functional Logic

**Program memory is 12 bits wide. The 1650 has 512 words of program memory. As illustrated in Table 15-1, other variations may have 256 or 1024 words of program memory.** All program memory is read-only memory. There are currently no EPROM or EAROM program memory versions of the 1650. For development purposes, there is the 1664, which has no on-chip program memory; rather, it generates a memory Address Bus and a program memory Data Bus via a 64-pin DIP, so that external program memory can be accessed. Note that General Instrument has strong EAROM (Electrically Alterable Read-Only Memory) technology, but no significant EPROM (Erasable Programmable Read-Only Memory) technology. EPROMs and EAROMs are described in Volume 3.

**1650 PROGRAM MEMORY**

**I/O ports of 1650 series microcomputers are connected directly to 8-bit registers which can also be accessed as general purpose registers.** In Figure 15-2, Registers R5, R6, R7, and R8 are shown connected to four 8-bit bidirectional I/O ports. **I/O variations for other 1650 options are summarized in Table 15-1. Register connections for these other options are defined in Table 15-2.**

**1650 I/O PORT REGISTERS**

**1650 I/O PIN LOGIC**

**Those 1650 series microcomputer I/O pins which are defined as bidirectional are, in reality, pseudo-bidirectional. Pin logic is illustrated in Figure 15-3.** The logic illustrated in this figure has become standard pseudo-bidirectional pin logic for one-chip microcomputers. The 3870 and 8048 have similar logic.

When outputting data to a 1650 I/O port pin, the data is applied to the D input of a D-type flip-flop, which is clocked by an internal WRITE control signal. The reason for having two sets of gates on the flip-flop output is to provide a high voltage from $V_{XX}$ when switching a pin low. $V_{CC}$ sources 100 microamps. Thus, external logic connected to a high-level pin need only sink 100 microamps in order to pull a high pin low. External logic that attempts to write a 1 to a pin that is outputting 0 must pull-up Q2, which will be on and connected to ground; this is not feasible. Therefore, as was the case for other one-chip microcomputers, the CPU can output a 0 or a 1 to any pin, but a pin that is going to receive input must first have a 1 written to it. External logic can now leave 1 at the pin, or can pull the 1 to a 0. External logic cannot write a 1 to a pin that is outputting 0.

**For a complete discussion of this pseudo-bidirectional logic, refer to the 8048 functional overview presented in Chapter 6.**

## 1650 SERIES MICROCOMPUTER PROGRAMMABLE REGISTERS

**All of the 1650 series microcomputers have a single 8-bit Accumulator plus a register file, as illustrated in Figure 15-2.**

All registers in the register file are eight bits wide, with the exception of the Program Counter and the Status register.

**1650 ACCUMULATOR**

**The Accumulator, which is referred to in General Instrument's literature as the W register, is a primary Accumulator,** as described for other microcomputers in this book. It is the source of one operand for two-operand instructions, and an optional destination for any instruction that moves or operates on data.

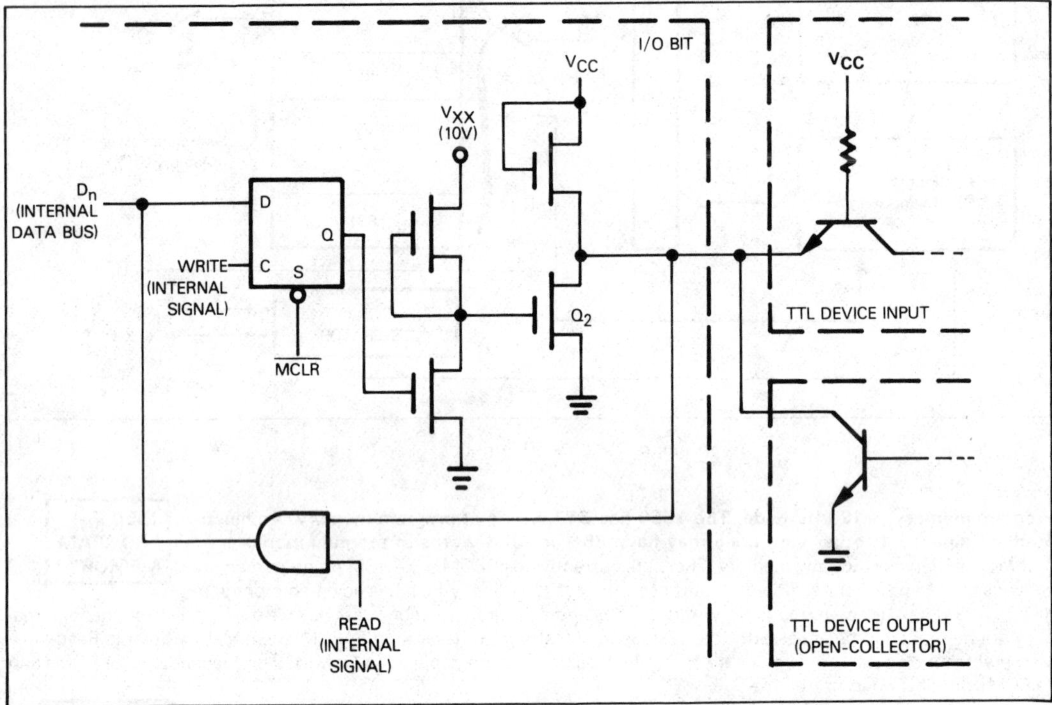


Figure 15-3. 1650 Series Microcomputer Bidirectional I/O Port Pin Logic

**Register 0 does not exist. When identified by any instruction, implied register addressing via Register 4 is assumed.** That is to say, when Register 0 is specified as a source or destination, the register identified by R4 will be selected instead. For example, suppose R4 contains $0F_{16}$. An instruction which selects R0 will then, in fact, access R15.

Register R1 can be used as a general purpose register unless you are making use of 1650 real-time clock/counter logic. **Every high-to-low transition of the $\overline{RTCC}$ input increments the contents of R1.**

**1650 PROGRAM COUNTER**

**Register R2 is the Program Counter.** The bit width of Register R2 depends on program memory size. For 1650 series microcomputers that have 512 words of program memory, R2 will be nine bits wide. The 1670 one-chip microcomputer will have a 10-bit R2 register, while the 1645 will have an 8-bit R2 register. **R2 is a write-only location;** however, it is otherwise treated as a general purpose register. Thus, any instruction that specifies a general purpose register as a destination, without specifying the same general purpose register as a source, can select Register R2. But note that all data manipulations operate on eight bits of data only. Thus, to a limited extent, 1650 series microcomputer program memory is divided into 256-word pages.

**1650 STATUS REGISTER**

**Register R3 is the Status register. This register is only three bits wide and contains the following status flags:**

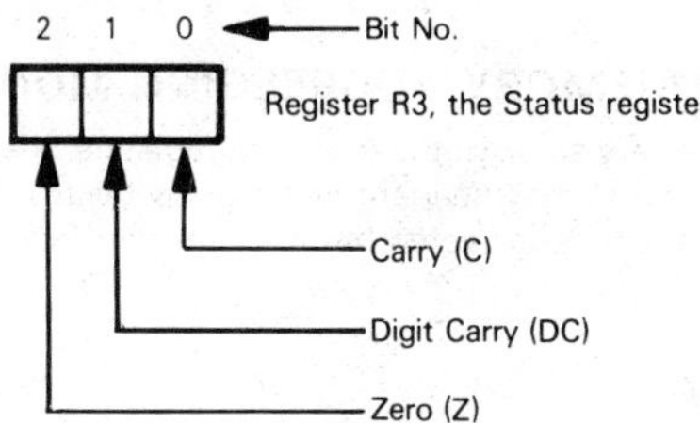


The Carry status is absolutely standard. It reflects a carry out of the high-order bit following an arithmetic operation. When a subtract instruction is executed, the Carry status is set if twos complement addition causes a carry out of the high-order result bit.

The Digit Carry status is an Auxiliary Carry; it identifies any carry from bit 3 to bit 4:

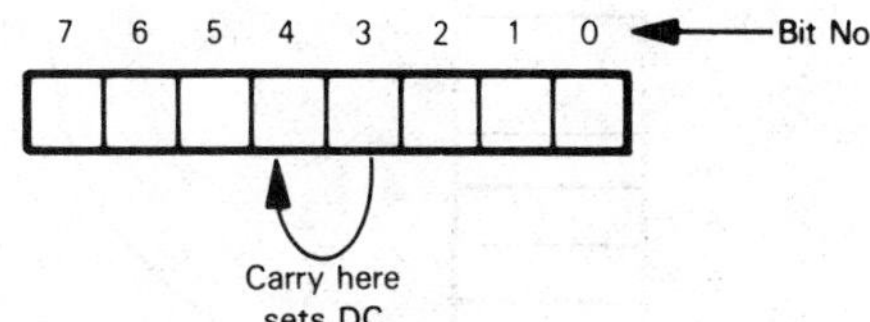


The Zero status is set to 1 when an arithmetic operation produces a 0 result; it is reset to 0 when an arithmetic operation generates a non-zero result.

Register R3 is a read/write location. Instructions can identify R3 as a source or destination for data. When reading the contents of R3, bits 3 through 7 will be read as 1 bits. When writing to R3, bits 3 through 7 will be lost.

**Register R4 is a register pointer** similar to the ISAR register described for the 3870. Register R4 is an 8-bit register; however, the low-order five bits are interpreted as a register select whenever an instruction identifies R0 (which does not exist).

Table 15-2. 1650 Series Microcomputer Register Designations

| REGISTER | FUNCTION | | | |
|---|---|---|---|---|
| | 1650 | 1655 | 1670 | 1645 |
| R0 | Not implemented. Specifies implied register addressing via R4 | | | |
| R1 | Real-time clock/counter register | | | |
| R2 | Program Counter | | | |
| R3 | Status register | | | |
| R4 | File Select register, holds implied register address | | | |
| R5 | I/O Port A | I/O Port A | I/O Port A | I/O Port A (bits 0-3 only) |
| R6 | I/O Port B | Output Port B | I/O Port B | Output Port B (bits 0-3 only) |
| R7 | I/O Port C | Input Port C (bits 0-3 only) | I/O Port C | Input Port C (bits 0-3 only) |
| R8 | I/O Port D | Scratchpad register | I/O Port D | Scratchpad register |
| R9-R19 | Scratchpad registers present in all versions | | | |
| R20-R23 | Scratchpad registers | | | Not present |
| R24-R31 | Scratchpad registers | | | Not present |
| R32-R47 | Not present | | Scratchpad registers | Not present |

**Registers R5 through R8 are connected to I/O ports in various ways for different members of the 1650 family, as defined in Table 15-2.** When you write to any one of these four registers, associated I/O port pins, if they contain output logic, will generate a high output level for a 1 and a low output level for a 0. When you read the contents of Register R5, R6, R7, or R8, then each register bit that is connected to an I/O port input pin will reflect the level of the most recently input data. For an I/O pin, if no data has been input, then the most recently output data will be read back. Any register bit that is not connected to an I/O port pin becomes a standard Scratchpad register bit. Whatever was most recently written to this bit will be read back.

**Beginning with Register R9, remaining registers are general Scratchpad registers.** Different 1650 versions provide different numbers of Scratchpad registers.

## 1650 SERIES MICROCOMPUTER MEMORY ADDRESSING MODES

Since the 1650 series microcomputers have a very small number of data registers, they have very simple data memory addressing options. Scratchpad registers up to R31 may be identified directly by any instruction that operates on data. If Register R0 is identified, however, then the register selected by the low-order five bits of Register R4 will in fact be selected. This may be illustrated as follows:

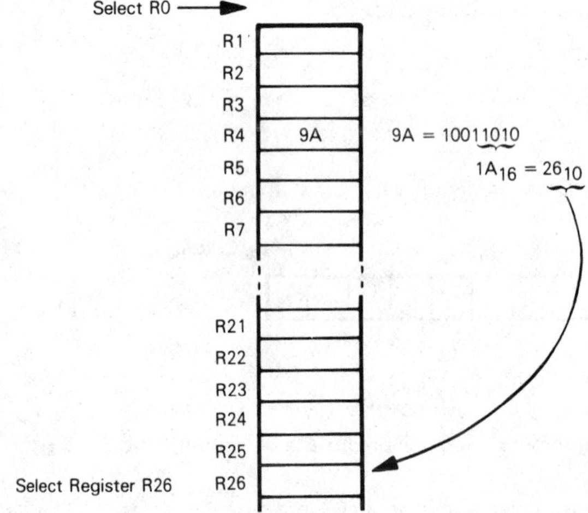


For the 1670 only, six bits of Register R4 are active address bits. This is necessary since the 1670 has general purpose registers numbered up to $47_{10}$. Note that **for the 1670, general-purpose registers R32 through R47 can be accessed only via Register R4, using indirect addressing.**

**Program memory is addressed by Jump instructions and Jump-to-Subroutine instructions, using direct addressing only.**

Jump instructions can identify any 9-bit address — covering the 512 words of program memory.

The Jump-to-Subroutine instruction can directly address only the first 256 words of program memory; all subroutines must therefore be origined in the first 256 words of program memory, although a subroutine can be called from any memory word.

**1650 STACK**

**The 1670 one-chip microcomputer has a four-level Stack; other 1650 series one-chip microcomputers have a two-level or three-level Stack.** Thus, with the exception of the 1670 and the 1645, only a single level of subroutine nesting is allowed. The 1670 allows three levels of subroutine nesting, the 1645, two. For a program that can only be 512 words long, two levels of subroutine nesting are probably quite sufficient.

## 1650 SERIES MICROCOMPUTER PINS AND SIGNALS

**Figure 15-4 illustrates pins and signals for the 1650 microcomputer.**

**1645 pin assignments are not available at the present time.**

The 1650 series microcomputers communicate with external logic via their I/O ports. **In Figure 15-4, three types of I/O pins are identified: pseudo-bidirectional, input-only, and output-only pins.** We have already described the logic of pseudo-bidirectional pins. Input-only and output-only pins, as their names imply, are limited to receiving data from external logic only or transmitting data to external logic only.

The 1650 series microcomputers have just two control signals: $\overline{\text{MCLR}}$ and $\overline{\text{RTCC}}$.

$\overline{\text{MCLR}}$ is a master reset control input. This signal should be held low for at least 1 millisecond after the power supply is valid. It forces all output pins to a high level and it sets all Program Counter bits to 1. Therefore, the first instruction executed following a reset will be located at the highest program memory location.

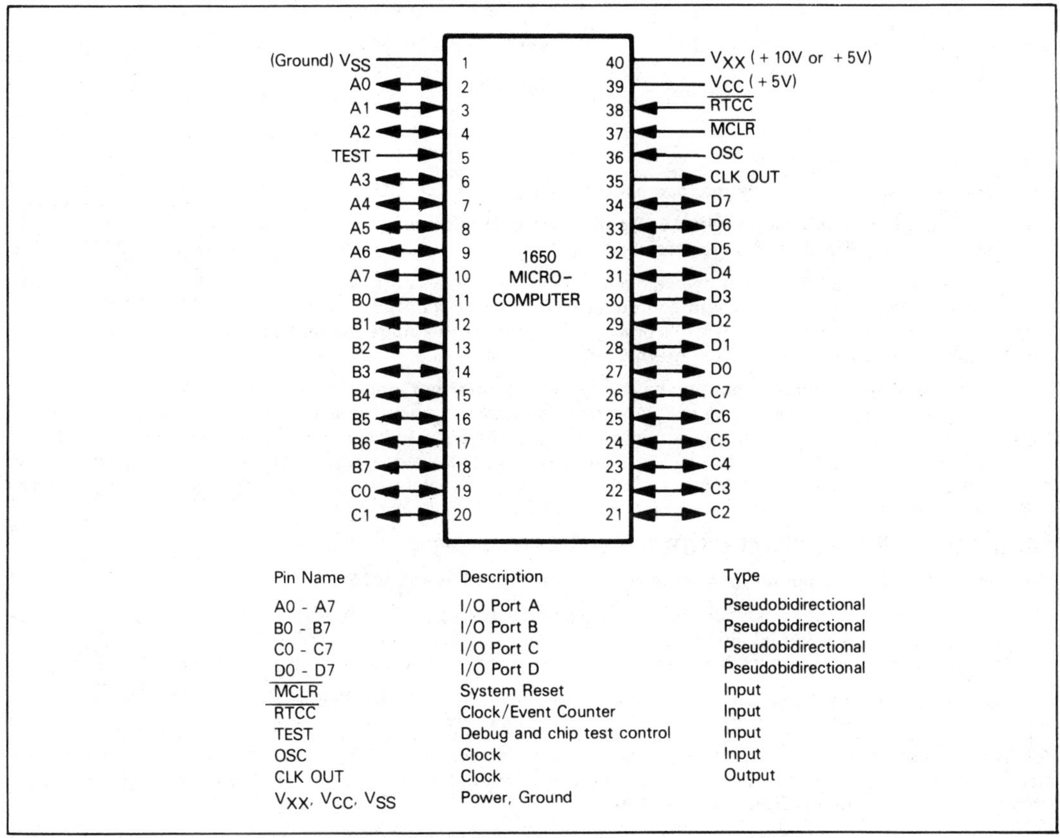


| Pin Name | Description | Type |
|---|---|---|
| A0 - A7 | I/O Port A | Pseudobidirectional |
| B0 - B7 | I/O Port B | Pseudobidirectional |
| C0 - C7 | I/O Port C | Pseudobidirectional |
| D0 - D7 | I/O Port D | Pseudobidirectional |
| $\overline{\text{MCLR}}$ | System Reset | Input |
| $\overline{\text{RTCC}}$ | Clock/Event Counter | Input |
| TEST | Debug and chip test control | Input |
| OSC | Clock | Input |
| CLK OUT | Clock | Output |
| $V_{XX}$, $V_{CC}$, $V_{SS}$ | Power, Ground | |

Figure 15-4. 1650 Microcomputer Signals and Pin Assignments

**1650 COUNTER/ TIMER LOGIC**

**On high-to-low transitions of $\overline{\text{RTCC}}$, the contents of Register R1 are incremented.** $\overline{\text{RTCC}}$ will not respond to a frequency that is greater than 250 KHz. That is all there is to 1650 counter/timer logic. No interrupts are generated on a time-out, nor is there any special logic associated with reading the contents of Register R1 or writing to this register. A program will access Register R1 as it would any other register, and $\overline{\text{RTCC}}$ will increment register contents without regard to events internal to the microcomputer.

If you are not using counter/timer logic, it is a good idea to ground the $\overline{\text{RTCC}}$ pin.

**TEST is a control input used to read the contents of program memory as data.** General Instrument purposely provides no information on the TEST pin or how it is used, since they do not want customers using this pin.

Two pins are associated with clock logic: the OSC input and the CLK OUT output. For very precise execution frequency, an external oscillator signal can be input via OSC. For less precise input, an RC network may generate the input as follows:

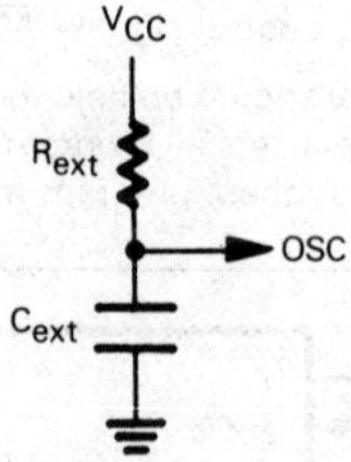


$R_{ext}$ and $C_{ext}$ options are described in the data sheets at the end of this chapter.

**The clock signal which drives the microcomputer is output via CLK OUT.**

**1650 TIMING**

**The very simple timing associated with 1650 series one-chip microcomputers is given in the data sheets at the end of this chapter.**

**1650 $V_{XX}$ POWER SUPPLY**

Although you can run any 1650 series one-chip microcomputer with a single +5V power supply, it is sometimes desirable to have **an additional +10V power supply** connected to the $V_{XX}$ input. As illustrated in Figure 15-3, this power supply **allows the bidirectional I/O port pins to sink more current,** typically to drive higher current loads such as LED displays.

**None of the 1650 series microcomputers have any DMA or interrupt logic.** The absence of DMA logic makes a lot of sense; the whole concept of Direct Memory Access is ridiculous when your data memory consists of 39 bytes or less. The absence of interrupt logic is simply a designer's choice. There are plenty of arguments for including interrupt logic in a one-chip microcomputer, since this allows external devices to influence event sequences asynchronously within the one-chip microcomputer. In the absence of interrupt logic, a program executed by a 1650 series microcomputer must test an input pin looking for a high or low level to trigger specific events.

## 1650 SERIES MICROCOMPUTER INSTRUCTION SET

**The 1650 series microcomputer instruction set is summarized in Table 15-3.**

We have arbitrarily chosen to classify instructions which access registers as memory reference instructions. These are also I/O instructions if Register R5, R6, R7, or R8 is identified. If Register R3 is identified, they become status instructions. Furthermore, any of these instructions could also be classified as register-register instructions.

Instructions that test, set, and clear bits become I/O instructions if a bit of Register R5, R6, R7, or R8 is specified; they are Status registers if Register R3 is specified.

The more you look at the 1650 instruction set, the more multifaceted many of the instructions become. General Instrument recognized this fact by creating **assembly language instruction mnemonics to identify special cases** of instructions. These **are summarized in Table 15-4.**

**There are two anomalies in the 1650 instruction set which you must guard against.**

**There is no Add-with-Carry instruction.** This makes it difficult to handle multi-byte arithmetic. Consider 16-bit binary addition.

You can start off simply enough by adding the two low-order bytes; this will generate a carry for the two high-order bytes:

```
   1 <-------- C
  31    EA
  24    6B
 ----------
        55
```

On first inspection, adding the two high-order bytes looks like no problem. You can add the carry to the augend:

```
 0 <---------- C
  32    EA
  24    6B
 ----------
        55
```

Then you add the high-order addend byte to the sum of the high-order augend byte plus the carry:

```
0 <-------- C
  32   EA
  24   6B
  -------
  56   55
```

A problem arises if the high-order augend byte happens to be FF. Now when you add a carry to FF, you get 00 and the carry is reset:

```
   1 <-------- C --------> 1
  FF   EA            00   EA
  24   6B            24   6B
  -------            -------
       55                 55
```

Upon adding the high-order addend byte, the Carry status will be cleared erroneously:

```
0 <-------- C (should be 1)
  00   EA
  24   6B
  -------
  24   55
```

This becomes a significant problem when dealing with numbers that are three or more bytes long, since you can no longer guarantee that the correct carry will be generated for the second and higher-order bytes. There are ways around this problem, but they lead to more complex programs. Fortunately the problem is not particularly severe, since in an application that is limited to a data memory as small as that of the 1650 you are most unlikely to have much multi-byte arithmetic anyway.

Note that **any time you return from a subroutine you will modify the contents of the Accumulator.**

**Table 15-5 summarizes 1650 instruction object codes and execution times.**

## THE 1650 BENCHMARK PROGRAM

**Our standard benchmark program is of little use with the 1650 microcomputers.** Given the very small amount of data memory available, moving blocks of data around makes no sense. **We therefore illustrate a modified benchmark program in which a number of data bytes are input via I/O Port A and then output via I/O Port B.** The first data byte input identifies the length of the data block which follows.

We are going to use bit 0 of I/O Port C to provide handshaking controls between the 1650 and external logic. Whenever external logic transmits new data to I/O Port A, it resets bit 0 of I/O Port C low. The 1650 program tests this bit before attempting to read data from I/O Port A. As soon as the program outputs data to I/O Port B, it sets I/O Port C bit 0 high again. Thus, external logic can wait until it detects I/O Port C bit 0 high before attempting to input new data — which will be followed by I/O Port C bit 0 being pulled low by external logic.

Here is the necessary instruction sequence:

```
        MOVLW   FF       INITIALIZE PORT A FOR INPUT BY
        MOVWF   R5       OUTPUTTING ALL HIGH BITS
        BSF     R7,0     SET PORT C BIT 0 HIGH
L1      BTFSC   R7,0     IF PORT C BIT 0 IS 0, READ FIRST DATA BYTE
        GOTO    L1
        MOVF    R5       INPUT FIRST BYTE
        MOVWF   R9       STORE AS A COUNTER IN R9
LOOP    BSF     R7,0     SET PORT C BIT 0 HIGH
L2      BTFSC   R7,0     IF PORT C BIT 0 IS 0, READ NEXT DATA BYTE
        GOTO    L2
        MOVF    R5,0     INPUT NEXT DATA BYTE FROM PORT A
        MOVWF   R6       OUTPUT VIA PORT B
        MOVLW   FF       PREPARE PORT A FOR NEW INPUT
        MOVWF   R5
        DECFSZ  R9       DECREMENT R9
        GOTO    LOOP     IF NOT ZERO, RETURN FOR NEXT BYTE
```

These abbreviations are used in Tables 15-3 and 15-4:

| | |
|---|---|
| R | Any register |
| W | Accumulator, or W register |
| d | Destination identifier digit; must be 0 or 1. |
| [$\overline{R}$] | Ones complement of Register R contents |
| DATA | Immediate 8-bit data value |
| LABEL9 | Program memory address (9 bits) |
| [STACK]← | Push onto Stack |
| ←[STACK] | Pop off Stack |
| n | A bit identification number, in the range 0 through 7. (0 low-order, 7 high-order) |

Table 15-3. A Summary of the 1650 Series Microcomputer Instruction Set

| TYPE | MNEMONIC | OPERAND(S) | BYTES | STATUSES C | DC | Z | | | | OPERATION PERFORMED |
|---|---|---|---|---|---|---|---|---|---|---|
| I/O, PRIMARY MEMORY REFERENCE AND REGISTER-REGISTER MOVE | MOVF | R,O | 1 | | | X | | | | [W]←[R]<br>Move register (or I/O port) contents to Accumulator. |
| | MOVWF | R | 1 | | | | | | | [R]←[W]<br>Move Accumulator contents to register or I/O port. |
| SECONDARY I/O, MEMORY OR REGISTER REFERENCE/OPERATE | ADDWF | R,d | 1 | X | X | X | | | | [W]←[W] + [R] if d=0. [R]←[W] + [R] if d=1.<br>Add Accumulator and register contents. Store sum in the Accumulator or source register. |
| | ANDWF | R,d | 1 | | | X | | | | [W]←[W] AND [R] if d=0. [R]←[W] AND [R] if d=1<br>AND Accumulator and register contents. Store result in the Accumulator or source register. |
| | CLRF | R | 1 | | | 1 | | | | [R]←0<br>Zero Register R contents. |
| | COMF | R,d | 1 | | | X | | | | [W]←[$\overline{R}$] if d=0. [R]←[$\overline{R}$] if d=1<br>Store the ones complement of register contents in the Accumulator, or back in the register. |
| | DECF | R,d | 1 | | | X | | | | [W]←[R] - 1 if d=0. [R]←[R] - 1 if d=1<br>Store decremented register contents in the Accumulator, or back in the register. |
| | INCF | R,d | 1 | | | X | | | | [W]←[R] + 1 if d=0. [R]←[R] + 1 if d=1<br>Store incremented register contents in the Accumulator, or back in the register. |
| | IORWF | R,d | 1 | | | X | | | | [W]←[R] OR [W] if d=0. [R]←[R] OR [W] if d=1.<br>OR Accumulator and register contents. Store result in the Accumulator or Source register. |
| | RLF | R,d | 1 | X | | | | | | Left rotate register contents. Store result in Accumulator if d=0 or in register if d=1.<br>C<br>Register contents |
| | RRF | R,d | 1 | X | | | | | | Right rotate register contents. Store result in Accumulator if d=0 or in register if d=1.<br>C<br>Register contents |

Table 15-3. A Summary of the 1650 Series Microcomputer Instruction Set (Continued)

| TYPE | MNEMONIC | OPERAND(S) | BYTES | STATUSES C | DC | Z | | | | OPERATION PERFORMED |
|---|---|---|---|---|---|---|---|---|---|---|
| SECONDARY I/O, MEMORY OR REGISTER REFERENCE [OPERATE | SUBWF | R,d | 1 | X | X | X | | | | [W]←[R] - [W] if d=0. [R]←[R] - [W] if d=1<br>Subtract Accumulator contents from register contents. Store result in Accumulator or source register. |
| | SWAPF | R,d | 1 | | | | | | | Swap register nibbles. Store result in Accumulator if d=0 or in register if d=1.<br>Register contents |
| | XORWF | R,d | 1 | | | X | | | | Exclusive-OR Accumulator and register contents. Store result in Accumulator if d=0 or in register if d=1. |
| IMMEDIATE | MOVLW | DATA | 1 | | | | | | | [W]←DATA<br>Load immediate data into Accumulator. |
| JUMP | GOTO | LABEL9 | 1 | | | | | | | [R2]←LABEL9<br>Jump to instruction LABEL9, anywhere in 512 word program memory. |
| SUBROUTINE CALL AND RETURN | CALL | LABEL8 | 1 | | | | | | | [STACK]←[R2]+1, [R2]←LABEL8<br>Jump to subroutine origined at LABEL8, anywhere in first 256 words of program memory. Push return address onto Stack. |
| | RET | | 1 | | | | | | | [R2]←[STACK], [W]←0<br>Return from subroutine and clear Accumulator. |
| | RETLW | DATA | 1 | | | | | | | [R2]←[STACK], [W]←DATA<br>Return from subroutine and load immediate data into Accumulator. |
| IMMEDIATE OPERATE | ANDLW | DATA | 1 | | | X | | | | [W]←[W] AND DATA<br>AND Accumulator contents with immediate data. Store result in Accumulator. |
| | IORLW | DATA | 1 | | | X | | | | [W]←[W] OR DATA<br>OR Accumulator contents with immediate data. Store result in Accumulator. |
| | XORLW | DATA | 1 | | | X | | | | [W]←[W] XOR DATA<br>Exclusive-OR Accumulator contents with immediate data. Store result in Accumulator. |

Table 15-3. A Summary of the 1650 Series Microcomputer Instruction Set (Continued)

| TYPE | MNEMONIC | OPERAND(S) | BYTES | STATUSES C | DC | Z | | | | OPERATION PERFORMED |
|---|---|---|---|---|---|---|---|---|---|---|
| SKIP ON CONDITION | BTFSC | R,n | 1 | | | | | | | Test bit n of Register R. If it is 0, skip the next instruction. |
| | BTFSS | R,n | 1 | | | | | | | Test bit n of Register R. If it is 1, skip the next instruction. |
| | DECFSZ | R,d | 1 | | | | | | | Decrement Register R contents. If the result is zero, skip the next instruction. |
| | INCFSZ | R,d | 1 | | | | | | | Increment Register R contents. If the result is zero, skip the next instruction. |
| REGISTER OPERATE | CLRW | | | | | 1 | | | | [W]←0<br>Clear Accumulator. |
| STATUS AND BIT OPERATIONS | BCF | R,n | | | | | | | | Reset bit n of Register R to 0 |
| | BSF | R,n | | | | | | | | Set bit n of Register R to 1 |
| | NOP | | | | | | | | | No operation. |

Table 15-4. Mnemonics Recognized by the 1650 Assembler for Special Cases of General Instructions

| Special Mnemonic | Equivalent Mnemonic(s) | Status Affected | Function |
|---|---|---|---|
| CLRC | BCF 3,0 | - | Clear Carry |
| SETC | BSF 3,0 | - | Set Carry |
| CLRDC | BCF 3,1 | - | Clear Digit Carry |
| SETDC | BSF 3,1 | - | Set Digit Carry |
| CLRZ | BCF 3,2 | - | Clear Zero |
| SETZ | BSF 3,2 | - | Set Zero |
| SKPC | BTFSS 3,0 | - | Skip on Carry |
| SKPNC | BTFSC 3,0 | - | Skip on No Carry |
| SKPDC | BTFSS 3,1 | - | Skip on Digit Carry |
| SKPNDC | BTFSC 3,1 | - | Skip on No Digit Carry |
| SKPZ | BTFSS 3,2 | - | Skip on Zero |
| SKPNZ | BTFSC 3,2 | - | Skip on No Zero |
| TSTF R | MOVF R,1 | Z | Test File |
| MOVFW R | MOVF R,0 | Z | Move File to W |
| NEGF R,d | COMF R,1 | | Negate File |
| | INCF R,d | Z | |
| ADDCF R,d | BTFSC 3,0 | | Add Carry to File |
| | INCF R,d | Z | |
| SUBCF R,d | BTFSC 3,0 | | Subtract Carry from File |
| | DECF R,d | Z | |
| ADDDCF R,d | BTFSC 3,1 | | Add Digit Carry to File |
| | INCF R,d | Z | |
| SUBDCF R,d | BTFSC 3,1 | | Subtract Digit Carry from File |
| | DECF R,d | Z | |
| B LABEL9 | GO TO LABEL9 | - | Branch |
| BC LABEL9 | BTFSC 3,0 | | Branch on Carry |
| | GO TO LABEL9 | - | |
| BNC LABEL9 | BTFSS 3,0 | | Branch on No Carry |
| | GO TO LABEL9 | - | |
| BDC LABEL9 | BTFSC 3,1 | | Branch on Digit Carry |
| | GO TO LABEL9 | - | |
| BNDC LABEL9 | BTFSS 3,1 | | Branch on No Digit Carry |
| | GO TO LABEL9 | - | |
| BZ LABEL9 | BTFSC 3,2 | | Branch on Zero |
| | GO TO LABEL9 | - | |
| BNZ LABEL9 | BTFSS 3,2 | | Branch on No Zero |
| | GO TO LABEL9 | - | |

The following abbreviations are used in the "Object Code" column of Table 15-5:

C - a "don't care" binary digit

n - binary digits that identify a bit number

r - binary digits that represent a register number

x - any hexadecimal digit

a - binary digits of a nine-bit address

Abbreviations defined for Table 15-3 are preserved in the "Instruction" column of Table 15-5.

Table 15-5. 1650 Instruction Set Object Codes

| Instruction | | Object Code |
|---|---|---|
| ADDWF | R,d | 000111drrrrr |
| ANDLW | DATA | Exx |
| ANDWF | R,d | 000101drrrrr |
| BCF | R,n | 0100nnnrrrrr |
| BSF | R,n | 0101nnnrrrrr |
| BTFSC | R,n | 0110nnnrrrrr |
| BTFSS | R,n | 0111nnnrrrrr |
| CALL | LABEL | 9xx |
| CLRF | R | 0000011rrrrr |
| CLRW | | 0000010ccccc |
| COMF | R,d | 001001drrrrr |
| DECF | R,d | 000011drrrrr |
| DECFSZ | R,d | 001011drrrrr |
| GOTO | LABEL9 | 101aaaaaaaaa |
| INCF | R,d | 001010drrrrr |
| INCFSZ | R,d | 001111drrrrr |
| IORLW | DATA | Dxx |
| IORWF | R,d | 000100drrrrr |
| MOVF | R,d | 001000drrrrr |
| MOVLW | DATA | Cxx |
| MOVWF | R | 0000001rrrrr |
| NOP | | 000 |
| RET | | 800 |
| RETLW | DATA | 8xx |
| RLF | R,d | 001101drrrrr |
| RRF | R,d | 001100drrrrr |
| SUBWF | R,d | 000010drrrrr |
| SWAPF | R,d | 001110drrrrr |
| XORLW | DATA | Fxx |

All object codes occupy one 12-bit word.

All instructions execute in one machine cycle, with the exception of conditional Skip instructions, which execute in one machine cycle for no skip or two machine cycles to skip.

# DATA SHEETS

The following section contains electrical data for the 1650.

## 1650 ELECTRICAL CHARACTERISTICS

### MAXIMUM RATINGS*

Storage Temperature ....................................... −55°C to +150°C
Operating Temperature ......................................... 0°C to +70°C
$V_{CC}$, $V_{XX}$, and all other input/output
voltages with respect to $V_{SS}$ ................................. −0.3V to +12.0V

*Exceeding these ratings could cause permanent damage. Functional operation of this device at these conditions is not implied—operating ranges are specified below.

### STANDARD CONDITIONS (unless otherwise noted)

$V_{CC}$: +5V ± 5%
$V_{XX}$: +4.75V to 10.0V

| Characteristics | Sym | Min | Typ** | Max | Units | Conditions |
|---|---|---|---|---|---|---|
| **DC CHARACTERISTICS** | | | | | | |
| Power Supply Currents | $I_{CC}$ | — | 35 | 50 | mA | |
| | $I_{XX}$ | — | 1 | 5 | mA | |
| **Logic Inputs** | | | | | | |
| Low | $V_{IL}$ | 0 | — | .65 | V | |
| High | $V_{IH}$ | 2.4 | — | $V_{CC}$ | V | |
| **Logic Outputs** | | | | | | |
| Low (Note 1) | $V_{OL}$ | — | — | 0.45 | V | $V_{XX}$=5V @ $I_{OL}$=1.6mA |
| High | $V_{OH}$ | 2.4 | — | $V_{CC}$ | V | $I_{OH}$=100μA min. |
| **AC CHARACTERISTICS** | | | | | | |
| OSC Frequency | $f_{IN}$ | .2 | — | 1 | MHz | |
| RTCC Frequency | — | DC | — | 200 | KHz | |
| CLKOUT Frequency | — | .25 fin | — | — | — | |
| **CLK OUT** | | | | | | |
| Rise Time | $t_r$ | — | — | 200 | ns | 1 TTL load and 100 pF |
| Fall Time | $t_f$ | — | — | 200 | ns | |
| **I/O Registers A, B, C, D** | | | | | | |
| **Output Mode:** | | | | | | |
| Delay From CLKOUT | $t_{DD}$ | — | — | 500 | ns | 1 TTL load and 100 pF |
| **Input Mode** | | | | | | |
| Set-Up | $t_{IS}$ | 0 | — | — | ns | |
| hold | $t_{IH}$ | 100 | — | — | ns | |

### 1650 LED Direct Drive

$V_{XX}$ drives the gate of the output buffer, allowing adjustment of LED drive capability:

| $V_{XX}$ | $V_{OUT}$ | $I_{SINK}$ (typ.) |
|---|---|---|
| 5V | 0.4V | 2.5mA |
| 5V | 0.7V | 4.2mA |
| 10V | 0.4V | 5.8mA |
| 10V | 0.7V | 10.0mA |
| 10V | 1.0V | 14.1mA |

### 1650 OSCILLATOR INPUT

The oscillator input (OSC) can be driven directly by a crystal with compatible output or by an external RC network.

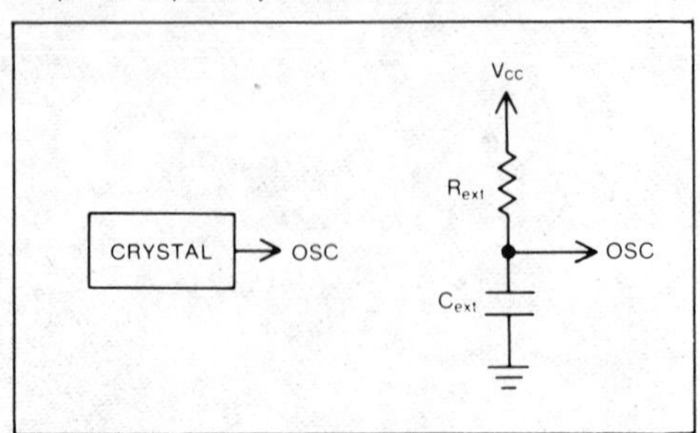


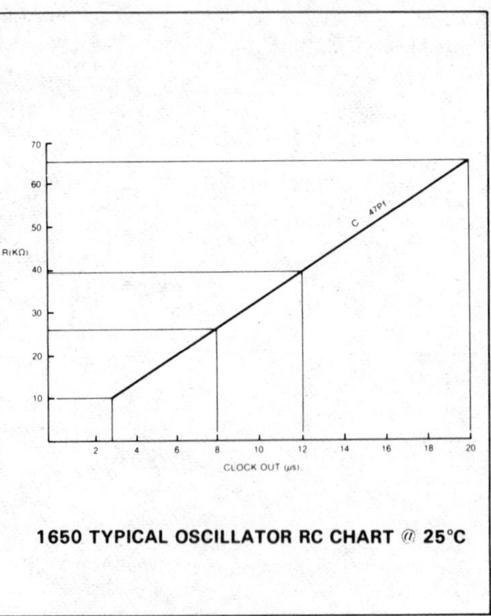


1650 TYPICAL OSCILLATOR RC CHART @ 25°C

We reprint data sheets on pages 15-D2 through 15-D3 by permission of General Instrument Corporation.

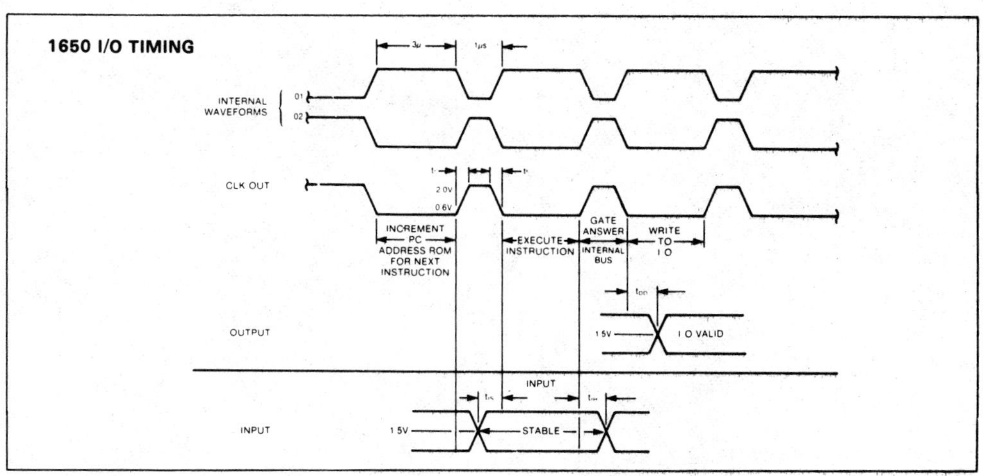

1650 I/O TIMING
INTERNAL WAVEFORMS
01
02
1μs
CLK OUT
2.0V
0.6V
INCREMENT PC
ADDRESS ROM FOR NEXT INSTRUCTION
EXECUTE INSTRUCTION
GATE ANSWER
INTERNAL BUS
WRITE TO I O
OUTPUT
1.5V
I O VALID
INPUT
STABLE
1.5V
INPUT

# INDEX

## OSBORNE/McGraw-Hill Books of Interest

**The 8086 Book**
by R. Rector and G. Alexy
**8080 Programming for Logic Design**
by Adam Osborne
**6800 Programming for Logic Design**
by Adam Osborne
**Z80 Programming for Logic Design**
by Adam Osborne

**8080A/8085 Assembly Language Programming**
by L. Leventhal
**6800 Assembly Language Programming**
by L. Leventhal
**Z80 Assembly Language Programming**
by L. Leventhal
**6502 Assembly Language Programming**
by L. Leventhal
**Z8000 Assembly Language Programming**
by L. Leventhal et al.
**Running Wild: The Next Industrial Revolution**
by Adam Osborne
**PET/CBM Personal Computer Guide — Second Edition**
by Adam Osborne and Carroll Donahue
**PET and the IEEE 488 Bus (GPIB)**
by E. Fisher and C. W. Jensen
**Practical Basic Programs**
by L. Poole et al.
**Some Common BASIC Programs**
by L. Poole and M. Borchers
**Payroll with Cost Accounting — CBASIC**
by Lon Poole et al.
**Accounts Payable and Accounts Receivable — CBASIC**
by Lon Poole et al.
**General Ledger — CBASIC**
by Lon Poole et al.

**Some Common Basic Programs — PET/CBM**
edited by Lon Poole et al.

## OSBORNE/McGraw-Hill
## Microprocessor Handbook Series

**OSBORNE 4 & 8-Bit Microprocessor Handbook**
by Adam Osborne and Gerry Kane

**OSBORNE 16-Bit Microprocessor Handbook**
by Adam Osborne and Gerry Kane

**An Introduction to Microcomputers: Volume 3 — Some Real Support Devices**
by Gerry Kane and Adam Osborne

**8089 I/O Processor Handbook**
by Adam Osborne

**CRT Controller Handbook**
by Gerry Kane

**68000 Microprocessor Handbook**
by Gerry Kane